2022/23

THE DIRECTORY OF GRANT MAKING TRUSTS

27th edition

Ian Pembridge, Rebecca Eddington, Abigail O'Loughlin, Emma Piper and Jessica Threlfall

Additional research by Rhiannon Doherty, Muna Farah, Abigail Hanley, Chester Howarth, Dean Renshaw, Lauren Shaw and Gabriele Zagnojute

Published by the Directory of Social Change (Registered Charity no. 800517 in England and Wales)
Office: Suite 103, 1 Old Hall Street, Liverpool L3 9HG
Tel: 020 4526 5995

Visit www.dsc.org.uk to find out more about our books, subscription funding website and training events. You can also sign up for e-newsletters so that you're always the first to hear about what's new.

The publisher welcomes suggestions and comments that will help to inform and improve future versions of this and all of our titles. Please give us your feedback by emailing publications@dsc.org.uk.

First published by Charities Aid Foundation 1968
Second edition 1971
Third edition 1974
Fourth edition 1975
Fifth edition 1977
Sixth edition 1978
Seventh edition 1981
Eighth edition 1983
Ninth edition 1985
Tenth edition 1987
Eleventh edition 1989
Twelfth edition 1991
Thirteenth edition 1993
Fourteenth edition 1995
Fifteenth edition 1997
Sixteenth edition 1999
Seventeenth edition published by Directory of Social Change 2001
Eighteenth edition 2003
Nineteenth edition 2005
Twentieth edition 2007
Twenty-first edition 2010
Twenty-second edition 2012
Twenty-third edition 2014
Twenty-fourth edition 2015
Twenty-fifth edition 2017
Twenty-sixth edition 2019
Twenty-seventh edition 2021

ISBN 978 1 78482 079 4

British Library Cataloguing in Publication Data
A catalogue record for this book is available from the British Library

Cover design by Kate Griffith
Text designed by Eugenie Dodd Typographics, London
Typeset by Marlinzo Services, Frome
Printed and bound in Great Britain by CPI Group, Croydon

Contents

Foreword

It has been an extraordinary 18 months navigating the COVID-19 pandemic. As fundraisers, we are starting to recalibrate our asks and areas of focus in a landscape which faces challenges unlike any we have seen before. I have spent a great deal of the last year and a half working with my team at Macmillan, and during my tenure as the chair of the Chartered Institute of Fundraising, thinking about where we might go next, as we start to look forward in a new and very different world.

An area of significant opportunity is grant-making trusts. In the UK alone, there are over 8,000 grant-making trusts giving a total in excess of £3 billion annually.[1] Trust funding is an area of fundraising that does not always get the attention it deserves. Trusts tend not to grab the attention of the UK public, provide splashy headlines or galvanise mass action, but that £3 billion adds up to a lot of impact for causes across the world, and is quietly transformative for many charities. During my career, I have been part of and witnessed some truly amazing projects and initiatives funded by trusts – from life-changing research projects, to social investment ventures in Africa and of course, most recently, in a sector-wide response to the global pandemic.

The Directory of Grant Making Trusts is a resource which is invaluable to both fundraisers new to trust funding and also the more seasoned fundraisers among us. In a highly competitive and difficult to navigate space, this guide is a key tool to get you started and help stay on the right track. Most importantly, it gives you the information to ensure that your approaches tick all the boxes for success and you're the right fit for funding.

The opportunities that grant-making trusts offer charities are diverse; from funding specific projects, to supporting research, to contributing to charities' running costs. The competition for funding in post-pandemic times will be even stronger, and, as fundraisers, it would be remiss of us to not take advantage of these opportunities. This guide is a critical weapon in your arsenal as you start to build your relationships with grant-makers, which hopefully will last for many years to come and provide you with the funding to achieve your ambitions and deliver your purpose.

Claire Rowney
Executive Director of Fundraising,
Marketing and Innovation, Macmillan Cancer Support

1 'Facts & Figures: Grant-Making Trusts' [web page], nfpSynergy, https://nfpsynergy.net/free-report/facts-figures-grant-making-trusts, 2 August 2017.

About the Directory of Social Change

At the Directory of Social Change (DSC), we believe that the world is made better by people coming together to serve their communities and each other. For us, an independent voluntary sector is at the heart of that social change and we exist to support charities, voluntary organisations and community groups in the work they do. Our role is to:

- **Provide practical information** on a range of topics from fundraising to project management in both our printed publications and our e-books
- **Offer training** through public courses, events and in-house services
- **Research funders** and maintain a subscription database, *Funds Online*, with details on funding from grant-making charities, companies and government sources
- **Offer bespoke research** to voluntary sector organisations in order to evaluate projects, identify new opportunities and help make sense of existing data
- **Stimulate debate and campaign** on key issues that affect the voluntary sector, particularly to champion the concerns of smaller charities

We are a registered charity ourselves but we self-fund most of our work. We charge for services, but cross-subsidise those which charities particularly need and cannot easily afford.

Visit our website **www.dsc.org.uk** to see how we can help you to help others and have a look at **www.fundsonline.org.uk** to see how DSC could improve your fundraising. Alternatively, call our friendly team at **020 4526 5995** to chat about your needs or drop us a line at **cs@dsc.org.uk**.

Introduction

Welcome to the 27th edition of *The Directory of Grant Making Trusts* (DGMT). This book covers over 2,000 of the largest grant-making charities that award grants to UK organisations. A lot has changed since the last edition and the charity sector has had to quickly adapt to the multiple challenges resulting from the COVID-19 pandemic. We saw many grant-making charities responding quickly to support the sector in different ways, such as providing emergency funding, simplifying application processes and offering grantees additional flexibility with grant conditions. As emergency response funds from the government dry up, and fundraising events continue to be cancelled or indefinitely postponed, many charities have become more reliant on grant-funding. We hope that the meticulously researched information provided in this directory allows you to continue achieving your organisation's goals during these challenging times.

The Charities Aid Foundation published the first edition of DGMT in 1968 and it has been researched and published by DSC since 2001. Over this time the title has gained a notable reputation as a comprehensive guide to UK grant-making charities and their funding policies. DSC's other guides include independent, sometimes critical, comments on and analysis of funders' activities. DGMT does not. Rather, it is a concise and to-the-point guide to grant-making charities. It is designed to provide a bridge between the grant-makers and fundraising communities in the UK. Today it is hard to imagine the difficulties which must have been encountered and the amount of time spent trying to obtain funds from these charities before DGMT brought together so many of them in one place.

This edition welcomes over 170 grant-making charities that are completely new to DGMT. Each individual funder listed in this guide annually gives over £50,000, with some giving significantly more and up to a staggering £759.5 million awarded by the Wellcome Trust. The combined giving of all the grant-makers totalled over £5.6 billion, of which £5.56 billion was given to organisations. This marks a slight increase of around £60 million from the last edition.

In the course of our research, we scrutinised each grant-maker's annual reports and accounts, mainly for the financial years 2019 and 2019/20. We also examined the content of other resources, such as charities' websites, social media accounts and application guidelines, in order to provide the most relevant information for our readers. In some cases we also made direct contact with the funders themselves.

Each of the records gives a figure for the annual grant total distributed by the charity and the amount awarded to organisations only. In the majority of cases the two figures will match because the grant-maker only gives to organisations; however, where support is given to both organisations and individuals, you will be able to see there are two separate totals. In some cases, we were unable to determine the breakdown, and both fields will show the same figure to reflect the charity's potential to give. In other instances, full accounts were not available to view online and we had to estimate the grant total based on the charity's spending or previous grant-making.

We value the opinions of our readers on all aspects of our work, including this directory. We are always looking to improve the guide and would welcome any feedback – positive or negative – which could be useful for future editions. Please email us at: research@dsc.org.uk with any comments you would like to make.

All in the Research Team at DSC wish you the very best of luck with your fundraising!

The grant-making charities we have listed

This directory aims to include the majority of UK-based grant-makers that are capable of giving at least around £50,000 a year to organisations. Many of their trustees and/or staff are extremely helpful and we have been able to access comprehensive information on current policies via their websites, published material or direct communication. However, not all are so open. Where we have found this to be the case and information is not readily available, the funder's details have been updated, where possible, using the information on the appropriate regulator's website. Grant-makers have been included in the index under the appropriate headings according to their own published guidelines, grant-making practices and/or annual reports. We have placed those for which we do not have such information under what we believe to be the most suitable categories based on the information available.

Some trustees have stated their wish for their charity not to be included in this book. However, we believe that our guides provide an invaluable bridge between the charitable community and the rest of the voluntary sector, and that charities in receipt of public funds should not attempt to draw a veil of secrecy over their activities, barring the most exceptional cases. Furthermore, we believe it is in the interests of the charitable sector to have information in the public domain about the activities of grant-makers as a group. Consequently, we have declined requests from grant-makers to be excluded from this directory. We are, though, happy to explain the reasons why the organisation may not be awarding grants or accepting applications, and we think this is more helpful than letting the charity remain an obscure name in the sea of funders.

In general we have included:

- charities with a grant-making capacity of at least around £50,000 per year which make grants to charities and voluntary organisations. This includes The National Lottery Community Fund and its programme Awards for All (which operate like grant-making charities). Please note that while grant totals of some of the funders listed here could be below £50,000 in the given year, their grant-making activities either have the potential to exceed this amount or vary significantly each year.

We have excluded:

- grant-makers which fund individuals only;
- grant-makers which fund one organisation exclusively;
- grant-makers which generally have a grant-making capacity of less than £50,000 (smaller grant-making charities are included on our funding website; for more information visit: fundsonline.org.uk);

- grant-makers which only fund work overseas;
- grant-makers which have ceased to exist or are being wound up with any remaining funds fully committed.

We continue to include grant-making charities which state that they do not respond to unsolicited applications. We believe that their inclusion benefits fundraisers by giving a broader overview of the grant-making community, and that the information could be important in building relationships with funders. We feel it benefits the grant-makers in helping them to communicate that they do not wish to receive applications, which fundraisers might not know if they identified that particular grant-maker through other avenues. This also reduces the number of ineligible applications that are submitted to very busy and often over-stretched grant-making charities. As outlined in DSC's Responsible Giving policy principle, clear and accessible information is essential for both funders and applicants and ensures effective use of time and charitable resources (please visit www.dsc.org.uk for more information).

Acknowledgements

We would like to thank Claire Rowney, Executive Director of Fundraising, Marketing and Innovation at Macmillan Cancer Support and former Chair of Trustees at the Chartered Institute of Fundraising, for contributing the foreword to this edition.

We would also like to thank all those trustees and staff of grant-making charities who strive to make their information openly available, and all those who help our research by responding to our communications and providing helpful comments.

How to use DGMT

The directory starts with four indexes:

- grant-makers by geographical area;
- grant-makers by field of interest and type of beneficiary;
- grant-makers by type of organisation;
- grant-makers by type of grant.

There is also an alphabetical listing of the top 150 grant-makers by grant total on page xix.

Using these indexes, readers should be able to make a shortlist of grant-makers whose funding policies match their needs.

Grant-makers by geographical area

This index enables you to see which grant-makers will consider applications from a charity or project in a particular geographical area. It contains two separate listings:

LIST OF GEOGRAPHICAL AREA HEADINGS

This is a complete list of all the geographical area headings used in DGMT.

LIST OF GRANT-MAKERS BY GEOGRAPHICAL AREA

These pages list grant-makers under the geographical areas where they will consider funding.

Grant-makers by field of interest and type of beneficiary

This index enables you to see which grant-makers are likely to fund a particular type of work to benefit a particular type of person. It lists grant-makers according to:

- the type of activity or work they are willing to fund – their fields of interest;
- who they want to benefit – their preferred beneficiaries.

These pages contain two separate listings:

CATEGORISATION OF FIELDS OF INTEREST AND TYPES OF BENEFICIARY

This lists all of the headings used in DGMT to categorise fields of interest and types of beneficiary. This listing should help you match your project with one – or more – of the categories used.

LIST OF GRANT-MAKERS BY FIELD OF INTEREST AND TYPE OF BENEFICIARY

These pages list grant-makers under the fields of interest and types of beneficiary where there is a stated preference, or that our research suggests they might be willing to support.

The index is structured hierarchically. This means that the general heading comes first, followed by more specific subject areas. For example, under 'Beneficial groups' you can find the 'Social and economic circumstances' category which is then split into further sub-headings, including 'People who are homeless/at risk of homelessness', 'Carers' and 'Victims of disasters and famine'.

So, if your project falls under a specific heading such as 'Victims of disasters and famine', it is also worth looking at the grant-makers which have expressed a general interest in funding 'Social and economic circumstances'. Grant-makers might be interested in funding your project even if they have not specifically expressed a preference for a particular field as long as it falls within the broad area they are supporting.

Grant-makers by type of organisation

This index enables you to see which grant-makers will consider funding a particular type of organisation. We have not listed grant-makers that will support registered, excepted or exempt charities as all the grant-makers listed in this guide will. The index contains two separate listings:

LIST OF TYPES OF ORGANISATION

This list contains all of the headings used in DGMT to categorise types of organisation.

LIST OF GRANT-MAKERS BY TYPE OF ORGANISATION

These pages list grant-makers under the types of organisation for which they have expressed a funding preference.

Grant-makers by type of grant

This index enables you to see which grant-makers can consider making the types of grant you are looking for. Grant-makers are listed under the type of grant that our research suggests they are willing or likely to make. These pages contain two separate listings:

LIST OF TYPES OF GRANT

This lists all of the headings used in DGMT to categorise types of grant.

LIST OF GRANT-MAKERS BY TYPE OF GRANT

These pages list grant-makers under the types of grant that they are willing or likely to make.

The largest grant-makers

On page xix we have listed the largest 150 grant-makers by the total of grants awarded to organisations in alphabetical order. Between them they account for around £4.47 billion, or about 80% of the funds available in the book. *Please do not* use this simply as a mailing list: these grant-makers cover a wide range of specialist interests and many of them will not fund your work.

We strongly recommend that you read each record carefully and compile your own list of those major grant-makers relevant to you. You can then set this list alongside the other lists generated from the other indexes in the directory. We believe this list should only be used as an effective way of ensuring that you do not omit any major grant-makers.

How to use DGMT
Key steps

STEP 1

Define the project, programme or work for which you are seeking funding.

STEP 2

Geographical area: find the area most local to your requirements (the geographical location of the people who will benefit from any funding received). Identify the relevant section of the index.

STEP 3

Field of interest and type of beneficiary: identify the categories that match your project. What charitable activities, facilities or services will the funding provide? What are the characteristics which best describe the people who will benefit from any funding received? Find the relevant sections of the index and funders listed there.

STEP 4

Type of organisation: identify the type of your organisation (or, if you are searching for funding on behalf of someone else, the type of organisation which would be receiving the funds). Find the relevant section of the index.

STEP 5

Type of grant: identify the type of grant you are looking for. Find the relevant section of the index and grant-makers listed there.

STEP 6

Compare the relevant sections of grant-makers identified through all of the indexes to find the funders which appear in more than one section. This way you will produce a list of those whose funding policies most closely match the characteristics of the project for which you are seeking funding.

If your list is too short you could include grant-makers that have a general interest in funding your area of work – while these may not define a specific field as a priority or preference, they will consider applications as long as they fall within the broad category.

STEP 7

Look up the records for the grant-makers identified, study their details carefully and pay close attention to 'What is funded', 'What is not funded' and the preferred method of communication or where further details may be found.

STEP 8

Look at the list of the top 150 grant-makers to make sure you do not miss any major funders. Look up the records for the grant-makers identified, study their details carefully and again pay particularly close attention to 'What is funded' and 'What is not funded'. Remember that these funders are likely to be more well-known and consequently over-subscribed.

EXAMPLE

Funding is being sought to purchase equipment for a children's hospice in North Wales.

- The geographical location is: United Kingdom → Wales → North Wales. You may want to look at the grant-makers listed under the broader region (Wales) as well, and it is also worth looking at grant-makers listed under United Kingdom. A grant-maker listed under a more general heading may be just as willing to fund activity in a specific region as another which states that it has a specific interest in that area.
- The service to be provided is: health. If you were looking for funding for a children's hospice, you would probably first look under 'Community health services' which can be found under 'Health'; however, grant-makers listed under the broader area of interest (health) are also worth looking at.
- The key characteristic of the people to benefit is that they are: children. If you look under 'Beneficial groups', you will find 'Children and young people', which is under 'Age'.
- The type of organisation is: hospice.
- The type of grant being sought is: capital costs.

The list you produce by following these steps will contain the grant-makers most accurately matching you project criteria; however, it is also worth considering funders that give for general charitable purposes, especially if they give in your local area.

A typical grant-making charity record

A complete record should contain information under the headings listed below. An explanation of the information which should appear in these fields is given alongside.

CC NO
Charity registration number

WHERE FUNDING CAN BE GIVEN
The village, town, borough, parish or other geographical area the trust is prepared to fund

WHAT IS FUNDED
Details of the types of project or activity the trust plans to fund and groups it intends to ultimately benefit

WHAT IS NOT FUNDED
The types of project or causes the trust does not fund, e.g. expeditions, scholarships

SAMPLE GRANTS
Examples of grants previously awarded by the trust

TRUSTEES
Names of the trustees

CONTACT DETAILS
Information on whom to contact for further details or, if appropriate, where applications should be sent

■ The Fictitious Trust

CC NO 123456 **ESTABLISHED** 1993
WHERE FUNDING CAN BE GIVEN UK.
WHO CAN BENEFIT Registered charities.
WHAT IS FUNDED Education and training.
WHAT IS NOT FUNDED Gap year activities.
TYPE OF GRANT One-off; capital costs; running costs.
RANGE OF GRANTS £250 to £5,000.
SAMPLE GRANTS A registered charity (£5,000); a CIC (£1,000); a museum (£800), a gallery and a university (£500 each); an exempted charity (£400); an excepted charity (£250).
FINANCES *Financial year end* 31/03/2018
Income £55,000 *Total grants* £60,000
Grants to organisations £50,000
Assets £800,000
TRUSTEES Ernestine Papadopoulos; Samuel Akintola; Grace O'Malley; Alistair Johnson; Dr Angelique Kidjo; Prof. Miriam Masekela.
OTHER INFORMATION Grants to individuals totalled £10,000.
HOW TO APPLY Apply in writing to the address below. An sae should be enclosed if an acknowledgement is required.
CONTACT DETAILS The Trust Secretary, The Old Barn, Main Street, New Town ZC48 2QQ *Tel.* 020 7123 4567 *Email* grantsteam@fictitioustrust.co.uk *Website* www.fictitioustrust.co.uk

ESTABLISHED
Year the trust was established

WHO CAN BENEFIT
The types of organisation that can be supported

TYPE OF GRANT
The types of grant or loan the trust is prepared to give, e.g. one-off, core costs, project costs

RANGE OF GRANTS
The typical size of grant normally given

FINANCES
The most recent financial information available, including the total amount given in grants during the year

OTHER INFORMATION
Any other information which might be useful to grant-seekers

HOW TO APPLY
Useful information to those preparing their grant application

The top 150 grant-makers by grant total

This is a list of the largest 150 grant-makers by the total of grants awarded to organisations in alphabetical order. Between them they account for around £4.47 billion, or about 80% of the funds available in the book. *Please do not* use this simply as a mailing list: these grant-makers cover a wide range of specialist interests and many of them will not fund your work.

We recommend that you read each record carefully and compile your own list of major grant-makers relevant to you. You can use this list alongside the other lists generated from the indexes in the directory. We believe this is the most effective way of ensuring that you do not omit any major grant-makers.

The 29th May 1961 Charitable Trust

The Aberdeen Foundation

ABF The Soldiers' Charity

AKO Foundation

The Alborada Trust

Allchurches Trust Ltd

Alzheimer's Research UK

Alzheimer's Society

Amabrill Ltd

Arcadia Fund

Ardbarron Trust Ltd

Armed Forces Covenant Fund Trust

Arts Council England

Arts Council of Northern Ireland

Arts Council of Wales (also known as Cyngor Celfyddydau Cymru)

The Asda Foundation

The Associated Board of the Royal Schools of Music

Keren Association Ltd

The Band Trust

BBC Children in Need

Benesco Charity Ltd

Asser Bishvil Foundation

Bloodwise

The Liz and Terry Bramall Foundation

Breast Cancer Now

British Heart Foundation (BHF)

Children with Cancer UK

The City Bridge Trust (Bridge House Estates)

The Clothworkers' Foundation

Denise Coates Foundation

Colyer-Fergusson Charitable Trust

Comic Relief

Corra Foundation

Council for World Mission (UK)

Creative Scotland

The D. G. Charitable Settlement

Diabetes UK

Dunard Fund

The Dunhill Medical Trust

John Ellerman Foundation

England and Wales Cricket Trust

Essex Community Foundation

Esmée Fairbairn Foundation

The February Foundation

The Fidelity UK Foundation

The Football Foundation

The Foyle Foundation

GambleAware

The Gannochy Trust

The Garfield Weston Foundation

The Gatsby Charitable Foundation

Goldman Sachs Gives (UK)

The Edward Gostling Foundation

The Grace Trust

Groundwork UK

Paul Hamlyn Foundation

The David and Claudia Harding Foundation

The Health Foundation

The Helping Foundation

Heritage Lottery Fund

Historic Environment Scotland

The Hunter Foundation

Impact Funding Partners Ltd

The Jagclif Charitable Trust

The Elton John Aids Foundation (EJAF)

The Jordan Charitable Foundation

The Kasner Charitable Trust

The Kennedy Trust for Rheumatology Research

Kidney Research UK

The Law Family Charitable Foundation

The Legal Education Foundation

Lempriere Pringle 2015

The Leverhulme Trust

The Linbury Trust

Lloyds Bank Foundation for England and Wales

Lloyd's Register Foundation
The London Community Foundation (LCF)
The London Marathon Charitable Trust Ltd
John Lyon's Charity
Masonic Charitable Foundation
The Master Charitable Trust
The Mercers' Charitable Foundation
Mind
The Mohn Westlake Foundation
The Monday Charitable Trust
Moondance Foundation
The Steve Morgan Foundation
The Alexander Mosley Charitable Trust
Motor Neurone Disease Association
Multiple Sclerosis Society
Muslim Hands
The National Lottery Community Fund
Nesta
The Nuffield Foundation
The P27 Trust
Parkinson's UK
The Pears Family Charitable Foundation
People's Health Trust
The Jack Petchey Foundation
Power to Change Trust
The Prince of Wales's Charitable Foundation
The Professional Footballers' Association Charity
Prostate Cancer UK
Rachel Charitable Trust
The Racing Foundation
The Rank Foundation Ltd
The Sigrid Rausing Trust
The Resolution Trust
Reuben Foundation
The Robertson Trust
Rosetrees Trust
The Rothschild Foundation
Rothschild Foundation (Hanadiv) Europe
The Joseph Rowntree Charitable Trust
The Joseph Rowntree Foundation
The Royal British Legion
The Royal Navy and Royal Marines Charity
Royal Society of Wildlife Trusts
Foundation Scotland
Scott (Eredine) Charitable Trust
Shetland Charitable Trust
Shulem B. Association Ltd
The Henry Smith Charity
The Sobell Foundation
The Souter Charitable Trust
The Michael and Sarah Spencer Foundation
St James's Place Charitable Foundation
Stewards Company Ltd
The Stoller Charitable Trust
The Stone Family Foundation
Suffolk Community Foundation
The Thompson Family Charitable Trust
The Constance Travis Charitable Trust
Trust For London
The Tudor Trust
Community Foundation serving Tyne and Wear and Northumberland
United Jewish Israel Appeal
The Michael Uren Foundation
The Veolia Environmental Trust
Versus Arthritis
Viridor Credits Environmental Company
The Vodafone Foundation
The Waterloo Foundation
The Wellcome Trust
Friends of Wiznitz Ltd
The Charles Wolfson Charitable Trust
The Wolfson Foundation
Yorkshire Cancer Research
Youth Music
The Zochonis Charitable Trust

Other publications and resources

The following publications and resources may also be of interest to readers of DGMT. They are all available directly from DSC by ringing 020 4526 5995 or visiting our website at www.dsc.org.uk.

Publications

The Guide to Grants for Individuals in Need

This best-selling funding guide gives details of a wide range of funds and other support available for the relief of individual poverty and hardship. It remains a key reference book for social workers, as well as the individuals themselves and those concerned with their welfare. It contains:

- Details on national and local charitable grant-makers which collectively give around £300 million a year towards the relief of individual poverty and hardship.
- Essential advice on applications for each source: eligibility; types of grant given; annual grant total; contact details.
- An example of how to make an effective application, and advice on finding the right sources to apply to.

The Guide to UK Company Giving

This invaluable guide offers insight into 400 companies in the UK that give a combined total of around £400 million in community contributions to voluntary and community organisations. It contains:

- Essential information on whom to contact within each company.
- Detailed information on cash and in-kind donations, employee-led support, sponsorship and details of CSR programmes.
- A section containing essential details on 160 corporate charities.

The Guide to the Major Trusts

The in-depth research and independent comment that this flagship title offers has made it an essential reference guide for all fundraisers. This guide is the only source of independent critical analysis of grant-makers in practice. It includes:

- Essential information on the 1,000 largest grant makers which together give a total of over £5 billion.
- Clear descriptions of charities' policies and practices, as well as details of grant programmes, contact details, eligibility criteria and information on how to apply.

The Guide to New Trusts

This popular guide offers essential details on newly established funders. It is a vital resource for anyone looking for fresh potential sources of funding for their organisation. The guide includes:

- Research on around 100 newly registered grant-making charities.
- Key funding guidelines, including grant-makers' aims and objectives, and stated policies.
- Contact details and any available information that could help tailor your appeal.

Funds Online

DSC's funding website, Funds Online (www.fundsonline.org.uk) contains information on over 8,000 funders which make grants to organisations and individuals.

Some of the great features include:

- Fast, intelligent and intuitive search function – locate the right funder for you within a few clicks.
- User dashboard – track funding you have applied for, see new funding opportunities, and save searches and funders with ease.
- Email alerts to let you know when funders you are interested in have been updated.
- Great data and insight for multi-user account administrators – see how your subscription is being used to inform your decision-making.

There are four subscription options:

Grant-making charities funding organisations – information on over 4,500 grant-making charities giving a combined total of over £5.8 billion to organisations.

Grant-making charities funding individuals – details on around 3,400 charities that give to individuals for educational and welfare purposes. Collectively they give over £350 million each year.

Company giving for organisations – information on over 460 companies giving over £400 million per year in UK cash donations and in-kind support.

Government and statutory support for organisations – funding from local, regional and central government, and European sources.

Grant-makers by geographical area

This index contains two separate listings:

Geographical area headings: This lists all of the geographical area headings used in DGMT.

Grant-makers by geographical area: This lists the funders appearing in DGMT under the geographical areas for which they have expressed a funding preference. Asterisks mark funders which have not been featured in DGMT before.

Grant-makers by geographical area

The index contains two separate listings:

Geographical area headings
This lists all of the geographical area headings used in DGMT.

Grant-makers by geographical area
This lists the funders appearing in DGMT under the geographical areas for which they have expressed a funding preference

Worldwide

The Aaronson Foundation
The Aberdeen Foundation
ABF The Soldiers' Charity
The Acacia Charitable Trust
The Bryan Adams Foundation
The Adlard Family Charitable Foundation
The Aimwell Charitable Trust
Ajahma Charitable Trust
The Alborada Trust
The Alchemy Foundation
The Aldama Foundation
Al-Fayed Charitable Foundation
The Derrill Allatt Foundation
The Allen & Overy Foundation
The Allen Trust
The Almond Trust
Amabrill Ltd
The Anchor Foundation
The Apax Foundation
Arcadia Fund
The Archer Trust
Ardbarron Trust Ltd
The Artemis Charitable Foundation
ArtSocial Foundation
The Ove Arup Foundation
The Ashden Trust
The Ashworth Charitable Trust
The Associated Board of the Royal Schools of Music
Atlas Memorial Ltd
The Scott Bader Commonwealth Ltd
The Austin Bailey Foundation
The Bamford Charitable Foundation
*Veronica and Lars Bane Foundation**
Robert Barr's Charitable Trust
The Batchworth Trust
BC Partners Foundation
Beauland Ltd
The Becht Family Charitable Trust
The Becker Family Charitable Trust
The John Beckwith Charitable Trust
Bedfordshire Charitable Trust Ltd
The Benham Charitable Settlement
The Michael Bishop Foundation
Lady Blakenham's Charity Trust
The Blandford Lake Trust
The Sir Victor Blank Charitable Settlement
The Bloom Foundation
*The Blyth Charitable Trust**
The Boltini Trust
Salo Bordon Charitable Trust
Friends of Boyan Trust
The British and Foreign School Society
British Council for Prevention of Blindness
The Rory and Elizabeth Brooks Foundation
*The Brothers Trust**
*Mary Brown Memorial Trust**
*The Brown Source Trust**
Brushmill Ltd
The Buffini Chao Foundation
*Bulb Foundation**
The Burberry Foundation
The Clara E. Burgess Charity
Burnie's Foundation
The Arnold Burton 1998 Charitable Trust
*The Candy Foundation**
Cannon Charitable Trust
Carlee Ltd
*The Antonio Carluccio Foundation**
Catholic Charitable Trust
The Charities Advisory Trust
Charitworth Ltd
Chartered Accountants' Livery Charity (CALC)
The Cheruby Trust
*The Childs Charitable Trust**
Christadelphian Samaritan Fund
The André Christian Trust
Chrysalis Trust
Clark Foundation
The Clothworkers' Foundation
Denise Coates Foundation
The Vivienne and Samuel Cohen Charitable Trust
The Coltstaple Trust
The Alice Ellen Cooper Dean Charitable Foundation
Michael Cornish Charitable Trust
The Evan Cornish Foundation
The Cornwell Charitable Trust
*Council for World Mission (UK)**
*The CPF Trust**
The Cross Trust
Oizer Dalim Trust
The Crispin Davis Family Trust
Dawat-E-Hadiyah Trust (United Kingdom)
The Roger De Haan Charitable Trust
The Delves Charitable Trust
The Desmond Foundation
The Laduma Dhamecha Charitable Trust
Donibristle Trust
Dromintee Trust
The Mildred Duveen Charitable Trust
The DWF Charitable Foundation
The James Dyson Foundation
The Economist Charitable Trust
The Gilbert and Eileen Edgar Foundation
Edupoor Ltd
The George Elias Charitable Trust
The Ellinson Foundation Ltd
Joseph Ettedgui Charitable Foundation
The Exilarch's Foundation
The Fairstead Trust
The Farthing Trust
Allan and Nesta Ferguson Charitable Settlement
Fine & Country Foundation
*The Fonthill Foundation**
Donald Forrester Trust
The Forte Charitable Trust
The Lord Forte Foundation
Four Acre Trust
*Foux Foundation**
The Foxglove Trust
The Freshfield Foundation
The Fulmer Charitable Trust
The Funding Network
The G. D. Charitable Trust
Gamma Trust
The Gatsby Charitable Foundation
The Jacqueline and Michael Gee Charitable Trust
The General Charity Fund
The Generations Foundation
The Steven Gerrard Foundation
The Gertner Charitable Trust
The Tara Getty Foundation
The Gibbs Charitable Trusts
The G. C. Gibson Charitable Trust
The Gloag Foundation
Sydney and Phyllis Goldberg Memorial Charitable Trust
The Golden Bottle Trust
The Goldman Sachs Charitable Gift Fund (UK)
Goldman Sachs Gives (UK)
The Goodman Foundation
The Hemraj Goyal Foundation
Grace Charitable Trust
The Grace Trust
Grahame Charitable Foundation Ltd
The Grant Foundation
The Kenneth and Susan Green Charitable Foundation
The Green Hall Foundation
Philip and Judith Green Trust
The Grimmitt Trust
The Gunter Charitable Trust
*The Guy Foundation**
H. C. D. Memorial Fund
Hadras Kodesh Trust
The Helen Hamlyn Trust
The Kathleen Hannay Memorial Charity

The Happold Foundation
The Haramead Trust
Harbinson Charitable Trust
The Harbour Foundation
The Hasluck Charitable Trust
The Maurice Hatter Foundation
The Heathside Charitable Trust
The Charlotte Heber-Percy Charitable Trust
The Michael Heller Charitable Foundation
The Simon Heller Charitable Settlement
The Highcroft Charitable Trust
Highway One Trust
The Hilden Charitable Fund
The Hillier Trust
R. G. Hills Charitable Trust
Hinchley Charitable Trust
The Hinduja Foundation
The Hintze Family Charity Foundation
The Hiscox Foundation
The Jane Hodge Foundation
The Holbeck Charitable Trust
The Holliday Foundation
Sir Harold Hood's Charitable Trust
Hope Trust
The Thomas J. Horne Memorial Trust
The Hunter Foundation
The Hutton Foundation
IGO Foundation Ltd
The Ingram Trust
The Innocent Foundation
*The Investindustrial Foundation**
The Invigorate Charitable Trust
The ITF Seafarers Trust
The J. A. R. Charitable Trust
*The Jagclif Charitable Trust**
John Jarrold Trust Ltd
The Jephcott Charitable Trust
The Jerusalem Trust
Jewish Child's Day (JCD)
Joffe Charitable Trust
The Christopher and Kirsty Johnston Charitable Trust
The Muriel Jones Foundation
The Cyril and Eve Jumbo Charitable Trust
The Jusaca Charitable Trust
The Michael and Ilse Katz Foundation
The Kennedy Trust for Rheumatology Research
The Kentown Wizard Foundation
The Nancy Kenyon Charitable Trust
E. and E. Kernkraut Charities Ltd
Kilpatrick Fraser Charitable Trust
*The Kilroot Foundation**
The Ernest Kleinwort Charitable Trust
Kolyom Trust Ltd
The K. P. Ladd Charitable Trust
The David Laing Foundation
The Kirby Laing Foundation
The Beatrice Laing Trust
The Lancashire Foundation
The Lauffer Family Charitable Foundation
Mrs F. B. Laurence Charitable Trust
The Betty Lawes Foundation
The William Leech Charity
The Leigh Trust
*The Ralph Levy Charitable Company Ltd**
*Cecil and Hilda Lewis Charitable Trust**
David and Ruth Lewis Family Charitable Trust
John Lewis Foundation
The Limbourne Trust
The Linbury Trust
The Second Joseph Aaron Littman Foundation
Lloyd's Charities Trust
Lloyd's Register Foundation
The Lower Green Foundation
The Henry Lumley Charitable Trust
The M. Y. A. Charitable Trust
The Mactaggart Third Fund
The Mallinckrodt Foundation
The Marchig Animal Welfare Trust
The Michael Marks Charitable Trust
Marmot Charitable Trust
The Martin Charitable Trust
The Geoffrey and Pauline Martin Trust
The Master Charitable Trust
*Material World Foundation**
*Gemma and Chris McGough Charitable Foundation CIO**
The Melow Charitable Trust
The Brian Mercer Charitable Trust
Mercury Phoenix Trust
T. and J. Meyer Family Foundation Ltd
The Mickel Fund
*The Mila Charitable Organisation**
The Millennium Oak Trust
Jean and Roger Miller's Charitable Trust
The Millichope Foundation
The Millward Charitable Trust
*The Milne Family Foundation**
Moondance Foundation
The Henry Moore Foundation
The Morel Charitable Trust
The Morris Charitable Trust
*The Mosawi Foundation**
Vyoel Moshe Charitable Trust
The Alexander Mosley Charitable Trust
Motor Neurone Disease Association
The Edwina Mountbatten and Leonora Children's Foundation
The Frederick Mulder Foundation
Brian Murtagh Charitable Trust
Muslim Hands
MW (CL) Foundation
MW (GK) Foundation
MW (HO) Foundation
MW (RH) Foundation
The NDL Foundation
Nemoral Ltd
Network for Social Change Charitable Trust
*NNS Foundation**
The Nomura Charitable Trust
The Northwick Trust
The Norton Rose Fulbright Charitable Foundation
The Sir Peter O'Sullevan Charitable Trust
The Oakdale Trust
*Ocean Family Foundation**
The Ogle Christian Trust
Old Possum's Practical Trust
*The Olwyn Foundation**
*Orange Tree Trust**
*Otsar Trust**
The Ovo Charitable Foundation
*The P27 Trust**
The Paget Charitable Trust
The Gerald Palmer Eling Trust Company
Susanna Peake Charitable Trust
The Pears Family Charitable Foundation
Personal Assurance Charitable Trust
Petplan Charitable Trust
The Pharsalia Charitable Trust
The Pickwell Foundation
Pink Ribbon Foundation
Polden-Puckham Charitable Foundation
The Priory Foundation
The Privy Purse Charitable Trust
The Puebla Charitable Trust
Quintessentially Foundation
R. S. Charitable Trust
Rachel Charitable Trust
The Bishop Radford Trust
The Rainford Trust
*The Randal Charitable Foundation**
The Sigrid Rausing Trust
The Reso Charitable Foundation

Reuben Foundation
RG Foundation*
Rhodi Charitable Trust
The Rhododendron Trust
Riada Trust
Ridgesave Ltd
The River Farm Foundation
Rivers Foundation
Robyn Charitable Trust
The Roddick Foundation
Mrs L. D. Rope's Third Charitable Settlement
The Eranda Rothschild Foundation
The Roughley Charitable Trust
Rowanville Ltd
The Joseph Rowntree Charitable Trust
The Royal Foundation of the Duke and Duchess of Cambridge
RSM UK Foundation*
The Dr Mortimer and Theresa Sackler Foundation
The Jean Sainsbury Animal Welfare Trust
Saint Sarkis Charity Trust
The M. J. Samuel Charitable Trust
The Samworth Foundation
The Sandhu Charitable Foundation
The Sands Family Trust
The Anthony Scholefield Foundation*
Schroder Charity Trust
The Schroder Foundation
Scouloudi Foundation
The SDL Foundation
Seedfield Trust
The Shanly Foundation
The Shears Foundation
The Archie Sherman Charitable Trust
Shlomo Memorial Fund Ltd
Shulem B. Association Ltd
The Simmons & Simmons Charitable Foundation
The Thomas Sivewright Catto Charitable Settlement
The Slaughter and May Charitable Trust
Rita and David Slowe Charitable Trust
The SMB Trust
Smith Bradbeer Charitable Trust*
Stanley Smith UK Horticultural Trust
The Sobell Foundation
Societe Generale UK Foundation*
The Souter Charitable Trust
W. F. Southall Trust
Sparquote Ltd
The Michael and Sarah Spencer Foundation*
Rosalyn and Nicholas Springer Charitable Trust
St James's Place Charitable Foundation
Standard Life Aberdeen Charitable Foundation
Staples Trust
Starlow Charities Ltd
The Peter Stebbings Memorial Charity
C. E. K. Stern Charitable Trust
Stewards Company Ltd
Sir Halley Stewart Trust
The Stone Family Foundation
Peter Stormonth Darling Charitable Trust
The Street Foundation
Surgo Foundation UK Ltd
The Sutasoma Trust
The Hugh Symons Charitable Trust*
Stephen Taylor Foundation
Scott Thomson Charitable Trust
The Tomoro Foundation*
The Tory Family Foundation
The Toy Trust
The Toye Foundation
David William Traill Cargill Fund
The Tresanton Trust*
The Trusthouse Charitable Foundation
Ulting Overseas Trust
The Ulverscroft Foundation
The Michael Uren Foundation
The David Uri Memorial Trust
Utermann Charitable Trust*
The Utley Foundation
The Vail Foundation
The Valentine Charitable Trust
The Albert Van Den Bergh Charitable Trust
The Van Mesdag Fund*
The Van Neste Foundation
The Vardy Foundation
The Vaughan Williams Charitable Trust
Virgin Atlantic Foundation
The Vodafone Foundation
The Georg and Emily Von Opel Foundation*
The Waterloo Foundation
G. R. Waters Charitable Trust 2000
The Watson Family Charitable Trust
The Wellcome Trust
Westhill Endowment
The Norman Whiteley Trust
The Williams Charitable Trust
The HDH Wills 1965 Charitable Trust
Dame Violet Wills Charitable Trust
The Wimbledon Foundation
The Wingate Foundation
The Charles Wolfson Charitable Trust
The Woodward Charitable Trust
WWDP (World day of Prayer National Committee for England, Wales and Northern Ireland)
Yankov Charitable Trust
The Zochonis Charitable Trust
Zurich Community Trust (UK) Ltd

Africa

Anglo American Group Foundation
The Baring Foundation
The Boltini Trust
BOOST Charitable Trust
The Breadsticks Foundation
The Brenley Trust
The Consuelo and Anthony Brooke Charitable Trust
The Noel Buxton Trust
William A. Cadbury Charitable Trust
The Childwick Trust
J. A. Clark Charitable Trust
Comic Relief
Corra Foundation
Council for World Mission (UK)*
Credit Suisse EMEA Foundation
The Dashlight Foundation*
The Davis Foundation
Didymus
The Dulverton Trust
The Ecology Trust
The Gilbert and Eileen Edgar Foundation
The Eighty Eight Foundation
The Estelle Trust
The ExPat Foundation
The Gatsby Charitable Foundation
The James Grace Trust*
H. C. D. Memorial Fund
The Charles Hayward Foundation
The Headley Trust
IBM United Kingdom Trust
The Indigo Trust
The J. J. Charitable Trust
The Frank Jackson Foundation
The Jerusalem Trust
The Elton John Aids Foundation (EJAF)
The Labone Charitable Trust*
Maurice and Hilda Laing Charitable Trust

The Kirby Laing Foundation
Lancaster Foundation
*The Leeward Trust**
The Light Fund Company
*The Livingston Charitable Trust**
Lord and Lady Lurgan Trust
Medical Research Foundation
The Morel Charitable Trust
Morgan Stanley International Foundation
The Miles Morland Foundation
*NNS Foundation**
David and Elaine Potter Foundation
*The Raindance Charitable Trust**
The Eleanor Rathbone Charitable Trust
The Reso Charitable Foundation
Rivers Foundation
The Alan and Babette Sainsbury Charitable Fund
Rita and David Slowe Charitable Trust
*The Sterry Family Foundation**
Mark Stolkin Foundation
The Gay and Keith Talbot Trust
Mrs R. P. Tindall's Charitable Trust
The Tolkien Trust
Tropical Health And Education Trust
The True Colours Trust
The Tudor Trust
The Union Of The Sisters Of Mercy Of Great Britain
The Scurrah Wainwright Charity
The Wood Foundation
*The Edward and Catherine Wray Charitable Trust**
The Zochonis Charitable Trust

Asia (excluding Israel)

AKO Foundation
Alliance Family Foundation Ltd
The Arah Foundation
The Bagri Foundation
Bairdwatson Charitable Trust
The Bestway Foundation
The Boltini Trust
The Breadsticks Foundation
William A. Cadbury Charitable Trust
*CareTech Foundation**
J. A. Clark Charitable Trust
Comic Relief
Corra Foundation
*Council for World Mission (UK)**
Credit Suisse EMEA Foundation
The Daiwa Anglo-Japanese Foundation
The Ecology Trust
The James Grace Trust
The Great Britain Sasakawa Foundation
The Walter Guinness Charitable Trust
H. C. D. Memorial Fund
Paul Hamlyn Foundation
The Helen Hamlyn Trust
The Hinduja Foundation
IBM United Kingdom Trust
The Jerusalem Trust
The Elton John Aids Foundation (EJAF)
J. E. Joseph Charitable Fund
Kusuma Trust UK
*The Labone Charitable Trust**
The Kirby Laing Foundation
*The Leeward Trust**
*The Livingston Charitable Trust**
The Matliwala Family Charitable Trust
The Mittal Foundation
Morgan Stanley International Foundation
Ostro Fayre Share Foundation
*Quadstar Charitable Foundation**
The Queen Anne's Gate Foundation
The Eleanor Rathbone Charitable Trust
Rhodi Charitable Trust
Rivers Foundation
Savannah Wisdom
The Sino-British Fellowship Trust
*The Support Foundation**
Surgo Foundation UK Ltd
The Gay and Keith Talbot Trust
Tropical Health and Education Trust

Israel

4 Charity Foundation
A. W. Charitable Trust
The Aaronson Foundation
Alliance Family Foundation Ltd
The Ardwick Trust
Keren Association Ltd
Atkin Charitable Foundation
The Andrew Balint Charitable Trust
The Max Barney Foundation
The Beaverbrooks Charitable Trust
Ruth Berkowitz Charitable Trust
The Beth Hamedrash Satmar Trust (BHST)
The John Black Charitable Foundation
The Bloom Foundation
The Bluston Charitable Settlement
Salo Bordon Charitable Trust
Charitworth Ltd
Closehelm Ltd
CMZ Ltd
The Vivienne and Samuel Cohen Charitable Trust
The Gershon Coren Charitable Foundation (also known as The Muriel and Gus Coren Charitable Foundation)
The Craps Charitable Trust
Itzchok Meyer Cymerman Trust Ltd
*The Manny and Brigitta Davidson Charitable Foundation**
The Davis Foundation
The Henry and Suzanne Davis Foundation
Debmar Benevolent Trust Ltd
The Djanogly Foundation
Dollond Charitable Trust
The Doughty Charity Trust
Dushinsky Trust Ltd
Entindale Ltd
The Exilarch's Foundation
Extonglen Ltd
Famos Foundation Trust
The Isaac and Freda Frankel Memorial Charitable Trust
The Gertner Charitable Trust
The Gould Charitable Trust
M. and R. Gross Charities Ltd
The N. and R. Grunbaum Charitable Trust
The Harbour Charitable Trust
The Harbour Foundation
The Maurice Hatter Foundation
The Humanitarian Trust
The Huntingdon Foundation Ltd
Investream Charitable Trust
Jewish Child's Day (JCD)
J. E. Joseph Charitable Fund
The Jusaca Charitable Trust
The Ian Karten Charitable Trust
The Kasner Charitable Trust
Kupath Gemach Chaim Bechesed Viznitz Trust
Largsmount Ltd
The Lauffer Family Charitable Foundation
The Kennedy Leigh Charitable Trust
Joseph Levy Foundation
*Cecil and Hilda Lewis Charitable Trust**
Jack Livingstone Charitable Trust
The Locker Foundation
The M. Y. A. Charitable Trust

The Manackerman Charitable Trust
*The Manson Family Charitable Trust**
Marbeh Torah Trust
The Stella and Alexander Margulies Charitable Trust
The Marks Family Charitable Trust
Mayfair Charities Ltd
Mayheights Ltd
Melodor Ltd
The Melow Charitable Trust
Mercaz Torah Vechesed Ltd
The Mutual Trust Group
Ner Foundation
Newpier Charity Ltd
The Polonsky Foundation
Premishlaner Charitable Trust
The Rayne Trust
Reuben Foundation
The Rofeh Trust
Rowanville Ltd
The Jeremy and John Sacher Charitable Trust
Saint Sarkis Charity Trust
Sam and Bella Sebba Charitable Trust
Sellata Ltd
Shlomo Memorial Fund Ltd
The Sobell Foundation
The E. C. Sosnow Charitable Trust
The Steinberg Family Charitable Trust
C. E. K. Stern Charitable Trust
The Sir Sigmund Sternberg Charitable Foundation
The David Tannen Charitable Trust
Mrs R. P. Tindall's Charitable Trust
Tzedakah
United Jewish Israel Appeal
The Vail Foundation
*The Velvet Foundation**
VHLT Ltd
The Linda and Michael Weinstein Charitable Trust
Friends of Wiznitz Ltd
The Maurice Wohl Charitable Foundation
The Wolfson Family Charitable Trust

Central and South America

Anglo American Group Foundation
William A. Cadbury Charitable Trust
Didymus
H. C. D. Memorial Fund
*The Karlsson Jativa Charitable Foundation**
*The Leeward Trust**
The Sunrise Foundation CIO

North America

AKO Foundation
Alliance Family Foundation Ltd
Anglo American Group Foundation
Keren Association Ltd
The Becht Family Charitable Trust
Bennett Lowell Ltd
Breast Cancer Now
Bridgepoint Charitable Trust
*The Brothers Trust**
The G. W. Cadbury Charitable Trust
CMZ Ltd
The Exilarch's Foundation
*Family Philanthropy Ltd**
The Christina Mary Hendrie Trust
The Hinduja Foundation
*The Investindustrial Foundation**
The Kennedy Charitable Foundation
Kupath Gemach Chaim Bechesed Viznitz Trust
The Lauffer Family Charitable Foundation
Melodor Ltd
The Mittal Foundation
The Mutual Trust Group
*NNS Foundation**
*Partners Global Foundation**
The Polonsky Foundation
The Reso Charitable Foundation
*RG Foundation**
The Dr Mortimer and Theresa Sackler Foundation
Sam and Bella Sebba Charitable Trust
Shlomo Memorial Fund Ltd
The St James's Trust Settlement
Friends of Wiznitz Ltd

Oceania

Anglo American Group Foundation
The Girdlers' Company Charitable Trust
*RG Foundation**

Europe

AKO Foundation
Alliance Family Foundation Ltd
ArtSocial Foundation
The Andrew Balint Charitable Trust
Bridgepoint Charitable Trust
The Consuelo and Anthony Brooke Charitable Trust
The CIBC World Markets Children's Foundation
*Council for World Mission (UK)**
Credit Suisse EMEA Foundation
Donibristle Trust
The Ecology Trust
The Headley Trust
The Hinduja Foundation
IBM United Kingdom Trust
*The Investindustrial Foundation**
The Elton John Aids Foundation (EJAF)
*The Karlsson Jativa Charitable Foundation**
Kusuma Trust UK
*The Labone Charitable Trust**
The Martin Laing Foundation
Merchant Navy Welfare Board
Morgan Stanley International Foundation
The Polonsky Foundation
QBE European Operations Foundation
The Joseph and Lena Randall Charitable Trust
Rothschild Foundation (Hanadiv) Europe
Saint Sarkis Charity Trust
Sofronie Foundation
The Tolkien Trust
The Union of the Sisters of Mercy of Great Britain
The Veneziana Fund
Wellington Management UK Foundation

United Kingdom

The 29th May 1961 Charitable Trust
The 3Ts Charitable Trust
4 Charity Foundation
The 4814 Trust
The A. B. Charitable Trust
The A. Team Foundation Ltd
The Aaronson Foundation
The Abbeyfield Research Foundation
The Aberdeen Foundation
ABF The Soldiers' Charity
The Acacia Charitable Trust
Access Sport CIO
The Access to Justice Foundation*
Action Medical Research
The Bryan Adams Foundation
The Adint Charitable Trust
The AIM Foundation
The Aimwell Charitable Trust
Sylvia Aitken's Charitable Trust
Ajahma Charitable Trust
The Alborada Trust
The Alchemy Foundation
The Aldama Foundation
Al-Fayed Charitable Foundation
AlixPartners (UK) Charitable Foundation
The All Saints Educational Trust
The Derrill Allatt Foundation
Allchurches Trust Ltd
D. C. R. Allen Charitable Trust
Alliance Family Foundation Ltd
The Almond Trust
Alzheimer's Research UK
Alzheimer's Society
Amabrill Ltd
The Ampersand Foundation*
The AMW Charitable Trust
The Anchor Foundation
Andor Charitable Trust
Anglo American Group Foundation
The Annandale Charitable Trust
The Anson Charitable Trust
The Apax Foundation
The Archer Trust
The Architectural Heritage Fund
Ardbarron Trust Ltd
The Ardeola Charitable Trust
The Ardwick Trust
The Armed Forces Covenant Fund Trust*
Armed Forces Education Trust
The Armourers' and Brasiers' Gauntlet Trust
The Art Fund
The Artemis Charitable Foundation
Douglas Arter Foundation
ArtSocial Foundation
The Ove Arup Foundation
Ove Arup Partnership Charitable Trust
The Ashburnham Thanksgiving Trust
The Ashden Trust
The Ashworth Charitable Trust
The Ian Askew Charitable Trust
The Associated Board of the Royal Schools of Music
Keren Association Ltd
Asthma UK
The Astor Foundation
John Atcheson Foundation*
Atkin Charitable Foundation
The Atlas Fund
The Aurelius Charitable Trust
Backstage Trust
The Scott Bader Commonwealth Ltd
The Bagri Foundation
The Baily Thomas Charitable Fund
The Balcombe Charitable Trust
The Balfour Beatty Charitable Trust
The Andrew Balint Charitable Trust
The Bamford Charitable Foundation
The Roger and Sarah Bancroft Clark Charitable Trust
The Band Trust
Veronica and Lars Bane Foundation*
The Banister Charitable Trust
The Barbers' Company General Charities
The Barbour Foundation
The Barclay Foundation
The Baring Foundation
The Barker-Mill Foundation
The Michael Barnard Charitable Trust*
Lord Barnby's Foundation
The Barnsbury Charitable Trust
Misses Barrie Charitable Trust
Robert Barr's Charitable Trust
The Paul Bassham Charitable Trust
BBC Children in Need
BC Partners Foundation
Bear Mordechai Ltd
The Beaverbrook Foundation
The Beaverbrooks Charitable Trust
The Becht Family Charitable Trust
The John Beckwith Charitable Trust
AJ Bell Trust*
Benesco Charity Ltd
The Benham Charitable Settlement
Bennett Lowell Ltd
Ruth Berkowitz Charitable Trust
The Bestway Foundation
The Beth Hamedrash Satmar Trust (BHST)
Biffa Award
The Big Yellow Foundation*
The Billmeir Charitable Trust
The Percy Bilton Charity
The Michael Bishop Foundation
Maria Bjornson Memorial Fund*
The John Black Charitable Foundation
The Sydney Black Charitable Trust
Lady Blakenham's Charity Trust
The Sir Victor Blank Charitable Settlement
Bloodwise
The Bloom Foundation
The Bloomfield Charitable Trust
Bluespark Foundation
The Bluston Charitable Settlement
The BNA Charitable Incorporated Organisation*
The Boltini Trust
The Bonamy Charitable Trust
The Charlotte Bonham-Carter Charitable Trust
BOOST Charitable Trust
Salo Bordon Charitable Trust
The Oliver Borthwick Memorial Trust
The Bothwell Charitable Trust
Sir Clive Bourne Family Trust
Bourneheights Ltd
The Bowerman Charitable Trust
G. and K. Boyes Charitable Trust
The William Brake Charitable Trust
The Liz and Terry Bramall Foundation
The Breadsticks Foundation
Breast Cancer Now
The Breast Cancer Research Trust (BCRT)
The Brenley Trust
Bridgepoint Charitable Trust
Bristol Charities
The BRIT Trust
The Britford Bridge Trust
The British and Foreign School Society
British Eye Research Foundation (Fight for Sight)
British Heart Foundation (BHF)
British Humane Association
British Lung Foundation

British Motor Sports Training Trust
The Bromley Trust
The Brook Trust
The Consuelo and Anthony Brooke Charitable Trust
The Rory and Elizabeth Brooks Foundation
*The Brothers Trust**
Bill Brown 1989 Charitable Trust
*Mary Brown Memorial Trust**
*The Brown Source Trust**
R. S. Brownless Charitable Trust
The T. B. H. Brunner's Charitable Settlement
Brushmill Ltd
Buckingham Trust
The Buffini Chao Foundation
Building & Civil Engineering Charitable Trust
*Bulb Foundation**
The Bulldog Trust Ltd
BUPA UK Foundation
The Burberry Foundation
The Burden Trust
The Burdett Trust for Nursing
The Clara E. Burgess Charity
Burnie's Foundation
The Arnold Burton 1998 Charitable Trust
Miss Margaret Butters Reekie Charitable Trust
Byrne Family Foundation
C. and F. Charitable Trust
The G. W. Cadbury Charitable Trust
William A. Cadbury Charitable Trust
The Cadbury Foundation
The Barrow Cadbury Trust
The Cadogan Charity
The Frederick and Phyllis Cann Trust
Cannon Charitable Trust
*Card Factory Foundation**
*CareTech Foundation**
*The Antonio Carluccio Foundation**
The Carne Trust
The Carpenters' Company Charitable Trust
The Carrington Charitable Trust
The Leslie Mary Carter Charitable Trust
The Casey Trust
The Castanea Trust
The Castang Foundation
Catholic Charitable Trust
The Cayo Foundation
Elizabeth Cayzer Charitable Trust
The B. G. S. Cayzer Charitable Trust
The Cazenove Charitable Trust
CBRE Charitable Trust
CEO Sleepout
The Amelia Chadwick Trust
Champneys Charitable Foundation
Chapman Charitable Trust
The Charities Advisory Trust
Charitworth Ltd
The Charter 600 Charity
Chartered Accountants' Livery Charity (CALC)
The Cheruby Trust
The Chetwode Foundation
Children with Cancer UK
Children's Liver Disease Foundation
*The Childs Charitable Trust**
CHK Foundation
Christadelphian Samaritan Fund
The André Christian Trust
Chrysalis Trust
The Churchill Foundation
The CIBC World Markets Children's Foundation
J. A. Clark Charitable Trust
Clark Foundation
The Clore Duffield Foundation
Closehelm Ltd
The Clothworkers' Foundation
The Clover Trust
The Robert Clutterbuck Charitable Trust
Clydpride Ltd
CMZ Ltd
The Francis Coales Charitable Foundation
Denise Coates Foundation
The Vivienne and Samuel Cohen Charitable Trust
The John S. Cohen Foundation
Sir Jeremiah Colman Gift Trust
The Colt Foundation
Colwinston Charitable Trust
Comic Relief
The Comino Foundation
Congregational and General Charitable Trust
The Ernest Cook Trust
The Cooks Charity
The Catherine Cookson Charitable Trust
The Keith Coombs Trust
Mabel Cooper Charity
The Alice Ellen Cooper Dean Charitable Foundation
Co-operative Community Investment Foundation
The Worshipful Company of Cordwainers Charitable Trusts (Minges Gift)
The Gershon Coren Charitable Foundation (also known as The Muriel and Gus Coren Charitable Foundation)
The Cornwell Charitable Trust
The Corporation of Trinity House of Deptford Strond
The Costa Family Charitable Trust
*The Cotswold Primrose Charitable Trust**
*Countypier Ltd**
Coutts Charitable Foundation
*The Noel Coward Foundation**
Dudley and Geoffrey Cox Charitable Trust
The Lord Cozens-Hardy Trust
*The CPF Trust**
The Craignish Trust
The Craps Charitable Trust
CRASH
The Elizabeth Creak Charitable Trust
Credit Suisse EMEA Foundation
The Crescent Trust
The Cross Trust
CSIS Charity Fund
The Dennis Curry Charitable Trust
Itzchok Meyer Cymerman Trust Ltd
The D. G. Charitable Settlement
The D'Oyly Carte Charitable Trust
The Daiwa Anglo-Japanese Foundation
Oizer Dalim Trust
*The Dashlight Foundation**
*The Manny and Brigitta Davidson Charitable Foundation**
The Davidson Family Charitable Trust
Michael Davies Charitable Settlement
Dawat-E-Hadiyah Trust (United Kingdom)
The De Laszlo Foundation
William Dean Countryside and Educational Trust
Debmar Benevolent Trust Ltd
The Delves Charitable Trust
The Demigryphon Trust
Dentons UKMEA LLP Charitable Trust
The J. N. Derbyshire Trust
The Desmond Foundation
The Laduma Dhamecha Charitable Trust
Diabetes UK
Dinwoodie Charitable Company
The Djanogly Foundation
The DLM Charitable Trust
*The Ken Dodd Charitable Foundation**
Dollond Charitable Trust
Donibristle Trust
The Dorfman Foundation

The Hadley Trust
Hamamelis Trust
Paul Hamlyn Foundation
The Helen Hamlyn Trust
The Kathleen Hannay Memorial Charity
The Haramead Trust
Harbinson Charitable Trust
The Harbour Foundation
The David and Claudia Harding Foundation
The Harding Trust
The Harebell Centenary Fund
The Harris Family Charitable Trust
The Edith Lilian Harrison 2000 Foundation
The Peter Harrison Foundation
The Harrison-Frank Family Foundation (UK) Ltd
The Hasluck Charitable Trust
The Maurice Hatter Foundation
The Hawthorne Charitable Trust
The Charles Hayward Foundation
The Headley Trust
The Health Foundation
Heart Research UK
The Heathside Charitable Trust
The Charlotte Heber-Percy Charitable Trust
Ernest Hecht Charitable Foundation
The Percy Hedley 1990 Charitable Trust
The Hedley Foundation
The Michael Heller Charitable Foundation
The Simon Heller Charitable Settlement
Help the Homeless Ltd
The Helping Foundation
Henley Royal Regatta Charitable Trust
The G. D. Herbert Charitable Trust
Heritage Lottery Fund
P. and C. Hickinbotham Charitable Trust
The Highcroft Charitable Trust
Highway One Trust
The Hilden Charitable Fund
The Derek Hill Foundation
R. G. Hills Charitable Trust
Hinchley Charitable Trust
The Hinduja Foundation
The Hinrichsen Foundation
The Hiscox Foundation
The Henry C. Hoare Charitable Trust
The Hobson Charity Ltd
Hockerill Educational Foundation
The Jane Hodge Foundation
The Holbeck Charitable Trust
The Holden Charitable Trust
Hollick Family Foundation
The Holliday Foundation
Dorothy Holmes Charitable Trust
Homelands Charitable Trust
The Mary Homfray Charitable Trust
Sir Harold Hood's Charitable Trust
The Thomas J. Horne Memorial Trust
The Horse Trust
Horwich Shotter Charitable Trust
Hospice UK
The Hospital Saturday Fund
The Reta Lila Howard Foundation
James T. Howat Charitable Trust
The Huggard Charitable Trust
The Humanitarian Trust
Michael and Shirley Hunt Charitable Trust
The Albert Hunt Trust
The Hunter Foundation
The Huntingdon Foundation Ltd
*The Hurley Partners Charitable Trust**
The Hutchinson Charitable Trust
The Hutton Foundation
The Nani Huyu Charitable Trust
IBM United Kingdom Trust
Ibrahim Foundation Ltd
The Iceland Foods Charitable Foundation
The Idlewild Trust
The Iliffe Family Charitable Trust
Imagine Foundation
Impetus
The Indigo Trust
The Ingram Trust
The Inlight Trust
The Inman Charity
The Institute for Policy Research
The International Bankers Charitable Trust
The Inverforth Charitable Trust
Investream Charitable Trust
The Invigorate Charitable Trust
The Ireland Fund of Great Britain
Irish Youth Foundation (UK) Ltd (incorporating The Lawlor Foundation)
*The Irving Memorial Trust**
*The Isla Foundation**
The ITF Seafarers Trust
The J. J. Charitable Trust
The Jabbs Foundation
The Frank Jackson Foundation
*The Jagclif Charitable Trust**
*JD Foundation**
Rees Jeffreys Road Fund
The Jenour Foundation
The Jephcott Charitable Trust
The Jerusalem Trust
Jewish Child's Day (JCD)
The Jewish Youth Fund
The Elton John Aids Foundation (EJAF)
Lillie Johnson Charitable Trust
Johnnie Johnson Trust
The Christopher and Kirsty Johnston Charitable Trust
The Muriel Jones Foundation
The Jordan Charitable Foundation
The Joron Charitable Trust
Anton Jurgens Charitable Trust
The Jusaca Charitable Trust
*Kantor Charitable Foundation**
The Boris Karloff Charitable Foundation
*The Karlsson Jativa Charitable Foundation**
The Ian Karten Charitable Trust
The Kasner Charitable Trust
The Michael and Ilse Katz Foundation
C. S. Kaufman Charitable Trust
The Emmanuel Kaye Foundation
The Kelly Family Charitable Trust
The Kay Kendall Leukaemia Fund
The Kennedy Charitable Foundation
The Kennel Club Charitable Trust
The Kentown Wizard Foundation
The Nancy Kenyon Charitable Trust
E. and E. Kernkraut Charities Ltd
*KFC Foundation**
Kidney Research UK
Kilpatrick Fraser Charitable Trust
*The Kilroot Foundation**
The Mary Kinross Charitable Trust
Laura Kinsella Foundation
The Graham Kirkham Foundation
The Kirschel Foundation
The Ernest Kleinwort Charitable Trust
The Kobler Trust
The KPMG Foundation
The Kreitman Foundation
Kupath Gemach Chaim Bechesed Viznitz Trust

Kusuma Trust UK
The Kyte Charitable Trust
Ladbrokes Coral Trust
The K. P. Ladd Charitable Trust
John Laing Charitable Trust
Maurice and Hilda Laing Charitable Trust
Christopher Laing Foundation
The David Laing Foundation
The Kirby Laing Foundation
The Martin Laing Foundation
The Lake House Charity
The Lancashire Foundation
Lancaster Foundation
LandAid Charitable Trust (LandAid)
The Allen Lane Foundation
Langdale Trust
Largsmount Ltd
Mrs M. A. Lascelles Charitable Trust
The Lauffer Family Charitable Foundation
Mrs F. B. Laurence Charitable Trust
The Kathleen Laurence Trust
The Law Family Charitable Foundation
The Betty Lawes Foundation
The Richard Lawes Foundation
The Edgar E. Lawley Foundation
Lawson Beckman Charitable Trust
The Leach Fourteenth Trust
The David Lean Foundation
The Leathersellers' Company Charitable Fund
The Leche Trust
The Arnold Lee Charitable Trust
Leeds Building Society Charitable Foundation
*The Leeward Trust**
The Legal Education Foundation
The Kennedy Leigh Charitable Trust
The Leigh Trust
The Mark Leonard Trust
The Leri Charitable Trust
The Leverhulme Trust
Lord Leverhulme's Charitable Trust
*The Ralph Levy Charitable Company Ltd**
Joseph Levy Foundation
*Cecil and Hilda Lewis Charitable Trust**
Bernard Lewis Family Charitable Trust
David and Ruth Lewis Family Charitable Trust
John Lewis Foundation
The Sir Edward Lewis Foundation
*The Charles Lewis Foundation**
The Light Fund Company
The Limbourne Trust
Limoges Charitable Trust
The Linbury Trust
The Linden Charitable Trust
The Linder Foundation
The Frank Litchfield Charitable Trust
The Charles Littlewood Hill Trust
The Second Joseph Aaron Littman Foundation
The George John and Sheilah Livanos Charitable Trust
*The Livingston Charitable Trust**
Jack Livingstone Charitable Trust
The Ian and Natalie Livingstone Charitable Trust
The Elaine and Angus Lloyd Charitable Trust
The Andrew Lloyd Webber Foundation
Local Trent Ltd
The Locker Foundation
Loftus Charitable Trust
The William and Katherine Longman Trust
The Lord's Taverners
The C. L. Loyd Charitable Trust
LPW Ltd
Robert Luff Foundation Ltd
The Henry Lumley Charitable Trust
Lord and Lady Lurgan Trust
The Lyndal Tree Foundation
M. and C. Trust
M. B. Foundation
The M. Y. A. Charitable Trust
The Macdonald-Buchanan Charitable Trust
Mace Foundation
The Mackay and Brewer Charitable Trust
The Mackintosh Foundation
The MacRobert Trust 2019
The Mactaggart Third Fund
The Ian Mactaggart Trust (The Mactaggart Second Fund)
*The Mageni Trust**
The Mahoro Charitable Trust
Makers of Playing Cards Charity
Making a Difference Locally Ltd
The Mallinckrodt Foundation
Man Group plc Charitable Trust
The Manackerman Charitable Trust
The W. M. Mann Foundation
*The Manson Family Charitable Trust**
*The Marandi Foundation**
Marbeh Torah Trust
The Stella and Alexander Margulies Charitable Trust
The Michael Marks Charitable Trust
The Marks Family Charitable Trust
The J. P. Marland Charitable Trust
Marmot Charitable Trust
*The Marque Foundation**
The Marsh Christian Trust
Charlotte Marshall Charitable Trust
D. G. Marshall of Cambridge Trust
The Kristina Martin Charitable Trust
The Martin Charitable Trust
The Dan Maskell Tennis Trust
The Master Charitable Trust
Matchroom Sport Charitable Foundation
*Material World Foundation**
The Matliwala Family Charitable Trust
The Violet Mauray Charitable Trust
Mayfair Charities Ltd
The Mayfield Valley Arts Trust
Maypride Ltd
Mazars Charitable Trust
The Robert McAlpine Foundation
McGreevy No. 5 Settlement
D. D. McPhail Charitable Settlement
Medical Research Foundation
The Medlock Charitable Trust
The Melow Charitable Trust
Meningitis Research Foundation
Menuchar Ltd
The Brian Mercer Charitable Trust
The Mercers' Charitable Foundation
Merchant Navy Welfare Board
The Merchant Taylors' Company Charities Fund
Mercury Phoenix Trust
T. and J. Meyer Family Foundation Ltd
The Mickel Fund
The Mickleham Trust
The Gerald Micklem Charitable Trust
*The Mila Charitable Organisation**
The Millennium Oak Trust
The Ronald Miller Foundation
Jean and Roger Miller's Charitable Trust

The Millichope Foundation
Mills and Reeve Charitable Trust
The Millward Charitable Trust
The Milne Family Foundation*
The James Milner Foundation
Minton Charitable Trust
The Mishcon Family Charitable Trust
The Brian Mitchell Charitable Settlement
The Mittal Foundation
Keren Mitzvah Trust
The Mizpah Trust
Mole Charitable Trust
The Monday Charitable Trust*
Moondance Foundation
The Henry Moore Foundation
The Morel Charitable Trust
The Morgan Charitable Foundation
The Miles Morland Foundation
The Morris Charitable Trust
The Willie and Mabel Morris Charitable Trust
G. M. Morrison Charitable Trust
The Ken and Edna Morrison Charitable Trust
The Morton Charitable Trust (Dundee)
The Mosawi Foundation*
The Moshal Charitable Trust
Vyoel Moshe Charitable Trust
The Alexander Mosley Charitable Trust
The Mosselson Charitable Trust
Moto in the Community
Motor Neurone Disease Association
The Edwina Mountbatten and Leonora Children's Foundation
The Mowgli Trust*
The MSE Charity
The Mulberry Trust
The Frederick Mulder Foundation
Multiple Sclerosis Society
Edith Murphy Foundation
Murphy-Neumann Charity Company Ltd
The John R. Murray Charitable Trust
Brian Murtagh Charitable Trust
Music Sales Charitable Trust
Muslim Hands
The Mutual Trust Group
MW (CL) Foundation
MW (GK) Foundation
MW (RH) Foundation
The Janet Nash Charitable Settlement
The National Churches Trust
The National Express Foundation
The National Garden Scheme
Friends of the National Libraries*
The National Lottery Community Fund
The National Manuscripts Conservation Trust
The Nationwide Foundation
The NDL Foundation
Nemoral Ltd
Ner Foundation
Nesswall Ltd
Nesta
Network for Social Change Charitable Trust
Newby Trust Ltd
The Frances and Augustus Newman Foundation
Newpier Charity Ltd
The NFU Mutual Charitable Trust
The Nineveh Charitable Trust
NNS Foundation*
The Nomura Charitable Trust
Normanby Charitable Trust
The Northwick Trust
The Norton Foundation
The Norton Rose Fulbright Charitable Foundation
The Nuffield Foundation
The Sir Peter O'Sullevan Charitable Trust
The Oakdale Trust
Odin Charitable Trust
The Ofenheim Charitable Trust
The Ogle Christian Trust
Oizer Charitable Trust
Old Possum's Practical Trust
The Olwyn Foundation*
Orange Tree Trust*
Orthopaedic Research UK
Ostro Fayre Share Foundation
The O'Sullivan Family Charitable Trust
Otsar Trust*
The Owen Family Trust
The Doris Pacey Charitable Foundation
The Paget Charitable Trust
The Gerald Palmer Eling Trust Company
The Panacea Charitable Trust
The Paphitis Charitable Trust
The Paragon Trust
The Samuel and Freda Parkinson Charitable Trust*
Parkinson's UK
Peacock Charitable Trust
David Pearlman Charitable Foundation
The Pears Family Charitable Foundation
The Pell Charitable Trust
The Pennycress Trust
Dina Perelman Trust Ltd*
The Performing Right Society Foundation
B. E. Perl Charitable Trust
Petplan Charitable Trust
The Pets at Home Foundation
The Pharsalia Charitable Trust
The Phillips and Rubens Charitable Trust
Betty Phillips Charitable Trust
The Phillips Charitable Trust
The Phillips Family Charitable Trust
The Pickwell Foundation
The Pilgrim Trust
Elise Pilkington Charitable Trust*
Cecil Pilkington Charitable Trust
Pilkington Charities Fund
The Austin and Hope Pilkington Trust
Miss A. M. Pilkington's Charitable Trust
PIMCO Foundation Europe
Pink Ribbon Foundation
The Pitt-Rivers Charitable Trust
The Pixel Fund
Thomas Pocklington Trust
Polden-Puckham Charitable Foundation
The George and Esme Pollitzer Charitable Settlement
The Polonsky Foundation
The Porta Pia 2012 Foundation
David and Elaine Potter Foundation
Poundland Foundation*
Premierquote Ltd
Premishlaner Charitable Trust
The Pret Foundation
The Primrose Trust
The Prince of Wales's Charitable Foundation
The Prince's Countryside Fund
The Princess Anne's Charities
The Priory Foundation
Prison Service Charity Fund
The Privy Purse Charitable Trust
The Professional Footballers' Association Charity
The Progress Foundation
Prostate Cancer UK
The Puebla Charitable Trust
Catkin Pussywillow Charitable Trust
The PwC Foundation
Mr and Mrs J. A. Pye's Charitable Settlement
QBE European Operations Foundation
Quadstar Charitable Foundation*

The Queen Anne's Gate Foundation
Queen Mary's Roehampton Trust
The Quilter Foundation*
Quintessentially Foundation
R. S. Charitable Trust
The Monica Rabagliati Charitable Trust
The Racing Foundation
The Radcliffe Trust
Richard Radcliffe Trust
The Bishop Radford Trust
The Rainford Trust
The Randal Charitable Foundation*
The Joseph and Lena Randall Charitable Trust
Randeree Charitable Trust*
The Rank Foundation Ltd
The Joseph Rank Trust
The Ranworth Trust
The Ratcliff Foundation
The Rathbone Brothers Foundation
Elizabeth Rathbone Charity
The Sigrid Rausing Trust
The Roger Raymond Charitable Trust
The Rayne Foundation
The Rayne Trust
The John Rayner Charitable Trust
The Sir James Reckitt Charity
C. A. Redfern Charitable Foundation
The Reso Charitable Foundation
The Resolution Trust
The Rest-Harrow Trust
Reuben Foundation
RG Foundation*
Rhodi Charitable Trust
The Rhododendron Trust
Riada Trust
The Sir Cliff Richard Charitable Trust
Ridgesave Ltd
Rigby Foundation
The Sir John Ritblat Family Foundation
The River Farm Foundation
The River Trust
Rivers Foundation
RNID (The Royal National Institute for Deaf People)
The Roan Charitable Trust
Rockcliffe Charitable Trust
The Roddick Foundation
The Rofeh Trust
The Sir James Roll Charitable Trust
The Helen Roll Charity
Mrs L. D. Rope's Third Charitable Settlement
Rosa Fund
The Rose Animal Welfare Trust CIO*
The Cecil Rosen Foundation
The David Ross Foundation
The Rothermere Foundation
The Rothschild Foundation
Rowanville Ltd
The Rowlands Trust
The Joseph Rowntree Charitable Trust
The Joseph Rowntree Foundation
Royal Artillery Charitable Fund
The Royal British Legion
The Royal Foundation of the Duke and Duchess of Cambridge
The Royal Navy and Royal Marines Charity
Royal Society of Wildlife Trusts
RSM UK Foundation*
The Rubin Foundation Charitable Trust
The Ruddock Foundation for the Arts
The Russell Trust
The RVW Trust
The Jeremy and John Sacher Charitable Trust
The Michael and Nicola Sacher Charitable Trust
The Saddlers' Company Charitable Fund
The Jean Sainsbury Animal Welfare Trust
The Alan and Babette Sainsbury Charitable Fund
Saint Sarkis Charity Trust
The Saintbury Trust
The Saints and Sinners Trust Ltd
The Salamander Charitable Trust
Salisbury Pool Charity
Salters' Charitable Foundation
The Basil Samuel Charitable Trust
The M. J. Samuel Charitable Trust
The Peter Samuel Charitable Trust
The Samworth Foundation
The Sandhu Charitable Foundation
Sandra Charitable Trust
The Sands Family Trust
Santander UK Foundation Ltd
Savannah Wisdom
The Savoy Educational Trust
The Scarfe Charitable Trust
Schass Foundation
The Annie Schiff Charitable Trust
The Anthony Scholefield Foundation*
Schroder Charity Trust
The Schroder Foundation
Sir Samuel Scott of Yews Trust
The Ina Scott Sutherland Charitable Foundation*
The Scottish Power Foundation
Scouloudi Foundation
The Screwfix Foundation
The SDL Foundation
Seafarers UK (King George's Fund for Sailors)
The Searchlight Electric Charitable Trust
Sam and Bella Sebba Charitable Trust
Seedfield Trust
The Selfridges Group Foundation*
Leslie Sell Charitable Trust
Sellata Ltd
The Cyril Shack Trust
The Jean Shanks Foundation
ShareGift (The Orr Mackintosh Foundation)
The Sharp Foundation*
The Shears Foundation
The Sheepdrove Trust
The Sheldon Trust
The Patricia and Donald Shepherd Charitable Trust
The Sherling Charitable Trust
The Bassil Shippam and Alsford Trust
The Shipwrights' Charitable Fund
Shlomo Memorial Fund Ltd
The Shoe Zone Trust
The Florence Shute Millennium Trust
The Simmons & Simmons Charitable Foundation
The Singer Foundation*
The Sino-British Fellowship Trust
The Thomas Sivewright Catto Charitable Settlement
The Charles Skey Charitable Trust
Skipton Building Society Charitable Foundation
The John Slater Foundation
The Slaughter and May Charitable Trust
Sloane Robinson Foundation
Rita and David Slowe Charitable Trust
Smallwood Trust
The SMB Trust
Smith Bradbeer Charitable Trust*
The N. Smith Charitable Settlement
The Peter Smith Charitable Trust for Nature
The Henry Smith Charity
The Martin Smith Foundation

The Leslie Smith Foundation
The W. H. Smith Group Charitable Trust
Stanley Smith UK Horticultural Trust
Philip Smith's Charitable Trust
Social Business Trust
Social Investment Business Foundation
Social Tech Trust
Societe Generale UK Foundation*
Sodexo Stop Hunger Foundation
Sofronie Foundation
David Solomons Charitable Trust
The E. C. Sosnow Charitable Trust
The Souter Charitable Trust
The Stephen R. and Philippa H. Southall Charitable Trust
W. F. Southall Trust
Peter Sowerby Foundation
Spar Charitable Fund
Sparks Charity
The Spear Charitable Trust
The Michael and Sarah Spencer Foundation*
The Jessie Spencer Trust
Rosalyn and Nicholas Springer Charitable Trust
The Spurrell Charitable Trust
The Geoff and Fiona Squire Foundation
The St James's Trust Settlement
St James's Place Charitable Foundation
St Luke's College Foundation
Stadium Charitable Trust
The Stafford Trust
Standard Life Foundation
Stanley Foundation Ltd
Staples Trust
The Peter Stebbings Memorial Charity
The Steel Charitable Trust
The Steinberg Family Charitable Trust
C. E. K. Stern Charitable Trust
The Sir Sigmund Sternberg Charitable Foundation
The Sterry Family Foundation*
Stervon Ltd
Stevenson Family's Charitable Trust
Sir Halley Stewart Trust
The Stewarts Law Foundation
The Stobart Newlands Charitable Trust
The Stone Family Foundation
The Stoneygate Trust
The Samuel Storey Family Charitable Trust
Peter Stormonth Darling Charitable Trust
Peter Storrs Trust
The WO Street Charitable Foundation
The Street Foundation
StreetSmart – Action for the Homeless
Sumner Wilson Charitable Trust
The Sunrise Foundation CIO
The Support Foundation*
Surgo Foundation UK Ltd
The Sutasoma Trust
Sabina Sutherland Charitable Trust
Swan Mountain Trust
The Swann-Morton Foundation
The John Swire (1989) Charitable Trust
The Swire Charitable Trust
The Adrian Swire Charitable Trust
The Sir Hugh and Lady Sykes Charitable Trust
The Charles and Elsie Sykes Trust
The Hugh Symons Charitable Trust*
The Syncona Foundation
T. and S. Trust Fund
The T.K. Maxx and Homesense Foundation
The Tabhair Charitable Trust
The Tajtelbaum Charitable Trust
Talteg Ltd
The David Tannen Charitable Trust
Tanner Trust
Tay Charitable Trust
C. B. and H. H. Taylor 1984 Trust
The Taylor Family Foundation
The Tedworth Charitable Trust
Tegham Ltd
Tenovus Cancer Care
The Thales Charitable Trust
the7stars Foundation*
The Theatres Trust Charitable Fund
The David Thomas Charitable Trust
The Thompson Family Charitable Trust
Scott Thomson Charitable Trust
Sir Jules Thorn Charitable Trust
The Thornton Foundation
The Three Guineas Trust
Three Monkies Trust
The Thriplow Charitable Trust
Mrs R. P. Tindall's Charitable Trust
The Tolkien Trust
The Tomoro Foundation*
The Tompkins Foundation
The Toy Trust
The Toye Foundation
Toyota Manufacturing UK Charitable Trust
David William Traill Cargill Fund
Annie Tranmer Charitable Trust
The Constance Travis Charitable Trust
The Treeside Trust
The Trefoil Trust
The Tresanton Trust*
The Triangle Trust (1949) Fund
Tropical Health and Education Trust
The True Colours Trust
Truedene Co. Ltd
The Truemark Trust
Truemart Ltd
Trumros Ltd
The Trusthouse Charitable Foundation
The James Tudor Foundation
The Tudor Trust
The Tufton Charitable Trust
The Tuixen Foundation
The Florence Turner Trust
Tzedakah
Ufi VocTech Trust
Ulting Overseas Trust
The Ulverscroft Foundation
The Underwood Trust
The Union of Orthodox Hebrew Congregations
United Jewish Israel Appeal
The United Reformed Church (Wessex) Trust Ltd
Universal Music UK Sound Foundation
UnLtd (Foundation for Social Entrepreneurs)
UPP Foundation
The Michael Uren Foundation
Utermann Charitable Trust*
The Utley Foundation
The Vail Foundation
The Valentine Charitable Trust
The Albert Van Den Bergh Charitable Trust
The Van Mesdag Fund*
The Van Neste Foundation
The Vandervell Foundation
The Vardy Foundation
Variety, the Children's Charity
The Vaughan Williams Charitable Trust
The Veneziana Fund
The William and Patricia Venton Charitable Trust
The Veolia Environmental Trust
Versus Arthritis
The Veterans' Foundation
Vinci UK Foundation*
Nigel Vinson Charitable Trust

England

England and Wales Cricket Trust
Esher House Charitable Trust
*The Fieldrose Charitable Trust**
The Football Association National Sports Centre Trust
The Football Foundation
The Fort Foundation
Ian M. Foulerton Charitable Trust
*The Fraxinus Charitable Trust**
*The Joyce and Norman Freed Charitable Trust**
GambleAware
The Gaudio Family Foundation (UK) Ltd
Martin Geddes Charitable Trust
The General Nursing Council for England and Wales Trust
The Girdlers' Company Charitable Trust
The Goshen Trust
The Granada Foundation
*The Grand Trust CIO**
Gordon Gray Trust
The Lennox Hannay Charitable Trust
*The Peter and Teresa Harris Charitable Trust**
Hays Travel Foundation
The Hearth Foundation
The Tim Henman Foundation
The Hintze Family Charity Foundation
Historic Houses Foundation
Hurdale Charity Ltd
*The Inflexion Foundation**
*The Investindustrial Foundation**
The J. and J. Benevolent Foundation
The Kennedy Trust for Rheumatology Research
*The Labone Charitable Trust**
The Herd Lawson and Muriel Lawson Charitable Trust
The Lindley Foundation (TLF)
Lloyds Bank Foundation for England and Wales
Lloyd's Patriotic Fund
The Lockwood Charitable Foundation
Longleigh Foundation
Lord and Lady Lurgan Trust
Charity of John Marshall
Masonic Charitable Foundation
*The Mather Family Charitable Trust**
*The Mikheev Charitable Trust**
*Millie's Watch**
*Mind**
*The Mohn Westlake Foundation**
The Morrisons Foundation
*The Mulchand Foundation**
*The Gareth Neame Foundation**
Newby Trust Ltd
Northern Land Trust
The Norwood and Newton Settlement
The Oakley Charitable Trust
Oglesby Charitable Trust
The Ouseley Church Music Trust
Ovingdean Hall Foundation
P. F. Charitable Trust
*The Pantheon Charitable Trust**
Parabola Foundation
The Pargiter Trust
*Partners Global Foundation**
*Rosanna Pearson's 1987 Charity Trust**
People's Health Trust
The Persimmon Charitable Foundation
*The Points Family Trust**
The Portrack Charitable Trust
Postcode Society Trust (formerly Postcode Dream Trust)
Power to Change Trust
*The Raindance Charitable Trust**
Rentrust Foundation Ltd
The Revere Charitable Trust
Riverside Charitable Trust Ltd
Rix Thompson Rothenberg Foundation
RJM Charity Trust
*The Rockspring Charitable Trust**
Rosetrees Trust
Royal Masonic Trust for Girls and Boys
S. and R. Charitable Trust
The Dr Mortimer and Theresa Sackler Foundation
*The Sanderson Foundation**
O. and G. Schreiber Charitable Trust
Scott (Eredine) Charitable Trust
The Segelman Trust
Sloane Robinson Foundation
The DS Smith Charitable Foundation
*Arabella and Julian Smith Family Trust**
The Sobell Foundation
Mark Stolkin Foundation
The Strangward Trust
*The Joseph Strong Frazer Trust**
The Bernard Sunley Foundation
*The Ashley Tabor-King Foundation**
Stephen Taylor Foundation
*The Thirty Percy Foundation**
The Thornton Trust
*The Troutsdale Charitable Trust**
UKH Foundation
The Union of the Sisters of Mercy of Great Britain
*The Velvet Foundation**
Viridor Credits Environmental Company
Robert and Felicity Waley-Cohen Charitable Trust
*The Welland Trust**
Wembley National Stadium Trust
The Wheeler Family Charitable Trust
The Melanie White Foundation Ltd
The Wigoder Family Foundation
*Joan Wilkinson Charitable Trust**
The Francis Winham Foundation
Wychville Ltd
The Wyfold Charitable Trust
The Yapp Charitable Trust
Youth Music

East Midlands

Axis Foundation
Church Urban Fund
The Coalfields Regeneration Trust
The Helen Jean Cope Charity
The Haramead Trust
The Hearth Foundation
Johnnie Johnson Trust
The Patrick Trust
The Ratcliff Foundation
The Samworth Foundation
The Jessie Spencer Trust
*The Vichai Srivaddhanaprabha Foundation**
The Whitaker Charitable Trust
The Wilmcote Charitrust

■ Derbyshire

The Bamford Charitable Foundation
The Bingham Trust
The Harry Bottom Charitable Trust
The Chetwode Foundation
The Evan Cornish Foundation
William Dean Countryside and Educational Trust
Foundation Derbyshire
Provincial Grand Charity of the Province of Derbyshire

The Duke of Devonshire's Charitable Trust
Gay and Peter Hartley's Hillards Charitable Trust
May Hearnshaw's Charity
The Sir Hugh and Lady Sykes Charitable Trust
Toyota Manufacturing UK Charitable Trust
Woodroffe Benton Foundation

■ Leicestershire

The Carlton Hayes Mental Health Charity
The Chetwode Foundation
The Ernest Cook Trust
The Helen Jean Cope Charity
The J. Reginald Corah Foundation Fund
Coventry Building Society Charitable Foundation
Dromintee Trust
The Maud Elkington Charitable Trust
The Everard Foundation
Gay and Peter Hartley's Hillards Charitable Trust
P. and C. Hickinbotham Charitable Trust
The David Laing Foundation
Leicestershire and Rutland Masonic Charity Association
Leicestershire, Leicester and Rutland Community Foundation
Edith Murphy Foundation
Alderman Newton's Educational Foundation
The Jack Patston Charitable Trust
The Shoe Zone Trust
The Florence Turner Trust

■ Lincolnshire

The BNA Charitable Incorporated Organisation*
Alan Boswell Group Charitable Trust*
Michael Cornish Charitable Trust
The Evan Cornish Foundation
Gay and Peter Hartley's Hillards Charitable Trust
May Hearnshaw's Charity
Help for Health
Lincolnshire Community Foundation
Charity of John Marshall
The Medlock Charitable Trust
The Mercers' Charitable Foundation
The Rugby Group Benevolent Fund Ltd
Charity of Sir Richard Whittington
Worth Waynflete Foundation

■ Northamptonshire

The Benham Charitable Settlement
The Frederick and Phyllis Cann Trust
The Childwick Trust
The Francis Coales Charitable Foundation
The Compton Charitable Trust
Douglas Compton James Charitable Trust
Coventry Building Society Charitable Foundation
The Maud Elkington Charitable Trust
Ford Britain Trust
Gay and Peter Hartley's Hillards Charitable Trust
The David Laing Foundation
The Macdonald-Buchanan Charitable Trust
Northamptonshire Community Foundation
The Phillips Charitable Trust
The Clive and Sylvia Richards Charity Ltd
The Strangward Trust
The Sudborough Foundation
The Constance Travis Charitable Trust
Robert and Felicity Waley-Cohen Charitable Trust
The Wilson Foundation

■ Nottinghamshire

Bauer Radio's Cash for Kids Charities
The BNA Charitable Incorporated Organisation*
Boots Charitable Trust
The Chetwode Foundation
The Evan Cornish Foundation
Coventry Building Society Charitable Foundation
The J. N. Derbyshire Trust
The Dunn Family Charitable Trust
Sir John Eastwood Foundation
The Thomas Farr Charity
The Fifty Fund
The Forman Hardy Charitable Trust
The Gray Trust
Gay and Peter Hartley's Hillards Charitable Trust
May Hearnshaw's Charity
The Lady Hind Trust
The Jones 1986 Charitable Trust
The Charles Littlewood Hill Trust
Nottinghamshire Community Foundation
The Mary Potter Convent Hospital Trust
The Clive and Sylvia Richards Charity Ltd
The Skerritt Trust

■ Rutland

The Carlton Hayes Mental Health Charity
The J. Reginald Corah Foundation Fund
Coventry Building Society Charitable Foundation
The Maud Elkington Charitable Trust
P. and C. Hickinbotham Charitable Trust
Leicestershire and Rutland Masonic Charity Association
Leicestershire, Leicester and Rutland Community Foundation
The Shoe Zone Trust

East of England

Red Hill Charitable Trust
The Strangward Trust

■ Bedfordshire

The John Apthorp Charity
The Bedfordshire and Hertfordshire Historic Churches Trust
Bedfordshire and Luton Community Foundation
Bedfordshire Charitable Trust Ltd
The Childwick Trust
Church Urban Fund
The Francis Coales Charitable Foundation
The Connolly Foundation*
The Gale Family Charity Trust
The Harpur Trust
House of Industry Estate
The Eranda Rothschild Foundation
The Rugby Group Benevolent Fund Ltd
The Steel Charitable Trust
The Strangward Trust
The Wixamtree Trust

■ Cambridgeshire

Alan Boswell Group Charitable Trust*
The Broomton Foundation
The Cambridgeshire Community Foundation
The Childwick Trust
Church Urban Fund
The John Coates Charitable Trust
The Cole Charitable Trust
Douglas Compton James Charitable Trust
Eastern Counties Educational Trust Ltd
The Evelyn Trust
The Earl Fitzwilliam Charitable Trust
The Simon Gibson Charitable Trust
Gay and Peter Hartley's Hillards Charitable Trust
The Hudson Foundation
Huntingdon Freemen's Trust
The Hutchinson Charitable Trust
The Frank Litchfield Charitable Trust
D. G. Marshall of Cambridge Trust
Mills and Reeve Charitable Trust
The Jack Patston Charitable Trust
The Pye Foundation
The Rugby Group Benevolent Fund Ltd
The Mrs Smith and Mount Trust
The Strangward Trust
Annie Tranmer Charitable Trust

■ Essex

Andrews Charitable Trust
The Michael Barnard Charitable Trust*
The Boltini Trust
The Broomton Foundation
The Leslie Mary Carter Charitable Trust
The Childwick Trust
The Christabella Charitable Trust
The Christabella Charitable Trust
Colchester Catalyst Charity
Eastern Counties Educational Trust Ltd
The Essex and Southend Sports Trust
Friends of Essex Churches Trust
Essex Community Foundation
The Essex Heritage Trust
Ford Britain Trust
Fowler Smith and Jones Trust
Charles S. French Charitable Trust
The Grange Farm Centre Trust
Hockerill Educational Foundation
The Martin Laing Foundation
The Frank Litchfield Charitable Trust
London Legal Support Trust (LLST)
The Mulberry Trust
Notting Hill Genesis Community Foundation
The Jack Petchey Foundation
The Priory Foundation
Rosca Trust
The Rugby Group Benevolent Fund Ltd
The Mrs Smith and Mount Trust
Tabeel Trust
Annie Tranmer Charitable Trust
The Tudwick Foundation*

■ Hertfordshire

Andrews Charitable Trust
The John Apthorp Charity
The Arsenal Foundation
The Bedfordshire and Hertfordshire Historic Churches Trust
The Boltini Trust
The Childwick Trust
The Robert Clutterbuck Charitable Trust
The Francis Coales Charitable Foundation
Eastern Counties Educational Trust Ltd
The Follett Trust
The Simon Gibson Charitable Trust
The Gretna Charitable Trust
Hertfordshire Community Foundation
Hockerill Educational Foundation
Christopher Laing Foundation
The Martin Laing Foundation
The Frank Litchfield Charitable Trust
London Legal Support Trust (LLST)
The Masonic Province of Middlesex Charitable Trust (Middlesex Masonic Charity)
B. E. Perl Charitable Trust
The Priory Foundation
Salisbury Pool Charity
The Shanly Foundation
The Mrs Smith and Mount Trust
The Stevenage Community Trust
The Valiant Charitable Trust
West Herts Charity Trust Ltd*

■ Norfolk

Anguish's Educational Foundation
The Paul Bassham Charitable Trust
Alan Boswell Group Charitable Trust*
The Broomton Foundation
The Leslie Mary Carter Charitable Trust
The Childwick Trust
The Clan Trust Ltd
The John Coates Charitable Trust
The Lord Cozens-Hardy Trust
Eastern Counties Educational Trust Ltd
The Ellerdale Trust
Anne French Memorial Trust
The Simon Gibson Charitable Trust
The Lady Hind Trust
John Jarrold Trust Ltd
The Martin Laing Foundation
The Charles Littlewood Hill Trust
The Mercers' Charitable Foundation
The Mickleham Trust
Mills and Reeve Charitable Trust
The Norfolk Churches Trust Ltd
Norfolk Community Foundation
Educational Foundation of Alderman John Norman
Norwich Town Close Estate Charity
The Pennycress Trust
The Ranworth Trust
The Mrs Smith and Mount Trust
The R. C. Snelling Charitable Trust
The Spurrell Charitable Trust
Annie Tranmer Charitable Trust
The Virgin Money Foundation
The Geoffrey Watling Charity
Charity of Sir Richard Whittington

■ Suffolk

The Broomton Foundation
The Leslie Mary Carter Charitable Trust
The John Coates Charitable Trust
Eastern Counties Educational Trust Ltd

The Ganzoni Charitable Trust
The Simon Gibson Charitable Trust
The Frank Jackson Foundation
Music Sales Charitable Trust
Notting Hill Genesis Community Foundation
The Pargiter Trust
Mrs L. D. Rope's Third Charitable Settlement
The Scarfe Charitable Trust
The Mrs Smith and Mount Trust
Suffolk Community Foundation
The Suffolk Historic Churches Trust
Annie Tranmer Charitable Trust
The Tudwick Foundation*
The Geoffrey Watling Charity
Alfred Williams Charitable Trust

Greater London

A. W. Charitable Trust
Access Sport CIO
The Allen & Overy Foundation
Andrews Charitable Trust
Anpride Ltd
The Arah Foundation
The Armourers' and Brasiers' Gauntlet Trust
The Ashendene Trust
Lawrence Atwell's Charity (Skinners' Company)
Axis Foundation
Bauer Radio's Cash for Kids Charities
The Berkeley Foundation
Asser Bishvil Foundation
The Bowerman Charitable Trust
The Cadogan Charity
The Calleva Foundation
Canary Wharf Contractors Fund
The Carpenters' Company Charitable Trust
The Carr-Gregory Trust
Chapman Charitable Trust
The Charterhouse Charitable Trust
The Childhood Trust
The Childwick Trust
The Christabella Charitable Trust
Church Urban Fund
The City Bridge Trust (Bridge House Estates)
The John Coates Charitable Trust
The Cooks Charity
Dudley and Geoffrey Cox Charitable Trust
The Peter Cruddas Foundation
Drapers' Charitable Fund
The Ellinson Foundation Ltd
The Fidelity UK Foundation
The Goldsmiths' Company Charity
The Gould Charitable Trust
The Grange Farm Centre Trust
The Gretna Charitable Trust
The Harbour Charitable Trust
The Heritage of London Trust Ltd
The Horners Charity Fund
Inner London Magistrates Court Poor Box and Feeder Charity
The International Bankers Charitable Trust
J. E. Joseph Charitable Fund
The Kasner Charitable Trust
William Kendall's Charity (Wax Chandlers' Company)
Robert Kitchin (Saddlers' Company)
The Leathersellers' Company Charitable Fund
Lloyd's Charities Trust
London Catalyst
The London Community Foundation (LCF)
London Freemasons Charity
London Housing Foundation Ltd (LHF)
London Legal Support Trust (LLST)
The London Marathon Charitable Trust Ltd
Lord and Lady Lurgan Trust
The Mercers' Charitable Foundation
The Merchant Taylors' Company Charities Fund
The Masonic Province of Middlesex Charitable Trust (Middlesex Masonic Charity)
Mills and Reeve Charitable Trust
The Morel Charitable Trust
The Mulberry Trust
Music Sales Charitable Trust
The Nomura Charitable Trust
Notting Hill Genesis Community Foundation
The Jack Petchey Foundation
The Progress Foundation
Quintessentially Foundation
Red Hill Charitable Trust
The Rose Foundation
Saint Sarkis Charity Trust
Salters' Charitable Foundation
Schass Foundation
The Sheldon Trust
The Shipwrights' Charitable Fund
The Mrs Smith and Mount Trust
The Peter Stebbings Memorial Charity
T. and S. Trust Fund
Tallow Chandlers Benevolent Fund No. 2
The Tobacco Pipe Makers and Tobacco Trade Benevolent Fund
Trust For London
VHLT Ltd
The Vintners' Foundation
The Virgin Money Foundation
Vision Foundation*
The William Wates Memorial Trust
Wellington Management UK Foundation
Charity of Sir Richard Whittington
W. Wing Yip and Brothers Foundation
The Victoria Wood Foundation*
The William Allen Young Charitable Trust

■ Barking and Dagenham

Friends of Essex Churches Trust
Ford Britain Trust
Charles S. French Charitable Trust

■ Barnet

The Arsenal Foundation
The Eighteen Fund
Edward Harvist Trust (The Harvist Estate)
Jesus Hospital Charity
John Lyon's Charity
Mayheights Ltd
Mercaz Torah Vechesed Ltd
Notting Hill Genesis Community Foundation
B. E. Perl Charitable Trust
The David Tannen Charitable Trust
Tegham Ltd

■ Bexley

William Kendall's Charity (Wax Chandlers' Company)
Maudsley Charity

■ Brent

The Christabella Charitable Trust
Edward Harvist Trust (The Harvist Estate)
The Huntingdon Foundation Ltd
Hyde Charitable Trust

The Leri Charitable Trust
John Lyon's Charity
The Manackerman Charitable Trust
Melodor Ltd
Notting Hill Genesis Community Foundation
B. E. Perl Charitable Trust
Sellata Ltd
Wembley National Stadium Trust

■ Camden

The Arsenal Foundation
Camden Giving*
The Charterhouse Charitable Trust
Fishmongers' Company's Charitable Trust
The Hampstead Wells and Campden Trust
Edward Harvist Trust (The Harvist Estate)
Hollick Family Foundation
The Huntingdon Foundation Ltd
John Lyon's Charity
Notting Hill Genesis Community Foundation
The Portal Trust
Richard Reeve's Foundation

■ City of London

Aldgate and Allhallows Foundation
The Barbers' Company General Charities
The Charterhouse Charitable Trust
The Worshipful Company of Cordwainers Charitable Trusts (Minges Gift)
Cripplegate Foundation
East End Community Foundation
Fishmongers' Company's Charitable Trust
Charles S. French Charitable Trust
The Worshipful Company of Gardeners of London Charity
The B. and P. Glasser Charitable Trust
Worshipful Company of Glovers of London Charitable Trust
Worshipful Company of Gold and Silver Wyre Drawers Second Charitable Trust Fund
HFC Help For Children UK LTD
The Holbeck Charitable Trust
The Sir Joseph Hotung Charitable Settlement
The International Bankers Charitable Trust
Robert Kitchin (Saddlers' Company)
John Lyon's Charity
Makers of Playing Cards Charity
The Portal Trust
Richard Reeve's Foundation
The Saddlers' Company Charitable Fund
The Shipwrights' Charitable Fund
The Mrs Smith and Mount Trust
Tallow Chandlers Benevolent Fund No. 2
Wakefield and Tetley Trust

■ City of Westminster

The Charterhouse Charitable Trust
The Dischma Charitable Trust
Fishmongers' Company's Charitable Trust
M. and R. Gross Charities Ltd
Edward Harvist Trust (The Harvist Estate)
Hyde Park Place Estate Charity
John Lyon's Charity
Notting Hill Genesis Community Foundation
The Portal Trust
Strand Parishes Trust
Westminster Almshouses Foundation
Westminster Amalgamated Charity
Westminster Foundation

■ Croydon

Ros Harding Trust
Hyde Charitable Trust
Maudsley Charity
W. Wing Yip and Brothers Foundation

■ Ealing

Heathrow Community Trust
Housing Pathways Trust
John Lyon's Charity
Notting Hill Genesis Community Foundation

■ Greenwich

Sir William Boreman's Foundation
Hyde Charitable Trust
Maudsley Charity
The Portal Trust

■ Hackney

The Arsenal Foundation
The Charterhouse Charitable Trust
East End Community Foundation
The Englefield Charitable Trust
Fishmongers' Company's Charitable Trust
Ford Britain Trust
Charles S. French Charitable Trust
Hackney Parochial Charities
Hadras Kodesh Trust
The Manackerman Charitable Trust
Mayheights Ltd
Melodor Ltd
Notting Hill Genesis Community Foundation
B. E. Perl Charitable Trust
The Portal Trust
Sellata Ltd
The David Tannen Charitable Trust
Friends of Wiznitz Ltd

■ Hammersmith and Fulham

Dr Edwards Bishop King's Fulham Endowment Fund
The Girdlers' Company Charitable Trust
Hammersmith United Charities
John Lyon's Charity
Notting Hill Genesis Community Foundation
The Portal Trust

■ Haringey

Charles S. French Charitable Trust
Sellata Ltd
The David Tannen Charitable Trust
The Tottenham Grammar School Foundation
Friends of Wiznitz Ltd

■ Harrow

Edward Harvist Trust (The Harvist Estate)
John Lyon's Charity

Havering

Friends of Essex Churches Trust
Ford Britain Trust
Charles S. French Charitable Trust
The Norwood and Newton Settlement

Hillingdon

Heathrow Community Trust
A. P. Taylor Trust

Hounslow

Heathrow Community Trust
Housing Pathways Trust

Islington

The Arsenal Foundation
The Charterhouse Charitable Trust
Cloudesley
Cripplegate Foundation
Fishmongers' Company's Charitable Trust
Charles S. French Charitable Trust
Hyde Charitable Trust
The Portal Trust
Richard Reeve's Foundation

Kensington and Chelsea

The Campden Charities Trustee
Hollick Family Foundation
The Kensington and Chelsea Foundation
John Lyon's Charity
The Portal Trust
Westway Trust

Lambeth

The Battersea Power Station Foundation
The Charterhouse Charitable Trust
Fishmongers' Company's Charitable Trust
Hyde Charitable Trust
Maudsley Charity
The Peter Minet Trust
The Portal Trust
Sir Walter St John's Educational Charity
The Walcot Foundation

Lewisham

Sir William Boreman's Foundation
Hyde Charitable Trust
Maudsley Charity
The Portal Trust

Merton

The Vernon N. Ely Charitable Trust
The Generations Foundation
Maudsley Charity
The Taylor Family Foundation
The Wimbledon Foundation

Newham

East End Community Foundation
Friends of Essex Churches Trust
Fishmongers' Company's Charitable Trust
Ford Britain Trust
Charles S. French Charitable Trust
Notting Hill Genesis Community Foundation
The Portal Trust
Royal Docks Trust (London)

Redbridge

Friends of Essex Churches Trust
Ford Britain Trust
Charles S. French Charitable Trust

Richmond

*The Barnes Fund**
Hampton Fund
Heathrow Community Trust
Maudsley Charity
Richmond Parish Lands Charity

Southwark

The Charterhouse Charitable Trust
Fishmongers' Company's Charitable Trust
The Girdlers' Company Charitable Trust
The Hintze Family Charity Foundation
Hyde Charitable Trust
Charity of John Marshall
Maudsley Charity
The Peter Minet Trust
Newcomen Collett Foundation
The Portal Trust
The Alan and Babette Sainsbury Charitable Fund
St Olave's and St Saviour's Schools Foundation
United St Saviour's Charity
Wakefield and Tetley Trust

Tower Hamlets

Aldgate and Allhallows Foundation
The Charterhouse Charitable Trust
East End Community Foundation
Fishmongers' Company's Charitable Trust
Ford Britain Trust
Charles S. French Charitable Trust
Morgan Stanley International Foundation
Notting Hill Genesis Community Foundation
The Portal Trust
Tower Hill Trust
Wakefield and Tetley Trust

Waltham Forest

The Arsenal Foundation
Friends of Essex Churches Trust
Ford Britain Trust
Charles S. French Charitable Trust

Wandsworth

The Battersea Power Station Foundation
Maudsley Charity
The Portal Trust
Sir Walter St John's Educational Charity
The Wimbledon Foundation

North East England

The 1989 Willan Charitable Trust
The Roy and Pixie Baker Charitable Trust
The Ballinger Charitable Trust
The Barbour Foundation
Bauer Radio's Cash for Kids Charities
The Tony Bramall Charitable Trust
*Bright Red Charity**
Chrysalis Trust
The Coalfields Regeneration Trust

The Catherine Cookson Charitable Trust
The Evan Cornish Foundation
The Ellinson Foundation Ltd
The Goshen Trust
The Greggs Foundation
The Hearth Foundation
The Hospital of God at Greatham
The William Leech Charity
R. W. Mann Trust
The Mercers' Charitable Foundation
The Millfield House Foundation (1)
The National Churches Trust
Normanby Charitable Trust
North East Area Miners' Social Welfare Trust Fund
Oglesby Charitable Trust
The Reece Foundation
The Rothley Trust
The Shears Foundation
SHINE (Support and Help in Education)
The Vardy Foundation
The Virgin Money Foundation
The Watson Family Charitable Trust
The William Webster Charitable Trust
Charity of Sir Richard Whittington
*The Victoria Wood Foundation**
*Sir Graham Wylie Foundation**

■ County Durham

The Evan Cornish Foundation
The Sir Tom Cowie Charitable Trust
The Gillian Dickinson Trust
County Durham Community Foundation
Jill Franklin Trust
The Hadrian Trust
The W. A. Handley Charity Trust
The Hospital of God at Greatham
Sir James Knott Trust
Lempriere Pringle 2015
R. W. Mann Trust
The Millfield House Foundation (1)
North East Area Miners' Social Welfare Trust Fund
The Northumbria Historic Churches Trust
The JGW Patterson Foundation
Sir John Priestman Charity Trust
The Reece Foundation
The Rothley Trust

■ Northumberland

E. C. Graham Belford Charitable Settlement
The Evan Cornish Foundation
The Gillian Dickinson Trust
Jill Franklin Trust
The Hadrian Trust
The W. A. Handley Charity Trust
The Percy Hedley 1990 Charitable Trust
The Hospital of God at Greatham
The Joicey Trust
Sir James Knott Trust
R. W. Mann Trust
The Millfield House Foundation (1)
North East Area Miners' Social Welfare Trust Fund
The Northumbria Historic Churches Trust
The JGW Patterson Foundation
The Reece Foundation
The Rothley Trust
Shaftoe Educational Foundation
The Shears Foundation
The St Hilda's Trust
Community Foundation serving Tyne and Wear and Northumberland

■ North Yorkshire (formerly Cleveland)

Jill Franklin Trust
North East Area Miners' Social Welfare Trust Fund
The Rothley Trust
Sirius Minerals Foundation
Tees Valley Community Foundation
The Hospital of God at Greatham

■ Tyne and Wear

The Evan Cornish Foundation
The Sir Tom Cowie Charitable Trust
The Gillian Dickinson Trust
Jill Franklin Trust
The Hadrian Trust
The W. A. Handley Charity Trust
The Hospital of God at Greatham
The Joicey Trust
Sir James Knott Trust
R. W. Mann Trust
The Millfield House Foundation (1)
North East Area Miners' Social Welfare Trust Fund
The JGW Patterson Foundation
Sir John Priestman Charity Trust
The Reece Foundation
The Rothley Trust
The Shears Foundation
The St Hilda's Trust
T. and S. Trust Fund
Community Foundation serving Tyne and Wear and Northumberland

North West England

*The Tim Bacon Foundation**
The Philip Barker Charity
Bauer Radio's Cash for Kids Charities
The Bonamy Charitable Trust
The Bowland Charitable Trust
The Tony Bramall Charitable Trust
*Bright Red Charity**
The Coalfields Regeneration Trust
The Evan Cornish Foundation
The Eventhall Family Charitable Trust
The Granada Foundation
The Hearth Foundation
The Medicash Foundation
The Brian Mercer Charitable Trust
North West Cancer Research
Oglesby Charitable Trust
SHINE (Support and Help in Education)
The John Slater Foundation
The Steinberg Family Charitable Trust
The Stoller Charitable Trust
UKH Foundation
The Watson Family Charitable Trust
*The Victoria Wood Foundation**
The Eric Wright Charitable Trust

■ Cheshire

The Marjory Boddy Charitable Trust
Cheshire Community Foundation Ltd
Cheshire Freemason's Charity
The Robert Clutterbuck Charitable Trust
The Evan Cornish Foundation
*CRH Charitable Trust**
William Dean Countryside and Educational Trust

The Anne Duchess of Westminster's Charity
The Hamilton Davies Trust
May Hearnshaw's Charity
The Ursula Keyes Trust
Lord Leverhulme's Charitable Trust
Manchester Airport Community Trust Fund
MBNA General Foundation
John Moores Foundation
The Steve Morgan Foundation
The Dowager Countess Eleanor Peel Trust
The Pennycress Trust
Toyota Manufacturing UK Charitable Trust
The Ward Blenkinsop Trust
Westminster Foundation
The Williams Family Foundation
Brian Wilson Charitable Trust

■ Cumbria

The Harold and Alice Bridges Charity
Clark Foundation
The Evan Cornish Foundation
*CRH Charitable Trust**
Cumbria Community Foundation
Sir John Fisher Foundation
The Hadfield Charitable Trust
The W. A. Handley Charity Trust
*The Karlsson Jativa Charitable Foundation**
The Herd Lawson and Muriel Lawson Charitable Trust
*The Samuel and Freda Parkinson Charitable Trust**
The JGW Patterson Foundation
The Dowager Countess Eleanor Peel Trust
Francis C. Scott Charitable Trust
The Frieda Scott Charitable Trust
The Norman Whiteley Trust
The Yorkshire Dales Millennium Trust

■ Greater Manchester

A. W. Charitable Trust
Access Sport CIO
Beauland Ltd
Asser Bishvil Foundation
The Booth Charities
*Alan Boswell Group Charitable Trust**
The Bruntwood Charity
*Barbara and Derek Calrow Charitable Foundation**
The Chadwick Educational Foundation
Cheshire Freemason's Charity
Church Urban Fund
The Evan Cornish Foundation
*CRH Charitable Trust**
Ford Britain Trust
Forever Manchester
The Greater Manchester High Sheriff's Police Trust
The Hamilton Davies Trust
William Harding's Charity
Horwich Shotter Charitable Trust
J. E. Joseph Charitable Fund
The Kasner Charitable Trust
The Peter Kershaw Trust
Duchy of Lancaster Benevolent Fund
The Leri Charitable Trust
Jack Livingstone Charitable Trust
Local Trent Ltd
M. B. Foundation
The Manackerman Charitable Trust
Manchester Airport Community Trust Fund
The Manchester Guardian Society Charitable Trust
Charity of John Marshall
Melodor Ltd
Mills and Reeve Charitable Trust
Mole Charitable Trust
MW (HO) Foundation
Oizer Charitable Trust
The Dowager Countess Eleanor Peel Trust
Samjo Ltd
Schass Foundation
The Searchlight Electric Charitable Trust
The Shears Foundation
The Skelton Bounty
The Stoller Charitable Trust
T. and S. Trust Fund
The Treeside Trust
The Virgin Money Foundation
The Ward Blenkinsop Trust
The Whinfell Charitable Fund
W. Wing Yip and Brothers Foundation
The Zochonis Charitable Trust

■ Lancashire

The Harold and Alice Bridges Charity
The Chadwick Educational Foundation
Church Urban Fund
The Evan Cornish Foundation
*CRH Charitable Trust**
William Dean Countryside and Educational Trust
The Fort Foundation
*The Halsall Foundation**
May Hearnshaw's Charity
Community Foundations for Lancashire and Merseyside
Lancashire Environmental Fund Ltd
Duchy of Lancaster Benevolent Fund
Lord Leverhulme's Charitable Trust
The W. M. and B. W. Lloyd Trust
The Brian Mercer Charitable Trust
John Moores Foundation
*The Samuel and Freda Parkinson Charitable Trust**
The Dowager Countess Eleanor Peel Trust
Rhodi Charitable Trust
Riverside Charitable Trust Ltd
Schass Foundation
Francis C. Scott Charitable Trust
The Skelton Bounty
The WO Street Charitable Foundation
Mrs Waterhouse Charitable Trust
Westminster Foundation

■ Merseyside

The Marjory Boddy Charitable Trust
The Charles Brotherton Trust
The Bruntwood Charity
The Amelia Chadwick Trust
Cheshire Freemason's Charity
The Evan Cornish Foundation
William Dean Countryside and Educational Trust
*The Ken Dodd Charitable Foundation**
Ford Britain Trust
The General Charity Fund
The Steven Gerrard Foundation
The Hemby Charitable Trust
P. H. Holt Foundation
The Johnson Foundation
Community Foundations for Lancashire and Merseyside
Duchy of Lancaster Benevolent Fund
Lord Leverhulme's Charitable Trust
Liverpool Charity and Voluntary Services (LCVS)
*The Geoffrey and Pauline Martin Trust**
MBNA General Foundation
John Moores Foundation
The Steve Morgan Foundation
The Dowager Countess Eleanor Peel Trust

Pilkington Charities Fund
The Sir Harry Pilkington Trust Fund
Price Parry Charitable Trust*
The Rainford Trust
The Eleanor Rathbone Charitable Trust
Elizabeth Rathbone Charity
The Ravensdale Trust
The Clive and Sylvia Richards Charity Ltd
The Skelton Bounty
The Ward Blenkinsop Trust
West Derby Waste Lands Charity

South East England

The Ammco Trust
Axis Foundation
The Rowan Bentall Charitable Trust
The Berkeley Foundation
Bill Brown 1989 Charitable Trust
Chapman Charitable Trust
The Childwick Trust
The John Coates Charitable Trust
Dudley and Geoffrey Cox Charitable Trust
The Eight Foundation*
The Fonthill Foundation*
The Simon Gibson Charitable Trust
HFC Help For Children UK LTD
The Roger and Jean Jefcoate Trust
The Leach Fourteenth Trust
Notting Hill Genesis Community Foundation
The Pell Charitable Trust
Red Hill Charitable Trust
Mrs L. D. Rope's Third Charitable Settlement
Sandra Charitable Trust
The Shanly Foundation
The Syder Foundation
The Wates Foundation
The William Wates Memorial Trust

■ Berkshire

The Louis Baylis (Maidenhead Advertiser) Charitable Trust
The Earley Charity
The Eight Foundation*
The Englefield Charitable Trust
Greenham Trust Ltd
The Peter Harrison Foundation
Heathrow Community Trust
Henley Educational Trust
London Legal Support Trust (LLST)
The Masonic Province of Middlesex Charitable Trust (Middlesex Masonic Charity)
Mobbs Memorial Trust Ltd
The Gerald Palmer Eling Trust Company
The Pargiter Trust
Payne-Gallwey 1989 Charitable Trust
The Clive and Sylvia Richards Charity Ltd
The Peter Samuel Charitable Trust
The Shanly Foundation
The Singer Foundation*
The Spoore, Merry and Rixman Foundation
The Syder Foundation
The Tompkins Foundation

■ Buckinghamshire

Andrews Charitable Trust
The Anson Charitable Trust
The John Apthorp Charity
The Louis Baylis (Maidenhead Advertiser) Charitable Trust
The Boltini Trust
Buckinghamshire Community Foundation
The Buckinghamshire Historic Churches Trust
The Carrington Charitable Trust
The Childwick Trust
The Francis Coales Charitable Foundation
The Ernest Cook Trust
Coventry Building Society Charitable Foundation
The Louis and Valerie Freedman Charitable Settlement
William Harding's Charity
The Peter Harrison Foundation
Heathrow Community Trust
The Roger and Jean Jefcoate Trust
London Legal Support Trust (LLST)
Milton Keynes Community Foundation Ltd
Mobbs Memorial Trust Ltd
The Rothschild Foundation
The Eranda Rothschild Foundation
The Shanly Foundation
The Sherling Charitable Trust
The Syder Foundation

■ East Sussex

Andrews Charitable Trust
The Ian Askew Charitable Trust
The Isabel Blackman Foundation
The Blagrave Trust
The Bloom Foundation
The Harry Bottom Charitable Trust
The Bowerman Charitable Trust
The Chalk Cliff Trust
The Childwick Trust
The Derek and Eileen Dodgson Foundation
Gatwick Airport Community Trust
The Peter Harrison Foundation
Hollick Family Foundation
Hyde Charitable Trust
The Ernest Kleinwort Charitable Trust
The Lawson Trust CIO
The Magdalen and Lasher Charity (General Fund)
The Ofenheim Charitable Trust
The Pebbles Trust
The River Trust
Robertson Hall Trust
The Romney Marsh Historic Churches Trust
The Rugby Group Benevolent Fund Ltd
Southover Manor General Education Trust Ltd
The Sussex Community Foundation

■ Hampshire

The Barker-Mill Foundation
Bauer Radio's Cash for Kids Charities
The Blagrave Trust
The Charlotte Bonham-Carter Charitable Trust
The Calleva Foundation
The Childwick Trust
Colefax Charitable Trust
John and Freda Coleman Charitable Trust
Sir Jeremiah Colman Gift Trust
The Alice Ellen Cooper Dean Charitable Foundation
The Dibden Allotments Fund
The Eight Foundation*
Ford Britain Trust
Greenham Trust Ltd
Hampshire and Isle of Wight Community Foundation
The Peter Harrison Foundation
The Emmanuel Kaye Foundation
The Gerald Micklem Charitable Trust

Sarum St Michael Educational Charity
The Selwood Charitable Trust*
The Shanly Foundation
The Syder Foundation
Zurich Community Trust (UK) Ltd

Isle of Wight

The Blagrave Trust
Hampshire and Isle of Wight Community Foundation
The Peter Harrison Foundation
Isle of Wight Foundation
Daisie Rich Trust

Kent

Lawrence Atwell's Charity (Skinners' Company)
The Boltini Trust
The William Brake Charitable Trust
The Frank Brake Charitable Trust
The Childwick Trust
The Coalfields Regeneration Trust
The Cobtree Charity Trust Ltd
The Cole Charitable Trust
Colyer-Fergusson Charitable Trust
The Roger De Haan Charitable Trust
The Fidelity UK Foundation
Gatwick Airport Community Trust
The Gibbons Family Trust
The Godinton Charitable Trust
The Great Stone Bridge Trust of Edenbridge
The Peter Harrison Foundation
R. G. Hills Charitable Trust
Hollick Family Foundation
Hyde Charitable Trust
The Friends of Kent Churches
Kent Community Foundation
The Lawson Trust CIO
The Elaine and Angus Lloyd Charitable Trust
London Legal Support Trust (LLST)
Charity of John Marshall
Henry Oldfield Trust
The Pargiter Trust
The Romney Marsh Historic Churches Trust
The Rugby Group Benevolent Fund Ltd
The Mrs Smith and Mount Trust
The Tory Family Foundation

Oxfordshire

Access Sport CIO
The Ammco Trust
Andrews Charitable Trust
The Barnsbury Charitable Trust
The T. B. H. Brunner's Charitable Settlement
The Wilfrid and Constance Cave Foundation
The Childwick Trust
The Ernest Cook Trust
Coventry Building Society Charitable Foundation
The DLM Charitable Trust
The Lord Faringdon Charitable Trust
Doris Field Charitable Trust
The Simon Gibson Charitable Trust
The Peter Harrison Foundation
Henley Educational Trust
Christopher Laing Foundation
The David Laing Foundation
The C. L. Loyd Charitable Trust
The Mosawi Foundation*
Oxfordshire Community Foundation
Oxfordshire Historic Churches Trust (2016)
The Pharsalia Charitable Trust
Mr and Mrs J. A. Pye's Charitable Settlement
The Clive and Sylvia Richards Charity Ltd
The Rugby Group Benevolent Fund Ltd
Sarum St Michael Educational Charity
The Shanly Foundation
The Singer Foundation*
Staples Trust
The Syder Foundation
Tanner Trust
The Tolkien Trust
Robert and Felicity Waley-Cohen Charitable Trust

Surrey

Andrews Charitable Trust
Misses Barrie Charitable Trust
The Billmeir Charitable Trust
The Boltini Trust
The Childwick Trust
John and Freda Coleman Charitable Trust
The Earley Charity
The Eight Foundation*
The Fidelity UK Foundation
Gatwick Airport Community Trust
Hamamelis Trust
Ros Harding Trust
The Peter Harrison Foundation
Heathrow Community Trust
Henley Educational Trust
The Ingram Trust
The Sir Edward Lewis Foundation
The Elaine and Angus Lloyd Charitable Trust
London Legal Support Trust (LLST)
The London Marathon Charitable Trust Ltd
Charity of John Marshall
The Masonic Province of Middlesex Charitable Trust (Middlesex Masonic Charity)
The Pargiter Trust
Humphrey Richardson Taylor Charitable Trust
The Shanly Foundation
The Mrs Smith and Mount Trust
Community Foundation for Surrey
The Syder Foundation
Walton on Thames Charity

West Sussex

Andrews Charitable Trust
The Ian Askew Charitable Trust
The Blagrave Trust
The Boltini Trust
The Bowerman Charitable Trust
The Childwick Trust
The Derek and Eileen Dodgson Foundation
The Eight Foundation*
Friarsgate Trust
Gatwick Airport Community Trust
The F. Glenister Woodger Trust
The Peter Harrison Foundation
Heathrow Community Trust
Hyde Charitable Trust
The Ernest Kleinwort Charitable Trust
The Lawson Trust CIO
The Gerald Micklem Charitable Trust
The River Trust
The Shanly Foundation
The Bassil Shippam and Alsford Trust
Southover Manor General Education Trust Ltd
The Sussex Community Foundation
The Tompkins Foundation

South West England

Axis Foundation
The Rowan Bentall Charitable Trust
The Berkeley Foundation
Bill Brown 1989 Charitable Trust
The John Coates Charitable Trust
G. F. Eyre Charitable Trust
The Joyce Fletcher Charitable Trust
The Marjorie and Geoffrey Jones Charitable Trust
The Leonard Laity Stoate Charitable Trust
The Leach Fourteenth Trust
The Clare Milne Trust
The Norman Family Charitable Trust
Susanna Peake Charitable Trust
The Pell Charitable Trust
The Portishead Nautical Trust
Postcode Local Trust
The Clive and Sylvia Richards Charity Ltd
Spielman Charitable Trust
St Monica Trust
The Wates Foundation
The Elizabeth and Prince Zaiger Trust

■ Bristol

Coventry Building Society Charitable Foundation
Denman Charitable Trust
The Gloucestershire Historic Churches Trust
The Nani Huyu Charitable Trust
John James Bristol Foundation
The Leonard Laity Stoate Charitable Trust
McGreevy No. 5 Settlement
The Merchant Venturers' Charity
The Morel Charitable Trust
The Nisbet Trust
The Portishead Nautical Trust
Quartet Community Foundation
*The Singer Foundation**
Spielman Charitable Trust
St Monica Trust
The Sunrise Foundation CIO
The Dame Violet Wills Will Trust

■ Cornwall

The Wilfrid and Constance Cave Foundation
Cornwall Community Foundation
The Duke of Cornwall's Benevolent Fund
Duchy Health Charity Ltd
The Heathcoat Trust
The Leonard Laity Stoate Charitable Trust
The Clare Milne Trust
The Norman Family Charitable Trust
The Patrick Trust
The Charles Skey Charitable Trust
St Luke's College Foundation
Tanner Trust

■ Devon

Viscount Amory's Charitable Trust
The Ashworth Charitable Trust
Bideford Bridge Trust
The Wilfrid and Constance Cave Foundation
Mabel Cooper Charity
Devon Community Foundation
The Devon Historic Churches
The Gibbons Family Trust
The David Gibbons Foundation
The Heathcoat Trust
The Marjorie and Geoffrey Jones Charitable Trust
The Leonard Laity Stoate Charitable Trust
The Clare Milne Trust
The Norman Family Charitable Trust
Sarum St Michael Educational Charity
The Charles Skey Charitable Trust
St Luke's College Foundation

■ Dorset

Battens Charitable Trust
The Burry Charitable Trust
The Wilfrid and Constance Cave Foundation
The Clover Trust
The Ernest Cook Trust
The Alice Ellen Cooper Dean Charitable Foundation
Dorset Community Foundation
The Dorset Historic Churches Trust
*The Eight Foundation**
Dorothy Holmes Charitable Trust
The Leonard Laity Stoate Charitable Trust
The Pitt-Rivers Charitable Trust
Salisbury Pool Charity
Sarum St Michael Educational Charity
The Sherling Charitable Trust
The Talbot Village Trust
Mrs R. P. Tindall's Charitable Trust
The Valentine Charitable Trust
The Elizabeth and Prince Zaiger Trust

■ Gloucestershire

Andrews Charitable Trust
Douglas Arter Foundation
The Ashendene Trust
The Avon and Somerset Police Community Trust
Barnwood Trust
Bristol Archdeaconry Charity
The J. and M. Britton Charitable Trust
The George Cadbury Trust
The Wilfrid and Constance Cave Foundation
The Chipping Sodbury Town Lands Charity
*The Cotswold Primrose Charitable Trust**
Coventry Building Society Charitable Foundation
Denman Charitable Trust
County of Gloucestershire Community Foundation
The Gloucestershire Historic Churches Trust
Gordon Gray Trust
The Nani Huyu Charitable Trust
The Charles Irving Charitable Trust
Sylvanus Lysons Charity
The Nisbet Trust
The Notgrove Trust
Susanna Peake Charitable Trust
The Portishead Nautical Trust
Quartet Community Foundation
The Rowlands Trust
The Saintbury Trust
The Florence Shute Millennium Trust
*The Singer Foundation**
Philip Smith's Charitable Trust
St Monica Trust
The Summerfield Charitable Trust
The Dame Violet Wills Will Trust
Zurich Community Trust (UK) Ltd

■ Somerset

Andrews Charitable Trust
Douglas Arter Foundation

The Avon and Somerset Police Community Trust
The Roger and Sarah Bancroft Clark Charitable Trust
Battens Charitable Trust
The J. and M. Britton Charitable Trust
The Brownsword Charitable Foundation
The Wilfrid and Constance Cave Foundation
Clark Foundation
Coventry Building Society Charitable Foundation
Denman Charitable Trust
The Foxglove Trust
The Nani Huyu Charitable Trust
The Leonard Laity Stoate Charitable Trust
McGreevy No. 5 Settlement
The Medlock Charitable Trust
The Nisbet Trust
The Norman Family Charitable Trust
The Portishead Nautical Trust
Quartet Community Foundation
The Peter Samuel Charitable Trust
Sarum St Michael Educational Charity
The Charles Skey Charitable Trust
Somerset Community Foundation
St John's Foundation Est. 1174
St Monica Trust
The Dame Violet Wills Will Trust
The Elizabeth and Prince Zaiger Trust

Wiltshire

The Ashendene Trust
Battens Charitable Trust
The Blagrave Trust
The Wilfrid and Constance Cave Foundation
Chippenham Borough Lands Charity
Community First
Coventry Building Society Charitable Foundation
The James Dyson Foundation
*The Eight Foundation**
Samuel William Farmer Trust
The Fulmer Charitable Trust
The Walter Guinness Charitable Trust
The Pargiter Trust
Sarum St Michael Educational Charity
*The Singer Foundation**
The Syder Foundation
Mrs R. P. Tindall's Charitable Trust
Wiltshire Community Foundation
Zurich Community Trust (UK) Ltd

West Midlands Region

Axis Foundation
The Berkeley Foundation
The Edward Cadbury Charitable Trust
William A. Cadbury Charitable Trust
The Edward and Dorothy Cadbury Trust
The Coalfields Regeneration Trust
The Keith Coombs Trust
Coventry Building Society Charitable Foundation
Baron Davenport's Charity
The Eveson Charitable Trust
G. M. C. Trust
The Grantham Yorke Trust
Gay and Peter Hartley's Hillards Charitable Trust
Heart of England Community Foundation
The Hearth Foundation
The Jabbs Foundation
Johnnie Johnson Trust
The Edgar E. Lawley Foundation
The Michael Marsh Charitable Trust
*Millie's Watch**
The National Express Foundation
The Oakley Charitable Trust
The Owen Family Trust
The Patrick Trust
Quothquan Trust
The Ratcliff Foundation
The Clive and Sylvia Richards Charity Ltd
The Rowlands Trust
C. B. and H. H. Taylor 1984 Trust
The Warwickshire Masonic Charitable Association Ltd
The Wilmcote Charitrust

Herefordshire

The Hawthorne Charitable Trust
Herefordshire Community Foundation
The Herefordshire Historic Churches Trust
The Huntingdon Foundation Ltd
The Rowlands Trust
The Stephen R. and Philippa H. Southall Charitable Trust
St Peter's Saltley Trust

Shropshire

The Edward Cadbury Charitable Trust
The Lady Forester Trust
MBNA General Foundation
The Millichope Foundation
The Rowlands Trust
The Walker Trust
The Westcroft Trust

Staffordshire

The Bamford Charitable Foundation
Consolidated Charity of Burton upon Trent
The Edward Cadbury Charitable Trust
The Chartley Foundation
Coventry Building Society Charitable Foundation
William Dean Countryside and Educational Trust
The Wilfred and Elsie Elkes Charity Fund
The Harding Trust
May Hearnshaw's Charity
The Michael Marsh Charitable Trust
St Peter's Saltley Trust
The Community Foundation for Staffordshire

Warwickshire

The 29th May 1961 Charitable Trust
The Aylesford Family Charitable Trust
Misses Barrie Charitable Trust
Birmingham International Airport Community Trust Fund
The Edward Cadbury Charitable Trust
Coventry Building Society Charitable Foundation
The Elizabeth Creak Charitable Trust
Dumbreck Charity
Heart of England Community Foundation
The Alan Edward Higgs Charity
The King Henry VIII Endowed Trust – Warwick
The Michael Marsh Charitable Trust
The Norton Foundation
The Rowlands Trust

The Rugby Group Benevolent Fund Ltd
The Saintbury Trust
The Singer Foundation*
Stratford-upon-Avon Town Trust
Robert and Felicity Waley-Cohen Charitable Trust
Warwick Relief in Need Charity
The Warwickshire Masonic Charitable Association Ltd

West Midlands Metropolitan Area

The Lord Austin Trust
The Aylesford Family Charitable Trust
The James Beattie Charitable Trust
Birmingham International Airport Community Trust Fund
The Edward Cadbury Charitable Trust
The Barrow Cadbury Trust
The George Cadbury Trust
Church Urban Fund
Dumbreck Charity
The Eveson Charitable Trust
The Grimmitt Trust
The Alfred Haines Charitable Trust
Harborne Parish Lands Charity
Heart of England Community Foundation
The Alan Edward Higgs Charity
The Sir Barry Jackson County Fund
Lillie Johnson Charitable Trust
The Michael Marsh Charitable Trust
The Rowlands Trust
The Saintbury Trust
The Sheldon Trust
The Roger and Douglas Turner Charitable Trust

Worcestershire

Misses Barrie Charitable Trust
The Bransford Trust*
The Edward Cadbury Charitable Trust
The Wilfrid and Constance Cave Foundation
Dumbreck Charity
The Elmley Foundation
The Eveson Charitable Trust
Gordon Gray Trust
The Hawthorne Charitable Trust
The Kildare Trust
Laslett's (Hinton) Charity
The Michael Marsh Charitable Trust
John Martin's Charity
The Rowlands Trust
The Saintbury Trust
The Singer Foundation*
St Peter's Saltley Trust
The Roger and Douglas Turner Charitable Trust
Worcester Municipal Charities (CIO)
Worcestershire Community Foundation*

Yorkshire and the Humber

Bauer Radio's Cash for Kids Charities
The Liz and Terry Bramall Foundation
The Arnold Burton 1998 Charitable Trust
The Holbeck Charitable Trust
The Lyndal Tree Foundation
The Mayfield Valley Arts Trust
The Rose Animal Welfare Trust CIO*
SHINE (Support and Help in Education)
The Scurrah Wainwright Charity

East Riding of Yorkshire

The Tony Bramall Charitable Trust
The Brelms Trust CIO
The Joseph and Annie Cattle Trust
The Evan Cornish Foundation
The Dashlight Foundation*
Help for Health
The Hull and East Riding Charitable Trust
The Ken and Lynne Morrison Charitable Trust
The Ken and Edna Morrison Charitable Trust
The Sir James Reckitt Charity
Two Ridings Community Foundation
Yorkshire Cancer Research
The Yorkshire Historic Churches Trust

North Yorkshire

The Tony Bramall Charitable Trust
The Brelms Trust CIO
The Charles Brotherton Trust
The Jack Brunton Charitable Trust
The Evan Cornish Foundation
The Dashlight Foundation*
The Duke of Devonshire's Charitable Trust
The A. M. Fenton Trust
The Feoffees of St Michael's Spurriergate York
Hampton Fund
Gay and Peter Hartley's Hillards Charitable Trust
Heathrow Community Trust
Sir George Martin Trust
Maudsley Charity
The George A. Moore Foundation
The Ken and Lynne Morrison Charitable Trust
The Ken and Edna Morrison Charitable Trust
Normanby Charitable Trust
Sir John Priestman Charity Trust
The Purey Cust Trust CIO
Richmond Parish Lands Charity
The Shears Foundation
The Sylvia and Colin Shepherd Charitable Trust
The Patricia and Donald Shepherd Charitable Trust
Sirius Minerals Foundation
Peter Sowerby Foundation
Two Ridings Community Foundation
York Children's Trust
Yorkshire Cancer Research
The Yorkshire Dales Millennium Trust
The Yorkshire Historic Churches Trust

South Yorkshire

The Harry Bottom Charitable Trust
The Tony Bramall Charitable Trust
The Brelms Trust CIO
The Church Burgesses Educational Foundation
Church Burgesses Trust
The Evan Cornish Foundation
Coventry Building Society Charitable Foundation
The Dashlight Foundation*
The Earl Fitzwilliam Charitable Trust
The Freshgate Trust Foundation
The J. G. Graves Charitable Trust
Gay and Peter Hartley's Hillards Charitable Trust
May Hearnshaw's Charity
The Ken and Lynne Morrison Charitable Trust
The Ken and Edna Morrison Charitable Trust
The Sheffield Town Trust

■ West Yorkshire

Channel Islands

Isle of Man

Scotland

The Aberbrothock Skea Trust
Adam Family Foundation*
The AEB Charitable Trust
Sylvia Aitken's Charitable Trust
The AMW Charitable Trust
The Baird Trust
Bairdwatson Charitable Trust
Bank of Scotland Foundation
Barcapel Foundation Ltd
Barchester Healthcare Foundation
Misses Barrie Charitable Trust
Binks Trust
British Gas Energy Trust
Building & Civil Engineering Charitable Trust
Miss Margaret Butters Reekie Charitable Trust
The Noel Buxton Trust
The Cadogan Charity
Callendar Charitable Trust
W. A. Cargill Charitable Trust
The Castansa Trust
Cattanach
The Coalfields Regeneration Trust
Marjorie Coote Animal Charity Trust
Corra Foundation
The Craignish Trust
The Cray Trust
Creative Scotland
The Crerar Trust
Crisis UK
Cruden Foundation Ltd
The Cunningham Trust
The Daniell Trust*
Digital Xtra Fund*
The Dulverton Trust
Dunard Fund
Dunlossit and Islay Community Trust*
The Robert Fleming Hannay Memorial Charity
The Gordon Fraser Charitable Trust
The Hugh Fraser Foundation
The Joyce and Norman Freed Charitable Trust*
GambleAware
Gamma Trust
The Gannochy Trust
The Graham Trust
Dr Guthrie's Association
The Lennox Hannay Charitable Trust
The Christina Mary Hendrie Trust
Historic Environment Scotland*
Hope Trust
Miss Agnes H. Hunter's Trust
Impact Funding Partners Ltd
Lady Eda Jardine Charitable Trust
Jeffrey Charitable Trust*
Kilpatrick Fraser Charitable Trust
The Labone Charitable Trust*
The R. J. Larg Family Trust
Mrs M. A. Lascelles Charitable Trust
The Lyndal Tree Foundation
The R. S. Macdonald Charitable Trust
The MacRobert Trust 2019
The Manackerman Charitable Trust
The W. M. Mann Foundation
The Martin Charitable Trust
Nancie Massey Charitable Trust
Medical Research Scotland
The Meikle Foundation
Merchants' House of Glasgow
Hugh and Mary Miller Bequest Trust
The Ronald Miller Foundation
Jean and Roger Miller's Charitable Trust
The Milne Family Foundation*
The Morrisons Foundation
The Morton Charitable Trust (Dundee)
The Orrin Charitable Trust
P. F. Charitable Trust
Miss M. E. S. Paterson's Charitable Trust
People's Health Trust
People's Postcode Trust
The Persimmon Charitable Foundation
Miss A. M. Pilkington's Charitable Trust
The Portrack Charitable Trust
Postcode Society Trust (formerly Postcode Dream Trust)
Rentrust Foundation Ltd
The Robertson Trust
Rosetrees Trust
Foundation Scotland
The John Scott Trust Fund
Scottish Coal Industry Special Welfare Fund
Scottish Property Industry Festival of Christmas (SPIFOX)
The Souter Charitable Trust
The Stafford Trust
Standard Life Foundation
The Hugh Stenhouse Foundation
Talteg Ltd
Tay Charitable Trust
Tenovus Scotland
The Trades House of Glasgow
David William Traill Cargill Fund
The Triangle Trust (1949) Fund
The Turtleton Charitable Trust
The Union of the Sisters of Mercy of Great Britain
Viridor Credits Environmental Company
Volant Charitable Trust
John Watson's Trust
The Colin Weir Charitable Foundation*
The Weir Charitable Trust
The Whitaker Charitable Trust
J. and J. R. Wilson Trust
Women's Fund for Scotland*
The James Wood Bequest Fund
The Wood Foundation
Youth Music

Ayreshire and Arran

Bairdwatson Charitable Trust
Walton Foundation
The James Weir Foundation

Dumfries and Galloway

The Castansa Trust
Dumfriesshire East Community Benefit Group SCIO*
The Holywood Trust

Dunbartonshire and Argyll and Bute

Dunlossit and Islay Community Trust*
The Pastoral Care Trust – The St Nicholas Care Fund
Walton Foundation

Fife

The Carnegie Dunfermline Trust
KPE4 Charitable Trust*
The R. J. Larg Family Trust
Mathew Trust
The Meikle Foundation
The Alexander Moncur Trust
The Morton Charitable Trust (Dundee)
The Russell Trust

Glasgow

Robert Barr's Charitable Trust
The Bellahouston Bequest Fund

The W. A. Cargill Fund
The Castansa Trust
The Endrick Trust
James T. Howat Charitable Trust
Merchants' House of Glasgow
Morgan Stanley International Foundation
The Pastoral Care Trust – The St Nicholas Care Fund
The Templeton Goodwill Trust
The Trades House of Glasgow
The Virgin Money Foundation
Walton Foundation
The James Weir Foundation
Zurich Community Trust (UK) Ltd

Highlands and Western Isles

The Anne Duchess of Westminster's Charity
The Englefield Charitable Trust
The Peter Samuel Charitable Trust
Strathnairn Community Benefit Fund Ltd
Westminster Foundation

Lanarkshire

Bairdwatson Charitable Trust
The Pastoral Care Trust – The St Nicholas Care Fund
Walton Foundation

Lothian

The AEB Charitable Trust
The Castansa Trust
The Cray Trust
Edinburgh Children's Holiday Fund
Dr Guthrie's Association
*KPE4 Charitable Trust**
Nancie Massey Charitable Trust
*North Berwick Trust**
The Row Fogo Charitable Trust
The Virgin Money Foundation
John Watson's Trust

Orkney and Shetland

Shetland Charitable Trust

Renfrewshire

The Pastoral Care Trust – The St Nicholas Care Fund
Walton Foundation

Scottish Borders

The AEB Charitable Trust
The Joicey Trust

Tayside

*The Nine Incorporated Trades of Dundee General Fund Charity**
The Gannochy Trust
The R. J. Larg Family Trust
Leng Charitable Trust
Mathew Trust
The Alexander Moncur Trust
The Morton Charitable Trust (Dundee)
Northwood Charitable Trust
Tay Charitable Trust

Wales

The Sylvia Adams Charitable Trust
The Adlard Family Charitable Foundation
*The Aitken Family Charitable Trust**
*Alpkit Foundation**
The Annandale Charitable Trust
The Arah Foundation
The John Armitage Charitable Trust
Arts Council of Wales (also known as Cyngor Celfyddydau Cymru)
The Asda Foundation
The Ashley Family Foundation
Lawrence Atwell's Charity (Skinners' Company)
Axis Foundation
The Rachel Baker Memorial Charity
*The Kamini and Vindi Banga Family Trust**
Barchester Healthcare Foundation
The Max Barney Foundation
Belljoe Tzedoko Ltd
Birthday House Trust
Blakemore Foundation
The Boodle & Dunthorne Charitable Trust
The Borrows Charitable Trust
The Boshier-Hinton Foundation
British Gas Energy Trust
Building & Civil Engineering Charitable Trust
The Noel Buxton Trust
The Wilfrid and Constance Cave Foundation
Chalfords Ltd
Chartered Accountants' Livery Charity (CALC)
Christie Foundation
CLA Charitable Trust
The Coalfields Regeneration Trust
Colwinston Charitable Trust
Coventry Building Society Charitable Foundation
Michael Crawford Children's Charity
Crisis UK
The Peter Cruddas Foundation
D. M. H. Educational Trust Ltd
*The Daniell Trust**
Margaret Davies Charity
The Henry and Suzanne Davis Foundation
The De Brye Charitable Trust
Didymus
*William and Frances Dobie Charitable Foundation**
Drapers' Charitable Fund
The Dulverton Trust

England and Wales Cricket Trust
Esher House Charitable Trust
The Fieldrose Charitable Trust*
The Football Foundation
The Fort Foundation
Ian M. Foulerton Charitable Trust
The Fraxinus Charitable Trust*
The Joyce and Norman Freed Charitable Trust*
The Patrick and Helena Frost Foundation
GambleAware
The Gaudio Family Foundation (UK) Ltd
Martin Geddes Charitable Trust
The General Nursing Council for England and Wales Trust
The Gibbs Charitable Trusts
The Simon Gibson Charitable Trust
The Goshen Trust
The Grand Trust CIO*
The Lennox Hannay Charitable Trust
The Peter and Teresa Harris Charitable Trust*
The Hearth Foundation
The Tim Henman Foundation
The Hintze Family Charity Foundation
Historic Houses Foundation
The Jane Hodge Foundation
The Mary Homfray Charitable Trust
The Huggard Charitable Trust
Hurdale Charity Ltd
The Inflexion Foundation*
The Investindustrial Foundation*
The Jenour Foundation
The Herd Lawson and Muriel Lawson Charitable Trust
The Lindley Foundation (TLF)
Lloyds Bank Foundation for England and Wales
Lloyd's Patriotic Fund
The Lockwood Charitable Foundation
Charity of John Marshall
The Geoffrey and Pauline Martin Trust*
Masonic Charitable Foundation
The Mather Family Charitable Trust*
The Mikheev Charitable Trust*
Millennium Stadium Charitable Trust (Ymddiriedolaeth Elusennol Stadiwm y Mileniwm)
Millie's Watch*
Mind*
The Mohn Westlake Foundation*
Moondance Foundation
The Steve Morgan Foundation
The Morrisons Foundation
The Mulchand Foundation*
The National Churches Trust
The Gareth Neame Foundation*
North West Cancer Research
The Norwood and Newton Settlement
The Oakdale Trust
The Oakley Charitable Trust
The Ouseley Church Music Trust
P. F. Charitable Trust
The Pantheon Charitable Trust*
The James Pantyfedwen Foundation (Ymddiriedolaeth James Pantyfedwen)
Partners Global Foundation*
Rosanna Pearson's 1987 Charity Trust*
People's Health Trust
The Persimmon Charitable Foundation
The Points Family Trust*
The Portrack Charitable Trust
Postcode Community Trust
Postcode Society Trust (formerly Postcode Dream Trust)
The Raindance Charitable Trust*
Rentrust Foundation Ltd
The Revere Charitable Trust
Riverside Charitable Trust Ltd
Rix Thompson Rothenberg Foundation
RJM Charity Trust
The Dezna Robins Jones Charitable Foundation
The Rockspring Charitable Trust*
Rosetrees Trust
Royal Masonic Trust for Girls and Boys
The Dr Mortimer and Theresa Sackler Foundation
The Sanderson Foundation*
O. and G. Schreiber Charitable Trust
Scott (Eredine) Charitable Trust
The Segelman Trust
Sloane Robinson Foundation
The DS Smith Charitable Foundation
Arabella and Julian Smith Family Trust*
The Sobell Foundation
Mark Stolkin Foundation
The Joseph Strong Frazer Trust*
The Bernard Sunley Foundation
The Ashley Tabor-King Foundation*
Stephen Taylor Foundation
Tenovus Cancer Care
The Thirty Percy Foundation*
The Thornton Trust
The Triangle Trust (1949) Fund
UKH Foundation
The Union of the Sisters of Mercy of Great Britain
The Velvet Foundation*
The Community Foundation in Wales
Robert and Felicity Waley-Cohen Charitable Trust
The Waterloo Foundation
The Welland Trust*
The Wheeler Family Charitable Trust
The Wigoder Family Foundation
Wychville Ltd
The Wyfold Charitable Trust
The Yapp Charitable Trust
Youth Music

Mid and West Wales

The County Council of Dyfed Welsh Church Fund
Garthgwynion Charities
The Simon Gibson Charitable Trust
The Morel Charitable Trust
Swansea and Brecon Diocesan Board of Finance Ltd

North Wales

The Blandford Lake Trust
The Marjory Boddy Charitable Trust
Chapman Charitable Trust
The Earl Fitzwilliam Charitable Trust
P. and C. Hickinbotham Charitable Trust
The Isle of Anglesey Charitable Trust
The Geoffrey and Pauline Martin Trust*
MBNA General Foundation
The Steve Morgan Foundation
North West Cancer Research
The Ratcliff Foundation
Toyota Manufacturing UK Charitable Trust

South Wales

The Austin Bailey Foundation
Ford Britain Trust
The Simon Gibson Charitable Trust
The Huggard Charitable Trust
The Monmouthshire County Council Welsh Church Act Fund
The Dezna Robins Jones Charitable Foundation
The Florence Shute Millennium Trust
Swansea and Brecon Diocesan Board of Finance Ltd
The Virgin Money Foundation
The Welsh Church Act Fund

Northern Ireland

Arts Council of Northern Ireland
*John Atcheson Foundation**
The Roger and Sarah Bancroft Clark Charitable Trust
Bauer Radio's Cash for Kids Charities
*Maureen Boal Charitable Trust**
Building & Civil Engineering Charitable Trust
Church of Ireland Priorities Fund
Marjorie Coote Animal Charity Trust
Donibristle Trust
The Enkalon Foundation
Halifax Foundation for Northern Ireland
P. and C. Hickinbotham Charitable Trust
The Reta Lila Howard Foundation
Integrated Education Fund
The Ireland Fund of Great Britain
The Kennedy Charitable Foundation
Lord and Lady Lurgan Trust
The Esmé Mitchell Trust
John Moores Foundation
The National Churches Trust
Community Foundation for Northern Ireland
Northern Pharmacies Ltd Trust Fund
The O'Sullivan Family Charitable Trust
Rix Thompson Rothenberg Foundation
The T.K. Maxx and Homesense Foundation
Taca
The Triangle Trust (1949) Fund
Ulster Garden Villages Ltd

Republic of Ireland

Allchurches Trust Ltd
The Scott Bader Commonwealth Ltd
Breast Cancer Now
William A. Cadbury Charitable Trust
The Cadbury Foundation
Elizabeth Cayzer Charitable Trust
Church of Ireland Priorities Fund
The Duke of Devonshire's Charitable Trust
Marc Fitch Fund
The Goodman Foundation
Calouste Gulbenkian Foundation – UK Branch
H. C. D. Memorial Fund
The Charles Hayward Foundation
Hinchley Charitable Trust
The Hospital Saturday Fund
The Ireland Fund of Great Britain
The Ian Karten Charitable Trust
The Kennedy Charitable Foundation
Ladbrokes Coral Trust
The O'Sullivan Family Charitable Trust
The Ouseley Church Music Trust
The Phillips Charitable Trust
*The Selfridges Group Foundation**
ShareGift (The Orr Mackintosh Foundation)
Sodexo Stop Hunger Foundation
The T.K. Maxx and Homesense Foundation
The Tabhair Charitable Trust
C. B. and H. H. Taylor 1984 Trust
Mrs R. P. Tindall's Charitable Trust
The Toy Trust
Universal Music UK Sound Foundation
*Vinci UK Foundation**
Wellbeing of Women
Wooden Spoon Society

Grant-makers by field of interest and type of beneficiary

This index contains two separate listings:

Categorisation of fields of interest and types of beneficiary: This lists all of the headings used in DGMT to categorise fields of interest and types of beneficiary.

Grant-makers by field of interest and type of beneficiary: This lists funders under the fields of interest and types of beneficiary for which they have expressed a funding preference. Asterisks mark funders which have not been featured in DGMT before.

Grant-makers by field of interest and type of beneficiary

These pages contain two separate listings:

Categorisation of fields of interest and types of beneficiary
This lists all of the headings used in DGMT to categorise fields of interest and types of beneficiary

Grant-makers by field of interest and type of beneficiary
This lists funders under the fields of interest and types of beneficiary for which they have expressed a funding preference

Animals

The Bryan Adams Foundation
The Adlard Family Charitable Foundation
Sylvia Aitken's Charitable Trust
The Alborada Trust
Al-Fayed Charitable Foundation
The Banister Charitable Trust
The Barclay Foundation
Lord Barnby's Foundation
Burnie's Foundation
The Edward and Dorothy Cadbury Trust
The Frederick and Phyllis Cann Trust
The Leslie Mary Carter Charitable Trust
Marjorie Coote Animal Charity Trust
The Demigryphon Trust
The Anne Duchess of Westminster's Charity
Audrey Earle Charitable Trust
The Emerald Foundation
The Enkalon Foundation
The Lord Faringdon Charitable Trust
Donald Forrester Trust
The Gordon Fraser Charitable Trust
The G. D. Charitable Trust
The Graham Trust
The Gunter Charitable Trust
Hamamelis Trust
The Lennox Hannay Charitable Trust
The Hawthorne Charitable Trust
The Charlotte Heber-Percy Charitable Trust
The Henry C. Hoare Charitable Trust
The Hobson Charity Ltd
The Mary Homfray Charitable Trust
The Muriel Jones Foundation
The Kennel Club Charitable Trust
The Graham Kirkham Foundation
The Ernest Kleinwort Charitable Trust
Sir James Knott Trust
The Leonard Laity Stoate Charitable Trust
Langdale Trust
Mrs F. B. Laurence Charitable Trust
The Herd Lawson and Muriel Lawson Charitable Trust
Limoges Charitable Trust
The Lindley Foundation (TLF)
The Macdonald-Buchanan Charitable Trust
The Mactaggart Third Fund
The W. M. Mann Foundation
R. W. Mann Trust
The Marsh Christian Trust
The Martin Charitable Trust
The Geoffrey and Pauline Martin Trust*
The Master Charitable Trust
The Ronald Miller Foundation
Jean and Roger Miller's Charitable Trust
The Millichope Foundation
The Oakdale Trust
The Paget Charitable Trust
The Gerald Palmer Eling Trust Company
The Jack Patston Charitable Trust
Susanna Peake Charitable Trust
Petplan Charitable Trust
The Pitt-Rivers Charitable Trust
The Prince of Wales's Charitable Foundation
The Princess Anne's Charities
The Revere Charitable Trust
The Royal Foundation of the Duke and Duchess of Cambridge
Royal Society Of Wildlife Trusts
The Saddlers' Company Charitable Fund
Salisbury Pool Charity
The M. J. Samuel Charitable Trust
Sandra Charitable Trust
Scott (Eredine) Charitable Trust
ShareGift (The Orr Mackintosh Foundation)
The Sheepdrove Trust
The John Slater Foundation
Ruth Smart Foundation
The SMB Trust
The N. Smith Charitable Settlement
The Spear Charitable Trust
The Joseph Strong Frazer Trust*
Sabina Sutherland Charitable Trust
The Constance Travis Charitable Trust
The Underwood Trust
The Michael Uren Foundation
The Van Mesdag Fund*
Sylvia Waddilove Foundation UK
The HDH Wills 1965 Charitable Trust

Animal conservation

The AEB Charitable Trust
The Alborada Trust
The Derrill Allatt Foundation
The Ian Askew Charitable Trust
The Banister Charitable Trust
Battens Charitable Trust
The Becht Family Charitable Trust
Biffa Award
Birmingham International Airport Community Trust Fund
Burnie's Foundation
The Wilfrid and Constance Cave Foundation
The Charities Advisory Trust
CLA Charitable Trust
Marjorie Coote Animal Charity Trust
The Daniell Trust*
The Dashlight Foundation*
William Dean Countryside and Educational Trust
The Earl Fitzwilliam Charitable Trust
Michael and Shirley Hunt Charitable Trust
The Iliffe Family Charitable Trust
Langdale Trust
Mrs M. A. Lascelles Charitable Trust
The R. S. Macdonald Charitable Trust
The Marchig Animal Welfare Trust
The Michael Marks Charitable Trust
The Norman Family Charitable Trust
The Oakdale Trust
The Ofenheim Charitable Trust
The Owen Family Trust
The Samuel and Freda Parkinson Charitable Trust*
The Jack Patston Charitable Trust
The Primrose Trust
The Prince of Wales's Charitable Foundation
Quintessentially Foundation
The Ranworth Trust
The Royal Foundation of the Duke and Duchess of Cambridge
The Michael and Nicola Sacher Charitable Trust
The Jean Sainsbury Animal Welfare Trust
Ruth Smart Foundation
Sylvia Waddilove Foundation UK
Whitley Animal Protection Trust
The HDH Wills 1965 Charitable Trust
J. and J. R. Wilson Trust
The William Allen Young Charitable Trust

Animal health care/veterinary practice

Animal welfare

Arts, culture and heritage

The 29th May 1961 Charitable Trust
The Acacia Charitable Trust
Adam Family Foundation*
The Adlard Family Charitable Foundation
The AEB Charitable Trust
Sylvia Aitken's Charitable Trust
AKO Foundation
The Aldama Foundation
Aldgate and Allhallows Foundation
The Derrill Allatt Foundation
D. C. R. Allen Charitable Trust
The Allen Trust
The Ammco Trust
The Anchor Foundation
Andor Charitable Trust
The Anson Charitable Trust
The Arah Foundation
The Architectural Heritage Fund
The John Armitage Charitable Trust
The Armourers' and Brasiers' Gauntlet Trust
Arts Council England
Arts Council of Northern Ireland
Arts Council of Wales (also known as Cyngor Celfyddydau Cymru)
ArtSocial Foundation
The Ashendene Trust
The Ashley Family Foundation
The Astor Foundation
Atkin Charitable Foundation
The Aurelius Charitable Trust
Backstage Trust
The Bagri Foundation
The Ballinger Charitable Trust
The Roger and Sarah Bancroft Clark Charitable Trust
The Band Trust
Veronica and Lars Bane Foundation*
The Kamini and Vindi Banga Family Trust*
Barchester Healthcare Foundation
The Baring Foundation
The Barker-Mill Foundation
Misses Barrie Charitable Trust
Robert Barr's Charitable Trust
Battens Charitable Trust
BC Partners Foundation
The Beaverbrook Foundation
AJ Bell Trust*
The Benham Charitable Settlement
Bennett Lowell Ltd
The Billmeir Charitable Trust
The Bingham Trust
Birthday House Trust
The Michael Bishop Foundation
Maria Bjornson Memorial Fund*
The Sir Victor Blank Charitable Settlement
The Boltini Trust
The Charlotte Bonham-Carter Charitable Trust
The Borrows Charitable Trust
The Bowerman Charitable Trust
The Bowland Charitable Trust
The Liz and Terry Bramall Foundation
The Bransford Trust*
The Brelms Trust CIO
The Britford Bridge Trust
The J. and M. Britton Charitable Trust
The Consuelo and Anthony Brooke Charitable Trust
The Charles Brotherton Trust
The Brownsword Charitable Foundation
The T. B. H. Brunner's Charitable Settlement
The Jack Brunton Charitable Trust
The Arnold Burton 1998 Charitable Trust
The Edward Cadbury Charitable Trust
William A. Cadbury Charitable Trust
The Edward and Dorothy Cadbury Trust
The George Cadbury Trust
Camden Giving*
W. A. Cargill Charitable Trust
The Carnegie Dunfermline Trust
The Castansa Trust
The Wilfrid and Constance Cave Foundation
Elizabeth Cayzer Charitable Trust
The B. G. S. Cayzer Charitable Trust
The Amelia Chadwick Trust
The Chalk Cliff Trust
Chapman Charitable Trust
The Chartley Foundation
The Childhood Trust
Chippenham Borough Lands Charity
The Church Burgesses Educational Foundation
The City Bridge Trust (Bridge House Estates)
Clark Foundation
The Clore Duffield Foundation
The John Coates Charitable Trust
The Vivienne and Samuel Cohen Charitable Trust
The John S. Cohen Foundation
The Cole Charitable Trust
Sir Jeremiah Colman Gift Trust
The Catherine Cookson Charitable Trust
The Worshipful Company of Cordwainers Charitable Trusts (Minges Gift)
The Duke of Cornwall's Benevolent Fund
The County Council of Dyfed Welsh Church Fund
The Craps Charitable Trust
Creative Scotland
The Crescent Trust
Cruden Foundation Ltd
Cumbria Community Foundation
The D'Oyly Carte Charitable Trust
The Daiwa Anglo-Japanese Foundation
The Manny and Brigitta Davidson Charitable Foundation*
The Davidson Family Charitable Trust
Michael Davies Charitable Settlement
Margaret Davies Charity
The Davis Foundation
The Henry and Suzanne Davis Foundation
The Roger De Haan Charitable Trust
The De Laszlo Foundation
Foundation Derbyshire
Provincial Grand Charity of the Province of Derbyshire
Devon Community Foundation
The Gillian Dickinson Trust
Didymus
The Dischma Charitable Trust
The Djanogly Foundation
William and Frances Dobie Charitable Foundation*
The Dorfman Foundation
Dorset Community Foundation
Drapers' Charitable Fund
Dumbreck Charity
Dumfriesshire East Community Benefit Group SCIO*
Dunard Fund
The Nine Incorporated Trades of Dundee General Fund Charity*
Dunlossit and Islay Community Trust*
The Charles Dunstone Charitable Trust
County Durham Community Foundation
The Dyers' Company Charitable Trust

The Earley Charity
The Gilbert and Eileen Edgar Foundation
The Eighty Eight Foundation
John Ellerman Foundation
The Elmley Foundation
The Emerton-Christie Charity
The Englefield Charitable Trust
The Enkalon Foundation
The Estelle Trust
Esmée Fairbairn Foundation
The Lord Faringdon Charitable Trust
The Fidelity UK Foundation
The Finnis Scott Foundation
Sir John Fisher Foundation
The Earl Fitzwilliam Charitable Trust
The Robert Fleming Hannay Memorial Charity
The Joyce Fletcher Charitable Trust
The Follett Trust
Oliver Ford Foundation
The Fort Foundation
The Foxglove Trust
The Foyle Foundation
The Elizabeth Frankland Moore and Star Foundation
The Gordon Fraser Charitable Trust
The Freelands Foundation Ltd
Charles S. French Charitable Trust
The Freshgate Trust Foundation
Gamma Trust
The Gannochy Trust
Garfield Weston Foundation
Gatwick Airport Community Trust
The Jacqueline and Michael Gee Charitable Trust
Sir Robert Geffery's Almshouse Trust
The Gibbs Charitable Trusts
The Simon Gibson Charitable Trust
The G. C. Gibson Charitable Trust
The Glass-House Trust
Worshipful Company of Gold and Silver Wyre Drawers Second Charitable Trust Fund
The Golden Bottle Trust
The Goldman Sachs Charitable Gift Fund (UK)
Goldman Sachs Gives (UK)
The Goldsmiths' Company Charity
The Golsoncott Foundation
Nicholas and Judith Goodison's Charitable Settlement
Gowling WLG (UK) Charitable Trust
The Graham Trust
The Granada Foundation
The J. G. Graves Charitable Trust
The Great Britain Sasakawa Foundation
The Kenneth and Susan Green Charitable Foundation
Greenham Trust Ltd
The Grimmitt Trust
The Grocers' Charity
Calouste Gulbenkian Foundation – UK Branch
The Hadfield Charitable Trust
The Hadrian Trust
Paul Hamlyn Foundation
The Helen Hamlyn Trust
Hampton Fund
The W. A. Handley Charity Trust
The Lennox Hannay Charitable Trust
The Kathleen Hannay Memorial Charity
The Harbour Charitable Trust
The Harbour Foundation
The David and Claudia Harding Foundation
William Harding's Charity
The Harrison-Frank Family Foundation (UK) Ltd
The Hawthorne Charitable Trust
Hays Travel Foundation
The Headley Trust
Heart of England Community Foundation
The Heathside Charitable Trust
The Charlotte Heber-Percy Charitable Trust
Ernest Hecht Charitable Foundation
The Percy Hedley 1990 Charitable Trust
The Hemby Charitable Trust
Herefordshire Community Foundation
Heritage Lottery Fund
P. and C. Hickinbotham Charitable Trust
The Derek Hill Foundation
The Hillier Trust
The Lady Hind Trust
The Hinduja Foundation
The Hinrichsen Foundation
The Hintze Family Charity Foundation
The Hiscox Foundation
The Henry C. Hoare Charitable Trust
The Hobson Charity Ltd
The Holbeck Charitable Trust
Hollick Family Foundation
The Holliday Foundation
P. H. Holt Foundation
The Holywood Trust
The Mary Homfray Charitable Trust
Huntingdon Freemen's Trust
Ibrahim Foundation Ltd
The Idlewild Trust
The Inverforth Charitable Trust
*The Investindustrial Foundation**
The Invigorate Charitable Trust
The Ireland Fund of Great Britain
Irish Youth Foundation (UK) Ltd (incorporating The Lawlor Foundation)
The Isle of Anglesey Charitable Trust
Lady Eda Jardine Charitable Trust
John Jarrold Trust Ltd
The Jenour Foundation
The Jewish Youth Fund
The Marjorie and Geoffrey Jones Charitable Trust
The Cyril and Eve Jumbo Charitable Trust
The Jusaca Charitable Trust
*Kantor Charitable Foundation**
The Kensington and Chelsea Foundation
Kilpatrick Fraser Charitable Trust
Laura Kinsella Foundation
The Graham Kirkham Foundation
Sir James Knott Trust
The Kobler Trust
*KPE4 Charitable Trust**
The Kyte Charitable Trust
The David Laing Foundation
The Martin Laing Foundation
The Leonard Laity Stoate Charitable Trust
Langdale Trust
The R. J. Larg Family Trust
Mrs M. A. Lascelles Charitable Trust
The Lauffer Family Charitable Foundation
The Law Family Charitable Foundation
The Edgar E. Lawley Foundation
The Lawson Trust CIO
The Leach Fourteenth Trust
The Leathersellers' Company Charitable Fund
*The Leeward Trust**
The Kennedy Leigh Charitable Trust
The Leri Charitable Trust
The Leverhulme Trust
Lord Leverhulme's Charitable Trust

*The Ralph Levy Charitable Company Ltd**
*Cecil and Hilda Lewis Charitable Trust**
The Limbourne Trust
Limoges Charitable Trust
The Linbury Trust
The Linden Charitable Trust
The Linder Foundation
The Lindley Foundation (TLF)
The Charles Littlewood Hill Trust
Liverpool Charity and Voluntary Services (LCVS)
The Elaine and Angus Lloyd Charitable Trust
The Andrew Lloyd Webber Foundation
The Lockwood Charitable Foundation
The London Community Foundation (LCF)
The C. L. Loyd Charitable Trust
Lord and Lady Lurgan Trust
Mace Foundation
The Mactaggart Third Fund
The Ian Mactaggart Trust (The Mactaggart Second Fund)
*The Mageni Trust**
The Manchester Guardian Society Charitable Trust
The W. M. Mann Foundation
R. W. Mann Trust
*The Marandi Foundation**
The Stella and Alexander Margulies Charitable Trust
The Michael Marks Charitable Trust
The Marks Family Charitable Trust
The J. P. Marland Charitable Trust
The Marsh Christian Trust
Charity of John Marshall
The Martin Charitable Trust
Sir George Martin Trust
Nancie Massey Charitable Trust
The Master Charitable Trust
*Material World Foundation**
The Meikle Foundation
The Merchant Taylors' Company Charities Fund
The Merchant Venturers' Charity
Merchants' House of Glasgow
The Mickel Fund
*The Mikheev Charitable Trust**
*The Mila Charitable Organisation**
Millennium Stadium Charitable Trust (Ymddiriedclaeth Elusennol Stadiwm y Mileniwm)
The Ronald Miller Foundation
Jean and Roger Miller's Charitable Trust
The Millichope Foundation
Milton Keynes Community Foundation Ltd
The Brian Mitchell Charitable Settlement
The Esmé Mitchell Trust
The Mittal Foundation
*The Mohn Westlake Foundation**
The Alexander Moncur Trust
The Monmouthshire County Council Welsh Church Act Fund
The Henry Moore Foundation
The Morel Charitable Trust
The Morris Charitable Trust
G. M. Morrison Charitable Trust
The Morrisons Foundation
The Mulberry Trust
The John R. Murray Charitable Trust
Music Sales Charitable Trust
*Friends of the National Libraries**
The National Manuscripts Conservation Trust
The NDL Foundation
Nesta
Network for Social Change Charitable Trust
The Nisbet Trust
Normanby Charitable Trust
Community Foundation for Northern Ireland
Northwood Charitable Trust
The Norton Foundation
Norwich Town Close Estate Charity
The Norwood and Newton Settlement
The Notgrove Trust
The Oakdale Trust
The Oakley Charitable Trust
Odin Charitable Trust
The Ofenheim Charitable Trust
Oglesby Charitable Trust
Old Possum's Practical Trust
Henry Oldfield Trust
The Owen Family Trust
Oxfordshire Community Foundation
P. F. Charitable Trust
The Gerald Palmer Eling Trust Company
Parabola Foundation
*Partners Global Foundation**
The Patrick Trust
David Pearlman Charitable Foundation
The Pebbles Trust
The Persimmon Charitable Foundation
The Phillips and Rubens Charitable Trust
The Phillips Family Charitable Trust
The Pilgrim Trust
Cecil Pilkington Charitable Trust
The Austin and Hope Pilkington Trust
The Sir Harry Pilkington Trust Fund
PIMCO Foundation Europe
The Pitt-Rivers Charitable Trust
The Polonsky Foundation
The Portrack Charitable Trust
David and Elaine Potter Foundation
Mr and Mrs J. A. Pye's Charitable Settlement
Quartet Community Foundation
The Radcliffe Trust
Richard Radcliffe Trust
The Rainford Trust
The Ranworth Trust
The Ravensdale Trust
The Rayne Foundation
The Rayne Trust
The John Rayner Charitable Trust
The Revere Charitable Trust
The Rhododendron Trust
Daisie Rich Trust
The Clive and Sylvia Richards Charity Ltd
Rigby Foundation
The Sir John Ritblat Family Foundation
Rivers Foundation
*The Rockspring Charitable Trust**
The Roddick Foundation
The Gerald and Gail Ronson Family Foundation
The David Ross Foundation
The Rothermere Foundation
The Rothschild Foundation
The Eranda Rothschild Foundation
Rothschild Foundation (Hanadiv) Europe
The Roughley Charitable Trust
The Rowlands Trust
Royal Docks Trust (London)
The Rubin Foundation Charitable Trust
The Ruddock Foundation for the Arts
The Russell Trust
The Jeremy and John Sacher Charitable Trust
The Michael and Nicola Sacher Charitable Trust
The Dr Mortimer and Theresa Sackler Foundation
The Saddlers' Company Charitable Fund

The Saintbury Trust
The Salamander Charitable Trust
The Basil Samuel Charitable Trust
The M. J. Samuel Charitable Trust
The Scarfe Charitable Trust
Schroder Charity Trust
The Schroder Foundation
Foundation Scotland
The Frieda Scott Charitable Trust
Scottish Coal Industry Special Welfare Fund
The Scottish Power Foundation
Scouloudi Foundation
ShareGift (The Orr Mackintosh Foundation)
*The Sharp Foundation**
The Shears Foundation
The Sheepdrove Trust
The Sheffield Town Trust
The Sylvia and Colin Shepherd Charitable Trust
The Archie Sherman Charitable Trust
Shetland Charitable Trust
The Bassil Shippam and Alsford Trust
The Thomas Sivewright Catto Charitable Settlement
The Charles Skey Charitable Trust
The N. Smith Charitable Settlement
The E. C. Sosnow Charitable Trust
The Stephen R. and Philippa H. Southall Charitable Trust
Peter Sowerby Foundation
Spielman Charitable Trust
Rosalyn and Nicholas Springer Charitable Trust
The St James's Trust Settlement
St Olave's and St Saviour's Schools Foundation
Stanley Foundation Ltd
Staples Trust
The Steel Charitable Trust
The Hugh Stenhouse Foundation
*The Sterry Family Foundation**
Stevenson Family's Charitable Trust
The Summerfield Charitable Trust
Sumner Wilson Charitable Trust
The Sutasoma Trust
Sabina Sutherland Charitable Trust
Sutton Coldfield Charitable Trust
The John Swire (1989) Charitable Trust
The Swire Charitable Trust
The Charles and Elsie Sykes Trust
Tay Charitable Trust
C. B. and H. H. Taylor 1984 Trust
The Taylor Family Foundation
A. P. Taylor Trust
The Tedworth Charitable Trust
The Theatres Trust Charitable Fund
The Tolkien Trust
The Tompkins Foundation
The Constance Travis Charitable Trust
The Trefoil Trust
The Roger and Douglas Turner Charitable Trust
The Turtleton Charitable Trust
Ulster Garden Villages Ltd
The Underwood Trust
The Albert Van Den Bergh Charitable Trust
The Vandervell Foundation
The Vardy Foundation
The Veneziana Fund
Viridor Credits Environmental Company
Sylvia Waddilove Foundation UK
Wade's Charity
Robert and Felicity Waley-Cohen Charitable Trust
The Ward Blenkinsop Trust
The Barbara Ward Children's Foundation
Mrs Waterhouse Charitable Trust
The William Wates Memorial Trust
The Geoffrey Watling Charity
Blyth Watson Charitable Trust
The Weinstock Fund
The Welsh Church Act Fund
Westway Trust
The Barbara Whatmore Charitable Trust
The Williams Charitable Trust
The Williams Family Foundation
The Wingate Foundation
The Wixamtree Trust
The Wolfson Family Charitable Trust
The Lord Leonard and Lady Estelle Wolfson Foundation
The Wolfson Foundation
*The Victoria Wood Foundation**
The Woodward Charitable Trust
The Wyseliot Rose Charitable Trust
The William Allen Young Charitable Trust
Youth Music

Access to the arts

The Art Fund
The Bagri Foundation
Barchester Healthcare Foundation
The Louis Baylis (Maidenhead Advertiser) Charitable Trust
Binks Trust
*Maria Bjornson Memorial Fund**
The Cayo Foundation
Elizabeth Cayzer Charitable Trust
Chapman Charitable Trust
The Chetwode Foundation
The Clore Duffield Foundation
*The Noel Coward Foundation**
The Elmley Foundation
The Finnis Scott Foundation
The Joyce Fletcher Charitable Trust
Fowler Smith and Jones Trust
The Freelands Foundation Ltd
Charles S. French Charitable Trust
The Garrick Charitable Trust
The Gatsby Charitable Foundation
The Robert Gavron Charitable Trust
The General Charity Fund
The Golsoncott Foundation
The Helen Hamlyn Trust
The Harbour Foundation
The Headley Trust
The Heritage of London Trust Ltd
P. H. Holt Foundation
The Idlewild Trust
The Ireland Fund of Great Britain
The Sir Barry Jackson County Fund
The London Community Foundation (LCF)
John Lyon's Charity
*Material World Foundation**
The Mayfield Valley Arts Trust
The Brian Mercer Charitable Trust
Millennium Stadium Charitable Trust (Ymddiriedclaeth Elusennol Stadiwm y Mileniwm)
*The Mohn Westlake Foundation**
The Henry Moore Foundation
The Morel Charitable Trust
Norwich Town Close Estate Charity

Nottinghamshire Community Foundation
The Rainford Trust
Rix Thompson Rothenberg Foundation
The Ruddock Foundation for the Arts
The Alan and Babette Sainsbury Charitable Fund
The Taylor Family Foundation
The Theatres Trust Charitable Fund
Three Monkies Trust
The Lord Leonard and Lady Estelle Wolfson Foundation
The Woodward Charitable Trust
Youth Music

Arts and cultures of specific communities

Arcadia Fund
The Art Fund
The Bagri Foundation
Binks Trust
The Cayo Foundation
The Noel Coward Foundation*
The Daiwa Anglo-Japanese Foundation
The Great Britain Sasakawa Foundation
The Helen Hamlyn Trust
The Ireland Fund of Great Britain
The Allen Lane Foundation
The London Community Foundation (LCF)
Material World Foundation*
The Miles Morland Foundation
The James Pantyfedwen Foundation (Ymddiriedolaeth James Pantyfedwen)
The Rayne Trust
The Ruddock Foundation for the Arts
The Sino-British Fellowship Trust
Taca
The Weir Charitable Trust
W. Wing Yip and Brothers Foundation
Youth Music

Crafts

The Carpenters' Company Charitable Trust
The Worshipful Company of Cordwainers Charitable Trusts (Minges Gift)
The Nine Incorporated Trades of Dundee General Fund Charity*
The Dyers' Company Charitable Trust
The Elmley Foundation
Worshipful Company of Glovers of London Charitable Trust
Worshipful Company of Gold and Silver Wyre Drawers Second Charitable Trust Fund
The Headley Trust
The Idlewild Trust
The Kirby Laing Foundation
The Leathersellers' Company Charitable Fund
The Leche Trust
The Saddlers' Company Charitable Fund
The Weavers' Company Benevolent Fund

Heritage

The Adlard Family Charitable Foundation
Allchurches Trust Ltd
The Architectural Heritage Fund
The Art Fund
The Ian Askew Charitable Trust
Atlas Memorial Ltd
The Baird Trust
The Roy and Pixie Baker Charitable Trust
The Barbour Foundation
Barcapel Foundation Ltd
The Barclay Foundation
The Beaverbrook Foundation
The Bedfordshire and Hertfordshire Historic Churches Trust
The Bellahouston Bequest Fund
The Benham Charitable Settlement
Bennett Lowell Ltd
The Rowan Bentall Charitable Trust
Birmingham International Airport Community Trust Fund
The Michael Bishop Foundation
G. and K. Boyes Charitable Trust
The Consuelo and Anthony Brooke Charitable Trust
The T. B. H. Brunner's Charitable Settlement
Buckingham Trust
The Buckinghamshire Historic Churches Trust
The Arnold Burton 1998 Charitable Trust
The Leslie Mary Carter Charitable Trust
Elizabeth Cayzer Charitable Trust
The Francis Coales Charitable Foundation
The Francis Coales Charitable Foundation
The John Coates Charitable Trust
Sir Jeremiah Colman Gift Trust
Colwinston Charitable Trust
Community First
Congregational and General Charitable Trust
The Duke of Cornwall's Benevolent Fund
The County Council of Dyfed Welsh Church Fund
Cruden Foundation Ltd
The D'Oyly Carte Charitable Trust
The Henry and Suzanne Davis Foundation
The Roger De Haan Charitable Trust
The Devon Historic Churches
The Dischma Charitable Trust
The Dorset Historic Churches Trust
Drapers' Charitable Fund
The Dulverton Trust
The Charles Dunstone Charitable Trust
The Englefield Charitable Trust
Friends of Essex Churches Trust
The Essex Heritage Trust
G. F. Eyre Charitable Trust
The Lord Faringdon Charitable Trust
The A. M. Fenton Trust
The Feoffees of St Michael's Spurriergate York
The Fidelity UK Foundation
Marc Fitch Fund
The Earl Fitzwilliam Charitable Trust
Ian M. Foulerton Charitable Trust
Jill Franklin Trust
The Gordon Fraser Charitable Trust
The Freshgate Trust Foundation
Frognal Trust
The Simon Gibson Charitable Trust
The Gloucestershire Historic Churches Trust
The Goldsmiths' Company Charity
The Graham Trust

The J. G. Graves Charitable Trust
The Grocers' Charity
The Helen Hamlyn Trust
The W. A. Handley Charity Trust
The Charles Hayward Foundation
The Headley Trust
The Herefordshire Historic Churches Trust
Heritage Lottery Fund
The Heritage of London Trust Ltd
Historic Environment Scotland*
Historic Houses Foundation
The Henry C. Hoare Charitable Trust
The Holbeck Charitable Trust
The Idlewild Trust
The Investindustrial Foundation*
The Isle of Anglesey Charitable Trust
John Jarrold Trust Ltd
The Friends of Kent Churches
The Kilroot Foundation*
The King Henry VIII Endowed Trust – Warwick
Laura Kinsella Foundation
The Graham Kirkham Foundation
Sir James Knott Trust
Laslett's (Hinton) Charity
Mrs F. B. Laurence Charitable Trust
The Lawson Trust CIO
The Leach Fourteenth Trust
The Leche Trust
Limoges Charitable Trust
The Linbury Trust
The Charles Littlewood Hill Trust
The Lockwood Charitable Foundation
Manchester Airport Community Trust Fund
The Michael Marks Charitable Trust
The Marsh Christian Trust
Charity of John Marshall
Sir George Martin Trust
The Master Charitable Trust
Gemma and Chris McGough Charitable Foundation CIO*
The Millichope Foundation
The Esmé Mitchell Trust
The Monmouthshire County Council Welsh Church Act Fund
The Henry Moore Foundation
G. M. Morrison Charitable Trust
The John R. Murray Charitable Trust
The National Churches Trust
Friends of the National Libraries*
The National Manuscripts Conservation Trust
The Norfolk Churches Trust Ltd
Normanby Charitable Trust
The Northumbria Historic Churches Trust
Norwich Town Close Estate Charity
The Norwood and Newton Settlement
Old Possum's Practical Trust
Henry Oldfield Trust
The Owen Family Trust
Oxfordshire Historic Churches Trust (2016)
The Gerald Palmer Eling Trust Company
The James Pantyfedwen Foundation (Ymddiriedolaeth James Pantyfedwen)
Miss M. E. S. Paterson's Charitable Trust
The Jack Patston Charitable Trust
David Pearlman Charitable Foundation
The Pilgrim Trust
Postcode Local Trust
Sir John Priestman Charity Trust
The Prince of Wales's Charitable Foundation
The Professional Footballers' Association Charity
Mr and Mrs J. A. Pye's Charitable Settlement
The Racing Foundation
The Joseph Rank Trust
The Clive and Sylvia Richards Charity Ltd
Rigby Foundation
The Sir John Ritblat Family Foundation
Rockcliffe Charitable Trust
The Romney Marsh Historic Churches Trust
The Rose Foundation
The David Ross Foundation
Rothschild Foundation (Hanadiv) Europe
The Roughley Charitable Trust
The Rowlands Trust
Royal Docks Trust (London)
The Ruddock Foundation for the Arts
Salisbury Pool Charity
The Peter Samuel Charitable Trust
The Scarfe Charitable Trust
Schroder Charity Trust
ShareGift (The Orr Mackintosh Foundation)
The Sheffield Town Trust
The Sylvia and Colin Shepherd Charitable Trust
The Shipwrights' Charitable Fund
Stanley Foundation Ltd
Stevenson Family's Charitable Trust
Mark Stolkin Foundation
Peter Stormonth Darling Charitable Trust
The Suffolk Historic Churches Trust
The Summerfield Charitable Trust
The Swire Charitable Trust
The Adrian Swire Charitable Trust
Tanner Trust
The Theatres Trust Charitable Fund
The Roger and Douglas Turner Charitable Trust
The Turtleton Charitable Trust
Ulster Garden Villages Ltd
The Michael Uren Foundation
The Veneziana Fund
Sylvia Waddilove Foundation UK
War Memorials Trust*
Mrs Waterhouse Charitable Trust
The Geoffrey Watling Charity
The Welsh Church Act Fund
The Barbara Whatmore Charitable Trust
Colonel W. H. Whitbread Charitable Trust
Alfred Williams Charitable Trust
The Wolfson Foundation
Worth Waynflete Foundation
The Yorkshire Dales Millennium Trust
The Yorkshire Historic Churches Trust

Literature

The Clore Duffield Foundation
The Elmley Foundation
The Garrick Charitable Trust
The Granada Foundation
The Derek Hill Foundation
The Graham Kirkham Foundation
The Limbourne Trust
The Marsh Christian Trust
The Miles Morland Foundation
Friends of the National Libraries*
The Wingate Foundation

Media (including TV, film, publishing and radio)

The Daiwa Anglo-Japanese Foundation
The Elmley Foundation
The J. J. Charitable Trust
The Jerusalem Trust
The David Lean Foundation
The Miles Morland Foundation
*Quadstar Charitable Foundation**
The Roddick Foundation
Ufi VocTech Trust

Performing arts

The AMW Charitable Trust
The Associated Board Of The Royal Schools Of Music
Backstage Trust
The Bagri Foundation
The Rachel Baker Memorial Charity
*The Kamini and Vindi Banga Family Trust**
The Louis Baylis (Maidenhead Advertiser) Charitable Trust
Bennett Lowell Ltd
Binks Trust
*Maria Bjornson Memorial Fund**
Bluespark Foundation
The Marjory Boddy Charitable Trust
The Bowerman Charitable Trust
*The Bransford Trust**
The BRIT Trust
The Jack Brunton Charitable Trust
The Carne Trust
The Carr-Gregory Trust
The Cayo Foundation
The Church Burgesses Educational Foundation
The Clore Duffield Foundation
Colwinston Charitable Trust
*The Noel Coward Foundation**
Margaret Davies Charity
The De Laszlo Foundation
Dunard Fund
The Gilbert and Eileen Edgar Foundation
The Gilbert and Eileen Edgar Foundation
John Ellerman Foundation
The Elmley Foundation
The Emerald Foundation
*Equity Charitable Trust**
The Lord Faringdon Charitable Trust
The Fidelio Charitable Trust
The Joyce Fletcher Charitable Trust
Fowler Smith and Jones Trust
The Foyle Foundation
The Gordon Fraser Charitable Trust
The Hugh Fraser Foundation
Charles S. French Charitable Trust
The Freshgate Trust Foundation
The Garrick Charitable Trust
The Gatsby Charitable Foundation
The General Charity Fund
The G. C. Gibson Charitable Trust
Worshipful Company of Gold and Silver Wyre Drawers Second Charitable Trust Fund
The Golsoncott Foundation
The Granada Foundation
Dr Guthrie's Association
The Helen Hamlyn Trust
The W. A. Handley Charity Trust
The David and Claudia Harding Foundation
The Harding Trust
Henley Educational Trust
The Tim Henman Foundation
The Derek Hill Foundation
The Hinrichsen Foundation
The Hobson Charity Ltd
The Holbeck Charitable Trust
The Idlewild Trust
The Inverforth Charitable Trust
The Sir Barry Jackson County Fund
The Boris Karloff Charitable Foundation
*The Karlsson Jativa Charitable Foundation**
The Michael and Ilse Katz Foundation
The Emmanuel Kaye Foundation
The Kildare Trust
The Graham Kirkham Foundation
The Kirby Laing Foundation
The David Lean Foundation
The Leche Trust
The Mark Leonard Trust
The Limbourne Trust
The Limbourne Trust
The Linbury Trust
The Linder Foundation
The Linder Foundation
John Lyon's Charity
The Mackintosh Foundation
Sir George Martin Trust
*Material World Foundation**
The Mayfield Valley Arts Trust
The Brian Mercer Charitable Trust
Merchants' House of Glasgow
Millennium Stadium Charitable Trust (Ymddiriedclaeth Elusennol Stadiwm y Mileniwm)
The Millward Charitable Trust
The Henry Moore Foundation
The Morel Charitable Trust
G. M. Morrison Charitable Trust
Norwich Town Close Estate Charity
Nottinghamshire Community Foundation
The Ofenheim Charitable Trust
The Ouseley Church Music Trust
The Patrick Trust
The Pell Charitable Trust
The Performing Right Society Foundation
The Polonsky Foundation
The Radcliffe Trust
The Rainford Trust
Richard Reeve's Foundation
Humphrey Richardson Taylor Charitable Trust
Rix Thompson Rothenberg Foundation
The Rowlands Trust
The Ruddock Foundation for the Arts
The RVW Trust
The Saddlers' Company Charitable Fund
The Alan and Babette Sainsbury Charitable Fund
The Sands Family Trust
The Scarfe Charitable Trust
The Martin Smith Foundation
Mark Stolkin Foundation
The Taylor Family Foundation
The Theatres Trust Charitable Fund
Three Monkies Trust
Mrs R. P. Tindall's Charitable Trust
Universal Music UK Sound Foundation
The Utley Foundation
The Vandervell Foundation
The Vaughan Williams Charitable Trust
Sylvia Waddilove Foundation UK
Robert and Felicity Waley-Cohen Charitable Trust
The Whitaker Charitable Trust
Alfred Williams Charitable Trust
The Wingate Foundation
The Lord Leonard and Lady Estelle Wolfson Foundation

The Wolfson Foundation
Youth Music

Visual arts

*The Ampersand Foundation**
The Art Fund
The Louis Baylis (Maidenhead Advertiser) Charitable Trust
Binks Trust
*Maria Bjornson Memorial Fund**
The Rory and Elizabeth Brooks Foundation
The Cayo Foundation
Colwinston Charitable Trust
*The Noel Coward Foundation**
Margaret Davies Charity
The De Laszlo Foundation
Dunard Fund
The Elmley Foundation
The Finnis Scott Foundation
Fowler Smith and Jones Trust
The Foyle Foundation
The Gordon Fraser Charitable Trust
The Hugh Fraser Foundation
The Freelands Foundation Ltd
Charles S. French Charitable Trust
The Gatsby Charitable Foundation
The General Charity Fund
The Golsoncott Foundation
The Granada Foundation
Dr Guthrie's Association
The Holbeck Charitable Trust
The Idlewild Trust
The David Lean Foundation
The Linbury Trust
The Linder Foundation
John Lyon's Charity
*Material World Foundation**
The Brian Mercer Charitable Trust
Millennium Stadium Charitable Trust (Ymddiriedclaeth Elusennol Stadiwm y Mileniwm)
The Henry Moore Foundation
Nottinghamshire Community Foundation
The Ruddock Foundation for the Arts
The Alan and Babette Sainsbury Charitable Fund
Mark Stolkin Foundation
Three Monkies Trust
Sylvia Waddilove Foundation UK
The Lord Leonard and Lady Estelle Wolfson Foundation

Community services and development

The 1989 Willan Charitable Trust
The 4814 Trust
*Adam Family Foundation**
The Aimwell Charitable Trust
The Aldama Foundation
Allchurches Trust Ltd
The Anchor Foundation
The Anson Charitable Trust
The Armourers' and Brasiers' Gauntlet Trust
Ove Arup Partnership Charitable Trust
The Asda Foundation
The Ashley Family Foundation
The Avon and Somerset Police Community Trust
Bairdwatson Charitable Trust
Bank of Scotland Foundation
Barchester Healthcare Foundation
The Philip Barker Charity
*The Barnes Fund**
Barnwood Trust
The Battersea Power Station Foundation
BBC Children in Need
The James Beattie Charitable Trust
Bedfordshire and Luton Community Foundation
The Berkeley Foundation
Biffa Award
*The Big Yellow Foundation**
Birthday House Trust
The Blagrave Trust
The Boltini Trust
Boots Charitable Trust
The Borrows Charitable Trust
*Alan Boswell Group Charitable Trust**
The Liz and Terry Bramall Foundation
*The Bransford Trust**
The Brelms Trust CIO
The Harold and Alice Bridges Charity
British Gas Energy Trust
British Humane Association
*Mary Brown Memorial Trust**
R. S. Brownless Charitable Trust
The Brownsword Charitable Foundation
The Jack Brunton Charitable Trust
Buckinghamshire Community Foundation
The Burges Salmon Charitable Trust
Consolidated Charity of Burton upon Trent
The Edward Cadbury Charitable Trust
William A. Cadbury Charitable Trust
The Edward and Dorothy Cadbury Trust
Community Foundation for Calderdale
The Calleva Foundation
The Cambridgeshire Community Foundation
*Camden Giving**
The Campden Charities Trustee
*Card Factory Foundation**
*CareTech Foundation**
The W. A. Cargill Fund
*The Antonio Carluccio Foundation**
The Carnegie Dunfermline Trust
The Castansa Trust
The Wilfrid and Constance Cave Foundation
The Charter 600 Charity
Cheshire Community Foundation Ltd
The Childhood Trust
Chippenham Borough Lands Charity
The Chipping Sodbury Town Lands Charity
Church Urban Fund
The Churchill Foundation
The City Bridge Trust (Bridge House Estates)
The Clan Trust Ltd
The Clothworkers' Foundation
The John Coates Charitable Trust
Denise Coates Foundation
The Cole Charitable Trust
Colyer-Fergusson Charitable Trust
Comic Relief
Community First
*The Connolly Foundation**
The J. Reginald Corah Foundation Fund
Corra Foundation
Coventry Building Society Charitable Foundation
Cripplegate Foundation
The Peter Cruddas Foundation
Cumbria Community Foundation
The Roger De Haan Charitable Trust
The Demigryphon Trust
Devon Community Foundation
The Dibden Allotments Fund
Donibristle Trust
Dorset Community Foundation
The Anne Duchess of Westminster's Charity
The Dulverton Trust

*Dumfriesshire East Community Benefit Group SCIO**
*The Nine Incorporated Trades of Dundee General Fund Charity**
*Dunlossit and Islay Community Trust**
County Durham Community Foundation
The Endrick Trust
The Englefield Charitable Trust
The Enkalon Foundation
Esher House Charitable Trust
Essex Community Foundation
*The Ethos Foundation**
The Everard Foundation
Esmée Fairbairn Foundation
The Thomas Farr Charity
The Fermanagh Trust
The Fidelity UK Foundation
Sir John Fisher Foundation
The Football Association National Sports Centre Trust
The Football Foundation
Ford Britain Trust
Forever Manchester
Donald Forrester Trust
Fowler Smith and Jones Trust
Charles S. French Charitable Trust
Friarsgate Trust
Friends Provident Charitable Foundation
The Gannochy Trust
Garfield Weston Foundation
Gatwick Airport Community Trust
The Tara Getty Foundation
The G. C. Gibson Charitable Trust
County of Gloucestershire Community Foundation
The Golden Bottle Trust
The Goldsmiths' Company Charity
The Mike Gooley Trailfinders Charity
The Gosling Foundation Ltd
The Grace Trust
The Grantham Yorke Trust
The J. G. Graves Charitable Trust
The Great Stone Bridge Trust of Edenbridge
The Greater Manchester High Sheriff's Police Trust
Greenham Trust Ltd
The Grimmitt Trust
Groundwork UK
H. C. D. Memorial Fund
The Hadfield Charitable Trust
The Alfred Haines Charitable Trust
Halifax Foundation for Northern Ireland
The Hamilton Davies Trust
Paul Hamlyn Foundation
Hammersmith United Charities
Hampshire and Isle of Wight Community Foundation
Hampton Fund
The W. A. Handley Charity Trust
The Lennox Hannay Charitable Trust
Harborne Parish Lands Charity
Ros Harding Trust
William Harding's Charity
Gay and Peter Hartley's Hillards Charitable Trust
The Hasluck Charitable Trust
Heart of England Community Foundation
The Heathcoat Trust
Heathrow Community Trust
The Hemby Charitable Trust
Herefordshire Community Foundation
Hertfordshire Community Foundation
P. and C. Hickinbotham Charitable Trust
The Lady Hind Trust
The Henry C. Hoare Charitable Trust
The Hobson Charity Ltd
The Holbeck Charitable Trust
Hollick Family Foundation
P. H. Holt Foundation
The Holywood Trust
The Mary Homfray Charitable Trust
The Hospital of God at Greatham
Hyde Charitable Trust
Hyde Park Place Estate Charity
Imagine Foundation
Impact Funding Partners Ltd
Impetus
The Indigo Trust
The Innocent Foundation
The International Bankers Charitable Trust
The Inverforth Charitable Trust
The Invigorate Charitable Trust
The Ireland Fund of Great Britain
Irish Youth Foundation (UK) Ltd (incorporating The Lawlor Foundation)
The Charles Irving Charitable Trust
The Isle of Anglesey Charitable Trust
Isle of Wight Foundation
John Jarrold Trust Ltd
Rees Jeffreys Road Fund
The Jones 1986 Charitable Trust
Kent Community Foundation
Kilpatrick Fraser Charitable Trust
The King Henry VIII Endowed Trust – Warwick
The Mary Kinross Charitable Trust
Sir James Knott Trust
*KPE4 Charitable Trust**
The KPMG Foundation
Kusuma Trust UK
Ladbrokes Coral Trust
The Martin Laing Foundation
The Leonard Laity Stoate Charitable Trust
The Lake House Charity
Community Foundations for Lancashire and Merseyside
Lancashire Environmental Fund Ltd
Duchy of Lancaster Benevolent Fund
The Allen Lane Foundation
The R. J. Larg Family Trust
Mrs F. B. Laurence Charitable Trust
The Edgar E. Lawley Foundation
The Lawson Trust CIO
Leeds Building Society Charitable Foundation
*The Leeward Trust**
Lempriere Pringle 2015
The Leri Charitable Trust
Lord Leverhulme's Charitable Trust
*The Charles Lewis Foundation**
The Limbourne Trust
The Lindley Foundation (TLF)
The Charles Littlewood Hill Trust
Liverpool Charity and Voluntary Services (LCVS)
Jack Livingstone Charitable Trust
Lloyds Bank Foundation for the Channel Islands
London Catalyst
The London Community Foundation (LCF)
The London Marathon Charitable Trust Ltd
Longleigh Foundation
Sylvanus Lysons Charity
The Mackintosh Foundation
The MacRobert Trust 2019
The Magdalen and Lasher Charity (General Fund)
Making a Difference Locally Ltd
Manchester Airport Community Trust Fund
The Manchester Guardian Society Charitable Trust
The W. M. Mann Foundation
R. W. Mann Trust

Ulster Garden Villages Ltd
United St Saviour's Charity
UnLtd (Foundation for Social Entrepreneurs)
UPP Foundation
The Van Neste Foundation
The Vardy Foundation
The Veolia Environmental Trust
*Vinci UK Foundation**
Nigel Vinson Charitable Trust
The Virgin Money Foundation
Viridor Credits Environmental Company
Volant Charitable Trust
Wade's Charity
The Wakeham Trust
The Community Foundation in Wales
Walton Foundation
Walton on Thames Charity
G. R. Waters Charitable Trust 2000
The Wates Foundation
The Weavers' Company Benevolent Fund
West Derby Waste Lands Charity
Westhill Endowment
Westminster Amalgamated Charity
Westminster Foundation
Alfred Williams Charitable Trust
Wiltshire Community Foundation
The Wimbledon Foundation
W. Wing Yip and Brothers Foundation
The Wolfson Family Charitable Trust
The Wood Foundation
Wooden Spoon Society
The Woodward Charitable Trust
*Sir Graham Wylie Foundation**
The Yorkshire Dales Millennium Trust
The Zochonis Charitable Trust
Zurich Community Trust (UK) Ltd

Advice and counselling services

ABF The Soldiers' Charity
*The Access to Justice Foundation**
Bairdwatson Charitable Trust
Bank of Scotland Foundation
The James Beattie Charitable Trust
*AJ Bell Trust**
*The Big Yellow Foundation**
The Bowerman Charitable Trust
The Liz and Terry Bramall Foundation
British Gas Energy Trust
William A. Cadbury Charitable Trust
*Camden Giving**
The Campden Charities Trustee
The Childhood Trust
The City Bridge Trust (Bridge House Estates)
The Clothworkers' Foundation
Colyer-Fergusson Charitable Trust
Cripplegate Foundation
Devon Community Foundation
County Durham Community Foundation
Jill Franklin Trust
Charles S. French Charitable Trust
Friends Provident Charitable Foundation
Global Charities
The Goldsmiths' Company Charity
The Grantham Yorke Trust
Dr Guthrie's Association
The Hadfield Charitable Trust
The Hadrian Trust
The Alfred Haines Charitable Trust
Hammersmith United Charities
Hampshire and Isle of Wight Community Foundation
The Hemby Charitable Trust
The Hobson Charity Ltd
Miss Agnes H. Hunter's Trust
The Charles Irving Charitable Trust
Isle of Wight Foundation
Kilpatrick Fraser Charitable Trust
The Leathersellers' Company Charitable Fund
The Legal Education Foundation
The Leigh Trust
The London Community Foundation (LCF)
London Legal Support Trust (LLST)
Merchants' House of Glasgow
The Mickleham Trust
G. M. Morrison Charitable Trust
The MSE Charity
The Mulberry Trust
The Norton Rose Fulbright Charitable Foundation
Notting Hill Genesis Community Foundation
The Pixel Fund
The Portishead Nautical Trust
David and Elaine Potter Foundation
The Progress Foundation
The PwC Foundation
Quartet Community Foundation
The Queen Anne's Gate Foundation
*The Quilter Foundation**
The Sigrid Rausing Trust
The Rayne Foundation
*RG Foundation**
The Robertson Trust
The Roughley Charitable Trust
The Royal British Legion
*RSM UK Foundation**
The Simmons & Simmons Charitable Foundation
*The Singer Foundation**
Sirius Minerals Foundation
The Slaughter and May Charitable Trust
The Mrs Smith and Mount Trust
The Stewarts Law Foundation
C. B. and H. H. Taylor 1984 Trust
Trust for London
The Trusthouse Charitable Foundation
Ulster Garden Villages Ltd
The Vardy Foundation
The Veterans' Foundation
*Vinci UK Foundation**
Volant Charitable Trust
Wakefield and Tetley Trust
Warwick Relief in Need Charity
The Waterloo Foundation
The Wates Foundation
The Wixamtree Trust
The Woodward Charitable Trust
Worcester Municipal Charities (CIO)

Citizenship

The A. B. Charitable Trust
The Aldama Foundation
The Asda Foundation
The Blagrave Trust
The Britford Bridge Trust
*Mary Brown Memorial Trust**
The Cayo Foundation
The City Bridge Trust (Bridge House Estates)
The John Coates Charitable Trust
Cripplegate Foundation
The Davis Foundation
*Dumfriesshire East Community Benefit Group SCIO**
*The Nine Incorporated Trades of Dundee General Fund Charity**
*Dunlossit and Islay Community Trust**

The Endrick Trust
The Enkalon Foundation
The Fairness Foundation
The Fort Foundation
Charles S. French Charitable Trust
The Gannochy Trust
The Golden Bottle Trust
Paul Hamlyn Foundation
The Lennox Hannay Charitable Trust
The Charles Hayward Foundation
The Hedley Foundation
The Henry C. Hoare Charitable Trust
The Hunter Foundation
The Invigorate Charitable Trust
Kilpatrick Fraser Charitable Trust
KPE4 Charitable Trust*
The KPMG Foundation
The R. J. Larg Family Trust
The Leeward Trust*
The Legal Education Foundation
The Leigh Trust
The Northwick Trust
Polden-Puckham Charitable Foundation
Richard Radcliffe Trust
The Sigrid Rausing Trust
The Joseph Rowntree Charitable Trust
The Saintbury Trust
Salters' Charitable Foundation
The Scottish Power Foundation
The Simmons & Simmons Charitable Foundation
The Charles Skey Charitable Trust
The South Yorkshire Community Foundation
W. F. Southall Trust
The Triangle Trust (1949) Fund
Trust for London
UPP Foundation
Nigel Vinson Charitable Trust

Community enterprise and social entrepreneurship

D. C. R. Allen Charitable Trust
Anglo American Group Foundation
The Apax Foundation
The Asda Foundation
BC Partners Foundation
The James Beattie Charitable Trust
Bedfordshire and Luton Community Foundation
Ruth Berkowitz Charitable Trust
The Bingham Trust
Birmingham International Airport Community Trust Fund
The Harold and Alice Bridges Charity
The Britford Bridge Trust
The Consuelo and Anthony Brooke Charitable Trust
The Noel Buxton Trust
Camden Giving*
The Chalk Cliff Trust
The Coalfields Regeneration Trust
The Cole Charitable Trust
Co-operative Community Investment Foundation
Michael Cornish Charitable Trust
Cripplegate Foundation
Cumbria Community Foundation
The Delves Charitable Trust
Foundation Derbyshire
County Durham Community Foundation
East End Community Foundation
The Ecology Trust
The Englefield Charitable Trust
The ExPat Foundation
Esmée Fairbairn Foundation
Allan and Nesta Ferguson Charitable Settlement
The Fidelity UK Foundation
The Football Foundation
The Fort Foundation
Charles S. French Charitable Trust
Friends Provident Charitable Foundation
The Goldman Sachs Charitable Gift Fund (UK)
Goldman Sachs Gives (UK)
GrantScape
The Greggs Foundation
The Grimmitt Trust
H. C. D. Memorial Fund
The Hadrian Trust
Hammersmith United Charities
Hampton Fund
The David and Claudia Harding Foundation
The Charles Hayward Foundation
Heathrow Community Trust
The Alan Edward Higgs Charity
The Hilden Charitable Fund
Housing Pathways Trust
The Hunter Foundation
Hyde Charitable Trust
Imagine Foundation
The Indigo Trust
The Innocent Foundation
Investream Charitable Trust
The Isle of Anglesey Charitable Trust
The J. J. Charitable Trust
The Johnson Foundation
The Cyril and Eve Jumbo Charitable Trust
The Kensington and Chelsea Foundation
Kilpatrick Fraser Charitable Trust
John Laing Charitable Trust
Community Foundations for Lancashire and Merseyside
The W. M. and B. W. Lloyd Trust
The London Community Foundation (LCF)
Mace Foundation
The Mactaggart Third Fund
Making a Difference Locally Ltd
D. G. Marshall of Cambridge Trust
The Master Charitable Trust
The Mercers' Charitable Foundation
I. and J. Meyer Family Foundation Ltd
Millennium Stadium Charitable Trust (Ymddiriedclaeth Elusennol Stadiwm y Mileniwm)
The Monmouthshire County Council Welsh Church Act Fund
Vyoel Moshe Charitable Trust
The MSE Charity
The Nomura Charitable Trust
Community Foundation for Northern Ireland
Notting Hill Genesis Community Foundation
Henry Oldfield Trust
Oxfordshire Community Foundation
The Pebbles Trust
The Jack Petchey Foundation
Power to Change Trust
The Prince of Wales's Charitable Foundation
Quartet Community Foundation
Elizabeth Rathbone Charity
Richmond Parish Lands Charity
The Rothley Trust
Royal Docks Trust (London)
The Rugby Group Benevolent Fund Ltd
The Scottish Power Foundation
The Shears Foundation
The Singer Foundation*
The Henry Smith Charity
Social Business Trust
Somerset Community Foundation

The South Yorkshire Community Foundation
Stanley Foundation Ltd
Sir Halley Stewart Trust
The Bernard Sunley Foundation
*The Thirty Percy Foundation**
The Truemark Trust
Trust for London
The Trusthouse Charitable Foundation
The Tudor Trust
United St Saviour's Charity
UnLtd (Foundation for Social Entrepreneurs)
The Veolia Environmental Trust
*Vinci UK Foundation**
The Virgin Money Foundation
Wakefield and Tetley Trust
Wates Family Enterprise Trust
Westway Trust
White Stuff Foundation
Wiltshire Community Foundation
Worcester Municipal Charities (CIO)
Worth Waynflete Foundation
The Yorkshire Dales Millennium Trust
The William Allen Young Charitable Trust

Community transport

The Liz and Terry Bramall Foundation
The Jack Brunton Charitable Trust
Community First
Hampton Fund
Hertfordshire Community Foundation
Rees Jeffreys Road Fund
The Lord's Taverners
Millennium Stadium Charitable Trust (Ymddiriedclaeth Elusennol Stadiwm y Mileniwm)
The Morrisons Foundation
Foundation Scotland
The Frieda Scott Charitable Trust
Shetland Charitable Trust
Ulster Garden Villages Ltd
*West Herts Charity Trust Ltd**

Rural communities

The Aberbrothock Skea Trust
The Ashley Family Foundation
The Banister Charitable Trust
Biffa Award
The Liz and Terry Bramall Foundation
The Noel Buxton Trust
Community First
The Dulverton Trust
The Ecology Trust
The Earl Fitzwilliam Charitable Trust
The Tara Getty Foundation
The Hamilton Davies Trust
The Innocent Foundation
The Limbourne Trust
Sir George Martin Trust
Millennium Stadium Charitable Trust (Ymddiriedclaeth Elusennol Stadiwm y Mileniwm)
The NFU Mutual Charitable Trust
The Jack Patston Charitable Trust
Power to Change Trust
The Prince's Countryside Fund
Quartet Community Foundation
The Ranworth Trust
The Robertson Trust
The Shears Foundation
The Sheffield Town Trust
Shetland Charitable Trust
The Stafford Trust
Tanner Trust
The Tedworth Charitable Trust
The Trusthouse Charitable Foundation
Worth Waynflete Foundation

Support services

The A. B. Charitable Trust
The Liz and Terry Bramall Foundation
The Noel Buxton Trust
The City Bridge Trust (Bridge House Estates)
The John Coates Charitable Trust
Cripplegate Foundation
The Fairness Foundation
Charles S. French Charitable Trust
Michael and Shirley Hunt Charitable Trust
The Allen Lane Foundation
The Leathersellers' Company Charitable Fund
The London Community Foundation (LCF)
The Merchant Venturers' Charity
The Mickleham Trust
Rix Thompson Rothenberg Foundation
The Saintbury Trust
The Sheldon Trust
Sirius Minerals Foundation
The Skelton Bounty
The South Yorkshire Community Foundation
The Vardy Foundation
The Woodward Charitable Trust

Urban communities

The Battersea Power Station Foundation
Biffa Award
The Liz and Terry Bramall Foundation
The Noel Buxton Trust
Community First
Cripplegate Foundation
Charles S. French Charitable Trust
The Hamilton Davies Trust
Rees Jeffreys Road Fund
The Mercers' Charitable Foundation
The Morel Charitable Trust
The Morris Charitable Trust
The Persimmon Charitable Foundation
Power to Change Trust
The Stafford Trust
Stephen Taylor Foundation
The Trusthouse Charitable Foundation

Education and training

The 1989 Willan Charitable Trust
The 29th May 1961 Charitable Trust
4 Charity Foundation
The Aaronson Foundation
The Aberdeen Foundation
ABF The Soldiers' Charity
The Acacia Charitable Trust
Adam Family Foundation*
The Bryan Adams Foundation
Adenfirst Ltd
The Aimwell Charitable Trust
The Aitken Family Charitable Trust*
Sylvia Aitken's Charitable Trust
AKO Foundation
The Alborada Trust
The Aldama Foundation
Aldgate and Allhallows Foundation
Al-Fayed Charitable Foundation
The All Saints Educational Trust
The Derrill Allatt Foundation
The Allen & Overy Foundation
D. C. R. Allen Charitable Trust
Alliance Family Foundation Ltd
Viscount Amory's Charitable Trust
Andor Charitable Trust
Anglo American Group Foundation
Anguish's Educational Foundation
The Apax Foundation
The John Apthorp Charity
The Arah Foundation
Ardbarron Trust Ltd
The Ardwick Trust
The Armed Forces Covenant Fund Trust*
Armed Forces Education Trust
The John Armitage Charitable Trust
The Armourers' and Brasiers' Gauntlet Trust
The Arsenal Foundation
The Ove Arup Foundation
Ove Arup Partnership Charitable Trust
The Asda Foundation
The Ashendene Trust
The Ian Askew Charitable Trust
Keren Association Ltd
Atkin Charitable Foundation
Atlas Memorial Ltd
Lawrence Atwell's Charity (Skinners' Company)
The Lord Austin Trust
The Scott Bader Commonwealth Ltd
The Bagri Foundation
Bairdwatson Charitable Trust
The Roy and Pixie Baker Charitable Trust
The Balcombe Charitable Trust
The Balfour Beatty Charitable Trust
The Roger and Sarah Bancroft Clark Charitable Trust
The Band Trust
Veronica and Lars Bane Foundation*
The Kamini and Vindi Banga Family Trust*
The Barbers' Company General Charities
The Barbour Foundation
The Philip Barker Charity
The Barker-Mill Foundation
The Barnes Fund*
Battens Charitable Trust
BC Partners Foundation
The James Beattie Charitable Trust
The Beaverbrooks Charitable Trust
The Becht Family Charitable Trust
The John Beckwith Charitable Trust
AJ Bell Trust*
The Bellahouston Bequest Fund
Benesco Charity Ltd
The Benham Charitable Settlement
The Rowan Bentall Charitable Trust
The Berkeley Foundation
Ruth Berkowitz Charitable Trust
The Bestway Foundation
The Beth Hamedrash Satmar Trust (BHST)
Bideford Bridge Trust
The Big Yellow Foundation*
The Billmeir Charitable Trust
The Bingham Trust
The Michael Bishop Foundation
Asser Bishvil Foundation
The Sydney Black Charitable Trust
The Isabel Blackman Foundation
The Blagrave Trust
The Sir Victor Blank Charitable Settlement
Bluespark Foundation
The Bluston Charitable Settlement
The Boltini Trust
The Bonamy Charitable Trust
The Booth Charities
Boots Charitable Trust
Sir William Boreman's Foundation
The Borrows Charitable Trust
The Boshier-Hinton Foundation
Alan Boswell Group Charitable Trust*
The Harry Bottom Charitable Trust
The Bowerman Charitable Trust
The Bowland Charitable Trust
G. and K. Boyes Charitable Trust
The Liz and Terry Bramall Foundation
The Breadsticks Foundation
The Brelms Trust CIO
The Brenley Trust
Bridgepoint Charitable Trust
The Britford Bridge Trust
The British and Foreign School Society
British Heart Foundation (BHF)
British Motor Sports Training Trust
The J. and M. Britton Charitable Trust
The Brook Trust
The Consuelo and Anthony Brooke Charitable Trust
The Charles Brotherton Trust
Mary Brown Memorial Trust*
The Brownsword Charitable Foundation
Brushmill Ltd
The Buffini Chao Foundation
Building & Civil Engineering Charitable Trust
The Burberry Foundation
The Burden Trust
The Clara E. Burgess Charity
The Arnold Burton 1998 Charitable Trust
Consolidated Charity of Burton upon Trent
C. and F. Charitable Trust
The Edward Cadbury Charitable Trust
William A. Cadbury Charitable Trust
The Cadbury Foundation
The Edward and Dorothy Cadbury Trust
The Cadogan Charity
The Calleva Foundation
Camden Giving*
The Campden Charities Trustee
Canary Wharf Contractors Fund
The Frederick and Phyllis Cann Trust
CareTech Foundation*
W. A. Cargill Charitable Trust
The W. A. Cargill Fund
The Antonio Carluccio Foundation*
The Carnegie Dunfermline Trust

The Carpenters' Company Charitable Trust
The Carr-Gregory Trust
The Castansa Trust
The Wilfrid and Constance Cave Foundation
The Cayo Foundation
The B. G. S. Cayzer Charitable Trust
The Chadwick Educational Foundation
The Amelia Chadwick Trust
Chalfords Ltd
Charitworth Ltd
Chartered Accountants' Livery Charity (CALC)
The Charterhouse Charitable Trust
The Cheruby Trust
Cheshire Community Foundation Ltd
The Chetwode Foundation
The Childhood Trust
The Childwick Trust
Chippenham Borough Lands Charity
The Chipping Sodbury Town Lands Charity
The Christabella Charitable Trust
The André Christian Trust
The Church Burgesses Educational Foundation
The CIBC World Markets Children's Foundation
The City Bridge Trust (Bridge House Estates)
The Clan Trust Ltd
The Clothworkers' Foundation
The Robert Clutterbuck Charitable Trust
The Coalfields Regeneration Trust
The John Coates Charitable Trust
Denise Coates Foundation
The Vivienne and Samuel Cohen Charitable Trust
The John S. Cohen Foundation
The Cole Charitable Trust
John and Freda Coleman Charitable Trust
Sir Jeremiah Colman Gift Trust
Comic Relief
The Comino Foundation
Douglas Compton James Charitable Trust
*The Connolly Foundation**
The Ernest Cook Trust
The Cooks Charity
The Catherine Cookson Charitable Trust
The Keith Coombs Trust
The Alice Ellen Cooper Dean Charitable Foundation
The J. Reginald Corah Foundation Fund
The Worshipful Company of Cordwainers Charitable Trusts (Minges Gift)
The Evan Cornish Foundation
The Duke of Cornwall's Benevolent Fund
The Corporation of Trinity House of Deptford Strond
*The Cotswold Primrose Charitable Trust**
*Council for World Mission (UK)**
The County Council of Dyfed Welsh Church Fund
Dudley and Geoffrey Cox Charitable Trust
The Lord Cozens-Hardy Trust
The Craps Charitable Trust
The Elizabeth Creak Charitable Trust
Credit Suisse EMEA Foundation
The Cross Trust
The Peter Cruddas Foundation
Cruden Foundation Ltd
Cumbria Community Foundation
Itzchok Meyer Cymerman Trust Ltd
D. M. H. Educational Trust Ltd
Oizer Dalim Trust
*The Daniell Trust**
*The Dashlight Foundation**
The Davidson Family Charitable Trust
Michael Davies Charitable Settlement
Margaret Davies Charity
The Crispin Davis Family Trust
The Henry and Suzanne Davis Foundation
Dawat-E-Hadiyah Trust (United Kingdom)
The Roger De Haan Charitable Trust
William Dean Countryside and Educational Trust
The Demigryphon Trust
The J. N. Derbyshire Trust
Devon Community Foundation
The Laduma Dhamecha Charitable Trust
The Dibden Allotments Fund
Didymus
The Dischma Charitable Trust
The Djanogly Foundation
*William and Frances Dobie Charitable Foundation**
Donibristle Trust
Dorset Community Foundation
The Double 'O' Charity Ltd
Drapers' Charitable Fund
The Anne Duchess of Westminster's Charity
*Dumfriesshire East Community Benefit Group SCIO**
County Durham Community Foundation
The DWF Charitable Foundation
The Dyers' Company Charitable Trust
The Earley Charity
East End Community Foundation
The Economist Charitable Trust
The Gilbert and Eileen Edgar Foundation
The Edge Foundation
Edinburgh Trust No. 2 Account
Edupoor Ltd
*The Eight Foundation**
The Eighteen Fund
The Eighty Eight Foundation
The George Elias Charitable Trust
*The Elie Trust**
The Elmley Foundation
The Emerton-Christie Charity
The Englefield Charitable Trust
The Enkalon Foundation
Entindale Ltd
The EQ Foundation
Esher House Charitable Trust
The Essex Youth Trust
The Estelle Trust
The Exilarch's Foundation
The ExPat Foundation
Extonglen Ltd
*Family Philanthropy Ltd**
The Lord Faringdon Charitable Trust
Samuel William Farmer Trust
The Thomas Farr Charity
The Farthing Trust
The George Fentham Birmingham Charity
The Feoffees of St Michael's Spurriergate York
Allan and Nesta Ferguson Charitable Settlement
The Fidelity UK Foundation
The Finborough Foundation
The Finnis Scott Foundation
Sir John Fisher Foundation
Fishmongers' Company's Charitable Trust
The Follett Trust
*The Fonthill Foundation**
The Football Foundation
Ford Britain Trust
Oliver Ford Foundation
Forest Hill Charitable Trust
Donald Forrester Trust
Gwyneth Forrester Trust
The Fort Foundation
Four Acre Trust
*Foux Foundation**
The Foyle Foundation

The Elizabeth Frankland Moore and Star Foundation
The Gordon Fraser Charitable Trust
The Hugh Fraser Foundation
The Joyce and Norman Freed Charitable Trust*
Charles S. French Charitable Trust
The Freshfield Foundation
The Freshgate Trust Foundation
Friarsgate Trust
The Fulmer Charitable Trust
The Funding Network
GambleAware
Gamma Trust
The Gannochy Trust
The Worshipful Company of Gardeners of London Charity
Garfield Weston Foundation
The Gatsby Charitable Foundation
The Gaudio Family Foundation (UK) Ltd
The Robert Gavron Charitable Trust
The Jacqueline and Michael Gee Charitable Trust
Sir Robert Geffery's Almshouse Trust
General Charity (Coventry)
The Tara Getty Foundation
The Gibbons Family Trust
The Gibbs Charitable Trusts
The G. C. Gibson Charitable Trust
The Girdlers' Company Charitable Trust
The Glass-House Trust
The Gloag Foundation
Worshipful Company of Gold and Silver Wyre Drawers Second Charitable Trust Fund
The Golden Bottle Trust
The Goldman Sachs Charitable Gift Fund (UK)
Goldman Sachs Gives (UK)
The Goldsmiths' Company Charity
The Mike Gooley Trailfinders Charity
The Gosling Foundation Ltd
The Gould Charitable Trust
Gowling WLG (UK) Charitable Trust
The Hemraj Goyal Foundation
Grace Charitable Trust
The Grace Trust
The James Grace Trust*
The Granada Foundation
The Grant Foundation
The Grantham Yorke Trust
The J. G. Graves Charitable Trust
The Great Britain Sasakawa Foundation
The Great Stone Bridge Trust of Edenbridge
The Greater Manchester High Sheriff's Police Trust
The Kenneth and Susan Green Charitable Foundation
Philip and Judith Green Trust
Greenham Trust Ltd
The Greenslade Family Foundation*
The Grimmitt Trust
The Grocers' Charity
M. and R. Gross Charities Ltd
Groundwork UK
The Walter Guinness Charitable Trust
Dr Guthrie's Association
H. C. D. Memorial Fund
H. C. Foundation
Hackney Parochial Charities
The Hadrian Trust
The Alfred Haines Charitable Trust
Halifax Foundation for Northern Ireland
The Hamilton Davies Trust
Paul Hamlyn Foundation
The Helen Hamlyn Trust
Hampshire and Isle of Wight Community Foundation
The W. A. Handley Charity Trust
The Lennox Hannay Charitable Trust
The Haramead Trust
Harbinson Charitable Trust
Harborne Parish Lands Charity
The Harbour Charitable Trust
The Harbour Foundation
The David and Claudia Harding Foundation
William Harding's Charity
The Harebell Centenary Fund
The Harpur Trust
The Harrison-Frank Family Foundation (UK) Ltd
The Harry and Mary Foundation*
Gay and Peter Hartley's Hillards Charitable Trust
Edward Harvist Trust (The Harvist Estate)
The Maurice Hatter Foundation
Hays Travel Foundation
The Headley Trust
The Health Foundation
May Hearnshaw's Charity
Heart of England Community Foundation
Heart Research UK
The Heathcoat Trust
Heathrow Community Trust
The Heathside Charitable Trust
The Charlotte Heber-Percy Charitable Trust
The Percy Hedley 1990 Charitable Trust
The Hedley Foundation
The Simon Heller Charitable Settlement
The Helping Foundation
The Hemby Charitable Trust
Henley Educational Trust
Henley Royal Regatta Charitable Trust
The Tim Henman Foundation
Herefordshire Community Foundation
Hertfordshire Community Foundation
P. and C. Hickinbotham Charitable Trust
The Alan Edward Higgs Charity
The Highcroft Charitable Trust
The Hilden Charitable Fund
The Derek Hill Foundation
The Hillier Trust
R. G. Hills Charitable Trust
The Lady Hind Trust
The Hinduja Foundation
The Hintze Family Charity Foundation
The Hiscox Foundation
The Henry C. Hoare Charitable Trust
The Hobson Charity Ltd
Hockerill Educational Foundation
The Jane Hodge Foundation
The Holbeck Charitable Trust
The Holden Charitable Trust
Hollick Family Foundation
The Holliday Foundation
P. H. Holt Foundation
The Mary Homfray Charitable Trust
The Horners Charity Fund
The Horse Trust
Hospice UK
The Sir Joseph Hotung Charitable Settlement
House of Industry Estate
Housing Pathways Trust
The Reta Lila Howard Foundation
The Humanitarian Trust
The Hunter Foundation
Miss Agnes H. Hunter's Trust
The Huntingdon Foundation Ltd
Huntingdon Freemen's Trust
The Hutchinson Charitable Trust
The Nani Huyu Charitable Trust
Hyde Park Place Estate Charity
IBM United Kingdom Trust
Ibrahim Foundation Ltd

The Iliffe Family Charitable Trust
Impetus
Integrated Education Fund
The International Bankers Charitable Trust
The Inverforth Charitable Trust
*The Investindustrial Foundation**
Investream Charitable Trust
The Invigorate Charitable Trust
The Ireland Fund of Great Britain
Irish Youth Foundation (UK) Ltd (incorporating The Lawlor Foundation)
The Isle of Anglesey Charitable Trust
The ITF Seafarers Trust
The J. and J. Benevolent Foundation
The J. A. R. Charitable Trust
The Jabbs Foundation
The Frank Jackson Foundation
John James Bristol Foundation
John Jarrold Trust Ltd
Rees Jeffreys Road Fund
The Jephcott Charitable Trust
The Jerusalem Trust
The Jewish Youth Fund
The Johnson Foundation
The Marjorie and Geoffrey Jones Charitable Trust
The Jordan Charitable Foundation
The Joron Charitable Trust
J. E. Joseph Charitable Fund
The Cyril and Eve Jumbo Charitable Trust
The Jusaca Charitable Trust
*Kantor Charitable Foundation**
The Kasner Charitable Trust
C. S. Kaufman Charitable Trust
The Emmanuel Kaye Foundation
William Kendall's Charity (Wax Chandlers' Company)
The Kensington and Chelsea Foundation
E. and E. Kernkraut Charities Ltd
The Peter Kershaw Trust
The King Henry VIII Endowed Trust – Warwick
The Graham Kirkham Foundation
The Kirschel Foundation
Robert Kitchin (Saddlers' Company)
Sir James Knott Trust
Kolyom Trust Ltd
*KPE4 Charitable Trust**
The KPMG Foundation
The Kreitman Foundation
Kusuma Trust UK
The Kyte Charitable Trust
*The Labone Charitable Trust**
Ladbrokes Coral Trust
John Laing Charitable Trust
The Kirby Laing Foundation
The Beatrice Laing Trust
The Lake House Charity
Community Foundations for Lancashire and Merseyside
The Lancashire Foundation
Duchy of Lancaster Benevolent Fund
The R. J. Larg Family Trust
Mrs F. B. Laurence Charitable Trust
The Law Family Charitable Foundation
The Edgar E. Lawley Foundation
Lawson Beckman Charitable Trust
The Lawson Trust CIO
The David Lean Foundation
The Leathersellers' Company Charitable Fund
The Leche Trust
*The Leeward Trust**
The Legal Education Foundation
The Kennedy Leigh Charitable Trust
The Leigh Trust
The Leri Charitable Trust
The Leverhulme Trust
Lord Leverhulme's Charitable Trust
*Cecil and Hilda Lewis Charitable Trust**
Bernard Lewis Family Charitable Trust
David and Ruth Lewis Family Charitable Trust
John Lewis Foundation
The Limbourne Trust
Limoges Charitable Trust
The Linbury Trust
The Linder Foundation
The Lindley Foundation (TLF)
The Charles Littlewood Hill Trust
The Second Joseph Aaron Littman Foundation
Liverpool Charity and Voluntary Services (LCVS)
*The Livingston Charitable Trust**
The Elaine and Angus Lloyd Charitable Trust
The W. M. and B. W. Lloyd Trust
Local Trent Ltd
The Locker Foundation
The Lockwood Charitable Foundation
Loftus Charitable Trust
The London Community Foundation (LCF)
London Freemasons Charity
Longleigh Foundation
LPW Ltd
The Henry Lumley Charitable Trust
Lord and Lady Lurgan Trust
John Lyon's Charity
M. and C. Trust
The M. Y. A. Charitable Trust
The Macdonald-Buchanan Charitable Trust
Mace Foundation
The Mackintosh Foundation
The MacRobert Trust 2019
Makers of Playing Cards Charity
Making a Difference Locally Ltd
Man Group plc Charitable Trust
The Manackerman Charitable Trust
The Manchester Guardian Society Charitable Trust
The W. M. Mann Foundation
R. W. Mann Trust
*The Manson Family Charitable Trust**
*The Marandi Foundation**
The Stella and Alexander Margulies Charitable Trust
The Marks Family Charitable Trust
The J. P. Marland Charitable Trust
*The Marque Foundation**
The Michael Marsh Charitable Trust
The Marsh Christian Trust
Charlotte Marshall Charitable Trust
D. G. Marshall of Cambridge Trust
The Martin Charitable Trust
Sir George Martin Trust
John Martin's Charity
Nancie Massey Charitable Trust
The Master Charitable Trust
Mathew Trust
The Matliwala Family Charitable Trust
The Robert McAlpine Foundation
*Gemma and Chris McGough Charitable Foundation CIO**
The Medlock Charitable Trust
Melodor Ltd
The Melow Charitable Trust
The Mercers' Charitable Foundation
The Merchant Taylors' Company Charities Fund

The Merchant Venturers' Charity
Merchants' House of Glasgow
T. and J. Meyer Family Foundation Ltd
The Mickel Fund
The Masonic Province of Middlesex Charitable Trust (Middlesex Masonic Charity)
The Mikheev Charitable Trust*
The Millennium Oak Trust
The Ronald Miller Foundation
Jean and Roger Miller's Charitable Trust
The Millichope Foundation
The Millward Charitable Trust
The Milne Family Foundation*
The James Milner Foundation
Milton Keynes Community Foundation Ltd
Minton Charitable Trust
The Brian Mitchell Charitable Settlement
The Mittal Foundation
Keren Mitzvah Trust
The Mizpah Trust
The Mohn Westlake Foundation*
Mole Charitable Trust
The Alexander Moncur Trust
The Monday Charitable Trust*
The Monmouthshire County Council Welsh Church Act Fund
Moondance Foundation
The Henry Moore Foundation
John Moores Foundation
The Steve Morgan Foundation
Morgan Stanley International Foundation
The Morris Charitable Trust
The Ken and Lynne Morrison Charitable Trust
G. M. Morrison Charitable Trust
The Ken and Edna Morrison Charitable Trust
The Morrisons Foundation
The Morton Charitable Trust (Dundee)
The Mosawi Foundation*
The Moshal Charitable Trust
Vyoel Moshe Charitable Trust
The Mosselson Charitable Trust
Moto in the Community
Motor Neurone Disease Association
The Mulberry Trust
The John R. Murray Charitable Trust
Brian Murtagh Charitable Trust
Music Sales Charitable Trust
Muslim Hands
The Mutual Trust Group
MW (CL) Foundation
MW (GK) Foundation
MW (HO) Foundation
MW (RH) Foundation
The National Express Foundation
The National Garden Scheme
The NDL Foundation
Ner Foundation
Nesta
Network for Social Change Charitable Trust
Newby Trust Ltd
Alderman Newton's Educational Foundation
The NFU Mutual Charitable Trust
The Nineveh Charitable Trust
The Nisbet Trust
NNS Foundation*
The Nomura Charitable Trust
Norfolk Community Foundation
Educational Foundation of Alderman John Norman
The Norman Family Charitable Trust
Normanby Charitable Trust
North Berwick Trust*
Northamptonshire Community Foundation
Community Foundation for Northern Ireland
Northwood Charitable Trust
The Norton Foundation
The Norton Rose Fulbright Charitable Foundation
Norwich Town Close Estate Charity
Notting Hill Genesis Community Foundation
The Nuffield Foundation
The Oakley Charitable Trust
Oglesby Charitable Trust
Oizer Charitable Trust
The Olwyn Foundation*
Orthopaedic Research UK
The O'Sullivan Family Charitable Trust
Ovingdean Hall Foundation
The Ovo Charitable Foundation
The Owen Family Trust
The Paget Charitable Trust
The Paphitis Charitable Trust
The Paragon Trust
Partners Global Foundation*
The Pastoral Care Trust – The St Nicholas Care Fund
The Patrick Trust
Peacock Charitable Trust
Susanna Peake Charitable Trust
David Pearlman Charitable Foundation
The Pears Family Charitable Foundation
The Pebbles Trust
People's Postcode Trust
Dina Perelman Trust Ltd*
B. E. Perl Charitable Trust
The Persimmon Charitable Foundation
Personal Assurance Charitable Trust
The Jack Petchey Foundation
Petplan Charitable Trust
The Phillips and Rubens Charitable Trust
The Phillips Family Charitable Trust
The Pilgrim Trust
Cecil Pilkington Charitable Trust
PIMCO Foundation Europe
The Pitt-Rivers Charitable Trust
The George and Esme Pollitzer Charitable Settlement
The Polonsky Foundation
The Portal Trust
The Portishead Nautical Trust
Postcode Society Trust (formerly Postcode Dream Trust)
David and Elaine Potter Foundation
The Pret Foundation
The Prince of Wales's Charitable Foundation
The Priory Foundation
The Professional Footballers' Association Charity
The Progress Foundation
Catkin Pussywillow Charitable Trust
The PwC Foundation
The Pye Foundation
Mr and Mrs J. A. Pye's Charitable Settlement
QBE European Operations Foundation
Quadstar Charitable Foundation*
Quartet Community Foundation
The Queen Anne's Gate Foundation
The Quilter Foundation*
Quintessentially Foundation
R. S. Charitable Trust
The Monica Rabagliati Charitable Trust
Rachel Charitable Trust
Richard Radcliffe Trust
The Rainford Trust
Randeree Charitable Trust*
The Rank Foundation Ltd
The Joseph Rank Trust
The Ranworth Trust
The Eleanor Rathbone Charitable Trust
Elizabeth Rathbone Charity
The Ravensdale Trust
The Roger Raymond Charitable Trust

The Rayne Foundation
The Rayne Trust
The Sir James Reckitt Charity
Red Hill Charitable Trust
The Reece Foundation
Richard Reeve's Foundation
Rentrust Foundation Ltd
Reuben Foundation
*RG Foundation**
The Clive and Sylvia Richards Charity Ltd
Humphrey Richardson Taylor Charitable Trust
Richmond Parish Lands Charity
Ridgesave Ltd
Rigby Foundation
The River Farm Foundation
Rivers Foundation
Riverside Charitable Trust Ltd
Rix Thompson Rothenberg Foundation
The Roan Charitable Trust
The Robertson Trust
The Dezna Robins Jones Charitable Foundation
Robyn Charitable Trust
*The Rockspring Charitable Trust**
The Roddick Foundation
The Gerald and Gail Ronson Family Foundation
Mrs L. D. Rope's Third Charitable Settlement
The Cecil Rosen Foundation
The David Ross Foundation
The Rothermere Foundation
The Rothley Trust
The Rothschild Foundation
The Eranda Rothschild Foundation
The Roughley Charitable Trust
Rowanville Ltd
The Rowlands Trust
The Royal British Legion
Royal Docks Trust (London)
The Royal Foundation of the Duke and Duchess of Cambridge
Royal Masonic Trust for Girls and Boys
*RSM UK Foundation**
The Russell Trust
The Saddlers' Company Charitable Fund
The Alan and Babette Sainsbury Charitable Fund
The Saintbury Trust
The Salamander Charitable Trust
Salters' Charitable Foundation
Samjo Ltd
The Basil Samuel Charitable Trust
The M. J. Samuel Charitable Trust
*The Sanderson Foundation**
The Sandhu Charitable Foundation
The Sands Family Trust
Santander UK Foundation Ltd
O. and G. Schreiber Charitable Trust
Schroder Charity Trust
The Schroder Foundation
Foundation Scotland
Francis C. Scott Charitable Trust
The Scottish Power Foundation
Scottish Property Industry Festival of Christmas (SPIFOX)
Scouloudi Foundation
The SDL Foundation
Seafarers UK (King George's Fund for Sailors)
Sam and Bella Sebba Charitable Trust
Shaftoe Educational Foundation
The Shanly Foundation
ShareGift (The Orr Mackintosh Foundation)
The Shears Foundation
The Sheepdrove Trust
The Sheldon Trust
The Sherling Charitable Trust
The Archie Sherman Charitable Trust
SHINE (Support and Help in Education)
The Bassil Shippam and Alsford Trust
The Shipwrights' Charitable Fund
Shlomo Memorial Fund Ltd
The Shoe Zone Trust
Shulem B. Association Ltd
*The Singer Foundation**
Sirius Minerals Foundation
The Charles Skey Charitable Trust
Skipton Building Society Charitable Foundation
The Slaughter and May Charitable Trust
Sloane Robinson Foundation
The SMB Trust
The Mrs Smith and Mount Trust
The DS Smith Charitable Foundation
The N. Smith Charitable Settlement
*Arabella and Julian Smith Family Trust**
The Martin Smith Foundation
The Leslie Smith Foundation
Philip Smith's Charitable Trust
The R. C. Snelling Charitable Trust
The Sobell Foundation
*Societe Generale UK Foundation**
Sodexo Stop Hunger Foundation
Sofronie Foundation
Somerset Community Foundation
The E. C. Sosnow Charitable Trust
The South Yorkshire Community Foundation
The Stephen R. and Philippa H. Southall Charitable Trust
Southover Manor General Education Trust Ltd
Peter Sowerby Foundation
Sparquote Ltd
*The Michael and Sarah Spencer Foundation**
Spielman Charitable Trust
The Spoore, Merry and Rixman Foundation
Rosalyn and Nicholas Springer Charitable Trust
The Geoff and Fiona Squire Foundation
The St James's Trust Settlement
Sir Walter St John's Educational Charity
St John's Foundation Est. 1174
St Olave's and St Saviour's Schools Foundation
The Community Foundation for Staffordshire
Standard Life Foundation
Stanley Foundation Ltd
Staples Trust
The Peter Stebbings Memorial Charity
The Steel Charitable Trust
The Steinberg Family Charitable Trust
C. E. K. Stern Charitable Trust
*The Sterry Family Foundation**
Stevenson Family's Charitable Trust
Sir Halley Stewart Trust
The Stewarts Law Foundation
Mark Stolkin Foundation
The Stoneygate Trust
Peter Stormonth Darling Charitable Trust
Peter Storrs Trust
Strand Parishes Trust
Stratford-upon-Avon Town Trust
The WO Street Charitable Foundation
The Street Foundation
StreetSmart – Action for the Homeless
*The Joseph Strong Frazer Trust**
The Sudborough Foundation

The Summerfield Charitable Trust
The Bernard Sunley Foundation
The Support Foundation*
The Sutasoma Trust
Sutton Coldfield Charitable Trust
The Swann-Morton Foundation
The John Swire (1989) Charitable Trust
The Swire Charitable Trust
The Adrian Swire Charitable Trust
The Charles and Elsie Sykes Trust
The T.K. Maxx and Homesense Foundation
The Tabhair Charitable Trust
Taca
The Tajtelbaum Charitable Trust
The Talbot Village Trust
Tallow Chandlers Benevolent Fund No. 2
Talteg Ltd
The David Tannen Charitable Trust
Tay Charitable Trust
C. B. and H. H. Taylor 1984 Trust
The Taylor Family Foundation
Stephen Taylor Foundation
The Thales Charitable Trust
Scott Thomson Charitable Trust
The Thornton Trust
The Thriplow Charitable Trust
Mrs R. P. Tindall's Charitable Trust
The Tobacco Pipe Makers and Tobacco Trade Benevolent Fund
The Tolkien Trust
The Tomoro Foundation*
The Tompkins Foundation
The Tory Family Foundation
The Tottenham Grammar School Foundation
Tower Hill Trust
Toyota Manufacturing UK Charitable Trust
The Trades House of Glasgow
The Troutsdale Charitable Trust*
Trumros Ltd
Trust for London
The James Tudor Foundation
The Tudwick Foundation*
The Tuixen Foundation
The Turtleton Charitable Trust
Ufi VocTech Trust
Ulster Garden Villages Ltd
The Underwood Trust
The Union Of The Sisters Of Mercy Of Great Britain
The Michael Uren Foundation
The Van Mesdag Fund*
The Vandervell Foundation
The Vardy Foundation
The Velvet Foundation*
The Veterans' Foundation
Nigel Vinson Charitable Trust
The Vintners' Foundation
Virgin Atlantic Foundation
The Vodafone Foundation
Sylvia Waddilove Foundation UK
The Wakeham Trust
The Walcot Foundation
The Walker Trust
Walton Foundation
The Barbara Ward Children's Foundation
The Waterloo Foundation
Wates Family Enterprise Trust
The Wates Foundation
The William Wates Memorial Trust
The Geoffrey Watling Charity
John Watson's Trust
The Weavers' Company Benevolent Fund
The Weinstock Fund
The James Weir Foundation
The Welland Trust*
Wellington Management UK Foundation
The Welsh Church Act Fund
Westminster Almshouses Foundation
The Barbara Whatmore Charitable Trust
The Wheeler Family Charitable Trust
The Whinfell Charitable Fund
Charity Of Sir Richard Whittington
Joan Wilkinson Charitable Trust*
The Williams Charitable Trust
The Willmott Dixon Foundation
The Wilson Foundation
The Wimbledon Foundation
W. Wing Yip and Brothers Foundation
The Michael and Anna Wix Charitable Trust
The Wixamtree Trust
The Maurice Wohl Charitable Foundation
The Charles Wolfson Charitable Trust
The Wolfson Family Charitable Trust
The Wolfson Foundation
The Wood Foundation
Woodroffe Benton Foundation
The Woodward Charitable Trust
The Woosnam Foundation
Worcester Municipal Charities (CIO)
The Eric Wright Charitable Trust
Wychville Ltd
Sir Graham Wylie Foundation*
Yankov Charitable Trust
The Yapp Charitable Trust
York Children's Trust
The William Allen Young Charitable Trust
The Elizabeth and Prince Zaiger Trust
The Zochonis Charitable Trust

Preschool education

Henley Educational Trust
Richard Reeve's Foundation
SHINE (Support and Help in Education)

Primary education

The Chadwick Educational Foundation
The Foyle Foundation
Henley Educational Trust
The J. J. Charitable Trust
Newcomen Collett Foundation
SHINE (Support and Help in Education)

Secondary education

The Harry Bottom Charitable Trust
Bristol Charities
The Chadwick Educational Foundation
The Dibden Allotments Fund
The Foyle Foundation
Hadras Kodesh Trust
Heathrow Community Trust
Henley Educational Trust
Integrated Education Fund
The J. J. Charitable Trust
The Peter Kershaw Trust
The Charles Littlewood Hill Trust
Nesta
Newcomen Collett Foundation
The Owen Family Trust
Richard Reeve's Foundation
Sarum St Michael Educational Charity
SHINE (Support and Help in Education)
Colonel W. H. Whitbread Charitable Trust
The Wolfson Foundation

Higher education

Bloodwise
The Harry Bottom Charitable Trust
The Rory and Elizabeth Brooks Foundation
The Chadwick Educational Foundation
The Elizabeth Creak Charitable Trust
The Simon Heller Charitable Settlement
Henley Educational Trust
The Holbeck Charitable Trust
Huntingdon Freemen's Trust
The International Bankers Charitable Trust
The Ireland Fund of Great Britain
Rees Jeffreys Road Fund
The Ian Karten Charitable Trust
The Leathersellers' Company Charitable Fund
The Leche Trust
The Masonic Province of Middlesex Charitable Trust (Middlesex Masonic Charity)
The National Express Foundation
The Nuffield Foundation
The James Pantyfedwen Foundation (Ymddiriedolaeth James Pantyfedwen)
The Pears Family Charitable Foundation
The Pharsalia Charitable Trust
The Polonsky Foundation
Richard Reeve's Foundation
Humphrey Richardson Taylor Charitable Trust
Rothschild Foundation (Hanadiv) Europe
The Thriplow Charitable Trust
UPP Foundation
The Wolfson Foundation

Vocational training and apprenticeships

Bairdwatson Charitable Trust
The Max Barney Foundation
The Bestway Foundation
Building & Civil Engineering Charitable Trust
John and Freda Coleman Charitable Trust
The Finnis Scott Foundation
The Girdlers' Company Charitable Trust
The Ian Karten Charitable Trust
The Kirby Laing Foundation
The Allen Lane Foundation
Mathew Trust
The National Garden Scheme
The Pears Family Charitable Foundation
People's Postcode Trust
The Jack Petchey Foundation
The Pilgrim Trust
The Professional Footballers' Association Charity
The Racing Foundation
The Reece Foundation
Seafarers UK (King George's Fund for Sailors)
The Shipwrights' Charitable Fund
Ufi VocTech Trust

Adult education and training

Bairdwatson Charitable Trust
The Big Yellow Foundation*
The Blagrave Trust
Boots Charitable Trust
Building & Civil Engineering Charitable Trust
The Cooks Charity
GambleAware
The Alfred Haines Charitable Trust
The Lady Hind Trust
The Jerusalem Trust
The London Community Foundation (LCF)
Mathew Trust
John Moores Foundation
The Pret Foundation
The Professional Footballers' Association Charity
Richard Reeve's Foundation
The Robertson Trust
The Royal British Legion
The Royal Foundation of the Duke and Duchess of Cambridge
StreetSmart – Action for the Homeless
C. B. and H. H. Taylor 1984 Trust
Trust for London
Ufi VocTech Trust

Special educational needs

ArtSocial Foundation
The Boshier-Hinton Foundation
The J. Reginald Corah Foundation Fund
Eastern Counties Educational Trust Ltd
The Joyce Fletcher Charitable Trust
The Forbes Charitable Foundation
The J. G. Graves Charitable Trust
The J. J. Charitable Trust
The Ian Karten Charitable Trust
The Kasner Charitable Trust
The Lord's Taverners
The Ken and Lynne Morrison Charitable Trust
The Morrisons Foundation
The Pears Family Charitable Foundation
Red Hill Charitable Trust
Rix Thompson Rothenberg Foundation
The Sheldon Trust
The Leslie Smith Foundation
Westminster Almshouses Foundation
The Wolfson Foundation
The Woodward Charitable Trust

Extracurricular activities

The Ernest Cook Trust
Newcomen Collett Foundation
The Woodward Charitable Trust

Integrated education

Integrated Education Fund

Arts, humanities and social sciences

The Ove Arup Foundation
The Associated Board of the Royal Schools of Music
The Aurelius Charitable Trust
The BRIT Trust
The Burberry Foundation
The Clore Duffield Foundation
The Daiwa Anglo-Japanese Foundation
The De Laszlo Foundation
The Elmley Foundation
The Enkalon Foundation
The Finborough Foundation
The Finnis Scott Foundation
Marc Fitch Fund

Nicholas and Judith Goodison's Charitable Settlement
The Great Britain Sasakawa Foundation
Paul Hamlyn Foundation
The Harbour Foundation
The Institute for Policy Research
*The Karlsson Jativa Charitable Foundation**
The Leche Trust
The Legal Education Foundation
The Leverhulme Trust
The Linder Foundation
The Mayfield Valley Arts Trust
*The Mikheev Charitable Trust**
The Miles Morland Foundation
The Nuffield Foundation
*Orange Tree Trust**
The Ouseley Church Music Trust
The Performing Right Society Foundation
The Pitt-Rivers Charitable Trust
The Polonsky Foundation
David and Elaine Potter Foundation
The Radcliffe Trust
Richard Reeve's Foundation
The Resolution Trust
The RVW Trust
Universal Music UK Sound Foundation
UPP Foundation
Nigel Vinson Charitable Trust
Wates Family Enterprise Trust
The Wellcome Trust
The Wolfson Foundation
Youth Music

Literacy

The Elmley Foundation
The Girdlers' Company Charitable Trust
The J. J. Charitable Trust
The Linbury Trust
Lloyds Bank Foundation for the Channel Islands
Man Group plc Charitable Trust
The Marsh Christian Trust
The Miles Morland Foundation
The Morrisons Foundation
Old Possum's Practical Trust
Richard Reeve's Foundation
The W. H. Smith Group Charitable Trust
Ulster Garden Villages Ltd

Formal sciences

The Borrows Charitable Trust
The Burberry Foundation
*Digital Xtra Fund**
The Finborough Foundation
The Golden Bottle Trust
The Graham Trust
IBM United Kingdom Trust
Ibrahim Foundation Ltd
The Invigorate Charitable Trust
The Graham Kirkham Foundation
The Leri Charitable Trust
*The Mikheev Charitable Trust**
*The Mila Charitable Organisation**
The John R. Murray Charitable Trust
The Reece Foundation
The Rowlands Trust
The Charles Skey Charitable Trust
The Wolfson Foundation

Natural sciences

The Burberry Foundation
The Elizabeth Creak Charitable Trust
The Finborough Foundation
The Granada Foundation
The Great Britain Sasakawa Foundation
The Harbour Foundation
The Invigorate Charitable Trust
The Frank Jackson Foundation
John Jarrold Trust Ltd
The Rowlands Trust
Salters' Charitable Foundation
The Sylvia and Colin Shepherd Charitable Trust
The Wellcome Trust

Professional and applied sciences

The Ove Arup Foundation
The Barbers' Company General Charities
British Heart Foundation (BHF)
Building & Civil Engineering Charitable Trust
*The Antonio Carluccio Foundation**
The Corporation of Trinity House of Deptford Strond
The Elizabeth Creak Charitable Trust
The James Dyson Foundation
The Exilarch's Foundation
The Finnis Scott Foundation
The Lord Forte Foundation
The Freshgate Trust Foundation
The Happold Foundation
Help for Health
The International Bankers Charitable Trust
The Legal Education Foundation
The Linder Foundation
Lloyd's Register Foundation
The MacRobert Trust 2019
The National Garden Scheme
North East Area Miners' Social Welfare Trust Fund
The Nuffield Foundation
The Prince of Wales's Charitable Foundation
The Professional Footballers' Association Charity
The Reece Foundation
Salisbury Pool Charity
The Savoy Educational Trust
Seafarers UK (King George's Fund for Sailors)
The Sheepdrove Trust
The Shipwrights' Charitable Fund
The Simmons & Simmons Charitable Foundation
Peter Sowerby Foundation
The Whitaker Charitable Trust
The Wolfson Foundation

Skilled crafts

The Worshipful Company of Cordwainers Charitable Trusts (Minges Gift)
*The Nine Incorporated Trades of Dundee General Fund Charity**
The Dyers' Company Charitable Trust
Worshipful Company of Glovers of London Charitable Trust
The Idlewild Trust
The Kirby Laing Foundation
The Leathersellers' Company Charitable Fund
The Leche Trust
The Saddlers' Company Charitable Fund

Emergency response/relief

The Adlard Family Charitable Foundation
The Alborada Trust
Ardbarron Trust Ltd
The Roger and Sarah Bancroft Clark Charitable Trust
The Barbour Foundation
Bauer Radio's Cash for Kids Charities
Blakemore Foundation
The Boltini Trust
Community Foundation for Calderdale
The Charterhouse Charitable Trust
The Clothworkers' Foundation
Devon Community Foundation
Forest Hill Charitable Trust
The Tara Getty Foundation
The Grace Trust
The Kenneth and Susan Green Charitable Foundation
Greenham Trust Ltd
The Lennox Hannay Charitable Trust
The Albert Hunt Trust
IBM United Kingdom Trust
The Innocent Foundation
International Bible Students Association
*JD Foundation**
The Elton John Aids Foundation (EJAF)
Community Foundations for Lancashire and Merseyside
Mrs M. A. Lascelles Charitable Trust
The Leathersellers' Company Charitable Fund
Limoges Charitable Trust
The Linbury Trust
Milton Keynes Community Foundation Ltd
The Monmouthshire County Council Welsh Church Act Fund
The Steve Morgan Foundation
The Morrisons Foundation
Norfolk Community Foundation
The Norman Family Charitable Trust
The Norton Rose Fulbright Charitable Foundation
Oxfordshire Community Foundation
*The Samuel and Freda Parkinson Charitable Trust**
The Pets at Home Foundation
The Prince's Countryside Fund
The Puebla Charitable Trust
Quartet Community Foundation
Rhodi Charitable Trust
Richmond Parish Lands Charity
The Sir James Roll Charitable Trust
The Royal Foundation of the Duke and Duchess of Cambridge
The Saintbury Trust
Salters' Charitable Foundation
Seafarers UK (King George's Fund for Sailors)
The Shanly Foundation
Somerset Community Foundation
The South Yorkshire Community Foundation
Spar Charitable Fund
*The Ashley Tabor-King Foundation**
Community Foundation serving Tyne and Wear and Northumberland
The Welsh Church Act Fund
The Will Charitable Trust
The Zochonis Charitable Trust

Air ambulance

The Alborada Trust
The Liz and Terry Bramall Foundation
The Grace Trust
The Notgrove Trust
The Spurrell Charitable Trust
*The Ashley Tabor-King Foundation**

Emergency relief

The Alborada Trust
The Artemis Charitable Foundation
Bauer Radio's Cash for Kids Charities
Community Foundation for Calderdale
The Clothworkers' Foundation
Denise Coates Foundation
Forest Hill Charitable Trust
House of Industry Estate
The Albert Hunt Trust
The Innocent Foundation
International Bible Students Association
The Elton John Aids Foundation (EJAF)
Community Foundations for Lancashire and Merseyside
The Leathersellers' Company Charitable Fund
*Cecil and Hilda Lewis Charitable Trust**
The Ogle Christian Trust
The Pets at Home Foundation
The Prince's Countryside Fund
The Shanly Foundation
The SMB Trust
The South Yorkshire Community Foundation
*The Ashley Tabor-King Foundation**
The Gay and Keith Talbot Trust
Community Foundation serving Tyne and Wear and Northumberland
The Will Charitable Trust

Lifeboats

Mrs F. B. Laurence Charitable Trust
The R. S. Macdonald Charitable Trust
The MacRobert Trust 2019
The Phillips Charitable Trust
Seafarers UK (King George's Fund for Sailors)
The Spurrell Charitable Trust
*The Ashley Tabor-King Foundation**

Moutain rescue

*JD Foundation**
*The Ashley Tabor-King Foundation**

Environment

The 29th May 1961 Charitable Trust
The A. Team Foundation Ltd
The Bryan Adams Foundation
The Adlard Family Charitable Foundation
The AEB Charitable Trust
The AIM Foundation
Sylvia Aitken's Charitable Trust
The Aldama Foundation
Alpkit Foundation*
Anglo American Group Foundation
The Anson Charitable Trust
Arcadia Fund
The Artemis Charitable Foundation
Ove Arup Partnership Charitable Trust
The Ashden Trust
The Ashendene Trust
The Ian Askew Charitable Trust
The Astor Foundation
The Scott Bader Commonwealth Ltd
The Balcombe Charitable Trust
The Banister Charitable Trust
The Barbour Foundation
The Barclay Foundation
Lord Barnby's Foundation
Robert Barr's Charitable Trust
BC Partners Foundation
The Becht Family Charitable Trust
The Benham Charitable Settlement
The Rowan Bentall Charitable Trust
Biffa Award
Birmingham International Airport Community Trust Fund
Birthday House Trust
The Isabel Blackman Foundation
Blakemore Foundation
The Boltini Trust
The Charlotte Bonham-Carter Charitable Trust
The Bowland Charitable Trust
G. and K. Boyes Charitable Trust
The Liz and Terry Bramall Foundation
Bridgepoint Charitable Trust
The Britford Bridge Trust
The Brown Source Trust*
The Edward Cadbury Charitable Trust
The Edward and Dorothy Cadbury Trust
The Cadogan Charity
The Cambridgeshire Community Foundation
Camden Giving*
The Leslie Mary Carter Charitable Trust
The Castansa Trust
The B. G. S. Cayzer Charitable Trust
The Amelia Chadwick Trust
The Chalk Cliff Trust
Chapman Charitable Trust
The Charities Advisory Trust
The Chartley Foundation
CHK Foundation
The City Bridge Trust (Bridge House Estates)
CLA Charitable Trust
J. A. Clark Charitable Trust
Clark Foundation
The John Coates Charitable Trust
The John S. Cohen Foundation
The Cole Charitable Trust
Community First
The Ernest Cook Trust
The Sir Tom Cowie Charitable Trust
The Craignish Trust
The Craps Charitable Trust
The Crescent Trust
Cumbria Community Foundation
The Dennis Curry Charitable Trust
The D. G. Charitable Settlement
The D'Oyly Carte Charitable Trust
The Daniell Trust*
The Roger De Haan Charitable Trust
William Dean Countryside and Educational Trust
The Delves Charitable Trust
The Demigryphon Trust
The Dischma Charitable Trust
The Dulverton Trust
Dumfriesshire East Community Benefit Group SCIO*
Dunard Fund
Dunlossit and Islay Community Trust*
County Durham Community Foundation
The DWF Charitable Foundation
Audrey Earle Charitable Trust
The Ecology Trust
John Ellerman Foundation
The Emerton-Christie Charity
The Enkalon Foundation
The Everard Foundation
Esmée Fairbairn Foundation
The Fairness Foundation
Family Philanthropy Ltd*
The Lord Faringdon Charitable Trust
Samuel William Farmer Trust
The February Foundation
The A. M. Fenton Trust
The Fidelity UK Foundation
The Finborough Foundation
The Finnis Scott Foundation
The Earl Fitzwilliam Charitable Trust
Forever Manchester
The Fort Foundation
The Gordon Fraser Charitable Trust
The Hugh Fraser Foundation
The Freshfield Foundation
The Freshgate Trust Foundation
The Funding Network
The G. D. Charitable Trust
The Gannochy Trust
The Worshipful Company of Gardeners of London Charity
Garfield Weston Foundation
The Gatsby Charitable Foundation
Gatwick Airport Community Trust
The General Charity Fund
The Generations Foundation
The Tara Getty Foundation
The Simon Gibson Charitable Trust
The Golden Bottle Trust
GrantScape
Gordon Gray Trust
The Great Britain Sasakawa Foundation
Greenham Trust Ltd
The Greggs Foundation
The Grocers' Charity
Groundwork UK
The Gunter Charitable Trust
H. C. D. Memorial Fund
The Hadfield Charitable Trust
The Hadrian Trust
The W. A. Handley Charity Trust
The Lennox Hannay Charitable Trust
The Harrison-Frank Family Foundation (UK) Ltd
The Hawthorne Charitable Trust
Heathrow Community Trust
The Charlotte Heber-Percy Charitable Trust
The Percy Hedley 1990 Charitable Trust
The Hemby Charitable Trust
The G. D. Herbert Charitable Trust
Herefordshire Community Foundation
The Lady Hind Trust
The Hinduja Foundation
The Henry C. Hoare Charitable Trust
The Hobson Charity Ltd

P. H. Holt Foundation
The Mary Homfray Charitable Trust
The Iceland Foods Charitable Foundation
The Iliffe Family Charitable Trust
The Inflexion Foundation*
The Investindustrial Foundation*
The Ireland Fund of Great Britain
The Isle of Anglesey Charitable Trust
The J. J. Charitable Trust
The Jabbs Foundation
The Frank Jackson Foundation
Lady Eda Jardine Charitable Trust
John Jarrold Trust Ltd
Rees Jeffreys Road Fund
The Jephcott Charitable Trust
The Marjorie and Geoffrey Jones Charitable Trust
The Muriel Jones Foundation
The Kilroot Foundation*
The Ernest Kleinwort Charitable Trust
Sir James Knott Trust
KPE4 Charitable Trust*
Christopher Laing Foundation
The Martin Laing Foundation
The Kirby Laing Foundation
The Leonard Laity Stoate Charitable Trust
Lancashire Environmental Fund Ltd
Langdale Trust
Mrs M. A. Lascelles Charitable Trust
Mrs F. B. Laurence Charitable Trust
The Law Family Charitable Foundation
The Lawson Trust CIO
The Leach Fourteenth Trust
The Leeward Trust*
The Mark Leonard Trust
The Leri Charitable Trust
Lord Leverhulme's Charitable Trust
John Lewis Foundation
The Limbourne Trust
Limoges Charitable Trust
The Linbury Trust
The Linder Foundation
The Lindley Foundation (TLF)
The Charles Littlewood Hill Trust
The London Community Foundation (LCF)
The Mackintosh Foundation
The Mactaggart Third Fund
Manchester Airport Community Trust Fund
R. W. Mann Trust
The Michael Marks Charitable Trust
Marmot Charitable Trust
The Marsh Christian Trust
Sir George Martin Trust
The Master Charitable Trust
Gemma and Chris McGough Charitable Foundation CIO*
The Medlock Charitable Trust
The Merchant Venturers' Charity
Merchants' House of Glasgow
T. and J. Meyer Family Foundation Ltd
The Gerald Micklem Charitable Trust
The Mila Charitable Organisation*
The Millennium Oak Trust
Millennium Stadium Charitable Trust (Ymddiriedclaeth Elusennol Stadiwm y Mileniwm)
The Ronald Miller Foundation
Jean and Roger Miller's Charitable Trust
The Millichope Foundation
Moondance Foundation
The Morrisons Foundation
Moto in the Community
The Mulberry Trust
The John R. Murray Charitable Trust
The National Garden Scheme
Nesta
Network for Social Change Charitable Trust
The Nineveh Charitable Trust
The Norman Family Charitable Trust
Community Foundation for Northern Ireland
The Northwick Trust
The Oakdale Trust
The Ofenheim Charitable Trust
Oglesby Charitable Trust
One Community Foundation Ltd
The Ovo Charitable Foundation
The Owen Family Trust
Oxfordshire Community Foundation
P. F. Charitable Trust
The Paget Charitable Trust
The Gerald Palmer Eling Trust Company
The Paragon Trust
The Jack Patston Charitable Trust
Susanna Peake Charitable Trust
People's Postcode Trust
The Persimmon Charitable Foundation
The Phillips Charitable Trust
Cecil Pilkington Charitable Trust
PIMCO Foundation Europe
Polden-Puckham Charitable Foundation
The George and Esme Pollitzer Charitable Settlement
The Portrack Charitable Trust
Postcode Local Trust
Postcode Society Trust (formerly Postcode Dream Trust)
The Prince of Wales's Charitable Foundation
The Prince's Countryside Fund
The Princess Anne's Charities
Mr and Mrs J. A. Pye's Charitable Settlement
Quartet Community Foundation
Richard Radcliffe Trust
The Rainford Trust
The Ranworth Trust
The Sigrid Rausing Trust
The Sir James Reckitt Charity
The Revere Charitable Trust
The Rhododendron Trust
Daisie Rich Trust
Rockcliffe Charitable Trust
The Roddick Foundation
The Rothschild Foundation
The Roughley Charitable Trust
The Rowlands Trust
The Joseph Rowntree Charitable Trust
Royal Docks Trust (London)
The Royal Foundation of the Duke and Duchess of Cambridge
Royal Society of Wildlife Trusts
RSM UK Foundation*
The Russell Trust
The Saintbury Trust
Salisbury Pool Charity
The M. J. Samuel Charitable Trust
The Samworth Foundation
Sandra Charitable Trust
The Scarfe Charitable Trust
Schroder Charity Trust
The Schroder Foundation
Foundation Scotland
The Scottish Power Foundation
Scouloudi Foundation
The SDL Foundation
Sam and Bella Sebba Charitable Trust
The Shanly Foundation
The Shears Foundation
The Sheepdrove Trust
The Sheffield Town Trust
The Sylvia and Colin Shepherd Charitable Trust
Sirius Minerals Foundation
Ruth Smart Foundation
The SMB Trust

The DS Smith Charitable Foundation
The N. Smith Charitable Settlement
The Martin Smith Foundation
The Leslie Smith Foundation
Stanley Smith UK Horticultural Trust
Philip Smith's Charitable Trust
The Sobell Foundation
Societe Generale UK Foundation*
The South Yorkshire Community Foundation
The Stephen R. and Philippa H. Southall Charitable Trust
W. F. Southall Trust
Peter Sowerby Foundation
The Spear Charitable Trust
The Michael and Sarah Spencer Foundation*
Staples Trust
The Steel Charitable Trust
Stevenson Family's Charitable Trust
The Joseph Strong Frazer Trust*
The Summerfield Charitable Trust
Sumner Wilson Charitable Trust
Community Foundation for Surrey
Sabina Sutherland Charitable Trust
The John Swire (1989) Charitable Trust
The Swire Charitable Trust
The Adrian Swire Charitable Trust
The Hugh Symons Charitable Trust*
C. B. and H. H. Taylor 1984 Trust
Stephen Taylor Foundation
The Tedworth Charitable Trust
The Thirty Percy Foundation*
The Thriplow Charitable Trust
The Tolkien Trust
The Tomoro Foundation*
Tower Hill Trust
Toyota Manufacturing UK Charitable Trust
The Constance Travis Charitable Trust
The Tresanton Trust*
The Roger and Douglas Turner Charitable Trust
Ulster Garden Villages Ltd
The Underwood Trust
The Michael Uren Foundation
The Valentine Charitable Trust
The Albert Van Den Bergh Charitable Trust
The Van Neste Foundation
The Vandervell Foundation
The Veolia Environmental Trust
Nigel Vinson Charitable Trust
Viridor Credits Environmental Company
The Georg and Emily Von Opel Foundation*
Sylvia Waddilove Foundation UK
Mrs Waterhouse Charitable Trust
The Waterloo Foundation
Wales Family Enterprise Trust
The Geoffrey Watling Charity
Westway Trust
The Barbara Whatmore Charitable Trust
Colonel W. H. Whitbread Charitable Trust
Whitley Animal Protection Trust
The Williams Charitable Trust
Alfred Williams Charitable Trust
The Williams Family Foundation
The HDH Wills 1965 Charitable Trust
The Wixamtree Trust
Woodroffe Benton Foundation
The Yorkshire Dales Millennium Trust

Agriculture and farming

The A. Team Foundation Ltd
The Ashden Trust
The Ian Askew Charitable Trust
The Scott Bader Commonwealth Ltd
Birmingham International Airport Community Trust Fund
The Cadbury Foundation
The Castansa Trust
The Chalk Cliff Trust
CLA Charitable Trust
The Clan Trust Ltd
Community First
The Ernest Cook Trust
The Elizabeth Creak Charitable Trust
The Ecology Trust
The Englefield Charitable Trust
The Worshipful Company of Gardeners of London Charity
The Great Britain Sasakawa Foundation
The Hutchinson Charitable Trust
The Innocent Foundation
The J. J. Charitable Trust
The Mark Leonard Trust
The Limbourne Trust
The MacRobert Trust 2019
Network for Social Change Charitable Trust
The NFU Mutual Charitable Trust
The Nineveh Charitable Trust
Oglesby Charitable Trust
Oxfordshire Community Foundation
The Prince of Wales's Charitable Foundation
The Prince's Countryside Fund
Quartet Community Foundation
Salisbury Pool Charity
The Shears Foundation
The Sheepdrove Trust
Tanner Trust
The Thirty Percy Foundation*
The Whitaker Charitable Trust
The HDH Wills 1965 Charitable Trust

Biodiversity

Anglo American Group Foundation
The Becht Family Charitable Trust
Biffa Award
The Delves Charitable Trust
The Ecology Trust
John Ellerman Foundation
Family Philanthropy Ltd*
The Finnis Scott Foundation
Hamamelis Trust
Lancashire Environmental Fund Ltd
The Peter Samuel Charitable Trust
The Samworth Foundation
Ruth Smart Foundation
The Swire Charitable Trust
Tower Hill Trust

Climate change

The Ashden Trust
The Scott Bader Commonwealth Ltd
Bulb Foundation*
J. A. Clark Charitable Trust
The Ecology Trust
The Freshfield Foundation
The Funding Network
The Tara Getty Foundation
Calouste Gulbenkian Foundation – UK Branch
H. C. D. Memorial Fund
The J. J. Charitable Trust
The Kreitman Foundation
The Mark Leonard Trust
The Limbourne Trust
The Frederick Mulder Foundation
The Nineveh Charitable Trust
The Pickwell Foundation

The Samworth Foundation
*Societe Generale UK Foundation**
The Summerfield Charitable Trust
*The Thirty Percy Foundation**

Coastal/marine

The Becht Family Charitable Trust
*The Dashlight Foundation**
John Ellerman Foundation
The Tara Getty Foundation
Calouste Gulbenkian Foundation – UK Branch
*Ocean Family Foundation**
The Shipwrights' Charitable Fund
The Stafford Trust
*The Tomoro Foundation**

Energy

Ove Arup Partnership Charitable Trust
The Ashden Trust
County Durham Community Foundation
The J. J. Charitable Trust
The Mark Leonard Trust
The Limbourne Trust
Nesta
The Ovo Charitable Foundation
Postcode Local Trust
The Rothley Trust
The South Yorkshire Community Foundation
*The Thirty Percy Foundation**

Forestry

The Ashden Trust
Hamamelis Trust
The J. J. Charitable Trust
The Jabbs Foundation
The MacRobert Trust 2019
The Nineveh Charitable Trust
The Peter Samuel Charitable Trust
The Shanly Foundation
The Whitaker Charitable Trust

Fresh water (e.g. streams, rivers and lakes)

Esmée Fairbairn Foundation
The Nineveh Charitable Trust

Waste management and recycling

The Burberry Foundation

General charitable purposes

The 1989 Willan Charitable Trust
The 3Ts Charitable Trust
4 Charity Foundation
The 4814 Trust
The Aaronson Foundation
The Aberdeen Foundation
The Acacia Charitable Trust
The Adlard Family Charitable Foundation
*The Aitken Family Charitable Trust**
Sylvia Aitken's Charitable Trust
AlixPartners (UK) Charitable Foundation
D. C. R. Allen Charitable Trust
The Allen Trust
The Ammco Trust
Viscount Amory's Charitable Trust
The AMW Charitable Trust
The Annandale Charitable Trust
The Anson Charitable Trust
The Arah Foundation
The Archer Trust
The Ardeola Charitable Trust
The Ardwick Trust
The John Armitage Charitable Trust
The Arsenal Foundation
Ove Arup Partnership Charitable Trust
The Asda Foundation
The Ashburnham Thanksgiving Trust
The Ashendene Trust
The Ian Askew Charitable Trust
Keren Association Ltd
Atkin Charitable Foundation
The Atlas Fund
The Lord Austin Trust
Axis Foundation
The Aylesford Family Charitable Trust
The Bagri Foundation
The Andrew Balint Charitable Trust
The Bamford Charitable Foundation
Banbury Charities
The Roger and Sarah Bancroft Clark Charitable Trust
The Band Trust
*The Kamini and Vindi Banga Family Trust**
The Barbers' Company General Charities
The Barbour Foundation
The Barclay Foundation
The Barker-Mill Foundation
Lord Barnby's Foundation
*The Barnes Fund**

The Max Barney Foundation
The Barnsbury Charitable Trust
Misses Barrie Charitable Trust
Robert Barr's Charitable Trust
The Paul Bassham Charitable Trust
Battens Charitable Trust
The Battersea Power Station Foundation
Bauer Radio's Cash for Kids Charities
The Bay Tree Charitable Trust
The Louis Baylis (Maidenhead Advertiser) Charitable Trust
Bear Mordechai Ltd
Bearder Charity
The James Beattie Charitable Trust
The Beaverbrook Foundation
The Beaverbrooks Charitable Trust
The Becker Family Charitable Trust
Bedfordshire and Luton Community Foundation
Bedfordshire Charitable Trust Ltd
E. C. Graham Belford Charitable Settlement
The Benham Charitable Settlement
Bennett Lowell Ltd
The Rowan Bentall Charitable Trust
The Berkshire Community Foundation
The Bilmeir Charitable Trust
The Bingham Trust
Binks Trust
Birthday House Trust
The Michael Bishop Foundation
*Maria Bjornson Memorial Fund**
Blakemore Foundation
Lady Blakenham's Charity Trust
The Sir Victor Blank Charitable Settlement
The Bloom Foundation
The Bloomfield Charitable Trust
The Bluston Charitable Settlement
*The Blyth Charitable Trust**
*The BNA Charitable Incorporated Organisation**
The Marjory Boddy Charitable Trust
The Charlotte Bonham-Carter Charitable Trust
The Boodle & Dunthorne Charitable Trust
The Bothwell Charitable Trust
The Bowland Charitable Trust
The William Brake Charitable Trust
The Frank Brake Charitable Trust
The Liz and Terry Bramall Foundation
The Harold and Alice Bridges Charity
Bristol Charities
British Humane Association
The J. and M. Britton Charitable Trust
The Broomton Foundation
*The Brothers Trust**
*The Brown Source Trust**
R. S. Brownless Charitable Trust
The T. B. H. Brunner's Charitable Settlement
The Jack Brunton Charitable Trust
The Bruntwood Charity
Buckinghamshire Community Foundation
The Bulldog Trust Ltd
The Burges Salmon Charitable Trust
The Burry Charitable Trust
Byrne Family Foundation
The G. W. Cadbury Charitable Trust
The Edward and Dorothy Cadbury Trust
The George Cadbury Trust
Community Foundation for Calderdale
Callendar Charitable Trust
*Barbara and Derek Calrow Charitable Foundation**
The Cambridgeshire Community Foundation
*Camden Giving**
*The Candy Foundation**
The Frederick and Phyllis Cann Trust
*Card Factory Foundation**
The W. A. Cargill Fund
The Carpenters' Company Charitable Trust
The Carrington Charitable Trust
The Casey Trust
The Castanea Trust
The Joseph and Annie Cattle Trust
The Wilfrid and Constance Cave Foundation
The B. G. S. Cayzer Charitable Trust
The Cazenove Charitable Trust
CBRE Charitable Trust
The Amelia Chadwick Trust
The Charities Advisory Trust
The Charter 600 Charity
Chartered Accountants' Livery Charity (CALC)
The Charterhouse Charitable Trust
The Cheruby Trust
Cheshire Community Foundation Ltd
Cheshire Freemason's Charity
The Chetwode Foundation
Chippenham Borough Lands Charity
The Chipping Sodbury Town Lands Charity
Christie Foundation
The Church Burgesses Educational Foundation
Church Burgesses Trust
The Clover Trust
Clydpride Ltd
The Coalfields Regeneration Trust
The John Coates Charitable Trust
The Cobtree Charity Trust Ltd
Colefax Charitable Trust
*The George Collins Charity**
Sir Jeremiah Colman Gift Trust
The Compton Charitable Trust
Douglas Compton James Charitable Trust
The Cooks Charity
The Catherine Cookson Charitable Trust
The Keith Coombs Trust
Mabel Cooper Charity
The Alice Ellen Cooper Dean Charitable Foundation
The Helen Jean Cope Charity
The Gershon Coren Charitable Foundation (also known as The Muriel and Gus Coren Charitable Foundation)
Michael Cornish Charitable Trust
Cornwall Community Foundation
The Cornwell Charitable Trust
The Costa Family Charitable Trust
The County Council of Dyfed Welsh Church Fund
Coventry Building Society Charitable Foundation
The Sir Tom Cowie Charitable Trust
The Lord Cozens-Hardy Trust
*The CPF Trust**
The Craignish Trust
The Craps Charitable Trust
The Cray Trust
The Crerar Trust
The Crescent Trust
Cripplegate Foundation
Cumbria Community Foundation
The Dennis Curry Charitable Trust

Itzchok Meyer Cymerman Trust Ltd
The D. G. Charitable Settlement
*The Dashlight Foundation**
Michael Davies Charitable Settlement
Margaret Davies Charity
The Crispin Davis Family Trust
The Henry and Suzanne Davis Foundation
The De Brye Charitable Trust
Denman Charitable Trust
Dentons UKMEA LLP Charitable Trust
Foundation Derbyshire
Provincial Grand Charity of the Province of Derbyshire
The J. N. Derbyshire Trust
The Desmond Foundation
Devon Community Foundation
The Duke of Devonshire's Charitable Trust
The Laduma Dhamecha Charitable Trust
The Dischma Charitable Trust
The DLM Charitable Trust
*William and Frances Dobie Charitable Foundation**
The Dorfman Foundation
Dorset Community Foundation
The Double 'O' Charity Ltd
Dromintee Trust
The Dulverton Trust
Dumbreck Charity
The Dunn Family Charitable Trust
The Charles Dunstone Charitable Trust
County Durham Community Foundation
The Mildred Duveen Charitable Trust
The James Dyson Foundation
Audrey Earle Charitable Trust
The Earley Charity
Sir John Eastwood Foundation
Edinburgh Trust No. 2 Account
Edupoor Ltd
*The Eight Foundation**
The Eighteen Fund
The Eighty Eight Foundation
The Wilfred and Elsie Elkes Charity Fund
The Maud Elkington Charitable Trust
The Ellerdale Trust
The Vernon N. Ely Charitable Trust
The Englefield Charitable Trust
The EQ Foundation
Essex Community Foundation
*The Ethos Foundation**
Joseph Ettedgui Charitable Foundation
The Eventhall Family Charitable Trust
The Everard Foundation
Eversheds Sutherland (International) Charitable Trust
The Exilarch's Foundation
G. F. Eyre Charitable Trust
The Fairness Foundation
The Fairstead Trust
The Lord Faringdon Charitable Trust
The Farthing Trust
The February Foundation
The A. M. Fenton Trust
The Feoffees of St Michael's Spurriergate York
The Fermanagh Trust
Doris Field Charitable Trust
*The Fieldrose Charitable Trust**
Dixie Rose Findlay Charitable Trust
Sir John Fisher Foundation
The Earl Fitzwilliam Charitable Trust
The Robert Fleming Hannay Memorial Charity
The Follett Trust
Fordeve Ltd
Forest Hill Charitable Trust
Forever Manchester
The Forman Hardy Charitable Trust
Donald Forrester Trust
Gwyneth Forrester Trust
The Fort Foundation
The Forte Charitable Trust
*Foux Foundation**
Fowler Smith and Jones Trust
The Foxglove Trust
The Elizabeth Frankland Moore and Star Foundation
The Gordon Fraser Charitable Trust
The Hugh Fraser Foundation
*The Fraxinus Charitable Trust**
*The Joyce and Norman Freed Charitable Trust**
Anne French Memorial Trust
Frognal Trust
The Patrick and Helena Frost Foundation
The Fulmer Charitable Trust
The Funding Network
G. M. C. Trust
The Gale Family Charity Trust
Gamma Trust
The Ganzoni Charitable Trust
The Worshipful Company of Gardeners of London Charity
Garthgwynion Charities
Gatwick Airport Community Trust
The Gaudio Family Foundation (UK) Ltd
The Robert Gavron Charitable Trust
The Jacqueline and Michael Gee Charitable Trust
The Steven Gerrard Foundation
The Gertner Charitable Trust
The Simon Gibson Charitable Trust
The G. C. Gibson Charitable Trust
The B. and P. Glasser Charitable Trust
The F. Glenister Woodger Trust
County of Gloucestershire Community Foundation
Worshipful Company of Glovers of London Charitable Trust
The Godinton Charitable Trust
Worshipful Company of Gold and Silver Wyre Drawers Second Charitable Trust Fund
*The Goldcrest Charitable Trust**
The Golden Bottle Trust
The Goldman Sachs Charitable Gift Fund (UK)
Goldman Sachs Gives (UK)
The Goldsmiths' Company Charity
The Goodman Foundation
The Gosling Foundation Ltd
The Gould Charitable Trust
Gowling WLG (UK) Charitable Trust
The Hemraj Goyal Foundation
Grace Charitable Trust
The Grace Trust
*The Grand Trust CIO**
The Grant Foundation
GrantScape
The J. G. Graves Charitable Trust
The Gray Trust
The Great Stone Bridge Trust of Edenbridge
The Kenneth and Susan Green Charitable Foundation
The Green Hall Foundation
The Greggs Foundation
The Gretna Charitable Trust
The Grimmitt Trust
Groundwork UK
The Walter Guinness Charitable Trust
The Gunter Charitable Trust
H. C. D. Memorial Fund
*The Halsall Foundation**
Hampshire and Isle of Wight Community Foundation
Hampton Fund
The W. A. Handley Charity Trust

The Lennox Hannay Charitable Trust
The Kathleen Hannay Memorial Charity
The Haramead Trust
Harborne Parish Lands Charity
The Harbour Charitable Trust
The Harbour Foundation
The David and Claudia Harding Foundation
William Harding's Charity
The Harebell Centenary Fund
The Peter and Teresa Harris Charitable Trust*
The Edith Lilian Harrison 2000 Foundation
The Harrison-Frank Family Foundation (UK) Ltd
Gay and Peter Hartley's Hillards Charitable Trust
Edward Harvist Trust (The Harvist Estate)
The Hasluck Charitable Trust
The Maurice Hatter Foundation
The Hawthorne Charitable Trust
The Charles Hayward Foundation
Heart of England Community Foundation
The Hearth Foundation
The Heathcoat Trust
The Heathside Charitable Trust
The Charlotte Heber-Percy Charitable Trust
The Percy Hedley 1990 Charitable Trust
The Michael Heller Charitable Foundation
The Helping Foundation
The Hemby Charitable Trust
The Tim Henman Foundation
The G. D. Herbert Charitable Trust
Herefordshire Community Foundation
Hertfordshire Community Foundation
P. and C. Hickinbotham Charitable Trust
The Alan Edward Higgs Charity
The Hilden Charitable Fund
R. G. Hills Charitable Trust
The Hintze Family Charity Foundation
The Hiscox Foundation
The Henry C. Hoare Charitable Trust
The Hobson Charity Ltd
The Holbeck Charitable Trust
Hollick Family Foundation
The Holliday Foundation
Dorothy Holmes Charitable Trust
P. H. Holt Foundation
The Mary Homfray Charitable Trust
The Horners Charity Fund
The Hospital of God at Greatham
The Sir Joseph Hotung Charitable Settlement
House of Industry Estate
The Reta Lila Howard Foundation
James T. Howat Charitable Trust
The Hudson Foundation
The Huggard Charitable Trust
The Hull and East Riding Charitable Trust
Michael and Shirley Hunt Charitable Trust
The Hunting Horn General Charitable Trust
The Hutchinson Charitable Trust
The Hutton Foundation
The Nani Huyu Charitable Trust
Ibrahim Foundation Ltd
The Iceland Foods Charitable Foundation
The Iliffe Family Charitable Trust
The Inflexion Foundation*
The Ingram Trust
The Inman Charity
The Inverforth Charitable Trust
The Investindustrial Foundation*
Investream Charitable Trust
The Charles Irving Charitable Trust
The Irving Memorial Trust*
The Isle of Anglesey Charitable Trust
The J. and J. Benevolent Foundation
The J. J. Charitable Trust
The Jagclif Charitable Trust*
John James Bristol Foundation
Lady Eda Jardine Charitable Trust
John Jarrold Trust Ltd
The Jenour Foundation
The Jephcott Charitable Trust
Lillie Johnson Charitable Trust
The Johnson Foundation
The Christopher and Kirsty Johnston Charitable Trust
The Joicey Trust
The Marjorie and Geoffrey Jones Charitable Trust
The Muriel Jones Foundation
The Joron Charitable Trust
J. E. Joseph Charitable Fund
The Cyril and Eve Jumbo Charitable Trust
Kantor Charitable Foundation*
The Kasner Charitable Trust
The Michael and Ilse Katz Foundation
The Emmanuel Kaye Foundation
William Kendall's Charity (Wax Chandlers' Company)
The Kennedy Charitable Foundation
Kent Community Foundation
The Nancy Kenyon Charitable Trust
E. and E. Kernkraut Charities Ltd
The Ursula Keyes Trust
The Kildare Trust
Kilpatrick Fraser Charitable Trust
The King Henry VIII Endowed Trust – Warwick
The Mary Kinross Charitable Trust
Laura Kinsella Foundation
The Graham Kirkham Foundation
Robert Kitchin (Saddlers' Company)
The Ernest Kleinwort Charitable Trust
Sir James Knott Trust
The Kobler Trust
Kollel and Co. Ltd
The Kyte Charitable Trust
Ladbrokes Coral Trust
The David Laing Foundation
The Kirby Laing Foundation
The Martin Laing Foundation
The Leonard Laity Stoate Charitable Trust
The Lake House Charity
Community Foundations for Lancashire and Merseyside
The Lancashire Foundation
Duchy of Lancaster Benevolent Fund
Langdale Trust
Mrs M. A. Lascelles Charitable Trust
The Lauffer Family Charitable Foundation
Mrs F. B. Laurence Charitable Trust
The Kathleen Laurence Trust
The Law Family Charitable Foundation
The Betty Lawes Foundation
The Richard Lawes Foundation
The Edgar E. Lawley Foundation
The Herd Lawson and Muriel Lawson Charitable Trust
Lawson Beckman Charitable Trust
The Leach Fourteenth Trust
The Leathersellers' Company Charitable Fund

The Arnold Lee Charitable Trust
The William Leech Charity
Leeds Community Foundation (LCF)
Leicestershire and Rutland Masonic Charity Association
Leicestershire, Leicester and Rutland Community Foundation
The Kennedy Leigh Charitable Trust
Leng Charitable Trust
The Leri Charitable Trust
*The Ralph Levy Charitable Company Ltd**
*Cecil and Hilda Lewis Charitable Trust**
Bernard Lewis Family Charitable Trust
David and Ruth Lewis Family Charitable Trust
The Sir Edward Lewis Foundation
*The Charles Lewis Foundation**
The Light Fund Company
The Limbourne Trust
Limoges Charitable Trust
Lincolnshire Community Foundation
The Linden Charitable Trust
The Linder Foundation
The Lindley Foundation (TLF)
The Frank Litchfield Charitable Trust
The Charles Littlewood Hill Trust
The George John and Sheilah Livanos Charitable Trust
Liverpool Charity and Voluntary Services (LCVS)
Jack Livingstone Charitable Trust
The Elaine and Angus Lloyd Charitable Trust
The W. M. and B. W. Lloyd Trust
Local Trent Ltd
The Lockwood Charitable Foundation
The London Community Foundation (LCF)
London Freemasons Charity
The William and Katherine Longman Trust
The Lower Green Foundation
The C. L. Loyd Charitable Trust
LPW Ltd
The Henry Lumley Charitable Trust
Lord and Lady Lurgan Trust
M. and C. Trust
The Mackay and Brewer Charitable Trust
The Mackintosh Foundation
The Mactaggart Third Fund
The Ian Mactaggart Trust (The Mactaggart Second Fund)
*The Mageni Trust**
The Mahoro Charitable Trust
Makers of Playing Cards Charity
Making a Difference Locally Ltd
The Mallinckrodt Foundation
The Manackerman Charitable Trust
Manchester Airport Community Trust Fund
The Manchester Guardian Society Charitable Trust
The W. M. Mann Foundation
R. W. Mann Trust
*The Manson Family Charitable Trust**
The J. P. Marland Charitable Trust
*The Marque Foundation**
The Michael Marsh Charitable Trust
The Marsh Christian Trust
Charlotte Marshall Charitable Trust
D. G. Marshall of Cambridge Trust
The Kristina Martin Charitable Trust
The Martin Charitable Trust
*The Geoffrey and Pauline Martin Trust**
Matchroom Sport Charitable Foundation
*The Mather Family Charitable Trust**
The Violet Mauray Charitable Trust
Mayheights Ltd
Mazars Charitable Trust
MBNA General Foundation
The Robert McAlpine Foundation
*Gemma and Chris McGough Charitable Foundation CIO**
McGreevy No. 5 Settlement
The Medlock Charitable Trust
The Meikle Foundation
The Melow Charitable Trust
The Merchant Venturers' Charity
Merchants' House of Glasgow
The Masonic Province of Middlesex Charitable Trust (Middlesex Masonic Charity)
*The Mikheev Charitable Trust**
*The Mila Charitable Organisation**
The Millennium Oak Trust
Hugh and Mary Miller Bequest Trust
The Ronald Miller Foundation
Jean and Roger Miller's Charitable Trust
The Millichope Foundation
*Millie's Watch**
Mills and Reeve Charitable Trust
The Millward Charitable Trust
The Clare Milne Trust
Milton Keynes Community Foundation Ltd
The Mishcon Family Charitable Trust
The Esmé Mitchell Trust
The Mittal Foundation
Keren Mitzvah Trust
The Mizpah Trust
Mobbs Memorial Trust Ltd
*The Mohn Westlake Foundation**
Mole Charitable Trust
The Alexander Moncur Trust
The Monmouthshire County Council Welsh Church Act Fund
The George A. Moore Foundation
The Morgan Charitable Foundation
The Steve Morgan Foundation
The Morris Charitable Trust
The Willie and Mabel Morris Charitable Trust
The Ken and Lynne Morrison Charitable Trust
G. M. Morrison Charitable Trust
The Ken and Edna Morrison Charitable Trust
The Morrisons Foundation
The Morton Charitable Trust (Dundee)
The Moshal Charitable Trust
Vyoel Moshe Charitable Trust
The Alexander Mosley Charitable Trust
Moto in the Community
*The Mowgli Trust**
The Mulberry Trust
*The Mulchand Foundation**
The John R. Murray Charitable Trust
Music Sales Charitable Trust
Muslim Hands
The Janet Nash Charitable Settlement
The National Express Foundation
The National Lottery Community Fund
The NDL Foundation
*The Gareth Neame Foundation**
Ner Foundation
Network for Social Change Charitable Trust

Norfolk Community Foundation
The Norman Family Charitable Trust
Normanby Charitable Trust
Northamptonshire Community Foundation
Community Foundation for Northern Ireland
The Northwick Trust
Northwood Charitable Trust
The Notgrove Trust
Nottinghamshire Community Foundation
Odin Charitable Trust
The Ofenheim Charitable Trust
Oglesby Charitable Trust
Oizer Charitable Trust
One Community Foundation Ltd
The Orrin Charitable Trust
Ostro Fayre Share Foundation
The Owen Family Trust
Oxfordshire Community Foundation
P. F. Charitable Trust
The Paget Charitable Trust
*The Pantheon Charitable Trust**
The James Pantyfedwen Foundation (Ymddiriedolaeth James Pantyfedwen)
The Paphitis Charitable Trust
Parabola Foundation
The Paragon Trust
*The Samuel and Freda Parkinson Charitable Trust**
*Partners Global Foundation**
The Pastoral Care Trust – The St Nicholas Care Fund
Miss M. E. S. Paterson's Charitable Trust
The Patrick Trust
Payne-Gallwey 1989 Charitable Trust
Peacock Charitable Trust
Susanna Peake Charitable Trust
David Pearlman Charitable Foundation
*Rosanna Pearson's 1987 Charity Trust**
The Pebbles Trust
The Pennycress Trust
People's Health Trust
People's Postcode Trust
*Dina Perelman Trust Ltd**
B. E. Perl Charitable Trust
The Persimmon Charitable Foundation
Personal Assurance Charitable Trust
The Pharsalia Charitable Trust
The Phillips Family Charitable Trust
Bernard Piggott Charitable Trust
Cecil Pilkington Charitable Trust
The Sir Harry Pilkington Trust Fund
Miss A. M. Pilkington's Charitable Trust
The Pitt-Rivers Charitable Trust
*The Points Family Trust**
The Porta Pia 2012 Foundation
Postcode Society Trust (formerly Postcode Dream Trust)
*Price Parry Charitable Trust**
Sir John Priestman Charity Trust
The Primrose Trust
The Princess Anne's Charities
The Priory Foundation
The Privy Purse Charitable Trust
The Puebla Charitable Trust
Catkin Pussywillow Charitable Trust
The PwC Foundation
The Pye Foundation
Mr and Mrs J. A. Pye's Charitable Settlement
Quartet Community Foundation
The Queen Anne's Gate Foundation
Quintessentially Foundation
The Monica Rabagliati Charitable Trust
Rachel Charitable Trust
The Racing Foundation
*The Raindance Charitable Trust**
The Rainford Trust
The Joseph and Lena Randall Charitable Trust
The Rank Foundation Ltd
The Ratcliff Foundation
The Rathbone Brothers Foundation
The Ravensdale Trust
The Roger Raymond Charitable Trust
The Sir James Reckitt Charity
C. A. Redfern Charitable Foundation
Rentrust Foundation Ltd
The Reso Charitable Foundation
The Rest-Harrow Trust
Reuben Foundation
The Rhododendron Trust
Riada Trust
Daisie Rich Trust
Richmond Parish Lands Charity
Rigby Foundation
The Sir John Ritblat Family Foundation
The River Farm Foundation
Rivers Foundation
Riverside Charitable Trust Ltd
The Roan Charitable Trust
The Dezna Robins Jones Charitable Foundation
Robyn Charitable Trust
Rockcliffe Charitable Trust
*The Rockspring Charitable Trust**
The Rofeh Trust
The Sir James Roll Charitable Trust
The Helen Roll Charity
The Gerald and Gail Ronson Family Foundation
Mrs L. D. Rope's Third Charitable Settlement
Rosca Trust
The Rose Foundation
The Rothermere Foundation
The Rothley Trust
The Rowlands Trust
Royal Artillery Charitable Fund
Royal Docks Trust (London)
The Rubin Foundation Charitable Trust
The Rugby Group Benevolent Fund Ltd
The Russell Trust
S. and R. Charitable Trust
The Jeremy and John Sacher Charitable Trust
The Saddlers' Company Charitable Fund
The Saintbury Trust
The Saints and Sinners Trust Ltd
The Salamander Charitable Trust
Salisbury Pool Charity
Salters' Charitable Foundation
The Basil Samuel Charitable Trust
The M. J. Samuel Charitable Trust
The Peter Samuel Charitable Trust
*The Sanderson Foundation**
The Sandhu Charitable Foundation
Sandra Charitable Trust
The Sands Family Trust
The Scarfe Charitable Trust
Schass Foundation
*The Anthony Scholefield Foundation**
O. and G. Schreiber Charitable Trust
Foundation Scotland
Scott (Eredine) Charitable Trust
*The Ina Scott Sutherland Charitable Foundation**
The John Scott Trust Fund
The Scottish Power Foundation

Scottish Property Industry Festival of Christmas (SPIFOX)
Scouloudi Foundation
The SDL Foundation
The Searchlight Electric Charitable Trust
Sam and Bella Sebba Charitable Trust
*The Selwood Charitable Trust**
The Cyril Shack Trust
The Shanly Foundation
*The Sharp Foundation**
The Sheepdrove Trust
The Sheldon Trust
The Patricia and Donald Shepherd Charitable Trust
The Sylvia and Colin Shepherd Charitable Trust
The Sherling Charitable Trust
The Archie Sherman Charitable Trust
Shlomo Memorial Fund Ltd
Shulem B. Association Ltd
The Florence Shute Millennium Trust
The Thomas Sivewright Catto Charitable Settlement
The Charles Skey Charitable Trust
The John Slater Foundation
The Slaughter and May Charitable Trust
Rita and David Slowe Charitable Trust
The SMB Trust
The N. Smith Charitable Settlement
*Arabella and Julian Smith Family Trust**
The W. H. Smith Group Charitable Trust
The R. C. Snelling Charitable Trust
Social Business Trust
Social Investment Business Foundation
*Societe Generale UK Foundation**
Sodexo Stop Hunger Foundation
Somerset Community Foundation
The South Yorkshire Community Foundation
The Stephen R. and Philippa H. Southall Charitable Trust
W. F. Southall Trust
Spar Charitable Fund
Sparquote Ltd
The Spear Charitable Trust
The Jessie Spencer Trust
Spielman Charitable Trust
Rosalyn and Nicholas Springer Charitable Trust
The Spurrell Charitable Trust
The Geoff and Fiona Squire Foundation
*The Vichai Srivaddhanaprabha Foundation**
The St James's Trust Settlement
Stadium Charitable Trust
The Stafford Trust
The Community Foundation for Staffordshire
Standard Life Aberdeen Charitable Foundation
Staples Trust
The Peter Stebbings Memorial Charity
The Hugh Stenhouse Foundation
The Stevenage Community Trust
Stevenson Family's Charitable Trust
The Stoller Charitable Trust
The Samuel Storey Family Charitable Trust
Peter Stormonth Darling Charitable Trust
Peter Storrs Trust
Stratford-upon-Avon Town Trust
Strathnairn Community Benefit Fund Ltd
*The Joseph Strong Frazer Trust**
The Sudborough Foundation
Suffolk Community Foundation
*The Support Foundation**
Community Foundation for Surrey
The Sussex Community Foundation
Sabina Sutherland Charitable Trust
Sutton Coldfield Charitable Trust
The Swann-Morton Foundation
The John Swire (1989) Charitable Trust
The Adrian Swire Charitable Trust
The Syder Foundation
The Sir Hugh and Lady Sykes Charitable Trust
The Charles and Elsie Sykes Trust
The T.K. Maxx and Homesense Foundation
*The Ashley Tabor-King Foundation**
The Talbot Village Trust
Tallow Chandlers Benevolent Fund No. 2
Tay Charitable Trust
Stephen Taylor Foundation
A. P. Taylor Trust
The Tedworth Charitable Trust
Tees Valley Community Foundation
The Templeton Goodwill Trust
The Thales Charitable Trust
The David Thomas Charitable Trust
The Thompson Family Charitable Trust
The Thornton Foundation
The Three Guineas Trust
Mrs R. P. Tindall's Charitable Trust
The Tobacco Pipe Makers and Tobacco Trade Benevolent Fund
The Tompkins Foundation
The Toye Foundation
Toyota Manufacturing UK Charitable Trust
The Trades House of Glasgow
David William Traill Cargill Fund
Annie Tranmer Charitable Trust
The Treeside Trust
The Truemark Trust
Truemart Ltd
The Tudor Trust
The Tuixen Foundation
G. J. W. Turner Trust
The Florence Turner Trust
Two Ridings Community Foundation
Community Foundation serving Tyne and Wear and Northumberland
Tzedakah
The Udlington Trust
UnLtd (Foundation for Social Entrepreneurs)
The David Uri Memorial Trust
*Utermann Charitable Trust**
The Utley Foundation
The Vail Foundation
The Valentine Charitable Trust
The Valiant Charitable Trust
The Albert Van Den Bergh Charitable Trust
*The Van Mesdag Fund**
The Vandervell Foundation
The Vardy Foundation
*The Velvet Foundation**
VHLT Ltd
Nigel Vinson Charitable Trust
The Vintners' Foundation
Virgin Atlantic Foundation
The Community Foundation in Wales
Robert and Felicity Waley-Cohen Charitable Trust
Walton Foundation
The Ward Blenkinsop Trust
The Warwickshire Masonic Charitable Association Ltd
G. R. Waters Charitable Trust 2000
The Geoffrey Watling Charity
Blyth Watson Charitable Trust

The William Webster Charitable Trust
The Linda and Michael Weinstein Charitable Trust
The Colin Weir Charitable Foundation*
The James Weir Foundation
The Welsh Church Act Fund
West Derby Waste Lands Charity
Westminster Foundation
The Whinfoll Charitable Fund
The Whitaker Charitable Trust
The Melanie White Foundation Ltd
White Stuff Foundation
Charity Of Sir Richard Whittington
The Wigoder Family Foundation
The Williams Charitable Trust
The HDH Wills 1965 Charitable Trust
The Dame Violet Wills Will Trust
The Wilmcote Charitrust
Brian Wilson Charitable Trust
Wiltshire Community Foundation
The Benjamin Winegarten Charitable Trust
W. Wing Yip and Brothers Foundation
The Wingate Foundation
The Michael and Anna Wix Charitable Trust
The James Wood Bequest Fund
Worcestershire Community Foundation*
Worth Waynflete Foundation
The Edward and Catherine Wray Charitable Trust*
Wychdale Ltd
Wychville Ltd
The Wyfold Charitable Trust
The Wyndham Charitable Trust
Yorkshire Building Society Charitable Foundation
The Elizabeth and Prince Zaiger Trust
The Marjorie and Arnold Ziff Charitable Foundation
The Zochonis Charitable Trust
Zurich Community Trust (UK) Ltd

Health

The 1989 Willan Charitable Trust
The 29th May 1961 Charitable Trust
4 Charity Foundation
The 4814 Trust
The Aaronson Foundation
The Aberbrothock Skea Trust
The Aberdeen Foundation
ABF The Soldiers' Charity
The Sylvia Adams Charitable Trust
Adenfirst Ltd
The Adint Charitable Trust
The AEB Charitable Trust
The AIM Foundation
The Aimwell Charitable Trust
Ajahma Charitable Trust
The Alchemy Foundation
The Aldama Foundation
Al-Fayed Charitable Foundation
The Derrill Allatt Foundation
Alliance Family Foundation Ltd
The Ammco Trust
The AMW Charitable Trust
Andor Charitable Trust
Anglo American Group Foundation
Ardbarron Trust Ltd
The Ardwick Trust
The Armed Forces Covenant Fund Trust*
The Artemis Charitable Foundation
Douglas Arter Foundation
ArtSocial Foundation
Ove Arup Partnership Charitable Trust
The Asda Foundation
The Astor Foundation
John Atcheson Foundation*
Atkin Charitable Foundation
The Lord Austin Trust
The Scott Bader Commonwealth Ltd
The Bagri Foundation
The Baily Thomas Charitable Fund
The Roy and Pixie Baker Charitable Trust
The Balcombe Charitable Trust
The Ballinger Charitable Trust
The Roger and Sarah Bancroft Clark Charitable Trust
Veronica and Lars Bane Foundation*
The Kamini and Vindi Banga Family Trust*
The Barbour Foundation
Barcapel Foundation Ltd
Barchester Healthcare Foundation
The Barnes Fund*
Barnwood Trust
Misses Barrie Charitable Trust
Robert Barr's Charitable Trust
The Batchworth Trust
Battens Charitable Trust
Bauer Radio's Cash for Kids Charities
The Bay Tree Charitable Trust
BBC Children in Need
The James Beattie Charitable Trust
The Beaverbrook Foundation
The Beaverbrooks Charitable Trust
Bedfordshire Charitable Trust Ltd
AJ Bell Trust*
The Bellahouston Bequest Fund
Benesco Charity Ltd
The Benham Charitable Settlement
The Rowan Bentall Charitable Trust
The Bestway Foundation
Bideford Bridge Trust
The Billmeir Charitable Trust
The Michael Bishop Foundation
Maria Bjornson Memorial Fund*
The John Black Charitable Foundation
The Isabel Blackman Foundation
Blakemore Foundation
Lady Blakenham's Charity Trust
The Sir Victor Blank Charitable Settlement
The Bloom Foundation
The Bluston Charitable Settlement
Maureen Boal Charitable Trust*
The Marjory Boddy Charitable Trust
The Boltini Trust
The Booth Charities
Boots Charitable Trust
The Borrows Charitable Trust
Alan Boswell Group Charitable Trust*
The Bothwell Charitable Trust
The Harry Bottom Charitable Trust
Sir Clive Bourne Family Trust
The Bowerman Charitable Trust
The Frank Brake Charitable Trust
The Tony Bramall Charitable Trust
The Liz and Terry Bramall Foundation
The Bransford Trust*
The Breadsticks Foundation
The Brelms Trust CIO

Bridgepoint Charitable Trust
*Bright Red Charity**
The Britford Bridge Trust
British Council for Prevention of Blindness
British Eye Research Foundation (Fight for Sight)
British Humane Association
British Lung Foundation
The J. and M. Britton Charitable Trust
The Consuelo and Anthony Brooke Charitable Trust
*The Brothers Trust**
*Mary Brown Memorial Trust**
R. S. Brownless Charitable Trust
The Jack Brunton Charitable Trust
Buckingham Trust
E. F. Bulmer Trust
BUPA UK Foundation
The Burden Trust
The Clara E. Burgess Charity
Consolidated Charity of Burton upon Trent
Miss Margaret Butters Reekie Charitable Trust
William A. Cadbury Charitable Trust
The Edward and Dorothy Cadbury Trust
The George Cadbury Trust
Callendar Charitable Trust
*Camden Giving**
Canary Wharf Contractors Fund
W. A. Cargill Charitable Trust
The W. A. Cargill Fund
*The Antonio Carluccio Foundation**
The Carr-Gregory Trust
The Leslie Mary Carter Charitable Trust
The Castanea Trust
The Joseph and Annie Cattle Trust
The Wilfrid and Constance Cave Foundation
Champneys Charitable Foundation
The Charterhouse Charitable Trust
Children with Cancer UK
The Childwick Trust
The Christabella Charitable Trust
The André Christian Trust
Chrysalis Trust
The Churchill Foundation
The CIBC World Markets Children's Foundation
The City Bridge Trust (Bridge House Estates)
Clark Foundation
The Clothworkers' Foundation
Cloudesley
The Clover Trust
*FB Coales No4 (Family) Trust**
The Coalfields Regeneration Trust
The John Coates Charitable Trust
Denise Coates Foundation
The Vivienne and Samuel Cohen Charitable Trust
The John S. Cohen Foundation
Colchester Catalyst Charity
*The George Collins Charity**
Sir Jeremiah Colman Gift Trust
The Colt Foundation
Colyer-Fergusson Charitable Trust
Comic Relief
The Catherine Cookson Charitable Trust
The Keith Coombs Trust
The Alice Ellen Cooper Dean Charitable Foundation
The J. Reginald Corah Foundation Fund
The Worshipful Company of Cordwainers Charitable Trusts (Minges Gift)
The Gershon Coren Charitable Foundation (also known as The Muriel and Gus Coren Charitable Foundation)
Michael Cornish Charitable Trust
The Evan Cornish Foundation
Corra Foundation
The Lord Cozens-Hardy Trust
The Craps Charitable Trust
Michael Crawford Children's Charity
*CRH Charitable Trust**
Cripplegate Foundation
The Croydon Relief in Need Charities
CSIS Charity Fund
Cumbria Community Foundation
Itzchok Meyer Cymerman Trust Ltd
The D. G. Charitable Settlement
The D'Oyly Carte Charitable Trust
Baron Davenport's Charity
The Davidson Family Charitable Trust
Margaret Davies Charity
The Crispin Davis Family Trust
Dawat-E-Hadiyah Trust (United Kingdom)
The Roger De Haan Charitable Trust
The Demigryphon Trust
Provincial Grand Charity of the Province of Derbyshire
The J. N. Derbyshire Trust
Devon Community Foundation
The Laduma Dhamecha Charitable Trust
The Dibden Allotments Fund
The Dischma Charitable Trust
The Djanogly Foundation
*William and Frances Dobie Charitable Foundation**
The Derek and Eileen Dodgson Foundation
Donibristle Trust
Dorset Community Foundation
The Double 'O' Charity Ltd
Dromintee Trust
The Anne Duchess of Westminster's Charity
Duchy Health Charity Ltd
Dumbreck Charity
*The Nine Incorporated Trades of Dundee General Fund Charity**
*Dunlossit and Islay Community Trust**
The Dunn Family Charitable Trust
County Durham Community Foundation
The DWF Charitable Foundation
The Dyers' Company Charitable Trust
Sir John Eastwood Foundation
The Gilbert and Eileen Edgar Foundation
Edupoor Ltd
*The Eight Foundation**
The Eighteen Fund
The Eighty Eight Foundation
*The Elie Trust**
The Marian Elizabeth Trust
The Wilfred and Elsie Elkes Charity Fund
The Ellerdale Trust
The Emerton-Christie Charity
The Enkalon Foundation
The EQ Foundation
Esher House Charitable Trust
The Evelyn Trust
The Eveson Charitable Trust
The Exilarch's Foundation
*Family Philanthropy Ltd**
The Lord Faringdon Charitable Trust
Samuel William Farmer Trust
The Thomas Farr Charity
The Farthing Trust
The A. M. Fenton Trust
The Fidelity UK Foundation
Dixie Rose Findlay Charitable Trust
Sir John Fisher Foundation
The Earl Fitzwilliam Charitable Trust
The Robert Fleming Hannay Memorial Charity
The Follett Trust
Forest Hill Charitable Trust

The Lady Forester Trust
Forever Manchester
The Forman Hardy Charitable Trust
Donald Forrester Trust
The Fort Foundation
The Forte Charitable Trust
Foux Foundation*
Fowler Smith and Jones Trust
The Gordon Fraser Charitable Trust
The Joyce and Norman Freed Charitable Trust*
Charles S. French Charitable Trust
The Freshfield Foundation
The Freshgate Trust Foundation
Friarsgate Trust
The Funding Network
Gamma Trust
The Ganzoni Charitable Trust
Garfield Weston Foundation
The Robert Gavron Charitable Trust
Martin Geddes Charitable Trust
The Jacqueline and Michael Gee Charitable Trust
General Charity (Coventry)
The General Charity Fund
The General Nursing Council for England and Wales Trust
The Tara Getty Foundation
The David Gibbons Foundation
The Gibbs Charitable Trusts
The Simon Gibson Charitable Trust
The G. C. Gibson Charitable Trust
The B. and P. Glasser Charitable Trust
The Gloag Foundation
County of Gloucestershire Community Foundation
Worshipful Company of Gold and Silver Wyre Drawers Second Charitable Trust Fund
Sydney and Phyllis Goldberg Memorial Charitable Trust
The Goldcrest Charitable Trust*
The Golden Bottle Trust
The Goldman Sachs Charitable Gift Fund (UK)
Goldman Sachs Gives (UK)
The Goldsmiths' Company Charity
The Goodman Foundation
The Edward Gostling Foundation
The Gould Charitable Trust
Gowling WLG (UK) Charitable Trust
Grace Charitable Trust
The Grace Trust
The Graham Trust
The J. G. Graves Charitable Trust
Gordon Gray Trust
The Gray Trust
The Great Britain Sasakawa Foundation
The Great Stone Bridge Trust of Edenbridge
The Kenneth and Susan Green Charitable Foundation
The Green Hall Foundation
Philip and Judith Green Trust
Greenham Trust Ltd
The Greggs Foundation
The Grimmitt Trust
The Gunter Charitable Trust
H. C. D. Memorial Fund
H. C. Foundation
The Hadley Trust
The Alfred Haines Charitable Trust
Paul Hamlyn Foundation
The Helen Hamlyn Trust
The Hampstead Wells and Campden Trust
Hampton Fund
The W. A. Handley Charity Trust
The Lennox Hannay Charitable Trust
The Kathleen Hannay Memorial Charity
The Haramead Trust
Harborne Parish Lands Charity
The Harbour Charitable Trust
The Harbour Foundation
The Harding Trust
The Harpur Trust
The Harris Family Charitable Trust
The Edith Lilian Harrison 2000 Foundation
The Harrison-Frank Family Foundation (UK) Ltd
The Harry and Mary Foundation*
Gay and Peter Hartley's Hillards Charitable Trust
Edward Harvist Trust (The Harvist Estate)
The Hasluck Charitable Trust
The Maurice Hatter Foundation
The Hawthorne Charitable Trust
Hays Travel Foundation
The Headley Trust
The Health Foundation
May Hearnshaw's Charity
Heart of England Community Foundation
The Heathcoat Trust
The Heathside Charitable Trust
The Charlotte Heber-Percy Charitable Trust
Ernest Hecht Charitable Foundation
The Percy Hedley 1990 Charitable Trust
The Hedley Foundation
Help for Health
The Christina Mary Hendrie Trust
The Tim Henman Foundation
The G. D. Herbert Charitable Trust
Herefordshire Community Foundation
P. and C. Hickinbotham Charitable Trust
The Alan Edward Higgs Charity
The Hilden Charitable Fund
R. G. Hills Charitable Trust
The Lady Hind Trust
The Hinduja Foundation
The Hintze Family Charity Foundation
The Henry C. Hoare Charitable Trust
The Hobson Charity Ltd
The Jane Hodge Foundation
The Holbeck Charitable Trust
Hollick Family Foundation
P. H. Holt Foundation
The Mary Homfray Charitable Trust
The Thomas J. Horne Memorial Trust
The Horners Charity Fund
Hospice UK
The Hospital of God at Greatham
The Hudson Foundation
The Huggard Charitable Trust
The Humanitarian Trust
The Albert Hunt Trust
Huntingdon Freemen's Trust
The Hurley Partners Charitable Trust*
The Nani Huyu Charitable Trust
Hyde Charitable Trust
IBM United Kingdom Trust
The Iceland Foods Charitable Foundation
The Iliffe Family Charitable Trust
The Inflexion Foundation*
The Inman Charity
The Inverforth Charitable Trust
Investream Charitable Trust
The Ireland Fund of Great Britain
The Charles Irving Charitable Trust
The Isle of Anglesey Charitable Trust
The ITF Seafarers Trust
John James Bristol Foundation

Lady Eda Jardine Charitable Trust
John Jarrold Trust Ltd
The Roger and Jean Jefcoate Trust
The Jenour Foundation
The Jephcott Charitable Trust
The Elton John Aids Foundation (EJAF)
Lillie Johnson Charitable Trust
The Johnson Foundation
The Jones 1986 Charitable Trust
The Marjorie and Geoffrey Jones Charitable Trust
The Muriel Jones Foundation
J. E. Joseph Charitable Fund
The Cyril and Eve Jumbo Charitable Trust
The Jusaca Charitable Trust
*Kantor Charitable Foundation**
The Kasner Charitable Trust
The Michael and Ilse Katz Foundation
The Emmanuel Kaye Foundation
The Kennedy Charitable Foundation
The Kennedy Trust for Rheumatology Research
The Kentown Wizard Foundation
The Peter Kershaw Trust
The Ursula Keyes Trust
The Kildare Trust
Kilpatrick Fraser Charitable Trust
The Mary Kinross Charitable Trust
The Graham Kirkham Foundation
Sir James Knott Trust
The Kobler Trust
*KPE4 Charitable Trust**
The Kreitman Foundation
Kupath Gemach Chaim Bechesed Viznitz Trust
Kusuma Trust UK
The Kyte Charitable Trust
Ladbrokes Coral Trust
Christopher Laing Foundation
The David Laing Foundation
The Kirby Laing Foundation
The Martin Laing Foundation
The Beatrice Laing Trust
The Leonard Laity Stoate Charitable Trust
The Lake House Charity
Community Foundations for Lancashire and Merseyside
The Lancashire Foundation
Duchy of Lancaster Benevolent Fund
Lancaster Foundation
Langdale Trust
The R. J. Larg Family Trust
Mrs M. A. Lascelles Charitable Trust
Laslett's (Hinton) Charity
Mrs F. B. Laurence Charitable Trust
The Kathleen Laurence Trust
The Law Family Charitable Foundation
The Richard Lawes Foundation
The Edgar E. Lawley Foundation
Lawson Beckman Charitable Trust
The Lawson Trust CIO
The Leach Fourteenth Trust
The Leathersellers' Company Charitable Fund
Leeds Building Society Charitable Foundation
The Kennedy Leigh Charitable Trust
The Leri Charitable Trust
Lord Leverhulme's Charitable Trust
*The Ralph Levy Charitable Company Ltd**
Joseph Levy Foundation
*Cecil and Hilda Lewis Charitable Trust**
Bernard Lewis Family Charitable Trust
John Lewis Foundation
The Light Fund Company
The Limbourne Trust
Limoges Charitable Trust
The Linbury Trust
Lincolnshire Community Foundation
The Linden Charitable Trust
The Linder Foundation
The Lindley Foundation (TLF)
The Frank Litchfield Charitable Trust
The Charles Littlewood Hill Trust
Liverpool Charity and Voluntary Services (LCVS)
*The Livingston Charitable Trust**
Jack Livingstone Charitable Trust
The Ian and Natalie Livingstone Charitable Trust
The Elaine and Angus Lloyd Charitable Trust
The W. M. and B. W. Lloyd Trust
Lloyds Bank Foundation for England and Wales
Lloyds Bank Foundation for the Channel Islands
The Locker Foundation
The Lockwood Charitable Foundation
London Catalyst
The London Community Foundation (LCF)
The C. L. Loyd Charitable Trust
Robert Luff Foundation Ltd
The Henry Lumley Charitable Trust
The Lyndal Tree Foundation
M. and C. Trust
The Macdonald-Buchanan Charitable Trust
Mace Foundation
The Mactaggart Third Fund
The Ian Mactaggart Trust (The Mactaggart Second Fund)
*The Mageni Trust**
The Mahoro Charitable Trust
Making a Difference Locally Ltd
The Manackerman Charitable Trust
The Manchester Guardian Society Charitable Trust
R. W. Mann Trust
*The Manson Family Charitable Trust**
*The Marandi Foundation**
The Marks Family Charitable Trust
The J. P. Marland Charitable Trust
*The Marque Foundation**
The Michael Marsh Charitable Trust
The Marsh Christian Trust
Charlotte Marshall Charitable Trust
D. G. Marshall of Cambridge Trust
The Kristina Martin Charitable Trust
The Martin Charitable Trust
Sir George Martin Trust
Masonic Charitable Foundation
Nancie Massey Charitable Trust
The Master Charitable Trust
Matchroom Sport Charitable Foundation
The Matliwala Family Charitable Trust
The Violet Mauray Charitable Trust
Mayheights Ltd
MBNA General Foundation
*Gemma and Chris McGough Charitable Foundation CIO**
The Medicash Foundation
The Medlock Charitable Trust
The Meikle Foundation
The Brian Mercer Charitable Trust
The Merchant Taylors' Company Charities Fund
The Merchant Venturers' Charity

T. and J. Meyer Family Foundation Ltd
The Mickel Fund
The Mickleham Trust
The Gerald Micklem Charitable Trust
The Masonic Province of Middlesex Charitable Trust (Middlesex Masonic Charity)
The Millennium Oak Trust
The Ronald Miller Foundation
Jean and Roger Miller's Charitable Trust
The Milne Family Foundation*
The James Milner Foundation
The Mishcon Family Charitable Trust
The Brian Mitchell Charitable Settlement
Keren Mitzvah Trust
The Mohn Westlake Foundation*
The Alexander Moncur Trust
The Monmouthshire County Council Welsh Church Act Fund
Moondance Foundation
The Morel Charitable Trust
The Morgan Charitable Foundation
The Steve Morgan Foundation
Morgan Stanley International Foundation
The Morris Charitable Trust
The Willie and Mabel Morris Charitable Trust
G. M. Morrison Charitable Trust
The Ken and Edna Morrison Charitable Trust
The Morrisons Foundation
The Morton Charitable Trust (Dundee)
The Mosawi Foundation*
Vyoel Moshe Charitable Trust
The Edwina Mountbatten and Leonora Children's Foundation
The Mulberry Trust
Edith Murphy Foundation
Murphy-Neumann Charity Company Ltd
The John R. Murray Charitable Trust
Brian Murtagh Charitable Trust
Music Sales Charitable Trust
Muslim Hands
The Janet Nash Charitable Settlement
The National Garden Scheme
The NDL Foundation
Ner Foundation
Nesta
Network for Social Change Charitable Trust
Newby Trust Ltd
The Nineveh Charitable Trust
NNS Foundation*
Norfolk Community Foundation
The Norman Family Charitable Trust
Normanby Charitable Trust
North Berwick Trust*
North East Area Miners' Social Welfare Trust Fund
Northamptonshire Community Foundation
Community Foundation for Northern Ireland
Northern Pharmacies Ltd Trust Fund
The Northwick Trust
Northwood Charitable Trust
The Norton Foundation
The Norton Rose Fulbright Charitable Foundation
The Notgrove Trust
Notting Hill Genesis Community Foundation
Nottinghamshire Community Foundation
The Ofenheim Charitable Trust
Oizer Charitable Trust
The O'Sullivan Family Charitable Trust
The Owen Family Trust
The Paget Charitable Trust
The Gerald Palmer Eling Trust Company
The Paphitis Charitable Trust
The Paragon Trust
Partners Global Foundation*
The Pastoral Care Trust – The St Nicholas Care Fund
The Patrick Trust
Peacock Charitable Trust
Susanna Peake Charitable Trust
David Pearlman Charitable Foundation
The Pears Family Charitable Foundation
People's Postcode Trust
The Persimmon Charitable Foundation
Personal Assurance Charitable Trust
The Pharsalia Charitable Trust
The Phillips and Rubens Charitable Trust
The Phillips Charitable Trust
Cecil Pilkington Charitable Trust
Pilkington Charities Fund
The Sir Harry Pilkington Trust Fund
PIMCO Foundation Europe
Pink Ribbon Foundation
The Pitt-Rivers Charitable Trust
The Pixel Fund
The George and Esme Pollitzer Charitable Settlement
The Portrack Charitable Trust
Postcode Community Trust
Postcode Society Trust (formerly Postcode Dream Trust)
The Mary Potter Convent Hospital Trust
The Prince of Wales's Charitable Foundation
The Princess Anne's Charities
The Priory Foundation
Prison Service Charity Fund
The Professional Footballers' Association Charity
Catkin Pussywillow Charitable Trust
The PwC Foundation
The Pye Foundation
Mr and Mrs J. A. Pye's Charitable Settlement
QBE European Operations Foundation
The Queen Anne's Gate Foundation
Queen Mary's Roehampton Trust
The Quilter Foundation*
Quintessentially Foundation
The Monica Rabagliati Charitable Trust
Richard Radcliffe Trust
The Randal Charitable Foundation*
The Joseph and Lena Randall Charitable Trust
The Eleanor Rathbone Charitable Trust
Elizabeth Rathbone Charity
The Ravensdale Trust
The Rayne Foundation
The Rayne Trust
The John Rayner Charitable Trust
The Sir James Reckitt Charity
C. A. Redfern Charitable Foundation
Rentrust Foundation Ltd
The Rest-Harrow Trust
The Revere Charitable Trust
RG Foundation*
The Rhododendron Trust
Riada Trust
Daisie Rich Trust
Rigby Foundation
The River Farm Foundation
The Dezna Robins Jones Charitable Foundation
Robyn Charitable Trust
Rockcliffe Charitable Trust
The Rockspring Charitable Trust*
The Roddick Foundation
The Gerald and Gail Ronson Family Foundation

Rosca Trust
The Cecil Rosen Foundation
The Rothley Trust
The Roughley Charitable Trust
The Rowlands Trust
The Royal Foundation of the Duke and Duchess of Cambridge
The Rubin Foundation Charitable Trust
The Russell Trust
S. and R. Charitable Trust
The Jeremy and John Sacher Charitable Trust
The Michael and Nicola Sacher Charitable Trust
The Saintbury Trust
The Saints and Sinners Trust Ltd
The Salamander Charitable Trust
Salters' Charitable Foundation
Samjo Ltd
The Basil Samuel Charitable Trust
The M. J. Samuel Charitable Trust
The Sandhu Charitable Foundation
Sandra Charitable Trust
Savannah Wisdom
Schroder Charity Trust
The Schroder Foundation
Scott (Eredine) Charitable Trust
The Frieda Scott Charitable Trust
The John Scott Trust Fund
Scouloudi Foundation
Sam and Bella Sebba Charitable Trust
*The Selfridges Group Foundation**
The Shanly Foundation
ShareGift (The Orr Mackintosh Foundation)
The Shears Foundation
The Sylvia and Colin Shepherd Charitable Trust
The Sherling Charitable Trust
Shetland Charitable Trust
The Florence Shute Millennium Trust
Sirius Minerals Foundation
The Thomas Sivewright Catto Charitable Settlement
The Charles Skey Charitable Trust
The Mrs Smith and Mount Trust
*Arabella and Julian Smith Family Trust**
The Leslie Smith Foundation
The R. C. Snelling Charitable Trust
The Sobell Foundation
Sodexo Stop Hunger Foundation
Somerset Community Foundation
The E. C. Sosnow Charitable Trust
The South Yorkshire Community Foundation
Peter Sowerby Foundation
Sparquote Ltd
The Spear Charitable Trust
*The Michael and Sarah Spencer Foundation**
Rosalyn and Nicholas Springer Charitable Trust
The Spurrell Charitable Trust
The Geoff and Fiona Squire Foundation
*The Vichai Srivaddhanaprabha Foundation**
The St James's Trust Settlement
St John's Foundation Est. 1174
St Monica Trust
Stadium Charitable Trust
The Stafford Trust
The Community Foundation for Staffordshire
Stanley Foundation Ltd
The Peter Stebbings Memorial Charity
The Steel Charitable Trust
*The Sterry Family Foundation**
Stevenson Family's Charitable Trust
Sir Halley Stewart Trust
The Stewarts Law Foundation
Mark Stolkin Foundation
The Stoneygate Trust
Peter Stormonth Darling Charitable Trust
The Strangward Trust
Stratford-upon-Avon Town Trust
The WO Street Charitable Foundation
*The Joseph Strong Frazer Trust**
Suffolk Community Foundation
Sumner Wilson Charitable Trust
The Bernard Sunley Foundation
The Sunrise Foundation CIO
*The Support Foundation**
Surgo Foundation UK Ltd
Community Foundation for Surrey
Sutton Coldfield Charitable Trust
The Swann-Morton Foundation
The John Swire (1989) Charitable Trust
The Swire Charitable Trust
The Charles and Elsie Sykes Trust
*The Hugh Symons Charitable Trust**
The Syncona Foundation
*The Ashley Tabor-King Foundation**
The Tajtelbaum Charitable Trust
The Talbot Trusts
Tanner Trust
Tay Charitable Trust
C. B. and H. H. Taylor 1984 Trust
The Taylor Family Foundation
A. P. Taylor Trust
The Thales Charitable Trust
Sir Jules Thorn Charitable Trust
The Thornton Trust
Mrs R. P. Tindall's Charitable Trust
The Tolkien Trust
*The Tomoro Foundation**
The Tompkins Foundation
The Tory Family Foundation
The Toy Trust
Toyota Manufacturing UK Charitable Trust
Annie Tranmer Charitable Trust
The Constance Travis Charitable Trust
The Trefoil Trust
The True Colours Trust
Trumros Ltd
The James Tudor Foundation
*The Tudwick Foundation**
The Tufton Charitable Trust
The Tuixen Foundation
The Roger and Douglas Turner Charitable Trust
UKH Foundation
Ulster Garden Villages Ltd
The Underwood Trust
The Valentine Charitable Trust
The Albert Van Den Bergh Charitable Trust
*The Van Mesdag Fund**
The Vardy Foundation
Variety, the Children's Charity
*The Velvet Foundation**
The Veterans' Foundation
Virgin Atlantic Foundation
The Vodafone Foundation
Volant Charitable Trust
Sylvia Waddilove Foundation UK
Wakefield and Tetley Trust
Robert and Felicity Waley-Cohen Charitable Trust
The Walker Trust
Walton Foundation
The Ward Blenkinsop Trust
The Barbara Ward Children's Foundation
The Warwickshire Masonic Charitable Association Ltd

Mrs Waterhouse Charitable Trust
Wates Family Enterprise Trust
The Wates Foundation
The Geoffrey Watling Charity
Blyth Watson Charitable Trust
The Watson Family Charitable Trust
The Weinstock Fund
The Weir Charitable Trust
The James Weir Foundation
The Welsh Church Act Fund
The Westfield Health Charitable Trust
Westminster Amalgamated Charity
The Whinfell Charitable Fund
The Melanie White Foundation Ltd
The Williams Charitable Trust
The Williams Family Foundation
The Dame Violet Wills Will Trust
The Wilmcote Charitrust
The Francis Winham Foundation
The Michael and Anna Wix Charitable Trust
The Wixamtree Trust
Friends of Wiznitz Ltd
The Maurice Wohl Charitable Foundation
The Charles Wolfson Charitable Trust
The Wolfson Family Charitable Trust
The Wolfson Foundation
The Wood Foundation
Wooden Spoon Society
The Eric Wright Charitable Trust
*Sir Graham Wylie Foundation**
The Wyseliot Rose Charitable Trust
The Yapp Charitable Trust
York Children's Trust
Yorkshire Building Society Charitable Foundation
Yorkshire Cancer Research
The William Allen Young Charitable Trust
The Elizabeth and Prince Zaiger Trust
The Marjorie and Arnold Ziff Charitable Foundation
The Zochonis Charitable Trust
Zurich Community Trust (UK) Ltd

Clinical treatment/care

The 4814 Trust
The Abbeyfield Research Foundation
The Aberbrothock Skea Trust
The Bryan Adams Foundation
The Aimwell Charitable Trust
The Alborada Trust
The Alchemy Foundation
*Beryl Alexander Charity**
D. C. R. Allen Charitable Trust
Alliance Family Foundation Ltd
The John Armitage Charitable Trust
The Armourers' and Brasiers' Gauntlet Trust
The Astor Foundation
The Baily Thomas Charitable Fund
The Barbers' Company General Charities
The Barclay Foundation
The Birmingham District Nursing Charitable Trust
*Maria Bjornson Memorial Fund**
The Boltini Trust
The Boshier-Hinton Foundation
G. and K. Boyes Charitable Trust
The Tony Bramall Charitable Trust
*Bright Red Charity**
British Lung Foundation
Bill Brown 1989 Charitable Trust
The Brownsword Charitable Foundation
The Burden Trust
The Burdett Trust for Nursing
Miss Margaret Butters Reekie Charitable Trust
The Edward Cadbury Charitable Trust
Cattanach
The B. G. S. Cayzer Charitable Trust
The Charities Advisory Trust
Children with Cancer UK
Children's Liver Disease Foundation
The Colt Foundation
The Keith Coombs Trust
Cruden Foundation Ltd
Michael Davies Charitable Settlement
The De Laszlo Foundation
The Delves Charitable Trust
Dinwoodie Charitable Company
The Charles Dunstone Charitable Trust
The Gilbert and Eileen Edgar Foundation
W. G. Edwards Charitable Foundation
The Eighty Eight Foundation
The Ellerdale Trust
The Englefield Charitable Trust
The Evelyn Trust
The Eveson Charitable Trust
*Family Philanthropy Ltd**
The Lord Faringdon Charitable Trust
The February Foundation
Sir John Fisher Foundation
The Forbes Charitable Foundation
The Anna Rosa Forster Charitable Trust
The Elizabeth Frankland Moore and Star Foundation
Jill Franklin Trust
The Hugh Fraser Foundation
The Louis and Valerie Freedman Charitable Settlement
The Freshgate Trust Foundation
Frognal Trust
Garthgwynion Charities
The General Charity Fund
The General Nursing Council for England and Wales Trust
Sydney and Phyllis Goldberg Memorial Charitable Trust
The Goldsmiths' Company Charity
The Great Britain Sasakawa Foundation
The Grocers' Charity
The Walter Guinness Charitable Trust
The Alfred Haines Charitable Trust
The Harris Family Charitable Trust
The Charles Hayward Foundation
The Health Foundation
The Michael Heller Charitable Foundation
The Simon Heller Charitable Settlement
Help for Health
The Hemby Charitable Trust
The Hintze Family Charity Foundation
The Holbeck Charitable Trust
Homelands Charitable Trust
The Hospital Saturday Fund
The Sir Joseph Hotung Charitable Settlement
Miss Agnes H. Hunter's Trust
*Jeffrey Charitable Trust**
The Peter Kershaw Trust
The Kirschel Foundation
The Ernest Kleinwort Charitable Trust

Kollel and Co. Ltd
Kupath Gemach Chaim Bechesed Viznitz Trust
The Lake House Charity
Lancaster Foundation
Langdale Trust
The Linder Foundation
The Charles Littlewood Hill Trust
The Lockwood Charitable Foundation
Robert Luff Foundation Ltd
Lord and Lady Lurgan Trust
The W. M. Mann Foundation
*The Marque Foundation**
Nancie Massey Charitable Trust
The Robert McAlpine Foundation
D. D. McPhail Charitable Settlement
The Mosselson Charitable Trust
The Edwina Mountbatten and Leonora Children's Foundation
The National Garden Scheme
The Frances and Augustus Newman Foundation
Oglesby Charitable Trust
*The Samuel and Freda Parkinson Charitable Trust**
Payne-Gallwey 1989 Charitable Trust
The Pharsalia Charitable Trust
Prostate Cancer UK
Mr and Mrs J. A. Pye's Charitable Settlement
Queen Mary's Roehampton Trust
The Monica Rabagliati Charitable Trust
The Ranworth Trust
Reuben Foundation
The Revere Charitable Trust
The Clive and Sylvia Richards Charity Ltd
Riverside Charitable Trust Ltd
The Roan Charitable Trust
Rosetrees Trust
The Eranda Rothschild Foundation
The Row Fogo Charitable Trust
The Dr Mortimer and Theresa Sackler Foundation
The Peter Samuel Charitable Trust
The Schroder Foundation
The Jean Shanks Foundation
The Sheepdrove Trust
The SMB Trust
The N. Smith Charitable Settlement
The Leslie Smith Foundation
David Solomons Charitable Trust
Peter Sowerby Foundation
Sparks Charity
The Spear Charitable Trust
Spielman Charitable Trust
The Stafford Trust
The Steinberg Family Charitable Trust
Sir Halley Stewart Trust
The Stoller Charitable Trust
*The Support Foundation**
Surgo Foundation UK Ltd
The Charles and Elsie Sykes Trust
The Syncona Foundation
The Gay and Keith Talbot Trust
Tallow Chandlers Benevolent Fund No. 2
Tanner Trust
The Templeton Goodwill Trust
Tenovus Cancer Care
Tenovus Scotland
Sir Jules Thorn Charitable Trust
The Three Guineas Trust
The Tolkien Trust
David William Traill Cargill Fund
The Trefoil Trust
Tropical Health and Education Trust
The True Colours Trust
The James Tudor Foundation
The Roger and Douglas Turner Charitable Trust
The Michael Uren Foundation
The Albert Van Den Bergh Charitable Trust
The Vandervell Foundation
Versus Arthritis
*Vinci UK Foundation**
*Vision Foundation**
The Wellcome Trust
The Welsh Church Act Fund
The Westcroft Trust
The Felicity Wilde Charitable Trust
W. Wing Yip and Brothers Foundation
The Francis Winham Foundation
The Lord Leonard and Lady Estelle Wolfson Foundation
The Wolfson Foundation
Yorkshire Cancer Research

Community health services

The 1989 Willan Charitable Trust
Allchurches Trust Ltd
The Anchor Foundation
The Archer Trust
Barchester Healthcare Foundation
Barnwood Trust
CRASH
The Anne Duchess of Westminster's Charity
The Evelyn Trust
Sir John Fisher Foundation
The Forbes Charitable Foundation
Jill Franklin Trust
The Hugh Fraser Foundation
The Louis and Valerie Freedman Charitable Settlement
Charles S. French Charitable Trust
The General Nursing Council for England and Wales Trust
The Girdlers' Company Charitable Trust
Sydney and Phyllis Goldberg Memorial Charitable Trust
The Grimmitt Trust
The Hamilton Davies Trust
Paul Hamlyn Foundation
Gay and Peter Hartley's Hillards Charitable Trust
The Hawthorne Charitable Trust
The Lady Hind Trust
P. H. Holt Foundation
The Hudson Foundation
Michael and Shirley Hunt Charitable Trust
The Albert Hunt Trust
Irish Youth Foundation (UK) Ltd (incorporating The Lawlor Foundation)
The Charles Irving Charitable Trust
*Jeffrey Charitable Trust**
The Kentown Wizard Foundation
The Allen Lane Foundation
London Catalyst
The London Community Foundation (LCF)
The Mackintosh Foundation
The Magdalen and Lasher Charity (General Fund)
Sir George Martin Trust
The Gerald Micklem Charitable Trust
North East Area Miners' Social Welfare Trust Fund
Odin Charitable Trust
People's Health Trust
The George and Esme Pollitzer Charitable Settlement
Postcode Community Trust
The Mary Potter Convent Hospital Trust
Richard Radcliffe Trust
Elizabeth Rathbone Charity
Richmond Parish Lands Charity

The Sir James Roll Charitable Trust
Salisbury Pool Charity
The Frieda Scott Charitable Trust
The Sheldon Trust
The Stafford Trust
Swan Mountain Trust
The Talbot Trusts
The Three Guineas Trust
The James Tudor Foundation
The Utley Foundation
The Vardy Foundation
Variety, the Children's Charity
*Vinci UK Foundation**
The Vintners' Foundation
Viridor Credits Environmental Company
*Vision Foundation**
Wade's Charity
The Bruce Wake Charitable Trust
The Will Charitable Trust
*Sir Graham Wylie Foundation**
Yorkshire Cancer Research

Health advice and support

The Anchor Foundation
The Avon and Somerset Police Community Trust
The Baily Thomas Charitable Fund
British Lung Foundation
Building & Civil Engineering Charitable Trust
BUPA UK Foundation
*Camden Giving**
Cattanach
The City Bridge Trust (Bridge House Estates)
The Colt Foundation
Colyer-Fergusson Charitable Trust
Cripplegate Foundation
The Charles Dunstone Charitable Trust
The Evelyn Trust
The Eveson Charitable Trust
The February Foundation
The Louis and Valerie Freedman Charitable Settlement
Charles S. French Charitable Trust
GambleAware
The Green Hall Foundation
Hammersmith United Charities
HFC Help For Children UK LTD
Housing Pathways Trust
The Huggard Charitable Trust
Miss Agnes H. Hunter's Trust
The Charles Irving Charitable Trust
The Roger and Jean Jefcoate Trust
The Kelly Family Charitable Trust
The Kirschel Foundation
The Leathersellers' Company Charitable Fund
London Catalyst
The London Community Foundation (LCF)
Longleigh Foundation
The Mackintosh Foundation
The Magdalen and Lasher Charity (General Fund)
The Kristina Martin Charitable Trust
The Mickleham Trust
The Monmouthshire County Council Welsh Church Act Fund
The Morrisons Foundation
The National Garden Scheme
The Nisbet Trust
The Northwick Trust
The Pastoral Care Trust – The St Nicholas Care Fund
Miss M. E. S. Paterson's Charitable Trust
People's Health Trust
The Portishead Nautical Trust
Queen Mary's Roehampton Trust
The Rayne Foundation
Red Hill Charitable Trust
The Rothley Trust
The Michael and Nicola Sacher Charitable Trust
Salisbury Pool Charity
The Frieda Scott Charitable Trust
The Sheldon Trust
David Solomons Charitable Trust
The Souter Charitable Trust
St Monica Trust
The Stafford Trust
The Charles and Elsie Sykes Trust
The Talbot Trusts
The Templeton Goodwill Trust
The Three Guineas Trust
The True Colours Trust
*Vision Foundation**
The VTCT Foundation
Charity Of Sir Richard Whittington
The Woodward Charitable Trust
The Zochonis Charitable Trust

Health awareness/promotion

The Alchemy Foundation
The Baily Thomas Charitable Fund
Birmingham International Airport Community Trust Fund
Building & Civil Engineering Charitable Trust
BUPA UK Foundation
*The Antonio Carluccio Foundation**
Cattanach
Colyer-Fergusson Charitable Trust
The Evelyn Trust
The Eveson Charitable Trust
The Louis and Valerie Freedman Charitable Settlement
GambleAware
The Greggs Foundation
The Health Foundation
Heart Research UK
The Lady Hind Trust
Hope Trust
The Hospital Saturday Fund
Housing Pathways Trust
Impact Funding Partners Ltd
The Innocent Foundation
The Kelly Family Charitable Trust
The Leathersellers' Company Charitable Fund
The Linder Foundation
The London Community Foundation (LCF)
The Kristina Martin Charitable Trust
Maudsley Charity
Mercury Phoenix Trust
The Mickleham Trust
Northwood Charitable Trust
The Pastoral Care Trust – The St Nicholas Care Fund
People's Health Trust
Prostate Cancer UK
The Purey Cust Trust CIO
The Rayne Trust
Rosca Trust
The Roughley Charitable Trust
The Shears Foundation
Sodexo Stop Hunger Foundation
The Souter Charitable Trust
The Stafford Trust
Stratford-upon-Avon Town Trust
The Charles and Elsie Sykes Trust
Tenovus Cancer Care
The Three Guineas Trust
Tropical Health and Education Trust
*Vision Foundation**

The Wellcome Trust
The Lord Leonard and Lady Estelle Wolfson Foundation
Yorkshire Cancer Research

Mental health and well-being

ABF The Soldiers' Charity
Beryl Alexander Charity*
ArtSocial Foundation
The Baily Thomas Charitable Fund
The Barnes Fund*
Barnwood Trust
BUPA UK Foundation
Camden Giving*
The Carlton Hayes Mental Health Charity
Chapman Charitable Trust
Cheshire Community Foundation Ltd
The Childhood Trust
The Childwick Trust
The Churchill Foundation
The City Bridge Trust (Bridge House Estates)
Comic Relief
Co-operative Community Investment Foundation
CRH Charitable Trust*
Cripplegate Foundation
The Dashlight Foundation*
The Anne Duchess of Westminster's Charity
County Durham Community Foundation
The Ellerdale Trust
The Evelyn Trust
The Eveson Charitable Trust
The Fairness Foundation
Fishmongers' Company's Charitable Trust
Gwyneth Forrester Trust
Jill Franklin Trust
GambleAware
The Tara Getty Foundation
The Girdlers' Company Charitable Trust
Global Charities
The J. G. Graves Charitable Trust
Hampton Fund
Harborne Parish Lands Charity
Herefordshire Community Foundation
HFC Help For Children UK LTD
The Hobson Charity Ltd
The Jane Hodge Foundation
Hollick Family Foundation
The Hospital of God at Greatham
Hyde Charitable Trust
The Inverforth Charitable Trust
The Charles Irving Charitable Trust
JD Foundation*
The Roger and Jean Jefcoate Trust
The Ian Karten Charitable Trust
The Richard Lawes Foundation
The London Community Foundation (LCF)
Longleigh Foundation
John Lyon's Charity
The Kristina Martin Charitable Trust
Maudsley Charity
The Mercers' Charitable Foundation
The Millennium Oak Trust
Mind*
John Moores Foundation
G. M. Morrison Charitable Trust
The Mulberry Trust
The National Garden Scheme
Northwood Charitable Trust
One Community Foundation Ltd
Orange Tree Trust*
The Pears Family Charitable Foundation
The Pixel Fund
The Prince of Wales's Charitable Foundation
The Priory Foundation
The Purey Cust Trust CIO
The Randal Charitable Foundation*
The Rayne Trust
Red Hill Charitable Trust
The Rhododendron Trust
The Robertson Trust
The Roughley Charitable Trust
The Royal Foundation of the Duke and Duchess of Cambridge
Francis C. Scott Charitable Trust
The Frieda Scott Charitable Trust
Sam and Bella Sebba Charitable Trust
The Mrs Smith and Mount Trust
The South Yorkshire Community Foundation
St James's Place Charitable Foundation
The Peter Stebbings Memorial Charity
The Stone Family Foundation
Stratford-upon-Avon Town Trust
StreetSmart – Action for the Homeless
Swan Mountain Trust
The Ashley Tabor-King Foundation*
The Talbot Trusts
C. B. and H. H. Taylor 1984 Trust
The Tuixen Foundation
UKH Foundation
Ulster Garden Villages Ltd
The Veterans' Foundation
Volant Charitable Trust
Wakefield and Tetley Trust
Charity Of Sir Richard Whittington
The Lord Leonard and Lady Estelle Wolfson Foundation
The Wolfson Foundation
The Yapp Charitable Trust

Respite/breaks/ convalescence

The Alchemy Foundation
Bauer Radio's Cash for Kids Charities
The Birmingham District Nursing Charitable Trust
Edinburgh Children's Holiday Fund
The Ellerdale Trust
Charles S. French Charitable Trust
The Girdlers' Company Charitable Trust
The Edward Gostling Foundation
Hackney Parochial Charities
The Alfred Haines Charitable Trust
The Hampstead Wells and Campden Trust
The Hedley Foundation
The Charles Irving Charitable Trust
The Linder Foundation
The Gerald Micklem Charitable Trust
The Eleanor Rathbone Charitable Trust
The Sheldon Trust
The Will Charitable Trust
The Eric Wright Charitable Trust

Housing and homelessness

The 29th May 1961 Charitable Trust
The 4814 Trust
ABF The Soldiers' Charity
Adam Family Foundation*
The Alchemy Foundation
Allchurches Trust Ltd
Andrews Charitable Trust
The Barbour Foundation
The Berkeley Foundation
Blakemore Foundation
The Brelms Trust CIO
R. S. Brownless Charitable Trust
Community Foundation for Calderdale
CEO Sleepout
Chrysalis Trust
The City Bridge Trust (Bridge House Estates)
Clark Foundation
The Clothworkers' Foundation
The Cole Charitable Trust
The Coltstaple Trust
Michael Crawford Children's Charity
Crisis UK
The D. G. Charitable Settlement
Baron Davenport's Charity
Foundation Derbyshire
Dorset Community Foundation
Drapers' Charitable Fund
County Durham Community Foundation
The Eveson Charitable Trust
The Thomas Farr Charity
The Feoffees of St Michael's Spurriergate York
Fine & Country Foundation
Oliver Ford Foundation
The Elizabeth Frankland Moore and Star Foundation
The Freshfield Foundation
The G. D. Charitable Trust
The Goldsmiths' Company Charity
The Green Hall Foundation
The Greggs Foundation
The Hadrian Trust
The Alfred Haines Charitable Trust
Hammersmith United Charities
Hampton Fund
The Haramead Trust
The Harbour Foundation
William Harding's Charity
The Harrison-Frank Family Foundation (UK) Ltd
The Hasluck Charitable Trust
Help the Homeless Ltd
The Hemby Charitable Trust
P. and C. Hickinbotham Charitable Trust
Highway One Trust
The Lady Hind Trust
The Hobson Charity Ltd
The Jane Hodge Foundation
Hollick Family Foundation
The Mary Homfray Charitable Trust
The Thomas J. Horne Memorial Trust
The Hospital of God at Greatham
The Huggard Charitable Trust
The Albert Hunt Trust
The Nani Huyu Charitable Trust
Irish Youth Foundation (UK) Ltd (incorporating The Lawlor Foundation)
The Charles Irving Charitable Trust
The Isla Foundation*
John Jarrold Trust Ltd
JD Foundation*
The Jusaca Charitable Trust
Kent Community Foundation
The Graham Kirkham Foundation
Sir James Knott Trust
John Laing Charitable Trust
The Beatrice Laing Trust
LandAid Charitable Trust (LandAid)
Laslett's (Hinton) Charity
Mrs F. B. Laurence Charitable Trust
The Leathersellers' Company Charitable Fund
Leeds Building Society Charitable Foundation
The Linbury Trust
The Charles Littlewood Hill Trust
Lloyds Bank Foundation for the Channel Islands
London Housing Foundation Ltd (LHF)
Longleigh Foundation
Making a Difference Locally Ltd
R. W. Mann Trust
The Medlock Charitable Trust
The Mercers' Charitable Foundation
Jean and Roger Miller's Charitable Trust
The Monday Charitable Trust*
John Moores Foundation
The Morgan Charitable Foundation
The Steve Morgan Foundation
G. M. Morrison Charitable Trust
Muslim Hands
The Nationwide Foundation
Norfolk Community Foundation
The Norman Family Charitable Trust
Community Foundation for Northern Ireland
The Norton Foundation
Nottinghamshire Community Foundation
Odin Charitable Trust
Henry Oldfield Trust
Orange Tree Trust*
The Ovo Charitable Foundation
The Persimmon Charitable Foundation
The Phillips and Rubens Charitable Trust
The Austin and Hope Pilkington Trust
PIMCO Foundation Europe
The George and Esme Pollitzer Charitable Settlement
The Pret Foundation
The Raindance Charitable Trust*
The Eleanor Rathbone Charitable Trust
The Rhododendron Trust
Richmond Parish Lands Charity
The River Farm Foundation
Mrs L. D. Rope's Third Charitable Settlement
The Royal British Legion
The Saintbury Trust
Francis C. Scott Charitable Trust
Sam and Bella Sebba Charitable Trust
Rita and David Slowe Charitable Trust
The Mrs Smith and Mount Trust
The Sobell Foundation
St John's Foundation Est. 1174
Standard Life Foundation
The Peter Stebbings Memorial Charity
The Talbot Trusts
C. B. and H. H. Taylor 1984 Trust
The Constance Travis Charitable Trust
Trust For London
The Tudor Trust
The Tuixen Foundation
Ulster Garden Villages Ltd
The Albert Van Den Bergh Charitable Trust
The Veterans' Foundation
Vinci UK Foundation*
The Vintners' Foundation
The Virgin Money Foundation
Sylvia Waddilove Foundation UK
Walton on Thames Charity
The Welland Trust*

Westminster Amalgamated Charity
Charity of Sir Richard Whittington
The Wood Foundation
*Sir Graham Wylie Foundation**
Yorkshire Building Society Charitable Foundation
The Zochonis Charitable Trust

Almshouses

Baron Davenport's Charity
Hammersmith United Charities
The Hospital of God at Greatham
Laslett's (Hinton) Charity
The Mickleham Trust

Homelessness outreach

ABF The Soldiers' Charity
The DWF Charitable Foundation
The Thomas J. Horne Memorial Trust
*The Isla Foundation**
The London Community Foundation (LCF)
The Mickleham Trust
Rita and David Slowe Charitable Trust
The Peter Stebbings Memorial Charity
The Virgin Money Foundation
*The Welland Trust**

Hostels/shelters

The Oliver Borthwick Memorial Trust
CRASH
The Elizabeth Frankland Moore and Star Foundation
The Hilden Charitable Fund
The Mickleham Trust
The Nisbet Trust
Rita and David Slowe Charitable Trust
The Mrs Smith and Mount Trust
StreetSmart – Action for the Homeless

Housing advice

The Hilden Charitable Fund
The Charles Littlewood Hill Trust
The Nationwide Foundation
The Nisbet Trust
The Robertson Trust
StreetSmart – Action for the Homeless
Three Monkies Trust
Trust for London

Social housing

Longleigh Foundation
The Nationwide Foundation

Supported accommodation

The Hospital of God at Greatham
The Allen Lane Foundation
The Charles Littlewood Hill Trust
The Mickleham Trust
The Skerritt Trust
St Monica Trust
Ulster Garden Villages Ltd
Westminster Almshouses Foundation

Religion

Adenfirst Ltd
Sylvia Aitken's Charitable Trust
The All Saints Educational Trust
Alliance Family Foundation Ltd
Viscount Amory's Charitable Trust
Ardbarron Trust Ltd
The John Armitage Charitable Trust
The Asda Foundation
The Ashendene Trust
The Austin Bailey Foundation
The Roger and Sarah Bancroft Clark Charitable Trust
The Philip Barker Charity
Bear Mordechai Ltd
Beauland Ltd
The Bellahouston Bequest Fund
Benesco Charity Ltd
The Billmeir Charitable Trust
The Bingham Trust
Birthday House Trust
*Mary Brown Memorial Trust**
Buckingham Trust
Consolidated Charity of Burton upon Trent
C. and F. Charitable Trust
Callendar Charitable Trust
Cannon Charitable Trust
The W. A. Cargill Fund
The Carpenters' Company Charitable Trust
The B. G. S. Cayzer Charitable Trust
Chalfords Ltd
Charitworth Ltd
Church Burgesses Trust
Church of Ireland Priorities Fund
Clark Foundation
CMZ Ltd
The Catherine Cookson Charitable Trust
The Alice Ellen Cooper Dean Charitable Foundation
The Worshipful Company of Cordwainers Charitable Trusts (Minges Gift)
The Duke of Cornwall's Benevolent Fund
The Cross Trust
The Demigryphon Trust
Didymus
Dorset Community Foundation
*The Nine Incorporated Trades of Dundee General Fund Charity**
The Gilbert and Eileen Edgar Foundation
The Eighteen Fund
The Englefield Charitable Trust
The Farthing Trust

The Robert Fleming Hannay Memorial Charity
The Fort Foundation
The Gordon Fraser Charitable Trust
The Hugh Fraser Foundation
Garfield Weston Foundation
The Jacqueline and Michael Gee Charitable Trust
The Simon Gibson Charitable Trust
The G. C. Gibson Charitable Trust
The Gloag Foundation
The Golden Bottle Trust
The Gosling Foundation Ltd
The James Grace Trust*
The Great Stone Bridge Trust of Edenbridge
The Lennox Hannay Charitable Trust
Harbinson Charitable Trust
The Harbour Foundation
The Maurice Hatter Foundation
The Herefordshire Historic Churches Trust
Highway One Trust
The Lady Hind Trust
The Hinduja Foundation
The Henry C. Hoare Charitable Trust
The Hobson Charity Ltd
The Jane Hodge Foundation
The Holden Charitable Trust
The Mary Homfray Charitable Trust
Sir Harold Hood's Charitable Trust
The Reta Lila Howard Foundation
The Huggard Charitable Trust
Hyde Park Place Estate Charity
The Inlight Trust
International Bible Students Association
The Invigorate Charitable Trust
John Jarrold Trust Ltd
The Labone Charitable Trust*
The David Laing Foundation
The Kirby Laing Foundation
The Beatrice Laing Trust
Duchy of Lancaster Benevolent Fund
The Lauffer Family Charitable Foundation
Mrs F. B. Laurence Charitable Trust
Lempriere Pringle 2015
Lord Leverhulme's Charitable Trust
The Locker Foundation
The Mactaggart Third Fund
The Marque Foundation*
Charity of John Marshall
The Master Charitable Trust
The Mikheev Charitable Trust*
Jean and Roger Miller's Charitable Trust
The Millward Charitable Trust
The Monmouthshire County Council Welsh Church Act Fund
G. M. Morrison Charitable Trust
The Mulberry Trust
Music Sales Charitable Trust
The Norwood and Newton Settlement
P. F. Charitable Trust
The Gerald Palmer Eling Trust Company
The Paragon Trust
The Pitt-Rivers Charitable Trust
The Prince of Wales's Charitable Foundation
The Privy Purse Charitable Trust
The Joseph Rank Trust
Rentrust Foundation Ltd
The Rothermere Foundation
S. and R. Charitable Trust
ShareGift (The Orr Mackintosh Foundation)
The Charles Skey Charitable Trust
Smith Bradbeer Charitable Trust*
The Henry Smith Charity
The Martin Smith Foundation
Stewards Company Ltd
Sir Halley Stewart Trust
The Street Foundation
The Joseph Strong Frazer Trust*
Sumner Wilson Charitable Trust
Sabina Sutherland Charitable Trust
Sutton Coldfield Charitable Trust
Tay Charitable Trust
C. B. and H. H. Taylor 1984 Trust
Mrs R. P. Tindall's Charitable Trust
The Tompkins Foundation
The Constance Travis Charitable Trust
The United Reformed Church (Wessex) Trust Ltd
Westhill Endowment
The Wingate Foundation
Friends of Wiznitz Ltd

Christianity

Allchurches Trust Ltd
The Allen Trust
The Almond Trust
Viscount Amory's Charitable Trust
The Anchor Foundation
Andrews Charitable Trust
The John Apthorp Charity
The Archer Trust
Ardbarron Trust Ltd
The Ashburnham Thanksgiving Trust
The Baird Trust
The Roger and Sarah Bancroft Clark Charitable Trust
The Philip Barker Charity
The Bedfordshire and Hertfordshire Historic Churches Trust
The Benham Charitable Settlement
The Sydney Black Charitable Trust
The Isabel Blackman Foundation
The Blandford Lake Trust
The Harry Bottom Charitable Trust
The Bowerman Charitable Trust
The Bowland Charitable Trust
The Liz and Terry Bramall Foundation
Bristol Archdeaconry Charity
Mary Brown Memorial Trust*
The T. B. H. Brunner's Charitable Settlement
Buckingham Trust
Byrne Family Foundation
Catholic Charitable Trust
The Childs Charitable Trust*
The Christabella Charitable Trust
The André Christian Trust
The Church Burgesses Educational Foundation
Church Burgesses Trust
Church Urban Fund
Cloudesley
The Clover Trust
Sir Jeremiah Colman Gift Trust
Congregational and General Charitable Trust
The Costa Family Charitable Trust
Council for World Mission (UK)*
The County Council of Dyfed Welsh Church Fund
Donibristle Trust
The Elie Trust*
The Farthing Trust
The Feoffees of St Michael's Spurriergate York
The Earl Fitzwilliam Charitable Trust
Forest Hill Charitable Trust
The Forte Charitable Trust
Anne French Memorial Trust
The Fulmer Charitable Trust
Gamma Trust
The Ganzoni Charitable Trust

The Gibbs Charitable Trusts
The Gloag Foundation
The Gloucestershire Historic Churches Trust
The Goshen Trust
Grace Charitable Trust
The Grace Trust
*The James Grace Trust**
The Grant Foundation
Philip and Judith Green Trust
The Alfred Haines Charitable Trust
Ros Harding Trust
Gay and Peter Hartley's Hillards Charitable Trust
May Hearnshaw's Charity
P. and C. Hickinbotham Charitable Trust
Highway One Trust
The Hillier Trust
Hinchley Charitable Trust
The Hintze Family Charity Foundation
Hockerill Educational Foundation
The Holbeck Charitable Trust
Homelands Charitable Trust
Sir Harold Hood's Charitable Trust
Hope Trust
The Reta Lila Howard Foundation
The Hunting Horn General Charitable Trust
Hyde Park Place Estate Charity
The Iliffe Family Charitable Trust
International Bible Students Association
The Invigorate Charitable Trust
The J. A. R. Charitable Trust
The Jenour Foundation
The Kennedy Charitable Foundation
The Friends of Kent Churches
The Nancy Kenyon Charitable Trust
The King Henry VIII Endowed Trust – Warwick
The K. P. Ladd Charitable Trust
Maurice and Hilda Laing Charitable Trust
The Kirby Laing Foundation
The Martin Laing Foundation
The Beatrice Laing Trust
The Leonard Laity Stoate Charitable Trust
Lancaster Foundation
Langdale Trust
Laslett's (Hinton) Charity
The Herd Lawson and Muriel Lawson Charitable Trust
Lempriere Pringle 2015
The Charles Littlewood Hill Trust
The Elaine and Angus Lloyd Charitable Trust
The Lockwood Charitable Foundation
Sylvanus Lysons Charity
The Mallinckrodt Foundation
Charity of John Marshall
Charlotte Marshall Charitable Trust
D. G. Marshall of Cambridge Trust
The Mercers' Charitable Foundation
The Merchant Taylors' Company Charities Fund
*The Milne Family Foundation**
The Mizpah Trust
The Monmouthshire County Council Welsh Church Act Fund
The Mulberry Trust
The National Churches Trust
The Norfolk Churches Trust Ltd
The Northumbria Historic Churches Trust
The Norwood and Newton Settlement
The Ogle Christian Trust
*Otsar Trust**
The Ouseley Church Music Trust
The Owen Family Trust
Oxfordshire Historic Churches Trust (2016)
*The P27 Trust**
The Panacea Charitable Trust
The James Pantyfedwen Foundation (Ymddiriedolaeth James Pantyfedwen)
Miss M. E. S. Paterson's Charitable Trust
The Jack Patston Charitable Trust
Sir John Priestman Charity Trust
Quothquan Trust
The Bishop Radford Trust
The Rank Foundation Ltd
The Joseph Rank Trust
The Sir James Reckitt Charity
Riada Trust
The Sir Cliff Richard Charitable Trust
The River Trust
Robertson Hall Trust
Mrs L. D. Rope's Third Charitable Settlement
The Saddlers' Company Charitable Fund
Saint Sarkis Charity Trust
The Salamander Charitable Trust
Sarum St Michael Educational Charity
Seedfield Trust
The Bassil Shippam and Alsford Trust
The SMB Trust
*Smith Bradbeer Charitable Trust**
The Henry Smith Charity
The R. C. Snelling Charitable Trust
The Souter Charitable Trust
W. F. Southall Trust
St Peter's Saltley Trust
Stewards Company Ltd
Sir Halley Stewart Trust
The Stobart Newlands Charitable Trust
Mark Stolkin Foundation
Stratford-upon-Avon Town Trust
Sabina Sutherland Charitable Trust
Swansea and Brecon Diocesan Board of Finance Ltd
Tabeel Trust
Scott Thomson Charitable Trust
The Thornton Trust
Mrs R. P. Tindall's Charitable Trust
The Tory Family Foundation
The Toye Foundation
The Tufton Charitable Trust
Ulting Overseas Trust
The Union Of The Sisters Of Mercy Of Great Britain
The Vardy Foundation
Nigel Vinson Charitable Trust
*The Georg and Emily Von Opel Foundation**
Mrs Waterhouse Charitable Trust
The Welsh Church Act Fund
The Westcroft Trust
The Whinfell Charitable Fund
The Norman Whiteley Trust
Dame Violet Wills Charitable Trust
The Wilmcote Charitrust
The James Wood Bequest Fund
WWDP (World Day of Prayer National Committee for England, Wales and Northern Ireland)
The Yorkshire Historic Churches Trust

Interfaith activities/understanding

The Rayne Trust
The Sir James Roll Charitable Trust
The Jeremy and John Sacher Charitable Trust

The Alan and Babette Sainsbury Charitable Fund
The Sir Sigmund Sternberg Charitable Foundation
The Tolkien Trust
The Wingate Foundation

Islam

Dawat-E-Hadiyah Trust (United Kingdom)
The Matliwala Family Charitable Trust
Muslim Hands
*Randeree Charitable Trust**

Judaism

4 Charity Foundation
A. W. Charitable Trust
The Aaronson Foundation
The Aberdeen Foundation
The Acacia Charitable Trust
Adenfirst Ltd
The Aimwell Charitable Trust
Alliance Family Foundation Ltd
Amabrill Ltd
Anpride Ltd
The Ardwick Trust
Keren Association Ltd
Atlas Memorial Ltd
The Andrew Balint Charitable Trust
Bay Charitable Trust
Bear Mordechai Ltd
Beauland Ltd
The Becker Family Charitable Trust
Belljoe Tzedoko Ltd
Benesco Charity Ltd
Ruth Berkowitz Charitable Trust
The Beth Hamedrash Satmar Trust (BHST)
Asser Bishvil Foundation
The Sir Victor Blank Charitable Settlement
The Bloom Foundation
The Bluston Charitable Settlement
The Bonamy Charitable Trust
Salo Bordon Charitable Trust
Sir Clive Bourne Family Trust
Bourneheights Ltd
Friends of Boyan Trust
Brushmill Ltd
C. and F. Charitable Trust
Cannon Charitable Trust
Carlee Ltd
Chalfords Ltd
Charitworth Ltd
The Childwick Trust
The Clore Duffield Foundation
Closehelm Ltd
Clydpride Ltd
The Vivienne and Samuel Cohen Charitable Trust
The Gershon Coren Charitable Foundation (also known as The Muriel and Gus Coren Charitable Foundation)
*Countypier Ltd**
The Craps Charitable Trust
Itzchok Meyer Cymerman Trust Ltd
D. M. H. Educational Trust Ltd
Oizer Dalim Trust
The Davidson Family Charitable Trust
The Davis Foundation
Debmar Benevolent Trust Ltd
The Djanogly Foundation
Dollond Charitable Trust
The Dorfman Foundation
The Doughty Charity Trust
Dushinsky Trust Ltd
Elanore Ltd
The George Elias Charitable Trust
The Ellinson Foundation Ltd
Entindale Ltd
Esher House Charitable Trust
The Eventhall Family Charitable Trust
The Exilarch's Foundation
Extonglen Ltd
Famos Foundation Trust
Fordeve Ltd
The Isaac and Freda Frankel Memorial Charitable Trust
The Jacqueline and Michael Gee Charitable Trust
The Gertner Charitable Trust
Grahame Charitable Foundation Ltd
M. and R. Gross Charities Ltd
The N. and R. Grunbaum Charitable Trust
H. C. Foundation
Hadras Kodesh Trust
The Harbour Charitable Trust
The Harbour Foundation
The Maurice Hatter Foundation
The Heathside Charitable Trust
The Simon Heller Charitable Settlement
The Helping Foundation
The Highcroft Charitable Trust
The Holden Charitable Trust
Horwich Shotter Charitable Trust
The Humanitarian Trust
The Huntingdon Foundation Ltd
Hurdale Charity Ltd
IGO Foundation Ltd
Investream Charitable Trust
The J. and J. Benevolent Foundation
Jewish Child's Day (JCD)
The Jewish Youth Fund
J. E. Joseph Charitable Fund
The Jusaca Charitable Trust
*Kantor Charitable Foundation**
The Kasner Charitable Trust
The Michael and Ilse Katz Foundation
C. S. Kaufman Charitable Trust
E. and E. Kernkraut Charities Ltd
The Kirschel Foundation
The Kobler Trust
Kollel and Co. Ltd
Kolyom Trust Ltd
Kupath Gemach Chaim Bechesed Viznitz Trust
The Kyte Charitable Trust
Largsmount Ltd
The Lauffer Family Charitable Foundation
Lawson Beckman Charitable Trust
The Arnold Lee Charitable Trust
The Kennedy Leigh Charitable Trust
Bernard Lewis Family Charitable Trust
David and Ruth Lewis Family Charitable Trust
The Second Joseph Aaron Littman Foundation
Jack Livingstone Charitable Trust
Local Trent Ltd
The Locker Foundation
Loftus Charitable Trust
LPW Ltd
M. and C. Trust
M. B. Foundation
The M. Y. A. Charitable Trust
The Manackerman Charitable Trust
*The Manson Family Charitable Trust**
Marbeh Torah Trust
The Stella and Alexander Margulies Charitable Trust
The Marks Family Charitable Trust
*The Marque Foundation**
The Violet Mauray Charitable Trust
Mayfair Charities Ltd
Mayheights Ltd
Maypride Ltd
Melodor Ltd
The Melow Charitable Trust
Menuchar Ltd
Mercaz Torah Vechesed Ltd
The Mishcon Family Charitable Trust
Keren Mitzvah Trust
Mole Charitable Trust
The Morgan Charitable Foundation

The Moshal Charitable Trust
Vyoel Moshe Charitable Trust
The Mosselson Charitable Trust
The Mutual Trust Group
MW (CL) Foundation
MW (GK) Foundation
MW (HO) Foundation
MW (RH) Foundation
Nemoral Ltd
Ner Foundation
Nesswall Ltd
Newpier Charity Ltd
Northern Land Trust
Oizer Charitable Trust
The Doris Pacey Charitable Foundation
David Pearlman Charitable Foundation
The Pears Family Charitable Foundation
*Dina Perelman Trust Ltd**
B. E. Perl Charitable Trust
The Phillips and Rubens Charitable Trust
The Phillips Family Charitable Trust
The Polonsky Foundation
Premierquote Ltd
Premishlaner Charitable Trust
R. S. Charitable Trust
Rachel Charitable Trust
The Rayne Trust
The Rest-Harrow Trust
Reuben Foundation
Ridgesave Ltd
The Sir John Ritblat Family Foundation
The Rofeh Trust
The Gerald and Gail Ronson Family Foundation
The Cecil Rosen Foundation
Rothschild Foundation (Hanadiv) Europe
Rowanville Ltd
The Rubin Foundation Charitable Trust
S. and R. Charitable Trust
The Jeremy and John Sacher Charitable Trust
The Michael and Nicola Sacher Charitable Trust
Samjo Ltd
The Peter Samuel Charitable Trust
Schass Foundation
The Annie Schiff Charitable Trust
O. and G. Schreiber Charitable Trust
The Searchlight Electric Charitable Trust
Sam and Bella Sebba Charitable Trust
Sellata Ltd
The Archie Sherman Charitable Trust
Shlomo Memorial Fund Ltd
Shulem B. Association Ltd
The Sobell Foundation
The E. C. Sosnow Charitable Trust
Sparquote Ltd
Rosalyn and Nicholas Springer Charitable Trust
Starlow Charities Ltd
The Steinberg Family Charitable Trust
C. E. K. Stern Charitable Trust
The Sir Sigmund Sternberg Charitable Foundation
Stervon Ltd
T. and S. Trust Fund
The Tajtelbaum Charitable Trust
Talteg Ltd
The David Tannen Charitable Trust
Tegham Ltd
Truedene Co. Ltd
Truemart Ltd
Trumros Ltd
Tzedakah
The Union of Orthodox Hebrew Congregations
United Jewish Israel Appeal
The David Uri Memorial Trust
The Vail Foundation
*The Velvet Foundation**
VHLT Ltd
Vivdale Ltd
The Linda and Michael Weinstein Charitable Trust
The Wigoder Family Foundation
The Benjamin Winegarten Charitable Trust
The Wingate Foundation
The Michael and Anna Wix Charitable Trust
Friends of Wiznitz Ltd
The Maurice Wohl Charitable Foundation
The Charles Wolfson Charitable Trust
The Wolfson Family Charitable Trust
Woodlands Green Ltd
Wychdale Ltd
Wychville Ltd
Yankov Charitable Trust
The Marjorie and Arnold Ziff Charitable Foundation

Research

Environmental research

The A. Team Foundation Ltd
The Alborada Trust
The Aldama Foundation
The Ove Arup Foundation
The Ashden Trust
The Ian Askew Charitable Trust
The Scott Bader Commonwealth Ltd
Birmingham International Airport Community Trust Fund
The Castansa Trust
The Chalk Cliff Trust
CLA Charitable Trust
Community First
The Elizabeth Creak Charitable Trust
The Ecology Trust
The Fidelity UK Foundation
The Tara Getty Foundation
The Great Britain Sasakawa Foundation
The Greggs Foundation
Hamamelis Trust
Heathrow Community Trust
The Jabbs Foundation
The Frank Jackson Foundation
Marmot Charitable Trust
Nesta
Network for Social Change Charitable Trust
The NFU Mutual Charitable Trust
The Nineveh Charitable Trust
Oglesby Charitable Trust
Oxfordshire Community Foundation
The Prince of Wales's Charitable Foundation
Quartet Community Foundation
The Racing Foundation
The Samworth Foundation
The Shears Foundation
The Sheepdrove Trust
The Martin Smith Foundation
The Sobell Foundation
*The Thirty Percy Foundation**
The Thriplow Charitable Trust

Humanities and social sciences

The Ove Arup Foundation
The Aurelius Charitable Trust
The Burberry Foundation
The Clore Duffield Foundation
The Daiwa Anglo-Japanese Foundation
The De Laszlo Foundation

John Ellerman Foundation
The Elmley Foundation
The Enkalon Foundation
The Finborough Foundation
The Finnis Scott Foundation
Marc Fitch Fund
Nicholas and Judith Goodison's Charitable Settlement
The Great Britain Sasakawa Foundation
Paul Hamlyn Foundation
The Harbour Foundation
The Institute for Policy Research
The Leche Trust
The Legal Education Foundation
The Leverhulme Trust
The Linder Foundation
The Mayfield Valley Arts Trust
The Mikheev Charitable Trust*
The Mohn Westlake Foundation*
The Miles Morland Foundation
The Nuffield Foundation
Orange Tree Trust*
The Pilgrim Trust
The Pitt-Rivers Charitable Trust
The Polonsky Foundation
David and Elaine Potter Foundation
The Resolution Trust
UPP Foundation
Nigel Vinson Charitable Trust
Wates Family Enterprise Trust
The Wellcome Trust
The Wolfson Foundation

Medical research

The Abbeyfield Research Foundation
The Aberbrothock Skea Trust
Action Medical Research
The Bryan Adams Foundation
Sylvia Aitken's Charitable Trust
The Alborada Trust
The Alchemy Foundation
D. C. R. Allen Charitable Trust
Alzheimer's Research UK
Alzheimer's Society
Andor Charitable Trust
The Anson Charitable Trust
The John Armitage Charitable Trust
The Armourers' and Brasiers' Gauntlet Trust
Asthma UK
The Astor Foundation
The Tim Bacon Foundation*
The Baily Thomas Charitable Fund
The Roy and Pixie Baker Charitable Trust
The Roger and Sarah Bancroft Clark Charitable Trust
The Kamini and Vindi Banga Family Trust*
The Barbour Foundation
The Barclay Foundation
The Batchworth Trust
AJ Bell Trust*
Ruth Berkowitz Charitable Trust
The Bestway Foundation
The Bingham Trust
Maria Bjornson Memorial Fund*
The John Black Charitable Foundation
Blakemore Foundation
Lady Blakenham's Charity Trust
Bloodwise
The Bluston Charitable Settlement
The Boltini Trust
The Bothwell Charitable Trust
The Harry Bottom Charitable Trust
The Bowerman Charitable Trust
G. and K. Boyes Charitable Trust
The Tony Bramall Charitable Trust
Bright Red Charity*
British Council for Prevention of Blindness
British Eye Research Foundation (Fight for Sight)
British Heart Foundation (BHF)
British Lung Foundation
Bill Brown 1989 Charitable Trust
The Brownsword Charitable Foundation
The Burden Trust
Miss Margaret Butters Reekie Charitable Trust
William A. Cadbury Charitable Trust
The Cadogan Charity
The Calleva Foundation
The Castang Foundation
The Cayo Foundation
The B. G. S. Cayzer Charitable Trust
The Charities Advisory Trust
Children with Cancer UK
Children's Liver Disease Foundation
The Childwick Trust
Denise Coates Foundation
The Colt Foundation
Dudley and Geoffrey Cox Charitable Trust
CRH Charitable Trust*
Cruden Foundation Ltd
The Cunningham Trust
Michael Davies Charitable Settlement
The De Laszlo Foundation
The Delves Charitable Trust
Diabetes UK
Dinwoodie Charitable Company
Dromintee Trust
The Anne Duchess of Westminster's Charity
The Dunhill Medical Trust
The James Dyson Foundation
The Gilbert and Eileen Edgar Foundation
The Eighty Eight Foundation
The Englefield Charitable Trust
Epilepsy Research UK
The Evelyn Trust
The Eveson Charitable Trust
G. F. Eyre Charitable Trust
The Fairness Foundation
Sir John Fisher Foundation
Donald Forrester Trust
The Anna Rosa Forster Charitable Trust
The Elizabeth Frankland Moore and Star Foundation
The Hugh Fraser Foundation
The Louis and Valerie Freedman Charitable Settlement
The Freshfield Foundation
Frognal Trust
Gamma Trust
Garthgwynion Charities
The Gatsby Charitable Foundation
General Charity (Coventry)
The Tara Getty Foundation
The G. C. Gibson Charitable Trust
Sydney and Phyllis Goldberg Memorial Charitable Trust
The Mike Gooley Trailfinders Charity
The Grace Trust
The Great Britain Sasakawa Foundation
The Grocers' Charity
The Walter Guinness Charitable Trust
The Guy Foundation*
Hamamelis Trust
The Harbour Foundation
The Maurice Hatter Foundation
The Health Foundation
The Michael Heller Charitable Foundation
The Simon Heller Charitable Settlement
Help for Health
The Hinduja Foundation
The Jane Hodge Foundation
The Holbeck Charitable Trust
Dorothy Holmes Charitable Trust
Homelands Charitable Trust

The Hospital Saturday Fund
The Sir Joseph Hotung Charitable Settlement
The Iceland Foods Charitable Foundation
The Jabbs Foundation
John Jarrold Trust Ltd
*Jeffrey Charitable Trust**
The Elton John Aids Foundation (EJAF)
The Joron Charitable Trust
The Emmanuel Kaye Foundation
The Kay Kendall Leukaemia Fund
The Kennedy Trust for Rheumatology Research
The Peter Kershaw Trust
Kidney Research UK
Kilpatrick Fraser Charitable Trust
The Mary Kinross Charitable Trust
The Graham Kirkham Foundation
The Kirschel Foundation
The Ernest Kleinwort Charitable Trust
Kollel and Co. Ltd
The Kirby Laing Foundation
The Kathleen Laurence Trust
The Richard Lawes Foundation
The Leach Fourteenth Trust
The William Leech Charity
*Cecil and Hilda Lewis Charitable Trust**
David and Ruth Lewis Family Charitable Trust
The Linder Foundation
The Frank Litchfield Charitable Trust
The Charles Littlewood Hill Trust
The Second Joseph Aaron Littman Foundation
Robert Luff Foundation Ltd
The Henry Lumley Charitable Trust
Lord and Lady Lurgan Trust
The Lyndal Tree Foundation
The MacRobert Trust 2019
The W. M. Mann Foundation
The Stella and Alexander Margulies Charitable Trust
Masonic Charitable Foundation
Nancie Massey Charitable Trust
The Robert McAlpine Foundation
D. D. McPhail Charitable Settlement
Medical Research Foundation
Medical Research Scotland
Meningitis Research Foundation
Merchants' House of Glasgow
Mercury Phoenix Trust
Mills and Reeve Charitable Trust
G. M. Morrison Charitable Trust
The Mosselson Charitable Trust
Motor Neurone Disease Association
Multiple Sclerosis Society
The Frances and Augustus Newman Foundation
The Norman Family Charitable Trust
North West Cancer Research
Northern Pharmacies Ltd Trust Fund
The Norton Rose Fulbright Charitable Foundation
The Nuffield Foundation
The Ofenheim Charitable Trust
Oglesby Charitable Trust
*Orange Tree Trust**
The O'Sullivan Family Charitable Trust
P. F. Charitable Trust
The Paragon Trust
Parkinson's UK
The JGW Patterson Foundation
Peacock Charitable Trust
The Dowager Countess Eleanor Peel Trust
The Pharsalia Charitable Trust
The Phillips and Rubens Charitable Trust
The George and Esme Pollitzer Charitable Settlement
Queen Mary's Roehampton Trust
The Ranworth Trust
Reuben Foundation
The Revere Charitable Trust
RNID (The Royal National Institute for Deaf People)
The Roan Charitable Trust
The Cecil Rosen Foundation
Rosetrees Trust
The Rothermere Foundation
The Rothley Trust
The Eranda Rothschild Foundation
The Row Fogo Charitable Trust
The Rowlands Trust
The Dr Mortimer and Theresa Sackler Foundation
The Alan and Babette Sainsbury Charitable Fund
The Salamander Charitable Trust
The Peter Samuel Charitable Trust
The Schroder Foundation
Sir Samuel Scott of Yews Trust
The Jean Shanks Foundation
The Shears Foundation
The Sheepdrove Trust
The Bassil Shippam and Alsford Trust
The Florence Shute Millennium Trust
The Charles Skey Charitable Trust
The SMB Trust
The N. Smith Charitable Settlement
The Souter Charitable Trust
Peter Sowerby Foundation
Sparks Charity
The Stafford Trust
The Peter Stebbings Memorial Charity
Sir Halley Stewart Trust
The Stoller Charitable Trust
The Stoneygate Trust
Peter Stormonth Darling Charitable Trust
*The Joseph Strong Frazer Trust**
The Swann-Morton Foundation
The Charles and Elsie Sykes Trust
The Syncona Foundation
The Gay and Keith Talbot Trust
Tallow Chandlers Benevolent Fund No. 2
Tanner Trust
The Templeton Goodwill Trust
Tenovus Cancer Care
Tenovus Scotland
Sir Jules Thorn Charitable Trust
The Thriplow Charitable Trust
The Tolkien Trust
Toyota Manufacturing UK Charitable Trust
The Trefoil Trust
*The Tresanton Trust**
*The Troutsdale Charitable Trust**
The James Tudor Foundation
The Roger and Douglas Turner Charitable Trust
Ulster Garden Villages Ltd
The Ulverscroft Foundation
The Underwood Trust
The Michael Uren Foundation
The Albert Van Den Bergh Charitable Trust
The Vandervell Foundation
*The Velvet Foundation**
Versus Arthritis
The VTCT Foundation
Sylvia Waddilove Foundation UK
Wellbeing of Women
The Wellcome Trust
The Welsh Church Act Fund
The Felicity Wilde Charitable Trust
W. Wing Yip and Brothers Foundation

The Wingate Foundation
Friends of Wiznitz Ltd
The Charles Wolfson Charitable Trust
The Wolfson Family Charitable Trust
The Lord Leonard and Lady Estelle Wolfson Foundation
The Wolfson Foundation
The Woosnam Foundation
The Wyndham Charitable Trust
Yorkshire Cancer Research

Social justice

The Alchemy Foundation
The Allen & Overy Foundation
The John Armitage Charitable Trust
The Roger and Sarah Bancroft Clark Charitable Trust
The Baring Foundation
The Michael Bishop Foundation
The Blagrave Trust
The Rory and Elizabeth Brooks Foundation
The Edward Cadbury Charitable Trust
The Barrow Cadbury Trust
*Camden Giving**
The W. A. Cargill Fund
The City Bridge Trust (Bridge House Estates)
Comic Relief
The Evan Cornish Foundation
Cripplegate Foundation
The Henry and Suzanne Davis Foundation
The Demigryphon Trust
Didymus
County Durham Community Foundation
John Ellerman Foundation
The Emerton-Christie Charity
Esmée Fairbairn Foundation
The Fairness Foundation
The Robert Fleming Hannay Memorial Charity
The Funding Network
The Gloag Foundation
The Golden Bottle Trust
The Goldsmiths' Company Charity
The Greggs Foundation
H. C. D. Memorial Fund
The Hadley Trust
The Lennox Hannay Charitable Trust
The Charles Hayward Foundation
Highway One Trust
Michael and Shirley Hunt Charitable Trust
Ibrahim Foundation Ltd
Impact Funding Partners Ltd
The Indigo Trust
The Invigorate Charitable Trust
The Ireland Fund of Great Britain
Joffe Charitable Trust
The Elton John Aids Foundation (EJAF)
The Muriel Jones Foundation
The Emmanuel Kaye Foundation
The Mary Kinross Charitable Trust
The Kreitman Foundation
Community Foundations for Lancashire and Merseyside
The Allen Lane Foundation
The Leathersellers' Company Charitable Fund
The Legal Education Foundation
The Leigh Trust
The Leri Charitable Trust
The Mactaggart Third Fund
*Gemma and Chris McGough Charitable Foundation CIO**
Jean and Roger Miller's Charitable Trust
The Morel Charitable Trust
The Frederick Mulder Foundation
Muslim Hands
Network for Social Change Charitable Trust
Community Foundation for Northern Ireland
The Nuffield Foundation
The Oakdale Trust
*The Olwyn Foundation**
The Pastoral Care Trust – The St Nicholas Care Fund
People's Postcode Trust
Polden-Puckham Charitable Foundation
David and Elaine Potter Foundation
The Eleanor Rathbone Charitable Trust
The Sigrid Rausing Trust
The Roddick Foundation
Rosa Fund
The Joseph Rowntree Charitable Trust
The Joseph Rowntree Foundation
The Samworth Foundation
Sam and Bella Sebba Charitable Trust
The St James's Trust Settlement
The Stewarts Law Foundation
Sumner Wilson Charitable Trust
C. B. and H. H. Taylor 1984 Trust
Stephen Taylor Foundation
The Three Guineas Trust
*The Tresanton Trust**
Trust for London
The Tudor Trust
United St Saviour's Charity
UPP Foundation
The Van Neste Foundation
The Scurrah Wainwright Charity
G. R. Waters Charitable Trust 2000
Blyth Watson Charitable Trust
Youth Music

Conflict resolution

The Demigryphon Trust
The Dulverton Trust
Allan and Nesta Ferguson Charitable Settlement
The Jacqueline and Michael Gee Charitable Trust
The Golden Bottle Trust
H. C. D. Memorial Fund
The Ireland Fund of Great Britain
*KPE4 Charitable Trust**
The Kennedy Leigh Charitable Trust
The Leri Charitable Trust
Marmot Charitable Trust
Jean and Roger Miller's Charitable Trust
Network for Social Change Charitable Trust
The Northwick Trust
Ostro Fayre Share Foundation
Polden-Puckham Charitable Foundation
The Sigrid Rausing Trust
The Rayne Trust
The Joseph Rowntree Charitable Trust
Savannah Wisdom
W. F. Southall Trust
The Westcroft Trust

Human rights

The A. B. Charitable Trust
Ajahma Charitable Trust
The Arah Foundation
*Veronica and Lars Bane Foundation**
British Humane Association
The Bromley Trust
Chrysalis Trust
The City Bridge Trust (Bridge House Estates)
The Evan Cornish Foundation
The Craignish Trust
The D. G. Charitable Settlement
The Henry and Suzanne Davis Foundation
The Demigryphon Trust
Didymus
Dunard Fund
John Ellerman Foundation
The Fairness Foundation
The Farthing Trust
The Robert Fleming Hannay Memorial Charity
The Elizabeth Frankland Moore and Star Foundation
The Funding Network
The Robert Gavron Charitable Trust
The Golden Bottle Trust
Greenham Trust Ltd
The Greggs Foundation
The Helen Hamlyn Trust
The Lennox Hannay Charitable Trust
The Harrison-Frank Family Foundation (UK) Ltd
The Sir Joseph Hotung Charitable Settlement
Ibrahim Foundation Ltd
The Indigo Trust
The Invigorate Charitable Trust
The ITF Seafarers Trust
Joffe Charitable Trust
The Muriel Jones Foundation
The Mary Kinross Charitable Trust
Laura Kinsella Foundation
*KPE4 Charitable Trust**
The Kreitman Foundation
The Legal Education Foundation
The Kennedy Leigh Charitable Trust
The Leri Charitable Trust
The Master Charitable Trust
Jean and Roger Miller's Charitable Trust
The Miles Morland Foundation
Network for Social Change Charitable Trust
The Norton Rose Fulbright Charitable Foundation
P. F. Charitable Trust
People's Postcode Trust
Polden-Puckham Charitable Foundation
The Eleanor Rathbone Charitable Trust
The Sigrid Rausing Trust
The Robertson Trust
The Roddick Foundation
The Joseph Rowntree Charitable Trust
The Alan and Babette Sainsbury Charitable Fund
The Samworth Foundation
Savannah Wisdom
Sam and Bella Sebba Charitable Trust
The Simmons & Simmons Charitable Foundation
Staples Trust
The Street Foundation
Trust for London
UPP Foundation
G. R. Waters Charitable Trust 2000
Blyth Watson Charitable Trust
The Westcroft Trust
The Wyndham Charitable Trust
The William Allen Young Charitable Trust

Social welfare

The 1989 Willan Charitable Trust
The 29th May 1961 Charitable Trust
4 Charity Foundation
The 4814 Trust
A. W. Charitable Trust
The Aaronson Foundation
The Aberdeen Foundation
ABF The Soldiers' Charity
The Acacia Charitable Trust
*Adam Family Foundation**
The Bryan Adams Foundation
Adenfirst Ltd
The Adint Charitable Trust
The AEB Charitable Trust
Sylvia Aitken's Charitable Trust
Ajahma Charitable Trust
The Alchemy Foundation
Al-Fayed Charitable Foundation
The Derrill Allatt Foundation
Allchurches Trust Ltd
D. C. R. Allen Charitable Trust
The Allen Trust
Alliance Family Foundation Ltd
Amabrill Ltd
The Ammco Trust
Viscount Amory's Charitable Trust
Andrews Charitable Trust
Anpride Ltd
The Apax Foundation
The John Apthorp Charity
The Archer Trust
Ardbarron Trust Ltd
The Ardwick Trust
*The Armed Forces Covenant Fund Trust**
The John Armitage Charitable Trust
The Armourers' and Brasiers' Gauntlet Trust
The Arsenal Foundation
The Artemis Charitable Foundation
ArtSocial Foundation
Ove Arup Partnership Charitable Trust
The Asda Foundation
The Ashburnham Thanksgiving Trust
The Ashendene Trust
The Ashworth Charitable Trust
*John Atcheson Foundation**
Atkin Charitable Foundation
The Lord Austin Trust
Axis Foundation
The Scott Bader Commonwealth Ltd
The Austin Bailey Foundation
The Roy and Pixie Baker Charitable Trust
The Balcombe Charitable Trust
The Ballinger Charitable Trust
Bank of Scotland Foundation

The Barbour Foundation
Barcapel Foundation Ltd
Barchester Healthcare Foundation
The Barclay Foundation
The Philip Barker Charity
The Michael Barnard Charitable Trust*
Lord Barnby's Foundation
The Barnes Fund*
Barnwood Trust
Robert Barr's Charitable Trust
The Batchworth Trust
Battens Charitable Trust
Bauer Radio's Cash for Kids Charities
Bay Charitable Trust
The Bay Tree Charitable Trust
BBC Children in Need
Bear Mordechai Ltd
Bearder Charity
Beauland Ltd
The Beaverbrook Foundation
The Beaverbrooks Charitable Trust
The Becker Family Charitable Trust
Bedfordshire and Luton Community Foundation
Bedfordshire Charitable Trust Ltd
AJ Bell Trust*
The Bellahouston Bequest Fund
Belljoe Tzedoko Ltd
Benesco Charity Ltd
The Benham Charitable Settlement
The Rowan Bentall Charitable Trust
The Berkeley Foundation
The Bestway Foundation
The Beth Hamedrash Satmar Trust (BHST)
Bideford Bridge Trust
The Billmeir Charitable Trust
The Percy Bilton Charity
The Bingham Trust
Binks Trust
Birmingham International Airport Community Trust Fund
Asser Bishvil Foundation
The Sydney Black Charitable Trust
The Isabel Blackman Foundation
Lady Blakenham's Charity Trust
The Sir Victor Blank Charitable Settlement
The Bloom Foundation
The Bluston Charitable Settlement
Maureen Boal Charitable Trust*
The Bonamy Charitable Trust
The Booth Charities
Boots Charitable Trust
Salo Bordon Charitable Trust
The Borrows Charitable Trust
Alan Boswell Group Charitable Trust*
The Bothwell Charitable Trust
The Harry Bottom Charitable Trust
Bourneheights Ltd
The Bowerman Charitable Trust
The Tony Bramall Charitable Trust
The Liz and Terry Bramall Foundation
The Brelms Trust CIO
The Brenley Trust
Bristol Charities
The Britford Bridge Trust
British Gas Energy Trust
British Humane Association
The J. and M. Britton Charitable Trust
The Bromley Trust
The Brook Trust
The Brothers Trust*
The Charles Brotherton Trust
Bill Brown 1989 Charitable Trust
Mary Brown Memorial Trust*
R. S. Brownless Charitable Trust
The Bruntwood Charity
Brushmill Ltd
Buckingham Trust
Buckinghamshire Community Foundation
E. F. Bulmer Trust
BUPA UK Foundation
The Burberry Foundation
The Burden Trust
The Clara E. Burgess Charity
The Arnold Burton 1998 Charitable Trust
Byrne Family Foundation
The Edward Cadbury Charitable Trust
The Edward and Dorothy Cadbury Trust
The Cadogan Charity
Community Foundation for Calderdale
Callendar Charitable Trust
The Calleva Foundation
The Cambridgeshire Community Foundation
The Campden Charities Trustee
Canary Wharf Contractors Fund
Cannon Charitable Trust
W. A. Cargill Charitable Trust
The W. A. Cargill Fund
The Carr-Gregory Trust
The Leslie Mary Carter Charitable Trust
The Casey Trust
The Castanea Trust
Cattanach
The Joseph and Annie Cattle Trust
The Cayo Foundation
The B. G. S. Cayzer Charitable Trust
The Amelia Chadwick Trust
Chalfords Ltd
The Chalk Cliff Trust
Charitworth Ltd
The Charter 600 Charity
Chartered Accountants' Livery Charity (CALC)
The Charterhouse Charitable Trust
The Cheruby Trust
Cheshire Community Foundation Ltd
The Childhood Trust
Children with Cancer UK
The Childwick Trust
Chippenham Borough Lands Charity
The Chipping Sodbury Town Lands Charity
CHK Foundation
The Christabella Charitable Trust
The André Christian Trust
Chrysalis Trust
Church Urban Fund
The Churchill Foundation
The CIBC World Markets Children's Foundation
The City Bridge Trust (Bridge House Estates)
The Clan Trust Ltd
Clark Foundation
Closehelm Ltd
The Clothworkers' Foundation
Cloudesley
The Clover Trust
Clydpride Ltd
CMZ Ltd
The Coalfields Regeneration Trust
Denise Coates Foundation
The Vivienne and Samuel Cohen Charitable Trust
The John S. Cohen Foundation
The Cole Charitable Trust
The Coltstaple Trust
Colyer-Fergusson Charitable Trust
Comic Relief
Douglas Compton James Charitable Trust
The Cooks Charity
The Alice Ellen Cooper Dean Charitable Foundation
Co-operative Community Investment Foundation

The J. Reginald Corah Foundation Fund
The Worshipful Company of Cordwainers Charitable Trusts (Minges Gift)
The Evan Cornish Foundation
Cornwall Community Foundation
The Duke of Cornwall's Benevolent Fund
The Corporation of Trinity House of Deptford Strond
Corra Foundation
The County Council of Dyfed Welsh Church Fund
*Countypier Ltd**
Coventry Building Society Charitable Foundation
The Sir Tom Cowie Charitable Trust
Dudley and Geoffrey Cox Charitable Trust
The Lord Cozens-Hardy Trust
The Craps Charitable Trust
CRASH
Michael Crawford Children's Charity
*CRH Charitable Trust**
Cripplegate Foundation
Crisis UK
The Cross Trust
The Croydon Relief in Need Charities
The Peter Cruddas Foundation
Cruden Foundation Ltd
CSIS Charity Fund
Cumbria Community Foundation
Itzchok Meyer Cymerman Trust Ltd
D. M. H. Educational Trust Ltd
Oizer Dalim Trust
*The Daniell Trust**
*The Dashlight Foundation**
Baron Davenport's Charity
*The Manny and Brigitta Davidson Charitable Foundation**
The Davidson Family Charitable Trust
Margaret Davies Charity
The Davis Foundation
Dawat-E-Hadiyah Trust (United Kingdom)
The De Brye Charitable Trust
The Roger De Haan Charitable Trust
Debmar Benevolent Trust Ltd
Foundation Derbyshire
Provincial Grand Charity of the Province of Derbyshire
The J. N. Derbyshire Trust
Devon Community Foundation
The Dibden Allotments Fund
The Dischma Charitable Trust
The Djanogly Foundation
*The Ken Dodd Charitable Foundation**
The Derek and Eileen Dodgson Foundation
Dorset Community Foundation
The Double 'O' Charity Ltd
Drapers' Charitable Fund
Dromintee Trust
The Anne Duchess of Westminster's Charity
The Dulverton Trust
Dumbreck Charity
*The Nine Incorporated Trades of Dundee General Fund Charity**
*Dunlossit and Islay Community Trust**
The Dunn Family Charitable Trust
County Durham Community Foundation
Dushinsky Trust Ltd
The James Dyson Foundation
The Earley Charity
East End Community Foundation
EBM Charitable Trust
The Ecology Trust
The Gilbert and Eileen Edgar Foundation
Edupoor Ltd
Dr Edwards Bishop King's Fulham Endowment Fund
W. G. Edwards Charitable Foundation
*The Eight Foundation**
The Eighteen Fund
The Eighty Eight Foundation
The George Elias Charitable Trust
*The Elie Trust**
The Maud Elkington Charitable Trust
The Ellerdale Trust
The Endrick Trust
The Englefield Charitable Trust
The Enkalon Foundation
Entindale Ltd
The EQ Foundation
Esher House Charitable Trust
Essex Community Foundation
The Essex Youth Trust
The Estelle Trust
The Exilarch's Foundation
The ExPat Foundation
G. F. Eyre Charitable Trust
Esmée Fairbairn Foundation
*Family Philanthropy Ltd**
The Lord Faringdon Charitable Trust
Samuel William Farmer Trust
The Thomas Farr Charity
The Farthing Trust
The George Fentham Birmingham Charity
The A. M. Fenton Trust
The Feoffees of St Michael's Spurriergate York
The Fermanagh Trust
The Fifty Fund
Dixie Rose Findlay Charitable Trust
Sir John Fisher Foundation
The Earl Fitzwilliam Charitable Trust
The Robert Fleming Hannay Memorial Charity
Ford Britain Trust
Forest Hill Charitable Trust
Forever Manchester
The Forman Hardy Charitable Trust
Donald Forrester Trust
The Fort Foundation
Four Acre Trust
*Foux Foundation**
The Isaac and Freda Frankel Memorial Charitable Trust
The Elizabeth Frankland Moore and Star Foundation
The Hugh Fraser Foundation
The Louis and Valerie Freedman Charitable Settlement
Charles S. French Charitable Trust
The Freshfield Foundation
The Freshgate Trust Foundation
Friarsgate Trust
Frognal Trust
The G. D. Charitable Trust
Gamma Trust
The Gannochy Trust
The Ganzoni Charitable Trust
Garfield Weston Foundation
Garthgwynion Charities
The Gaudio Family Foundation (UK) Ltd
Martin Geddes Charitable Trust
General Charity (Coventry)
The General Charity Fund
The Generations Foundation
The Steven Gerrard Foundation
The Tara Getty Foundation
The Gibbons Family Trust
The David Gibbons Foundation
The Gibbs Charitable Trusts
The Simon Gibson Charitable Trust
The Girdlers' Company Charitable Trust
The B. and P. Glasser Charitable Trust
The Gloag Foundation
County of Gloucestershire Community Foundation
Worshipful Company of Gold and Silver Wyre Drawers Second Charitable Trust Fund

Sydney and Phyllis Goldberg Memorial Charitable Trust
The Golden Bottle Trust
The Goldman Sachs Charitable Gift Fund (UK)
Goldman Sachs Gives (UK)
The Goldsmiths' Company Charity
The Goodman Foundation
The Gosling Foundation Ltd
The Edward Gostling Foundation
Gowling WLG (UK) Charitable Trust
The Hemraj Goyal Foundation
Grace Charitable Trust
The Grace Trust
The James Grace Trust*
The Graham Trust
The Grant Foundation
The Grantham Yorke Trust
GrantScape
Gordon Gray Trust
The Greater Manchester High Sheriff's Police Trust
The Kenneth and Susan Green Charitable Foundation
The Green Hall Foundation
Greenham Trust Ltd
The Greenslade Family Foundation*
The Greggs Foundation
The Grocers' Charity
M. and R. Gross Charities Ltd
The Walter Guinness Charitable Trust
Dr Guthrie's Association
H. C. D. Memorial Fund
H. C. Foundation
Hackney Parochial Charities
The Hadfield Charitable Trust
The Hadley Trust
The Hadrian Trust
The Alfred Haines Charitable Trust
Halifax Foundation for Northern Ireland
The Halsall Foundation*
The Helen Hamlyn Trust
Hammersmith United Charities
Hampshire and Isle of Wight Community Foundation
The Hampstead Wells and Campden Trust
Hampton Fund
The W. A. Handley Charity Trust
The Haramead Trust
Harbinson Charitable Trust
Harborne Parish Lands Charity
The Harbour Foundation
Ros Harding Trust
William Harding's Charity
The Harpur Trust
The Edith Lilian Harrison 2000 Foundation
The Peter Harrison Foundation
The Harrison-Frank Family Foundation (UK) Ltd
The Harry and Mary Foundation*
Gay and Peter Hartley's Hillards Charitable Trust
Edward Harvist Trust (The Harvist Estate)
The Hasluck Charitable Trust
The Maurice Hatter Foundation
The Hawthorne Charitable Trust
Hays Travel Foundation
The Charles Hayward Foundation
The Headley Trust
May Hearnshaw's Charity
Heart of England Community Foundation
The Heathcoat Trust
The Heathside Charitable Trust
The Charlotte Heber-Percy Charitable Trust
The Hedley Foundation
The Helping Foundation
The Hemby Charitable Trust
The Christina Mary Hendrie Trust
The Tim Henman Foundation
The G. D. Herbert Charitable Trust
Herefordshire Community Foundation
Hertfordshire Community Foundation
HFC Help For Children UK LTD
P. and C. Hickinbotham Charitable Trust
The Alan Edward Higgs Charity
The Highcroft Charitable Trust
The Hilden Charitable Fund
The Hillier Trust
R. G. Hills Charitable Trust
The Lady Hind Trust
The Hinduja Foundation
The Hiscox Foundation
The Henry C. Hoare Charitable Trust
The Hobson Charity Ltd
The Jane Hodge Foundation
The Holbeck Charitable Trust
The Holywood Trust
Homelands Charitable Trust
The Thomas J. Horne Memorial Trust
The Hospital of God at Greatham
House of Industry Estate
Housing Pathways Trust
The Reta Lila Howard Foundation
The Hudson Foundation
The Humanitarian Trust
The Albert Hunt Trust
The Hunter Foundation
Huntingdon Freemen's Trust
The Hutchinson Charitable Trust
The Nani Huyu Charitable Trust
Hyde Charitable Trust
Hyde Park Place Estate Charity
IBM United Kingdom Trust
Ibrahim Foundation Ltd
The Iliffe Family Charitable Trust
Imagine Foundation
Impact Funding Partners Ltd
The Inman Charity
Inner London Magistrates Court Poor Box and Feeder Charity
Investream Charitable Trust
The Invigorate Charitable Trust
The Ireland Fund of Great Britain
Irish Youth Foundation (UK) Ltd (incorporating The Lawlor Foundation)
The Isla Foundation*
The ITF Seafarers Trust
The J. and J. Benevolent Foundation
The J. A. R. Charitable Trust
The Jabbs Foundation
Jeffrey Charitable Trust*
The Jenour Foundation
Jesus Hospital Charity
Jewish Child's Day (JCD)
The Elton John Aids Foundation (EJAF)
The Johnson Foundation
Johnnie Johnson Trust
The Jones 1986 Charitable Trust
The Marjorie and Geoffrey Jones Charitable Trust
The Muriel Jones Foundation
The Cyril and Eve Jumbo Charitable Trust
Anton Jurgens Charitable Trust
The Jusaca Charitable Trust
The Ian Karten Charitable Trust
The Kasner Charitable Trust
The Michael and Ilse Katz Foundation
The Emmanuel Kaye Foundation
The Kelly Family Charitable Trust
William Kendall's Charity (Wax Chandlers' Company)
The Kensington and Chelsea Foundation
Kent Community Foundation
The Kentown Wizard Foundation
The Nancy Kenyon Charitable Trust
The Peter Kershaw Trust
KFC Foundation*

The King Henry VIII Endowed Trust – Warwick
The Mary Kinross Charitable Trust
Laura Kinsella Foundation
The Graham Kirkham Foundation
The Ernest Kleinwort Charitable Trust
Sir James Knott Trust
Kollel and Co. Ltd
Kolyom Trust Ltd
*KPE4 Charitable Trust**
The KPMG Foundation
*The Labone Charitable Trust**
Ladbrokes Coral Trust
John Laing Charitable Trust
Maurice and Hilda Laing Charitable Trust
Christopher Laing Foundation
The David Laing Foundation
The Martin Laing Foundation
The Beatrice Laing Trust
The Leonard Laity Stoate Charitable Trust
The Lake House Charity
Community Foundations for Lancashire and Merseyside
The Lancashire Foundation
Duchy of Lancaster Benevolent Fund
Lancaster Foundation
The Allen Lane Foundation
Langdale Trust
The R. J. Larg Family Trust
Largsmount Ltd
Mrs M. A. Lascelles Charitable Trust
Laslett's (Hinton) Charity
The Herd Lawson and Muriel Lawson Charitable Trust
Lawson Beckman Charitable Trust
The Lawson Trust CIO
The Leathersellers' Company Charitable Fund
The William Leech Charity
Leeds Building Society Charitable Foundation
*The Leeward Trust**
The Kennedy Leigh Charitable Trust
The Leri Charitable Trust
*The Ralph Levy Charitable Company Ltd**
Joseph Levy Foundation
*Cecil and Hilda Lewis Charitable Trust**
Bernard Lewis Family Charitable Trust
David and Ruth Lewis Family Charitable Trust
The Limbourne Trust
The Linbury Trust
Lincolnshire Community Foundation
The Linden Charitable Trust
The Linder Foundation
The Lindley Foundation (TLF)
The Charles Littlewood Hill Trust
The Second Joseph Aaron Littman Foundation
The George John and Sheilah Livanos Charitable Trust
Liverpool Charity and Voluntary Services (LCVS)
*The Livingston Charitable Trust**
The Ian and Natalie Livingstone Charitable Trust
The Elaine and Angus Lloyd Charitable Trust
The W. M. and B. W. Lloyd Trust
Lloyd's Charities Trust
Lloyds Bank Foundation for England and Wales
Lloyds Bank Foundation for the Channel Islands
Local Trent Ltd
The Locker Foundation
Loftus Charitable Trust
London Catalyst
The London Community Foundation (LCF)
London Freemasons Charity
London Housing Foundation Ltd (LHF)
The C. L. Loyd Charitable Trust
LPW Ltd
The Henry Lumley Charitable Trust
The Lyndal Tree Foundation
John Lyon's Charity
Sylvanus Lysons Charity
M. and C. Trust
M. B. Foundation
The M. Y. A. Charitable Trust
The R. S. Macdonald Charitable Trust
Mace Foundation
The MacRobert Trust 2019
The Mactaggart Third Fund
The Ian Mactaggart Trust (The Mactaggart Second Fund)
The Magdalen and Lasher Charity (General Fund)
The Mahoro Charitable Trust
The Manackerman Charitable Trust
Manchester Airport Community Trust Fund
The Manchester Guardian Society Charitable Trust
R. W. Mann Trust
Marbeh Torah Trust
*The Marque Foundation**
The Michael Marsh Charitable Trust
The Marsh Christian Trust
Charlotte Marshall Charitable Trust
D. G. Marshall of Cambridge Trust
Sir George Martin Trust
Masonic Charitable Foundation
Nancie Massey Charitable Trust
The Master Charitable Trust
*Material World Foundation**
The Matliwala Family Charitable Trust
Mayfair Charities Ltd
Mayheights Ltd
MBNA General Foundation
The Robert McAlpine Foundation
*Gemma and Chris McGough Charitable Foundation CIO**
The Medlock Charitable Trust
Melodor Ltd
The Melow Charitable Trust
The Brian Mercer Charitable Trust
The Mercers' Charitable Foundation
Merchant Navy Welfare Board
The Merchant Venturers' Charity
Merchants' House of Glasgow
The Mickel Fund
The Mickleham Trust
The Gerald Micklem Charitable Trust
The Masonic Province of Middlesex Charitable Trust (Middlesex Masonic Charity)
The Millennium Oak Trust
The Ronald Miller Foundation
Jean and Roger Miller's Charitable Trust
The Millward Charitable Trust
*The Milne Family Foundation**
Milton Keynes Community Foundation Ltd
The Peter Minet Trust
The Mishcon Family Charitable Trust
The Brian Mitchell Charitable Settlement
The Mittal Foundation
Keren Mitzvah Trust
The Mizpah Trust
*The Mohn Westlake Foundation**
The Alexander Moncur Trust
*The Monday Charitable Trust**
The Monmouthshire County Council Welsh Church Act Fund
Moondance Foundation
John Moores Foundation
The Morel Charitable Trust
The Morgan Charitable Foundation

The Steve Morgan Foundation
Morgan Stanley International Foundation
The Miles Morland Foundation
The Morris Charitable Trust
G. M. Morrison Charitable Trust
The Morrisons Foundation
The Morton Charitable Trust (Dundee)
The Mosawi Foundation*
Vyoel Moshe Charitable Trust
The Mosselson Charitable Trust
The Mulberry Trust
The Frederick Mulder Foundation
Edith Murphy Foundation
Murphy-Neumann Charity Company Ltd
The John R. Murray Charitable Trust
Brian Murtagh Charitable Trust
Music Sales Charitable Trust
Muslim Hands
The Mutual Trust Group
MW (CL) Foundation
MW (GK) Foundation
MW (HO) Foundation
MW (RH) Foundation
The Janet Nash Charitable Settlement
The National Express Foundation
The Nationwide Foundation
Nemoral Ltd
Ner Foundation
Nesta
Newby Trust Ltd
The Frances and Augustus Newman Foundation
The NFU Mutual Charitable Trust
The Nineveh Charitable Trust
Norfolk Community Foundation
The Norman Family Charitable Trust
Normanby Charitable Trust
North Berwick Trust*
North East Area Miners' Social Welfare Trust Fund
Northamptonshire Community Foundation
Community Foundation for Northern Ireland
The Northwick Trust
Northwood Charitable Trust
The Norton Foundation
The Norton Rose Fulbright Charitable Foundation
Norwich Town Close Estate Charity
Notting Hill Genesis Community Foundation
Nottinghamshire Community Foundation
The Nuffield Foundation
The Oakdale Trust
The Oakley Charitable Trust
Odin Charitable Trust
The Ofenheim Charitable Trust
Oglesby Charitable Trust
Henry Oldfield Trust
One Community Foundation Ltd
The O'Sullivan Family Charitable Trust
Otsar Trust*
The Ovo Charitable Foundation
The Owen Family Trust
Oxfordshire Community Foundation
The Paget Charitable Trust
The Gerald Palmer Eling Trust Company
The Panacea Charitable Trust
The Paphitis Charitable Trust
The Paragon Trust
The Pargiter Trust
The Pastoral Care Trust – The St Nicholas Care Fund
The Patrick Trust
Peacock Charitable Trust
David Pearlman Charitable Foundation
The Pears Family Charitable Foundation
The Dowager Countess Eleanor Peel Trust
People's Postcode Trust
The Persimmon Charitable Foundation
Personal Assurance Charitable Trust
The Pharsalia Charitable Trust
The Phillips and Rubens Charitable Trust
The Phillips Charitable Trust
The Phillips Family Charitable Trust
The Pickwell Foundation
The Pilgrim Trust
Cecil Pilkington Charitable Trust
Pilkington Charities Fund
The Austin and Hope Pilkington Trust
The Sir Harry Pilkington Trust Fund
The Pitt-Rivers Charitable Trust
The Pixel Fund
The George and Esmé Pollitzer Charitable Settlement
The Porta Pia 2012 Foundation
The Portishead Nautical Trust
The Portrack Charitable Trust
Postcode Society Trust (formerly Postcode Dream Trust)
Premierquote Ltd
The Pret Foundation
Sir John Priestman Charity Trust
The Prince of Wales's Charitable Foundation
The Princess Anne's Charities
The Professional Footballers' Association Charity
The Puebla Charitable Trust
The Purey Cust Trust CIO
Catkin Pussywillow Charitable Trust
The Pye Foundation
Mr and Mrs J. A. Pye's Charitable Settlement
QBE European Operations Foundation
Quadstar Charitable Foundation*
Quartet Community Foundation
The Queen Anne's Gate Foundation
Quintessentially Foundation
Quothquan Trust
R. S. Charitable Trust
The Monica Rabagliati Charitable Trust
Rachel Charitable Trust
The Racing Foundation
The Raindance Charitable Trust*
The Rainford Trust
The Randal Charitable Foundation*
The Joseph and Lena Randall Charitable Trust
The Rank Foundation Ltd
The Ranworth Trust
The Eleanor Rathbone Charitable Trust
Elizabeth Rathbone Charity
The Ravensdale Trust
The Rayne Foundation
The Rayne Trust
The John Rayner Charitable Trust
The Sir James Reckitt Charity
C. A. Redfern Charitable Foundation
The Rest-Harrow Trust
The Revere Charitable Trust
RG Foundation*
The Rhododendron Trust
Daisie Rich Trust
The Sir Cliff Richard Charitable Trust
Richmond Parish Lands Charity
Ridgesave Ltd
Rigby Foundation
The River Farm Foundation
The River Trust
Rivers Foundation
Riverside Charitable Trust Ltd
The Roan Charitable Trust
The Robertson Trust
Robyn Charitable Trust
Rockcliffe Charitable Trust

The Roddick Foundation
The Gerald and Gail Ronson Family Foundation
Mrs L. D. Rope's Third Charitable Settlement
Rosca Trust
The Cecil Rosen Foundation
The Rothschild Foundation
The Eranda Rothschild Foundation
The Roughley Charitable Trust
The Row Fogo Charitable Trust
The Rowlands Trust
The Joseph Rowntree Foundation
Royal Artillery Charitable Fund
Royal Docks Trust (London)
The Royal Foundation of the Duke and Duchess of Cambridge
Royal Masonic Trust for Girls and Boys
The Royal Navy and Royal Marines Charity
*RSM UK Foundation**
The Rugby Group Benevolent Fund Ltd
The Russell Trust
S. and R. Charitable Trust
The Michael and Nicola Sacher Charitable Trust
The Saintbury Trust
The Saints and Sinners Trust Ltd
The Salamander Charitable Trust
Salters' Charitable Foundation
Samjo Ltd
The Basil Samuel Charitable Trust
The M. J. Samuel Charitable Trust
The Peter Samuel Charitable Trust
The Sandhu Charitable Foundation
Sandra Charitable Trust
O. and G. Schreiber Charitable Trust
Schroder Charity Trust
The Schroder Foundation
Foundation Scotland
Francis C. Scott Charitable Trust
The Frieda Scott Charitable Trust
The John Scott Trust Fund
Scottish Coal Industry Special Welfare Fund
The Scottish Power Foundation
Scottish Property Industry Festival of Christmas (SPIFOX)
Scouloudi Foundation
The SDL Foundation
Seafarers UK (King George's Fund for Sailors)
The Searchlight Electric Charitable Trust
Sam and Bella Sebba Charitable Trust
Seedfield Trust
The Segelman Trust
Sellata Ltd
The Shanly Foundation
The Shears Foundation
The Sheldon Trust
The Sylvia and Colin Shepherd Charitable Trust
The Archie Sherman Charitable Trust
The Bassil Shippam and Alsford Trust
The Shoe Zone Trust
The Simmons & Simmons Charitable Foundation
Sirius Minerals Foundation
The Skelton Bounty
The Charles Skey Charitable Trust
Skipton Building Society Charitable Foundation
The John Slater Foundation
Rita and David Slowe Charitable Trust
Smallwood Trust
The SMB Trust
The Mrs Smith and Mount Trust
*Smith Bradbeer Charitable Trust**
The N. Smith Charitable Settlement
The Henry Smith Charity
*Arabella and Julian Smith Family Trust**
The Martin Smith Foundation
The Leslie Smith Foundation
Philip Smith's Charitable Trust
The R. C. Snelling Charitable Trust
The Sobell Foundation
Social Tech Trust
Sodexo Stop Hunger Foundation
Somerset Community Foundation
The E. C. Sosnow Charitable Trust
The Souter Charitable Trust
The South Yorkshire Community Foundation
W. F. Southall Trust
Sparquote Ltd
*The Michael and Sarah Spencer Foundation**
Spielman Charitable Trust
The Spoore, Merry and Rixman Foundation
Rosalyn and Nicholas Springer Charitable Trust
The Spurrell Charitable Trust
The Geoff and Fiona Squire Foundation
The St Hilda's Trust
The St James's Trust Settlement
St James's Place Charitable Foundation
St John's Foundation Est. 1174
The Stafford Trust
The Community Foundation for Staffordshire
Standard Life Foundation
Stanley Foundation Ltd
Starlow Charities Ltd
The Peter Stebbings Memorial Charity
The Steel Charitable Trust
The Steinberg Family Charitable Trust
The Hugh Stenhouse Foundation
Sir Halley Stewart Trust
The Stewarts Law Foundation
Mark Stolkin Foundation
The Stone Family Foundation
The Stoneygate Trust
Strand Parishes Trust
Stratford-upon-Avon Town Trust
The WO Street Charitable Foundation
The Street Foundation
StreetSmart – Action for the Homeless
*The Joseph Strong Frazer Trust**
Suffolk Community Foundation
The Summerfield Charitable Trust
The Bernard Sunley Foundation
The Sunrise Foundation CIO
Community Foundation for Surrey
Sabina Sutherland Charitable Trust
Sutton Coldfield Charitable Trust
Swan Mountain Trust
The Swann-Morton Foundation
The John Swire (1989) Charitable Trust
The Swire Charitable Trust
The Charles and Elsie Sykes Trust
*The Hugh Symons Charitable Trust**
The T.K. Maxx and Homesense Foundation
The Tabhair Charitable Trust
The Tajtelbaum Charitable Trust
The Talbot Trusts
The Talbot Village Trust

Tallow Chandlers Benevolent Fund No. 2
Talteg Ltd
The David Tannen Charitable Trust
Tanner Trust
C. B. and H. H. Taylor 1984 Trust
The Taylor Family Foundation
Tegham Ltd
the7stars Foundation*
Scott Thomson Charitable Trust
Sir Jules Thorn Charitable Trust
Three Monkies Trust
Mrs R. P. Tindall's Charitable Trust
The Tobacco Pipe Makers and Tobacco Trade Benevolent Fund
The Tomoro Foundation*
The Tompkins Foundation
The Tory Family Foundation
Tower Hill Trust
The Toy Trust
Toyota Manufacturing UK Charitable Trust
The Trades House of Glasgow
David William Traill Cargill Fund
Annie Tranmer Charitable Trust
The Constance Travis Charitable Trust
The Trefoil Trust
The Tresanton Trust*
The Troutsdale Charitable Trust*
The Truemark Trust
Trumros Ltd
Trust for London
The Trusthouse Charitable Foundation
The Tudor Trust
The Tudwick Foundation*
The Tuixen Foundation
The Roger and Douglas Turner Charitable Trust
The Turtleton Charitable Trust
Tzedakah
Ulster Garden Villages Ltd
The Underwood Trust
The Union Of The Sisters Of Mercy Of Great Britain
United Jewish Israel Appeal
United St Saviour's Charity
The Valentine Charitable Trust
The Albert Van Den Bergh Charitable Trust
The Van Mesdag Fund*
The Van Neste Foundation
The Vandervell Foundation
The Vardy Foundation
The Velvet Foundation*
The William and Patricia Venton Charitable Trust
The Veterans' Foundation
VHLT Ltd
Vinci UK Foundation*
The Vintners' Foundation
Virgin Atlantic Foundation
The Virgin Money Foundation
Vision Foundation*
Volant Charitable Trust
The Georg and Emily Von Opel Foundation*
Wade's Charity
The Scurrah Wainwright Charity
Wakefield and Tetley Trust
The Walcot Foundation
Robert and Felicity Waley-Cohen Charitable Trust
The Walker Trust
Walton on Thames Charity
The Barbara Ward Children's Foundation
Warwick Relief in Need Charity
The Warwickshire Masonic Charitable Association Ltd
Mrs Waterhouse Charitable Trust
The Waterloo Foundation
Wates Family Enterprise Trust
The Wates Foundation
The William Wates Memorial Trust
The Geoffrey Watling Charity
Blyth Watson Charitable Trust
The Weinstock Fund
The Welland Trust*
The Welsh Church Act Fund
West Derby Waste Lands Charity
The Westcroft Trust
Westhill Endowment
Westminster Almshouses Foundation
Westminster Amalgamated Charity
Westminster Foundation
Westway Trust
The Melanie White Foundation Ltd
White Stuff Foundation
The Norman Whiteley Trust
The Felicity Wilde Charitable Trust
Joan Wilkinson Charitable Trust*
The Williams Family Foundation
The Willmott Dixon Foundation
J. and J. R. Wilson Trust
Wiltshire Community Foundation
The Wimbledon Foundation
The Benjamin Winegarten Charitable Trust
W. Wing Yip and Brothers Foundation
The Francis Winham Foundation
The Michael and Anna Wix Charitable Trust
The Wixamtree Trust
Friends of Wiznitz Ltd
The Charles Wolfson Charitable Trust
The Wolfson Foundation
Women's Fund for Scotland*
The Wood Foundation
Wooden Spoon Society
Woodlands Green Ltd
Woodroffe Benton Foundation
The Woodward Charitable Trust
Worcester Municipal Charities (CIO)
The Eric Wright Charitable Trust
Sir Graham Wylie Foundation*
The Wyseliot Rose Charitable Trust
The Yapp Charitable Trust
York Children's Trust
Yorkshire Building Society Charitable Foundation
The William Allen Young Charitable Trust
Youth Music
The Elizabeth and Prince Zaiger Trust
The Marjorie and Arnold Ziff Charitable Foundation
The Zochonis Charitable Trust
Zurich Community Trust (UK) Ltd

Sports and recreation

The 29th May 1961 Charitable Trust
*Adam Family Foundation**
The Bryan Adams Foundation
The Aldama Foundation
*Alpkit Foundation**
The Ammco Trust
*The Armed Forces Covenant Fund Trust**
The Arsenal Foundation
The Astor Foundation
*The Barnes Fund**
Barnwood Trust
The James Beattie Charitable Trust
*AJ Bell Trust**
Bideford Bridge Trust
Birmingham International Airport Community Trust Fund
The Isabel Blackman Foundation
Blakemore Foundation
Bluespark Foundation
BOOST Charitable Trust
The Booth Charities
*Alan Boswell Group Charitable Trust**
The Bowland Charitable Trust
*The Bransford Trust**
The Brelms Trust CIO
British Motor Sports Training Trust
The Jack Brunton Charitable Trust
The Cadbury Foundation
*Camden Giving**
The Carnegie Dunfermline Trust
The Chartley Foundation
Chippenham Borough Lands Charity
The Robert Clutterbuck Charitable Trust
The Coalfields Regeneration Trust
The Vivienne and Samuel Cohen Charitable Trust
Community First
Michael Cornish Charitable Trust
*The Cotswold Primrose Charitable Trust**
Cumbria Community Foundation
The Roger De Haan Charitable Trust
Provincial Grand Charity of the Province of Derbyshire
County Durham Community Foundation
The Earley Charity
Edinburgh Children's Holiday Fund
England and Wales Cricket Trust
The Englefield Charitable Trust
The Enkalon Foundation
The Essex and Southend Sports Trust
The Essex Youth Trust
The Lord Faringdon Charitable Trust
The Football Association National Sports Centre Trust
The Football Foundation
The Foxglove Trust
Charles S. French Charitable Trust
The Freshgate Trust Foundation
The Gannochy Trust
Gatwick Airport Community Trust
The Girdlers' Company Charitable Trust
The Grange Farm Centre Trust
The Grantham Yorke Trust
GrantScape
The J. G. Graves Charitable Trust
Greenham Trust Ltd
*The Greenslade Family Foundation**
Dr Guthrie's Association
The Hadrian Trust
The Alfred Haines Charitable Trust
The Hamilton Davies Trust
Hampshire and Isle of Wight Community Foundation
Hampton Fund
The Lennox Hannay Charitable Trust
The Harpur Trust
The Peter Harrison Foundation
Edward Harvist Trust (The Harvist Estate)
Hays Travel Foundation
The Hedley Foundation
Henley Educational Trust
Henley Royal Regatta Charitable Trust
The Tim Henman Foundation
The Holbeck Charitable Trust
The Holywood Trust
The Mary Homfray Charitable Trust
Huntingdon Freemen's Trust
Ibrahim Foundation Ltd
The Isle of Anglesey Charitable Trust
Johnnie Johnson Trust
Kilpatrick Fraser Charitable Trust
The King Henry VIII Endowed Trust – Warwick
Sir James Knott Trust
*KPE4 Charitable Trust**
The Kyte Charitable Trust
The Lake House Charity
The Leathersellers' Company Charitable Fund
John Lewis Foundation
The Lindley Foundation (TLF)
The Charles Littlewood Hill Trust
The London Marathon Charitable Trust Ltd
The Lord's Taverners
Making a Difference Locally Ltd
The J. P. Marland Charitable Trust
The Martin Charitable Trust
Sir George Martin Trust
The Dan Maskell Tennis Trust
The Master Charitable Trust
Matchroom Sport Charitable Foundation
The Mickel Fund
Millennium Stadium Charitable Trust (Ymddiriedclaeth Elusennol Stadiwm Y. Mileniwm)
Jean and Roger Miller's Charitable Trust
The James Milner Foundation
Minton Charitable Trust
*The Mohn Westlake Foundation**
The Morton Charitable Trust (Dundee)
The National Express Foundation
The Nisbet Trust
The Norman Family Charitable Trust
*North Berwick Trust**
North East Area Miners' Social Welfare Trust Fund
Northamptonshire Community Foundation
Community Foundation for Northern Ireland
One Community Foundation Ltd
Oxfordshire Community Foundation
The Paphitis Charitable Trust
The Pastoral Care Trust – The St Nicholas Care Fund
Payne-Gallwey 1989 Charitable Trust
People's Postcode Trust
The Persimmon Charitable Foundation
The Porta Pia 2012 Foundation
Postcode Community Trust
Postcode Society Trust (formerly Postcode Dream Trust)

Poundland Foundation*
The Priory Foundation
The Professional Footballers' Association Charity
Quadstar Charitable Foundation*
Quartet Community Foundation
The John Rayner Charitable Trust
Riada Trust
The David Ross Foundation
The Rothermere Foundation
Royal Docks Trust (London)
The Rugby Group Benevolent Fund Ltd
The Russell Trust
The Saintbury Trust
The Frieda Scott Charitable Trust
The Sheffield Town Trust
The Sherling Charitable Trust
The Shipwrights' Charitable Fund
The Charles Skey Charitable Trust
The Martin Smith Foundation
St Olave's and St Saviour's Schools Foundation
Stadium Charitable Trust
The Sterry Family Foundation*
Peter Stormonth Darling Charitable Trust
The Summerfield Charitable Trust
The John Swire (1989) Charitable Trust
Tay Charitable Trust
A. P. Taylor Trust
The Tompkins Foundation
Tower Hill Trust
The Toy Trust
The Trusthouse Charitable Foundation
The Albert Van Den Bergh Charitable Trust
The Bruce Wake Charitable Trust
Wates Family Enterprise Trust
The William Wates Memorial Trust
The Geoffrey Watling Charity
The Weir Charitable Trust
The Welsh Church Act Fund
Wembley National Stadium Trust
Westway Trust
The Wilson Foundation
The Wimbledon Foundation
The Wixamtree Trust
Wooden Spoon Society
York Children's Trust

Recreational activities and clubs

The 29th May 1961 Charitable Trust
The Ammco Trust
The Barnes Fund*
Bauer Radio's Cash for Kids Charities
The James Beattie Charitable Trust
Bideford Bridge Trust
The Jack Brunton Charitable Trust
The Carnegie Dunfermline Trust
The Chipping Sodbury Town Lands Charity
The Clan Trust Ltd
The Peter Cruddas Foundation
Dumfriesshire East Community Benefit Group SCIO*
The Earley Charity
The Gilbert and Eileen Edgar Foundation
Edinburgh Children's Holiday Fund
The Essex Youth Trust
The Football Association National Sports Centre Trust
The Football Foundation
The Freshgate Trust Foundation
The Gannochy Trust
The Gibbons Family Trust
The Girdlers' Company Charitable Trust
The Granada Foundation
The Grange Farm Centre Trust
The Grantham Yorke Trust
The J. G. Graves Charitable Trust
The Alfred Haines Charitable Trust
The Peter Harrison Foundation
Henley Educational Trust
The Heritage of London Trust Ltd
The Holbeck Charitable Trust
The Holywood Trust
Huntingdon Freemen's Trust
The Isle of Anglesey Charitable Trust
The Jewish Youth Fund
KFC Foundation*
The Graham Kirkham Foundation
KPE4 Charitable Trust*
Lancashire Environmental Fund Ltd
The Charles Littlewood Hill Trust
The London Community Foundation (LCF)
The Lord's Taverners
R. W. Mann Trust
The Merchant Venturers' Charity
The Masonic Province of Middlesex Charitable Trust (Middlesex Masonic Charity)
The Millennium Oak Trust
The Mohn Westlake Foundation*
The Monmouthshire County Council Welsh Church Act Fund
The National Garden Scheme
North Berwick Trust*
North East Area Miners' Social Welfare Trust Fund
One Community Foundation Ltd
The Persimmon Charitable Foundation
The Jack Petchey Foundation
Postcode Local Trust
Daisie Rich Trust
Humphrey Richardson Taylor Charitable Trust
Richmond Parish Lands Charity
The Roughley Charitable Trust
The Rugby Group Benevolent Fund Ltd
The Shanly Foundation
The Sheldon Trust
The Shipwrights' Charitable Fund
The Skelton Bounty
The R. C. Snelling Charitable Trust
Peter Stormonth Darling Charitable Trust
Community Foundation for Surrey
Tanner Trust
Stephen Taylor Foundation
A. P. Taylor Trust
The Tompkins Foundation
Tower Hill Trust
Variety, the Children's Charity
The Veolia Environmental Trust
Viridor Credits Environmental Company
Wade's Charity
The Bruce Wake Charitable Trust
The Welsh Church Act Fund
Westway Trust
The Wilson Foundation
The Wimbledon Foundation
Wooden Spoon Society
The Woodward Charitable Trust
York Children's Trust
Youth Music

Sports

The Britford Bridge Trust
British Motor Sports Training Trust
England and Wales Cricket Trust
The Essex Youth Trust
The Football Association National Sports Centre Trust
The Football Foundation
The Freshgate Trust Foundation
The Great Britain Sasakawa Foundation
Hampton Fund
Henley Educational Trust
Henley Royal Regatta Charitable Trust
The Holbeck Charitable Trust
The Kyte Charitable Trust
The London Marathon Charitable Trust Ltd
The Lord's Taverners
Minton Charitable Trust
One Community Foundation Ltd
The Sheffield Town Trust
Peter Stormonth Darling Charitable Trust
The Welsh Church Act Fund
Wooden Spoon Society

Specific sports

The Childwick Trust
The Emerald Foundation
England and Wales Cricket Trust
The Football Association National Sports Centre Trust
The Football Foundation
The Golf Foundation Ltd
Henley Royal Regatta Charitable Trust
Johnnie Johnson Trust
The Boris Karloff Charitable Foundation
The Lord's Taverners
The Dan Maskell Tennis Trust
The Sir Peter O'Sullevan Charitable Trust
The Professional Footballers' Association Charity
The Racing Foundation
Riada Trust
The Saddlers' Company Charitable Fund
The Shipwrights' Charitable Fund
The Wimbledon Foundation
Wooden Spoon Society

Work outside the UK

The Bryan Adams Foundation
The Alborada Trust
The Allen & Overy Foundation
The Allen Trust
The Archer Trust
*The Armed Forces Covenant Fund Trust**
The Artemis Charitable Foundation
The Ashworth Charitable Trust
The Austin Bailey Foundation
The Roger and Sarah Bancroft Clark Charitable Trust
The Becht Family Charitable Trust
The John Beckwith Charitable Trust
The Bestway Foundation
Lady Blakenham's Charity Trust
The Bloom Foundation
The Boltini Trust
The Consuelo and Anthony Brooke Charitable Trust
The Rory and Elizabeth Brooks Foundation
*The Brown Source Trust**
The Noel Buxton Trust
William A. Cadbury Charitable Trust
The Calleva Foundation
The André Christian Trust
Clark Foundation
The Clothworkers' Foundation
The Alice Ellen Cooper Dean Charitable Foundation
Corra Foundation
Credit Suisse EMEA Foundation
The D. G. Charitable Settlement
*The Dashlight Foundation**
Donibristle Trust
Dromintee Trust
Dunard Fund
The Englefield Charitable Trust
The Estelle Trust
The ExPat Foundation
Allan and Nesta Ferguson Charitable Settlement
Forest Hill Charitable Trust
The Forte Charitable Trust
The Foxglove Trust
The Freshfield Foundation
The Gatsby Charitable Foundation
The Jacqueline and Michael Gee Charitable Trust
The Gibbs Charitable Trusts
The Gloag Foundation
Sydney and Phyllis Goldberg Memorial Charitable Trust
The Golden Bottle Trust
The Goldman Sachs Charitable Gift Fund (UK)
The Goodman Foundation
The Hemraj Goyal Foundation
The Grace Trust
The Grant Foundation
The Great Britain Sasakawa Foundation
The Green Hall Foundation
The Grimmitt Trust
H. C. D. Memorial Fund
The Alfred Haines Charitable Trust
The Helen Hamlyn Trust
Harbinson Charitable Trust
The Hasluck Charitable Trust
The Hawthorne Charitable Trust
The Headley Trust
The Charlotte Heber-Percy Charitable Trust
The Jane Hodge Foundation
The Holbeck Charitable Trust
The Thomas J. Horne Memorial Trust
The Indigo Trust
The Innocent Foundation
The Inverforth Charitable Trust
The Invigorate Charitable Trust
The J. J. Charitable Trust
The Frank Jackson Foundation
John Jarrold Trust Ltd
The Jephcott Charitable Trust
The Jerusalem Trust
The Elton John Aids Foundation (EJAF)
The Cyril and Eve Jumbo Charitable Trust
The Nancy Kenyon Charitable Trust
The Kyte Charitable Trust
Maurice and Hilda Laing Charitable Trust
The Kirby Laing Foundation
The Martin Laing Foundation
The Leonard Laity Stoate Charitable Trust
The Lancashire Foundation
Langdale Trust
Mrs M. A. Lascelles Charitable Trust
The Leach Fourteenth Trust
The William Leech Charity
John Lewis Foundation
The Linbury Trust
*The Manson Family Charitable Trust**
The Brian Mercer Charitable Trust
The Millennium Oak Trust
The Millichope Foundation
The Morel Charitable Trust
The Morgan Charitable Foundation
The Miles Morland Foundation

The Edwina Mountbatten and Leonora Children's Foundation
Music Sales Charitable Trust
The NDL Foundation
Network for Social Change Charitable Trust
The Northwick Trust
The Olwyn Foundation*
The Gerald Palmer Eling Trust Company
Susanna Peake Charitable Trust
The Pears Family Charitable Foundation
The Pharsalia Charitable Trust
The Pitt-Rivers Charitable Trust
The Portrack Charitable Trust
The Prince of Wales's Charitable Foundation
The Priory Foundation
The Puebla Charitable Trust
The Quilter Foundation*
The Raindance Charitable Trust*
The Ranworth Trust
The Eleanor Rathbone Charitable Trust
The Rhododendron Trust
Riada Trust
The Roan Charitable Trust
The Roddick Foundation
Mrs L. D. Rope's Third Charitable Settlement
The M. J. Samuel Charitable Trust
The Samworth Foundation
The Schroder Foundation
The SDL Foundation
Seedfield Trust
The Archie Sherman Charitable Trust
The Thomas Sivewright Catto Charitable Settlement
Rita and David Slowe Charitable Trust
The SMB Trust
The N. Smith Charitable Settlement
The Sobell Foundation
W. F. Southall Trust
Staples Trust
Stewards Company Ltd
The Support Foundation*
Surgo Foundation UK Ltd
The Hugh Symons Charitable Trust*
C. B. and H. H. Taylor 1984 Trust
The Toy Trust
Tropical Health and Education Trust
The Ulverscroft Foundation
The Albert Van Den Bergh Charitable Trust
The Van Neste Foundation
The Vodafone Foundation
Volant Charitable Trust
The Waterloo Foundation
The Norman Whiteley Trust
The Wimbledon Foundation
The Wixamtree Trust
The Zochonis Charitable Trust
Zurich Community Trust (UK) Ltd

Conflict resolution, peace-building, and disarmament

Allan and Nesta Ferguson Charitable Settlement
The Jacqueline and Michael Gee Charitable Trust
The Golden Bottle Trust
H. C. D. Memorial Fund
Network for Social Change Charitable Trust
The Northwick Trust
The Tolkien Trust
W. F. Southall Trust

Education

The Bestway Foundation
The British and Foreign School Society
The Dashlight Foundation*
Allan and Nesta Ferguson Charitable Settlement
The Gloag Foundation
The Grace Trust
The Headley Trust
The Frank Jackson Foundation
The Jephcott Charitable Trust
John Lewis Foundation
Charity of John Marshall
The Northwick Trust
Riada Trust
The Alan and Babette Sainsbury Charitable Fund
The John Slater Foundation
Standard Life Aberdeen Charitable Foundation
The Sutasoma Trust
C. B. and H. H. Taylor 1984 Trust
The Vodafone Foundation
The Georg and Emily Von Opel Foundation*

Humanitarian aid

The Roger and Sarah Bancroft Clark Charitable Trust
The Bestway Foundation
The Grace Trust
The Northwick Trust
The Samworth Foundation
Seedfield Trust
The Alborada Trust
The Becht Family Charitable Trust
The Allen Trust
The Jacqueline and Michael Gee Charitable Trust
The Gloag Foundation
The Goldman Sachs Charitable Gift Fund (UK)
The Helen Hamlyn Trust
Harbinson Charitable Trust
The Roddick Foundation
The Cyril and Eve Jumbo Charitable Trust
The Ashworth Charitable Trust
The Kyte Charitable Trust
The SMB Trust
The N. Smith Charitable Settlement
Music Sales Charitable Trust
The Pharsalia Charitable Trust
The Eleanor Rathbone Charitable Trust
The Brown Source Trust*
Mrs L. D. Rope's Third Charitable Settlement
The Archie Sherman Charitable Trust
The Rhododendron Trust
The Forte Charitable Trust
The Foxglove Trust
The Goodman Foundation
The Alfred Haines Charitable Trust
The Innocent Foundation
The Elton John Aids Foundation (EJAF)
The Morel Charitable Trust
The Norman Whiteley Trust

Water, sanitation and hygiene

The Alchemy Foundation
Chrysalis Trust
Four Acre Trust
The Headley Trust
The Jephcott Charitable Trust
The Livingston Charitable Trust*
The Eleanor Rathbone Charitable Trust
Seedfield Trust
The Peter Stebbings Memorial Charity
The Stone Family Foundation
Surgo Foundation UK Ltd

Age

Children and young people

The 1989 Willan Charitable Trust
The 4814 Trust
The Aberbrothock Skea Trust
Access Sport CIO
Action Medical Research
*Adam Family Foundation**
The Sylvia Adams Charitable Trust
The Bryan Adams Foundation
The Adint Charitable Trust
The AIM Foundation
The Aimwell Charitable Trust
Sylvia Aitken's Charitable Trust
The Alchemy Foundation
Aldgate and Allhallows Foundation
Al-Fayed Charitable Foundation
The Derrill Allatt Foundation
D. C. R. Allen Charitable Trust
Viscount Amory's Charitable Trust
The AMW Charitable Trust
The Annandale Charitable Trust
The John Apthorp Charity
The Archer Trust
The Ardwick Trust
*The Armed Forces Covenant Fund Trust**
Armed Forces Education Trust
The John Armitage Charitable Trust
The Armourers' and Brasiers' Gauntlet Trust
Arts Council of Wales (also known as Cyngor Celfyddydau Cymru)
ArtSocial Foundation
Ove Arup Partnership Charitable Trust
Keren Association Ltd
The Astor Foundation
Lawrence Atwell's Charity (Skinners' Company)
The Aylesford Family Charitable Trust
Backstage Trust
The Scott Bader Commonwealth Ltd
The Austin Bailey Foundation
Bairdwatson Charitable Trust
The Roy and Pixie Baker Charitable Trust
The Balfour Beatty Charitable Trust
The Ballinger Charitable Trust
The Roger and Sarah Bancroft Clark Charitable Trust
The Band Trust
*Veronica and Lars Bane Foundation**
Bank of Scotland Foundation
The Barbour Foundation
Barcapel Foundation Ltd
The Barclay Foundation
The Philip Barker Charity
The Barker-Mill Foundation
Lord Barnby's Foundation
*The Barnes Fund**
The Barnsbury Charitable Trust
Barnwood Trust
Misses Barrie Charitable Trust
The Batchworth Trust
Battens Charitable Trust
Bauer Radio's Cash for Kids Charities
Bay Charitable Trust
The Louis Baylis (Maidenhead Advertiser) Charitable Trust
Bearder Charity
The James Beattie Charitable Trust
The Beaverbrooks Charitable Trust
The John Beckwith Charitable Trust
Bedfordshire and Luton Community Foundation
Bedfordshire Charitable Trust Ltd
*AJ Bell Trust**
The Benham Charitable Settlement
The Rowan Bentall Charitable Trust
The Berkeley Foundation
Ruth Berkowitz Charitable Trust
The Berkshire Community Foundation
Bideford Bridge Trust
The Percy Bilton Charity
Birmingham International Airport Community Trust Fund
The Sydney Black Charitable Trust
The Isabel Blackman Foundation
The Blagrave Trust
Lady Blakenham's Charity Trust
The Blandford Lake Trust
Bluespark Foundation
The Bluston Charitable Settlement
The Marjory Boddy Charitable Trust
The Boltini Trust
The Bonamy Charitable Trust
The Charlotte Bonham-Carter Charitable Trust
The Boodle & Dunthorne Charitable Trust
Sir William Boreman's Foundation
The Borrows Charitable Trust
The Boshier-Hinton Foundation
*Alan Boswell Group Charitable Trust**
The Bothwell Charitable Trust
The Bowerman Charitable Trust
The Bowland Charitable Trust
The Breadsticks Foundation
The Brelms Trust CIO
The Brenley Trust
Bristol Charities
The BRIT Trust
The British and Foreign School Society
The Brook Trust
*The Brothers Trust**
The Charles Brotherton Trust
The Brownsword Charitable Foundation
The Jack Brunton Charitable Trust
The Buffini Chao Foundation
The Clara E. Burgess Charity
The Burry Charitable Trust
Consolidated Charity of Burton upon Trent
Miss Margaret Butters Reekie Charitable Trust
Byrne Family Foundation
The Cadogan Charity
Community Foundation for Calderdale
The Calleva Foundation
The Cambridgeshire Community Foundation
The Campden Charities Trustee
The Frederick and Phyllis Cann Trust
W. A. Cargill Charitable Trust
The W. A. Cargill Fund
The Carnegie Dunfermline Trust
The Carpenters' Company Charitable Trust
The Casey Trust
The Castanea Trust
The Castang Foundation
The Castansa Trust
Cattanach
The Joseph and Annie Cattle Trust
The Cayo Foundation
The Chadwick Educational Foundation
The Chalk Cliff Trust
Chapman Charitable Trust
The Charter 600 Charity
Chartered Accountants' Livery Charity (CALC)
Cheshire Community Foundation Ltd
The Chetwode Foundation

The Childhood Trust
Children's Liver Disease Foundation
The Childwick Trust
Chippenham Borough Lands Charity
The Chipping Sodbury Town Lands Charity
CHK Foundation
The Church Burgesses Educational Foundation
Church Burgesses Trust
The Churchill Foundation
The CIBC World Markets Children's Foundation
The City Bridge Trust (Bridge House Estates)
CLA Charitable Trust
The Clan Trust Ltd
Clark Foundation
The Clothworkers' Foundation
The Robert Clutterbuck Charitable Trust
FB Coales No4 (Family) Trust*
Colchester Catalyst Charity
The Cole Charitable Trust
John and Freda Coleman Charitable Trust
Colyer-Fergusson Charitable Trust
Comic Relief
Community First
The Connolly Foundation*
The Ernest Cook Trust
The Cooks Charity
The Catherine Cookson Charitable Trust
The Keith Coombs Trust
Co-operative Community Investment Foundation
The J. Reginald Corah Foundation Fund
The Worshipful Company of Cordwainers Charitable Trusts (Minges Gift)
Michael Cornish Charitable Trust
The Evan Cornish Foundation
The Corporation of Trinity House of Deptford Strond
Corra Foundation
Council for World Mission (UK)*
Coutts Charitable Foundation
The Sir Tom Cowie Charitable Trust
Dudley and Geoffrey Cox Charitable Trust
Michael Crawford Children's Charity
Credit Suisse EMEA Foundation
CRH Charitable Trust*
Cripplegate Foundation
The Peter Cruddas Foundation
Cumbria Community Foundation
Itzchok Meyer Cymerman Trust Ltd
The D'Oyly Carte Charitable Trust
Oizer Dalim Trust
The Daniell Trust*
Baron Davenport's Charity
Margaret Davies Charity
The Crispin Davis Family Trust
The Davis Foundation
The De Brye Charitable Trust
The Roger De Haan Charitable Trust
Foundation Derbyshire
Provincial Grand Charity of the Province of Derbyshire
The J. N. Derbyshire Trust
The Dibden Allotments Fund
The Gillian Dickinson Trust
Digital Xtra Fund*
Dorset Community Foundation
Drapers' Charitable Fund
Dromintee Trust
The Anne Duchess of Westminster's Charity
The Dulverton Trust
Dumbreck Charity
Dunlossit and Islay Community Trust*
The Charles Dunstone Charitable Trust
County Durham Community Foundation
The Dyers' Company Charitable Trust
East End Community Foundation
Eastern Counties Educational Trust Ltd
The Gilbert and Eileen Edgar Foundation
Edinburgh Children's Holiday Fund
Dr Edwards Bishop King's Fulham Endowment Fund
The Eight Foundation*
The Eighteen Fund
Elanore Ltd
The Elie Trust*
The Marian Elizabeth Trust
The Wilfred and Elsie Elkes Charity Fund
The Maud Elkington Charitable Trust
The Ellerdale Trust
John Ellerman Foundation
The Emerald Foundation
England and Wales Cricket Trust
The Englefield Charitable Trust
The EQ Foundation
The Essex and Southend Sports Trust
The Essex Youth Trust
The Estelle Trust
The Evelyn Trust
The Everard Foundation
The Eveson Charitable Trust
The ExPat Foundation
Extonglen Ltd
Esmée Fairbairn Foundation
The Fairness Foundation
The Thomas Farr Charity
The George Fentham Birmingham Charity
The Finborough Foundation
Dixie Rose Findlay Charitable Trust
The Fonthill Foundation*
Ford Britain Trust
Oliver Ford Foundation
Forest Hill Charitable Trust
Forever Manchester
Donald Forrester Trust
Four Acre Trust
Fowler Smith and Jones Trust
The Isaac and Freda Frankel Memorial Charitable Trust
The Elizabeth Frankland Moore and Star Foundation
Jill Franklin Trust
The Gordon Fraser Charitable Trust
The Hugh Fraser Foundation
The Louis and Valerie Freedman Charitable Settlement
Charles S. French Charitable Trust
Friarsgate Trust
The Fulmer Charitable Trust
The G. D. Charitable Trust
The Gale Family Charity Trust
The Gannochy Trust
Garfield Weston Foundation
Gatwick Airport Community Trust
The Gaudio Family Foundation (UK) Ltd
Martin Geddes Charitable Trust
Sir Robert Geffery's Almshouse Trust
General Charity (Coventry)
The Generations Foundation
The Steven Gerrard Foundation
The Tara Getty Foundation
The Gibbons Family Trust
The David Gibbons Foundation
The Simon Gibson Charitable Trust
The Glass-House Trust
The Gloag Foundation
Global Charities
County of Gloucestershire Community Foundation
Worshipful Company of Gold and Silver Wyre Drawers Second Charitable Trust Fund

The Golden Bottle Trust
The Goldsmiths' Company Charity
The Golf Foundation Ltd
The Golsoncott Foundation
The Goodman Foundation
The Mike Gooley Trailfinders Charity
Gowling WLG (UK) Charitable Trust
The Hemraj Goyal Foundation
The Grace Trust
The Grant Foundation
The Grantham Yorke Trust
The Gray Trust
Gordon Gray Trust
The Great Stone Bridge Trust of Edenbridge
Philip and Judith Green Trust
Greenham Trust Ltd
*The Greenslade Family Foundation**
The Greggs Foundation
The Gretna Charitable Trust
The Grimmitt Trust
The Grocers' Charity
M. and R. Gross Charities Ltd
The Walter Guinness Charitable Trust
Dr Guthrie's Association
The Hadfield Charitable Trust
The Hadley Trust
The Hadrian Trust
The Alfred Haines Charitable Trust
Halifax Foundation for Northern Ireland
*The Halsall Foundation**
The Hamilton Davies Trust
Paul Hamlyn Foundation
The Helen Hamlyn Trust
Hammersmith United Charities
Hampshire and Isle of Wight Community Foundation
Hampton Fund
The W. A. Handley Charity Trust
The Lennox Hannay Charitable Trust
The Kathleen Hannay Memorial Charity
The Happold Foundation
The Haramead Trust
Harborne Parish Lands Charity
The David and Claudia Harding Foundation
Ros Harding Trust
William Harding's Charity
The Harebell Centenary Fund
The Harpur Trust
The Peter Harrison Foundation
*The Harry and Mary Foundation**
Gay and Peter Hartley's Hillards Charitable Trust
The Hasluck Charitable Trust
The Hawthorne Charitable Trust
Hays Travel Foundation
The Charles Hayward Foundation
The Headley Trust
Heart of England Community Foundation
The Hearth Foundation
Heathrow Community Trust
The Charlotte Heber-Percy Charitable Trust
The Percy Hedley 1990 Charitable Trust
The Hedley Foundation
The Hemby Charitable Trust
The Christina Mary Hendrie Trust
Henley Educational Trust
Henley Royal Regatta Charitable Trust
The Tim Henman Foundation
The G. D. Herbert Charitable Trust
Herefordshire Community Foundation
Hertfordshire Community Foundation
HFC Help For Children UK LTD
P. and C. Hickinbotham Charitable Trust
The Alan Edward Higgs Charity
The Hilden Charitable Fund
R. G. Hills Charitable Trust
Hinchley Charitable Trust
The Hiscox Foundation
The Henry C. Hoare Charitable Trust
The Hobson Charity Ltd
The Holbeck Charitable Trust
Hollick Family Foundation
The Holliday Foundation
Dorothy Holmes Charitable Trust
The Holywood Trust
Homelands Charitable Trust
The Mary Homfray Charitable Trust
Sir Harold Hood's Charitable Trust
The Horners Charity Fund
The Hospital of God at Greatham
Housing Pathways Trust
The Reta Lila Howard Foundation
James T. Howat Charitable Trust
The Hull and East Riding Charitable Trust
The Humanitarian Trust
The Hunter Foundation
Miss Agnes H. Hunter's Trust
The Huntingdon Foundation Ltd
Huntingdon Freemen's Trust
The Nani Huyu Charitable Trust
Hyde Charitable Trust
Hyde Park Place Estate Charity
Ibrahim Foundation Ltd
The Iliffe Family Charitable Trust
Impetus
The Inlight Trust
The Innocent Foundation
Integrated Education Fund
The International Bankers Charitable Trust
International Bible Students Association
The Inverforth Charitable Trust
Investream Charitable Trust
The Invigorate Charitable Trust
The Ireland Fund of Great Britain
Irish Youth Foundation (UK) Ltd (incorporating The Lawlor Foundation)
The J. A. R. Charitable Trust
The J. J. Charitable Trust
The Sir Barry Jackson County Fund
The Frank Jackson Foundation
Lady Eda Jardine Charitable Trust
John Jarrold Trust Ltd
*JD Foundation**
The Jerusalem Trust
Jewish Child's Day (JCD)
The Jewish Youth Fund
Lillie Johnson Charitable Trust
Johnnie Johnson Trust
The Jones 1986 Charitable Trust
The Marjorie and Geoffrey Jones Charitable Trust
The Jordan Charitable Foundation
The Joron Charitable Trust
J. E. Joseph Charitable Fund
The Cyril and Eve Jumbo Charitable Trust
The Boris Karloff Charitable Foundation
*The Karlsson Jativa Charitable Foundation**
The Ian Karten Charitable Trust
The Kasner Charitable Trust
The Emmanuel Kaye Foundation
William Kendall's Charity (Wax Chandlers' Company)
The Kensington and Chelsea Foundation
Kent Community Foundation
The Kentown Wizard Foundation
The Peter Kershaw Trust
*KFC Foundation**
Kidney Research UK

Kilpatrick Fraser Charitable Trust
*The Kilroot Foundation**
The Mary Kinross Charitable Trust
The Kirschel Foundation
Robert Kitchin (Saddlers' Company)
The Ernest Kleinwort Charitable Trust
Sir James Knott Trust
The Kobler Trust
Kolyom Trust Ltd
The KPMG Foundation
The Kreitman Foundation
Kupath Gemach Chaim Bechesed Viznitz Trust
Kusuma Trust UK
The Kyte Charitable Trust
Ladbrokes Coral Trust
John Laing Charitable Trust
Maurice and Hilda Laing Charitable Trust
Christopher Laing Foundation
The David Laing Foundation
The Kirby Laing Foundation
The Martin Laing Foundation
The Beatrice Laing Trust
The Lake House Charity
Community Foundations for Lancashire and Merseyside
Lancashire Environmental Fund Ltd
The Lancashire Foundation
Duchy of Lancaster Benevolent Fund
Lancaster Foundation
LandAid Charitable Trust (LandAid)
Langdale Trust
Largsmount Ltd
Laslett's (Hinton) Charity
Mrs F. B. Laurence Charitable Trust
The Kathleen Laurence Trust
The Law Family Charitable Foundation
The Edgar E. Lawley Foundation
Lawson Beckman Charitable Trust
The Lawson Trust CIO
The David Lean Foundation
The William Leech Charity
Leeds Community Foundation (LCF)
Leicestershire and Rutland Masonic Charity Association
The Leigh Trust
Lempriere Pringle 2015
Leng Charitable Trust
The Mark Leonard Trust
The Leri Charitable Trust
Joseph Levy Foundation
*Cecil and Hilda Lewis Charitable Trust**
Bernard Lewis Family Charitable Trust
David and Ruth Lewis Family Charitable Trust
*The Charles Lewis Foundation**
The Light Fund Company
Limoges Charitable Trust
The Linbury Trust
Lincolnshire Community Foundation
The Linden Charitable Trust
The Linder Foundation
The Frank Litchfield Charitable Trust
Jack Livingstone Charitable Trust
The Ian and Natalie Livingstone Charitable Trust
The Elaine and Angus Lloyd Charitable Trust
The Andrew Lloyd Webber Foundation
Lloyd's Charities Trust
Lloyds Bank Foundation for England and Wales
Lloyds Bank Foundation for the Channel Islands
Lloyd's Patriotic Fund
Local Trent Ltd
The Locker Foundation
Loftus Charitable Trust
London Freemasons Charity
London Housing Foundation Ltd (LHF)
London Legal Support Trust (LLST)
The London Marathon Charitable Trust Ltd
Longleigh Foundation
The Lord's Taverners
LPW Ltd
Lord and Lady Lurgan Trust
The Lyndal Tree Foundation
John Lyon's Charity
Sylvanus Lysons Charity
M. and C. Trust
M. B. Foundation
The R. S. Macdonald Charitable Trust
Mace Foundation
The MacRobert Trust 2019
Makers of Playing Cards Charity
Man Group plc Charitable Trust
The Manackerman Charitable Trust
The Manchester Guardian Society Charitable Trust
R. W. Mann Trust
*The Manson Family Charitable Trust**
Marbeh Torah Trust
The Marks Family Charitable Trust
Marmot Charitable Trust
The Michael Marsh Charitable Trust
D. G. Marshall of Cambridge Trust
The Martin Charitable Trust
Sir George Martin Trust
The Dan Maskell Tennis Trust
Masonic Charitable Foundation
Nancie Massey Charitable Trust
The Master Charitable Trust
Matchroom Sport Charitable Foundation
*The Mather Family Charitable Trust**
The Matliwala Family Charitable Trust
Mayfair Charities Ltd
Mayheights Ltd
Maypride Ltd
MBNA General Foundation
The Robert McAlpine Foundation
McGreevy No. 5 Settlement
D. D. McPhail Charitable Settlement
The Medlock Charitable Trust
The Meikle Foundation
Melodor Ltd
Menuchar Ltd
The Brian Mercer Charitable Trust
The Mercers' Charitable Foundation
The Merchant Venturers' Charity
Merchants' House of Glasgow
T. and J. Meyer Family Foundation Ltd
The Mickel Fund
The Mickleham Trust
The Gerald Micklem Charitable Trust
The Masonic Province of Middlesex Charitable Trust (Middlesex Masonic Charity)
The Millennium Oak Trust
The Ronald Miller Foundation
Mills and Reeve Charitable Trust
The James Milner Foundation
Milton Keynes Community Foundation Ltd
The Peter Minet Trust
Minton Charitable Trust
The Mishcon Family Charitable Trust
The Esmé Mitchell Trust
The Mittal Foundation
*The Mohn Westlake Foundation**
Mole Charitable Trust

*The Monday Charitable Trust**
The Monmouthshire County Council Welsh Church Act Fund
Moondance Foundation
John Moores Foundation
The Steve Morgan Foundation
Morgan Stanley International Foundation
The Morris Charitable Trust
G. M. Morrison Charitable Trust
*The Mosawi Foundation**
Vyoel Moshe Charitable Trust
The Mosselson Charitable Trust
Moto in the Community
Motor Neurone Disease Association
The Edwina Mountbatten and Leonora Children's Foundation
The MSE Charity
The Mulberry Trust
Edith Murphy Foundation
Murphy-Neumann Charity Company Ltd
Brian Murtagh Charitable Trust
Music Sales Charitable Trust
Muslim Hands
The National Express Foundation
The National Lottery Community Fund
The NDL Foundation
Nemoral Ltd
Ner Foundation
Nesswall Ltd
Nesta
Network for Social Change Charitable Trust
Newby Trust Ltd
Newcomen Collett Foundation
Newpier Charity Ltd
The NFU Mutual Charitable Trust
The Nisbet Trust
The Nomura Charitable Trust
Norfolk Community Foundation
Educational Foundation of Alderman John Norman
The Norman Family Charitable Trust
Normanby Charitable Trust
Northamptonshire Community Foundation
Community Foundation for Northern Ireland
The Norton Foundation
Nottinghamshire Community Foundation
Odin Charitable Trust
The Ofenheim Charitable Trust
Oglesby Charitable Trust
Oizer Charitable Trust
Old Possum's Practical Trust
Henry Oldfield Trust
*The Olwyn Foundation**
Ostro Fayre Share Foundation
The O'Sullivan Family Charitable Trust
Ovingdean Hall Foundation
The Ovo Charitable Foundation
The Doris Pacey Charitable Foundation
The Paget Charitable Trust
The James Pantyfedwen Foundation (Ymddiriedolaeth James Pantyfedwen)
The Paphitis Charitable Trust
The Paragon Trust
The Pastoral Care Trust – The St Nicholas Care Fund
Miss M. E. S. Paterson's Charitable Trust
The Patrick Trust
Peacock Charitable Trust
Susanna Peake Charitable Trust
The Pears Family Charitable Foundation
The Pebbles Trust
People's Postcode Trust
The Persimmon Charitable Foundation
The Jack Petchey Foundation
The Phillips and Rubens Charitable Trust
Bernard Piggott Charitable Trust
Pilkington Charities Fund
The Austin and Hope Pilkington Trust
The Sir Harry Pilkington Trust Fund
Miss A. M. Pilkington's Charitable Trust
PIMCO Foundation Europe
The Pixel Fund
The George and Esme Pollitzer Charitable Settlement
The Porta Pia 2012 Foundation
The Portal Trust
The Portishead Nautical Trust
The Portrack Charitable Trust
Postcode Community Trust
Postcode Local Trust
Postcode Society Trust (formerly Postcode Dream Trust)
*Poundland Foundation**
Premierquote Ltd
*Price Parry Charitable Trust**
Sir John Priestman Charity Trust
The Prince of Wales's Charitable Foundation
The Prince's Countryside Fund
The Princess Anne's Charities
The Priory Foundation
Prison Service Charity Fund
The Privy Purse Charitable Trust
The Professional Footballers' Association Charity
The Progress Foundation
Mr and Mrs J. A. Pye's Charitable Settlement
The Queen Anne's Gate Foundation
*The Quilter Foundation**
Quintessentially Foundation
The Monica Rabagliati Charitable Trust
The Radcliffe Trust
Richard Radcliffe Trust
*The Raindance Charitable Trust**
The Rainford Trust
*Randeree Charitable Trust**
The Rathbone Brothers Foundation
The Eleanor Rathbone Charitable Trust
Elizabeth Rathbone Charity
The Ravensdale Trust
The Roger Raymond Charitable Trust
The Rayne Foundation
The John Rayner Charitable Trust
The Sir James Reckitt Charity
Red Hill Charitable Trust
The Reece Foundation
Richard Reeve's Foundation
The Revere Charitable Trust
The Rhododendron Trust
Riada Trust
Humphrey Richardson Taylor Charitable Trust
Richmond Parish Lands Charity
The River Farm Foundation
Rivers Foundation
Rix Thompson Rothenberg Foundation
The Robertson Trust
Robyn Charitable Trust
Rockcliffe Charitable Trust
The Sir James Roll Charitable Trust
The Gerald and Gail Ronson Family Foundation
Rosa Fund
Rosca Trust
The David Ross Foundation
The Rothermere Foundation
The Rothley Trust
The Eranda Rothschild Foundation
The Roughley Charitable Trust
Royal Docks Trust (London)
The Royal Foundation of the Duke and Duchess of Cambridge
Royal Masonic Trust for Girls and Boys

The Royal Navy and Royal Marines Charity
Royal Society of Wildlife Trusts
The Saddlers' Company Charitable Fund
The Alan and Babette Sainsbury Charitable Fund
The Saintbury Trust
The Salamander Charitable Trust
Salters' Charitable Foundation
Samjo Ltd
The Samworth Foundation
The Sandhu Charitable Foundation
Sarum St Michael Educational Charity
The Savoy Educational Trust
Schroder Charity Trust
Foundation Scotland
Francis C. Scott Charitable Trust
The Frieda Scott Charitable Trust
The John Scott Trust Fund
Scottish Property Industry Festival of Christmas (SPIFOX)
Scouloudi Foundation
Seedfield Trust
Leslie Sell Charitable Trust
Shaftoe Educational Foundation
The Shanly Foundation
ShareGift (The Orr Mackintosh Foundation)
The Sheffield Town Trust
The Sheldon Trust
The Patricia and Donald Shepherd Charitable Trust
The Sylvia and Colin Shepherd Charitable Trust
Shetland Charitable Trust
SHINE (Support and Help in Education)
The Bassil Shippam and Alsford Trust
The Shipwrights' Charitable Fund
The Shoe Zone Trust
Sirius Minerals Foundation
The Skelton Bounty
The Charles Skey Charitable Trust
Skipton Building Society Charitable Foundation
The Slaughter and May Charitable Trust
Sloane Robinson Foundation
The Mrs Smith and Mount Trust
The DS Smith Charitable Foundation
The N. Smith Charitable Settlement
Arabella and Julian Smith Family Trust*
The Leslie Smith Foundation
The W. H. Smith Group Charitable Trust
The Sobell Foundation
Sofronie Foundation
Somerset Community Foundation
The South Yorkshire Community Foundation
Southover Manor General Education Trust Ltd
Sparks Charity
Spielman Charitable Trust
The Spoore, Merry and Rixman Foundation
The Spurrell Charitable Trust
The Geoff and Fiona Squire Foundation
The St Hilda's Trust
St James's Place Charitable Foundation
Sir Walter St John's Educational Charity
St John's Foundation Est. 1174
St Olave's and St Saviour's Schools Foundation
St Peter's Saltley Trust
The Stafford Trust
The Community Foundation for Staffordshire
Standard Life Aberdeen Charitable Foundation
The Steinberg Family Charitable Trust
The Hugh Stenhouse Foundation
The Stevenage Community Trust
Stevenson Family's Charitable Trust
Mark Stolkin Foundation
The Stoller Charitable Trust
The Stone Family Foundation
The Samuel Storey Family Charitable Trust
Strand Parishes Trust
Stratford-upon-Avon Town Trust
The WO Street Charitable Foundation
The Street Foundation
The Joseph Strong Frazer Trust*
Suffolk Community Foundation
The Bernard Sunley Foundation
The Support Foundation*
The Sussex Community Foundation
Swan Mountain Trust
The Swann-Morton Foundation
The John Swire (1989) Charitable Trust
The Swire Charitable Trust
The Charles and Elsie Sykes Trust
The T.K. Maxx and Homesense Foundation
The Ashley Tabor-King Foundation*
Taca
The Talbot Trusts
The Talbot Village Trust
Tallow Chandlers Benevolent Fund No. 2
Tanner Trust
Tay Charitable Trust
C. B. and H. H. Taylor 1984 Trust
The Taylor Family Foundation
Stephen Taylor Foundation
A. P. Taylor Trust
The Tedworth Charitable Trust
The Thales Charitable Trust
the7stars Foundation*
The Thornton Trust
The Three Guineas Trust
Three Monkies Trust
Mrs R. P. Tindall's Charitable Trust
The Tolkien Trust
The Tomoro Foundation*
The Tompkins Foundation
Tower Hill Trust
The Toy Trust
The Trades House of Glasgow
Annie Tranmer Charitable Trust
The Trefoil Trust
The Tresanton Trust*
The Triangle Trust (1949) Fund
The Troutsdale Charitable Trust*
The True Colours Trust
Truedene Co. Ltd
Truemart Ltd
Trumros Ltd
The Trusthouse Charitable Foundation
The Tudor Trust
The Tuixen Foundation
The Roger and Douglas Turner Charitable Trust
Two Ridings Community Foundation
Community Foundation serving Tyne and Wear and Northumberland
Tzedakah
UKH Foundation
Ulster Garden Villages Ltd
The Ulverscroft Foundation
The Union of the Sisters of Mercy of Great Britain
United Jewish Israel Appeal
Universal Music UK Sound Foundation
UPP Foundation
The Utley Foundation
The Albert Van Den Bergh Charitable Trust

The Van Neste Foundation
The Vardy Foundation
Variety, the Children's Charity
VHLT Ltd
Nigel Vinson Charitable Trust
The Vintners' Foundation
The Virgin Money Foundation
Vivdale Ltd
Volant Charitable Trust
Wade's Charity
Wakefield and Tetley Trust
Robert and Felicity Waley-Cohen Charitable Trust
Warwick Relief in Need Charity
Mrs Waterhouse Charitable Trust
The Waterloo Foundation
The William Wates Memorial Trust
John Watson's Trust
The Weavers' Company Benevolent Fund
The Weinstock Fund
Wembley National Stadium Trust
West Derby Waste Lands Charity
Westhill Endowment
Westminster Almshouses Foundation
Westminster Amalgamated Charity
Westminster Foundation
Westway Trust
The Barbara Whatmore Charitable Trust
Colonel W. H. Whitbread Charitable Trust
Charity of Sir Richard Whittington
Joan Wilkinson Charitable Trust*
Alfred Williams Charitable Trust
The Williams Family Foundation
The Willmott Dixon Foundation
The Dame Violet Wills Will Trust
The Wilmcote Charitrust
The Wilson Foundation
Wiltshire Community Foundation
The Wimbledon Foundation
The Michael and Anna Wix Charitable Trust
The Lord Leonard and Lady Estelle Wolfson Foundation
The Wolfson Foundation
The Wood Foundation
Wooden Spoon Society
Woodlands Green Ltd
Woodroffe Benton Foundation
The Woodward Charitable Trust
Worth Waynflete Foundation
The Eric Wright Charitable Trust
Wychdale Ltd
The Wyfold Charitable Trust
The Wyndham Charitable Trust
The Wyseliot Rose Charitable Trust
The Yapp Charitable Trust
York Children's Trust
Yorkshire Building Society Charitable Foundation
Youth Music
The Elizabeth and Prince Zaiger Trust
The Marjorie and Arnold Ziff Charitable Foundation
The Zochonis Charitable Trust
Zurich Community Trust (UK) Ltd

Older people

The 1989 Willan Charitable Trust
The 29th May 1961 Charitable Trust
The 4814 Trust
ABF The Soldiers' Charity
Adam Family Foundation*
The Bryan Adams Foundation
The Adint Charitable Trust
The Aimwell Charitable Trust
Sylvia Aitken's Charitable Trust
The Annandale Charitable Trust
The John Apthorp Charity
The Archer Trust
The Armed Forces Covenant Fund Trust*
The John Armitage Charitable Trust
Keren Association Ltd
John Atcheson Foundation*
The Aylesford Family Charitable Trust
The Scott Bader Commonwealth Ltd
The Austin Bailey Foundation
The Ballinger Charitable Trust
The Roger and Sarah Bancroft Clark Charitable Trust
The Band Trust
Bank of Scotland Foundation
Barchester Healthcare Foundation
The Barclay Foundation
Lord Barnby's Foundation
The Barnes Fund*
Misses Barrie Charitable Trust
The Batchworth Trust
Bay Charitable Trust
The Louis Baylis (Maidenhead Advertiser) Charitable Trust
Bearder Charity
The Beaverbrook Foundation
The Beaverbrooks Charitable Trust
Bedfordshire and Luton Community Foundation
Bedfordshire Charitable Trust Ltd
The Benham Charitable Settlement
The Rowan Bentall Charitable Trust
The Berkshire Community Foundation
Bideford Bridge Trust
The Percy Bilton Charity
Birmingham International Airport Community Trust Fund
The Sydney Black Charitable Trust
The Isabel Blackman Foundation
Lady Blakenham's Charity Trust
The Boltini Trust
The Charlotte Bonham-Carter Charitable Trust
The Booth Charities
The Borrows Charitable Trust
The Boshier-Hinton Foundation
The Bothwell Charitable Trust
The Harry Bottom Charitable Trust
The Brelms Trust CIO
Bristol Charities
The Charles Brotherton Trust
Bill Brown 1989 Charitable Trust
R. S. Brownless Charitable Trust
The Brownsword Charitable Foundation
The Jack Brunton Charitable Trust
Buckingham Trust
The Burden Trust
The Burry Charitable Trust
Miss Margaret Butters Reekie Charitable Trust
Community Foundation for Calderdale
Callendar Charitable Trust
W. A. Cargill Charitable Trust
The W. A. Cargill Fund
The Carpenters' Company Charitable Trust
The Castanea Trust
The Castansa Trust
The Joseph and Annie Cattle Trust
The Chalk Cliff Trust
Cheshire Community Foundation Ltd
The Childwick Trust
Chippenham Borough Lands Charity
Church Burgesses Trust

The Churchill Foundation
The City Bridge Trust (Bridge House Estates)
The Clan Trust Ltd
The Clothworkers' Foundation
The Robert Clutterbuck Charitable Trust
Colchester Catalyst Charity
The Cole Charitable Trust
*The George Collins Charity**
*The Connolly Foundation**
The Catherine Cookson Charitable Trust
The J. Reginald Corah Foundation Fund
The Worshipful Company of Cordwainers Charitable Trusts (Minges Gift)
The Cray Trust
Cripplegate Foundation
CSIS Charity Fund
Cumbria Community Foundation
Itzchok Meyer Cymerman Trust Ltd
The D. G. Charitable Settlement
Oizer Dalim Trust
Baron Davenport's Charity
The Davis Foundation
The De Brye Charitable Trust
The Roger De Haan Charitable Trust
The Demigryphon Trust
Provincial Grand Charity of the Province of Derbyshire
The J. N. Derbyshire Trust
The Derek and Eileen Dodgson Foundation
Dromintee Trust
The Anne Duchess of Westminster's Charity
The Dunhill Medical Trust
*Dunlossit and Islay Community Trust**
County Durham Community Foundation
The Gilbert and Eileen Edgar Foundation
Edupoor Ltd
W. G. Edwards Charitable Foundation
*The Eight Foundation**
The Eighteen Fund
The Eighty Eight Foundation
Elanore Ltd
*The Elie Trust**
The Maud Elkington Charitable Trust
John Ellerman Foundation
The Englefield Charitable Trust
The EQ Foundation
The Evelyn Trust
The Everard Foundation
The Eveson Charitable Trust
The ExPat Foundation
Extonglen Ltd
The Fairness Foundation
The Lord Faringdon Charitable Trust
The Thomas Farr Charity
The George Fentham Birmingham Charity
Oliver Ford Foundation
Forever Manchester
Donald Forrester Trust
The Forte Charitable Trust
The Isaac and Freda Frankel Memorial Charitable Trust
The Elizabeth Frankland Moore and Star Foundation
Jill Franklin Trust
The Hugh Fraser Foundation
Charles S. French Charitable Trust
Friarsgate Trust
The Fulmer Charitable Trust
The Gale Family Charity Trust
Gatwick Airport Community Trust
Martin Geddes Charitable Trust
General Charity (Coventry)
The David Gibbons Foundation
The Simon Gibson Charitable Trust
County of Gloucestershire Community Foundation
The Golden Bottle Trust
The Goldsmiths' Company Charity
The Goodman Foundation
Gowling WLG (UK) Charitable Trust
The Graham Trust
The Gray Trust
Gordon Gray Trust
The Green Hall Foundation
Greenham Trust Ltd
The Greggs Foundation
The Gretna Charitable Trust
The Grimmitt Trust
The Grocers' Charity
M. and R. Gross Charities Ltd
The Walter Guinness Charitable Trust
Calouste Gulbenkian Foundation – UK Branch
The Hadfield Charitable Trust
The Hadrian Trust
The Alfred Haines Charitable Trust
*The Halsall Foundation**
The Helen Hamlyn Trust
Hampshire and Isle of Wight Community Foundation
The Hampstead Wells and Campden Trust
Hampton Fund
The W. A. Handley Charity Trust
The Lennox Hannay Charitable Trust
Harborne Parish Lands Charity
Ros Harding Trust
The Edith Lilian Harrison 2000 Foundation
Gay and Peter Hartley's Hillards Charitable Trust
Edward Harvist Trust (The Harvist Estate)
The Hasluck Charitable Trust
The Hawthorne Charitable Trust
The Charles Hayward Foundation
The Headley Trust
Heart of England Community Foundation
The Percy Hedley 1990 Charitable Trust
The Hedley Foundation
The Helping Foundation
The Hemby Charitable Trust
The Christina Mary Hendrie Trust
The G. D. Herbert Charitable Trust
Herefordshire Community Foundation
R. G. Hills Charitable Trust
The Hiscox Foundation
The Henry C. Hoare Charitable Trust
The Hobson Charity Ltd
Dorothy Holmes Charitable Trust
The Mary Homfray Charitable Trust
The Hospital of God at Greatham
Housing Pathways Trust
James T. Howat Charitable Trust
The Hudson Foundation
The Huggard Charitable Trust
The Huntingdon Foundation Ltd
Huntingdon Freemen's Trust
The Nani Huyu Charitable Trust
Ibrahim Foundation Ltd
The Iliffe Family Charitable Trust
The Inlight Trust
The Inman Charity
International Bible Students Association
Investream Charitable Trust
The Invigorate Charitable Trust
The Ireland Fund of Great Britain
The Charles Irving Charitable Trust
The J. A. R. Charitable Trust
John James Bristol Foundation
John Jarrold Trust Ltd
Lillie Johnson Charitable Trust

The Jones 1986 Charitable Trust
The Marjorie and Geoffrey Jones Charitable Trust
The Joron Charitable Trust
J. E. Joseph Charitable Fund
The Kensington and Chelsea Foundation
Kent Community Foundation
The Peter Kershaw Trust
Kidney Research UK
Kilpatrick Fraser Charitable Trust
The Kirschel Foundation
The Ernest Kleinwort Charitable Trust
Sir James Knott Trust
Kolyom Trust Ltd
Kupath Gemach Chaim Bechesed Viznitz Trust
Kusuma Trust UK
Ladbrokes Coral Trust
Maurice and Hilda Laing Charitable Trust
The Kirby Laing Foundation
The Martin Laing Foundation
The Beatrice Laing Trust
The Lake House Charity
Community Foundations for Lancashire and Merseyside
Lancashire Environmental Fund Ltd
Duchy of Lancaster Benevolent Fund
Lancaster Foundation
The Allen Lane Foundation
Langdale Trust
Largsmount Ltd
Laslett's (Hinton) Charity
Mrs F. B. Laurence Charitable Trust
The Edgar E. Lawley Foundation
The Herd Lawson and Muriel Lawson Charitable Trust
Lawson Beckman Charitable Trust
The Lawson Trust CIO
Leeds Community Foundation (LCF)
The Leeward Trust*
Leicestershire and Rutland Masonic Charity Association
Lempriere Pringle 2015
Leng Charitable Trust
The Leri Charitable Trust
Cecil and Hilda Lewis Charitable Trust*
Bernard Lewis Family Charitable Trust
David and Ruth Lewis Family Charitable Trust
The Linbury Trust
Lincolnshire Community Foundation
The Frank Litchfield Charitable Trust
Jack Livingstone Charitable Trust
Lloyd's Charities Trust
Lloyds Bank Foundation for England and Wales
Lloyds Bank Foundation for the Channel Islands
Lloyd's Patriotic Fund
Local Trent Ltd
The Locker Foundation
Loftus Charitable Trust
London Freemasons Charity
London Legal Support Trust (LLST)
The London Marathon Charitable Trust Ltd
Longleigh Foundation
The C. L. Loyd Charitable Trust
LPW Ltd
Lord and Lady Lurgan Trust
M. and C. Trust
M. B. Foundation
The Magdalen and Lasher Charity (General Fund)
The Manchester Guardian Society Charitable Trust
R. W. Mann Trust
Marbeh Torah Trust
Marmot Charitable Trust
The Michael Marsh Charitable Trust
The Martin Charitable Trust
Sir George Martin Trust
The Dan Maskell Tennis Trust
Masonic Charitable Foundation
Nancie Massey Charitable Trust
The Master Charitable Trust
The Matliwala Family Charitable Trust
Mayfair Charities Ltd
Mayheights Ltd
Maypride Ltd
MBNA General Foundation
The Robert McAlpine Foundation
D. D. McPhail Charitable Settlement
The Medlock Charitable Trust
The Meikle Foundation
Melodor Ltd
Menuchar Ltd
The Brian Mercer Charitable Trust
The Mercers' Charitable Foundation
The Merchant Venturers' Charity
Merchants' House of Glasgow
T. and J. Meyer Family Foundation Ltd
The Mickel Fund
The Mickleham Trust
The Gerald Micklem Charitable Trust
The Millennium Oak Trust
Mills and Reeve Charitable Trust
Milton Keynes Community Foundation Ltd
The Peter Minet Trust
Minton Charitable Trust
The Esmé Mitchell Trust
Mole Charitable Trust
The Monday Charitable Trust*
The Monmouthshire County Council Welsh Church Act Fund
Moondance Foundation
John Moores Foundation
The Steve Morgan Foundation
The Morris Charitable Trust
G. M. Morrison Charitable Trust
Vyoel Moshe Charitable Trust
The Mulberry Trust
Edith Murphy Foundation
Murphy-Neumann Charity Company Ltd
Muslim Hands
The National Lottery Community Fund
Nemoral Ltd
Ner Foundation
Nesswall Ltd
Nesta
Network for Social Change Charitable Trust
Newby Trust Ltd
Newpier Charity Ltd
Norfolk Community Foundation
Normanby Charitable Trust
Northamptonshire Community Foundation
Community Foundation for Northern Ireland
Notting Hill Genesis Community Foundation
Nottinghamshire Community Foundation
Odin Charitable Trust
The Ofenheim Charitable Trust
Oglesby Charitable Trust
Oizer Charitable Trust
Old Possum's Practical Trust
The Paget Charitable Trust
The Paphitis Charitable Trust
The Paragon Trust
The Pargiter Trust
The Pastoral Care Trust – The St Nicholas Care Fund
Miss M. E. S. Paterson's Charitable Trust
The Patrick Trust
Susanna Peake Charitable Trust
The Dowager Countess Eleanor Peel Trust

The Persimmon Charitable Foundation
The Phillips and Rubens Charitable Trust
The Phillips Family Charitable Trust
Bernard Piggott Charitable Trust
Elise Pilkington Charitable Trust*
Pilkington Charities Fund
The Sir Harry Pilkington Trust Fund
Miss A. M. Pilkington's Charitable Trust
The George and Esme Pollitzer Charitable Settlement
The Porta Pia 2012 Foundation
The Portrack Charitable Trust
Postcode Community Trust
Postcode Local Trust
Postcode Society Trust (formerly Postcode Dream Trust)
Premierquote Ltd
Price Parry Charitable Trust*
Sir John Priestman Charity Trust
The Prince of Wales's Charitable Foundation
The Pye Foundation
Mr and Mrs J. A. Pye's Charitable Settlement
Quothquan Trust
The Rainford Trust
The Ravensdale Trust
The Rayne Foundation
The John Rayner Charitable Trust
The Sir James Reckitt Charity
The Revere Charitable Trust
The Rhododendron Trust
Richmond Parish Lands Charity
Riverside Charitable Trust Ltd
Rockcliffe Charitable Trust
Rosca Trust
The Rothley Trust
The Eranda Rothschild Foundation
The Roughley Charitable Trust
The Row Fogo Charitable Trust
The Rowlands Trust
The Royal Navy and Royal Marines Charity
The Saddlers' Company Charitable Fund
The Saintbury Trust
The Salamander Charitable Trust
Samjo Ltd
The Frieda Scott Charitable Trust
The Searchlight Electric Charitable Trust
The Shanly Foundation
The Sheffield Town Trust
The Sylvia and Colin Shepherd Charitable Trust
Shetland Charitable Trust
The Bassil Shippam and Alsford Trust
Sirius Minerals Foundation
The Skelton Bounty
The Skerritt Trust
The Charles Skey Charitable Trust
Skipton Building Society Charitable Foundation
The Mrs Smith and Mount Trust
The Sobell Foundation
Somerset Community Foundation
The South Yorkshire Community Foundation
Spielman Charitable Trust
St Monica Trust
The Stafford Trust
The Community Foundation for Staffordshire
The Steinberg Family Charitable Trust
The Stevenage Community Trust
The WO Street Charitable Foundation
The Joseph Strong Frazer Trust*
Suffolk Community Foundation
The Bernard Sunley Foundation
The Support Foundation*
The Sussex Community Foundation
The John Swire (1989) Charitable Trust
The Charles and Elsie Sykes Trust
The Talbot Trusts
The Talbot Village Trust
Tanner Trust
Tay Charitable Trust
C. B. and H. H. Taylor 1984 Trust
A. P. Taylor Trust
The Thornton Trust
The Tolkien Trust
Tower Hill Trust
David William Traill Cargill Fund
Truedene Co. Ltd
Truemart Ltd
Trumros Ltd
The Trusthouse Charitable Foundation
The Tudor Trust
Two Ridings Community Foundation
Community Foundation serving Tyne and Wear and Northumberland
Tzedakah
UKH Foundation
Ulster Garden Villages Ltd
The Union of the Sisters of Mercy of Great Britain
United St Saviour's Charity
The Albert Van Den Bergh Charitable Trust
The William and Patricia Venton Charitable Trust
VHLT Ltd
Nigel Vinson Charitable Trust
Vivdale Ltd
Wade's Charity
Wakefield and Tetley Trust
Warwick Relief in Need Charity
The Welsh Church Act Fund
West Derby Waste Lands Charity
Westminster Almshouses Foundation
Westminster Amalgamated Charity
Charity of Sir Richard Whittington
The Williams Family Foundation
The Wilmcote Charitrust
J. and J. R. Wilson Trust
Wiltshire Community Foundation
The Francis Winham Foundation
The Michael and Anna Wix Charitable Trust
The Wolfson Family Charitable Trust
The Lord Leonard and Lady Estelle Wolfson Foundation
The Wolfson Foundation
Woodlands Green Ltd
Woodroffe Benton Foundation
Worth Waynflete Foundation
The Eric Wright Charitable Trust
Wychdale Ltd
The Wyfold Charitable Trust
The Wyseliot Rose Charitable Trust
The Yapp Charitable Trust
Yorkshire Building Society Charitable Foundation
The Elizabeth and Prince Zaiger Trust
The Marjorie and Arnold Ziff Charitable Foundation
The Zochonis Charitable Trust
Zurich Community Trust (UK) Ltd

Beneficial groups

Disability

The 29th May 1961 Charitable Trust
The 4814 Trust
The Aberbrothock Skea Trust
Access Sport CIO
The Adint Charitable Trust
The Aimwell Charitable Trust
Sylvia Aitken's Charitable Trust
The Alchemy Foundation
D. C. R. Allen Charitable Trust
The Ammco Trust
The AMW Charitable Trust
Andor Charitable Trust
The Anson Charitable Trust
The Archer Trust
The Ardwick Trust
The Arsenal Foundation
Douglas Arter Foundation
ArtSocial Foundation
The Astor Foundation
John Atcheson Foundation*
Axis Foundation
The Baily Thomas Charitable Fund
The Band Trust
Barchester Healthcare Foundation
The Barclay Foundation
The Barker-Mill Foundation
The Barnsbury Charitable Trust
Barnwood Trust
Misses Barrie Charitable Trust
The Batchworth Trust
Battens Charitable Trust
The Battersea Power Station Foundation
Bauer Radio's Cash for Kids Charities
The James Beattie Charitable Trust
Bedfordshire and Luton Community Foundation
AJ Bell Trust*
The Benham Charitable Settlement
The Rowan Bentall Charitable Trust
The Berkeley Foundation
Bideford Bridge Trust
The Big Yellow Foundation*
The Percy Bilton Charity
Birmingham International Airport Community Trust Fund
The Michael Bishop Foundation
Maria Bjornson Memorial Fund*
Lady Blakenham's Charity Trust
The Marjory Boddy Charitable Trust
BOOST Charitable Trust
The Boshier-Hinton Foundation
The Bothwell Charitable Trust
The Harry Bottom Charitable Trust
The Liz and Terry Bramall Foundation
The Brelms Trust CIO
Bristol Charities
The Britford Bridge Trust
British Council for Prevention of Blindness
British Eye Research Foundation (Fight for Sight)
Bill Brown 1989 Charitable Trust
R. S. Brownless Charitable Trust
The Brownsword Charitable Foundation
The Jack Brunton Charitable Trust
The Bruntwood Charity
Miss Margaret Butters Reekie Charitable Trust
William A. Cadbury Charitable Trust
CareTech Foundation*
The W. A. Cargill Fund
The Leslie Mary Carter Charitable Trust
The Casey Trust
The Joseph and Annie Cattle Trust
The Amelia Chadwick Trust
Champneys Charitable Foundation
The Charities Advisory Trust
Cheshire Community Foundation Ltd
The Childwick Trust
Chippenham Borough Lands Charity
The Chipping Sodbury Town Lands Charity
The Christabella Charitable Trust
Chrysalis Trust
The Churchill Foundation
The City Bridge Trust (Bridge House Estates)
CLA Charitable Trust
The Clan Trust Ltd
The Clothworkers' Foundation
The Clover Trust
The Vivienne and Samuel Cohen Charitable Trust
Colchester Catalyst Charity
The Catherine Cookson Charitable Trust
The J. Reginald Corah Foundation Fund
The Worshipful Company of Cordwainers Charitable Trusts (Minges Gift)
Michael Cornish Charitable Trust
Cornwall Community Foundation
Corra Foundation
The Sir William Coxen Trust Fund
The Lord Cozens-Hardy Trust
Michael Crawford Children's Charity
CRH Charitable Trust*
Cruden Foundation Ltd
The D'Oyly Carte Charitable Trust
The Daniell Trust*
The Davis Foundation
The De Brye Charitable Trust
The Roger De Haan Charitable Trust
Provincial Grand Charity of the Province of Derbyshire
The J. N. Derbyshire Trust
Devon Community Foundation
The Dibden Allotments Fund
The Gillian Dickinson Trust
The Dischma Charitable Trust
William and Frances Dobie Charitable Foundation*
Dorset Community Foundation
Drapers' Charitable Fund
The Anne Duchess of Westminster's Charity
Dumbreck Charity
Dunlossit and Islay Community Trust*
The Charles Dunstone Charitable Trust
County Durham Community Foundation
Eastern Counties Educational Trust Ltd
EBM Charitable Trust
Edupoor Ltd
The Eight Foundation*
The Eighteen Fund
The Elie Trust*
The Marian Elizabeth Trust
The Wilfred and Elsie Elkes Charity Fund
The Ellerdale Trust
The Emerton-Christie Charity
The EQ Foundation
The Everard Foundation
The Eveson Charitable Trust
The Fairness Foundation
The Fairstead Trust
The Lord Faringdon Charitable Trust
Samuel William Farmer Trust
The Thomas Farr Charity
The February Foundation
The George Fentham Birmingham Charity
The A. M. Fenton Trust
The Feoffees of St Michael's Spurriergate York

The Fidelity UK Foundation
Dixie Rose Findlay Charitable Trust
Sir John Fisher Foundation
The Earl Fitzwilliam Charitable Trust
The Robert Fleming Hannay Memorial Charity
The Joyce Fletcher Charitable Trust
The Follett Trust
The Forbes Charitable Foundation
Ford Britain Trust
Oliver Ford Foundation
Forest Hill Charitable Trust
The Lady Forester Trust
The Forman Hardy Charitable Trust
Donald Forrester Trust
Foux Foundation*
Fowler Smith and Jones Trust
The Foyle Foundation
The Gordon Fraser Charitable Trust
The Hugh Fraser Foundation
The Joyce and Norman Freed Charitable Trust*
The Louis and Valerie Freedman Charitable Settlement
Charles S. French Charitable Trust
Friarsgate Trust
Frognal Trust
The Patrick and Helena Frost Foundation
The Fulmer Charitable Trust
The G. D. Charitable Trust
Gatwick Airport Community Trust
The Robert Gavron Charitable Trust
General Charity (Coventry)
The Generations Foundation
The Steven Gerrard Foundation
The Tara Getty Foundation
The David Gibbons Foundation
The B. and P. Glasser Charitable Trust
County of Gloucestershire Community Foundation
Sydney and Phyllis Goldberg Memorial Charitable Trust
The Goldcrest Charitable Trust*
The Golden Bottle Trust
The Goldsmiths' Company Charity
The Goodman Foundation
The Gosling Foundation Ltd
The Edward Gostling Foundation
Gowling WLG (UK) Charitable Trust
The Hemraj Goyal Foundation
The Grace Trust
The Graham Trust
The Green Hall Foundation
Greenham Trust Ltd
The Greggs Foundation
The Grocers' Charity
The Walter Guinness Charitable Trust
The Hadley Trust
The Hadrian Trust
The Alfred Haines Charitable Trust
Halifax Foundation for Northern Ireland
The Halsall Foundation*
Hampshire and Isle of Wight Community Foundation
The Hampstead Wells and Campden Trust
Hampton Fund
The W. A. Handley Charity Trust
The Lennox Hannay Charitable Trust
The Haramead Trust
Harborne Parish Lands Charity
The Harbour Foundation
William Harding's Charity
The Harebell Centenary Fund
The Harris Family Charitable Trust
The Edith Lilian Harrison 2000 Foundation
The Peter Harrison Foundation
The Harrison-Frank Family Foundation (UK) Ltd
Gay and Peter Hartley's Hillards Charitable Trust
The Hasluck Charitable Trust
The Maurice Hatter Foundation
The Hawthorne Charitable Trust
The Headley Trust
May Hearnshaw's Charity
Heart of England Community Foundation
The Hedley Foundation
Help for Health
The Hemby Charitable Trust
The Tim Henman Foundation
The G. D. Herbert Charitable Trust
Herefordshire Community Foundation
The Hillier Trust
R. G. Hills Charitable Trust
The Lady Hind Trust
The Henry C. Hoare Charitable Trust
The Hobson Charity Ltd
The Jane Hodge Foundation
Hollick Family Foundation
Dorothy Holmes Charitable Trust
The Holywood Trust
The Mary Homfray Charitable Trust
The Thomas J. Horne Memorial Trust
The Horners Charity Fund
The Hospital of God at Greatham
The Hospital Saturday Fund
Housing Pathways Trust
The Hudson Foundation
The Huggard Charitable Trust
The Humanitarian Trust
The Albert Hunt Trust
Miss Agnes H. Hunter's Trust
IBM United Kingdom Trust
The Iliffe Family Charitable Trust
The Inflexion Foundation*
The Inman Charity
Investream Charitable Trust
The Invigorate Charitable Trust
Irish Youth Foundation (UK) Ltd (incorporating The Lawlor Foundation)
The Charles Irving Charitable Trust
The J. and J. Benevolent Foundation
Lady Eda Jardine Charitable Trust
John Jarrold Trust Ltd
The Roger and Jean Jefcoate Trust
Jeffrey Charitable Trust*
Jewish Child's Day (JCD)
Lillie Johnson Charitable Trust
The Johnson Foundation
Johnnie Johnson Trust
The Jones 1986 Charitable Trust
The Marjorie and Geoffrey Jones Charitable Trust
The Muriel Jones Foundation
J. E. Joseph Charitable Fund
The Cyril and Eve Jumbo Charitable Trust
Anton Jurgens Charitable Trust
The Ian Karten Charitable Trust
The Michael and Ilse Katz Foundation
The Kennedy Trust for Rheumatology Research
The Kensington and Chelsea Foundation
Kent Community Foundation
The Kentown Wizard Foundation
The Peter Kershaw Trust
The Ursula Keyes Trust
Kilpatrick Fraser Charitable Trust
The Graham Kirkham Foundation
The Kirschel Foundation

The Ernest Kleinwort Charitable Trust
Sir James Knott Trust
The Kobler Trust
Ladbrokes Coral Trust
Christopher Laing Foundation
The David Laing Foundation
The Beatrice Laing Trust
The Leonard Laity Stoate Charitable Trust
The Lake House Charity
Duchy of Lancaster Benevolent Fund
The R. J. Larg Family Trust
Mrs F. B. Laurence Charitable Trust
The Law Family Charitable Foundation
The Edgar E. Lawley Foundation
The Lawson Trust CIO
The Leach Fourteenth Trust
The Leathersellers' Company Charitable Fund
Leeds Building Society Charitable Foundation
*The Leeward Trust**
Leicestershire and Rutland Masonic Charity Association
The Kennedy Leigh Charitable Trust
The Leri Charitable Trust
*Cecil and Hilda Lewis Charitable Trust**
David and Ruth Lewis Family Charitable Trust
The Linbury Trust
The Linden Charitable Trust
The Linder Foundation
The Lindley Foundation (TLF)
The Frank Litchfield Charitable Trust
The Charles Littlewood Hill Trust
Jack Livingstone Charitable Trust
The Elaine and Angus Lloyd Charitable Trust
The W. M. and B. W. Lloyd Trust
Lloyds Bank Foundation for England and Wales
Lloyds Bank Foundation for the Channel Islands
The Locker Foundation
London Catalyst
The London Community Foundation (LCF)
Longleigh Foundation
The Lord's Taverners
The Henry Lumley Charitable Trust
Lord and Lady Lurgan Trust
The Lyndal Tree Foundation
John Lyon's Charity
M. and C. Trust
The R. S. Macdonald Charitable Trust
The Macdonald-Buchanan Charitable Trust
The Manackerman Charitable Trust
The Manchester Guardian Society Charitable Trust
R. W. Mann Trust
*The Manson Family Charitable Trust**
*The Marandi Foundation**
The Michael Marsh Charitable Trust
The Marsh Christian Trust
Charlotte Marshall Charitable Trust
D. G. Marshall of Cambridge Trust
The Martin Charitable Trust
Sir George Martin Trust
John Martin's Charity
The Dan Maskell Tennis Trust
Nancie Massey Charitable Trust
The Master Charitable Trust
*Material World Foundation**
*The Mather Family Charitable Trust**
MBNA General Foundation
The Robert McAlpine Foundation
*Gemma and Chris McGough Charitable Foundation CIO**
D. D. McPhail Charitable Settlement
The Medicash Foundation
Merchants' House of Glasgow
T. and J. Meyer Family Foundation Ltd
The Mickleham Trust
The Gerald Micklem Charitable Trust
Hugh and Mary Miller Bequest Trust
The Ronald Miller Foundation
The Clare Milne Trust
Milton Keynes Community Foundation Ltd
The Mishcon Family Charitable Trust
The Brian Mitchell Charitable Settlement
Keren Mitzvah Trust
Mobbs Memorial Trust Ltd
Mole Charitable Trust
The Monmouthshire County Council Welsh Church Act Fund
The Morgan Charitable Foundation
The Steve Morgan Foundation
The Morris Charitable Trust
The Ken and Lynne Morrison Charitable Trust
G. M. Morrison Charitable Trust
The Ken and Edna Morrison Charitable Trust
The Morrisons Foundation
The Morton Charitable Trust (Dundee)
The Mosselson Charitable Trust
The MSE Charity
The Mulberry Trust
Edith Murphy Foundation
Murphy-Neumann Charity Company Ltd
Brian Murtagh Charitable Trust
Music Sales Charitable Trust
Muslim Hands
The Janet Nash Charitable Settlement
Newby Trust Ltd
Norfolk Community Foundation
The Norman Family Charitable Trust
North East Area Miners' Social Welfare Trust Fund
Northamptonshire Community Foundation
Community Foundation for Northern Ireland
The Northwick Trust
The Norton Foundation
Norwich Town Close Estate Charity
The Oakdale Trust
Odin Charitable Trust
Oizer Charitable Trust
One Community Foundation Ltd
The O'Sullivan Family Charitable Trust
Ovingdean Hall Foundation
The Owen Family Trust
Oxfordshire Community Foundation
The Paragon Trust
The Pastoral Care Trust – The St Nicholas Care Fund
Miss M. E. S. Paterson's Charitable Trust
The Patrick Trust
Payne-Gallwey 1989 Charitable Trust
Susanna Peake Charitable Trust
The Pears Family Charitable Foundation
People's Postcode Trust
The Pharsalia Charitable Trust
The Phillips and Rubens Charitable Trust
The Phillips Family Charitable Trust
Bernard Piggott Charitable Trust
PIMCO Foundation Europe

The George and Esme Pollitzer Charitable Settlement
The Portishead Nautical Trust
The Portrack Charitable Trust
The Prince of Wales's Charitable Foundation
Prison Service Charity Fund
The Professional Footballers' Association Charity
The Purey Cust Trust CIO
Mr and Mrs J. A. Pye's Charitable Settlement
QBE European Operations Foundation
Quartet Community Foundation
Queen Mary's Roehampton Trust
The Monica Rabagliati Charitable Trust
The Radcliffe Trust
Richard Radcliffe Trust
The Rainford Trust
Elizabeth Rathbone Charity
The Rayne Foundation
The John Rayner Charitable Trust
C. A. Redfern Charitable Foundation
The Rest-Harrow Trust
Reuben Foundation
The Rhododendron Trust
The Clive and Sylvia Richards Charity Ltd
Richmond Parish Lands Charity
Rigby Foundation
RNID (The Royal National Institute for Deaf People)
The Robertson Trust
The Dezna Robins Jones Charitable Foundation
The Sir James Roll Charitable Trust
Mrs L. D. Rope's Third Charitable Settlement
Rosca Trust
The Rothley Trust
The Eranda Rothschild Foundation
The Roughley Charitable Trust
The Rowlands Trust
Royal Docks Trust (London)
S. and R. Charitable Trust
The Jeremy and John Sacher Charitable Trust
The Saddlers' Company Charitable Fund
The Saintbury Trust
The Saints and Sinners Trust Ltd
The Salamander Charitable Trust
Samjo Ltd
The Basil Samuel Charitable Trust
The Sandhu Charitable Foundation
O. and G. Schreiber Charitable Trust
Scott (Eredine) Charitable Trust
The Frieda Scott Charitable Trust
The John Scott Trust Fund
The Scottish Power Foundation
Scottish Property Industry Festival of Christmas (SPIFOX)
Scouloudi Foundation
Sam and Bella Sebba Charitable Trust
The Shanly Foundation
The Shears Foundation
The Sheffield Town Trust
The Sheldon Trust
The Shipwrights' Charitable Fund
The Thomas Sivewright Catto Charitable Settlement
The Skelton Bounty
The Charles Skey Charitable Trust
The Mrs Smith and Mount Trust
The N. Smith Charitable Settlement
The R. C. Snelling Charitable Trust
The Sobell Foundation
David Solomons Charitable Trust
Spielman Charitable Trust
The Spurrell Charitable Trust
The Geoff and Fiona Squire Foundation
St James's Place Charitable Foundation
St Monica Trust
The Peter Stebbings Memorial Charity
The Steinberg Family Charitable Trust
The Sir Sigmund Sternberg Charitable Foundation
The Stewarts Law Foundation
Strand Parishes Trust
The Strangward Trust
The WO Street Charitable Foundation
The Street Foundation
The Joseph Strong Frazer Trust*
The Summerfield Charitable Trust
The Bernard Sunley Foundation
The Swann-Morton Foundation
The Swire Charitable Trust
The Charles and Elsie Sykes Trust
The Talbot Trusts
The Talbot Village Trust
Tallow Chandlers Benevolent Fund No. 2
Tanner Trust
Tay Charitable Trust
C. B. and H. H. Taylor 1984 Trust
A. P. Taylor Trust
The Thales Charitable Trust
Sir Jules Thorn Charitable Trust
The Three Guineas Trust
The Tobacco Pipe Makers and Tobacco Trade Benevolent Fund
The Tory Family Foundation
Tower Hill Trust
The Toy Trust
Annie Tranmer Charitable Trust
The Constance Travis Charitable Trust
The Trefoil Trust
The James Tudor Foundation
The Tudor Trust
The Tuixen Foundation
The Roger and Douglas Turner Charitable Trust
UKH Foundation
Ulster Garden Villages Ltd
The Ulverscroft Foundation
The Valiant Charitable Trust
The Albert Van Den Bergh Charitable Trust
The Van Mesdag Fund*
Variety, the Children's Charity
Vinci UK Foundation*
Nigel Vinson Charitable Trust
Sylvia Waddilove Foundation UK
The Bruce Wake Charitable Trust
Wakefield and Tetley Trust
The Walker Trust
The Barbara Ward Children's Foundation
The Warwickshire Masonic Charitable Association Ltd
Mrs Waterhouse Charitable Trust
G. R. Waters Charitable Trust 2000
Wates Family Enterprise Trust
The Wates Foundation
John Watson's Trust
The William Webster Charitable Trust
The Weinstock Fund
The James Weir Foundation
The Welsh Church Act Fund
Wembley National Stadium Trust
The Westcroft Trust
The Westfield Health Charitable Trust
Westminster Amalgamated Charity
The Whinfell Charitable Fund

White Stuff Foundation
The Will Charitable Trust
The Williams Family Foundation
The Willmott Dixon Foundation
The Francis Winham Foundation
The Michael and Anna Wix Charitable Trust
The Wolfson Family Charitable Trust
The Lord Leonard and Lady Estelle Wolfson Foundation
The Wolfson Foundation
Wooden Spoon Society
The Woodward Charitable Trust
Worth Waynflete Foundation
The Wyseliot Rose Charitable Trust
The Yapp Charitable Trust
York Children's Trust
Yorkshire Building Society Charitable Foundation
Youth Music
The Elizabeth and Prince Zaiger Trust
Zurich Community Trust (UK) Ltd

■ People with a cognitive or learning disability

Douglas Arter Foundation
The Baily Thomas Charitable Fund
The Battersea Power Station Foundation
*The Big Yellow Foundation**
The Percy Bilton Charity
*Maria Bjornson Memorial Fund**
The Boshier-Hinton Foundation
*CareTech Foundation**
The Clothworkers' Foundation
Colchester Catalyst Charity
The J. Reginald Corah Foundation Fund
*CRH Charitable Trust**
*The Daniell Trust**
Eastern Counties Educational Trust Ltd
EBM Charitable Trust
The Ellerdale Trust
The Eveson Charitable Trust
The Forbes Charitable Foundation
Oliver Ford Foundation
The Foyle Foundation
Halifax Foundation for Northern Ireland
The Peter Harrison Foundation
Help for Health
The Albert Hunt Trust
The Charles Irving Charitable Trust
The J. J. Charitable Trust
The Muriel Jones Foundation
The Ian Karten Charitable Trust
Kilpatrick Fraser Charitable Trust
The Mark Leonard Trust
Lloyds Bank Foundation for England and Wales
The Lord's Taverners
John Lyon's Charity
Sir George Martin Trust
The Dan Maskell Tennis Trust
*Material World Foundation**
*The Mather Family Charitable Trust**
The MSE Charity
The Norman Family Charitable Trust
Odin Charitable Trust
The Portishead Nautical Trust
The Purey Cust Trust CIO
Mr and Mrs J. A. Pye's Charitable Settlement
Queen Mary's Roehampton Trust
Rix Thompson Rothenberg Foundation
The Sir James Roll Charitable Trust
The Roughley Charitable Trust
The Saddlers' Company Charitable Fund
Scottish Property Industry Festival of Christmas (SPIFOX)
The Sheldon Trust
The Mrs Smith and Mount Trust
The Leslie Smith Foundation
David Solomons Charitable Trust
The Strangward Trust
*The Joseph Strong Frazer Trust**
The Charles and Elsie Sykes Trust
The Templeton Goodwill Trust
The Three Guineas Trust
The True Colours Trust
The Tuixen Foundation
Ulster Garden Villages Ltd
The Barbara Ward Children's Foundation
The Will Charitable Trust
The Lord Leonard and Lady Estelle Wolfson Foundation

■ People with a physical disability

The 29th May 1961 Charitable Trust
The Adint Charitable Trust
Douglas Arter Foundation
ArtSocial Foundation
The Barker-Mill Foundation
The Barnsbury Charitable Trust
The Benham Charitable Settlement
*The Big Yellow Foundation**
The Percy Bilton Charity
*Maria Bjornson Memorial Fund**
Lady Blakenham's Charity Trust
The Boshier-Hinton Foundation
British Council for Prevention of Blindness
British Eye Research Foundation (Fight for Sight)
*CareTech Foundation**
The Charities Advisory Trust
The Clothworkers' Foundation
The J. Reginald Corah Foundation Fund
The Worshipful Company of Cordwainers Charitable Trusts (Minges Gift)
*CRH Charitable Trust**
The De Brye Charitable Trust
The Dibden Allotments Fund
EBM Charitable Trust
The Wilfred and Elsie Elkes Charity Fund
The Ellerdale Trust
The Eveson Charitable Trust
Worshipful Company of Glovers of London Charitable Trust
The Greggs Foundation
The Peter Harrison Foundation
Help for Health
The Albert Hunt Trust
The Charles Irving Charitable Trust
The Roger and Jean Jefcoate Trust
The Ian Karten Charitable Trust
*Cecil and Hilda Lewis Charitable Trust**
The Frank Litchfield Charitable Trust
Lloyds Bank Foundation for England and Wales
The Lord's Taverners
John Lyon's Charity
The R. S. Macdonald Charitable Trust
Sir George Martin Trust
The Dan Maskell Tennis Trust
*Material World Foundation**
*The Mather Family Charitable Trust**
Brian Murtagh Charitable Trust
Newby Trust Ltd
The Norman Family Charitable Trust

Payne-Gallwey 1989 Charitable Trust
The Purey Cust Trust CIO
Mr and Mrs J. A. Pye's Charitable Settlement
Queen Mary's Roehampton Trust
Richard Radcliffe Trust
Riada Trust
Rosca Trust
The Saddlers' Company Charitable Fund
Scottish Property Industry Festival of Christmas (SPIFOX)
The Strangward Trust
*The Joseph Strong Frazer Trust**
The Charles and Elsie Sykes Trust
The Talbot Trusts
The Templeton Goodwill Trust
The True Colours Trust
The Tuixen Foundation
Ulster Garden Villages Ltd
The Ulverscroft Foundation
*Vision Foundation**
The Welsh Church Act Fund
The Will Charitable Trust
The Elizabeth and Prince Zaiger Trust

Gender and sexuality

The Scott Bader Commonwealth Ltd
The Baring Foundation
Cornwall Community Foundation
Coutts Charitable Foundation
The J. N. Derbyshire Trust
The Dischma Charitable Trust
The Hemraj Goyal Foundation
*The Gynaecological Cancer Fund**
The Hadrian Trust
Paul Hamlyn Foundation
Harborne Parish Lands Charity
P. and C. Hickinbotham Charitable Trust
The Hilden Charitable Fund
Impact Funding Partners Ltd
The Elton John Aids Foundation (EJAF)
The Kreitman Foundation
The Beatrice Laing Trust
The Allen Lane Foundation
Moondance Foundation
The Mosselson Charitable Trust
The NDL Foundation
Community Foundation for Northern Ireland
The Pilgrim Trust
PIMCO Foundation Europe
The Eleanor Rathbone Charitable Trust
Elizabeth Rathbone Charity
Rosa Fund
The Alan and Babette Sainsbury Charitable Fund
Smallwood Trust
Staples Trust
The Peter Stebbings Memorial Charity
A. P. Taylor Trust
Volant Charitable Trust
Wakefield and Tetley Trust
Wembley National Stadium Trust
WWDP (World Day of Prayer National Committee for England, Wales and Northern Ireland)

■ LGBTQ+

The Baring Foundation
The Fairness Foundation
The Elton John Aids Foundation (EJAF)
The Kreitman Foundation
The London Community Foundation (LCF)
The Mishcon Family Charitable Trust
The Sigrid Rausing Trust
The Stafford Trust

■ Women and girls

The Scott Bader Commonwealth Ltd
The Brook Trust
Comic Relief
Cornwall Community Foundation
Coutts Charitable Foundation
The J. N. Derbyshire Trust
The Dischma Charitable Trust
The Fairness Foundation
The Hemraj Goyal Foundation
*The Gynaecological Cancer Fund**
The Hadrian Trust
Paul Hamlyn Foundation
Harborne Parish Lands Charity
P. and C. Hickinbotham Charitable Trust
The Hilden Charitable Fund
Hollick Family Foundation
P. H. Holt Foundation
Impact Funding Partners Ltd
The Elton John Aids Foundation (EJAF)
The Beatrice Laing Trust
The Allen Lane Foundation
The Leathersellers' Company Charitable Fund
The London Community Foundation (LCF)
The Marsh Christian Trust
Moondance Foundation
John Moores Foundation
The Mosselson Charitable Trust
The NDL Foundation
Community Foundation for Northern Ireland
*The Olwyn Foundation**
The Pilgrim Trust
PIMCO Foundation Europe
The Eleanor Rathbone Charitable Trust
Elizabeth Rathbone Charity
The Sigrid Rausing Trust
The Rayne Foundation
The Robertson Trust
Rosa Fund
The Alan and Babette Sainsbury Charitable Fund
Smallwood Trust
The Stafford Trust
Staples Trust
The Peter Stebbings Memorial Charity
A. P. Taylor Trust
Volant Charitable Trust
Wakefield and Tetley Trust
Wellbeing of Women
Wembley National Stadium Trust
*Women's Fund for Scotland**
The Woodward Charitable Trust
WWDP (World Day of Prayer National Committee for England, Wales and Northern Ireland)

Health

The 29th May 1961 Charitable Trust
4 Charity Foundation
The 4814 Trust
The Aberbrothock Skea Trust
The Aberdeen Foundation
The Sylvia Adams Charitable Trust
The Adint Charitable Trust
The AEB Charitable Trust
The Aimwell Charitable Trust
The Alborada Trust
The Alchemy Foundation
Al-Fayed Charitable Foundation
The Derrill Allatt Foundation
D. C. R. Allen Charitable Trust
Alliance Family Foundation Ltd
The AMW Charitable Trust
Andor Charitable Trust
The Annandale Charitable Trust
The Anson Charitable Trust
The Ardeola Charitable Trust

The Ardwick Trust
The Arsenal Foundation
The Artemis Charitable Foundation
ArtSocial Foundation
Ove Arup Partnership Charitable Trust
Asthma UK
The Lord Austin Trust
The Scott Bader Commonwealth Ltd
The Balcombe Charitable Trust
The Band Trust
The Barbers' Company General Charities
The Barbour Foundation
Barcapel Foundation Ltd
The Barker-Mill Foundation
The Barnes Fund*
The Barnsbury Charitable Trust
Barnwood Trust
Misses Barrie Charitable Trust
The Batchworth Trust
Battens Charitable Trust
Bauer Radio's Cash for Kids Charities
The Bay Tree Charitable Trust
Bearder Charity
The Beaverbrook Foundation
The Beaverbrooks Charitable Trust
AJ Bell Trust*
The Bellahouston Bequest Fund
Benesco Charity Ltd
The Benham Charitable Settlement
Ruth Berkowitz Charitable Trust
The Bestway Foundation
Bideford Bridge Trust
The Percy Bilton Charity
The Bingham Trust
The Birmingham District Nursing Charitable Trust
Maria Bjornson Memorial Fund*
The John Black Charitable Foundation
The Isabel Blackman Foundation
Lady Blakenham's Charity Trust
Bloodwise
The Bluston Charitable Settlement
The Boltini Trust
The Booth Charities
The Harry Bottom Charitable Trust
Sir Clive Bourne Family Trust
The Bowerman Charitable Trust
The Tony Bramall Charitable Trust
The Liz and Terry Bramall Foundation
The Breadsticks Foundation
The Breast Cancer Research Trust (BCRT)
Bristol Charities
The Britford Bridge Trust
British Council for Prevention of Blindness
British Heart Foundation (BHF)
British Lung Foundation
Bill Brown 1989 Charitable Trust
R. S. Brownless Charitable Trust
The Bruntwood Charity
E. F. Bulmer Trust
BUPA UK Foundation
The Burden Trust
The Burdett Trust for Nursing
Consolidated Charity of Burton upon Trent
Miss Margaret Butters Reekie Charitable Trust
The Edward and Dorothy Cadbury Trust
Callendar Charitable Trust
The Cambridgeshire Community Foundation
W. A. Cargill Charitable Trust
The Carr-Gregory Trust
The Leslie Mary Carter Charitable Trust
The Castanea Trust
The Castansa Trust
The Joseph and Annie Cattle Trust
The Wilfrid and Constance Cave Foundation
The B. G. S. Cayzer Charitable Trust
The Amelia Chadwick Trust
The Chalk Cliff Trust
Champneys Charitable Foundation
Children with Cancer UK
The Childwick Trust
Chippenham Borough Lands Charity
CHK Foundation
The Churchill Foundation
The City Bridge Trust (Bridge House Estates)
The Clover Trust
The John Coates Charitable Trust
The Cobtree Charity Trust Ltd
The Vivienne and Samuel Cohen Charitable Trust
Colchester Catalyst Charity
The Colt Foundation
Comic Relief
The J. Reginald Corah Foundation Fund
The Worshipful Company of Cordwainers Charitable Trusts (Minges Gift)
The Gershon Coren Charitable Foundation (also known as The Muriel and Gus Coren Charitable Foundation)
Corra Foundation
Dudley and Geoffrey Cox Charitable Trust
The Sir William Coxen Trust Fund
The Lord Cozens-Hardy Trust
The Craps Charitable Trust
CRASH
Michael Crawford Children's Charity
CRH Charitable Trust*
Cripplegate Foundation
The Croydon Relief in Need Charities
Cruden Foundation Ltd
The Cunningham Trust
The D. G. Charitable Settlement
The D'Oyly Carte Charitable Trust
The Roger De Haan Charitable Trust
The Demigryphon Trust
Provincial Grand Charity of the Province of Derbyshire
The J. N. Derbyshire Trust
The Laduma Dhamecha Charitable Trust
Diabetes UK
Dinwoodie Charitable Company
The Dischma Charitable Trust
Dromintee Trust
The Anne Duchess of Westminster's Charity
Duchy Health Charity Ltd
Dunlossit and Islay Community Trust*
County Durham Community Foundation
The Earley Charity
Eastern Counties Educational Trust Ltd
The Gilbert and Eileen Edgar Foundation
Edupoor Ltd
The Eight Foundation*
The Eighteen Fund
The Elie Trust*
The Wilfred and Elsie Elkes Charity Fund
The Ellerdale Trust
The Englefield Charitable Trust
The Enkalon Foundation
The Evelyn Trust
The Everard Foundation
The Exilarch's Foundation
G. F. Eyre Charitable Trust
The Fairness Foundation

The Lord Faringdon Charitable Trust
Samuel William Farmer Trust
The Thomas Farr Charity
The February Foundation
The George Fentham Birmingham Charity
The A. M. Fenton Trust
Dixie Rose Findlay Charitable Trust
Sir John Fisher Foundation
The Earl Fitzwilliam Charitable Trust
The Follett Trust
Forest Hill Charitable Trust
The Lady Forester Trust
The Forman Hardy Charitable Trust
Donald Forrester Trust
Gwyneth Forrester Trust
The Fort Foundation
The Forte Charitable Trust
*Foux Foundation**
Fowler Smith and Jones Trust
The Elizabeth Frankland Moore and Star Foundation
The Gordon Fraser Charitable Trust
The Hugh Fraser Foundation
*The Joyce and Norman Freed Charitable Trust**
The Louis and Valerie Freedman Charitable Settlement
Charles S. French Charitable Trust
The Freshfield Foundation
The Freshgate Trust Foundation
Friarsgate Trust
The Patrick and Helena Frost Foundation
The Fulmer Charitable Trust
G. M. C. Trust
Gamma Trust
The Ganzoni Charitable Trust
Garfield Weston Foundation
Garthgwynion Charities
Martin Geddes Charitable Trust
The Jacqueline and Michael Gee Charitable Trust
General Charity (Coventry)
The General Nursing Council for England and Wales Trust
The Generations Foundation
The Tara Getty Foundation
The David Gibbons Foundation
The Girdlers' Company Charitable Trust
The B. and P. Glasser Charitable Trust
The Gloag Foundation
Global Charities
Worshipful Company of Gold and Silver Wyre Drawers Second Charitable Trust Fund
Sydney and Phyllis Goldberg Memorial Charitable Trust
The Goldsmiths' Company Charity
The Goodman Foundation
The Gosling Foundation Ltd
The Edward Gostling Foundation
Gowling WLG (UK) Charitable Trust
Grace Charitable Trust
The Grace Trust
The Graham Trust
The Green Hall Foundation
Philip and Judith Green Trust
Greenham Trust Ltd
The Greggs Foundation
The Grimmitt Trust
The Hadley Trust
The Hadrian Trust
Hamamelis Trust
The Helen Hamlyn Trust
Hampshire and Isle of Wight Community Foundation
The Hampstead Wells and Campden Trust
Hampton Fund
The W. A. Handley Charity Trust
The Lennox Hannay Charitable Trust
The Kathleen Hannay Memorial Charity
The Haramead Trust
Harborne Parish Lands Charity
The Harbour Charitable Trust
The Harding Trust
The Harebell Centenary Fund
The Harris Family Charitable Trust
The Edith Lilian Harrison 2000 Foundation
The Peter Harrison Foundation
The Harrison-Frank Family Foundation (UK) Ltd
Gay and Peter Hartley's Hillards Charitable Trust
Edward Harvist Trust (The Harvist Estate)
The Hasluck Charitable Trust
The Hawthorne Charitable Trust
The Charles Hayward Foundation
The Headley Trust
The Health Foundation
May Hearnshaw's Charity
Heart of England Community Foundation
Heart Research UK
The Heathcoat Trust
The Hedley Foundation
Help for Health
The Hemby Charitable Trust
The Tim Henman Foundation
The G. D. Herbert Charitable Trust
Herefordshire Community Foundation
P. and C. Hickinbotham Charitable Trust
R. G. Hills Charitable Trust
The Hintze Family Charity Foundation
The Henry C. Hoare Charitable Trust
The Hobson Charity Ltd
The Jane Hodge Foundation
The Holbeck Charitable Trust
Hollick Family Foundation
P. H. Holt Foundation
Sir Harold Hood's Charitable Trust
Hope Trust
The Thomas J. Horne Memorial Trust
Hospice UK
The Hospital of God at Greatham
The Hospital Saturday Fund
The Hudson Foundation
The Hull and East Riding Charitable Trust
The Humanitarian Trust
The Albert Hunt Trust
Miss Agnes H. Hunter's Trust
Huntingdon Freemen's Trust
*The Hurley Partners Charitable Trust**
The Nani Huyu Charitable Trust
Hyde Park Place Estate Charity
The Iliffe Family Charitable Trust
*The Inflexion Foundation**
The Inman Charity
The Inverforth Charitable Trust
Investream Charitable Trust
The Ireland Fund of Great Britain
The Charles Irving Charitable Trust
The J. and J. Benevolent Foundation
John Jarrold Trust Ltd
*JD Foundation**
The Roger and Jean Jefcoate Trust
*Jeffrey Charitable Trust**
The Jenour Foundation
The Elton John Aids Foundation (EJAF)
Lillie Johnson Charitable Trust
The Johnson Foundation
The Jones 1986 Charitable Trust
The Muriel Jones Foundation
Anton Jurgens Charitable Trust
The Jusaca Charitable Trust

The Ian Karten Charitable Trust
The Michael and Ilse Katz Foundation
The Kennedy Trust for Rheumatology Research
The Kensington and Chelsea Foundation
Kent Community Foundation
The Peter Kershaw Trust
The Ursula Keyes Trust
The Kildare Trust
Kilpatrick Fraser Charitable Trust
The Mary Kinross Charitable Trust
The Graham Kirkham Foundation
The Ernest Kleinwort Charitable Trust
Sir James Knott Trust
The Kobler Trust
Kollel and Co. Ltd
KPE4 Charitable Trust*
Kupath Gemach Chaim Bechesed Viznitz Trust
Kusuma Trust UK
Ladbrokes Coral Trust
Christopher Laing Foundation
The Kirby Laing Foundation
The Martin Laing Foundation
The Beatrice Laing Trust
The Leonard Laity Stoate Charitable Trust
The Lake House Charity
Community Foundations for Lancashire and Merseyside
Duchy of Lancaster Benevolent Fund
Lancaster Foundation
The Allen Lane Foundation
The R. J. Larg Family Trust
The Richard Lawes Foundation
The Edgar E. Lawley Foundation
The Leach Fourteenth Trust
The Leathersellers' Company Charitable Fund
Leeds Building Society Charitable Foundation
The Leeward Trust*
Leicestershire and Rutland Masonic Charity Association
The Kennedy Leigh Charitable Trust
The Leigh Trust
Lord Leverhulme's Charitable Trust
Limoges Charitable Trust
The Linbury Trust
Lincolnshire Community Foundation
The Linden Charitable Trust
The Linder Foundation
The Frank Litchfield Charitable Trust
The Charles Littlewood Hill Trust
Liverpool Charity and Voluntary Services (LCVS)
Jack Livingstone Charitable Trust
The Ian and Natalie Livingstone Charitable Trust
The Elaine and Angus Lloyd Charitable Trust
Lloyds Bank Foundation for England and Wales
Lloyds Bank Foundation for the Channel Islands
The Locker Foundation
London Catalyst
The London Community Foundation (LCF)
The Lord's Taverners
The C. L. Loyd Charitable Trust
The Henry Lumley Charitable Trust
Lord and Lady Lurgan Trust
The Lyndal Tree Foundation
John Lyon's Charity
M. and C. Trust
The Mageni Trust*
The Manackerman Charitable Trust
The Manchester Guardian Society Charitable Trust
R. W. Mann Trust
The Manson Family Charitable Trust*
The Marsh Christian Trust
Charlotte Marshall Charitable Trust
D. G. Marshall of Cambridge Trust
The Kristina Martin Charitable Trust
The Martin Charitable Trust
Sir George Martin Trust
The Geoffrey and Pauline Martin Trust*
John Martin's Charity
Masonic Charitable Foundation
Nancie Massey Charitable Trust
The Master Charitable Trust
Matchroom Sport Charitable Foundation
The Matliwala Family Charitable Trust
Maudsley Charity
The Violet Mauray Charitable Trust
The Robert McAlpine Foundation
Gemma and Chris McGough Charitable Foundation CIO*
D. D. McPhail Charitable Settlement
The Medicash Foundation
The Medlock Charitable Trust
The Mercers' Charitable Foundation
The Merchant Taylors' Company Charities Fund
The Merchant Venturers' Charity
Merchants' House of Glasgow
Mercury Phoenix Trust
T. and J. Meyer Family Foundation Ltd
The Mickleham Trust
The Gerald Micklem Charitable Trust
The Ronald Miller Foundation
The Clare Milne Trust
The James Milner Foundation
Milton Keynes Community Foundation Ltd
Mind*
The Mishcon Family Charitable Trust
The Brian Mitchell Charitable Settlement
Keren Mitzvah Trust
The Monmouthshire County Council Welsh Church Act Fund
Moondance Foundation
John Moores Foundation
The Morris Charitable Trust
The Willie and Mabel Morris Charitable Trust
G. M. Morrison Charitable Trust
The Morrisons Foundation
Motor Neurone Disease Association
The Edwina Mountbatten and Leonora Children's Foundation
The MSE Charity
The Mulberry Trust
Multiple Sclerosis Society
Edith Murphy Foundation
The John R. Murray Charitable Trust
Brian Murtagh Charitable Trust
Music Sales Charitable Trust
The Janet Nash Charitable Settlement
The National Garden Scheme
Newby Trust Ltd
The Frances and Augustus Newman Foundation
Norfolk Community Foundation
The Norman Family Charitable Trust
Normanby Charitable Trust
North East Area Miners' Social Welfare Trust Fund
North West Cancer Research
Community Foundation for Northern Ireland
Northern Pharmacies Ltd Trust Fund

The Northwick Trust
The Norton Rose Fulbright Charitable Foundation
Nottinghamshire Community Foundation
The Nuffield Foundation
The Oakdale Trust
One Community Foundation Ltd
Orthopaedic Research UK
P. F. Charitable Trust
The Paget Charitable Trust
The Gerald Palmer Eling Trust Company
The Panacea Charitable Trust
The Paragon Trust
Parkinson's UK
Partners Global Foundation*
Miss M. E. S. Paterson's Charitable Trust
The JGW Patterson Foundation
Susanna Peake Charitable Trust
The Pears Family Charitable Foundation
Personal Assurance Charitable Trust
The Pharsalia Charitable Trust
Bernard Piggott Charitable Trust
Pilkington Charities Fund
PIMCO Foundation Europe
Pink Ribbon Foundation
The Pitt-Rivers Charitable Trust
The Pixel Fund
The Mary Potter Convent Hospital Trust
The Prince of Wales's Charitable Foundation
Prison Service Charity Fund
The Professional Footballers' Association Charity
Prostate Cancer UK
The Purey Cust Trust CIO
The PwC Foundation
Mr and Mrs J. A. Pye's Charitable Settlement
QBE European Operations Foundation
Quartet Community Foundation
Quothquan Trust
The Monica Rabagliati Charitable Trust
Richard Radcliffe Trust
The Rainford Trust
The Randal Charitable Foundation*
Elizabeth Rathbone Charity
The Ravensdale Trust
The Rayne Foundation
The John Rayner Charitable Trust
Red Hill Charitable Trust
C. A. Redfern Charitable Foundation
The Rest-Harrow Trust
Reuben Foundation
The Revere Charitable Trust
The Rhododendron Trust
Daisie Rich Trust
The Clive and Sylvia Richards Charity Ltd
Richmond Parish Lands Charity
Rigby Foundation
Riverside Charitable Trust Ltd
RNID (The Royal National Institute for Deaf People)
The Dezna Robins Jones Charitable Foundation
The Cecil Rosen Foundation
Rosetrees Trust
The Rothermere Foundation
The Eranda Rothschild Foundation
The Roughley Charitable Trust
The Rowlands Trust
The Royal Foundation of the Duke and Duchess of Cambridge
The Jeremy and John Sacher Charitable Trust
The Michael and Nicola Sacher Charitable Trust
The Alan and Babette Sainsbury Charitable Fund
The Saintbury Trust
The Saints and Sinners Trust Ltd
The Salamander Charitable Trust
Samjo Ltd
The Basil Samuel Charitable Trust
The Sandhu Charitable Foundation
Sandra Charitable Trust
Schroder Charity Trust
Francis C. Scott Charitable Trust
The Frieda Scott Charitable Trust
The John Scott Trust Fund
Scouloudi Foundation
The Searchlight Electric Charitable Trust
Sam and Bella Sebba Charitable Trust
The Selfridges Group Foundation*
The Jean Shanks Foundation
The Shanly Foundation
ShareGift (The Orr Mackintosh Foundation)
The Shears Foundation
The Florence Shute Millennium Trust
The Thomas Sivewright Catto Charitable Settlement
Skipton Building Society Charitable Foundation
The Mrs Smith and Mount Trust
The N. Smith Charitable Settlement
Arabella and Julian Smith Family Trust*
Philip Smith's Charitable Trust
Somerset Community Foundation
The E. C. Sosnow Charitable Trust
The South Yorkshire Community Foundation
The Stephen R. and Philippa H. Southall Charitable Trust
Sparks Charity
Sparquote Ltd
The Spear Charitable Trust
Spielman Charitable Trust
Rosalyn and Nicholas Springer Charitable Trust
The St James's Trust Settlement
St James's Place Charitable Foundation
The Stafford Trust
The Peter Stebbings Memorial Charity
The Hugh Stenhouse Foundation
The Sir Sigmund Sternberg Charitable Foundation
The Sterry Family Foundation*
Sir Halley Stewart Trust
The Stoller Charitable Trust
The Stone Family Foundation
Stratford-upon-Avon Town Trust
The WO Street Charitable Foundation
The Joseph Strong Frazer Trust*
Sumner Wilson Charitable Trust
Community Foundation for Surrey
Swan Mountain Trust
The Swann-Morton Foundation
The Charles and Elsie Sykes Trust
The Tajtelbaum Charitable Trust
The Gay and Keith Talbot Trust
The Talbot Trusts
Tallow Chandlers Benevolent Fund No. 2
Tanner Trust
Tay Charitable Trust
C. B. and H. H. Taylor 1984 Trust
A. P. Taylor Trust
The Templeton Goodwill Trust
Tenovus Cancer Care
The Thales Charitable Trust
Sir Jules Thorn Charitable Trust
The Thornton Trust
The Tolkien Trust
The Tory Family Foundation

The Toy Trust
Toyota Manufacturing UK Charitable Trust
David William Traill Cargill Fund
The Constance Travis Charitable Trust
The Trefoil Trust
Tropical Health and Education Trust
The James Tudor Foundation
The Tudor Trust
The Tuixen Foundation
UKH Foundation
Ulster Garden Villages Ltd
The Underwood Trust
The Union of the Sisters of Mercy of Great Britain
The Utley Foundation
The Albert Van Den Bergh Charitable Trust
*The Van Mesdag Fund**
The Vandervell Foundation
Variety, the Children's Charity
Versus Arthritis
The Vintners' Foundation
Virgin Atlantic Foundation
The Vodafone Foundation
Robert and Felicity Waley-Cohen Charitable Trust
The Warwickshire Masonic Charitable Association Ltd
Mrs Waterhouse Charitable Trust
The Geoffrey Watling Charity
Blyth Watson Charitable Trust
The Weir Charitable Trust
Wellbeing of Women
The Welsh Church Act Fund
The Westfield Health Charitable Trust
The Whinfell Charitable Fund
The Melanie White Foundation Ltd
White Stuff Foundation
The Felicity Wilde Charitable Trust
The Will Charitable Trust
The Wilmcote Charitrust
The Michael and Anna Wix Charitable Trust
The Wolfson Family Charitable Trust
The Lord Leonard and Lady Estelle Wolfson Foundation
The Wolfson Foundation
The Wyseliot Rose Charitable Trust
The Yapp Charitable Trust
Yorkshire Building Society Charitable Foundation
Yorkshire Cancer Research
The Elizabeth and Prince Zaiger Trust
The Zochonis Charitable Trust
Zurich Community Trust (UK) Ltd

■ Mental health

The Adint Charitable Trust
*Beryl Alexander Charity**
ArtSocial Foundation
Barnwood Trust
The Benham Charitable Settlement
The Percy Bilton Charity
BUPA UK Foundation
The Carlton Hayes Mental Health Charity
CHK Foundation
The City Bridge Trust (Bridge House Estates)
Comic Relief
*CRH Charitable Trust**
Cripplegate Foundation
*The Dashlight Foundation**
The Dischma Charitable Trust
County Durham Community Foundation
Eastern Counties Educational Trust Ltd
The Ellerdale Trust
The Evelyn Trust
The Fairness Foundation
Gwyneth Forrester Trust
G. M. C. Trust
The Girdlers' Company Charitable Trust
Global Charities
Hampton Fund
Harborne Parish Lands Charity
The Peter Harrison Foundation
The Hospital of God at Greatham
The Albert Hunt Trust
The Ireland Fund of Great Britain
The Charles Irving Charitable Trust
*JD Foundation**
The Roger and Jean Jefcoate Trust
The Ian Karten Charitable Trust
The Kensington and Chelsea Foundation
The Mary Kinross Charitable Trust
The Beatrice Laing Trust
The Allen Lane Foundation
The Richard Lawes Foundation
Lloyds Bank Foundation for England and Wales
The London Community Foundation (LCF)
John Lyon's Charity
The Kristina Martin Charitable Trust
Sir George Martin Trust
Maudsley Charity
The Mercers' Charitable Foundation
The Mickleham Trust
*Mind**
John Moores Foundation
G. M. Morrison Charitable Trust
The MSE Charity
The National Garden Scheme
Newby Trust Ltd
Norfolk Community Foundation
The Norman Family Charitable Trust
Community Foundation for Northern Ireland
The Northwick Trust
Nottinghamshire Community Foundation
One Community Foundation Ltd
The Paragon Trust
The Pixel Fund
The Priory Foundation
The Purey Cust Trust CIO
The PwC Foundation
Mr and Mrs J. A. Pye's Charitable Settlement
*The Randal Charitable Foundation**
The Rayne Foundation
The Rayne Trust
Red Hill Charitable Trust
The Rhododendron Trust
The Royal Foundation of the Duke and Duchess of Cambridge
Francis C. Scott Charitable Trust
Sam and Bella Sebba Charitable Trust
The Mrs Smith and Mount Trust
*Arabella and Julian Smith Family Trust**
The South Yorkshire Community Foundation
The Stephen R. and Philippa H. Southall Charitable Trust
Rosalyn and Nicholas Springer Charitable Trust
The Peter Stebbings Memorial Charity
The Stone Family Foundation
Stratford-upon-Avon Town Trust
*The Joseph Strong Frazer Trust**
Community Foundation for Surrey
Swan Mountain Trust
The Charles and Elsie Sykes Trust
The Talbot Trusts
The Templeton Goodwill Trust
The Tudor Trust
The Tuixen Foundation
UKH Foundation

Robert and Felicity Waley-Cohen Charitable Trust
Mrs Waterhouse Charitable Trust
The Lord Leonard and Lady Estelle Wolfson Foundation
The Yapp Charitable Trust

■ People with specific conditions

The 4814 Trust
The Sylvia Adams Charitable Trust
The Adint Charitable Trust
The AEB Charitable Trust
Al-Fayed Charitable Foundation
The Anson Charitable Trust
The Ardeola Charitable Trust
ArtSocial Foundation
Asthma UK
The Barker-Mill Foundation
Bearder Charity
The Bellahouston Bequest Fund
The Benham Charitable Settlement
The Bingham Trust
Maria Bjornson Memorial Fund*
Bloodwise
The Marjory Boddy Charitable Trust
Sir Clive Bourne Family Trust
The Breast Cancer Research Trust (BCRT)
Bright Red Charity*
British Council for Prevention of Blindness
British Eye Research Foundation (Fight for Sight)
British Heart Foundation (BHF)
British Lung Foundation
The Castansa Trust
Children with Cancer UK
The Cobtree Charity Trust Ltd
The Keith Coombs Trust
The Worshipful Company of Cordwainers Charitable Trusts (Minges Gift)
The D. G. Charitable Settlement
Diabetes UK
The Wilfred and Elsie Elkes Charity Fund
The Evelyn Trust
The Forte Charitable Trust
Sydney and Phyllis Goldberg Memorial Charitable Trust
Philip and Judith Green Trust
The Peter Harrison Foundation
The Headley Trust
Heart Research UK
Highway One Trust
Miss Agnes H. Hunter's Trust
The Roger and Jean Jefcoate Trust
The Elton John Aids Foundation (EJAF)
The Kentown Wizard Foundation
Kilpatrick Fraser Charitable Trust
The Kirby Laing Foundation
Joseph Levy Foundation
The Frank Litchfield Charitable Trust
The R. S. Macdonald Charitable Trust
The Mackintosh Foundation
The Geoffrey and Pauline Martin Trust*
Nancie Massey Charitable Trust
The Mather Family Charitable Trust*
Merchants' House of Glasgow
Mercury Phoenix Trust
The Mickleham Trust
The Gerald Micklem Charitable Trust
The Clare Milne Trust
The Willie and Mabel Morris Charitable Trust
The Ken and Lynne Morrison Charitable Trust
The Ken and Edna Morrison Charitable Trust
Motor Neurone Disease Association
The MSE Charity
Multiple Sclerosis Society
Murphy-Neumann Charity Company Ltd
North West Cancer Research
The Nuffield Foundation
The O'Sullivan Family Charitable Trust
Ovingdean Hall Foundation
The Paragon Trust
Parkinson's UK
The JGW Patterson Foundation
Payne-Gallwey 1989 Charitable Trust
The Dowager Countess Eleanor Peel Trust
Pink Ribbon Foundation
Prison Service Charity Fund
Prostate Cancer UK
The Purey Cust Trust CIO
Richard Radcliffe Trust
Red Hill Charitable Trust
The Revere Charitable Trust
The Alan and Babette Sainsbury Charitable Fund
The Selfridges Group Foundation*
Skipton Building Society Charitable Foundation
The Leslie Smith Foundation
The South Yorkshire Community Foundation
St James's Place Charitable Foundation
The Joseph Strong Frazer Trust*
The Charles and Elsie Sykes Trust
The Syncona Foundation
Tanner Trust
Tay Charitable Trust
The Templeton Goodwill Trust
Tenovus Cancer Care
The Three Guineas Trust
The True Colours Trust
The James Tudor Foundation
The Ulverscroft Foundation
The Utley Foundation
Versus Arthritis
The VTCT Foundation
The Will Charitable Trust
The Lord Leonard and Lady Estelle Wolfson Foundation
Yorkshire Cancer Research

■ Substance misusers and abusers

The Brelms Trust CIO
The Chetwode Foundation
Corra Foundation
County Durham Community Foundation
Forest Hill Charitable Trust
Martin Geddes Charitable Trust
The General Charity Fund
The Greater Manchester High Sheriff's Police Trust
The Alfred Haines Charitable Trust
The Peter Harrison Foundation
P. and C. Hickinbotham Charitable Trust
Hope Trust
The Hospital of God at Greatham
Inner London Magistrates Court Poor Box and Feeder Charity
The Elton John Aids Foundation (EJAF)
The Kelly Family Charitable Trust
The Peter Kershaw Trust
The Graham Kirkham Foundation
Laslett's (Hinton) Charity
The Leigh Trust
The Linbury Trust
Lloyds Bank Foundation for England and Wales
Lloyds Bank Foundation for the Channel Islands
Merchants' House of Glasgow

The Mickleham Trust
The Miles Morland Foundation
Norfolk Community Foundation
The Norman Family Charitable Trust
Henry Oldfield Trust
The Pastoral Care Trust – The St Nicholas Care Fund
*The Randal Charitable Foundation**
The Rhododendron Trust
The Roughley Charitable Trust
The Frieda Scott Charitable Trust
The Souter Charitable Trust
The Peter Stebbings Memorial Charity
The Trusthouse Charitable Foundation
Ulster Garden Villages Ltd
The Vintners' Foundation
Volant Charitable Trust
The Woodward Charitable Trust

Occupation and membership groups

■ Armed forces

The Aberbrothock Skea Trust
ABF The Soldiers' Charity
The Adint Charitable Trust
The AEB Charitable Trust
*The Armed Forces Covenant Fund Trust**
Armed Forces Education Trust
The Armourers' and Brasiers' Gauntlet Trust
The Band Trust
The Benham Charitable Settlement
*The Big Yellow Foundation**
Blakemore Foundation
The Borrows Charitable Trust
The Cadogan Charity
Callendar Charitable Trust
The Castanea Trust
The Cayo Foundation
Chartered Accountants' Livery Charity (CALC)
The Childwick Trust
The Robert Clutterbuck Charitable Trust
The Worshipful Company of Cordwainers Charitable Trusts (Minges Gift)
The Demigryphon Trust
Drapers' Charitable Fund
The Anne Duchess of Westminster's Charity
The Dyers' Company Charitable Trust
Edinburgh Trust No. 2 Account
The Englefield Charitable Trust
The Everard Foundation
Donald Forrester Trust
The Elizabeth Frankland Moore and Star Foundation
Worshipful Company of Gold and Silver Wyre Drawers Second Charitable Trust Fund
The Golden Bottle Trust
The Mike Gooley Trailfinders Charity
The Gosling Foundation Ltd
The Gray Trust
Greenham Trust Ltd
The Grocers' Charity
The Walter Guinness Charitable Trust
The W. A. Handley Charity Trust
The Lennox Hannay Charitable Trust
The Christina Mary Hendrie Trust
The Hintze Family Charity Foundation
The Hobson Charity Ltd
The Inman Charity
The Inverforth Charitable Trust
The Michael and Ilse Katz Foundation
The Graham Kirkham Foundation
Sir James Knott Trust
The Beatrice Laing Trust
Mrs F. B. Laurence Charitable Trust
The Lawson Trust CIO
The Charles Littlewood Hill Trust
Lloyd's Patriotic Fund
The MacRobert Trust 2019
Nancie Massey Charitable Trust
The Master Charitable Trust
The Norman Family Charitable Trust
P. F. Charitable Trust
The Paragon Trust
Susanna Peake Charitable Trust
The George and Esme Pollitzer Charitable Settlement
The Princess Anne's Charities
Queen Mary's Roehampton Trust
Riada Trust
Rigby Foundation
The Rothley Trust
The Rowlands Trust
Royal Artillery Charitable Fund
The Royal British Legion
The Royal Foundation of the Duke and Duchess of Cambridge
The Royal Navy and Royal Marines Charity
The Saddlers' Company Charitable Fund
Salters' Charitable Foundation
Schroder Charity Trust
Scott (Eredine) Charitable Trust
Scouloudi Foundation
Seafarers UK (King George's Fund for Sailors)
The Charles Skey Charitable Trust
Philip Smith's Charitable Trust
The Stafford Trust
*The Joseph Strong Frazer Trust**
The Swire Charitable Trust
The Charles and Elsie Sykes Trust
The Trefoil Trust
The Michael Uren Foundation
The Utley Foundation
The Albert Van Den Bergh Charitable Trust
The Veterans' Foundation
G. R. Waters Charitable Trust 2000
Colonel W. H. Whitbread Charitable Trust
The Wilmcote Charitrust
The Zochonis Charitable Trust

■ Arts, culture and heritage

The Architectural Heritage Fund
The John Armitage Charitable Trust
Arts Council of Northern Ireland
The Associated Board of the Royal Schools of Music
The Bagri Foundation
The Rachel Baker Memorial Charity
The Band Trust
The Bowerman Charitable Trust
W. A. Cargill Charitable Trust
The W. A. Cargill Fund
The Carne Trust
Creative Scotland
The Daiwa Anglo-Japanese Foundation
Drapers' Charitable Fund
The Gilbert and Eileen Edgar Foundation
The Eighty Eight Foundation
The Elmley Foundation
*Equity Charitable Trust**
The Fidelio Charitable Trust
Sir John Fisher Foundation
Oliver Ford Foundation
The Foyle Foundation

The Freelands Foundation Ltd
The Garrick Charitable Trust
Gatwick Airport Community Trust
The Golsoncott Foundation
Nicholas and Judith Goodison's Charitable Settlement
The Helen Hamlyn Trust
The Harding Trust
The Headley Trust
P. and C. Hickinbotham Charitable Trust
The Hinrichsen Foundation
Historic Houses Foundation
The Hobson Charity Ltd
P. H. Holt Foundation
The Hull and East Riding Charitable Trust
The Idlewild Trust
The Inverforth Charitable Trust
The Sir Barry Jackson County Fund
The Boris Karloff Charitable Foundation
The David Laing Foundation
The David Lean Foundation
The Leche Trust
The Light Fund Company
Limoges Charitable Trust
The Linder Foundation
Lord and Lady Lurgan Trust
*The Mageni Trust**
The Mayfield Valley Arts Trust
The Henry Moore Foundation
The Miles Morland Foundation
G. M. Morrison Charitable Trust
The Nisbet Trust
The Ouseley Church Music Trust
Parabola Foundation
The Pebbles Trust
The Performing Right Society Foundation
The Pilgrim Trust
The Pitt-Rivers Charitable Trust
The Polonsky Foundation
David and Elaine Potter Foundation
The Prince of Wales's Charitable Foundation
Mr and Mrs J. A. Pye's Charitable Settlement
Humphrey Richardson Taylor Charitable Trust
The Ruddock Foundation for the Arts
The RVW Trust
The Scottish Power Foundation
ShareGift (The Orr Mackintosh Foundation)
The St James's Trust Settlement
Sumner Wilson Charitable Trust
The Theatres Trust Charitable Fund
The Underwood Trust
The Michael Uren Foundation
The Valiant Charitable Trust
The Vaughan Williams Charitable Trust
The Veneziana Fund
Viridor Credits Environmental Company
The Wingate Foundation
The Lord Leonard and Lady Estelle Wolfson Foundation
Youth Music

■ Environment, agriculture and animals

The A. Team Foundation Ltd
The Alborada Trust
Ove Arup Partnership Charitable Trust
Burnie's Foundation
Consolidated Charity of Burton upon Trent
The Frederick and Phyllis Cann Trust
The Wilfrid and Constance Cave Foundation
The Clan Trust Ltd
The Elizabeth Creak Charitable Trust
The Worshipful Company of Gardeners of London Charity
Gatwick Airport Community Trust
The Tara Getty Foundation
P. and C. Hickinbotham Charitable Trust
The Hobson Charity Ltd
P. H. Holt Foundation
The Hutchinson Charitable Trust
Rees Jeffreys Road Fund
The Muriel Jones Foundation
The Graham Kirkham Foundation
The MacRobert Trust 2019
The Martin Charitable Trust
The Master Charitable Trust
Moto in the Community
The National Garden Scheme
The NFU Mutual Charitable Trust
The Nineveh Charitable Trust
One Community Foundation Ltd
The Paragon Trust
People's Postcode Trust
Betty Phillips Charitable Trust
The Phillips Charitable Trust
The Primrose Trust
The Prince of Wales's Charitable Foundation
The Prince's Countryside Fund
The Princess Anne's Charities
The Jean Sainsbury Animal Welfare Trust
Sandra Charitable Trust
ShareGift (The Orr Mackintosh Foundation)
Sumner Wilson Charitable Trust
The Underwood Trust
The Michael Uren Foundation
Viridor Credits Environmental Company

■ Freemasons

Douglas Compton James Charitable Trust
Provincial Grand Charity of the Province of Derbyshire
Leicestershire and Rutland Masonic Charity Association
London Freemasons Charity

■ Manufacturing

The Worshipful Company of Cordwainers Charitable Trusts (Minges Gift)
Worshipful Company of Glovers of London Charitable Trust
The Horners Charity Fund
Makers of Playing Cards Charity
Daisie Rich Trust
Riverside Charitable Trust Ltd
The Savoy Educational Trust
The South Yorkshire Community Foundation

■ Medicine and health

The Alborada Trust
The Barbers' Company General Charities
The Birmingham District Nursing Charitable Trust
The John Black Charitable Foundation
Bloodwise
The Boltini Trust
British Heart Foundation (BHF)
British Lung Foundation
The Burdett Trust for Nursing
The Colt Foundation
The Cunningham Trust
Dinwoodie Charitable Company
The James Dyson Foundation
The Gilbert and Eileen Edgar Foundation

The General Nursing Council for England and Wales Trust
The Health Foundation
The Jane Hodge Foundation
The Holbeck Charitable Trust
Hospice UK
The Inman Charity
The Ursula Keyes Trust
The Linder Foundation
The Medlock Charitable Trust
G. M. Morrison Charitable Trust
The Edwina Mountbatten and Leonora Children's Foundation
The National Garden Scheme
Northern Pharmacies Ltd Trust Fund
Orthopaedic Research UK
The Paragon Trust
Susanna Peake Charitable Trust
The Pharsalia Charitable Trust
The Purey Cust Trust CIO
The Royal Foundation of the Duke and Duchess of Cambridge
Sandra Charitable Trust
The Jean Shanks Foundation
Tropical Health and Education Trust
The James Tudor Foundation
The Underwood Trust
The Michael Uren Foundation
The Melanie White Foundation Ltd

■ Seafarers and ex-seafarers

The Frederick and Phyllis Cann Trust
The Corporation of Trinity House of Deptford Strond
Sir John Fisher Foundation
The Gosling Foundation Ltd
The W. A. Handley Charity Trust
The ITF Seafarers Trust
Sir James Knott Trust
Mrs F. B. Laurence Charitable Trust
The MacRobert Trust 2019
Merchant Navy Welfare Board
The Norman Family Charitable Trust
The Phillips Charitable Trust
The Royal Navy and Royal Marines Charity
Scouloudi Foundation
Seafarers UK (King George's Fund for Sailors)
The Shipwrights' Charitable Fund
*The Joseph Strong Frazer Trust**

■ Science, technology and engineering

Building & Civil Engineering Charitable Trust
The W. A. Cargill Fund
The Colt Foundation
The James Dyson Foundation
Heart Research UK

■ Service industry

The Cooks Charity
The Lord Forte Foundation
Makers of Playing Cards Charity
Daisie Rich Trust
Riverside Charitable Trust Ltd
The Savoy Educational Trust

■ Social or sporting clubs

Bauer Radio's Cash for Kids Charities
The James Beattie Charitable Trust
Bedfordshire and Luton Community Foundation
British Motor Sports Training Trust
The Jack Brunton Charitable Trust
Buckinghamshire Community Foundation
The Chartley Foundation
Cheshire Freemason's Charity
The Childhood Trust
The Church Burgesses Educational Foundation
Cumbria Community Foundation
Provincial Grand Charity of the Province of Derbyshire
County Durham Community Foundation
The Football Association National Sports Centre Trust
The Football Foundation
The Fort Foundation
The Forte Charitable Trust
The Girdlers' Company Charitable Trust
The Grange Farm Centre Trust
The Grantham Yorke Trust
Hampshire and Isle of Wight Community Foundation
The Peter Harrison Foundation
The Heathcoat Trust
Henley Educational Trust
Henley Royal Regatta Charitable Trust
The Lady Hind Trust
The Isle of Anglesey Charitable Trust
Leicestershire and Rutland Masonic Charity Association
The Charles Littlewood Hill Trust
The London Marathon Charitable Trust Ltd
Making a Difference Locally Ltd
Oxfordshire Community Foundation
The Persimmon Charitable Foundation
The Jack Petchey Foundation
The Racing Foundation
Daisie Rich Trust
A. P. Taylor Trust
Toyota Manufacturing UK Charitable Trust
York Children's Trust

People of a particular heritage/ethnic origin

The Scott Bader Commonwealth Ltd
The Bagri Foundation
The Clothworkers' Foundation
The Daiwa Anglo-Japanese Foundation
The Eighty Eight Foundation
The Grace Trust
The Hadrian Trust
Harborne Parish Lands Charity
The Hinduja Foundation
Integrated Education Fund
The Ireland Fund of Great Britain
Irish Youth Foundation (UK) Ltd (incorporating The Lawlor Foundation)
John Moores Foundation
The Miles Morland Foundation
Norfolk Community Foundation
Odin Charitable Trust
The Austin and Hope Pilkington Trust
Quartet Community Foundation
The Eleanor Rathbone Charitable Trust
The Sigrid Rausing Trust
Rentrust Foundation Ltd
The Robertson Trust
Rosca Trust
The Joseph Rowntree Charitable Trust
Saint Sarkis Charity Trust

The Sino-British Fellowship Trust
Staples Trust
Taca
Tees Valley Community Foundation
Volant Charitable Trust
Wakefield and Tetley Trust
The Wates Foundation
W. Wing Yip and Brothers Foundation
Youth Music

Relationships

Al-Fayed Charitable Foundation
The Clara E. Burgess Charity
The Noel Buxton Trust
The Cambridgeshire Community Foundation
Cumbria Community Foundation
The De Brye Charitable Trust
The Ellerdale Trust
Jill Franklin Trust
Global Charities
The Grantham Yorke Trust
The Walter Guinness Charitable Trust
The Alfred Haines Charitable Trust
Hammersmith United Charities
The Headley Trust
The Alan Edward Higgs Charity
Inner London Magistrates Court Poor Box and Feeder Charity
The Jabbs Foundation
The Johnson Foundation
The Kelly Family Charitable Trust
The Kensington and Chelsea Foundation
Kollel and Co. Ltd
The Beatrice Laing Trust
Community Foundations for Lancashire and Merseyside
The Richard Lawes Foundation
The Marsh Christian Trust
Charlotte Marshall Charitable Trust
The MSE Charity
The Mulberry Trust
Muslim Hands
The George and Esme Pollitzer Charitable Settlement
Quothquan Trust
The Eleanor Rathbone Charitable Trust
The Robertson Trust
The Roughley Charitable Trust
The Segelman Trust
Somerset Community Foundation
The Stafford Trust
The Peter Stebbings Memorial Charity
Volant Charitable Trust
Wakefield and Tetley Trust
The Walker Trust
Charity of Sir Richard Whittington
The Zochonis Charitable Trust

■ Bereavement

The Ellerdale Trust
Jill Franklin Trust
Global Charities
The Hobson Charity Ltd
The Richard Lawes Foundation
The Kristina Martin Charitable Trust
The MSE Charity
The Roughley Charitable Trust

■ Families

The Brook Trust
The Noel Buxton Trust
The Cambridgeshire Community Foundation
Colyer-Fergusson Charitable Trust
Cumbria Community Foundation
Devon Community Foundation
County Durham Community Foundation
The Ellerdale Trust
The Fifty Fund
County of Gloucestershire Community Foundation
The Grantham Yorke Trust
The Walter Guinness Charitable Trust
Hackney Parochial Charities
The Alfred Haines Charitable Trust
The Halsall Foundation*
Hammersmith United Charities
Hampshire and Isle of Wight Community Foundation
The Headley Trust
HFC Help For Children UK LTD
The Alan Edward Higgs Charity
Inner London Magistrates Court Poor Box and Feeder Charity
The Jabbs Foundation
The Johnson Foundation
The Kelly Family Charitable Trust
The Kensington and Chelsea Foundation
The Beatrice Laing Trust
Community Foundations for Lancashire and Merseyside
Laslett's (Hinton) Charity
Lloyds Bank Foundation for England and Wales
The London Community Foundation (LCF)
John Lyon's Charity
The R. S. Macdonald Charitable Trust
Charlotte Marshall Charitable Trust
The Steve Morgan Foundation
G. M. Morrison Charitable Trust
The MSE Charity
The Mulberry Trust
The George and Esme Pollitzer Charitable Settlement
Quothquan Trust
The Rayne Foundation
The Robertson Trust
The Royal British Legion
The Segelman Trust
Somerset Community Foundation
The South Yorkshire Community Foundation
The Peter Stebbings Memorial Charity
The WO Street Charitable Foundation
The Tedworth Charitable Trust
The Trusthouse Charitable Foundation
Volant Charitable Trust
Wakefield and Tetley Trust
The Walker Trust
The Welland Trust*
Charity of Sir Richard Whittington
The Woodward Charitable Trust

■ Orphans

Al-Fayed Charitable Foundation
The Clara E. Burgess Charity
The De Brye Charitable Trust
Kollel and Co. Ltd
Muslim Hands
The Eleanor Rathbone Charitable Trust
The Leslie Smith Foundation
The Walker Trust

Religion

4 Charity Foundation
A. W. Charitable Trust
The Aaronson Foundation
The Aberdeen Foundation
The Acacia Charitable Trust
Adenfirst Ltd
The All Saints Educational Trust
Allchurches Trust Ltd
Alliance Family Foundation Ltd

The Almond Trust
Amabrill Ltd
Viscount Amory's Charitable Trust
The AMW Charitable Trust
The Anchor Foundation
Andrews Charitable Trust
Anpride Ltd
The John Apthorp Charity
The Ardwick Trust
The John Armitage Charitable Trust
The Ashburnham Thanksgiving Trust
Keren Association Ltd
The Baird Trust
The Andrew Balint Charitable Trust
The Roger and Sarah Bancroft Clark Charitable Trust
Bay Charitable Trust
Bear Mordechai Ltd
Beauland Ltd
The Beaverbrooks Charitable Trust
The Becker Family Charitable Trust
The Bellahouston Bequest Fund
Belljoe Tzedoko Ltd
Benesco Charity Ltd
The Beth Hamedrash Satmar Trust (BHST)
Bideford Bridge Trust
Asser Bishvil Foundation
The Blandford Lake Trust
The Bloom Foundation
The Bluston Charitable Settlement
The Bonamy Charitable Trust
The Harry Bottom Charitable Trust
Sir Clive Bourne Family Trust
Bourneheights Ltd
Friends of Boyan Trust
Bristol Archdeaconry Charity
Mary Brown Memorial Trust*
Brushmill Ltd
Buckingham Trust
Consolidated Charity of Burton upon Trent
Byrne Family Foundation
C. and F. Charitable Trust
The W. A. Cargill Fund
Carlee Ltd
Catholic Charitable Trust
Chalfords Ltd
Chartered Accountants' Livery Charity (CALC)
The Childs Charitable Trust*
The Childwick Trust
Church Burgesses Trust
Church of Ireland Priorities Fund
Cloudesley
The Clover Trust
Clydpride Ltd
CMZ Ltd
Congregational and General Charitable Trust
The Gershon Coren Charitable Foundation (also known as The Muriel and Gus Coren Charitable Foundation)
The Costa Family Charitable Trust
Council for World Mission (UK)*
The County Council of Dyfed Welsh Church Fund
The Craps Charitable Trust
Itzchok Meyer Cymerman Trust Ltd
D. M. H. Educational Trust Ltd
Oizer Dalim Trust
The Davidson Family Charitable Trust
The Davis Foundation
Dawat-E-Hadiyah Trust (United Kingdom)
Debmar Benevolent Trust Ltd
The Djanogly Foundation
The Dorfman Foundation
The Doughty Charity Trust
The Gilbert and Eileen Edgar Foundation
Elanore Ltd
The George Elias Charitable Trust
The Ellinson Foundation Ltd
The Eventhall Family Charitable Trust
The Exilarch's Foundation
Famos Foundation Trust
The Feoffees of St Michael's Spurriergate York
The Robert Fleming Hannay Memorial Charity
Fordeve Ltd
Forest Hill Charitable Trust
The Forte Charitable Trust
The Isaac and Freda Frankel Memorial Charitable Trust
Anne French Memorial Trust
Gamma Trust
The Ganzoni Charitable Trust
The Jacqueline and Michael Gee Charitable Trust
The Gertner Charitable Trust
The Gibbs Charitable Trusts
The B. and P. Glasser Charitable Trust
The Gloag Foundation
The Goshen Trust
The Gould Charitable Trust
Grace Charitable Trust
The Grace Trust
The Grant Foundation
Philip and Judith Green Trust
M. and R. Gross Charities Ltd
The N. and R. Grunbaum Charitable Trust
Hadras Kodesh Trust
The Harbour Charitable Trust
The Helping Foundation
The Highcroft Charitable Trust
Highway One Trust
The Hinduja Foundation
The Hintze Family Charity Foundation
Hockerill Educational Foundation
The Holden Charitable Trust
Homelands Charitable Trust
Sir Harold Hood's Charitable Trust
Hope Trust
Horwich Shotter Charitable Trust
The Humanitarian Trust
The Huntingdon Foundation Ltd
Ibrahim Foundation Ltd
The Inlight Trust
Integrated Education Fund
International Bible Students Association
Investream Charitable Trust
The J. and J. Benevolent Foundation
The J. A. R. Charitable Trust
The Jerusalem Trust
Jewish Child's Day (JCD)
The Jewish Youth Fund
J. E. Joseph Charitable Fund
The Jusaca Charitable Trust
The Kasner Charitable Trust
The Michael and Ilse Katz Foundation
C. S. Kaufman Charitable Trust
The Kennedy Charitable Foundation
The Friends of Kent Churches
E. and E. Kernkraut Charities Ltd
The Kirschel Foundation
The Kobler Trust
Kollel and Co. Ltd
Kolyom Trust Ltd
Kupath Gemach Chaim Bechesed Viznitz Trust
The Labone Charitable Trust*
The Kirby Laing Foundation
Largsmount Ltd
The Lauffer Family Charitable Foundation
The Herd Lawson and Muriel Lawson Charitable Trust
Lawson Beckman Charitable Trust
The Arnold Lee Charitable Trust
Leicestershire and Rutland Masonic Charity Association
Bernard Lewis Family Charitable Trust

David and Ruth Lewis Family Charitable Trust
The Charles Littlewood Hill Trust
The Second Joseph Aaron Littman Foundation
Jack Livingstone Charitable Trust
Local Trent Ltd
The Locker Foundation
Loftus Charitable Trust
LPW Ltd
M. and C. Trust
M. B. Foundation
The Mallinckrodt Foundation
Marbeh Torah Trust
Charity of John Marshall
Charlotte Marshall Charitable Trust
John Martin's Charity
The Master Charitable Trust
The Violet Mauray Charitable Trust
Mayfair Charities Ltd
Mayheights Ltd
Maypride Ltd
Melodor Ltd
The Melow Charitable Trust
Menuchar Ltd
Mercaz Torah Vechesed Ltd
Keren Mitzvah Trust
The Mizpah Trust
Mole Charitable Trust
Vyoel Moshe Charitable Trust
The Mosselson Charitable Trust
The Mulberry Trust
The John R. Murray Charitable Trust
Muslim Hands
The Mutual Trust Group
MW (CL) Foundation
MW (GK) Foundation
MW (HO) Foundation
MW (RH) Foundation
The National Churches Trust
Nemoral Ltd
Ner Foundation
Nesswall Ltd
Newpier Charity Ltd
The Norwood and Newton Settlement
Oizer Charitable Trust
The Ouseley Church Music Trust
The Doris Pacey Charitable Foundation
The Gerald Palmer Eling Trust Company
The Panacea Charitable Trust
Miss M. E. S. Paterson's Charitable Trust
David Pearlman Charitable Foundation
The Pears Family Charitable Foundation
B. E. Perl Charitable Trust
The Phillips and Rubens Charitable Trust
The Pitt-Rivers Charitable Trust
The George and Esme Pollitzer Charitable Settlement
David and Elaine Potter Foundation
Premierquote Ltd
Premishlaner Charitable Trust
The Prince of Wales's Charitable Foundation
Quothquan Trust
R. S. Charitable Trust
Rachel Charitable Trust
The Bishop Radford Trust
The Joseph Rank Trust
The Sir James Reckitt Charity
Reuben Foundation
Richmond Parish Lands Charity
Ridgesave Ltd
Robertson Hall Trust
The Gerald and Gail Ronson Family Foundation
Mrs L. D. Rope's Third Charitable Settlement
Rothschild Foundation (Hanadiv) Europe
Rowanville Ltd
S. and R. Charitable Trust
The Jeremy and John Sacher Charitable Trust
Samjo Ltd
Sarum St Michael Educational Charity
Schass Foundation
The Annie Schiff Charitable Trust
O. and G. Schreiber Charitable Trust
Sam and Bella Sebba Charitable Trust
Sellata Ltd
The Cyril Shack Trust
ShareGift (The Orr Mackintosh Foundation)
The Archie Sherman Charitable Trust
Shlomo Memorial Fund Ltd
Shulem B. Association Ltd
*Smith Bradbeer Charitable Trust**
The Henry Smith Charity
The E. C. Sosnow Charitable Trust
The Souter Charitable Trust
The Stephen R. and Philippa H. Southall Charitable Trust
W. F. Southall Trust
Sparquote Ltd
Rosalyn and Nicholas Springer Charitable Trust
St Peter's Saltley Trust
Starlow Charities Ltd
C. E. K. Stern Charitable Trust
Stervon Ltd
Stewards Company Ltd
Sir Halley Stewart Trust
Sumner Wilson Charitable Trust
Swansea and Brecon Diocesan Board of Finance Ltd
T. and S. Trust Fund
The Tajtelbaum Charitable Trust
Talteg Ltd
The David Tannen Charitable Trust
The Thornton Trust
Mrs R. P. Tindall's Charitable Trust
The Tory Family Foundation
The Toye Foundation
Truedene Co. Ltd
Truemart Ltd
Trumros Ltd
The Tufton Charitable Trust
Tzedakah
Ulting Overseas Trust
The Union of Orthodox Hebrew Congregations
The Union of the Sisters of Mercy of Great Britain
United Jewish Israel Appeal
The United Reformed Church (Wessex) Trust Ltd
The David Uri Memorial Trust
The Vail Foundation
VHLT Ltd
Vivdale Ltd
The Welsh Church Act Fund
Westhill Endowment
The Wigoder Family Foundation
Dame Violet Wills Charitable Trust
The Wingate Foundation
The Maurice Wohl Charitable Foundation
The Charles Wolfson Charitable Trust
The James Wood Bequest Fund
Woodlands Green Ltd
WWDP (World Day of Prayer National Committee for England, Wales and Northern Ireland)
Wychdale Ltd
Wychville Ltd
Yankov Charitable Trust

People of the Christian faith

The All Saints Educational Trust
Allchurches Trust Ltd
The Almond Trust
The Anchor Foundation
Andrews Charitable Trust
The John Apthorp Charity
Ardbarron Trust Ltd

The Ashburnham Thanksgiving Trust
The Baird Trust
The Roger and Sarah Bancroft Clark Charitable Trust
The Bellahouston Bequest Fund
The Benham Charitable Settlement
The Sydney Black Charitable Trust
The Harry Bottom Charitable Trust
The Bowerman Charitable Trust
The Liz and Terry Bramall Foundation
Bristol Archdeaconry Charity
*Mary Brown Memorial Trust**
Buckingham Trust
Byrne Family Foundation
Catholic Charitable Trust
*The Childs Charitable Trust**
The Christabella Charitable Trust
The Church Burgesses Educational Foundation
Church of Ireland Priorities Fund
Cloudesley
The Clover Trust
Congregational and General Charitable Trust
The Costa Family Charitable Trust
*Council for World Mission (UK)**
The County Council of Dyfed Welsh Church Fund
The Feoffees of St Michael's Spurriergate York
Forest Hill Charitable Trust
The Forte Charitable Trust
Gamma Trust
The Ganzoni Charitable Trust
The Gibbs Charitable Trusts
The Gloag Foundation
The Goshen Trust
Grace Charitable Trust
The Grace Trust
The Grant Foundation
Philip and Judith Green Trust
Ros Harding Trust
Highway One Trust
Hinchley Charitable Trust
The Hintze Family Charity Foundation
Hockerill Educational Foundation
The Holbeck Charitable Trust
Homelands Charitable Trust
Sir Harold Hood's Charitable Trust
Hope Trust
The Hunting Horn General Charitable Trust
Integrated Education Fund
International Bible Students Association
The J. A. R. Charitable Trust
The Jerusalem Trust
The Kennedy Charitable Foundation
The Friends of Kent Churches
*The Labone Charitable Trust**
The K. P. Ladd Charitable Trust
The Kirby Laing Foundation
The Leonard Laity Stoate Charitable Trust
Lancaster Foundation
The Herd Lawson and Muriel Lawson Charitable Trust
The Charles Littlewood Hill Trust
The Mallinckrodt Foundation
Charity of John Marshall
Charlotte Marshall Charitable Trust
John Martin's Charity
*The Milne Family Foundation**
The Mizpah Trust
The Mulberry Trust
The National Churches Trust
The Norfolk Churches Trust Ltd
The Norwood and Newton Settlement
The Ogle Christian Trust
The Ouseley Church Music Trust
*The P27 Trust**
The Gerald Palmer Eling Trust Company
The Panacea Charitable Trust
Miss M. E. S. Paterson's Charitable Trust
Sir John Priestman Charity Trust
The Privy Purse Charitable Trust
Quothquan Trust
The Bishop Radford Trust
The Joseph Rank Trust
The Sir James Reckitt Charity
Riada Trust
The River Trust
Robertson Hall Trust
Mrs L. D. Rope's Third Charitable Settlement
Rosca Trust
The Saddlers' Company Charitable Fund
Sarum St Michael Educational Charity
Seedfield Trust
The SMB Trust
*Smith Bradbeer Charitable Trust**
The Souter Charitable Trust
W. F. Southall Trust
St Peter's Saltley Trust
Stewards Company Ltd
Sir Halley Stewart Trust
The Stobart Newlands Charitable Trust
Sabina Sutherland Charitable Trust
Swansea and Brecon Diocesan Board of Finance Ltd
C. B. and H. H. Taylor 1984 Trust
The Thornton Trust
The Tory Family Foundation
The Toye Foundation
The Tufton Charitable Trust
The Union of the Sisters of Mercy of Great Britain
The Welsh Church Act Fund
Westhill Endowment
The Norman Whiteley Trust
Dame Violet Wills Charitable Trust
The James Wood Bequest Fund
WWDP (World Day of Prayer National Committee for England, Wales and Northern Ireland)

■ People of the Jewish faith

4 Charity Foundation
A. W. Charitable Trust
The Aaronson Foundation
The Aberdeen Foundation
The Acacia Charitable Trust
Adenfirst Ltd
The Aimwell Charitable Trust
Alliance Family Foundation Ltd
Amabrill Ltd
Anpride Ltd
The Ardwick Trust
Keren Association Ltd
Atkin Charitable Foundation
Atlas Memorial Ltd
The Andrew Balint Charitable Trust
Bay Charitable Trust
Bear Mordechai Ltd
Beauland Ltd
The Beaverbrooks Charitable Trust
The Becker Family Charitable Trust
Belljoe Tzedoko Ltd
Benesco Charity Ltd
Ruth Berkowitz Charitable Trust
The Beth Hamedrash Satmar Trust (BHST)
Asser Bishvil Foundation
The Bloom Foundation
The Bluston Charitable Settlement
The Bonamy Charitable Trust
Salo Bordon Charitable Trust
Sir Clive Bourne Family Trust

Bourneheights Ltd
Friends of Boyan Trust
Brushmill Ltd
C. and F. Charitable Trust
Carlee Ltd
Chalfords Ltd
Charitworth Ltd
The Childwick Trust
The Clore Duffield Foundation
Closehelm Ltd
Clydpride Ltd
CMZ Ltd
The Vivienne and Samuel Cohen Charitable Trust
The Gershon Coren Charitable Foundation (also known as The Muriel and Gus Coren Charitable Foundation)
Countypier Ltd*
The Craps Charitable Trust
Itzchok Meyer Cymerman Trust Ltd
D. M. H. Educational Trust Ltd
Oizer Dalim Trust
The Davidson Family Charitable Trust
The Davis Foundation
Debmar Benevolent Trust Ltd
The Djanogly Foundation
Dollond Charitable Trust
The Dorfman Foundation
The Doughty Charity Trust
Dushinsky Trust Ltd
Elanore Ltd
The George Elias Charitable Trust
The Ellinson Foundation Ltd
Entindale Ltd
Esher House Charitable Trust
The Eventhall Family Charitable Trust
The Exilarch's Foundation
Extonglen Ltd
Famos Foundation Trust
Fordeve Ltd
The Isaac and Freda Frankel Memorial Charitable Trust
The Jacqueline and Michael Gee Charitable Trust
The Gertner Charitable Trust
The B. and P. Glasser Charitable Trust
The Gould Charitable Trust
Grahame Charitable Foundation Ltd
M. and R. Gross Charities Ltd
The N. and R. Grunbaum Charitable Trust
H. C. Foundation
Hadras Kodesh Trust
The Harbour Charitable Trust
The Simon Heller Charitable Settlement
The Helping Foundation
The Highcroft Charitable Trust
The Holden Charitable Trust
Horwich Shotter Charitable Trust
The Humanitarian Trust
The Huntingdon Foundation Ltd
Hurdale Charity Ltd
IGO Foundation Ltd
Investream Charitable Trust
The J. and J. Benevolent Foundation
Jewish Child's Day (JCD)
The Jewish Youth Fund
J. E. Joseph Charitable Fund
The Jusaca Charitable Trust
The Kasner Charitable Trust
The Michael and Ilse Katz Foundation
C. S. Kaufman Charitable Trust
E. and E. Kernkraut Charities Ltd
The Kirschel Foundation
The Kobler Trust
Kollel and Co. Ltd
Kolyom Trust Ltd
Kupath Gemach Chaim Bechesed Viznitz Trust
The Kyte Charitable Trust
Largsmount Ltd
The Lauffer Family Charitable Foundation
Lawson Beckman Charitable Trust
The Arnold Lee Charitable Trust
The Kennedy Leigh Charitable Trust
Cecil and Hilda Lewis Charitable Trust*
Bernard Lewis Family Charitable Trust
David and Ruth Lewis Family Charitable Trust
The Second Joseph Aaron Littman Foundation
Jack Livingstone Charitable Trust
Local Trent Ltd
The Locker Foundation
Loftus Charitable Trust
LPW Ltd
M. and C. Trust
M. B. Foundation
The M. Y. A. Charitable Trust
The Manackerman Charitable Trust
The Manson Family Charitable Trust*
Marbeh Torah Trust
The Stella and Alexander Margulies Charitable Trust
The Marks Family Charitable Trust
The Violet Mauray Charitable Trust
Mayfair Charities Ltd
Mayheights Ltd
Maypride Ltd
Melodor Ltd
The Melow Charitable Trust
Menuchar Ltd
Mercaz Torah Vechesed Ltd
The Mishcon Family Charitable Trust
Keren Mitzvah Trust
Mole Charitable Trust
The Morgan Charitable Foundation
The Moshal Charitable Trust
Vyoel Moshe Charitable Trust
The Mosselson Charitable Trust
The Mutual Trust Group
MW (CL) Foundation
MW (GK) Foundation
MW (HO) Foundation
MW (RH) Foundation
Nemoral Ltd
Ner Foundation
Nesswall Ltd
Newpier Charity Ltd
Northern Land Trust
Oizer Charitable Trust
The Doris Pacey Charitable Foundation
David Pearlman Charitable Foundation
The Pears Family Charitable Foundation
Dina Perelman Trust Ltd*
B. E. Perl Charitable Trust
The Phillips and Rubens Charitable Trust
The Phillips Family Charitable Trust
The George and Esme Pollitzer Charitable Settlement
Premierquote Ltd
Premishlaner Charitable Trust
R. S. Charitable Trust
Rachel Charitable Trust
The Rayne Trust
Rentrust Foundation Ltd
The Rest-Harrow Trust
Reuben Foundation
Richmond Parish Lands Charity
Ridgesave Ltd
The Rofeh Trust
The Gerald and Gail Ronson Family Foundation
Rothschild Foundation (Hanadiv) Europe
Rowanville Ltd
The Rubin Foundation Charitable Trust
S. and R. Charitable Trust
The Jeremy and John Sacher Charitable Trust
The Michael and Nicola Sacher Charitable Trust
Samjo Ltd

The Peter Samuel Charitable Trust
Schass Foundation
The Annie Schiff Charitable Trust
O. and G. Schreiber Charitable Trust
The Searchlight Electric Charitable Trust
Sam and Bella Sebba Charitable Trust
Sellata Ltd
The Cyril Shack Trust
The Archie Sherman Charitable Trust
Shlomo Memorial Fund Ltd
Shulem B. Association Ltd
The Sobell Foundation
The E. C. Sosnow Charitable Trust
Sparquote Ltd
Rosalyn and Nicholas Springer Charitable Trust
Starlow Charities Ltd
The Steinberg Family Charitable Trust
C. E. K. Stern Charitable Trust
Stervon Ltd
T. and S. Trust Fund
The Tajtelbaum Charitable Trust
Talteg Ltd
The David Tannen Charitable Trust
Tegham Ltd
Truedene Co. Ltd
Truemart Ltd
Trumros Ltd
Tzedakah
The Union of Orthodox Hebrew Congregations
United Jewish Israel Appeal
The David Uri Memorial Trust
The Vail Foundation
*The Velvet Foundation**
VHLT Ltd
Vivdale Ltd
The Linda and Michael Weinstein Charitable Trust
The Wigoder Family Foundation
The Benjamin Winegarten Charitable Trust
The Wingate Foundation
Friends of Wiznitz Ltd
The Maurice Wohl Charitable Foundation
The Charles Wolfson Charitable Trust
The Wolfson Family Charitable Trust
Woodlands Green Ltd
Wychdale Ltd
Wychville Ltd
Yankov Charitable Trust
The Marjorie and Arnold Ziff Charitable Foundation

■ People of the Muslim faith

Dawat-E-Hadiyah Trust (United Kingdom)
The Matliwala Family Charitable Trust
Muslim Hands

Social and economic circumstances

The 29th May 1961 Charitable Trust
The 4814 Trust
The A. B. Charitable Trust
The Aberdeen Foundation
ABF The Soldiers' Charity
Access Sport CIO
*The Access to Justice Foundation**
The Adint Charitable Trust
Sylvia Aitken's Charitable Trust
Ajahma Charitable Trust
The Alborada Trust
The Alchemy Foundation
The Aldama Foundation
The Derrill Allatt Foundation
Allchurches Trust Ltd
The Allen & Overy Foundation
D. C. R. Allen Charitable Trust
Alliance Family Foundation Ltd
*Alpkit Foundation**
The AMW Charitable Trust
The Anchor Foundation
Andrews Charitable Trust
Anguish's Educational Foundation
The Apax Foundation
The John Apthorp Charity
The Archer Trust
Ardbarron Trust Ltd
The Ardwick Trust
The John Armitage Charitable Trust
The Arsenal Foundation
The Artemis Charitable Foundation
Ove Arup Partnership Charitable Trust
The Ashburnham Thanksgiving Trust
The Ashworth Charitable Trust
The Lord Austin Trust
Axis Foundation
The Scott Bader Commonwealth Ltd
The Austin Bailey Foundation
Bairdwatson Charitable Trust
The Roy and Pixie Baker Charitable Trust
The Balcombe Charitable Trust
The Balfour Beatty Charitable Trust
The Roger and Sarah Bancroft Clark Charitable Trust
Bank of Scotland Foundation
The Barbour Foundation
*The Barnes Fund**
The Barnsbury Charitable Trust
Barnwood Trust
Misses Barrie Charitable Trust
The Batchworth Trust
Bauer Radio's Cash for Kids Charities
Bay Charitable Trust
The Bay Tree Charitable Trust
BBC Children in Need
Bearder Charity
The James Beattie Charitable Trust
Beauland Ltd
The Beaverbrooks Charitable Trust
The John Beckwith Charitable Trust
Bedfordshire and Luton Community Foundation
Bedfordshire Charitable Trust Ltd
*AJ Bell Trust**
The Bellahouston Bequest Fund
The Benham Charitable Settlement
The Rowan Bentall Charitable Trust
The Berkeley Foundation
The Bestway Foundation
The Beth Hamedrash Satmar Trust (BHST)
Bideford Bridge Trust
*The Big Yellow Foundation**
The Percy Bilton Charity
The Bingham Trust
Birmingham International Airport Community Trust Fund
The Sydney Black Charitable Trust
The Isabel Blackman Foundation
Lady Blakenham's Charity Trust
The Blandford Lake Trust
The Boltini Trust
BOOST Charitable Trust
The Booth Charities
Boots Charitable Trust
The Oliver Borthwick Memorial Trust
The Harry Bottom Charitable Trust
The Bowerman Charitable Trust
The Liz and Terry Bramall Foundation
The Breadsticks Foundation
The Brelms Trust CIO
The Brenley Trust

Bristol Charities
The Britford Bridge Trust
The British and Foreign School Society
British Gas Energy Trust
British Humane Association
The J. and M. Britton Charitable Trust
The Brook Trust
Bill Brown 1989 Charitable Trust
R. S. Brownless Charitable Trust
Brushmill Ltd
Buckinghamshire Community Foundation
Building & Civil Engineering Charitable Trust
E. F. Bulmer Trust
The Arnold Burton 1998 Charitable Trust
Consolidated Charity of Burton upon Trent
The Noel Buxton Trust
Byrne Family Foundation
The Barrow Cadbury Trust
The Edward and Dorothy Cadbury Trust
Community Foundation for Calderdale
Callendar Charitable Trust
The Cambridgeshire Community Foundation
Camden Giving*
The Campden Charities Trustee
Canary Wharf Contractors Fund
The W. A. Cargill Fund
The Antonio Carluccio Foundation*
The Carr-Gregory Trust
The Joseph and Annie Cattle Trust
The Wilfrid and Constance Cave Foundation
The B. G. S. Cayzer Charitable Trust
CEO Sleepout
The Amelia Chadwick Trust
The Chalk Cliff Trust
The Charities Advisory Trust
The Charterhouse Charitable Trust
Cheshire Community Foundation Ltd
The Chetwode Foundation
The Childhood Trust
Chippenham Borough Lands Charity
CHK Foundation
Christadelphian Samaritan Fund
The André Christian Trust
Chrysalis Trust
The Church Burgesses Educational Foundation
The City Bridge Trust (Bridge House Estates)
CLA Charitable Trust
J. A. Clark Charitable Trust
The Clore Duffield Foundation
The Clothworkers' Foundation
Cloudesley
The Clover Trust
The John Coates Charitable Trust
The Vivienne and Samuel Cohen Charitable Trust
The John S. Cohen Foundation
The Cole Charitable Trust
The Coltstaple Trust
Colyer-Fergusson Charitable Trust
Comic Relief
Community First
The Cooks Charity
The Alice Ellen Cooper Dean Charitable Foundation
The Worshipful Company of Cordwainers Charitable Trusts (Minges Gift)
The Gershon Coren Charitable Foundation (also known as The Muriel and Gus Coren Charitable Foundation)
The Evan Cornish Foundation
Corra Foundation
Coventry Building Society Charitable Foundation
The Lord Cozens-Hardy Trust
Michael Crawford Children's Charity
CRH Charitable Trust*
Cripplegate Foundation
Crisis UK
The Cross Trust
The Croydon Relief in Need Charities
Cruden Foundation Ltd
Cumbria Community Foundation
The D. G. Charitable Settlement
The D'Oyly Carte Charitable Trust
Dawat-E-Hadiyah Trust (United Kingdom)
The Roger De Haan Charitable Trust
Foundation Derbyshire
The J. N. Derbyshire Trust
The Gillian Dickinson Trust
Didymus
The Ken Dodd Charitable Foundation*
Dorset Community Foundation
The Double 'O' Charity Ltd
The Doughty Charity Trust
Drapers' Charitable Fund
Dromintee Trust
The Anne Duchess of Westminster's Charity
The Dulverton Trust
The Charles Dunstone Charitable Trust
County Durham Community Foundation
The Dyers' Company Charitable Trust
The Earley Charity
EBM Charitable Trust
Edinburgh Children's Holiday Fund
Edupoor Ltd
The Eight Foundation*
The George Elias Charitable Trust
The Wilfred and Elsie Elkes Charity Fund
The Ellerdale Trust
The Endrick Trust
The Englefield Charitable Trust
The Enkalon Foundation
Entindale Ltd
The EQ Foundation
Essex Community Foundation
The Estelle Trust
The Eventhall Family Charitable Trust
The Everard Foundation
The Eveson Charitable Trust
The Exilarch's Foundation
The ExPat Foundation
G. F. Eyre Charitable Trust
The Lord Faringdon Charitable Trust
Samuel William Farmer Trust
The Farthing Trust
The February Foundation
The George Fentham Birmingham Charity
Allan and Nesta Ferguson Charitable Settlement
The Fifty Fund
The Finborough Foundation
Fine & Country Foundation
The Earl Fitzwilliam Charitable Trust
The Robert Fleming Hannay Memorial Charity
The Follett Trust
Forest Hill Charitable Trust
Forever Manchester
The Forman Hardy Charitable Trust
Donald Forrester Trust
The Anna Rosa Forster Charitable Trust
Foux Foundation*
The Foyle Foundation
The Elizabeth Frankland Moore and Star Foundation
Jill Franklin Trust
The Gordon Fraser Charitable Trust
The Hugh Fraser Foundation

The Louis and Valerie Freedman Charitable Settlement
Charles S. French Charitable Trust
The Freshgate Trust Foundation
Friends Provident Charitable Foundation
The Patrick and Helena Frost Foundation
The Fulmer Charitable Trust
The G. D. Charitable Trust
Gamma Trust
The Gannochy Trust
Garfield Weston Foundation
Garthgwynion Charities
General Charity (Coventry)
The General Charity Fund
The Generations Foundation
The Steven Gerrard Foundation
The Tara Getty Foundation
The David Gibbons Foundation
The Gibbs Charitable Trusts
The Girdlers' Company Charitable Trust
The Gloag Foundation
Global Charities
County of Gloucestershire Community Foundation
Sydney and Phyllis Goldberg Memorial Charitable Trust
The Goldsmiths' Company Charity
The Goodman Foundation
The Gosling Foundation Ltd
The Edward Gostling Foundation
Gowling WLG (UK) Charitable Trust
The Hemraj Goyal Foundation
Grace Charitable Trust
The Grace Trust
The Graham Trust
The Grant Foundation
The Grantham Yorke Trust
The J. G. Graves Charitable Trust
The Green Hall Foundation
Philip and Judith Green Trust
Greenham Trust Ltd
The Greggs Foundation
The Walter Guinness Charitable Trust
H. C. D. Memorial Fund
Hackney Parochial Charities
The Hadley Trust
The Hadrian Trust
The Alfred Haines Charitable Trust
Paul Hamlyn Foundation
The Helen Hamlyn Trust
Hammersmith United Charities
Hampshire and Isle of Wight Community Foundation
The Hampstead Wells and Campden Trust
Hampton Fund
The W. A. Handley Charity Trust
The Lennox Hannay Charitable Trust
The Haramead Trust
Harborne Parish Lands Charity
The Harbour Foundation
William Harding's Charity
The Harpur Trust
The Edith Lilian Harrison 2000 Foundation
The Peter Harrison Foundation
The Harrison-Frank Family Foundation (UK) Ltd
The Harry and Mary Foundation*
Edward Harvist Trust (The Harvist Estate)
The Hasluck Charitable Trust
The Hawthorne Charitable Trust
The Charles Hayward Foundation
The Headley Trust
May Hearnshaw's Charity
Heart of England Community Foundation
The Hedley Foundation
The Helping Foundation
The Hemby Charitable Trust
Henley Educational Trust
The Tim Henman Foundation
Herefordshire Community Foundation
Hertfordshire Community Foundation
P. and C. Hickinbotham Charitable Trust
The Alan Edward Higgs Charity
Highway One Trust
The Hilden Charitable Fund
The Hillier Trust
R. G. Hills Charitable Trust
The Lady Hind Trust
The Hinduja Foundation
The Hiscox Foundation
The Henry C. Hoare Charitable Trust
The Hobson Charity Ltd
The Holbeck Charitable Trust
Hollick Family Foundation
P. H. Holt Foundation
The Holywood Trust
The Mary Homfray Charitable Trust
Sir Harold Hood's Charitable Trust
The Thomas J. Horne Memorial Trust
The Hospital of God at Greatham
House of Industry Estate
Housing Pathways Trust
The Huggard Charitable Trust
The Hull and East Riding Charitable Trust
The Humanitarian Trust
The Hunter Foundation
Huntingdon Freemen's Trust
The Nani Huyu Charitable Trust
Hyde Charitable Trust
Ibrahim Foundation Ltd
Imagine Foundation
Impact Funding Partners Ltd
Impetus
The Inflexion Foundation*
Inner London Magistrates Court Poor Box and Feeder Charity
The Innocent Foundation
The International Bankers Charitable Trust
Investream Charitable Trust
The Invigorate Charitable Trust
The Ireland Fund of Great Britain
Irish Youth Foundation (UK) Ltd (incorporating The Lawlor Foundation)
The Charles Irving Charitable Trust
Isle of Wight Foundation
The J. and J. Benevolent Foundation
The J. A. R. Charitable Trust
The Jabbs Foundation
The Frank Jackson Foundation
John Jarrold Trust Ltd
JD Foundation*
The Jenour Foundation
The Elton John Aids Foundation (EJAF)
The Johnson Foundation
Johnnie Johnson Trust
The Jones 1986 Charitable Trust
The Muriel Jones Foundation
J. E. Joseph Charitable Fund
The Cyril and Eve Jumbo Charitable Trust
Anton Jurgens Charitable Trust
The Jusaca Charitable Trust
The Michael and Ilse Katz Foundation
The Emmanuel Kaye Foundation
The Kelly Family Charitable Trust
William Kendall's Charity (Wax Chandlers' Company)
The Kensington and Chelsea Foundation
Kent Community Foundation
The Nancy Kenyon Charitable Trust
KFC Foundation*
Kilpatrick Fraser Charitable Trust

The Graham Kirkham Foundation
The Kirschel Foundation
Sir James Knott Trust
Kollel and Co. Ltd
KPE4 Charitable Trust*
The KPMG Foundation
Kupath Gemach Chaim Bechesed Viznitz Trust
Kusuma Trust UK
Ladbrokes Coral Trust
Maurice and Hilda Laing Charitable Trust
The Martin Laing Foundation
The Beatrice Laing Trust
The Leonard Laity Stoate Charitable Trust
The Lake House Charity
Community Foundations for Lancashire and Merseyside
The Lancashire Foundation
Duchy of Lancaster Benevolent Fund
Lancaster Foundation
LandAid Charitable Trust (LandAid)
The Allen Lane Foundation
The R. J. Larg Family Trust
Largsmount Ltd
Laslett's (Hinton) Charity
Mrs F. B. Laurence Charitable Trust
The Edgar E. Lawley Foundation
The Herd Lawson and Muriel Lawson Charitable Trust
Lawson Beckman Charitable Trust
The Lawson Trust CIO
The Leach Fourteenth Trust
The Leathersellers' Company Charitable Fund
Leeds Building Society Charitable Foundation
Leeds Community Foundation (LCF)
The Leeward Trust*
The Legal Education Foundation
Leicestershire and Rutland Masonic Charity Association
The Kennedy Leigh Charitable Trust
The Leigh Trust
Bernard Lewis Family Charitable Trust
David and Ruth Lewis Family Charitable Trust
The Limbourne Trust
The Linbury Trust
Lincolnshire Community Foundation
The Linder Foundation
The Frank Litchfield Charitable Trust
The Charles Littlewood Hill Trust
The Second Joseph Aaron Littman Foundation
The Ian and Natalie Livingstone Charitable Trust
The Elaine and Angus Lloyd Charitable Trust
The W. M. and B. W. Lloyd Trust
Lloyds Bank Foundation for England and Wales
Lloyds Bank Foundation for the Channel Islands
Lloyd's Patriotic Fund
Local Trent Ltd
Loftus Charitable Trust
London Catalyst
London Housing Foundation Ltd (LHF)
London Legal Support Trust (LLST)
Longleigh Foundation
The Lord's Taverners
The C. L. Loyd Charitable Trust
The Henry Lumley Charitable Trust
The Lyndal Tree Foundation
John Lyon's Charity
Sylvanus Lysons Charity
M. and C. Trust
The R. S. Macdonald Charitable Trust
Mace Foundation
The Magdalen and Lasher Charity (General Fund)
Makers of Playing Cards Charity
The Manchester Guardian Society Charitable Trust
R. W. Mann Trust
The Marandi Foundation*
Marbeh Torah Trust
Marmot Charitable Trust
The Michael Marsh Charitable Trust
The Marsh Christian Trust
Charlotte Marshall Charitable Trust
D. G. Marshall of Cambridge Trust
Sir George Martin Trust
John Martin's Charity
Nancie Massey Charitable Trust
The Master Charitable Trust
The Mather Family Charitable Trust*
Mathew Trust
The Matliwala Family Charitable Trust
Mayfair Charities Ltd
Gemma and Chris McGough Charitable Foundation CIO*
The Medlock Charitable Trust
Melodor Ltd
The Melow Charitable Trust
Mercaz Torah Vechesed Ltd
The Brian Mercer Charitable Trust
The Mercers' Charitable Foundation
The Merchant Taylors' Company Charities Fund
The Merchant Venturers' Charity
Merchants' House of Glasgow
T. and J. Meyer Family Foundation Ltd
The Mickel Fund
The Mickleham Trust
The Gerald Micklem Charitable Trust
The Millennium Oak Trust
Jean and Roger Miller's Charitable Trust
The Millfield House Foundation (1)
Mills and Reeve Charitable Trust
Milton Keynes Community Foundation Ltd
The Peter Minet Trust
The Mishcon Family Charitable Trust
The Brian Mitchell Charitable Settlement
Keren Mitzvah Trust
The Mizpah Trust
The Monday Charitable Trust*
The Monmouthshire County Council Welsh Church Act Fund
Moondance Foundation
John Moores Foundation
The Morgan Charitable Foundation
The Steve Morgan Foundation
The Morris Charitable Trust
G. M. Morrison Charitable Trust
The Morrisons Foundation
The Morton Charitable Trust (Dundee)
Moto in the Community
The MSE Charity
The Mulberry Trust
Edith Murphy Foundation
Murphy-Neumann Charity Company Ltd
The John R. Murray Charitable Trust
Brian Murtagh Charitable Trust
Muslim Hands
The Janet Nash Charitable Settlement
The National Express Foundation
The National Garden Scheme
The Nationwide Foundation
The NDL Foundation
Nemoral Ltd

Network for Social Change Charitable Trust
Newby Trust Ltd
Newpier Charity Ltd
The NFU Mutual Charitable Trust
The Nisbet Trust
The Nomura Charitable Trust
Norfolk Community Foundation
The Norman Family Charitable Trust
Normanby Charitable Trust
North East Area Miners' Social Welfare Trust Fund
Northamptonshire Community Foundation
Community Foundation for Northern Ireland
The Northwick Trust
The Norton Foundation
The Norton Rose Fulbright Charitable Foundation
Norwich Town Close Estate Charity
Notting Hill Genesis Community Foundation
Nottinghamshire Community Foundation
The Nuffield Foundation
Odin Charitable Trust
The Ogle Christian Trust
Henry Oldfield Trust
One Community Foundation Ltd
Oxfordshire Community Foundation
P. F. Charitable Trust
The Paget Charitable Trust
The Gerald Palmer Eling Trust Company
The Panacea Charitable Trust
The Paragon Trust
The Pargiter Trust
*Partners Global Foundation**
The Pastoral Care Trust – The St Nicholas Care Fund
Payne-Gallwey 1989 Charitable Trust
The Dowager Countess Eleanor Peel Trust
People's Health Trust
People's Postcode Trust
Personal Assurance Charitable Trust
The Pharsalia Charitable Trust
The Pilgrim Trust
Pilkington Charities Fund
PIMCO Foundation Europe
The Pitt-Rivers Charitable Trust
Polden-Puckham Charitable Foundation
The George and Esme Pollitzer Charitable Settlement
The Porta Pia 2012 Foundation
The Portishead Nautical Trust
Postcode Local Trust
Postcode Society Trust (formerly Postcode Dream Trust)
David and Elaine Potter Foundation
Premierquote Ltd
The Pret Foundation
Sir John Priestman Charity Trust
The Prince of Wales's Charitable Foundation
The Prince's Countryside Fund
The Princess Anne's Charities
The Privy Purse Charitable Trust
The Professional Footballers' Association Charity
The Progress Foundation
The PwC Foundation
The Pye Foundation
Mr and Mrs J. A. Pye's Charitable Settlement
QBE European Operations Foundation
*Quadstar Charitable Foundation**
Quartet Community Foundation
The Queen Anne's Gate Foundation
*The Quilter Foundation**
Quothquan Trust
R. S. Charitable Trust
The Monica Rabagliati Charitable Trust
Rachel Charitable Trust
Richard Radcliffe Trust
The Rainford Trust
The Eleanor Rathbone Charitable Trust
Elizabeth Rathbone Charity
The Ravensdale Trust
The Rayne Foundation
The Sir James Reckitt Charity
C. A. Redfern Charitable Foundation
The Resolution Trust
The Rest-Harrow Trust
Reuben Foundation
Rhodi Charitable Trust
The Rhododendron Trust
Riada Trust
Daisie Rich Trust
Richmond Parish Lands Charity
Rigby Foundation
Riverside Charitable Trust Ltd
The Robertson Trust
The Sir James Roll Charitable Trust
Mrs L. D. Rope's Third Charitable Settlement
Rosca Trust
The Eranda Rothschild Foundation
The Roughley Charitable Trust
The Rowlands Trust
The Joseph Rowntree Charitable Trust
The Royal British Legion
Royal Docks Trust (London)
The Rugby Group Benevolent Fund Ltd
S. and R. Charitable Trust
The Jeremy and John Sacher Charitable Trust
The Michael and Nicola Sacher Charitable Trust
The Saddlers' Company Charitable Fund
The Alan and Babette Sainsbury Charitable Fund
The Saintbury Trust
The Salamander Charitable Trust
Salters' Charitable Foundation
The Basil Samuel Charitable Trust
The Samworth Foundation
The Sandhu Charitable Foundation
The Savoy Educational Trust
O. and G. Schreiber Charitable Trust
Schroder Charity Trust
Foundation Scotland
Francis C. Scott Charitable Trust
The Frieda Scott Charitable Trust
The John Scott Trust Fund
Scottish Coal Industry Special Welfare Fund
The Scottish Power Foundation
Scouloudi Foundation
The SDL Foundation
Sam and Bella Sebba Charitable Trust
Seedfield Trust
The Segelman Trust
The Shanly Foundation
The Shears Foundation
The Sheldon Trust
Shetland Charitable Trust
SHINE (Support and Help in Education)
The Bassil Shippam and Alsford Trust
The Shipwrights' Charitable Fund
The Shoe Zone Trust
The Simmons & Simmons Charitable Foundation
The Thomas Sivewright Catto Charitable Settlement
The Skelton Bounty
Rita and David Slowe Charitable Trust
The SMB Trust
The Mrs Smith and Mount Trust
The Henry Smith Charity

Arabella and Julian Smith Family Trust*
Philip Smith's Charitable Trust
The Sobell Foundation
Social Tech Trust
Sodexo Stop Hunger Foundation
Sofronie Foundation
Somerset Community Foundation
The E. C. Sosnow Charitable Trust
The Souter Charitable Trust
The South Yorkshire Community Foundation
W. F. Southall Trust
Sparquote Ltd
The Spear Charitable Trust
Spielman Charitable Trust
Rosalyn and Nicholas Springer Charitable Trust
The St Hilda's Trust
The St James's Trust Settlement
Sir Walter St John's Educational Charity
The Stafford Trust
The Community Foundation for Staffordshire
Standard Life Foundation
The Peter Stebbings Memorial Charity
The Hugh Stenhouse Foundation
Stervon Ltd
Sir Halley Stewart Trust
The Stone Family Foundation
Strand Parishes Trust
Stratford-upon-Avon Town Trust
The WO Street Charitable Foundation
The Street Foundation
StreetSmart – Action for the Homeless
Suffolk Community Foundation
The Summerfield Charitable Trust
The Bernard Sunley Foundation
The Sunrise Foundation CIO
Community Foundation for Surrey
Sutton Coldfield Charitable Trust
Swan Mountain Trust
The Swann-Morton Foundation
The Swire Charitable Trust
The Charles and Elsie Sykes Trust
The Tabhair Charitable Trust
The Talbot Trusts
The Talbot Village Trust
Tallow Chandlers Benevolent Fund No. 2
The Taylor Family Foundation
Tegham Ltd
the7stars Foundation*
Scott Thomson Charitable Trust
Sir Jules Thorn Charitable Trust
The Thornton Trust
The Tobacco Pipe Makers and Tobacco Trade Benevolent Fund
The Tolkien Trust
Tower Hill Trust
The Toy Trust
Toyota Manufacturing UK Charitable Trust
The Trades House of Glasgow
Annie Tranmer Charitable Trust
The Constance Travis Charitable Trust
The Triangle Trust (1949) Fund
The Truemark Trust
Trust for London
The Trusthouse Charitable Foundation
The Tudor Trust
The Tuixen Foundation
The Turtleton Charitable Trust
Two Ridings Community Foundation
Tzedakah
Ulster Garden Villages Ltd
The Underwood Trust
The Union of the Sisters of Mercy of Great Britain
United St Saviour's Charity
UPP Foundation
The Albert Van Den Bergh Charitable Trust
The Van Neste Foundation
The Vandervell Foundation
The Vardy Foundation
The Vintners' Foundation
Virgin Atlantic Foundation
The Virgin Money Foundation
The Vodafone Foundation
Volant Charitable Trust
The Georg and Emily Von Opel Foundation*
Sylvia Waddilove Foundation UK
The Scurrah Wainwright Charity
Wakefield and Tetley Trust
The Wakeham Trust
The Walcot Foundation
The Walker Trust
Walton on Thames Charity
Warwick Relief in Need Charity
The Warwickshire Masonic Charitable Association Ltd
Mrs Waterhouse Charitable Trust
Wates Family Enterprise Trust
The Wates Foundation
The William Wates Memorial Trust
The Geoffrey Watling Charity
Blyth Watson Charitable Trust
John Watson's Trust
The Weavers' Company Benevolent Fund
The William Webster Charitable Trust
Wellington Management UK Foundation
The Welsh Church Act Fund
West Derby Waste Lands Charity
Westminster Almshouses Foundation
Westminster Foundation
Westway Trust
The Melanie White Foundation Ltd
White Stuff Foundation
Charity of Sir Richard Whittington
The Wilson Foundation
Wiltshire Community Foundation
The Wimbledon Foundation
The Benjamin Winegarten Charitable Trust
The Michael and Anna Wix Charitable Trust
The Wixamtree Trust
Friends of Wiznitz Ltd
The Maurice Wohl Charitable Foundation
The Wood Foundation
Wooden Spoon Society
Woodlands Green Ltd
Woodroffe Benton Foundation
The Woodward Charitable Trust
Worcester Municipal Charities (CIO)
The Eric Wright Charitable Trust
Sir Graham Wylie Foundation*
The Wyseliot Rose Charitable Trust
The Yapp Charitable Trust
York Children's Trust
Yorkshire Building Society Charitable Foundation
Youth Music
The Elizabeth and Prince Zaiger Trust
The Zochonis Charitable Trust
Zurich Community Trust (UK) Ltd

Asylum seekers/internally displaced peoples/refugees

The A. B. Charitable Trust
The Alborada Trust
The Apax Foundation
The Roger and Sarah Bancroft Clark Charitable Trust
The Big Yellow Foundation*
The Bromley Trust

The Noel Buxton Trust
William A. Cadbury Charitable Trust
The Charities Advisory Trust
The City Bridge Trust (Bridge House Estates)
J. A. Clark Charitable Trust
The Evan Cornish Foundation
The D. G. Charitable Settlement
The Dashlight Foundation*
The Emerton-Christie Charity
The EQ Foundation
The Fairness Foundation
Gwyneth Forrester Trust
Jill Franklin Trust
Gamma Trust
The Gloag Foundation
H. C. D. Memorial Fund
Paul Hamlyn Foundation
The Harbour Foundation
P. and C. Hickinbotham Charitable Trust
The Hilden Charitable Fund
The Holbeck Charitable Trust
P. H. Holt Foundation
The Hospital of God at Greatham
Inner London Magistrates Court Poor Box and Feeder Charity
The Allen Lane Foundation
The Leigh Trust
The Mark Leonard Trust
The Leri Charitable Trust
The Limbourne Trust
The Linbury Trust
Lloyds Bank Foundation for England and Wales
The London Community Foundation (LCF)
The Marks Family Charitable Trust
The Marsh Christian Trust
The Mercers' Charitable Foundation
The Mickleham Trust
Network for Social Change Charitable Trust
Newby Trust Ltd
Community Foundation for Northern Ireland
The Northwick Trust
Odin Charitable Trust
Orange Tree Trust*
The Pastoral Care Trust – The St Nicholas Care Fund
People's Postcode Trust
The Pickwell Foundation
The Austin and Hope Pilkington Trust
The Eleanor Rathbone Charitable Trust
The Sigrid Rausing Trust
The Rayne Foundation
The Robertson Trust
Rosca Trust
The Roughley Charitable Trust
The Joseph Rowntree Charitable Trust
The Alan and Babette Sainsbury Charitable Fund
Sam and Bella Sebba Charitable Trust
Swan Mountain Trust
The Gay and Keith Talbot Trust
The Talbot Trusts
The Tolkien Trust
The Union of the Sisters of Mercy of Great Britain
The Vodafone Foundation
Volant Charitable Trust
Wakefield and Tetley Trust
The Woodward Charitable Trust

Carers

The Alchemy Foundation
The Astor Foundation
The Barnes Fund*
The Birmingham District Nursing Charitable Trust
The Charlotte Bonham-Carter Charitable Trust
BUPA UK Foundation
CHK Foundation
The City Bridge Trust (Bridge House Estates)
The Clothworkers' Foundation
Colchester Catalyst Charity
The D'Oyly Carte Charitable Trust
The Anne Duchess of Westminster's Charity
County Durham Community Foundation
The Forbes Charitable Foundation
Jill Franklin Trust
The Girdlers' Company Charitable Trust
Global Charities
The Goldsmiths' Company Charity
The Greggs Foundation
The Hadrian Trust
Hampton Fund
Harborne Parish Lands Charity
The Headley Trust
The Hedley Foundation
P. and C. Hickinbotham Charitable Trust
The Hobson Charity Ltd
Hospice UK
The Roger and Jean Jefcoate Trust
KFC Foundation*
The Martin Laing Foundation
The Leach Fourteenth Trust
The Linder Foundation
Lloyds Bank Foundation for the Channel Islands
The Lord's Taverners
The Lyndal Tree Foundation
The R. S. Macdonald Charitable Trust
The MacRobert Trust 2019
The Mercers' Charitable Foundation
The Mickleham Trust
The Gerald Micklem Charitable Trust
John Moores Foundation
The Morrisons Foundation
The MSE Charity
Norfolk Community Foundation
The Quilter Foundation*
The Rayne Foundation
The Rhododendron Trust
Rix Thompson Rothenberg Foundation
The Robertson Trust
The Roughley Charitable Trust
The Frieda Scott Charitable Trust
The Skelton Bounty
The Tedworth Charitable Trust
the7stars Foundation*
The Triangle Trust (1949) Fund
Ulster Garden Villages Ltd
Walton on Thames Charity
The Waterloo Foundation
The Will Charitable Trust
The Eric Wright Charitable Trust

Disadvantaged and socially excluded people

The 29th May 1961 Charitable Trust
The 4814 Trust
The Aberdeen Foundation
Access Sport CIO
The Access to Justice Foundation*
The Derrill Allatt Foundation
D. C. R. Allen Charitable Trust
The AMW Charitable Trust
The Anchor Foundation
Anpride Ltd
The John Apthorp Charity
The Ardwick Trust
The John Armitage Charitable Trust
The Arsenal Foundation
The Ashworth Charitable Trust
Axis Foundation
The Austin Bailey Foundation
The Balcombe Charitable Trust
The Roger and Sarah Bancroft Clark Charitable Trust
Bank of Scotland Foundation
The Baring Foundation
Barnwood Trust

Bauer Radio's Cash for Kids Charities
Bay Charitable Trust
The Bay Tree Charitable Trust
BBC Children in Need
Bearder Charity
The James Beattie Charitable Trust
Beauland Ltd
The John Beckwith Charitable Trust
Bedfordshire and Luton Community Foundation
Bedfordshire Charitable Trust Ltd
*AJ Bell Trust**
The Benham Charitable Settlement
The Berkeley Foundation
The Percy Bilton Charity
The Bingham Trust
Birmingham International Airport Community Trust Fund
Boots Charitable Trust
The Liz and Terry Bramall Foundation
The Brelms Trust CIO
The Brenley Trust
Bristol Charities
The British and Foreign School Society
British Gas Energy Trust
British Humane Association
Bill Brown 1989 Charitable Trust
R. S. Brownless Charitable Trust
Buckinghamshire Community Foundation
The Bulldog Trust Ltd
Consolidated Charity of Burton upon Trent
Byrne Family Foundation
C. and F. Charitable Trust
William A. Cadbury Charitable Trust
The Edward and Dorothy Cadbury Trust
Callendar Charitable Trust
The Campden Charities Trustee
Canary Wharf Contractors Fund
The W. A. Cargill Fund
*The Antonio Carluccio Foundation**
The Carr-Gregory Trust
The Amelia Chadwick Trust
The Charterhouse Charitable Trust
The Chetwode Foundation
The Childhood Trust
Chippenham Borough Lands Charity
The City Bridge Trust (Bridge House Estates)
The Clothworkers' Foundation
Cloudesley
The John Coates Charitable Trust
The Cooks Charity
Co-operative Community Investment Foundation
The Worshipful Company of Cordwainers Charitable Trusts (Minges Gift)
Corra Foundation
The Lord Cozens-Hardy Trust
The Craps Charitable Trust
*CRH Charitable Trust**
The Cross Trust
The Croydon Relief in Need Charities
Foundation Derbyshire
The J. N. Derbyshire Trust
The Gillian Dickinson Trust
Didymus
Drapers' Charitable Fund
The Anne Duchess of Westminster's Charity
The Dulverton Trust
The Charles Dunstone Charitable Trust
The Dyers' Company Charitable Trust
The Earley Charity
Edinburgh Children's Holiday Fund
Edupoor Ltd
*The Eight Foundation**
The EQ Foundation
The Eventhall Family Charitable Trust
The Everard Foundation
The Robert Fleming Hannay Memorial Charity
*Foux Foundation**
The Elizabeth Frankland Moore and Star Foundation
Charles S. French Charitable Trust
The Freshfield Foundation
Friends Provident Charitable Foundation
The Gannochy Trust
General Charity (Coventry)
The General Charity Fund
The Steven Gerrard Foundation
The Tara Getty Foundation
The Gibbs Charitable Trusts
The Girdlers' Company Charitable Trust
Global Charities
County of Gloucestershire Community Foundation
The Hemraj Goyal Foundation
Grace Charitable Trust
The Grace Trust
The Graham Trust
The Grant Foundation
The Grantham Yorke Trust
The J. G. Graves Charitable Trust
The Green Hall Foundation
Greenham Trust Ltd
The Greggs Foundation
Hackney Parochial Charities
Halifax Foundation for Northern Ireland
Hammersmith United Charities
Harborne Parish Lands Charity
William Harding's Charity
The Harrison-Frank Family Foundation (UK) Ltd
Hays Travel Foundation
Heathrow Community Trust
The Hedley Foundation
Hertfordshire Community Foundation
P. and C. Hickinbotham Charitable Trust
The Alan Edward Higgs Charity
The Hillier Trust
The Lady Hind Trust
The Hiscox Foundation
P. H. Holt Foundation
The Holywood Trust
House of Industry Estate
The Huggard Charitable Trust
The Albert Hunt Trust
The Hunter Foundation
Hyde Charitable Trust
Ibrahim Foundation Ltd
Imagine Foundation
Impact Funding Partners Ltd
*The Inflexion Foundation**
Inner London Magistrates Court Poor Box and Feeder Charity
The Invigorate Charitable Trust
The Ireland Fund of Great Britain
Irish Youth Foundation (UK) Ltd (incorporating The Lawlor Foundation)
Isle of Wight Foundation
The Frank Jackson Foundation
The Johnson Foundation
Johnnie Johnson Trust
The Jones 1986 Charitable Trust
The Muriel Jones Foundation
Anton Jurgens Charitable Trust
The Kelly Family Charitable Trust
The Kensington and Chelsea Foundation
The Graham Kirkham Foundation
The Kirschel Foundation
Sir James Knott Trust
*KPE4 Charitable Trust**
Ladbrokes Coral Trust
The Martin Laing Foundation
The Leonard Laity Stoate Charitable Trust
The Lancashire Foundation

LandAid Charitable Trust (LandAid)
Laslett's (Hinton) Charity
Mrs F. B. Laurence Charitable Trust
The Lawson Trust CIO
The Leathersellers' Company Charitable Fund
Leeds Building Society Charitable Foundation
Leeds Community Foundation (LCF)
*The Leeward Trust**
The Mark Leonard Trust
Bernard Lewis Family Charitable Trust
The Charles Littlewood Hill Trust
The Ian and Natalie Livingstone Charitable Trust
The Elaine and Angus Lloyd Charitable Trust
The W. M. and B. W. Lloyd Trust
Lloyds Bank Foundation for England and Wales
London Catalyst
The London Community Foundation (LCF)
London Housing Foundation Ltd (LHF)
London Legal Support Trust (LLST)
The Lord's Taverners
Sylvanus Lysons Charity
The R. S. Macdonald Charitable Trust
Mace Foundation
Makers of Playing Cards Charity
R. W. Mann Trust
The Master Charitable Trust
*Gemma and Chris McGough Charitable Foundation CIO**
The Brian Mercer Charitable Trust
The Mercers' Charitable Foundation
The Mickleham Trust
Jean and Roger Miller's Charitable Trust
The Millfield House Foundation (1)
Mills and Reeve Charitable Trust
Milton Keynes Community Foundation Ltd
The Peter Minet Trust
John Moores Foundation
The Morgan Charitable Foundation
The Steve Morgan Foundation
The Mulberry Trust
Murphy-Neumann Charity Company Ltd
The John R. Murray Charitable Trust
The Janet Nash Charitable Settlement
Newby Trust Ltd
The Norton Foundation
The Norton Rose Fulbright Charitable Foundation
Norwich Town Close Estate Charity
The Nuffield Foundation
Oglesby Charitable Trust
Henry Oldfield Trust
Oxfordshire Community Foundation
The Gerald Palmer Eling Trust Company
The Panacea Charitable Trust
The Pargiter Trust
Payne-Gallwey 1989 Charitable Trust
People's Health Trust
People's Postcode Trust
Personal Assurance Charitable Trust
The Pharsalia Charitable Trust
The Pilgrim Trust
The George and Esme Pollitzer Charitable Settlement
Postcode Local Trust
Postcode Society Trust (formerly Postcode Dream Trust)
*Price Parry Charitable Trust**
The Professional Footballers' Association Charity
The Progress Foundation
The PwC Foundation
The Pye Foundation
The Monica Rabagliati Charitable Trust
The Rainford Trust
*The Randal Charitable Foundation**
*Randeree Charitable Trust**
The Eleanor Rathbone Charitable Trust
The Rayne Foundation
The Rayne Trust
Reuben Foundation
Rhodi Charitable Trust
The Rhododendron Trust
Daisie Rich Trust
Rigby Foundation
The River Farm Foundation
The Sir James Roll Charitable Trust
Rosca Trust
The Roughley Charitable Trust
The Joseph Rowntree Charitable Trust
S. and R. Charitable Trust
The Jeremy and John Sacher Charitable Trust
The Michael and Nicola Sacher Charitable Trust
Foundation Scotland
Francis C. Scott Charitable Trust
The John Scott Trust Fund
Scottish Coal Industry Special Welfare Fund
The SDL Foundation
The Segelman Trust
The Shanly Foundation
The Shears Foundation
The Sheldon Trust
SHINE (Support and Help in Education)
The Shipwrights' Charitable Fund
The Simmons & Simmons Charitable Foundation
The Skelton Bounty
The Charles Skey Charitable Trust
The Henry Smith Charity
The Sobell Foundation
Sofronie Foundation
Somerset Community Foundation
The Souter Charitable Trust
W. F. Southall Trust
The St Hilda's Trust
The St James's Trust Settlement
Sir Walter St John's Educational Charity
The Community Foundation for Staffordshire
Standard Life Foundation
The Hugh Stenhouse Foundation
Strand Parishes Trust
Stratford-upon-Avon Town Trust
The Bernard Sunley Foundation
The Sunrise Foundation CIO
The Swire Charitable Trust
The Charles and Elsie Sykes Trust
The Tabhair Charitable Trust
The Talbot Village Trust
Tallow Chandlers Benevolent Fund No. 2
C. B. and H. H. Taylor 1984 Trust
*the7stars Foundation**
Sir Jules Thorn Charitable Trust
Three Monkies Trust
Tower Hill Trust
The Constance Travis Charitable Trust
The Trusthouse Charitable Foundation
The Turtleton Charitable Trust
The Vandervell Foundation
*Vinci UK Foundation**
The Vintners' Foundation
The Virgin Money Foundation
The Vodafone Foundation

Volant Charitable Trust
Sylvia Waddilove Foundation UK
The Scurrah Wainwright Charity
Wakefield and Tetley Trust
The Wakeham Trust
Walton on Thames Charity
Mrs Waterhouse Charitable Trust
Wates Family Enterprise Trust
The Wates Foundation
The William Wates Memorial Trust
The Geoffrey Watling Charity
Blyth Watson Charitable Trust
John Watson's Trust
The Weavers' Company Benevolent Fund
The William Webster Charitable Trust
Wellington Management UK Foundation
Westway Trust
White Stuff Foundation
Charity of Sir Richard Whittington
Wiltshire Community Foundation
The Wingate Foundation
The Wixamtree Trust
Friends of Wiznitz Ltd
Wooden Spoon Society
Woodroffe Benton Foundation
The Woodward Charitable Trust
Worcester Municipal Charities (CIO)
The Yapp Charitable Trust
Youth Music
The Zochonis Charitable Trust
Zurich Community Trust (UK) Ltd

■ Ex-offenders/offenders/at risk of offending

The 29th May 1961 Charitable Trust
The A. B. Charitable Trust
The Alchemy Foundation
The John Armitage Charitable Trust
The Roger and Sarah Bancroft Clark Charitable Trust
The Big Yellow Foundation*
The Sydney Black Charitable Trust
The Bowerman Charitable Trust
The Bowland Charitable Trust
The Bromley Trust
The Noel Buxton Trust
William A. Cadbury Charitable Trust
The Chetwode Foundation
CHK Foundation
The City Bridge Trust (Bridge House Estates)
The Clothworkers' Foundation
The John Coates Charitable Trust
Colyer-Fergusson Charitable Trust
The Evan Cornish Foundation
The D. G. Charitable Settlement
Drapers' Charitable Fund
The Emerton-Christie Charity
The Fairness Foundation
Fishmongers' Company's Charitable Trust
Jill Franklin Trust
Gamma Trust
The Girdlers' Company Charitable Trust
The Goldsmiths' Company Charity
The Greater Manchester High Sheriff's Police Trust
The Walter Guinness Charitable Trust
H. C. D. Memorial Fund
The Hadley Trust
The Hadrian Trust
Paul Hamlyn Foundation
The Helen Hamlyn Trust
The Charles Hayward Foundation
The Hedley Foundation
P. and C. Hickinbotham Charitable Trust
The Hilden Charitable Fund
P. H. Holt Foundation
The Hospital of God at Greatham
Michael and Shirley Hunt Charitable Trust
Inner London Magistrates Court Poor Box and Feeder Charity
The Charles Irving Charitable Trust
The Jabbs Foundation
The Jerusalem Trust
The Emmanuel Kaye Foundation
The Kelly Family Charitable Trust
The Kensington and Chelsea Foundation
KFC Foundation*
The Mary Kinross Charitable Trust
Maurice and Hilda Laing Charitable Trust
The Beatrice Laing Trust
The Allen Lane Foundation
The Leigh Trust
The Mark Leonard Trust
The Linbury Trust
The Linder Foundation
Lloyds Bank Foundation for England and Wales
Lloyds Bank Foundation for the Channel Islands
The MacRobert Trust 2019
The Merchant Venturers' Charity
The Miles Morland Foundation
G. M. Morrison Charitable Trust
The MSE Charity
The Norman Family Charitable Trust
The Northwick Trust
The Oakdale Trust
Odin Charitable Trust
Henry Oldfield Trust
People's Postcode Trust
The Portishead Nautical Trust
The Sigrid Rausing Trust
The Rayne Foundation
The Rhododendron Trust
The Sir James Roll Charitable Trust
The Roughley Charitable Trust
Saint Sarkis Charity Trust
Francis C. Scott Charitable Trust
The Frieda Scott Charitable Trust
The Swire Charitable Trust
C. B. and H. H. Taylor 1984 Trust
The Triangle Trust (1949) Fund
Ulster Garden Villages Ltd
Volant Charitable Trust
The Weavers' Company Benevolent Fund
The Welsh Church Act Fund
The Woodward Charitable Trust

■ Migrants

The A. B. Charitable Trust
The Roger and Sarah Bancroft Clark Charitable Trust
The Barrow Cadbury Trust
The Evan Cornish Foundation
The Fairness Foundation
Paul Hamlyn Foundation
The Allen Lane Foundation
The Linbury Trust
The London Community Foundation (LCF)
The MSE Charity
The Sigrid Rausing Trust
The Rayne Foundation
The Roughley Charitable Trust
The Union of the Sisters of Mercy of Great Britain

People who are educationally disadvantaged

The 29th May 1961 Charitable Trust
The 4814 Trust
The Allen & Overy Foundation
Anguish's Educational Foundation
The John Armitage Charitable Trust
Lawrence Atwell's Charity (Skinners' Company)
The Balcombe Charitable Trust
The Roger and Sarah Bancroft Clark Charitable Trust
The Max Barney Foundation
AJ Bell Trust*
The Berkeley Foundation
The Bestway Foundation
The Boshier-Hinton Foundation
The British and Foreign School Society
The Chetwode Foundation
The Church Burgesses Educational Foundation
The Clothworkers' Foundation
The John Coates Charitable Trust
Colyer-Fergusson Charitable Trust
The Demigryphon Trust
The Eight Foundation*
The Estelle Trust
Allan and Nesta Ferguson Charitable Settlement
The Hugh Fraser Foundation
The Girdlers' Company Charitable Trust
The Gloag Foundation
The Grace Trust
The Grantham Yorke Trust
H. C. D. Memorial Fund
The Hadfield Charitable Trust
The Hadley Trust
Paul Hamlyn Foundation
Harbinson Charitable Trust
Harborne Parish Lands Charity
The Hemby Charitable Trust
Henley Educational Trust
The Alan Edward Higgs Charity
The Holbeck Charitable Trust
Housing Pathways Trust
The Hunter Foundation
The International Bankers Charitable Trust
The Ireland Fund of Great Britain
Isle of Wight Foundation
The Kensington and Chelsea Foundation
Kilpatrick Fraser Charitable Trust
Robert Kitchin (Saddlers' Company)
The KPMG Foundation
The Beatrice Laing Trust
Community Foundations for Lancashire and Merseyside
Cecil and Hilda Lewis Charitable Trust*
Lloyds Bank Foundation for the Channel Islands
The London Community Foundation (LCF)
Longleigh Foundation
Man Group plc Charitable Trust
The Merchant Venturers' Charity
Jean and Roger Miller's Charitable Trust
The James Milner Foundation
John Moores Foundation
The Ken and Lynne Morrison Charitable Trust
The Ken and Edna Morrison Charitable Trust
The Morrisons Foundation
Newby Trust Ltd
The Nuffield Foundation
People's Postcode Trust
The Progress Foundation
The PwC Foundation
Richard Radcliffe Trust
RG Foundation*
Richmond Parish Lands Charity
The Robertson Trust
The Gerald and Gail Ronson Family Foundation
The Alan and Babette Sainsbury Charitable Fund
Foundation Scotland
Francis C. Scott Charitable Trust
The Sheldon Trust
SHINE (Support and Help in Education)
Arabella and Julian Smith Family Trust*
The Stephen R. and Philippa H. Southall Charitable Trust
The Stewarts Law Foundation
Strand Parishes Trust
The Swire Charitable Trust
The Trusthouse Charitable Foundation
The Virgin Money Foundation
The Vodafone Foundation
Wellington Management UK Foundation
Westminster Almshouses Foundation

People who are homeless/ at risk of homelessness

The 29th May 1961 Charitable Trust
The 4814 Trust
ABF The Soldiers' Charity
The Adint Charitable Trust
The Alchemy Foundation
The Balcombe Charitable Trust
The Barbour Foundation
The Barnsbury Charitable Trust
The Berkeley Foundation
The Oliver Borthwick Memorial Trust
The Brelms Trust CIO
CEO Sleepout
The Charities Advisory Trust
Chrysalis Trust
The Clothworkers' Foundation
The Cole Charitable Trust
The Coltstaple Trust
The Evan Cornish Foundation
CRASH
Crisis UK
The D. G. Charitable Settlement
Foundation Derbyshire
Dorset Community Foundation
Drapers' Charitable Fund
The Anne Duchess of Westminster's Charity
The Eveson Charitable Trust
The Feoffees of St Michael's Spurriergate York
The Finborough Foundation
Fine & Country Foundation
The Elizabeth Frankland Moore and Star Foundation
The Hugh Fraser Foundation
Charles S. French Charitable Trust
The Freshfield Foundation
The G. D. Charitable Trust
The Goldsmiths' Company Charity
The Greggs Foundation
The Hadrian Trust
The Alfred Haines Charitable Trust
Hammersmith United Charities
Hampton Fund
The Haramead Trust
The Harbour Foundation
The Peter Harrison Foundation
Help the Homeless Ltd
P. and C. Hickinbotham Charitable Trust
Highway One Trust
The Hilden Charitable Fund
The Hobson Charity Ltd
Hollick Family Foundation
The Thomas J. Horne Memorial Trust
Housing Pathways Trust
The Huggard Charitable Trust
The Albert Hunt Trust
Inner London Magistrates Court Poor Box and Feeder Charity

Irish Youth Foundation (UK) Ltd (incorporating The Lawlor Foundation)
The Charles Irving Charitable Trust
*The Isla Foundation**
John Jarrold Trust Ltd
*JD Foundation**
The Jusaca Charitable Trust
The Kensington and Chelsea Foundation
Kent Community Foundation
*KFC Foundation**
Ladbrokes Coral Trust
John Laing Charitable Trust
Maurice and Hilda Laing Charitable Trust
The Beatrice Laing Trust
LandAid Charitable Trust (LandAid)
Laslett's (Hinton) Charity
Leeds Building Society Charitable Foundation
Lloyds Bank Foundation for England and Wales
Lloyds Bank Foundation for the Channel Islands
The London Community Foundation (LCF)
London Housing Foundation Ltd (LHF)
Longleigh Foundation
The Mackintosh Foundation
R. W. Mann Trust
The Mercers' Charitable Foundation
The Merchant Venturers' Charity
Merchants' House of Glasgow
The Mickleham Trust
Jean and Roger Miller's Charitable Trust
*The Monday Charitable Trust**
John Moores Foundation
G. M. Morrison Charitable Trust
The MSE Charity
The Nationwide Foundation
The Nisbet Trust
Norfolk Community Foundation
The Norman Family Charitable Trust
Community Foundation for Northern Ireland
Nottinghamshire Community Foundation
Odin Charitable Trust
Henry Oldfield Trust
*Orange Tree Trust**
The Ovo Charitable Foundation
People's Postcode Trust
The Austin and Hope Pilkington Trust
PIMCO Foundation Europe
The Portishead Nautical Trust
The Pret Foundation
Quartet Community Foundation
Richard Radcliffe Trust
The Rhododendron Trust
Richmond Parish Lands Charity
The River Farm Foundation
Mrs L. D. Rope's Third Charitable Settlement
The Roughley Charitable Trust
The Royal British Legion
Royal Docks Trust (London)
The Saintbury Trust
The Salamander Charitable Trust
Francis C. Scott Charitable Trust
Rita and David Slowe Charitable Trust
The Mrs Smith and Mount Trust
The Peter Stebbings Memorial Charity
Sir Halley Stewart Trust
Strand Parishes Trust
StreetSmart – Action for the Homeless
The Swire Charitable Trust
The Talbot Trusts
C. B. and H. H. Taylor 1984 Trust
The Taylor Family Foundation
*the7stars Foundation**
The Tolkien Trust
The Tuixen Foundation
The Albert Van Den Bergh Charitable Trust
*Vinci UK Foundation**
The Virgin Money Foundation
Walton on Thames Charity
Charity of Sir Richard Whittington
*Sir Graham Wylie Foundation**
Yorkshire Building Society Charitable Foundation

People who are isolated

*AJ Bell Trust**
*Camden Giving**
*The George Collins Charity**
The Goldsmiths' Company Charity
The Greggs Foundation
*The Halsall Foundation**
Hammersmith United Charities
Ros Harding Trust
The Harpur Trust
Inner London Magistrates Court Poor Box and Feeder Charity
The Ireland Fund of Great Britain
The Kensington and Chelsea Foundation
Kusuma Trust UK
Community Foundations for Lancashire and Merseyside
The Linden Charitable Trust
The London Community Foundation (LCF)
Norfolk Community Foundation
People's Postcode Trust
Postcode Local Trust
The Prince of Wales's Charitable Foundation
Foundation Scotland
Francis C. Scott Charitable Trust
SHINE (Support and Help in Education)
The South Yorkshire Community Foundation
Community Foundation for Surrey
The Trusthouse Charitable Foundation
Walton on Thames Charity
Charity of Sir Richard Whittington
The Woodward Charitable Trust

People on low incomes and/or benefits

The 29th May 1961 Charitable Trust
The Archer Trust
The Artemis Charitable Foundation
The Roger and Sarah Bancroft Clark Charitable Trust
*The Barnes Fund**
Bauer Radio's Cash for Kids Charities
*AJ Bell Trust**
The Bellahouston Bequest Fund
The Berkeley Foundation
The Sydney Black Charitable Trust
The Harry Bottom Charitable Trust
The Bowerman Charitable Trust
British Gas Energy Trust
The J. and M. Britton Charitable Trust
Brushmill Ltd
The Campden Charities Trustee
The Chetwode Foundation
The Childhood Trust
Chippenham Borough Lands Charity
CLA Charitable Trust
Cloudesley
The Cole Charitable Trust
Colyer-Fergusson Charitable Trust

Community First
Michael Crawford Children's Charity
The Double 'O' Charity Ltd
The Doughty Charity Trust
EBM Charitable Trust
Dr Edwards Bishop King's Fulham Endowment Fund
The George Elias Charitable Trust
The Enkalon Foundation
The Fifty Fund
The Robert Fleming Hannay Memorial Charity
The Hugh Fraser Foundation
The Tara Getty Foundation
The David Gibbons Foundation
The Gloag Foundation
County of Gloucestershire Community Foundation
The Goodman Foundation
The Gosling Foundation Ltd
The Graham Trust
H. C. D. Memorial Fund
Hackney Parochial Charities
The Hadley Trust
The Hadrian Trust
The Alfred Haines Charitable Trust
Paul Hamlyn Foundation
Hampton Fund
Harborne Parish Lands Charity
The Harpur Trust
The Edith Lilian Harrison 2000 Foundation
Edward Harvist Trust (The Harvist Estate)
The Hawthorne Charitable Trust
May Hearnshaw's Charity
The Heathcoat Trust
The Helping Foundation
Henley Educational Trust
The Tim Henman Foundation
Herefordshire Community Foundation
Highway One Trust
The Hinduja Foundation
The Henry C. Hoare Charitable Trust
The Hobson Charity Ltd
The Holbeck Charitable Trust
The Hospital of God at Greatham
Housing Pathways Trust
The Hunter Foundation
Huntingdon Freemen's Trust
Inner London Magistrates Court Poor Box and Feeder Charity
The Innocent Foundation
The Ireland Fund of Great Britain
The Charles Irving Charitable Trust
The J. and J. Benevolent Foundation
The J. A. R. Charitable Trust
J. E. Joseph Charitable Fund
The Cyril and Eve Jumbo Charitable Trust
The Jusaca Charitable Trust
William Kendall's Charity (Wax Chandlers' Company)
The Peter Kershaw Trust
Kilpatrick Fraser Charitable Trust
The Graham Kirkham Foundation
Kupath Gemach Chaim Bechesed Viznitz Trust
Kusuma Trust UK
The Beatrice Laing Trust
Community Foundations for Lancashire and Merseyside
Largsmount Ltd
Lawson Beckman Charitable Trust
The Lawson Trust CIO
The Leri Charitable Trust
*Cecil and Hilda Lewis Charitable Trust**
The Linder Foundation
The Frank Litchfield Charitable Trust
Local Trent Ltd
Loftus Charitable Trust
London Catalyst
London Legal Support Trust (LLST)
Longleigh Foundation
The Henry Lumley Charitable Trust
The Magdalen and Lasher Charity (General Fund)
Marbeh Torah Trust
Mayfair Charities Ltd
Melodor Ltd
The Melow Charitable Trust
Mercaz Torah Vechesed Ltd
The Merchant Taylors' Company Charities Fund
The Merchant Venturers' Charity
Merchants' House of Glasgow
T. and J. Meyer Family Foundation Ltd
Jean and Roger Miller's Charitable Trust
Keren Mitzvah Trust
The Mizpah Trust
The Monmouthshire County Council Welsh Church Act Fund
The Morris Charitable Trust
The MSE Charity
Edith Murphy Foundation
Muslim Hands
Newpier Charity Ltd
Norfolk Community Foundation
The Nuffield Foundation
The Ogle Christian Trust
Payne-Gallwey 1989 Charitable Trust
People's Postcode Trust
Pilkington Charities Fund
The Portishead Nautical Trust
Premierquote Ltd
The Pret Foundation
The Pye Foundation
Quartet Community Foundation
Quothquan Trust
Rachel Charitable Trust
Richard Radcliffe Trust
The Eleanor Rathbone Charitable Trust
Richmond Parish Lands Charity
Riverside Charitable Trust Ltd
The Robertson Trust
Mrs L. D. Rope's Third Charitable Settlement
Samjo Ltd
Francis C. Scott Charitable Trust
The SDL Foundation
Sam and Bella Sebba Charitable Trust
SHINE (Support and Help in Education)
Shlomo Memorial Fund Ltd
Sparquote Ltd
Standard Life Foundation
The Peter Stebbings Memorial Charity
Stervon Ltd
Strand Parishes Trust
Sabina Sutherland Charitable Trust
The Swire Charitable Trust
Tegham Ltd
Scott Thomson Charitable Trust
The Thornton Trust
The Tuixen Foundation
Tzedakah
The Union of the Sisters of Mercy of Great Britain
The Walcot Foundation
The Walker Trust
The Welsh Church Act Fund
West Derby Waste Lands Charity
Westminster Almshouses Foundation
The Maurice Wohl Charitable Foundation
Woodlands Green Ltd
Yorkshire Building Society Charitable Foundation

■ People who are unemployed

Bairdwatson Charitable Trust
The Max Barney Foundation
The James Beattie Charitable Trust

*AJ Bell Trust**
The Berkeley Foundation
Colyer-Fergusson Charitable Trust
The Enkalon Foundation
Dr Guthrie's Association
H. C. D. Memorial Fund
The Hadfield Charitable Trust
The Alfred Haines Charitable Trust
Housing Pathways Trust
Inner London Magistrates Court Poor Box and Feeder Charity
Isle of Wight Foundation
The Kensington and Chelsea Foundation
Kilpatrick Fraser Charitable Trust
The KPMG Foundation
Kusuma Trust UK
The Leathersellers' Company Charitable Fund
The London Community Foundation (LCF)
Longleigh Foundation
Mathew Trust
The MSE Charity
People's Postcode Trust
The Prince's Countryside Fund
The Progress Foundation
The Robertson Trust
The Gerald and Gail Ronson Family Foundation
*Arabella and Julian Smith Family Trust**
Standard Life Foundation
The Trusthouse Charitable Foundation
UPP Foundation
*Vinci UK Foundation**

■ People who have been affected by crime

The Avon and Somerset Police Community Trust
The Greater Manchester High Sheriff's Police Trust
The Hadley Trust
Inner London Magistrates Court Poor Box and Feeder Charity
The Charles Irving Charitable Trust
The Kensington and Chelsea Foundation
The London Community Foundation (LCF)
The Trusthouse Charitable Foundation

■ People who have been affected by violence, abuse or neglect

The Adint Charitable Trust
The Roger and Sarah Bancroft Clark Charitable Trust
Bauer Radio's Cash for Kids Charities
The Brelms Trust CIO
The Bromley Trust
The Brook Trust
The Noel Buxton Trust
The Chetwode Foundation
The City Bridge Trust (Bridge House Estates)
The Clothworkers' Foundation
County Durham Community Foundation
The Ellerdale Trust
The Fairness Foundation
The Finborough Foundation
Forest Hill Charitable Trust
Gwyneth Forrester Trust
The Tara Getty Foundation
The Gloag Foundation
Global Charities
Sydney and Phyllis Goldberg Memorial Charitable Trust
The Hadrian Trust
P. and C. Hickinbotham Charitable Trust
The Hospital of God at Greatham
Housing Pathways Trust
Inner London Magistrates Court Poor Box and Feeder Charity
The Charles Irving Charitable Trust
The Jabbs Foundation
Jewish Child's Day (JCD)
The Emmanuel Kaye Foundation
The Kelly Family Charitable Trust
The Lake House Charity
The Allen Lane Foundation
The Leathersellers' Company Charitable Fund
Lloyds Bank Foundation for England and Wales
Lloyds Bank Foundation for the Channel Islands
The London Community Foundation (LCF)
Longleigh Foundation
The R. S. Macdonald Charitable Trust
The Mickleham Trust
The MSE Charity
The NDL Foundation
The Norton Foundation
People's Postcode Trust
The Pilgrim Trust
The Portishead Nautical Trust
The Sigrid Rausing Trust
The Rayne Foundation
The Robertson Trust
The Roughley Charitable Trust
The Samworth Foundation
Francis C. Scott Charitable Trust
The Frieda Scott Charitable Trust
The Mrs Smith and Mount Trust
The South Yorkshire Community Foundation
Staples Trust
The Peter Stebbings Memorial Charity
The Swire Charitable Trust
The Talbot Trusts
*the7stars Foundation**
The Three Guineas Trust
The Trusthouse Charitable Foundation
Volant Charitable Trust
The Woodward Charitable Trust
The Yapp Charitable Trust

■ Roma and Travellers

The Allen Lane Foundation
Odin Charitable Trust
The Sigrid Rausing Trust
The Rayne Foundation
The Woodward Charitable Trust

■ Sex workers

P. and C. Hickinbotham Charitable Trust
The Elton John Aids Foundation (EJAF)
The London Community Foundation (LCF)
The Samworth Foundation
The Swire Charitable Trust

■ Victims of disasters and famine

The Alchemy Foundation
The Allen & Overy Foundation
Ove Arup Partnership Charitable Trust
The Ashworth Charitable Trust
The Austin Bailey Foundation
The Roy and Pixie Baker Charitable Trust
The Rowan Bentall Charitable Trust
The Bestway Foundation
Lady Blakenham's Charity Trust

The Blandford Lake Trust
Christadelphian Samaritan Fund
The Coltstaple Trust
The Anna Rosa Forster Charitable Trust
The Freshfield Foundation
The Tara Getty Foundation
The Goodman Foundation
The Grace Trust
The Harbour Foundation
The Holbeck Charitable Trust
The Millichope Foundation
The Monmouthshire County Council Welsh Church Act Fund
Muslim Hands
The Ogle Christian Trust
The Pharsalia Charitable Trust
The Privy Purse Charitable Trust
Rhodi Charitable Trust
Seedfield Trust
Sumner Wilson Charitable Trust
The Constance Travis Charitable Trust

Grant-makers by type of organisation

This index contains two separate listings:

List of types of organisation: This lists all the headings used in DGMT to categorise types of organisation.

Grant-makers by type of organisation: This lists funders under the types of organisation for which they have expressed a funding preference. Asterisks mark funders which have not been featured in DGMT before.

Grant-makers by type of organisation

These pages contain two separate listings:

List of types of organisation
This lists all the headings used in DGMT to categorise types of organisation.

Grant-makers by type of organisation
This lists funders under the types of organisation for which they have expressed a funding preference. Asterisks mark funders which have not been featured in DGMT before.

Community Interest Companies (CICs)

The 4814 Trust
ABF The Soldiers' Charity
The Sylvia Adams Charitable Trust
The Allen & Overy Foundation
Anguish's Educational Foundation
The Architectural Heritage Fund
The Art Fund
Arts Council England
Arts Council of Wales (also known as Cyngor Celfyddydau Cymru)
The Ove Arup Foundation
Ove Arup Partnership Charitable Trust
The Austin Bailey Foundation
Bairdwatson Charitable Trust
The Barbour Foundation
Barchester Healthcare Foundation
The Barnes Fund*
Barnwood Trust
Robert Barr's Charitable Trust
BBC Children in Need
Bedfordshire and Luton Community Foundation
The Rowan Bentall Charitable Trust
The Berkeley Foundation
The Berkshire Community Foundation
Biffa Award
The Percy Bilton Charity
The Bingham Trust
Birmingham International Airport Community Trust Fund
The Blagrave Trust
Bluespark Foundation
The Boshier-Hinton Foundation
The Harry Bottom Charitable Trust
The Bransford Trust*
The Harold and Alice Bridges Charity
Buckinghamshire Community Foundation
The Bulldog Trust Ltd
E. F. Bulmer Trust
BUPA UK Foundation
Community Foundation for Calderdale
The Cambridgeshire Community Foundation
Camden Giving*
The Frederick and Phyllis Cann Trust
Card Factory Foundation*
Cheshire Community Foundation Ltd
Church Urban Fund
The City Bridge Trust (Bridge House Estates)
CLA Charitable Trust
The Clothworkers' Foundation
The Coalfields Regeneration Trust
Colchester Catalyst Charity
John and Freda Coleman Charitable Trust
Sir Jeremiah Colman Gift Trust
Colyer-Fergusson Charitable Trust
Community First
The Catherine Cookson Charitable Trust
Co-operative Community Investment Foundation
The Evan Cornish Foundation
Cornwall Community Foundation
The Duke of Cornwall's Benevolent Fund
The Corporation of Trinity House of Deptford Strond
Corra Foundation
Cripplegate Foundation
Cumbria Community Foundation
Baron Davenport's Charity
The Roger De Haan Charitable Trust
Foundation Derbyshire
Devon Community Foundation
The Duke of Devonshire's Charitable Trust
The Gillian Dickinson Trust
Digital Xtra Fund*
Dorset Community Foundation
The Anne Duchess of Westminster's Charity
Dumfriesshire East Community Benefit Group SCIO*
The Nine Incorporated Trades of Dundee General Fund Charity*
The Dunhill Medical Trust
Dunlossit and Islay Community Trust*
County Durham Community Foundation
East End Community Foundation
The Edge Foundation
The EQ Foundation
The Essex and Southend Sports Trust
Essex Community Foundation
The Evelyn Trust
Esmée Fairbairn Foundation
The Thomas Farr Charity
The Fermanagh Trust
The Finnis Scott Foundation
Sir John Fisher Foundation
Fishmongers' Company's Charitable Trust
The Earl Fitzwilliam Charitable Trust
The Football Foundation
Forever Manchester
The Freshgate Trust Foundation
Friends Provident Charitable Foundation
The Funding Network
Garfield Weston Foundation
The David Gibbons Foundation
The Gibbs Charitable Trusts
The Simon Gibson Charitable Trust
County of Gloucestershire Community Foundation
The Golden Bottle Trust
Goldman Sachs Gives (UK)
The Golsoncott Foundation
The Grace Trust
The Grange Farm Centre Trust
The Grantham Yorke Trust
GrantScape
The J. G. Graves Charitable Trust
The Greggs Foundation
Groundwork UK
Calouste Gulbenkian Foundation – UK Branch
Dr Guthrie's Association
Hackney Parochial Charities
The Hadfield Charitable Trust
The Hadrian Trust
The Hamilton Davies Trust
Paul Hamlyn Foundation
Hammersmith United Charities
Hampshire and Isle of Wight Community Foundation
Hampton Fund
The Happold Foundation
Harborne Parish Lands Charity
William Harding's Charity
The Harpur Trust
Edward Harvist Trust (The Harvist Estate)
Hays Travel Foundation
Heart of England Community Foundation
Heart Research UK
The Hearth Foundation
Heathrow Community Trust
Herefordshire Community Foundation
Hertfordshire Community Foundation
HFC Help For Children UK Ltd
Highway One Trust
The Hilden Charitable Fund
The Lady Hind Trust
The Holywood Trust
The Hospital of God at Greatham
Housing Pathways Trust
Hyde Charitable Trust
Impact Funding Partners Ltd
The Isla Foundation*

Isle of Wight Foundation
The Sir Barry Jackson County Fund
John James Bristol Foundation
John Jarrold Trust Ltd
Rees Jeffreys Road Fund
The Joicey Trust
The Jones 1986 Charitable Trust
The Marjorie and Geoffrey Jones Charitable Trust
The Kelly Family Charitable Trust
The Kensington and Chelsea Foundation
KFC Foundation*
The Mary Kinross Charitable Trust
The Kirschel Foundation
John Laing Charitable Trust
Community Foundations for Lancashire and Merseyside
Lancashire Environmental Fund Ltd
Duchy of Lancaster Benevolent Fund
The Allen Lane Foundation
The Law Family Charitable Foundation
The Legal Education Foundation
Leicestershire, Leicester and Rutland Community Foundation
John Lewis Foundation
Lincolnshire Community Foundation
The W. M. and B. W. Lloyd Trust
The Andrew Lloyd Webber Foundation
Lloyd's Charities Trust
Lloyds Bank Foundation for the Channel Islands
London Catalyst
The London Community Foundation (LCF)
The London Marathon Charitable Trust Ltd
The R. S. Macdonald Charitable Trust
Making a Difference Locally Ltd
Manchester Airport Community Trust Fund
R. W. Mann Trust
The Michael Marsh Charitable Trust
Mathew Trust
Maudsley Charity
The Merchant Venturers' Charity
Millennium Stadium Charitable Trust (Ymddiriedclaeth Elusennol Stadiwm Y. Mileniwm)
Milton Keynes Community Foundation Ltd
Moondance Foundation
John Moores Foundation
The Steve Morgan Foundation
The MSE Charity
The National Express Foundation
The National Garden Scheme
The National Lottery Community Fund
Nesta
Network for Social Change Charitable Trust
Newcomen Collett Foundation
The Nineveh Charitable Trust
The Nisbet Trust
Norfolk Community Foundation
The Norman Family Charitable Trust
North Berwick Trust*
Northamptonshire Community Foundation
Community Foundation for Northern Ireland
Northwood Charitable Trust
Norwich Town Close Estate Charity
Notting Hill Genesis Community Foundation
Nottinghamshire Community Foundation
The Oakdale Trust
Oglesby Charitable Trust
One Community Foundation Ltd
Oxfordshire Community Foundation
The Pears Family Charitable Foundation
The Pebbles Trust
People's Health Trust
People's Postcode Trust
The Persimmon Charitable Foundation
Personal Assurance Charitable Trust
The Pets at Home Foundation
The Pickwell Foundation
Bernard Piggott Charitable Trust
Pilkington Charities Fund
Pink Ribbon Foundation
Polden-Puckham Charitable Foundation
Postcode Community Trust
Postcode Local Trust
Postcode Society Trust (formerly Postcode Dream Trust)
The Mary Potter Convent Hospital Trust
Poundland Foundation*
Power to Change Trust
The Prince's Countryside Fund
The PwC Foundation
Quadstar Charitable Foundation*
Quartet Community Foundation
The Rainford Trust
The Eleanor Rathbone Charitable Trust
The Sir James Reckitt Charity
Richard Reeve's Foundation
Rhodi Charitable Trust
Richmond Parish Lands Charity
Rigby Foundation
Rix Thompson Rothenberg Foundation
The Robertson Trust
Rosa Fund
Rosca Trust
The Rothley Trust
The Rothschild Foundation
The Rowlands Trust
The Joseph Rowntree Charitable Trust
The Joseph Rowntree Foundation
The Royal Navy and Royal Marines Charity
Royal Society of Wildlife Trusts
The Russell Trust
The RVW Trust
Santander UK Foundation Ltd
Foundation Scotland
Francis C. Scott Charitable Trust
Seafarers UK (King George's Fund for Sailors)
The Sheffield Town Trust
The Sheldon Trust
SHINE (Support and Help in Education)
The Shipwrights' Charitable Fund
Sirius Minerals Foundation
Smallwood Trust
The Henry Smith Charity
Social Business Trust
Social Investment Business Foundation
Social Tech Trust
Somerset Community Foundation
The South Yorkshire Community Foundation
The Stephen R. and Philippa H. Southall Charitable Trust
Peter Sowerby Foundation
The Jessie Spencer Trust
The St Hilda's Trust
Sir Walter St John's Educational Charity
St John's Foundation Est. 1174
The Community Foundation for Staffordshire
Standard Life Foundation
Staples Trust
The Steel Charitable Trust
Stratford-upon-Avon Town Trust

Strathnairn Community Benefit Fund Ltd
The WO Street Charitable Foundation
StreetSmart – Action for the Homeless
Suffolk Community Foundation
The Summerfield Charitable Trust
Community Foundation for Surrey
The Sussex Community Foundation
The Talbot Trusts
Tanner Trust
The Tedworth Charitable Trust
Tees Valley Community Foundation
The Theatres Trust Charitable Fund
The Thirty Percy Foundation*
Three Monkies Trust
The Toye Foundation
The Triangle Trust (1949) Fund
The True Colours Trust
Trust For London
The Trusthouse Charitable Foundation
The Tudor Trust
The Tuixen Foundation
Two Ridings Community Foundation
Community Foundation serving Tyne and Wear and Northumberland
Ufi VocTech Trust
The Ulverscroft Foundation
United St Saviour's Charity
UPP Foundation
The Van Neste Foundation
The Vardy Foundation
Variety, the Children's Charity
The Veolia Environmental Trust
Vinci UK Foundation*
The Virgin Money Foundation
Vision Foundation*
Volant Charitable Trust
Sylvia Waddilove Foundation UK
The Scurrah Wainwright Charity
The Bruce Wake Charitable Trust
Wakefield and Tetley Trust
The Community Foundation in Wales
Walton on Thames Charity
The Waterloo Foundation
Wates Family Enterprise Trust
The Wates Foundation
The Welsh Church Act Fund
Wembley National Stadium Trust
Westminster Foundation
Westway Trust
Alfred Williams Charitable Trust
The Wilson Foundation
Wiltshire Community Foundation
The Woodward Charitable Trust
Worcestershire Community Foundation*
Youth Music
Zurich Community Trust (UK) Ltd

Hospices

The 3Ts Charitable Trust
ABF The Soldiers' Charity
The Acacia Charitable Trust
Al-Fayed Charitable Foundation
Allchurches Trust Ltd
The Almond Trust
Andor Charitable Trust
The Anson Charitable Trust
The John Apthorp Charity
The Ardwick Trust
The Armourers' and Brasiers' Gauntlet Trust
The Arsenal Foundation
Ove Arup Partnership Charitable Trust
The Asda Foundation
The Ian Askew Charitable Trust
John Atcheson Foundation*
Atkin Charitable Foundation
The Lord Austin Trust
The Aylesford Family Charitable Trust
The Austin Bailey Foundation
Banbury Charities
The Roger and Sarah Bancroft Clark Charitable Trust
Bank of Scotland Foundation
The Barbers' Company General Charities
The Barbour Foundation
Misses Barrie Charitable Trust
Robert Barr's Charitable Trust
The Paul Bassham Charitable Trust
The Batchworth Trust
Battens Charitable Trust
Bauer Radio's Cash for Kids Charities
The Louis Baylis (Maidenhead Advertiser) Charitable Trust
Bearder Charity
The Beaverbrook Foundation
The Beaverbrooks Charitable Trust
Bedfordshire Charitable Trust Ltd
The Bellahouston Bequest Fund
Benesco Charity Ltd
The Rowan Bentall Charitable Trust
The Bestway Foundation
Bideford Bridge Trust
The Percy Bilton Charity
Binks Trust
Birmingham International Airport Community Trust Fund
The Sydney Black Charitable Trust
The Isabel Blackman Foundation
Blakemore Foundation
The Sir Victor Blank Charitable Settlement

*Maureen Boal Charitable Trust**
The Marjory Boddy Charitable Trust
The Boltini Trust
The Booth Charities
Boots Charitable Trust
The Borrows Charitable Trust
The Boshier-Hinton Foundation
The Bothwell Charitable Trust
The Frank Brake Charitable Trust
The William Brake Charitable Trust
The Tony Bramall Charitable Trust
The Liz and Terry Bramall Foundation
*The Bransford Trust**
The Breadsticks Foundation
The Brenley Trust
The Harold and Alice Bridges Charity
*Bright Red Charity**
The J. and M. Britton Charitable Trust
Bill Brown 1989 Charitable Trust
R. S. Brownless Charitable Trust
The Jack Brunton Charitable Trust
Buckinghamshire Community Foundation
E. F. Bulmer Trust
The Burdett Trust for Nursing
The Clara E. Burgess Charity
The Burry Charitable Trust
Miss Margaret Butters Reekie Charitable Trust
Byrne Family Foundation
William A. Cadbury Charitable Trust
The Cadbury Foundation
The Edward and Dorothy Cadbury Trust
The George Cadbury Trust
Community Foundation for Calderdale
Callendar Charitable Trust
The Cambridgeshire Community Foundation
The Frederick and Phyllis Cann Trust
W. A. Cargill Charitable Trust
The W. A. Cargill Fund
The Carlton Hayes Mental Health Charity
The Carrington Charitable Trust
The Leslie Mary Carter Charitable Trust
The Castanea Trust
The Wilfrid and Constance Cave Foundation
CBRE Charitable Trust
The Amelia Chadwick Trust
Cheshire Freemason's Charity
Children with Cancer UK
The Childwick Trust
Chippenham Borough Lands Charity
The Clan Trust Ltd
Clark Foundation
Closehelm Ltd
Denise Coates Foundation
The Cobtree Charity Trust Ltd
The Vivienne and Samuel Cohen Charitable Trust
Colchester Catalyst Charity
Sir Jeremiah Colman Gift Trust
Colyer-Fergusson Charitable Trust
*The Connolly Foundation**
The Catherine Cookson Charitable Trust
Mabel Cooper Charity
The Gershon Coren Charitable Foundation (also known as The Muriel and Gus Coren Charitable Foundation)
Michael Cornish Charitable Trust
The Duke of Cornwall's Benevolent Fund
The Cornwell Charitable Trust
The Sir Tom Cowie Charitable Trust
Dudley and Geoffrey Cox Charitable Trust
The Sir William Coxen Trust Fund
The Craps Charitable Trust
CRASH
The Crerar Trust
The Croydon Relief in Need Charities
CSIS Charity Fund
Cumbria Community Foundation
The D'Oyly Carte Charitable Trust
Baron Davenport's Charity
Michael Davies Charitable Settlement
The Roger De Haan Charitable Trust
The De Laszlo Foundation
Dentons UKMEA LLP Charitable Trust
Foundation Derbyshire
Provincial Grand Charity of the Province of Derbyshire
Devon Community Foundation
The Laduma Dhamecha Charitable Trust
The Dibden Allotments Fund
*The Ken Dodd Charitable Foundation**
The Derek and Eileen Dodgson Foundation
The Anne Duchess of Westminster's Charity
Duchy Health Charity Ltd
The Mildred Duveen Charitable Trust
Sir John Eastwood Foundation
EBM Charitable Trust
The Gilbert and Eileen Edgar Foundation
W. G. Edwards Charitable Foundation
*The Elie Trust**
The Marian Elizabeth Trust
The Wilfred and Elsie Elkes Charity Fund
Esher House Charitable Trust
Essex Community Foundation
The Evelyn Trust
The Eveson Charitable Trust
The Exilarch's Foundation
G. F. Eyre Charitable Trust
The Fairstead Trust
The Lord Faringdon Charitable Trust
Samuel William Farmer Trust
The February Foundation
The George Fentham Birmingham Charity
The A. M. Fenton Trust
Doris Field Charitable Trust
The Fifty Fund
Dixie Rose Findlay Charitable Trust
The Finnis Scott Foundation
Sir John Fisher Foundation
The Earl Fitzwilliam Charitable Trust
Ford Britain Trust
The Lady Forester Trust
The Forte Charitable Trust
Fowler Smith and Jones Trust
The Elizabeth Frankland Moore and Star Foundation
Jill Franklin Trust
The Hugh Fraser Foundation
Charles S. French Charitable Trust
The Freshgate Trust Foundation
Friarsgate Trust
The Patrick and Helena Frost Foundation
The Funding Network
The G. D. Charitable Trust
Gamma Trust
The Ganzoni Charitable Trust
Garfield Weston Foundation
Gatwick Airport Community Trust
The Jacqueline and Michael Gee Charitable Trust
General Charity (Coventry)
The Generations Foundation
The Gibbons Family Trust
The David Gibbons Foundation

The Simon Gibson Charitable Trust
The G. C. Gibson Charitable Trust
The B. and P. Glasser Charitable Trust
The F. Glenister Woodger Trust
The Godinton Charitable Trust
Worshipful Company of Gold and Silver Wyre Drawers Second Charitable Trust Fund
The Golden Bottle Trust
Goldman Sachs Gives (UK)
The Goshen Trust
Gowling WLG (UK) Charitable Trust
The Grace Trust
The Grange Farm Centre Trust
The Grant Foundation
The Grantham Yorke Trust
The J. G. Graves Charitable Trust
The Gray Trust
Gordon Gray Trust
The Green Hall Foundation
Greenham Trust Ltd
The Greggs Foundation
The Grimmitt Trust
The Walter Guinness Charitable Trust
Hackney Parochial Charities
The Hadfield Charitable Trust
The Hadley Trust
The Hadrian Trust
Hampshire and Isle of Wight Community Foundation
Hampton Fund
The W. A. Handley Charity Trust
The Lennox Hannay Charitable Trust
The Kathleen Hannay Memorial Charity
Harborne Parish Lands Charity
The Harding Trust
Ros Harding Trust
The Harebell Centenary Fund
The Harris Family Charitable Trust
The Edith Lilian Harrison 2000 Foundation
Edward Harvist Trust (The Harvist Estate)
The Hasluck Charitable Trust
The Hawthorne Charitable Trust
Hays Travel Foundation
The Health Foundation
May Hearnshaw's Charity
Heathrow Community Trust
The Charlotte Heber-Percy Charitable Trust
Ernest Hecht Charitable Foundation
Help for Health
The Christina Mary Hendrie Trust
The Tim Henman Foundation
The G. D. Herbert Charitable Trust
Herefordshire Community Foundation
The Heritage of London Trust Ltd
The Lady Hind Trust
The Hiscox Foundation
The Hobson Charity Ltd
The Jane Hodge Foundation
Dorothy Holmes Charitable Trust
The Holywood Trust
Homelands Charitable Trust
The Mary Homfray Charitable Trust
Sir Harold Hood's Charitable Trust
The Thomas J. Horne Memorial Trust
Horwich Shotter Charitable Trust
Hospice UK
The Hospital of God at Greatham
The Hospital Saturday Fund
The Albert Hunt Trust
Hyde Park Place Estate Charity
The Iceland Foods Charitable Foundation
The Iliffe Family Charitable Trust
The Inman Charity
The Inverforth Charitable Trust
The Charles Irving Charitable Trust
John James Bristol Foundation
Lady Eda Jardine Charitable Trust
John Jarrold Trust Ltd
The Roger and Jean Jefcoate Trust
Jeffrey Charitable Trust*
The Jenour Foundation
Lillie Johnson Charitable Trust
The Johnson Foundation
The Christopher and Kirsty Johnston Charitable Trust
The Jones 1986 Charitable Trust
Anton Jurgens Charitable Trust
The Jusaca Charitable Trust
The Michael and Ilse Katz Foundation
The Kennedy Charitable Foundation
The Kensington and Chelsea Foundation
The Kentown Wizard Foundation
The Ursula Keyes Trust
The Kildare Trust
Kilpatrick Fraser Charitable Trust
The King Henry VIII Endowed Trust – Warwick
The Graham Kirkham Foundation
The Kirschel Foundation
The Ernest Kleinwort Charitable Trust
Sir James Knott Trust
The Kobler Trust
Kusuma Trust UK
Ladbrokes Coral Trust
Christopher Laing Foundation
The Beatrice Laing Trust
Duchy of Lancaster Benevolent Fund
Langdale Trust
The R. J. Larg Family Trust
Laslett's (Hinton) Charity
The Edgar E. Lawley Foundation
The Herd Lawson and Muriel Lawson Charitable Trust
The Lawson Trust CIO
Leicestershire and Rutland Masonic Charity Association
Leicestershire, Leicester and Rutland Community Foundation
Leng Charitable Trust
The Ralph Levy Charitable Company Ltd*
John Lewis Foundation
Limoges Charitable Trust
Lincolnshire Community Foundation
The Linden Charitable Trust
The Linder Foundation
The Frank Litchfield Charitable Trust
The Charles Littlewood Hill Trust
The Second Joseph Aaron Littman Foundation
The Elaine and Angus Lloyd Charitable Trust
The W. M. and B. W. Lloyd Trust
The Locker Foundation
The Lockwood Charitable Foundation
London Catalyst
London Freemasons Charity
The C. L. Loyd Charitable Trust
Robert Luff Foundation Ltd
The Henry Lumley Charitable Trust
Lord and Lady Lurgan Trust
The Lyndal Tree Foundation
M. and C. Trust
The Mageni Trust*
Making a Difference Locally Ltd

The Manchester Guardian Society Charitable Trust
The W. M. Mann Foundation
R. W. Mann Trust
The Michael Marsh Charitable Trust
Charlotte Marshall Charitable Trust
D. G. Marshall of Cambridge Trust
Sir George Martin Trust
Masonic Charitable Foundation
Nancie Massey Charitable Trust
The Master Charitable Trust
Matchroom Sport Charitable Foundation
Maudsley Charity
The Violet Mauray Charitable Trust
Mazars Charitable Trust
MBNA General Foundation
The Robert McAlpine Foundation
D. D. McPhail Charitable Settlement
The Medicash Foundation
The Medlock Charitable Trust
The Gerald Micklem Charitable Trust
The Masonic Province of Middlesex Charitable Trust (Middlesex Masonic Charity)
The Millenium Oak Trust
The Millichope Foundation
The Millward Charitable Trust
The Clare Milne Trust
Milton Keynes Community Foundation Ltd
The Brian Mitchell Charitable Settlement
Mobbs Memorial Trust Ltd
Moondance Foundation
The George A. Moore Foundation
The Willie and Mabel Morris Charitable Trust
G. M. Morrison Charitable Trust
Moto in the Community
The Edwina Mountbatten and Leonora Children's Foundation
The Mulberry Trust
The National Garden Scheme
The National Lottery Community Fund
The NFU Mutual Charitable Trust
Norfolk Community Foundation
Educational Foundation of Alderman John Norman
The Norman Family Charitable Trust
Normanby Charitable Trust
North Berwick Trust*
Northern Pharmacies Ltd Trust Fund
Norwich Town Close Estate Charity
The Notgrove Trust
Notting Hill Genesis Community Foundation
Nottinghamshire Community Foundation
Odin Charitable Trust
The Ofenheim Charitable Trust
Oglesby Charitable Trust
Henry Oldfield Trust
The Orrin Charitable Trust
The Paget Charitable Trust
The Paragon Trust
Miss M. E. S. Paterson's Charitable Trust
The Patrick Trust
The Jack Patston Charitable Trust
The JGW Patterson Foundation
Payne-Gallwey 1989 Charitable Trust
Susanna Peake Charitable Trust
The Pears Family Charitable Foundation
The Pebbles Trust
The Dowager Countess Eleanor Peel Trust
The Persimmon Charitable Foundation
Personal Assurance Charitable Trust
Bernard Piggott Charitable Trust
Elise Pilkington Charitable Trust*
Miss A. M. Pilkington's Charitable Trust
Pink Ribbon Foundation
The George and Esme Pollitzer Charitable Settlement
The Mary Potter Convent Hospital Trust
Sir John Priestman Charity Trust
The Prince of Wales's Charitable Foundation
Prison Service Charity Fund
The Purey Cust Trust CIO
Mr and Mrs J. A. Pye's Charitable Settlement
Quartet Community Foundation
Richard Radcliffe Trust
The Rainford Trust
The Ratcliff Foundation
The Rathbone Brothers Foundation
The Ravensdale Trust
The Sir James Reckitt Charity
C. A. Redfern Charitable Foundation
The Reso Charitable Foundation
The Revere Charitable Trust
Riada Trust
The Clive and Sylvia Richards Charity Ltd
Richmond Parish Lands Charity
Rigby Foundation
The Roan Charitable Trust
The Dezna Robins Jones Charitable Foundation
Rockcliffe Charitable Trust
The Gerald and Gail Ronson Family Foundation
Rosca Trust
The Rose Foundation
The David Ross Foundation
The Rothermere Foundation
The Row Fogo Charitable Trust
The Rowlands Trust
Royal Masonic Trust for Girls and Boys
The Rugby Group Benevolent Fund Ltd
S. and R. Charitable Trust
The Saintbury Trust
Salisbury Pool Charity
Samjo Ltd
The Basil Samuel Charitable Trust
Sandra Charitable Trust
Schroder Charity Trust
Foundation Scotland
The John Scott Trust Fund
Scouloudi Foundation
Sam and Bella Sebba Charitable Trust
The Sheffield Town Trust
The Sylvia and Colin Shepherd Charitable Trust
The Sherling Charitable Trust
The Bassil Shippam and Alsford Trust
The Shoe Zone Trust
The Charles Skey Charitable Trust
Skipton Building Society Charitable Foundation
The John Slater Foundation
The Leslie Smith Foundation
The W. H. Smith Group Charitable Trust
Philip Smith's Charitable Trust
The R. C. Snelling Charitable Trust
The Sobell Foundation
Societe Generale UK Foundation*
Somerset Community Foundation
The Stephen R. and Philippa H. Southall Charitable Trust
Peter Sowerby Foundation
The Spear Charitable Trust
The Jessie Spencer Trust
Spielman Charitable Trust

The Spurrell Charitable Trust
The Geoff and Fiona Squire Foundation
The Vichai Srivaddhanaprabha Foundation*
St James's Place Charitable Foundation
St John's Foundation Est. 1174
St Monica Trust
The Community Foundation for Staffordshire
The Peter Stebbings Memorial Charity
The Steel Charitable Trust
The Stevenage Community Trust
Stevenson Family's Charitable Trust
The Stoneygate Trust
The Samuel Storey Family Charitable Trust
Peter Stormonth Darling Charitable Trust
Strand Parishes Trust
Stratford-upon-Avon Town Trust
The Street Foundation
The Joseph Strong Frazer Trust*
The Summerfield Charitable Trust
Sumner Wilson Charitable Trust
The Bernard Sunley Foundation
Community Foundation for Surrey
The Sussex Community Foundation
The Swann-Morton Foundation
The John Swire (1989) Charitable Trust
The Adrian Swire Charitable Trust
The Charles and Elsie Sykes Trust
The Hugh Symons Charitable Trust*
The Talbot Village Trust
Tanner Trust
C. B. and H. H. Taylor 1984 Trust
The Thompson Family Charitable Trust
Sir Jules Thorn Charitable Trust
The Tompkins Foundation
The Toy Trust
Toyota Manufacturing UK Charitable Trust
The Trades House of Glasgow
David William Traill Cargill Fund
Annie Tranmer Charitable Trust
The Trefoil Trust
Tropical Health and Education Trust
The True Colours Trust
The Truemark Trust
The James Tudor Foundation
The Tudwick Foundation*
The Tufton Charitable Trust
The Tuixen Foundation
The Roger and Douglas Turner Charitable Trust
Two Ridings Community Foundation
UKH Foundation
Ulster Garden Villages Ltd
The Ulverscroft Foundation
The Union of the Sisters of Mercy of Great Britain
The Valentine Charitable Trust
The Valiant Charitable Trust
The Albert Van Den Bergh Charitable Trust
Variety, the Children's Charity
Sylvia Waddilove Foundation UK
The Bruce Wake Charitable Trust
The Walker Trust
The Barbara Ward Children's Foundation
The Warwickshire Masonic Charitable Association Ltd
Mrs Waterhouse Charitable Trust
Wates Family Enterprise Trust
The Geoffrey Watling Charity
Blyth Watson Charitable Trust
The Wellcome Trust
West Herts Charity Trust Ltd*
The Westfield Health Charitable Trust
Westminster Amalgamated Charity
Westway Trust
The Whinfell Charitable Fund
Charity of Sir Richard Whittington
The Felicity Wilde Charitable Trust
Joan Wilkinson Charitable Trust*
The Will Charitable Trust
The Williams Family Foundation
The Willmott Dixon Foundation
The Dame Violet Wills Will Trust
Brian Wilson Charitable Trust
J. and J. R. Wilson Trust
Wiltshire Community Foundation
The Francis Winham Foundation
The Charles Wolfson Charitable Trust
The Wolfson Family Charitable Trust
The Wolfson Foundation
Worcestershire Community Foundation*
Worth Waynflete Foundation
The Wyndham Charitable Trust
York Children's Trust
Yorkshire Building Society Charitable Foundation
The William Allen Young Charitable Trust
The Elizabeth and Prince Zaiger Trust
Zurich Community Trust (UK) Ltd

Hospitals

The 29th May 1961 Charitable Trust
The Abbeyfield Research Foundation
ABF The Soldiers' Charity
Action Medical Research
The AEB Charitable Trust
*The Aitken Family Charitable Trust**
Al-Fayed Charitable Foundation
Allchurches Trust Ltd
Alzheimer's Research UK
Alzheimer's Society
The Ardwick Trust
The John Armitage Charitable Trust
The Armourers' and Brasiers' Gauntlet Trust
Ove Arup Partnership Charitable Trust
Asthma UK
Atkin Charitable Foundation
The Lord Austin Trust
The Bamford Charitable Foundation
The Band Trust
The Barbers' Company General Charities
The Barclay Foundation
The Barker-Mill Foundation
Lord Barnby's Foundation
Robert Barr's Charitable Trust
The Batchworth Trust
Battens Charitable Trust
Bauer Radio's Cash for Kids Charities
BC Partners Foundation
The James Beattie Charitable Trust
The Beaverbrook Foundation
The Beaverbrooks Charitable Trust
The John Beckwith Charitable Trust
Benesco Charity Ltd
The Rowan Bentall Charitable Trust
The Bestway Foundation
The Percy Bilton Charity
The Bingham Trust
Binks Trust
The Birmingham District Nursing Charitable Trust
Birmingham International Airport Community Trust Fund
The Sydney Black Charitable Trust
The Isabel Blackman Foundation
Blakemore Foundation
Bloodwise
The Marjory Boddy Charitable Trust
The Boltini Trust
The Boshier-Hinton Foundation
The Tony Bramall Charitable Trust
The Breadsticks Foundation
Breast Cancer Now
The Breast Cancer Research Trust (BCRT)
*Bright Red Charity**
British Council for Prevention of Blindness
British Eye Research Foundation (Fight for Sight)
British Heart Foundation (BHF)
British Lung Foundation
The T. B. H. Brunner's Charitable Settlement
The Jack Brunton Charitable Trust
The Burden Trust
The Burry Charitable Trust
Miss Margaret Butters Reekie Charitable Trust
The G. W. Cadbury Charitable Trust
The Cambridgeshire Community Foundation
The Frederick and Phyllis Cann Trust
The Carlton Hayes Mental Health Charity
The Carrington Charitable Trust
The Castang Foundation
The Wilfrid and Constance Cave Foundation
Cheshire Freemason's Charity
Children with Cancer UK
Children's Liver Disease Foundation
Clark Foundation
The Clore Duffield Foundation
The Vivienne and Samuel Cohen Charitable Trust
Colchester Catalyst Charity
Colefax Charitable Trust
Sir Jeremiah Colman Gift Trust
Dudley and Geoffrey Cox Charitable Trust
The Sir William Coxen Trust Fund
The Craps Charitable Trust
The Croydon Relief in Need Charities
CSIS Charity Fund
The Cunningham Trust
The Roger De Haan Charitable Trust
The Laduma Dhamecha Charitable Trust
The Dibden Allotments Fund
Dinwoodie Charitable Company
*The Ken Dodd Charitable Foundation**
The Derek and Eileen Dodgson Foundation
Duchy Health Charity Ltd
Dumbreck Charity
The Dunhill Medical Trust
The Charles Dunstone Charitable Trust
The Mildred Duveen Charitable Trust
Sir John Eastwood Foundation
EBM Charitable Trust
The Gilbert and Eileen Edgar Foundation
*The Elie Trust**
The Maud Elkington Charitable Trust
Epilepsy Research UK
Esher House Charitable Trust
Joseph Ettedgui Charitable Foundation
The Evelyn Trust
The Eventhall Family Charitable Trust
The Eveson Charitable Trust
The Exilarch's Foundation
The Fairstead Trust
*Family Philanthropy Ltd**
The Lord Faringdon Charitable Trust
Samuel William Farmer Trust
The Thomas Farr Charity
The George Fentham Birmingham Charity
The Fifty Fund
The Lady Forester Trust
The Fort Foundation
The Forte Charitable Trust
Fowler Smith and Jones Trust
The Elizabeth Frankland Moore and Star Foundation
Jill Franklin Trust
The Hugh Fraser Foundation
The Freshgate Trust Foundation
The Funding Network
The G. D. Charitable Trust
The Gale Family Charity Trust
GambleAware
Gamma Trust
The Ganzoni Charitable Trust
Garfield Weston Foundation
The Robert Gavron Charitable Trust
General Charity (Coventry)
The Generations Foundation
The Gibbs Charitable Trusts
The Simon Gibson Charitable Trust
The G. C. Gibson Charitable Trust
The B. and P. Glasser Charitable Trust
The F. Glenister Woodger Trust
Worshipful Company of Glovers of London Charitable Trust
Sydney and Phyllis Goldberg Memorial Charitable Trust
Goldman Sachs Gives (UK)

Grace Charitable Trust
The Grace Trust
The Grange Farm Centre Trust
The Green Hall Foundation
The Greggs Foundation
The Grimmitt Trust
The Walter Guinness Charitable Trust
The Gunter Charitable Trust
The Gynaecological Cancer Fund*
Hackney Parochial Charities
The Hadfield Charitable Trust
Hampton Fund
Ros Harding Trust
The Harris Family Charitable Trust
The Harry and Mary Foundation*
The Health Foundation
May Hearnshaw's Charity
Heart Research UK
The Michael Heller Charitable Foundation
Help for Health
The Heritage of London Trust Ltd
The Hintze Family Charity Foundation
The Hiscox Foundation
The Hobson Charity Ltd
Dorothy Holmes Charitable Trust
Homelands Charitable Trust
The Mary Homfray Charitable Trust
Sir Harold Hood's Charitable Trust
The Hospital Saturday Fund
The Albert Hunt Trust
The Hurley Partners Charitable Trust*
IBM United Kingdom Trust
The Iliffe Family Charitable Trust
The Inverforth Charitable Trust
John Jarrold Trust Ltd
Jeffrey Charitable Trust*
Lillie Johnson Charitable Trust
The Johnson Foundation
The Joron Charitable Trust
Kantor Charitable Foundation*
The Kay Kendall Leukaemia Fund
The Kennedy Trust for Rheumatology Research
The Kensington and Chelsea Foundation
The Kentown Wizard Foundation
The Ursula Keyes Trust
Kidney Research UK
Kilpatrick Fraser Charitable Trust
The King Henry VIII Endowed Trust – Warwick
The Kirschel Foundation
Kusuma Trust UK
Ladbrokes Coral Trust
The Edgar E. Lawley Foundation
The William Leech Charity
The Leverhulme Trust
Lord Leverhulme's Charitable Trust
David and Ruth Lewis Family Charitable Trust
The Linder Foundation
The Second Joseph Aaron Littman Foundation
The Elaine and Angus Lloyd Charitable Trust
The W. M. and B. W. Lloyd Trust
London Freemasons Charity
The William and Katherine Longman Trust
Robert Luff Foundation Ltd
The Henry Lumley Charitable Trust
Lord and Lady Lurgan Trust
M. and C. Trust
Mace Foundation
The Mageni Trust*
The Manackerman Charitable Trust
The W. M. Mann Foundation
R. W. Mann Trust
The J. P. Marland Charitable Trust
The Michael Marsh Charitable Trust
D. G. Marshall of Cambridge Trust
The Geoffrey and Pauline Martin Trust*
Maudsley Charity
The Robert McAlpine Foundation
T. and J. Meyer Family Foundation Ltd
The Masonic Province of Middlesex Charitable Trust (Middlesex Masonic Charity)
Moondance Foundation
The George A. Moore Foundation
G. M. Morrison Charitable Trust
Motor Neurone Disease Association
The Edwina Mountbatten and Leonora Children's Foundation
The Janet Nash Charitable Settlement
The National Garden Scheme
The Frances and Augustus Newman Foundation
The Norman Family Charitable Trust
Normanby Charitable Trust
Oglesby Charitable Trust
The Orrin Charitable Trust
Orthopaedic Research UK
The Paragon Trust
Parkinson's UK
The JGW Patterson Foundation
Payne-Gallwey 1989 Charitable Trust
The Pears Family Charitable Foundation
Miss A. M. Pilkington's Charitable Trust
Pink Ribbon Foundation
Thomas Pocklington Trust
The George and Esme Pollitzer Charitable Settlement
The Mary Potter Convent Hospital Trust
Sir John Priestman Charity Trust
The Prince of Wales's Charitable Foundation
Prison Service Charity Fund
Prostate Cancer UK
Mr and Mrs J. A. Pye's Charitable Settlement
Queen Mary's Roehampton Trust
The Sir James Reckitt Charity
Riada Trust
The Clive and Sylvia Richards Charity Ltd
Rigby Foundation
RNID (The Royal National Institute for Deaf People)
The Dezna Robins Jones Charitable Foundation
Rockcliffe Charitable Trust
The Gerald and Gail Ronson Family Foundation
Rosca Trust
The Cecil Rosen Foundation
Rosetrees Trust
The Row Fogo Charitable Trust
Samjo Ltd
The Basil Samuel Charitable Trust
Sandra Charitable Trust
Sir Samuel Scott of Yews Trust
The Selfridges Group Foundation*
The Jean Shanks Foundation
The Bassil Shippam and Alsford Trust
The W. H. Smith Group Charitable Trust
Societe Generale UK Foundation*
Somerset Community Foundation
Peter Sowerby Foundation
Sparks Charity
The Jessie Spencer Trust

Rosalyn and Nicholas Springer Charitable Trust
The Geoff and Fiona Squire Foundation
*The Vichai Srivaddhanaprabha Foundation**
St Monica Trust
The Peter Stebbings Memorial Charity
The Steel Charitable Trust
Mark Stolkin Foundation
The Stoller Charitable Trust
The Stoneygate Trust
Peter Stormonth Darling Charitable Trust
Stratford-upon-Avon Town Trust
*The Joseph Strong Frazer Trust**
The Sunrise Foundation CIO
Sutton Coldfield Charitable Trust
The Swann-Morton Foundation
The Adrian Swire Charitable Trust
The Charles and Elsie Sykes Trust
The Talbot Trusts
Tanner Trust
Tenovus Cancer Care
Tenovus Scotland
The Thompson Family Charitable Trust
Sir Jules Thorn Charitable Trust
The Tompkins Foundation
David William Traill Cargill Fund
Annie Tranmer Charitable Trust
The Constance Travis Charitable Trust
Tropical Health and Education Trust
The Tuixen Foundation
Ulster Garden Villages Ltd
The Ulverscroft Foundation
The Underwood Trust
The Michael Uren Foundation
The Valentine Charitable Trust
The Valiant Charitable Trust
Variety, the Children's Charity
The Veterans' Foundation
Sylvia Waddilove Foundation UK
Robert and Felicity Waley-Cohen Charitable Trust
The Warwickshire Masonic Charitable Association Ltd
Mrs Waterhouse Charitable Trust
The Wellcome Trust
The Westfield Health Charitable Trust
The Dame Violet Wills Will Trust
The Francis Winham Foundation
The Charles Wolfson Charitable Trust
The Wolfson Family Charitable Trust
The Lord Leonard and Lady Estelle Wolfson Foundation
The Wyndham Charitable Trust
York Children's Trust
Yorkshire Cancer Research
The William Allen Young Charitable Trust
The Elizabeth and Prince Zaiger Trust
Zurich Community Trust (UK) Ltd

Museums, libraries and galleries

The 29th May 1961 Charitable Trust
The 4814 Trust
The Bryan Adams Foundation
The AEB Charitable Trust
The Alborada Trust
Viscount Amory's Charitable Trust
*The Ampersand Foundation**
The John Armitage Charitable Trust
The Art Fund
Arts Council England
Arts Council of Wales (also known as Cyngor Celfyddydau Cymru)
ArtSocial Foundation
Atkin Charitable Foundation
The Bagri Foundation
*The Kamini and Vindi Banga Family Trust**
The Baring Foundation
The Barnsbury Charitable Trust
Robert Barr's Charitable Trust
The Louis Baylis (Maidenhead Advertiser) Charitable Trust
The Beaverbrook Foundation
The Beaverbrooks Charitable Trust
Bennett Lowell Ltd
Bideford Bridge Trust
The Michael Bishop Foundation
The Boltini Trust
The William Brake Charitable Trust
The Liz and Terry Bramall Foundation
The J. and M. Britton Charitable Trust
The Arnold Burton 1998 Charitable Trust
Community Foundation for Calderdale
The Wilfrid and Constance Cave Foundation
Elizabeth Cayzer Charitable Trust
Chapman Charitable Trust
The Charities Advisory Trust
The Chipping Sodbury Town Lands Charity
The Clore Duffield Foundation
Denise Coates Foundation
The John S. Cohen Foundation
Colwinston Charitable Trust
The County Council of Dyfed Welsh Church Fund
The Sir Tom Cowie Charitable Trust
The Crescent Trust
The D'Oyly Carte Charitable Trust

The Daiwa Anglo-Japanese Foundation
The Roger De Haan Charitable Trust
The Gillian Dickinson Trust
The Dorfman Foundation
John Ellerman Foundation
The Elmley Foundation
The Emerald Foundation
Esmée Fairbairn Foundation
*Family Philanthropy Ltd**
The Lord Faringdon Charitable Trust
The Thomas Farr Charity
The Finnis Scott Foundation
Sir John Fisher Foundation
Fishmongers' Company's Charitable Trust
Marc Fitch Fund
Oliver Ford Foundation
Ian M. Foulerton Charitable Trust
Fowler Smith and Jones Trust
The Freelands Foundation Ltd
Garfield Weston Foundation
Nicholas and Judith Goodison's Charitable Settlement
The Grantham Yorke Trust
The J. G. Graves Charitable Trust
The Helen Hamlyn Trust
The Lennox Hannay Charitable Trust
The Headley Trust
The Heathcoat Trust
The Charlotte Heber-Percy Charitable Trust
Heritage Lottery Fund
The Heritage of London Trust Ltd
The Derek Hill Foundation
The Lady Hind Trust
The Hinduja Foundation
The Hintze Family Charity Foundation
*Historic Environment Scotland**
The Hobson Charity Ltd
The Idlewild Trust
The Ireland Fund of Great Britain
Sir James Knott Trust
The Kirby Laing Foundation
Duchy of Lancaster Benevolent Fund
Langdale Trust
Mrs M. A. Lascelles Charitable Trust
Lord Leverhulme's Charitable Trust
*Cecil and Hilda Lewis Charitable Trust**
The Linbury Trust
The Linder Foundation
Jack Livingstone Charitable Trust
The W. M. and B. W. Lloyd Trust
The Lockwood Charitable Foundation
The MacRobert Trust 2019
The Ian Mactaggart Trust (The Mactaggart Second Fund)
The W. M. Mann Foundation
The Michael Marks Charitable Trust
The Marks Family Charitable Trust
Sir George Martin Trust
Nancie Massey Charitable Trust
The Mickel Fund
*The Mikheev Charitable Trust**
The Esmé Mitchell Trust
The Monmouthshire County Council Welsh Church Act Fund
The Henry Moore Foundation
G. M. Morrison Charitable Trust
The Alexander Mosley Charitable Trust
*Friends of the National Libraries**
The National Manuscripts Conservation Trust
Normanby Charitable Trust
Norwich Town Close Estate Charity
The Ofenheim Charitable Trust
Oglesby Charitable Trust
Old Possum's Practical Trust
Henry Oldfield Trust
The Orrin Charitable Trust
The Owen Family Trust
Oxfordshire Community Foundation
Parabola Foundation
The Patrick Trust
The Pears Family Charitable Foundation
The Phillips and Rubens Charitable Trust
The Pilgrim Trust
Miss A. M. Pilkington's Charitable Trust
The Pitt-Rivers Charitable Trust
The Polonsky Foundation
Catkin Pussywillow Charitable Trust
Richmond Parish Lands Charity
The River Farm Foundation
Rix Thompson Rothenberg Foundation
Rockcliffe Charitable Trust
The Rose Foundation
The Rothermere Foundation
The Rothschild Foundation
Rothschild Foundation (Hanadiv) Europe
The Rowlands Trust
Royal Artillery Charitable Fund
The Ruddock Foundation for the Arts
The Jeremy and John Sacher Charitable Trust
The Michael and Nicola Sacher Charitable Trust
The Alan and Babette Sainsbury Charitable Fund
Saint Sarkis Charity Trust
Salisbury Pool Charity
Schroder Charity Trust
*The Sharp Foundation**
The Sheffield Town Trust
Stanley Smith UK Horticultural Trust
Philip Smith's Charitable Trust
The Stephen R. and Philippa H. Southall Charitable Trust
Rosalyn and Nicholas Springer Charitable Trust
Stanley Foundation Ltd
Staples Trust
The Steel Charitable Trust
Stevenson Family's Charitable Trust
The Samuel Storey Family Charitable Trust
Peter Stormonth Darling Charitable Trust
Suffolk Community Foundation
C. B. and H. H. Taylor 1984 Trust
The Roger and Douglas Turner Charitable Trust
Two Ridings Community Foundation
The Ulverscroft Foundation
Robert and Felicity Waley-Cohen Charitable Trust
The Welsh Church Act Fund
The Wingate Foundation
The Wolfson Family Charitable Trust
The Lord Leonard and Lady Estelle Wolfson Foundation
The Wolfson Foundation
*Worcestershire Community Foundation**
The William Allen Young Charitable Trust

Non-registered charities/ voluntary groups

The Aberdeen Foundation
ABF The Soldiers' Charity
Access Sport CIO
*Adam Family Foundation**
The Sylvia Adams Charitable Trust
The Aimwell Charitable Trust
Sylvia Aitken's Charitable Trust
*Alpkit Foundation**
*The Ampersand Foundation**
Anguish's Educational Foundation
The Apax Foundation
The Arsenal Foundation
The Artemis Charitable Foundation
Arts Council England
Ove Arup Partnership Charitable Trust
The Asda Foundation
The Ashendene Trust
The Ashley Family Foundation
The Associated Board of the Royal Schools of Music
The Aurelius Charitable Trust
The Avon and Somerset Police Community Trust
The Bagri Foundation
Bairdwatson Charitable Trust
The Ballinger Charitable Trust
Barchester Healthcare Foundation
The Philip Barker Charity
*The Barnes Fund**
The Max Barney Foundation
Barnwood Trust
Misses Barrie Charitable Trust
Robert Barr's Charitable Trust
The Battersea Power Station Foundation
Bauer Radio's Cash for Kids Charities
BBC Children in Need
The James Beattie Charitable Trust
Bedfordshire and Luton Community Foundation
*AJ Bell Trust**
The Rowan Bentall Charitable Trust
The Berkshire Community Foundation
The Bestway Foundation
Bideford Bridge Trust
Biffa Award
The Percy Bilton Charity
Binks Trust
Blakemore Foundation
Bluespark Foundation
BOOST Charitable Trust
Boots Charitable Trust
*Alan Boswell Group Charitable Trust**
*The Bransford Trust**
The Breadsticks Foundation
The Harold and Alice Bridges Charity
British Gas Energy Trust
British Motor Sports Training Trust
*Mary Brown Memorial Trust**
The Jack Brunton Charitable Trust
Buckingham Trust
Buckinghamshire Community Foundation
Building & Civil Engineering Charitable Trust
The Bulldog Trust Ltd
E. F. Bulmer Trust
Burnie's Foundation
Consolidated Charity of Burton upon Trent
Byrne Family Foundation
The Barrow Cadbury Trust
Community Foundation for Calderdale
The Cambridgeshire Community Foundation
*Camden Giving**
Canary Wharf Contractors Fund
The Frederick and Phyllis Cann Trust
*Card Factory Foundation**
W. A. Cargill Charitable Trust
The Carnegie Dunfermline Trust
The Carpenters' Company Charitable Trust
Chalfords Ltd
The Chartley Foundation
Cheshire Community Foundation Ltd
Chippenham Borough Lands Charity
The Chipping Sodbury Town Lands Charity
CHK Foundation
The Churchill Foundation
The Clan Trust Ltd
Clark Foundation
Cloudesley
The Coalfields Regeneration Trust
Denise Coates Foundation
John and Freda Coleman Charitable Trust
Comic Relief
The Comino Foundation
Community First
The Ernest Cook Trust
The Catherine Cookson Charitable Trust
Mabel Cooper Charity
Co-operative Community Investment Foundation
The Evan Cornish Foundation
Cornwall Community Foundation
The Duke of Cornwall's Benevolent Fund
Coventry Building Society Charitable Foundation
The Craps Charitable Trust
Creative Scotland
Cripplegate Foundation
Crisis UK
The Cross Trust
CSIS Charity Fund
Cumbria Community Foundation
The D. G. Charitable Settlement
Baron Davenport's Charity
The Roger De Haan Charitable Trust
Foundation Derbyshire
Devon Community Foundation
The Dibden Allotments Fund
*Digital Xtra Fund**
The Dorfman Foundation
Dorset Community Foundation
The Anne Duchess of Westminster's Charity
*Dumfriesshire East Community Benefit Group SCIO**
*The Nine Incorporated Trades of Dundee General Fund Charity**
*Dunlossit and Islay Community Trust**
County Durham Community Foundation
The Earley Charity
East End Community Foundation
Eastern Counties Educational Trust Ltd
The Eighty Eight Foundation
The Elmley Foundation
The Vernon N. Ely Charitable Trust
The Emerald Foundation
England and Wales Cricket Trust
The Enkalon Foundation
Essex Community Foundation
The Essex Youth Trust
The Evelyn Trust
Esmée Fairbairn Foundation
The George Fentham Birmingham Charity
Doris Field Charitable Trust
Sir John Fisher Foundation
The Football Association National Sports Centre Trust
The Football Foundation
Ford Britain Trust
Forever Manchester
The Forman Hardy Charitable Trust
The Fort Foundation

The Forte Charitable Trust
Fowler Smith and Jones Trust
Jill Franklin Trust
The Freshgate Trust Foundation
Friends Provident Charitable Foundation
The Funding Network
GambleAware
Garfield Weston Foundation
Gatwick Airport Community Trust
The Generations Foundation
The David Gibbons Foundation
The F. Glenister Woodger Trust
County of Gloucestershire Community Foundation
The Grace Trust
The Granada Foundation
The Grange Farm Centre Trust
The Gray Trust
Greenham Trust Ltd
The Greggs Foundation
The Grimmitt Trust
Groundwork UK
The Walter Guinness Charitable Trust
Calouste Gulbenkian Foundation – UK Branch
Hadras Kodesh Trust
The Alfred Haines Charitable Trust
The Hamilton Davies Trust
Hammersmith United Charities
Hampshire and Isle of Wight Community Foundation
The Hampstead Wells and Campden Trust
Hampton Fund
The Happold Foundation
The Harding Trust
Ros Harding Trust
The Harpur Trust
Gay and Peter Hartley's Hillards Charitable Trust
Edward Harvist Trust (The Harvist Estate)
The Health Foundation
Heart of England Community Foundation
Heart Research UK
The Hearth Foundation
The Heathcoat Trust
Heathrow Community Trust
The Hemby Charitable Trust
Henley Educational Trust
Henley Royal Regatta Charitable Trust
Herefordshire Community Foundation
The Heritage of London Trust Ltd
Hertfordshire Community Foundation
The Hilden Charitable Fund
The Lady Hind Trust
The Hiscox Foundation
Historic Environment Scotland*
Hockerill Educational Foundation
The Holywood Trust
The Hospital of God at Greatham
The Sir Joseph Hotung Charitable Settlement
House of Industry Estate
Housing Pathways Trust
The Hull and East Riding Charitable Trust
Huntingdon Freemen's Trust
Hyde Charitable Trust
IBM United Kingdom Trust
Ibrahim Foundation Ltd
Imagine Foundation
Impact Funding Partners Ltd
The Institute for Policy Research
Integrated Education Fund
The Ireland Fund of Great Britain
The Isla Foundation*
The Isle of Anglesey Charitable Trust
Isle of Wight Foundation
The Sir Barry Jackson County Fund
John James Bristol Foundation
Lady Eda Jardine Charitable Trust
John Jarrold Trust Ltd
Rees Jeffreys Road Fund
The Elton John Aids Foundation (EJAF)
The Christopher and Kirsty Johnston Charitable Trust
The Joicey Trust
The Kensington and Chelsea Foundation
Kent Community Foundation
KFC Foundation*
Kidney Research UK
Kilpatrick Fraser Charitable Trust
The King Henry VIII Endowed Trust – Warwick
The Graham Kirkham Foundation
Robert Kitchin (Saddlers' Company)
Sir James Knott Trust
The Kreitman Foundation
Ladbrokes Coral Trust
Community Foundations for Lancashire and Merseyside
Lancashire Environmental Fund Ltd
Duchy of Lancaster Benevolent Fund
The Allen Lane Foundation
Mrs M. A. Lascelles Charitable Trust
The Lauffer Family Charitable Foundation
The Richard Lawes Foundation
The Edgar E. Lawley Foundation
The David Lean Foundation
The William Leech Charity
Leeds Community Foundation (LCF)
Leicestershire and Rutland Masonic Charity Association
Leicestershire, Leicester and Rutland Community Foundation
Leng Charitable Trust
David and Ruth Lewis Family Charitable Trust
John Lewis Foundation
Lincolnshire Community Foundation
The Frank Litchfield Charitable Trust
The Second Joseph Aaron Littman Foundation
The W. M. and B. W. Lloyd Trust
London Catalyst
The London Community Foundation (LCF)
London Housing Foundation Ltd (LHF)
London Legal Support Trust (LLST)
The London Marathon Charitable Trust Ltd
The Lord's Taverners
LPW Ltd
Making a Difference Locally Ltd
Manchester Airport Community Trust Fund
The Manchester Guardian Society Charitable Trust
R. W. Mann Trust
The Dan Maskell Tennis Trust
The Master Charitable Trust
Maudsley Charity
MBNA General Foundation
The Medlock Charitable Trust
The Mercers' Charitable Foundation
The Millenium Oak Trust
Jean and Roger Miller's Charitable Trust
The Millichope Foundation
Milton Keynes Community Foundation Ltd
Mobbs Memorial Trust Ltd
The Monmouthshire County Council Welsh Church Act Fund
Moondance Foundation
The Henry Moore Foundation
John Moores Foundation
The Miles Morland Foundation

The Willie and Mabel Morris Charitable Trust
The Alexander Mosley Charitable Trust
Moto in the Community
The Frederick Mulder Foundation
The National Express Foundation
The National Garden Scheme
The Nationwide Foundation
Nesta
Newcomen Collett Foundation
The NFU Mutual Charitable Trust
The Nisbet Trust
The Nomura Charitable Trust
Norfolk Community Foundation
Educational Foundation of Alderman John Norman
The Norman Family Charitable Trust
*North Berwick Trust**
North East Area Miners' Social Welfare Trust Fund
Northamptonshire Community Foundation
Community Foundation for Northern Ireland
Northern Pharmacies Ltd Trust Fund
The Norton Foundation
Norwich Town Close Estate Charity
The Notgrove Trust
Nottinghamshire Community Foundation
The Nuffield Foundation
The Oakdale Trust
*Ocean Family Foundation**
Henry Oldfield Trust
One Community Foundation Ltd
Orthopaedic Research UK
*Otsar Trust**
The Ouseley Church Music Trust
Ovingdean Hall Foundation
The James Pantyfedwen Foundation (Ymddiriedolaeth James Pantyfedwen)
The Pastoral Care Trust – The St Nicholas Care Fund
The Jack Patston Charitable Trust
The Pears Family Charitable Foundation
The Pell Charitable Trust
People's Health Trust
The Performing Right Society Foundation
The Persimmon Charitable Foundation
The Jack Petchey Foundation
The Pets at Home Foundation
The Pharsalia Charitable Trust
The Pickwell Foundation
Miss A. M. Pilkington's Charitable Trust
The Pitt-Rivers Charitable Trust
*The Points Family Trust**
The Portal Trust
Postcode Local Trust
Postcode Society Trust (formerly Postcode Dream Trust)
The Mary Potter Convent Hospital Trust
*Poundland Foundation**
Power to Change Trust
*Price Parry Charitable Trust**
*Quadstar Charitable Foundation**
Quartet Community Foundation
*The Quilter Foundation**
The Rainford Trust
The Eleanor Rathbone Charitable Trust
The Sigrid Rausing Trust
The Sir James Reckitt Charity
The Reece Foundation
Richard Reeve's Foundation
Rhodi Charitable Trust
Riada Trust
Daisie Rich Trust
Humphrey Richardson Taylor Charitable Trust
Richmond Parish Lands Charity
Rigby Foundation
The Sir John Ritblat Family Foundation
Riverside Charitable Trust Ltd
Rix Thompson Rothenberg Foundation
The Robertson Trust
Robyn Charitable Trust
The Sir James Roll Charitable Trust
Mrs L. D. Rope's Third Charitable Settlement
Rosca Trust
The Rose Foundation
The David Ross Foundation
The Rothley Trust
The Rowlands Trust
The Joseph Rowntree Charitable Trust
Royal Docks Trust (London)
The Rugby Group Benevolent Fund Ltd
The Russell Trust
The RVW Trust
Santander UK Foundation Ltd
Savannah Wisdom
Foundation Scotland
Francis C. Scott Charitable Trust
The Frieda Scott Charitable Trust
The John Scott Trust Fund
The Screwfix Foundation
Seafarers UK (King George's Fund for Sailors)
Sam and Bella Sebba Charitable Trust
Leslie Sell Charitable Trust
Shaftoe Educational Foundation
The Shanly Foundation
The Sheffield Town Trust
The Bassil Shippam and Alsford Trust
The Shipwrights' Charitable Fund
Sirius Minerals Foundation
The Skelton Bounty
Skipton Building Society Charitable Foundation
The Slaughter and May Charitable Trust
Smallwood Trust
The Henry Smith Charity
The R. C. Snelling Charitable Trust
The Sobell Foundation
Sofronie Foundation
Somerset Community Foundation
The South Yorkshire Community Foundation
Southover Manor General Education Trust Ltd
*The Vichai Srivaddhanaprabha Foundation**
The St Hilda's Trust
Sir Walter St John's Educational Charity
St John's Foundation Est. 1174
St Olave's and St Saviour's Schools Foundation
St Peter's Saltley Trust
The Community Foundation for Staffordshire
The Stevenage Community Trust
Stewards Company Ltd
Stratford-upon-Avon Town Trust
Strathnairn Community Benefit Fund Ltd
The WO Street Charitable Foundation
*The Joseph Strong Frazer Trust**
Suffolk Community Foundation
The Summerfield Charitable Trust
The Sunrise Foundation CIO
Community Foundation for Surrey
The Sussex Community Foundation
Sutton Coldfield Charitable Trust
The Talbot Trusts
Tees Valley Community Foundation

Tenovus Scotland
The Theatres Trust Charitable Fund
Three Monkies Trust
Tower Hill Trust
The Toy Trust
Toyota Manufacturing UK Charitable Trust
The Treeside Trust
Tropical Health and Education Trust
Trust For London
The Tudor Trust
*The Tudwick Foundation**
The Tuixen Foundation
Two Ridings Community Foundation
Community Foundation serving Tyne and Wear and Northumberland
Ufi VocTech Trust
The Ulverscroft Foundation
United St Saviour's Charity
UPP Foundation
Variety, the Children's Charity
The Veolia Environmental Trust
The Virgin Money Foundation
Viridor Credits Environmental Company
*Vision Foundation**
The Vodafone Foundation
Sylvia Waddilove Foundation UK
Wade's Charity
The Scurrah Wainwright Charity
Wakefield and Tetley Trust
The Walcot Foundation
The Community Foundation in Wales
The Walker Trust
*War Memorials Trust**
Wates Family Enterprise Trust
The Wates Foundation
The William Wates Memorial Trust
The Geoffrey Watling Charity
The Watson Family Charitable Trust
The William Webster Charitable Trust
The Linda and Michael Weinstein Charitable Trust
The Weir Charitable Trust
The Welsh Church Act Fund
Wembley National Stadium Trust
*West Herts Charity Trust Ltd**
The Westfield Health Charitable Trust
Westway Trust
The Whitaker Charitable Trust
Charity of Sir Richard Whittington
The Wigoder Family Foundation
The Wilson Foundation
Wiltshire Community Foundation
The Wimbledon Foundation
The Wolfson Family Charitable Trust
The Wolfson Foundation
*Women's Fund for Scotland**
*The Victoria Wood Foundation**
Woodroffe Benton Foundation
The Woodward Charitable Trust
*Worcestershire Community Foundation**
Worth Waynflete Foundation
York Children's Trust
The Yorkshire Dales Millennium Trust
Youth Music
Zurich Community Trust (UK) Ltd

Places of worship

The Aaronson Foundation
Allchurches Trust Ltd
The Almond Trust
Viscount Amory's Charitable Trust
The AMW Charitable Trust
The Anchor Foundation
Andrews Charitable Trust
The John Armitage Charitable Trust
The Armourers' and Brasiers' Gauntlet Trust
The Ashburnham Thanksgiving Trust
The Ashendene Trust
The Ian Askew Charitable Trust
The Astor Foundation
*John Atcheson Foundation**
The Atlas Fund
Atlas Memorial Ltd
The Aurelius Charitable Trust
The Aylesford Family Charitable Trust
The Austin Bailey Foundation
The Baird Trust
Banbury Charities
The Roger and Sarah Bancroft Clark Charitable Trust
The Barker-Mill Foundation
Lord Barnby's Foundation
*The Barnes Fund**
The Barnsbury Charitable Trust
The Paul Bassham Charitable Trust
The Louis Baylis (Maidenhead Advertiser) Charitable Trust
BBC Children in Need
Bearder Charity
The James Beattie Charitable Trust
The Bedfordshire and Hertfordshire Historic Churches Trust
The Bellahouston Bequest Fund
The Benham Charitable Settlement
The Rowan Bentall Charitable Trust
The Beth Hamedrash Satmar Trust (BHST)
Bideford Bridge Trust
Biffa Award
The Bingham Trust
Binks Trust
Birmingham International Airport Community Trust Fund
The Isabel Blackman Foundation
The Bluston Charitable Settlement
The Boltini Trust
The Bonamy Charitable Trust
The Booth Charities

The Bowerman Charitable Trust
The Bowland Charitable Trust
The Liz and Terry Bramall Foundation
The Harold and Alice Bridges Charity
Bristol Archdeaconry Charity
The T. B. H. Brunner's Charitable Settlement
The Jack Brunton Charitable Trust
Buckingham Trust
The Buckinghamshire Historic Churches Trust
Consolidated Charity of Burton upon Trent
William A. Cadbury Charitable Trust
The Edward and Dorothy Cadbury Trust
Community Foundation for Calderdale
Callendar Charitable Trust
The Cambridgeshire Community Foundation
The Frederick and Phyllis Cann Trust
Cannon Charitable Trust
The Carrington Charitable Trust
The Leslie Mary Carter Charitable Trust
Catholic Charitable Trust
CEO Sleepout
The Chadwick Educational Foundation
Chippenham Borough Lands Charity
The Chipping Sodbury Town Lands Charity
The André Christian Trust
The Church Burgesses Educational Foundation
Church Burgesses Trust
Church of Ireland Priorities Fund
Church Urban Fund
Clark Foundation
The Clore Duffield Foundation
Cloudesley
The Robert Clutterbuck Charitable Trust
CMZ Ltd
The Francis Coales Charitable Foundation
The Coalfields Regeneration Trust
The Cobtree Charity Trust Ltd
The Vivienne and Samuel Cohen Charitable Trust
Sir Jeremiah Colman Gift Trust
Community First
Congregational and General Charitable Trust
The Catherine Cookson Charitable Trust
The Helen Jean Cope Charity
The Worshipful Company of Cordwainers Charitable Trusts (Minges Gift)
The Duke of Cornwall's Benevolent Fund
The Costa Family Charitable Trust
*Council for World Mission (UK)**
The County Council of Dyfed Welsh Church Fund
The Sir Tom Cowie Charitable Trust
The Cross Trust
The Croydon Relief in Need Charities
D. M. H. Educational Trust Ltd
Baron Davenport's Charity
The Davis Foundation
The De Brye Charitable Trust
The Roger De Haan Charitable Trust
The Devon Historic Churches
The Duke of Devonshire's Charitable Trust
The Derek and Eileen Dodgson Foundation
Donibristle Trust
Dorset Community Foundation
The Dorset Historic Churches Trust
Dromintee Trust
Dumbreck Charity
*Dumfriesshire East Community Benefit Group SCIO**
*The Nine Incorporated Trades of Dundee General Fund Charity**
The Dyers' Company Charitable Trust
The Gilbert and Eileen Edgar Foundation
Edinburgh Trust No. 2 Account
The Eighteen Fund
*The Elie Trust**
The Maud Elkington Charitable Trust
The Emerald Foundation
The Englefield Charitable Trust
The Enkalon Foundation
Entindale Ltd
Esher House Charitable Trust
Friends of Essex Churches Trust
The Essex Heritage Trust
The Everard Foundation
The Eveson Charitable Trust
G. F. Eyre Charitable Trust
The Fairstead Trust
Famos Foundation Trust
The Thomas Farr Charity
The Farthing Trust
The A. M. Fenton Trust
The Feoffees of St Michael's Spurriergate York
Allan and Nesta Ferguson Charitable Settlement
Doris Field Charitable Trust
The Fifty Fund
Dixie Rose Findlay Charitable Trust
The Forte Charitable Trust
Ian M. Foulerton Charitable Trust
Fowler Smith and Jones Trust
Jill Franklin Trust
The Gale Family Charity Trust
Gamma Trust
The Ganzoni Charitable Trust
Garfield Weston Foundation
Gatwick Airport Community Trust
The Jacqueline and Michael Gee Charitable Trust
General Charity (Coventry)
The Gibbs Charitable Trusts
The Simon Gibson Charitable Trust
The Gloucestershire Historic Churches Trust
Worshipful Company of Glovers of London Charitable Trust
The Godinton Charitable Trust
The Golsoncott Foundation
The Goshen Trust
Grace Charitable Trust
The Grace Trust
The Grange Farm Centre Trust
The Grant Foundation
The Grantham Yorke Trust
The J. G. Graves Charitable Trust
The Gray Trust
The Green Hall Foundation
Philip and Judith Green Trust
The Grocers' Charity
Hackney Parochial Charities
Hadras Kodesh Trust
The Alfred Haines Charitable Trust
The Hamilton Davies Trust
Hampton Fund
The W. A. Handley Charity Trust
The Lennox Hannay Charitable Trust
Harborne Parish Lands Charity
The David and Claudia Harding Foundation
Ros Harding Trust
Gay and Peter Hartley's Hillards Charitable Trust
The Headley Trust
The Heathcoat Trust
The Charlotte Heber-Percy Charitable Trust
Help the Homeless Ltd
The Helping Foundation

The Herefordshire Historic Churches Trust
Heritage Lottery Fund
The Heritage of London Trust Ltd
The Hillier Trust
The Lady Hind Trust
The Hintze Family Charity Foundation
*Historic Environment Scotland**
The Hobson Charity Ltd
Hockerill Educational Foundation
The Jane Hodge Foundation
The Holbeck Charitable Trust
The Holden Charitable Trust
Dorothy Holmes Charitable Trust
Homelands Charitable Trust
The Mary Homfray Charitable Trust
Sir Harold Hood's Charitable Trust
Hope Trust
The Hospital of God at Greatham
Housing Pathways Trust
The Hudson Foundation
The Humanitarian Trust
The Albert Hunt Trust
The Hunting Horn General Charitable Trust
Huntingdon Freemen's Trust
Hyde Park Place Estate Charity
The Idlewild Trust
The Iliffe Family Charitable Trust
International Bible Students Association
*The Isla Foundation**
The J. and J. Benevolent Foundation
The J. A. R. Charitable Trust
John James Bristol Foundation
Lady Eda Jardine Charitable Trust
John Jarrold Trust Ltd
The Jenour Foundation
The Jerusalem Trust
The Joicey Trust
The Jusaca Charitable Trust
The Kasner Charitable Trust
The Kennedy Charitable Foundation
The Friends of Kent Churches
The Nancy Kenyon Charitable Trust
The Kildare Trust
The King Henry VIII Endowed Trust – Warwick
The Kirschel Foundation
Sir James Knott Trust
Kollel and Co. Ltd
Kolyom Trust Ltd
The K. P. Ladd Charitable Trust
Maurice and Hilda Laing Charitable Trust
The Kirby Laing Foundation
The Martin Laing Foundation
The Beatrice Laing Trust
The Leonard Laity Stoate Charitable Trust
Lancashire Environmental Fund Ltd
Duchy of Lancaster Benevolent Fund
Lancaster Foundation
The R. J. Larg Family Trust
Laslett's (Hinton) Charity
The Herd Lawson and Muriel Lawson Charitable Trust
The Leche Trust
The William Leech Charity
Leicestershire and Rutland Masonic Charity Association
Leicestershire, Leicester and Rutland Community Foundation
Lempriere Pringle 2015
Leng Charitable Trust
Lord Leverhulme's Charitable Trust
Limoges Charitable Trust
The Linbury Trust
Lincolnshire Community Foundation
The Charles Littlewood Hill Trust
The Second Joseph Aaron Littman Foundation
Jack Livingstone Charitable Trust
The Elaine and Angus Lloyd Charitable Trust
The W. M. and B. W. Lloyd Trust
The Locker Foundation
The Lockwood Charitable Foundation
Loftus Charitable Trust
London Catalyst
The C. L. Loyd Charitable Trust
Sylvanus Lysons Charity
The Mactaggart Third Fund
The Magdalen and Lasher Charity (General Fund)
Making a Difference Locally Ltd
R. W. Mann Trust
The Michael Marsh Charitable Trust
Charity of John Marshall
Charlotte Marshall Charitable Trust
D. G. Marshall of Cambridge Trust
The Kristina Martin Charitable Trust
Sir George Martin Trust
John Martin's Charity
Nancie Massey Charitable Trust
Maudsley Charity
Mayheights Ltd
Maypride Ltd
The Medlock Charitable Trust
The Mercers' Charitable Foundation
The Merchant Taylors' Company Charities Fund
The Merchant Venturers' Charity
The Millichope Foundation
The Millward Charitable Trust
*The Milne Family Foundation**
Milton Keynes Community Foundation Ltd
The Esmé Mitchell Trust
Mobbs Memorial Trust Ltd
Mole Charitable Trust
The Monmouthshire County Council Welsh Church Act Fund
The Morel Charitable Trust
G. M. Morrison Charitable Trust
Vyoel Moshe Charitable Trust
Music Sales Charitable Trust
The National Churches Trust
The National Express Foundation
The National Lottery Community Fund
The Norfolk Churches Trust Ltd
Norfolk Community Foundation
Normanby Charitable Trust
Northamptonshire Community Foundation
The Northumbria Historic Churches Trust
Northwood Charitable Trust
Norwich Town Close Estate Charity
The Norwood and Newton Settlement
The Notgrove Trust
The Ofenheim Charitable Trust
The Ogle Christian Trust
Oglesby Charitable Trust
Old Possum's Practical Trust
Henry Oldfield Trust
The Orrin Charitable Trust
*Otsar Trust**
The Ouseley Church Music Trust
The Owen Family Trust
Oxfordshire Historic Churches Trust (2016)
*The P27 Trust**
The Gerald Palmer Eling Trust Company

The James Pantyfedwen Foundation (Ymddiriedolaeth James Pantyfedwen)
The Paragon Trust
Miss M. E. S. Paterson's Charitable Trust
The Jack Patston Charitable Trust
Payne-Gallwey 1989 Charitable Trust
Susanna Peake Charitable Trust
The Pears Family Charitable Foundation
*Dina Perelman Trust Ltd**
The Persimmon Charitable Foundation
The Phillips and Rubens Charitable Trust
The Pilgrim Trust
Miss A. M. Pilkington's Charitable Trust
The Mary Potter Convent Hospital Trust
Sir John Priestman Charity Trust
The Privy Purse Charitable Trust
Quothquan Trust
The Bishop Radford Trust
The Rank Foundation Ltd
The Joseph Rank Trust
The Ratcliff Foundation
The Rathbone Brothers Foundation
The Sir James Reckitt Charity
Daisie Rich Trust
The Clive and Sylvia Richards Charity Ltd
Richmond Parish Lands Charity
Rigby Foundation
The River Trust
Robertson Hall Trust
The Romney Marsh Historic Churches Trust
Mrs L. D. Rope's Third Charitable Settlement
Rosca Trust
The Rose Foundation
The Cecil Rosen Foundation
The Rothermere Foundation
The Rowlands Trust
The Joseph Rowntree Charitable Trust
Royal Society of Wildlife Trusts
The Rugby Group Benevolent Fund Ltd
S. and R. Charitable Trust
The Saddlers' Company Charitable Fund
Saint Sarkis Charity Trust
The Salamander Charitable Trust
Salisbury Pool Charity
The Basil Samuel Charitable Trust
The Peter Samuel Charitable Trust
*The Sanderson Foundation**
Sandra Charitable Trust
Sarum St Michael Educational Charity
The Scarfe Charitable Trust
Schroder Charity Trust
Foundation Scotland
Sam and Bella Sebba Charitable Trust
Seedfield Trust
The Shanly Foundation
The Sheffield Town Trust
The Sylvia and Colin Shepherd Charitable Trust
The Bassil Shippam and Alsford Trust
The Skelton Bounty
The Charles Skey Charitable Trust
*Smith Bradbeer Charitable Trust**
The Henry Smith Charity
The R. C. Snelling Charitable Trust
The Stephen R. and Philippa H. Southall Charitable Trust
The Jessie Spencer Trust
Rosalyn and Nicholas Springer Charitable Trust
The Spurrell Charitable Trust
The St Hilda's Trust
St Luke's College Foundation
St Olave's and St Saviour's Schools Foundation
St Peter's Saltley Trust
Starlow Charities Ltd
The Hugh Stenhouse Foundation
Stewards Company Ltd
The Stobart Newlands Charitable Trust
Mark Stolkin Foundation
The Samuel Storey Family Charitable Trust
Stratford-upon-Avon Town Trust
The Street Foundation
*The Joseph Strong Frazer Trust**
The Suffolk Historic Churches Trust
The Summerfield Charitable Trust
The Bernard Sunley Foundation
Sabina Sutherland Charitable Trust
Sutton Coldfield Charitable Trust
Swansea and Brecon Diocesan Board of Finance Ltd
The Adrian Swire Charitable Trust
Tabeel Trust
The Tajtelbaum Charitable Trust
The Talbot Village Trust
Tallow Chandlers Benevolent Fund No. 2
Tanner Trust
C. B. and H. H. Taylor 1984 Trust
Scott Thomson Charitable Trust
Mrs R. P. Tindall's Charitable Trust
The Tompkins Foundation
The Toye Foundation
The Constance Travis Charitable Trust
The Treeside Trust
*The Troutsdale Charitable Trust**
The Truemark Trust
Trust For London
The Tudor Trust
The Tufton Charitable Trust
Community Foundation serving Tyne and Wear and Northumberland
Ulting Overseas Trust
The Union of the Sisters of Mercy of Great Britain
The United Reformed Church (Wessex) Trust Ltd
United St Saviour's Charity
The Vail Foundation
The Albert Van Den Bergh Charitable Trust
The Vardy Foundation
The Veneziana Fund
Nigel Vinson Charitable Trust
Viridor Credits Environmental Company
Robert and Felicity Waley-Cohen Charitable Trust
Warwick Relief in Need Charity
Wates Family Enterprise Trust
The Wates Foundation
The Geoffrey Watling Charity
The William Webster Charitable Trust
The Linda and Michael Weinstein Charitable Trust
The Welsh Church Act Fund
West Derby Waste Lands Charity
The Westcroft Trust
Westhill Endowment
Westminster Foundation
The Whinfell Charitable Fund
The Whitaker Charitable Trust
The Norman Whiteley Trust
Charity of Sir Richard Whittington
Dame Violet Wills Charitable Trust
The Wilmcote Charitrust

The Benjamin Winegarten Charitable Trust
The Wixamtree Trust
Friends of Wiznitz Ltd
The Wolfson Family Charitable Trust
The Wolfson Foundation
The James Wood Bequest Fund
Worth Waynflete Foundation
WWDP (World Day of Prayer National Committee for England, Wales and Northern Ireland)
The Wyndham Charitable Trust
The Yorkshire Historic Churches Trust
The William Allen Young Charitable Trust
The Marjorie and Arnold Ziff Charitable Foundation
Zurich Community Trust (UK) Ltd

Schools and colleges

The 29th May 1961 Charitable Trust
The Acacia Charitable Trust
The Bryan Adams Foundation
The Adlard Family Charitable Foundation
The Alborada Trust
Aldgate and Allhallows Foundation
Al-Fayed Charitable Foundation
Allchurches Trust Ltd
Alpkit Foundation*
Viscount Amory's Charitable Trust
Anguish's Educational Foundation
The Ardwick Trust
Armed Forces Education Trust
The John Armitage Charitable Trust
The Armourers' and Brasiers' Gauntlet Trust
Arts Council of Wales (also known as Cyngor Celfyddydau Cymru)
The Ove Arup Foundation
The Asda Foundation
The Ian Askew Charitable Trust
The Associated Board of the Royal Schools of Music
John Atcheson Foundation*
The Atlas Fund
Lawrence Atwell's Charity (Skinners' Company)
The Avon and Somerset Police Community Trust
Axis Foundation
The Aylesford Family Charitable Trust
Backstage Trust
The Baily Thomas Charitable Fund
Banbury Charities
The Baring Foundation
The Barker-Mill Foundation
Lord Barnby's Foundation
The Barnes Fund*
The Barnsbury Charitable Trust
Barnwood Trust
Robert Barr's Charitable Trust
Battens Charitable Trust
The Battersea Power Station Foundation
Bauer Radio's Cash for Kids Charities
Bay Charitable Trust
The Louis Baylis (Maidenhead Advertiser) Charitable Trust
BBC Children in Need
BC Partners Foundation
Bear Mordechai Ltd
The James Beattie Charitable Trust
Beauland Ltd
The Beaverbrooks Charitable Trust
Benesco Charity Ltd
The Benham Charitable Settlement
The Rowan Bentall Charitable Trust
The Berkshire Community Foundation
The Bestway Foundation
Bideford Bridge Trust
Biffa Award
The Percy Bilton Charity
The Bingham Trust
Binks Trust
Birmingham International Airport Community Trust Fund
Birthday House Trust
The Michael Bishop Foundation
The Sydney Black Charitable Trust
The Isabel Blackman Foundation
Blakemore Foundation
The Bloom Foundation
Bluespark Foundation
The Boltini Trust
The Bonamy Charitable Trust
The Booth Charities
Sir William Boreman's Foundation
The Boshier-Hinton Foundation
Alan Boswell Group Charitable Trust*
The Bowerman Charitable Trust
The Bowland Charitable Trust
The Liz and Terry Bramall Foundation
The Breadsticks Foundation
The Brenley Trust
The Harold and Alice Bridges Charity
Bristol Charities
The BRIT Trust
The British and Foreign School Society
The J. and M. Britton Charitable Trust
R. S. Brownless Charitable Trust
The Jack Brunton Charitable Trust
Buckingham Trust
The Buffini Chao Foundation
E. F. Bulmer Trust
The Burden Trust
The Clara E. Burgess Charity
The Burry Charitable Trust
Consolidated Charity of Burton upon Trent
Byrne Family Foundation

The Grace Trust
Grahame Charitable Foundation Ltd
The Grange Farm Centre Trust
The Grantham Yorke Trust
GrantScape
The J. G. Graves Charitable Trust
The Gray Trust
The Great Britain Sasakawa Foundation
The Great Stone Bridge Trust of Edenbridge
Greenham Trust Ltd
The Greenslade Family Foundation*
The Greggs Foundation
The Grimmitt Trust
The Grocers' Charity
Groundwork UK
Dr Guthrie's Association
Hackney Parochial Charities
Hadras Kodesh Trust
The Hadrian Trust
The Hamilton Davies Trust
Paul Hamlyn Foundation
The Helen Hamlyn Trust
Hammersmith United Charities
Hampshire and Isle of Wight Community Foundation
The W. A. Handley Charity Trust
The Happold Foundation
Harbinson Charitable Trust
Harborne Parish Lands Charity
The David and Claudia Harding Foundation
William Harding's Charity
The Harebell Centenary Fund
The Harpur Trust
The Peter Harrison Foundation
Edward Harvist Trust (The Harvist Estate)
The Heathcoat Trust
Heathrow Community Trust
The Charlotte Heber-Percy Charitable Trust
Ernest Hecht Charitable Foundation
The Helping Foundation
Henley Educational Trust
The Tim Henman Foundation
Herefordshire Community Foundation
The Heritage of London Trust Ltd
The Highcroft Charitable Trust
The Hilden Charitable Fund
The Lady Hind Trust
The Hinduja Foundation
The Hintze Family Charity Foundation
The Hobson Charity Ltd
The Jane Hodge Foundation
The Holbeck Charitable Trust
The Holden Charitable Trust
The Holywood Trust
The Mary Homfray Charitable Trust
Sir Harold Hood's Charitable Trust
The Horners Charity Fund
The Horse Trust
Horwich Shotter Charitable Trust
Housing Pathways Trust
The Hudson Foundation
The Hull and East Riding Charitable Trust
The Hunter Foundation
The Huntingdon Foundation Ltd
Hurdale Charity Ltd
Hyde Charitable Trust
Hyde Park Place Estate Charity
IBM United Kingdom Trust
Imagine Foundation
Integrated Education Fund
The International Bankers Charitable Trust
The Ireland Fund of Great Britain
Irish Youth Foundation (UK) Ltd (incorporating The Lawlor Foundation)
The ITF Seafarers Trust
The Frank Jackson Foundation
John James Bristol Foundation
John Jarrold Trust Ltd
Jeffrey Charitable Trust*
The Jenour Foundation
The Jerusalem Trust
The Johnson Foundation
Johnnie Johnson Trust
The Jones 1986 Charitable Trust
The Muriel Jones Foundation
The Jusaca Charitable Trust
Kantor Charitable Foundation*
The Karlsson Jativa Charitable Foundation*
The Ian Karten Charitable Trust
The Kasner Charitable Trust
C. S. Kaufman Charitable Trust
William Kendall's Charity (Wax Chandlers' Company)
The Kennedy Charitable Foundation
The Kensington and Chelsea Foundation
The Nancy Kenyon Charitable Trust
The Peter Kershaw Trust
The Ursula Keyes Trust
The King Henry VIII Endowed Trust – Warwick
The Kirschel Foundation
Robert Kitchin (Saddlers' Company)
Sir James Knott Trust
Kollel and Co. Ltd
KPE4 Charitable Trust*
The KPMG Foundation
Kusuma Trust UK
The Kyte Charitable Trust
The Kirby Laing Foundation
The Beatrice Laing Trust
Community Foundations for Lancashire and Merseyside
The Lancashire Foundation
Duchy of Lancaster Benevolent Fund
Lancaster Foundation
The R. J. Larg Family Trust
The Lauffer Family Charitable Foundation
The Edgar E. Lawley Foundation
Lawson Beckman Charitable Trust
The Lawson Trust CIO
The David Lean Foundation
The Leathersellers' Company Charitable Fund
The Legal Education Foundation
Leicestershire, Leicester and Rutland Community Foundation
The Leverhulme Trust
Lord Leverhulme's Charitable Trust
Cecil and Hilda Lewis Charitable Trust*
The Linbury Trust
Lincolnshire Community Foundation
The Linden Charitable Trust
The Charles Littlewood Hill Trust
The Second Joseph Aaron Littman Foundation
Jack Livingstone Charitable Trust
The Elaine and Angus Lloyd Charitable Trust
The W. M. and B. W. Lloyd Trust
Local Trent Ltd
The Locker Foundation
London Freemasons Charity
The London Marathon Charitable Trust Ltd
The Lord's Taverners
The Henry Lumley Charitable Trust
Lord and Lady Lurgan Trust
John Lyon's Charity
M. and C. Trust
M. B. Foundation
Mace Foundation
The Mackintosh Foundation
The MacRobert Trust 2019
The Mactaggart Third Fund
The Magdalen and Lasher Charity (General Fund)

Scottish Property Industry Festival of Christmas (SPIFOX)
Sam and Bella Sebba Charitable Trust
Shaftoe Educational Foundation
The Jean Shanks Foundation
The Shanly Foundation
The Shears Foundation
The Sheepdrove Trust
The Sheffield Town Trust
The Sheldon Trust
The Sylvia and Colin Shepherd Charitable Trust
SHINE (Support and Help in Education)
The Bassil Shippam and Alsford Trust
The Shipwrights' Charitable Fund
Shulem B. Association Ltd
The Sino-British Fellowship Trust
Sirius Minerals Foundation
The Charles Skey Charitable Trust
The John Slater Foundation
The Slaughter and May Charitable Trust
Sloane Robinson Foundation
The Henry Smith Charity
The Leslie Smith Foundation
The W. H. Smith Group Charitable Trust
Stanley Smith UK Horticultural Trust
The R. C. Snelling Charitable Trust
Societe Generale UK Foundation*
David Solomons Charitable Trust
Somerset Community Foundation
The South Yorkshire Community Foundation
Southover Manor General Education Trust Ltd
The Spear Charitable Trust
Spielman Charitable Trust
The Spoore, Merry and Rixman Foundation
Rosalyn and Nicholas Springer Charitable Trust
St James's Place Charitable Foundation
Sir Walter St John's Educational Charity
St John's Foundation Est. 1174
St Luke's College Foundation
St Olave's and St Saviour's Schools Foundation
St Peter's Saltley Trust
The Community Foundation for Staffordshire
Starlow Charities Ltd
The Steel Charitable Trust
The Stevenage Community Trust
Mark Stolkin Foundation
The Samuel Storey Family Charitable Trust
Peter Stormonth Darling Charitable Trust
Strand Parishes Trust
Stratford-upon-Avon Town Trust
Strathnairn Community Benefit Fund Ltd
The Joseph Strong Frazer Trust*
The Sudborough Foundation
Suffolk Community Foundation
The Summerfield Charitable Trust
The Bernard Sunley Foundation
Community Foundation for Surrey
The Sussex Community Foundation
The Sutasoma Trust
Sutton Coldfield Charitable Trust
The John Swire (1989) Charitable Trust
The Adrian Swire Charitable Trust
The Charles and Elsie Sykes Trust
Taca
The Tajtelbaum Charitable Trust
The Talbot Village Trust
Tallow Chandlers Benevolent Fund No. 2
The David Tannen Charitable Trust
Tanner Trust
C. B. and H. H. Taylor 1984 Trust
Stephen Taylor Foundation
The Tedworth Charitable Trust
Tees Valley Community Foundation
The Thompson Family Charitable Trust
Mrs R. P. Tindall's Charitable Trust
The Tompkins Foundation
The Tottenham Grammar School Foundation
Tower Hill Trust
The Toy Trust
Toyota Manufacturing UK Charitable Trust
The Constance Travis Charitable Trust
The Treeside Trust
The Trefoil Trust
Trumros Ltd
The Tufton Charitable Trust
The Tuixen Foundation
Ufi VocTech Trust
Ulster Garden Villages Ltd
Ulting Overseas Trust
The Ulverscroft Foundation
United Jewish Israel Appeal
Universal Music UK Sound Foundation
The Vail Foundation
The Vandervell Foundation
Variety, the Children's Charity
The Vintners' Foundation
Vivdale Ltd
The Walcot Foundation
The Barbara Ward Children's Foundation
G. R. Waters Charitable Trust 2000
Wates Family Enterprise Trust
John Watson's Trust
The Linda and Michael Weinstein Charitable Trust
Wembley National Stadium Trust
West Derby Waste Lands Charity
West Herts Charity Trust Ltd*
Westhill Endowment
Westminster Foundation
Westway Trust
Dame Violet Wills Charitable Trust
Brian Wilson Charitable Trust
The Wilson Foundation
W. Wing Yip and Brothers Foundation
Friends of Wiznitz Ltd
The Maurice Wohl Charitable Foundation
The Charles Wolfson Charitable Trust
The Wolfson Family Charitable Trust
The Wolfson Foundation
The Wood Foundation
Wooden Spoon Society
Woodroffe Benton Foundation
Worth Waynflete Foundation
Yankov Charitable Trust
York Children's Trust
The William Allen Young Charitable Trust
Youth Music
Zurich Community Trust (UK) Ltd

Social enterprises

The 29th May 1961 Charitable Trust
ABF The Soldiers' Charity
The Sylvia Adams Charitable Trust
AKO Foundation
Anguish's Educational Foundation
The Anson Charitable Trust
The Apax Foundation
The Armourers' and Brasiers' Gauntlet Trust
The Art Fund
Arts Council England
Arts Council of Wales (also known as Cyngor Celfyddydau Cymru)
Bairdwatson Charitable Trust
The Ballinger Charitable Trust
The Barbour Foundation
Lord Barnby's Foundation
*The Barnes Fund**
The Max Barney Foundation
Barnwood Trust
Misses Barrie Charitable Trust
Robert Barr's Charitable Trust
BBC Children in Need
Bedfordshire and Luton Community Foundation
Benesco Charity Ltd
The Berkshire Community Foundation
Biffa Award
The Percy Bilton Charity
The Bingham Trust
Birmingham International Airport Community Trust Fund
Bluespark Foundation
BOOST Charitable Trust
Boots Charitable Trust
The Harold and Alice Bridges Charity
The Jack Brunton Charitable Trust
Buckinghamshire Community Foundation
The Bulldog Trust Ltd
E. F. Bulmer Trust
BUPA UK Foundation
Consolidated Charity of Burton upon Trent
Community Foundation for Calderdale
The Cambridgeshire Community Foundation
*Camden Giving**
Canary Wharf Contractors Fund
*Card Factory Foundation**
*CareTech Foundation**
Cheshire Community Foundation Ltd
Church Urban Fund
The City Bridge Trust (Bridge House Estates)
CLA Charitable Trust
J. A. Clark Charitable Trust
The Clothworkers' Foundation
The Coalfields Regeneration Trust
The Cobtree Charity Trust Ltd
Colchester Catalyst Charity
John and Freda Coleman Charitable Trust
Comic Relief
The Comino Foundation
Community First
The Catherine Cookson Charitable Trust
Co-operative Community Investment Foundation
The Evan Cornish Foundation
Cornwall Community Foundation
The Duke of Cornwall's Benevolent Fund
Corra Foundation
Cripplegate Foundation
Crisis UK
Cumbria Community Foundation
Baron Davenport's Charity
Foundation Derbyshire
Devon Community Foundation
*Digital Xtra Fund**
Dorset Community Foundation
The Dunhill Medical Trust
*Dunlossit and Islay Community Trust**
County Durham Community Foundation
East End Community Foundation
Eastern Counties Educational Trust Ltd
The Edge Foundation
The Elmley Foundation
The Enkalon Foundation
Essex Community Foundation
The Evelyn Trust
Esmée Fairbairn Foundation
The Finnis Scott Foundation
Fishmongers' Company's Charitable Trust
The Football Foundation
The Forbes Charitable Foundation
Forever Manchester
The Forman Hardy Charitable Trust
The Freshgate Trust Foundation
Friends Provident Charitable Foundation
The Funding Network
Garfield Weston Foundation
Gatwick Airport Community Trust
The F. Glenister Woodger Trust
County of Gloucestershire Community Foundation
Worshipful Company of Gold and Silver Wyre Drawers Second Charitable Trust Fund
Sydney and Phyllis Goldberg Memorial Charitable Trust
The Grace Trust
The Granada Foundation
The Grange Farm Centre Trust
The Greggs Foundation
Groundwork UK
Calouste Gulbenkian Foundation – UK Branch
The Hadfield Charitable Trust
The Hadrian Trust
Halifax Foundation for Northern Ireland
The Hamilton Davies Trust
Hampshire and Isle of Wight Community Foundation
Hampton Fund
The Happold Foundation
Harbinson Charitable Trust
Harborne Parish Lands Charity
William Harding's Charity
The Harpur Trust
Edward Harvist Trust (The Harvist Estate)
Heart of England Community Foundation
Heart Research UK
Heathrow Community Trust
Help the Homeless Ltd
Herefordshire Community Foundation
Heritage Lottery Fund
The Heritage of London Trust Ltd
Hertfordshire Community Foundation
Highway One Trust
The Hilden Charitable Fund
*Historic Environment Scotland**
The Holywood Trust
The Hospital of God at Greatham
Housing Pathways Trust
The Hunter Foundation
Hyde Charitable Trust
Ibrahim Foundation Ltd
Imagine Foundation
Impact Funding Partners Ltd
Impetus
The Innocent Foundation
*The Isla Foundation**
Isle of Wight Foundation
John James Bristol Foundation
John Jarrold Trust Ltd
The Kensington and Chelsea Foundation
Kent Community Foundation
The Mary Kinross Charitable Trust
Sir James Knott Trust
The KPMG Foundation

Kusuma Trust UK
Community Foundations for Lancashire and Merseyside
Lancashire Environmental Fund Ltd
Lancaster Foundation
The Allen Lane Foundation
Leeds Community Foundation (LCF)
The Legal Education Foundation
Lincolnshire Community Foundation
The Frank Litchfield Charitable Trust
The W. M. and B. W. Lloyd Trust
Lloyd's Charities Trust
The London Community Foundation (LCF)
The London Marathon Charitable Trust Ltd
Making a Difference Locally Ltd
R. W. Mann Trust
The J. P. Marland Charitable Trust
Mathew Trust
Maudsley Charity
MBNA General Foundation
The Mercers' Charitable Foundation
The Masonic Province of Middlesex Charitable Trust (Middlesex Masonic Charity)
The Millennium Oak Trust
Millennium Stadium Charitable Trust (Ymddiriedclaeth Elusennol Stadiwm y Mileniwm)
Milton Keynes Community Foundation Ltd
*The Mohn Westlake Foundation**
The Monmouthshire County Council Welsh Church Act Fund
Moondance Foundation
John Moores Foundation
The Steve Morgan Foundation
The MSE Charity
The Frederick Mulder Foundation
The National Express Foundation
The National Lottery Community Fund
The Nationwide Foundation
Nesta
Network for Social Change Charitable Trust
Newcomen Collett Foundation
The Nineveh Charitable Trust
The Nisbet Trust
Norfolk Community Foundation
The Norman Family Charitable Trust
Northamptonshire Community Foundation
Northern Pharmacies Ltd Trust Fund
Norwich Town Close Estate Charity
Notting Hill Genesis Community Foundation
Nottinghamshire Community Foundation
Ovingdean Hall Foundation
Oxfordshire Community Foundation
The Pastoral Care Trust – The St Nicholas Care Fund
The Pears Family Charitable Foundation
People's Health Trust
People's Postcode Trust
Bernard Piggott Charitable Trust
Pilkington Charities Fund
Pink Ribbon Foundation
Polden-Puckham Charitable Foundation
Postcode Community Trust
Postcode Local Trust
Postcode Society Trust (formerly Postcode Dream Trust)
The Mary Potter Convent Hospital Trust
Power to Change Trust
The Prince's Countryside Fund
The Progress Foundation
The PwC Foundation
*Quadstar Charitable Foundation**
Quartet Community Foundation
The Eleanor Rathbone Charitable Trust
The Sigrid Rausing Trust
The Reece Foundation
Richard Reeve's Foundation
Richmond Parish Lands Charity
The Roddick Foundation
Rosca Trust
The Joseph Rowntree Charitable Trust
The Joseph Rowntree Foundation
Royal Docks Trust (London)
The Royal Navy and Royal Marines Charity
Royal Society of Wildlife Trusts
The Russell Trust
The RVW Trust
Santander UK Foundation Ltd
Savannah Wisdom
The Savoy Educational Trust
Foundation Scotland
Francis C. Scott Charitable Trust
The SDL Foundation
Sam and Bella Sebba Charitable Trust
The Cyril Shack Trust
The Sheffield Town Trust
Sirius Minerals Foundation
The John Slater Foundation
Smallwood Trust
The Henry Smith Charity
Social Business Trust
Social Investment Business Foundation
Social Tech Trust
*Societe Generale UK Foundation**
Sodexo Stop Hunger Foundation
Somerset Community Foundation
The South Yorkshire Community Foundation
The Spurrell Charitable Trust
The St Hilda's Trust
Sir Walter St John's Educational Charity
The Community Foundation for Staffordshire
Standard Life Foundation
The Stone Family Foundation
Stratford-upon-Avon Town Trust
The WO Street Charitable Foundation
StreetSmart – Action for the Homeless
Suffolk Community Foundation
The Summerfield Charitable Trust
Surgo Foundation UK Ltd
Community Foundation for Surrey
The Sussex Community Foundation
Tallow Chandlers Benevolent Fund No. 2
Tees Valley Community Foundation
The Theatres Trust Charitable Fund
*The Thirty Percy Foundation**
Tower Hill Trust
The Triangle Trust (1949) Fund
Trust For London
The Trusthouse Charitable Foundation
The Tudor Trust
The Tuixen Foundation
Two Ridings Community Foundation
Community Foundation serving Tyne and Wear and Northumberland
Ufi VocTech Trust
The Ulverscroft Foundation
United St Saviour's Charity
UnLtd (Foundation for Social Entrepreneurs)
UPP Foundation

The Vardy Foundation
The Veolia Environmental Trust
*Vinci UK Foundation**
The Virgin Money Foundation
*Vision Foundation**
The Vodafone Foundation
The Scurrah Wainwright Charity
The Bruce Wake Charitable Trust
The Walcot Foundation
The Community Foundation in Wales
Walton on Thames Charity
The Warwickshire Masonic Charitable Association Ltd
The Waterloo Foundation
Wates Family Enterprise Trust
The Wates Foundation
The William Wates Memorial Trust
The Geoffrey Watling Charity
Wembley National Stadium Trust
Westminster Amalgamated Charity
Westway Trust
The Wilmcote Charitrust
The Wilson Foundation
The Wood Foundation
Wooden Spoon Society
The Woodward Charitable Trust
The Wyseliot Rose Charitable Trust
Youth Music
Zurich Community Trust (UK) Ltd

Uniformed groups

Banbury Charities
Misses Barrie Charitable Trust
The Louis Baylis (Maidenhead Advertiser) Charitable Trust
Bideford Bridge Trust
The Marjory Boddy Charitable Trust
The Harold and Alice Bridges Charity
The Jack Brunton Charitable Trust
*CareTech Foundation**
The Leslie Mary Carter Charitable Trust
Church Burgesses Trust
The Corporation of Trinity House of Deptford Strond
CSIS Charity Fund
The Roger De Haan Charitable Trust
The Dibden Allotments Fund
*Dumfriesshire East Community Benefit Group SCIO**
*The Nine Incorporated Trades of Dundee General Fund Charity**
Essex Community Foundation
Sir John Fisher Foundation
The Gibbons Family Trust
The Simon Gibson Charitable Trust
Worshipful Company of Gold and Silver Wyre Drawers Second Charitable Trust Fund
The Gosling Foundation Ltd
Dr Guthrie's Association
Edward Harvist Trust (The Harvist Estate)
Heathrow Community Trust
The Lady Hind Trust
The Hudson Foundation
The Iceland Foods Charitable Foundation
Sir James Knott Trust
Lancashire Environmental Fund Ltd
Duchy of Lancaster Benevolent Fund
The R. J. Larg Family Trust
Limoges Charitable Trust
Lincolnshire Community Foundation
The MacRobert Trust 2019
The Magdalen and Lasher Charity (General Fund)
Manchester Airport Community Trust Fund
The Manchester Guardian Society Charitable Trust
The W. M. Mann Foundation
R. W. Mann Trust
MBNA General Foundation
Milton Keynes Community Foundation Ltd
Mobbs Memorial Trust Ltd
Moondance Foundation
Norfolk Community Foundation
Normanby Charitable Trust
The Notgrove Trust
The Patrick Trust
Susanna Peake Charitable Trust
The Persimmon Charitable Foundation
Miss A. M. Pilkington's Charitable Trust
The Rainford Trust
The Sir James Reckitt Charity
Rigby Foundation
The Rowlands Trust
The Royal Foundation of the Duke and Duchess of Cambridge
The Rugby Group Benevolent Fund Ltd
Foundation Scotland
The Frieda Scott Charitable Trust
Leslie Sell Charitable Trust
Shaftoe Educational Foundation
The Shanly Foundation
The Sheffield Town Trust
The Sheldon Trust
The Patricia and Donald Shepherd Charitable Trust
Sirius Minerals Foundation
The Skelton Bounty
The Henry Smith Charity
The W. H. Smith Group Charitable Trust
The R. C. Snelling Charitable Trust
The South Yorkshire Community Foundation
Spielman Charitable Trust
St Olave's and St Saviour's Schools Foundation
Community Foundation for Surrey
The Charles and Elsie Sykes Trust
The Talbot Village Trust
*The Tudwick Foundation**
Two Ridings Community Foundation
Variety, the Children's Charity
The Veolia Environmental Trust
Wembley National Stadium Trust
West Derby Waste Lands Charity
*West Herts Charity Trust Ltd**
Wiltshire Community Foundation
York Children's Trust

Universities

The 29th May 1961 Charitable Trust
The 3Ts Charitable Trust
The Abbeyfield Research Foundation
Action Medical Research
The AEB Charitable Trust
The AIM Foundation
AKO Foundation
The Alborada Trust
The All Saints Educational Trust
Allchurches Trust Ltd
Alliance Family Foundation Ltd
Alzheimer's Research UK
Alzheimer's Society
The AMW Charitable Trust
Anglo American Group Foundation
Arcadia Fund
The Ardeola Charitable Trust
The Ardwick Trust
The John Armitage Charitable Trust
The Armourers' and Brasiers' Gauntlet Trust
The Art Fund
The Ove Arup Foundation
The Associated Board of the Royal Schools of Music
Asthma UK
The Astor Foundation
Atkin Charitable Foundation
The Atlas Fund
The Aurelius Charitable Trust
The Aylesford Family Charitable Trust
The Baily Thomas Charitable Fund
The Roger and Sarah Bancroft Clark Charitable Trust
The Kamini and Vindi Banga Family Trust*
The Barbers' Company General Charities
The Barclay Foundation
The Baring Foundation
The Philip Barker Charity
Misses Barrie Charitable Trust
Robert Barr's Charitable Trust
BC Partners Foundation
The Bellahouston Bequest Fund
Benesco Charity Ltd
The Bestway Foundation
Binks Trust
The John Black Charitable Foundation
Blakemore Foundation
The Sir Victor Blank Charitable Settlement
Bloodwise
The Bluston Charitable Settlement
The Boltini Trust
Sir William Boreman's Foundation
The Borrows Charitable Trust
The Boshier-Hinton Foundation
The William Brake Charitable Trust
The Tony Bramall Charitable Trust
The Liz and Terry Bramall Foundation
Breast Cancer Now
The Breast Cancer Research Trust (BCRT)
The Harold and Alice Bridges Charity
Bright Red Charity*
British Council for Prevention of Blindness
British Eye Research Foundation (Fight for Sight)
British Heart Foundation (BHF)
British Lung Foundation
The Rory and Elizabeth Brooks Foundation
Buckingham Trust
Building & Civil Engineering Charitable Trust
E. F. Bulmer Trust
The Burdett Trust for Nursing
The G. W. Cadbury Charitable Trust
The Barrow Cadbury Trust
The Calleva Foundation
Cannon Charitable Trust
CareTech Foundation*
W. A. Cargill Charitable Trust
The W. A. Cargill Fund
The Carne Trust
The Carpenters' Company Charitable Trust
The Castang Foundation
Chapman Charitable Trust
Chartered Accountants' Livery Charity (CALC)
Children with Cancer UK
Children's Liver Disease Foundation
The Clan Trust Ltd
The Clore Duffield Foundation
Denise Coates Foundation
The Vivienne and Samuel Cohen Charitable Trust
The John S. Cohen Foundation
Colchester Catalyst Charity
The Colt Foundation
The Comino Foundation
Marjorie Coote Animal Charity Trust
The Worshipful Company of Cordwainers Charitable Trusts (Minges Gift)
Dudley and Geoffrey Cox Charitable Trust
The Craps Charitable Trust
The Elizabeth Creak Charitable Trust
CRH Charitable Trust*
The Cunningham Trust
The Daiwa Anglo-Japanese Foundation
Michael Davies Charitable Settlement
Margaret Davies Charity
The Davis Foundation
The De Laszlo Foundation
The Demigryphon Trust
Diabetes UK
Digital Xtra Fund*
Dinwoodie Charitable Company
The Dischma Charitable Trust
The Djanogly Foundation
The Dorfman Foundation
Drapers' Charitable Fund
The Nine Incorporated Trades of Dundee General Fund Charity*
The Dunhill Medical Trust
The Mildred Duveen Charitable Trust
The Dyers' Company Charitable Trust
The James Dyson Foundation
Eastern Counties Educational Trust Ltd
The Gilbert and Eileen Edgar Foundation
The Edge Foundation
The Elmley Foundation
The Emerald Foundation
Entindale Ltd
Epilepsy Research UK
The Evelyn Trust
The Eveson Charitable Trust
The Exilarch's Foundation
The Lord Faringdon Charitable Trust
The Thomas Farr Charity
Allan and Nesta Ferguson Charitable Settlement
The Fidelio Charitable Trust
The Finnis Scott Foundation
Sir John Fisher Foundation
Marc Fitch Fund
The Football Foundation
The Forman Hardy Charitable Trust
The Fort Foundation
The Lord Forte Foundation
The Foyle Foundation
The Hugh Fraser Foundation
The Freelands Foundation Ltd
The Freshgate Trust Foundation
Friends Provident Charitable Foundation
The Funding Network
GambleAware
Gamma Trust
Garfield Weston Foundation
Garthgwynion Charities
The Gatsby Charitable Foundation

The Robert Gavron Charitable Trust
The Jacqueline and Michael Gee Charitable Trust
The General Charity Fund
The General Nursing Council for England and Wales Trust
The F. Glenister Woodger Trust
Worshipful Company of Glovers of London Charitable Trust
Worshipful Company of Gold and Silver Wyre Drawers Second Charitable Trust Fund
The Golden Bottle Trust
The Goldman Sachs Charitable Gift Fund (UK)
Goldman Sachs Gives (UK)
The Goldsmiths' Company Charity
The Golsoncott Foundation
Nicholas and Judith Goodison's Charitable Settlement
The Mike Gooley Trailfinders Charity
The Gould Charitable Trust
Gowling WLG (UK) Charitable Trust
The Grace Trust
The Grange Farm Centre Trust
The Great Britain Sasakawa Foundation
Philip and Judith Green Trust
The Grimmitt Trust
The Grocers' Charity
The Guy Foundation*
The Hadfield Charitable Trust
Hamamelis Trust
The Hamilton Davies Trust
The Helen Hamlyn Trust
The Lennox Hannay Charitable Trust
The Happold Foundation
The Haramead Trust
The Harbour Foundation
The David and Claudia Harding Foundation
The Harpur Trust
The Peter Harrison Foundation
The Maurice Hatter Foundation
The Health Foundation
May Hearnshaw's Charity
Heart Research UK
The Michael Heller Charitable Foundation
The Simon Heller Charitable Settlement
Help for Health
The Helping Foundation
Heritage Lottery Fund
The Heritage of London Trust Ltd
The Lady Hind Trust
The Hinduja Foundation
The Hintze Family Charity Foundation
Historic Houses Foundation
The Hobson Charity Ltd
The Jane Hodge Foundation
The Holbeck Charitable Trust
P. H. Holt Foundation
Hope Trust
The Horse Trust
The Sir Joseph Hotung Charitable Settlement
Housing Pathways Trust
James T. Howat Charitable Trust
The Humanitarian Trust
The Hunter Foundation
The Huntingdon Foundation Ltd
Hyde Park Place Estate Charity
IBM United Kingdom Trust
Ibrahim Foundation Ltd
The Iceland Foods Charitable Foundation
The Inman Charity
The Innocent Foundation
The Institute for Policy Research
The International Bankers Charitable Trust
The Ireland Fund of Great Britain
Irish Youth Foundation (UK) Ltd (incorporating The Lawlor Foundation)
The ITF Seafarers Trust
The Jabbs Foundation
The Frank Jackson Foundation
John James Bristol Foundation
Lady Eda Jardine Charitable Trust
John Jarrold Trust Ltd
Rees Jeffreys Road Fund
The Jerusalem Trust
The Johnson Foundation
The Jusaca Charitable Trust
Kantor Charitable Foundation*
The Ian Karten Charitable Trust
C. S. Kaufman Charitable Trust
The Kay Kendall Leukaemia Fund
The Kennedy Trust for Rheumatology Research
The Kennel Club Charitable Trust
Kidney Research UK
The Mary Kinross Charitable Trust
Robert Kitchin (Saddlers' Company)
Sir James Knott Trust
Kollel and Co. Ltd
The KPMG Foundation
Kusuma Trust UK
The Kirby Laing Foundation
Duchy of Lancaster Benevolent Fund
The R. J. Larg Family Trust
The Lauffer Family Charitable Foundation
The Law Family Charitable Foundation
The Edgar E. Lawley Foundation
The Lawson Trust CIO
The David Lean Foundation
The Leathersellers' Company Charitable Fund
The Leche Trust
The William Leech Charity
The Legal Education Foundation
Leicestershire and Rutland Masonic Charity Association
Leng Charitable Trust
The Leverhulme Trust
Cecil and Hilda Lewis Charitable Trust*
David and Ruth Lewis Family Charitable Trust
Limoges Charitable Trust
The Linbury Trust
The Linder Foundation
The Charles Littlewood Hill Trust
The Second Joseph Aaron Littman Foundation
The W. M. and B. W. Lloyd Trust
Lloyd's Register Foundation
The Henry Lumley Charitable Trust
Lord and Lady Lurgan Trust
The R. S. Macdonald Charitable Trust
The MacRobert Trust 2019
The Mactaggart Third Fund
The Ian Mactaggart Trust (The Mactaggart Second Fund)
The Mallinckrodt Foundation
The W. M. Mann Foundation
R. W. Mann Trust
Marbeh Torah Trust
The Marchig Animal Welfare Trust
The Michael Marks Charitable Trust
The Michael Marsh Charitable Trust
Sir George Martin Trust
Masonic Charitable Foundation
Nancie Massey Charitable Trust
The Master Charitable Trust
Mathew Trust
Maudsley Charity
Mayfair Charities Ltd
Maypride Ltd

D. D. McPhail Charitable Settlement
Medical Research Foundation
Medical Research Scotland
The Medlock Charitable Trust
Melodor Ltd
Meningitis Research Foundation
The Mercers' Charitable Foundation
The Merchant Venturers' Charity
Merchants' House of Glasgow
The Mickel Fund
The Masonic Province of Middlesex Charitable Trust (Middlesex Masonic Charity)
The Mikheev Charitable Trust*
The Millfield House Foundation (1)
The Millichope Foundation
Mills and Reeve Charitable Trust
The Millward Charitable Trust
Mind*
The Mittal Foundation
Mole Charitable Trust
The Henry Moore Foundation
The Miles Morland Foundation
G. M. Morrison Charitable Trust
The Moshal Charitable Trust
The Alexander Mosley Charitable Trust
Motor Neurone Disease Association
Multiple Sclerosis Society
Edith Murphy Foundation
The John R. Murray Charitable Trust
The National Express Foundation
Friends of the National Libraries*
The National Manuscripts Conservation Trust
The Nationwide Foundation
Nesta
The Frances and Augustus Newman Foundation
The NFU Mutual Charitable Trust
The Nineveh Charitable Trust
Alice Noakes Memorial Charitable Trust
The Norman Family Charitable Trust
Normanby Charitable Trust
North West Cancer Research
Northern Pharmacies Ltd Trust Fund
Northwood Charitable Trust
The Nuffield Foundation
Oglesby Charitable Trust
Orange Tree Trust*
Orthopaedic Research UK
The O'Sullivan Family Charitable Trust
Ovingdean Hall Foundation
The Panacea Charitable Trust
Parabola Foundation
Parkinson's UK
The JGW Patterson Foundation
The Pears Family Charitable Foundation
The Dowager Countess Eleanor Peel Trust
B. E. Perl Charitable Trust
Petplan Charitable Trust
The Pharsalia Charitable Trust
The Pilgrim Trust
Thomas Pocklington Trust
The Polonsky Foundation
The Portal Trust
The Mary Potter Convent Hospital Trust
David and Elaine Potter Foundation
Prostate Cancer UK
Mr and Mrs J. A. Pye's Charitable Settlement
Queen Mary's Roehampton Trust
The Racing Foundation
Randeree Charitable Trust*
The Sir James Reckitt Charity
The Reece Foundation
The Resolution Trust
Reuben Foundation
Humphrey Richardson Taylor Charitable Trust
Rix Thompson Rothenberg Foundation
RNID (The Royal National Institute for Deaf People)
The Roan Charitable Trust
The Dezna Robins Jones Charitable Foundation
Rockcliffe Charitable Trust
The Gerald and Gail Ronson Family Foundation
The Rose Foundation
The Cecil Rosen Foundation
Rosetrees Trust
The Rothermere Foundation
The Rothschild Foundation
The Eranda Rothschild Foundation
Rothschild Foundation (Hanadiv) Europe
The Row Fogo Charitable Trust
The Rowlands Trust
The Joseph Rowntree Charitable Trust
The Joseph Rowntree Foundation
The Royal Foundation of the Duke and Duchess of Cambridge
Royal Society of Wildlife Trusts
The Rubin Foundation Charitable Trust
The Ruddock Foundation for the Arts
The Russell Trust
The Dr Mortimer and Theresa Sackler Foundation
The Alan and Babette Sainsbury Charitable Fund
The Saintbury Trust
The Basil Samuel Charitable Trust
Sarum St Michael Educational Charity
The Savoy Educational Trust
Sir Samuel Scott of Yews Trust
The Scottish Power Foundation
Sam and Bella Sebba Charitable Trust
The Selfridges Group Foundation*
The Jean Shanks Foundation
The Sheepdrove Trust
The Sheffield Town Trust
The Sylvia and Colin Shepherd Charitable Trust
The Shipwrights' Charitable Fund
The Sino-British Fellowship Trust
The Charles Skey Charitable Trust
The John Slater Foundation
Sloane Robinson Foundation
The W. H. Smith Group Charitable Trust
Stanley Smith UK Horticultural Trust
Social Tech Trust
Peter Sowerby Foundation
Sparks Charity
The Spear Charitable Trust
The Michael and Sarah Spencer Foundation*
St Luke's College Foundation
St Peter's Saltley Trust
Standard Life Foundation
Stanley Foundation Ltd
Staples Trust
The Steel Charitable Trust
The Sir Sigmund Sternberg Charitable Foundation
Stevenson Family's Charitable Trust
Sir Halley Stewart Trust
Mark Stolkin Foundation
The Stoneygate Trust
The Samuel Storey Family Charitable Trust
Peter Stormonth Darling Charitable Trust
The Joseph Strong Frazer Trust*
The Sudborough Foundation

The Summerfield Charitable Trust
Surgo Foundation UK Ltd
The Sutasoma Trust
The John Swire (1989) Charitable Trust
The Adrian Swire Charitable Trust
The Charles and Elsie Sykes Trust
The Talbot Village Trust
Tallow Chandlers Benevolent Fund No. 2
C. B. and H. H. Taylor 1984 Trust
Stephen Taylor Foundation
The Tedworth Charitable Trust
Tenovus Cancer Care
Tenovus Scotland
*The Thirty Percy Foundation**
The Thompson Family Charitable Trust
Sir Jules Thorn Charitable Trust
The Three Guineas Trust
The Thriplow Charitable Trust
The Tolkien Trust
David William Traill Cargill Fund
The Constance Travis Charitable Trust
The Treeside Trust
Tropical Health and Education Trust
The Tuixen Foundation
Ufi VocTech Trust
Ulster Garden Villages Ltd
Ulting Overseas Trust
The Ulverscroft Foundation
United Jewish Israel Appeal
UPP Foundation
The Michael Uren Foundation
*Utermann Charitable Trust**
The Vandervell Foundation
Versus Arthritis
Nigel Vinson Charitable Trust
The VTCT Foundation
Walton Foundation
Wates Family Enterprise Trust
John Watson's Trust
The Linda and Michael Weinstein Charitable Trust
Wellbeing of Women
The Wellcome Trust
Dame Violet Wills Charitable Trust
W. Wing Yip and Brothers Foundation
The Wingate Foundation
The Maurice Wohl Charitable Foundation
The Charles Wolfson Charitable Trust
The Wolfson Family Charitable Trust
The Lord Leonard and Lady Estelle Wolfson Foundation
The Wolfson Foundation
The Wood Foundation
Woodroffe Benton Foundation
The Wyndham Charitable Trust
Yorkshire Cancer Research
The Marjorie and Arnold Ziff Charitable Foundation
Zurich Community Trust (UK) Ltd

Grant-makers by type of grant

This index contains two separate listings:

List of types of grant: This lists all the headings used in DGMT to categorise types of grant.

Grant-makers by type of grant: This lists funders under the types of grant for which they have expressed a funding preference. Asterisks mark funders which have not been featured in DGMT before.

Grant-makers by type of grant

These pages contain two separate listings:

List of types of grant
This lists all of the headings used in DGMT to categorise types of grant

Grant-makers by type of grant
This lists funders under the types of grant for which they have expressed a funding preference

Campaigning

The AIM Foundation
The Bloom Foundation
Friends Provident Charitable Foundation
Royal Society of Wildlife Trusts
Trust for London

Capacity building

Children with Cancer UK
Council for World Mission (UK)*
The Dunhill Medical Trust
The Jerusalem Trust
The Kirby Laing Foundation
John Lyon's Charity
John Moores Foundation
Muslim Hands
Norwich Town Close Estate Charity
The Robertson Trust
The Royal British Legion
Sam and Bella Sebba Charitable Trust
The Theatres Trust Charitable Fund
The VTCT Foundation
The Eric Wright Charitable Trust

Capital costs

The 29th May 1961 Charitable Trust
The Sylvia Adams Charitable Trust
The Bryan Adams Foundation
The Adint Charitable Trust
Al-Fayed Charitable Foundation
Allchurches Trust Ltd
D. C. R. Allen Charitable Trust
Alpkit Foundation*
Amabrill Ltd
The Ammco Trust
The Anchor Foundation
Anguish's Educational Foundation
The Anson Charitable Trust
The John Apthorp Charity
Arts Council of Wales (also known as Cyngor Celfyddydau Cymru)
The Ashley Family Foundation
Keren Association Ltd
The Astor Foundation
Atlas Memorial Ltd
Backstage Trust
The Scott Bader Commonwealth Ltd
The Baily Thomas Charitable Fund
The Baird Trust
Bairdwatson Charitable Trust
The Rachel Baker Memorial Charity
The Ballinger Charitable Trust
Banbury Charities
The Banister Charitable Trust
Bank of Scotland Foundation
The Barbers' Company General Charities
Barchester Healthcare Foundation
The Barnes Fund*
Barnwood Trust
Robert Barr's Charitable Trust
The Paul Bassham Charitable Trust
Bauer Radio's Cash for Kids Charities
BBC Children in Need
BC Partners Foundation
The James Beattie Charitable Trust
The Beaverbrook Foundation
The Bedfordshire and Hertfordshire Historic Churches Trust
The Bellahouston Bequest Fund
Benesco Charity Ltd
The Berkshire Community Foundation
Biffa Award
The Percy Bilton Charity
The Bingham Trust

Birmingham International Airport Community Trust Fund
The Michael Bishop Foundation
The John Black Charitable Foundation
Blakemore Foundation
Bloodwise
Bluespark Foundation
The Marjory Boddy Charitable Trust
BOOST Charitable Trust
The Booth Charities
Boots Charitable Trust
The Oliver Borthwick Memorial Trust
The Boshier-Hinton Foundation
Alan Boswell Group Charitable Trust*
The Harry Bottom Charitable Trust
The Harold and Alice Bridges Charity
Bristol Charities
The British and Foreign School Society
British Council for Prevention of Blindness
British Eye Research Foundation (Fight for Sight)
British Gas Energy Trust
British Heart Foundation (BHF)
British Lung Foundation
British Motor Sports Training Trust
The Broomton Foundation
Mary Brown Memorial Trust*
The Jack Brunton Charitable Trust
Buckinghamshire Community Foundation
The Buckinghamshire Historic Churches Trust
The Buffini Chao Foundation
E. F. Bulmer Trust
Consolidated Charity of Burton upon Trent
Community Foundation for Calderdale
The Cambridgeshire Community Foundation
The Campden Charities Trustee
The Frederick and Phyllis Cann Trust
Card Factory Foundation*
The Leslie Mary Carter Charitable Trust
The Joseph and Annie Cattle Trust
The Wilfrid and Constance Cave Foundation
Elizabeth Cayzer Charitable Trust
The Chadwick Educational Foundation
Chalfords Ltd
The Chalk Cliff Trust
The Chetwode Foundation
Children with Cancer UK
The Childwick Trust
Chippenham Borough Lands Charity
The Chipping Sodbury Town Lands Charity
Chrysalis Trust
The Church Burgesses Educational Foundation
Church Burgesses Trust
Church of Ireland Priorities Fund
The City Bridge Trust (Bridge House Estates)
CLA Charitable Trust
The Clan Trust Ltd
Clark Foundation
The Clothworkers' Foundation
Cloudesley
The Robert Clutterbuck Charitable Trust
The Francis Coales Charitable Foundation
The John Coates Charitable Trust
Denise Coates Foundation
Colchester Catalyst Charity
The Cole Charitable Trust
Community First
Congregational and General Charitable Trust
The Cooks Charity
Marjorie Coote Animal Charity Trust
The Helen Jean Cope Charity
The Worshipful Company of Cordwainers Charitable Trusts (Minges Gift)
Cornwall Community Foundation
The Corporation of Trinity House of Deptford Strond
Council for World Mission (UK)*
The County Council of Dyfed Welsh Church Fund
The Sir Tom Cowie Charitable Trust
The Lord Cozens-Hardy Trust
The Craignish Trust
CRASH
The Crerar Trust
Cruden Foundation Ltd
Cumbria Community Foundation
Baron Davenport's Charity
The Manny and Brigitta Davidson Charitable Foundation*
The Davidson Family Charitable Trust
Margaret Davies Charity
The Roger De Haan Charitable Trust
The De Laszlo Foundation
The Delves Charitable Trust
Foundation Derbyshire
The Devon Historic Churches
Diabetes UK
The Gillian Dickinson Trust
Dorset Community Foundation
Duchy Health Charity Ltd
The Dulverton Trust
The Dunhill Medical Trust
County Durham Community Foundation
The Earley Charity
Dr Edwards Bishop King's Fulham Endowment Fund
W. G. Edwards Charitable Foundation
The Marian Elizabeth Trust
The Elmley Foundation
England and Wales Cricket Trust
The Englefield Charitable Trust
The Enkalon Foundation
The Essex and Southend Sports Trust
Essex Community Foundation
The Essex Heritage Trust
The Essex Youth Trust
The Evelyn Trust
The Eventhall Family Charitable Trust
The Eveson Charitable Trust
Samuel William Farmer Trust
The February Foundation
The Feoffees of St Michael's Spurriergate York
The Fidelity UK Foundation
Fine & Country Foundation
The Finnis Scott Foundation
Sir John Fisher Foundation
The Joyce Fletcher Charitable Trust
The Football Association National Sports Centre Trust
The Forbes Charitable Foundation
Ford Britain Trust
Oliver Ford Foundation
Donald Forrester Trust
Gwyneth Forrester Trust
Ian M. Foulerton Charitable Trust
Four Acre Trust
Fowler Smith and Jones Trust
The Foyle Foundation
Mrs D. M. France-Hayhurst Foundation
The Gordon Fraser Charitable Trust
The Hugh Fraser Foundation
The Freshgate Trust Foundation

Friarsgate Trust
G. M. C. Trust
The Gannochy Trust
The Ganzoni Charitable Trust
Garfield Weston Foundation
Gatwick Airport Community Trust
General Charity (Coventry)
The General Charity Fund
The Generations Foundation
The Gibbons Family Trust
The Gibbs Charitable Trusts
The G. C. Gibson Charitable Trust
The F. Glenister Woodger Trust
Global Charities
The Gloucestershire Historic Churches Trust
The Godinton Charitable Trust
Nicholas and Judith Goodison's Charitable Settlement
Grace Charitable Trust
The Granada Foundation
The Grant Foundation
The Grantham Yorke Trust
GrantScape
The J. G. Graves Charitable Trust
The Gray Trust
The Great Stone Bridge Trust of Edenbridge
The Green Hall Foundation
Groundwork UK
H. C. D. Memorial Fund
The Hadfield Charitable Trust
The Hadley Trust
The Hadrian Trust
The Alfred Haines Charitable Trust
Halifax Foundation for Northern Ireland
The Halsall Foundation*
The Hamilton Davies Trust
The Hampstead Wells and Campden Trust
Harborne Parish Lands Charity
The Harebell Centenary Fund
The Harpur Trust
The Peter Harrison Foundation
Edward Harvist Trust (The Harvist Estate)
Hays Travel Foundation
The Charles Hayward Foundation
The Headley Trust
Heart of England Community Foundation
Heart Research UK
Heathrow Community Trust
Ernest Hecht Charitable Foundation
The Percy Hedley 1990 Charitable Trust
The Hedley Foundation
Help for Health
Help the Homeless Ltd
The Hemby Charitable Trust
Henley Educational Trust
The Tim Henman Foundation
Herefordshire Community Foundation
The Herefordshire Historic Churches Trust
Heritage Lottery Fund
Hertfordshire Community Foundation
P. and C. Hickinbotham Charitable Trust
The Alan Edward Higgs Charity
Highway One Trust
The Hinduja Foundation
The Hintze Family Charity Foundation
Historic Environment Scotland*
Historic Houses Foundation
P. H. Holt Foundation
The Holywood Trust
Hospice UK
The Hospital Saturday Fund
House of Industry Estate
The Hudson Foundation
The Hull and East Riding Charitable Trust
The Albert Hunt Trust
Huntingdon Freemen's Trust
The Hurley Partners Charitable Trust*
Hyde Park Place Estate Charity
IBM United Kingdom Trust
Ibrahim Foundation Ltd
The Iceland Foods Charitable Foundation
The Ingram Trust
Integrated Education Fund
International Bible Students Association
Irish Youth Foundation (UK) Ltd (incorporating The Lawlor Foundation)
The Charles Irving Charitable Trust
The Isla Foundation*
The Isle of Anglesey Charitable Trust
Isle of Wight Foundation
The ITF Seafarers Trust
The Jabbs Foundation
The Sir Barry Jackson County Fund
John James Bristol Foundation
John Jarrold Trust Ltd
The Roger and Jean Jefcoate Trust
Jeffrey Charitable Trust*
Rees Jeffreys Road Fund
The Jenour Foundation
The Jephcott Charitable Trust
The Jerusalem Trust
Jewish Child's Day (JCD)
The Jewish Youth Fund
Johnnie Johnson Trust
The Joicey Trust
The Jones 1986 Charitable Trust
The Jordan Charitable Foundation
The Joron Charitable Trust
The Cyril and Eve Jumbo Charitable Trust
The Jusaca Charitable Trust
The Ian Karten Charitable Trust
The Kelly Family Charitable Trust
The Kay Kendall Leukaemia Fund
The Kennel Club Charitable Trust
The Friends of Kent Churches
Kent Community Foundation
The Ursula Keyes Trust
KFC Foundation*
Kilpatrick Fraser Charitable Trust
The King Henry VIII Endowed Trust – Warwick
The Mary Kinross Charitable Trust
The Kirschel Foundation
The Ernest Kleinwort Charitable Trust
Sir James Knott Trust
Kollel and Co. Ltd
The K. P. Ladd Charitable Trust
John Laing Charitable Trust
Maurice and Hilda Laing Charitable Trust
Christopher Laing Foundation
The David Laing Foundation
The Kirby Laing Foundation
The Martin Laing Foundation
The Beatrice Laing Trust
The Leonard Laity Stoate Charitable Trust
Lancashire Environmental Fund Ltd
LandAid Charitable Trust (LandAid)
The Richard Lawes Foundation
The Leathersellers' Company Charitable Fund
Leeds Building Society Charitable Foundation
Leeds Community Foundation (LCF)
The Legal Education Foundation
The Kennedy Leigh Charitable Trust
The Mark Leonard Trust
Joseph Levy Foundation
The Sir Edward Lewis Foundation
The Light Fund Company
The Limbourne Trust

The Linbury Trust
Lincolnshire Community Foundation
The Charles Littlewood Hill Trust
Liverpool Charity and Voluntary Services (LCVS)
The Ian and Natalie Livingstone Charitable Trust
The W. M. and B. W. Lloyd Trust
Lloyds Bank Foundation for the Channel Islands
London Catalyst
The London Community Foundation (LCF)
The London Marathon Charitable Trust Ltd
Longleigh Foundation
The Lord's Taverners
John Lyon's Charity
The R. S. Macdonald Charitable Trust
The Mackintosh Foundation
The MacRobert Trust 2019
Manchester Airport Community Trust Fund
The Manchester Guardian Society Charitable Trust
R. W. Mann Trust
The Marchig Animal Welfare Trust
The Michael Marsh Charitable Trust
Charity of John Marshall
Sir George Martin Trust
John Martin's Charity
The Dan Maskell Tennis Trust
Mayfair Charities Ltd
The Robert McAlpine Foundation
Medical Research Foundation
Merchant Navy Welfare Board
The Merchant Venturers' Charity
Merchants' House of Glasgow
The Mickel Fund
The Gerald Micklem Charitable Trust
The Masonic Province of Middlesex Charitable Trust (Middlesex Masonic Charity)
Millennium Stadium Charitable Trust (Ymddiriedclaeth Elusennol Stadiwm y Mileniwm)
Milton Keynes Community Foundation Ltd
Minton Charitable Trust
Mobbs Memorial Trust Ltd
The Monmouthshire County Council Welsh Church Act Fund
John Moores Foundation
The Steve Morgan Foundation
Morgan Stanley International Foundation
The Morris Charitable Trust
The Morrisons Foundation
Motor Neurone Disease Association
Muslim Hands
The National Churches Trust
The National Lottery Community Fund
The Nationwide Foundation
Network for Social Change Charitable Trust
Newby Trust Ltd
Newcomen Collett Foundation
The Frances and Augustus Newman Foundation
Alderman Newton's Educational Foundation
The Nineveh Charitable Trust
The Nisbet Trust
Alice Noakes Memorial Charitable Trust
The Norfolk Churches Trust Ltd
The Norman Family Charitable Trust
North East Area Miners' Social Welfare Trust Fund
North West Cancer Research
The Northumbria Historic Churches Trust
The Norton Foundation
Norwich Town Close Estate Charity
The Norwood and Newton Settlement
The Sir Peter O'Sullevan Charitable Trust
The Oakdale Trust
The Oakley Charitable Trust
Oglesby Charitable Trust
One Community Foundation Ltd
*Orange Tree Trust**
The Ouseley Church Music Trust
Ovingdean Hall Foundation
Oxfordshire Historic Churches Trust (2016)
P. F. Charitable Trust
The Paget Charitable Trust
The Pastoral Care Trust – The St Nicholas Care Fund
Miss M. E. S. Paterson's Charitable Trust
The Patrick Trust
The Jack Patston Charitable Trust
The Pears Family Charitable Foundation
The Pebbles Trust
The Dowager Countess Eleanor Peel Trust
People's Health Trust
People's Postcode Trust
The Persimmon Charitable Foundation
Petplan Charitable Trust
The Pets at Home Foundation
The Pilgrim Trust
*Elise Pilkington Charitable Trust**
Pilkington Charities Fund
Pink Ribbon Foundation
The Portal Trust
Postcode Community Trust
Postcode Local Trust
The Mary Potter Convent Hospital Trust
Power to Change Trust
Sir John Priestman Charity Trust
The Primrose Trust
The Prince's Countryside Fund
The Professional Footballers' Association Charity
The Purey Cust Trust CIO
*Quadstar Charitable Foundation**
Quartet Community Foundation
Queen Mary's Roehampton Trust
The Racing Foundation
The Rainford Trust
The Joseph Rank Trust
The Rathbone Brothers Foundation
The Rayne Foundation
The Sir James Reckitt Charity
Red Hill Charitable Trust
Richard Reeve's Foundation
The Rest-Harrow Trust
Riada Trust
The Clive and Sylvia Richards Charity Ltd
Humphrey Richardson Taylor Charitable Trust
Richmond Parish Lands Charity
Rivers Foundation
Robertson Hall Trust
The Robertson Trust
The Roddick Foundation
The Gerald and Gail Ronson Family Foundation
Rosca Trust
The Rose Foundation
The Cecil Rosen Foundation
The Rothley Trust
The Rowlands Trust
Royal Artillery Charitable Fund
The Royal British Legion
Royal Docks Trust (London)
The Royal Foundation of the Duke and Duchess of Cambridge
The Royal Navy and Royal Marines Charity
The Rugby Group Benevolent Fund Ltd
The Saddlers' Company Charitable Fund

The Jean Sainsbury Animal Welfare Trust
The Alan and Babette Sainsbury Charitable Fund
Savannah Wisdom
The Savoy Educational Trust
The Scarfe Charitable Trust
Foundation Scotland
Scott (Eredine) Charitable Trust
Francis C. Scott Charitable Trust
The Frieda Scott Charitable Trust
The Scottish Power Foundation
Scottish Property Industry Festival of Christmas (SPIFOX)
The Screwfix Foundation
Seafarers UK (King George's Fund for Sailors)
Sam and Bella Sebba Charitable Trust
Leslie Sell Charitable Trust
Shaftoe Educational Foundation
The Shanly Foundation
The Sheldon Trust
The Archie Sherman Charitable Trust
Shetland Charitable Trust
The Shipwrights' Charitable Fund
Shulem B. Association Ltd
The Skelton Bounty
The Skerritt Trust
The Charles Skey Charitable Trust
Skipton Building Society Charitable Foundation
The Mrs Smith and Mount Trust
The Leslie Smith Foundation
The R. C. Snelling Charitable Trust
The Sobell Foundation
Somerset Community Foundation
The South Yorkshire Community Foundation
W. F. Southall Trust
Southover Manor General Education Trust Ltd
Peter Sowerby Foundation
The Jessie Spencer Trust
The Spoore, Merry and Rixman Foundation
The St James's Trust Settlement
St James's Place Charitable Foundation
Sir Walter St John's Educational Charity
St Monica Trust
The Stafford Trust
Staples Trust
The Steel Charitable Trust
The Stevenage Community Trust
Strand Parishes Trust
Stratford-upon-Avon Town Trust
Strathnairn Community Benefit Fund Ltd
StreetSmart – Action for the Homeless
Suffolk Community Foundation
The Suffolk Historic Churches Trust
The Summerfield Charitable Trust
Sumner Wilson Charitable Trust
The Bernard Sunley Foundation
Community Foundation for Surrey
The Sussex Community Foundation
Swansea and Brecon Diocesan Board of Finance Ltd
The Swire Charitable Trust
The Adrian Swire Charitable Trust
The Syder Foundation
Tabeel Trust
Taca
The Gay and Keith Talbot Trust
The Talbot Trusts
The Talbot Village Trust
Tanner Trust
Stephen Taylor Foundation
Tenovus Scotland
The Theatres Trust Charitable Fund
Sir Jules Thorn Charitable Trust
Mrs R. P. Tindall's Charitable Trust
The Tory Family Foundation
The Tottenham Grammar School Foundation
Tower Hill Trust
The Toy Trust
The Trades House of Glasgow
The Constance Travis Charitable Trust
The Treeside Trust
The True Colours Trust
Truemart Ltd
Trumros Ltd
Trust for London
The Tudor Trust
The Roger and Douglas Turner Charitable Trust
Community Foundation serving Tyne and Wear and Northumberland
Ulster Garden Villages Ltd
The Ulverscroft Foundation
The Underwood Trust
The United Reformed Church (Wessex) Trust Ltd
United St Saviour's Charity
Universal Music UK Sound Foundation
The Valiant Charitable Trust
Variety, the Children's Charity
The Veneziana Fund
The Veolia Environmental Trust
Versus Arthritis
The Veterans' Foundation
*Vinci UK Foundation**
Virgin Atlantic Foundation
Viridor Credits Environmental Company
Volant Charitable Trust
The VTCT Foundation
Sylvia Waddilove Foundation UK
Wade's Charity
The Scurrah Wainwright Charity
The Walker Trust
G. R. Waters Charitable Trust 2000
John Watson's Trust
The Weavers' Company Benevolent Fund
The William Webster Charitable Trust
The Weinstock Fund
The Weir Charitable Trust
The James Weir Foundation
The Wellcome Trust
The Welsh Church Act Fund
Wembley National Stadium Trust
The Westfield Health Charitable Trust
Westminster Almshouses Foundation
Westminster Amalgamated Charity
Westway Trust
The Will Charitable Trust
Alfred Williams Charitable Trust
The Williams Family Foundation
The HDH Wills 1965 Charitable Trust
The Wilson Foundation
J. and J. R. Wilson Trust
Wiltshire Community Foundation
The Charles Wolfson Charitable Trust
The Wolfson Family Charitable Trust
The Wolfson Foundation
The James Wood Bequest Fund
Wooden Spoon Society
The Eric Wright Charitable Trust
The Wyndham Charitable Trust
The Wyseliot Rose Charitable Trust

Yorkshire Building Society Charitable Foundation
The Yorkshire Dales Millennium Trust
The Yorkshire Historic Churches Trust
Youth Music
The Marjorie and Arnold Ziff Charitable Foundation
Zurich Community Trust (UK) Ltd

Collection and acquistion

*The Ampersand Foundation**
The Art Fund
The Beaverbrook Foundation
Denise Coates Foundation
*The Manny and Brigitta Davidson Charitable Foundation**
The De Laszlo Foundation
The Lord Faringdon Charitable Trust
Nicholas and Judith Goodison's Charitable Settlement
The Headley Trust
The Leche Trust
The Linbury Trust
The Ruddock Foundation for the Arts

Core/revenue costs

The 29th May 1961 Charitable Trust
ABF The Soldiers' Charity
The Sylvia Adams Charitable Trust
The Adint Charitable Trust
The AEB Charitable Trust
The AIM Foundation
The Alborada Trust
The Ammco Trust
The Anchor Foundation
The Anson Charitable Trust
The Ashley Family Foundation
The Astor Foundation
The Avon and Somerset Police Community Trust
The Austin Bailey Foundation
The Baily Thomas Charitable Fund
Bairdwatson Charitable Trust
The Barbour Foundation
Barcapel Foundation Ltd
*The Barnes Fund**
The Battersea Power Station Foundation
BBC Children in Need
BC Partners Foundation
The James Beattie Charitable Trust
The Beaverbrook Foundation
The Berkeley Foundation
Bideford Bridge Trust
Birmingham International Airport Community Trust Fund
The Michael Bishop Foundation
The Blagrave Trust
The Blandford Lake Trust
The Marjory Boddy Charitable Trust
The Oliver Borthwick Memorial Trust
The Harry Bottom Charitable Trust
Buckinghamshire Community Foundation
E. F. Bulmer Trust
Consolidated Charity of Burton upon Trent
The Noel Buxton Trust
The Barrow Cadbury Trust
Community Foundation for Calderdale
The Cambridgeshire Community Foundation
Cattanach
The Wilfrid and Constance Cave Foundation
The B. G. S. Cayzer Charitable Trust
Chalfords Ltd

Chartered Accountants' Livery Charity (CALC)
Chrysalis Trust
The City Bridge Trust (Bridge House Estates)
The Robert Clutterbuck Charitable Trust
The John Coates Charitable Trust
Community First
Cornwall Community Foundation
The Lord Cozens-Hardy Trust
The Craignish Trust
Cripplegate Foundation
Cruden Foundation Ltd
Cumbria Community Foundation
Baron Davenport's Charity
Foundation Derbyshire
Dorset Community Foundation
The Anne Duchess of Westminster's Charity
Duchy Health Charity Ltd
The Dulverton Trust
County Durham Community Foundation
East End Community Foundation
The Ecology Trust
John Ellerman Foundation
The Englefield Charitable Trust
The Enkalon Foundation
Essex Community Foundation
The Essex Heritage Trust
The Essex Youth Trust
The Eveson Charitable Trust
The ExPat Foundation
The Feoffees of St Michael's Spurriergate York
The Finnis Scott Foundation
Sir John Fisher Foundation
The Joyce Fletcher Charitable Trust
The Forbes Charitable Foundation
Forever Manchester
Donald Forrester Trust
Gwyneth Forrester Trust
Four Acre Trust
Fowler Smith and Jones Trust
The Foyle Foundation
The Gordon Fraser Charitable Trust
The Hugh Fraser Foundation
The Freshgate Trust Foundation
Friends Provident Charitable Foundation
G. M. C. Trust
Garfield Weston Foundation
Grace Charitable Trust
The J. G. Graves Charitable Trust
The Gray Trust
The Great Stone Bridge Trust of Edenbridge
The Greggs Foundation
The Grimmitt Trust
Groundwork UK
Calouste Gulbenkian Foundation – UK Branch
H. C. D. Memorial Fund
Hackney Parochial Charities
The Hadfield Charitable Trust
The Hadrian Trust
*The Halsall Foundation**
The Hampstead Wells and Campden Trust
William Harding's Charity
The Harebell Centenary Fund
The Peter Harrison Foundation
Heathrow Community Trust
The Percy Hedley 1990 Charitable Trust
The Hemby Charitable Trust
The Christina Mary Hendrie Trust
Herefordshire Community Foundation
The Alan Edward Higgs Charity
The Hilden Charitable Fund
The Hintze Family Charity Foundation
The Hospital Saturday Fund
James T. Howat Charitable Trust
The Hudson Foundation
The Albert Hunt Trust
The Indigo Trust
The Charles Irving Charitable Trust
The Isle of Anglesey Charitable Trust
John Jarrold Trust Ltd
The Roger and Jean Jefcoate Trust
*Jeffrey Charitable Trust**
The Joicey Trust
The Jones 1986 Charitable Trust
The Jordan Charitable Foundation
The Joron Charitable Trust
The Jusaca Charitable Trust
The Kelly Family Charitable Trust
The King Henry VIII Endowed Trust – Warwick
The Mary Kinross Charitable Trust
The Kirschel Foundation
The Ernest Kleinwort Charitable Trust
The K. P. Ladd Charitable Trust
The Leonard Laity Stoate Charitable Trust
The Allen Lane Foundation
Leicestershire, Leicester and Rutland Community Foundation
The Leverhulme Trust
The Sir Edward Lewis Foundation
The Light Fund Company
Lincolnshire Community Foundation
Lloyds Bank Foundation for the Channel Islands
London Catalyst
The London Community Foundation (LCF)
John Lyon's Charity
The R. S. Macdonald Charitable Trust
The Marsh Christian Trust
Sir George Martin Trust
Mayfair Charities Ltd
The Robert McAlpine Foundation
The Merchant Venturers' Charity
Merchants' House of Glasgow
Millennium Stadium Charitable Trust (Ymddiriedolaeth Elusennol Stadiwm y Mileniwm)
The Alexander Moncur Trust
John Moores Foundation
The Steve Morgan Foundation
G. M. Morrison Charitable Trust
Motor Neurone Disease Association
The Frederick Mulder Foundation
Muslim Hands
The National Lottery Community Fund
Network for Social Change Charitable Trust
Newby Trust Ltd
Newcomen Collett Foundation
The Norman Family Charitable Trust
The Oakdale Trust
*The Olwyn Foundation**
One Community Foundation Ltd
P. F. Charitable Trust
The Paget Charitable Trust
People's Postcode Trust
The Pets at Home Foundation
The Pilgrim Trust
Pink Ribbon Foundation
Polden-Puckham Charitable Foundation
The Portal Trust
The Mary Potter Convent Hospital Trust
David and Elaine Potter Foundation
Quartet Community Foundation

The Eleanor Rathbone Charitable Trust
The Rayne Foundation
Daisie Rich Trust
Robertson Hall Trust
The Robertson Trust
Rosa Fund
Rothschild Foundation (Hanadiv) Europe
The Roughley Charitable Trust
The Joseph Rowntree Charitable Trust
Royal Masonic Trust for Girls and Boys
The Royal Navy and Royal Marines Charity
The Alan and Babette Sainsbury Charitable Fund
Savannah Wisdom
Schroder Charity Trust
Foundation Scotland
Francis C. Scott Charitable Trust
The Frieda Scott Charitable Trust
Seafarers UK (King George's Fund for Sailors)
Sam and Bella Sebba Charitable Trust
Shaftoe Educational Foundation
The Shears Foundation
The Sheldon Trust
Shetland Charitable Trust
SHINE (Support and Help in Education)
The Shipwrights' Charitable Fund
Shulem B. Association Ltd
The Charles Skey Charitable Trust
The Henry Smith Charity
The R. C. Snelling Charitable Trust
Somerset Community Foundation
The Souter Charitable Trust
W. F. Southall Trust
The Jessie Spencer Trust
St James's Place Charitable Foundation
St Monica Trust
Strand Parishes Trust
Stratford-upon-Avon Town Trust
Community Foundation for Surrey
The Sussex Community Foundation
The Adrian Swire Charitable Trust
Taca
Tay Charitable Trust
The Tedworth Charitable Trust
Tenovus Scotland
Sir Jules Thorn Charitable Trust
The Thriplow Charitable Trust
Mrs R. P. Tindall's Charitable Trust
The Constance Travis Charitable Trust
The Treeside Trust
The Triangle Trust (1949) Fund
The True Colours Trust
Trust for London
The Trusthouse Charitable Foundation
The James Tudor Foundation
The Tudor Trust
*The Tudwick Foundation**
The Tuixen Foundation
The Roger and Douglas Turner Charitable Trust
Community Foundation serving Tyne and Wear and Northumberland
The Underwood Trust
The United Reformed Church (Wessex) Trust Ltd
United St Saviour's Charity
The Valentine Charitable Trust
The Virgin Money Foundation
*Vision Foundation**
Volant Charitable Trust
The Scurrah Wainwright Charity
Wakefield and Tetley Trust
The Walcot Foundation
Walton on Thames Charity
G. R. Waters Charitable Trust 2000
Wates Family Enterprise Trust
The Wates Foundation
The Weavers' Company Benevolent Fund
The Weinstock Fund
The Weir Charitable Trust
The James Weir Foundation
Westminster Amalgamated Charity
Westminster Foundation
Westway Trust
Whitley Animal Protection Trust
The HDH Wills 1965 Charitable Trust
J. and J. R. Wilson Trust
Wiltshire Community Foundation
Wooden Spoon Society
Woodroffe Benton Foundation
The Woodward Charitable Trust
Worcester Municipal Charities (CIO)
Worth Waynflete Foundation
The Eric Wright Charitable Trust
WWDP (World Day of Prayer National Committee for England, Wales and Northern Ireland)
The Wyndham Charitable Trust
The Wyseliot Rose Charitable Trust
The Yapp Charitable Trust
Youth Music
Zurich Community Trust (UK) Ltd

Development funding

The Architectural Heritage Fund
Keren Association Ltd
Backstage Trust
The Philip Barker Charity
The Paul Bassham Charitable Trust
Benesco Charity Ltd
The Berkeley Foundation
British Lung Foundation
The Buffini Chao Foundation
William A. Cadbury Charitable Trust
The Worshipful Company of Cordwainers Charitable Trusts (Minges Gift)
The Corporation of Trinity House of Deptford Strond
Credit Suisse EMEA Foundation
The Roger De Haan Charitable Trust
Donibristle Trust
The Dunhill Medical Trust
The Marian Elizabeth Trust
England and Wales Cricket Trust
The Estelle Trust
The George Fentham Birmingham Charity
The Fidelity UK Foundation
The Forbes Charitable Foundation
Friends Provident Charitable Foundation
The Generations Foundation
The Glass-House Trust
The Hadley Trust
The Tim Henman Foundation
Hinchley Charitable Trust
Hospice UK
The Hunter Foundation
The Iceland Foods Charitable Foundation
The Innocent Foundation
The J. J. Charitable Trust
Joffe Charitable Trust
The Mark Leonard Trust
The Linbury Trust
The James Milner Foundation
The Mutual Trust Group
The National Garden Scheme
Nesta
The Nineveh Charitable Trust
The Patrick Trust
The Pilgrim Trust
Thomas Pocklington Trust
The Portal Trust
The Professional Footballers' Association Charity
The Progress Foundation
The Rayne Trust
Sam and Bella Sebba Charitable Trust
The Mrs Smith and Mount Trust
Peter Sowerby Foundation
St Peter's Saltley Trust
The Stone Family Foundation
The WO Street Charitable Foundation
Swansea and Brecon Diocesan Board of Finance Ltd
Tanner Trust
C. B. and H. H. Taylor 1984 Trust
Stephen Taylor Foundation
The Triangle Trust (1949) Fund
The True Colours Trust
Truemart Ltd
Trumros Ltd
The Tudor Trust
Ufi VocTech Trust
The Valentine Charitable Trust
The Veterans' Foundation
Virgin Atlantic Foundation
The Wingate Foundation
WWDP (World Day of Prayer National Committee for England, Wales and Northern Ireland)
Yorkshire Cancer Research
Youth Music

Loan finance/ social investment

Esmée Fairbairn Foundation
Nesta
Equity Charitable Trust*
The Maurice Hatter Foundation
The Herefordshire Historic Churches Trust
The Jewish Youth Fund
Kupath Gemach Chaim Bechesed Viznitz Trust
The William Leech Charity
The Ranworth Trust
The Rayne Foundation
The Romney Marsh Historic Churches Trust
Social Investment Business Foundation
The Talbot Village Trust
Ulster Garden Villages Ltd
The Charles Wolfson Charitable Trust

Project funding

The Abbeyfield Research Foundation
The Acacia Charitable Trust
Access Sport CIO
Alpkit Foundation*
The Armed Forces Covenant Fund Trust*
Armed Forces Education Trust
Douglas Arter Foundation
Arts Council England
Arts Council of Wales (also known as Cyngor Celfyddydau Cymru)
ArtSocial Foundation
The Ashden Trust
The Ashworth Charitable Trust
The Associated Board of the Royal Schools of Music
Keren Association Ltd
The Astor Foundation
Lawrence Atwell's Charity (Skinners' Company)
The Avon and Somerset Police Community Trust
Backstage Trust
The Austin Bailey Foundation
Bairdwatson Charitable Trust
The Ballinger Charitable Trust
Banbury Charities
Veronica and Lars Bane Foundation*
The Banister Charitable Trust
Bank of Scotland Foundation
The Barbers' Company General Charities
Barchester Healthcare Foundation
The Philip Barker Charity
The Barnes Fund*
Barnwood Trust
The Paul Bassham Charitable Trust
The Battersea Power Station Foundation
Bauer Radio's Cash for Kids Charities
BBC Children in Need
BC Partners Foundation
The James Beattie Charitable Trust
The Beaverbrook Foundation
Benesco Charity Ltd
The Berkeley Foundation
The Berkshire Community Foundation
Biffa Award
The Percy Bilton Charity
The Michael Bishop Foundation
Maria Bjornson Memorial Fund*
The John Black Charitable Foundation
The Blagrave Trust
The Blandford Lake Trust
Bloodwise
The Bloom Foundation
The Bloomfield Charitable Trust
Bluespark Foundation
The BNA Charitable Incorporated Organisation*
The Charlotte Bonham-Carter Charitable Trust
BOOST Charitable Trust
The Booth Charities
Boots Charitable Trust
Sir William Boreman's Foundation
Alan Boswell Group Charitable Trust*
The Liz and Terry Bramall Foundation
The Breadsticks Foundation
The Brelms Trust CIO
Bridgepoint Charitable Trust
Bristol Archdeaconry Charity
Bristol Charities
The BRIT Trust
The British and Foreign School Society
British Council for Prevention of Blindness
British Eye Research Foundation (Fight for Sight)
British Gas Energy Trust
British Heart Foundation (BHF)
British Lung Foundation
British Motor Sports Training Trust
The Brook Trust
The Broomton Foundation
Bill Brown 1989 Charitable Trust
Mary Brown Memorial Trust*
The Brown Source Trust*
R. S. Brownless Charitable Trust
The Jack Brunton Charitable Trust
The Bruntwood Charity
Buckinghamshire Community Foundation
The Buffini Chao Foundation
Building & Civil Engineering Charitable Trust
Bulb Foundation*
BUPA UK Foundation
The Burdett Trust for Nursing
The Burges Salmon Charitable Trust
Burnie's Foundation
Consolidated Charity of Burton upon Trent
The Noel Buxton Trust
The Edward Cadbury Charitable Trust
William A. Cadbury Charitable Trust
The Barrow Cadbury Trust
Community Foundation for Calderdale
The Calleva Foundation
The Cambridgeshire Community Foundation
Camden Giving*
The Campden Charities Trustee
Canary Wharf Contractors Fund
Card Factory Foundation*
The Carlton Hayes Mental Health Charity
The Leslie Mary Carter Charitable Trust
The Casey Trust
The Castang Foundation
Cattanach
The Joseph and Annie Cattle Trust
The Wilfrid and Constance Cave Foundation
Elizabeth Cayzer Charitable Trust
The B. G. S. Cayzer Charitable Trust
The Chalk Cliff Trust
The Charter 600 Charity
Chartered Accountants' Livery Charity (CALC)
The Charterhouse Charitable Trust
The Chetwode Foundation
The Childhood Trust
Children with Cancer UK
Children's Liver Disease Foundation
The Childs Charitable Trust*
Chippenham Borough Lands Charity
The Chipping Sodbury Town Lands Charity
The Church Burgesses Educational Foundation
Church of Ireland Priorities Fund
Church Urban Fund
CLA Charitable Trust
The Clan Trust Ltd
J. A. Clark Charitable Trust
Cloudesley
The John Coates Charitable Trust
Denise Coates Foundation
Colchester Catalyst Charity
John and Freda Coleman Charitable Trust
The George Collins Charity*
The Colt Foundation
Colwinston Charitable Trust
Colyer-Fergusson Charitable Trust
The Comino Foundation
Community First
Congregational and General Charitable Trust
The Cooks Charity

The Alice Ellen Cooper Dean Charitable Foundation
Marjorie Coote Animal Charity Trust
The Helen Jean Cope Charity
The Worshipful Company of Cordwainers Charitable Trusts (Minges Gift)
Michael Cornish Charitable Trust
The Evan Cornish Foundation
Cornwall Community Foundation
The Corporation of Trinity House of Deptford Strond
Corra Foundation
The County Council of Dyfed Welsh Church Fund
The Noel Coward Foundation*
The Sir Tom Cowie Charitable Trust
The Craignish Trust
Creative Scotland
Credit Suisse EMEA Foundation
The Crerar Trust
Cripplegate Foundation
Cruden Foundation Ltd
Cumbria Community Foundation
The Cunningham Trust
The D'Oyly Carte Charitable Trust
The Daiwa Anglo-Japanese Foundation
Baron Davenport's Charity
The Roger De Haan Charitable Trust
The Delves Charitable Trust
Denman Charitable Trust
Foundation Derbyshire
Devon Community Foundation
The Devon Historic Churches
Digital Xtra Fund*
Dinwoodie Charitable Company
The Djanogly Foundation
Donibristle Trust
Dorset Community Foundation
Drapers' Charitable Fund
The Anne Duchess of Westminster's Charity
Duchy Health Charity Ltd
The Dulverton Trust
Dunard Fund
The Dunhill Medical Trust
County Durham Community Foundation
The DWF Charitable Foundation
The James Dyson Foundation
The Earley Charity
East End Community Foundation
EBM Charitable Trust
The Economist Charitable Trust
The Gilbert and Eileen Edgar Foundation
The Edge Foundation
Dr Edwards Bishop King's Fulham Endowment Fund
W. G. Edwards Charitable Foundation
The George Elias Charitable Trust
The Maud Elkington Charitable Trust
John Ellerman Foundation
The Endrick Trust
England and Wales Cricket Trust
The Enkalon Foundation
Epilepsy Research UK
The EQ Foundation
Essex Community Foundation
The Essex Youth Trust
The Estelle Trust
The Evelyn Trust
The Eventhall Family Charitable Trust
The Lord Faringdon Charitable Trust
The Thomas Farr Charity
The February Foundation
The George Fentham Birmingham Charity
The Feoffees of St Michael's Spurriergate York
Allan and Nesta Ferguson Charitable Settlement
The Fidelio Charitable Trust
Fine & Country Foundation
Sir John Fisher Foundation
Fishmongers' Company's Charitable Trust
Oliver Ford Foundation
Forever Manchester
Donald Forrester Trust
Gwyneth Forrester Trust
The Lord Forte Foundation
Fowler Smith and Jones Trust
The Foyle Foundation
Mrs D. M. France-Hayhurst Foundation
The Gordon Fraser Charitable Trust
The Louis and Valerie Freedman Charitable Settlement
The Freelands Foundation Ltd
Friarsgate Trust
Friends Provident Charitable Foundation
The Fulmer Charitable Trust
The Funding Network
The Gale Family Charity Trust
The Gannochy Trust
Garfield Weston Foundation
The Gatsby Charitable Foundation
Gatwick Airport Community Trust
Martin Geddes Charitable Trust
Sir Robert Geffery's Almshouse Trust
General Charity (Coventry)
The General Charity Fund
The Generations Foundation
The Gibbons Family Trust
The Simon Gibson Charitable Trust
The G. C. Gibson Charitable Trust
The Glass-House Trust
Global Charities
Worshipful Company of Glovers of London Charitable Trust
Sydney and Phyllis Goldberg Memorial Charitable Trust
Goldman Sachs Gives (UK)
The Golsoncott Foundation
Nicholas and Judith Goodison's Charitable Settlement
The Goshen Trust
The Edward Gostling Foundation
The Granada Foundation
The Grant Foundation
GrantScape
The Great Stone Bridge Trust of Edenbridge
The Greater Manchester High Sheriff's Police Trust
The Green Hall Foundation
Greenham Trust Ltd
The Greggs Foundation
The Grimmitt Trust
The Grocers' Charity
Groundwork UK
Calouste Gulbenkian Foundation – UK Branch
The Guy Foundation*
H. C. D. Memorial Fund
Hackney Parochial Charities
The Hadfield Charitable Trust
The Hadley Trust
The Hadrian Trust
The Alfred Haines Charitable Trust
Halifax Foundation for Northern Ireland
The Helen Hamlyn Trust
Hammersmith United Charities
The Hampstead Wells and Campden Trust
The Happold Foundation
Harborne Parish Lands Charity
The Harding Trust
The Harpur Trust
The Harris Family Charitable Trust
The Peter Harrison Foundation
Edward Harvist Trust (The Harvist Estate)
Hays Travel Foundation

The Charles Hayward Foundation
The Headley Trust
The Health Foundation
Heart of England Community Foundation
Heart Research UK
Heathrow Community Trust
Ernest Hecht Charitable Foundation
The Michael Heller Charitable Foundation
The Simon Heller Charitable Settlement
Help for Health
The Helping Foundation
Henley Educational Trust
Henley Royal Regatta Charitable Trust
The Tim Henman Foundation
Herefordshire Community Foundation
The Herefordshire Historic Churches Trust
Heritage Lottery Fund
Hertfordshire Community Foundation
HFC Help For Children UK LTD
Highway One Trust
The Hilden Charitable Fund
Hinchley Charitable Trust
The Hinduja Foundation
The Hinrichsen Foundation
Historic Environment Scotland*
Historic Houses Foundation
The Hobson Charity Ltd
Hockerill Educational Foundation
The Jane Hodge Foundation
The Holbeck Charitable Trust
P. H. Holt Foundation
The Holywood Trust
Hospice UK
The Hospital of God at Greatham
House of Industry Estate
Housing Pathways Trust
James T. Howat Charitable Trust
The Huggard Charitable Trust
The Hull and East Riding Charitable Trust
The Hunter Foundation
Miss Agnes H. Hunter's Trust
Huntingdon Freemen's Trust
Hyde Charitable Trust
IBM United Kingdom Trust
Ibrahim Foundation Ltd
The Idlewild Trust
Imagine Foundation
The Indigo Trust
The Ingram Trust
The Innocent Foundation
The Institute for Policy Research
Integrated Education Fund
The International Bankers Charitable Trust
The Investindustrial Foundation*
The Ireland Fund of Great Britain
The Charles Irving Charitable Trust
The Isla Foundation*
Isle of Wight Foundation
The ITF Seafarers Trust
The J. J. Charitable Trust
The Sir Barry Jackson County Fund
John Jarrold Trust Ltd
The Roger and Jean Jefcoate Trust
Rees Jeffreys Road Fund
The Jephcott Charitable Trust
The Jerusalem Trust
Jewish Child's Day (JCD)
The Jewish Youth Fund
Joffe Charitable Trust
The Johnson Foundation
The Joron Charitable Trust
Anton Jurgens Charitable Trust
The Ian Karten Charitable Trust
The Kennel Club Charitable Trust
The Kensington and Chelsea Foundation
The Kentown Wizard Foundation
The Peter Kershaw Trust
KFC Foundation*
Kilpatrick Fraser Charitable Trust
The King Henry VIII Endowed Trust – Warwick
The Mary Kinross Charitable Trust
The Kirschel Foundation
Robert Kitchin (Saddlers' Company)
The Ernest Kleinwort Charitable Trust
Kollel and Co. Ltd
The KPMG Foundation
The Kreitman Foundation
Kusuma Trust UK
The K. P. Ladd Charitable Trust
John Laing Charitable Trust
Maurice and Hilda Laing Charitable Trust
Christopher Laing Foundation
The Kirby Laing Foundation
The Lake House Charity
Community Foundations for Lancashire and Merseyside
Lancashire Environmental Fund Ltd
LandAid Charitable Trust (LandAid)
The Richard Lawes Foundation
The Lawson Trust CIO
The Leach Fourteenth Trust
The Leche Trust
The William Leech Charity
Leeds Community Foundation (LCF)
The Legal Education Foundation
Leicestershire, Leicester and Rutland Community Foundation
The Leverhulme Trust
Joseph Levy Foundation
The Charles Lewis Foundation*
The Light Fund Company
The Limbourne Trust
The Linbury Trust
Lincolnshire Community Foundation
The Linder Foundation
The Frank Litchfield Charitable Trust
Liverpool Charity and Voluntary Services (LCVS)
The Ian and Natalie Livingstone Charitable Trust
The Andrew Lloyd Webber Foundation
Lloyd's Charities Trust
Lloyds Bank Foundation for the Channel Islands
Lloyd's Patriotic Fund
Lloyd's Register Foundation
The Locker Foundation
London Catalyst
The London Community Foundation (LCF)
London Housing Foundation Ltd (LHF)
The London Marathon Charitable Trust Ltd
The Lord's Taverners
John Lyon's Charity
The R. S. Macdonald Charitable Trust
Mace Foundation
The Mackintosh Foundation
The Magdalen and Lasher Charity (General Fund)
Man Group plc Charitable Trust
The Marandi Foundation*
The Marchig Animal Welfare Trust
The Michael Marsh Charitable Trust
John Martin's Charity
Masonic Charitable Foundation
Mathew Trust
Maudsley Charity
The Robert McAlpine Foundation
Gemma and Chris McGough Charitable Foundation CIO*

D. D. McPhail Charitable Settlement
The Brian Mercer Charitable Trust
The Mercers' Charitable Foundation
Merchants' House of Glasgow
Mercury Phoenix Trust
The Mickel Fund
The Masonic Province of Middlesex Charitable Trust (Middlesex Masonic Charity)
Millennium Stadium Charitable Trust (Ymddiriedclaeth Elusennol Stadiwm y Mileniwm)
The Millfield House Foundation (1)
Mills and Reeve Charitable Trust
The James Milner Foundation
Milton Keynes Community Foundation Ltd
Minton Charitable Trust
Moondance Foundation
The George A. Moore Foundation
John Moores Foundation
The Morel Charitable Trust
Morgan Stanley International Foundation
The Miles Morland Foundation
The Morrisons Foundation
Motor Neurone Disease Association
The Edwina Mountbatten and Leonora Children's Foundation
The MSE Charity
The Frederick Mulder Foundation
Muslim Hands
The National Express Foundation
The National Garden Scheme
The National Lottery Community Fund
The Nationwide Foundation
Network for Social Change Charitable Trust
Newby Trust Ltd
Alderman Newton's Educational Foundation
The NFU Mutual Charitable Trust
The Nineveh Charitable Trust
The Nisbet Trust
Alice Noakes Memorial Charitable Trust
The Nomura Charitable Trust
North West Cancer Research
Northern Pharmacies Ltd Trust Fund
Norwich Town Close Estate Charity
The Nuffield Foundation
The Sir Peter O'Sullevan Charitable Trust
The Oakdale Trust
Old Possum's Practical Trust
The Olwyn Foundation*
One Community Foundation Ltd
Orange Tree Trust*
Orthopaedic Research UK
Ostro Fayre Share Foundation
The O'Sullivan Family Charitable Trust
Ovingdean Hall Foundation
The Ovo Charitable Foundation
P. F. Charitable Trust
The Panacea Charitable Trust
Parabola Foundation
The Pastoral Care Trust – The St Nicholas Care Fund
Miss M. E. S. Paterson's Charitable Trust
The JGW Patterson Foundation
The Pears Family Charitable Foundation
The Pebbles Trust
The Dowager Countess Eleanor Peel Trust
People's Health Trust
People's Postcode Trust
The Performing Right Society Foundation
The Persimmon Charitable Foundation
The Jack Petchey Foundation
Petplan Charitable Trust
The Pets at Home Foundation
The Pickwell Foundation
The Pilgrim Trust
Elise Pilkington Charitable Trust*
Pilkington Charities Fund
The Austin and Hope Pilkington Trust
Pink Ribbon Foundation
The Pixel Fund
Polden-Puckham Charitable Foundation
The Portal Trust
Postcode Community Trust
Postcode Local Trust
Postcode Society Trust (formerly Postcode Dream Trust)
The Mary Potter Convent Hospital Trust
David and Elaine Potter Foundation
Power to Change Trust
The Pret Foundation
Sir John Priestman Charity Trust
The Primrose Trust
The Prince of Wales's Charitable Foundation
The Professional Footballers' Association Charity
The Progress Foundation
Prostate Cancer UK
QBE European Operations Foundation
Quadstar Charitable Foundation*
Quartet Community Foundation
The Queen Anne's Gate Foundation
Queen Mary's Roehampton Trust
Quintessentially Foundation
The Racing Foundation
The Radcliffe Trust
The Bishop Radford Trust
The Rainford Trust
The Joseph Rank Trust
The Rathbone Brothers Foundation
The Eleanor Rathbone Charitable Trust
The Sigrid Rausing Trust
The Ravensdale Trust
The Rayne Foundation
The Rayne Trust
The John Rayner Charitable Trust
Red Hill Charitable Trust
Richard Reeve's Foundation
The Resolution Trust
The Rest-Harrow Trust
The Rhododendron Trust
Daisie Rich Trust
Richmond Parish Lands Charity
Rivers Foundation
The Robertson Trust
The Roddick Foundation
The Helen Roll Charity
Rosa Fund
Rosca Trust
Rothschild Foundation (Hanadiv) Europe
The Rowlands Trust
The Joseph Rowntree Charitable Trust
The Joseph Rowntree Foundation
The Royal British Legion
Royal Docks Trust (London)
The Royal Foundation of the Duke and Duchess of Cambridge
Royal Masonic Trust for Girls and Boys
The Royal Navy and Royal Marines Charity
Royal Society of Wildlife Trusts
The Ruddock Foundation for the Arts
The Russell Trust
The RVW Trust
The Saddlers' Company Charitable Fund

The Jean Sainsbury Animal Welfare Trust
The Alan and Babette Sainsbury Charitable Fund
Salters' Charitable Foundation
Santander UK Foundation Ltd
Savannah Wisdom
The Savoy Educational Trust
The Scarfe Charitable Trust
Schroder Charity Trust
Foundation Scotland
Scott (Eredine) Charitable Trust
Francis C. Scott Charitable Trust
The Frieda Scott Charitable Trust
The Scottish Power Foundation
Seafarers UK (King George's Fund for Sailors)
Sam and Bella Sebba Charitable Trust
Seedfield Trust
The Shears Foundation
The Sheffield Town Trust
The Sheldon Trust
The Sylvia and Colin Shepherd Charitable Trust
The Archie Sherman Charitable Trust
Shetland Charitable Trust
SHINE (Support and Help in Education)
The Shipwrights' Charitable Fund
Smallwood Trust
The Mrs Smith and Mount Trust
The Henry Smith Charity
*Arabella and Julian Smith Family Trust**
The Leslie Smith Foundation
The W. H. Smith Group Charitable Trust
Stanley Smith UK Horticultural Trust
The R. C. Snelling Charitable Trust
The Sobell Foundation
Social Tech Trust
*Societe Generale UK Foundation**
Sofronie Foundation
Somerset Community Foundation
The Souter Charitable Trust
The South Yorkshire Community Foundation
Southover Manor General Education Trust Ltd
Peter Sowerby Foundation
The Spoore, Merry and Rixman Foundation
The St Hilda's Trust
The St James's Trust Settlement
St James's Place Charitable Foundation
Sir Walter St John's Educational Charity
St Olave's and St Saviour's Schools Foundation
St Peter's Saltley Trust
The Community Foundation for Staffordshire
Standard Life Aberdeen Charitable Foundation
Standard Life Foundation
Staples Trust
The Peter Stebbings Memorial Charity
The Steel Charitable Trust
The Hugh Stenhouse Foundation
The Stevenage Community Trust
The Stone Family Foundation
Strand Parishes Trust
Stratford-upon-Avon Town Trust
Strathnairn Community Benefit Fund Ltd
The WO Street Charitable Foundation
StreetSmart – Action for the Homeless
Suffolk Community Foundation
Surgo Foundation UK Ltd
Community Foundation for Surrey
The Sussex Community Foundation
The Sutasoma Trust
Sutton Coldfield Charitable Trust
The Swann-Morton Foundation
Swansea and Brecon Diocesan Board of Finance Ltd
The Swire Charitable Trust
The T.K. Maxx and Homesense Foundation
The Tabhair Charitable Trust
The Gay and Keith Talbot Trust
The Talbot Trusts
Tanner Trust
C. B. and H. H. Taylor 1984 Trust
The Taylor Family Foundation
Stephen Taylor Foundation
The Tedworth Charitable Trust
Tenovus Cancer Care
*the7stars Foundation**
*The Thirty Percy Foundation**
Sir Jules Thorn Charitable Trust
The Three Guineas Trust
The Thriplow Charitable Trust
Mrs R. P. Tindall's Charitable Trust
The Tottenham Grammar School Foundation
Tower Hill Trust
The Toy Trust
The Trades House of Glasgow
Tropical Health and Education Trust
The True Colours Trust
Truemart Ltd
Trumros Ltd
The Trusthouse Charitable Foundation
The James Tudor Foundation
The Tudor Trust
*The Tudwick Foundation**
The Tuixen Foundation
Community Foundation serving Tyne and Wear and Northumberland
Ufi VocTech Trust
Ulster Garden Villages Ltd
The Ulverscroft Foundation
The Underwood Trust
The United Reformed Church (Wessex) Trust Ltd
United St Saviour's Charity
UPP Foundation
The Michael Uren Foundation
The Valentine Charitable Trust
The Valiant Charitable Trust
The Vaughan Williams Charitable Trust
Versus Arthritis
The Veterans' Foundation
The Vintners' Foundation
Virgin Atlantic Foundation
The Virgin Money Foundation
Viridor Credits Environmental Company
*Vision Foundation**
Volant Charitable Trust
The VTCT Foundation
Wade's Charity
Wakefield and Tetley Trust
The Walcot Foundation
Walton on Thames Charity
Warwick Relief in Need Charity
The Waterloo Foundation
G. R. Waters Charitable Trust 2000
Wates Family Enterprise Trust
The Wates Foundation
The William Wates Memorial Trust
The Geoffrey Watling Charity
The Weavers' Company Benevolent Fund
The Weir Charitable Trust
*The Welland Trust**
The Welsh Church Act Fund
Wembley National Stadium Trust
The Westfield Health Charitable Trust
Westhill Endowment
Westminster Almshouses Foundation
Westway Trust
The Barbara Whatmore Charitable Trust

The Will Charitable Trust
The Williams Family Foundation
The Willmott Dixon Foundation
J. and J. R. Wilson Trust
Wiltshire Community Foundation
The Charles Wolfson Charitable Trust
The Lord Leonard and Lady Estelle Wolfson Foundation
Women's Fund for Scotland*
The James Wood Bequest Fund
The Wood Foundation
Wooden Spoon Society
Woodroffe Benton Foundation
WWDP (World Day of Prayer National Committee for England, Wales and Northern Ireland)
The Wyseliot Rose Charitable Trust
Yorkshire Building Society Charitable Foundation
The Yorkshire Dales Millennium Trust
Youth Music
Zurich Community Trust (UK) Ltd

Research funding

Action Medical Research
The Bryan Adams Foundation
The AEB Charitable Trust
The AIM Foundation
The Aimwell Charitable Trust
The Alborada Trust
The Alchemy Foundation
Alzheimer's Society
The John Apthorp Charity
The Ove Arup Foundation
The Ashden Trust
Asthma UK
The Astor Foundation
The Tim Bacon Foundation*
The Baily Thomas Charitable Fund
The Paul Bassham Charitable Trust
The Bloom Foundation
Breast Cancer Now
The Breast Cancer Research Trust (BCRT)
Bright Red Charity*
British Council for Prevention of Blindness
British Heart Foundation (BHF)
Bill Brown 1989 Charitable Trust
The Edward Cadbury Charitable Trust
The Barrow Cadbury Trust
The Castang Foundation
Children with Cancer UK
Children's Liver Disease Foundation
The Childs Charitable Trust*
The Childwick Trust
Christadelphian Samaritan Fund
The Clan Trust Ltd
Denise Coates Foundation
The Cunningham Trust
The De Laszlo Foundation
Diabetes UK
Dinwoodie Charitable Company
The Dunhill Medical Trust
The James Dyson Foundation
EBM Charitable Trust
The EQ Foundation
The Evelyn Trust
The Lord Faringdon Charitable Trust
Sir John Fisher Foundation
Marc Fitch Fund
The Louis and Valerie Freedman Charitable Settlement
The Freelands Foundation Ltd
Friends Provident Charitable Foundation
GambleAware
The Gatsby Charitable Foundation
The General Nursing Council for England and Wales Trust
The Glass-House Trust
The Great Britain Sasakawa Foundation
The Grocers' Charity
The Guy Foundation*
The Helen Hamlyn Trust
The Happold Foundation
The Health Foundation
Heart Research UK
Help for Health
HFC Help For Children UK LTD
The Hinduja Foundation
The Hinrichsen Foundation
Hockerill Educational Foundation
The Jane Hodge Foundation
The Holbeck Charitable Trust
The Horse Trust
The Hospital Saturday Fund
James T. Howat Charitable Trust
IBM United Kingdom Trust
The Iceland Foods Charitable Foundation
The Innocent Foundation
Integrated Education Fund
The ITF Seafarers Trust
The Jabbs Foundation
The Frank Jackson Foundation
Jeffrey Charitable Trust*
The Johnson Foundation
The Kay Kendall Leukaemia Fund
The Kennedy Trust for Rheumatology Research
The Kennel Club Charitable Trust
Kilpatrick Fraser Charitable Trust
Kusuma Trust UK
The Kirby Laing Foundation
The William Leech Charity
The Leverhulme Trust
Joseph Levy Foundation
David and Ruth Lewis Family Charitable Trust
The Linder Foundation
The Frank Litchfield Charitable Trust
The Second Joseph Aaron Littman Foundation
Lloyd's Register Foundation
London Housing Foundation Ltd (LHF)
Robert Luff Foundation Ltd
The Mackintosh Foundation
The MacRobert Trust 2019
The Robert McAlpine Foundation
D. D. McPhail Charitable Settlement
Medical Research Foundation

Meningitis Research Foundation
The Millfield House Foundation (1)
Mills and Reeve Charitable Trust
The Henry Moore Foundation
Motor Neurone Disease Association
Multiple Sclerosis Society
Edith Murphy Foundation
Murphy-Neumann Charity Company Ltd
The Nationwide Foundation
Nesta
The Frances and Augustus Newman Foundation
The Nineveh Charitable Trust
Alice Noakes Memorial Charitable Trust
North West Cancer Research
Northern Pharmacies Ltd Trust Fund
The Nuffield Foundation
The Oakley Charitable Trust
Oglesby Charitable Trust
Orthopaedic Research UK
The O'Sullivan Family Charitable Trust
Ovingdean Hall Foundation
P. F. Charitable Trust
Parkinson's UK
The JGW Patterson Foundation
The Pears Family Charitable Foundation
The Dowager Countess Eleanor Peel Trust
Petplan Charitable Trust
The Pilgrim Trust
Pink Ribbon Foundation
Thomas Pocklington Trust
Prostate Cancer UK
The Racing Foundation
The Resolution Trust
RNID (The Royal National Institute for Deaf People)
The Gerald and Gail Ronson Family Foundation
Rosetrees Trust
The Rowlands Trust
The Joseph Rowntree Foundation
The Ruddock Foundation for the Arts
The Alan and Babette Sainsbury Charitable Fund
Scouloudi Foundation
Sam and Bella Sebba Charitable Trust
*The Selfridges Group Foundation**
The Jean Shanks Foundation
The Sino-British Fellowship Trust
*Arabella and Julian Smith Family Trust**
Stanley Smith UK Horticultural Trust
Peter Sowerby Foundation
Sparks Charity
The Steel Charitable Trust
Sir Halley Stewart Trust
The Swann-Morton Foundation
The Gay and Keith Talbot Trust
Tenovus Cancer Care
Tenovus Scotland
Sir Jules Thorn Charitable Trust
The Three Guineas Trust
The Tory Family Foundation
Trust for London
The Michael Uren Foundation
Versus Arthritis
The VTCT Foundation
The Wellcome Trust
The Lord Leonard and Lady Estelle Wolfson Foundation
The Woosnam Foundation
Yankov Charitable Trust
Yorkshire Cancer Research

Salaries

The AIM Foundation
The Alchemy Foundation
The Ashden Trust
The Baily Thomas Charitable Fund
The Philip Barker Charity
Birmingham International Airport Community Trust Fund
The Blandford Lake Trust
The Booth Charities
The Breast Cancer Research Trust (BCRT)
The Charter 600 Charity
Corra Foundation
Credit Suisse EMEA Foundation
Drapers' Charitable Fund
The Ecology Trust
The Essex Youth Trust
Oliver Ford Foundation
The Gatsby Charitable Foundation
The Glass-House Trust
The Hadrian Trust
Harborne Parish Lands Charity
The Peter Harrison Foundation
The Charles Hayward Foundation
The Headley Trust
Heart of England Community Foundation
Heritage Lottery Fund
Hinchley Charitable Trust
The Hintze Family Charity Foundation
The Holbeck Charitable Trust
The Holywood Trust
The Inlight Trust
Integrated Education Fund
Irish Youth Foundation (UK) Ltd (incorporating The Lawlor Foundation)
Isle of Wight Foundation
The Jabbs Foundation
*Jeffrey Charitable Trust**
The Jerusalem Trust
The Peter Kershaw Trust
Sir James Knott Trust
The Legal Education Foundation
The Leverhulme Trust
Joseph Levy Foundation
Liverpool Charity and Voluntary Services (LCVS)
The London Community Foundation (LCF)
Man Group plc Charitable Trust
The Mercers' Charitable Foundation
The National Manuscripts Conservation Trust
The Frances and Augustus Newman Foundation

The Nineveh Charitable Trust
North East Area Miners' Social Welfare Trust Fund
Northern Pharmacies Ltd Trust Fund
*The Olwyn Foundation**
Ovingdean Hall Foundation
The Pilgrim Trust
*Elise Pilkington Charitable Trust**
Power to Change Trust
The Racing Foundation
The Rayne Foundation
The Rayne Trust
Richmond Parish Lands Charity
Robertson Hall Trust
The Robertson Trust
Rosetrees Trust
Royal Masonic Trust for Girls and Boys
Savannah Wisdom
The Shears Foundation
The Sheldon Trust
The Henry Smith Charity
The South Yorkshire Community Foundation
St James's Place Charitable Foundation
The Stafford Trust
Sir Halley Stewart Trust
The Swire Charitable Trust
The Adrian Swire Charitable Trust
The Tedworth Charitable Trust
Tenovus Cancer Care
Tenovus Scotland
Trust for London
The Trusthouse Charitable Foundation
Community Foundation serving Tyne and Wear and Northumberland
Versus Arthritis
The Wates Foundation
The Weir Charitable Trust
Wooden Spoon Society
Worcester Municipal Charities (CIO)
Youth Music
Zurich Community Trust (UK) Ltd

Seed funding/ start-up funding

ABF The Soldiers' Charity
The Sylvia Adams Charitable Trust
The John Apthorp Charity
The Ove Arup Foundation
The Austin Bailey Foundation
The Barbour Foundation
Barcapel Foundation Ltd
Barnwood Trust
The Michael Bishop Foundation
The Oliver Borthwick Memorial Trust
The Boshier-Hinton Foundation
The Harry Bottom Charitable Trust
Bristol Charities
Buckinghamshire Community Foundation
E. F. Bulmer Trust
Community Foundation for Calderdale
The Casey Trust
The Wilfrid and Constance Cave Foundation
The Christabella Charitable Trust
The André Christian Trust
Church Burgesses Trust
Church of Ireland Priorities Fund
Church Urban Fund
The Clan Trust Ltd
The Craignish Trust
Cumbria Community Foundation
The Dulverton Trust
County Durham Community Foundation
The Elmley Foundation
The Essex and Southend Sports Trust
The Estelle Trust
Samuel William Farmer Trust
The Gordon Fraser Charitable Trust
The Hugh Fraser Foundation
The Freshgate Trust Foundation
The Funding Network
G. M. C. Trust
Gatwick Airport Community Trust
The F. Glenister Woodger Trust
Grace Charitable Trust
The J. G. Graves Charitable Trust
The Great Stone Bridge Trust of Edenbridge
H. C. D. Memorial Fund
The Hadrian Trust
*The Halsall Foundation**
William Harding's Charity
Heart of England Community Foundation
Herefordshire Community Foundation
P. and C. Hickinbotham Charitable Trust
The Alan Edward Higgs Charity
Hockerill Educational Foundation
Hollick Family Foundation
P. H. Holt Foundation
Housing Pathways Trust
James T. Howat Charitable Trust
The Hunter Foundation
The Indigo Trust
Integrated Education Fund
Irish Youth Foundation (UK) Ltd (incorporating The Lawlor Foundation)
The J. J. Charitable Trust
John James Bristol Foundation
*Jeffrey Charitable Trust**
The Jewish Youth Fund
Joffe Charitable Trust
The Jusaca Charitable Trust
The Peter Kershaw Trust
The King Henry VIII Endowed Trust – Warwick
The Mary Kinross Charitable Trust
The Ernest Kleinwort Charitable Trust
Sir James Knott Trust
The K. P. Ladd Charitable Trust
The Leonard Laity Stoate Charitable Trust
Community Foundations for Lancashire and Merseyside
The Allen Lane Foundation
Mrs F. B. Laurence Charitable Trust
The Kennedy Leigh Charitable Trust
The Mark Leonard Trust
Joseph Levy Foundation
Lincolnshire Community Foundation
The Linder Foundation
Lloyds Bank Foundation for the Channel Islands
London Catalyst
The London Community Foundation (LCF)
The R. S. Macdonald Charitable Trust
The Michael Marsh Charitable Trust
Merchant Navy Welfare Board
Millennium Stadium Charitable Trust (Ymddiriedclaeth Elusennol Stadiwm y Mileniwm)
The Frederick Mulder Foundation

The National Lottery Community Fund
Network for Social Change Charitable Trust
Newcomen Collett Foundation
The Nuffield Foundation
The Oakdale Trust
Orthopaedic Research UK
The Ouseley Church Music Trust
The Pears Family Charitable Foundation
People's Postcode Trust
Pink Ribbon Foundation
Polden-Puckham Charitable Foundation
The Mary Potter Convent Hospital Trust
Power to Change Trust
Quartet Community Foundation
The Eleanor Rathbone Charitable Trust
The Rayne Foundation
The Rayne Trust
The Sir James Reckitt Charity
The Clive and Sylvia Richards Charity Ltd
Richmond Parish Lands Charity
Rosetrees Trust
The Rothley Trust
The Roughley Charitable Trust
The Joseph Rowntree Charitable Trust
Royal Docks Trust (London)
The Royal Foundation of the Duke and Duchess of Cambridge
The Royal Navy and Royal Marines Charity
Francis C. Scott Charitable Trust
Seafarers UK (King George's Fund for Sailors)
The Segelman Trust
SHINE (Support and Help in Education)
The Shipwrights' Charitable Fund
The Charles Skey Charitable Trust
The R. C. Snelling Charitable Trust
Somerset Community Foundation
W. F. Southall Trust
Sir Walter St John's Educational Charity
Sir Halley Stewart Trust
Strathnairn Community Benefit Fund Ltd
The Summerfield Charitable Trust
Community Foundation for Surrey
The Sussex Community Foundation
Swansea and Brecon Diocesan Board of Finance Ltd
Tabeel Trust
Tay Charitable Trust
Tenovus Scotland
The Thriplow Charitable Trust
The Triangle Trust (1949) Fund
Ufi VocTech Trust
The VTCT Foundation
Wade's Charity
The Scurrah Wainwright Charity
Wakefield and Tetley Trust
The Wakeham Trust
Walton on Thames Charity
The Westcroft Trust
Alfred Williams Charitable Trust
J. and J. R. Wilson Trust
Worth Waynflete Foundation
Zurich Community Trust (UK) Ltd

Strategic funding

The Astor Foundation
Backstage Trust
The Ballinger Charitable Trust
The Michael Bishop Foundation
Bloodwise
The Bloom Foundation
British Motor Sports Training Trust
The Buffini Chao Foundation
Cloudesley
Colwinston Charitable Trust
The Corporation of Trinity House of Deptford Strond
Donibristle Trust
Dorset Community Foundation
The Evelyn Trust
The George Fentham Birmingham Charity
The Fidelity UK Foundation
The Funding Network
The Harding Trust
Hinchley Charitable Trust
The Hunter Foundation
Impetus
The International Bankers Charitable Trust
Longleigh Foundation
Mace Foundation
Mercury Phoenix Trust
Nesta
The Nuffield Foundation
The Pears Family Charitable Foundation
People's Health Trust
The Prince of Wales's Charitable Foundation
The Professional Footballers' Association Charity
Sam and Bella Sebba Charitable Trust
Social Investment Business Foundation
The Tedworth Charitable Trust
The Thirty Percy Foundation*
Truemart Ltd
Trumros Ltd
The United Reformed Church (Wessex) Trust Ltd
United St Saviour's Charity
The Valentine Charitable Trust
The Veterans' Foundation
Wembley National Stadium Trust
Yorkshire Cancer Research

The alphabetical register of grant-making charities

This section lists the individual records for the grant-making charities.

The 1989 Willan Charitable Trust

CC NO 802749 **ESTABLISHED** 1989
WHERE FUNDING CAN BE GIVEN Tyne and Wear, Northumberland, County Durham and Teesside.
WHO CAN BENEFIT Registered charities.
WHAT IS FUNDED General charitable purposes including: growth and employment; children and young people; health; community cohesion; older people.
WHAT IS NOT FUNDED Trips abroad; individuals except for Project Trust applications from residents of the benefit area; projects focused on heritage and the environment, scientific and/or medical research unless these address deprivation and/or enrich local communities, or improve local quality of life; beneficiaries that did not provide feedback on previous awards.
TYPE OF GRANT Core costs and project funding.
RANGE OF GRANTS £1,000 to £10,000.
SAMPLE GRANTS A full list of grants awarded is available on request from the Tyne and Wear Community Foundation.
FINANCES *Financial year end* 30/09/2019 *Income* £568,300 *Total grants* £509,400 *Grants to organisations* £507,400 *Assets* £20,750,000
TRUSTEES Francis Chapman; Alex Ohlsson; Willan Trustee Ltd.
OTHER INFORMATION The 2018/19 accounts were the latest available at the time of writing (June 2021). Grants were awarded to 87 organisations and individuals during the year.
HOW TO APPLY Applications can be made in writing to the correspondent, further details of how to apply and what to include can be found on the Community Foundation's website. The trustees meet in March, June, September and December. Applications will generally be considered at the next scheduled trustees' meeting, provided they are received by the 15th of the preceding month. Applicants are encouraged to submit their applications as early as possible to ensure they are considered at the next available trustees' meeting.
CONTACT DETAILS The Trustees, c/o Community Foundation, Philanthropy House, Gosforth, Newcastle upon Tyne, Tyne and Wear NE3 1DD *Tel.* 0191 222 0945 *Email* general@communityfoundation.org.uk *Website* https://www.communityfoundation.org.uk/group_grant/the-1989-willan-charitable-trust

The 29th May 1961 Charitable Trust

CC NO 200198 **ESTABLISHED** 1961
WHERE FUNDING CAN BE GIVEN UK, with a preference for the Warwickshire and Coventry area.
WHO CAN BENEFIT Registered charities; social enterprises; universities.
WHAT IS FUNDED The arts; museums; conservation; employment, education and training; homelessness and housing; leisure and recreation; young people; health; offenders; social welfare.
WHAT IS NOT FUNDED Individuals; unregistered charities.
TYPE OF GRANT Capital costs; core/revenue costs; unrestricted funding.
RANGE OF GRANTS Up to £250,000 but typically £6,000 to £40,000.
SAMPLE GRANTS Albany Theatre Trust (£260,000); Lord Leycester Hospital (£210,000); Opera North (£50,000); Philharmonia Ltd (£25,000); Kiln Theatre and World Heartbeat Music Academy (£15,000 each); National Art Collections Fund and Sir John Soane's Museum (£10,000 each); Coventry Gang Show Ltd and Parish of Boston (£5,000 each).
FINANCES *Financial year end* 05/04/2020 *Income* £3,140,000 *Total grants* £4,300,000 *Grants to organisations* £4,300,000 *Assets* £101,310,000
TRUSTEES Paul Varney; Andrew Jones; Elizabeth Rantzen; Geoffrey Cox; Charles Martin.
OTHER INFORMATION Grants were awarded to 373 organisations during the year. Of these, 174 were in the Midlands area. Grants were distributed as follows: social welfare (£1.61 million); art and museums (£632,000); leisure, recreation and youth (£604,000); homelessness and housing (£380,500); medical causes (£303,500); employment, education and training (£296,000); conservation and protection (£281,500). Beneficiaries receiving under £5,000 were not listed in the 2019/20 accounts.
HOW TO APPLY Apply in writing to the correspondent, enclosing the most recent annual report and accounts. Follow-up visits to charities may be requested to better understand applicants' requirements. Trustees typically meet in February, May, August and November. Due to the large number of applications received, applications are not acknowledged and unsuccessful applicants are not notified.
CONTACT DETAILS The Trustees, One Eastwood, Bilney Business Park, Coventry CV3 2UB *Tel.* 020 7024 9034 *Email* enquiries@29may1961charity.org.uk

The 3Ts Charitable Trust

CC NO 1109733 **ESTABLISHED** 2005
WHERE FUNDING CAN BE GIVEN UK and overseas.
WHO CAN BENEFIT Registered charities.
WHAT IS FUNDED General charitable purposes.
RANGE OF GRANTS Up to £50,000.
SAMPLE GRANTS Seaview Project (£51,000); Imperial College SCI and Médecins Sans Frontières (£40,000 each); Marie Curie Cancer Care and St Mungo's (£25,000 each); Fair Trials International, Hardman Trust and The Big Issue Foundation (£10,000 each); Envision (£1,000); Lupus UK (£100).
FINANCES *Financial year end* 31/03/2020 *Income* £1,510,000 *Total grants* £499,600 *Grants to organisations* £499,600 *Assets* £11,000,000
TRUSTEES Charles Sherwood; Rosemary Sherwood; William Medlicott; Tim Sherwood; Tabitha Sherwood; Tatiana Sherwood.
OTHER INFORMATION In 2019/20 the trust made grants to 27 organisations.
HOW TO APPLY The trustees adopt a proactive approach in seeking worthy causes requiring support.
CONTACT DETAILS The Trustees, PO Box 68, Knebworth, Hertfordshire SG3 6UZ *Tel.* 01892 701743 *Email* info@3tscharitabletrust.com

4 Charity Foundation

CC NO 1077143 **ESTABLISHED** 1999
WHERE FUNDING CAN BE GIVEN UK and Israel.
WHO CAN BENEFIT Mainly Jewish charities and causes.
WHAT IS FUNDED General charitable purposes; social welfare; education; health; Jewish causes.
RANGE OF GRANTS Up to £1.6 million.
SAMPLE GRANTS Previous beneficiaries have included: Achisomoch Aid Company Ltd

(£1.2 million); The Marque Foundation (£900,000); Farmwood Charitable Foundation (£550,000); Tikva UK (£335,400); Covenant and Conversation Trust (£73,800); Asser Bishvil Foundation (£28,000); Baba Sali Trust (£17,600); Mizrachi UK (£10,000).

FINANCES *Financial year end* 31/03/2019 *Income* £517,600 *Total grants* £4,080,000 *Grants to organisations* £4,080,000 *Assets* £7,270,000

TRUSTEES Jacob Schimmel; Verette Schimmel; Jonathan Schimmel.

OTHER INFORMATION The 2018/19 accounts were the latest available at the time of writing (January 2021). Grants of under £25,000 totalled £142,100.

HOW TO APPLY The foundation does not accept unsolicited applications.

CONTACT DETAILS Jacob Schimmel, Trustee, 121 Princes Park Avenue, London NW11 0JS *Tel.* 020 8455 0100 *Email* four4charities@gmail.com

■ The 4814 Trust

CC NO 1162714 **ESTABLISHED** 2014

WHERE FUNDING CAN BE GIVEN UK.

WHO CAN BENEFIT Small innovative UK charities which deliver significant benefit from limited resources and funds.

WHAT IS FUNDED General charitable purposes, including: social welfare, health, disability, young people, older people, economic disadvantage, disability.

RANGE OF GRANTS Typically £500 to £10,000.

SAMPLE GRANTS Dorset Community Foundation (£25,000); Alzheimer's Society, Climbing Out and Diverse Abilities Plus Ltd (£10,000 each); Batley Community Outreach Centre and Foresight Gardening Enterprises CIC (£5,000 each); British Liver Trust (£3,600); Young Carers Development Trust (£3,500).

FINANCES *Financial year end* 31/12/2019 *Income* £246,200 *Total grants* £177,200 *Grants to organisations* £163,600 *Assets* £4,010,000

TRUSTEES Carole Bedwell; Chris Bedwell; Chris Gardner.

OTHER INFORMATION In 2019, the trust awarded grants totalling £163,600 to 16 organisations. Grants totalling £13,600 were awarded to six individuals.

HOW TO APPLY Applications should be made in writing and sent via email or post to the correspondent. The trustees ask that you include a copy of your latest accounts, any supporting literature and an overview of your plans for the next 12 months. The trustees will contact successful applicants or applicants from whom more information is required.

CONTACT DETAILS Chris Bedwell, Chair of Trustees, PO Box 96, Somerton TA11 9BS *Email* grants@the4814trust.org *Website* www.the4814trust.com

The A. B. Charitable Trust

CC NO 1000147 **ESTABLISHED** 1990

WHERE FUNDING CAN BE GIVEN UK.

WHO CAN BENEFIT Registered charities. The trust favours those charities with an annual income between £150,000 and £1.5 million, which do not have substantial free reserves.

WHAT IS FUNDED Migrants and refugees; criminal justice and penal reform; human rights, particularly access to justice.

WHAT IS NOT FUNDED Individuals; organisations that are not registered charities.

TYPE OF GRANT Project funding; core costs.

RANGE OF GRANTS Typically £10,000 to £20,000.

SAMPLE GRANTS Legal Education Foundation (£250,000); The Justice Initiative (£125,000); Prison Reform Trust (£40,000); Circles UK, Hackney Migrant Centre and Safe Passage International (£20,000 each); ASSIST Sheffield and UK Lesbian and Gay Immigration Group (£15,000 each); Criminal Justice Alliance and Room to Heal (£10,000 each).

FINANCES *Financial year end* 30/04/2020 *Income* £3,040,000 *Total grants* £2,980,000 *Grants to organisations* £2,980,000 *Assets* £500,300

TRUSTEE ABCT Trustee Ltd.

OTHER INFORMATION In 2019/20 the trust ran three programmes: the Open Programme (£1.79 million); the Special Initiatives programme (invitation only; £672,000); and the Anchor Programme (invitation only; £270,000). Grants by cause were distributed as follows: human rights (£1.25 million), migrants and refugees (£1.17 million) and criminal justice (£570,000).

HOW TO APPLY Applications can be completed online via the trust's website. Application deadlines are typically in January, April, July and October. Full guidelines and answers to frequently asked questions are available on the trust's website.

CONTACT DETAILS Havva Hassan, Grants Administrator, c/o Woodsford, 3rd Floor, 8 Bloomsbury Street, London WC1B 3SR *Tel.* 020 7313 8070 *Email* mail@abcharitabletrust.org.uk *Website* www.abcharitabletrust.org.uk

The A Team Foundation Ltd

CC NO 1077094 **ESTABLISHED** 1999

WHERE FUNDING CAN BE GIVEN UK.

WHO CAN BENEFIT Charitable organisations.

WHAT IS FUNDED Food and land projects that are ecologically, economically and socially conscious.

RANGE OF GRANTS Typically £1,000 to £50,000.

SAMPLE GRANTS Landworker's Alliance (£67,000); New Venture Fund (Agroecology Fund) (£40,000); Sustain (£25,000); Sustainable Food Trust (£15,000); Beyond GM (£10,000); The Gaia Foundation (£5,000); Soil Association (£1,000).

FINANCES *Financial year end* 05/04/2020 *Income* £577,600 *Total grants* £447,700 *Grants to organisations* £447,700 *Assets* £14,620,000

TRUSTEES Benjamin Arbib; Tamara Arbib.

OTHER INFORMATION In 2019/20 the trust awarded grants totalling £447,700 to 26 organisations.

HOW TO APPLY The trust was not accepting unsolicited applications at the time of writing (March 2021). Visit the foundation's website for more information.

CONTACT DETAILS The Trustees, 61 Grosvenor Street, London W1K 3JE *Tel.* 020 3011 1100 *Email* info@ateamfoundation.org *Website* www.ateamfoundation.org

A. W. Charitable Trust

CC NO 283322 **ESTABLISHED** 1961

WHERE FUNDING CAN BE GIVEN London, Gateshead, Manchester and Salford; Israel.

WHO CAN BENEFIT Registered charities.

WHAT IS FUNDED Orthodox Jewish causes; social welfare.

SAMPLE GRANTS Previous beneficiaries have included: Asser Bishvil Foundation; Beenstock Home; British Friends of Kupat Ha'ir; Chevras Oneg Shabbos-Yomtov; Friends of Mir; Purim Fund; Toimchei Shabbos Manchester; Zoreya Tzedokos.

FINANCES *Financial year end* 30/06/2019 *Income* £17,770,000 *Total grants* £830,000 *Grants to organisations* £830,000 *Assets* £201,520,000

TRUSTEES Rabbi Aubrey Weis; Rachel Weis; Sir Weis.

OTHER INFORMATION The 2018/19 accounts were the latest available at the time of writing (June 2021).

HOW TO APPLY Contact the correspondent for further information.

CONTACT DETAILS Rabbi Aubrey Weis, Trustee, 66 Waterpark Road, Manchester M7 4JL *Tel.* 0161 740 0116

The Aaronson Foundation

CC NO 1159385 **ESTABLISHED** 2014

WHERE FUNDING CAN BE GIVEN UK and overseas.

WHO CAN BENEFIT Charitable organisations.

WHAT IS FUNDED General charitable purposes; education and training; health and medical research; social welfare; the Jewish religion.

RANGE OF GRANTS Up to £150,000.

SAMPLE GRANTS Netivei Itzhak (£148,000); Lev Chana Synagogue (£19,500); The Jewish Book Trust UK (£6,500).

FINANCES *Financial year end* 31/07/2019 *Income* £163,500 *Total grants* £210,600 *Grants to organisations* £210,600 *Assets* £122,000

TRUSTEES David Rodney; Michael Aaronson.

OTHER INFORMATION Grants were distributed as follows: education (£196,300); medical research (£10,100); social welfare (£7,000). Beneficiaries in receipt of less than £5,000 were not listed. The 2018/19 accounts were the latest available at the time of writing (February 2021).

HOW TO APPLY Contact the correspondent for further information.

CONTACT DETAILS The Trustees, First Floor, Winston House, 349 Regents Park Road, London N3 1DH *Tel.* 020 3411 2001 *Email* LFAFoundation@citroenwells.co.uk

■ The Abbeyfield Research Foundation

CC NO 1167685 **ESTABLISHED** 2016

WHERE FUNDING CAN BE GIVEN UK.

WHO CAN BENEFIT Organisations, mainly universities.

WHAT IS FUNDED Research relating to the quality of life and provision of care for older people.

WHAT IS NOT FUNDED Research using animals.

TYPE OF GRANT PhD studentships; project costs.

RANGE OF GRANTS PhD studentships of up to £30,000 per year; small project grants of up to £50,000 per year; pump-priming grants of up to £20,000 for one year.

SAMPLE GRANTS University of York (£120,900); University of the West of England Bristol (£65,900); University of the West of Scotland (£63,800); University of West London (£19,400).

FINANCES *Financial year end* 31/03/2020 *Income* £354,500 *Total grants* £269,900 *Grants to organisations* £269,900 *Assets* £39,600

TRUSTEES Prof. Brian Williams; Prof. Cameron Swift; Keith Fowler; Kenneth Staveley; Robin Means.

OTHER INFORMATION In 2019 the foundation made grants to four organisations, all of which were universities. Research priorities for the year are highlighted on the foundation's website.

HOW TO APPLY The foundation invites applications annually, typically in October. Application forms can be downloaded from the foundation's website and returned via email. Successful applicants at stage one are invited to complete a second stage.

CONTACT DETAILS The Trustees, St Peter's House, 2 Bricket Road, St Albans, Hertfordshire AL1 3JW *Tel.* 01727 734067 *Email* research@abbeyfield.com *Website* www.abbeyfieldresearchfoundation.org

■ The Aberbrothock Skea Trust

OSCR NO SC039202 **ESTABLISHED** 2007

WHERE FUNDING CAN BE GIVEN East of Scotland, north of the Firth of Tay.

WHO CAN BENEFIT Charitable organisations.

WHAT IS FUNDED General charitable purposes, including: health; children and young people; wildlife; the armed forces.

TYPE OF GRANT Typically one-off grants.

RANGE OF GRANTS Mostly under £5,000.

SAMPLE GRANTS Patrick Allan-Fraser of Hospitalfield Trust (£25,000); Kettins Parish Hall (£5,000).

FINANCES *Financial year end* 31/01/2020 *Income* £153,900 *Total grants* £146,800 *Grants to organisations* £146,800 *Assets* £4,910,000

OTHER INFORMATION Beneficiaries of grants of under £5,000 are not listed.

HOW TO APPLY Apply in writing to the correspondent. The trustees meet to consider grants in March, August and December.

CONTACT DETAILS The Trustees, c/o Thorntons Law LLP, Brothockbank House, Arbroath, Angus DD11 1NE

■ The Aberdeen Foundation

CC NO 1151506 **ESTABLISHED** 2013

WHERE FUNDING CAN BE GIVEN UK and overseas.

WHO CAN BENEFIT Charitable organisations.

WHAT IS FUNDED Jewish causes; education and training; health; social welfare; general charitable purposes.

RANGE OF GRANTS Typically up to £1 million.

SAMPLE GRANTS Yedidut Toronto (£6.82 million); Career 21 (£899,700); Colegio Maimonides (£638,800); Encyclopedia Talmudit (£573,000); Friedberg Economic Institute (£221,800); Harchavat Hamaagalim (£181,800); Vehechezakta (£86,600).

FINANCES *Financial year end* 31/03/2020 *Income* £774,500 *Total grants* £9,390,000 *Grants to organisations* £9,390,000 *Assets* £27,720,000

TRUSTEES Chaya Spitz; Albert Friedberg; Nancy Friedberg; Paul Staszewski; Shraga Zaltzman; Michael Shumacher.

OTHER INFORMATION In 2019/20 the foundation made grants of over £54,000 to eight organisations; beneficiaries below this amount were not listed. Grants were distributed as follows: education (£5.58 million); health (£3.17 million); social welfare (£641,800). The financial information has been converted from USD using the exchange rate at the time of writing (March 2021).

HOW TO APPLY Unsolicited applications are not accepted.

CONTACT DETAILS The Trustees, New Burlington House, 1075 Finchley Road, London NW11 0PU *Email* aberdeenfoundation@gmail.com

■ ABF The Soldiers' Charity

CC NO 1146420 **ESTABLISHED** 1944

WHERE FUNDING CAN BE GIVEN UK and overseas.

WHO CAN BENEFIT Parental regimental or corps associations dealing with former soldiers; charitable organisations with a preference for members of COBSEO/Veterans Scotland; other not-for-profit organisations; community projects; housing associations.

WHAT IS FUNDED Support for British Army soldiers, veterans and their immediate families. This includes: welfare; employment, education and training; care of older people; housing; disability; well-being.

WHAT IS NOT FUNDED Organisations that do not support serving soldiers, veterans and their immediate families, and/or the wider Army community; funding requests made within 12 months of the outcome of a previous application; gap years, study trips, fundraising expeditions or sponsorship; specific posts and salaries (however, the trustees will consider contributing to an organisation's core operating costs); full cost recovery; multi-year grants; umbrella organisations.

TYPE OF GRANT Core/revenue costs; seed funding/start-up funding; unrestricted funding.

RANGE OF GRANTS Up to £150,000.

SAMPLE GRANTS Erskine Hospital (£150,000); Care for Veterans – Queen Alexandra Hospital Home (£69,300) Regular Forces Employment Association (£60,000); SSAFA Central Office (£50,000); CAIS – Change Step (£45,000); Victory Services Club (£35,000); Poppy Scotland (£25,000); Forces in the Community (£10,000).

FINANCES *Financial year end* 31/03/2020 *Income* £14,710,000 *Total grants* £5,860,000 *Grants to organisations* £5,860,000 *Assets* £77,870,000

TRUSTEES Simon Newton Heale; Amanda Metcalfe; Anthony Scott; Mary Fagan; Maj. Gen. Malcolm Wood; David London; Simon Martin; Lt. Gen. Philip Jones; Paul Hearn; James Rous; Maj. Gen. Neil Sexton; Lisa Worley; Rachel Booth; Rowena Fell; Gavin Paton.

HOW TO APPLY Application forms are available from the charity's website and should be returned by email to externalgrants@soldierscharity.org.

Application deadlines can be found on the funder's website.

CONTACT DETAILS The Trustees, Mountbarrow House, 6–20 Elizabeth Street, London SW1W 9RB *Tel.* 020 7901 8900 *Email* externalgrants@soldierscharity.org *Website* www.soldierscharity.org

■ The Acacia Charitable Trust

CC NO 274275 **ESTABLISHED** 1977

WHERE FUNDING CAN BE GIVEN UK.

WHO CAN BENEFIT Registered charities.

WHAT IS FUNDED Arts and culture; community and welfare; overseas aid; health and disability; education; the environment; Jewish causes.

WHAT IS NOT FUNDED Grants are not awarded for individuals.

TYPE OF GRANT Core and project costs will be considered.

RANGE OF GRANTS From £100 to £36,000.

SAMPLE GRANTS Jewish Museum (£36,000); World Jewish Relief (£6,500); Spanish and Portuguese Jews' Synagogue (£4,500); Jewish Care (£3,000); Magen David Adom UK, Nightingale Hammerson and St John's Hospice (£2,000 each); Great Ormond Street Hospital Children's Charity and The Wiener Holocaust Library (£500); North London Hospice (£200); The Autism Group, The Mount Camphill Community Ltd and The Society of Recorder Players (£100 each).

FINANCES *Financial year end* 05/04/2019 *Income* £80,000 *Total grants* £61,400 *Grants to organisations* £61,400 *Assets* £1,780,000

TRUSTEES Angela Rubens; Simon Rubens; Paul Rubens.

OTHER INFORMATION The 2018/19 accounts were the latest available at the time of writing (June 2021). A total of 47 grants were awarded to organisations.

HOW TO APPLY Contact the correspondent for further information.

CONTACT DETAILS The Trustees, c/o H. W Fisher and Company, Acre House, 11–15 William Road, London NW1 3ER *Tel.* 020 7486 1884 *Email* acacia@dircon.co.uk

■ Access Sport CIO

CC NO 1156819 **ESTABLISHED** 2004

WHERE FUNDING CAN BE GIVEN UK, in practice: London, Bristol, Manchester and Oxford.

WHO CAN BENEFIT Sports clubs; registered charities.

WHAT IS FUNDED Improving access to sport for young people in disadvantaged communities, with a strong emphasis on supporting young people with disabilities.

TYPE OF GRANT Project costs.

SAMPLE GRANTS A list of beneficiaries was not included in the annual report and accounts.

FINANCES *Financial year end* 31/03/2019 *Income* £1,260,000 *Total grants* £205,000 *Grants to organisations* £205,000 *Assets* £617,600

TRUSTEES Martin McPhee; David Ascott; Christine Gibbons; Mandans Pour; John Baker; Nichola Janvier; Mark Burgess; Paul Lee.

OTHER INFORMATION The 2018/19 accounts were the latest available at the time of writing (June 2021). Support is given through three core programmes: Making Trax Cycling Inclusion Programme (formerly known as BMX Legacy Programme), Social Inclusion Programme and Ignite Programme. See the charity's website for details.

HOW TO APPLY Contact information and details on how to apply for each of the charity's current projects can be found on the website.

CONTACT DETAILS The Trustees, 3 Durham Yard, Teesdale Street, London E2 6QF *Tel.* 020 7993 9883 *Email* info@accesssport.co.uk *Website* www.accesssport.org.uk

■ The Access to Justice Foundation

CC NO 1126147 **ESTABLISHED** 2008

WHERE FUNDING CAN BE GIVEN UK.

WHO CAN BENEFIT Legal advice charities.

WHAT IS FUNDED The provision of legal assistance to people in need.

SAMPLE GRANTS Support Through Court (£540,400); RCJ Advice (£436,500); Suffolk Law Centre (£60,000); Law Centres Network (£15,000); Citizens Advice – York (£1,100).

FINANCES *Financial year end* 31/12/2019 *Income* £2,440,000 *Total grants* £1,910,000 *Grants to organisations* £1,910,000 *Assets* £494,700

TRUSTEES Lance Ashworth; Nicola Sawford; Rebecca Samaras; Frances Edwards; Alice Coping; Jeffrey Forrest; Andrew Seager; Lord Goldsmith; Natalie Rymaszewska; Toby Brown; Joe Snape; Audrey Haaxman; Dame Janet Smith; Sarah Stephens; Laurance Harris.

HOW TO APPLY Visit the foundation's website for the latest information on funding opportunities.

CONTACT DETAILS The Trustees, PO Box 64162, London WC2A 9AN *Tel.* 020 7092 3973 *Email* enquiries@atjf.org.uk *Website* https://atjf.org.uk

■ Action Medical Research

CC NO 208701 **ESTABLISHED** 1952

WHERE FUNDING CAN BE GIVEN UK.

WHO CAN BENEFIT University departments, hospitals and research institutes.

WHAT IS FUNDED Medical research focusing on child health including research into premature birth, cerebral palsy, childhood infections, juvenile arthritis, leukaemia and other rare conditions. Research into medical engineering is also supported.

WHAT IS NOT FUNDED A full list of exclusions can be found on the charity's website.

TYPE OF GRANT Project funding; research training fellowships.

RANGE OF GRANTS Up to £250,000.

SAMPLE GRANTS University College London and University of Manchester (£250,000 each); Brunel University – London (£205,300); Swansea University (£164,700); University of Oxford (£148,200); University of Cambridge (£138,100); University NHS Trust – London (£107,900); King's College London (£57,800).

FINANCES *Financial year end* 31/12/2019 *Income* £5,610,000 *Total grants* £2,250,000 *Grants to organisations* £2,250,000 *Assets* £6,050,000

TRUSTEES Richard Stoneham-Buck; Philip Hodkinson; Kathy Harvey; Prof. David Edwards; Esther Alderson; Karen Last; Prof. David Rowitch; Sarah Bray; Richard Wild; Luck Batchelor Bordewich.

HOW TO APPLY Full details of applying for both project and research grants are given on the charity's website along with current closing dates.

CONTACT DETAILS The Trustees, Vincent House, 31 North Parade, Horsham, West Sussex RH12 2DP *Tel.* 01403 210406 *Email* info@action.org.uk *Website* www.action.org.uk

■ Adam Family Foundation

OSCR NO SC046468 **ESTABLISHED** 2016

WHERE FUNDING CAN BE GIVEN Scotland, mainly Moray.

WHO CAN BENEFIT Charitable organisations.

WHAT IS FUNDED Community facilities; community development; social welfare; homelessness and housing; education; sport; the arts; older people; children and young people.

SAMPLE GRANTS A list of beneficiaries was not included in the 2019/20 annual report and accounts.

FINANCES *Financial year end* 30/04/2020 *Income* £175,000 *Total grants* £199,100 *Grants to organisations* £199,100 *Assets* £39,300

HOW TO APPLY Contact the correspondent for further information.

CONTACT DETAILS The Trustees, 10 Southfield Drive, Elgin IV30 6GR

■ The Sylvia Adams Charitable Trust

CC NO 1050678 **ESTABLISHED** 1995

WHERE FUNDING CAN BE GIVEN England and Wales.

WHO CAN BENEFIT Registered charities; unregistered charities; CICs; social enterprises.

WHAT IS FUNDED Projects improving the life chances of disadvantaged 0–3 year olds in England and Wales; work supporting and informing families and communities affected by genetic conditions, particularly autosomal recessive conditions.

TYPE OF GRANT Capital costs; core/revenue costs; seed/start-up funding; project funding; unrestricted funding. Funding available for up to three years.

RANGE OF GRANTS Up to £50,000.

SAMPLE GRANTS Nofas UK (£120,000); Cued Speech Association UK (£50,000); Child Dynamix (£35,100); Growing Together Northampton (£25,700); Plymouth Music Zone (£15,000); Minority Rights Group International (£9,000); Special Stars Foundation (£3,000); Birmingham Royal Ballet (£1,000).

FINANCES *Financial year end* 31/03/2020 *Income* £241,900 *Total grants* £972,800 *Grants to organisations* £972,800 *Assets* £3,120,000

TRUSTEES Matthew McBryde; Alexandra Butler; Anthony Copsey.

OTHER INFORMATION Grants were made to 52 organisations during the year. The trust is currently in the process of winding down and anticipates that by March 2023 it will have spent out its assets.

HOW TO APPLY Priority will be given to charities the trust has already supported; however, the website states that the trustees will consider supporting new organisations through its Breaking Down Barriers programme (aimed at supporting people with genetic conditions). See the website for further information.

CONTACT DETAILS Jane Young, Director, PO Box 599, Welwyn, Hertfordshire AL7 9QB *Tel.* 07775 793432 *Email* info@sylvia-adams.org.uk *Website* www.sylvia-adams.org.uk

■ The Bryan Adams Foundation

CC NO 1117863 **ESTABLISHED** 2006

WHERE FUNDING CAN BE GIVEN UK; overseas.

WHO CAN BENEFIT Registered charities.

WHAT IS FUNDED Education of children and young people; older people; animal welfare; conservation; disaster relief; museums and galleries; recreational facilities; health; medical research.

TYPE OF GRANT Capital costs; project funding; research.

RANGE OF GRANTS Mostly £1,000 to £5,000.

SAMPLE GRANTS Park Walk Primary School (£247,500); The Royal Foundation (£12,000); Big Issue Foundation (£10,000); VSPCA (£500).

FINANCES *Financial year end* 31/03/2020 *Income* £301,000 *Total grants* £304,000 *Grants to organisations* £304,000 *Assets* £354,400

TRUSTEES Bryan Adams; John Armitage; Rafi Manoukian; Alicia Grimaldi.

OTHER INFORMATION Grants were made to 12 organisations during the year.

HOW TO APPLY At the time of writing (March 2021) the foundation was closed for applications. Check the foundation's website for the latest information.

CONTACT DETAILS Alicia Grimaldi, Trustee, 8 Apollo Place, London SW10 0ET *Email* Foundation@bryanadams.com *Website* www.thebryanadamsfoundation.com

■ Adenfirst Ltd

CC NO 291647 **ESTABLISHED** 1984

WHERE FUNDING CAN BE GIVEN Worldwide.

WHO CAN BENEFIT Mainly Jewish organisations.

WHAT IS FUNDED Education, health, relief of poverty and the advancement of religion, with a preference for Jewish causes.

RANGE OF GRANTS Up to £100,000.

SAMPLE GRANTS Russian Immigrant Aid Fund Ltd (£102,000); Friends of Gur Foundation Israel (£29,000); Yeshivas Lev Simcha Ltd (£16,000); Society Friends of the Torah Ltd (£14,000).

FINANCES *Financial year end* 31/12/2019 *Income* £294,100 *Total grants* £172,600 *Grants to organisations* £172,600 *Assets* £5,270,000

TRUSTEES Sarah Heitner; Leonard Bondi; Allan Becker; Chaim Friedmann; Sylvia Cymerman; Michael Cymerman; Mrs H. F. Bondi; Ian Heitner.

HOW TO APPLY Contact the correspondent for further information.

CONTACT DETAILS Mrs H. F. Bondi, Company Secretary, c/o 479 Holloway Road, London N7 6LE *Tel.* 020 7272 2255 *Email* mail@cohenarnold.com

■ The Adint Charitable Trust

CC NO 265290 **ESTABLISHED** 1973

WHERE FUNDING CAN BE GIVEN UK.

WHO CAN BENEFIT Registered charities.

WHAT IS FUNDED General charitable purposes, with a preference for: health and health research, social welfare, disability, housing and homelessness.

WHAT IS NOT FUNDED Individuals.

TYPE OF GRANT Capital costs; core/revenue costs; project funding; unrestricted funding.

RANGE OF GRANTS Typically £5,000 to £10,000.

SAMPLE GRANTS PM Trust (£20,000); Alzheimer's Society, St Mary-le-Bow Young Homeless

Charity, Starlight Children's Foundation and The Hospital of St John and St Elizabeth (£10,000); Age UK, Meningitis Research Foundation and Thomas Coram Foundation for Children (£5,000).

FINANCES *Financial year end* 05/04/2020 *Income* £193,400 *Total grants* £300,000 *Grants to organisations* £300,000 *Assets* £7,800,000

TRUSTEES Anthony Edwards; Douglas Oram; Brian Pate; Claire Edwards.

OTHER INFORMATION The trust made grants to 41 organisations in 2019/20.

HOW TO APPLY Apply in writing to the correspondent, including full details of the charity for which the funding is requested. Unsuccessful applicants will not be notified.

CONTACT DETAILS The Trustees, Suite 512, 571 Finchley Road, London NW3 7BN *Email* adintct@btinternet.com

■ The Adlard Family Charitable Foundation

CC NO 1164276 **ESTABLISHED** 2015

WHERE FUNDING CAN BE GIVEN Worldwide, predominantly England and Wales.

WHO CAN BENEFIT Charitable organisations.

WHAT IS FUNDED General charitable purposes; the environment, conservation and heritage.

RANGE OF GRANTS £1,000 to £30,000.

SAMPLE GRANTS The Greenpeace Environmental Trust (£55,000 in two grants); Ellesmore College and International Fund for Animal Welfare (£10,000 each); Cartoon Art Museum of California (£5,300); Leeds Comic Festival (£5,000); RNLI (£2,000); Pentabus Theatre Company and The Wales Air Ambulance Service (£1,000 each).

FINANCES *Financial year end* 09/09/2019 *Income* £54,100 *Total grants* £111,300 *Grants to organisations* £111,300 *Assets* £157,700

TRUSTEES Ludlow Trust Company Ltd; Charles Adlard; Elsa Adlard.

OTHER INFORMATION The 2018/19 accounts were the latest available at the time of writing (June 2021). During the year, the foundation awarded 14 grants to charitable organisations.

HOW TO APPLY Apply in writing to the correspondent. The trustees meet regularly to consider grants.

CONTACT DETAILS The Trustees, 1st Floor, Tower Wharf, Cheese Lane, Bristol BS2 0JJ *Tel.* 0117 313 8200 *Email* charitabletrusts@ludlowtrust.com

■ The AEB Charitable Trust

OSCR NO SC028858 **ESTABLISHED** 1998

WHERE FUNDING CAN BE GIVEN Scotland with a preference for the Lothian and Borders regions.

WHO CAN BENEFIT Registered charities; galleries; museums; hospitals; universities.

WHAT IS FUNDED Wildlife, ecology and nature; health, particularly research into and treatment of Alzheimer's and the care of the elderly; museums and galleries; music and the arts; emergency services and the armed forces.

WHAT IS NOT FUNDED Individuals.

TYPE OF GRANT Research costs; project funding; core/revenue costs. One-off and multi-year grants.

RANGE OF GRANTS Mostly £1,000 to £10,000. Larger grants are available in limited circumstances at the trustees' discretion.

SAMPLE GRANTS University of Aberdeen Development Trust and Horatio's Garden (£20,000 each); Hearts and Minds (£10,000); The Royal (Dick) School of Veterinary Studies (£8,250); National Galleries of Scotland Foundation and War Memorials Trust (£5,000); Euan's Guide and The National Trust for Scotland (£3,000); Butterfly Conservation Trust (£2,000).

FINANCES *Financial year end* 31/03/2020 *Income* £117,000 *Total grants* £114,500 *Grants to organisations* £114,500 *Assets* £2,350,000

OTHER INFORMATION In 2019/20, grants were distributed as follows: health (£65,300); arts, museums and historic sites (£26,000); wildlife and nature (£18,300); elderly and retired people (£5,000).

HOW TO APPLY Apply in writing or via email to the correspondent by the deadline stated on the trust's website (typically in November). The trustees meet once a year in spring and normally pay grants prior to 31 March.

CONTACT DETAILS The Trustees, c/o Turcan Connell, Princes Exchange, 1 Earl Grey Street, Edinburgh EH3 9EE *Tel.* 0131 228 8111 *Email* enquiries@turcanconnell.com *Website* https://www.turcanconnell.com/the-aeb-charitable-trust

■ The AIM Foundation

CC NO 263294 **ESTABLISHED** 1971

WHERE FUNDING CAN BE GIVEN UK.

WHO CAN BENEFIT Charitable organisations.

WHAT IS FUNDED Nutrition for health and well-being; children and young people; the environment.

TYPE OF GRANT Revenue grants: core costs and salaries; campaigning and research.

RANGE OF GRANTS Mostly between £1,000 and £25,000.

SAMPLE GRANTS Impetus-PEF (£50,000); Nutritank (£35,000); The Wave Trust (£25,000); College of Medicine (£10,000); British Red Cross (£1,000).

FINANCES *Financial year end* 31/08/2020 *Income* £394,600 *Total grants* £773,300 *Grants to organisations* £773,300 *Assets* £11,310,000

TRUSTEES Philippa Bailey; Caroline Marks; Nicholas Marks; Joanna Precious; Angela Marks.

HOW TO APPLY The foundation is 'highly proactive' in seeking out potential partners and does not accept unsolicited applications.

CONTACT DETAILS The Trustees, PKF Francis Clark, Peninsula Park, Centenary House, Rydon Lane, Exeter, Devon EX2 7XE *Tel.* 01392 667000 *Email* info@francisclark.co.uk

■ The Aimwell Charitable Trust

CC NO 1039415 **ESTABLISHED** 1994

WHERE FUNDING CAN BE GIVEN UK and overseas.

WHO CAN BENEFIT Charitable organisations; educational organisations.

WHAT IS FUNDED Education; social welfare; health; community development and services; Jewish causes.

TYPE OF GRANT Research.

RANGE OF GRANTS Mostly up to £50,000.

SAMPLE GRANTS British Friends of the Hebrew University (£249,600); Portland Trust (£155,400); Community Security Trust (£100,000); Jewish Care and Kessler Foundation (£50,000).

FINANCES *Financial year end* 31/03/2020
Income £350,300 *Total grants* £945,500
Grants to organisations £945,500
Assets £13,860,000

TRUSTEES Isaac Kaye; Steven Kaye; Geoffrey Jayson; Warren Roiter; Craig Cowan.

OTHER INFORMATION Grants were awarded to 42 organisations in 2019/20. Only the five beneficiaries receiving more than £50,000 were listed in the annual report.

HOW TO APPLY Contact the correspondent for further information.

CONTACT DETAILS Geoffrey Jayson, Trustee, c/o Baystone Associates, 3rd Floor, 52 Conduit Street, London W1S 2YX *Tel.* 020 7317 8980 *Email* geoffrey@jaysonconsulting.co.uk

■ The Aitken Family Charitable Trust

CC NO 1168153 **ESTABLISHED** 2016

WHERE FUNDING CAN BE GIVEN England and Wales.

WHO CAN BENEFIT Charities; educational organisations; hospitals.

WHAT IS FUNDED General charitable purposes; education.

RANGE OF GRANTS Up to £100,000.

SAMPLE GRANTS Chelsea and Westminster Hospital (£100,000); St Paul's Girls' School Bursary Fund (£50,000); St Anne's College Oxford (£30,000); First Story (£15,000).

FINANCES *Financial year end* 16/02/2020
Income £915,300 *Total grants* £195,000
Grants to organisations £195,000
Assets £619,200

TRUSTEES Katharine Aitken; Peter Aitken; Anna Aitken; Jane Aitken; Alexandra Aitken; Lucy Aitken; Coutts & Co.

OTHER INFORMATION During 2019/20, grants were made to four organisations.

HOW TO APPLY Apply by letter to the correspondent

CONTACT DETAILS The Trustees, Coutts & Co. Trustee Department, 1st Floor, Trinity Quay 1, Avon Street, Bristol BS2 0PT *Tel.* 0345 304 2424

■ Sylvia Aitken's Charitable Trust

OSCR NO SC010556 **ESTABLISHED** 1985

WHERE FUNDING CAN BE GIVEN UK, with a preference for Scotland.

WHO CAN BENEFIT Charitable organisations.

WHAT IS FUNDED Medical research; children and young people; older people; the environment; wildlife and animals; education; culture and religion; disability; social welfare.

SAMPLE GRANTS Previous beneficiaries have included: Association for International Cancer Research; Barn Owl Trust; British Lung Foundation; British Stammering Association; Disabled Living Foundation; Epilepsy Research Trust; Friends of the Lake District; Motor Neurone Disease Association; Network for Surviving Stalking; Royal Scots Dragoon Guards Museum Trust; Roy Castle Lung Cancer Foundation; Scottish Child Psychotherapy Trust; Sense Scotland; Tall Ships Youth Trust; Tenovus Scotland; Wood Green Animal Shelters; YoungMinds.

FINANCES *Financial year end* 05/04/2020
Income £68,100 *Total grants* £185,500
Grants to organisations £185,500
Assets £1,370,000

HOW TO APPLY Contact the correspondent for further information.

CONTACT DETAILS The Trustees, c/o Fergusons Chartered Accountants, 24 Woodside, Houston, Renfrewshire PA6 7DD

■ Ajahma Charitable Trust

CC NO 273823 **ESTABLISHED** 1977

WHERE FUNDING CAN BE GIVEN UK and overseas.

WHO CAN BENEFIT Registered charities.

WHAT IS FUNDED General charitable purposes including: health, welfare and human rights.

RANGE OF GRANTS £12,000 to £60,000.

SAMPLE GRANTS Afghanaid (£150,000); African Prisons Project, Farm Africa and Transparency International (£60,000 each); Camden Carers Centre, Hillingdon Carers Centres and North London Cares (£12,000 each); Redbridge Carers Support Centre (£9,000).

FINANCES *Financial year end* 30/09/2019
Income £27,000 *Total grants* £552,100
Grants to organisations £552,100
Assets £1,360,000

TRUSTEES Roger Paffard; Prof. Elizabeth Simpson; Jenny Sheridan; James Taylor; Carole Pound.

OTHER INFORMATION The 2018/19 accounts were the latest available at the time of writing (June 2021). Grants were made to 14 organisations during the year.

HOW TO APPLY The trust's 2018/19 annual report states: 'The trustees have adopted a policy of seeking and considering applications for charitable funding generally from established charities. They seek to maintain a reasonable balance between charitable activities overseas and in the United Kingdom.'

CONTACT DETAILS Suzanne Hunt, Administrator, 275 Dover House Road, London SW15 5BP *Tel.* 020 8788 5388

■ AKO Foundation

CC NO 1151815 **ESTABLISHED** 2013

WHERE FUNDING CAN BE GIVEN England; Germany; Denmark; Norway; Sri Lanka; USA.

WHO CAN BENEFIT Registered charities.

WHAT IS FUNDED Education; the arts.

RANGE OF GRANTS Typically between £8,000 and £1 million.

SAMPLE GRANTS AKO Kunststiftelse (£11.9 million); Foundation to Educate Girls Globally (£2.4 million); Hampstead Theatre (£304,000); British Museum (£410,000); FareShare (£80,000); Turner Contemporary (£50,000); Little Sun Foundation (£29,600); Moderna Museet (£8,300).

FINANCES *Financial year end* 31/12/2019
Income £49,970,000
Total grants £27,000,000
Grants to organisations £27,000,000
Assets £120,510,000

TRUSTEES David Woodburn; Henrik Syse; Sally Procopis.

OTHER INFORMATION Over 38 grants were made during the year and were distributed as follows: art (£13.1 million); education (£10.1 million); climate change (£3.2 million); AKO Give Back Initiative (£340,000); Local projects (£312,900).

HOW TO APPLY Unsolicited applications are not accepted.

CONTACT DETAILS The Trustees, c/o Ako Capital LLP, 61 Conduit Street, London W1S 2GB *Tel.* 020 7070 2400 *Email* akofoundation@akocapital.com *Website* https://www.akofoundation.org

■ The Alborada Trust

CC NO 1091660 **ESTABLISHED** 2001

WHERE FUNDING CAN BE GIVEN UK and overseas.

WHO CAN BENEFIT Charitable organisations; universities; colleges.

WHAT IS FUNDED Medical and veterinary causes, research and education; health; welfare of animals; disaster relief; refugee aid.

WHAT IS NOT FUNDED Each funding stream has its own exclusions, see the trust's website for further information.

TYPE OF GRANT Research; general funding; revenue costs.

RANGE OF GRANTS Typically £25,000 to £500,000.

SAMPLE GRANTS Alzheimer's Research UK (£1 million); University of Cambridge – Africa Project (£500,000); Médecins Sans Frontières (£445,200); The Brooke Hospital for Animals (£251,800); Animal Health Trust (£100,000); RVC – Josh Slater (£58,400); The Horse Trust (£40,000); World Horse Welfare (£25,000); Unity Schools Partnership (£18,000); The Wavertree Charitable Trust (£10,000).

FINANCES *Financial year end* 31/12/2019 *Income* £10,110,000 *Total grants* £4,900,000 *Grants to organisations* £4,900,000 *Assets* (£4,880,000)

TRUSTEES Eva Rausing; James Nicholson; Roland Lerner; Robert Goff; Larry Pillard.

OTHER INFORMATION Grants were awarded to 36 organisations in 2019.

HOW TO APPLY Details of how to apply can be found on the trust's website. The trustees meet twice a year in April and December so completed applications should be received by March or November to make the agenda at the appropriate meetings.

CONTACT DETAILS Jeremy Richardson, Secretary, Lanwades Stud, Moulton, Newmarket, Suffolk CB8 8QS *Tel.* 01638 750222 *Email* secretary@alboradatrust.com *Website* www.alboradatrust.com

■ The Alchemy Foundation

CC NO 292500 **ESTABLISHED** 1985

WHERE FUNDING CAN BE GIVEN UK and overseas.

WHO CAN BENEFIT Community projects; voluntary organisations; registered charities.

WHAT IS FUNDED Disability (particularly mobility, access, helplines and communications); social welfare (inner city community projects, disaffected youth, family mediation, homelessness); penal reform (work with prisoners, especially young prisoners and their families); medical research and aid (especially in areas of 'blindness and disfigurement'); individual enterprise (by helping Raleigh International and similar organisations to give opportunities to young people according to need); respite for carers; water projects in the financially developing world. The foundation also delivers the Alchemist Scheme which funds the costs of fundraisers assigned to other charities to assist with their fundraising efforts.

TYPE OF GRANT Salaries; project funding; medical research.

SAMPLE GRANTS A list of beneficiaries was not included in the annual report and accounts.

FINANCES *Financial year end* 05/04/2020 *Income* £244,400 *Total grants* £566,200 *Grants to organisations* £552,500 *Assets* £1,520,000

TRUSTEES Dr Jemima Stilgoe; Holly Stilgoe; Jack Stilgoe; Rufus Stilgoe; Sir Richard Stilgoe; Alexander Armitage; Andrew Murison; Lady Annabel Stilgoe; Joseph Stilgoe; Antoun Elias; Caroline Pedley.

OTHER INFORMATION During the year, the foundation awarded 604 grants, distributed as follows: inner city community projects (£165,600); The Alchemist Scheme (£165,600); disability (£100,700); other (£45,400); respite for carers (£24,700); penal reform (£20,700); individuals on behalf of registered charities (£13,700); medical research and aid (£9,400) and water projects (£500).

HOW TO APPLY Contact the correspondent for further information.

CONTACT DETAILS The Trustees, Trevereux Manor, Trevereux Hill, Limpsfield Chart, Oxted, Surrey RH8 0TL

■ The Aldama Foundation

CC NO 1126791 **ESTABLISHED** 2008

WHERE FUNDING CAN BE GIVEN UK and overseas.

WHO CAN BENEFIT Charitable organisations.

WHAT IS FUNDED Social welfare; education; health; citizenship and community development; arts, culture, heritage or science; amateur sport; environmental protection or improvement.

RANGE OF GRANTS Typically up to £25,000.

SAMPLE GRANTS John Paul II Foundation for Sport and SAVE (£30,000 each over three years); National Gallery (£25,000); Royal College of Music (£24,000 over two years); Sussex Community Foundation and World Monuments Fund (£10,000 each); AIDS Ark (£5,000); Garden Museum (£700).

FINANCES *Financial year end* 05/04/2020 *Income* £68,400 *Total grants* £346,000 *Grants to organisations* £346,000 *Assets* £5,100,000

TRUSTEE The Dickinson Trust Ltd.

OTHER INFORMATION During the year, grants were distributed in the following areas: art, culture, heritage or science (£223,400); health and saving lives (£81,600); social welfare (£12,500); education (£10,800); citizenship/community development (£10,000); relief of poverty (£7,700). In previous years, the foundation has also awarded grants for amateur sport and the environment.

HOW TO APPLY Contact the correspondent for further information.

CONTACT DETAILS The Trustee, 4th Floor, 10 Bruton Street, London W1J 6PX *Tel.* 020 7907 2100 *Email* charity@mfs.co.uk

■ Aldgate and Allhallows Foundation

CC NO 312500 **ESTABLISHED** 1893

WHERE FUNDING CAN BE GIVEN City of London and the London Borough of Tower Hamlets.

WHO CAN BENEFIT Registered charities; schools; individuals.

WHAT IS FUNDED Education of children and young people. The foundation can only consider applications for education projects that will benefit children or young people who are: under the age of 30, residents of Tower Hamlets or the City of London, in full-time education or studying for a recognised qualification, and from disadvantaged backgrounds or areas of high deprivation.

WHAT IS NOT FUNDED Equipment or teachers' salaries that are the responsibility of statutory authorities; youth groups; supplementary schools or mother tongue teaching; the purchase, repair or furnishing of buildings; conferences or seminars; stage, film, publication or video production costs; performances or exhibitions; retrospective requests (i.e. any activity that has already taken place); requests to substitute for the withdrawal or reduction of statutory funding; general fundraising campaigns or appeals.

TYPE OF GRANT Project funding.

RANGE OF GRANTS £10,000 to £60,000.

SAMPLE GRANTS Hermitage Primary School (£60,000); Magic Me (£35,000); The Brilliant Club (£15,000); Sound Connections, Shadwell Basin Outdoor Activity Centre, London Symphony Orchestra and Clio's Company (£10,000 each).

FINANCES *Financial year end* 31/12/2019 *Income* £226,800 *Total grants* £228,800 *Grants to organisations* £193,800 *Assets* £8,550,000

TRUSTEES Cllr Denise Jones; David Mash; Robin Hazlewood; John Hall; William Hamilton-Hinds; Marianne Fredericks; Billy Whitbread; Susan Knowles; Cllr Sirajul Islam; Kevin Everett; Col Michael O'Dwyer; Revd Laura Jørgensen.

OTHER INFORMATION During 2019 there were 15 grants made to organisations totalling £193,800 and 28 grants made to individuals totalling £35,000.

HOW TO APPLY Initial enquiries should be made to the foundation. Full details of what information to include can be found on the website. Applications can be submitted throughout the year. There is no closing date, but applications must be received in good time before the next trustees' meeting. Decisions are made twice a year, in April and September.

CONTACT DETAILS Richard Foley, Clerk to the Governors (Chief Executive), 31 Jewry Street, London EC3N 2EY *Tel.* 07787 371761 *Email* aldgateandallhallows@sirjohncass.org *Website* www.aldgateallhallows.org.uk

■ Beryl Alexander Charity

CC NO 1179895 **ESTABLISHED** 2016

WHERE FUNDING CAN BE GIVEN England.

WHO CAN BENEFIT Registered charities.

WHAT IS FUNDED Mental health.

SAMPLE GRANTS Great Ormond Street Hospital Children's Charity: Psychological Well-being and Mental Health Drop-In Centre (£357,400).

FINANCES *Financial year end* 31/12/2019 *Income* £2,970,000 *Total grants* £357,400 *Grants to organisations* £357,400 *Assets* £2,590,000

TRUSTEES Joshua Alton; Jeremy Alton; Ruby Alton; Dr Stanley Lions.

HOW TO APPLY Contact the correspondent for further information.

CONTACT DETAILS The Trustees, 4 London Road, Stanmore, HA7 4NZ

■ Al-Fayed Charitable Foundation

CC NO 297114 **ESTABLISHED** 1987

WHERE FUNDING CAN BE GIVEN Mainly in the UK, but also worldwide.

WHO CAN BENEFIT Registered charities; schools; hospices; hospitals; medical centres; individuals.

WHAT IS FUNDED Disadvantaged children and children living with life-threatening illnesses. One-off grants are given to medical centres and individuals for specialist equipment. Grants are also given to support causes that transform the lives of maltreated and endangered animals.

TYPE OF GRANT Project funding; capital costs; core costs.

RANGE OF GRANTS Up to £120,000 but typically £1,000 to £90,000.

SAMPLE GRANTS Zoe's Place (£90,000); FACE for Children in Need and Imperial Health Charity (£50,000 each); Cancer Research UK (£14,000); World Animal Protection (£10,000); Nowzad Dogs (£5,000); English National Ballet (£3,400); Harrod's Ltd (£2,800).

FINANCES *Financial year end* 31/12/2019 *Income* £311,400 *Total grants* £329,700 *Grants to organisations* £329,700 *Assets* £75,600

TRUSTEES Mohamed Al-Fayed; Camilla Fayed; Heini Fayed; Omar Fayed.

OTHER INFORMATION During 2019, the foundation awarded 11 grants.

HOW TO APPLY Apply in writing to the correspondent via email or post. Include an sae if applying by post.

CONTACT DETAILS Charity Manager, 55 Park Lane, London W1K 1NA *Tel.* 020 7409 9350 *Email* acf@alfayed.com *Website* www.the-acf.com

■ AlixPartners (UK) Charitable Foundation

CC NO 1134913 **ESTABLISHED** 2010

WHERE FUNDING CAN BE GIVEN UK.

WHO CAN BENEFIT Registered charities.

WHAT IS FUNDED General charitable purposes.

RANGE OF GRANTS Up to £21,000.

SAMPLE GRANTS Birkbeck (£17,500); Legs4Africa (£15,100); Magic Breakfast (£10,000); Arnold Foundation for Rugby School (£2,000); NSPCC (£1,200); Heart of England Community Boxing Club (£1,000); Salvation Army (£500); Amnesty International (£150).

FINANCES *Financial year end* 31/03/2020 *Income* £99,000 *Total grants* £80,300 *Grants to organisations* £80,300 *Assets* £152,400

TRUSTEES Alastair Beveridge; Lindsey Hornby; Liam Colley; Paul Kelly; Mark Veldon.

OTHER INFORMATION Grants totalling £80,300 were made to 59 organisations during 2019/20.

HOW TO APPLY Contact the correspondent for further information.

CONTACT DETAILS The Trustees, AlixPartners, 6 New Street Square, London EC4A 3BF *Tel.* 020 7098 7400 *Email* fviti@alixpartners.com *Website* https://www.alixpartners.com/about-alixpartners

■ The All Saints Educational Trust

CC NO 312934 **ESTABLISHED** 1978

WHERE FUNDING CAN BE GIVEN UK and overseas.

WHO CAN BENEFIT Charities; educational organisations; individuals.

WHAT IS FUNDED Projects which support religious education or home economics teaching, or the development of education, in schools or in the community.

WHAT IS NOT FUNDED Salaries.

TYPE OF GRANT Project funding; multi-year.

RANGE OF GRANTS Up to £26,000.

SAMPLE GRANTS Bangor University (£26,000); Wesley's Chapel (£20,000); Faith in Media (£15,000); Canterbury Christ Church (£13,300); Bishop Grosseteste University (£8,400); Wulugu Project (£4,200); Priory School (£750).

FINANCES *Financial year end* 30/06/2020
Income £760,700 *Total grants* £7,700
Grants to organisations £5,500
Assets £12,140,000

TRUSTEES Dr Augur Pearce; Stephanie Valentine; Prof. Anthony Leeds; Revd Tim Elbourne; The Revd Dr Keith Riglin; Derek Holloway; Dorothy Garland; Allan Kanu; Frances Smith; Barbara Harvey; Stephen Brooker; Diane McCrea; Michael Jacob; Louise Davies; David Trillo.

OTHER INFORMATION Due to COVID-19, the trust suspended the making of new grants in the year 2020/21 for students and organisations, resulting in a low grant total. However, in the previous year grants to organisations totalled £978,400. According to its website, the trust is confident it will resume making grants during the 2021/22 academic year and potential applicants are advised to contact the Clerk to discuss their proposed projects.

HOW TO APPLY Application forms can be downloaded from the trust's website. Applicants are invited to discuss their ideas informally with the clerk before making an application. Completed applications are put before the awards committee in April/May, with final decisions made in June. Visit the website for current deadlines.

CONTACT DETAILS Mr K. D. Mitchell, Clerk to the Trustees, Knightrider House, 2 Knightrider Court, London EC4V 5AR *Tel.* 020 7248 8380 *Email* aset@aset.org.uk *Website* www.aset.org.uk

■ The Derrill Allatt Foundation

CC NO 1148440 **ESTABLISHED** 2012

WHERE FUNDING CAN BE GIVEN Worldwide.

WHO CAN BENEFIT Registered charities.

WHAT IS FUNDED Social welfare; social inclusion; health; training; the arts; animals.

RANGE OF GRANTS £100 to £50,000.

SAMPLE GRANTS Calvert Trust Exmoor (£50,800); Children on the Edge (£50,000); Hearings Dogs for Deaf People (£20,000); Oxford Lieder (£15,000); National Youth Choirs of Great Britain and Contemporary Applied Arts (£10,000 each); Central School of Ballet Charitable Trust (£8,000); Leonard Cheshire (£6,000); The Lunch People (£5,000); London Youth Choir (£3,000); Ballet Central – The Live Theatre Winchester Trust Ltd (£100).

FINANCES *Financial year end* 05/04/2019
Income £34,100 *Total grants* £390,200
Grants to organisations £390,200
Assets £687,700

TRUSTEES Diana Hargreaves; Clare Matthews; Payne Hicks Beach Trust Corporation Ltd.

OTHER INFORMATION The 2018/19 accounts were the latest available at the time of writing (June 2021). Grants were awarded to 24 organisations during the year.

HOW TO APPLY Unsolicited applications are not accepted.

CONTACT DETAILS The Trustees, Payne Hicks Beach, 10 New Square, Lincoln's Inn, London WC2A 3QG *Tel.* 020 7465 4300

■ Allchurches Trust Ltd

CC NO 263960 **ESTABLISHED** 1972

WHERE FUNDING CAN BE GIVEN UK and Ireland.

WHO CAN BENEFIT Registered charities; schools; hospitals; hospices; religious bodies/ organisations.

WHAT IS FUNDED The repair, restoration and protection of churches and Christian places of worship; social issues such as homelessness, poverty, climate change and cultural cohesion; promoting the Christian faith.

WHAT IS NOT FUNDED Overseas projects or charities; running costs except when assisting the launch of new or transformative projects; individuals or causes that will benefit only one person; healthcare projects, although hospices can apply for funding towards the provision of chapel and chaplaincy space; animal welfare or rescue; work that is primarily the responsibility of statutory authorities; retrospective grants; one-off events that benefit only a few people. A detailed list of exclusions can be found on the trust's website.

TYPE OF GRANT Capital costs; project funding.

RANGE OF GRANTS Most grants are £1,000 to £15,000 but larger grants are considered.

SAMPLE GRANTS Methodist Connexion (£910,000); The Diocese of London (£422,000); The Diocese of Leeds (£318,000); Just Finance Foundation (£250,000); Transforming Lives for Good (£178,000); Exeter Cathedral (£125,000); St Patrick's Cathedral, Dublin (£111,000); The Archbishops' Council, London (£61,000); The Representative Body of the Church in Wales (£15,000).

FINANCES *Financial year end* 31/12/2019
Income £38,980,000
Total grants £17,850,000
Grants to organisations £17,850,000
Assets £618,790,000

TRUSTEES Caroline Banszky; Sir Laurance Magnus; Canon Michael Arlington; Revd Jane Hedges Canon; Timothy Carroll; Steven Hudson; The Venerable Karen Lund; Chris Moulder; Sir Stephen Lamport; Revd Paul Davis.

OTHER INFORMATION The trust's income is derived from its wholly-owned subsidiary company Ecclesiastical Insurance Office plc.

HOW TO APPLY Applications should be submitted online via the trust's website. Applications can be submitted at any time.

CONTACT DETAILS Iain Hearn, Beaufort House, Brunswick Road, Gloucester, Gloucestershire GL1 1JZ *Tel.* 01452 873189 *Email* atl@allchurches.co.uk *Website* www.allchurches.co.uk

■ The Allen & Overy Foundation

CC NO 1153738 **ESTABLISHED** 2013

WHERE FUNDING CAN BE GIVEN London; UK; worldwide.

WHO CAN BENEFIT Registered charities.

WHAT IS FUNDED Disaster relief; access to justice; access to education, employment and training.

TYPE OF GRANT Project and core costs.

RANGE OF GRANTS Local grants programme: typically between £5,000 and £10,000. Global Grants Programme: typically £50,000.

SAMPLE GRANTS Hope and Homes for Children – the foundation's global charity partner 2018–2021 (£339,800); Equal Education Law Centre (£50,000); The Access to Justice Foundation and The London Community Foundation (£25,000 each); Islington People's Rights and Reach out Youth (£10,000 each); The Dash Charity (£5,000); Cambridge Cyrenians (£2,500); Syria Relief (£330).

FINANCES *Financial year end* 30/04/2020
Income £1,840,000 *Total grants* £1,450,000
Grants to organisations £1,450,000
Assets £679,700

TRUSTEES Mark Mansell; Andrew Wedderburn-Day; Philip Mansfield; Brendan Hannigan; Angela

Clist; Joanna Page; Hilde van der Bann; Mary Johnston; Franz Ranero.

OTHER INFORMATION This is the corporate charity of Allen & Overy LLP. There are two grant programmes: The Global Grants Programme which supports three or four charities each year under core themes; and the Local Charitable Giving (London) programme which supports projects that benefit people in Tower Hamlets and Hackney. The foundation also makes a large annual donation to its global charity partner. For further information on each grant programme see the foundation's helpful website.

HOW TO APPLY The Allen & Overy Foundation (London) – Application forms are available from the correspondent by email. Application guidelines are on the foundation's website, along with the next deadline. The committee meets to consider grants in March and October. Global Grants Programme – Applications should be made in a letter of no more than two pages – details of what to include are given on the website. Refer to the website for information on when the next round of funding will open.

CONTACT DETAILS The Trustees, One Bishops Square, London E1 6AD *Tel.* 020 3088 0000 *Email* allenoveryfoundation@allenovery.com *Website* https://www.allenovery.com/en-gb/global/about_us/corporate_responsibility/charitable_giving

■ D. C. R. Allen Charitable Trust

CC NO 277293 **ESTABLISHED** 1979

WHERE FUNDING CAN BE GIVEN UK.

WHO CAN BENEFIT Registered charities.

WHAT IS FUNDED General charitable purposes, especially disadvantaged young people. There is a preference for small to medium-sized charities.

WHAT IS NOT FUNDED Individuals; funding of services usually provided by statutory sources; causes outside the UK; evangelical or worship activities; animal welfare; medical research; heritage conservation/preservation; arts or collections and performing arts.

TYPE OF GRANT Capital costs; project funding; unrestricted funding.

RANGE OF GRANTS From £2,000 to £20,000. Larger amounts may be considered, especially for innovative or capital projects.

SAMPLE GRANTS Previous beneficiaries have included: Centrepoint and NORPIP – The Northamptonshire Parent Infant Partnership (£25,000 each); Designability (£20,000); Greenham Community Trust and Operation New World (£10,000 each); Bright Ideas Trust (£5,000); Young Asian Voices (£2,000); Great Ormond Street (£1,000); St Leonard's Church – Aston-le-Wells (£500).

FINANCES *Financial year end* 05/04/2019 *Income* £249,900 *Total grants* £291,000 *Grants to organisations* £291,000 *Assets* £5,410,000

TRUSTEES Julie Frusher; Tristram Allen; Colin Allen.

OTHER INFORMATION Grants were broken down as follows: youth projects (£167,500); education (£54,000); medical causes (£39,500); disability (£28,000). The 2018/19 accounts were the latest available at the time of writing (January 2021).

HOW TO APPLY Applications should be made by email to the correspondent and should include a copy of your latest accounts and your official charity number. The trustees normally meet monthly, so decisions can be made promptly. It is not possible for the trustees to respond to unsuccessful applicants, so if no positive response has been received within eight weeks of the application date, then applicants may assume that they have not been successful.

CONTACT DETAILS Julie Frusher, Trustee, Estate Office, Edgcote House, Edgcote, Banbury, Oxfordshire OX17 1AG *Email* juile.frusher@edgecote.com

■ The Allen Trust

CC NO 1146388 **ESTABLISHED** 2012

WHERE FUNDING CAN BE GIVEN Worldwide.

WHO CAN BENEFIT Registered charities.

WHAT IS FUNDED General charitable purposes with a preference for Christian causes and social welfare.

RANGE OF GRANTS Typically between £250 and £12,500. It appears that one large grant of over £100,000 is made per year.

SAMPLE GRANTS African Revival (£142,000); Friends of African International Christian Ministry and Mission Aviation Fellowship (£12,500 each); Grange Park Opera (£11,800); Cinnamon Network (£10,000); Queen Elizabeth Castle of Mey Trust (£3,500); Hospices of Hope (£2,000); Royal Hospital for Neuro Disability (£1,000); Salvation Army (£500); Friends of Chatter (£250).

FINANCES *Financial year end* 31/03/2020 *Income* £54,400 *Total grants* £215,000 *Grants to organisations* £215,000 *Assets* £2,530,000

TRUSTEES Tony Allen; Melanie Pollitt.

OTHER INFORMATION Grants were awarded to 16 organisations during the year.

HOW TO APPLY Contact the correspondent for further information.

CONTACT DETAILS The Trustees, Oakmead Farm, Ockham Lane, Cobham, Surrey KTLL 1LY *Tel.* 07704 475257

■ Alliance Family Foundation Ltd

CC NO 258721 **ESTABLISHED** 1968

WHERE FUNDING CAN BE GIVEN UK; Israel; Iran; Serbia; USA.

WHO CAN BENEFIT Charitable organisations, particularly Jewish organisations benefitting young people and people disadvantaged by poverty; individuals.

WHAT IS FUNDED Jewish causes; the relief of poverty; advancement of religion; education.

RANGE OF GRANTS Up to £50,000.

SAMPLE GRANTS Community Security Trust (£25,000); Spanish and Portuguese Sephardi Community Synagogue (£14,900); Sheffield Children's Hospital Charity (£11,000).

FINANCES *Financial year end* 31/03/2020 *Income* £1,330,000 *Total grants* £152,300 *Grants to organisations* £86,300 *Assets* (£061,700)

TRUSTEES Lord David Alliance; Hon. Sara Esterkin; Hon. Joshua Alliance.

OTHER INFORMATION There were 59 grants made to organisations and individuals during the year. Grants to individuals for educational and medical/care costs totalled £66,000. Only beneficiaries that received grants representing 5% or more of the foundation's total expenditure for the year were reported in the accounts.

HOW TO APPLY Apply in writing to the trustees.

CONTACT DETAILS The Trustees, Spencer House, 27 St James's Place, London SW1A 1NR *Tel.* 020 7493 7735 *Email* aff@alliance.me

The Almond Trust

CC NO 328583 **ESTABLISHED** 1990

WHERE FUNDING CAN BE GIVEN UK and overseas.

WHO CAN BENEFIT Mostly organisations of which the trustees have personal knowledge, particularly those benefitting Christians and evangelists.

WHAT IS FUNDED Christian evangelism; the advancement of the translation, reading, study and teaching of the Bible.

RANGE OF GRANTS Typically £5,000 to £15,000.

SAMPLE GRANTS Warbleton Parish Church Council (£15,000); BMS World Mission, Christian Solidarity Worldwide and Tear Fund (£10,000 each); Arab Vision and The Bible Network (£5,000 each); Oxford Inter-Collegiate Christian Union (£4,000).

FINANCES *Financial year end* 31/03/2020
Income £375,700 *Total grants* £229,000
Grants to organisations £229,000
Assets £556,800

TRUSTEES Sir Jeremy Cooke; Jonathan Cooke; Lady Cooke.

OTHER INFORMATION Grants were awarded to 27 organisations during the year.

HOW TO APPLY The trust's 2019/20 accounts state that it rarely responds to uninvited applications.

CONTACT DETAILS Sir Jeremy Cooke, Trustee, White Birch Farm, White Birch Lane, Warbleton, East Sussex, TN21 9BE *Tel.* 01435 830883

Alpkit Foundation

CC NO 1162585 **ESTABLISHED** 2015

WHERE FUNDING CAN BE GIVEN England and Wales.

WHO CAN BENEFIT Individuals; groups; schools; organisations.

WHAT IS FUNDED Outdoor experiences; outdoor educational programs and training (i.e. first aid or mountain leader training); the environment and conservation.

WHAT IS NOT FUNDED Charity challenges; commercially led travel expeditions that are not focused the great outdoors (e.g. rebuilding schools, overseas medicine); scout jamborees; holidays; retrospective applications.

TYPE OF GRANT Transport costs; capital costs (equipment); project costs.

SAMPLE GRANTS A list of beneficiaries was not included in the annual report and accounts.

FINANCES *Financial year end* 31/10/2019
Income £74,800 *Total grants* £60,500
Grants to organisations £60,500
Assets £28,200

TRUSTEES David Hanney; Colin Stocker; Kenneth Stocker; Nicholas Smith; Adge Last; Liam Reeves; Louise Bailey; Eloise Marie Cundill; Caroline Fry; Rehna Yaseen.

OTHER INFORMATION This is the corporate charity of Alpkit, an outdoor clothing and equipment company. The foundation's website provides examples of activities likely to be supported. The 2018/19 accounts were the latest available at the time of writing (January 2021).

HOW TO APPLY Application forms are available on the foundation's website. The trustees meet every two months to consider applications.

CONTACT DETAILS The Trustees, Alpkit Ltd, Unit 12–14 Oak House, Moorgreen Industrial Park, Engine Lane, Newthorpe, Nottinghamshire NG16 3QU *Tel.* 01773 417007 *Email* akf@alpkit.com *Website* https://www.alpkit.com/foundation

Alzheimer's Research UK

CC NO 1077089 **ESTABLISHED** 1998

WHERE FUNDING CAN BE GIVEN UK.

WHO CAN BENEFIT Universities; charities; hospitals; research institutions.

WHAT IS FUNDED Research into the cause, diagnosis/detection of, prevention and treatment of Alzheimer's disease and other dementias.

SAMPLE GRANTS Imperial College London (£3.06 million); University of Cambridge (£2.33 million); Cardiff University (£350,000); Crawford Works (£10,000); University of Aberdeen (£1,800).

FINANCES *Financial year end* 31/03/2020
Income £40,060,000
Total grants £18,430,000
Grants to organisations £18,430,000
Assets £7,080,000

TRUSTEES Shirley Cramer; Rupert Evenett; Prof. Rob Howard; David Mayhew; Michael Cooper; Nicholas Antill; Christopher Carter; Caroline van den Brul; Giles Dennison; Dr Ruth McKernan.

HOW TO APPLY Full details of all available grant schemes including deadlines, eligibility criteria and application procedures are available on the charity's website.

CONTACT DETAILS The Trustees, 3 Riverside, Granta Park, Cambridge CB21 6AD *Tel.* 0300 111 5555 *Email* enquiries@alzheimersresearchuk.org *Website* www.alzheimersresearchuk.org

Alzheimer's Society

CC NO 296645 **ESTABLISHED** 1987

WHERE FUNDING CAN BE GIVEN UK.

WHO CAN BENEFIT Universities; hospitals; research institutions.

WHAT IS FUNDED Research into dementia.

WHAT IS NOT FUNDED Refer to the website for exclusions from individual funding schemes.

TYPE OF GRANT Research funding; fellowships, studentships, bursaries.

SAMPLE GRANTS University College London (£1.9 million); Dementia Research Institute (£1 million); University of Exeter (£643,000); University of Leeds (£75,000); King's College London (£4,000); University of Glasgow (£1,000).

FINANCES *Financial year end* 31/03/2020
Income £113,890,000
Total grants £6,470,000
Grants to organisations £6,470,000
Assets £31,790,000

TRUSTEES Caroline Fawcett; Alison Harrison; Manish Shah; Andrew Lynch; Stephen Hill; Sarah Weir; Prof. McKenna; Duncan Jones.

HOW TO APPLY For information on how to apply to one of Alzheimer's Society's current grant schemes, refer to the website. Funding calls are advertised on the website and applications should be submitted online.

CONTACT DETAILS Research Team, 43–44 Crutched Friars, London EC3N 2AE *Tel.* 0330 333 0804 *Email* grantenquiries@alzheimer's.org.uk *Website* www.alzheimer's.org.uk

Amabrill Ltd

CC NO 1078968 **ESTABLISHED** 2000

WHERE FUNDING CAN BE GIVEN UK and overseas.

WHO CAN BENEFIT Jewish charities.

WHAT IS FUNDED The advancement of education and religious practice in accordance with the

teachings of the Orthodox Jewish faith; social welfare.
TYPE OF GRANT Capital costs; core costs.
SAMPLE GRANTS Kahal Chasidim Bobov (£411,600); Achisomoch Aid Company Ltd (£205,100); Amud Hatzdokoh Trust (£96,500); Dover Sholom Community Trust (£50,000).
FINANCES *Financial year end* 29/02/2020
Income £3,890,000 *Total grants* £4,700,000
Grants to organisations £4,700,000
Assets £26,370,000
TRUSTEES Mr C. Lerner; Frances Lerner; Israel Grossnass; Irving Lerner.
OTHER INFORMATION Grants were distributed as follows: educational grants (£1.8 million); relief of poverty (£1.4 million); advancement of the Jewish faith (£1.3 million). Grants of under £50,000 totalled £2.36 million.
HOW TO APPLY Apply in writing to the correspondent. The 2019/20 annual report explains: 'Appeal letters are received from, and personal visits made by representatives of Jewish charitable, religious and educational institutions. These requests are then considered by the trustees and grants are made in accordance with the trustees decisions.'
CONTACT DETAILS Frances Lerner, Trustee, 1 Golders Manor Drive, London NW11 9HU *Tel.* 020 8455 6785 *Email* mail@venittandgreaves.com

■ The Ammco Trust

CC NO 327962 **ESTABLISHED** 1988
WHERE FUNDING CAN BE GIVEN Oxfordshire and adjoining counties.
WHO CAN BENEFIT Registered charities.
WHAT IS FUNDED General charitable purposes, with a preference for disability.
WHAT IS NOT FUNDED Individuals; students; research.
TYPE OF GRANT Capital costs; core/revenue costs.
RANGE OF GRANTS Between £200 and £2,000.
SAMPLE GRANTS Able Kids; Animal Antiks; Cyclists Fighting Cancer; Full Circle; Hargreaves Narrow Boat Trust; National Children's Research Centre; Pegasus Theatre; Rivertime Boat Trust; Sunny Days Children's Fund; Soundabout.
FINANCES *Financial year end* 05/04/2020
Income £152,300 *Total grants* £52,900
Grants to organisations £52,900
Assets £1,790,000
TRUSTEES Esther Lewis; Rowena Vickers; Nicholas Cobbold; Clare Luck.
OTHER INFORMATION The trust's annual report provides the following breakdown of grants awarded: disability (£40,300); welfare (£11,800); other (£900). A list of beneficiaries was available in the accounts but grant totals were not included.
HOW TO APPLY Apply in writing to the correspondent. Applications are reviewed quarterly.
CONTACT DETAILS The Trustees, Wallon, Drewsteignton, Exeter, Devon EX6 6PZ *Tel.* 01647 272847

■ Viscount Amory's Charitable Trust

CC NO 204958 **ESTABLISHED** 1962
WHERE FUNDING CAN BE GIVEN UK, with a strong preference for Devon.
WHO CAN BENEFIT Registered charities; churches; schools.
WHAT IS FUNDED General charitable purposes with a preference for education and religion.
WHAT IS NOT FUNDED Applications from individuals for poverty relief; applications for grants or short-term loans for individuals.
RANGE OF GRANTS Mainly under £30,000.
SAMPLE GRANTS Rona Sailing Project (£95,700); Exeter Cathedral School (£40,100); Devon Community Foundation (£30,000); Exeter Northcott Theatre (£15,000); Exeter School (£7,500); Birkenhead School (£6,000); Churches Housing Action Team (£5,000).
FINANCES *Financial year end* 05/04/2020
Income £474,200 *Total grants* £422,700
Grants to organisations £407,600
Assets £12,380,000
TRUSTEES Sir Ian Amory; Catherine Cavender.
OTHER INFORMATION Grants totalling £15,100 were made to 26 individuals during 2019/20. Only organisations receiving grants of over £5,000 were listed as beneficiaries in the trust's accounts.
HOW TO APPLY Apply in writing to the correspondent – applications should not be sent by email. Applications should include: address, email, general background information of the appeal, the nature of the sponsoring or associated organisation, the total amount to be raised, how much has been raised, proposal for any shortfall and any other relevant information.
CONTACT DETAILS Mrs S. Curtis, The Island, Lowman Green, Tiverton, Devon EX16 4LA *Tel.* 01884 242200 *Email* office@vact.org.uk *Website* www.vact.org.uk

■ The Ampersand Foundation

CC NO 1167018 **ESTABLISHED** 2011
WHERE FUNDING CAN BE GIVEN UK.
WHO CAN BENEFIT Arts organisations; museums and galleries.
WHAT IS FUNDED Visual arts projects including exhibitions, acquisitions and commissions.
TYPE OF GRANT Project funding; exhibitions; acquisitions.
SAMPLE GRANTS A list of beneficiaries was not included in the annual report and accounts.
FINANCES *Financial year end* 31/03/2020
Income £1,400,000 *Total grants* £532,300
Grants to organisations £532,300
Assets £4,020,000
TRUSTEES John Kirkland; Victoria Siddall; Thiago Carvalho; Alastair Sooke; Simon Conway.
OTHER INFORMATION It is a requirement that all exhibitions supported by The Ampersand Foundation should be free to the public at least one whole day per week.
HOW TO APPLY Apply in writing to the correspondent. Full details of the application process including deadlines can be found on the foundation's website.
CONTACT DETAILS The Trustees, Third Floor, 21 Conduit Street, London W1S 2XP
Email info@theampersandfoundation.com
Website www.theampersandfoundation.com

■ The AMW Charitable Trust

OSCR NO SC006959 **ESTABLISHED** 1974
WHERE FUNDING CAN BE GIVEN UK, with a preference for the west of Scotland.
WHO CAN BENEFIT Charitable organisations; universities.
WHAT IS FUNDED General charitable purposes, with a focus on young people, music and health.
RANGE OF GRANTS Typically between £2,000 and £5,000.

SAMPLE GRANTS University of Glasgow and University of Strathclyde (£25,000 each); Abbeyfield Strathaven and District Society (£5,000); Sepsis Research (FEAT) (£4,000); Bethany Christian Trust, Inspire Foundation and Versus Arthritis (£2,500 each); Canine Partners and Volunteer Glasgow (£2,000 each).
FINANCES *Financial year end* 05/04/2020 *Income* £213,000 *Total grants* £198,000 *Grants to organisations* £198,000 *Assets* £4,000,000
OTHER INFORMATION The trust awarded 53 grants during the year.
HOW TO APPLY Apply in writing to the correspondent. The trustees normally meet twice a year to consider applications.
CONTACT DETAILS The Trustees, c/o KPMG LLP, 319 St Vincent Street, Glasgow G2 5AS

■ The Anchor Foundation

CC NO 1082485 **ESTABLISHED** 2000
WHERE FUNDING CAN BE GIVEN UK and overseas.
WHO CAN BENEFIT Christian charities.
WHAT IS FUNDED Social inclusion, particularly through ministries and the arts.
WHAT IS NOT FUNDED Individuals.
TYPE OF GRANT Applications for capital and revenue funding are considered. Only in very exceptional circumstances will grants be given for building work. It is not the normal practice of the charity to support the same project for more than three years (projects which have had three years funding may apply again two years from the payment of the last grant).
RANGE OF GRANTS £500 to £10,000.
SAMPLE GRANTS Riding Lights Theatre Company (£9,200); Castlemilk Parish Church (£7,500); Christian Solidarity Worldwide, Embracing Age and The Toybox Charity (£5,000 each); Hope Into Action (£3,000); Art Action UK (£2,000); Church Pastoral Aid Society (£1,000).
FINANCES *Financial year end* 31/03/2020 *Income* £253,100 *Total grants* £238,800 *Grants to organisations* £238,800 *Assets* £7,120,000
TRUSTEES Revd Michael Mitton; Revd Robin Anker-Petersen; Nina Stewart; Sue Mayfield.
OTHER INFORMATION Grants were awarded to 48 charities during the year. The trustees look favourably on organisations whose boards demonstrate equal opportunities.
HOW TO APPLY An initial application form can be completed online at the Anchor Foundation website. Applications are considered at trustees' meetings held twice a year in April and October and need to be received by 31 January and 31 July respectively. Full guidelines and criteria for applicants are also available on the foundation's helpful website.
CONTACT DETAILS Secretary, PO Box 7689, Perth, Perthshire PH2 1JX *Tel.* 0115 950 0055 *Email* secretary@theanchorfoundation.org.uk *Website* www.theanchorfoundation.org.uk

■ Andor Charitable Trust

CC NO 1083572 **ESTABLISHED** 1996
WHERE FUNDING CAN BE GIVEN UK and overseas.
WHO CAN BENEFIT Charitable organisations.
WHAT IS FUNDED Health; medical research; the arts; social welfare; education; older people; people with disabilities.
RANGE OF GRANTS Up to £5,000 but mostly £1,000 to £3,000.
SAMPLE GRANTS Multiple Sclerosis Society (£5,000); Motor Neurone Disease Association (£3,000); WaterAid (£2,000); English National Opera and Theatres Trust (£1,000 each).
FINANCES *Financial year end* 05/04/2020 *Income* £88,000 *Total grants* £190,000 *Grants to organisations* £190,000 *Assets* £2,890,000
TRUSTEES David Rothenberg; Nicholas Lederer; Dr Claire Walford; Karen Andor.
OTHER INFORMATION There were 78 grants made during the year.
HOW TO APPLY Contact the correspondent for further information.
CONTACT DETAILS The Trustees, c/o Blick Rothenberg Chartered Accountants, 16 Great Queen Street, Covent Garden, London WC2B 5AH *Tel.* 020 7544 8865 *Email* robin@blickrothenberg.com

■ Andrews Charitable Trust

CC NO 1174706 **ESTABLISHED** 1965
WHERE FUNDING CAN BE GIVEN Bristol; South Gloucester; Bath and North East Somerset; Gloucestershire; Oxfordshire; London; Surrey; West Sussex; Essex; Buckinghamshire; Hertfordshire; East Sussex.
WHO CAN BENEFIT Christian organisations; churches.
WHAT IS FUNDED Housing; social welfare; Christian community projects supporting disadvantaged or marginalised people.
TYPE OF GRANT Project funding.
SAMPLE GRANTS Dementia Adventure (£102,000); The Together Group (£70,000); 2nd Chance (£50,000); Ekklesia (£34,500).
FINANCES *Financial year end* 31/12/2019 *Income* £26,460,000 *Total grants* £219,000 *Grants to organisations* £219,000 *Assets* £19,570,000
TRUSTEES Nicholas Wright; Paul Heal; David Westgate; Helen Battrick; Alastair Page; Ami Davis; Ruth Knagg; Alison Kelly; Elizabeth Hughes; Alexandra McDonald.
HOW TO APPLY The trust only accepts applications for its Christian Innovation Grants programme which provides small grants to Christian organisations that promote the Christian faith and provide practical help for disadvantaged and marginalised people within communities. Applications to this programme can be made online via The Cinnamon Network.
CONTACT DETAILS The Trustees, The Clockhouse, Bath Hill, Keynsham, Bristol BS31 1HL *Tel.* 0117 946 1834 *Email* info@andrewscharitabletrust.org.uk *Website* www.andrewscharitabletrust.org.uk

■ Anglo American Group Foundation

CC NO 1111719 **ESTABLISHED** 2005
WHERE FUNDING CAN BE GIVEN UK; Australia; Botswana; Brazil; Canada; Chile; Colombia; Peru; South Africa; Zimbabwe.
WHO CAN BENEFIT Registered charities.
WHAT IS FUNDED Community development; education and training; the environment; health (particularly HIV/AIDS) and social welfare.
SAMPLE GRANTS A full list of beneficiaries was not available.
FINANCES *Financial year end* 31/12/2019 *Income* £2,500,000 *Total grants* £2,300,000 *Grants to organisations* £2,300,000 *Assets* £309,700

TRUSTEES Jonathan Samuel; Norman Mbazima; Yvonne Mfolo; Anik Michaud-Ahmed.

OTHER INFORMATION The foundation was established in 2005 by Anglo American plc, a large multinational mining company. Grants were broken down as follows: other social investments (£813,100); community development (£776,400); education and training (£356,900); health and welfare (£250,000); environmental (£76,600); employee matched funding (£23,800).

HOW TO APPLY Contact the correspondent for further information.

CONTACT DETAILS The Trustees, Anglo American House, 20 Carlton House Terrace, London SW1Y 5AN *Tel.* 020 7968 8888 *Email* aagf@angloamerican.com *Website* www.angloamericangroupfoundation.org

■ Anguish's Educational Foundation

CC NO 311288 **ESTABLISHED** 1605

WHERE FUNDING CAN BE GIVEN Norwich and the parishes of Costessey, Hellesdon, Catton, Sprowston, Thorpe-next-Norwich and Corpusty.

WHO CAN BENEFIT Registered charities; schools; individuals.

WHAT IS FUNDED The education of children and young people (under 25 years old).

TYPE OF GRANT Core costs; capital costs; project funding.

SAMPLE GRANTS NORCA and Sistema in Norwich (£40,000); Norwich International Youth Project (£12,500); Catton Grove Primary School (£9,000).

FINANCES *Financial year end* 31/03/2020 *Income* £950,200 *Total grants* £1,190,000 *Grants to organisations* £661,700 *Assets* £24,020,000

TRUSTEES Boyd Taylor; Michael Flynn; Cllr Karen Davies; Laura McCartney-Gray; Philip Davies; Adam Giles; John Garside; Prof. Mioshi; David Fullman; Vivien Thomas; Sally Button; Jacqueline Hanlon; Philip Blanchflower; Jeanne Southgate.

OTHER INFORMATION In 2019/20 the foundation awarded two exceptional grants of £200,000 to Into Opera and YMCA Norwich to fund educational programmes aimed at disadvantaged young people in the beneficial area. Grants to individuals totalled £523,000.

HOW TO APPLY The foundation shares its administration with the Norwich Consolidated Charites and Norwich Freemen's Charity (also known as the Nowich Town Close Estate Charity). Due to the impact of COVID-19, the charities have temporarily adapted the application process and broadened the criteria of what they may consider to fund. Applicants must first read the information on the Norwich Charitable Trusts website and then contact the correspondent. If successful, applicants will be invited to make an application via the 'Flexigrant' application portal.

CONTACT DETAILS David Hynes, CEO of Norwich Charitable Trusts, 1 Woolgate Court, St Benedicts Street, Norwich, Norfolk NR2 4AP *Tel.* 01603 621023 *Email* david.hynes@norwichcharitabletrusts.org.uk *Website* www.norwichcharitabletrusts.org.uk

■ The Annandale Charitable Trust

CC NO 1049193 **ESTABLISHED** 1995

WHERE FUNDING CAN BE GIVEN UK.

WHO CAN BENEFIT Registered charities; voluntary groups.

WHAT IS FUNDED General charitable purposes.

RANGE OF GRANTS £1,600 to £10,000.

SAMPLE GRANTS Cornwall Air Ambulance Trust (£10,000); Chestnut Tree House Hospice (£6,700); Abby's Heroes and Activity Club for Children (£3,000 each); Forget Me Not Children's Hospice and Ruby's Fund (£1,600 each).

FINANCES *Financial year end* 05/04/2020 *Income* £408,400 *Total grants* £412,100 *Grants to organisations* £412,100 *Assets* £12,170,000

TRUSTEE HSBC Trust Company (UK) Ltd.

OTHER INFORMATION A total of 186 grants were made to charitable organisations during the year.

HOW TO APPLY Contact the correspondent for further information.

CONTACT DETAILS The Trustees, HSBC Trust Company UK Ltd, Forum 1, Second Floor, Parkway, Whiteley, Fareham, Hampshire PO15 7PA *Tel.* 023 8199 9231

■ Anpride Ltd

CC NO 288978 **ESTABLISHED** 1984

WHERE FUNDING CAN BE GIVEN London.

WHO CAN BENEFIT Registered charities.

WHAT IS FUNDED Advancement of the Jewish faith; social welfare.

SAMPLE GRANTS A list of beneficiaries was not included in the annual report and accounts.

FINANCES *Financial year end* 30/09/2019 *Income* £481,100 *Total grants* £145,200 *Grants to organisations* £145,200 *Assets* £857,000

TRUSTEES Chaim Benedikt; Golda Benedikt.

HOW TO APPLY Contact the correspondent for further information.

CONTACT DETAILS Golda Benedikt, Trustee, 99 Geldeston Road, London E5 8RS *Tel.* 020 8806 1011

■ The Anson Charitable Trust

CC NO 1111010 **ESTABLISHED** 2005

WHERE FUNDING CAN BE GIVEN UK, with a preference for Buckinghamshire.

WHO CAN BENEFIT Registered charities; social enterprises; hospices.

WHAT IS FUNDED Arts and culture; medical research and the sciences; community development; the environment and ecology.

WHAT IS NOT FUNDED Individuals.

TYPE OF GRANT Capital costs; core/revenue costs; project funding; unrestricted funding.

RANGE OF GRANTS Grants range from £50 to £12,000.

SAMPLE GRANTS The Pace Centre (£12,000); Watts Gallery (£10,000); Youth Concern (£6,000); Willen Hospice (£5,000); Wycombe Youth Action (£3,000); Shelter (£2,000); The Country Food Trust (£500).

FINANCES *Financial year end* 05/04/2020 *Income* £250,000 *Total grants* £330,900 *Grants to organisations* £330,900 *Assets* £86,000

TRUSTEES George Anson; Kirsty Anson.

HOW TO APPLY Application forms can be downloaded from the charity's website.

CONTACT DETAILS The Trustees, The Lilies, High Street, Weedon, Aylesbury, Buckinghamshire HP22 4NS *Tel.* 01296 640331 *Email* mail@ansoncharitabletrust.org.uk *Website* https://www.ansoncharitabletrust.org.uk

■ The Apax Foundation

CC NO 1112845 **ESTABLISHED** 2006

WHERE FUNDING CAN BE GIVEN UK and overseas, with a focus on disadvantaged communities.

WHO CAN BENEFIT Registered charities and community groups.

WHAT IS FUNDED Social entrepreneurship; relief of poverty; education; refugees.

RANGE OF GRANTS Mostly under £10,000. Larger grants are offered from around £10,000 to £100,000.

SAMPLE GRANTS The Opportunity Network (£377,900); Grameen America (£229,100); The AGA Khan Foundation (£101,000); St Paul's Girls' School (£70,000); The Prince's Trust – Mosaic Programme (£50,000); Children of the Fallen Patriots Foundation (£39,500); St Luke's Foundation (£19,700).

FINANCES *Financial year end* 31/12/2019 *Income* £1,620,000 *Total grants* £1,850,000 *Grants to organisations* £1,850,000 *Assets* £56,640,000

TRUSTEES Sir Ronald Cohen; Dr Peter Englander; David Marks; Simon Cresswell; Mitch Truwit; Shashank Singh; Rohan Haldea; Jason Wright.

OTHER INFORMATION The foundation is the corporate charity of Apax Partners LLP.

HOW TO APPLY Contact the correspondent for further information.

CONTACT DETAILS Kate Albert, Foundation Manager, Apax Partners, 33 Jermyn Street, London SW1Y 6DN *Tel.* 020 7872 6300 *Email* foundation@apax.com *Website* www.apax.com/responsibility/apax-foundation

■ The John Apthorp Charity

CC NO 1102472 **ESTABLISHED** 2003

WHERE FUNDING CAN BE GIVEN Hertfordshire, Bedfordshire and Buckinghamshire.

WHO CAN BENEFIT Registered charities.

WHAT IS FUNDED Education; religion; social welfare.

WHAT IS NOT FUNDED Projects outside the geographical catchment area; charities that have unrestricted reserves; core funding; any institution which is not a registered charity; any institution which has recently received funding from the charity.

TYPE OF GRANT Capital costs; seed funding/start-up funding; project funding; research.

RANGE OF GRANTS Grants range from £500 to £100,000.

SAMPLE GRANTS Autism Bedfordshire (£100,000); Luton Culture (£80,800); Westoning Village Hall (£50,000); Hospice of St Francis (£31,400); Rennie Grove Hospice Care (£16,200); Wycombe Youth Action (£2,400); Friends for Life Bedfordshire (£500).

FINANCES *Financial year end* 31/12/2019 *Income* £547,300 *Total grants* £812,000 *Grants to organisations* £812,000 *Assets* £12,740,000

TRUSTEES John Apthorp; Duncan Apthorp; Justin Apthorp; Kate Arnold.

OTHER INFORMATION In total, 38 organisations were awarded grants throughout the year.

HOW TO APPLY Applicants are asked to read the eligibility criteria on the charity's website before applying. The charity recommends that applications are sent via email. As the charity supports such a wide range of projects there is no application form; however, details of what to include in the email are on its website.

CONTACT DETAILS The Trustees, 29 Newlands Avenue, Radlett, Hertfordshire WD7 8 EJ *Tel.* 01923 855727 *Email* johnapthorpcharity@hotmail.com *Website* https://www.johnapthorpcharity.org

■ The Arah Foundation

CC NO 1154244 **ESTABLISHED** 2013

WHERE FUNDING CAN BE GIVEN England and Wales; St Vincent and the Grenadines; Turkey.

WHO CAN BENEFIT Registered charities.

WHAT IS FUNDED General charitable purposes; education and training; arts and culture; human rights; religious and racial harmony.

SAMPLE GRANTS A list of beneficiaries was not included in the annual report and accounts.

FINANCES *Financial year end* 31/03/2020 *Income* £936 *Total grants* £326,800 *Grants to organisations* £326,800

TRUSTEES Asli Arah; William Arah.

OTHER INFORMATION Full accounts were not available to view on the Charity Commission's website due to the foundation's low income. We have therefore estimated the grant total based on the foundation's total expenditure.

HOW TO APPLY Apply in writing to the correspondent.

CONTACT DETAILS The Trustees, c/o MacFarlanes LLP, 10 Norwich Street, London EC4A 1 BD *Tel.* 07435 883224 *Email* info@arahfoundation.org

■ Arcadia Fund

ESTABLISHED 2001

WHERE FUNDING CAN BE GIVEN Worldwide.

WHO CAN BENEFIT Registered charities; educational organisations.

WHAT IS FUNDED Preserving endangered culture; protecting endangered nature; promoting open access to information.

WHAT IS NOT FUNDED Individuals.

SAMPLE GRANTS University of Oxford (£3.07 million); Global Witness (£1.39 million); Chickenshed NYC (£73,700).

FINANCES *Financial year end* 31/12/2020 *Total grants* £21,750,000 *Grants to organisations* £21,750,000

OTHER INFORMATION Full accounts were not available to view. The grant total was taken from the grant-maker's Grant Directory page on its website and converted to GBP using the exchange rate at the time of writing (January 2021).

HOW TO APPLY Unsolicited applications are not accepted.

CONTACT DETAILS Grants Team, Sixth Floor, 5 Young Street, London W8 5EH *Email* info@arcadiafund.org.uk *Website* www.arcadiafund.org.uk

■ The Archer Trust

CC NO 1033534 **ESTABLISHED** 1994

WHERE FUNDING CAN BE GIVEN UK and overseas.

WHO CAN BENEFIT Small Christian charities. Preference is given to organisations working in areas with high unemployment and deprivation in the UK, and organisations that make 'good use' of volunteers.

WHAT IS FUNDED Provision of aid or support to people in need, people with disabilities or people who are disadvantaged. The trust will also fund overseas projects.
WHAT IS NOT FUNDED Individuals; conservation, heritage and environmental projects; conversions for disabled access; charities supporting animals; research.
TYPE OF GRANT Project funding.
RANGE OF GRANTS £500 to £4,000.
SAMPLE GRANTS MIND and Silverline (£10,000 each); Strive Café (£5,000); Giving World and Lilias Graham Charitable Trust (£4,000 each); Ashford Place (£3,000); Wigan Stars (£500).
FINANCES *Financial year end* 05/04/2020 *Income* £151,600 *Total grants* £240,800 *Grants to organisations* £240,800 *Assets* £2,100,000
TRUSTEES Catherine Archer; Lyn Packman; James Archer; Michael Baker; Dr Charlotte Wilson.
HOW TO APPLY Apply in writing to the correspondent. Unsuccessful applicants will not receive a response, even if an sae is enclosed.
CONTACT DETAILS The Secretary, Bourne House, Wadesmill, Ware, Hertfordshire SG12 0TT *Tel.* 01920 462312 *Website* www.archertrust.org.uk

■ The Architectural Heritage Fund

CC NO 266780 **ESTABLISHED** 1976
WHERE FUNDING CAN BE GIVEN UK.
WHO CAN BENEFIT Registered charities; not-for-profit organisations; CICs; benefit societies; parish and town councils; community councils (in Scotland and Wales).
WHAT IS FUNDED Historic buildings; conservation; encouraging the use of historic buildings for public benefit.
WHAT IS NOT FUNDED Individuals; unincorporated trusts or associations; local authorities and other public sector bodies; for-profit companies unless in a partnership led by incorporated charity community business or social enterprise; churches or other places of worship where the building will remain in use primarily as a place of religious worship.
TYPE OF GRANT Project funding; development funding.
RANGE OF GRANTS Grants range from £1,500 to £25,000.
SAMPLE GRANTS St Ives Community Land Trust (£73,800); Always Ahead (£30,000); Arkwright Society (£15,000); The Landmark Trust (£7,000); Ederney Community Development Trust (£5,000); St John's House Trust (Bridgend) (£700).
FINANCES *Financial year end* 31/03/2020 *Income* £7,950,000 *Total grants* £3,750,000 *Grants to organisations* £3,750,000 *Assets* £15,580,000
TRUSTEES Dr Neal Sashore; Gregory Pickup; Carole-Anne Davies; Kate Dickson; Myra Barnes; Elizabeth Peace; David Hunter; Suzanne Snowden; Susan Brown; Adebayo Alao; Karen Latimer; Eleanor McAlliser; Roy Hodson; Graham Fisher; James Bowdidge.
HOW TO APPLY Online applications can be completed from the helpful website. Guidance notes on the stages of the application process are also available from the website.
CONTACT DETAILS The Trustees, 3 Spital Yard, Spitalfields, London E1 6AQ *Tel.* 020 7925 0199 *Email* ahf@ahfund.org.uk *Website* www.ahfund.org.uk

■ Ardbarron Trust Ltd

CCNI NO NIC101111 **ESTABLISHED** 1985
WHERE FUNDING CAN BE GIVEN UK and overseas.
WHO CAN BENEFIT Registered charities.
WHAT IS FUNDED Awareness and understanding of the Christian gospel; social welfare; healthcare; literacy.
SAMPLE GRANTS Barnabas Fund; Christian Missions Charitable Trust; Echoes of Service; Gideons International; Operation Mobilisation; Tear Fund; Youth for Christ Northern Ireland.
FINANCES *Financial year end* 31/12/2019 *Income* £5,030,000 *Total grants* £4,258,000 *Grants to organisations* £4,230,000 *Assets* £171,910,000
TRUSTEES Martin Agnew; Geoffrey Agnew; John Agnew; Malcolm Johnston.
OTHER INFORMATION Grants were made to 315 institutions throughout the year.
HOW TO APPLY Contact the correspondent for further information.
CONTACT DETAILS The Trustees, PO Box 49, Hightown Avenue, Newtownabbey, County Antrim BT36 4RT *Tel.* 028 9034 2733

■ The Ardeola Charitable Trust

CC NO 1124380 **ESTABLISHED** 2008
WHERE FUNDING CAN BE GIVEN UK.
WHO CAN BENEFIT Registered charities.
WHAT IS FUNDED General charitable purposes, although the main beneficiary each year is Target Ovarian Cancer.
RANGE OF GRANTS Mostly under £5,000.
SAMPLE GRANTS Target Ovarian Cancer (£200,000); Elizabeth Montagu Correspondence Online (£100,000); British Museum (£30,000); Thames Hospice, National Theatre (£25,000 each); British Library (£8,800); Windsor Benefit Trust (£2,000).
FINANCES *Financial year end* 31/05/2019 *Income* £392,000 *Total grants* £470,300 *Grants to organisations* £470,300 *Assets* £7,970,000
TRUSTEES Graham Barker; Joanna Barker; William Hiscocks; Prof. John Cornwall; Coutts & Co.
OTHER INFORMATION The 2018/19 accounts were the latest available at the time of writing (February 2021).
HOW TO APPLY Apply in writing to the correspondent.
CONTACT DETAILS The Trustees, Coutts & Co. Trustee Department, 1st Floor, Trinity Quay 1, Avon Street, Bristol BS2 0PT *Tel.* 0345 304 2424

■ The Ardwick Trust

CC NO 266981 **ESTABLISHED** 1975
WHERE FUNDING CAN BE GIVEN UK and Israel.
WHO CAN BENEFIT Charitable organisations.
WHAT IS FUNDED General charitable purposes with a focus on Jewish causes; social welfare; health; disability; older people; children and young people.
RANGE OF GRANTS Up to £1,000; mostly £100 to £500.
SAMPLE GRANTS Jewish Care (£1,000); Anthony Nolan and Cancer Research UK (£1,000 each); Combat Stress (£500); Different Strokes (£200); Step by Step (£100).
FINANCES *Financial year end* 05/04/2020 *Income* £88,400 *Total grants* £72,800 *Grants to organisations* £72,800 *Assets* £1,100,000

TRUSTEES Janet Bloch; Dominic Flynn; Judith Portrait.
HOW TO APPLY Contact the correspondent for further information.
CONTACT DETAILS The Trustees, Office Suite 1, Haslemere House, Lower Street, Haslemere, Surrey GU27 2HR *Tel.* 01428 652788 *Email* haslemere@knoxcropper.com

■ The Armed Forces Covenant Fund Trust

CC NO 1177627 **ESTABLISHED** 2018
WHERE FUNDING CAN BE GIVEN UK.
WHO CAN BENEFIT Organisations that support the armed forces community.
WHAT IS FUNDED Support for the armed forces community, including: social welfare; mental and physical health; education; employment; criminal justice.
TYPE OF GRANT Typically core and project costs.
RANGE OF GRANTS Typically less than £50,000, depending on programme.
SAMPLE GRANTS A full list of beneficiaries can be found on the website.
FINANCES *Financial year end* 31/03/2020 *Income* £10,040,000 *Total grants* £21,380,000 *Grants to organisations* £21,380,000 *Assets* £13,190,000
TRUSTEES Helen Helliwell; Wendy Cartwright; Commodore Rex Cox; General Sir John McColl; Gerald Oppenheim; John Pitt Brooke; Prof. David Rose; Anna Wright; Maj. General David Eastman; Cerys Gage; Lesley O'Rourke; John Mooney.
OTHER INFORMATION During the year, grants were distributed from three main funds: the Covenant Fund (£9.3 million), the Veterans' Mental Health and Well-being Fund (£9.2 million) and the Veterans' Community Centres Fund (£2.8 million). Open funding programmes are advertised on the website.
HOW TO APPLY Check the trust's website for current programmes and apply via the website.
CONTACT DETAILS Carol Stone, Director of Grants, 7 Hatherley Street, London SW1P 2QN *Tel.* 020 7154 1725 *Email* admin@covenantfund.org.uk *Website* https://www.covenantfund.org.uk

■ Armed Forces Education Trust

CC NO 1167682 **ESTABLISHED** 2016
WHERE FUNDING CAN BE GIVEN UK.
WHO CAN BENEFIT Schools/education providers (must be a registered charity or not-for-profit); individuals.
WHAT IS FUNDED Education of people under 25 who are or were dependants of serving or former members of the armed forces.
WHAT IS NOT FUNDED Capital projects; activities that should be funded by the Service Pupil Premium (in England); activities that the state has a legal obligation to provide.
TYPE OF GRANT Project funding.
SAMPLE GRANTS Salisbury Plain Academies (£42,700); Mayhill School (£23,000); Kinloss Primary School (£9,000); Newton Tony Primary (£1,300).
FINANCES *Financial year end* 31/08/2020 *Income* £403,300 *Total grants* £191,200 *Grants to organisations* £191,200 *Assets* £13,360,000
TRUSTEES Merrick Willis; Iain Buckle; Janet Melson; Alan Behagg; Jenny Lycett; Dominic Toriati; Maria Clohessy; Lucy Robinson; Tim Flesher.
OTHER INFORMATION Grants were paid to fifteen organisations during the year.
HOW TO APPLY Eligible organisations can submit applications via the trust's website.
CONTACT DETAILS The Trustees, PO Box 684, Farnham, Surrey GU9 1LP *Tel.* 07464 732000 *Email* admin@armedforceseducation.org *Website* https://www.armedforceseducation.org

■ The John Armitage Charitable Trust

CC NO 1079688 **ESTABLISHED** 2000
WHERE FUNDING CAN BE GIVEN England and Wales.
WHO CAN BENEFIT Registered charitable organisations.
WHAT IS FUNDED Disadvantaged children and youth support; education; medical care; research; arts and culture, prisoners and young offenders; religion.
TYPE OF GRANT Project funding.
RANGE OF GRANTS Grants up to £300,000.
SAMPLE GRANTS Harris Federation (£300,000); Shine (£80,000); Save Britain's Heritage, Cleanup UK and UK Community Foundation (£60,000 each).
FINANCES *Financial year end* 05/04/2020 *Income* £13,930,000 *Total grants* £2,970,000 *Grants to organisations* £2,970,000 *Assets* £109,520,000
TRUSTEES John Armitage; Catherine Armitage; William Francklin; Celina Francklin; Robert MacInnes.
OTHER INFORMATION Only the beneficiaries of the three largest grants were listed in the accounts. In total, 90 organisations were awarded grants.
HOW TO APPLY The trust does not accept unsolicited applications.
CONTACT DETAILS The Trustees, c/o Sampson West, Forum House, First Floor, 15–18 Lime Street, London EC3M 7AN *Tel.* 020 7404 5040

■ The Armourers' and Brasiers' Gauntlet Trust

CC NO 279204 **ESTABLISHED** 1979
WHERE FUNDING CAN BE GIVEN UK, with some preference for London.
WHO CAN BENEFIT Registered charities; small charities; schools; colleges; universities.
WHAT IS FUNDED Materials science; community projects; the armed forces; children and young people; education; health and medical research; the arts; arms or armour.
WHAT IS NOT FUNDED Maintenance, repair or restoration of buildings; individuals; projects outside the UK.
TYPE OF GRANT Core costs; project funding.
RANGE OF GRANTS £500 to £1,500.
SAMPLE GRANTS Wicked Weather Watch (£9,000); The Ulysses Trust (£2,000); Royal Armouries Museum (£250); United Guilds Service (£180).
FINANCES *Financial year end* 31/03/2020 *Income* £1,290,000 *Total grants* £286,500 *Grants to organisations* £218,600 *Assets* £8,450,000
TRUSTEES Prof. William Bonfield; Christopher Weston-Simons; Colonel David Davies; Edward Pitt; Michael Goulette; Nicola Davies.
OTHER INFORMATION In 2019/20 grants were awarded to 84 organisations and a further 141

grants totalling £67,900 were awarded to individuals.

HOW TO APPLY Apply via the charity's website.

CONTACT DETAILS Secretary, Armourers' Hall, 81 Coleman Street, London EC2R 5BJ *Tel.* 020 7374 4000 *Email* charities@armourershall.co.uk *Website* https://www.armourershall.co.uk/funding-grants

■ The Arsenal Foundation

CC NO 1145668 **ESTABLISHED** 2012

WHERE FUNDING CAN BE GIVEN Islington; Camden; Hackney; Barnet; Walthamstow; Hertsmere.

WHO CAN BENEFIT Charitable organisations and individuals.

WHAT IS FUNDED Social welfare; the provision of sports facilities; education of younger people.

SAMPLE GRANTS Save the Children (£597,200); Islington Giving and Willow (£50,000 each).

FINANCES *Financial year end* 31/05/2020 *Income* £386,000 *Total grants* £1,300,000 *Grants to organisations* £1,300,000 *Assets* £1,100,000

TRUSTEES Kenneth Friar; Vinaichandra Venkatesman; Andrew Jolly; David Miles; Svenja Geissmar; Frederick Hudson; Alan Sefton.

OTHER INFORMATION Grants are predominantly made through the Gunners Fund which supports local projects and good causes in the boroughs of Islington, Camden and Hackney by offering smaller grants of up to £2,500. During the year, the foundation awarded £56,200 through the Gunners Fund.

HOW TO APPLY Application forms are available to download from the foundation's website, along with grant-making guidelines. The foundation states that it is unable to respond to all of the applications it receives, so if you do not receive a response within one month, you should assume that you have been unsuccessful. Gunners fund application guidelines are available online at: www.arsenal.com/arsenalfoundation/local-giving/gunners-fund.

CONTACT DETAILS Samir Singh, Highbury House, 75 Drayton Park, London N5 1BU *Tel.* 020 7704 4406 *Email* ssingh@arsenal.co.uk *Website* www.arsenal.com/thearsenalfoundation

■ The Art Fund

CC NO 209174 **ESTABLISHED** 1903

WHERE FUNDING CAN BE GIVEN UK.

WHO CAN BENEFIT Public museums, galleries, historic houses, libraries and archives that are: open for at least half the week for at least six months a year; are fully or provisionally accredited under the Arts Council Scheme.

WHAT IS FUNDED The purchase of works of art; funding to borrow works from collections; funding for curators towards travel and other costs, to enable collections and exhibition research projects; grants for small projects which focus on: audience development; equality, diversity and inclusion; projects outside London; new partnerships.

WHAT IS NOT FUNDED A comprehensive list of exclusions can be found on the fund's helpful website.

TYPE OF GRANT Collections and acquisitions; training and development; display of art through tours and exhibitions.

RANGE OF GRANTS There is no fixed upper or lower limit to the size of grant the committee may offer. The charity usually only funds part of an acquisition.

SAMPLE GRANTS John Ruskin Library (£500,000 in two grants); Grosvenor Museum (£100,000); The Fruitmarket Gallery (£50,000); Headstone Manor and Museum (£650).

FINANCES *Financial year end* 31/12/2019 *Income* £17,000,000 *Total grants* £3,800,000 *Grants to organisations* £3,800,000 *Assets* £59,080,000

TRUSTEES Jeremy Palmer; Chris Smith; Anupam Ganguli; Axel Ruger; Alastair Laing; Madeleine Kennedy; Isaac Julien; Prof. Marcia Pointon; Prof. Marica Pointon; Katrina Brown; Tessa Jackson; Satish Padiyar; Monisha Shah; Dame Liz Forgan; Susan Rees; Philippa Glanville.

HOW TO APPLY Applications can be made via the charity's website.

CONTACT DETAILS Museum Services, 2 Granary Square, King's Cross, London N1C 4BH *Tel.* 020 7225 4800 *Email* info@artfund.org *Website* www.artfund.org

■ The Artemis Charitable Foundation

OSCR NO SC037857 **ESTABLISHED** 2007

WHERE FUNDING CAN BE GIVEN Worldwide.

WHO CAN BENEFIT UK registered charities.

WHAT IS FUNDED Health; social welfare; education and training; the environment; global disasters and emergency appeals.

SAMPLE GRANTS City Harvest (£128,100); The Robertson Trust (£70,200); Cool Earth (£50,400); Crisis (£20,000); Mary's Meals (£5,500); The Clink (£350).

FINANCES *Financial year end* 31/12/2019 *Income* £1,160,000 *Total grants* £1,230,000 *Grants to organisations* £1,230,000 *Assets* £670,000

OTHER INFORMATION According to the foundation's 2019 accounts, 'the foundation aims to have a primary core charity in each category and a junior core charity receiving less funding, with the option that this level of funding may be split over more than one junior charity in that activity.' The foundation is the corporate charity of Artemis Investment Management LLP.

HOW TO APPLY Apply in writing via email. Full details of what should be included in an application can be found on the foundation's website.

CONTACT DETAILS Marisa Charoskey, 6th Floor, Exchange Plaza, 50 Lothian Road, Edinburgh EH3 9BY *Email* charitablefoundation@artemisfunds.com *Website* https://www.artemisfunds.com/en/about-artemis/artemis-charitable-foundation

■ Douglas Arter Foundation

CC NO 201794 **ESTABLISHED** 1960

WHERE FUNDING CAN BE GIVEN UK, with a preference for Bristol, Somerset and Gloucestershire.

WHO CAN BENEFIT Registered charities only.

WHAT IS FUNDED Projects supporting people with disabilities.

WHAT IS NOT FUNDED Research; core costs; major funding appeals.

TYPE OF GRANT Project funding.

RANGE OF GRANTS Mostly between £250 and £500 but can be up to £2,500.

SAMPLE GRANTS Previous beneficiaries have included: Assist Trust, Build Charity, Challenge, Climbing Out, Deafway, Hamlet, Listening Books, REACT (Rapid Effective Assistance for Children with potentially Terminal illness), Wheely Boat and Willow Foundation.

FINANCES *Financial year end* 31/12/2019
Income £114,100 *Total grants* £86,800
Grants to organisations £86,800
Assets £3,450,000

TRUSTEES Geoffrey Arter; Belinda Arter; John Gurney; John Hudd; Peter Yardley.

OTHER INFORMATION The foundation received 358 applications and made 148 grants during the year.

HOW TO APPLY Apply in writing by post or email to the correspondent. Applications must include: the objectives of the appeal; funding already available; details of self-help; a timetable for the project; a copy of the latest audited accounts. Appeals should be for specific projects. Only successful applicants will be acknowledged. The trustees meet four times a year in the first week of March, June, September and December and cheques for grants will be sent by the second week of those months.

CONTACT DETAILS Belinda Arter, Trustee and Secretary to the Trustees, Fern Villa, Melksham Road, Patterdown, Chippenham, Wiltshire SN15 2NR *Tel.* 01249 448252 *Email* dafbristol@aol.com

■ Arts Council England

CC NO 1036733 **ESTABLISHED** 1994

WHERE FUNDING CAN BE GIVEN England.

WHO CAN BENEFIT Arts organisations; galleries; museums; libraries; artists and creative professionals.

WHAT IS FUNDED Developing, sustaining and promoting the arts.

WHAT IS NOT FUNDED Exclusions may vary depending upon the specific grant programme.

TYPE OF GRANT Mostly project funding.

RANGE OF GRANTS £1,000 to £100,000.

SAMPLE GRANTS A list of beneficiaries was not included in the annual report and accounts.

FINANCES *Financial year end* 31/03/2020
Income £760,960,000
Total grants £655,000,000
Grants to organisations £655,000,000
Assets £27,820,000

TRUSTEES Daren Henley; Laura Dyer; Simon Mellor; Liz Bushell; Mags Patten; Richard Bushell; Francis Runacres.

HOW TO APPLY There is a helpful 'Funding finder' facility on the council's website which allows users to browse the funding programmes operated by the council. This facility provides links to application forms and guidance as well as details about eligibility criteria and deadlines.

CONTACT DETAILS Enquiries Team, 21 Bloomsbury Street, London WC1B 3HF *Tel.* 0161 934 4317 *Website* www.artscouncil.org.uk

■ Arts Council of Northern Ireland

ESTABLISHED 1995

WHERE FUNDING CAN BE GIVEN Northern Ireland.

WHO CAN BENEFIT Artists; arts organisations.

WHAT IS FUNDED The Arts Council of Northern Ireland (ACNI) is the development and funding agency for the Arts in Northern Ireland. It distributes public money and National Lottery funds to develop and deliver a wide variety of arts projects, events and initiatives across Northern Ireland.

SAMPLE GRANTS Examples of projects supported by the council can be found on its website.

FINANCES *Financial year end* 31/03/2020
Income £1,660,000 *Total grants* £11,650,000
Grants to organisations £11,650,000
Assets (£3,060,000)

TRUSTEES Liam Hannaway; William Leatham; Julie Andrews; Lynne Best; Paul Boyle; Paul Brolly; Joe Dougan; Sean Kelly; Laura McCorry; Una McRory; Máirtín Ó Muilleoir; Dr Gearoid Trimble.

OTHER INFORMATION Details of all funding programmes and grants awarded can be found on the council's website. We took the grant total to be 'Expenditure on the arts', listed in the 2019/20 accounts.

HOW TO APPLY Information on what funding is currently available, guidelines and full details of how to apply can be found at the Arts Council of Northern Ireland website.

CONTACT DETAILS The Arts Development Department, 1 The Sidings, Antrim Road, Lisburn, County Antrim BT28 3AJ *Tel.* 028 9262 3555 *Email* info@artscouncil-ni.org *Website* www.artscouncil-ni.org

■ Arts Council of Wales (also known as Cyngor Celfyddydau Cymru)

CC NO 1034245 **ESTABLISHED** 1994

WHERE FUNDING CAN BE GIVEN Wales.

WHO CAN BENEFIT Arts organisations; schools; individuals.

WHAT IS FUNDED Arts activities and projects including: theatre; arts centres; opera; visual arts; dance; music; arts and young people; community arts; literature; circus and carnivals; disability arts.

TYPE OF GRANT Project funding; capital costs; training.

SAMPLE GRANTS Arts Active Trust (£185,200); Theatre Brycheiniog (£30,000); Company of Sirens (£21,000); Brecon Beacons Music Trust (£13,000); Dawns i Bawb (£5,400).

FINANCES *Financial year end* 31/03/2020
Income £35,790,000
Total grants £10,710,000
Grants to organisations £10,710,000
Assets £2,840,000

TRUSTEES Dr Sarah Younan; Phillip George; Kate Eden; Keith Murrell; Ruth Fabby; Prudence Thimbleby; Dafydd Gwyn Rhys; Lhosa Daly; Ceri Davies; Victoria Provis; Gwennan Jones; Elen Robert; Alison Mears; Devinda De Silva; Tafsila Khan; Iwan Bala; Yr Athro Tudur Hallam; Andrew Eagle.

HOW TO APPLY Details of the application process and application deadlines for each programme can be found on the council's website.

CONTACT DETAILS Grants and Information Department, Bute Place, Cardiff CF10 5AL *Tel.* 0330 124 2733 *Email* Contact form on website *Website* www.arts.wales

■ ArtSocial Foundation

CC NO 1163100 **ESTABLISHED** 2015

WHERE FUNDING CAN BE GIVEN Worldwide, with a preference for the UK and Russia.

WHO CAN BENEFIT Registered charities; museums and galleries.

WHAT IS FUNDED The use of art and arts therapies to transform the lives of disadvantaged and vulnerable young people with special needs, life-limiting health conditions or psychological trauma.

WHAT IS NOT FUNDED Individuals; for-profit organisations; unregistered charitable organisations.
TYPE OF GRANT Project funding; developmental funding.
RANGE OF GRANTS Up to £25,000.
SAMPLE GRANTS Otakar Kraus Music Trust (£22,400); Imperial Health Charity (£10,300); The V&A Museum (£9,100); Artcity Nights (£5,000); Koleso Obozrenia (£3,200); Revine Vozmozhnosti (£1,800); Latimer Community Art Therapy (£570).
FINANCES *Financial year end* 31/08/2019
Income £97,500 *Total grants* £52,300
Grants to organisations £52,300
Assets £70,700
TRUSTEES Alina Uspenskaya; Alina Davey; Anna Siakotos; Liza Oliver; Lali Margania.
OTHER INFORMATION Seven organisations were awarded grants during the year. The 2018/19 accounts were the latest available at the time of writing (January 2021).
HOW TO APPLY Contact the correspondent for further information.
CONTACT DETAILS Alina Uspenskaya, Trustee and Director, LCLB Suite 1756, Ground Floor, 95 Mortimer Street, London W1W 7GB *Email* info@artsocial.uk *Website* artsocial.uk

■ The Ove Arup Foundation

CC NO 328138 **ESTABLISHED** 1989
WHERE FUNDING CAN BE GIVEN UK and overseas.
WHO CAN BENEFIT Charitable organisations; universities; research organisations; CICs.
WHAT IS FUNDED The built environment, engineering, architecture, education.
WHAT IS NOT FUNDED Individuals.
TYPE OF GRANT Research and project costs, including start-up and feasibility costs.
RANGE OF GRANTS Mainly up to £48,000.
SAMPLE GRANTS University of Cambridge (£276,700); Terreform (£41,200); Landmark West (£8,200); The Institute of Fiscal Studies (£8,000); Arts Depot and The Designing and Making Educational Trust (£5,000 each); The Anglo–Danish Society (£2,500).
FINANCES *Financial year end* 31/03/2020
Income £523,800 *Total grants* £405,100
Grants to organisations £405,100
Assets £4,480,000
TRUSTEES Caroline Cole; Terry Hill; Gregory Hodkinson; Dr Andrew Chan; Faith Wainwright; Tim Chapman; Kate West; Alan Belfield.
HOW TO APPLY Application forms are available to download from the website. The trustees' meetings are held quarterly – early December, March, June and September. The trustees will consider applications received by the secretary by the middle of the preceding month.
CONTACT DETAILS John Ward, Secretary, Ove Arup and Partners, 13 Fitzroy Street, London W1T 4BQ *Tel.* 020 7636 1531
Email foundation@ovearupfoundation.org
Website www.ovearupfoundation.org

■ Ove Arup Partnership Charitable Trust

CC NO 1038737 **ESTABLISHED** 1978
WHERE FUNDING CAN BE GIVEN UK and overseas.
WHO CAN BENEFIT Registered charities; non-profit organisations in the UK and overseas; hospices; hospitals.
WHAT IS FUNDED Education; social care; health and welfare; disaster relief and poverty alleviation; local community development; sustainability; the environment and technology.
WHAT IS NOT FUNDED Individuals.
RANGE OF GRANTS Typically £500 to £60,000.
SAMPLE GRANTS The Ove Arup Foundation (£300,000); Frank Water (£60,000); The World's Big Sleep Out Trust (£45,000); Earthlinks UK (£31,900); International Development Enterprises – UK (£23,700); Class of Your Own and Social Mobility Foundation (£20,000 each); Northern Ireland Hospice (£1,000); MS Trust (£577); Birmingham Children's Hospital (£500).
FINANCES *Financial year end* 31/03/2020
Income £683,900 *Total grants* £709,300
Grants to organisations £709,300
Assets £20,400
TRUSTEE Ove Arup Partnership Trust Corporation Ltd.
OTHER INFORMATION The trust makes an annual donation to its sister charity, The Ove Arup Foundation. A further 16 organisations were supported in 2019/20.
HOW TO APPLY Apply in writing to the correspondent.
CONTACT DETAILS The Trustees, Ove Arup and Partners Ltd, 13 Fitzroy Street, London W1T 4BQ *Tel.* 020 7636 1531
Email foundation@ovearupfoundation.com

■ The Asda Foundation

CC NO 1124268 **ESTABLISHED** 2008
WHERE FUNDING CAN BE GIVEN England and Wales.
WHO CAN BENEFIT Registered charities and voluntary sector organisations.
WHAT IS FUNDED Community development.
RANGE OF GRANTS Up to £250,000.
SAMPLE GRANTS A list of beneficiaries was not included in the annual report and accounts. The foundation's website has some examples of good causes it has supported.
FINANCES *Financial year end* 31/12/2019
Income £4,110,000 *Total grants* £4,430,000
Grants to organisations £4,430,000
Assets £6,280,000
TRUSTEES Jane Earnshaw; Andrew Murray; Jason Martin; Susan Hennessey; John Cookman; Simon Lewis; Rukia Hussain; Jodie Tate; Patricia Mitchell.
OTHER INFORMATION The Asda Foundation is Asda's corporate charity. It supplements the good causes that colleagues support locally, as well as a number of bigger ad-hoc projects in local communities.
HOW TO APPLY Further information on how to apply for grants can be found on the foundation's website.
CONTACT DETAILS Grants Team, Asda House, Great Wilson Street, Leeds, West Yorkshire LS11 5AD
Email asdafoundation@asda.co.uk
Website www.asdafoundation.org

■ The Ashburnham Thanksgiving Trust

CC NO 249109 **ESTABLISHED** 1965
WHERE FUNDING CAN BE GIVEN UK and worldwide.
WHO CAN BENEFIT Individuals and Christian missions.
WHAT IS FUNDED Only Christian work already known to the trustees is supported, particularly evangelical overseas missionary work.
WHAT IS NOT FUNDED Building costs.
RANGE OF GRANTS £500 to £9,800.

SAMPLE GRANTS New Destiny Trust (£9,800); Ashburnham Christian Trust (£5,500); St Stephen's Society (£4,500); Wycliffe Bible Translators (£3,800); Stewards Trust (£2,000); Penhurst Retreat Centre (£1,500); RZIM Zacharias Trust (£1,600); Sharing Christ Internationally (£1,100); Titus Trust (£1,000); Swiss Church in London (£500).
FINANCES *Financial year end* 05/04/2020 *Income* £277,200 *Total grants* £104,900 *Grants to organisations* £81,600 *Assets* £7,810,000
TRUSTEES Edward Bickersteth; Robert Bickersteth; Dr Charles Warren.
OTHER INFORMATION Grants were awarded to 71 organisations and 13 individuals during the year.
HOW TO APPLY Unsolicited applications are not accepted.
CONTACT DETAILS The Trustees, Agmerhurst House, Kitchenham Road, Ashburnham, Battle, East Sussex TN33 9NB *Tel.* 01424 892253 *Email* att@lookingforward.biz

■ The Ashden Trust

CC NO 802623 **ESTABLISHED** 1989
WHERE FUNDING CAN BE GIVEN UK and overseas.
WHO CAN BENEFIT Registered charities.
WHAT IS FUNDED Tackling climate change. The trust has four programme areas: connecting people with nature; sustainable farming; stopping deforestation; aligning financial markets with the Paris Agreement.
WHAT IS NOT FUNDED Individuals.
TYPE OF GRANT Project funding; core costs, including salaries; research.
SAMPLE GRANTS Soil Association (£125,000); Amazon Watch (£65,900); Client Earth (£50,000); Sustain (£20,000); City Harvest (£1,000).
FINANCES *Financial year end* 05/04/2020 *Income* £1,370,000 *Total grants* £1,250,000 *Grants to organisations* £1,250,000 *Assets* £33,850,000
TRUSTEES Sarah Butler-Sloss; Claire Birch; Grace Yu.
OTHER INFORMATION The trust is one of the Sainsbury Family Charitable Trusts which share a common administration – see www.sftc.org.uk for more information.
HOW TO APPLY The trust does not generally accept unsolicited applications. However, the trust's website states: 'We may put out a "Call for Proposals" to expand one of our programme areas – this will set out what activities and type and size of organisation we are looking to fund.'
CONTACT DETAILS The Trustees, The Peak, 5 Wilton Road, London SW1V 1AP *Tel.* 020 7410 0330 *Email* ashdentrust@sfct.org.uk *Website* www.ashdentrust.org.uk

■ The Ashendene Trust

CC NO 270749 **ESTABLISHED** 1975
WHERE FUNDING CAN BE GIVEN London, Gloucestershire; West Berkshire; Wiltshire.
WHO CAN BENEFIT Registered charities.
WHAT IS FUNDED General charitable purposes; arts, culture, heritage, science; the environment/conservation/heritage; education and training; social welfare; religious activities; children and young people; older people.
WHAT IS NOT FUNDED Buildings; individuals.
RANGE OF GRANTS Generally up to £7,000.
SAMPLE GRANTS Whitley Fund for Nature (£7,000); P3 – People Potential Possibilities (£5,900); Enmore School, Outside in Art and RHS (£5,000 each).
FINANCES *Financial year end* 05/04/2019 *Income* £54,100 *Total grants* £54,200 *Grants to organisations* £54,200 *Assets* £1,270,000
TRUSTEES Nicholas Hornby; Camilla Pugh; James Spence.
OTHER INFORMATION The 2018/19 accounts were the latest available at the time of writing (January 2021).
HOW TO APPLY Contact the correspondent for further information.
CONTACT DETAILS The Trustees, 34 Sackville Street, London W1S 3ED *Tel.* 020 7036 4110

■ The Ashley Family Foundation

CC NO 288099 **ESTABLISHED** 1985
WHERE FUNDING CAN BE GIVEN England and Wales, with a preference for Wales.
WHO CAN BENEFIT Registered charities; unregistered charities supported by a registered charity.
WHAT IS FUNDED Development of rural communities; participation in the arts; community projects.
WHAT IS NOT FUNDED Individuals; business ventures; overseas projects; projects in the field of religion; dance-related projects; direct funding toward schools; retrospective funding for activities that have already taken place.
TYPE OF GRANT Revenue proposals are favoured over capital requests. Funding is generally awarded to one-off projects but the trustees will consider funding a project over a number of years (up to three).
RANGE OF GRANTS Mostly under £10,000.
SAMPLE GRANTS Black Mountains College (£45,000); Green Man and Outside Edge Theatre Company (£10,000 each); Brighton Fringe (£5,000); Pembrokeshire Remakery (£4,100); Belfield Farms (£980).
FINANCES *Financial year end* 30/09/2019 *Income* £346,300 *Total grants* £373,500 *Grants to organisations* £373,500 *Assets* £13,710,000
TRUSTEES Anita George; Emma Shuckburgh; Jeremy McIlroy; Alexis Korner; Julian Ashley; Laura Ashley; Prof. Oriana Bradley.
OTHER INFORMATION The 2018/19 accounts were the latest available at the time of writing (June 2021).
HOW TO APPLY Applications can be made online through the foundation's website. Applicants are encouraged to read the grants criteria on the website and speak to the foundation before applying. If you would like to discuss your application in Welsh, please call Ffion Roberts at the Community Foundation in Wales, on 029 2037 9580.
CONTACT DETAILS The Administrator, 6 Trull Farm Buildings, Trull, Tetbury, Gloucestershire GL8 8SQ *Tel.* 0303 040 1005 *Email* info@ashleyfamilyfoundation.org.uk *Website* www.ashleyfamilyfoundation.org.uk

■ The Ashworth Charitable Trust

CC NO 1045492 **ESTABLISHED** 1995
WHERE FUNDING CAN BE GIVEN UK; Devon; overseas.
WHO CAN BENEFIT Charitable organisations.
WHAT IS FUNDED Humanitarian causes; social welfare.
WHAT IS NOT FUNDED Charities which are not UK-registered; individuals; charities with a turnover

of over £1 million; charities with disproportionately large reserves, unless there is an exceptional reason; animal welfare; projects promoting religious proselytization or partisan political activities; charities mainly involved in research; heritage; museums; UK hospices.

TYPE OF GRANT Project funding.

RANGE OF GRANTS £2,500 to £5,000.

SAMPLE GRANTS Network for a Better World (£10,000); Adventure Ashram (£4,000); Dartmouth Caring and Refugee Support – Devon (£3,000 each); Golden Oldies (£1,000).

FINANCES *Financial year end* 05/04/2020 *Income* £202,700 *Total grants* £178,500 *Grants to organisations* £178,500 *Assets* £4,980,000

TRUSTEES Sharareh Rouhipour; Katherine Gray; Kian Golestani; Ian Miles; Hoshmand Rouhipour; Dr Wendi Momen.

OTHER INFORMATION Grants were awarded to 53 organisations.

HOW TO APPLY Apply online via the trust's website. The website states: 'Our solicitors should only be contacted as a last resort in the event of a genuine complication or crisis, as they are not in a position to comment on the progress of an application or the decision of the trustees.'

CONTACT DETAILS Trish O'Neill, Veale Wasbrough Vizards LLP, Second Floor, 3 Brindleyplace, Birmingham B1 2JB *Email* admin@ashworthtrust.org *Website* www.ashworthtrust.org

■ The Ian Askew Charitable Trust

CC NO 264515 **ESTABLISHED** 1972

WHERE FUNDING CAN BE GIVEN UK, with a preference for Sussex.

WHO CAN BENEFIT Charitable organisations; schools; churches, chapels and other historically significant buildings; individuals.

WHAT IS FUNDED General charitable purposes; education; conservation and restoration of historic buildings; agriculture, horticulture and arboriculture.

RANGE OF GRANTS Generally up to £2,000.

SAMPLE GRANTS The Sussex Community Foundation (£25,000); Ringmer Area Community Land Trust (£10,000); Berwick (Sussex) Conservation Trust (£4,000); Jamie's Farm (£2,000); Care For Veterans and Clowns in the Sky (£1,000 each); Saltdean Lido Trust (£500); The Sussex Historic Churches Trust (£100).

FINANCES *Financial year end* 05/04/2020 *Income* £492,700 *Total grants* £175,800 *Grants to organisations* £175,800 *Assets* £20,640,000

TRUSTEES Rory Askew; James Rank; John Hecks; Henriette Marshall; Venetia Harrison; Keith Buckland.

OTHER INFORMATION The trust made a larger grant of £25,000 to Sussex Community Foundation which was then distributed to several beneficiaries in grants ranging from £1,000 to £3,000.

HOW TO APPLY Contact the correspondent for further information.

CONTACT DETAILS The Trustees, Coney Hall, Sharpsbridge Lane, Newick, East Sussex BN8 4SA *Tel.* 01825 723302 *Email* carruthers@mistral.co.uk

■ The Associated Board of the Royal Schools of Music

CC NO 292182 **ESTABLISHED** 1985

WHERE FUNDING CAN BE GIVEN UK; overseas.

WHO CAN BENEFIT Registered charities.

WHAT IS FUNDED Music education.

TYPE OF GRANT Project funding.

RANGE OF GRANTS £5,000 to £25,000.

SAMPLE GRANTS National Youth Orchestra (£31,000); Commonwealth Resounds and Young Urban Arts Foundation (£10,000 each); Tinderbox Project (£8,000); Southbank Sinfonia (£6,000).

FINANCES *Financial year end* 31/01/2020 *Income* £49,780,000 *Total grants* £7,000,000 *Grants to organisations* £5,982,000 *Assets* (£1,730,000)

TRUSTEES Prof. Colin Lawson; Prof. Jeffrey Sharkey; Prof. Linda Merrick; Kevin Porter; Judith Barber; John Cunningham; Douglas Gardner; Alan Smith; David Roper; Damian Wisniewski; Jeremy Heap; Prof. Jonathan Attwood.

OTHER INFORMATION Grants were broken down as follows: support for the four Royal Schools of Music (£5.6 million); scholarships (£1.05 million); music education (£382,000).

HOW TO APPLY Visit the charity's website for the latest information.

CONTACT DETAILS The Trustees, Associated Board of the Royal Schools of Music, 4 London Wall Place, London EC2Y 5AU *Tel.* 020 7636 5400 *Email* abrsm@abrsm.ac.uk *Website* www.abrsm.org

■ Keren Association Ltd

CC NO 313119 **ESTABLISHED** 1961

WHERE FUNDING CAN BE GIVEN UK and overseas.

WHO CAN BENEFIT Charitable organisations, mainly those benefitting Jewish people.

WHAT IS FUNDED General charitable purposes, including the advancement of education, the provision of religious instruction and training in Orthodox Judaism and the relief of need.

TYPE OF GRANT Capital costs; project funding; development funding.

RANGE OF GRANTS Up to £1 million.

SAMPLE GRANTS Friends of Mercaz Hatorah Belz Macnivka (£2.6 million); China Vechisda (£1.3 million); Achisomoch Aid Company Ltd (£1.1 million); Heichalei Hakodesh (£751,000); Parkwill Ltd (£550,000); United Talmudical Associates Ltd (£356,000); Society of Friends of the Torah Ltd (£167,000); Agudat Yeshivat Belz Machnovk (£125,000); Emuno Educational Centre Ltd (£69,000); Ezer Viznitz Foundation (£59,000).

FINANCES *Financial year end* 31/03/2020 *Income* £2,910,000 *Total grants* £13,840,000 *Grants to organisations* £13,840,000 *Assets* £3,850,000

TRUSTEES A Perlman; Mrs H. Weiss; Mr E. Englander; Mrs N. Weiss; I. Englander; S. Englander; J. Stern; Mr S. Englander; P. Englander.

OTHER INFORMATION Only beneficiaries of grants over £50,000 were listed in the accounts. Grants below £50,000 totalled £1.49 million.

HOW TO APPLY Contact the correspondent for further information. The annual report for 2019/20 states: 'The trustees consider all requests which they receive and make donations based on the level of funds available to charities whose purpose fall within the objects of the Charitable Company.'

CONTACT DETAILS The Trustees, 129 Stamford Hill, London N16 5TW *Tel.* 020 8800 9677 *Email* mail@cohenarnold.com

■ Asthma UK

CC NO 802364 **ESTABLISHED** 1990

WHERE FUNDING CAN BE GIVEN UK.

WHO CAN BENEFIT Research organisations; universities; medical and academic professionals.

WHAT IS FUNDED Research into asthma. Priority areas can be broadly split into six themes: asthma biology; asthma types; asthma management; asthma diagnosis; asthma prevention; asthma treatments.

TYPE OF GRANT Project grants; research; fellowships and studentships.

SAMPLE GRANTS University of Edinburgh (£2 million); Kings College London and University of Leicester (£250,000 each).

FINANCES *Financial year end* 30/09/2019 *Income* £8,441,000 *Total grants* £2,750,000 *Grants to organisations* £2,750,000 *Assets* £8,518,000

TRUSTEES Prof. Ian Hall; John Tucker; Martin Sinclair; George Anson; Dr Paul Anson; Dr Paul Hodgkin; Prof. Sir Lewis Ritchie; Jean-Francois Bessiron; James Bowes; Katherine Morgan; Dr Yvonne Braun; Prof. Ian Sabroe; Niren Patel.

OTHER INFORMATION The 2018/19 accounts were the latest available at the time of writing (January 2021).

HOW TO APPLY Details of current funding opportunities can be found on the website. Applications are accepted through the charity's online research management system.

CONTACT DETAILS Research Team, 18 Mansell Street, London E1 8AA *Tel.* 0300 222 5800 *Email* research@asthma.org.uk *Website* https://www.asthma.org.uk/research/researchers

■ The Astor Foundation

CC NO 225708 **ESTABLISHED** 1963

WHERE FUNDING CAN BE GIVEN UK.

WHO CAN BENEFIT Medical research organisations and registered charities.

WHAT IS FUNDED Medical research; children and young people; disability; the countryside; the arts; sports; carers groups; animal welfare.

TYPE OF GRANT Research; core/revenue costs; project funding; capital costs; strategic funding.

RANGE OF GRANTS Generally between £250 and £2,000.

SAMPLE GRANTS The Destitution Project (£77,000); Alzheimer's Society (£3,000); Action on Elder Abuse (£1,000); Erb's Palsy Group and Perthes Association (£500 each).

FINANCES *Financial year end* 05/04/2020 *Income* £123,500 *Total grants* £113,000 *Grants to organisations* £113,000 *Assets* £4,040,000

TRUSTEES The Hon. Tania Astor; Lord Latymer; Prof. Sir John Cunningham; Robert Astor; Charles Astor.

HOW TO APPLY Applications should be in writing to the correspondent and must include accounts and an annual report if available. The trustees meet twice yearly, usually in October and April. If the appeal arrives too late for one meeting it will automatically be carried over for consideration at the next. An acknowledgement will be sent on receipt of an appeal. No further communication will be entered into unless the trustees raise any queries regarding the appeal, or unless the appeal is subsequently successful.

CONTACT DETAILS Mrs L. Rothwell-Orr, Secretary, PO Box 168, Bideford EX39 6WB *Tel.* 07957 954507 *Email* astor.foundation@gmail.com

■ John Atcheson Foundation

CCNI NO NIC103846 **ESTABLISHED** 1993

WHERE FUNDING CAN BE GIVEN UK, with a preference for Northern Ireland.

WHO CAN BENEFIT Charitable organisations.

WHAT IS FUNDED Social welfare; people with disabilities; older people.

SAMPLE GRANTS Marie Curie (£20,000); The Prince's Trust (£12,000); Air Ambulance (£11,000); Northern Ireland Polio Fellowship and The Linenhall Library (£2,500 each).

FINANCES *Financial year end* 05/04/2019 *Income* £141,000 *Total grants* £125,000 *Grants to organisations* £125,000 *Assets* £3,640,000

TRUSTEES David McCleane; Aileen Martin; John Knaggs; Rosemary O'Callaghan; Mark Regan.

OTHER INFORMATION The 2018/19 accounts were the latest available at the time of writing (May 2021).

HOW TO APPLY Contact the correspondent for further information.

CONTACT DETAILS Christopher McClean, c/o Cunningham Coates Stockbrokers, 32–38 Linehall Street, Belfast BT2 8BG *Tel.* 028 9072 3000

■ Atkin Charitable Foundation

CC NO 1112925 **ESTABLISHED** 2006

WHERE FUNDING CAN BE GIVEN UK; Israel.

WHO CAN BENEFIT Registered charities; hospices; hospitals; museums and galleries; universities.

WHAT IS FUNDED General charitable purposes; Jewish causes.

RANGE OF GRANTS Mostly up to £10,000; some grants of up to £100,000.

SAMPLE GRANTS Roundhouse Trust (£85,000); JAMI (£50,000); Jewish Care (£35,000); Great Ormond Street Hospital Children's Charity (£20,000); Design Museum and National Holocaust Centre and Museum (£10,000 each); Royal Academy of Art (£8,400).

FINANCES *Financial year end* 05/04/2019 *Income* £638,600 *Total grants* £814,400 *Grants to organisations* £814,400 *Assets* £5,270,000

TRUSTEES Barry Gold; Raymond Harris; Ross Atkin; Celia Atkin; Edward Atkin; Lara Atkin.

OTHER INFORMATION Grants of under £8,000 totalled £125,500. The 2018/19 accounts were the latest available at the time of writing (January 2021).

HOW TO APPLY Contact the correspondent for further information.

CONTACT DETAILS Raymond Harris, Trustee, 16 Rosemont Road, London NW3 6NE *Tel.* 020 7472 6500

■ The Atlas Fund

CC NO 278030 **ESTABLISHED** 1979

WHERE FUNDING CAN BE GIVEN UK.

WHO CAN BENEFIT Registered charities; churches; schools.

WHAT IS FUNDED General charitable purposes.

RANGE OF GRANTS Generally £1,000 to £5,000.

SAMPLE GRANTS Alzheimer's Society (£5,000); Oxfam (£3,000); Amber Foundation (£2,000); Age UK and Marie Curie (£1,000 each).
FINANCES *Financial year end* 31/03/2020 *Income* £85,600 *Total grants* £84,000 *Grants to organisations* £84,000 *Assets* £2,500,000
TRUSTEES Lady Hester Touche; Peter Touche; Helen Hoffman; Mr W. G. Touche.
HOW TO APPLY Contact the correspondent for further information.
CONTACT DETAILS The Trustees, Stane House, Stane Street, Ockley, Dorking, Surrey RH5 5TQ *Tel.* 01306 627397 *Email* toucheockley@btinternet.com

■ Atlas Memorial Ltd

CCNI NO NIC101043 **ESTABLISHED** 2015
WHERE FUNDING CAN BE GIVEN Worldwide.
WHO CAN BENEFIT Jewish organisations; places of worship.
WHAT IS FUNDED Jewish religion and religious education; relief of poverty for Jewish communities; maintenance of buildings used for religious practice.
TYPE OF GRANT General funding; capital costs (including maintenance).
RANGE OF GRANTS Up to £500,000, mostly up to £50,000.
SAMPLE GRANTS Asser Bishvil Foundation (£412,200); United Talmudical Association (£340,000); Kollel Shomrei Hachomos (£120,000); Chaim Charitable Company Ltd (£77,000); Inspirations (£65,000); Bayis Lepleitos (£51,000).
FINANCES *Financial year end* 31/01/2020 *Income* £1,440,000 *Total grants* £2,160,000 *Grants to organisations* £2,160,000 *Assets* £4,120,000
TRUSTEES Joel Gross; Abraham Gross; Israel Gross; Berish Gross.
OTHER INFORMATION Grants of under £50,000 totalled £643,500 during the year.
HOW TO APPLY Contact the correspondent for further information.
CONTACT DETAILS Michael Salomon, 86 Filey Avenue, London N16 6JJ *Tel.* 020 8806 0088

■ Lawrence Atwell's Charity (Skinners' Company)

CC NO 210773 **ESTABLISHED** 1988
WHERE FUNDING CAN BE GIVEN England and Wales with priority given to London and Kent.
WHO CAN BENEFIT Charitable organisations; individuals.
WHAT IS FUNDED Education and training for young people from low income backgrounds.
WHAT IS NOT FUNDED See the grant-maker's website for a full list of exclusions.
TYPE OF GRANT Project funding. Up to three years.
RANGE OF GRANTS Up to £10,000.
SAMPLE GRANTS Catch22 (£20,000); Prisoners' Education Trust (£15,000); Camden Spear Trust and The Big House (£10,000 each); The Treloar Trust (£8,400).
FINANCES *Financial year end* 30/06/2020 *Income* £826,500 *Total grants* £489,200 *Grants to organisations* £316,500 *Assets* £17,210,000
TRUSTEE The Worshipful Company of Skinners.
OTHER INFORMATION Grants to individuals totalled £172,700.
HOW TO APPLY For the Charities Programme, the trust asks applicants to contact them by email with a short outline of the project. If you are eligible, the charity will be in touch with full details of how to apply. Further information including application deadlines can be found on the charity's website.
CONTACT DETAILS Grants Officer, Skinners' Hall, 8 Dowgate Hill, London EC4R 2SP *Tel.* 020 7236 5629 *Email* atwell@skinners.org.uk *Website* https://www.skinners.org.uk/grants-and-trusts/atwell

■ The Aurelius Charitable Trust

CC NO 271333 **ESTABLISHED** 1975
WHERE FUNDING CAN BE GIVEN UK.
WHO CAN BENEFIT Registered charities; unregistered charities; universities; religious bodies/institutions.
WHAT IS FUNDED Conservation/preservation of culture inherited from the past; the dissemination of knowledge, particularly in the humanities field; research or publications.
WHAT IS NOT FUNDED Individuals.
RANGE OF GRANTS Mostly £2,000 to £5,000.
SAMPLE GRANTS The College of Arms (£4,800); Berwick Conservation Trust (£4,500); Textile Conservation Trust (£2,500); Minehead Museum (£500).
FINANCES *Financial year end* 05/04/2020 *Income* £94,600 *Total grants* £93,000 *Grants to organisations* £93,000 *Assets* £2,120,000
TRUSTEES William Wallis; Philip Haynes.
HOW TO APPLY Apply in writing to the correspondent. Grants are generally made on the recommendation of the trust's board of advisors. Unsolicited applications will only be responded to if an sae is included. The trustees meet twice a year.
CONTACT DETAILS The Trustees, Briarsmead, Old Road, Buckland, Betchworth, Surrey RH3 7DU *Tel.* 01737 842186 *Email* philip.haynes@tiscali.co.uk

■ The Lord Austin Trust

CC NO 208394 **ESTABLISHED** 1937
WHERE FUNDING CAN BE GIVEN Birmingham City, Dudley, Sandwell, Solihull, Walsall.
WHO CAN BENEFIT Hospitals, medical organisations and charities in England, restricted to: local charities based in Birmingham and West Midlands; national organisations (but not their provincial branches).
WHAT IS FUNDED General charitable purposes; health; medical research; the welfare and education of disadvantaged children; older people; community projects.
WHAT IS NOT FUNDED Individuals.
SAMPLE GRANTS Previous beneficiaries have included: Acorns Children's Hospice Trust; All Saints Youth Project; Army Benevolent Fund; Avoncroft Museum; Birmingham St Mary's Hospice; Broadening Choices for Older People; Children's Heart Foundation; City of Birmingham Symphony Orchestra; Queen Elizabeth Hospital Birmingham; Saltley Neighbourhood Pensioner's Centre; St Martin's Centre for Health and Healing; Tamworth Nursery (Special Needs).
FINANCES *Financial year end* 31/03/2020 *Income* £132,200 *Total grants* £103,800 *Grants to organisations* £103,800 *Assets* £3,560,000

TRUSTEES Rodney Spencer Kettel; Keith Dudley; Neil Andrews; Robert Hunt.

OTHER INFORMATION Grants were made to 65 organisations and can be broken down as follows: miscellaneous (£34,300); medical causes (£32,000); children and young people (£30,500); older people (£7,000).

HOW TO APPLY Apply in writing to the correspondent, including a set of recent accounts. The trustees meet twice a year to consider grants.

CONTACT DETAILS Chrissy Norgrove, Administrator, The Estate Office, Wharf Cottage, Broombank, Tenbury Wells, Worcestershire WR15 8NY *Tel.* 07799 784019 *Email* chrissy@lordaustintrust.org.uk

■ The Avon and Somerset Police Community Trust

CC NO 1076770 **ESTABLISHED** 1999

WHERE FUNDING CAN BE GIVEN The Avon and Somerset Constabulary area.

WHO CAN BENEFIT Charitable organisations; community and voluntary organisations.

WHAT IS FUNDED Projects that work towards reducing crime in the local community.

WHAT IS NOT FUNDED Individuals; expeditions and trips; bursaries or scholarships; replacements of statutory funding and salaries; projects that fall outside the Avon and Somerset Constabulary area; building costs are given a very low priority; further applications within a period of three years (for the General fund).

TYPE OF GRANT Project funding; core/revenue costs.

RANGE OF GRANTS Usually up to £50,000.

SAMPLE GRANTS A list of beneficiaries was not included in the annual report and accounts.

FINANCES *Financial year end* 31/03/2020 *Income* £287,200 *Total grants* £211,100 *Grants to organisations* £211,100 *Assets* £538,300

TRUSTEES Patricia Hunt; Paul Hooper; Andy Marsh; Sue Mountstevens; James Makepeace; David Wood; Roger Opie; Robert Bernays.

HOW TO APPLY Applications are made through the funder's website. See each fund's page for criteria, guidance and deadlines.

CONTACT DETAILS Trust Manager, PO Box 37, Valley Road, Portishead, Bristol BS20 8QJ *Tel.* 01278 646650 *Email* policecommunitytrust@avonandsomerset.police.uk *Website* https://www.avonandsomerset.police.uk/services/police-community-trust

■ Axis Foundation

CC NO 1126117 **ESTABLISHED** 2009

WHERE FUNDING CAN BE GIVEN London; South of England; Midlands; Wales.

WHO CAN BENEFIT Registered charities; community organisations; schools; individuals.

WHAT IS FUNDED General charitable purposes; small/local projects or causes.

WHAT IS NOT FUNDED National appeals; projects that are non-inclusive and are not open to all individuals and communities irrespective of gender, race or faith; the advancement of religion or religious groups unless they offer a non-religious service to the local community; work outside the UK; replacement of statutory funding; projects of a political nature; animal welfare.

RANGE OF GRANTS Generally up to £10,000.

SAMPLE GRANTS Demelza Hospice (£68,400); Sparks Charity (£12,400); For Jimmy (£10,000); Swale Gloves (£6,000); Choir with No Name, Imber Metz, Stepney City Farm and TAG Youth Club (£5,000 each).

FINANCES *Financial year end* 31/03/2019 *Income* £375,000 *Total grants* £167,700 *Grants to organisations* £167,700 *Assets* £274,800

TRUSTEES Peter Varney; John Hayes; Michael Hayes; Timothy Hayes; Maurice Gertsky; Sandra Ryan; Yusef Ibrahim.

OTHER INFORMATION Only organisations receiving grants of over £5,000 were listed as beneficiaries in the charity's accounts. Grants of under £5,000 totalled £51,000 and were awarded to 29 organisations. The 2018/19 accounts were the latest available at the time of writing (January 2021).

HOW TO APPLY Applications can be made via the foundation's website.

CONTACT DETAILS The Trustees, Tramway House, 3 Tramway Avenue, Stratford E15 4PN *Tel.* 020 7564 2100 *Email* info@axisfoundation.com *Website* https://www.axisfoundation.org

■ The Aylesford Family Charitable Trust

CC NO 328299 **ESTABLISHED** 1989

WHERE FUNDING CAN BE GIVEN West Midlands and Warwickshire.

WHO CAN BENEFIT Registered charities; hospices; universities; schools; churches.

WHAT IS FUNDED General charitable purposes.

WHAT IS NOT FUNDED Individuals.

RANGE OF GRANTS Typically £250 to £5,000.

SAMPLE GRANTS St James' Church – Great Packington (£8,500); Trinity College Cambridge (£1,500); West London Free School Primary (£1,000); Bumblebee Conservation Trust, The Friendship Project and The Institute of Cancer Research (£500 each); Cancer Research and The Royal British Legion (£250 each).

FINANCES *Financial year end* 05/04/2020 *Income* £65,300 *Total grants* £72,700 *Grants to organisations* £72,700 *Assets* £1,970,000

TRUSTEES Lord Charles Aylesford; Lady Aylesford.

OTHER INFORMATION In 2019/20 the trust made grants to 100 organisations.

HOW TO APPLY Apply in writing to the correspondent.

CONTACT DETAILS The Trustees, Packington Hall, Meriden, Warwickshire CV7 7HF *Tel.* 01676 522020 *Email* sam@packingtonestate.co.uk

■ Backstage Trust

CC NO 1145887 **ESTABLISHED** 2012

WHERE FUNDING CAN BE GIVEN UK.

WHO CAN BENEFIT Registered charities; theatres.

WHAT IS FUNDED Supports theatre, music and the performing arts for disadvantaged and young people.

WHAT IS NOT FUNDED Individuals.

TYPE OF GRANT Core costs; capital costs; project funding; strategic funding; development funding.

RANGE OF GRANTS Up to £500,000.

SAMPLE GRANTS Roundhouse Theatre (£500,000); Royal Academy of Music (£385,000); Old Vic Theatre (£200,000); Roots Theatre (£100,000); World Heart Beat Music (£75,000); Liverpool Everyman and Playhouse (£50,000); Arts & Business Cymru (£40,000).

FINANCES *Financial year end* 05/04/2020 *Income* £4,200,000 *Total grants* £4,110,000 *Grants to organisations* £4,110,000 *Assets* £2,100,000

TRUSTEES Lady Susan Sainsbury; Dominic Flynn; David Wood.

OTHER INFORMATION Only organisations receiving grants of over £35,000 were listed as beneficiaries in the charity's accounts. Grants of under £35,000 totalled £651,00.

HOW TO APPLY Apply in writing to the correspondent.

CONTACT DETAILS The Trustees, North House, 27 Great Peter Street, London SW1P 3LN *Tel.* 020 7072 4498 *Email* info@backstagetrust.org.uk

■ The Tim Bacon Foundation

CC NO 1173108 **ESTABLISHED** 2006

WHERE FUNDING CAN BE GIVEN The North West.

WHO CAN BENEFIT Registered charities.

WHAT IS FUNDED Cancer research.

TYPE OF GRANT Research.

SAMPLE GRANTS Kidscan (£99,000); Prevent Breast Cancer (£46,800) Maggie's (£18,400).

FINANCES *Financial year end* 31/03/2020 *Income* £135,000 *Total grants* £164,200 *Grants to organisations* £164,200 *Assets* £219,800

TRUSTEES Michelle Gandy; Chris Hill; Peter Martin; Alec Gutherie; Jeremy Roberts; David Mansbridge; Michael Perls.

HOW TO APPLY Applications can be made via the foundation's website. Applications are reviewed annually. The deadline for receipt of applications is 31 December.

CONTACT DETAILS The Trustees, 98 King Street, Knutsford, Cheshire WA16 6HQ *Tel.* 01565 631234 *Email* info@timbaconfoundation.co.uk *Website* www.timbaconfoundation.co.uk

■ The Scott Bader Commonwealth Ltd

CC NO 206391 **ESTABLISHED** 1951

WHERE FUNDING CAN BE GIVEN Worldwide.

WHO CAN BENEFIT Charitable organisations.

WHAT IS FUNDED Social welfare, education and training, overseas aid, conservation, children and young people, socially excluded and disadvantaged people, women and minority communities.

WHAT IS NOT FUNDED Animal welfare; individual sponsorships; travel and adventure schemes; arts projects; any form of advertising; medical research and equipment; amateur sports clubs; general charitable appeals; construction/renovation/maintenance of buildings in the UK.

TYPE OF GRANT Capital and core costs.

SAMPLE GRANTS Rock UK, Rockingham Forest Trust and Wollaston Heritage Association (£2,000 each); Wollaston Primary School (£1,800); Adrenaline Alley (£500).

FINANCES *Financial year end* 31/12/2019 *Income* £343,000 *Total grants* £235,800 *Grants to organisations* £235,800 *Assets* £1,390,000

TRUSTEES Robert Gibson; David Harris; Hansi Manning; Agne Bengtsson; Jessica Clark; Prof. Heather Davidson; Paul Smith: David Black; Andrew Bell.

OTHER INFORMATION Grants made to UK organisations totalled £45,700, of which £36,200 was awarded through the nomination scheme whereby staff of Scott Bader can nominate a charity of their choice.

HOW TO APPLY Information regarding the application process and deadlines for the large project funding scheme, as well as assessment criteria and application forms, can be found via the fund's website.

CONTACT DETAILS Hayley Sutherland, Secretary, Scott Bader Commonwealth Ltd, Wollaston, Wellingborough, Northamptonshire NN29 7RL *Tel.* 01933 666755 *Website* https://www.scottbader.com/humanity/our-society/how-to-access-funds

■ The Bagri Foundation

CC NO 1000219 **ESTABLISHED** 1990

WHERE FUNDING CAN BE GIVEN Mainly UK and India.

WHO CAN BENEFIT Charitable organisations; individuals.

WHAT IS FUNDED Artistic, cultural, research and digital projects that celebrate and promote Asian culture; innovative cross-disciplinary projects that examine traditional and contemporary Asian culture; support for emerging artists from Asia; education; health.

SAMPLE GRANTS A list of beneficiaries was not available in the accounts.

FINANCES *Financial year end* 30/06/2019 *Income* £617,000 *Total grants* £543,200 *Grants to organisations* £535,800 *Assets* £13,210,000

TRUSTEES Lady Bagri; Hon. Mr A. Bagri; Hon. Mrs A. Bagri; Amisha Bagri; Aditi Malhotra.

OTHER INFORMATION The 2018/19 accounts were the latest available at the time of writing (June 2021). Grants to organisations were broken down as follows: culture (£345,700), education (£134,000), health (£56,200). In addition, grants to individuals totalled £7,400. Previous beneficiaries and current projects can be seen on the website.

HOW TO APPLY Apply in writing to the correspondent.

CONTACT DETAILS The Trustees, c/o Ferguson Maidment and Co., 167 Fleet street, London EC4A 2EA *Tel.* 020 7280 0000 *Email* enquiries@bagrifoundation.org *Website* bagrifoundation.org

The Austin Bailey Foundation

CC NO 514912 **ESTABLISHED** 1984

WHERE FUNDING CAN BE GIVEN Swansea and overseas.

WHO CAN BENEFIT Registered charities; CICs; hospices; churches.

WHAT IS FUNDED Social welfare and Christian churches in Swansea; overseas aid and relief.

WHAT IS NOT FUNDED Medical research, apart from in exceptional circumstances; individuals; organisations which are not registered charities or churches; building or refurbishment projects.

TYPE OF GRANT Core/revenue costs; project funding; seed funding/start-up funding.

RANGE OF GRANTS £500 to £1,000.

SAMPLE GRANTS Pump Aid (£4,000); St Thomas Church – Swansea (£2,500); Temwa (£1,000); Surfability (£1,000); Kids Cancer Charity (£550); Clydach Community Garden (£500).

FINANCES *Financial year end* 05/04/2020 *Income* £367,400 *Total grants* £111,500 *Grants to organisations* £111,500 *Assets* £1,210,000

TRUSTEES Dr Sourour Mikhail; Revd Steven Buting; James Leach; Sandra Morton; Sian Popper; Sally Goldstone; Eleanor Norton; Clive Bailey.

HOW TO APPLY Application forms are available to download from the trust's website and should be submitted by email. The trustees normally meet in April, September and December. Applications should be submitted by the middle of the month before the next meeting.

CONTACT DETAILS Sandra Morton, Trustee, Eastmoor Resource Centre, St Barnabas Church, Hawthorne Avenue, Swansea SA2 0LP *Tel.* 01792 473569 *Email* localcharities@austinbaileyfoundation.org *Website* www.austinbaileyfoundation.org

The Baily Thomas Charitable Fund

CC NO 262334 **ESTABLISHED** 1971

WHERE FUNDING CAN BE GIVEN UK.

WHO CAN BENEFIT Registered and exempt charities; schools and parent teacher associations. Applications for research grants will only be considered from university departments.

WHAT IS FUNDED Research into learning disabilities (mainly the development of initial-stage research projects); the care and relief of those affected by learning disabilities.

WHAT IS NOT FUNDED Individuals; CICs; statutory funding. A full list of exclusions is available on the fund's helpful website.

TYPE OF GRANT Capital and revenue costs for both specific projects and for general running/core costs; research costs, including salaries; fellowships.

RANGE OF GRANTS Small grants: £250 to £10,000; general grants: £10,000 to £100,000.

SAMPLE GRANTS King's College London (£111,900); University of Cambridge (£51,900); University of Sheffield (£40,200); The Hextol Foundation (£30,000); The Chronicle Sunshine Fund (£25,500); Abbey Court School Trust and Pennyhooks Farm Trust (£20,000 each).

FINANCES *Financial year end* 30/09/2020 *Income* £2,270,000 *Total grants* £2,460,000 *Grants to organisations* £2,460,000 *Assets* £83,840,000

TRUSTEES Suzanne Marriott; Kenneth Young; Prof. Sally-Ann Cooper; Prof. Anne Farmer; Jonathan Snow.

OTHER INFORMATION Only beneficiaries of grants of £20,000 and above were listed in the accounts. Grants of under £20,000 totalled £1.75 million. See the fund's website for up-to-date details of its funding programmes.

HOW TO APPLY Applications should be made using the fund's online application form. There are no submission deadlines for applicants seeking funding up to £10,000. Grants under £5,000 are considered solely by the Chair. Grants above £10,000 considered at Main Grant Board meetings, details of which can be found on the website along with comprehensive guidelines for each grant scheme.

CONTACT DETAILS Ann Cooper, Secretary to the Trustees, c/o TMF Global Services (UK) Ltd, 960 Capability Green, Luton, Bedfordshire LU1 3PE *Tel.* 01582 439225 *Email* info@bailythomas.org.uk *Website* www.bailythomas.org.uk

The Baird Trust

OSCR NO SC016549 **ESTABLISHED** 1873

WHERE FUNDING CAN BE GIVEN Scotland.

WHO CAN BENEFIT Churches.

WHAT IS FUNDED Maintenance and repair of churches; educational activities of churches.

WHAT IS NOT FUNDED Churches with adequate unrestricted and/or designated funds that could cover the costs; work that is already underway or has already taken place; applications without some contribution from the congregation.

TYPE OF GRANT Capital costs; general funding.

RANGE OF GRANTS Typically £1,000 to £10,000.

SAMPLE GRANTS A list of beneficiaries was not included in the annual report and accounts.

FINANCES *Financial year end* 31/12/2019 *Income* £421,600 *Total grants* £409,700 *Grants to organisations* £409,700 *Assets* £448,200

TRUSTEES Cmdr. Charles Ball; The Hon. Mary Coltman; Col. J. M. K. Erskine; Revd Dr Johnston McKay; Alan Borthwick; Dr Alison Elliot; Luke Borwick; Walter Barbour; Lt. Col. Richard Callander.

HOW TO APPLY Application forms can be downloaded from the website and must be accompanied by the latest annual accounts. Submissions are usually by either email or post; however, at the time of writing (March 2021) postal applications will not be received due to the closure of the trust's office.

CONTACT DETAILS Iain Mowat, Secretary, 182 Bath Street, Glasgow G2 4HG *Tel.* 0141 332 0476 *Email* info@bairdtrust.org.uk *Website* www.bairdtrust.org.uk

Bairdwatson Charitable Trust

OSCR NO SC038468 **ESTABLISHED** 2007

WHERE FUNDING CAN BE GIVEN Scotland with a strong preference for Ayr and Airdrie; West Bengal.

WHO CAN BENEFIT Registered charities; social enterprises; charitable organisations; individuals.

WHAT IS FUNDED Education or training for employment; re-training; supporting people into work; vocational training, especially for young people.

WHAT IS NOT FUNDED Hospices and palliative care; appliances for illness or disability; organisations concerned with specific diseases; medical research; animal charities; projects in England, Wales or Northern Ireland, large projects where the trust's contribution would not make a material difference.

TYPE OF GRANT Revenue/core costs; capital funding, project funding.
RANGE OF GRANTS Generally up to £12,000.
SAMPLE GRANTS One Parent Families Scotland (£11,500); Save UK – India (£10,500); The Prince's Foundation (£10,400); CVO East Ayrshire and Girvan Youth Trust (£10,000 each); Right Track (£9,000); Lanarkshire Enterprise Services Ltd (£6,000).
FINANCES *Financial year end* 31/03/2020 *Income* £64,700 *Total grants* £67,400 *Grants to organisations* £67,400 *Assets* £2,220,000
TRUSTEES Robert Kerr; John Ramsay; Jacqueline Leslie.
HOW TO APPLY Application forms are available from the trust's website and can be returned by email or post. The trustees meet three times a year in January, May and September. Application deadlines are posted on the trust's website.
CONTACT DETAILS Linda Anderson, Grant Assessor, 27 Balfour Terrace, Murray, East Kilbride, Lanarkshire G75 0JQ *Tel.* 07982 915666 *Email* linda@bairdwatson.org.uk *Website* www.bairdwatson.org.uk

The Roy and Pixie Baker Charitable Trust

CC NO 1101988 **ESTABLISHED** 1995
WHERE FUNDING CAN BE GIVEN The North East.
WHO CAN BENEFIT Registered charities.
WHAT IS FUNDED Health and medical research; education of young people; heritage; social welfare; disaster relief.
WHAT IS NOT FUNDED Individuals.
RANGE OF GRANTS Up to £5,000.
SAMPLE GRANTS Daft as a Brush (£10,000); NE Youth (£5,000); Washington Riding Centre for the Disabled (£4,000); Durham Association of Boys and Girls Clubs (£2,500); Northumberland Rugby Union (£1,500); Be Inspired To (£1,000); Northumbria Deaf Mission (£500); SAFE (£200).
FINANCES *Financial year end* 05/04/2020 *Income* £74,700 *Total grants* £68,200 *Grants to organisations* £68,200 *Assets* £3,070,000
TRUSTEES Tony Glenton; George Straker; Leslie Caisley; Bill Dryden.
OTHER INFORMATION Grants were made to 26 organisations during the year in the following categories: health and medicine (£30,500); education (£20,000); people in need (£11,700); architectural preservation (£6,000).
HOW TO APPLY Apply in writing to the correspondent, providing full back-up information. The trustees meet twice a year.
CONTACT DETAILS The Trustees, c/o Ryecroft Glenton, 32 Portland Terrace, Newcastle upon Tyne, Tyne and Wear NE2 1QP *Tel.* 0191 281 1292 *Email* bakercharitabletrust@ryecroftglenton.com

The Rachel Baker Memorial Charity

CC NO 1162913 **ESTABLISHED** 2009
WHERE FUNDING CAN BE GIVEN England and Wales.
WHO CAN BENEFIT Charitable organisations.
WHAT IS FUNDED Classical music.
WHAT IS NOT FUNDED Retrospective costs.
TYPE OF GRANT Long-term capital projects.
SAMPLE GRANTS Previous beneficiaries have included: City of Birmingham Symphony Orchestra and Young Classical Artists Trust (£125,000 each).
FINANCES *Financial year end* 05/04/2020 *Income* £13,900 *Total grants* £290,900 *Grants to organisations* £290,900
TRUSTEES Hugh Richards; Nicholas Moxon; Robin Daniels.
OTHER INFORMATION Full accounts were not available to view on the Charity Commission's website due to the charity's low income. We have therefore estimated the grant total based on the charity's total expenditure.
HOW TO APPLY Details of how to apply for grants are available from the clerk. Applications must be on the charity's standard application form. Application forms should be completed and returned along with any relevant information to the clerk at least four weeks before the meeting at which the application is to be considered. The trustees usually meet at the end of May and at the end of October.
CONTACT DETAILS Kirsty McEwen, Trust Administrator, Higgs and Sons, Unit 3, Waterfront Business Park, Dudley Road, Brierley Hill, West Midlands DY5 1LX *Tel.* 01384 327322 *Email* kirsty.mcewen@higgsandsons.co.uk

The Balcombe Charitable Trust

CC NO 267172 **ESTABLISHED** 1975
WHERE FUNDING CAN BE GIVEN UK.
WHO CAN BENEFIT Registered charities.
WHAT IS FUNDED Education; the environment; health and welfare.
RANGE OF GRANTS Typically £1,000 to £35,000.
SAMPLE GRANTS Blue Ventures Conservation (£95,000); YMCA – Burton and District (£35,000); Association for Young Peoples' Health (£15,000); Prison Radio Association (£10,000); Calibre Audio Library (£5,000); Coram Fields (£1,300); Crisis UK (£1,000).
FINANCES *Financial year end* 05/04/2020 *Income* £701,700 *Total grants* £254,100 *Grants to organisations* £254,100 *Assets* £32,030,000
TRUSTEES R. A. Kreitman; Patricia Kreitman; Edward Brown.
OTHER INFORMATION In 2019/20 the trust made grants totalling £254,100 to 13 organisations, distributed across the following areas: the environment (£120,000), education (£76,800) and health and welfare (£57,300).
HOW TO APPLY At the time of writing (March 2021), the trust is not currently accepting applications. Check the trust's website for updates.
CONTACT DETAILS The Trustees, c/o Citroen Wells and Partners, Devonshire House, 1 Devonshire Street, London W1W 5DR *Tel.* 020 7304 2000 *Email* jonathan@balcombetrust.org.uk *Website* www.balcombetrust.org.uk

The Balfour Beatty Charitable Trust

CC NO 1127453 **ESTABLISHED** 2009
WHERE FUNDING CAN BE GIVEN UK.
WHO CAN BENEFIT Registered charities.
WHAT IS FUNDED Projects that help young people develop their skills, capacities and capabilities for work, education and training.
RANGE OF GRANTS Up to £50,000.
SAMPLE GRANTS The Prince's Trust (£50,000); Barnardo's (£20,500); The Thomas Coram Foundation (£19,000).

FINANCES *Financial year end* 31/12/2019
Income £107,100 *Total grants* £89,500
Grants to organisations £89,500
Assets £190,500

TRUSTEES Paul Raby; Andrea Holt; Louise McCulloch; Nicola Kane; Tony Ellender; Bekir Andrews; Paul Woodhams.

OTHER INFORMATION This trust is the corporate charity of Balfour Beatty plc. In 2019 the trust made grants totalling £89,500 to three organisations, all of which also received funding in 2018.

HOW TO APPLY Apply in writing to the correspondent. The trustees work together with the Balfour Beatty Community Engagement Working Group (CEWG) to identify suitable charities to support.

CONTACT DETAILS The Trustees, The Curve, Axis Business Park, Hurricane Way, Langley, Slough, Berkshire SL3 8AG *Tel.* 01753 211121 *Email* sbf@balfourbeatty.com *Website* https://www.balfourbeatty.com/sustainability

The Andrew Balint Charitable Trust

CC NO 273691 **ESTABLISHED** 1961

WHERE FUNDING CAN BE GIVEN UK, Israel, Hungary and Romania.

WHO CAN BENEFIT Charitable organisations.

WHAT IS FUNDED General charitable purposes; Jewish causes.

RANGE OF GRANTS £1,000 to £20,000.

SAMPLE GRANTS American Jewish Joint Distribution Committee (£20,000); United Jewish Israel appeal (£12,500); University of Bristol (£10,000); The Trust for Former Employees (£5,000); Leket Israel (£1,000).

FINANCES *Financial year end* 05/04/2020
Income £52,900 *Total grants* £72,300
Grants to organisations £72,300
Assets £1,710,000

TRUSTEES Dr Gabriel Balint-Kurti; Roy Balint-Kurti; Daniel Balint-Kurti; Peter Balint-Kurti.

HOW TO APPLY Contact the correspondent for further information.

CONTACT DETAILS The Trustees, Carter Backer Winter LLP, Kingsfield House, 66 Prescot Street, London E1 8NN *Tel.* 020 7309 3800 *Email* balintcharitabletrust@gmail.com

The Ballinger Charitable Trust

CC NO 1121739 **ESTABLISHED** 2007

WHERE FUNDING CAN BE GIVEN The North East.

WHO CAN BENEFIT Registered charities.

WHAT IS FUNDED The health, development and well-being of young people; older people; cultural/arts projects based in the North East.

WHAT IS NOT FUNDED Individuals.

TYPE OF GRANT Strategic funding; capital costs; project funding.

RANGE OF GRANTS Typically less than £20,000.

SAMPLE GRANTS Age UK North Tyneside (£189,200); Dementia Matters (£103,300); Save the Children (£83,300); Stanley Area Youth Consortium (£40,000); Cramlington Voluntary Youth Project (£32,000); Royal Voluntary Service (£22,500).

FINANCES *Financial year end* 31/12/2019
Income £3,570,000 *Total grants* £2,270,000
Grants to organisations £2,270,000
Assets £42,860,000

TRUSTEES Diana Ballinger; John Flynn; Andrew Ballinger; Nicola Crowther.

OTHER INFORMATION Beneficiaries of less than £20,000 were not listed.

HOW TO APPLY Applications can be made through the trust's website. At the time of writing (March 2021), the application process has been suspended due to COVID-19.

CONTACT DETAILS Joanne Thomas, Co-ordinator, PO Box 166, Ponteland, Newcastle upon Tyne, Tyne and Wear NE20 2BL *Tel.* 07578 197886 *Email* info@ballingercharitabletrust.org.uk *Website* www.ballingercharitabletrust.org.uk

The Bamford Charitable Foundation

CC NO 279848 **ESTABLISHED** 1979

WHERE FUNDING CAN BE GIVEN UK and overseas, but mainly within a 40-mile radius of Rocester.

WHO CAN BENEFIT Charitable organisations.

WHAT IS FUNDED General charitable purposes.

RANGE OF GRANTS Up to £100,000.

SAMPLE GRANTS Imperial War Museum (£2 million); The Barbados Children's Trust (£160,200); The Felix Project (£40,000); Racing Welfare (£20,000); Wonderdale Care (£10,000); St Wilfrid's Church – Egginton Derby (£5,000); Eternity Gala Event (£3,000); Child Bereavement UK (£400).

FINANCES *Financial year end* 31/03/2020
Income £53,200 *Total grants* £2,720,000
Grants to organisations £2,720,000
Assets £1,680,000

TRUSTEES Lord Bamford; Lady Bamford.

OTHER INFORMATION During 2019/20 grants were made to 22 organisations including an exceptional grant of £2 million to the Imperial War Museum.

HOW TO APPLY Apply in writing to the correspondent.

CONTACT DETAILS The Trustees, J. C. Bamford Excavators Ltd, Lakeside Works, Denstone Road, Rocester, Uttoxeter, Staffordshire ST14 5JP *Tel.* 01889 593140

Banbury Charities

CC NO 201418 **ESTABLISHED** 1961

WHERE FUNDING CAN BE GIVEN Within a ten mile radius of Banbury.

WHO CAN BENEFIT Charitable organisations; schools; churches; uniformed groups; individuals.

WHAT IS FUNDED General charitable purposes.

TYPE OF GRANT Project funding; capital costs.

RANGE OF GRANTS Generally up to £10,000.

SAMPLE GRANTS Banbury Welfare Trust (£26,000); Banbury Cricket Club (£15,000); Cherwell DC: Youth and Community Centre (£10,000); Katherine House Hospice (£7,800); All Saints Church Middleton Cheney (£5,000); Royal Air Force Air Cadets (£3,000); The Warriner School (£2,000); The Sunshine Centre (£1,100).

FINANCES *Financial year end* 31/12/2019
Income £749,400 *Total grants* £208,200
Grants to organisations £146,500
Assets £8,000,000

TRUSTEES Judy May; Julia Colegrave; Angela Heritage; Colin Clarke; Martin Humphris; Jamie Briggs; Kieron Mallon; Valerie Fisher; Tom Blinkhorn; Sandra Williams; John Donaldson.

OTHER INFORMATION Grants were awarded to 66 organisations. Only organisations receiving grants of over £1,000 were listed as beneficiaries in the charity's accounts. Grants of under £1,000 totalled £11,700 and were awarded to 32 organisations. There were 146 grants made to individuals totalling £61,700.

HOW TO APPLY Contact the correspondent for further information.

CONTACT DETAILS Mrs M. Tarrant, Clerk to the Trustees, 36 West Bar, Banbury, Oxfordshire OX16 9RU *Tel.* 01295 251234

The Roger and Sarah Bancroft Clark Charitable Trust

CC NO 211513 **ESTABLISHED** 1960

WHERE FUNDING CAN BE GIVEN UK, with a preference for Somerset.

WHO CAN BENEFIT Charitable organisations; universities.

WHAT IS FUNDED General charitable purposes with a preference for Quaker causes, heritage and education (particularly postgraduate).

WHAT IS NOT FUNDED Individuals.

RANGE OF GRANTS Mostly under £10,000.

SAMPLE GRANTS The Alfred Gillett Trust (£260,100); Street Quaker (£10,000); OXFAM (£6,000); The Society for the Protection of Ancient Buildings (£4,000); Arthritis Research UK and Médecins Sans Frontières (£2,000 each); Amnesty International and Prisoner Education Trust (£1,000 each).

FINANCES *Financial year end* 31/12/2019 *Income* £162,700 *Total grants* £341,500 *Grants to organisations* £341,500 *Assets* £11,690,000

TRUSTEES Alice Clark; Martin Lovell; Caroline Gould; Priscilla Goldby; Robert Robertson.

OTHER INFORMATION Grants were made to 58 organisations during 2019. Grants were distributed within the following categories: Restricted grants (to one organisation) (£260,100); educational grants (£32,900); religious grants (£24,500); other grants (£16,000); Somerset grants (£8,000). Grants of under £1,500 totalled £20,400.

HOW TO APPLY Apply in writing to the correspondent. The trustees meet regularly to consider applications.

CONTACT DETAILS Mel Park, c/o C. and J. Clark Ltd, Box 1, 40 High Street, Street, Somerset BA16 0EQ *Tel.* 01458 842121 *Email* mel.park@clarks.com

The Band Trust

CC NO 279802 **ESTABLISHED** 1976

WHERE FUNDING CAN BE GIVEN UK.

WHO CAN BENEFIT UK-registered charities; individuals.

WHAT IS FUNDED General charitable purposes including: the armed forces; children and young people; disability; education; the arts; older people; nursing care.

WHAT IS NOT FUNDED Political activities; commercial ventures or publications; retrospective grants or loans; direct replacement of statutory funding or activities that are primarily the responsibility of central or local government.

RANGE OF GRANTS Typically under £150,000.

SAMPLE GRANTS Maggie's (£1 million); National Gallery (£400,000); British Library and The Norfolk Hospice (£100,000 each); Temple Bar Trust (£50,000); The Not Forgotten Association (£25,000); Friends of the Elderly (£12,000); The Commonwealth Walkway Trust (£5,000); Friends of the Courtauld Institute (£1,100).

FINANCES *Financial year end* 31/03/2020 *Income* £1,020,000 *Total grants* £5,040,000 *Grants to organisations* £5,040,000 *Assets* £21,750,000

TRUSTEES Richard Mason; Bartholomew Peerless; The Hon. Nicholas Wallop; The Hon. Mrs Nicholas Wallop; Victoria Wallop; Henry Wallop.

OTHER INFORMATION Over 43 grants were awarded to organisations during 2019/20. Miscellaneous grants of up to £2,000 totalled £22,000.

HOW TO APPLY Unsolicited applications are not accepted – only make an application if you have been invited to do so.

CONTACT DETAILS Richard Mason, Trustee, BM Box 2144, London WC1N 3XX *Tel.* 020 7702 4243 *Email* rjsmason32@gmail.com *Website* www.bandtrust.co.uk

Veronica and Lars Bane Foundation

CC NO 1183391 **ESTABLISHED** 2019

WHERE FUNDING CAN BE GIVEN UK; overseas.

WHO CAN BENEFIT Registered charities.

WHAT IS FUNDED Young people; education; human rights; health and well-being; arts and culture.

TYPE OF GRANT Project funding.

SAMPLE GRANTS Previous beneficiaries have included: EMpower; Fistula Foundation; Hampstead Theatre; Hand in Hand; Human Rights Watch; London Academy of Excellence; The Roundhouse.

FINANCES *Financial year end* 31/12/2019 *Income* £2,410,000 *Total grants* £90,000 *Grants to organisations* £90,000 *Assets* £2,170,000

TRUSTEES Georg Kjallgren; Lars Erik Bane; Martin Wiwen-Nilsson; Veronica Bane.

HOW TO APPLY Unsolicited applications are not accepted.

CONTACT DETAILS The Trustees, 98 Frognal, London NW3 6XB *Tel.* 07921 894842 *Email* grants@banefoundation.org *Website* https://banefoundation.org

The Kamini and Vindi Banga Family Trust

CC NO 1171409 **ESTABLISHED** 2017

WHERE FUNDING CAN BE GIVEN England and Wales.

WHO CAN BENEFIT Charitable organisations; universities.

WHAT IS FUNDED General charitable purposes; support for cancer research and education through the performing arts.

RANGE OF GRANTS £500 to £50,000.

SAMPLE GRANTS University of Southampton (£50,000); Cancer Research (£46,200); Almeida Theatre Company (£25,000); Chance to Shine and The Poetry School (£10,000 each); Southbank Centre (£1,000); Marie Curie and Room to Read (£500 each).

FINANCES *Financial year end* 05/04/2020 *Income* £1,380,000 *Total grants* £218,200 *Grants to organisations* £218,200 *Assets* £3,550,000

TRUSTEES Kamini Banga; Prof. Roy Anderson; Manvinder Banga; Baroness Patience Wheatcroft.

HOW TO APPLY Apply in writing to the correspondent. The trustees hold at least two meetings each year.

CONTACT DETAILS The Trustees, c/o Handelsbanken Wealth Management, 77 Mount Ephraim, Tunbridge Wells, Kent TN4 8BS *Tel.* 01892 701801

■ The Banister Charitable Trust

CC NO 1102320 **ESTABLISHED** 2004

WHERE FUNDING CAN BE GIVEN UK.

WHO CAN BENEFIT Charitable organisations.

WHAT IS FUNDED Conservation, protection and improvement of the physical and natural environment.

TYPE OF GRANT Core costs; project costs and capital costs.

SAMPLE GRANTS The Woodland Trust (£800,000); Lincolnshire Wildlife Trust (£150,000); Gwent Wildlife Trust (£75,000); Amphibian and Reptile Conservation Trust (£50,000); Bumblebee Conservation Trust (£35,000); Severn Rivers Trust (£21,500); Forest of Avon Trust (£4,000); Welcome to Our Future (£2,000).

FINANCES *Financial year end* 31/12/2019 *Income* £1,260,000 *Total grants* £3,090,000 *Grants to organisations* £3,090,000 *Assets* £11,060,000

TRUSTEES Christopher Banister; Huw Banister; Coutts and Co.

HOW TO APPLY Apply by letter to the correspondent.

CONTACT DETAILS The Trustees, Coutts & Co. Trustee Department, 1st Floor, Trinity Quay 1, Avon Street, Bristol BS2 0PT *Tel.* 0345 304 2424

■ Bank of Scotland Foundation

OSCR NO SC032942 **ESTABLISHED** 2002

WHERE FUNDING CAN BE GIVEN Scotland.

WHO CAN BENEFIT OSCR-registered charities.

WHAT IS FUNDED Social disadvantage or exclusion; developing and improving local communities; financial literacy and financial inclusion.

WHAT IS NOT FUNDED Political organisations; animal welfare; the promotion of religion; medical research; organisations that redistribute funding for subsequent grant-making to other organisations and/or individuals; individuals; advertising; sponsorship; foreign travel; overseas projects; newly registered charities that have been operating for less than one year.

TYPE OF GRANT Core costs; capital costs; project funding.

RANGE OF GRANTS Dependent on funding programme.

SAMPLE GRANTS The Moira Anderson Foundation (£145,200); REACH Lanarkshire Autism (£64,200); Beatson Cancer Charity (£40,000); Salvesen Mindroom Centre (£29,900); Cerebral Palsy Scotland (£26,900); Mikeysline (£25,100); Rosemount Lifelong Learning (£20,900).

FINANCES *Financial year end* 31/12/2020 *Income* £5,310,000 *Total grants* £4,050,000 *Grants to organisations* £4,050,000 *Assets* £2,450,000

TRUSTEES Philip Grant; Martin Fleming; Graham Blair; Alison Macdonald; Graeme Thompson; Karen Watt.

OTHER INFORMATION The foundation also operates a Matched Giving Programme whereby Lloyds Banking Group colleagues can receive matched funding for their fundraising activities. In 2020 the foundation awarded 351 grants for social exclusion and disadvantage totalling £4.1 million. This included COVID-19 Contingency Grants awarded to existing grant recipients. A further £304,900 was awarded through the Matched Giving Programme. Only organisations receiving grants of over £20,000 were listed in the foundation's accounts. A full list of all grants awarded during the year is available on the foundation's website.

HOW TO APPLY Check the foundation's website for current deadlines and fund opening dates. Further information on each grant programme is available on the website.

CONTACT DETAILS Sinead Finnie, Grants Manager, The Mound, Edinburgh EH1 1YZ *Tel.* 0345 124 1351 *Email* enquiries@bankofscotlandfoundation.co.uk *Website* www.bankofscotlandfoundation.org

■ The Barbers' Company General Charities

CC NO 265579 **ESTABLISHED** 1973

WHERE FUNDING CAN BE GIVEN UK, with some preference for the City of London.

WHO CAN BENEFIT Hospitals; hospices; educational organisations; charitable organisations; individuals.

WHAT IS FUNDED Education, particularly medical education; social welfare.

WHAT IS NOT FUNDED Medical research; large, well-endowed charities; large projects.

TYPE OF GRANT Project costs; capital costs.

RANGE OF GRANTS Mainly between £1,000 and £50,000.

SAMPLE GRANTS Phyllis Tuckwell Hospice (£109,400); Royal College of Surgeons (£50,000); Kings College London (£15,600); Treloar Trust (£5,000); ABF The Soldiers' Charity, Florence Nightingale Museum and Theodora Children's Charity (£1,000 each).

FINANCES *Financial year end* 31/08/2020 *Income* £201,500 *Total grants* £229,800 *Grants to organisations* £227,500 *Assets* £1,900,000

TRUSTEE Worshipful Company of Barbers.

OTHER INFORMATION Grants to individuals totalled £2,300 in 2019/20.

HOW TO APPLY Apply in writing, directly to the Worshipful Company of Barbers. Guidelines are provided on the website.

CONTACT DETAILS Malachy Doran, Clerk, The Worshipful Company of Barbers, Barber-Surgeons' Hall, 1A Monkwell Square, Wood Street, London EC2Y 5BL *Tel.* 020 7606 0741 *Email* clerk@barberscompany.org *Website* barberscompany.org.uk

■ The Barbour Foundation

CC NO 328081 **ESTABLISHED** 1988

WHERE FUNDING CAN BE GIVEN UK with a strong preference for the North East.

WHO CAN BENEFIT Registered charities; CICs; social enterprises; amateur sports clubs; hospices.

WHAT IS FUNDED Social welfare; education and employability; homelessness; research into the cause and treatment of chronic illness or disease and the provision of medical equipment; protection and preservation of buildings and countryside of environmental, historical or architectural interest; national and international disaster relief.

WHAT IS NOT FUNDED Organisations outside the beneficial area; educational organisations; capital grants for building projects; individuals.

TYPE OF GRANT Core/revenue costs; seed funding/start-up funding; unrestricted funding.

RANGE OF GRANTS Up to £150,000 but mainly between £1,000 and £5,000.

SAMPLE GRANTS Newcastle University Faculty Of Medical Sciences (£1 million); North Music Trust (£150,000); Hospitality and Hope (£30,000); Veterans At Ease (£10,000); Single

Homeless Action Initiative Durham and Versus Arthritis (£5,000 each); Together For Short Lives (£3,000); National Kidney Federation, Theatre Space and Wallsend Sea Cadets (£1,000 each).

FINANCES *Financial year end* 05/04/2020 *Income* £6,290,000 *Total grants* £2,400,000 *Grants to organisations* £2,400,000 *Assets* £13,320,000

TRUSTEES Helen Barbour; Dame Margaret Barbour; Nichola Bellaby.

OTHER INFORMATION In 2019/20 grants were made in the following areas: community welfare; youth/children; medical causes; disability; older people; conservation; heritage/museums; service charities; the arts; housing/homelessness; maritime charities; animal welfare; special appeals. Grants of under £1,000 totalled £40,100 and were awarded to 336 organisations.

HOW TO APPLY Apply in writing to the correspondent. Full details of what should be included in an application can be found on the foundation's website. Applications for the main grants are considered at quarterly meetings and applications for the small grant applications are considered at meetings every six weeks.

CONTACT DETAILS Edith Howse, Executive Secretary, Simonside, South Shields, Tyne and Wear NE34 9PD *Tel.* 0191 427 4217 *Email* barbour.foundation@barbour.com *Website* https://www.barbour.com/uk/the-barbour-foundation

Barcapel Foundation Ltd

OSCR NO SC009211 **ESTABLISHED** 1964

WHERE FUNDING CAN BE GIVEN UK, mainly Scotland.

WHO CAN BENEFIT Registered charities.

WHAT IS FUNDED Health, particularly complementary and alternative therapies; arts, culture and heritage, particularly the built environment; young people from socially disadvantaged backgrounds.

WHAT IS NOT FUNDED Individual applications for travel or similar; organisations or individuals engaged in promoting religious or political beliefs; applications for funding costs for feasibility studies or similar.

TYPE OF GRANT Core/revenue costs; seed funding/start-up funding.

RANGE OF GRANTS Up to £100,000.

SAMPLE GRANTS The Little Sparta Trust (£30,000); Grassmarket Community Project (£20,000); The Prince's Trust for Scotland (£15,000) Ardgowan Hospice (£10,000); Scottish Opera (£8,000); The Daisy Garland (£5,000); Tall Ships Youth Trust (£3,000).

FINANCES *Financial year end* 31/12/2019 *Income* £88,200 *Total grants* £419,500 *Grants to organisations* £419,500 *Assets* £3,121,000

TRUSTEES Robert Wilson; Amanda Richards; Jed Wilson; Clement Wilson.

OTHER INFORMATION The foundation awarded grants to 93 organisations.

HOW TO APPLY Application forms are available from the foundation's website. These should be returned by post with a covering letter and a copy of your annual accounts, but note that the trustees ask you do not send any additional information at this stage. If you have particularly important further documents and information refer to them in the covering letter so the trustees can request them if required. The foundation does not accept applications by email. Application deadlines are posted on the foundation's website.

CONTACT DETAILS Mia McCartney, Secretary, The Mews, Skelmorlie Castle, Skelmorlie, Ayrshire PA17 5EY *Tel.* 01475 521616 *Email* admin@barcapelfoundation.org *Website* www.barcapelfoundation.org

Barchester Healthcare Foundation

CC NO 1083272 **ESTABLISHED** 2000

WHERE FUNDING CAN BE GIVEN England, Scotland and Wales.

WHO CAN BENEFIT Charitable organisations; CICs; individuals.

WHAT IS FUNDED Improve independence, mobility and quality of life for people with disabilities and older people.

WHAT IS NOT FUNDED Core/running costs; salaries; indirect services such as help lines, newsletters, leaflets or research; major building projects or large capital projects; training of staff and volunteers.

TYPE OF GRANT One-off; capital costs; project funding.

RANGE OF GRANTS Up to £5,000.

SAMPLE GRANTS Barton and St Marychurch Childminders and Gateway into the Community (£1,500 each); East Park Activity Group, Martineau Gardens and With Music in Mind CIC (£1,000 each).

FINANCES *Financial year end* 31/12/2019 *Income* £317,000 *Total grants* £136,000 *Grants to organisations* £70,000 *Assets* £152,000

TRUSTEES David Walden; Andrew Cozens; Ann Mackay; Caroline Baker; Pete Calvely; Fiona McGill; Jamie Hodgson.

OTHER INFORMATION The 2019 annual report states that 20% of the 898 applications received were successful, with 90 grants awarded to organisations and a further 87 grants totalling £66,000 made to individuals.

HOW TO APPLY Applications can be made via the foundation's website.

CONTACT DETAILS Grants Management Team, Third Floor, The Aspect, 12 Finsbury Square, London EC2A 1AS *Tel.* 0800 328 3328 *Email* info@bhcfoundation.org.uk *Website* www.bhcfoundation.org.uk

The Barclay Foundation

CC NO 803696 **ESTABLISHED** 1990

WHERE FUNDING CAN BE GIVEN UK.

WHO CAN BENEFIT Registered charities; hospitals; universities; individuals.

WHAT IS FUNDED Medical research; young people; people with disabilities; people with illnesses; people who are disadvantaged.

SAMPLE GRANTS The Frederick Hugh Trust (£150,000).

FINANCES *Financial year end* 31/12/2019 *Income* £149,100 *Total grants* £150,000 *Grants to organisations* £150,000 *Assets* £230

TRUSTEES Sir David Barclay; Sir Frederick Barclay; Aidan Barclay; Howard Barclay.

HOW TO APPLY Applications should be in writing, clearly outlining the details of the proposed project, (for medical research, as far as possible in lay terms). The total cost and duration of the project should be stated; also the amount, if any, which has already been raised. Following an initial screening, applications are selected according to their merits, suitability and funds available. Visits are usually made to projects where substantial funds are involved. The foundation welcomes reports as to progress and requires these on the completion of a project.

CONTACT DETAILS Michael Seal, Administrator, 2nd Floor, 14 St George Street, London W1S 1FE *Tel.* 020 7915 0915 *Email* barclayfoundation@ellerman.co.uk

■ The Baring Foundation

CC NO 258583 **ESTABLISHED** 1969

WHERE FUNDING CAN BE GIVEN UK and overseas.

WHO CAN BENEFIT Charitable organisations; UK charities working with NGO partners in financially developing countries.

WHAT IS FUNDED Arts – promoting the role of creativity in the lives of people with mental health problems; International Development – empowering LGBTQ+ communities in sub-Saharan Africa; Strengthening the Voluntary Sector – supporting human rights and legal initiatives.

TYPE OF GRANT Core costs.

RANGE OF GRANTS Grants range from £500 up to £300,000.

SAMPLE GRANTS Initiative Sankofa d'Afrique de l'Ouest (£300,000); Manchester Museum (£250,000); Arts Council of Northern Ireland (£150,000); National Activity Providers Association (£40,000); Maternity Action (£18,600); Spare Tyre (£5,000); Redress Trust (£500).

FINANCES *Financial year end* 31/12/2019 *Income* £2,330,000 *Total grants* £2,380,000 *Grants to organisations* £2,380,000 *Assets* £102,680,000

TRUSTEES David Elliot; Dr Robert Berkeley; Lucy de Groot; Andrew Hind; Rhys Pullen; Poonam Joshi; Victoria Amedume; James Jenkins; Samuel Thorne; Emebet Wuhib-Mutungi; Asif Afridi; Francois Matarasso; Jillian Popkins; Shauneen Lambe.

HOW TO APPLY Check the foundation's website for the latest information on open programmes.

CONTACT DETAILS The Trustees, 8–10 Moorgate, London EC2R 6DA *Tel.* 020 7767 1348 *Email* baring.foundation@uk.ing.com *Website* https://baringfoundation.org.uk

■ The Philip Barker Charity

CC NO 1000227 **ESTABLISHED** 1990

WHERE FUNDING CAN BE GIVEN Cheshire.

WHO CAN BENEFIT Registered charities; community organisations; universities.

WHAT IS FUNDED General charitable purposes; young people and youth activities; community development; social welfare; education and employment; Christianity.

WHAT IS NOT FUNDED Individuals requesting funding for gap year activities.

TYPE OF GRANT Core costs; salaries; project funding; development funding.

RANGE OF GRANTS £12,000 to £20,000, with an exceptional grant of £100,000.

SAMPLE GRANTS The University of Chester (£100,000); Youth Federation (two grants totalling £32,000); Chester Storyhouse and Chester Zoological Society (£15,000 each).

FINANCES *Financial year end* 31/10/2019 *Income* £47,000 *Total grants* £162,000 *Grants to organisations* £162,000 *Assets* £1,200,000

TRUSTEES Sir Edmund Burton; Janet Groves; Terry Groves.

OTHER INFORMATION The 2018/19 accounts were the latest available at the time of writing (May 2021). A small number of grants are made each year. In 2018/19 five grants were made to four organisations in support of local youth activities. A significant grant of £100,000 was made to the University of Chester for a second year running to enable the establishment of the Philip Barker Centre for Creative Learning.

HOW TO APPLY Contact the correspondent for further information.

CONTACT DETAILS The Trustees, Bay Tree Cottage, Barbary Close, South Cheriton, Templecombe, Somerset BA8 0BG *Tel.* 07967 204685

■ The Barker-Mill Foundation

CC NO 1045479 **ESTABLISHED** 1995

WHERE FUNDING CAN BE GIVEN UK, with a strong preference for south west Hampshire, including Southampton.

WHO CAN BENEFIT Charitable organisations; local groups; schools; individuals.

WHAT IS FUNDED General charitable purposes, including: education; health; performing arts and culture; sport and leisure; animal welfare.

WHAT IS NOT FUNDED Only in exceptional circumstances does the foundation make grants to national charities.

RANGE OF GRANTS Grants are usually no more than £5,000.

SAMPLE GRANTS The Murray Parish Trust and Southampton Hospital Charity (General intensive Care Unit) (£100,000 each); Breast Cancer Haven (£24,000); Hampshire and Isle of Wight Wildlife Trust (£10,000); Raybel Charters (£4,000); Friends of Hazel Wood (£2,000); Colbury Memorial Hall Remembrance Concert (£500).

FINANCES *Financial year end* 31/03/2020 *Income* £59,200 *Total grants* £320,600 *Grants to organisations* £320,600 *Assets* £2,030,000

TRUSTEES Christopher Gwyn-Evans; Tim Jobling; Richard Moyse.

OTHER INFORMATION Grants were made to 37 organisations and individuals during the year.

HOW TO APPLY Applications should be made through the foundation's website. Guidelines are also available on the site. The trustees meet quarterly to consider applications.

CONTACT DETAILS Chris Gwyn-Evans, Trustee and administrator, The Estate Office, Longdown, Marchwood, Southampton, Hampshire SO40 4UH *Tel.* 023 8029 2107 *Email* info@barkermillfoundation.com *Website* www.barkermillfoundation.com

■ The Michael Barnard Charitable Trust

CC NO 1157878 **ESTABLISHED** 2014

WHERE FUNDING CAN BE GIVEN UK, with a preference for Basildon.

WHO CAN BENEFIT Charitable organisations.

WHAT IS FUNDED Social welfare.

SAMPLE GRANTS Acid Survivors Trust; Basildon Mind; CALM; Craig Tyler Trust; Hot Line Meals; Mustard Tree; My New Hair; St Francis Hospice; SANDS.

FINANCES *Financial year end* 31/03/2020 *Income* £34,800 *Total grants* £336,100 *Grants to organisations* £336,100 *Assets* £1,200,000

TRUSTEES Michael Barnard; John Summerton; John Caulcutt.

HOW TO APPLY Contact the correspondent for further information.

CONTACT DETAILS The Trustees, 85 Pound Lane, Laindon, Basildon, Essex SS15 5SP *Tel.* 07977 403704

■ Lord Barnby's Foundation

CC NO 251016 **ESTABLISHED** 1966

WHERE FUNDING CAN BE GIVEN UK.

WHO CAN BENEFIT Registered charities.

WHAT IS FUNDED General charitable purposes.

WHAT IS NOT FUNDED Individuals.

RANGE OF GRANTS Grants range from £250 to £12,000.

SAMPLE GRANTS Age UK (£12,000); Red Squirrel Trust (£10,000); Farms For City Children (£5,000); Selby Abbey (£3,000); Agoonoree Scout Camp (£2,500); Gurkha Welfare Trust (£2,000); Myeloma UK (£1,000); Get Kids Going (£500).

FINANCES *Financial year end* 31/03/2020 *Income* £294,700 *Total grants* £313,000 *Grants to organisations* £313,000 *Assets* £4,300,000

TRUSTEES The Hon. George Lopes; The Countess Peel; David Cecil; E. Smith-Maxwell; Laura Greenall.

OTHER INFORMATION The foundation has established a permanent list of beneficiaries that it supports each year, with the remaining funds then distributed to other charities.

HOW TO APPLY Applications will only be considered if received in writing accompanied by a set of your latest accounts. Contact the correspondent for further information.

CONTACT DETAILS The Trustees, PO Box 442, Market Drayton, Shropshire TF9 9EQ *Tel.* 07835 441100 *Email* lordbarnbyfoundation@gmail.com

■ The Barnes Fund

CC NO 200103 **ESTABLISHED** 1970

WHERE FUNDING CAN BE GIVEN Ancient parish of Barnes only (broadly the SW13 postal district).

WHO CAN BENEFIT Charitable organisations.

WHAT IS FUNDED Social welfare; older people and their carers; disability; health and mental health; carers; recreational facilities; educational facilities and opportunities. Grants are also made to individuals through referral agencies for educational purposes and for the relief of hardship.

WHAT IS NOT FUNDED National organisations.

TYPE OF GRANT Capital revenue grants; core funding; specific one-off projects, schemes or equipment.

RANGE OF GRANTS Organisational grants up to £40,000, most below £10,000. Welfare grants for individuals are generally limited to up to £500 per year for up to three years.

SAMPLE GRANTS Castelnau Centre Project (£41,800); Richmond Citizens Advice (£38,600); Richmond Carers Centre (£19,700); Off the Record (£12,600); Orange Tree Theatre (£5,000); Holly Lodge Centre (£3,000); Richmond Music Trust (£1,300); Barnes Children's Literature (£500).

FINANCES *Financial year end* 31/12/2019 *Income* £702,500 *Total grants* £259,200 *Grants to organisations* £234,900 *Assets* £13,170,000

TRUSTEE The Barnes Fund Trustee Ltd.

OTHER INFORMATION Grants were made to 40 organisations in 2019, of which two were for capital purposes. In addition, grants totalling £24,300 were awarded to individuals for the relief of poverty (61 grants) and for educational purposes (11 grants). As well as grant-making, the fund manages almshouses for older people (over 60) and people with disabilities.

HOW TO APPLY Organisations should apply using the online form on the fund's website and are advised to first read the eligibility guidelines on the website. Applications from organisations are considered at trustees' meetings in February, May, July and October each year. Applications must be received by the 6th of the month preceding a meeting to be considered.

CONTACT DETAILS Katy Makepeace-Gray, Executive Director, PO Box 347, Hampton TW12 9ED *Tel.* 07484 146 802 (Monday to Thursday) *Email* executivedirector@thebarnesfund.org.uk *Website* www.barnesworkhousefund.org.uk

■ The Max Barney Foundation

CC NO 1164583 **ESTABLISHED** 2014

WHERE FUNDING CAN BE GIVEN England and Wales; Israel.

WHO CAN BENEFIT Registered charities; social enterprises; Jewish organisations.

WHAT IS FUNDED General charitable purposes; relief for unemployment through vocational training and job creation, particularly among the Jewish community.

RANGE OF GRANTS Up to £100,000.

SAMPLE GRANTS Previous beneficiaries have included: The Work Avenue and World Jewish Relief (£100,000 each); London School of Jewish Studies (£50,000); Employment Resource (£42,000); Community Security Trust (£25,000); One Voice (£20,000).

FINANCES *Financial year end* 31/05/2020 *Income* £2,250,000 *Total grants* £1,640,000 *Grants to organisations* £1,640,000 *Assets* £918,600

TRUSTEES Alexander Bard; Michael Goldstein; Gary Phillips.

HOW TO APPLY Contact the correspondent for further information.

CONTACT DETAILS The Trustees, 4th Floor, 168 Shoreditch High Street, London E1 6HU *Tel.* 020 7583 5555 *Email* shraga@maxbarney.com

■ The Barnsbury Charitable Trust

CC NO 241383 **ESTABLISHED** 1964

WHERE FUNDING CAN BE GIVEN UK, with a strong preference for Oxfordshire.

WHO CAN BENEFIT Charitable organisations.

WHAT IS FUNDED General charitable purposes.

WHAT IS NOT FUNDED Individuals.

RANGE OF GRANTS Typically less than £11,000.

SAMPLE GRANTS Oxfordshire Community Foundation (£11,000); Oxfordshire Historic Churches Trust (£10,000); Friends of Abingdon Abbey Building Trust, Museum of Oxford Development Trust, (£5,000 each); Oxford Winter Night Shelter, Soldiers of Oxfordshire Museum (£2,500 each); SW Coast Path Association (£40).

FINANCES *Financial year end* 05/04/2020 *Income* £153,700 *Total grants* £118,500 *Grants to organisations* £118,500 *Assets* £6,130,000

TRUSTEES Mary Brunner; Isabel Sharp; Sir Hugh Brunner.

OTHER INFORMATION The trust awarded grants to 38 organisations.

HOW TO APPLY Contact the correspondent for further information.
CONTACT DETAILS The Trustees, 26 Norham Road, Oxford, Oxfordshire OX2 6SF *Tel.* 01865 554821 *Email* hmrbrunner@gmail.com

■ Barnwood Trust

CC NO 1162855 **ESTABLISHED** 2015
WHERE FUNDING CAN BE GIVEN Gloucestershire.
WHO CAN BENEFIT Charitable organisations and community groups; schools and colleges; individuals.
WHAT IS FUNDED Improving the quality of life of people in Gloucestershire with disabilities and mental health challenges. At the time of writing (January 2021) grants were being awarded to support community spaces affected by COVID-19 and to fund COVID-19 response projects.
WHAT IS NOT FUNDED People or organisations outside Gloucestershire. Specific exclusions and criteria apply to each of the grant programmes which are published on the trust's website.
TYPE OF GRANT Project costs; start-up costs; equipment; holiday and play schemes; capital costs.
RANGE OF GRANTS Up to £5,000.
SAMPLE GRANTS The Milestone School (£5,400); Gloucester Rowing Club (£4,800); Gloucestershire College (£3,300); Independence Trust (£2,300); 2gether NHS Foundation Trust (£2,000).
FINANCES *Financial year end* 31/12/2019 *Income* £3,190,000 *Total grants* £1,369,600 *Grants to organisations* £129,600 *Assets* £99,260,000
TRUSTEES Sally Pullen; Ann Santry; Lucy Floyer-Aclan; Michael North; Dr Jean Waters; Suzanne Beech; Shaun Parson; Rachel Robinson; Edward Payne; Benjamin Preece-Smith.
OTHER INFORMATION Grants to individuals totalled £1.24 million in 2019.
HOW TO APPLY Check the website for information on how to apply for each of the grant programmes. The trust has an online grant portal for most grant applications.
CONTACT DETAILS The Grants Team, Overton House, Overton Road, Cheltenham GL50 3BN *Tel.* 01242 539935 *Email* grants@barnwoodtrust.org *Website* www.barnwoodtrust.org

■ Misses Barrie Charitable Trust

CC NO 279459 **ESTABLISHED** 1979
WHERE FUNDING CAN BE GIVEN UK, with a particular interest in Surrey, Warwickshire, Worcestershire and Scotland.
WHO CAN BENEFIT Registered charities.
WHAT IS FUNDED General charitable purposes.
WHAT IS NOT FUNDED Individuals.
RANGE OF GRANTS Usually £1,000 to £3,000.
SAMPLE GRANTS National Youth Orchestra of Great Britain (£8,000); University of Oxford (£7,500) Scottish Opera (£3,500); Birnam Arts (£2,800); Alzheimer Scotland and Marine Conservation Society (£2,000 each); Braes Storehouse Food Bank and Yorkshire Air Ambulance (£1,500 each); Mid-Surrey Mencap and St John Ambulance (£1,000 each).
FINANCES *Financial year end* 05/04/2020 *Income* £233,700 *Total grants* £138,000 *Grants to organisations* £138,000 *Assets* £6,220,000
TRUSTEES John Carter; Rachel Fraser; Sally Abell; Charlotte Carter; Suzanne Fraser.
OTHER INFORMATION The trustees prefer to support small to medium-sized charities.
HOW TO APPLY Apply in writing to the correspondent accompanied by up-to-date accounts or financial information. The trustees are unable to notify unsuccessful applicants.
CONTACT DETAILS The Trustees, 34 Victoria Road, Dartmouth, Devon TQ6 9SA *Tel.* 01737 248065 *Email* charlotte@raymondcarter.co.uk

■ Robert Barr's Charitable Trust

OSCR NO SC007613 **ESTABLISHED** 1970
WHERE FUNDING CAN BE GIVEN UK and overseas with a preference for Scotland.
WHO CAN BENEFIT Charitable organisations; hospitals; schools; universities; CICs.
WHAT IS FUNDED General charitable purposes; welfare; health; the arts; conservation; research.
TYPE OF GRANT The trustees will not normally support any charity more often than once every three years and favour capital projects rather than running costs.
RANGE OF GRANTS £5,000 to £100,000.
SAMPLE GRANTS Keep Scotland Beautiful (£100,000); The Royal College of Surgeons of Edinburgh (£50,000); The Mark Scott Foundation (£40,000); Linlithgow Community Development Trust (£30,000); Team Jak Foundation and The Bread Maker (£20,000 each); The Fraser Centre Community Trust (£15,000); Provan Hall Community Trust (£10,000); Islay and Jura Community Enterprises Ltd (£5,000).
FINANCES *Financial year end* 05/04/2020 *Income* £911,600 *Total grants* £678,000 *Grants to organisations* £678,000 *Assets* £1,420,000
OTHER INFORMATION In 2019/20 grants were distributed in the following categories: adult and child welfare (£380,000 in 20 grants); medical research (£135,000 in six grants); conservation (£120,000 in seven grants); arts (£23,000 in three grants); animal welfare, environmental (£10,000 in one grant).
HOW TO APPLY Contact the correspondent for further information.
CONTACT DETAILS The Trustees, c/o Dentons UK and Middle East LLP, 1 George Square, Glasgow G2 1AL

■ The Paul Bassham Charitable Trust

CC NO 266842 **ESTABLISHED** 1973
WHERE FUNDING CAN BE GIVEN UK, with a preference for Norfolk.
WHO CAN BENEFIT UK-registered charities; charitable bodies that are exempt from registration.
WHAT IS FUNDED General charitable purposes.
WHAT IS NOT FUNDED Individuals.
TYPE OF GRANT Capital costs; development funding; project costs; research.
RANGE OF GRANTS Up to £50,000.
SAMPLE GRANTS EACH and YMCA Norfolk (£50,000 each); The Big C Appeal Ltd – Nearer to Home Appeal (£30,000); Matthew Project (£19,300); Build the Nest (£15,000); 46th Norwich Scout Group and Norwich Cathedral (£10,000 each); Norfolk and Norwich Festival and Shrublands Youth and Adult Centre Charitable Trust (£5,000 each).

FINANCES *Financial year end* 05/04/2020 *Income* £446,700 *Total grants* £407,600 *Grants to organisations* £407,600 *Assets* £12,150,000

OTHER INFORMATION Only organisations receiving grants of over £5,000 were listed as beneficiaries in the trust's accounts. Grants of under £5,000 totalled £163,300.

HOW TO APPLY Apply in writing to the correspondent. The trustees will only consider written applications and meet quarterly to discuss such applications.

CONTACT DETAILS Morris Peacock, Trust Correspondent, c/o Howes Percival LLP, Flint Buildings, 1 Bedding Lane, Norwich, Norfolk NR3 1RG *Tel.* 01603 762103

■ The Batchworth Trust

CC NO 245061 **ESTABLISHED** 1965

WHERE FUNDING CAN BE GIVEN Worldwide.

WHO CAN BENEFIT Major UK and international charities.

WHAT IS FUNDED General charitable purposes with a preference for health and social welfare.

RANGE OF GRANTS Grants are up to £90,000 but generally £1,000 to £25,000.

SAMPLE GRANTS Music for My Mind (£90,000); Médecins Sans Frontières (£55,000); Lorica Trust (£30,000); Above and Beyond (£20,000); International Justice Mission (£10,000); 1 Voice (£5,000).

FINANCES *Financial year end* 05/04/2020 *Income* £484,700 *Total grants* £1,100,000 *Grants to organisations* £1,100,000 *Assets* £12,610,000

TRUSTEE Lockwell Trustees Ltd.

OTHER INFORMATION Grants were made to 75 charities during the year.

HOW TO APPLY Contact the correspondent for further information.

CONTACT DETAILS James Peach, c/o Kreston Reeves LLP, Springfield House, Springfield Road, Horsham, West Sussex RH12 2RG *Tel.* 01293 776152 *Email* james.peach@krestonreeves.com

■ Battens Charitable Trust

CC NO 293500 **ESTABLISHED** 1985

WHERE FUNDING CAN BE GIVEN Somerset, Dorset and surrounding areas.

WHO CAN BENEFIT Registered charities and local charitable organisations.

WHAT IS FUNDED General charitable purposes.

SAMPLE GRANTS Previous beneficiaries have included: Dorset Wildlife Trust (£13,500); LV Streetwise Safety Centre (£10,000); Citizens Advice, Dorset Somerset Air Ambulance and RSPB (£5,000 each).

FINANCES *Financial year end* 05/04/2020 *Income* £120,600 *Total grants* £62,700 *Grants to organisations* £62,700 *Assets* £524,500

TRUSTEES Raymond Edwards; Stuart Allen; Robert Randall; Naomi Dyer; Katherine Gilmour; James Owen.

HOW TO APPLY Contact the correspondent for further information.

CONTACT DETAILS The Trustees, c/o Battens Solicitors, Mansion House, 54–58 Princes Street, Yeovil, Somerset BA20 1EP *Tel.* 01935 846000 *Email* matthew.kinder@battens.co.uk *Website* https://www.battens.co.uk/battens-charitable-trust

■ The Battersea Power Station Foundation

CC NO 1161232 **ESTABLISHED** 2014

WHERE FUNDING CAN BE GIVEN Lambeth; Wandsworth.

WHO CAN BENEFIT Charitable organisations.

WHAT IS FUNDED General charitable purposes; community services and development.

WHAT IS NOT FUNDED Individuals; general appeals; promotion of religion or places of worship; other grant-makers; medical research; educational initiatives linked to the national curriculum. More details on exclusions can be found on the foundation's helpful website.

TYPE OF GRANT Core/revenue costs; project funding.

SAMPLE GRANTS Oasis Hub Waterloo (£357,800); Cyber Hive at Caius House (£258,800); SEN Talk (£75,000); LPWP (£45,000); Rotary Club of Battersea Park (£5,000); Connaught Opera (£1,500).

FINANCES *Financial year end* 31/12/2019 *Income* £1,000,000 *Total grants* £960,000 *Grants to organisations* £960,000 *Assets* £534,400

TRUSTEES Marquess of Salisbury Robert Cecil; Right Hon. Lord Strathclyde; Datuk Wong Tuck Wai.

OTHER INFORMATION In total, 16 grants were awarded in 2019. Grants were awarded through two schemes; The Spring Fund and The Evolve Fund. The Spring Fund aims to help communities in Lambeth and Wandsworth with projects that bring together residents, volunteers, businesses and local authorities. The Evolve Fund is for selected organisations which are working towards longer-term goals that match the foundation's own vision for the future.

HOW TO APPLY Applications can be made through the foundation's website. Detailed guidance, FAQs and other information is provided on the website. The Evolve Fund is a closed programme and does not accept unsolicited applications.

CONTACT DETAILS The Trustees, 7 Circus Road West, Battersea Power Station, London SW11 8EZ *Tel.* 020 7501 0707 *Email* info@bpsfoundation.org.uk *Website* bpsfoundation.org.uk

■ Bauer Radio's Cash for Kids Charities

CC NO 1122062 **ESTABLISHED** 2007

WHERE FUNDING CAN BE GIVEN 23 areas around the UK where Bauer Radio has a local radio station.

WHO CAN BENEFIT Registered charities; schools; community groups; health organisations; individuals.

WHAT IS FUNDED Disadvantaged children and young people up to the age of 18. A full list of activities the charity will fund can be found in the Grants Eligibility Criteria document, available to download from the 'Grants' section of the website.

WHAT IS NOT FUNDED A list of exclusions is available in the Grants Eligibility Criteria document.

TYPE OF GRANT Equipment; project costs.

RANGE OF GRANTS Typically £1,000 to £3,000.

SAMPLE GRANTS A list of beneficiaries was not included in the annual report and accounts.

FINANCES *Financial year end* 31/12/2019 *Income* £14,740,000 *Total grants* £2,430,000 *Grants to organisations* £2,430,000 *Assets* £2,520,000

TRUSTEES Sally Aitchison; Martin Ball; Sean Marley; Danny Simpson; Susan Voss; Gary Stein; David Tighe; Sarah Barnes.

OTHER INFORMATION This is the corporate umbrella charity for Bauer Radio who own radio stations In 23 areas of the UK. Each station has its own charity and operates a grant-making strategy to benefit children in the local area. The grant total includes grants made to individuals and organisations but we were unable to determine the exact amount awarded to individuals. The charity gave a further £10.93 million in gifts in kind through its Mission Christmas appeal and its Big Day Out event.

HOW TO APPLY To apply for a grant, first visit the locations page of the charity's website to find your local radio station and grant team. Application forms, eligibility criteria and deadlines are available on the local websites. The charity encourages you to discuss your application with your local grant team.

CONTACT DETAILS The Trustees, Hampdon House, Unit 3 Falcon Court, Preston Farm, Stockton-on-Tees, County Durham TS18 3TS *Tel.* 01642 675788 *Email* info@cashforkids.uk.com *Website* www.cashforkids.uk.com

■ Bay Charitable Trust

CC NO 1060537 **ESTABLISHED** 1997

WHERE FUNDING CAN BE GIVEN UK and overseas.

WHO CAN BENEFIT Registered charities; Orthodox Jewish organisations.

WHAT IS FUNDED Social welfare; the advancement of traditions of the Orthodox Jewish Religion and the study of Torah.

SAMPLE GRANTS A list of beneficiaries was not included in the annual report and accounts.

FINANCES *Financial year end* 31/12/2019 *Income* £697,500 *Total grants* £791,000 *Grants to organisations* £791,000 *Assets* £92,600

TRUSTEES Ian Kreditor; Michael Lisser.

OTHER INFORMATION The grant total includes awards made to individuals.

HOW TO APPLY Contact the correspondent for further information.

CONTACT DETAILS Ian Kreditor, Trustee, 21 Woodlands Close, London NW11 9QR *Tel.* 020 8810 4321

■ The Bay Tree Charitable Trust

CC NO 1044091 **ESTABLISHED** 1994

WHERE FUNDING CAN BE GIVEN UK.

WHO CAN BENEFIT Charitable organisations.

WHAT IS FUNDED General charitable purposes including: development work; health; social welfare.

WHAT IS NOT FUNDED Grants are not made to individuals.

RANGE OF GRANTS Grants range from £5,000 to £20,000.

SAMPLE GRANTS Médecins Sans Frontières, Maggie's – Cheltenham and St Mungo's (£20,000 each); Cruse Bereavement and International Rescue Committee (£10,000 each); Putney Arts Theatre (£5,000).

FINANCES *Financial year end* 31/12/2019 *Income* £150,000 *Total grants* £140,000 *Grants to organisations* £140,000 *Assets* £6,020,000

TRUSTEES Ian Benton; Emma Benton; Paul Benton.

OTHER INFORMATION Grants were made to 11 organisations during the year.

HOW TO APPLY Apply in writing to the correspondent. All appeals should contain the following: aims and objectives of the charity, nature of appeal, total target if for a specific project, contributions received against target, registered charity number and any other relevant factors. Applications should include a copy of your latest accounts.

CONTACT DETAILS The Trustees, PO Box 53983, London SW15 1VT *Tel.* 020 7465 4300

■ The Louis Baylis (Maidenhead Advertiser) Charitable Trust

CC NO 210533 **ESTABLISHED** 1962

WHERE FUNDING CAN BE GIVEN Berkshire and South Buckinghamshire (the areas served by the publications of Baylis Media Ltd).

WHO CAN BENEFIT Registered charities.

WHAT IS FUNDED General charitable purposes with a preference for projects supporting older people, children and young people and the arts.

WHAT IS NOT FUNDED Individuals.

RANGE OF GRANTS Grants are typically less than £3,000.

SAMPLE GRANTS Maidenhead Citizens Advice (£25,000); People to Places (£12,500); Relate (£4,000); Buckinghamshire Mind and Great Ormond Street Hospital Children's Charity (£2,000 each); Target Ovarian Cancer (£1,000); Berkshire Community Foundation (£300).

FINANCES *Financial year end* 31/03/2020 *Income* £2,020,000 *Total grants* £229,800 *Grants to organisations* £229,800 *Assets* £13,410,000

TRUSTEES John Robertson; Peter Sands; Peter Murcott; Patricia Lattimer.

OTHER INFORMATION During the year, 86% of grants were to local charities, 11% to regional charities and 3% to national charities.

HOW TO APPLY Application forms are available to download on the website and should be returned to the trust by email or post. The trustees meet four times a year to consider grants.

CONTACT DETAILS Richard Curry, The Administrator, PO Box 4832, Maidenhead, Berkshire SL60 1JQ *Tel.* 01628 626333 *Email* lbctrust@baylismedia.co.uk *Website* www.baylis-trust.org.uk

■ BBC Children in Need

CC NO 802052 **ESTABLISHED** 1989

WHERE FUNDING CAN BE GIVEN UK.

WHO CAN BENEFIT Voluntary projects; community groups; registered charities; not-for-profit organisations; churches; schools.

WHAT IS FUNDED Children and young people under the age of 18 experiencing disadvantage through illness, distress, abuse or neglect, any kind of disability, behavioural or psychological difficulties or who are living in poverty and/or experiencing deprivation.

TYPE OF GRANT Capital costs; project funding; core/revenue funding.

RANGE OF GRANTS Generally up to £100,000 for main grants and up to £10,000 for small grants.

SAMPLE GRANTS A list of beneficiaries was not included in the annual report and accounts.

FINANCES *Financial year end* 30/06/2020
Income £85,790,000
Total grants £48,800,000
Grants to organisations £48,800,000
Assets £42,810,000

TRUSTEES Rosie Millard; Jonathan Munro; Bob Shennan; Luke Mayhew; Gillian Sheldon; Matthew Baker; Joanna Berry; Kenny Imafidon; Suzy Lamb; Rhona Burns; Ade Adepitan; Kieran Clifton; Trevor Bradley.

HOW TO APPLY Applications can be made via the charity's website which also has information on eligibility criteria, application deadlines and exclusions. If you have a general enquiry, are unsure about anything you have read, or are looking for support regarding your application, contact the charity via phone or email. You can also contact your local regional or national office.

CONTACT DETAILS Grants Team, PO Box 649, Salford, Greater Manchester M5 0LD *Tel.* 0345 609 0015 *Email* pudseygrants@bbc.co.uk *Website* https://www.bbcchildreninneed.co.uk

■ BC Partners Foundation

CC NO 1136956 **ESTABLISHED** 2010

WHERE FUNDING CAN BE GIVEN UK and overseas.

WHO CAN BENEFIT Registered charities; schools; universities; hospitals; local authorities.

WHAT IS FUNDED Community development; conservation of the environment; the arts; education.

TYPE OF GRANT Capital costs; project funding; core/revenue costs.

RANGE OF GRANTS Mostly up to £100,000.

SAMPLE GRANTS BCPF Inc. (£128,000); Dulwich College (£28,000); Fine Cell Work (£10,000); Operation Smile (£2,900); Daisy Trust (£1,300); Carers UK (£60).

FINANCES *Financial year end* 31/12/2019
Income £398,700 *Total grants* £394,900
Grants to organisations £394,900
Assets £571,600

TRUSTEES Matthew Evans; Francesco Loredan; Cedric Dubourdieu; Jan Kengelbach; Nikos Stathopoulos.

OTHER INFORMATION This is the corporate charity of private equity firm BC Partners.

HOW TO APPLY The foundation does not accept unsolicited applications. Charities are nominated by BC Partners employees or trustees of the foundation.

CONTACT DETAILS The Trustees, BC Partners LLP, 40 Portman Square, London W1H 6DA *Tel.* 020 7009 4800 *Website* https://www.bcpartners.com/about/foundation

■ Bear Mordechai Ltd

CC NO 286806 **ESTABLISHED** 1982

WHERE FUNDING CAN BE GIVEN UK.

WHO CAN BENEFIT Registered charities.

WHAT IS FUNDED Projects and organisations benefitting Jewish people.

RANGE OF GRANTS Up to £50,000.

SAMPLE GRANTS Yad Yemin (£50,700); Pinbent (£42,200); Tzedoko V'chesed (£26,000); Tevini Ltd (£13,200); Sellata (£7,000); Beis Chinuch Lebonos Girls School and Mir Charitable Trust (£5,000 each); Satmar Yeshiva (£1,000).

FINANCES *Financial year end* 31/03/2020
Income £206,700 *Total grants* £180,600
Grants to organisations £180,600
Assets £384,600

TRUSTEES Chaim Benedikt; Eliezer Benedikt; Yechiel Benedikt.

OTHER INFORMATION Only beneficiaries of grants of £1,000 and over were listed in the 2019/20 accounts (13 organisations). Small grants of less than £1,000 totalled £1,100.

HOW TO APPLY Contact the correspondent for further information.

CONTACT DETAILS The Trustees, 40 Fountayne Road, London N16 7DT *Tel.* 0161 792 9461 *Email* dp.whiteside@gmail.com

■ Bearder Charity

CC NO 1010529 **ESTABLISHED** 1992

WHERE FUNDING CAN BE GIVEN Calderdale.

WHO CAN BENEFIT Registered charities; individuals.

WHAT IS FUNDED Social welfare; general charitable purposes.

RANGE OF GRANTS £500 to £15,500.

SAMPLE GRANTS Smartmove (£15,500); Horton Housing (£14,500); WomenCentre (£6,000); Macmillan Cancer Support (£5,000); Cricket Asylum (£700); Brighouse Central Food Bank (£500).

FINANCES *Financial year end* 05/04/2020
Income £126,800 *Total grants* £307,100
Grants to organisations £93,600
Assets £3,140,000

TRUSTEES Richard Smithies; David Normanton; Trevor Simpson; Brendan Mowforth.

OTHER INFORMATION Grants were made to 38 organisations during the year. Grants to individuals totalled £213,500.

HOW TO APPLY Apply in writing to the correspondent. Trustee board meetings are held six times a year.

CONTACT DETAILS The Trustees, 5 King Street, Brighouse, West Yorkshire HD6 1NX *Tel.* 01484 710571 *Email* beardercharity@gmail.com

■ The James Beattie Charitable Trust

CC NO 265654 **ESTABLISHED** 1972

WHERE FUNDING CAN BE GIVEN Wolverhampton.

WHO CAN BENEFIT Local projects and organisations, hospitals, churches, schools, clubs (including Scout and Guide groups) and support services benefitting the people of Wolverhampton.

WHAT IS FUNDED General charitable purposes including youth and community work.

WHAT IS NOT FUNDED Individuals. The trust is unlikely to donate to national charities, even those that offer ringfencing for Wolverhampton.

TYPE OF GRANT Capital costs; project funding; revenue costs; one-off or recurring.

RANGE OF GRANTS £100 to £25,000.

SAMPLE GRANTS Bilbrook Initiatives Hub; Canal and River Trust; Edward's Trust; Hands On Wednesfield; Listening Books; Oasis Soup Kitchen; The Haven Wolverhampton; Theodora Children's Charity; West Midlands CARE Team; Wolverhampton Mencap.

FINANCES *Financial year end* 05/04/2020
Income £82,900 *Total grants* £151,900
Grants to organisations £151,900
Assets £3,710,000

TRUSTEES Jane Redshaw; Michael Redshaw; Kenneth Dolman; Susannah Norbury; Michael Boyce.

OTHER INFORMATION In total, 83 grants were awarded throughout the year. A list of beneficiaries was not available in the accounts, therefore a sample of beneficiaries has been taken from the website.

HOW TO APPLY Apply in writing to the correspondent, including a recent set of accounts, contact details, the grant size required and information about what the funding will be used for. Eligible applications are considered by the trustees once per month.

CONTACT DETAILS The Trustees, PO Box 12, Bridgnorth, Shropshire WV15 5LQ *Tel.* 0121 551 6021 *Website* https://jamesbeattietrust.org.uk

■ Beauland Ltd

CC NO 511374 **ESTABLISHED** 1981

WHERE FUNDING CAN BE GIVEN Worldwide, with some preference for the Manchester area.

WHO CAN BENEFIT Registered charities; Jewish educational institutions; religious institutions.

WHAT IS FUNDED Advancement of the Orthodox Jewish faith and Jewish religious education; social welfare.

RANGE OF GRANTS Between £2,000 and £100,000.

SAMPLE GRANTS Previous beneficiaries have included: Rosecare Foundation (£114,600); Yesoiday Hatorah School (£25,500); Cosmon (Belz) Ltd, Dover Sholem Community Trust and Moreshet Hatorah Ltd; (£25,000 each); Talmud Torah Chinuch Neorim (£10,000); The Manchester Eruv Committee (£5,000); Klal-Chazon Ltd (£2,000).

FINANCES *Financial year end* 05/04/2019 *Income* £927,700 *Total grants* £318,800 *Grants to organisations* £318,800 *Assets* £10,920,000

TRUSTEES Henry Neumann; Pinchas Neumann; Maurice Neumann; Mr Neumann; Esther Henry; Janet Bleier; Miriam Friedlander; Rebecca Delange; Hannah Roseman.

OTHER INFORMATION The 2018/19 accounts were the latest available at the time of writing (January 2021).

HOW TO APPLY Contact the correspondent for further information.

CONTACT DETAILS Maurice Neumann, Trustee, 32 Stanley Road, Salford, Greater Manchester M7 4ES *Tel.* 0161 720 6188

■ The Beaverbrook Foundation

CC NO 1153470 **ESTABLISHED** 1954

WHERE FUNDING CAN BE GIVEN UK.

WHO CAN BENEFIT Registered charities.

WHAT IS FUNDED General charitable purposes with a focus on: the improvement of church buildings; the purchase of books, papers, manuscripts or works of art; care of older people and people with illnesses; arts, culture and heritage.

WHAT IS NOT FUNDED Retrospective costs.

TYPE OF GRANT Capital costs; revenue and running costs; project funding; collections and acquisitions.

RANGE OF GRANTS Up to £40,000.

SAMPLE GRANTS Northwood House (£40,000); English National Ballet and RAF Museum – Hendon (£25,000 each); World House Welfare (£20,000); BASMOM and Battle of Britain Memorial Trust (£10,000 each); PDSA (£7,500); Charlotte's BAG (£6,500).

FINANCES *Financial year end* 30/09/2019 *Income* £86,500 *Total grants* £227,500 *Grants to organisations* £227,500 *Assets* £13,330,000

TRUSTEES Lord Beaverbrook; Lady Beaverbrook; The Hon. Laura Levi; John Kidd; The Hon. Rory Aitken; The Hon. Max Aitken; The Hon. Charlotte Aitken.

OTHER INFORMATION The 2018/19 accounts were the latest available at the time of writing (May 2021).

HOW TO APPLY Applications can be made via the foundation's website.

CONTACT DETAILS Jane Ford, Secretary, 19 Crown Passage, London SW1Y 6PP *Tel.* 020 3325 3987 *Email* jane@beaverbrookfoundation.org *Website* www.beaverbrookfoundation.org

■ The Beaverbrooks Charitable Trust

CC NO 1142857 **ESTABLISHED** 2011

WHERE FUNDING CAN BE GIVEN UK and Israel.

WHO CAN BENEFIT Charitable organisations.

WHAT IS FUNDED General charitable purposes including: education, welfare, health, mentoring and self-development.

RANGE OF GRANTS Grants range from £5,000 up to £310,500.

SAMPLE GRANTS The M. and A. Brown Charitable Trust (£200,000); Jewish Homes Emergency Appeal (£100,000); Fighting All Cancers Together £35,000); Royal Manchester Children's Hospital (£25,000); Business in the Community (£11,000); Rays of Sunshine (£10,000); MIND (£5,000).

FINANCES *Financial year end* 30/04/2020 *Income* £1,890,000 *Total grants* £1,850,000 *Grants to organisations* £1,850,000 *Assets* £8,380,000

TRUSTEES Mark Adlestone; Anna Blackburn; Susie Nicholas; Paul Holly.

HOW TO APPLY Contact the correspondent for further information.

CONTACT DETAILS The Trustees, Adele House, Park Road, St Annes-On-Sea, Lancashire FY8 1RE *Tel.* 01253 721262 *Email* Charitable.Trust@beaverbrooks.co.uk

■ The Becht Family Charitable Trust

CC NO 1116657 **ESTABLISHED** 2006

WHERE FUNDING CAN BE GIVEN Worldwide (UK, USA and elsewhere).

WHO CAN BENEFIT Charitable organisations.

WHAT IS FUNDED Protection and restoration of biodiversity and the natural environment, particularly through marine conservation; education (especially for activities related to the restoration of the natural environment); humanitarian aid.

WHAT IS NOT FUNDED Individuals; scholarships or tuition assistance for undergraduate or postgraduate students.

TYPE OF GRANT The trustees' are willing to consider restricted and unrestricted funding.

RANGE OF GRANTS Mostly up to £100,000.

SAMPLE GRANTS Save the Children (two grants totalling £2.04 million); Chelsea and Westminster Hospital (£100,000); Sightsavers and WaterAid (£50,000 each); Elemental Water Foundation (£13,400); Oxford Hospitals (£10,000); Head for the Cure Foundation (£4,100); Covenant Harbor Bible Camp (£3,800).

FINANCES *Financial year end* 03/10/2019 *Income* £6,190,000 *Total grants* £2,360,000 *Grants to organisations* £2,360,000 *Assets* £208,330,000

TRUSTEES Anne Becht; Lambertus Becht; David Poulter; R&H. Trust Co. (UK) Ltd.

OTHER INFORMATION The 2018/19 accounts were the latest available at the time of writing (June 2021). During the year, grants were awarded to 12 organisations. The largest single donation made in the year was £2 million awarded to Save the Children – Emergency Health Unit.

HOW TO APPLY An online grant application form is available on the trust's website. The trustees consider grants on a quarterly basis. All grant applications will be acknowledged but only successful applications will receive further consideration from the trustees.

CONTACT DETAILS The Trustees, c/o Rawlinson and Hunter, 8th Floor, 6 New Street Square, London EC4A 3AQ *Tel.* 020 7842 2000 *Email* thebfct@rawlinson-hunter.com *Website* https://bfct.org

■ The Becker Family Charitable Trust

CC NO 1047968 **ESTABLISHED** 1995

WHERE FUNDING CAN BE GIVEN UK and overseas.

WHO CAN BENEFIT Registered charities.

WHAT IS FUNDED Advancement of the Orthodox Jewish religion; social welfare.

SAMPLE GRANTS Previous beneficiaries have included: Keren Shabbas, Lolev CT, Menora Grammar School, Torah Temima and WST.

FINANCES *Financial year end* 05/04/2020 *Income* £233,300 *Total grants* £75,900 *Grants to organisations* £75,900 *Assets* £1,070,000

TRUSTEES Allan Becker; Ruth Becker; Deanna Fried; Andrew Guttentag.

HOW TO APPLY Contact the correspondent for further information.

CONTACT DETAILS The Trustees, 33 Sinclair Grove, London NW11 9JH *Tel.* 020 8455 6789

■ The John Beckwith Charitable Trust

CC NO 800276 **ESTABLISHED** 1987

WHERE FUNDING CAN BE GIVEN UK and overseas.

WHO CAN BENEFIT Registered charities.

WHAT IS FUNDED Education; social welfare; oversees aid; youth work.

RANGE OF GRANTS Grants are up to £40,000.

SAMPLE GRANTS David Ross Foundation (£40,000); Amelie and David Linsey Foundation (£25,000); Médecins Sans Frontières and Parkinson's Disease Society (£5,000 each); Hospice UK (£2,500); London Air Ambulance and Operation Smile UK (£1,000 each).

FINANCES *Financial year end* 05/04/2020 *Income* £311,200 *Total grants* £166,900 *Grants to organisations* £166,900 *Assets* £1,520,000

TRUSTEES Sir John Beckwith; Heather Beckwith; Christopher Meech.

OTHER INFORMATION In total, 56 grants were awarded throughout the year in the following categories: social welfare (42 grants), medical research (13 grants) and the arts (one grant).

HOW TO APPLY Apply in writing to the correspondent. The trustees aim to meet once a year to review grant applications.

CONTACT DETAILS The Trustees, 124 Sloane Street, London SW1X 9BW *Tel.* 020 7225 2250 *Email* info@beckwithlondon.com

■ The Bedfordshire and Hertfordshire Historic Churches Trust

CC NO 1005697 **ESTABLISHED** 1991

WHERE FUNDING CAN BE GIVEN Bedfordshire, Hertfordshire and the part of Barnet which falls within the Diocese of St Albans.

WHO CAN BENEFIT Places of active Christian worship.

WHAT IS FUNDED Restoration, maintenance, preservation, repair and reconstruction of churches and chapels.

WHAT IS NOT FUNDED Individuals.

TYPE OF GRANT Capital costs.

RANGE OF GRANTS Typically £1,000 to £5,000.

SAMPLE GRANTS St Lawrence – Abbots Langley (£10,000); St Mary Magdalene – Barkway and St Peter – Sharnbrook (£5,000 each); St Mary the Virgin – Keysoe and St Paul – Letchworth (£1,000 each).

FINANCES *Financial year end* 31/03/2020 *Income* £235,400 *Total grants* £197,000 *Grants to organisations* £197,000 *Assets* £337,000

TRUSTEES Stuart Russell; Dr Christopher Green; Jim May; Judith Howard; Madeline Russell; Richard Genochio; William Marsterson; David Mowbray; Revd Malcolm Grant; Revd Thomas Sander; Theresa Britt; Robert Sharp; Revd Paul Hughes.

OTHER INFORMATION The trust also acts as a distributive agent for church grants made by the Wixamtree Trust, Bedfordshire.

HOW TO APPLY Initial enquiries should be made to the Grants Secretary. Applications can only be made by members of the trust.

CONTACT DETAILS Archie Russell, Grants Secretary, Wychbrook, 31 Ivel Gardens, Biggleswade, Bedfordshire SG18 0AN *Tel.* 01767 312966 *Email* grants@bedshertshct.org.uk *Website* www.bedshertshct.org.uk

■ Bedfordshire and Luton Community Foundation

CC NO 1086516 **ESTABLISHED** 2001

WHERE FUNDING CAN BE GIVEN Bedfordshire and the borough of Luton.

WHO CAN BENEFIT Registered charities or other not-for-profit organisations (community groups/PTA's/sports groups, etc.). CICs and social enterprises should contact the foundation or review the specific guidance.

WHAT IS FUNDED General charitable purposes; community welfare.

WHAT IS NOT FUNDED Criteria for each of the foundation's grant programmes are available on the website, as well as a list of general exclusions.

TYPE OF GRANT Programme dependent.

RANGE OF GRANTS Mostly under £10,000, with the average grant of £5,000.

SAMPLE GRANTS The Safer Luton Partnership (£55,000); Bangladesh Youth League (£48,400); Anne Frank Trust UK (£21,300); Luton All Women's Centre (£10,000); Full House Theatre Company (£5,000); Happy Days Children's Charity (£3,200); Cruse Bereavement Care (£2,100); Arcadian Women's Group (£900).

FINANCES *Financial year end* 31/03/2020 *Income* £2,760,000 *Total grants* £785,400 *Grants to organisations* £785,400 *Assets* £2,780,000

TRUSTEES Judith Barker; Grafton Barbour; Vivianne Vayssieres; Jennifer Lascaris; Tarak Gorai;

Robert Houslin; Bina Briggs; Dr Joan Bailey; Rory Herbert.

OTHER INFORMATION This is one of the 46 UK community foundations, which distribute funding for a wide range of purposes. As with all community foundations, there are a number of donor-advised funds managed on behalf of individuals, families and charitable trusts. Grant schemes tend to change frequently – consult the foundation's website for details of current programmes and their up-to-date deadlines. Grants were awarded to over 125 organisations during the year.

HOW TO APPLY Application forms for the various funds are available on the foundation's website. If you wish to apply for more than one fund at the same time, you should first contact the foundation. The panel meets around five times a year.

CONTACT DETAILS Grants Administrator, Capability House, Wrest Park, Silsoe, Bedford, Bedfordshire MK45 4HR *Tel.* 01582 522422 *Email* administrator@blcf.org.uk *Website* www.blcf.org.uk

■ Bedfordshire Charitable Trust Ltd

CC NO 234329 **ESTABLISHED** 1964

WHERE FUNDING CAN BE GIVEN Bedford and overseas.

WHO CAN BENEFIT Charitable organisations.

WHAT IS FUNDED General charitable purposes, especially health and social welfare for older people and children.

RANGE OF GRANTS Up to £100,000, but mostly below £6,000.

SAMPLE GRANTS Bedfordshire Opportunities for Learning Disabilities – BOLD (£100,000); Macmillan – North Bedfordshire Hospice (£30,000); Motor Neurone Disease Association (£6,000); East Anglian Air Ambulance (£5,500); School Readers (£4,000); Keech Hospice (£2,500); The Kings Arms Project (£1,000).

FINANCES *Financial year end* 31/03/2019 *Income* £304,200 *Total grants* £174,600 *Grants to organisations* £174,600 *Assets* £16,040,000

TRUSTEES Clifton Ibbett; Mrs B. Plumby; Mr K. A Borneo; Christina Beddoes; Christopher Kilroy; Margaret Ibbett; Mark Thompson.

OTHER INFORMATION The 2018/19 accounts were the latest available at the time of writing (January 2021). Grants were made to 32 organisations during the year, with grants of less than £2,000 totalling £25,600. The trust also provides care homes and associated extra-care flats.

HOW TO APPLY Contact the correspondent for further information.

CONTACT DETAILS Christina Beddoes, Trustee and Secretary, Ladyslaude Court, Bramley Way, Bedford MK41 7FX *Tel.* 01234 352840 *Email* bedfordshire.charitable.trust@gmail.com

■ E. C. Graham Belford Charitable Settlement

CC NO 1014869 **ESTABLISHED** 1991

WHERE FUNDING CAN BE GIVEN Northumberland.

WHO CAN BENEFIT Smaller charities and branches of larger charities based in the area of benefit.

WHAT IS FUNDED General charitable purposes.

RANGE OF GRANTS Generally up to £15,000.

SAMPLE GRANTS Haltwhistle Youth Club (£25,000); Hexham Youth Initiative (£15,000); Rape Crisis Tyneside and North (£10,000); Tynedale Hospice at Home (£5,000); Royal Voluntary Service (£2,000); Blyth Stroke Support Group (£600).

FINANCES *Financial year end* 05/04/2020 *Income* £95,600 *Total grants* £158,100 *Grants to organisations* £158,100 *Assets* £7,670,000

TRUSTEES Anthony Thompson; Robert Hutchinson.

OTHER INFORMATION Grants were made to 21 organisations during the year.

HOW TO APPLY Contact the correspondent for further information.

CONTACT DETAILS Anthony Thompson, Trustee, Forsters LLP, 31 Hill Street, London SE1 2AU *Tel.* 020 7863 8333

■ AJ Bell Trust

CC NO 1141269 **ESTABLISHED** 2011

WHERE FUNDING CAN BE GIVEN UK.

WHO CAN BENEFIT Charitable organisations; individuals.

WHAT IS FUNDED Children and young people; disability; social welfare and inclusion; skills development; education and training; health and medical research.

SAMPLE GRANTS A list of beneficiaries was not included in the annual report and accounts.

FINANCES *Financial year end* 30/09/2020 *Income* £684,900 *Total grants* £296,600 *Grants to organisations* £296,600 *Assets* £2,360,000

TRUSTEES Andrew Bell; Tracey Bell; Paul Clements; Paul Barrow.

HOW TO APPLY Apply in writing to the correspondent.

CONTACT DETAILS Esther Speksnijder, Secretary, Blythe Hall, Blythe Lane, Lathom, Ormskirk L40 5TY *Email* moorhall@outlook.com *Website* https://www.ajbell.co.uk/about-us/corporate-social-responsibility

■ The Bellahouston Bequest Fund

OSCR NO SC011781 **ESTABLISHED** 1888

WHERE FUNDING CAN BE GIVEN Glasgow and district, but not more than five miles beyond the Glasgow city boundary.

WHO CAN BENEFIT Churches; registered charities; universities and educational institutions; hospices.

WHAT IS FUNDED Education; Protestant evangelical churches and associated schools, halls and clergy; social welfare; health.

TYPE OF GRANT Capital costs.

RANGE OF GRANTS Usually between £2,000 and £5,000.

SAMPLE GRANTS Prince and Princess of Wales Hospice (£10,000); Lodging House Mission (£7,000); Crossreach (£5,000); Good Morning Service (£3,000); KidsOut UK and Street Connect (£2,000 each); Visibility (£1,500); University of Glasgow (£250).

FINANCES *Financial year end* 30/06/2020 *Income* £197,900 *Total grants* £160,300 *Grants to organisations* £160,300 *Assets* £5,290,000

HOW TO APPLY Apply in writing to the correspondent. The trustees meet on a regular basis.

CONTACT DETAILS Eddie Barry, Administrator, c/o Mitchells Roberton Solicitors, George House, 36 North Hanover Street, Glasgow G1 2AD *Tel.* 0141 552 3422 *Email* emb@mitchells-roberton.co.uk

■ Belljoe Tzedoko Ltd

CC NO 282726 **ESTABLISHED** 1981

WHERE FUNDING CAN BE GIVEN England and Wales.

WHO CAN BENEFIT Registered charities.

WHAT IS FUNDED Advancement of the Orthodox Jewish faith; relief of poverty.

RANGE OF GRANTS Up to £30,000.

SAMPLE GRANTS Previous beneficiaries have included: Beis Brucha Ltd, CMZ Ltd, Kolyom Trust, The Gateshead Cheder Ltd, Viznitz and Yishaya Adler Memorial Fund.

FINANCES *Financial year end* 31/12/2019
Income £858,200 *Total grants* £450,100
Grants to organisations £450,100
Assets £8,250,000

TRUSTEES Morris Lobenstein; Karen Lobenstein; Benjamin Lobenstein.

OTHER INFORMATION All grants made during the year were for £30,000 or less. A list of beneficiaries was not available in the 2019 accounts.

HOW TO APPLY Contact the correspondent for further information.

CONTACT DETAILS The Trustees, 92 Fairholt Road, London N16 5NH *Tel.* 020 8455 6789

■ Benesco Charity Ltd

CC NO 269181 **ESTABLISHED** 1970

WHERE FUNDING CAN BE GIVEN UK.

WHO CAN BENEFIT Registered charities; hospitals; schools.

WHAT IS FUNDED Medicine; education; welfare; needs of the Jewish community.

WHAT IS NOT FUNDED Individuals.

TYPE OF GRANT General funding; development funding; capital costs; fixed term projects.

RANGE OF GRANTS Up to £50,000.

SAMPLE GRANTS A full list of beneficiaries was not available.

FINANCES *Financial year end* 05/04/2019
Income £8,920,000 *Total grants* £6,460,000
Grants to organisations £6,460,000
Assets £213,850,000

TRUSTEES Jonathan Ragol-Levy; Hon. Andrew Wolfson; David Wolfson.

OTHER INFORMATION A large proportion (£6.4 million) of the grant total was given to The Charles Wolfson Charitable Trust. The remaining £63,500 was donated to medicine, education and welfare charities, including to both Kishiron and the Institute for Policy Research. A full breakdown of beneficiaries was not provided in the 2018/19 annual report and accounts, which were the latest available at the time of writing (January 2021).

HOW TO APPLY Contact the correspondent for further information.

CONTACT DETAILS Michael Franks, Secretary, 8–10 Hallam Street, London W1W 6NS *Tel.* 020 7079 2506

■ The Benham Charitable Settlement

CC NO 239371 **ESTABLISHED** 1965

WHERE FUNDING CAN BE GIVEN UK and overseas, with a preference for Northamptonshire.

WHO CAN BENEFIT Registered charities; churches; schools.

WHAT IS FUNDED General charitable purposes; medical charities; Christian mission; disability; overseas aid; older people; children, schools and young people; conservation; art and sport; churches; animal welfare.

WHAT IS NOT FUNDED Individuals.

RANGE OF GRANTS Typically £1,000 to £2,000.

SAMPLE GRANTS Northampton Association of Youth Clubs (£45,000); The Filling Station Trust (£10,000); Sunningdale Hope Trust (£3,000); Katharine House Hospice, SportsAble and Voluntary Impact Northamptonshire (£2,000 each); Action on Poverty, Church Homeless Trust, Huntington's Disease Association and Samaritans (£1,000 each).

FINANCES *Financial year end* 05/04/2020
Income £261,600 *Total grants* £202,000
Grants to organisations £202,000
Assets £5,510,000

TRUSTEES Mrs M. Tittle; Lady Rosalind Hutton; David Tittle; Revd J. Nickols.

OTHER INFORMATION In 2019/20 the charity made 112 grants.

HOW TO APPLY Contact the correspondent for further information.

CONTACT DETAILS The Trustees, Norfolk Cottage, 1 Virginia Drive, Virginia Water, Surrey GU25 4RX *Tel.* 020 7631 4754

■ Bennett Lowell Ltd

CC NO 1149726 **ESTABLISHED** 2012

WHERE FUNDING CAN BE GIVEN UK and USA.

WHO CAN BENEFIT Registered charities; museums, theatres and arts organisations; USA tax-exempt organisations working in the UK.

WHAT IS FUNDED General charitable purposes, with a particular focus on the arts.

WHAT IS NOT FUNDED Individuals.

RANGE OF GRANTS Mostly up to £35,000, with some larger grants.

SAMPLE GRANTS The British Museum (two grants totalling £1.52 million); The Brunel Museum (£35,000); Selwyn College and Yorkshire Ballet Summer School (£20,000 each); The Swan Sanctuary (£15,000); The Royal Horticultural Society (£12,800); London Library (£8,800); Ark Franklin Primary School (£5,100); The Israel Philharmonic Orchestra (£2,000); The Old Royal Naval College (£600).

FINANCES *Financial year end* 31/12/2019
Income £4,650,000 *Total grants* £1,770,000
Grants to organisations £1,770,000
Assets £13,020,000

TRUSTEES David Borthwick; John Attree; Molly Borthwick; William Borthwick.

OTHER INFORMATION Grants were awarded to 21 organisations during the year. A large 'donation of investment' was made to The British Museum (£1.47 million).

HOW TO APPLY Contact the correspondent for further information.

CONTACT DETAILS The Trustees, c/o Charles Russell Speechlys LLP, 5 Fleet Place, London EC4M 7RD *Tel.* 020 7203 5000
Email information@crsblaw.com

■ The Rowan Bentall Charitable Trust

CC NO 273818 **ESTABLISHED** 1972

WHERE FUNDING CAN BE GIVEN Southern England.

WHO CAN BENEFIT Registered charities; churches; CICs; charitable organisations.

WHAT IS FUNDED Health and well-being; churches (repair, maintenance and improvement); children and young people; older people; people with disabilities; education; the environment; animal welfare and natural disasters.

RANGE OF GRANTS Mostly £250 to £1,000.

SAMPLE GRANTS Retail Trust (two grants totalling £28,000); Kingston and District Sea Cadet Corps (£3,000); Second Chance Children's Charity (£2,000); Fashion and Textile Children's Trust (£1,500); Help for Heroes and Surrey Cricket Foundation (£1,000 each); Combat Stress (£500); Butterfly Conservation and Young Epilepsy (£250 each); Ranelagh School (£100); The Rose Kingston Theatre Trust (£55).

FINANCES *Financial year end* 05/04/2020
Income £371,800 *Total grants* £78,700
Grants to organisations £78,700
Assets £2,480,000

TRUSTEES Leonard Bentall; Alastair Bentall; Kate Bentall; Abigail Shaw; Sarah Thompson; Holly Hunter; Sarah Haines.

OTHER INFORMATION The trust also provides support to any former Bentall's employee (including the employee of any subsidiary or associated company), their widows, widowers, children and dependants. During the year, 113 grants were awarded to 108 organisations in the following categories: older people (£32,800); health and saving lives (£12,100); education (£10,600); children and young people (£10,100); welfare (£4,100); other (£3,700); animal welfare (£2,300); the environment and churches (£1,500 each).

HOW TO APPLY Contact the correspondent for further information.

CONTACT DETAILS The Trustees, PO Box 109, Haslemere, Surrey GU27 9GW *Tel.* 01223 259043 *Email* rowanbentallcharitabletrust@hotmail.co.uk

■ The Berkeley Foundation

CC NO 1152596 **ESTABLISHED** 2013

WHERE FUNDING CAN BE GIVEN Greater London, Berkshire, Birmingham, Buckinghamshire, Hertfordshire, Oxfordshire, Surrey, Kent, Hampshire, West Sussex and Warwickshire.

WHO CAN BENEFIT Registered charities; CICs.

WHAT IS FUNDED Supporting young people with housing and homelessness; education, training and employment; health and well-being.

WHAT IS NOT FUNDED Individuals.

TYPE OF GRANT Project funding; core/revenue costs; development funding.

RANGE OF GRANTS Up to £70,000 for up to two years. Existing charity partners can apply to the Capacity Building Fund for up to £15,000 for a period of 1–2 years.

SAMPLE GRANTS Crisis (£1.26 million); The Change Foundation (£865,000); Chance UK (£88,600); No.5 Young People (£85,200); Oarsome Chance (£78,000); Skyway Charity (£59,900).

FINANCES *Financial year end* 30/04/2020
Income £4,730,000 *Total grants* £2,940,000
Grants to organisations £2,940,000
Assets £1,710,000

TRUSTEES Robert Perrins; Wendy Pritchard; Elaine Driver; Alison Dowsett.

OTHER INFORMATION The fund makes grants to its strategic partners, designated charities and invites applications to its Community Investment Fund which makes smaller grants to innovative programmes in line with the four key areas of housing, education, employment and health. Only recipients of more than £50,000 were listed.

HOW TO APPLY Applications are typically made online through the trust's website where details about upcoming deadlines can be found.

CONTACT DETAILS The Trustees, Berkeley House, 19 Portsmouth Road, Cobham, Surrey KT11 1JG *Email* info@berkeleyfoundation.org.uk *Website* www.berkeleyfoundation.org.uk

■ Ruth Berkowitz Charitable Trust

CC NO 1111673 **ESTABLISHED** 2005

WHERE FUNDING CAN BE GIVEN UK and Israel.

WHO CAN BENEFIT Mainly Jewish charitable organisations.

WHAT IS FUNDED General charitable purposes; welfare, education and security needs in the Jewish community; research money for major UK cancer charities.

RANGE OF GRANTS £5,000 to £50,000.

SAMPLE GRANTS Previous beneficiaries have included: University Jewish Chaplaincy (£50,000); World Jewish Relief (£45,000); Community Security Trust (£40,000); London School of Jewish Studies (£30,000); Marie Curie Cancer Care (£15,000); Aleh Charitable Foundation and Camp Simcha (£10,000 each); British Friends of United Hatzalah Israel and The Z.S.V. Trust (£7,500 each); Rimon Jewish Primary School (£5,000).

FINANCES *Financial year end* 05/04/2020
Income £22,100 *Total grants* £452,100
Grants to organisations £452,100

TRUSTEES Philip Beckman; Brian Beckman; Philip Goodman.

OTHER INFORMATION Full accounts were not available to view on the Charity Commission's website due to the trust's low income. We have therefore estimated the grant total based on the trust's total expenditure.

HOW TO APPLY According to the trust's accounts for 2018/19: 'As the Trust is not a reactive trust the Trustees will generally only make grants to charities which are known to them and will not normally respond to unsolicited requests for assistance.'

CONTACT DETAILS The Trustees, c/o Ruth Berkowitz Charitable Trust, 63–66 Hatton Garden, London EC1N 9LE *Tel.* 020 7408 8888 *Email* admin@ruthberkowitztrust.org

■ The Berkshire Community Foundation

CC NO 1155173 **ESTABLISHED** 1985

WHERE FUNDING CAN BE GIVEN Berkshire (the unitary authorities of Bracknell, Reading, Slough, Windsor and Maidenhead, West Berkshire and Wokingham).

WHO CAN BENEFIT Registered charities; unregistered charities; CICs; social enterprises; schools; PTAs; amateur sports clubs; individuals.

WHAT IS FUNDED General charitable purposes.

WHAT IS NOT FUNDED Refer to the website for specific exclusions under each grant programme.

TYPE OF GRANT Capital costs; project funding; unrestricted funding.

SAMPLE GRANTS Previous beneficiaries have included: Creativity in Sport (£25,000); Recovering in Mind (£19,000 each); Destiny Support CIC and Home-Start Reading (£15,000 each); Slough Refugee Support (£3,800); Living Paintings Trust (£1,000).

FINANCES *Financial year end* 31/03/2020
Income £1,640,000 *Total grants* £1,030,000
Grants to organisations £1,030,000
Assets £10,030,000

TRUSTEES Debra Allcock Tyler; Alexander Barfield; Stephen Howard; Jane Potter; Julie Elliott; Darren Browne; Geoff Ash; Susan Roberts; Margaret Haines; Camilla Horwood; Sean Taylor.

OTHER INFORMATION This is one of the 46 UK community foundations, which distribute funding for a wide range of purposes. As with all community foundations, there are a number of donor-advised funds managed on behalf of individuals, families and charitable trusts. Grant schemes tend to change frequently – consult the foundation's website for details of current programmes and up-to-date deadlines.
HOW TO APPLY Potential applicants are advised to visit the community foundation's website or contact its grants team to find the most suitable funding stream.
CONTACT DETAILS Grants Team, 100 Longwater Avenue, Green Park, Reading, Berkshire RG2 6GP *Tel.* 0118 930 3021 *Email* info@berkshirecf.org *Website* www.berkshirecf.org

■ The Bestway Foundation

CC NO 297178 **ESTABLISHED** 1987
WHERE FUNDING CAN BE GIVEN UK and overseas, particularly India, Pakistan, Bangladesh and Sri Lanka.
WHO CAN BENEFIT Registered charities; unregistered charitable organisations; individuals; educational establishments.
WHAT IS FUNDED Education and training; health, including building or endowing new hospitals, clinics or medical research establishments; social welfare; overseas and disaster aid. Grants, scholarships and loans are awarded to schoolchildren and students in the UK and overseas, particularly those of Indian, Pakistani, Bangladeshi or Sri Lankan origin.
RANGE OF GRANTS £500 to £100,000.
SAMPLE GRANTS Save the Children – Royal Ascot Charity (£100,000); Crimestoppers (£40,000); British Asian Trust (£30,000); Thames Hospice (£20,000); Duke of Edinburgh Awards (£15,000); Doncaster Flood Goods Donation (£7,100); Silver Star Diabetes (£2,500); Sickle Cell Society (£500).
FINANCES *Financial year end* 30/06/2020 *Income* £238,100 *Total grants* £402,000 *Grants to organisations* £217,600 *Assets* £5,780,000
TRUSTEES Mohammed Younus Sheikh; Sir Anwar Pervez; Lord Zameer Choudrey; Dawood Pervez; Rizwan Pervez.
OTHER INFORMATION Grants were made to 10 organisations in the UK during the year (£217,600). In addition, grants were awarded to 29 individuals (£184,400). Note that the grant total for individuals may include grants to overseas charitable organisations.
HOW TO APPLY Apply in writing to the correspondent. The foundation has previously noted that telephone calls are not invited.
CONTACT DETAILS Mohammed Younus Sheikh, Secretary and Trustee, Abbey Road, London NW10 7BW *Tel.* 020 8453 1234 *Email* zulfikaur.wajid-hasan@bestway.co.uk *Website* www.bestwaygroup.co.uk/responsibility/bestway-foundation

■ The Beth Hamedrash Satmar Trust (BHST)

CC NO 1004327 **ESTABLISHED** 1989
WHERE FUNDING CAN BE GIVEN UK; Israel.
WHO CAN BENEFIT Jewish organisations; individuals.
WHAT IS FUNDED Jewish charitable causes; social welfare; education.
RANGE OF GRANTS Up to £20,000.
SAMPLE GRANTS Friends of Yeshiva Daas Sholem Shotz and Talmud Torah Education Ltd (£20,000 each); Inspirations (£18,000); Wlodowa Charity and Rehabilitation Trust (£15,000 each); Kollel Torah Ve Yireh Ltd (£13,300); Jaster Ltd (£9,500); Binyen Torah Ltd (£9,000).
FINANCES *Financial year end* 31/03/2020 *Income* £714,200 *Total grants* £137,600 *Grants to organisations* £137,600 *Assets* £785,000
TRUSTEES Solomon Laufer; Joshua Sternlicht.
OTHER INFORMATION Grants of less than £5,000 totalled £32,800.
HOW TO APPLY Contact the correspondent for further information.
CONTACT DETAILS Solomon Laufer, Company Secretary, c/o Cohen Arnold, New Burlington House, 1075 Finchley Road, London NW11 0PU *Tel.* 020 8731 0777 *Email* mail@cohenarnold.com

■ Bideford Bridge Trust

CC NO 204536 **ESTABLISHED** 1973
WHERE FUNDING CAN BE GIVEN The parish of Bideford, Devon and the immediate neighbourhood.
WHO CAN BENEFIT Charitable organisations; individuals.
WHAT IS FUNDED General charitable purposes including: education; social welfare; health; amateur sports; business start-up schemes.
TYPE OF GRANT Core costs; running costs; unrestricted funding.
RANGE OF GRANTS £1,500 to £25,000.
SAMPLE GRANTS School Swimming Lessons – 1610 Ltd (£26,700); Torridge District Council – Playground Fund (£25,000); North Devon Hospice (£16,000); Bideford Methodist Church and North Devon Museum Trust (£10,000 each); South West Heritage Trust (£6,000); Bideford Amateur Rowing Club (£5,000); 1st Woolsery Scouts (£2,000).
FINANCES *Financial year end* 21/12/2019 *Income* £836,400 *Total grants* £424,700 *Grants to organisations* £172,600 *Assets* £17,920,700
TRUSTEES Jude Gubb; Oliver Chope; David Dark; Peter Christie; William Isaac; Elizabeth Junkison; Ruth Craigie; Angus Harper; Jamie McKenzie; Eric Hubber; Sally Ellis.
OTHER INFORMATION The 2018/19 accounts were the latest available at the time of writing (June 2021). Grants of under £1,500 to organisations totalled £57,100. Grants to individuals totalled £252,100.
HOW TO APPLY Application forms for each grant programme are available to download on the funder's website. Completed forms should be returned by post.
CONTACT DETAILS The Steward, 24 Bridgeland Street, Bideford, Devon EX39 2QB *Tel.* 01237 473122 *Email* info@bidefordbridgetrust.org.uk *Website* www.bidefordbridgetrust.org.uk

■ Biffa Award

ESTABLISHED 1997
WHERE FUNDING CAN BE GIVEN UK. Projects should be located near a Biffa operation and any licensed landfill site. There is a postcode checker on the website.
WHO CAN BENEFIT Charitable organisations.
WHAT IS FUNDED Biodiversity; community buildings; recreation.

WHAT IS NOT FUNDED The website details the specific exclusions for each theme.
TYPE OF GRANT Capital costs; project funding.
SAMPLE GRANTS Winchester Science Centre (£292,400); Staffordshire Wildlife Trust (£75,000); Swannington Play Area (£64,300); Stourbridge Scout Hut (£12,400).
FINANCES *Financial year end* 30/03/2020
Total grants £3,770,000
Grants to organisations £3,770,000
OTHER INFORMATION Full financial information was not available to view. The grant total has been taken from the grant-maker's 2019/20 annual review. Grants were broken down as follows: community buildings projects (£1.22 million); natural environment partnership grants (£1 million); built environment partnership grants (£960,000); rebuilding biodiversity (£388,400); recreation projects (£207,800).
HOW TO APPLY Applications can be made through the grant-maker's website. Check the website for application deadlines.
CONTACT DETAILS The Grants Team, The Wildlife Trusts, The Kiln, Mather Road, Newark NG24 1WT *Tel.* 01636 670000 *Email* biffa-award@wildlifetrusts.org *Website* www.biffa-award.org

■ The Big Yellow Foundation

CC NO 1171232 **ESTABLISHED** 2017
WHERE FUNDING CAN BE GIVEN Across the UK in areas where the Big Yellow Group plc operates.
WHO CAN BENEFIT Registered charities.
WHAT IS FUNDED Offenders and ex-offenders; health.
RANGE OF GRANTS £15,000 to £34,000.
SAMPLE GRANTS Breaking Barriers (£34,200); Down's Syndrome Association, St Giles Trust and Bounce Back (£20,000 each); Hire A Hero (£16,000); The Back-Up Trust (£15,000).
FINANCES *Financial year end* 31/03/2020
Income £170,600 *Total grants* £126,200
Grants to organisations £126,200
Assets £121,600
TRUSTEES Anthony Chenery; James Gibson; Jessica Pallot-Cook; Cheryl Hathaway.
OTHER INFORMATION This is the corporate charity of the Big Yellow Group plc. The foundation supports six charity partners each year.
HOW TO APPLY Grants are only made to the foundation's charity partners. Unsolicited applications are not accepted.
CONTACT DETAILS Gabriella Zepf, Head of CSR, Big Yellow Group, 1–2 The Deans, Bridge Road, Bagshot GU19 5AT *Tel.* 01276 477136 *Email* foundation@bigyellow.co.uk *Website* https://www.bigyellow.co.uk/foundation

■ The Billmeir Charitable Trust

CC NO 208561 **ESTABLISHED** 1956
WHERE FUNDING CAN BE GIVEN UK, with a preference for the Surrey area.
WHO CAN BENEFIT Charitable organisations.
WHAT IS FUNDED General charitable purposes; arts and culture; education; medical research and aid; religious activities; social welfare.
RANGE OF GRANTS Up to £20,000.
SAMPLE GRANTS Reed's School – Cobham (£20,000); ABF The Soldiers' Charity (£15,000); The Watts Gallery (£10,000); Surrey Community Foundation (£5,000); Challengers (£2,500); Home-start – Surrey (£2,000); Walk the Walk Worldwide (£1,000).
FINANCES *Financial year end* 05/04/2020
Income £232,100 *Total grants* £198,000
Grants to organisations £198,000
Assets £5,460,000
TRUSTEES Max Whitaker; Suzanne Marriott; Jason Whitaker.
OTHER INFORMATION In 2019/20 the trust made grants to 41 organisations totalling £198,000, distributed as follows: education (£62,500), social welfare (£37,000), general charitable purposes (£35,000), medical research and aid (£28,000), arts and culture (£22,500) and religious activities (£13,000).
HOW TO APPLY Unsolicited applications are not invited and rarely successful. Many of the trust's grants are to organisations that it supports on a regular basis.
CONTACT DETAILS Martin Fernandopulle, c/o BDO, 55 Baker Street, London W1U 7EU *Tel.* 020 7486 5888 *Email* charity.correspondence@bdo.co.uk

■ The Percy Bilton Charity

CC NO 1094720 **ESTABLISHED** 1962
WHERE FUNDING CAN BE GIVEN UK.
WHO CAN BENEFIT Registered charities; unregistered charities; social enterprises; CICs; PTAs; hospitals; hospices; individuals.
WHAT IS FUNDED General charitable purposes, particularly older people, children or adults with learning or physical disabilities or mental health problems and children and young people who are socially or educationally disadvantaged.
WHAT IS NOT FUNDED A full list of exclusions can be found on the charity's website.
TYPE OF GRANT Capital costs; project funding.
RANGE OF GRANTS Large grants £2,000 to £5,000; small grants up to £500.
SAMPLE GRANTS A list of beneficiaries was not included in the annual report and accounts.
FINANCES *Financial year end* 31/03/2020
Income £833,000 *Total grants* £800,800
Grants to organisations £486,300
Assets £24,510,000
TRUSTEES James Lee; Kim Lansdown; Hayley Bilton; Charles Sosna; Benjamin Chance.
OTHER INFORMATION During the year, grants were awarded to 175 organisations. Urgent one-off assistance is given to older people (over 65) and people with disabilities to purchase essential items. During the year, grants were awarded to 1,701 individuals totalling £314,500.
HOW TO APPLY Applications can be made online on the website and supporting documentation should be emailed or sent by post. Applicants should consult the charity's website for detailed guidance on how to make an application for each of the grant schemes.
CONTACT DETAILS The Trustees, Bilton House, 7 Culmington Road, Ealing, London W13 9NB *Tel.* 020 8579 2829 *Email* information@percybiltoncharity.org *Website* www.percy-bilton-charity.org

■ The Bingham Trust

CC NO 287636 **ESTABLISHED** 1977
WHERE FUNDING CAN BE GIVEN Buxton and surrounding SK17 postcode area.
WHO CAN BENEFIT Charitable organisations; individuals.
WHAT IS FUNDED General charitable purposes; social welfare; education; religious activity; community development.

WHAT IS NOT FUNDED Repayment of existing debts; businesses or profit-making organisations; higher education (university and college level); retrospective expenditure; revenue costs; organisations that have previously applied within the last 12 months.

TYPE OF GRANT The trust prefers to fund capital projects rather than revenue expenses.

RANGE OF GRANTS Capital costs.

SAMPLE GRANTS Previous beneficiaries have included: Good News Family Care (£37,500); Warslow Village Hall (£5,000); High Peak Foodbank (£4,900); Step By Step (£4,000); Buxton Community School and High Peak CVS (£3,100 each); Samaritans and Volunteer Centre Buxton (£2,000 each); Churches Together and Buxton Well Dressing (£1,000 each); PDSA (£50).

FINANCES *Financial year end* 05/04/2020
Income £158,000 *Total grants* £126,600
Grants to organisations £126,600
Assets £4,320,000

TRUSTEES Roger Horne; Alexandra Hurst; Eric Butterley; Helen Mirtle; Christine McMullen.

OTHER INFORMATION In 2019/20 the trust provided support to around 50 organisations and individuals. A list of beneficiaries for the year was not available.

HOW TO APPLY Application forms can be downloaded from the trust's website and returned via email or post. All applications are acknowledged and are typically reviewed in January, April, July and October – closing dates for the next funding round can be found on the trust's website. Refer to the trust's guidelines and frequently asked questions before submitting an application.

CONTACT DETAILS Ms E. Marshall, Trust Secretary, c/o BDO LLP, 55 Baker Street, London W1U 7EU *Tel.* 07966 378546 *Email* binghamtrust@aol.com *Website* www.binghamtrust.org.uk

■ Binks Trust

OSCR NO SC008849 **ESTABLISHED** 1973

WHERE FUNDING CAN BE GIVEN Scotland.

WHO CAN BENEFIT Registered charities.

WHAT IS FUNDED General charitable purposes with a preference for the arts, music and social welfare.

RANGE OF GRANTS £10,000 to £100,000.

SAMPLE GRANTS Capital Theatres, National Galleries of Scotland and Royal Botanic Garden of Edinburgh (£100,000 each); Dynamic Earth (£60,000); Freedom from Fistula Foundation (£50,000); Scottish Chamber Orchestra (£30,000); St Mary's Music School (£20,000); Cross Reach (£10,000).

FINANCES *Financial year end* 05/04/2020
Income £617,700 *Total grants* £1,170,000
Grants to organisations £1,170,000
Assets £9,280,000

OTHER INFORMATION Grants were awarded to 28 organisations during the year.

HOW TO APPLY Contact the correspondent for further information.

CONTACT DETAILS The Trustees, 61 Dublin Street, Edinburgh EH3 6NL

■ The Birmingham District Nursing Charitable Trust

CC NO 215652 **ESTABLISHED** 1963

WHERE FUNDING CAN BE GIVEN Within a 20-mile radius of the Council House in Birmingham.

WHO CAN BENEFIT Medical or nursing organisations; convalescent homes; Birmingham Domiciliary Nursing Service; hospitals.

WHAT IS FUNDED Health; amenities for patients and/or nursing staff.

WHAT IS NOT FUNDED Individuals.

RANGE OF GRANTS Typically £1,000 to £3,000.

SAMPLE GRANTS Birmingham Centre For Art Therapies and Freedom From Torture (£5,000 each); Better Pathways and Huntington's Disease (£3,000 each); Brain Tumour Support and Myton Hospice (£2,000 each); Breast Cancer Haven West Midlands and Ovacome (£1,000 each).

FINANCES *Financial year end* 18/07/2020
Income £73,100 *Total grants* £67,900
Grants to organisations £67,900
Assets £2,120,000

TRUSTEES Anthony Jones; Dr Peter Mayer; Stuart Reynolds; Joan Fox; Dr Mary Honeyman; Prof. Fiona Irvine; Jonathan Tuckey; Michael Hammond.

OTHER INFORMATION In 2019/20 the trust awarded grants to 28 organisations.

HOW TO APPLY Apply in writing to the correspondent, including a copy of your latest accounts. The trustees meet once per annum to consider applications.

CONTACT DETAILS Hannah Tait, Secretary, c/o Shakespeare Martineau LLP, Homer House, 8 Homer Road, Solihull, West Midlands B91 3QQ *Tel.* 0121 705 8151 *Email* hannah.tait@shma.co.uk

■ Birmingham International Airport Community Trust Fund

CC NO 1071176 **ESTABLISHED** 1998

WHERE FUNDING CAN BE GIVEN The areas affected by the airport's operation, particularly east Birmingham and north Solihull – a full list of postcodes is provided on the website.

WHO CAN BENEFIT Established, local non-profit organisations.

WHAT IS FUNDED Community; the environment; heritage; sport and recreation; health and well-being.

WHAT IS NOT FUNDED Individuals; organisations with statutory responsibilities; branches of national or international organisations; medical treatment; purchase of land or buildings; repair and maintenance; uniforms; sports kit; short-term projects e.g. trips or events; retrospective funding for projects.

TYPE OF GRANT Grants are awarded for capital or revenue projects, although the trust will not commit to recurrent or running costs, such as salaries.

RANGE OF GRANTS Up to £3,000.

SAMPLE GRANTS A list of beneficiaries was not included in the annual report and accounts.

FINANCES *Financial year end* 31/03/2019
Income £86,000 *Total grants* £84,900
Grants to organisations £84,900
Assets £20,000

TRUSTEES Cllr Michael Ward; Paul Orton; Andrew Holding; Edward Richards; Margaret Kennet; Cllr Majid Mahmood; David Cuthbert; Cllr Robert Grinsell; Cllr James Burn.

OTHER INFORMATION The 2018/19 accounts were the latest available at the time of writing (June 2021).

HOW TO APPLY Application packs can be requested from the correspondent.

CONTACT DETAILS Andy Holding, Trust Fund Secretary, Birmingham Airport, Birmingham, West Midlands B26 3QJ *Tel.* 0121 767 7448 *Email* andy.holding@birminghamairport.co.uk *Website* https://www.birminghamairport.co.uk/about-us/community-and-environment/community-investment/community-trust-fund

■ Birthday House Trust

CC NO 248028 **ESTABLISHED** 1966

WHERE FUNDING CAN BE GIVEN England and Wales.

WHO CAN BENEFIT Charitable organisations; individuals.

WHAT IS FUNDED General charitable purposes, including: religion; community development; arts and heritage; the environment; social welfare; promotion of the efficiency of emergency services.

RANGE OF GRANTS Up to £9,000.

SAMPLE GRANTS Cowdray Heritage Trust (£48,000); Greenpeace Environmental Trust (£10,000).

FINANCES *Financial year end* 05/04/2019 *Income* £158,800 *Total grants* £113,900 *Grants to organisations* £79,300 *Assets* £8,580,000

TRUSTEES The Dickinson Trust Ltd; Rathbone Trust Company Ltd.

OTHER INFORMATION Grants of under £9,000 totalled £55,900. The 2018/19 accounts were the latest available at the time of writing (January 2021).

HOW TO APPLY Contact the correspondent for further information.

CONTACT DETAILS The Trustees, 4th Floor, 10 Bruton Street, London W1J 6PX *Tel.* 020 7907 2100 *Email* charity@mfs.co.uk

■ The Michael Bishop Foundation

CC NO 297627 **ESTABLISHED** 1987

WHERE FUNDING CAN BE GIVEN Worldwide.

WHO CAN BENEFIT Registered charities.

WHAT IS FUNDED General charitable purposes; arts, culture and heritage; human rights, social justice and equality; advancement of health and medicine; education and training.

TYPE OF GRANT Project funding; capital costs; core/revenue costs; seed funding/start-up funding; strategic funding.

RANGE OF GRANTS £1,000 to £500,000.

SAMPLE GRANTS Glendonbrook Foundation (£250,000); Birmingham Royal Ballet (£100,000); Governor Phillip Scholarship (£57,400); Just Like Us (£25,000); Pimlico Opera (£15,000); Spinal Research Sundry (£10,000); Mission Mozambique (£5,000); Medical Detection Dogs (£1,000); Doorway (£600).

FINANCES *Financial year end* 05/04/2020 *Income* £3,420,000 *Total grants* £1,660,000 *Grants to organisations* £1,660,000 *Assets* £33,270,000

TRUSTEES Grahame Elliott; Baron Glendonbrook of Bowdon; Timothy Bye; Martin Ritchie.

OTHER INFORMATION During the year, the foundation awarded grants to 35 organisations. Grants were broken down as follows: arts and culture (£502,700); health and medicine (£434,500); general charitable purposes (£256,300); education and training (£238,800); human rights and social justice (£58,400); heritage (£57,500); relief of those in need (£25,000).

HOW TO APPLY The trustees do not accept unsolicited applications.

CONTACT DETAILS The Trustees, Staunton House, Ashby-de-la-Zouch, Leicestershire LE65 1RW *Tel.* 01530 564388 *Email* jo.furlong@btconnect.com

■ Asser Bishvil Foundation

CC NO 1112477 **ESTABLISHED** 2005

WHERE FUNDING CAN BE GIVEN Greater Manchester and London.

WHO CAN BENEFIT Registered charities.

WHAT IS FUNDED The relief of poverty among the Jewish community; the advancement of Jewish education and the Jewish faith.

SAMPLE GRANTS A list of beneficiaries was not included in the annual report and accounts.

FINANCES *Financial year end* 05/04/2020 *Income* £8,110,000 *Total grants* £8,230,000 *Grants to organisations* £8,230,000 *Assets* £1,670,000

TRUSTEES Rabbi Daniel Orzel; S. Orzel; Chaim Simche Ehrenteu.

OTHER INFORMATION Grants were distributed in the following categories: relief of poverty (£5.11 million); educational grants (£2.2 million); religious grants (£929,100).

HOW TO APPLY According to its 2019/20 annual report, 'the charity invites applications for funding through contacting local philanthropists to contribute towards projects that both the trustees and the philanthropists feel are appropriate for the charities objects'.

CONTACT DETAILS Daniel Orzel, Trustee, 2 New Hall Road, Salford M7 4EL *Tel.* 0161 792 1813 *Email* enquiries@asserbishvil.org.uk *Website* asserbishvil.org.uk

■ Maria Bjornson Memorial Fund

CC NO 1126096 **ESTABLISHED** 2008

WHERE FUNDING CAN BE GIVEN UK.

WHO CAN BENEFIT Registered charities.

WHAT IS FUNDED General charitable purposes including: medical and scientific research; social welfare; performing, visual and creative arts.

TYPE OF GRANT Project funding; core costs.

RANGE OF GRANTS Up to £80,000.

SAMPLE GRANTS New English Ballet Theatre (£80,000); Belarus Free Theatre (£40,000); Diverse Abilities (£10,000); Carers Trust (£5,000); Humanity and Inclusion (£1,500).

FINANCES *Financial year end* 31/12/2019 *Income* £446,200 *Total grants* £387,600 *Grants to organisations* £387,600 *Assets* £13,960,000

TRUSTEES Sir Richard Eyre; Simon Weil; Robert Crowley; Sir Michael Gifford.

OTHER INFORMATION Grants were made to 18 organisations.

HOW TO APPLY Contact the correspondent for further information.

CONTACT DETAILS The Trustees, Bircham Dyson Bell, 50 Broadway, London SW1H 0BL *Tel.* 020 7227 7000

The John Black Charitable Foundation

CC NO 1143431 **ESTABLISHED** 2011

WHERE FUNDING CAN BE GIVEN UK and Israel.

WHO CAN BENEFIT Universities; charitable organisations; individuals.

WHAT IS FUNDED Medical research (particularly Parkinson's disease and prostate cancer); general charitable purposes.

TYPE OF GRANT Capital costs; project funding.

RANGE OF GRANTS Grants previously up to £1.5 million.

SAMPLE GRANTS A list of beneficiaries was not included in the annual report and accounts.

FINANCES *Financial year end* 31/03/2020 *Income* £3,200,000 *Total grants* £3,450,000 *Grants to organisations* £3,450,000 *Assets* £82,260,000

TRUSTEES Stephen Conway; David Taglight.

OTHER INFORMATION During the year, long term grants were awarded to Oxford University and University College London for specific research into Parkinson's disease and prostate cancer. Grants were awarded for the following purposes: Parkinson's disease and prostate cancer (£2.45 million); other charitable purposes (£775,000).

HOW TO APPLY Contact the correspondent for further information.

CONTACT DETAILS The Trustees, 24 Old Burlington Street, London W1S 3AW *Tel.* 020 7734 0424

The Sydney Black Charitable Trust

CC NO 219855 **ESTABLISHED** 1949

WHERE FUNDING CAN BE GIVEN UK.

WHO CAN BENEFIT Registered charities; schools; amateur sports clubs; hospitals; hospices.

WHAT IS FUNDED Christianity; social welfare; older people; young people; education; prisoners' rights.

TYPE OF GRANT Unrestricted funding.

RANGE OF GRANTS £300 to £10,000.

SAMPLE GRANTS A list of beneficiaries was not included in the annual report and accounts.

FINANCES *Financial year end* 05/04/2020 *Income* £104,300 *Total grants* £108,100 *Grants to organisations* £108,100 *Assets* £3,420,000

TRUSTEES Hilary Dickenson; Stephen Crabtree; Philip Crabtree.

OTHER INFORMATION Grants were made to 164 organisations in the following categories: education and children (£58,900), social welfare (£24,900), religion (£12,400) and support for prisoners (£11,900).

HOW TO APPLY Applications should be made in writing to the correspondent.

CONTACT DETAILS The Trustees, PO Box 1251, St Albans, Hertfordshire AL1 9JU *Tel.* 07814 009039

The Isabel Blackman Foundation

CC NO 313577 **ESTABLISHED** 1966

WHERE FUNDING CAN BE GIVEN Hastings and St Leonards-on-Sea.

WHO CAN BENEFIT Charitable organisations; hospices; churches; schools; individuals.

WHAT IS FUNDED General charitable purposes including: health; social services; education; culture and recreation; youth clubs and organisations; religion; the environment.

WHAT IS NOT FUNDED Applications will only be considered from organisations based in Hastings and St Leonards district unless the applicant is able to satisfy the trustees that there is a direct or genuine connection with the people of Hastings and St Leonards-on-Sea.

RANGE OF GRANTS Up to £60,000 but generally £500 to £5,000.

SAMPLE GRANTS Friends of Conquest Hospital (£25,000); Hastings Advice & Representation Centre (£15,000); Rye Harbour Nature Reserve (£7,500); Hastings Music Festival (£5,000); Stepping Stones Pre-school (£3,500); The Fire Fighters Charity (£2,000); The Gap Project (£1,000); St Mary Star of the Sea Parish Community Club (£500); Christ Church Treasure Seekers (£300).

FINANCES *Financial year end* 05/04/2020 *Income* £296,500 *Total grants* £247,500 *Grants to organisations* £202,400 *Assets* £7,160,000

TRUSTEES David Harding; Denis Jukes; Patricia Connolly; John Lamplugh; Christine Deacon; Martin Holgate.

OTHER INFORMATION Grants were made to 68 organisations and broken down as follows: health (£95,300); social services (£73,600); education (£49,400); culture and recreation (£17,200); the environment (£9,500); religion (£1,500); youth clubs and organisations (£1,000). Grants to 34 individuals totalled £45,100.

HOW TO APPLY Contact the correspondent for further information.

CONTACT DETAILS The Trustees, Stonehenge, 13 Laton Road, Hastings, East Sussex TN34 2ES *Tel.* 01424 431756 *Email* ibfoundation@uwclub.net

The Blagrave Trust

CC NO 1164021 **ESTABLISHED** 2015

WHERE FUNDING CAN BE GIVEN South east Hampshire, the Isle of Wight, Sussex, Wiltshire and Berkshire. Occasionally, Somerset or Oxfordshire.

WHO CAN BENEFIT Registered charities; CICs.

WHAT IS FUNDED Helping disadvantaged young people develop the skills, experience and capabilities to successfully transition to adulthood; supporting young people's social change efforts; influencing policy on behalf of young people.

WHAT IS NOT FUNDED Capital grants or building projects; general recreational or social activities; one-off or short-term activities; promotion of religion.

TYPE OF GRANT Core/revenue costs; project funding.

RANGE OF GRANTS Typically between £10,000 and £80,000.

SAMPLE GRANTS Social Change Agency (£80,000); British Youth Council (£50,500); Youth Action Wiltshire (£40,000); Children England (£25,000); Homeless Link and Just for Kids Law (£20,000 each); Role Models Project and Seeds for Success (£10,000 each); The Shelia McKechnie Foundation (£5,000).

FINANCES *Financial year end* 31/12/2019 *Income* £2,300,000 *Total grants* £2,000,000 *Grants to organisations* £2,000,000 *Assets* £42,180,000

TRUSTEES Clare Cannock; Linda Epstein; Boudicca Pepper; Adaeze Aghaji; Segun Olowookere; Peter Babudu.

OTHER INFORMATION In 2019 the trust made grants totalling £2 million to 81 organisations.

HOW TO APPLY Applicants should complete the brief outline proposal form on the trust's website. Within a month, the trust invites successful applicants to complete the next steps, including a (virtual) meeting and sharing business, planning and financial documentation. Applications are then reviewed by trustees in March, July or November.

CONTACT DETAILS Jo Wells, Director, c/o Cripplegate Foundation, 13 Elliotts Place, London N1 8HX *Tel.* 020 7399 0370 *Email* jo.wells@blagravetrust.org *Website* https://www.blagravetrust.org

■ Blakemore Foundation

CC NO 1015938 **ESTABLISHED** 1992

WHERE FUNDING CAN BE GIVEN England and Wales excluding parts of the South West and northern England. There is a map on the foundation's website.

WHO CAN BENEFIT Local and national charitable organisations including: community groups, sports clubs, schools, hospices and hospitals.

WHAT IS FUNDED General charitable purpose including: sport and recreation; health; medical research; housing and homelessness; emergency services and armed forces; the environment.

WHAT IS NOT FUNDED Salaries; national charities (unless directly linked to an A.F. Blakemore employee or local branch); grants for an individual; good causes that fall outside A.F. Blakemore's trading area; overseas appeals; expeditions or overseas travel; sponsorship and marketing promotions; endowment and hardship funds; political causes.

TYPE OF GRANT Capital costs; core costs.

SAMPLE GRANTS A list of beneficiaries was not available in the annual report and accounts.

FINANCES *Financial year end* 30/04/2019
Income £364,500 *Total grants* £152,200
Grants to organisations £152,200
Assets £44,600

TRUSTEES Peter Blakemore; Ita McAuley.

OTHER INFORMATION Charities can also apply for in-kind support in the forms of goods for local charity and community events. The 2018/19 accounts were the latest available at the time of writing (January 2021).

HOW TO APPLY Applications can be made through the foundation's website. Applications are decided upon on the last Friday of every month.

CONTACT DETAILS Kate Senter, Community Affairs Officer, A. F. Blakemore and Sons Ltd, Longacre, Willenhall, West Midlands WV13 2JP *Tel.* 0121 568 2910 *Email* ksenter@afblakemore.com *Website* www.afblakemore.com/blakemore-foundation/blakemore-foundation

■ Lady Blakenham's Charity Trust

CC NO 266198 **ESTABLISHED** 1973

WHERE FUNDING CAN BE GIVEN Worldwide.

WHO CAN BENEFIT Charitable organisations.

WHAT IS FUNDED General charitable purposes; disability; medical welfare and research; overseas.

RANGE OF GRANTS Mostly £3,000 each.

SAMPLE GRANTS Previous beneficiaries have included: Maggie's (£20,000); 3H Fund, 4 Sight, Blind Veterans UK, Marie Curie Cancer Care and The National Brain Appeal (£3,000 each); Dodfords Children's Holiday Farm (£2,000).

FINANCES *Financial year end* 05/04/2020
Income £17,600 *Total grants* £60,000
Grants to organisations £60,000

TRUSTEES Hon. Mary-Anne Sergison-Brooke; Nicholas Brooke; Simon Cowell.

OTHER INFORMATION Full accounts were not available to view on the Charity Commission's website due to the trust's low income. We have therefore estimated the trust's grant total based on its total expenditure.

HOW TO APPLY Contact the correspondent for further information.

CONTACT DETAILS The Trustees, Chipping Warden Manor, Banbury, Oxfordshire OX17 1LB *Tel.* 01295 660227 *Email* Blakenham_Charity@tmf-group.com

■ The Blandford Lake Trust

CC NO 1069630 **ESTABLISHED** 1998

WHERE FUNDING CAN BE GIVEN North Wales and overseas.

WHO CAN BENEFIT Registered charities.

WHAT IS FUNDED Overseas aid and development; Christian outreach work in North Wales.

TYPE OF GRANT Project funding; core/revenue costs; salaries.

RANGE OF GRANTS Typically £1,000 to £10,000.

SAMPLE GRANTS Christian Aid (£30,000); Peace Direct, Send a Cow and Viva (£10,000 each); Urban Saints (£2,000); Scholarships for Street Kids (£1,000).

FINANCES *Financial year end* 31/12/2019
Income £71,000 *Total grants* £76,000
Grants to organisations £76,000 *Assets* £340

TRUSTEES Lucy Lake; Richard Lake; Jonathan Lake; Mathew Lake.

HOW TO APPLY Contact the correspondent for further information.

CONTACT DETAILS Mr R. M. Lake, Trust Secretary, The Courts, Park Street, Denbigh, Denbighshire LL16 3DE *Tel.* 01745 813174

■ The Sir Victor Blank Charitable Settlement

CC NO 1084187 **ESTABLISHED** 1979

WHERE FUNDING CAN BE GIVEN Worldwide.

WHO CAN BENEFIT Jewish organisations; registered charities.

WHAT IS FUNDED Jewish causes; general charitable purposes.

RANGE OF GRANTS Up to £25,000.

SAMPLE GRANTS Jewish Care (£25,000); Community Security Trust (CST) and The Henry Jackson Society (£15,000 each); University of Glasgow Trust (John Smith Centre); Women's Interfaith Network; Oxford Philharmonic Orchestra; British Academy and Best Beginnings (£10,000 each); Bodleian Libraries; Camp Simcha; Cancer Research UK and Holocaust Education Trust (£5,000 each); Crisis (£3,000); Hatzola; Maccabi UK and Ruth Strauss Foundation (£2,000 each).

FINANCES *Financial year end* 05/04/2020
Income £177,600 *Total grants* £215,300
Grants to organisations £215,300
Assets £2,540,000

TRUSTEES Lady Sylvia Blank; Simon Blank.

OTHER INFORMATION Grants of less than £1,000 totalled £9,500.

HOW TO APPLY Contact the correspondent for further information.

CONTACT DETAILS The Trustees, 2nd Floor, Regis House, 45 King William Street, London

EC4R 9AN *Tel.* 020 7403 1877 *Email* enquiries@sirvictorblankcharitablesettlement.com

■ Bloodwise

CC NO 216032 **ESTABLISHED** 1960

WHERE FUNDING CAN BE GIVEN UK.

WHO CAN BENEFIT Universities; hospitals; research institutions.

WHAT IS FUNDED Research into blood cancers, including: funding for laboratory-based research projects; training; career development awards; clinical trials.

TYPE OF GRANT Capital costs; core costs; project funding; strategic funding.

RANGE OF GRANTS Project grants are awarded for up to £250,000 and up to three years for clearly defined research projects.

SAMPLE GRANTS University of Birmingham (£2.34 million); University of Oxford (£845,000); CRUK Centre for Drug Development – London (£493,000); University College London (£250,000); UK Biobank – Salford (£15,000); University of Leeds (£102,000).

FINANCES *Financial year end* 31/03/2020 *Income* £14,460,000 *Total grants* £6,470,000 *Grants to organisations* £6,470,000 *Assets* £10,810,000

TRUSTEES John Ormerod; Simon Guild; Dr Jane Stevens; Prof. Fran Balkwill; Julia Whittaker; Steven Prescott-Jones; Tim Gillbanks; Aileen Thompson; Gemma Peters.

OTHER INFORMATION Criteria used to assess applications include: relevance to blood cancer and people living with and beyond blood cancer; quality of the research design and methodology; ability to deliver the proposed research; impact of the proposed research outputs; strength and make-up of the research team; value for money.

HOW TO APPLY Applications must be submitted via Grant Tracker. Further information on how to apply can be found on the charity's website.

CONTACT DETAILS Research Team, 39–40 Eagle Street, London WC1R 4TH *Tel.* 020 7504 2200 *Email* research@bloodwise.org.uk *Website* www.bloodwise.org.uk

■ The Bloom Foundation

CC NO 1166112 **ESTABLISHED** 2011

WHERE FUNDING CAN BE GIVEN UK, with a preference for Brighton; overseas with a preference for Israel.

WHO CAN BENEFIT Charities and not-for-profit organisations.

WHAT IS FUNDED Community development; Jewish causes; health and medical research; social welfare; international development.

TYPE OF GRANT Core grants; project funding; campaigning; advocacy; research; development and strategic funding.

RANGE OF GRANTS Mostly up to £100,000, with some exceptionally larger grants.

SAMPLE GRANTS Brighton and Hove Hebrew Congregation (£1.7 million); Overcoming Multiple Sclerosis (£600,000); Plan International UK (£100,000); The Work Avenue Foundation (£60,000); Campaign Against Living Miserably (£40,000); Grief Encounter Project (£30,000); East Africa Character Development Trust (£25,000); Solace Women's Aid (£20,000).

FINANCES *Financial year end* 30/06/2020 *Income* £5,080,000 *Total grants* £4,220,000 *Grants to organisations* £4,220,000 *Assets* £7,630,000

TRUSTEES Linda Bloom; Marc Sugarman; Marcelle Lester; Adam Franks; Anthony Bloom; Philip Saunders; Simon Johnson.

OTHER INFORMATION A total of 75 grants were distributed to organisations during the year. Grants were distributed for the following purposes: Brighton (£1.9 million); medical research and welfare (£831,000); Jewish community (£755,000); Israel (£393,000); disaster relief (£130,000); social welfare (£87,000); international development (£60,000); other (£34,000); animal welfare (£1,500). Grants below £20,000 totalled £172,700.

HOW TO APPLY Contact the correspondent for further information.

CONTACT DETAILS The Trustees, 34/36 Jamestown Road, London NW1 7BY *Tel.* 020 3014 9861 *Email* info@thebloomfoundation.com

■ The Bloomfield Charitable Trust

CC NO 1145866 **ESTABLISHED** 2012

WHERE FUNDING CAN BE GIVEN UK.

WHO CAN BENEFIT Registered charities.

WHAT IS FUNDED General charitable purposes.

TYPE OF GRANT Project funding.

SAMPLE GRANTS National Autistic Society (£150,000 in three grants); Action for Kids Charitable Trust (£47,500 in five grants); The Marketfield Trust (£12,900); Lancaster University (£1,200).

FINANCES *Financial year end* 06/02/2020 *Income* £4,460,000 *Total grants* £280,800 *Grants to organisations* £280,800 *Assets* £4,730,000

TRUSTEES Martin Hellawell; Mandy Hellawell; Coutts & Co.

OTHER INFORMATION The trust made grants to seven organisations.

HOW TO APPLY Apply by letter to the correspondent.

CONTACT DETAILS The Trustees, Coutts & Co. Trustee Department, 1st Floor, Trinity Quay 1, Avon Street, Bristol BS2 0PT *Tel.* 0345 304 2424

■ Bluespark Foundation

CC NO 1167172 **ESTABLISHED** 2016

WHERE FUNDING CAN BE GIVEN UK.

WHO CAN BENEFIT Charitable organisations; schools and education institutions; drama and music organisations; amateur sports clubs; youth organisations; individuals.

WHAT IS FUNDED Projects that support the education and development of children and young people. In previous years the following types of project have been supported: academic; drama; sport; outdoor activities; music, dance and singing; leadership and team building; educational excursions.

WHAT IS NOT FUNDED Projects for children or young people under the age of five or over the age of 22; life skill mentoring services; counselling services; holiday clubs or playgroups; construction, maintenance or repair of buildings; training adults who work with children or young people; student fees or maintenance.

TYPE OF GRANT Project funding; capital costs.

RANGE OF GRANTS Up to £5,000 but typically under £2,000.

SAMPLE GRANTS Previous beneficiaries have included: Bradford Academy; Braidwood School

for Deaf Children; Cerebral Palsy Plus; Get Set 4 Tennis CIC; Glee4Kidz; Hertford and Ware Sea Cadets and The Multi–Story Orchestra.
FINANCES *Financial year end* 31/03/2020 *Income* £104,100 *Total grants* £100,200 *Grants to organisations* £100,200 *Assets* £472,900
TRUSTEES Tim Davies; Robert Bartlett; Sarah Budnik.
HOW TO APPLY Applications can be made through the foundation's website.
CONTACT DETAILS The Trustees, 84A Upland Road, Sutton, Surrey SM2 5JB *Tel.* 020 8661 9997 *Email* contact@bluesparkfoundation.org.uk *Website* bluesparkfoundation.org.uk

■ The Bluston Charitable Settlement

CC NO 256691 **ESTABLISHED** 1968
WHERE FUNDING CAN BE GIVEN Mostly UK.
WHO CAN BENEFIT Registered charities; places of worship.
WHAT IS FUNDED General charitable purposes; education of children; social welfare; health; research; Jewish causes.
RANGE OF GRANTS Typically £10,000 to £50,000.
SAMPLE GRANTS Jerusalem Foundation re Aleh (£386,700); Chief Rabbinate Trust and Orchos Torah (£50,000 each); Golders Green Beth Hamedrash (£20,000); British Library and Youth Aliyah Child Rescue (£10,000 each); Farms for City Children (£5,000); Shunimi Engineering Ltd (£1,400).
FINANCES *Financial year end* 05/04/2020 *Income* £705,900 *Total grants* £1,410,000 *Grants to organisations* £1,410,000 *Assets* £21,050,000
TRUSTEES Daniel Dover; Martin Paisner; Prism Trustees Ltd.
OTHER INFORMATION In 2019/20 the trust made grants to 35 organisations.
HOW TO APPLY Apply in writing to the correspondent. The trustees meet twice a year to consider applications.
CONTACT DETAILS The Trustees, 20 Gloucester Place, London W1U 8HA *Tel.* 020 7486 7760

■ The Blyth Charitable Trust

CC NO 1176537 **ESTABLISHED** 2018
WHERE FUNDING CAN BE GIVEN Worldwide.
WHO CAN BENEFIT Charitable organisations.
WHAT IS FUNDED General charitable purposes.
RANGE OF GRANTS £1,000 to £50,000.
SAMPLE GRANTS Injured Jockeys Fund (£50,000); The Royal Academy of Engineering and World Horse Welfare Trust (£10,000 each); The Countryside Alliance Foundation (£5,000); Lord Leycester Hospital (£3,000); The Gloucestershire Society (£2,000); The Cayo Foundation (£1,000).
FINANCES *Financial year end* 18/12/2019 *Income* £222,800 *Total grants* £81,000 *Grants to organisations* £81,000 *Assets* £10,550,000
TRUSTEES The Hon. Abigail Blyth; Lady Pamela Blyth; Ludlow.
OTHER INFORMATION The trust awarded seven grants during the year. The 2018/19 accounts were the latest available at the time of writing (June 2021).
HOW TO APPLY Contact the correspondent for further information.
CONTACT DETAILS The Trustees, 1st Floor, Tower Wharf, Cheese Lane, Bristol BS2 0JJ *Tel.* 0117 313 8200 *Email* charitabletrusts@ludlowtrust.com

■ The BNA Charitable Incorporated Organisation

CC NO 1182500 **ESTABLISHED** 2019
WHERE FUNDING CAN BE GIVEN UK with a strong preference for Newark, Nottinghamshire, Lincoln, Lincolnshire and the surrounding area.
WHO CAN BENEFIT Registered charities.
WHAT IS FUNDED General charitable purposes.
WHAT IS NOT FUNDED Projects outside the UK; statutory authorities; projects which are primarily intended to promote political or religious beliefs; general appeals or circulars, including contributions to endowment funds.
TYPE OF GRANT Project funding.
SAMPLE GRANTS Newark Patriotic Fund (£100,000); Acts Trust and Bellamy's Charity (£10,000 each); Keyworth Sports Association (£5,000); Beanblock CIC (£1,000).
FINANCES *Financial year end* 30/06/2020 *Income* £19,900,000 *Total grants* £665,000 *Grants to organisations* £660,000 *Assets* £19,190,000
TRUSTEES Susan Fisher; Richard Vigar; Paul Simpson; Herman Kok; Keith Girling.
OTHER INFORMATION Grants to individuals totalled £5,000.
HOW TO APPLY Applications can be made via the charity's website.
CONTACT DETAILS The Trustees, c/o Wright Vicar Ltd, 15 Newland, Lincoln LN1 1XG *Website* https://www.bnacharity.com

■ Maureen Boal Charitable Trust

CCNI NO NIC105862 **ESTABLISHED** 1997
WHERE FUNDING CAN BE GIVEN Northern Ireland.
WHO CAN BENEFIT Charitable organisations.
WHAT IS FUNDED Health and saving lives; social welfare; animal welfare.
SAMPLE GRANTS Down's Syndrome Association NI; Mid-Antrim Animal Sanctuary; The Mae Murray Foundation.
FINANCES *Financial year end* 05/04/2019 *Income* £149,800 *Total grants* £120,000 *Grants to organisations* £120,000 *Assets* £2,860,000
TRUSTEE Northern Bank Executor and Trustee Company Ltd.
OTHER INFORMATION The 2018/19 were the latest available at the time of writing (May 2021).
HOW TO APPLY Contact the correspondent for further information.
CONTACT DETAILS Philip Donnan, PO Box 183, Donegall Square West, Belfast BT1 6JS *Tel.* 028 9004 8125 *Email* philip.donnan@danskebank.co.uk

■ The Marjory Boddy Charitable Trust

CC NO 1091356 **ESTABLISHED** 2002
WHERE FUNDING CAN BE GIVEN North Wales and the North West, in practice Cheshire and Wirral.
WHO CAN BENEFIT Registered charities; uniformed groups; hospices; hospitals.
WHAT IS FUNDED General charitable purposes; health; education; social welfare and the arts.
TYPE OF GRANT Capital costs; core/revenue costs.

RANGE OF GRANTS Normally £1,000 to £5,000.
SAMPLE GRANTS A list of beneficiaries was not included in the 2019/20 annual report and accounts.
FINANCES *Financial year end* 05/04/2020 *Income* £104,500 *Total grants* £66,200 *Grants to organisations* £66,200 *Assets* £3,564,000
TRUSTEES Edward Walton; Elizabeth Roberts; William Benoy; Hems de Winter.
OTHER INFORMATION Grants were awarded to 29 organisations across the following categories: cancer charities, hospices and hospitals (£39,000); support groups (£28,700); disability charities (£11,500); youth clubs (£8,100) and theatre groups (£2,000).
HOW TO APPLY Applications can be submitted via the form on the trust's website, by post or email. See the trust's website for further details. The trustees meet three times a year in February, June and October. Successful applicants will be notified within 28 days of the meetings.
CONTACT DETAILS The Trustees, c/o Morris and Co., Chester House, Lloyd Drive, Ellesmere Port, Cheshire CH65 9HQ *Tel.* 0151 348 8400 *Email* marjoryboddytrust@moco.co.uk *Website* https://marjoryboddy.co.uk

■ The Boltini Trust

CC NO 1123129 **ESTABLISHED** 2008
WHERE FUNDING CAN BE GIVEN UK, particularly Surrey and West Sussex, but also including other home counties and overseas.
WHO CAN BENEFIT Charitable organisations; hospitals; hospices; schools and colleges; universities; museums; churches.
WHAT IS FUNDED General charitable purposes; overseas causes; disadvantaged or disabled people; community development; education; medical research and institutions; disaster relief; environmental causes.
WHAT IS NOT FUNDED Individuals.
RANGE OF GRANTS Typically £2,500 to £15,000.
SAMPLE GRANTS Alike (£30,000); South Downs National Park (£15,000); David Knott Foundation, Midhurst Primary School and Microloan Foundation – Malawi and Zambia (£5,000 each); Great Ormond Street Hospital Children's Charity (£4,000); Chichester Information Shop for Young People (£2,000).
FINANCES *Financial year end* 31/03/2020 *Income* £477,500 *Total grants* £516,900 *Grants to organisations* £516,900 *Assets* £11,470,000
TRUSTEES Anthony Bolton; Sarah Bolton; James Nelson; Emma Nelson; Oliver Bolton; Benjamin Bolton; Fiona Bolton; Phoebe Bolton.
HOW TO APPLY Contact the correspondent for further information.
CONTACT DETAILS The Trustees, Woolbeding Glebe, Woolbeding, Midhurst, West Sussex GU29 9RR *Tel.* 01730 817324 *Email* boltinitrust@gmail.com

■ The Bonamy Charitable Trust

CC NO 326424 **ESTABLISHED** 1983
WHERE FUNDING CAN BE GIVEN UK, with a preference for the North West.
WHO CAN BENEFIT Charitable organisations.
WHAT IS FUNDED Advancement of the Jewish faith; Jewish education; social welfare.
RANGE OF GRANTS Around £5,000 to £15,000.
SAMPLE GRANTS Aish UK and Community Security Trust (£15,000 each); North Cheshire Jewish Primary School (£7,200); South Manchester Synagogue (£5,900); Langdon (£5,100).
FINANCES *Financial year end* 31/12/2019 *Income* £133,300 *Total grants* £109,900 *Grants to organisations* £104,900 *Assets* £512,900
TRUSTEES Max Moryoussef; James Moryoussef; Robert Moryoussef.
OTHER INFORMATION In 2019 the trust distributed grants across the following areas: Jewish welfare (£46,600); Jewish outreach and continuity (£33,200); synagogues (£13,700); Jewish education (£10,200); general poverty and welfare (£1,300).
HOW TO APPLY Contact the correspondent for further information.
CONTACT DETAILS The Trustees, Flat 2, Forrest Hills, South Downs Road, Altrincham, Cheshire WA14 3HD *Tel.* 01706 345868

■ The Charlotte Bonham-Carter Charitable Trust

CC NO 292839 **ESTABLISHED** 1985
WHERE FUNDING CAN BE GIVEN UK, with some preference for Hampshire.
WHO CAN BENEFIT Registered charities.
WHAT IS FUNDED General charitable purposes which were of particular concern to Lady Charlotte Bonham-Carter during her lifetime including: arts and culture; countryside preservation; young carers; older people; early intervention for children and young people.
WHAT IS NOT FUNDED Charities with religious or political objectives; uniformed groups; animal charities; large medical research charities; applications by/for the benefit of individuals, or sponsorship for individuals fundraising for charities; projects outside the UK.
TYPE OF GRANT Project funding.
RANGE OF GRANTS Mostly under £5,000.
SAMPLE GRANTS The National Trust (£10,000); Ashmolean Museum, Barons Court Project and Support Through Court (£4,000 each); Cavell Nurses Trust and Fry Art Gallery (£3,000 each); Friends of the National Library and Partnership for Children (£2,000 each); Rainbow Trust (£1,500); Shine (£1,000); Playhouse Foundation (£400).
FINANCES *Financial year end* 05/04/2020 *Income* £152,000 *Total grants* £127,100 *Grants to organisations* £127,100 *Assets* £5,050,000
TRUSTEES Sir Matthew Farrer; David Bonham-Carter; Georgina Nayler; Eliza Bonham-Carter; Mary Grimond.
OTHER INFORMATION Grants were awarded to 55 charities during the year. The trust supports a number of charities on a regular basis, as well in response to applications.
HOW TO APPLY According to the website, applications must be made by letter accompanied by a completed Application Covering Sheet (available to download from the website) and should explain what your charity does, the purpose of the application, funds raised so far and the timescale involved. The application should include a copy of your latest accounts. Applications should be sent by post, with supporting documents printed single sided (with the exception of accounts where this is not possible) and should be submitted by 1 January or 1 September, for meetings in March and October respectively. Applications are not acknowledged on receipt and successful

applicants will be notified by the end of March or October.

CONTACT DETAILS Jenny Cannon, Charity Administrator, Chelwood, Rectory Road, East Carleton, Norwich, Norfolk NR14 8HT *Tel.* 01508 571230 *Email* admin@charlottebonhamcartercharitabletrust.org.uk *Website* https://charlottebonhamcartercharitabletrust.org.uk

The Boodle & Dunthorne Charitable Trust

CC NO 1077748 **ESTABLISHED** 1999

WHERE FUNDING CAN BE GIVEN UK and overseas.

WHO CAN BENEFIT Registered charities.

WHAT IS FUNDED General charitable purposes.

WHAT IS NOT FUNDED Individuals.

RANGE OF GRANTS Typically around £5,000 to £20,000.

SAMPLE GRANTS Street Child (£50,000); Hopes and Homes for Children (£30,000); Shining Faces in India (£18,000); Rainbow Trust (£14,400); Brighter Futures Ltd (£12,500); Halow Project (£10,000); Marina Dalglish Appeal (£6,000).

FINANCES *Financial year end* 05/04/2020 *Income* £302,700 *Total grants* £178,700 *Grants to organisations* £178,700 *Assets* £1,080,000

TRUSTEES Nicholas Wainwright; Michael Wainwright.

OTHER INFORMATION Established in 1999, this is the corporate charity of Boodles, a family jewellers based in North West England.

HOW TO APPLY Contact the correspondent for further information.

CONTACT DETAILS The Trustees, Boodles House, 35 Lord Street, Liverpool, Merseyside L2 9SQ *Tel.* 0151 224 0580

BOOST Charitable Trust

CC NO 1111961 **ESTABLISHED** 2005

WHERE FUNDING CAN BE GIVEN England and Wales; Eswatini.

WHO CAN BENEFIT Registered charities; not-for-profit organisations involved in sports.

WHAT IS FUNDED Access to sport for disadvantaged individuals and people with disabilities.

TYPE OF GRANT Project funding; core costs; capital costs.

RANGE OF GRANTS Up to £15,000.

SAMPLE GRANTS CP Sport (£15,000); Running Charity Northern Project (£13,000); The Running Charity (£9,000); Level Water (£4,000); Butler Golf Academy (£3,400); Sports Aid (£2,000); Doncaster Foster Carer's Association (£1,000).

FINANCES *Financial year end* 30/09/2020 *Income* £154,400 *Total grants* £105,100 *Grants to organisations* £105,100 *Assets* £1,220,000

TRUSTEES Robert Houston; Alurie Dutton; Oliver Bartrum; Philippa Fine.

OTHER INFORMATION In 2019/20 grants were awarded to 15 organisations.

HOW TO APPLY Contact the correspondent via email or letter. Information on what to include can be found on the trust's website.

CONTACT DETAILS Liz Turtle, Trust Administrator, 5 St Bride Street, London EC4A 4AS *Tel.* 020 7078 1966 *Email* liz.turtle@boostct.org *Website* www.boostct.org

The Booth Charities

CC NO 221800 **ESTABLISHED** 1963

WHERE FUNDING CAN BE GIVEN Salford.

WHO CAN BENEFIT Organisations supporting the inhabitants of the City of Salford, especially older people; individuals.

WHAT IS FUNDED General charitable purposes; social welfare; sport and recreation; education.

TYPE OF GRANT Capital costs; project funding; salaries; one-off and up to three years.

RANGE OF GRANTS £100 to £60,000.

SAMPLE GRANTS Salford City Council – Holiday Hunger Project (two grants totalling £100,000); Salford Loaves and Fishes (two grants totalling £70,000); Lledr Mell Outdoor Education Centre (£45,000); The Fusilier Museum (£30,000); Start in Salford (£15,000); Challenge 4 Change (£10,000); Broughton House Veteran Care Village (£6,400); Frozen Light (£2,500); Worsley Village Community Association (£830); Manchester University Guild of Change Ringers (£100).

FINANCES *Financial year end* 31/03/2020 *Income* £1,630,000 *Total grants* £1,121,000 *Grants to organisations* £1,120,000 *Assets* £42,300,000

TRUSTEES John Willis; Barbara Griffin; Philip Okell; Richard Kershaw; Roger Weston; William Whittle; Richard Fildes; James Tully; Alan Dewhurst; Jonathan Shelmerdine.

OTHER INFORMATION Grants were awarded to 67 organisations during the year in the following categories: relief of distress and sickness (£608,000); educational facilities (£167,000); recreation/leisure facilities (£161,000); relief of older people or those experiencing financial hardship (£126,000); other (£34,000); Sacred Trinity Church (£24,000). In addition, grants totalling £1,000 were made to eight individuals.

HOW TO APPLY Contact the correspondent for further information.

CONTACT DETAILS The Trustees, c/o Butcher and Barlow LLP, 3 Royal Mews, Gadbrook Road, Northwich, Cheshire CW9 7UD *Tel.* 01606 334309 *Email* jaldersley@butcher-barlow.co.uk

Boots Charitable Trust

CC NO 1045927 **ESTABLISHED** 1971

WHERE FUNDING CAN BE GIVEN Nottinghamshire.

WHO CAN BENEFIT Registered charities; voluntary organisations that are too small to qualify for charitable status.

WHAT IS FUNDED Health; lifelong learning; community development; social care.

WHAT IS NOT FUNDED Projects benefitting people outside Nottinghamshire; individuals; organisations which are not registered charities and which have income or expenditure of more than £5,000 per year; charities seeking funds to redistribute to other charities; projects for which there is a legal statutory obligation or which replace statutory funding.

TYPE OF GRANT Project funding; capital costs; core costs.

RANGE OF GRANTS £100 to £10,000.

SAMPLE GRANTS SHE UK and Broxtowe Youth Homelessness (£10,000 each); Defence Medical Welfare Service (£9,700); Bulwell Forest Garden (£9,500); Open Minds (£6,400); Cornwater Evergreens (£5,000); Re-engage (£4,900); St Jude's Church – Mapperley (£3,000).

FINANCES *Financial year end* 31/08/2020 *Income* £254,200 *Total grants* £250,000 *Grants to organisations* £250,000 *Assets* £0

TRUSTEES Lavina Moxley; Peter Bowrey; Richard Bradley; Andrew Caplan; Felicity Walton-Bateson; Stuart Buchanan.

OTHER INFORMATION In 2019/20 the trust made a total of 28 grants which were broken down as follows: health (£102,000); social care (£69,400); lifelong learning (£49,200); community development (£29,400).

HOW TO APPLY There is an online application form on the website, alongside guidance on eligibility. Paper application forms can also be requested from the correspondent.

CONTACT DETAILS James Kirkpatrick, Funding Support, Boots UK Ltd, D90E S09, 1 Thane Road West, Nottingham, Nottinghamshire NG90 1BS *Tel.* 07739 835909 or 01159591285 *Email* james@fundingsupport.co.uk or Emma.Rowles@boots.co.uk *Website* www.boots-uk.com/corporate-social-responsibility/what-we-do/community/boots-charitable-trust

■ Salo Bordon Charitable Trust

CC NO 266439 **ESTABLISHED** 1973

WHERE FUNDING CAN BE GIVEN UK and overseas.

WHO CAN BENEFIT Charitable organisations, primarily Jewish organisations.

WHAT IS FUNDED Jewish causes; religious education; social welfare.

RANGE OF GRANTS Up to £34,000.

SAMPLE GRANTS Achisomoch Aid Company Ltd (£34,000); North London Welfare and Educational Foundation (£15,000); Project SEED Ltd (£7,500); Friends of Yeshiva Brisk (£2,500); Yishaya Adler Memorial Fund (£5,000); Shuvo Yisroel (£1,000).

FINANCES *Financial year end* 05/04/2020 *Income* £110,700 *Total grants* £88,000 *Grants to organisations* £88,000 *Assets* £7,280,000

TRUSTEES Marcel Bordon; Lilly Bordon.

HOW TO APPLY Contact the correspondent for more information.

CONTACT DETAILS The Trustees, 39 Gresham Gardens, London NW11 8PA *Tel.* 020 8458 6622

■ Sir William Boreman's Foundation

CC NO 312796 **ESTABLISHED** 1962

WHERE FUNDING CAN BE GIVEN Greenwich and Lewisham.

WHO CAN BENEFIT Registered charities; individuals; educational establishments.

WHAT IS FUNDED Educational projects for young people under the age of 25.

TYPE OF GRANT Project funding; bursaries; core costs.

RANGE OF GRANTS Up to £5,000.

SAMPLE GRANTS Superkidz (£10,000); Tall Ships Youth Trust (£8,400); Punchdrunk (£5,000); Chain Reaction (£3,000); Panathlon Foundation (£1,000).

FINANCES *Financial year end* 31/07/2020 *Income* £147,700 *Total grants* £80,600 *Grants to organisations* £80,600 *Assets* £4,410,000

TRUSTEE The Drapers' Company.

HOW TO APPLY Application forms can be downloaded from the foundation's website.

CONTACT DETAILS The Trustees, The Drapers' Company, Drapers' Hall, Throgmorton Avenue, London EC2N 2DQ *Tel.* 020 7588 5001 *Email* charities@thedrapers.co.uk *Website* https://thedrapers.co.uk/sir-william-boremans-foundation

■ The Borrows Charitable Trust

CC NO 1140591 **ESTABLISHED** 2011

WHERE FUNDING CAN BE GIVEN England and Wales.

WHO CAN BENEFIT Registered charities.

WHAT IS FUNDED General charitable purposes.

RANGE OF GRANTS Mostly up to £16,000, with some larger grants.

SAMPLE GRANTS The Royal Marsden Cancer Charity (£120,000); Community Foundation for Surrey (£80,000); Footsteps international (£44,300); The Eikon Charity (£16,000); Prostate Cancer UK and Royal Ballet School (£10,000 each); Caritas Anchor House (£6,000); Bowel Cancer UK, Learning Skills Research and University of Warwick (£5,000 each).

FINANCES *Financial year end* 31/03/2020 *Income* £116,600 *Total grants* £552,600 *Grants to organisations* £552,600 *Assets* £5,730,000

TRUSTEES Sally Borrows; Simon Borrows.

OTHER INFORMATION Grants were made to 110 organisations during the year in the following categories: social welfare (£172,400); health (£163,900); relief of poverty (£137,500); arts, culture, heritage or science (£52,800); education (£15,000); community development (£10,500); the armed forces (£500). Grants of less than £5,000 totalled £99,100 and were not listed in the accounts.

HOW TO APPLY Contact the correspondent for further information.

CONTACT DETAILS The Trustees, c/o Kingston Smith and Partners LLP, Devonshire House, 60 Goswell Road, London EC1M 7AD *Tel.* 020 7566 4000

■ The Oliver Borthwick Memorial Trust

CC NO 256206 **ESTABLISHED** 1968

WHERE FUNDING CAN BE GIVEN UK.

WHO CAN BENEFIT UK-registered charities.

WHAT IS FUNDED Health and well-being of individuals who are currently homeless or at risk of becoming homeless.

WHAT IS NOT FUNDED Individuals; non-charitable organisations; political or campaigning organisations; charities with an income over £500,000 (except in exceptional circumstances).

TYPE OF GRANT Capital costs; core/revenue costs; seed funding/start-up funding; unrestricted funding.

RANGE OF GRANTS £2,000 to £5,000.

SAMPLE GRANTS Ace of Clubs, Doncaster Housing for the Young and First Light Trust (£5,000 each); Homeless Care, Restore – York and The Good Soil Trust (£4,000 each); The Hope Hub and The Giving Hands Mission (£3,000 each).

FINANCES *Financial year end* 30/09/2019 *Income* £58,600 *Total grants* £56,000 *Grants to organisations* £56,000 *Assets* £1,320,000

TRUSTEES Sebastian Cresswell-Turner; Virginia Buckley; Andrew Impey; Sarah Mudd; The Earl Bathurst; George Impey; John Toth; David Scott.

OTHER INFORMATION The 2018/19 accounts were the latest available at the time of writing (April

2021). Grants were awarded to 13 organisations during the year.
HOW TO APPLY Application forms can be completed on the trust's website and are invited from 1 June to 31 March each year. The trustees meet in May to consider applications. Further information can be found on the trust's website.
CONTACT DETAILS Tony Blake, 2B Vicarage Drive, London SW14 8RX *Email* applications@obmt.org.uk *Website* https://obmt.org.uk

■ The Boshier-Hinton Foundation

CC NO 1108886 **ESTABLISHED** 2005
WHERE FUNDING CAN BE GIVEN England and Wales.
WHO CAN BENEFIT Registered charities; CICs; schools; universities; PTAs; hospitals; hospices.
WHAT IS FUNDED Work with children and adults with special educational needs.
WHAT IS NOT FUNDED Repeat grants within two years; retrospective grants; salaries; capital projects.
TYPE OF GRANT Capital costs; seed funding/start-up funding.
RANGE OF GRANTS Generally between £1,000 and £2,000.
SAMPLE GRANTS Designability (£15,000); English Touring Opera, Calverton Primary School and Hearing Dogs for Deaf People (£2,000 each); London Wheelchair Rugby Club and Plymouth Music Zone (£1,500 each); Shakespeare Schools Foundation (£1,000); My Life My Choice (£300); Brainwave Centre Ltd (£175).
FINANCES *Financial year end* 31/03/2020 *Income* £232,700 *Total grants* £238,600 *Grants to organisations* £238,600 *Assets* £1,160,000
TRUSTEES Thea Boshier; Dr Peter Boshier; Colin Flint.
OTHER INFORMATION The foundation awarded 166 grants during the year.
HOW TO APPLY Application forms can be downloaded from the foundation's website and should be returned by post. Guidance can be found on the application form. The correspondent can also be contacted via telephone or email for further information. There are no deadlines.
CONTACT DETAILS The Trustees, Whitegates, 32 Lower Street, Horning, Norfolk NR12 8AA *Tel.* 01692 630695 *Email* boshierhinton@yahoo.co.uk *Website* www.boshierhintonfoundation.org.uk

■ Alan Boswell Group Charitable Trust

CC NO 1183272 **ESTABLISHED** 2018
WHERE FUNDING CAN BE GIVEN Norwich; Bury; Peterborough; Grimsby; Boston; Cambridge.
WHO CAN BENEFIT Charitable organisations.
WHAT IS FUNDED Community sport and leisure; health and medical research; social welfare; education; children and young people.
TYPE OF GRANT Capital costs; project funding; core costs.
SAMPLE GRANTS A list of beneficiaries was not included in the 2019/20 annual report and accounts.
FINANCES *Financial year end* 31/03/2020 *Income* £271,900 *Total grants* £249,900 *Grants to organisations* £249,900 *Assets* £21,900
TRUSTEES Christopher Gibbs; Alexandra Bartram; Alan Boswell; Sarah Lusher; Alastair Drew; Lisa Adams.
OTHER INFORMATION Grants were broken down as follows: health and medical causes (£88,400); social welfare (£66,200); community sport and leisure (£56,400); youth and education (£39,000).
HOW TO APPLY Contact your local office for further information.
CONTACT DETAILS The Trustees, Prospect House, Rouen House, Norwich, Norfolk NR1 1RE *Tel.* 01603 218000 *Email* contact@alanboswelltrust.com *Website* https://www.alanboswell.com/about/corporate-social-responsibility

■ The Bothwell Charitable Trust

CC NO 299056 **ESTABLISHED** 1987
WHERE FUNDING CAN BE GIVEN UK.
WHO CAN BENEFIT Registered charities; hospices.
WHAT IS FUNDED General charitable purposes including: children's causes; hospices; medical research; disability and social welfare.
WHAT IS NOT FUNDED Individuals.
SAMPLE GRANTS Previous beneficiaries have included: Arthritis Research UK, Blackthorn Trust, British Heart Foundation, Friends of the Elderly and Leukaemia Research Fund (£2,000 each); Brain Research Trust, British Trust for Conservation Volunteers, Childlink Adoption Society, Multiple Sclerosis Society and Riding for the Disabled Association (£1,000 each).
FINANCES *Financial year end* 05/04/2020 *Income* £153,500 *Total grants* £351,000 *Grants to organisations* £351,000 *Assets* £3,250,000
TRUSTEES Paul James; Crispian Howard; Theresa McGregor.
OTHER INFORMATION During the year, grants were distributed as follows: medical research (£120,500); disability/social work (£98,500); childrens' causes (£97,000); hospices (£20,000); other (£15,000).
HOW TO APPLY Contact the correspondent for further information.
CONTACT DETAILS The Trustees, 69 Burrell Road, Compton, Newbury, Berkshire RG20 6QX *Tel.* 01925 757702 *Email* bct1987aa@gmail.com

■ The Harry Bottom Charitable Trust

CC NO 204675 **ESTABLISHED** 1960
WHERE FUNDING CAN BE GIVEN Sheffield, Rotherham, Barnsley and North East Derbyshire.
WHO CAN BENEFIT Registered charities; CICs.
WHAT IS FUNDED Health; religious activities; education.
TYPE OF GRANT Capital costs; core/revenue costs; seed funding/start-up funding.
RANGE OF GRANTS Typically between £2,000 and £10,000.
SAMPLE GRANTS Previous beneficiaries have included: Ashgate Hospice (£12,000); The Cavendish Hip Foundation (£10,000); University of Sheffield (£9,000); Snowdrop Project (£6,500); Homeless at Christmas (£3,000); Sheffield Methodist Church (£2,500); Stocksbridge Dementia (£2,000).
FINANCES *Financial year end* 30/06/2020 *Income* £247,100 *Total grants* £126,300 *Grants to organisations* £126,300 *Assets* £6,870,000
TRUSTEES Helen Woolley; Derek Handforth; Prof. Andrew Rawlinson; Revd William Shaw.

OTHER INFORMATION During the year, grants broken down as follows: religious activities (£55,900); educational and other activities (£51,300); medical activities (£19,200).

HOW TO APPLY Contact the correspondent for information regarding the application process.

CONTACT DETAILS The Trustees, c/o Lishmans LLP, 16–18 Station Road, Chapeltown, Sheffield, South Yorkshire S35 2XH *Tel.* 0114 246 5348 *Email* harrybottomtrust@lishmansllp.com

■ Sir Clive Bourne Family Trust

CC NO 290620 **ESTABLISHED** 1984

WHERE FUNDING CAN BE GIVEN UK.

WHO CAN BENEFIT Charities and voluntary bodies.

WHAT IS FUNDED The trustees favour Orthodox Jewish causes. A number of health and medical charities (particularly relating to cancer) have also benefitted.

SAMPLE GRANTS Previous beneficiaries have included: Prostate Cancer (£16,700); Jewish Care (£15,500); Magen David Adom UK (£10,000); Norwood (£9,300); Chai Community Care (£5,000); Chana (£1,800); Viscardi Center (£1,000); WIZO UK (£900); Simon Marks Primary School (£500).

FINANCES *Financial year end* 05/04/2020 *Income* £107,700 *Total grants* £80,100 *Grants to organisations* £80,100 *Assets* £5,790,000

TRUSTEES Lady Joy Bourne; Katie Cohen; Lucy Furman; Claire Lefton; Merryl Flitterman.

HOW TO APPLY Contact the correspondent for further information.

CONTACT DETAILS Ms J. Bater, Gardiner House, 6B Hemnall Street, Epping, Essex CM16 4LW *Tel.* 01992 560500 *Email* jbater@seabourne-group.com

■ Bourneheights Ltd

CC NO 298359 **ESTABLISHED** 1984

WHERE FUNDING CAN BE GIVEN UK.

WHO CAN BENEFIT Orthodox Jewish organisations and registered charities.

WHAT IS FUNDED Orthodox Jewish causes including education, welfare and advancement of the Orthodox Jewish faith.

RANGE OF GRANTS Up to £191,000.

SAMPLE GRANTS Tchabe Kollel Ltd (£191,000); Mosdos Chernobil (£138,300); Chasdei Sholom Trust (£70,000); Tchernobel Foundation Ltd (£64,000); Belz Foundation (£48,100); Dover Sholem (£20,000); Start Upright (£25,000); Clapton Support (£10,300); Adath Yisroel Bu (£10,000).

FINANCES *Financial year end* 30/11/2019 *Income* £2,820,000 *Total grants* £1,410,000 *Grants to organisations* £1,410,000 *Assets* £10,810,000

TRUSTEES Chaskel Rand; Erno Berger; Yechiel Chersky; Schloime Rand.

OTHER INFORMATION The 2018/19 accounts were the latest available at the time of writing (June 2021).

HOW TO APPLY Contact the correspondent for further information.

CONTACT DETAILS The Trustees, Flat 10, Palm Court, Queen Elizabeth's Walk, London N16 5XA *Tel.* 020 8800 1572

■ The Bowerman Charitable Trust

CC NO 289446 **ESTABLISHED** 1984

WHERE FUNDING CAN BE GIVEN UK, with a preference for Sussex and London.

WHO CAN BENEFIT Registered charities; places of worship; schools.

WHAT IS FUNDED General charitable purposes; Christian causes; relief of poverty; youth work; the arts and music; rehabilitation of offenders; education; medical care and research; social welfare.

RANGE OF GRANTS Up to £27,000.

SAMPLE GRANTS Emerging Futures (£13,700); Mary How Trust and Yehudi Menuhin School (£10,000 each); All Saints Wick (£7,500); Petworth Festival (£7,100); 4 Sight (£5,000).

FINANCES *Financial year end* 05/04/2020 *Income* £348,600 *Total grants* £84,900 *Grants to organisations* £73,100 *Assets* £15,980,000

TRUSTEES Anna Downham; Clarice Bowerman; Janet Taylor; Julyan Capper; Katharine Bowerman; Michael Follis.

OTHER INFORMATION During the year, grants to organisations were distributed as follows: the arts and music (£26,700); other (£25,700); religious causes (£14,600); medical charities (£6,100). In addition, grants totalling £11,800 were made to individuals. As well as making grants, the trust maintains a music room, art gallery, conference centre and campsite, and it operates Champs Hill Records, which aims to promote talented young musicians and raise awareness of classical music.

HOW TO APPLY Contact correspondent for further information. Grants are made at the discretion of the trustees and therefore unsolicited applications are unlikely to be accepted.

CONTACT DETAILS Yvonne Butterick, Trust Administrator, Champs Hill, Waltham Park Road, Coldwaltham, Pulborough, West Sussex RH20 1LY *Tel.* 01798 831205 *Website* https://www.thebct.org.uk/2

■ The Bowland Charitable Trust

CC NO 292027 **ESTABLISHED** 1985

WHERE FUNDING CAN BE GIVEN The North West.

WHO CAN BENEFIT Registered charities; charitable organisations.

WHAT IS FUNDED Religion; education; culture; rehabilitation of offenders; recreation; the environment; young people.

SAMPLE GRANTS Previous beneficiaries have included: Ron Clark Academy (£660,000); LEB Partnership (£306,000); The Brantwood Trust (£75,000); North Music Trust (£50,000); The Rosemere Cancer Foundation (£30,000); Blackburn Cathedral Trust (£25,000); Bowland High School (£20,000); Nazareth Unitarian Chapel (£15,000); The Lowry Centre Trust (£2,000); Ribble FM (£1,000).

FINANCES *Financial year end* 31/12/2018 *Income* £5,000,000 *Total grants* £1,300,000 *Grants to organisations* £1,300,000 *Assets* £7,680,000

TRUSTEES Tony Cann; Carole Fahy; Hugh Turner.

OTHER INFORMATION The 2018 accounts were the latest available at the time of writing (June 2021). Grants were broken down as follows: education (£961,200); religious activities (£243,200); young people (£52,200); cultural activities (£31,100); other grants (£7,700); rehabilitation of offenders (£3,000); recreational activities (£3,000).

HOW TO APPLY The charity invites applications for funding of projects from individuals, institutions and charitable organisations. The applications are made directly to the trustees, who meet regularly to assess them.

CONTACT DETAILS Carole Fahy, Bowland House, Philips Road, Blackburn, Lancashire BB1 5NA *Tel.* 01254 688051 *Email* carole.fahy@cannco.co.uk

■ Friends of Boyan Trust

CC NO 1114498 **ESTABLISHED** 2006

WHERE FUNDING CAN BE GIVEN Worldwide.

WHO CAN BENEFIT Orthodox Jewish organisations.

WHAT IS FUNDED Orthodox Jewish religious education and the relief of poverty in the Orthodox Jewish community.

RANGE OF GRANTS £2,500 to £434,200.

SAMPLE GRANTS Keren Hachessed Boyan (£434,200); Bais Rizhin Trust (£160,200); Yazoiree Boyan (£41,800); The Rehabilitation Trust (Wlodowa) (£22,000); The Lolev Charitable Trust (£15,000); Friends of Mercaz Hatorah Belz Macnivka (£5,000); Beis Ruchel D'Satmar (London) Ltd (£2,500).

FINANCES *Financial year end* 31/12/2018 *Income* £994,700 *Total grants* £889,200 *Grants to organisations* £758,200 *Assets* £93,900

TRUSTEES Jacob Getter; Mordechai Freund; Nathan Kuflik.

OTHER INFORMATION Grants to individuals totalled £131,000.

HOW TO APPLY Contact the correspondent for further information.

CONTACT DETAILS Jacob Getter, Trustee, 23 Durley Road, London N16 5JW *Tel.* 020 8809 6051

■ G. and K. Boyes Charitable Trust

CC NO 1166015 **ESTABLISHED** 2015

WHERE FUNDING CAN BE GIVEN UK.

WHO CAN BENEFIT Charitable organisations.

WHAT IS FUNDED The environment; education; medical research, in particular dementia and brain tumours; health; heritage.

RANGE OF GRANTS Up to £260,000.

SAMPLE GRANTS Royal Marsden Cancer Charity (£260,000); English National Ballet (£155,000); Susan's Farm (£62,200); London Zoological Society (£50,000); Cherubim (£30,000); Holland Park Opera (£20,000); David Shepherd Wildlife Trust (£10,000).

FINANCES *Financial year end* 05/04/2020 *Income* £22,200 *Total grants* £1,010,000 *Grants to organisations* £1,010,000 *Assets* £681,400

TRUSTEES Mr R. A. Henderson; Mrs A. Dalmahoy; Mark Cannon-Brookes; Cripps Trust Corporation Ltd.

OTHER INFORMATION Grants were made to 11 organisations during 2019/20.

HOW TO APPLY Apply in writing to the correspondent.

CONTACT DETAILS The Trustees, c/o Cripps Harries Hall LLP, 22 Mount Ephraim, Tunbridge Wells, Kent TN4 8AS *Tel.* 01892 765431 *Email* joanne.lee@cripps.co.uk

■ The William Brake Charitable Trust

CC NO 1023244 **ESTABLISHED** 1993

WHERE FUNDING CAN BE GIVEN UK, with a preference for Kent.

WHO CAN BENEFIT Registered charities; universities; hospices.

WHAT IS FUNDED General charitable purposes.

RANGE OF GRANTS £500 to £60,000.

SAMPLE GRANTS The Whitley Fund for Nature (£60,000); Child Bereavement UK (£50,000); Barnardo's (£15,000); Cure Parkinson's Trust and The National Portrait Gallery (£10,000 each); Farnham Youth Choir (£2,000); Royal Trinity Hospice (£1,000); The National Youth Choir of Great Britain (£500).

FINANCES *Financial year end* 31/03/2019 *Income* £111,600 *Total grants* £495,500 *Grants to organisations* £495,500 *Assets* £11,590,000

TRUSTEES Philip Wilson; Deborah Isaac; Penelope Lang; Michael Trigg.

OTHER INFORMATION The 2018/19 accounts were the latest available at the time of writing (May 2021).

HOW TO APPLY Apply in writing to the correspondent. The 2018/19 accounts note: 'The charity invites applications from the William Brake family for funding of worthy registered charities each year, with a particular emphasis on local charities where the family know the charity's representative.' The trustees hold two formal meetings each year to consider grants.

CONTACT DETAILS Michael Trigg, Chair and Trustee, c/o Gill Turner Tucker Solicitors, Colman House, King Street, Maidstone, Kent ME14 1JE *Tel.* 01622 759051 *Email* michael.trigg@gillturnertucker.com

■ The Frank Brake Charitable Trust

CC NO 1023245 **ESTABLISHED** 1993

WHERE FUNDING CAN BE GIVEN Kent.

WHO CAN BENEFIT Registered charities.

WHAT IS FUNDED General charitable purposes.

RANGE OF GRANTS £5,000 to £100,000.

SAMPLE GRANTS Parkinson's UK and Pilgrims Sport and Recreation Youth Trust (£100,000 each); Kent Community Foundation (£50,000); The Cure Parkinson's Trust (£25,000); Home-Start Ashford (£20,000); Motor Neurone Disease Association (£10,000); Demelza House Children's Hospice (£5,000).

FINANCES *Financial year end* 31/03/2019 *Income* £2,120,000 *Total grants* £455,000 *Grants to organisations* £455,000 *Assets* £13,620,000

TRUSTEES Philip Wilson; Michael Trigg; Michelle Leveridge; Richard Brake; Stephanie Senior.

OTHER INFORMATION The 2018/19 accounts were the latest available at the time of writing (May 2021). Grants were awarded to 15 organisations during the year, of which five had not been funded in the previous year.

HOW TO APPLY The 2018/19 accounts state that 'unsolicited direct applications to the Trust are not encouraged.'

CONTACT DETAILS Michael Trigg, Trustee, c/o Gill Turner Tucker, Colman House, King Street, Maidstone, Kent ME14 1JE *Tel.* 01622 759051 *Email* michael.trigg@gillturnertucker.com

■ The Tony Bramall Charitable Trust

CC NO 1001522 **ESTABLISHED** 1988

WHERE FUNDING CAN BE GIVEN Northern England with some preference for Yorkshire.

WHO CAN BENEFIT Charities; medical organisations; hospices; individuals.

WHAT IS FUNDED Medical research; care for people with illnesses; social welfare.

RANGE OF GRANTS Up to £60,000 but mostly under £5,000.

SAMPLE GRANTS St Michael's Hospice (£60,000); Shift MS (£18,000); Target Ovarian Cancer (£6,000); York Minster Fund (£5,000); All Saints Fabric Fund (£4,000); Cancer Support UK (£1,000); Hope and Homes for Children (£500).

FINANCES *Financial year end* 05/04/2020 *Income* £106,900 *Total grants* £131,100 *Grants to organisations* £131,100 *Assets* £4,210,000

TRUSTEES Anna Bramall; Tony Bramall; Geoffrey Tate; Karen Bramall Ogden.

HOW TO APPLY Apply in writing to the correspondent. The trustees review all applications. According to the 2019/20 annual report, 'certain fund requests are assessed by personal visits and discussions with the applicants'.

CONTACT DETAILS The Trustees, 12 Cardale Court, Cardale Park, Beckwith Head Road, Harrogate, North Yorkshire HG3 1RY *Tel.* 01423 535300 *Email* alison.lockwood@bramallproperties.co.uk

■ The Liz and Terry Bramall Foundation

CC NO 1121670 **ESTABLISHED** 2007

WHERE FUNDING CAN BE GIVEN UK with a strong preference for Yorkshire.

WHO CAN BENEFIT Charitable organisations; churches; hospices; schools; universities; cultural organisations.

WHAT IS FUNDED Christian causes; promotion of urban or rural regeneration in areas of social and economic deprivation; the environment; social welfare; health; education and training; arts and culture; preservation of historic buildings; prevention of crime. A detailed list of supported areas can be found on the foundation's website.

TYPE OF GRANT Project costs.

RANGE OF GRANTS £500 to £440,000.

SAMPLE GRANTS Forget-me-not Children's Hospice (£440,000); Leeds University (£385,800); Northern Ballet (£200,000); Bradford Cathedral (£50,000); Christians Against Poverty (£20,000); Harrogate Skills 4 Living Centre (£10,000); The Conservation Volunteers (£8,400); Paintings in Harrogate (£5,000); Cancer Research UK (£500).

FINANCES *Financial year end* 05/04/2020 *Income* £2,620,000 *Total grants* £7,130,000 *Grants to organisations* £7,130,000 *Assets* £99,680,000

TRUSTEES Dr Terence Bramall; Elizabeth Bramall; Suzannah Allard; Rebecca Bletcher; Rachel Tunnicliffe; Anthony Sharp.

OTHER INFORMATION During 2019/20 the trust made 182 grants. Some organisations received more than one grant.

HOW TO APPLY Applications should be made in writing to the correspondent and should be no more than 120 words. Details of what to include can be found on the website. Applications should be sent via post or email and they will be acknowledged within ten working days. The trustees meet four times a year usually in January, April, August and November. The acknowledgement letter will note the date on which the application will be considered.

CONTACT DETAILS The Trustees, c/o Raworths LLP, Eton House, 89 Station Parade, Harrogate, North Yorkshire HG1 1HF *Tel.* 01423 566666 *Email* bramallfoundation@raworths.co.uk *Website* https://www.bramallfoundation.org

■ The Bransford Trust

CC NO 1173809 **ESTABLISHED** 2004

WHERE FUNDING CAN BE GIVEN Worcester.

WHO CAN BENEFIT Charities; community groups.

WHAT IS FUNDED Culture; education; sport; community; healthcare.

SAMPLE GRANTS Previous beneficiaries have included: Elgar School of Music, St Richard's Hospice, Wildgoose Rural Training and Worcester Festival.

FINANCES *Financial year end* 05/04/2020 *Income* £3,960,000 *Total grants* £248,200 *Grants to organisations* £248,200 *Assets* £20,640,000

TRUSTEES John Yelland; Arthur Neil; Adam Freeman; Colin Kinnear; Duncan Sutcliffe; Clare Kinnear; Brenda Kinnear; Alastair Kinnear; Louisa Freeman; John Carver.

HOW TO APPLY Apply via the trust's website.

CONTACT DETAILS The Trustees, c/o Royal Porcelain Works, Royal Porcelain Works, Severn Street, Worcester, WR1 2NE *Email* Contact form on website *Website* https://www.bransfordtrust.org

■ The Breadsticks Foundation

CC NO 1125396 **ESTABLISHED** 2008

WHERE FUNDING CAN BE GIVEN UK; Africa; Asia.

WHO CAN BENEFIT Registered charities and community groups.

WHAT IS FUNDED Healthcare; education.

TYPE OF GRANT Core funding; project funding.

RANGE OF GRANTS Up to £300,000.

SAMPLE GRANTS Basic Need, Basic Rights – Kenya (£80,600); Brighton Oasis (£48,400); Three2Six (£37,000); School Home Support (£20,000); St Mary Islington Community Partnership (£8,000).

FINANCES *Financial year end* 30/09/2020 *Income* £200,300 *Total grants* £222,800 *Grants to organisations* £222,800 *Assets* £2,390,000

TRUSTEES Beatrix Payne; Dr Paul Ballantyne; Beatrice Roberts.

OTHER INFORMATION Throughout the year six grants were awarded.

HOW TO APPLY Applications are by invitation only and unsolicited applications will not be considered. See the foundation's website for more details.

CONTACT DETAILS The Trustees, 35 Canonbury Square, London N1 2AN *Email* info@breadsticksfoundation.org *Website* www.breadsticksfoundation.org

■ Breast Cancer Now

CC NO 1160558 **ESTABLISHED** 2014

WHERE FUNDING CAN BE GIVEN UK, Ireland and United States.

WHO CAN BENEFIT Research institutions.

WHAT IS FUNDED Breast cancer research.

TYPE OF GRANT Research grants; PhD studentships; fellowships.

SAMPLE GRANTS Institute of Cancer Research (£6.67 million); Queen Mary University of London (£1.02 million); King's College London (£847,000); Beatson Institute of Cancer Research (£600,000); University of Manchester (£330,000); University of Cardiff (£230,000); University of Leeds (£219,000).

FINANCES *Financial year end* 31/07/2020
Income £40,040,000
Total grants £11,470,000
Grants to organisations £11,470,000
Assets £16,090,000

TRUSTEES Dr Marion Lewis; Mark Astaire; Barbara Brown; Susan Gallone; Christopher Copeland; Pascale Alvanitakis-Guely; Prof. Powles; Prof. Adrian Harris; Ann Pickering; Jill Thompson; Andrew Moore; Sonia Gayle.

HOW TO APPLY Applications can be made through the charity's website. Refer to the website for application deadlines and guidelines.

CONTACT DETAILS The Research Team, 5th Floor, Ibex House, 42–47 Minories, London EC3N 1DY *Tel.* 0333 207 0300 *Email* grants_admin@breastcancernow.org *Website* www.breastcancernow.org

■ The Breast Cancer Research Trust (BCRT)

CC NO 272214 **ESTABLISHED** 1961

WHERE FUNDING CAN BE GIVEN UK.

WHO CAN BENEFIT Specific units in teaching hospitals; universities.

WHAT IS FUNDED Clinical and laboratory project research, undertaken in recognised cancer centres or research organisations in the UK, directly aimed at improving the prevention, early diagnosis and treatment of breast cancer.

WHAT IS NOT FUNDED No grants are awarded to students.

TYPE OF GRANT Project; research; core costs; salaries; up to a term of three years (reviewed annually).

RANGE OF GRANTS Mostly between £20,000 and £60,000.

SAMPLE GRANTS Edinburgh University, Kings College London (£25,000 each); Brighton University (£24,000); Nottingham University (£500).

FINANCES *Financial year end* 05/04/2019
Income £63,000 *Total grants* £74,500
Grants to organisations £74,500
Assets £238,700

TRUSTEES Susan Gallone; Jill Thompson; Baroness Delyth Morgan.

OTHER INFORMATION Grants were awarded to four universities during the year. The 2018/19 accounts were the latest available at the time of writing (June 2021).

HOW TO APPLY Application forms are available from the trust's website. Awards are made once or twice a year. Note that seven copies of the form are required. All appeals are assessed by a peer group of scientific and oncological experts in the field of breast cancer.

CONTACT DETAILS Rosemary Sutcliffe, Executive Administrator, Fifth Floor, Ibex House, 42–47 Minories, London EC3N 1DY *Tel.* 0333 207 0300 *Email* bcrtrust@btinternet.com *Website* www.breastcancerresearchtrust.org.uk

■ The Brelms Trust CIO

CC NO 1153372 **ESTABLISHED** 2013

WHERE FUNDING CAN BE GIVEN Yorkshire.

WHO CAN BENEFIT Registered charities. Mainly small to medium-sized charities with an income of less than £500,000 and usually with unrestricted reserves of six months or less.

WHAT IS FUNDED Arts, education and sport; carers; conservation; debt and benefits advice; domestic abuse and sexual violence; excluded young people; homelessness; older people facing isolation; people with physical or learning disabilities; prevention of re-offending; refugees, asylum seekers and ethnic minorities; rural isolation; substance misuse; support in bereavement; support for disadvantaged communities.

WHAT IS NOT FUNDED Organisations without charitable status; organisations not registered at the Charity Commission; large charitable organisations with an annual income of more than £500,000; national charities, unless the project is based in Yorkshire and for the specific benefit of the Yorkshire community, with clear evidence of embedded local management and financial control of budgetary spending and grant funding, usually evidenced by a set of accounts; applications from individuals or for student gap year costs; charities which send out general appeal letters for donations; organisations which advance religion or promote faith-based activities; party political organisations; animal welfare; medical research; retrospective funding.

TYPE OF GRANT Core costs and projects funding.

RANGE OF GRANTS Up to £15,000.

SAMPLE GRANTS Sight Support Ryedale (£15,000); City of Sanctuary (£14,600); Beverley Community Lift (£9,000); Esk Moors Active (£4,000); Sheffield Disabled Fishing Group (£3,000); York Women's Counselling Service (£2,700).

FINANCES *Financial year end* 30/11/2020
Income £386,900 *Total grants* £424,900
Grants to organisations £424,900
Assets £2,410,000

TRUSTEES Mary Cornish; Lesley Faithful; Juliet Kemp; Dr Glynis Jones; Stephen Stroud; Alan Wallace; Susan Brown; Jillian Malcomson.

OTHER INFORMATION Grants were made to 47 organisations during the year.

HOW TO APPLY Applications can be made via the trust's website.

CONTACT DETAILS The Trustees, Metro House, 57 Pepper Road, Leeds, West Yorkshire LS10 2RU *Email* admin@brelmstrust.org.uk *Website* https://www.brelmstrust.org.uk

■ The Brenley Trust

CC NO 1151128 **ESTABLISHED** 2013

WHERE FUNDING CAN BE GIVEN UK; southern Africa.

WHO CAN BENEFIT Charitable organisations.

WHAT IS FUNDED Social welfare; education.

SAMPLE GRANTS Bridge House School (£135,000); Help2Read (£60,000); Afrikids (£50,000); Explore (£5,000); Westfield School (£3,800).

FINANCES *Financial year end* 31/01/2020
Income £192,600 *Total grants* £852,200
Grants to organisations £672,000
Assets £12,350,000

TRUSTEES Patrick Riley; Mary-Louise Brennickmeyer; Robbert Zoet.

OTHER INFORMATION A total of 20 grants were made during the year.

HOW TO APPLY Contact the correspondent for further information.

CONTACT DETAILS The Trustees, 17 Princes Drive, Oxshott, Leatherhead, Surrey KT22 0UL *Tel.* 01372 841801 *Email* patrick.riley@btinternet.com

■ Bridgepoint Charitable Trust

CC NO 1134525 **ESTABLISHED** 2010

WHERE FUNDING CAN BE GIVEN UK; Europe; USA.

WHO CAN BENEFIT Registered charities.

WHAT IS FUNDED Education; the environment; health.

TYPE OF GRANT Project funding.

SAMPLE GRANTS Coup de Pouce CLÉ (£65,800); United World Schools (£46,200); NYC Harbour Foundation (£40,100); Dandelion Time (£34,500).

FINANCES *Financial year end* 31/12/2019 *Income* £789,500 *Total grants* £301,600 *Grants to organisations* £301,600 *Assets* £612,300

TRUSTEES William Paul; Michael Watson; Vanessa Delaage; James Murray; Paul Koziarski; Christina Magnusson; Benjamin Marten; David Nicholson.

OTHER INFORMATION The trust is linked to the international private equity firm Bridgepoint and supports charities in countries in which the company operates. Grants of under £25,000 totalled £35,900.

HOW TO APPLY Unsolicited applications are not accepted. The trust's website states that it 'provides support to charities nominated by our teams across our network and considered by trustees who are drawn from across the Firm'.

CONTACT DETAILS The Trustees, 95 Wigmore Street, London W1U 1FB *Tel.* 020 7034 3500 *Website* https://www.bridgepoint.eu/investing-responsibly/giving-back

■ The Harold and Alice Bridges Charity

CC NO 236654 **ESTABLISHED** 1963

WHERE FUNDING CAN BE GIVEN Lancashire and South Cumbria (particularly the River Ribble area and northwards, the Blackburn area and the South Lakes).

WHO CAN BENEFIT Registered charities; village halls; churches; voluntary/local organisations; CICs; hospices; scout groups. Charitable status preferred.

WHAT IS FUNDED General charitable purposes, with a preference for projects supporting rural and village life.

WHAT IS NOT FUNDED Grants are not normally awarded for running expenses.

TYPE OF GRANT Capital projects.

RANGE OF GRANTS Grants mostly up to £5,000.

SAMPLE GRANTS University of Cumbria (£16,000); Lake District Calvert Trust (£5,500); Emmanuel Parish Church – Southport (£5,000); Great Eccleston Cricket Club (£3,000); Piling Memorial Hall, Preston Sports Club (£2,000 each); St Andrew's Church Hall (£300).

FINANCES *Financial year end* 05/04/2020 *Income* £155,500 *Total grants* £133,300 *Grants to organisations* £133,300 *Assets* £3,400,000

TRUSTEES John Hinchliffe; Christopher Calvert.

OTHER INFORMATION During the year, grants were made to 68 organisations.

HOW TO APPLY Refer to the charity's website for full details, including a downloadable application form. Completed forms should be sent to the correspondent by post. The charity's website states: 'The application form has been designed to be straightforward to complete and it would be appreciated if the application could be confined to the application form itself and not include any attachments.' The application deadlines are 15 January, 15 May and 15 September each year.

CONTACT DETAILS The Trustees, c/o Linder Myers Solicitors, 21–23 Park Street, Lytham, Lancashire FY8 5LU *Tel.* 0844 984 6001 *Email* david.hinchliffe@lindermyers.co.uk *Website* www.haroldandalicebridgescharity.co.uk

■ Bright Red Charity

CC NO 1178566 **ESTABLISHED** 2018

WHERE FUNDING CAN BE GIVEN The north of England.

WHO CAN BENEFIT Charitable organisations; universities; research organisations; hospitals.

WHAT IS FUNDED Blood cancer research; the care of patients with blood cancer; education and training of healthcare professionals caring for patients with blood cancers.

TYPE OF GRANT Research; fellowships; studentships.

SAMPLE GRANTS A list of beneficiaries was not included in the annual report and accounts.

FINANCES *Financial year end* 31/12/2019 *Income* £584,500 *Total grants* £128,900 *Grants to organisations* £128,900 *Assets* £374,100

TRUSTEES Matthew Collin; Peter Towns; Peter Smith; Victoria Hervey; Gail Jones; Karen Richardson; Kathryn McRae; Ian Pedley; Charlotte Dickinson; Mark Thompson; David Thompkins; John Foggin.

OTHER INFORMATION Grants were broken down as follows: patient care grants (£108,700); research grants (£20,300).

HOW TO APPLY Application forms for research grants can be downloaded from the charity's website. Contact the correspondent for any other funding enquiries.

CONTACT DETAILS The Trustees, Ward 33, Northern Centre for Cancer Care, Freeman Hospital, Newcastle upon Tyne NE7 7DN *Email* info@brightred.org.uk *Website* https://brightred.org.uk

■ Bristol Archdeaconry Charity

CC NO 1058853 **ESTABLISHED** 1996

WHERE FUNDING CAN BE GIVEN Archdeaconry of Bristol and the surrounding area (including the Deanery of Kingswood in South Gloucestershire and the Benefice of Marshfield with Cold Ashton and Tormarton with West Littleton).

WHO CAN BENEFIT Churches; religious bodies.

WHAT IS FUNDED Church of England ministry and community projects.

TYPE OF GRANT Project funding; start-up funding.

RANGE OF GRANTS £1,000 to £100,000.

SAMPLE GRANTS Yate Christian Youth Project (£20,000); Bradley Stoke Parish (£12,000); St Oswald's Church (£10,000); Holy Trinity – Stapleton (£7,500); East Bristol Partnership (£5,000); Sisters of the Church (£4,000); St Michael and All Angels (£3,100); St Helen's Church – Alveston (£1,000).

FINANCES *Financial year end* 31/12/2019 *Income* £136,300 *Total grants* £211,300 *Grants to organisations* £211,300 *Assets* £4,050,000

TRUSTEES David Worthington; Roger Metcalfe; Peter Woolf; Nicholas Bacon; Revd Lee Barnes;

Stephen Gisby; Oliver Home; Revd Richard Croft; Amber May; Adrian Howkins; Revd Neil Warwick.

OTHER INFORMATION Grants were made to 22 organisations during 2019.

HOW TO APPLY Apply in writing to the correspondent. The trustees meet twice during the year.

CONTACT DETAILS Mrs A. Maddox, Clerk to the Trustees, All Saints Centre, 1 All Saints Court, Bristol BS1 1JN *Tel.* 0117 929 2709 *Email* ascl.charity@btconnect.com

■ Bristol Charities

CC NO 1109141 **ESTABLISHED** 1960

WHERE FUNDING CAN BE GIVEN In practice the City of Bristol, North Somerset and South Gloucestershire; mainly within a ten-mile radius of Bristol city centre.

WHO CAN BENEFIT Registered charities; schools; individuals; carers.

WHAT IS FUNDED Social welfare; disability; health; relief of carers; education.

TYPE OF GRANT Capital costs; project funding; start-up funding.

RANGE OF GRANTS Up to £75,000, mainly under £15,000.

SAMPLE GRANTS Bristol Grammar School (£74,700); Carers Support Centre (£14,100); Queen Elizabeth's Hospital School (£9,600); Clifton High School (£7,500); Age UK Help for New Carers (£5,000); Developing Health and Independence (DHI) Bath Reach Out 2020 (£3,700).

FINANCES *Financial year end* 31/03/2020 *Income* £2,270,000 *Total grants* £426,200 *Grants to organisations* £118,600 *Assets* £37,760,000

TRUSTEES Elizabeth Carrington-Porter; Richard Gore; Keith Low; Ian Dunn; Andrew Mennell; Rachel Howell; Jonathan O'Shea; Patrick Finch; Paul Staples; Nolan Webber; Olivia Spencer; Harriet Bosnell; Michelle Meredith.

OTHER INFORMATION In total, seven grants were awarded to organisations during 2019/20. The charity also provides almshouse accommodation for older people. Grants to individuals totalled £307,600.

HOW TO APPLY Application forms for each grant programme are available to download from the charity's website, together with full criteria and guidelines.

CONTACT DETAILS Anne Anketell, Chief Executive, 17 St Augustine's Parade, Bristol BS1 4UL *Tel.* 0117 930 0301 *Email* info@bristolcharities.org.uk *Website* www.bristolcharities.org.uk

■ The BRIT Trust

CC NO 1000413 **ESTABLISHED** 1989

WHERE FUNDING CAN BE GIVEN UK.

WHO CAN BENEFIT Charitable organisations.

WHAT IS FUNDED Music performance, education and appreciation.

TYPE OF GRANT Project funding.

RANGE OF GRANTS Mostly £5,000 to £60,000.

SAMPLE GRANTS The BRIT School (£562,000); Nordoff Robbins Music Therapy (£400,000); Mind (£100,000); Music for My Mind (£30,000).

FINANCES *Financial year end* 31/12/2018 *Income* £1,820,000 *Total grants* £1,560,000 *Grants to organisations* £1,560,000 *Assets* £10,370,000

TRUSTEES Paul Burger; Caroline Dollimore; Geoff Taylor; William Rowe; David Sharpe; Tony Wadsworth; David Munns; Henry Semmence; Mulika Sannie; Rita Broe; Angela Watts; Kwame Kwaten; Gerald Doherty.

OTHER INFORMATION The trust mainly supports The Brit School and Nordoff Robbins. However, the trustees sometimes make smaller grants to support additional charitable organisations and activities. These applications are considered at the November trustees' meeting.

HOW TO APPLY See the trust's website for the latest information on applications.

CONTACT DETAILS The Trustees, Riverside Building, County Hall, Westminster Bridge Road, London SE1 7JA *Email* brittrust@bpi.co.uk *Website* www.brittrust.co.uk

■ The Britford Bridge Trust

CC NO 1160012 **ESTABLISHED** 2014

WHERE FUNDING CAN BE GIVEN UK; overseas.

WHO CAN BENEFIT Registered charities.

WHAT IS FUNDED Social welfare; education; health; arts, science, culture and heritage; community development; sport; the environment.

RANGE OF GRANTS Up to £150,000; mostly £5,000 to £20,000.

SAMPLE GRANTS Coroner's Courts Support Service (£150,000); Museum of London (£100,000); Cambridge Science Centre (£40,000); Mary Rose Trust (£20,000); Tom's Trust (£10,000); Sheffield Wildlife Trust (£5,000).

FINANCES *Financial year end* 05/04/2020 *Income* £564,500 *Total grants* £1,040,000 *Grants to organisations* £1,040,000 *Assets* £22,680,000

TRUSTEES Brodies and Co. (Trustees) Ltd; Adrian Frost; Dr Margaret MacDougall.

OTHER INFORMATION Grants were made to 46 organisations during the year.

HOW TO APPLY Contact the correspondent to request an application form. The trustees meet to review applications every three months.

CONTACT DETAILS The Trustees, c/o Brodies LLP, Brodies House, 14–17 Atholl Crescent, Edinburgh EH3 8HA *Email* thebritfordbridgetrust@brodies.com

■ The British and Foreign School Society

CC NO 314286 **ESTABLISHED** 1964

WHERE FUNDING CAN BE GIVEN UK and overseas.

WHO CAN BENEFIT UK-registered charities; educational institutions.

WHAT IS FUNDED Access to education or the quality of education for vulnerable or deprived children and young people under the age of 25. In the UK the BFSS will support access to education or the quality of education for vulnerable or deprived children and young people under the age of 25. Internationally the BFSS supports projects to improve the quality, sustainability, and access to education for young people within international marginalised and deprived communities.

TYPE OF GRANT Capital costs; project funding; unrestricted funding.

RANGE OF GRANTS UK grants – £30,000 to £100,000; international grants – £5,000 to £60,000.

SAMPLE GRANTS Entraide (£30,000); A Second Chance (£19,600); Feed the Mind (£9,000); Saffron Hall Trust (£5,000); Theatre Unboxed (£1,200).

FINANCES *Financial year end* 31/12/2019 *Income* £800,900 *Total grants* £978,200 *Grants to organisations* £978,200 *Assets* £27,060,000

TRUSTEES Graham Kingsley; Leslie Stephen; Vic Craggs; Jane Creasy; David Baron; Stephen Wordsworth; Diana Hoy; Peter Miller; Karen Hughes; Prof. Joy Cooper; Andrew Gibbs.

HOW TO APPLY Apply via the BFSS website.

CONTACT DETAILS Belinda Lawrance, 7–14 Great Dover Street, London SE1 4YR *Email* grants@bfss.org.uk *Website* https://www.bfss.org.uk

British Council for Prevention of Blindness

CC NO 270941 **ESTABLISHED** 1976

WHERE FUNDING CAN BE GIVEN Worldwide.

WHO CAN BENEFIT Universities; hospitals; other research institutions; UK-based organisations only.

WHAT IS FUNDED Research which has the potential to make breakthroughs in understanding and treating currently incurable eye diseases and operational research aimed at improving best practice and delivery of eye care services.

WHAT IS NOT FUNDED Grants will not be awarded for: universities and hospitals outside the UK; completion of an existing project when previous funding has ended; laboratory-based research of a basic molecular or cell biological nature, unless the applicant can demonstrate relevance to the satisfaction of the grant-maker; research based in high income countries.

TYPE OF GRANT Capital costs; project funding; core costs; fellowships (over a maximum of three years); research grants (up to three years); research mentorship awards (over one year); studentships (up to three years).

RANGE OF GRANTS Dependent on the funding programme.

SAMPLE GRANTS International Centre for Eye Health (£190,000); Liverpool John Moores University (£60,000); International Centre for Eye Health and College of Ophthalmology of East Central and South Africa (£15,000).

FINANCES *Financial year end* 31/03/2020 *Income* £80,500 *Total grants* £332,500 *Grants to organisations* £332,500 *Assets* £168,200

TRUSTEE BCPB Management Ltd.

OTHER INFORMATION The grant-maker awards grants for research that has direct clinical or epidemiological relevance to the prevention of blindness in low and lower-middle countries (low and lower-middle as defined by the World Bank). The grant-maker focuses almost entirely on long-term interventions.

HOW TO APPLY Application forms are available on the grant-maker's website. See the relevant funding programme on the website for eligibility criteria.

CONTACT DETAILS Diana Bramson, Charity Manager, 4 Bloomsbury Square, London WC1A 2RP *Tel.* 020 7404 7114 *Email* info@bcpb.org *Website* www.bcpb.org

British Eye Research Foundation (Fight for Sight)

CC NO 1111438 **ESTABLISHED** 2005

WHERE FUNDING CAN BE GIVEN UK.

WHO CAN BENEFIT Universities; hospitals; other academic or medical organisations.

WHAT IS FUNDED Ophthalmology and research that addresses sight loss across all eye diseases and conditions.

WHAT IS NOT FUNDED Each individual scheme has its own exclusion criteria. See the charity's website for further information.

TYPE OF GRANT Project funding; core costs; capital costs; studentships.

RANGE OF GRANTS Programme dependent.

SAMPLE GRANTS University College London Institute of Ophthalmology (£858,000); University of Liverpool (£370,000); Queen's University Belfast (£276,000); Cardiff University (£121,000); University of Manchester (£99,000); University of St Andrews (£60,000); Imperial College Healthcare NHS Trust, University of Leicester and University of Nottingham (£15,000 each); University Hospital of Wales and University of Oxford (£5,000 each).

FINANCES *Financial year end* 31/03/2019 *Income* £2,910,000 *Total grants* £2,900,000 *Grants to organisations* £2,900,000 *Assets* £6,630,000

TRUSTEES Nigel Pantling; Steve Blackman; Thomas Bjorn; Prof. Francesca Cordeiro; Simon Craddock; Jonathon Grant; Ginny Greenwood; Alina Kessel; Barbara Merry; Sylvester Oppong; Prof. Roy Quinlan; Alistair Rae; Prof. David Spalton; Louisa Vincent; Jenny Williams.

OTHER INFORMATION Several grant programmes are offered by the grant-maker each year for research teams who are attached to recognised UK academic or medical institutions. According to its website these include: Small Grants (up to £15,000); Small Grant Awards (delivered in collaboration with other research partners); PhD Studentships (up to £100,000). See the grant-maker's website for further information on current grant programmes. Grants were awarded to 23 organisations during the year. The 2018/19 accounts were the latest available at the time of writing (January 2021).

HOW TO APPLY Information on how to apply can be found on the grant-maker's website.

CONTACT DETAILS Director of Finance and Resources, 18 Mansell Street, London E1 8AA *Tel.* 020 7264 3904 *Email* grants@fightforsight.org.uk *Website* www.fightforsight.org.uk

British Gas Energy Trust

CC NO 1179578 **ESTABLISHED** 2004

WHERE FUNDING CAN BE GIVEN England; Wales; Scotland.

WHO CAN BENEFIT Charitable organisations offering financial/debt advice; individuals.

WHAT IS FUNDED Emergency hardship relief for individuals in the form of clearing gas and electricity debts; grants to organisations that provide fuel debt advice services.

TYPE OF GRANT Project funding; capital costs; core costs.

SAMPLE GRANTS A list of beneficiaries was not included in the annual report and accounts.

FINANCES *Financial year end* 31/03/2020 *Income* £6,240,000 *Total grants* £4,660,000 *Grants to organisations* £3,140,000 *Assets* £2,800,000

TRUSTEES Helen Charlton; William Gillis; Albert Chong; Sheila Wheeler; Laurie Lee; Colin Trend.

OTHER INFORMATION The trust supports individuals though a hardship fund. Both British Gas customers and non-customers can apply for grants to clear domestic gas and electricity debts owed to British Gas or other suppliers.

HOW TO APPLY Applications can be made online via the trust's website.

CONTACT DETAILS The Trustees, Russell-Cooke Solicitors, 2 Putney Hill, London SW15 6AB *Tel.* 0121 348 7797 *Email* julie.collingham@russell-cooke.co.uk *Website* www.britishgasenergytrust.org.uk

■ British Heart Foundation (BHF)

CC NO 225971 **ESTABLISHED** 1961

WHERE FUNDING CAN BE GIVEN UK.

WHO CAN BENEFIT Universities; hospitals; charitable organisations related to cardiovascular research.

WHAT IS FUNDED Support for clinical and non-clinical cardiovascular researchers at all stages of their career.

TYPE OF GRANT Capital costs; core costs; project funding; fellowships; partnership funding.

RANGE OF GRANTS Ranges vary according to the grant programme.

SAMPLE GRANTS Health Data Research UK (£10 million); Kings College London (£7.2 million awarded in seven grants); University of Oxford (£5.2 million awarded in five grants); University College London (£4.4 million awarded in six grants); University of Edinburgh (£3.6 million awarded in five grants); University of Reading (£1.4 million); London School of Hygiene and Tropical Medicine (£400,000).

FINANCES *Financial year end* 31/03/2020 *Income* £139,900,000 *Total grants* £99,700,000 *Grants to organisations* £99,700,000 *Assets* £19,400,000

TRUSTEES Dr Sarah Clarke; Prof. Sir Munir Pirmohamed; Prof. Sir Kent Woods; Prof. John Iredale; Prof. David Lomas; Daryl Fielding; Mark FitzPatrick; Prof. Jill Pell; Karen Frank; Peter Phippen; Prof. Sussan Nourshargh; Dr Doug Gurr; Timothy Howe.

OTHER INFORMATION The foundation has several grant programmes with different levels of funding available. Further details can be found on the foundation's website. In 2019/20, the foundation awarded 217 new research grants worth £99.7 million, including supplements made to new and existing grants. Only the top 50 grants to organisations were listed in the foundation's accounts.

HOW TO APPLY Details on how to apply can be found on the foundation's website, along with guidelines and other useful information on the application process.

CONTACT DETAILS Research Funds Department, Greater London House (5th Floor), 180 Hampstead Road, London NW1 7AW *Tel.* 020 7554 0434 *Email* research@bhf.org.uk *Website* www.bhf.org.uk

■ British Humane Association

CC NO 207120 **ESTABLISHED** 1922

WHERE FUNDING CAN BE GIVEN UK.

WHO CAN BENEFIT Charitable organisations.

WHAT IS FUNDED General charitable purposes, with a preference for social welfare and human rights.

RANGE OF GRANTS £1,000 to £15,000.

SAMPLE GRANTS Apex Charitable Trust Ltd (£7,000); Friend of Meath and Gloucestershire Action for Refugees and Asylum Seekers (£6,000 each); Duke of Edinburgh Wales; Hot Line Meals Service and Step by Step (£5,000 each); Women's Aid Orkney (£3,000); Lothian Autistic Society (£2,000).

FINANCES *Financial year end* 31/12/2019 *Income* £175,200 *Total grants* £128,000 *Grants to organisations* £128,000 *Assets* £5,530,000

TRUSTEES Philip Gee; Duncan Cantlay; Anthony Chignell; Michael Nemko; Rachel Campbell-Johnston; Edward Campbell-Johnston; Dr John Smail; Anna Campbell-Johnston; Ann Holden.

OTHER INFORMATION Grants totalling £128,000 were awarded to 29 organisations in 2019.

HOW TO APPLY Applications made directly to the grant-maker are not considered. The 2019 annual report states: 'The directors of the Association have decided, that in order to increase the amount available for grant distribution to beneficiaries, they will transfer funds to other charitable organisations, which have in place systems for identifying and assisting deserving cases in need.'

CONTACT DETAILS Sarah Fox, Company Secretary, Suite One, 4 Bessemer Road, Cardiff CF11 8BA *Tel.* 029 2002 2143 *Email* secretary@britishhumaneassociation.co.uk

■ British Lung Foundation

CC NO 326730 **ESTABLISHED** 1984

WHERE FUNDING CAN BE GIVEN UK.

WHO CAN BENEFIT Hospitals; universities; other research institutions; charitable organisations involved with lung disease/respiratory diseases.

WHAT IS FUNDED Research into the causes of lung disease, cures, improved treatments, diagnostics and care.

WHAT IS NOT FUNDED Exclusion criteria may vary according to the programme being applied to. See the foundation's website for further information.

TYPE OF GRANT Project funding; core costs; capital costs; development funding.

RANGE OF GRANTS Ranges vary according to the grant programme.

SAMPLE GRANTS University of Leicester (£423,000); Papworth Hospital (£358,000); University of Cambridge (£203,000); King's College London (£150,000); University College London (£42,000); University of Exeter (£25,000); Ninewells Hospital and Medical School – Dundee (£21,000).

FINANCES *Financial year end* 30/06/2019 *Income* £8,510,000 *Total grants* £1,820,000 *Grants to organisations* £1,820,000 *Assets* £5,320,000

TRUSTEES Baroness Tessa Blackstone; Prof. Stephen Spiro; John Graham; Ralph Bernard; Teresa Burgoyne; Emily Bushby; Isabel DiVanna; Dr Francis Gilchrist; David Gill; John Loots; Richard Pettit.

OTHER INFORMATION The foundation offers multiple grant programmes for specific research projects in addition to travel awards which allow early-career researchers to travel to specific conferences. The 2018/19 accounts were the latest available at the time of writing (January 2021).

HOW TO APPLY Application forms and further information on the various grant programmes can be found on the foundation's website.

CONTACT DETAILS Research Team, 18 Mansell Street, London E1 8AA *Tel.* 020 7688 5555 *Website* https://www.blf.org.uk

■ British Motor Sports Training Trust

CC NO 273828 **ESTABLISHED** 1977

WHERE FUNDING CAN BE GIVEN UK.

WHO CAN BENEFIT Organisations involved with four-wheeled motor sports.

WHAT IS FUNDED Education and training, mainly focused on volunteer marshals and officials; grants for additional or enhanced safety improvements which comply with Motorsport UK requirements of regulations.

TYPE OF GRANT Capital costs; project funding; strategic funding.

RANGE OF GRANTS Safety development grants: up to £8,500; training projects and equipment: up to £12,200.

SAMPLE GRANTS British Motorsport Marshals Club Ltd (£19,000); Scottish Association of Motor Sports Club (£12,200); North of Scotland Kart Club (£8,500); Motor Sports Services Organisation (£6,000); Association Of Motorsport Recovery (£4,300); Goodwood Marshals Club Ltd (£2,000); Stoke Rescue Safety Group (£1,500); Association of North East Midlands Motor Club (£1,000).

FINANCES *Financial year end* 31/12/2019
Income £144,700 *Total grants* £297,200
Grants to organisations £297,200
Assets £3,820,000

TRUSTEES Prof. Richard Parry-jones; Jim Morris; Hugh Chambers; Peter Weall; Mr Nicky Moffitt; Dominic Ostrowski.

OTHER INFORMATION The trust has two main grant programmes: the Safety Development Fund which awards grants for safety at closed road and rally events, and the Volunteer and Marshals Training Day Programme which funds safety training projects. Further information on each programme can be found on the trust's website. Only organisations that received grants above £1,000 were listed in the 2019 accounts.

HOW TO APPLY Application forms and further information on the application process can be found on the trust's website. Application forms can either be downloaded and sent to the correspondent, or be filled out online.

CONTACT DETAILS Allan Dean-Lewis, Secretary, Birds Nest, 28 Tan y Bryn Road, Llandudno LL30 1UU *Tel.* 07801 591332 *Email* gensec@bmstt.org *Website* www.bmstt.org

■ The J. and M. Britton Charitable Trust

CC NO 1081979 **ESTABLISHED** 1996

WHERE FUNDING CAN BE GIVEN Mainly Bristol.

WHO CAN BENEFIT Local charitable organisations; individuals; hospices; educational organisations.

WHAT IS FUNDED General charitable purposes; education; relief of poverty.

RANGE OF GRANTS Typically up to £20,000 but mostly under £5,000.

SAMPLE GRANTS Bristol Music Trust (£145,000); Quartet Community Fund (£20,000); The Matthew Tree Project (£5,000); Clifton College (£4,000); Alabare Gloucestershire Homes for Veterans (£2,500); Penny Brohn Cancer Care (£2,000); Kinergy (£1,300).

FINANCES *Financial year end* 05/04/2020
Income £90,300 *Total grants* £238,300
Grants to organisations £238,300
Assets £3,090,000

TRUSTEES Richard Bernays; Lady Merrison; Alison Bernays; Caroline Duckworth; Annie Bernays.

OTHER INFORMATION During the year, grants of over £1,000 were awarded to 17 organisations. Grants of less than £1,000 totalled £34,700. No grants were awarded to individuals during the year.

HOW TO APPLY Apply in writing to the correspondent. The trustees meet regularly to consider applications.

CONTACT DETAILS The Trustees, 3A Merlin Haven, Wotton-Under-Edge, Gloucestershire GL12 7BA *Tel.* 01453 498044

■ The Bromley Trust

CC NO 801875 **ESTABLISHED** 1989

WHERE FUNDING CAN BE GIVEN UK.

WHO CAN BENEFIT UK-registered charities with an annual turnover of between £100,000 and £5 million.

WHAT IS FUNDED Human rights; prison reform.

WHAT IS NOT FUNDED See the trust's website for a full list of exclusions.

TYPE OF GRANT Unrestricted.

RANGE OF GRANTS Mostly £5,000 to £20,000.

SAMPLE GRANTS Mind in Camden (£30,000); Prison Reform Trust (£25,000); Music in Detention and Women in Prison (£10,000 each); Refugee Council (£5,000).

FINANCES *Financial year end* 31/03/2020
Income £645,000 *Total grants* £795,500
Grants to organisations £795,500
Assets £14,460,000

TRUSTEES Adam McCormack; Helen Curtis; Fiona Cramb; Anne-Marie Edgell; Terrence Davis; Susan Silk; Dr Judith Brett.

OTHER INFORMATION Grants were broken down as follows: prison reform (£393,000); human rights (£357,500); the environment (£45,000).

HOW TO APPLY Application forms and guidelines are available from the trust's helpful website. Unsolicited applications to the environmental funding stream are not accepted.

CONTACT DETAILS Grants Team, Unit K03, The Biscuit Factory, Drummond Road, London SE16 4DG *Email* enquiries@thebromleytrust.org.uk. *Website* www.thebromleytrust.org.uk

■ The Brook Trust

CC NO 1123562 **ESTABLISHED** 2008

WHERE FUNDING CAN BE GIVEN UK.

WHO CAN BENEFIT Registered charities.

WHAT IS FUNDED Women and children who are victims of violence; parenting, primarily in the context of social or economic deprivation; learning opportunities for any age group in play, arts, practical activities or sciences, particularly for the benefit of those who have limited opportunity owing to social or economic deprivation.

TYPE OF GRANT Core costs; front-line projects. Often multi-year.

SAMPLE GRANTS Refuge (£120,000); Kent Community Foundation (£110,000); Rape Crisis England and Wales (£75,000); Her Centre (£25,000); The Lions Part (£1,000).

FINANCES *Financial year end* 05/04/2020
Income £119,600 *Total grants* £1,160,000
Grants to organisations £1,160,000
Assets £5,510,000

TRUSTEES Tim Bull; Rosalind Riley; Dr Elinor Cleghorn.

HOW TO APPLY Unsolicited applications are not accepted; however, the trustees will consider initial enquiries which must be made by email to info@brooktrust.org.

CONTACT DETAILS The Trustees, PO Box 161, Cranbrook, Kent TN17 9BL *Email* info@brooktrust.org *Website* www.brooktrust.org

The Consuelo and Anthony Brooke Charitable Trust

CC NO 1150569 **ESTABLISHED** 2013

WHERE FUNDING CAN BE GIVEN UK; Europe; East Africa.

WHO CAN BENEFIT Charitable organisations.

WHAT IS FUNDED Education; the arts; community development; health.

SAMPLE GRANTS A list of beneficiaries was not included in the 2019/20 annual report and accounts.

FINANCES *Financial year end* 05/04/2020 *Income* £79,600 *Total grants* £120,200 *Grants to organisations* £120,200 *Assets* £39,700

TRUSTEES Carol Brooke; Anthony Brooke; Charlotte Eade; Alexander Brooke.

HOW TO APPLY Contact the correspondent for further information.

CONTACT DETAILS The Trustees, 20 Caroline Place, London W2 4AN *Tel.* 07802 796416 *Email* anthonylbrooke@btinternet.com

The Rory and Elizabeth Brooks Foundation

CC NO 1111587 **ESTABLISHED** 2005

WHERE FUNDING CAN BE GIVEN UK and overseas.

WHO CAN BENEFIT Charitable organisations.

WHAT IS FUNDED International development; poverty research; higher education; social justice; visual arts.

SAMPLE GRANTS University of Manchester (£355,000); Tate Gallery (£27,200); IntoUniversity (£40,000).

FINANCES *Financial year end* 31/01/2020 *Income* £500,000 *Total grants* £515,800 *Grants to organisations* £515,800 *Assets* £277,400

TRUSTEES Elizabeth Brooks; Roderick Brooks; Bridget Fury.

OTHER INFORMATION During the year, grants were awarded to 17 organisations. The 2019/20 accounts only named three principal beneficiaries.

HOW TO APPLY Contact the correspondent for further information.

CONTACT DETAILS Robyn Bryson, Orion House, 5 Upper St Martin's Lane, London WC2H 9EA *Tel.* 020 7024 2217 *Email* RBryson@mmlcapital.com *Website* https://www.brooks-foundation.org.uk

The Broomton Foundation

CC NO 1125386 **ESTABLISHED** 2008

WHERE FUNDING CAN BE GIVEN East Anglia.

WHO CAN BENEFIT Charitable organisations.

WHAT IS FUNDED General charitable purposes.

TYPE OF GRANT Capital and project costs.

SAMPLE GRANTS Pancreatic Cancer UK (£150,000); Walnut Tree (£13,600); Find Ipswich (£10,000); Pawsitive Squad (£6,000).

FINANCES *Financial year end* 05/04/2020 *Income* £827,200 *Total grants* £418,000 *Grants to organisations* £418,000 *Assets* £11,840,000

TRUSTEES Benedicta Chamberlain; Julius Chamberlain; Robert Chamberlain; Kate Lewis.

HOW TO APPLY Contact the correspondent for further information.

CONTACT DETAILS The Trustees, Providence House, 141–145 Princes Street, Ipswich, Suffolk IP1 1QJ *Tel.* 01473 232300 *Email* admin@broomton.org

The Brothers Trust

CC NO 1172675 **ESTABLISHED** 2017

WHERE FUNDING CAN BE GIVEN UK; USA; overseas.

WHO CAN BENEFIT Registered charities.

WHAT IS FUNDED General charitable purposes; social welfare; health.

SAMPLE GRANTS The Lunchbowl Network (£81,000); The John Foundation (£32,200); Tear Fund (£32,000); Story Book Dads (£30,000); Alex's Wish (£25,000).

FINANCES *Financial year end* 31/03/2020 *Income* £573,000 *Total grants* £434,600 *Grants to organisations* £434,600 *Assets* £130,800

TRUSTEES Nicola Holland; Dominic Holland; Thomas Holland; Gregory Cook; Janine Cook.

HOW TO APPLY Apply in writing to the correspondent. The trust's Charity Commission record states that it 'identifies needs itself and considers unsolicited applications for funds'.

CONTACT DETAILS The Trustees, c/o HW Fisher and Co., Acre House, 11–15 William Road, London NW1 3ER *Tel.* 020 7388 7000 *Website* https://www.thebrotherstrust.org

The Charles Brotherton Trust

CC NO 227067 **ESTABLISHED** 1940

WHERE FUNDING CAN BE GIVEN The cities of Birmingham, Leeds, Liverpool, Wakefield, York and Bebington in Wirral.

WHO CAN BENEFIT Charitable organisations.

WHAT IS FUNDED Education; organised recreational activities; older people; social welfare; children and young people.

WHAT IS NOT FUNDED Individuals.

RANGE OF GRANTS Generally up to £500.

SAMPLE GRANTS Brotherton Charity Trust (£1,300); Marie Curie Cancer Care (£400); Dogs for Good (£250); Northern Ballet (£200); Claire House (£175); Birmingham Festival Choir (£150); British Epilepsy Association (£100).

FINANCES *Financial year end* 31/03/2020 *Income* £79,000 *Total grants* £67,500 *Grants to organisations* £67,500 *Assets* £2,110,000

TRUSTEES Christopher Brotherton-Ratcliffe; David Brotherton; Helen Brotherton-Ratcliffe; Dominic Jones.

OTHER INFORMATION Grants were broken down as follows: Leeds (£27,000); Birmingham (£13,500); Liverpool, Wakefield, York and Bebington (£6,800 each). Most grants were for £250 or less.

HOW TO APPLY Apply in writing to the correspondent. The application should clearly show the organisation's activities, geographical area of operations and for what the funds are required. Applications should be accompanied by the organisation's most recent set of accounts. There is no formal application form and applications are not acknowledged. Grants are considered by the trustees at the start of the trust's accounting year in April and a single payment is made to successful applicants in October.

CONTACT DETAILS The Secretary, PO Box 374, Harrogate, North Yorkshire HG1 4YW

Email admin@charlesbrothertontrust.com
Website www.charlesbrothertontrust.com

■ Bill Brown 1989 Charitable Trust

CC NO 801756 **ESTABLISHED** 1989
WHERE FUNDING CAN BE GIVEN UK with a strong preference for the south of England.
WHO CAN BENEFIT UK-registered charities; hospices.
WHAT IS FUNDED Research into blindness; medical research; deaf and blind people; older people; people with disabilities; social welfare; hospices.
WHAT IS NOT FUNDED Individuals; animal welfare; small (local) charitable causes; appeals from regional branches of national charitable organisations; wildlife and environmental conservation; maintenance of buildings; religious charities.
TYPE OF GRANT Research funding; project funding.
RANGE OF GRANTS £5,000 to £15,000.
SAMPLE GRANTS Charities Aid Foundation (£75,000); Macmillan Cancer Support and Salvation Army (£15,000 each); Dementia UK and STUBS (£10,000 each); Alzheimer's Society, DEBRA and Treloar Trust (£7,500 each); RAF Benevolent Fund (£5,000); Richmond Borough MIND (£3,800).
FINANCES *Financial year end* 30/06/2019
Income £698,400 *Total grants* £207,500
Grants to organisations £207,500
Assets £16,030,000
TRUSTEES Graham Brown; Anthony Barnett.
OTHER INFORMATION The 2018/19 accounts were the latest available at the time of writing (June 2021).
HOW TO APPLY Apply by letter confirming your registered charity number, the aims and objectives of your charity, and a copy of your latest annual report and most recent audited accounts. The trustees will consider supporting specific projects, in this case applicants will be asked to provide details of the total amount required, contributions received to date and proposed timing to completion. Depending on the nature of the project, the trustees will sometimes make a grant commitment, but defer payment until assurances are received that sufficient funds have been raised or pledged. Applications must be received by the end of May or the end of October to be considered at the summer and winter meetings.
CONTACT DETAILS The Trustees, BM Box 4567, London WC1N 3XX *Tel.* 020 7465 4300 *Website* www.billbrowncharity.org

■ Mary Brown Memorial Trust

OSCR NO SC048591 **ESTABLISHED** 2018
WHERE FUNDING CAN BE GIVEN UK and overseas.
WHO CAN BENEFIT Charitable organisations.
WHAT IS FUNDED Advancement of the Christian faith; education, social welfare, health, citizenship and community development; religious and racial harmony; equality and diversity.
WHAT IS NOT FUNDED Non-charitable organisations; charities whose main aim is influencing policy or lobbying; general running costs of a project; political parties.
TYPE OF GRANT Project funding; capital costs; core costs.
RANGE OF GRANTS Small grants of up to £5,000; large grants of up to £50,000.
SAMPLE GRANTS Glasgow City Mission (£20,000); Parkhead Nazarene (£15,000); Pollokshaws Area Network (£10,000); Auldhouse Community Church and Scottish Christian Alliance (£7,500 each).
FINANCES *Financial year end* 31/12/2019
Income £873,700 *Total grants* £100,000
Grants to organisations £100,000
Assets £785,000
HOW TO APPLY Apply via the trust's website. The trustees meet three times per year.
CONTACT DETAILS The Trustees, 51 Netherauldhouse Road, Glasgow G43 2XG *Email* Contact form on website *Website* marybrowntrust.com

■ The Brown Source Trust

CC NO 1165158 **ESTABLISHED** 2016
WHERE FUNDING CAN BE GIVEN UK and overseas.
WHO CAN BENEFIT Charitable organisations.
WHAT IS FUNDED General charitable purposes, including social welfare, humanitarian aid and environmental needs.
TYPE OF GRANT Project funding; multi-year; unrestricted.
RANGE OF GRANTS Typically up to £15,000.
SAMPLE GRANTS Ebony Horse Club (£30,000 in two grants); Sponsored Arts for Education SAFE (£19,000 in two grants); The Snowdrop Project (£15,000); Refugee Support Network (£12,000); Rainforest Concern (£10,000); Christ's College Cambridge (£2,100); St Vincent de Paul Society Queensland (£560).
FINANCES *Financial year end* 21/11/2019
Income £26,800 *Total grants* £123,300
Grants to organisations £123,300
Assets £204,200
TRUSTEES Alan Brown; Chloe Noble; Hannah Brown; Harry Brown; Nicola Brown; Jack Brown; Coutts & Co.
OTHER INFORMATION The 2018/19 accounts were the latest available at the time of writing (June 2021). The trust awarded grants to 11 organisations during the period.
HOW TO APPLY The trust's website states the following: 'In general, we source most of the organisations we provide grants to from our own research. However, if you email harry@brown-source.com with some basic information about yourself then we will do our best to get back to you soon.'
CONTACT DETAILS The Trustees, Coutts & Co. Trustee Department, 1st Floor, Trinity Quay 1, Avon Street, Bristol BS2 0PT *Tel.* 0345 304 2424 *Email* harry@brown-source.com *Website* brownsourcetrust.org.uk

■ R. S. Brownless Charitable Trust

CC NO 1000320 **ESTABLISHED** 1990
WHERE FUNDING CAN BE GIVEN Mainly UK, occasionally overseas.
WHO CAN BENEFIT Registered charities; schools; amateur sports clubs; hospices; individuals.
WHAT IS FUNDED General charitable purposes including: disability, illness, social welfare and older people.
TYPE OF GRANT Project funding.
RANGE OF GRANTS Normally under £1,000.
SAMPLE GRANTS A list of beneficiaries was not included in the annual report and accounts.
FINANCES *Financial year end* 09/07/2020
Income £44,000 *Total grants* £52,400
Grants to organisations £52,400
Assets £1,370,000
TRUSTEES Frances Plummer; Philippa Nicolai.
HOW TO APPLY Contact the correspondent for further information.

CONTACT DETAILS The Trustees, Hennerton Holt, Hennerton, Wargrave, Reading, Berkshire RG10 8PD *Tel.* 0118 940 4029

■ The Brownsword Charitable Foundation

CC NO 1012615 **ESTABLISHED** 1992

WHERE FUNDING CAN BE GIVEN Bath and surrounding areas.

WHO CAN BENEFIT Charitable organisations.

WHAT IS FUNDED Children and young people; the arts; older people; community work; learning difficulties; education; medical research.

SAMPLE GRANTS Bath Abbey and Forever Friends (£200,000 each); St John Ambulance (£10,000); Teenage Cancer Trust (£2,000); Whizz-Kidz (£500).

FINANCES *Financial year end* 31/12/2019 *Income* £294,000 *Total grants* £443,800 *Grants to organisations* £443,800 *Assets* £9,420,000

TRUSTEES Andrew Brownsword; Robert Calleja; Peter Matthews; Allesandra Brownsword-Matthews.

OTHER INFORMATION Grants were made to 13 organisations.

HOW TO APPLY Contact the correspondent for further information.

CONTACT DETAILS The Trustees, 4 Queen Square, Bath, Somerset BA1 2HA *Tel.* 01225 339661

■ The T. B. H. Brunner's Charitable Settlement

CC NO 260604 **ESTABLISHED** 1969

WHERE FUNDING CAN BE GIVEN UK, with some preference for Oxfordshire.

WHO CAN BENEFIT Registered charities; individuals.

WHAT IS FUNDED Church of England preservation projects and other charities dealing with historical preservation, both local to Oxfordshire and nationally; the arts; music; general charitable purposes.

SAMPLE GRANTS Previous beneficiaries have included: Royal Opera House Foundation (£4,400); National Trust (£3,700); Rotherfield Greys PCC (£3,000); The London Library (£1,000); Friends of St Paul's Cathedral (£100).

FINANCES *Financial year end* 05/04/2020 *Income* £80,100 *Total grants* £80,200 *Grants to organisations* £80,200 *Assets* £2,790,000

TRUSTEES Helen Brunner; Dr Imogen Brunner; Timothy Brunner.

HOW TO APPLY Contact the correspondent for further information.

CONTACT DETAILS The Trustees, Flat 4, 2 Inverness Gardens, London W8 4RN *Tel.* 020 7727 6277 *Email* p.roberts@robco.uk.com

■ The Jack Brunton Charitable Trust

CC NO 518407 **ESTABLISHED** 1986

WHERE FUNDING CAN BE GIVEN North Riding area of Yorkshire – prior to the boundary changes in 1974.

WHO CAN BENEFIT Charities and community organisations, including: churches; scouts and girl guide groups; village halls; amateur sports clubs; social enterprises; hospital departments; drama, theatre and music groups; mountain rescue teams; schools; accessible transport services.

WHAT IS FUNDED General charitable purposes.

TYPE OF GRANT Capital costs, including medical, sports and leisure equipment; refurbishment and building costs for churches; project funding.

RANGE OF GRANTS Mostly up to £5,000.

SAMPLE GRANTS Great North Air Ambulance and Yorkshire Air Ambulance (£80,000 each); Russ Devereux Headlight Project (£10,000); East Cleveland Youth Housing Trust (£5,000); East Harlsey Village Hall (£3,200); Peasholme Charity – York (£3,000); Stokesley Methodist Church (£2,500); RNIB – North Yorkshire (£2,200).

FINANCES *Financial year end* 05/04/2020 *Income* £348,300 *Total grants* £351,700 *Grants to organisations* £351,700 *Assets* £9,250,000

TRUSTEES Derek Noble; James Lumb; David Swallow; Caroline Dickinson.

OTHER INFORMATION Grants were awarded to 104 organisations during the year. This includes 79 grants of £2,000 or less. Only the beneficiaries of grants above £2,000 were listed in the accounts.

HOW TO APPLY Application forms can be downloaded from the trust's website and should be signed before returning to the correspondent. The trustees meet on a quarterly basis to consider applications.

CONTACT DETAILS David Swallow, Administrator and Trustee, Commercial House, 10 Bridge Road, Stokesley, North Yorkshire TS9 5AA *Tel.* 01642 711407 *Website* www.jackbruntontrust.co.uk

■ The Bruntwood Charity

CC NO 1135777 **ESTABLISHED** 2010

WHERE FUNDING CAN BE GIVEN UK, mainly in Manchester, Leeds, Liverpool and Birmingham where the company has a presence.

WHO CAN BENEFIT Registered charities.

WHAT IS FUNDED General charitable purposes and social welfare, especially with regards to children and disability causes.

TYPE OF GRANT Project funding.

RANGE OF GRANTS £5,000 to £35,000.

SAMPLE GRANTS Factory Youth Zone – Harpurhey (£35,000); Factory Youth Zone – Godon (£25,000); Children's Liver Disease Foundation (£8,000); An Hour for Others (£5,000).

FINANCES *Financial year end* 30/09/2019 *Income* £55,500 *Total grants* £73,000 *Grants to organisations* £73,000 *Assets* £29,700

TRUSTEES Kate Vokes; Kathryn Graham; Peter Crowther.

OTHER INFORMATION This is the charity of Bruntwood Ltd, a company which owns and manages the commercial property and office space in Birmingham, Leeds, Manchester and Liverpool. At the time of writing (June 2021), the latest accounts that were available were the charity's 2018/19 accounts.

HOW TO APPLY Charities are chosen following discussions with the company and its employees. Funds are fully committed and therefore the trustees do not accept unsolicited applications.

CONTACT DETAILS The Trustees, Bruntwood Ltd, Union, Albert Square, Manchester M2 6LW *Tel.* 07387 417802

■ Brushmill Ltd

CC NO 285420 **ESTABLISHED** 1982
WHERE FUNDING CAN BE GIVEN UK and overseas.
WHO CAN BENEFIT Organisations benefitting Jewish people.
WHAT IS FUNDED Jewish education and places of worship for the Jewish community; social welfare; education.
RANGE OF GRANTS Up to £78,500.
SAMPLE GRANTS Ezer V'Hatzalah Ltd (£62,600); Friends of Boyan Trust (£59,400); Bais Rizhin Trust (£31,100); Hadras Kodesh Trust (£11,100); Comet Charities Ltd (£8,000); Friends of Yeshiva Luzern (£4,500).
FINANCES *Financial year end* 31/03/2019 *Income* £287,600 *Total grants* £271,400 *Grants to organisations* £271,400 *Assets* (£17,900)
TRUSTEES Mr C. Getter; Mr J. Weinberger; Mrs E. Weinberger.
OTHER INFORMATION Grants were awarded to 12 organisations during the year. Grants of under £3,000 totalled £24,000. The 2018/19 accounts were the latest available at the time of writing (January 2021).
HOW TO APPLY Apply in writing to the correspondent. The charity's 2018/19 accounts state: 'The Trustees consider all requests which they receive and make donations based on the level of funds available.'
CONTACT DETAILS Mrs M. Getter, Secretary, 76 Fairholt Road, London N16 5HN *Tel.* 020 8731 0777 *Email* mail@cohenarnold.com

■ Buckingham Trust

CC NO 237350 **ESTABLISHED** 1962
WHERE FUNDING CAN BE GIVEN UK.
WHO CAN BENEFIT Charitable organisations and churches.
WHAT IS FUNDED Advancement of religion (including missionary activities); social welfare; older people; health.
RANGE OF GRANTS Up to £10,000.
SAMPLE GRANTS The PCC of St Andrews (£17,900); Titus Trust (£13,200); Tear Fund (£9,000); New Life Church (£5,000); Battle Methodist Church (£4,000); Crosslinks (£3,000); Langham Partnership and Josiah Spiers Benevolent Fund (£1,000 each).
FINANCES *Financial year end* 05/04/2019 *Income* £193,500 *Total grants* £156,300 *Grants to organisations* £147,100 *Assets* £816,900
TRUSTEES Richard Foot; Christina Clay.
OTHER INFORMATION The trust acts mainly as an agency charity acting on behalf of other donors. During the year, grants were made to 14 churches and 19 charities, with grants for less than £1,000 totalling £36,700. In addition, grants to individuals totalled £9,200. The 2018/19 accounts were the latest available at the time of writing (January 2021).
HOW TO APPLY Apply in writing to the correspondent. Preference is given to charities of which the trustees have personal interest, knowledge, or association.
CONTACT DETAILS Christina Clay, Trustee, c/o Foot Davson Ltd, 17 Church Road, Tunbridge Wells, Kent TN1 1LG *Tel.* 01892 774774

■ Buckinghamshire Community Foundation

CC NO 1073861 **ESTABLISHED** 1998
WHERE FUNDING CAN BE GIVEN Buckinghamshire, excluding Milton Keynes.
WHO CAN BENEFIT Registered charities; unregistered charities; CICs limited by guarantee; social enterprises; clubs and societies; associations; amateur sports clubs; hospices; individuals; local authorities.
WHAT IS FUNDED General charitable purposes; community development; social welfare.
WHAT IS NOT FUNDED Organisations and/or projects operating solely outside Buckinghamshire, including Milton Keynes; activities promoting a particular religious belief; overseas travel; individuals; statutory organisations; CICs limited by shares; animal welfare; relief of statutory responsibilities; schools and private educational organisations; retrospective expenditure.
TYPE OF GRANT Capital costs; core/revenue costs; seed funding/start-up funding; project funding. Different types of grants are available through the funding programmes.
RANGE OF GRANTS Up to £20,000, but mostly between £1,000 and £5,000.
SAMPLE GRANTS Thames Hospice (£20,000); New Meaning Centre Bucks (£15,000); Citizens Advice Aylesbury and Empower to Cook CIC (£10,000 each).
FINANCES *Financial year end* 31/03/2019 *Income* £1,380,000 *Total grants* £631,400 *Grants to organisations* £619,100 *Assets* £7,100,000
TRUSTEES Moir Stewart; Joe Barclay; The Countess Howe; Linda Clegg; Lynda Marston-Weston; Philip Manktelow; Robert Taylor; Annalise Smith; Lucy Wood; Richard Collins; Mark Bradbury; Philippa Kirkbride.
OTHER INFORMATION This is one of the 46 UK community foundations, which distribute funding for a wide range of purposes. As with all community foundations, there are a number of donor-advised funds managed on behalf of individuals, families and charitable trusts. Grant schemes tend to change frequently – consult the foundation's website for details of current programmes and up-to-date deadlines. During the year, grants were awarded to 250 organisations. Only beneficiaries of grants of £10,000 and above were listed in the accounts. Grants to individuals totalled £12,300. The 2018/19 accounts were the latest available at the time of writing (January 2021).
HOW TO APPLY Potential applicants are advised to visit the community foundation's website or contact its grants team to find the most suitable funding stream.
CONTACT DETAILS The Trustees, Sunley House, 4th Floor, Oxford Road, Aylesbury, Buckinghamshire HP19 8FQ *Tel.* 01296 330134 *Email* info@bucksCF.org *Website* heartofbucks.org

■ The Buckinghamshire Historic Churches Trust

CC NO 206471 **ESTABLISHED** 1957
WHERE FUNDING CAN BE GIVEN Buckinghamshire (pre 1974 boundaries).
WHO CAN BENEFIT Religious bodies/institutions; places of worship.
WHAT IS FUNDED The preservation, repair, maintenance and upkeep of historic churches.
WHAT IS NOT FUNDED Bells, bell frames; organs; furnishings; work on heating; lighting; decoration

or churchyard structures; installation of kitchen facilities and lavatories.

TYPE OF GRANT Capital costs.

RANGE OF GRANTS £1,000 to £5,000.

SAMPLE GRANTS A list of beneficiaries was not included in the annual report and accounts.

FINANCES *Financial year end* 30/04/2020 *Income* £118,900 *Total grants* £95,500 *Grants to organisations* £95,500 *Assets* £908,700

TRUSTEES Caroline Aston; Sir Henry Fletcher; Mary Villiers; Mary Saunders; Caroline Abel-Smith; Sir David Lidington; Roger Evans; Marilynne Morgan; Vicky Peel; Robert Ruck-Keene; The Hon. Jenefer Farncombe; Andrew Finn-Kelcey; The Rt Revd Alan Wilson.

HOW TO APPLY Contact the secretary for a grant application form.

CONTACT DETAILS Penny Keens, Hon. Secretary, c/o Community Impact Buckinghamshire, 6 Centre Parade Parade, Place Farm Way, Monks Risborough, Princes Risborough, Buckinghamshire HP27 9JS *Tel.* 01908 242632 *Email* penny@pkeens.plus.com *Website* www.bucks-historic-churches.org

The Buffini Chao Foundation

CC NO 1111022 **ESTABLISHED** 2005

WHERE FUNDING CAN BE GIVEN UK; overseas.

WHO CAN BENEFIT Charitable organisations.

WHAT IS FUNDED Enhancing education and opportunity for children and young people.

TYPE OF GRANT Capital costs; project funding; development funding; strategic funding.

RANGE OF GRANTS Up to £100,000.

SAMPLE GRANTS National Theatre Connections (£100,000); Eastside Young Leaders Academy (£45,000); Lyric Theatre Hammersmith Ltd (£10,000); London Music Masters (£8,000); Hidden Tales Association (£1,900).

FINANCES *Financial year end* 05/04/2020 *Income* £857,500 *Total grants* £384,800 *Grants to organisations* £384,800 *Assets* £7,430,000

TRUSTEES Lady Buffini; Sir Damon Buffini; Maria Hindmarsh; Sue Gutierrez.

OTHER INFORMATION Grants were awarded to 17 organisations during the year.

HOW TO APPLY The foundation's support is primarily determined through experience, personal networks and the trustees' research. Charities that meet the foundation's core objectives can get in touch with the correspondent.

CONTACT DETAILS Alison Taylor, Foundation Secretary, PO Box 1427, Northampton, Northamptonshire NN1 9FP *Email* trustees@buffinichao.com *Website* https://www.buffinichao.com

Building & Civil Engineering Charitable Trust

CC NO 1004732 **ESTABLISHED** 1991

WHERE FUNDING CAN BE GIVEN UK.

WHO CAN BENEFIT Charitable organisations; not-for-profit organisations; research organisations; individuals.

WHAT IS FUNDED Education, training and retraining for operatives, past operatives and young people who want to start working in the construction industry; education, training and research for occupational health and safety initiatives in the construction industry; hardship grants for individuals who work, or have worked, in the construction industry.

WHAT IS NOT FUNDED Public sector bodies; overheads; project management fees.

TYPE OF GRANT Project funding; annual awards.

SAMPLE GRANTS Loughborough University – Occupational Health Research Award (£25,000); Barnardo's – ETS North Project (£20,500); Essex Youthbuild – Mowlem Award (£20,000); Corporate Television Networks – The WOW Show (£15,000).

FINANCES *Financial year end* 30/09/2019 *Income* £699,600 *Total grants* £302,200 *Grants to organisations* £212,100 *Assets* £72,000

TRUSTEES Robert Blackman Miosh; Stephen Terrell; David Smith; Patrick Heath-Lay; Chandrasekhar Ramamurthy.

OTHER INFORMATION This is the corporate charity of B&CE. During the year, 131 grants were awarded totalling £302,200, of which £90,100 was awarded to individuals. The 2018/19 accounts were the latest available at the time of writing (January 2021).

HOW TO APPLY Contact the correspondent for further information and an application form.

CONTACT DETAILS Karen Palfrey, Secretary, Manor Royal, Crawley, West Sussex RH10 9QP *Tel.* 0300 200 0600 *Email* charitabletrust@bandce.co.uk *Website* https://bandce.co.uk/corporate-responsibility/the-charitable-trust

Bulb Foundation

CC NO 1183235 **ESTABLISHED** 2019

WHERE FUNDING CAN BE GIVEN UK; overseas.

WHO CAN BENEFIT Charitable organisations.

WHAT IS FUNDED Climate change.

TYPE OF GRANT Project funding.

SAMPLE GRANTS Third Generation Environmentalism (£247,300); Carbon Tracker Initiative (£100,000).

FINANCES *Financial year end* 31/03/2020 *Income* £1,340,000 *Total grants* £347,300 *Grants to organisations* £347,300 *Assets* £928,800

TRUSTEES Amit Gudka; Dr Amal-Lee Amin; Sophie Pullan; Hayden Wood; Dr Alexander Edwards.

OTHER INFORMATION The foundation is associated with green energy supplier Bulb Energy Ltd.

HOW TO APPLY The foundation's website states: 'We don't accept unsolicited applications for funding. Instead, we develop projects with partners that fit our strategic approach.'

CONTACT DETAILS The Trustees, 155 Bishopsgate, London EC2M 3TQ *Email* bulbfoundation@bulb.co.uk *Website* https://bulb.co.uk/foundation

The Bulldog Trust Ltd

CC NO 1123081 **ESTABLISHED** 2008

WHERE FUNDING CAN BE GIVEN UK.

WHO CAN BENEFIT Registered charities; CICs; Community Benefit Societies.

WHAT IS FUNDED General charitable purposes. The Fore's website states: 'The Fore is particularly looking to fund small organisations working with marginalised groups and led by people in the community that may have found it hard to access trust and foundation funding in the past.'

TYPE OF GRANT Unrestricted.

RANGE OF GRANTS Up to £30,000.

SAMPLE GRANTS Head2Head Theatre and We Are Family Adoption (£30,000 each); Play Physio

(£28,000); Crosslight Advice (£25,800); Huckleberries Nurture Farm (£21,700).

FINANCES *Financial year end* 30/06/2020 *Income* £2,920,000 *Total grants* £1,910,000 *Grants to organisations* £1,910,000 *Assets* £9,100,000

TRUSTEES Brian Smouha; Alex Williams; Charles Hoare; Charles Jackson; Hamish McPherson.

OTHER INFORMATION The Fore Trust is a grant-making initiative of the Bulldog Trust. All financial information is for the Bulldog Trust.

HOW TO APPLY Apply via The Fore's website where application deadlines can also be found.

CONTACT DETAILS The Trustees, 2 Temple Place, London WC2R 3BD *Tel.* 020 7240 6044 *Email* info@bulldogtrust.org *Website* www.thefore.org/or bulldogtrust.org/grant-making

■ E. F. Bulmer Trust

CC NO 1188978 **ESTABLISHED** 1938

WHERE FUNDING CAN BE GIVEN Herefordshire.

WHO CAN BENEFIT Registered charities; unregistered charities; social enterprises; CICs; schools; universities; hospices; individuals.

WHAT IS FUNDED Social welfare; health. Former employees of H P Bulmer Holdings plc and individuals who are in need.

WHAT IS NOT FUNDED Large UK charities and those from outside Herefordshire are unlikely to be supported.

TYPE OF GRANT Capital costs; core and revenue costs; seed funding and start-up funding; unrestricted funding.

RANGE OF GRANTS Mostly under £2,500.

SAMPLE GRANTS Brightspace Foundation (£35,000); Plynlimon Trust (£30,000); Look UK (£19,300); Herefordshire Mind, St Michael's Hospice and Wellbeing Future Generations (£10,000); Hereford Sea Cadets (£5,000); Walford Parish Council (£3,000).

FINANCES *Financial year end* 05/04/2019 *Income* £466,600 *Total grants* £499,300 *Grants to organisations* £427,000 *Assets* £16,150,000

TRUSTEES Timothy Bulmer; Penelope Murray; Andrew Murray; Gillian Bulmer; Susan Bulmer; Jocelyn Wood; Andrew Patten.

OTHER INFORMATION A total of 78 organisations were supported during the year. Grants to individuals totalled £72,300. The 2018/19 accounts were the latest available at the time of writing (February 2021).

HOW TO APPLY Application forms are available to download from the fund's website. Hard copies should be returned with a detailed two page application, organisational budget, project budget and most recent audited accounts (if not available online).

CONTACT DETAILS Paddy Nugent, Chief Operating Officer, Fred Bulmer Centre, Wall Street, Hereford, Herefordshire HR4 9HP *Tel.* 01432 271293 *Email* efbulmer@gmail.com *Website* www.efbulmer.co.uk

■ Bupa UK Foundation

CC NO 1162759 **ESTABLISHED** 2015

WHERE FUNDING CAN BE GIVEN UK.

WHO CAN BENEFIT Registered charities; social enterprises, CICs and for-profit organisations delivering a charitable project may also apply as long as: the organisation is legally constituted; the proposed project is clearly for public benefit; the project fits the focus of an open funding programme.

WHAT IS FUNDED Health and well-being, including: mental health; ageing; prevention of long-term conditions; healthy living and behaviour change to improve health and well-being.

WHAT IS NOT FUNDED Exclusions are made available on the foundation's website when a programme opens for applications.

TYPE OF GRANT Project funding.

RANGE OF GRANTS £1,000 to £115,000.

SAMPLE GRANTS Asthma UK (£115,000); Muscular Dystrophy UK (£45,300); Single Homeless Project (£23,000); Cruse Bereavement Care (£22,800); Salford Foundation (£22,300); Bike for Good and Cardiff Community Trust (£1,000 each).

FINANCES *Financial year end* 31/12/2019 *Income* £1,140,000 *Total grants* £1,150,000 *Grants to organisations* £1,150,000 *Assets* £97,100

TRUSTEES Paula Franklin; Helen Cliffe; Sally Pain; Charles Richardson; Andrea Spyropoulos; Tom Webber; Alexandra Cole; Mark Davies; Robert Edmundson.

OTHER INFORMATION Grants were awarded according to four themes: mid-life mental health (£696,000); caring for carers (£292,000); healthy futures (supporting young adults who live with ongoing health challenges) (£160,300); training and development (£2,000). Grants were awarded to 48 organisations during the year.

HOW TO APPLY Information on how to apply will be available from the foundation's website when a programme opens. See the foundation's website for further information.

CONTACT DETAILS The Trustees, Battle Bridge House, 300–306 Gray's Inn Road, London WC1X 8DU *Email* bupafoundation@bupa.com *Website* www.bupaukfoundation.org

■ The Burberry Foundation

CC NO 1154468 **ESTABLISHED** 2013

WHERE FUNDING CAN BE GIVEN Worldwide, with a strong preference for communities where Burberry employees live and work.

WHO CAN BENEFIT Registered charities.

WHAT IS FUNDED STEAM education; educational equality; waste reduction; social and economic development.

SAMPLE GRANTS Oxfam (£850,200); Ideas Foundation (£404,000); Teach First (£300,000); MyKindaFuture (£132,100); King's College (£50,000).

FINANCES *Financial year end* 31/03/2020 *Income* £1,280,000 *Total grants* £2,950,000 *Grants to organisations* £2,950,000 *Assets* £4,680,000

TRUSTEES Christopher Holmes; Marco Gobbetti; Edward Rash; Pamela Batty.

OTHER INFORMATION Grants were awarded to 14 organisations and broken down as follows: UK (£2.33 million); USA (£340,000); France (£221,700); Italy (£57,000).

HOW TO APPLY Contact the correspondent for further information.

CONTACT DETAILS Pamela Batty, Secretary, Burberry Ltd, Horseferry House, Horseferry Road, London SW1P 2AW *Tel.* 020 7806 1328 *Email* enquiries@burberryfoundation.com *Website* https://www.burberryplc.com/en/responsibility/policies/communities/the-burberry-foundation.html

The Burden Trust

CC NO 235859 **ESTABLISHED** 1913

WHERE FUNDING CAN BE GIVEN UK, mainly Bristol.

WHO CAN BENEFIT Charitable organisations; hospitals; retirement homes; schools and training institutions.

WHAT IS FUNDED Medical research; social welfare.

SAMPLE GRANTS Oxford Centre for Mission Studies (£20,000); Easton Families Project (£15,000); Incredible Kids (£5,000); YMCA Bristol (£4,000); Personal Support Unit (£3,500).

FINANCES *Financial year end* 31/03/2020 *Income* £189,800 *Total grants* £181,800 *Grants to organisations* £181,800 *Assets* £4,250,000

TRUSTEES Prof. Andrew Halestrap; Annie Crawley; Dr Sheena Tranter; Colin Havill; Anthony Miles.

OTHER INFORMATION Grants were distributed as follows: support of the marginalised (£93,000); schools and training institutions (£64,800); organisations for care and training of young people (£24,000). The trust's website states: 'The trustees prefer to build a relationship with the organisation concerned and always look to see how best any project that is funded can be effectively sustained for the future.'

HOW TO APPLY Applications can be made using the online form available on the trust's website and should be submitted by 31 March each year in preparation for the trustees' meeting in June.

CONTACT DETAILS Patrick O'Conor, Secretary, 51 Downs Park West, Westbury Park, Bristol BS6 7QL *Email* Contact form on website *Website* www.burdentrustbristol.co.uk

The Burdett Trust for Nursing

CC NO 1089849 **ESTABLISHED** 2001

WHERE FUNDING CAN BE GIVEN UK and overseas.

WHO CAN BENEFIT Charities supporting nurses and research into nursing.

WHAT IS FUNDED Nursing.

WHAT IS NOT FUNDED General appeals; existing posts, although the trust will consider supporting new posts directly associated with a project/initiative; overhead costs of academic institutions or statutory agencies; organisations closely aligned to government departments where funding should properly be provided from statutory sources; retrospective expenditure; funding in lieu of statutory funding or as a replacement when it has run out or been withdrawn; significant capital appeals e.g. building costs or equipment.

TYPE OF GRANT Project funding. Small grants will be for one-off sums; no repeat or multi-year funding will be made.

RANGE OF GRANTS Usually £2,000 to £8,000.

SAMPLE GRANTS Global Health Network (£300,000); Winston Churchill Memorial Trust (£150,000); Foundation of Nursing Studies (£120,200); Bournemouth University (£59,000); Birmingham and Solihull TB Service (£5,000).

FINANCES *Financial year end* 31/12/2019 *Income* £2,080,000 *Total grants* £4,220,400 *Grants to organisations* £3,970,000 *Assets* £4,070,000

TRUSTEES Alan Gibbs; Audrey Ardern-Jones; Dame Christine Beasley; Prof. Ursula Gallagher; Andrew Gibbs; Dr Michael Gormley; Evy Hambro; Andrew Martin-Smith; David Sines; Prof. Tony Butterworth; Prof. Mary Lovegrove; Zoe Amasanti.

OTHER INFORMATION Grants to individuals totalled £250,400.

HOW TO APPLY See the trust's website for information on the current grant programmes and details on how to apply.

CONTACT DETAILS The Trustees, Rathbone Trust Company Ltd, 8 Finsbury Circus, London EC2M 7AZ *Tel.* 020 7399 0102 *Email* administrator@btfn.org.uk *Website* www.btfn.org.uk

The Burges Salmon Charitable Trust

CC NO 272522 **ESTABLISHED** 1976

WHERE FUNDING CAN BE GIVEN Priority is given to Bristol and the surrounding area.

WHO CAN BENEFIT Charities operating in Bristol and the surrounding regions. The trustees will generally support small to medium-sized charities rather than large national charities.

WHAT IS FUNDED Community projects.

TYPE OF GRANT Project funding.

RANGE OF GRANTS £500 to £26,000.

SAMPLE GRANTS Quartet Community Foundation (£26,000); Baby Bank Network, Barnardo's, Barton Hill and Easton Families (£3,000 each); Anchor Society, Dolphin Society and Grateful Society (£500 each).

FINANCES *Financial year end* 31/10/2019 *Income* £61,600 *Total grants* £62,900 *Grants to organisations* £62,900 *Assets* £18,400

TRUSTEES John Houlden; Mark Shepherd; Thomas Hewitt; Camilla Usher-Clark; Alice Honeywill; Catherine Elizabeth de Maid.

OTHER INFORMATION Grants were awarded to 94 organisations. Grants below £600 totalled £18,600. The 2018/19 accounts were the latest available at the time of writing (June 2021).

HOW TO APPLY Contact the correspondent for further information.

CONTACT DETAILS Alison Preece, Burges Salmon LLP, 1 Glass Wharf, Bristol BS2 0ZX *Tel.* 0117 902 2731 *Email* alison.preece@burges-salmon.com

The Clara E. Burgess Charity

CC NO 1072546 **ESTABLISHED** 1998

WHERE FUNDING CAN BE GIVEN UK and overseas.

WHO CAN BENEFIT Registered charities; schools; hospices.

WHAT IS FUNDED Children and young people; facilities and assistance for education, health and physical well-being. Preference may be given to younger children under the age of ten and children who have lost one or both parents.

RANGE OF GRANTS Mostly £1,000 to £5,000.

SAMPLE GRANTS Badcock's Wood E-ACT Academy (£20,400); Stanbridge Primary School (two grants totalling £10,000); Creating Better Futures and St Andrew's Children's Society (£5,000 each); Headstart4Babies and Right Now Foundation (£3,000 each); Vauxhall City Farm (£1,700); Kingswood School Association (£1,000).

FINANCES *Financial year end* 20/10/2019 *Income* £286,900 *Total grants* £284,900 *Grants to organisations* £284,900 *Assets* £11,580,000

TRUSTEE Ludlow Trust Company Ltd.

OTHER INFORMATION Grants were awarded to 79 organisations during the year. The 2018/19 accounts were the latest available at the time of writing (April 2021).

HOW TO APPLY Applications can be made in writing to the correspondent and are considered in January, April, July and October.
CONTACT DETAILS The Trustees, c/o Ludlow Trust Company Ltd, 1st Floor, Tower Wharf, Cheese Lane, Bristol BS2 0JJ *Tel.* 0117 313 8200 *Email* charitabletrusts@ludlowtrust.com

■ Burnie's Foundation

CC NO 1167997 **ESTABLISHED** 2016
WHERE FUNDING CAN BE GIVEN UK and overseas.
WHO CAN BENEFIT Charitable organisations.
WHAT IS FUNDED Animal welfare.
TYPE OF GRANT Project funding.
RANGE OF GRANTS £3,000 to £145,000.
SAMPLE GRANTS Animals Asia Foundation (£50,000); Cat Protection Pollensa – Spain (£15,000); Nowzad and Million of Friends Association – Romania (£10,000 each); Change for Animals Foundation (£5,000); Stray Dogs Campaign Foundation – Netherlands (£2,700).
FINANCES *Financial year end* 31/05/2019 *Income* £27,900 *Total grants* £115,000 *Grants to organisations* £115,000 *Assets* £684,300
TRUSTEES Kenneth Tonkin; Richard Thoburn; Bethann Sells.
OTHER INFORMATION In total, nine grants were awarded throughout the year. The 2018/19 accounts were the latest available at the time of writing (January 2021).
HOW TO APPLY At the time of writing (January 2021), the foundation is only accepting applications for project grants by invitation only.
CONTACT DETAILS Richard Thoburn, Trustee, 45 Britton Street, London EC1M 5NA *Tel.* 020 7250 7000 *Email* burnie@burniesfoundation.com *Website* www.burniesfoundation.com

■ The Burry Charitable Trust

CC NO 281045 **ESTABLISHED** 1961
WHERE FUNDING CAN BE GIVEN Mainly Highcliffe and the surrounding areas.
WHO CAN BENEFIT Charities, voluntary groups and other not-for-profit organisations.
WHAT IS FUNDED General charitable purposes.
RANGE OF GRANTS Up to £20,000; mostly £1,000 to £5,000.
SAMPLE GRANTS Arnewood School/Gryphon Trust (£69,500); Oakhaven Hospital Trust (£20,000); Canine Partners (£5,000); MS Society (£1,000).
FINANCES *Financial year end* 05/04/2020 *Income* £66,500 *Total grants* £124,000 *Grants to organisations* £124,000 *Assets* £1,830,000
TRUSTEES Robert Burry; Adrian Osman; Sarah Teague.
OTHER INFORMATION Grants were awarded to 16 organisations.
HOW TO APPLY Contact the correspondent for further information.
CONTACT DETAILS Sarah Teague, Trustee, 10 Hobrune Lane, Highcliffe, Christchurch, Dorset BH23 4HP *Tel.* 01425 277661 *Email* sarah.teague@hoburne.com

■ The Arnold Burton 1998 Charitable Trust

CC NO 1074633 **ESTABLISHED** 1998
WHERE FUNDING CAN BE GIVEN UK with a strong preference for Yorkshire; overseas.
WHO CAN BENEFIT Registered charities.
WHAT IS FUNDED Arts and amenities; education; health; heritage; social welfare; work overseas.
RANGE OF GRANTS Up to £15,000.
SAMPLE GRANTS Opera North (£20,000); Yorkshire Air Museum (£10,000); Moghissi Laser Research Fund (£5,000); Help Refugees (£2,000).
FINANCES *Financial year end* 05/04/2020 *Income* £158,600 *Total grants* £143,200 *Grants to organisations* £143,200 *Assets* £4,580,000
TRUSTEES Mark Burton; Jeremy Burton; Nicholas Burton.
OTHER INFORMATION There were 20 grants made during the year. Grants were broken down as follows: arts and amenities (£55,000); social welfare (£45,000); health (£25,000); heritage (£13,500); international (£4,000); education (£650).
HOW TO APPLY Contact the correspondent for further information.
CONTACT DETAILS The Trustees, Castlegarth, Scott Lane, Wetherby LS22 6LH *Tel.* 01937 585558

■ Consolidated Charity of Burton upon Trent

CC NO 239072 **ESTABLISHED** 2001
WHERE FUNDING CAN BE GIVEN Burton upon Trent and the parishes of Branston, Stretton and Outwoods.
WHO CAN BENEFIT Registered charities; voluntary groups; churches; individuals.
WHAT IS FUNDED Health; social welfare; sport and recreation; leisure; education; youth development; religion; community; the environment; heritage.
TYPE OF GRANT Capital costs; core/revenue costs; project funding.
SAMPLE GRANTS Previous beneficiaries have included: SARAC (£18,000); 16th Burton Scout Group (£6,600); St Mary's Church (£5,000); St Giles Hospice (£4,500); Fishing in Safe Hands, Little Theatre Company and Tutbury Pre-school (£2,000 each); Asthma Relief (£1,900).
FINANCES *Financial year end* 31/12/2019 *Income* £622,300 *Total grants* £238,600 *Grants to organisations* £148,000 *Assets* £14,810,000
TRUSTEES Cecilia Mahon; Ronald Clarke; Margaret Heather; George Fargher; Revd Robert Styles; Geoffrey Brown; Cllr Beryl Toon; Ben Robinson; Cllr Colin Wileman; Peter Davies; Keith Williamson; Patricia Ackroyd; Sandra Phillips; Cllr Julie Killoran; Nigel Powlson; Dennis Fletcher; Simon Gaskin; David Leese.
OTHER INFORMATION Grants to individuals totalled £90,600.
HOW TO APPLY Applications can be made through the charity's website.
CONTACT DETAILS Clerk of Trustees, 1st Floor, Gibraltar House, Crown Square, First Avenue, Burton upon Trent DE14 2WE *Tel.* 01283 527067 *Email* Contact form on website *Website* www.consolidatedcharityburton.org.uk

Miss Margaret Butters Reekie Charitable Trust

OSCR NO SC024696 **ESTABLISHED** 1996

WHERE FUNDING CAN BE GIVEN Mainly Scotland.

WHO CAN BENEFIT Registered charities; hospices.

WHAT IS FUNDED Health, medical research, people with disabilities; older people.

SAMPLE GRANTS Edinburgh Society for Relief of Indigent Old Men (£30,000); Postnatal Depression Borders (£20,000); Pain Association Scotland (£10,000); St Vincent's Hospice (£5,000); Leukaemia Care (£3,000); Children 1st (£2,000); Borders General Hospital (£170).

FINANCES *Financial year end* 08/04/2020 *Income* £174,400 *Total grants* £189,100 *Grants to organisations* £189,100 *Assets* £3,870,000

HOW TO APPLY Contact the correspondent for further information.

CONTACT DETAILS The Trustees, c/o Lindsays, Caledonian Exchange, 19A Canning Street, Edinburgh EH3 8HE *Tel.* 0131 229 1212

The Noel Buxton Trust

CC NO 220881 **ESTABLISHED** 1919

WHERE FUNDING CAN BE GIVEN UK, eastern and southern Africa.

WHO CAN BENEFIT Registered charities.

WHAT IS FUNDED Families affected by domestic violence; offenders and ex-offenders; sustainable and regenerative projects in Africa.

WHAT IS NOT FUNDED A full list of exclusions can be found on the trust's website. Each programme has further exclusions. Generally the trust does not fund individuals or capital/building costs.

TYPE OF GRANT Project funding; core/revenue costs.

RANGE OF GRANTS Grants range from £1,000 to £11,000.

SAMPLE GRANTS AFFORD (£11,000); Anglican International Development, CESA Uganda (£5,000 each); Insight (£4,000); Staying Put (£3,000); Fair Shares Gloucestershire (£2,000); SOFA Project (£1,000).

FINANCES *Financial year end* 31/12/2019 *Income* £129,400 *Total grants* £119,800 *Grants to organisations* £119,800 *Assets* £3,000,000

TRUSTEES Emma Compton-Burnett; Katie Aston; Katie Buxton; Simon Buxton; Brendan Gormley; Jo Tunnard; Tahera Aanchawan.

OTHER INFORMATION Grants were made to 39 organisations during the year under the following themes: families affected by domestic abuse (£47,000); offenders and ex-offenders (£39,000); African communities (£36,000).

HOW TO APPLY Visit the trust's website for guidance on how to apply to each programme.

CONTACT DETAILS Anne Murray, Manager, PO Box 520, Fleet, Hampshire GU51 9GX *Tel.* 01252 620841 *Website* www.noelbuxtontrust.org.uk

Byrne Family Foundation

CC NO 1137878 **ESTABLISHED** 2010

WHERE FUNDING CAN BE GIVEN UK.

WHO CAN BENEFIT Charitable organisations.

WHAT IS FUNDED General charitable purposes, including disadvantaged children and young people and Christian causes.

RANGE OF GRANTS Up to £148,000 but mostly £1,000 to £20,000.

SAMPLE GRANTS St Wilfrid's Hospice (£100,000); Hope House (£85,900); Christian Outreach Centre (£83,800); Global Compassion (£15,000); Chestnut Tree House (£2,800); Help for Harvey (£2,000); Lighthouse Foundation (£1,800).

FINANCES *Financial year end* 31/05/2019 *Income* £85,800 *Total grants* £291,500 *Grants to organisations* £291,500 *Assets* £5,370,000

TRUSTEES Kevin Byrne; Ruth Byrne; Lisa Byrne; David Harland. Emily Maple; Rachel Byrne.

OTHER INFORMATION The foundation was formerly know as the Checkatrade Foundation. Grants were made to seven organisations during the year. The 2018/19 accounts were the latest available at the time of writing (January 2021).

HOW TO APPLY Contact the correspondent for further information.

CONTACT DETAILS Kevin Byrne, Trustee, The Apple Building, Ellis Square, Selsey, Chichester, West Sussex PO20 0AF *Tel.* 07967 350212 *Email* kevin@byrneproperty.co.uk

C. and F. Charitable Trust

CC NO 274529 **ESTABLISHED** 1977
WHERE FUNDING CAN BE GIVEN UK.
WHO CAN BENEFIT Orthodox Jewish charities.
WHAT IS FUNDED Relief of poverty among the Jewish community; Orthodox Jewish causes.
RANGE OF GRANTS Up to £53,500.
SAMPLE GRANTS Ichud Mosdos Gur Ltd (£53,500); Friends of Gur Foundation Israel (£35,600); Emmunah Education (£28,000); Kollel Shomrei Hachomos (£16,000); Friends of Mercaz Hatorah Belz Macnivka (£13,000); Mifal Hachesed Vehatzedokoh (£12,000).
FINANCES *Financial year end* 05/04/2019 *Income* £95,900 *Total grants* £166,000 *Grants to organisations* £166,000 *Assets* £1,050,000
TRUSTEES Fradel Kaufman; Simon Kaufman.
OTHER INFORMATION Only organisations receiving grants of over £10,000 were listed as beneficiaries in the charity's accounts. Grants of under £10,000 totalled £8,000. The 2018/19 accounts were the latest available at the time of writing (January 2021).
HOW TO APPLY Contact the correspondent for further information.
CONTACT DETAILS Simon Kaufman, Trustee, 50 Keswick Street, Gateshead, Tyne and Wear NE8 1TQ *Tel.* 0191 490 0138

The Edward Cadbury Charitable Trust

CC NO 1160334 **ESTABLISHED** 2015
WHERE FUNDING CAN BE GIVEN The West Midlands with a preference for Herefordshire, Shropshire, Staffordshire, Warwickshire and Worcestershire.
WHO CAN BENEFIT Registered charities.
WHAT IS FUNDED Arts and culture; community projects; social welfare; the environment and conservation; social justice; religious activities such as interfaith and multi-faith relations; education and training; research.
WHAT IS NOT FUNDED Individuals.
TYPE OF GRANT Project costs and research.
RANGE OF GRANTS Up to £100,000 but mainly between £500 and £10,000.
SAMPLE GRANTS Birmingham Women's Hospital Charity (£100,000); Hill Street Youth and Community Centre – Coventry (£50,000); Sandwell Homeless/Resettlement Project (£11,000); Zoë's Place Baby Hospice – Coventry (£10,000); Access Project and Young People First Midlands (£5,000 each); Royal National College for the Blind – Hereford (£4,000); The Feast Youth Project and Nottinghamshire Wildlife Trusts (£3,000 each).
FINANCES *Financial year end* 05/04/2020 *Income* £1,240,000 *Total grants* £883,400 *Grants to organisations* £883,400 *Assets* £40,810,000
TRUSTEES Andrew Littleboy; Charles Gillett; Nigel Cadbury; Robert Marriott; Dr William Southall.
OTHER INFORMATION A total of 193 grants were awarded during 2019/20.
HOW TO APPLY Applications can be made by writing to the correspondent by post or email. Alternatively, applications can be made online through the trust's website. Applications are accepted all year round and are normally considered within a three-month timescale. Letters of application should provide a clear and concise description of the project requiring funding as well as the outcomes and benefits that are likely to be achieved. The trustees also require an outline budget and explanation of how the project is to be funded initially and in the future together with the latest annual report and accounts for the charity.
CONTACT DETAILS Susan Anderson, Trust Manager, Rokesley, University of Birmingham – Selly Oak, Bristol Road, Selly Oak, Birmingham, West Midlands B29 6QF *Tel.* 0121 472 1838 *Email* ecadburytrust@btconnect.com *Website* www.edwardcadburytrust.org.uk

The G. W. Cadbury Charitable Trust

CC NO 231861 **ESTABLISHED** 1922
WHERE FUNDING CAN BE GIVEN USA and UK.
WHO CAN BENEFIT Registered charities.
WHAT IS FUNDED General charitable purposes.
RANGE OF GRANTS Up to £20,000.
SAMPLE GRANTS Rotina UK (£60,000); Permaculture Association (£20,000); Magic Breakfast (£5,000); Bobath Centre (£3,000); Seattle Dance (£1,700).
FINANCES *Financial year end* 05/04/2020 *Income* £243,900 *Total grants* £201,300 *Grants to organisations* £201,300 *Assets* £6,640,000
TRUSTEES Caroline Woodroffe; Jessica Woodroffe; Nick Woodroffe; Peter Boal; Jennifer Boal; Lyndall Boal.
OTHER INFORMATION Grants were awarded to charities in the UK (£106,500) and the USA (£90,500) during the year.
HOW TO APPLY Contact the correspondent for further information.
CONTACT DETAILS The Trustees, c/o BDO LLP, Two Snowhill, Birmingham B4 6GA *Tel.* 0121 265 7288

William A. Cadbury Charitable Trust

CC NO 213629 **ESTABLISHED** 1923
WHERE FUNDING CAN BE GIVEN West Midlands, especially Birmingham and to a lesser extent the UK, Ireland and overseas.
WHO CAN BENEFIT Registered charities; CICs.
WHAT IS FUNDED Birmingham and the West Midlands: community action; vulnerable groups; advice, mediation and counselling; education and training; the environment and conservation; medical research and healthcare; the arts; people affected by the criminal justice system. In the UK – The Religious Society of Friends. Ireland – peace and reconciliation. International development – mainly focused on West Africa.
WHAT IS NOT FUNDED Individuals (whether for research, expeditions, educational purposes or medical treatment); projects concerned with travel, adventure, sports or recreation; organisations which are based outside the UK.
TYPE OF GRANT Core costs; development funding; project funding. Grants are normally one-off.
RANGE OF GRANTS Small grants up to £2,000; large grants usually range from £10,000 to £20,000.
SAMPLE GRANTS Trinity Christian Centre Trust (£42,000); United Purpose (£40,000); Big Brum Theatre in Education Company Ltd (£34,000);

West Mercia Women's Aid (£25,000); HALOW (Birmingham) (£12,000); Hereford Cathedral Perpetual Trust (£5,000); Dorset Opera (£3,000).

FINANCES *Financial year end* 31/03/2020 *Income* £1,280,000 *Total grants* £1,010,000 *Grants to organisations* £1,010,000 *Assets* £4,840,000

TRUSTEES Margaret Salmon; Rupert Cadbury; Sarah Stafford; Katherine Cadbury; Adrian Thomas; John Penny; Sophy Blandy; Janine Cobain; Victoria Mohan.

OTHER INFORMATION Grants were distributed as follows: West Midlands (79%); international development (8%); UK (6%); Ireland (4%). Grants for international development totalled £120,400 in 2019/20.

HOW TO APPLY Grant applications can be submitted on-line (preferred) or by post. Applications should include the following information: charity registration number; a description of the charity's aims and achievements; an outline and budget for the project; the grant programme to which the organisation is applying; details of projects previously funded by the trust (if applicable); details of funds raised to date and the current shortfall. Small grants (up to a maximum of £2,000) are awarded monthly. The trustees meet in May and November to award large grants ranging in value from £10,000 to £20,000 with an occasional maximum of £50,000. The cut-off for applications to the May meeting is early March while for November the cut-off is early to mid-September.

CONTACT DETAILS The Trustees, Rokesley, University of Birmingham, Bristol Road, Selly Oak, Birmingham, West Midlands B29 6QF *Tel.* 0121 472 1464 *Email* info@wa-cadbury.org.uk *Website* www.wa-cadbury.org.uk

■ The Cadbury Foundation

CC NO 1050482 **ESTABLISHED** 1935

WHERE FUNDING CAN BE GIVEN Charities close to Cadbury sites in the UK and Ireland.

WHO CAN BENEFIT Registered charities and voluntary organisations.

WHAT IS FUNDED Skill development; sustainability; disability sport.

SAMPLE GRANTS British Paralympic Association, Health for Life in Primary Schools (£100,000 each); Grocery Aid (£50,000); Bourneville Bookfest (£25,000); Age Concern Crediton (£5,000); Sandwell Advocacy (£2,500).

FINANCES *Financial year end* 31/12/2019 *Income* £642,000 *Total grants* £617,600 *Grants to organisations* £617,600 *Assets* £97,100

TRUSTEES Eoin Kellet; Denise Chester; Lisa Crane; Louise Stigant; Joshua Towson; Clive Jones.

OTHER INFORMATION The Cadbury Foundation was set up in 1935 in recognition of the company founders George and Richard Cadbury and their investment in the welfare of their employees and wider communities. In 2010 Kraft Foods Inc. gained control of Cadbury plc. In 2012 Kraft Foods Inc. was split into Kraft Food Group plc and Mondelēz which now funds the Cadbury Foundation.

HOW TO APPLY The trustees actively seek out projects to support and therefore do not accept any unsolicited requests for funding.

CONTACT DETAILS Kelly Farrell, Community Affairs Manager, PO Box 12, Bourneville, Birmingham, West Midlands B30 2LU *Tel.* 0121 787 2421 *Email* kelly.farrell@mdlz.com *Website* https://www.cadbury.co.uk/cadbury-foundation

■ The Barrow Cadbury Trust

CC NO 1115476 **ESTABLISHED** 1920

WHERE FUNDING CAN BE GIVEN UK and overseas, with a preference for Birmingham and the Black Country (Wolverhampton, Dudley, West Bromwich, Smethwick or Sandwell).

WHO CAN BENEFIT Charities; voluntary organisations; preferably grassroots community groups and user-led projects.

WHAT IS FUNDED Criminal justice; migration; social and economic justice.

TYPE OF GRANT Projects; recurring costs; running expenditure; research.

SAMPLE GRANTS A list of the trust's funded projects is provided on its website.

FINANCES *Financial year end* 31/03/2020 *Income* £3,950,000 *Total grants* £3,930,000 *Grants to organisations* £3,930,000 *Assets* £72,350,000

TRUSTEES Erica Cadbury; Nicola Cadbury; Esther McConnell; Cathy Pharoah; Tasmin Rupprechter; Harry Serle; Jack Serle; Steven Skakel; Anna Southall; Omar Khan.

OTHER INFORMATION The trust also provides social investment. It will consider investments which further the aims of the charity to promote social justice.

HOW TO APPLY Applicants should initially complete an enquiry form which is available on the trust's website. Applicants can then complete the application form once they have discussed the project with the trust and have been asked to make an application. Applications can be made at any time.

CONTACT DETAILS The Trustees, Kean House, 6 Kean Street, London WC2B 4AS *Tel.* 020 7632 9075 *Email* general@barrowcadbury.org.uk *Website* www.barrowcadbury.org.uk

■ The Edward and Dorothy Cadbury Trust

CC NO 1107327 **ESTABLISHED** 1928

WHERE FUNDING CAN BE GIVEN West Midlands and Worcestershire.

WHO CAN BENEFIT Registered charities.

WHAT IS FUNDED The trust continues to support, where appropriate, the interests of the founders and the particular charitable interests of the trustees. Grants are made under five main headings: arts and culture; community projects and integration; compassionate support; education and training and conservation and the environment.

WHAT IS NOT FUNDED Individuals.

TYPE OF GRANT Grants are usually made on a one-off basis for a specific purpose or part of a project.

RANGE OF GRANTS £500 to £5,000.

SAMPLE GRANTS Movement Centre – Shropshire (£5,100); Heart of England Community Foundation (£5,000); Birmingham Hippodrome (£4,000); Donna Louise Hospice (£3,300); Caring for Communities and People (£2,500); Special Olympics (£2,000); RSPB Sandwell Valley (£1,400); Hope for Justice and Sandwell Youth in Action (£1,000 each).

FINANCES *Financial year end* 05/04/2020 *Income* £224,600 *Total grants* £180,500 *Grants to organisations* £180,500 *Assets* £7,460,000

TRUSTEES Philippa Ward; Susan Anfilogoff; Julia Gillett; Julie Cadbury; Dr Johanna Russell; Jayne Higgins.

OTHER INFORMATION Grants were awarded to 111 organisations during 2019/20.

HOW TO APPLY Application forms can be downloaded from the trust's website and may be submitted at any time either online, by post or by email. The website states that application forms must be supported with the following: a letter detailing the funding required, the outcomes and benefits the project is intended to achieve, a project budget and a copy of the latest annual report and accounts (if these are not available on the Charity Commission's website). Applications are usually considered within three months. Applications that fall outside the trust's areas of interest may not be considered or acknowledged.
CONTACT DETAILS Susan Anderson, Trust Manager, Rokesley, University of Birmingham – Selly Oak, Bristol Road, Selly Oak, Birmingham, West Midlands B29 6QF *Tel.* 0121 472 1838 *Email* e-dcadburytrust@btconnect.com *Website* www.e-dcadburytrust.org.uk

■ The George Cadbury Trust

CC NO 1040999 **ESTABLISHED** 1924
WHERE FUNDING CAN BE GIVEN England, with a preference for the West Midlands and Gloucestershire.
WHO CAN BENEFIT Registered charities.
WHAT IS FUNDED General charitable purposes.
RANGE OF GRANTS Grants up to £25,000.
SAMPLE GRANTS Dean and Chapter Gloucester Cathedral For Dorothea Hoyland Choral (£25,000); Blood Bikes (£20,000); Avoncroft Museum (£13,000); UNICEF (£10,000); Worgan Trust (£5,000); Warwickshire Wildlife Trust (£3,000); Feedback Madagascar (£1,000).
FINANCES *Financial year end* 05/04/2020 *Income* £442,800 *Total grants* £317,100 *Grants to organisations* £317,100 *Assets* £15,200,000
TRUSTEES Roger Cadbury; Benedict Cadbury; Angela Cadbury; Mark Cadbury; Timothy Cadbury.
OTHER INFORMATION Grants were made to 119 charities during the year.
HOW TO APPLY Contact the correspondent for further information.
CONTACT DETAILS The Trustees, c/o BDO LLP, 2 Snow Hill, Birmingham B4 6GA *Tel.* 0121 265 7288

■ The Cadogan Charity

CC NO 247773 **ESTABLISHED** 1966
WHERE FUNDING CAN BE GIVEN UK, with a preference for London and Scotland.
WHO CAN BENEFIT Registered charities.
WHAT IS FUNDED Social welfare; medical research; military charities; conservation and the environment; education; animal welfare.
TYPE OF GRANT Support is usually given over one to two years, although some one-off grants may be made.
RANGE OF GRANTS Mostly £1,000 to £10,000.
SAMPLE GRANTS Natural History (£250,000); London Playing Fields Foundation (£140,000); Glass Door (£100,000); The Prince's Trust (£20,000); See Saw (£5,000).
FINANCES *Financial year end* 05/04/2020 *Income* £2,520,000 *Total grants* £2,480,000 *Grants to organisations* £2,480,000 *Assets* £65,240,000
TRUSTEES Lady Anna-Karina Thomson; Rt Hon. The Earl Cadogan; Countess Cadogan; Viscount Chelsea.
OTHER INFORMATION Grants were broken down as follows: social welfare (£824,000); military charities (£720,500); medical research (£308,000); conservation and the environment (£305,000).
HOW TO APPLY Apply in writing to the correspondent.
CONTACT DETAILS Paul Loutit, Secretary to the Trustees, 10 Duke of York Square, London SW3 4LY *Tel.* 020 7730 4567 *Email* paul.loutit@cadogan.co.uk

■ Community Foundation for Calderdale

CC NO 1002722 **ESTABLISHED** 1991
WHERE FUNDING CAN BE GIVEN Calderdale.
WHO CAN BENEFIT Registered charities; unregistered charities; CICs; social enterprises; hospices; places of worship; schools; individuals; PTAs.
WHAT IS FUNDED General charitable purposes including: homelessness and housing; poverty and disadvantage; community cohesion.
WHAT IS NOT FUNDED A list of exclusions can be found on the foundation's website.
TYPE OF GRANT Capital costs; project funding; seed funding/start-up funding; core/revenue costs.
SAMPLE GRANTS Space@FieldLane (£110,000); Calderdale Wellbeing (£74,700); Age UK Calderdale and Kirklees (£28,000); Ryburn United Junior FC (£10,000); Lovebread CIC (£5,000); All Saints Church (£3,000); Cycling Without Age (£1,500); Lee Mount Primary School (£400).
FINANCES *Financial year end* 30/06/2019 *Income* £2,000,000 *Total grants* £1,354,400 *Grants to organisations* £1,300,000 *Assets* £12,400,000
TRUSTEES Brenda Hodgson; Alison Haskins; Lee Kenny; Christopher Harris; Dr Roger Moore; Heidi Bingham; Rachel Dilley; Zohrah Zancudi; Richard Blackburn; Peter Sleigh.
OTHER INFORMATION This is one of the 46 UK community foundations, which distribute funding for a wide range of purposes. As with all community foundations, there are a number of donor-advised funds managed on behalf of individuals, families and charitable trusts. Grant schemes tend to change frequently; consult the foundation's website for details of current programmes and up-to-date deadlines. The 2018/19 accounts were the latest available at the time of writing (January 2021). Grants were made to 708 individuals and totalled £54,400.
HOW TO APPLY Potential applicants are advised to visit the community foundation's website or contact its grants team to find the most suitable funding stream.
CONTACT DETAILS The Trustees, The 1855 Building (first floor), Discovery Road, Halifax, West Yorkshire HX1 2NG *Tel.* 01422 438738 *Email* grants@cffc.co.uk *Website* www.cffc.co.uk

■ Callendar Charitable Trust

OSCR NO SC016609 **ESTABLISHED** 1072
WHERE FUNDING CAN BE GIVEN Scotland and other parts of the UK.
WHO CAN BENEFIT Charitable organisations; hospices; churches.
WHAT IS FUNDED General charitable purposes including: the advancement of religion; education; well-being; social welfare.
RANGE OF GRANTS Up to £7,000, but generally £2,000 and under.
SAMPLE GRANTS Strathcarron Hospice (£7,000); Church of Scotland and Thistle Foundation (£2,500 each); Capability Scotland and Seagull

Trust (£2,000 each); Coldstream Guards Charitable Trust (£1,500); Sense in Scotland and Sightsavers (£1,250 each); Médecins Sans Frontières (£750).

FINANCES *Financial year end* 05/04/2020
Income £87,000 *Total grants* £74,800
Grants to organisations £74,800
Assets £1,680,000

OTHER INFORMATION Grants were awarded to 38 organisations during the year.

HOW TO APPLY Contact the correspondent for further information.

CONTACT DETAILS The Trustees, c/o Anderson Strathern LLP, 1 Rutland Court, Edinburgh EH3 8EY

■ The Calleva Foundation

CC NO 1078808 **ESTABLISHED** 1999

WHERE FUNDING CAN BE GIVEN London; Hampshire.

WHO CAN BENEFIT Charitable organisations.

WHAT IS FUNDED Education and academic research; children's holidays; social services; medical research; international relief; the environment; animal welfare.

TYPE OF GRANT Project funding.

SAMPLE GRANTS Kew Phylogenomic Research Project (£400,000); Reading University (£200,000); House of Good Health (£30,000); Silchester Playground Association (£500).

FINANCES *Financial year end* 31/12/2019
Income £7,000,000 *Total grants* £2,120,000
Grants to organisations £2,120,000
Assets £4,150,000

TRUSTEES Caroline Butt; Stephen Butt.

OTHER INFORMATION Grants were broken down as follows: education and academic research (£1.95 million); international relief (£73,000); medical research (£33,400); social services (£25,600); the environment (£17,000); children's holidays (£13,500); animal welfare (£1,000).

HOW TO APPLY The foundation does not accept unsolicited applications.

CONTACT DETAILS The Trustees, PO Box 22554, London W8 5GN *Tel.* 020 8638 8653 *Email* contactcalleva@btopenworld.com

■ Barbara and Derek Calrow Charitable Foundation

CC NO 1178695 **ESTABLISHED** 2018

WHERE FUNDING CAN BE GIVEN Manchester and Bolton.

WHO CAN BENEFIT Charitable organisations.

WHAT IS FUNDED General charitable purposes.

SAMPLE GRANTS A list of beneficiaries was not included in the annual report and accounts.

FINANCES *Financial year end* 31/03/2020
Income £128,100 *Total grants* £130,200
Grants to organisations £130,200
Assets £32,400

TRUSTEES Robert Campbell; Robert Calrow; Barbara Calrow; Julie Jones.

HOW TO APPLY Contact the correspondent for further information.

CONTACT DETAILS The Trustees, 2 Stonehouse, Chapeltown Road, Bromley Cross, Bolton BL7 9NB *Tel.* 01204 309523 *Email* derekcalrow@me.com

■ The Cambridgeshire Community Foundation

CC NO 1103314 **ESTABLISHED** 2003

WHERE FUNDING CAN BE GIVEN Cambridgeshire.

WHO CAN BENEFIT Registered charities; CICs; social enterprises; schools; parent teacher associations; hospitals; hospices; religious bodies/institutions; local authorities; individuals.

WHAT IS FUNDED General charitable purposes including: social welfare; community development; health; children and young people; families; the environment.

WHAT IS NOT FUNDED See the foundation's website for a full list of exclusions.

TYPE OF GRANT Capital costs; core/revenue costs; project funding.

RANGE OF GRANTS The majority of the grants awarded are for small amounts of between £500 and £5,000.

SAMPLE GRANTS A list of beneficiaries was not included in the annual report and accounts.

FINANCES *Financial year end* 31/03/2020
Income £2,770,000 *Total grants* £2,310,000
Grants to organisations £2,310,000
Assets £7,800,000

TRUSTEES Simon Humphrey; Caroline Stenner; Linda Sinclair; Claire Davis; Stephen Catling; Dr Joanna Slota-Newson; Alison Griffiths; Elizabeth Damazer; Dr Gareth Thomas; Stuart Thompson; Christopher Parkhouse.

OTHER INFORMATION This is one of the 46 UK community foundations, which distribute funding for a wide range of purposes. As with all community foundations, there are a number of donor-advised funds managed on behalf of individuals, families and charitable trusts. Grant schemes tend to change frequently – consult the foundation's website for details of current programmes and up-to-date deadlines.

HOW TO APPLY Potential applicants are advised to visit the community foundation's website or contact its grants team to find the most suitable funding stream.

CONTACT DETAILS The Grants Team, Hangar One, The Airport, Newmarket Road, Cambridge CB5 8TG *Tel.* 01223 410535 *Email* info@cambscf.org.uk *Website* www.cambscf.org.uk

■ Camden Giving

CC NO 1174463 **ESTABLISHED** 2017

WHERE FUNDING CAN BE GIVEN Camden.

WHO CAN BENEFIT Registered charities; not-for-profit organisations; CICs; CIOs; schools; social enterprises.

WHAT IS FUNDED Activities that benefit the people who live and work in Camden including those that address: poverty and inequality; social isolation; employment; improving mental and physical health.

WHAT IS NOT FUNDED A full list of exclusions for each grant programme can be found on the website.

TYPE OF GRANT Project funding; core costs.

RANGE OF GRANTS Up to £100,000.

SAMPLE GRANTS Little Village (£100,000); Steel Pan Trust (£49,000); Samuel Lithgow Youth Centre (£33,000); Contemporary Dance Trust Ltd – The Place (£10,000); North London Cares (£5,900); Angel Community Canalboat Trust (£2,000); Somali Youth Development Resource Centre (£1,500); Hopscotch Asian Women's Centre (£771).

FINANCES *Financial year end* 31/03/2020 *Income* £2,980,000 *Total grants* £2,410,000 *Grants to organisations* £2,410,000 *Assets* £666,900

TRUSTEES Rose Alexander; Hafsa Mohammed; Mahfuz Sadique; Allan Sutherland; Dominic Pinkney; Simon Pitkeathley; Sue Wilby; Graham Dyer; Tom Holliss; Nathan Dyke; Jannah Mujib.

OTHER INFORMATION During 2019/20, 114 grants were awarded, with the majority of funding going to social cohesion projects. The charity acts as a hyperlocal community foundation for Camden, providing additional in-kind support for charities in the area.

HOW TO APPLY Information on eligibility and opening dates for funding rounds can be found on the website. The charity strongly advises that prospective applicants get in touch before making an application, to talk through the criteria for funding. This can be done by attending one of the charity's events, booking an appointment or by emailing admin@camdengiving.org.uk.

CONTACT DETAILS The Grants Team, 5–7 Buck Street, Camden Town, London NW1 8NJ *Tel.* 07872 534079 or 0771 759 5605 *Email* admin@camdengiving.org.uk *Website* https://www.camdengiving.org.uk

The Campden Charities Trustee

CC NO 1104616 **ESTABLISHED** 1629

WHERE FUNDING CAN BE GIVEN Kensington.

WHO CAN BENEFIT Registered charities.

WHAT IS FUNDED Social welfare; education and training; debt and money advice; employment advice.

TYPE OF GRANT Project funding; capital costs.

SAMPLE GRANTS Volunteer Centre (£132,500); Nova (£69,000); Nucleus Legal Advice Centre (£55,400); Westway Community Transport (£40,000); Turning Point (£36,000).

FINANCES *Financial year end* 31/03/2020 *Income* £4,040,000 *Total grants* £2,299,900 *Grants to organisations* £389,900 *Assets* £149,800,000

TRUSTEES Dr Christopher Townsley; Justine Soulieux; Sam Berwick; Dr Christopher Davis; Julie Mills; Richard Waller-Arnott; Robert Orr-Ewing; Frances Manthos; Charles Manners; David Banks; Marta Rodkina; Roberta Atkinson; Daniel Hawkins.

OTHER INFORMATION The charity funds partner organisations and has a referral funding programme. The referral funding works by proving funding to not-for-profit organisations for each individual they refer to the charity's grant programmes.

HOW TO APPLY Referral forms and further information on applications can be found on the charity's website.

CONTACT DETAILS The Trustees, Studios 3 and 4, 27A Pembridge Villas, London W11 3EP *Tel.* 020 7243 0551 *Email* Contact form on website *Website* www.campdencharities.org.uk

Canary Wharf Contractors Fund

CC NO 1097007 **ESTABLISHED** 2002

WHERE FUNDING CAN BE GIVEN East London.

WHO CAN BENEFIT Individuals; charities and community groups.

WHAT IS FUNDED Communities; social welfare; education; people engaged in the construction industry; sport and recreation.

TYPE OF GRANT Project costs.

RANGE OF GRANTS Up to £40,000 but usually between £500 and £20,000.

SAMPLE GRANTS University College Hospital London Cancer Fund (£40,000); London Air Ambulance (£20,000); Spread a Smile (£13,400); Construction Youth (£10,000); Oasis Hub Waterloo (£5,000); Stoke Newington Cricket Club (£4,000); South London Special League (£1,300).

FINANCES *Financial year end* 31/03/2020 *Income* £407,300 *Total grants* £297,300 *Grants to organisations* £297,300 *Assets* £241,600

TRUSTEES Giles Woolley; Nicholas Curran; Alec Vallintine.

OTHER INFORMATION In 2019/20, 24 grants were awarded.

HOW TO APPLY Contact the correspondent for further information.

CONTACT DETAILS Alan Ruddy, Secretary, Ruddy Joinery Ltd, Enterprise Way, Flitwick, Bedford MK45 5BS *Tel.* 07803 730360

The Candy Foundation

CC NO 1176337 **ESTABLISHED** 2017

WHERE FUNDING CAN BE GIVEN Worldwide.

WHO CAN BENEFIT Registered charities.

WHAT IS FUNDED General charitable purposes.

WHAT IS NOT FUNDED Individuals.

SAMPLE GRANTS A list of beneficiaries was not included in the annual report and accounts.

FINANCES *Financial year end* 31/12/2019 *Income* £200,000 *Total grants* £200,000 *Grants to organisations* £200,000 *Assets* £0

TRUSTEES Christopher Sullivan; Kevin Cahill; Nicholas Candy; David Williams; Holly Vukadinovic.

HOW TO APPLY Unsolicited applications are not accepted.

CONTACT DETAILS The Trustees, 49 Upper Brook Street, London W1K 2BR *Tel.* 020 3841 9008

The Frederick and Phyllis Cann Trust

CC NO 1087863 **ESTABLISHED** 1998

WHERE FUNDING CAN BE GIVEN UK, with a preference for Northamptonshire.

WHO CAN BENEFIT Registered charities; CICs; hospices; hospitals.

WHAT IS FUNDED Animal welfare; welfare of children; safety at sea.

TYPE OF GRANT Capital costs.

RANGE OF GRANTS £500 to £5,000.

SAMPLE GRANTS RNLI (£5,000); East Northants Community Services (£3,000); Lakeland Daycare Hospice and Starlight Children's Foundation (£2,000 each); RSPCA (£1,600); Cats Protection, Lymphoma Association and Tall Ships (£1,000 each); The Learning Bus (£500).

FINANCES *Financial year end* 05/04/2020 *Income* £62,900 *Total grants* £66,100 *Grants to organisations* £66,100 *Assets* £2,340,000

TRUSTEES Michael Percival; David Sharp; Keith Panter; Philip Saunderson; Ian James.

HOW TO APPLY Contact the correspondent for further information.

CONTACT DETAILS Angela Moon, c/o Hewitsons, Elgin House, Billing Road, Northampton, Northamptonshire NN1 5AU *Tel.* 01604 233233 *Email* angelamoon@hewitsons.com

■ Cannon Charitable Trust

CC NO 1080818 **ESTABLISHED** 2000
WHERE FUNDING CAN BE GIVEN UK; overseas.
WHO CAN BENEFIT Charitable organisations; individuals.
WHAT IS FUNDED Religious education; social welfare.
RANGE OF GRANTS Up to £80,000.
SAMPLE GRANTS Wlodowa Charity and Rehabilitation Trust (£80,000); The ABC Trust (£62,000); Karen Hatzolas Doros Alei Siach (£45,000); Bels Ruchel D'Satmer London (£34,500); Amut Hatzdokoh Trust (£33,000).
FINANCES *Financial year end* 31/01/2020 *Income* £758,100 *Total grants* £702,100 *Grants to organisations* £702,100 *Assets* £187,000
TRUSTEES Robert Tauber; Juliana Tauber.
HOW TO APPLY Contact the correspondent for further information.
CONTACT DETAILS The Trustees, Ashley Works, Ashley Road, Tottenham Hale, London N17 9LJ *Tel.* 020 8885 9430

■ Card Factory Foundation

CC NO 1180081 **ESTABLISHED** 2018
WHERE FUNDING CAN BE GIVEN UK.
WHO CAN BENEFIT Not-for-profit organisations, community groups and individuals.
WHAT IS FUNDED General charitable purposes.
TYPE OF GRANT Project funding; capital costs.
RANGE OF GRANTS Up to £2,500.
SAMPLE GRANTS A list of beneficiaries was not included in the annual report and accounts.
FINANCES *Financial year end* 28/02/2019 *Income* £1,454,000 *Total grants* £570,000 *Grants to organisations* £570,000 *Assets* £873,000
TRUSTEES Caroline Thompson-Hayes; Chris Beck; Geoff Pestel; Joanne Mary York; Julie Hardy; Nicola Louise Rogerson; Jane Rowney; Susan Glass.
OTHER INFORMATION The foundation's Community Grant fund supports charitable causes that benefit the communities of the company's colleagues and stores. The 2018/19 accounts were the latest available at the time of writing (June 2021).
HOW TO APPLY Applications can be made via the foundation's website.
CONTACT DETAILS The Trustees, Century House, Brunel Road, Wakefield 41 Industrial Estate, Wakefield, West Yorkshire WF2 0XG *Email* trustees@cardfactoryfoundation.org *Website* https://www.cardfactoryinvestors.com/foundation

■ CareTech Foundation

CC NO 1182567 **ESTABLISHED** 2017
WHERE FUNDING CAN BE GIVEN UK and Pakistan.
WHO CAN BENEFIT Registered charitable organisations.
WHAT IS FUNDED Disability; skills development; local community poverty relief projects.
RANGE OF GRANTS £5,000 to £100,000.
SAMPLE GRANTS British Asian Trust (£100,000); Birkbeck College (£83,300); EY Foundation (£30,000); National Care Force and Care Workers Charity (£12,500 each); Depaul UK (£9,500); Skills for Care (£6,900).
FINANCES *Financial year end* 30/09/2020 *Income* £4,950,000 *Total grants* £418,100 *Grants to organisations* £300,100 *Assets* £4,500,000
TRUSTEES Adrienne Kelbie; Michael Adams; Haroon Sheikh; Charles Cheffings; Farouq Sheikh; Akbar Sheikh; Navshir Jaffer; Jessica Taplin; Michael Pratt; Lucy Arciuolo; Christopher Dickinson.
OTHER INFORMATION Grants to individuals totalled £118,000.
HOW TO APPLY Each grant programme has an eligibility test, which should be completed by prospective applicants before making an application. If deemed eligible, applications can be made online. Paper or digital/word copies of the application form can be requested by email.
CONTACT DETAILS The Trustees, Metropolitan House, 3 Darkes Lane, Potters Lane EN6 1AG *Tel.* 01707 601800 *Email* info@caretechfoundation.org.uk *Website* https://www.caretechfoundation.org.uk

■ W. A. Cargill Charitable Trust

OSCR NO SC012076 **ESTABLISHED** 1992
WHERE FUNDING CAN BE GIVEN Scotland.
WHO CAN BENEFIT Registered charities.
WHAT IS FUNDED Care of the older people; care and support of children; medical research; education; art culture and heritage; science.
SAMPLE GRANTS A list of beneficiaries was not included in the annual report and accounts.
FINANCES *Financial year end* 30/11/2019 *Income* £178,900 *Total grants* £95,500 *Grants to organisations* £95,500 *Assets* £6,080,000
OTHER INFORMATION The 2018/19 accounts were the latest available at the time of writing (June 2021).
HOW TO APPLY Contact the correspondent for further information.
CONTACT DETAILS The Trustees, c/o Miller Beckett and Jackson Solicitors, 190 St Vincent Street, Glasgow G2 5SP

■ The W. A. Cargill Fund

OSCR NO SC008456 **ESTABLISHED** 1962
WHERE FUNDING CAN BE GIVEN Glasgow and the west of Scotland.
WHO CAN BENEFIT Registered charities; charitable organisations; hospices; schools.
WHAT IS FUNDED The prevention or relief of poverty; education; religion; the advancement of health; citizenship or community development; arts/culture/heritage; science; relief of older people; ill health; disability; social and economic disadvantage.
RANGE OF GRANTS Up to £50,000 but generally £500 to £5,000.
SAMPLE GRANTS A list of beneficiaries was not included in the annual report and accounts.
FINANCES *Financial year end* 30/11/2019 *Income* £633,900 *Total grants* £423,800 *Grants to organisations* £423,800 *Assets* £20,350,000
OTHER INFORMATION The 2018/19 accounts were the latest available at the time of writing (June 2021).The range is an estimation based on previous accounts. The most recent accounts (2018/19) do not give a full breakdown of grants made to organisations.
HOW TO APPLY Apply in writing to the correspondent, including a copy of your latest accounts or details of its financial position.
CONTACT DETAILS The Trustees, c/o Miller Beckett and Jackson Ltd, 190 St Vincent Street, Glasgow G2 5SP *Tel.* 0141 204 2833 *Email* nfyfe@millerbj.co.uk

■ Carlee Ltd

CC NO 282873 **ESTABLISHED** 1981
WHERE FUNDING CAN BE GIVEN Worldwide.
WHO CAN BENEFIT Jewish organisations.
WHAT IS FUNDED The advancement of religion in accordance with the Orthodox Jewish faith; the relief of poverty; general charitable purposes.
RANGE OF GRANTS £12,500 to £62,000.
SAMPLE GRANTS Mifal Hachesed Vehazdukeh (£62,000); Yeshivo Horomo (£52,400); Tevini Ltd (£38,500); Friends of Beis Chinuch Lebonos (£36,500); Yesamach Levav Trust (£36,000); Friends Of Beis Soroh Schneirer (£29,000); Congregation Sharei Sholom Tchabe Ltd (£27,500); Antryvale Ltd (£27,000); Chevraz Mo'ol Ladol (£25,000); Mercaz Hatorah Belz Machnivkah and Lev Echod One Heart (£22,000 each); Ben Anram Charitable Trust and Toldos Ahron Trust (£20,000 each); Bayis Lepleitos, Beis Ahron Trust, United Torah Association, VHLT Ltd, Yad Vochesed Association and MARS (£15,000 each); Friends Of Eidah Chareidis Jerusalem (£14,400); Ezer V'Hatzulah Ltd and The Toras Chesed Y (£12,500 each).
FINANCES *Financial year end* 31/03/2020
Income £532,350 *Total grants* £752,600
Grants to organisations £752,600
Assets £1,150,000
TRUSTEES Bernard Stroh; Ephraim Bleier; Alexandra Solomon Singer.
OTHER INFORMATION Grants were awarded to more than 23 organisations during the year.
HOW TO APPLY Contact the correspondent for further information.
CONTACT DETAILS The Trustee, 32 Paget Road, London N16 5NQ *Tel.* 020 8802 4782 *Email* admin@carleeltd.org

■ The Carlton Hayes Mental Health Charity

CC NO 219783 **ESTABLISHED** 1834
WHERE FUNDING CAN BE GIVEN Leicestershire; Leicester City; Rutland.
WHO CAN BENEFIT Charitable organisations.
WHAT IS FUNDED Mental health.
TYPE OF GRANT Project funding.
RANGE OF GRANTS Up to £55,000.
SAMPLE GRANTS Raising Health (£55,000); Leicester Charity Link (£30,000); Active Wesley Hall (£16,000); Schizophrenic Support Group (£2,000); Mosaic (£1,500).
FINANCES *Financial year end* 31/03/2020
Income £196,100 *Total grants* £176,400
Grants to organisations £176,400
Assets £5,210,000
TRUSTEES Mark Newcombe; Ashok Kataria; Rachael Stembridge; Richard Foster; William Liquorish; Edward Cassidy; Dr Penny Campling; Adam Lowe; Marie Bradley.
OTHER INFORMATION Grants were awarded to 14 organisations during the year.
HOW TO APPLY Application forms are available to download from the charity's website.
CONTACT DETAILS Helen Pole, Assistant to the Clerk, Shakespeare Martineau, Two Colton Square, Leicester LE1 1QH *Tel.* 0116 254 5454 ext 6235 *Email* Contact form on website *Website* www.carltonhayes.co.uk

■ The Antonio Carluccio Foundation

CC NO 1167646 **ESTABLISHED** 2016
WHERE FUNDING CAN BE GIVEN UK and overseas.
WHO CAN BENEFIT Charities; individuals.
WHAT IS FUNDED Prevention and relief of poverty and hunger; the training of chefs and cooks.
TYPE OF GRANT Project funding.
RANGE OF GRANTS £1,000 to £25,000.
SAMPLE GRANTS Action Against Hunger (£25,000); Magic Breakfast (£10,000); Community Drug and Alcohol Recovery Services (£9,000); Activiteens (£8,500); Body and Soul (£5,000); Clothe and Feed (£2,500); Nurture through Nature (£1,500); Sherbourne (£1,000).
FINANCES *Financial year end* 30/06/2020
Income £19,200 *Total grants* £674,700
Grants to organisations £674,700
Assets £319,600
TRUSTEES Andrea Stevenson; Steven Berry; Simon Kossoff.
OTHER INFORMATION During 2019/20 grants were awarded to 90 organisations and were distributed under the following headings: education/nutrition (66.2%) and feeding (33.8%).
HOW TO APPLY Contact the correspondent for further information.
CONTACT DETAILS The Trustees, Chamberlain Berry, 27–28 New Road, Chippenham SN15 1HS *Tel.* 01249 461999 *Email* trustees@theantoniocarlucciofoundation.org

■ The Carne Trust

CC NO 1115903 **ESTABLISHED** 2006
WHERE FUNDING CAN BE GIVEN UK.
WHO CAN BENEFIT Registered charities; arts institutions; educational establishments; individuals.
WHAT IS FUNDED Children and young people in the performing arts, especially music and theatre. A number of selected charities are supported on an ongoing basis.
SAMPLE GRANTS Royal Welsh College of Music and Drama (£225,000); Trinity Laban Conservatoire of Music and Dance (£25,000); Royal College of Music (£15,000); Pulp Rocket Theatre (£1,000).
FINANCES *Financial year end* 31/12/2019
Income £420,800 *Total grants* £397,000
Grants to organisations £397,000
Assets £525,400
TRUSTEES SG Kleinwort Hambros Trust Company (UK) Ltd; Philip Carne; Marjorie Carne.
HOW TO APPLY The trust has previously stated that it is the policy of trustees 'to consider all written appeals received, but only successful applications are notified of the trustees' decision'. Applications are considered at the annual trustees' meeting, normally held in June.
CONTACT DETAILS The Trustees, c/o Kleinwort Hambros Trust Company UK, 5th Floor, 8 St James's Square, London SW1Y 4JU *Tel.* 020 3207 7594 *Email* mike.considine@kleinworthambros.com

■ The Carnegie Dunfermline Trust

OSCR NO SC015710 **ESTABLISHED** 1903
WHERE FUNDING CAN BE GIVEN Dunfermline and surrounding areas.
WHO CAN BENEFIT Registered charities; voluntary sector organisations; schools; amateur sports clubs; societies.

WHAT IS FUNDED Projects, activities and schemes with social, community, educational, cultural, sport and recreational purposes.
WHAT IS NOT FUNDED Individuals; closed groups (with the exception of those catering for specialist needs); political, military or sectarian bodies; activities outside the geographic scope of the trust; medical organisations; routine running or salary costs; costs which are the responsibility of a government body.
RANGE OF GRANTS Between £300 and £10,000.
SAMPLE GRANTS Abbot House (£100,000); Fire Station Creative (£1,200); Fife Academy of Performing Arts (£1,000); Queen Anne High School (£800).
FINANCES *Financial year end* 31/12/2019 *Income* £555,500 *Total grants* £124,300 *Grants to organisations* £124,300 *Assets* £17,020,000
TRUSTEES Andrew Croxford; Dr Colin Firth; Cllr Helen Law; Danny McArthur; Janet McCauslin; Gillian Mann; George Murray; Cllr Tony Orton; Red. MaryAnn Rennie; Mike Reid; Fiona Robertson; J. Douglas Scott; David Walker; Ian Wilson; Cllr Derek Glen.
HOW TO APPLY Application forms are available to download from the trust's website.
CONTACT DETAILS Elaine Stewart, Grants Officer, Andrew Carnegie House, Pittencieff Street, Dunfermline, Fife KY12 8AW *Tel.* 01383 749789 *Email* grants@carnegietrust.com *Website* www.andrewcarnegie.co.uk

■ The Carpenters' Company Charitable Trust

CC NO 276996 **ESTABLISHED** 1978
WHERE FUNDING CAN BE GIVEN UK.
WHO CAN BENEFIT Individuals and schools, colleges, universities and other charitable organisations promoting the craft of carpentry.
WHAT IS FUNDED Education and general charitable purposes.
WHAT IS NOT FUNDED Grants are not normally made to individual churches or cathedrals, or to educational establishments having no association to the Carpenters' Company. Funds are usually only available to charities registered with the Charity Commission or exempt from registration.
SAMPLE GRANTS Building Crafts College (£994,200); Carpenters and Dockland Centre (£15,000); Carpenters Primary School (£7,800 each); Institute of Carpenters (£6,000).
FINANCES *Financial year end* 30/06/2019 *Income* £1,640,000 *Total grants* £1,160,000 *Grants to organisations* £1,160,000 *Assets* £31,920,000
TRUSTEES Michael Mathews; Martin Samuel; Alistair Gregory-Smith; Rachel Bower.
OTHER INFORMATION Grants were broken down as follows: craft activities (£1.1. million); religious organisations (£20,200); City of London (£15,300); youth and children's organisations (£9,500); miscellaneous (£1,000). The 2018/19 accounts were the latest available at the time of writing (February 2021).
HOW TO APPLY At the time of writing (March 2021) the trust's website states: 'All funds are currently committed and we are not considering any applications. The website will be updated should this position change.' Previously, the consideration of grants has been delegated to the Charitable Grants Committee which meets three times each year.
CONTACT DETAILS Clerk to the Carpenters' Company, Carpenters' Hall, 1 Throgmorton Avenue, London EC2N 2JJ *Tel.* 020 7588 7001 *Email* info@carpentersco.com *Website* https://www.carpentersco.com/charities/carpenters-company-charitable-trust

■ The Carr-Gregory Trust

CC NO 1085580 **ESTABLISHED** 2001
WHERE FUNDING CAN BE GIVEN London and Bristol.
WHO CAN BENEFIT Charitable organisations.
WHAT IS FUNDED Performing arts; health; social welfare; education.
WHAT IS NOT FUNDED Grants are not awarded for individuals.
SAMPLE GRANTS Royal Academy of Music (£22,500); Alzheimer's Research UK (£10,000); Prisoners' Education Trust (£7,500); National Opera Studio (£5,000); Barbican Centre Trust (£3,000); Great Western Air Ambulance (£2,500); Sound World (£1,000).
FINANCES *Financial year end* 31/12/2019 *Income* £109,600 *Total grants* £101,300 *Grants to organisations* £101,300 *Assets* £611,000
TRUSTEES Russ Carr; Heather Wheelhouse; Linda Carr.
OTHER INFORMATION Grants of over £1,000 were made to 32 organisations during the year. Grants were broken down as follows: education (£34,800); social needs (£24,800); health (£22,800); arts/culture (£19,000).
HOW TO APPLY Contact the correspondent for further information.
CONTACT DETAILS The Trustees, 56 Pembroke Road, Clifton, Bristol BS8 3DT *Tel.* 0117 973 7605

■ The Carrington Charitable Trust

CC NO 265824 **ESTABLISHED** 1973
WHERE FUNDING CAN BE GIVEN UK, with a preference for Buckinghamshire.
WHO CAN BENEFIT Registered charities.
WHAT IS FUNDED General charitable purposes.
RANGE OF GRANTS Mostly up to £1,000.
SAMPLE GRANTS Ashmolean Museum of Art and Archaeology and Royal Shakespeare Company (£10,000 each); Priscilla Bacon Centre for Palliative Care (£5,000); Blind Veterans UK (£1,000); Child Bereavement UK, Marlow Methodist Church and Calibre Audio Library (£500 each); Reeds Foundation (£100).
FINANCES *Financial year end* 05/04/2020 *Income* £111,000 *Total grants* £57,100 *Grants to organisations* £57,100 *Assets* £6,080,000
TRUSTEES Lord Carrington; Jeffrey Cloke; The Hon. Virginia Carrington.
HOW TO APPLY Contact the correspondent for further information.
CONTACT DETAILS Jeffrey Cloke, Trustee, The Courtyard, Manor Farm, Church End, Bledlow, Buckinghamshire HP27 9PD *Tel.* 01844 273508 *Email* clokejeff@gmail.com

■ The Leslie Mary Carter Charitable Trust

CC NO 284782 **ESTABLISHED** 1982
WHERE FUNDING CAN BE GIVEN UK with a strong preference for Norfolk, Suffolk and North Essex.
WHO CAN BENEFIT Registered charities; hospices; churches; uniformed groups.

WHAT IS FUNDED Conservation and restoration, the environment, social welfare; health.
WHAT IS NOT FUNDED Individuals.
TYPE OF GRANT Capital and project costs.
RANGE OF GRANTS Typically £200 to £10,000.
SAMPLE GRANTS Gainsborough's House and Norfolk Wildlife Trust (£10,000 each); Action Medical Research, Combat Stress and The Trussell Trust (£5,000 each); Marie Curie (£3,000); Barn Owl Trust and The Sir Joseph Banks Archive Project (£2,000 each); St John Ambulance (£200).
FINANCES *Financial year end* 31/12/2019
Income £116,900 *Total grants* £116,200
Grants to organisations £110,200
Assets £4,470,000
TRUSTEES Sam Wilson; Martyn Carr; Marycita Wilson; Sara Carr.
OTHER INFORMATION During 2019 the trust awarded grants to 28 organisations.
HOW TO APPLY Apply in writing to the correspondent. The trustees meet every six months to consider applications.
CONTACT DETAILS The Trustees, c/o Birketts LLP, Providence House, 141–145 Princes Street, Ipswich, Suffolk IP1 1QJ *Tel.* 01473 232300

■ The Casey Trust

CC NO 1055726 **ESTABLISHED** 1996
WHERE FUNDING CAN BE GIVEN UK and financially developing countries.
WHO CAN BENEFIT Registered charities.
WHAT IS FUNDED Children (up to the age of 18).
WHAT IS NOT FUNDED Individuals; unregistered organisations; projects that are not exclusively for children.
TYPE OF GRANT Project funding; seed funding/start-up funding. The trustees are looking for start-up projects or identifiable new initiatives within existing projects rather than contributing to recurring events or continuing events.
SAMPLE GRANTS Previous beneficiaries have included: Raw Material (£12,500); World Monuments Fund (£11,000); Buttle UK (£2,500); Acorns (£2,400); The Children's Adventure Farm Trust (£2,300); Lifelites (£2,100); Malaika Kids UK, Motability and Sightsavers (£2,000 each); Street Child – Liberia (£1,800); Perthes Association (£1,600); Sunny Days Children's Fund (£1,500); Edinburgh Young Carers Project and St Luke's Cares (£1,000 each).
FINANCES *Financial year end* 30/06/2019
Income £118,100 *Total grants* £150,500
Grants to organisations £150,500
Assets £4,060,000
TRUSTEES Kenneth Howard; Benjamin Shorten; Sam Howard; Alex Krikler.
OTHER INFORMATION Grants were awarded to 70 organisations during the year. The 2018/19 accounts were the latest available at the time of writing (February 2021).
HOW TO APPLY Appeals may be made in writing to the correspondent, providing a brief outline of your work and project for which the money is required as well as a clear budget and a recent set of accounts, if possible. The trustees ask that you enclose an sae.
CONTACT DETAILS The Trustees, 27 Arkwright Road, London NW3 6BJ *Tel.* 020 7435 9601 *Email* caseytrust@icloud.com *Website* www.caseytrust.org

■ The Castanea Trust

CC NO 1136180 **ESTABLISHED** 2010
WHERE FUNDING CAN BE GIVEN UK.
WHO CAN BENEFIT Registered charities.
WHAT IS FUNDED Ex-service personnel and their families; children who are sick; animal welfare; older people.
RANGE OF GRANTS Up to £10,000.
SAMPLE GRANTS Greek Animal Welfare Fund (£10,000); Blind Veterans UK (£6,000); The Woodland Trust (£4,000); The Royal Star and Garter Homes (£3,000); Katherine House Hospice (£2,000); Mind (£1,000).
FINANCES *Financial year end* 05/04/2020
Income £600,600 *Total grants* £145,000
Grants to organisations £145,000
Assets £9,870,000
TRUSTEES Mark Feeny; Geoffrey Wall; Ian Duncan.
HOW TO APPLY Contact the correspondent for further information.
CONTACT DETAILS Mark Feeny, Trustee, c/o Brabners LLP, Horton House, Exchange Flags, Liverpool, Merseyside L2 3YL *Email* mark.feeny@brabners.com

■ The Castang Foundation

CC NO 1003867 **ESTABLISHED** 1991
WHERE FUNDING CAN BE GIVEN UK.
WHO CAN BENEFIT Registered charities; universities; research institutions.
WHAT IS FUNDED Research into neurodevelopmental disorders in children. This includes research to help understand the causes of disability and research that focusses on the effectiveness of interventions to improve quality of life.
TYPE OF GRANT Research and project funding.
SAMPLE GRANTS Examples of research funded by the foundation can be found on its website.
FINANCES *Financial year end* 05/04/2020
Income £81,800 *Total grants* £149,000
Grants to organisations £149,000
Assets £1,540,000
TRUSTEES Dr Jeremy Parr; Michael Glynn; Dr Ian Burman.
HOW TO APPLY The foundation currently funds in partnership with the National Institute for Health Research and the British Academy of Childhood Disability. See the foundation's website for further details.
CONTACT DETAILS The Trustees, 2 More London Riverside, London SE1 2AP *Tel.* 020 7842 8000 *Email* info@castangfoundation.org.uk *Website* www.castangfoundation.org.uk

■ The Castansa Trust

OSCR NO SC037414 **ESTABLISHED** 2008
WHERE FUNDING CAN BE GIVEN Scotland, with a preference for the Lothians, Glasgow and Dumfries and Galloway.
WHO CAN BENEFIT Registered charities.
WHAT IS FUNDED Education; children and young people; people with dementia or cancer; social inclusion; arts and culture; health; the environment.
WHAT IS NOT FUNDED Individuals.
RANGE OF GRANTS £5,000 to £15,000.
SAMPLE GRANTS A lift of beneficiaries was not provided.
FINANCES *Financial year end* 25/07/2020
Income £1,040,000 *Total grants* £418,000
Grants to organisations £418,000
Assets £2,030,000

OTHER INFORMATION The average success rate for applicants is currently around 1 in 7.
HOW TO APPLY The trust no longer accepts unsolicited applications 'due to a significant number of existing commitments'.
CONTACT DETAILS The Trustees, c/o Turcan Connell, Princes Exchange, 1 Earl Grey Street, Edinburgh EH3 9EE *Website* https://www.turcanconnell.com/the-castansa-trust

■ Catholic Charitable Trust

CC NO 215553 **ESTABLISHED** 1935
WHERE FUNDING CAN BE GIVEN UK and overseas.
WHO CAN BENEFIT Catholic organisations.
WHAT IS FUNDED The traditional teachings of the Roman Catholic faith.
RANGE OF GRANTS Up to £40,000.
SAMPLE GRANTS Missio (£40,700); Society of Saint Pius X – England (£18,000); Little Sisters of the Poor (£6,000); Catholic Trust for England and Wales (£4,000); Hospice of St John and Elizabeth and St Francis Leprosy Guild (£2,000 each); Academy of Sacred Music (£1,500); St James Church – Spanish Place and St Peter's Church Winchester (£1,000 each).
FINANCES *Financial year end* 31/12/2019 *Income* £94,200 *Total grants* £112,500 *Grants to organisations* £112,500 *Assets* £3,010,000
TRUSTEES John Vernor-Miles; Wilfrid Vernor-Miles; David Orr; Jennifer Vernor-Miles.
OTHER INFORMATION During 2019 the made grants to 18 charities.
HOW TO APPLY Apply in writing to the correspondent. The trust's 2019 account state: 'The charity does not invite applications for grants but does consider unsolicited appeals.'
CONTACT DETAILS Wilfrid Vernor-Miles, Trustee, c/o Hunters Solicitors, 9 New Square, London WC2A 3QN *Tel.* 020 7412 0050 *Email* wilfrid.vernormiles@hunterslaw.com

■ Cattanach

OSCR NO SC049833 **ESTABLISHED** 1992
WHERE FUNDING CAN BE GIVEN Scotland.
WHO CAN BENEFIT Registered charities.
WHAT IS FUNDED Prenatal care; projects for children under the age of three; social welfare.
WHAT IS NOT FUNDED Individuals; personal study or travel; hospices and palliative care; animal charities; appliances for illness or disability; organisations concerned with specific diseases; large capital projects (more than £100,000); projects costing less than £3,000; crèches where parents are not involved; organisations or activities where religious content is compulsory for users; general appeals.
TYPE OF GRANT Project funding; core/revenue costs. Grants are often multi-year.
RANGE OF GRANTS From £3,000 to £25,000 with most being around £10,000.
SAMPLE GRANTS Saheliya (£56,000); Toybox Lee Avenue (£44,700); Home Link Family Support (£35,000); Citadel Youth Centre (£30,700); Glasgow Children's Hospital Charity (£17,000); Hilton Family Support (£8,500); Home-Start Clackmannanshire (£5,900); Isle of Jura Development Trust (£1,800).
FINANCES *Financial year end* 31/12/2019 *Income* £517,100 *Total grants* £574,000 *Grants to organisations* £574,000 *Assets* £21,870,000
TRUSTEES Alastair Wilson; Andrew Millington; Ian McLaughlan; Mafe Marwick; Steven Murray; Rory Marsh; Heather Coady; Jennifer Corrigan; Patricia Jackson; Caroline Murray.
HOW TO APPLY Applicants must first register on the trust's website and then a link to an application form will be sent via email. There is a useful list of FAQs on the trust's website. Applications must be made online (those sent on paper or by email are not accepted) and must be submitted along with supporting documents, which are listed on the form. The trustees meet four times a year, usually in February/March, May, August and November – meeting dates are posted on the website.
CONTACT DETAILS Jemma Slater, Grants Officer, Mansfield Traquair Centre, 15 Mansfield Place, 502 Gorgie Road, Edinburgh EH3 6BB *Tel.* 0131 474 6155 *Email* info@cattanach.org.uk *Website* www.cattanach.org.uk

■ The Joseph and Annie Cattle Trust

CC NO 262011 **ESTABLISHED** 1970
WHERE FUNDING CAN BE GIVEN Hull and East Yorkshire.
WHO CAN BENEFIT Charitable organisations.
WHAT IS FUNDED General charitable purposes including: older people; people with disabilities; health; social welfare; children with dyslexia.
TYPE OF GRANT Capital costs; project funding; one-off and recurring grants.
RANGE OF GRANTS Up to £1,000.
SAMPLE GRANTS A list of beneficiaries was not included in the annual report and accounts.
FINANCES *Financial year end* 05/04/2020 *Income* £324,400 *Total grants* £306,000 *Grants to organisations* £306,000 *Assets* £9,300,000
TRUSTEES Paul Edwards; Christopher Munday; S. C. Jowers; Ann Hughes.
HOW TO APPLY Application forms are available from the trust's website.
CONTACT DETAILS The Trustees, PO Box 23, Patrington, Hull, East Yorkshire HU12 0WF *Tel.* 07802 873991 *Email* rogercattletrust@protonmail.com *Website* www.jacattletrust.co.uk

■ The Wilfrid and Constance Cave Foundation

CC NO 241900 **ESTABLISHED** 1965
WHERE FUNDING CAN BE GIVEN England and Wales, with a preference for Cornwall, Devon, Somerset, Dorset, Wiltshire, Berkshire, Oxfordshire, Gloucestershire and Worcestershire.
WHO CAN BENEFIT Charitable organisations; registered charities; hospices; hospitals; schools and colleges; museums.
WHAT IS FUNDED General charitable purposes; education; the arts; culture; science; health; community development; animal conservation.
TYPE OF GRANT Capital costs; core/revenue costs; seed funding/start-up funding; project funding; unrestricted funding.
RANGE OF GRANTS Grants range from £1,000 up to £36,000.
SAMPLE GRANTS A list of beneficiaries was not included in the annual report and accounts.
FINANCES *Financial year end* 05/04/2020 *Income* £158,600 *Total grants* £164,100 *Grants to organisations* £164,100 *Assets* £4,340,000
TRUSTEES Mark Pickin; William Howells; Lucy Howells; Emily Pickin.

OTHER INFORMATION The Story Museum (£36,000); Exmoor Young Voices (£20,000); Thames Hospice (£12,000); Brushford Parish Hall Car Park (£10,000); King's Hall Adventure Playground (£5,000); Pilton Academy (£3,000); Henry Bissell Spinal Memorial Fund (£1,000).
HOW TO APPLY The foundation will not respond to unsolicited appeals.
CONTACT DETAILS Lorraine Olsen, Secretary, New Lodge Farm, Drift Road, Winkfield, Windsor, Berkshire SL4 4QQ *Tel.* 01344 890351 *Email* secretary@cavefoundation.org.uk *Website* https://www.cavefoundation.org.uk

■ The Cayo Foundation

CC NO 1080607 **ESTABLISHED** 1999
WHERE FUNDING CAN BE GIVEN UK.
WHO CAN BENEFIT Registered charities.
WHAT IS FUNDED General charitable purposes; medical research; crime prevention; children and young people; performing arts.
RANGE OF GRANTS £1,000 to £125,000.
SAMPLE GRANTS A list of beneficiaries was not included in the annual report and accounts.
FINANCES *Financial year end* 30/09/2019 *Income* £4,490,000 *Total grants* £706,900 *Grants to organisations* £706,900 *Assets* £1,120,000
TRUSTEES Angela McCarville; Stewart Harris.
OTHER INFORMATION The 2018/19 accounts were the latest available at the time of writing (February 2021).
HOW TO APPLY Contact the correspondent for further information.
CONTACT DETAILS The Trustees, Ground Floor, 3 Devonshire Square, London EC2M 4YA *Tel.* 020 7248 6700 *Website* cayofoundation.org.uk

■ Elizabeth Cayzer Charitable Trust

CC NO 1059265 **ESTABLISHED** 1996
WHERE FUNDING CAN BE GIVEN The British Isles.
WHO CAN BENEFIT Museums, galleries and other arts organisations and projects.
WHAT IS FUNDED Support to and promotion of the work of museums, galleries and the architectural heritage of the British Isles. This includes academic research and art history publications.
TYPE OF GRANT Project funding; capital costs; core costs.
RANGE OF GRANTS Up to £80,000.
SAMPLE GRANTS The British Museum (£80,000); Wentworth Woodhouse Preservation Trust (£50,000); Dulwich Picture Gallery (£30,000); The National Gallery (£12,300 in two grants – £6,900 towards exhibitions and catalogues and £5,400 towards research seminars, academic colloquia and workshops); The Landmark Trust (£9,600); The Wallace Collection (£8,300); Bath Preservation Trust (£7,100).
FINANCES *Financial year end* 31/03/2020 *Income* £200,400 *Total grants* £197,400 *Grants to organisations* £197,400 *Assets* £6,860,000
TRUSTEES The Hon. Elizabeth Gilmour; George Ponsonby; Dominic Gibbs; Diana Lloyd; Sonia Barry.
OTHER INFORMATION Grants were broken down as follows: archiving and cataloguing (£87,200); conservation and restoration (£59,600); conferences, exhibitions and colloquia (£50,600).
HOW TO APPLY Unsolicited applications are not accepted.
CONTACT DETAILS The Hon. Elizabeth Gilmour, Trustee, The Cayzer Trust Company Ltd, Cayzer House, 30 Buckingham Gate, London SW1E 6NN *Tel.* 020 7802 8080 *Email* admin@cayzertrust.com

■ The B. G. S. Cayzer Charitable Trust

CC NO 286063 **ESTABLISHED** 1982
WHERE FUNDING CAN BE GIVEN UK.
WHO CAN BENEFIT Registered charities.
WHAT IS FUNDED General charitable purposes; heritage, conservation and the environment; arts and culture; medical research, treatment and care; education and training; social welfare.
TYPE OF GRANT Project funding; core/revenue costs. One-off and multi-year grants.
RANGE OF GRANTS Up to £90,000.
SAMPLE GRANTS Kew Gardens Apprenticeship (£60,800); Opera Holland Park (£25,000); Bath Preservation Trust (£14,200); Avenues Youth Project and Charlie Waller Memorial Trust (£5,000 each); UK Sepsis Trust (£2,500); Friends of The Holy Land (£2,000).
FINANCES *Financial year end* 05/04/2020 *Income* £166,600 *Total grants* £148,500 *Grants to organisations* £148,500 *Assets* £4,360,000
TRUSTEES P. R. Davies; Mary Buckley; Arabella Hunter; Roseanna Leslie; Sonia Barry.
OTHER INFORMATION In 2019/20 the trust made grants to 30 organisations totalling £148,500, distributed across the following areas: heritage, conservation and the environment (£75,000); arts and culture (£25,000); medical research, treatment and care (£25,000); general charitable purposes (£18,500); education and training (£2,500); social welfare (£2,500). Only beneficiaries in receipt of over £2,000 were listed.
HOW TO APPLY The trustees do not accept unsolicited applications.
CONTACT DETAILS The Trustees, The Cayzer Trust Company Ltd, 30 Buckingham Gate, London SW1E 6NN *Tel.* 020 7802 8439 *Email* admin@cayzertrust.com

■ The Cazenove Charitable Trust

CC NO 1086899 **ESTABLISHED** 1969
WHERE FUNDING CAN BE GIVEN UK.
WHO CAN BENEFIT Charitable organisations.
WHAT IS FUNDED General charitable purposes.
SAMPLE GRANTS Great Ormond Street Hospital Children's Charity (£12,000); Alzheimer's Society (£6,800); Villers Park Educational Trust (£4,000); The Stroke Association (£2,000); EDP Drug and Alcohol Services and St George's Hospital Charity (£1,000 each).
FINANCES *Financial year end* 31/12/2019 *Income* £97,800 *Total grants* £60,300 *Grants to organisations* £60,300 *Assets* £3,210,000
TRUSTEES Michael Wentworth-Stanley; Michael Power; Lucinda Napier; David Mayhew; James Barker; John Mayne; Nicholas Hall; Damien Robinson.
OTHER INFORMATION Only organisations receiving grants of over £1,000 were listed as beneficiaries in the charity's accounts. Grants of

under £10,000 totalled £14,200. The trust primarily supports fundraising activities by employees and ex-employees of JP Morgan Cazenove and Cazenove Capital Management via a matched giving scheme.
HOW TO APPLY Contact the correspondent for further information.
CONTACT DETAILS The Trustees, Cazenove Capital Management Ltd, 12 Moorgate, London EC2R 6DA *Tel.* 020 7658 1178

■ CBRE Charitable Trust

CC NO 299026 **ESTABLISHED** 1987
WHERE FUNDING CAN BE GIVEN Mainly in the UK.
WHO CAN BENEFIT Registered charities.
WHAT IS FUNDED General charitable purposes.
RANGE OF GRANTS Mostly £100 to £2,000.
SAMPLE GRANTS Action for Children (£8,000); The Children's Trust (£1,500); British Heart Foundation (£1,000); Alzheimer's Society (£800); ABF The Soldiers' Charity and The Wave Project (£500 each); Bumblebee Conservation (£250); Chester Aid to the Homeless (£150); Trust Macmillan Cancer Support – Jersey (£50).
FINANCES *Financial year end* 31/10/2019 *Income* £62,700 *Total grants* £51,800 *Grants to organisations* £51,800 *Assets* £55,800
TRUSTEES Alex Naftis; Guy Gregory; Aimee Parkinson; Richard White; Sharvani Hindocha; Rajveer Bains.
OTHER INFORMATION Formerly known as the CB Richard Ellis Charitable Trust, this is the corporate charity of CBRE, a commercial property and real estate provider. Support is generally given to organisations that are recommended by CBRE's employees or whose work is closely aligned to that of CBRE. The 2018/19 accounts were the latest available at the time of writing (June 2021).
HOW TO APPLY The trust's 2018/19 accounts state: 'All requests for donations must be made in writing and are individually assessed, considered and approved by the Trustees prior to making any payments. Support is given in the form of financial donations, which are granted to recognised charitable causes only.'
CONTACT DETAILS Miss A. M. Pisaniak, Secretary to the Trustees, CBRE, St Martin's Court, 10 Paternoster Row, London EC4M 7HP *Tel.* 020 7182 3425

■ CEO Sleepout

CC NO 1154963 **ESTABLISHED** 2013
WHERE FUNDING CAN BE GIVEN UK.
WHO CAN BENEFIT Registered charities.
WHAT IS FUNDED Homelessness.
RANGE OF GRANTS Up to £121,000 but mainly between £100 and £24,000.
SAMPLE GRANTS The Fork In The Road (£121,900); YMCA Milton Keynes (£24,800); Buses 4 Homeless CIC (£11,300); First Stop Darlington (£6,500); Veterans in Crisis (£3,000); Carecent York (£2,000); Eva's Women's Aid (£200); Saltburn Food Bank (£60).
FINANCES *Financial year end* 31/03/2020 *Income* £489,700 *Total grants* £422,100 *Grants to organisations* £422,100 *Assets* £73,900
TRUSTEES Andy Preston; Niklas Tunley; Abu Ali.
HOW TO APPLY Contact the correspondent for further information.
CONTACT DETAILS The Trustees, Boho Number One, Bridge Street West, Middlesbrough, North Yorkshire TS2 1AE *Tel.* 07922 478994 *Email* info@ceosleepoutuk.com *Website* www.ceosleepoutuk.com

■ The Chadwick Educational Foundation

CC NO 526373 **ESTABLISHED** 1963
WHERE FUNDING CAN BE GIVEN The borough of Bolton and former urban district of Turton.
WHO CAN BENEFIT Schools; individuals.
WHAT IS FUNDED Education.
TYPE OF GRANT Mainly capital grants.
SAMPLE GRANTS Eagley Junior School (£25,800); Leverhulme Primary School (£21,000); Church Road Primary School (£18,100); Gaskell Community Primary School (£12,000); Devonshire Road Primary School (£9,600); St Thomas of Canterbury Roman Catholic Primary School (£4,800); Tall Ships Youth Trust (£1,500).
FINANCES *Financial year end* 31/12/2019 *Income* £208,300 *Total grants* £304,400 *Grants to organisations* £304,400 *Assets* £151,600
TRUSTEES Peter Liptrott; Revd Canon Dr Chris Bracegirdle; Esther Gelling; Ian Tomkin; Kathryn Hodgkiss; Diane Abbott.
OTHER INFORMATION Grants were awarded to 22 organisations during the year.
HOW TO APPLY The 2019 accounts state: 'The Charity invites applications for grants through headteachers at Bolton schools and with the co-operation of Bolton's Local Education Authority. Preference is given to the underprivileged.'
CONTACT DETAILS The Trustees, c/o R. P Smith and Co. Ltd, Hamill House, 112–116 Chorley New Road, Bolton BL1 4DH *Tel.* 01204 534421

■ The Amelia Chadwick Trust

CC NO 213795 **ESTABLISHED** 1960
WHERE FUNDING CAN BE GIVEN UK, with a preference for Merseyside.
WHO CAN BENEFIT Registered charities; hospices.
WHAT IS FUNDED General charitable purposes; education; health; the arts; social welfare; the environment.
WHAT IS NOT FUNDED Individuals.
RANGE OF GRANTS Mostly below £3,000.
SAMPLE GRANTS L'Arche Ltd (two grants totalling £14,500); Home-Start Wirral and North Liverpool Foodbank (£3,500 each); Prisoners' Education Trust (£2,000); Age Concern – Liverpool (£1,250); Liverpool Homeless Football Club and Relate (£1,000 each).
FINANCES *Financial year end* 05/04/2020 *Income* £195,200 *Total grants* £136,800 *Grants to organisations* £136,800 *Assets* £4,120,000
TRUSTEES Andrew Behrend; Matthew Dawson; Liverpool Charity and Voluntary Services.
OTHER INFORMATION Grants were awarded to 59 charities during the year ranging from £750 to £14,500. Only beneficiaries of grants of £1,000 and above were listed in the 2019/20 accounts.
HOW TO APPLY Grants are only made to charities known to the trustees and unsolicited applications are not considered.
CONTACT DETAILS The Trustees, c/o Liverpool Charity and Voluntary Services, 151 Dale Street, Liverpool, Merseyside L2 2AH *Tel.* 0151 227 5177 *Email* info@lcvs.org.uk

■ Chalfords Ltd

CC NO 287322 **ESTABLISHED** 1983
WHERE FUNDING CAN BE GIVEN England and Wales.
WHO CAN BENEFIT Jewish Orthodox institutions.
WHAT IS FUNDED Advancement of the Orthodox Jewish religion; advancement of Jewish religious education; social welfare.
TYPE OF GRANT Capital projects; revenue funding.
RANGE OF GRANTS Up to £172,000, but mostly £55,000 or less.
SAMPLE GRANTS Tchabe Kollel Ltd (£172,000); Keren Hatzolas Doros (£122,000); Vishnitz Girls School Ltd (£93,000); Care All Ltd and Edupoor Ltd (£55,000 each); College for Higher Rabbinical Studies, Friends of Beis Soroh Schneirer and One Heart-Lev Echod (£50,000 each); Friends of Seret Viznitz and The North West Community Patrol Trust (£25,000 each); Jewish Futures Trust Ltd (£22,500).
FINANCES *Financial year end* 31/12/2019 *Income* £4,280,000 *Total grants* £1,600,000 *Grants to organisations* £1,600,000 *Assets* £57,700,000
TRUSTEES Irwin Weiler; Riki Weiler; Mr A. Weiler; Mr M. Weiler.
OTHER INFORMATION Grants were distributed as follows: advancement of education (£1.13 million); grants to other grant making charities (£1.02 million); relief of poverty (£390,000); advancement of the Jewish religion (£86,300); other general purposes (£86,000). Only organisations receiving grants of over £20,000 were listed as beneficiaries in the charity's accounts. Grants of less than or equal to £20,000 totalled £243,900.
HOW TO APPLY Contact the correspondent for further information.
CONTACT DETAILS The Trustees, New Burlington House, 1075 Finchley Road, London NW11 0PU *Tel.* 020 8455 6075

■ The Chalk Cliff Trust

CC NO 1139102 **ESTABLISHED** 2010
WHERE FUNDING CAN BE GIVEN East Sussex.
WHO CAN BENEFIT Registered charities. Organisations pending registration or pressure groups will also be considered.
WHAT IS FUNDED Youth schemes and activities; social welfare; older people; people with learning difficulties or disabilities; overseas aid, particularly projects concerned with education, malnutrition or health; the environment; arts and culture.
TYPE OF GRANT Project funding; capital grants; core administration costs.
RANGE OF GRANTS Mostly £3,000 to £5,000.
SAMPLE GRANTS The Charleston Trust (£28,000); Towner (£20,000); Action Painting and Demelza House Children's Hospice (£10,000 each); Brighton Fringe and Impact Foundation (£5,000 each); East Addiction (£4,000); Christ Church with St Philip PCC, Deafkidz International and Vincent Dance Theatre (£3,000 each).
FINANCES *Financial year end* 31/03/2020 *Income* £3,270,000 *Total grants* £1,230,000 *Grants to organisations* £1,230,000 *Assets* £7,370,000
TRUSTEES Justine Senior; Sarah Hunter; Robert Senior; Rachel Senior; Hannah Senior.
OTHER INFORMATION Only organisations receiving grants of over £3,000 were listed as beneficiaries in the charity's accounts. Grants of under £3,000 totalled £112,900.
HOW TO APPLY Application forms can be downloaded from the trust's website and should be sent with supporting documents by email.
CONTACT DETAILS The Trustees, 18 Keere Street, Lewes, East Sussex BN7 1TY *Tel.* 01273 525354 *Email* apply@chalkclifftrust.org *Website* www.chalkclifftrust.org

■ Champneys Charitable Foundation

CC NO 1114429 **ESTABLISHED** 2006
WHERE FUNDING CAN BE GIVEN UK.
WHO CAN BENEFIT Charitable organisations.
WHAT IS FUNDED General charitable purposes including: health and disability.
RANGE OF GRANTS £500 to £18,000.
SAMPLE GRANTS Cancer Research (£185,100); Pink Ribbon Foundation (£17,700); Cancer HairCare and Cauldwell (£15,000 each); Crisis and Alzheimer Research (£14,800 each); Rainbow Trust (£500).
FINANCES *Financial year end* 30/04/2019 *Income* £417,200 *Total grants* £273,900 *Grants to organisations* £273,900 *Assets* £65,500
TRUSTEES Dorothy Purdew; Stephen Purdew; Alan Whiteley; Paul Mitchell.
OTHER INFORMATION Only seven organisations were listed as beneficiaries in the charity's accounts. The 2018/19 accounts were the latest available at the time of writing (January 2021).
HOW TO APPLY Apply in writing to the correspondent. The foundation's website states: 'Champneys Charitable Foundation particularly likes to support charities nominated by our guests and welcomes requests. Applications for grants can be made by email or in writing and will be discussed at the quarterly board meetings when trustees of the Charity decide how and who we can support.'
CONTACT DETAILS Bev Strong, Charity Administrator, Henlow Grange, Henlow, Bedfordshire SG16 6DB *Tel.* 01462 811111 *Email* charity@champneys.co.uk *Website* https://www.champneys.com/about-champneys/charity

■ Chapman Charitable Trust

CC NO 232791 **ESTABLISHED** 1963
WHERE FUNDING CAN BE GIVEN National charities operating across the UK; local charities operating in North Wales or South East England.
WHO CAN BENEFIT Registered charities; educational or research establishments with charitable status. The trust prefers to support charities which address the root causes of problems and it welcomes applications for research projects.
WHAT IS FUNDED Physical and mental well-being; conservation of the natural environment; sustainability; improving access to the arts, especially for young people.
WHAT IS NOT FUNDED Non UK registered charities; individuals, including sponsorship or education, research or travel; CICs; community amateur sports clubs; co-operative societies and not-for-profit organisations.
RANGE OF GRANTS Mostly £1,000 to £2,000.
SAMPLE GRANTS Ambitious about Autism (£16,000); Pesticide Action Network UK (£10,000); Action for Children and A Rocha UK (£6,000 each); Huntington Disease Association (£3,000); Bat Conservation Trust, Carers Trust and Earthwatch Institute (£2,000 each); Wellbeing of Women (£1,000); Amgueddfa'r Mor Porthmadog

Maritime Museum (£500). A full list of beneficiaries is available on the trust's website.

FINANCES *Financial year end* 05/04/2020 *Income* £371,900 *Total grants* £362,500 *Grants to organisations* £362,500 *Assets* £6,670,000

TRUSTEES Richard Chapman; Guy Chapman; Bryony Chapman; Thomas Williams.

OTHER INFORMATION Grants were broken down as follows: well-being (£119,000); the arts (£98,500); the environment (£78,000); care (£67,000).

HOW TO APPLY Apply online via the trust's website. The trustees meet twice a year in March and September.

CONTACT DETAILS Richard Chapman, Trustee, c/o RPG Crouch Chapman LLP, 62 Wilson Street, London EC2A 2BU *Tel.* 020 7782 0007 *Email* cct@chapmancharitabletrust.org.uk *Website* www.chapmancharitabletrust.org.uk

■ The Charities Advisory Trust

CC NO 1040487 **ESTABLISHED** 1994

WHERE FUNDING CAN BE GIVEN UK; overseas.

WHO CAN BENEFIT Charitable organisations.

WHAT IS FUNDED General charitable purposes.

WHAT IS NOT FUNDED Individuals; large fundraising charities.

SAMPLE GRANTS A list of beneficiaries was not included in the annual report and accounts.

FINANCES *Financial year end* 30/06/2019 *Income* £840,400 *Total grants* £416,100 *Grants to organisations* £416,100 *Assets* £2,980,000

TRUSTEES Rowena Dunn; David Russell; Leila Mactavish.

OTHER INFORMATION The 2018/19 accounts were the latest available at the time of writing (February 2021).

HOW TO APPLY Contact the correspondent for further information.

CONTACT DETAILS Dame Hilary Blume, Director, Radius Works, Back Lane, Hampstead, London NW3 1HL *Tel.* 020 7794 9835 *Email* people@charitiesadvisorytrust.org.uk *Website* www.charitiesadvisorytrust.org.uk

■ Charitworth Ltd

CC NO 286908 **ESTABLISHED** 1983

WHERE FUNDING CAN BE GIVEN Worldwide, mainly UK and Israel.

WHO CAN BENEFIT Charitable organisations; educational institutions.

WHAT IS FUNDED The advancement of Orthodox Jewish faith and education; the relief of poverty.

RANGE OF GRANTS Up to £220,000.

SAMPLE GRANTS Vishnitz Girls School Ltd (£230,000); Keren Hatzolas Doros Alei Siach (£150,000); Beis Chinuch Lebonos Ltd (£75,000); Entindale Ltd (£60,000); Friends of Beis Soroh Schneirer (£50,000); Care All Ltd and Edupoor Ltd (£35,000 each).

FINANCES *Financial year end* 31/03/2020 *Income* £1,790,000 *Total grants* £1,700,000 *Grants to organisations* £1,700,000 *Assets* £41,300,000

TRUSTEES Samuel Halpern; Sidney Halpern; David Halpern; Relly Halpern.

OTHER INFORMATION Only organisations receiving grants of £35,000 and above were listed as beneficiaries in the charity's accounts. Smaller grants totalled £439,700. During the year, all grants were paid in support of education or the relief of poverty.

HOW TO APPLY Contact the correspondent for further information.

CONTACT DETAILS David Halpern, Trustee, New Burlington House, 1075 Finchley Road, London NW11 0PU *Tel.* 020 8731 0777

■ The Charter 600 Charity

CC NO 1051146 **ESTABLISHED** 1994

WHERE FUNDING CAN BE GIVEN UK.

WHO CAN BENEFIT Registered charities; grassroots community organisations.

WHAT IS FUNDED A range of charitable purposes, with particular focus on young people and community.

TYPE OF GRANT Project funding; salaries.

RANGE OF GRANTS Between £10,000 and £25,000.

SAMPLE GRANTS Compassionate Friends, The Listening Place and The Daniel Spargo Mabbs Foundation (£25,000 each); Helford Rover Children's Sailing Trust and Renaissance Foundation (£10,000 each).

FINANCES *Financial year end* 31/03/2020 *Income* £105,700 *Total grants* £95,000 *Grants to organisations* £95,000 *Assets* £1,670,000

TRUSTEE The Mercers' Company.

OTHER INFORMATION This is the charitable arm of The Mercers' Company. Grants were awarded to five organisations during the year. After undergoing a full strategic review, the trust now focuses on making larger grants to 'grassroots' community organisations working in the areas of young people and community welfare, particularly those known by members or staff of the Mercers' Company. According to its 2019/20 annual report, the trust plans to award three large grants of £25,000 each in 2020/21.

HOW TO APPLY Applications for charitable grants will only be accepted when put forward by a member of the Mercers' Company. The charity does not consider unsolicited applications.

CONTACT DETAILS The Trustee, 6 Frederick's Place, London EC2R 8AB *Tel.* 020 7776 7200 *Email* info@mercers.co.uk *Website* https://www.mercers.co.uk/philanthropy

■ Chartered Accountants' Livery Charity (CALC)

CC NO 327681 **ESTABLISHED** 1988

WHERE FUNDING CAN BE GIVEN Unrestricted but primarily within England and Wales.

WHO CAN BENEFIT Registered charities; schools; universities.

WHAT IS FUNDED General charitable purposes including social welfare and education.

WHAT IS NOT FUNDED Causes that promote a single religion; political causes; animal welfare; medical research. The charity is unlikely to support individuals, sports events or projects where the grant will not make a significant difference to the cause supported.

TYPE OF GRANT Core/revenue costs; project funding.

RANGE OF GRANTS £100 to £5,000, but up to £250,000 for Major Project Awards.

SAMPLE GRANTS Lord Mayor's Appeal (£5,000); Treloar School Trust (£3,000); HMS Dundas – The Harrow and Wembley Sea Cadets and Leadership Through Sport and Business (£2,500 each); Islington Boat Club (£2,000); Alive and Kicking Theatre Company (£1,500); Royal Air Force Benevolent Fund (£1,000); Youth on the Move (£500); The City of London

Police Widows and Orphans Fund (£200); The Children's Society (£100).

FINANCES *Financial year end* 30/09/2019
Income £215,500 *Total grants* £157,700
Grants to organisations £157,700
Assets £2,270,000

TRUSTEES John Cardnell; Miles Hedges; Stephen Maslin; Andrew Pianca; William Martin Robinson; Sally-Ann Orton; Neeraj Kapur; Graeme Gordon; Dr Hilary Lindsay.

OTHER INFORMATION In total, 40 grants were awarded to organisations throughout the year. The charity supports one major project at a time. 'The Open University Youth Project Managing My Money' was supported between 2017 and 2019 and was awarded its final grant of £58,400 in 2019. The major project for 2020–2022 is a financial education programme for young carers delivered by Create. The 2018/19 accounts were the latest available at the time of writing (January 2021).

HOW TO APPLY Completed forms (available on the website) and accompanying applications may be sent by email to the Clerk to the Trustees, Barbara Brooks, at charity@accountantslivery.org or by post. The trustees meet quarterly, generally at the end of March, June, September and December to consider applications.

CONTACT DETAILS Barbara Brooks, Clerk to the Trustees, 18 Bosman Drive, Windlesham, Surrey GU20 6JW *Tel.* 01276 850195 *Email* charity@accountantslivery.org *Website* www.accountantslivery.org

The Charterhouse Charitable Trust

CC NO 210894 **ESTABLISHED** 1962

WHERE FUNDING CAN BE GIVEN London boroughs on the City of London perimeter.

WHO CAN BENEFIT Registered charities.

WHAT IS FUNDED Social welfare (providing opportunities for those from a deprived or disadvantaged background); education; health and well-being; general charitable purposes.

TYPE OF GRANT Mainly project funding or where it is thought the donation would make a difference.

RANGE OF GRANTS Up to £10,000.

SAMPLE GRANTS Australian Red Cross, St Mungo's and The Trussell Trust (£10,000 each); Lynda Jackson Macmillan Centre (£5,000); Policlinico di Milano – COVID-19 donation (£4,700); Mothers 2 Mothers (£1,500).

FINANCES *Financial year end* 30/06/2020
Income £56,000 *Total grants* £55,900
Grants to organisations £55,900
Assets £1,880,000

TRUSTEES Thomas Patrick; William Thomas; Willem Du Toit; Mirja Weidner.

OTHER INFORMATION Grants were awarded to eight organisations during the year. During the year, there were grants made to organisations working outside London in relation to specific global events, including the COVID-19 pandemic and Australian bushfires.

HOW TO APPLY Contact the correspondent for further information.

CONTACT DETAILS Irina Watson, Secretary, 6th Floor, Belgrave House, 76 Buckingham Palace Road, London SW1W 9TQ *Tel.* 020 7334 5322 *Email* irina.watson@charterhouse.co.uk *Website* www.charterhouse.co.uk

The Chartley Foundation

CC NO 1154637 **ESTABLISHED** 2013

WHERE FUNDING CAN BE GIVEN Staffordshire.

WHO CAN BENEFIT Charitable organisations; sports teams.

WHAT IS FUNDED General charitable purposes; the arts; amateur sport; the environment.

TYPE OF GRANT Unrestricted.

RANGE OF GRANTS Up to £40,000.

SAMPLE GRANTS The Outward Bound Trust (£39,700); Stoke Athletics (£29,200); Game and Wildlife Conservation Trust Tertiary Education (£26,500); Royal Forestry Society (£22,100); Staffordshire Clubs for Young People (£7,200).

FINANCES *Financial year end* 31/12/2019
Income £341,800 *Total grants* £124,800
Grants to organisations £124,800
Assets £10,950,000

TRUSTEES Anthony Reeves; David Johnson; Richard Poole; Lord Stafford.

OTHER INFORMATION Grants were awarded to five organisations during the year.

HOW TO APPLY Contact the correspondent for further information.

CONTACT DETAILS David Johnson, Trustee, The Bradshaws, Codsall, Wolverhampton, Staffordshire WV8 2HU *Tel.* 01902 754855 *Email* dedj@chartleyestates.co.uk

The Cheruby Trust

CC NO 327069 **ESTABLISHED** 1986

WHERE FUNDING CAN BE GIVEN UK and overseas.

WHO CAN BENEFIT Registered charities.

WHAT IS FUNDED General charitable purposes, including social welfare and education.

RANGE OF GRANTS Mostly under £5,000.

SAMPLE GRANTS British Friends of the Feuerstein Centre (£15,000); International Rescue Committee UK and World Jewish Relief (£5,000 each); FareShare and Sightsavers (£3,000 each); YoungMinds (£2,000); Woodland Trust (£1,500); The Stuart Low Trust (£1,000); Shabbaton Choir (£500).

FINANCES *Financial year end* 05/04/2020
Income £70,100 *Total grants* £105,800
Grants to organisations £105,800
Assets £29,700

TRUSTEES Alison Corob; Laura Corob; Christopher Cook; Sheila Wechsler; Tricia Corob.

OTHER INFORMATION Grants were awarded to 40 organisations during the year.

HOW TO APPLY Contact the correspondent for further information.

CONTACT DETAILS The Trustees, 62 Grosvenor Street, London W1K 3JF *Tel.* 020 7499 4301

Cheshire Community Foundation Ltd

CC NO 1143711 **ESTABLISHED** 2011

WHERE FUNDING CAN BE GIVEN Cheshire.

WHO CAN BENEFIT Registered charities; community and voluntary organisations; CICs; social enterprises.

WHAT IS FUNDED General charitable purposes including: mental health and well-being; poverty and disadvantage; education, skills and employment; stronger communities.

WHAT IS NOT FUNDED Check the foundation's website for programme specific exclusions.

TYPE OF GRANT Programme dependent.

RANGE OF GRANTS Programme dependent.

SAMPLE GRANTS A list of beneficiaries was not included in the annual report and accounts.
FINANCES *Financial year end* 31/12/2019 *Income* £1,470,000 *Total grants* £1,350,000 *Grants to organisations* £1,350,000 *Assets* £6,960,000
TRUSTEES Howard Platt; Andrew Butters; Jeannie France-Hayhurst; Terry Inns; Sarah Callander-Beckett; Sean Humphreys; Nicholas Mason; Diane Brown.
OTHER INFORMATION This is one of the 46 UK community foundations, which distribute funding for a wide range of purposes. As with all community foundations, there are a number of donor-advised funds managed on behalf of individuals, families and charitable trusts. Grant schemes tend to change frequently; consult the foundation's website for details of current programmes and up-to-date deadlines. Grants were made to around 155 organisations during the year.
HOW TO APPLY Potential applicants are advised to visit the community foundation's website or contact its grants team to find the most suitable funding stream.
CONTACT DETAILS Angela Richardson, Grants Director, Sension House, Denton Drive, Northwich, Cheshire CW9 7LU *Tel.* 01606 330607 *Email* grants@cheshirecommunityfoundation.org.uk *Website* www.cheshirecommunityfoundation.org.uk

■ Cheshire Freemason's Charity

CC NO 219177 **ESTABLISHED** 1963
WHERE FUNDING CAN BE GIVEN Cheshire; Stockport; Tameside; Trafford; Wirral.
WHO CAN BENEFIT Individuals; organisations benefitting Masons and their families; registered charities.
WHAT IS FUNDED General charitable purposes; social welfare; children and young people.
SAMPLE GRANTS A list of beneficiaries was not included in the annual report and accounts.
FINANCES *Financial year end* 30/04/2020 *Income* £408,400 *Total grants* £214,000 *Grants to organisations* £214,000 *Assets* £4,660,000
TRUSTEES Dennis Talbot; Peter Carroll; Graham Scott; Leo Saunders; Michael Ireland; Jonathan Shasha; Paul Crudge.
OTHER INFORMATION The charity's 2019/20 accounts state that grants totalling £214,000 were made to 'individuals, organisations and other charities'.
HOW TO APPLY Contact the correspondent for further information.
CONTACT DETAILS Harry Wright, Provincial Grand Charity Steward, Ashcroft House, 36 Clay Lane, Timperley, Altrincham, Cheshire WA15 7AB *Tel.* 0161 980 6090 *Email* harry.wright@cheshiremasons.co.uk *Website* www.cheshiremasons.co.uk

■ The Chetwode Foundation

CC NO 265950 **ESTABLISHED** 1973
WHERE FUNDING CAN BE GIVEN UK, with a preference for Nottinghamshire, Leicestershire and Derby.
WHO CAN BENEFIT Registered charities.
WHAT IS FUNDED General charitable purposes; disadvantaged children and young people (including education, employability, sport and art); training for youth workers; prisoners and ex-offenders.
WHAT IS NOT FUNDED Individuals; national charities; organisations outside the UK.
TYPE OF GRANT Project funding; capital costs; core costs; recurrent grants may be considered.
RANGE OF GRANTS Mostly under £5,000.
SAMPLE GRANTS Reach Learning Disability (£24,000); CRS Community Recording Studio (£10,000); Think Children (£6,600); Young Women's Trust (£5,000); Nottinghamshire Independent Domestic Abuse Services (NIDAS) (£4,000); Pintsize Theatre (£2,500); Trent District 1st Responders (£1,500); St Jude's PCC (£1,000).
FINANCES *Financial year end* 05/04/2020 *Income* £80,400 *Total grants* £106,000 *Grants to organisations* £106,000 *Assets* £2,150,000
TRUSTEES Lesley Samworth; Fiona Johnson; Russell Price.
OTHER INFORMATION Grants were awarded to 21 organisations during the year.
HOW TO APPLY An application form is available to download from the website or by contacting the trustees via email or post. The application form is basic, with the majority of detail to be included in a written statement outlining the project on no more than two sides of A4. Applications can be submitted at any time by email or post. The trustees aim to acknowledge all relevant applications within four weeks. If you are unsuccessful at the initial assessment you will be informed within eight weeks of receipt of your application.
CONTACT DETAILS Administrator, Farm Office, Stragglethorpe Grainstore, Nottingham Road, Cropwell Bishop, Nottingham NG12 2JU *Tel.* 0115 989 3722 *Email* info@thechetwodefoundation.co.uk *Website* www.thechetwodefoundation.co.uk

■ The Childhood Trust

CC NO 1154032 **ESTABLISHED** 2013
WHERE FUNDING CAN BE GIVEN London.
WHO CAN BENEFIT Registered charities.
WHAT IS FUNDED Children and young people (4–18 years); social welfare.
WHAT IS NOT FUNDED Statutory funding; capital costs; religious groups; accommodation for homeless children or families; retrospective expenditure; trips abroad; individuals, including hardship grants and educational bursaries. Full exclusions are available in the trust's grant-making policy, which is available to download from the website.
TYPE OF GRANT Project funding; matched funding.
RANGE OF GRANTS Up to £75,000 but mostly under £15,000.
SAMPLE GRANTS Greenhouse Sports Ltd (£75,000); Mayor's Fund for London (£50,000); Safe Families for Children (£30,000); IntoUniversity (£25,000); Refugee Support Network (£15,000); Lives Not Knives (£10,000); London Chamber Orchestra Trust (£5,000); The Kids' Cookery School (£2,000); Young Roots (£1,000); Immediate Theatre (£220).
FINANCES *Financial year end* 30/06/2020 *Income* £2,110,000 *Total grants* £1,510,000 *Grants to organisations* £1,510,000 *Assets* £298,500
TRUSTEES Rebecca Jacques; David Rhodes; Galiema Cloete; Karelia Ashman; Lesley O'Mara; Sonal Shenai; Grant Gordon; Dr Mathias Hink; Nicola Horlick; Andrei Popescu.
OTHER INFORMATION Grants were made to a total of 127 charities during the year. The trust funds projects through its bi-annual matched funding

campaigns. In 2019/20 funds were raised through two campaigns: The Christmas Challenge 2019 and Champions for Children 2020. In general, the trust looks to support projects in the following three areas: practical – ensuring that children have access to basic necessities; emotional – offering emotional support and motivation to break the cycle of poverty; inspirational – providing opportunities to try new experiences and develop new skills. The trust also offers added value support, such as workshops on successful campaigning, skills training and marketing advice, free of charge to its grantees.

HOW TO APPLY According to the website, 'all applications for The Childhood Trust's campaigns are processed through the Big Give platform.' To begin your application go to the 'Apply for funding' page of the trust's website and click 'begin application'. The application process comprises the following steps: 1) charities upload their project details onto The Big Give platform and submit their pledge donations; 2) The Big Give and The Childhood Trust carry out checks on applicant charities; 3) funding offers are sent out to the successful charities and the campaign begins. Contact the correspondent for any further information or use the contact form available on the website.

CONTACT DETAILS Laurence Guinness, Chief Executive and Secretary, 18 Buckingham Palace Road, London SW1W 0QP *Tel.* 07507 880109 *Email* info@childhoodtrust.org *Website* www.childhoodtrust.org.uk

■ Children with Cancer UK

CC NO 298405 **ESTABLISHED** 2003

WHERE FUNDING CAN BE GIVEN UK.

WHO CAN BENEFIT UK-based medical and scientific research centres; universities; hospitals; charities.

WHAT IS FUNDED Research into childhood cancer; welfare projects for young cancer patients and their families.

TYPE OF GRANT Research; project costs; capacity building; studentships.

RANGE OF GRANTS Up to £350,000.

SAMPLE GRANTS CLIC Sargent (£350,000); Ronald McDonald House Charities (£288,000); Beads of Courage (£280,000).

FINANCES *Financial year end* 31/12/2019
Income £17,330,000 *Total grants* £4,290,000
Grants to organisations £4,290,000
Assets £10,900,000

TRUSTEES Edward O'Gorman; Linda Robson; Sandra Mileham; Virna Midgley; David Gibbs; Ann Amaya-Torres; Dr Nicholas Goulden; Caroline Randerson.

OTHER INFORMATION During 2019, grants were broken down as follows: research into prevention and causes (£2.72 million); welfare (£918,000); research into treatment (£631,300); education (£18,400). Only a small number of beneficiary organisations were listed in the 2019 accounts.

HOW TO APPLY For information on current research funding opportunities and how to apply, refer to the charity's website. There is no open application process for welfare grants, the trustees determine which organisations are to be supported. Check the website for the latest information.

CONTACT DETAILS The Trustees, 51 Great Ormond Street, London WC1N 3JQ *Tel.* 0800 222 9000 *Email* research@childrenwithcancer.org.uk *Website* www.childrenwithcancer.org.uk

■ Children's Liver Disease Foundation

CC NO 1067331 **ESTABLISHED** 1980

WHERE FUNDING CAN BE GIVEN UK.

WHO CAN BENEFIT Hospitals; universities; research organisations.

WHAT IS FUNDED Clinical, laboratory-based and social research into childhood liver disease.

WHAT IS NOT FUNDED Support is not given to work based outside the UK or to retrospective projects.

TYPE OF GRANT Research and project funding.

RANGE OF GRANTS Up to £10,000 through the Main Grants Programme.

SAMPLE GRANTS A list of beneficiaries was not included in the annual report and accounts.

FINANCES *Financial year end* 31/12/2019
Income £853,000 *Total grants* £690,400
Grants to organisations £690,400
Assets £489,400

TRUSTEES Prof. James Neuberger; Dr Simon Colson; Mairi Everard; Kate Dinwiddy; Philip Orme; Georgina Sugden; Joel Glover.

HOW TO APPLY At the time of writing (January 2021) the foundation has suspended its £10,000 grant programme due to the challenges of COVID-19. Consult the foundation's website for up-to-date information.

CONTACT DETAILS The Trustees, 36 Great Charles Street, Queensway, Birmingham, West Midlands B3 3JY *Tel.* 0121 212 3839 *Email* info@childliverdisease.org *Website* www.childliverdisease.org

■ The Childs Charitable Trust

CC NO 1153327 **ESTABLISHED** 1962

WHERE FUNDING CAN BE GIVEN UK; overseas.

WHO CAN BENEFIT Christian UK-registered charities.

WHAT IS FUNDED Supporting Christian organisations which actively share the Christian gospel.

WHAT IS NOT FUNDED New builds, repair, refurbishment, renovation projects, or fixtures and fittings; salary costs for youth workers; foodbanks; street pastors/wardens; gap year projects.

TYPE OF GRANT Project funding; research.

SAMPLE GRANTS Igreja Baptist Church (£23,800); Off the Fence (£19,500); Life Bridging Works (£12,000); Orphaids (£6,000); Soldier's and Airmen's Scripture Readers Association (£2,500).

FINANCES *Financial year end* 31/12/2019
Income £451,400 *Total grants* £316,900
Grants to organisations £316,900
Assets £4,310,000

TRUSTEES Melanie Churchyard; Steve Puttock; Robert Peake; Christopher Large.

HOW TO APPLY Apply via the trust's website where application deadlines can also be found.

CONTACT DETAILS Melanie Churchyard, Chief Executive Officer, 11A Gildredge Road, Eastbourne, East Sussex BN21 4RB *Tel.* 01323 417944 *Email* info@childstrust.org *Website* childscharitabletrust.org

■ The Childwick Trust

CC NO 1150413 **ESTABLISHED** 1985

WHERE FUNDING CAN BE GIVEN Predominantly in the south and south east of the UK. A full list of the counties supported can be found on the trust's website. The trust also operates in South Africa.

WHO CAN BENEFIT Registered charities.

WHAT IS FUNDED In the UK: health, people with disabilities and older people; welfare in connection with the (horses) bloodstock industry; Jewish charities. In South Africa: education; childhood development.
WHAT IS NOT FUNDED A full list of exclusions can be found on the trust's helpful website.
TYPE OF GRANT Mainly one-off, project and capital funding for research and medical equipment.
RANGE OF GRANTS Typically £5,000 to £20,000.
SAMPLE GRANTS UK beneficiaries: Racing Welfare (£300,000); The British Racing School (£48,300); St Mark's Hospital Foundation (£25,000); Jewish Care, Kids in Action and Royal British Legion Industries (£20,000 each); Leonard Cheshire Disability (£17,000); Epilepsy Society and Wellbeing of Women (£15,000 each).
FINANCES *Financial year end* 31/03/2020 *Income* £2,220,000 *Total grants* £3,076,900 *Grants to organisations* £2,990,000 *Assets* £76,010,000
TRUSTEES Clare Maurice; Mark Farmar; John Wood; Peter Anwyl-Harris; Dr Alan Stranders; Michael Fiddes.
OTHER INFORMATION A total of 218 separate grants were awarded during the year. Grants were distributed as follows: health and associated causes – UK (£1.53 million); education – South Africa (£803,700); horseracing – UK (£435,400); Jewish charities – UK (£219,000). In addition, six individuals were awarded welfare grants. A full list of beneficiaries of grants above £15,000 is available on the website.
HOW TO APPLY Applications can be made through the trust's website. Applications are normally open in October and April each year and must be submitted by midnight on the 31st of the month.
CONTACT DETAILS Kirsty Jones, Trust Administrator, 9 Childwick Green, Childwicksbury, St Albans, Hertfordshire AL3 6JJ *Tel.* 01727 844666 *Email* kirsty@childwicktrust.org *Website* www.childwicktrust.org

■ Chippenham Borough Lands Charity

CC NO 270062 **ESTABLISHED** 1990
WHERE FUNDING CAN BE GIVEN Chippenham parish.
WHO CAN BENEFIT Individuals or community/charitable organisations.
WHAT IS FUNDED General charitable purposes; community projects, including arts projects; social welfare; education and training; work with young people.
WHAT IS NOT FUNDED Individual sports people; local authorities; retrospective applications; first degrees; the advancement of religion; animal welfare; political activities; salaries (except the proportion related to the delivery of the project); anything that can be obtained from statutory sources.
TYPE OF GRANT Project funding; capital costs; core costs.
RANGE OF GRANTS Typically under £10,000.
SAMPLE GRANTS Relate – Mid Wiltshire (£20,800); Home-Start (£10,800); Alzheimer's Support (£7,300); Waste Not Want Not (£8,600); The Rise Trust (£7,000); Wiltshire Community Foundation (£5,000); Salvation Army (£1,800); South Western Ambulance Charity (£1,600).
FINANCES *Financial year end* 31/03/2020 *Income* £626,100 *Total grants* £228,300 *Grants to organisations* £188,600 *Assets* £15,740,000
TRUSTEES Susan Lenihan; Marc Allum; Huw Thomas; David Sandberg; Mary Lanyon; Geraldine McKibbin; Donald Steele; Jim Cook; Philip Wren; Linda Candy; Richard Squires; Annette Foster.
OTHER INFORMATION Grants totalled £228,300 during the year. Of this amount, £188,600 was given to 157 organisations and the rest to individuals. Grants to organisations were broken down as follows: education and work with young people (£100,300); social welfare (£75,500); other charitable purposes (£12,800). The charity also rents out two community centres in the centre of Chippenham.
HOW TO APPLY Apply via a form available from the correspondent. Visit the charity's website for further guidelines. The trustees meet monthly.
CONTACT DETAILS The Trustees, Jubilee Building, 32 Market Place, Chippenham, Wiltshire SN15 3HP *Tel.* 01249 658180 *Email* admin@cblc.org.uk *Website* www.cblc.org.uk

■ The Chipping Sodbury Town Lands Charity

CC NO 236364 **ESTABLISHED** 1977
WHERE FUNDING CAN BE GIVEN Chipping Sodbury; Old Sodbury.
WHO CAN BENEFIT Individuals; schools; community groups; clubs and associations; places of worship; health authorities; leisure centres.
WHAT IS FUNDED General charitable purposes; welfare; education; leisure; community development.
WHAT IS NOT FUNDED Retrospective applications will not be considered.
TYPE OF GRANT Project funding; capital costs.
RANGE OF GRANTS £500 to £20,000.
SAMPLE GRANTS Chipping Sodbury Endowed School (£20,000); Chipping Sodbury Festival (£3,900); Sodbury Town Council Playscheme (£2,000); Chipping Sodbury Town Council – Town Floral Displays (£1,500); Abbeyfield Care Home (£800); Sodbury and District Twinning (£500).
FINANCES *Financial year end* 31/12/2019 *Income* £336,200 *Total grants* £70,500 *Grants to organisations* £58,100 *Assets* £10,860,000
TRUSTEES Elizabeth Lund; Stephen Hunter; Andrew Williams; Andrew Elmore; Brian Hardy; Scott Gibson; Wendy Whittle; Michael Reeves.
OTHER INFORMATION During 2019 the charity awarded £70,500 in grants, of which £58,400 was awarded to organisations. Grants to organisations were broken down as follows: education (£32,500); community support (£19,700); improvement of parish communal facilities (£6,000).
HOW TO APPLY Apply in writing to the correspondent. The trustees meet on the third week of each month except August.
CONTACT DETAILS Nicola Gideon, Clerk, Chipping Sodbury Town Hall, 57–59 Broad Street, Chipping Sodbury, Bristol, South Gloucestershire BS37 6AD *Tel.* 01454 852223 *Email* nicola.gideon@chippingsodburytownhall.co.uk

■ CHK Foundation

CC NO 1050900 **ESTABLISHED** 1995
WHERE FUNDING CAN BE GIVEN UK.
WHO CAN BENEFIT Registered charities.
WHAT IS FUNDED At risk young people aged 11–24. Priority is given to organisations supporting

young people affected by addiction, the criminal justice system or the care system.

TYPE OF GRANT Core costs; unrestricted.

SAMPLE GRANTS World Land Trust (£200,000); The Amber Foundation (£100,000); Cool Earth Action (£75,000); Prison Advice and Care Trust (£50,000); Access Project (£20,000); School for Social Entrepreneurs (£16,000); Caraline: Eating Disorders Counselling and Support Service (£5,000); Spark Inside (£3,800); Clinks (£500).

FINANCES *Financial year end* 31/01/2020 *Income* £3,030,000 *Total grants* £2,850,000 *Grants to organisations* £2,850,000 *Assets* £120,440,000

TRUSTEES Joanna Prest; Katherine Loyd; Lucy Morris; Rupert Prest; Dr Edward Peake; Diana Acland; Pandora Morris; Charles Kirwan-Taylor; Susanna Peake; Camilla Peake; Elisalex de Castro Peake.

OTHER INFORMATION CHK Foundation was formerly CHK Charities Ltd.

HOW TO APPLY The foundation's website states the following: 'Applications for funding are not invited. CHK Foundation undertakes its own research to identify the charities it wishes to support.'

CONTACT DETAILS The Trustees, PO Box 277, Royston, 8 St James's Square, London SG8 1EX *Tel.* 07592 806521 *Email* admin@chkcharities.co.uk *Website* www.chkcharities.co.uk

The Christabella Charitable Trust

CC NO 800610 **ESTABLISHED** 1988

WHERE FUNDING CAN BE GIVEN Essex, East London and France.

WHO CAN BENEFIT Registered charities; local organisations; individuals. There are several local organisations regularly supported, such as St Francis Parish Church in West Horndon.

WHAT IS FUNDED Christian causes; social welfare; education.

WHAT IS NOT FUNDED General running costs or building refurbishment; UK-wide or international charities.

TYPE OF GRANT 'Seed corn' funding of projects involving volunteers.

RANGE OF GRANTS Up to £26,000 but mostly £1,000 and under.

SAMPLE GRANTS National Gardens Scheme (£26,300); LDF Charitable Trust (£10,000); St Francis Parish Church (£8,700); The Children's Society (£1,600); Alzheimer's Society and Sunny Days Children's Society (£1,000 each); De Dion Bouton Club (£580).

FINANCES *Financial year end* 31/12/2019 *Income* £200,100 *Total grants* £83,300 *Grants to organisations* £54,700 *Assets* £7,560,000

TRUSTEES Christine Turner; Richard Hilburn; Ian Elliot; Robert Folwell.

OTHER INFORMATION This trust's primary objective is to maintain the charity's property at Barnards Farm in West Horndon as the house of the National Malus Collection. Only beneficiaries that received grants of over £200 were listed in the accounts. Grants to individuals totalled £28,600 during the year.

HOW TO APPLY A limited number of grants are awarded each year. Contact the correspondent by post if you believe your project would be of relevance or interest to the trust.

CONTACT DETAILS Robert Folwell, Trustee and Trust Administrator, 3 Burses Way, Hutton, Brentwood, Essex CM13 2PL *Tel.* 01277 514056 *Email* bobfolwell@hotmail.com *Website* www.barnardsfarm.eu

Christadelphian Samaritan Fund

CC NO 1004457 **ESTABLISHED** 1991

WHERE FUNDING CAN BE GIVEN UK and overseas.

WHO CAN BENEFIT Registered charities.

WHAT IS FUNDED Social welfare; humanitarian aid/emergency relief; medical research.

RANGE OF GRANTS Up to £16,000 but mostly £300 and under.

SAMPLE GRANTS Disasters Emergency Committee – Cyclone Idia (£16,100); Oxfam – Hidden Crises (£7,500); Disasters Emergency Committee – Cyclone Kenneth (£5,000); ActionAid, British Red Cross, Save the Children and ShelterBox Trust (£2,000 each); Jewish Clothing Relief and South Yorkshire Community Foundation (£1,000).

FINANCES *Financial year end* 31/12/2019 *Income* £116,300 *Total grants* £134,200 *Grants to organisations* £134,200 *Assets* £79,900

TRUSTEES David Ensell; John Buckler; Roger Miles; Pauline Bromage; Elisabeth Briley; Ruth Deedman; Mark Halstead; Mark Leinster.

HOW TO APPLY To apply, contact the correspondent by post and include details of what the charity does and what the appeal is for. Applications are considered quarterly in January, April, July and October.

CONTACT DETAILS Neville Moss, Secretary, Westhaven House, Arleston Way, Shirley, Solihull, West Midlands B90 4LH *Tel.* 0121 713 7100 *Email* Contact form on the website. *Website* https://christadelphiansf.com

The André Christian Trust

CC NO 248466 **ESTABLISHED** 1950

WHERE FUNDING CAN BE GIVEN UK and overseas.

WHO CAN BENEFIT Registered charities; religious bodies/institutions.

WHAT IS FUNDED Christian missionary work; promotion of Christianity; relief of sickness and poverty; advancement of education.

TYPE OF GRANT Seed funding/start-up funding.

RANGE OF GRANTS £1,000 to £24,000.

SAMPLE GRANTS Palm Tree Associates (£23,800); St Peter's Malawi Education Trust (£8,300); Care for the Family and Karis Kids (£5,000 each); South West Community Chaplaincy (£3,000); Life Words (£2,000); Tiverton Vineyard Church (£1,000).

FINANCES *Financial year end* 31/12/2019 *Income* £58,000 *Total grants* £59,400 *Grants to organisations* £59,400 *Assets* £1,900,000

TRUSTEES Andrew Mowll; Stephen Daykin; Peter Appleby.

OTHER INFORMATION Grants were awarded to 12 organisations during the year.

HOW TO APPLY Contact the correspondent for further information.

CONTACT DETAILS Andrew Mowll, Trustee, 24 Hellings Gardens, Broadclyst, Exeter, Devon EX5 3DX *Tel.* 01392 759836

■ Christie Foundation

CC NO 1151063 **ESTABLISHED** 2013

WHERE FUNDING CAN BE GIVEN England and Wales.

WHO CAN BENEFIT Charitable organisations.

WHAT IS FUNDED General charitable purposes.

RANGE OF GRANTS Up to £570,000.

SAMPLE GRANTS Social Finance (£570,000) Project Orchid Ltd (£250,000); Refugee Rights (£121,000); Strengths in Communities CIC Trading as Parents 1st (£60,000).

FINANCES *Financial year end* 29/02/2020 *Income* £186,600 *Total grants* £1,000,000 *Grants to organisations* £1,000,000 *Assets* £15,840,000

TRUSTEES Iain Abrahams; Alexandra Abrahams; Richard Stern.

OTHER INFORMATION In 2019/20 the foundation made grants to four organisations.

HOW TO APPLY Contact the correspondent for further information.

CONTACT DETAILS The Trustees, 1 Mercer Street, London WC2H 9QJ *Tel.* 020 3675 7721 *Email* info@thechristiefoundation.co.uk

■ Chrysalis Trust

CC NO 1133525 **ESTABLISHED** 2010

WHERE FUNDING CAN BE GIVEN UK and overseas with a preference for the North East.

WHO CAN BENEFIT Registered charities.

WHAT IS FUNDED The trust's current priorities are: the relief of poverty and disability; provision of access to shelter, education, healthcare and water; human rights.

WHAT IS NOT FUNDED Research – academic or medical; holidays or outings; arts or entertainment activities; animal welfare; local appeals outside the North East; general appeals.

TYPE OF GRANT Capital costs; core/revenue costs.

RANGE OF GRANTS £1,000 to £10,000.

SAMPLE GRANTS Previous beneficiaries have included: 700 Club, Children and Families Across Borders, Freedom from Torture, Gregg's Foundation, Huntington's Disease Association, Impact, Re-Cycle, Walkabout Foundation, Wamba Community Trust and YMCA North Tyneside.

FINANCES *Financial year end* 31/03/2020 *Income* £64,300 *Total grants* £71,400 *Grants to organisations* £71,400 *Assets* £1,830,000

TRUSTEES Mark Evans; Sarah Evans; Andrew Playle; Thomas Evans; Hannah Evans.

HOW TO APPLY Application forms are can be downloaded from the trust's website. Applications are considered twice a year, usually in June and January. The deadline for submissions are 15 May and 15 December respectively.

CONTACT DETAILS Sarah Evans, Secretary and Trustee, Piper Close House, Aydon Road, Corbridge, Northumberland NE45 5PW *Tel.* 01434 632038 *Email* info@chrysalis-trust.co.uk *Website* www.chrysalis-trust.co.uk

■ The Church Burgesses Educational Foundation

CC NO 529357 **ESTABLISHED** 1963

WHERE FUNDING CAN BE GIVEN Sheffield.

WHO CAN BENEFIT Charitable organisations; churches; individuals.

WHAT IS FUNDED Education (including social and physical training) of young people under 25; music activities.

WHAT IS NOT FUNDED Higher education courses.

TYPE OF GRANT Project funding; core costs; capital costs.

SAMPLE GRANTS A list of beneficiaries was not included in the annual report and accounts.

FINANCES *Financial year end* 31/12/2019 *Income* £212,900 *Total grants* £128,400 *Grants to organisations* £103,800 *Assets* £332,000

TRUSTEES David Booker; Mr D. Stanley; Revd Stephen Hunter; Revd W. Thomas; Mrs B. Hickman; Cllr. Garry Weatherall; David Quinney; Dr Linda Kirk.

OTHER INFORMATION The foundation is connected to the Sheffield Church Burgesses Trust. The foundation categorises grants awarded as: church schools grants (£38,200); one-off grants (£26,400); music in the city (£24,700); special individual grants (£19,000); families, youth and children's work (£12,000); individual grants for education (£5,600); youth organisations (£2,500). 'Music in the city' includes an instrumental music bursary scheme, grants to music organisations and choral training at Sheffield Cathedral.

HOW TO APPLY Application forms are available to download, together with criteria and guidelines, from the foundation's website. Forms should be returned to the correspondent by post. The trustees meet four times a year.

CONTACT DETAILS Ian Potter, Law Clerk, c/o Wrigleys Solicitors LLP, Derwent House, 150 Arundel Gate, Sheffield S1 2FN *Tel.* 0114 267 5588 *Email* ian.potter@wrigleys.co.uk *Website* www.sheffieldchurchburgesses.org.uk/educational.htm

■ Church Burgesses Trust

CC NO 221284 **ESTABLISHED** 1554

WHERE FUNDING CAN BE GIVEN Sheffield.

WHO CAN BENEFIT Registered charities; religious bodies/institutions.

WHAT IS FUNDED Social welfare; health; recreational facilities; Anglican churches.

TYPE OF GRANT Capital costs; seed funding/start-up funding.

RANGE OF GRANTS £500 to £10,000.

SAMPLE GRANTS Christ Church – Heeley (£17,500); Holy Cross Gleadless Valley (£12,500); Cathedral Archer Project (£8,000); Share Psychotherapy (£3,000); Weston Park Cancer Charity (£2,000); Dial a Ride Club (£1,900); St Mary the Virgin – Beighton (£490); Sheffield and District African Caribbean Community Association Men's Group (£300).

FINANCES *Financial year end* 31/12/2019 *Income* £1,930,000 *Total grants* £787,700 *Grants to organisations* £780,300 *Assets* £39,690,000

TRUSTEES Revd Sap Hunter; David Quinney; Stephen Eccleston; Dr Julie Banham; Nicholas Hutton; Dr Susan Gentle; Mrs B. R. Hickman; Ian Walker; Elizabeth Brownhill; Mr D. F. Booker; Mr D. Stanley.

OTHER INFORMATION The trust is connected to the Church Burgesses Educational Foundation. During 2019, grants were broken down as follows: Sheffield Cathedral expenditure (£487,600); ecclesiastical grants to organisations (£213,700); general charitable grants to organisations (£79,000). Clergy working expenses and support grants were awarded to 11 individuals totalling £7,400.

HOW TO APPLY Application forms can be downloaded from the relevant page on the trust's website. Completed applications and any supporting documents should be submitted by post or email to the correspondent before the beginning of the second week of December, March, June and September. Further guidance is available on the website.

CONTACT DETAILS Ian Potter, The Law Clerk, c/o Wrigleys Solicitors LLP, Derwent House, 150 Arundel Gate, Sheffield S1 2FN *Tel.* 0114 267 5588 *Email* ian.potter@wrigleys.co.uk *Website* www.sheffieldchurchburgesses.org.uk

■ Church of Ireland Priorities Fund

ESTABLISHED 1980

WHERE FUNDING CAN BE GIVEN The Republic of Ireland and Northern Ireland.

WHO CAN BENEFIT Church of Ireland churches.

WHAT IS FUNDED The following areas are supported by the grant-maker: training (lay and ordained); Christian education; outreach initiatives; innovative ministry projects in rural areas.

WHAT IS NOT FUNDED Projects which are still at the planning stage; recurrent grant aid; funding for salaries; financing debts; funding for cathedrals and churches; routine renovations and repairs.

TYPE OF GRANT Project funding; capital costs. Applications for seed funding are encouraged.

RANGE OF GRANTS Up to 40,000.

SAMPLE GRANTS Muckamore Parish Development Association (£40,800); Fivemiletown (£15,300); Parish of Kilroot (£9,200); St Catherine's Church (£1,300).

FINANCES *Financial year end* 31/12/2019 *Total grants* £625,700 *Grants to organisations* £625,700

OTHER INFORMATION Full accounts were not available to view. The grant total has been taken from the grant-maker's 2019 allocations. All financial information has been converted from Euros using the exchange rate at the time of writing (March 2020).

HOW TO APPLY Application forms are available from the grant-maker's website along with criteria and guidelines. Applications must be made by 31 October each year.

CONTACT DETAILS The Committee, Church of Ireland House, Church Avenue, Rathmines, Dublin D06 CF67 *Tel.* +353-(0)1-4125607 *Email* Contact form on website *Website* www.priorities.ireland.anglican.org

■ Church Urban Fund

CC NO 297483 **ESTABLISHED** 1988

WHERE FUNDING CAN BE GIVEN Lancashire; West Yorkshire; Greater Manchester; the Black Country; East Midlands; Birmingham; Peterborough; Luton; West London; East London.

WHO CAN BENEFIT Local faith-based organisations; voluntary groups; charities.

WHAT IS FUNDED Christian causes; community cohesion and development. The charity's Near Neighbours grants programme funds local groups which are working to bring together neighbours to develop relationships and to improve their communities.

WHAT IS NOT FUNDED See the website for specific exclusions.

TYPE OF GRANT Seed funding; project funding.

RANGE OF GRANTS £250 to £5,000.

SAMPLE GRANTS Centre for Theology and Community London (£128,000); King's Centre West London (£98,000); Faithful Neighbours – Bradford (£76,0000); Transforming Communities Together – Black Country (£58,000); St Philip's Centre Leicester (£55,000); Thrive Together Birmingham (£21,000).

FINANCES *Financial year end* 31/12/2019 *Income* £6,470,000 *Total grants* £1,370,000 *Grants to organisations* £1,370,000 *Assets* £2,820,000

TRUSTEES Andrew Barnett; Alec Spencer; Robert Hallam; Alison Grieve; Christina Rees; Susan Chalkley; Revd Dr Anderson Jeremiah; Philip Fletcher.

OTHER INFORMATION The charity administers the Near Neighbours Programme, through which it provides small grants of £250 to £5,000 to organisations. At the time of writing (June 2021) the programme was focusing on projects that support communities affected by the COVID-19 pandemic. During 2019/20, grants totalling £622,000 were awarded through the Windrush/ Christian Meditation grants and £750,000 through the Near Neighbours programme.

HOW TO APPLY Details of the application procedure for each programme can be found on the fund's website. Contact details of local Near Neighbours co-ordinates can be found on the Near Neighbours website.

CONTACT DETAILS The Near Neighbours Team, The Foundry, 17 Oval Way, London SE11 5RR *Tel.* 020 3752 5655 *Email* hello@cuf.org.uk *Website* www.cuf.org.uk

■ The Churchill Foundation

CC NO 1164320 **ESTABLISHED** 2015

WHERE FUNDING CAN BE GIVEN UK.

WHO CAN BENEFIT Local charities; community groups; national charities.

WHAT IS FUNDED Social welfare; health; older people; children and young people.

RANGE OF GRANTS The Small Grants programme offers grants between £50 and £2,000.

SAMPLE GRANTS Macmillan Cancer Support (£75,400); End Youth Homelessness (£75,300); James' Place (£52,700); Walking With the Wounded (£10,000); Willow Foundation (£2,500); The Rainbow Centre (£2,000); Harborough Community Bus and University of Leicester (£1,000 each).

FINANCES *Financial year end* 31/12/2019 *Income* £410,800 *Total grants* £292,800 *Grants to organisations* £292,800 *Assets* £211,400

TRUSTEES Clinton McCarthy; John Hatchard; Spencer McCarthy; Suzanne Revell; Lindsey Matthews.

OTHER INFORMATION Grants were awarded to 31 organisations during the year. The foundation has two programmes: Annual Partnership Programme – the trustees pick two or three charities each year to support financially and by generating exposure via Churchill Retirement employees, business partners, owners and Churchill Foundation events. Small Grants programme – grants of between £50 and £2,000 for applicants referred by Churchill Retirement colleagues, owners or business partners. Only beneficiaries of grants over £1,000 were detailed in the accounts. Grants below £1,000 totalled £20,300.

HOW TO APPLY Applications should be made in writing and be returned by email. The annual partnership programme is usually open for applications between August and September, with applicants being informed if they have been shortlisted by 1 November. The Small Grant application process is open all year round but applicants must be referred by Churchill Retirement colleagues, owners or business partners.

CONTACT DETAILS The Trustees, Churchill Retirement Living Ltd, Churchill House, Parkside, Ringwood, Hampshire BH24 3SG *Tel.* 01425 462100 *Email* enquiries@churchillfoundation.co.uk *Website* www.churchillfoundation.co.uk

■ The CIBC World Markets Children's Foundation

CC NO 1105094 **ESTABLISHED** 2004

WHERE FUNDING CAN BE GIVEN UK and Europe.

WHO CAN BENEFIT UK/European-registered charities.

WHAT IS FUNDED General charitable purposes; health; welfare; education.

WHAT IS NOT FUNDED Individuals; political or advocacy groups; private schools; groups that limit their activities to benefitting people of a designated ethnic or religious affiliation; endowments; multi-year projects or commitments; charities with an income of over £5 million; charities which have already been supported by the foundation in the last five years.

TYPE OF GRANT Two-year partnerships; unrestricted funding.

RANGE OF GRANTS Up to £56,000.

SAMPLE GRANTS Stem 4 and XLP (£56,000 each); Go Beyond (formerly known as CHICKS) and Honeypot (£28,000 each).

FINANCES *Financial year end* 31/03/2020 *Income* £164,100 *Total grants* £168,000 *Grants to organisations* £168,000 *Assets* £30,400

TRUSTEES Andrew Ryde; Samantha Orozco; Sarah Heavey; Sonia Beardsmore; Thomas Broad.

OTHER INFORMATION During the year, grants were awarded to four UK-registered 'Charities of the Year'.

HOW TO APPLY Application forms are available to download from the website and should be returned by email. Due to COVID-19, the foundation extended its current partnerships until 31 March 2022. See the website for updates on application openings.

CONTACT DETAILS The Trustees, c/o Canadian Imperial Bank of Commerce, 150 Cheapside, London EC2V 6ET *Tel.* 020 7234 6000 *Email* ukchildrensmiracle@cibc.co.uk *Website* https://www.cibc.com/ca/miracleday/international/childrens-foundation.html

■ The City Bridge Trust (Bridge House Estates)

CC NO 1035628 **ESTABLISHED** 1995

WHERE FUNDING CAN BE GIVEN Greater London.

WHO CAN BENEFIT Registered charities; CICs; CIOs; charitable companies; exempt or excepted charities; registered industrial and provident societies or co-operatives.

WHAT IS FUNDED Social welfare; mental health; the environment; inclusion; safety; older people; survivors of domestic and sexual abuse, modern day slavery, trafficking or hate crime; disability; offenders and ex-offenders; English language courses; advice and support services (debt and money, benefits, employment, housing or immigration status); strengthening the voluntary sector.

WHAT IS NOT FUNDED Political parties; political lobbying; non-charitable activities; work which does not benefit the inhabitants of Greater London; individuals (except through nominated agencies); grant-making bodies to make grants on the trust's behalf (except through a nominated agency); schools, PTAs, universities or other educational establishments; medical or academic research; churches or other religious bodies where the monies will be used for religious purposes; hospitals or primary healthcare providers; projects which have already taken place or building work which has already been completed; statutory bodies, such as local authorities; charities established/registered outside the UK; festivals or events which last no longer than a few days; residential care services; residential facilities (except where they provide short-term emergency accommodation).

TYPE OF GRANT Capital and core/revenue costs. Revenue grants can be for up to five years.

SAMPLE GRANTS Federation of London Youth Clubs (£390,000 over three years); Kingston Voluntary Action (£303,600 over two years); British Refugee Council (£220,800 over three years); Afghanistan and Central Asian Association (£121,000 over three years); Magpie Dance (£100,000 over three years); Fulham Good Neighbour Service (£28,200); Cripplegate Foundation (£25,000); The Spitz Charitable Trust (£9,400); Migrants Rights Network (£5,050); St Barnabas PCC (£980).

FINANCES *Financial year end* 31/03/2020 *Income* £46,600,000 *Total grants* £30,500,000 *Grants to organisations* £30,500,000 *Assets* £1,540,000

TRUSTEE The City of London Corporation.

OTHER INFORMATION The City Bridge Trust is the grant-making arm of the Bridge House Estates charity. Grants were made to 262 organisations during the year, supporting 277 projects. Details of all the grants approved are available on the website under the News and Events heading. Alternatively, a search tool is available on the website where you can search for active grants using different criteria.

HOW TO APPLY Applications have to be made through the online portal on the trust's website. To access the online form, you must first complete the eligibility quiz. Appeals sent by post, fax or email are not considered and any draft or initial proposals sent by email or via the enquiry form are not reviewed. See the website for a full list of supporting documents required and for detailed step-by-step guidance on the application process. The Grants Committee meets regularly and applications are accepted throughout the year for all current funding programmes.

CONTACT DETAILS The Grants Team, City of London Corporation, PO Box 270, Guildhall, London EC2P 2EJ *Tel.* 020 7332 3710 *Email* citybridgetrust@cityoflondon.gov.uk *Website* www.citybridgetrust.org.uk

■ CLA Charitable Trust

CC NO 280264 **ESTABLISHED** 1980

WHERE FUNDING CAN BE GIVEN England and Wales.

WHO CAN BENEFIT Registered charities; CICs.

WHAT IS FUNDED Education about the countryside for young people from towns and cities and those who are disadvantaged; to provide facilities for those who have disabilities or learning difficulties or who are in some way disadvantaged to enjoy the benefits of the countryside; to support the advancement of education in agriculture, horticulture and conservation for disadvantaged people, particularly the young.

WHAT IS NOT FUNDED Staff costs; sensory gardens or community allotments; state-funded schools or other organisations; organisations with substantial financial resources; organisations that have received a grant from the trust in the previous three years.

TYPE OF GRANT Specific projects or items rather than for ongoing running costs.

RANGE OF GRANTS Up to £21,000.

SAMPLE GRANTS Harper Adams University Scholarships (£20,000); High Mead (£7,500); The Country Trust, Farms for City Children, Langlands CIO and United Response (£5,000 each); Whirlow Hall Farm Trust (£3,000); Living Options Devon (£2,500); Open Doors CIC and Conquest Centre Devon (£2,200 each); Sheffield Wildlife Trust (£2,000).

FINANCES *Financial year end* 30/11/2019
Income £62,200 *Total grants* £64,400
Grants to organisations £64,400
Assets £405,300

TRUSTEES Bridget Biddell; Andrew Grant; Robin Clarke; Jane Lane; Roger Douglas; Giles Bowring.

OTHER INFORMATION The 2018/19 accounts were the latest available at the time of writing (June 2021).

HOW TO APPLY Application forms can be downloaded from the trust's website. The trustees meet three times a year.

CONTACT DETAILS Lisa Hofford, Trust Administrator, 16 Belgrave Square, London SW1X 8PQ *Tel.* 020 7235 0511 *Email* charitabletrust@cla.org.uk *Website* www.cla.org.uk

■ The Clan Trust Ltd

CC NO 803661 **ESTABLISHED** 1990

WHERE FUNDING CAN BE GIVEN Norfolk.

WHO CAN BENEFIT Individuals and organisations involved in agriculture and farming; community services, including activities and clubs, that benefit older people and people with disabilities.

WHAT IS FUNDED Agriculture and horticulture; agricultural education; scientific and innovative projects that advance farming; young farmers; older people; people with disabilities.

TYPE OF GRANT Capital costs (including equipment for young farmers); project funding; research and start-up costs.

RANGE OF GRANTS £200 to £15,000.

SAMPLE GRANTS Norfolk Young Farmers and Countrysiders (£15,000); University of East Anglia (£5,000); Agrifood Charities Partnership and The Royal Norfolk Agricultural Association (£4,000 each); North Norfolk Community Transport (£25,000); Pensthorpe Conservation Trust (£1,000); Aylsham Agricultural Show and Livability (£500 each); Ludham Village Hall (£200).

FINANCES *Financial year end* 31/03/2020
Income £227,000 *Total grants* £60,000
Grants to organisations £56,600
Assets £5,740,000

TRUSTEES Ian Alston; Richard Hirst; Stephen Oldfield; James Alson; Rob Alston; Timothy Papworth; Alison Ritchie; Henry Raker.

OTHER INFORMATION Grants were awarded to 29 organisations and four individuals during the year.

HOW TO APPLY Applications can be made through the trust's website. See the website for more information on its specific funds and awards.

CONTACT DETAILS Rob Hughes, c/o Brown and Co., Market Chambers, 25–26 Tuesday Market Place, King's Lynn, Norfolk PE30 1JJ *Tel.* 01553 770771 *Email* rob.hughes@brown-co.com *Website* www.theclantrust.co.uk

■ J. A. Clark Charitable Trust

CC NO 1010520 **ESTABLISHED** 1970

WHERE FUNDING CAN BE GIVEN UK and overseas.

WHO CAN BENEFIT UK and non-UK-registered charities and social enterprises.

WHAT IS FUNDED Climate change, in particular, people who have been forcibly displaced from their homes due to the climate crisis.

WHAT IS NOT FUNDED Individuals; emergency relief; research; the promotion of religious causes; core costs alone (but the trust will pay an appropriate share of core costs); academic research; organisations with an annual income of more than £10 million.

TYPE OF GRANT Project funding; one-off.

RANGE OF GRANTS Up to £30,000.

SAMPLE GRANTS Previous beneficiaries have included: Brave Hearts Foundation – Uganda; Cord Global; Lotus Flower Trust – India; Small Steps Project – Kenya and Ashden; The Ideas Partnership; Thousand Currents – Nigeria.

FINANCES *Financial year end* 31/12/2019
Income £289,800 *Total grants* £7,500
Grants to organisations £7,500
Assets £13,300,000

TRUSTEES William Pym; Thomas Clark; Aidan Pelly; Odette Clark Campbell.

OTHER INFORMATION In 2019 the trust underwent a strategic review and therefore did not make any new grants during the period. This resulted in a low grant total; however, grants to organisations the previous year totalled £406,500. The 2019 annual report states that grants were due to resume in 2020 under the new funding programme titled 'Climate Change and Displacement'. The trust provides an annual grant to the Eucalyptus Foundation and this was the only beneficiary during the year (£7,500).

HOW TO APPLY The trust has two funding rounds a year. All applications are submitted through an online system that opens four weeks before the deadline. Check the trust's website for the next deadline.

CONTACT DETAILS Lynette Cooper, Trust Secretary, 43B Grange Road, Street, Somerset BA16 0AY *Tel.* 01458 842374 *Email* hello@jaclarktrust.org *Website* https://jaclarktrust.org

■ Clark Foundation

CC NO 313143 **ESTABLISHED** 1959

WHERE FUNDING CAN BE GIVEN UK. Preference for areas where there are significant numbers of employees of C and J Clark and its subsidiaries.

WHO CAN BENEFIT Registered charities; schools; voluntary organisations; hospices; churches.

WHAT IS FUNDED Arts; countryside; education; housing; medicine; overseas aid; religion; social welfare; children.

TYPE OF GRANT One-off capital projects and start-up costs.

RANGE OF GRANTS Up to £60,000 but mostly £200 to £20,000.

SAMPLE GRANTS Whitstone School Academy Trust (£10,000); Carymoor Environmental Trust (£3,000); Aerospace Bristol (£2,000); Yeovil Netball Club (£200).

FINANCES *Financial year end* 31/03/2020
Income £11,890,000 *Total grants* £252,000
Grants to organisations £252,000
Assets £11,290,000

OTHER INFORMATION According to the trust's 2019/20 accounts, it generally makes grants 'to organisations which are close to significant numbers of C and J Clark Ltd employees or ex-employees. This includes organisations overseas which are near to where there are employees in companies supplying shoes to C and J Clark Ltd.'

HOW TO APPLY Contact the Trust Manager for further information.

CONTACT DETAILS The Trust Manager, Clarks International, 40 High Street, Somerset BA16 0EQ *Email* trustgrants@clarks.com

■ The Clore Duffield Foundation

CC NO 1084412 **ESTABLISHED** 2000

WHERE FUNDING CAN BE GIVEN UK, the larger grants go to London-based organisations.

WHO CAN BENEFIT Registered charities. Local authority cultural organisations are also eligible to apply.

WHAT IS FUNDED The cultural sector, in particular museums; galleries; performing arts learning spaces. Support is also given to the Jewish community.

WHAT IS NOT FUNDED The foundation does not fund projects retrospectively and will not accept (or respond to) applications from the following: individuals; general appeals and circulars; projects outside the UK. It should also be noted that the following are very rarely funded: staff posts; local branches of national charities; academic or project research; conference costs.

RANGE OF GRANTS Grants have ranged from £10,000 to £1 million.

SAMPLE GRANTS Previous beneficiaries have included: JW3 Trust Ltd (£1.6 million); New College, Oxford (£250,000); Grange Park Opera and Royal Academy of Arts (£200,000 each); National Theatre (£187,500); The Art Room (£133,000); Royal College of Art and Anna Freud National Centre for Children and Families (£100,000 each); University of Oxford Graduate Scholarship in the Humanities (£99,000); Tate Liverpool (£30,000); British Library and Tate (£5,000 each); Royal Trinity Hospice (£1,000).

FINANCES *Financial year end* 31/12/2019
Income £5,600 *Total grants* £3,700,000
Grants to organisations £3,700,000

OTHER INFORMATION Full accounts were not available to view on the Charity Commission's website due to the foundation's low income. We have therefore estimated the grant total based on the foundation's total expenditure.

HOW TO APPLY See the foundation's website of details of how to apply.

CONTACT DETAILS The Trustees, Unit 3, Chelsea Manor Studios, Flood Street, London SW3 5SR *Tel.* 020 7351 6061 *Email* info@cloreduffield.org.uk *Website* www.cloreduffield.org.uk

■ Closehelm Ltd

CC NO 291296 **ESTABLISHED** 1983

WHERE FUNDING CAN BE GIVEN UK and Israel.

WHO CAN BENEFIT Jewish organisations; individuals.

WHAT IS FUNDED The advancement of religion in accordance with the Jewish faith; the relief of poverty.

SAMPLE GRANTS A list of beneficiaries was not included in the annual report and accounts.

FINANCES *Financial year end* 30/03/2020
Income £308,800 *Total grants* £215,100
Grants to organisations £102,000
Assets £2,820,000

OTHER INFORMATION Grants to individuals totalled £113,100. Grants were made to ten organisations.

HOW TO APPLY Contact the correspondent for further information.

CONTACT DETAILS The Trustees, 30 Armitage Road, London NW11 8RD *Tel.* 020 8201 8688

■ The Clothworkers' Foundation

CC NO 274100 **ESTABLISHED** 1977

WHERE FUNDING CAN BE GIVEN UK and overseas.

WHO CAN BENEFIT Registered charities; social enterprises; CICs; special schools.

WHAT IS FUNDED People with disabilities; disadvantaged young people and minority communities; older people; domestic and sexual violence; homelessness; visual impairment; alcohol and substance misuse; prisoners and ex-offenders.

WHAT IS NOT FUNDED Refer to the foundation's website for a full list exclusions.

TYPE OF GRANT Capital costs.

RANGE OF GRANTS Large grants (over £100,000); Small grants (up to £10,000).

SAMPLE GRANTS Previous beneficiaries have included: The Aldingbourne Trust (£110,000); Ambitious about Autism (£100,000); North London Samaritans and Stable Family Home Trust (£50,000 each); Greenhouse Sports (£40,000); Ufton Court (£33,000); Sulgrave Club (£30,000); Buttle UK and Cardiff YMCA (£25,000 each).

FINANCES *Financial year end* 31/12/2019
Income £9,730,000 *Total grants* £7,360,000
Grants to organisations £7,360,000
Assets £228,490,000

OTHER INFORMATION During the year, the foundation awarded £7.59 million in grants distributed as follows: proactive programmes (£1.92 million); disabled people (£1.75 million); young people (£1.28 million); homelessness (£430,000); older people (£630,000); domestic and sexual violence (£293,000); visual impairment (£220,000); alcohol and substance misuse (£150,000); other (£90,000); prisoners and ex-offenders (£210,000); minority communities (£630,000).

HOW TO APPLY The foundation's website has an eligibility quiz, a list of frequently asked questions and further information on the application process.

CONTACT DETAILS The Trustees, Clothworkers' Hall, Dunster Court, Mincing Lane, London EC3R 7AH *Tel.* 020 7623 7041 *Email* foundation@clothworkers.co.uk *Website* https://www.clothworkersfoundation.org.uk

Cloudesley

CC NO 205959 **ESTABLISHED** 1517
WHERE FUNDING CAN BE GIVEN Islington.
WHO CAN BENEFIT Voluntary and charitable organisations; individuals; churches.
WHAT IS FUNDED Health; social welfare; the upkeep and repair of the 27 Church of England churches in the Islington Deanery.
TYPE OF GRANT Projects costs; strategic; small one-off grants; large multi-year grants; core funding; capital costs.
RANGE OF GRANTS Dependent on the grants programme, usually £5,000 to £50,000.
SAMPLE GRANTS Islington Law Centre (£168,000); Help on Your Doorstep (£107,000); St Saviour's – Hanley Road (£62,000); Islington Giving (£50,000); St Mary – Hornsey Rise (£22,900); Centre 404 (£10,000); The Maya Centre (£5,100); Our Most Holy Redeemer – Clerkenwell (£170).
FINANCES *Financial year end* 30/06/2020 *Income* £1,760,000 *Total grants* £981,700 *Grants to organisations* £804,900 *Assets* £53,360,000
TRUSTEE Richard Cloudesley Trustee Ltd.
OTHER INFORMATION During 2019/20, grants to churches totalled £444,800 and grants for health and social welfare totalled £360,100. The charity also makes health and welfare grants to individuals, via the Cloudesley Partners programme and these totalled £176,800.
HOW TO APPLY Applications can be completed online during open funding periods; applicants are advised to regularly check the charity's website for more information.
CONTACT DETAILS Yvonne Amar, Grants Manager, Office 1.1, Resource for London, 356 Holloway Road, London, N7 6PA *Tel.* 020 7697 4094 *Email* info@cloudesley.org.uk *Website* www.cloudesley.org.uk

The Clover Trust

CC NO 213578 **ESTABLISHED** 1961
WHERE FUNDING CAN BE GIVEN UK and overseas, with a slight preference for West Dorset.
WHO CAN BENEFIT Registered charities.
WHAT IS FUNDED Older people; young people; Catholicism; health; disability.
TYPE OF GRANT Up to three years.
RANGE OF GRANTS Typically £1,000 to £10,000.
SAMPLE GRANTS Friends of Children in Romania (£40,000); Farms of City Children (£15,000); The JOLT Trust (£10,000); 999 Club (£8,000); Kates Nursing Home, Children with Cancer (£7,000 each); The Southern Spinal Injuries Trust (£1,000).
FINANCES *Financial year end* 31/12/2019 *Income* £240,000 *Total grants* £219,500 *Grants to organisations* £219,500 *Assets* £6,000,000
TRUSTEES Sara Woodhouse; Benedict Woodhouse; Charlotte Morrison.
OTHER INFORMATION Grants were awarded to 38 organisations during the year.
HOW TO APPLY The trust's Charity Commission record states: 'The Trustees prefer to make regular donations to a designated selection of recipients and intend to continue with this policy for the foreseeable future. The trustees are currently not accepting any further applications for grant funding from other individuals or organisations.'
CONTACT DETAILS The Trustees, Box Tree House, 22 Martingale Road, Burbage, Marlborough, Wiltshire SN8 3TY

The Robert Clutterbuck Charitable Trust

CC NO 1010559 **ESTABLISHED** 1992
WHERE FUNDING CAN BE GIVEN UK, with a preference for Cheshire and Hertfordshire.
WHO CAN BENEFIT Registered charities; schools; places of worship.
WHAT IS FUNDED Personnel within the armed forces and ex-servicemen and women; sport and recreational facilities for young people in Cheshire and Hertfordshire; the welfare, protection and preservation of domestic animal life in Cheshire and Hertfordshire; natural history and wildlife.
WHAT IS NOT FUNDED Individuals; charities with an annual turnover exceeding £1 million (unless they are primarily concerned with the welfare of ex-service personnel or have previously received a grant from the trust).
TYPE OF GRANT Capital costs; core and revenue costs.
RANGE OF GRANTS Up to £5,000 but generally £1,000 to £3,000.
SAMPLE GRANTS Veterans at Ease (£3,000); Jubilee Sailing Trust (£2,000); Sandbach RAF Cadets (£1,800); Tall Ships Youth Trust (£1,200); Change Changing Lives, Live Music Now, Prader-Willi Syndrome Association and Suffolk Owl Charity (£1,000 each).
FINANCES *Financial year end* 05/04/2020 *Income* £68,800 *Total grants* £57,700 *Grants to organisations* £57,700 *Assets* £1,840,000
TRUSTEES Roger Pincham; Ian Pearson; Lucy Pitman; Tessa Lydekker.
OTHER INFORMATION Grants were made to 45 organisations during the 2019/20.
HOW TO APPLY The trust's website states: 'There are no application forms and charities wishing to apply should write to the Secretary giving details of what they propose to do with any grant made and of their current financial position.' The trustees usually meet twice a year in March and September to consider grants. The deadlines for the applications rounds are 30 June and 31 December each year.
CONTACT DETAILS George Wolfe, Secretary, 28 Brookfields, Calver, Hope Valley, Derbyshire S32 3XB *Tel.* 01433 631308 *Email* secretary@clutterbucktrust.org.uk *Website* www.clutterbucktrust.org.uk

Clydpride Ltd

CC NO 295393 **ESTABLISHED** 1982
WHERE FUNDING CAN BE GIVEN Worldwide.
WHO CAN BENEFIT Individuals and institutions benefitting Jewish people and people disadvantaged by poverty.
WHAT IS FUNDED Advancement of the Orthodox Jewish faith; relief of poverty; general charitable purposes.
RANGE OF GRANTS Generally up to £50,000.
SAMPLE GRANTS Tomchei Yotzei Anglia (£40,000); Comet Charities Ltd (£25,000).
FINANCES *Financial year end* 24/12/2019 *Income* £4,020,000 *Total grants* £287,200 *Grants to organisations* £284,800 *Assets* £30,440,000

TRUSTEES Leon Faust; Jacob Halpern; Jonathan Weinstein; Mr A. Faust.

OTHER INFORMATION Grants were broken down as follows: advancement of religion through education (£171,600); relief of poverty (£73,500); benefit of the Jewish community (£37,300). Only organisations receiving grants of over £15,000 were listed as beneficiaries in the charity's accounts. Grants of under £15,000 totalled £209,400. The 2018/19 accounts were the latest available at the time of writing (January 2021).

HOW TO APPLY Apply in writing to the correspondent. The charity considers all grant requests from organisations that fall within the criteria of the charity's objects.

CONTACT DETAILS Mrs T. Faust, Secretary, c/o Rayner Essex Accountants, Entrance D, Tavistock House South, Tavistock Square, London WC1H 9LG *Tel.* 020 8731 7744

■ CMZ Ltd

CC NO 1087870 **ESTABLISHED** 2001

WHERE FUNDING CAN BE GIVEN London, Israel and the United States.

WHO CAN BENEFIT Charitable organisations.

WHAT IS FUNDED Orthodox Jewish education and social welfare.

RANGE OF GRANTS £16,000 to £156,200.

SAMPLE GRANTS Mifal Hachesed Vehatzedokoh (£156,200); Support the Charity Worker (£155,900); Edupoor Ltd (£152,500); One Heart Lev Echod (£147,200); Amud Hatzdokoh Trust (£36,000); The Rehabilitation Trust (£135,700); Care All Ltd (£128,100); Friends of Beis Chinuch Lebonos Trust (£115,000); Keren Hatzolas Doros (£102,700); Friends of Wiznitz I td (£102,300); Lehachzikom (£96,100); Friends of Beis Soroh Schneirer (£90,100); Friends of Mercaz Hatorah Belz Macnivka (£72,000); Yesamach Levav (£39,200).

FINANCES *Financial year end* 31/03/2020
Income £3,940,000 *Total grants* £3,752,500
Grants to organisations £3,320,000
Assets £325,200

TRUSTEES Ephraim Gottesfeld; Mr P. Schneebalg; Samuel Steinmetz.

OTHER INFORMATION The charity offered 17 grants to organisations and individuals during the year.

HOW TO APPLY The charity offers grants and donations to registered charitable organisations and individuals, provided that a letter of approbation from a qualified Rabbi or Vaad Hatzdokoh is produced.

CONTACT DETAILS Mr B. Goldberg, Secretary, 206 High Road, London N15 4NP *Tel.* 020 8801 6038

■ The Francis Coales Charitable Foundation

CC NO 270718 **ESTABLISHED** 1975

WHERE FUNDING CAN BE GIVEN UK, with a preference for Bedfordshire, Buckinghamshire, Hertfordshire and Northamptonshire (including the Diocese of Peterborough).

WHO CAN BENEFIT Old buildings open to the public, usually churches, monuments and monumental brasses.

WHAT IS FUNDED The structural repair of ecclesiastical buildings (built before 1875) which are open to the public (preference is given to churches in the counties of Buckinghamshire, Bedfordshire, Hertfordshire and Northamptonshire); the conservation of monuments and monumental brasses (no geographical restriction); the publication of architectural and architectural books and papers; the purchase of documents and items for record offices and museums; archaeological research and related causes.

WHAT IS NOT FUNDED 'Domestic' items such as heating, lighting, wiring, installation of facilities, etc.

TYPE OF GRANT Largely one-off; capital costs (fabric repairs only).

RANGE OF GRANTS Mostly £500 to £5,000.

SAMPLE GRANTS Previous beneficiaries have included: Northamptonshire Victoria County History (£6,000); Smisby Derbyshire (£4,500); Hertfordshire Building Trust (£3,000); Chiltern Open Air Museum – Buckinghamshire (£1,000); London Record Society (£750); Monumental Brass Society (£500).

FINANCES *Financial year end* 31/12/2019
Income £144,600 *Total grants* £120,200
Grants to organisations £120,200
Assets £5,300,000

TRUSTEES Martin Stuchfield; Revd Brian Wilcox; Ian Barnett; Matthew Saunders; Pamela Ward.

OTHER INFORMATION In 2019 the foundation received 40 applications and awarded 20 grants.

HOW TO APPLY Application forms can be downloaded from the foundation's website. Once completed, these should be submitted to the foundation by post. The trustees normally meet three times a year to consider grants. The foundation's website offers the following guidance: 'In respect of a building or contents, include a copy of the relevant portion only of the architect's (or conservator's) specification showing the actual work proposed. Photographs illustrating this are a necessity, and only in exceptional circumstances will an application be considered without supporting photographs here. It is of help if six copies of any supporting documentation are submitted in order that each trustee may have a copy in advance of the meeting.'

CONTACT DETAILS David Edworthy, Administrator, The Old Rectory, Rectory Way, Lympsham, Weston-Super-Mare, Somerset BS24 0EW *Tel.* 01934 750817 *Email* administrator@franciscoales.uk *Website* franciscoales.co.uk

■ FB Coales No4 (Family) Trust

CC NO 1179856 **ESTABLISHED** 1964

WHERE FUNDING CAN BE GIVEN England and Wales.

WHO CAN BENEFIT Charitable organisations.

WHAT IS FUNDED Physical and mental health ; children and young people.

SAMPLE GRANTS A list of beneficiaries was not included in the annual report and accounts.

FINANCES *Financial year end* 05/02/2021
Income £125,000 *Total grants* £134,800
Grants to organisations £134,800
Assets £787,000

TRUSTEES Christopher Winn; John Burton; Andrew Sweeney.

HOW TO APPLY Contact the correspondent for further information.

CONTACT DETAILS The Trustees, c/o Winn and Coales (Denso) Ltd, Denso House, 33–35 Chapel Road, London SE27 0TR

The Coalfields Regeneration Trust

CC NO 1074930 **ESTABLISHED** 1999

WHERE FUNDING CAN BE GIVEN Coalfield and former coalfield communities in England, Scotland and Wales.

WHO CAN BENEFIT Most voluntary and community organisations and groups working to regenerate coalfield communities are eligible to apply for funding as long as they are not for personal profit. These include registered charities, companies limited by guarantee, community benefit societies, CICs, CIOs and community amateur sports clubs.

WHAT IS FUNDED Welfare of coalfield communities. The trust focuses on: improving health; proving opportunities for children and young people; employment, skills and training programmes; supporting community enterprise; practical help and community investment.

WHAT IS NOT FUNDED Individuals; private businesses/ business for personal profit; statutory bodies; national organisations without independent local branches; organisations that the trustees believe are in a poor financial position; 'friends of Groups' where the end beneficiary will clearly be a statutory body; organisations not established in the UK; organisations not based in or not working predominantly in eligible coalfield areas. Check the website for exclusions from any of the trust's programmes; the guidance notes provide a more detailed list.

RANGE OF GRANTS Grants up to £200,000.

SAMPLE GRANTS Previous beneficiaries have included: Aylesham Neighbourhood Project (£210,000); Haswell and District Mencap Society (£98,000); Derbyshire Rural Community Council (£89,000); The Cornforth Partnership (£75,000); Nottinghamshire Independent Domestic Abuse Link Workers (£66,000); Stoke-on-Trent and District Gingerbread Centre Ltd (£37,000); St John's Church (£10,000); Mansfield and Dukeries Irish Association (£5,000); City of Durham Air Cadets (£3,800); Thornycroft Art Club (£520).

FINANCES *Financial year end* 31/03/2020 *Income* £5,080,000 *Total grants* £1,400,000 *Grants to organisations* £1,400,000 *Assets* £37,620,000

TRUSTEES Peter McNestry; Nicholas Wilson; Michael Clapham; Robert Young; Trudie McGuinness; Sylvia Wileman; Wayne Thomas; Dawn Davies; Judith Kirton-Darling; Keith Cunliffe; Nicky Stubbs; Linda Rutter.

OTHER INFORMATION The trust provides advice, support and financial assistance to community and voluntary organisations which are working to tackle problems at a grass-roots level within coalfield communities.

HOW TO APPLY Application details are different for each programme; details can be found on the trust's website, where guidance notes are also available. Applicants can contact their regional teams to find out more information or to discuss an application.

CONTACT DETAILS The Trustees, 1 Waterside Park, Valley Way, Wombwell, Barnsley, South Yorkshire S73 0BB *Tel.* 01226 270800 *Email* info@coalfields-regen.org.uk *Website* www.coalfields-regen.org.uk

The John Coates Charitable Trust

CC NO 262057 **ESTABLISHED** 1969

WHERE FUNDING CAN BE GIVEN South East England; South West England; London; East Anglia.

WHO CAN BENEFIT Registered charities.

WHAT IS FUNDED Education for people with disabilities; outdoors education; prisoners' well-being; the arts; medicine/healthcare, including supporting service-users and funding research; heritage, conservation and the environment; societal and community cohesion.

WHAT IS NOT FUNDED Individuals; regional offices of national organisations; projects delivered overseas.

TYPE OF GRANT Capital costs; core/revenue costs; project funding.

RANGE OF GRANTS Grants range from £1,000 to £10,000.

SAMPLE GRANTS The Royal Marsden Cancer Charity and Sebastian's Action Trust (£10,000 each); Stroke Association and The British Red Cross Society (£5,000 each); Classics for All (£3,000); Dementia UK (£2,000); The Barn Owl Trust (£1,000).

FINANCES *Financial year end* 05/04/2020 *Income* £473,800 *Total grants* £382,000 *Grants to organisations* £382,000 *Assets* £12,600,000

TRUSTEES Catherine Kesley; Rebecca Lawes; Claire Cartledge; Susan Down; Antonia Youngman; Elspeth McGregor.

OTHER INFORMATION In total, 79 grants were awarded throughout the year.

HOW TO APPLY Applications can be made through the trust's website. The trustees meet twice a year usually in January and July to consider applications.

CONTACT DETAILS The Trustees, c/o The Trust Partnership Ltd, 6 Trull Farm Buildings, Trull, Tetbury, Gloucestershire GL8 8SQ *Tel.* 01285 719595 *Email* johncoates@thetrustpartnership.com *Website* https://johncoatescharitabletrust.org.uk

Denise Coates Foundation

CC NO 1149110 **ESTABLISHED** 2012

WHERE FUNDING CAN BE GIVEN UK and overseas.

WHO CAN BENEFIT Charities and community groups.

WHAT IS FUNDED Education and training; health and welfare; arts and culture; medical research and development; community development; disaster recovery.

TYPE OF GRANT Project funding; core costs; capital costs; research; collections and acquisitions.

SAMPLE GRANTS Sandbach Gymnastics Foundation (£2.18 million); Stonyhurst College (£1.6 million); mothers2mothers (£1 million); Leonard Cheshire Disability – Hill House (£552,700); Tate (£423,300); New Vic Theatre (£335,000); Douglas Macmillan Hospice (£283,800).

FINANCES *Financial year end* 29/03/2020 *Income* £88,710,000 *Total grants* £9,000,000 *Grants to organisations* £9,000,000 *Assets* £385,320,000

TRUSTEES Denise Coates; John Coates; Peter Coates; James White; Simon Galletley; Oliver Adams.

OTHER INFORMATION Grants were distributed as follows: community development (£2.61 million); health and welfare (£2.21 million); education and training (£2.1 million); medical research and development (£1.65 million); arts and culture (£423,300).

HOW TO APPLY Apply in writing to the correspondent.
CONTACT DETAILS The Trustees, bet365 House, Media Way, Stoke-on-Trent, Staffordshire ST1 5SZ *Tel.* 0845 600 0365

■ The Cobtree Charity Trust Ltd

CC NO 208455 **ESTABLISHED** 1951
WHERE FUNDING CAN BE GIVEN Maidstone and district.
WHO CAN BENEFIT Registered charities; churches; hospices.
WHAT IS FUNDED General charitable purposes by other charities in the Maidstone and district area.
RANGE OF GRANTS Grants are generally in the range of £1,000 to £5,000.
SAMPLE GRANTS Young Farmers (£15,900); Young Lives (£12,000); Teenage Cancer Trust (£6,000); Heart of Kent Hospice, Maidstone Winter Shelter (£5,000 each); Rainbow Trust Children's Charity (£2,000). Connect Church Maidstone (£800).
FINANCES *Financial year end* 05/04/2020 *Income* £226,300 *Total grants* £133,100 *Grants to organisations* £133,100 *Assets* £6,510,000
TRUSTEES John Fletcher; David Wigg; Lawrence Martin; Michael Startup; Stephen Beck; Stefan Jordan; Mike Sharp; Sandra Knatchbull.
OTHER INFORMATION Grants were awarded to 34 organisations during the year.
HOW TO APPLY Apply in writing to the correspondent. The trustees meet quarterly.
CONTACT DETAILS The Trustees, 3 Thurnham Oast, Aldington Lane, Thurnham, Maidstone, Kent ME14 3LL *Tel.* 01622 736865 *Email* cobtreecharitytrust@outlook.com *Website* https://www.cobtreecharitytrust.org

■ The Vivienne and Samuel Cohen Charitable Trust

CC NO 255496 **ESTABLISHED** 1965
WHERE FUNDING CAN BE GIVEN In practice, UK and Israel.
WHO CAN BENEFIT Charitable organisations, primarily Jewish causes.
WHAT IS FUNDED Jewish causes; health; education; religion; social welfare; culture and recreation.
WHAT IS NOT FUNDED Individuals.
RANGE OF GRANTS £1,000 to £5,000.
SAMPLE GRANTS Beit Moreshet Maale Adumin (£22,500 in three grants); Yishaya Adler Memorial Fund (£17,000 in three grants); Shirat Yisrael (£16,000 in two grants); Jerusalem Symphony Orchestra (£13,000 in two grants); Maarava (£8,000); Bayit Cham (£6,000 in three grants); World Jewish Relief (£5,000); University College London Development Office (£2,000); Age UK, Elimination of Leukaemia Fund, Hampstead Garden Suburb Synagogue, Jerusalem College of Technology, National Osteoporosis Society, Simon Marks Jewish Primary School and Union of Jewish Students (£1,000 each).
FINANCES *Financial year end* 05/04/2020 *Income* £164,500 *Total grants* £223,900 *Grants to organisations* £223,900 *Assets* £3,510,000
TRUSTEES Jonathan Lauffer; Gershon Cohen; Michael Ben-Gershon; Gideon Lauffer; Elizabeth Hacohen.
OTHER INFORMATION The charity made 137 grants during the year, distributed as follows: education (£72,400 in 34 grants); care and welfare (£68,200 in 52 grants); religious activities and communal (£41,700 in eight grants); medical care and welfare (£23,500 in 29 grants); cultural and recreation (£18,100 in 14 grants). There were 58 grants of less than £1,000, which totalled £18,700.
HOW TO APPLY Apply in writing to the correspondent.
CONTACT DETAILS The Trustees, Clayton Stark and Co., 5th Floor, Charles House, 108–110 Finchley Road, London NW3 5JJ *Tel.* 020 7431 4200 *Email* csco@claytonstark.co.uk

■ The John S. Cohen Foundation

CC NO 241598 **ESTABLISHED** 1965
WHERE FUNDING CAN BE GIVEN UK.
WHO CAN BENEFIT Registered charities; colleges and universities; museums.
WHAT IS FUNDED Arts; conservation and the environment; education and academia; social welfare and medical research.
SAMPLE GRANTS New Writing North (£65,000); British Museum (£13,400); Zoological Society of London (£10,000); Welsh National Opera (£5,000); Young Vic (£3,000); Bumblebee Conservation Trust (£500).
FINANCES *Financial year end* 31/03/2020 *Income* £628,800 *Total grants* £505,300 *Grants to organisations* £505,300 *Assets* £11,900,000
TRUSTEES Dr Imogen Cohen; Olivia Cohen; Jillian Cohen.
OTHER INFORMATION Grants were broken down as follows: the arts (£189,800); education and academia (£207,100); conservation and the environment (£28,000); social and medical causes (£10,500).
HOW TO APPLY Contact the correspondent for further information.
CONTACT DETAILS Diana Helme, Administrator, PO Box 21277, London W9 2YH *Tel.* 020 7286 6921

■ Colchester Catalyst Charity

CC NO 228352 **ESTABLISHED** 1963
WHERE FUNDING CAN BE GIVEN Northeast Essex.
WHO CAN BENEFIT Registered charities; CICs; social enterprises; universities; hospitals; hospices; individuals.
WHAT IS FUNDED Healthcare; respite breaks for carers.
WHAT IS NOT FUNDED Retrospective funding; statutory authorities; salaries or other running costs.
TYPE OF GRANT Project funding; capital costs.
SAMPLE GRANTS Age Concern (£33,000); The Befriending Scheme, Essex Sight (£20,000 each); Sports for Confidence (£15,000); Harwich Connexions and Tendring Community Transport (£10,000 each); PTSD Support (£5,000).
FINANCES *Financial year end* 31/12/2019 *Income* £416,100 *Total grants* £489,300 *Grants to organisations* £396,900 *Assets* £12,250,000
TRUSTEES Peter Fitt; Christine Hayward; Mark Pertwee; Dr Thilaka Rudra; Dr Max Hickman; Dr Naomi Busfield; Elizabeth Thrower; Keith Songhurst.
OTHER INFORMATION Grants were broken down as follows: charities (£233,200); respite care (£163,700); special individual needs (£92,400).
HOW TO APPLY Apply online via the charity's website. Application forms can also be sent out by post

on request. Application deadlines can be found on the charity's website.

CONTACT DETAILS Stephanie Grant, Administrator, 14 Dedham Vale Business Centre, Manningtree Road, Dedham, Colchester, Essex CO7 6BL *Tel.* 01206 323420 *Email* info@colchestercatalyst.co.uk *Website* www.colchestercatalyst.co.uk

■ The Cole Charitable Trust

CC NO 264033 **ESTABLISHED** 1972

WHERE FUNDING CAN BE GIVEN Greater Birmingham, Kent and Cambridge.

WHO CAN BENEFIT Registered charities.

WHAT IS FUNDED Social welfare; community development; environmental development; young people; community development.

WHAT IS NOT FUNDED National or regional organisations; organisations that are not registered charities; large building appeals; animal charities; research or further education; individuals.

TYPE OF GRANT Small capital or project grants; normally one-off; core costs.

SAMPLE GRANTS Hope Projects (West Midlands) Ltd (£63,100); Cambridge Cycling Campaign (£3,000); Spitfire Services (£2,000); Platform for Life, Hi Kent (£1,500 each); Acacia Family Support (£1,000); Walsall Community Church (£500).

FINANCES *Financial year end* 05/04/2020 *Income* £146,700 *Total grants* £155,600 *Grants to organisations* £155,600 *Assets* £4,050,000

TRUSTEES Ranjit Sondhi; Tim Cole; George Cole; Tom Cole; James Cole; Jont Cole; Jacqui Francis; Angie Cole; Katie Cole.

HOW TO APPLY Application forms are available to download from the trust's websites. Completed forms should be returned by email (preferred) or post along with a one page letter and a copy of your latest accounts if they are not available to view on the Charity Commission's website.

CONTACT DETAILS Lise Jackson, Administrator, PO Box 955, Haslingfield, Cambridge CB23 1WX *Tel.* 01223 871676 *Email* thecoletrust@gmail.com *Website* www.colecharitabletrust.org.uk

■ Colefax Charitable Trust

CC NO 1017285 **ESTABLISHED** 1993

WHERE FUNDING CAN BE GIVEN Berkshire and Hampshire.

WHO CAN BENEFIT Registered charities; hospitals; schools and charitable organisations.

WHAT IS FUNDED General charitable purposes.

WHAT IS NOT FUNDED Individuals.

SAMPLE GRANTS A list of beneficiaries was not included in the annual report and accounts.

FINANCES *Financial year end* 05/04/2020 *Income* £421,900 *Total grants* £158,700 *Grants to organisations* £158,700 *Assets* £15,690,000

TRUSTEES John Heath; Hans Krohn; Daniela Fiennes-Cox.

HOW TO APPLY Contact the correspondent for further information.

CONTACT DETAILS Hans Krohn, Trustee, Westbrook House, St Helens Gardens, The Pitchens, Wroughton, Swindon, Wiltshire SN4 0RD *Tel.* 01635 200415

■ John and Freda Coleman Charitable Trust

CC NO 278223 **ESTABLISHED** 1979

WHERE FUNDING CAN BE GIVEN Hampshire and Surrey.

WHO CAN BENEFIT Registered charities; unregistered charities; CICs; social enterprises; schools.

WHAT IS FUNDED Education and training for young people.

TYPE OF GRANT Project funding.

RANGE OF GRANTS Up to £25,000.

SAMPLE GRANTS Previous beneficiaries have included: Surrey SATRO (£25,000); Surrey Care Trust (£10,000); Therapy Garden – Green School (£6,000); Surrey Silkway (£4,000); Linkable (£3,000); Second Chance and Surrey Youth Focus (£2,500 each); Alton College STEM Outreach (£1,500); Ro-ro Sailing (£1,000).

FINANCES *Financial year end* 05/04/2020 *Income* £15,000 *Total grants* £80,000 *Grants to organisations* £80,000

TRUSTEES Paul Coleman; Jeanette Bird; Brian Coleman; Nicole Coleman.

OTHER INFORMATION Full accounts were not available to view on the Charity Commission's website due to the trust's low income. We have therefore estimated the grant total based on the trust's total expenditure.

HOW TO APPLY The trust's website states: 'If you would like to make an application for a grant either call us on 01428 681333 or email jeanette@thecolemantrust.co.uk.'

CONTACT DETAILS Jeanette Bird, Trustee, The Nest, 3 Gasden Drive, Witley, Godalming, Surrey GU8 5QQ *Tel.* 01428 681333 *Email* jeanette@thecolemantrust.co.uk *Website* https://thecolemantrust.co.uk

■ The George Collins Charity

CC NO 212268 **ESTABLISHED** 1959

WHERE FUNDING CAN BE GIVEN Within a 25 mile radius of Birmingham.

WHO CAN BENEFIT Local charitable organisations and local branches of registered national charities in Birmingham.

WHAT IS FUNDED General charitable purposes, with a preference for health; older people and projects tackling loneliness.

WHAT IS NOT FUNDED Individuals.

TYPE OF GRANT One-off project funding.

RANGE OF GRANTS £250 to £1,000.

SAMPLE GRANTS Previous beneficiaries have included: Acorns Children's Hospice, Bentley Beginnings, Birmingham Asian Resources Centre, Birmingham Repertory Theatre, Birmingham Royal Ballet, Coventry Resource Centre for the Blind, Edward's Trust, Martineau Gardens, Restore, Sutton Coldfield YMCA, Warwickshire Social Inclusion Partnership and Whole Person Health Trust.

FINANCES *Financial year end* 05/04/2020 *Income* £88,400 *Total grants* £94,200 *Grants to organisations* £94,200 *Assets* £17,230,000

TRUSTEES Anthony Collins; Sally Botteley; Peter Coggan; Roger Otto; Simon Field.

OTHER INFORMATION Grants were awarded to 86 organisations during the year.

HOW TO APPLY Apply in writing to the correspondent. The trustees usually meet in March, July and November.

CONTACT DETAILS Chrissy Norgrove, Clerk to the Trustees, The Estate Office, Wharf Cottage, Tenbury Wells, Worcestershire WR15 8NY *Tel.* 07799 784019 *Email* chrissy@georgehenrycollinscharity.org.uk

■ Sir Jeremiah Colman Gift Trust

CC NO 229553 **ESTABLISHED** 1920

WHERE FUNDING CAN BE GIVEN UK, with a preference for Hampshire, especially Basingstoke.

WHO CAN BENEFIT Registered charities; churches.

WHAT IS FUNDED General charitable purposes, with a preference for health, education and Christian causes.

RANGE OF GRANTS Grants are up to £20,000.

SAMPLE GRANTS Judd School (£15,000); Foundation for Educational Leadership (£10,000); Basingstoke Mencap Services and Severnside Building Appeal (£5,000 each); Mercy Ships (£3,000); Motiv8 (£1,500); Winchester Youth Counselling (£1,000).

FINANCES *Financial year end* 05/04/2020 *Income* £201,900 *Total grants* £163,300 *Grants to organisations* £163,300 *Assets* £7,290,000

TRUSTEES The Hon. Cynthia Colman; Jeremiah Colman; Lady Judith Colman; Oliver Colman; Sue Colman; Camilla Adeney; Louisa Mulvaney.

OTHER INFORMATION During the year, annual grants totalled £79,500; long-term grants totalled £56,500; new appeals totalled £27,100 and there were 'extra' grants which totalled £190.

HOW TO APPLY Unsolicited applications are not accepted.

CONTACT DETAILS Rose Persson, Secretary and Administrator to the Trustees, Malshanger, Basingstoke, Hampshire RG23 7EY *Tel.* 01963 240260 *Email* rosepersson@btinternet.com

■ The Colt Foundation

CC NO 277189 **ESTABLISHED** 1978

WHERE FUNDING CAN BE GIVEN UK.

WHO CAN BENEFIT Universities.

WHAT IS FUNDED Research projects in the field of occupational and environmental health, particularly those aimed at discovering the cause of illnesses arising from conditions at the place of work. The trustees are particularly keen to fund research that is likely to inform government policy or change working practices.

WHAT IS NOT FUNDED Grants are not made for the general funds of another charity, directly to individuals or for projects overseas.

TYPE OF GRANT Core costs; project funding.

SAMPLE GRANTS University of Edinburgh (£85,900); University College London/London School of Hygiene and Tropical Medicine (£64,9000; Imperial College (£52,000); University of Southampton (£40,600); British College (£10,100); St Mary's Cathedral Workshop (£3,900).

FINANCES *Financial year end* 31/12/2019 *Income* £805,000 *Total grants* £561,000 *Grants to organisations* £401,900 *Assets* £30,190,000

TRUSTEES Prof. David Coggon; Clare Gilchrist; Patricia Lebus; Dr Ira Madan; Prof. Anthony Taylor; Alan O'Hea; Jerome O'Hea; Peter O'Hea.

OTHER INFORMATION Grants were made to 12 organisations. Student fellowships totalled £120,200.

HOW TO APPLY Apply in writing to the correspondent. Full details of what should be included in an application can be found on the 'grants' section of the foundation's website. The trustees meet twice a year to review applications, in the spring and in the autumn, and applications normally need to be received approximately eight weeks beforehand to be considered at the meetings. Exact deadlines can be found on the foundation's website. Applicants can submit a single sheet lay summary at any time during the year prior to working on a full application, so that advice can be given on whether the work is likely to fall within the remit of the foundation.

CONTACT DETAILS Tash Heydon, Director, The Old Bank House, Market Square, Petworth, West Sussex GU28 0AH *Tel.* 01798 342831 *Email* tash@coltfoundation.org.uk *Website* www.coltfoundation.org.uk

■ The Coltstaple Trust

CC NO 1085500 **ESTABLISHED** 2001

WHERE FUNDING CAN BE GIVEN Worldwide.

WHO CAN BENEFIT Charitable organisations.

WHAT IS FUNDED Social welfare; people who are at risk of or experiencing homelessness; overseas aid.

SAMPLE GRANTS Oxfam (£250,000); Emmaus, Shelter and St Mungo's (£50,000 each).

FINANCES *Financial year end* 31/03/2020 *Income* £5,950,000 *Total grants* £400,000 *Grants to organisations* £400,000 *Assets* £12,500,000

TRUSTEES Matthew Oakeshott; Lord Stoneham of Droxford; Elaine Colville; Dr Philippa Oakeshott; Joseph Oakeshott; Leonard Baker.

OTHER INFORMATION Grants were awarded to four organisations during the year.

HOW TO APPLY Apply in writing to the correspondent. The trust tends to award grants to the same charities each year.

CONTACT DETAILS Matthew Oakeshott, Trustee, 15 Queen Anne's Gate, London SW1H 9BU *Tel.* 020 7647 6701 *Email* louise.blackmore@olimproperty.co.uk

■ Colwinston Charitable Trust

CC NO 1049189 **ESTABLISHED** 1995

WHERE FUNDING CAN BE GIVEN UK, with a preference for Wales.

WHO CAN BENEFIT UK-registered charities; arts organisations; libraries; archives.

WHAT IS FUNDED The trust seeks to sustain and support high quality artistic activities that add to the cultural life and experiences available in the UK and especially in Wales. Funding is particularly but not exclusively directed to the support of opera, music, the visual arts.

WHAT IS NOT FUNDED Organisations that are not registered with the Charity Commission; retrospective costs; individuals; research; general appeals; community or amateur arts groups; capital projects; commerical recordings (other than those benefitting emerging or mid-career Welsh composers).

TYPE OF GRANT Project funding; strategic funding.

RANGE OF GRANTS Up to £50,000 but mostly £5,000 to £20,000.

SAMPLE GRANTS Agatha Christie Trust for Children (£50,000); Sinfonia Cymru (£15,000); Music Theatre Wales (£30,000); National Youth Orchestra of Great Britain (£16,000); National Manuscripts Conservation Trust (£8,700); Llandeilo Fawr Festival of Music (£5,000); Longborough Festival Opera 18 (£3,000).

FINANCES *Financial year end* 31/03/2019 *Income* £560,100 *Total grants* £374,400 *Grants to organisations* £374,400 *Assets* £1,310,000

TRUSTEES Mathew Prichard; Martin Tinney; Sian Williams; Lucinda Prichard; Rebecca Evans.

OTHER INFORMATION The trust derives its income from the royalties from the West End production of The Mousetrap. Over 80% of funding goes to projects in Wales. In 2018/19 grants were awarded to 23 organisations. The 2018/19 accounts were the latest available at the time of writing (January 2021).

HOW TO APPLY Application forms and application guidelines can be found on the trust's website.

CONTACT DETAILS Mrs A. McMurray, Consultant Director, 14 Hanover Court, Midhope Road, Woking, Surrey GU22 7UX *Tel.* 020 7842 2000 *Email* colwinston.trust@ntlworld.com *Website* www.colwinston.org.uk

■ Colyer-Fergusson Charitable Trust

CC NO 258958 **ESTABLISHED** 1969

WHERE FUNDING CAN BE GIVEN Kent.

WHO CAN BENEFIT Registered charities; CICs; schools; hospices; individuals.

WHAT IS FUNDED Disadvantaged young people; disadvantaged families; community development; rehabilitation of offenders.

WHAT IS NOT FUNDED National charities receiving widespread support; statutory bodies; hospitals and health authorities; medical care, medical equipment or medical research; academic research, scholarships or bursaries, animal charities; the promotion of religion; the restoration or conservation of buildings; endowment appeals; retrospective funding; widely circulated appeals.

TYPE OF GRANT Project funding.

RANGE OF GRANTS Generally up to £100,000.

SAMPLE GRANTS ellenor Hospice (£2 million); RBLI (£500,000); Arts Education Exchange CIC (£50,000); East Kent Rape Crisis Centre (£30,000); Homeless Care (£15,000); Second Chance Charity (£9,000); Waltham Village Hall Charity (£5,000); Slough Fort Preservation Trust (£2,800).

FINANCES *Financial year end* 31/03/2020 *Income* £766,000 *Total grants* £5,010,500 *Grants to organisations* £4,930,400 *Assets* £32,460,000

TRUSTEES Nicholas Fisher; Ruth Murphy; Rosalind Riley; James Thorne; Barbara Long.

OTHER INFORMATION Grants to organisations were broken down as follows: 50th Anniversary Grants (£3.22 million); investing in young people (£544,700); investing in communities (£410,300); investing in families (£408,300); investing in rehabilitation (£353,600). Grants to individuals totalled £80,100.

HOW TO APPLY Full guidance and application forms are available on the trust's website.

CONTACT DETAILS Gilly Green, Grants Assessor, 34 Hill Street, Richmond, Surrey TW9 1TW *Tel.* 020 8948 3388 *Email* grantadmin@cfct.org.uk *Website* https://www.cfct.org.uk

■ Comic Relief

CC NO 326568 **ESTABLISHED** 1985

WHERE FUNDING CAN BE GIVEN UK, Sub-Saharan Africa and Asia, in particular: Bangladesh, Ghana, India, Kenya, Malawi, Nepal, Nigeria, Sierra Leone, South Africa, Rwanda, Tanzania, Uganda, Zambia and Zimbabwe.

WHO CAN BENEFIT UK-registered charities; voluntary organisations.

WHAT IS FUNDED Poverty and social injustice.

WHAT IS NOT FUNDED Activities which evangelise or proselytise; organisations which adopt a partisan political stance or activities which are party political; one-off conferences or workshops; general appeals, individual and group sponsorship; work where the long-term institutional care of children or young people is a preferred way of working (e.g. setting up or running orphanages); the delivery of services that are normally government's responsibility.

SAMPLE GRANTS A list of beneficiaries was not included in the annual report and accounts.

FINANCES *Financial year end* 31/07/2020 *Income* £65,140,000 *Total grants* £84,200,000 *Grants to organisations* £84,200,000 *Assets* £131,900,000

TRUSTEES Eric Salama; Jacqueline Onalo; Gautam Raju; Dr Sue Black; Jenny Hodgson; Charlotte Moar; Tom Shropshire; Matt Hyde; Tessy Ojo; Rupert Morley; Saul Klein; Fiona Campbell.

OTHER INFORMATION Grants were awarded to 465 organisations and 369 of those had not been supported previously. The 2019/20 annual report notes that over 60% of funding was awarded to overseas organisations. Grants totalling £27.1 million were also awarded to help support beneficiaries through the COVID-19 pandemic.

HOW TO APPLY Applications can be made online via the charity's website, where full guidance is also provided.

CONTACT DETAILS The Trustees, 1st Floor, 89 Albert Embankment, London SE1 7TP *Tel.* 020 7820 2000 *Email* Contact form on website *Website* www.comicrelief.com

■ The Comino Foundation

CC NO 312875 **ESTABLISHED** 1971

WHERE FUNDING CAN BE GIVEN UK.

WHO CAN BENEFIT Registered charities; unregistered charities; universities; social enterprises.

WHAT IS FUNDED Support of educational activities for young people which: improve practical and personal capabilities, enrich learning in science, engineering and technology; transform services for young people with complex needs; and improve social opportunity.

WHAT IS NOT FUNDED Research; activities outside the UK; individuals.

TYPE OF GRANT Project funding.

RANGE OF GRANTS Grants range from £400 to £60,000.

SAMPLE GRANTS University of Manchester (£60,000); University of Winchester (£45,000); Knowle West Media Centre (£37,300); Potential Trust (£12,000); Potential Plus (£8,400); Foundation for Science and Technology and 5x5x5 Creativity (£3,000 each).

FINANCES *Financial year end* 05/04/2020 *Income* £136,900 *Total grants* £288,500 *Grants to organisations* £288,500 *Assets* £3,180,000

TRUSTEES Anna Comino-James; David Perry; Amrit Singh; Mumtaz Bashir-Hanid.

HOW TO APPLY The foundation has a number of long-term funding commitments and a limited capacity to make grants. Potential applicants should refer to the foundation's website, where advice is given about what is currently being considered by the trustees. If you think that your project is suitable, you should apply to the trust's administrator, following the guidance on the website about what to include.

CONTACT DETAILS Sarah Mareschall, Administrator, 137 Thetford Road, Brandon, Suffolk IP27 0DB *Tel.* 07443 875920 *Email* sarah@cominofoundation.org.uk *Website* www.cominofoundation.org.uk

■ Community First

CC NO 288117 **ESTABLISHED** 1965
WHERE FUNDING CAN BE GIVEN Wiltshire and Swindon.
WHO CAN BENEFIT Charities; community organisations; parish or town councils.
WHAT IS FUNDED Community development; the arts; heritage; environmental projects; sport; transport; young carers.
TYPE OF GRANT Project funding; capital funding; core/revenue funding.
RANGE OF GRANTS Generally up to £15,000.
SAMPLE GRANTS Marlborough Golf Course (£60,000); Avebury Sports and Social Club Pavilion (£20,000); Lydiard Millicent PCC (£15,000); Goatacre Cricket Club (£13,000); Freshbrook Church and Ashton Keynes Village Hall (£10,000 each).
FINANCES *Financial year end* 31/03/2020 *Income* £2,300,000 *Total grants* £272,100 *Grants to organisations* £272,100 *Assets* £1,660,000
TRUSTEES Steve Boocock; Edward Heard; Jane Rowell; James Moody; Piers Dibben; Anthony Pooley; Jane James; Virginia Keen.
OTHER INFORMATION A total of 26 grants were awarded throughout the year. Only organisations receiving grants of over £10,000 were listed as beneficiaries in the charity's accounts. Grants of under £10,000 totalled £72,600 and were awarded to 19 organisations. Community First have five grant schemes: LEADER (heritage), Landfill Communities Fund, Lace Up Wiltshire (sport), Community Transport Development Fund and Building Bridges (youth).
HOW TO APPLY Each fund has a separate application process. See the charity's website for further details.
CONTACT DETAILS The Trustees, Unit C2 Brecon Business Centre, Hopton Park, Devizes, Wiltshire SN10 2EY *Tel.* 01380 722475 *Email* grants@communityfirst.org.uk *Website* www.communityfirst.org.uk

■ The Compton Charitable Trust

CC NO 280404 **ESTABLISHED** 1980
WHERE FUNDING CAN BE GIVEN Northamptonshire.
WHO CAN BENEFIT Charitable organisations, with a preference for those with a connection to the family estates of the Marquess of Northampton as well as those which the Marquess is a patron of.
WHAT IS FUNDED General charitable purposes.
RANGE OF GRANTS £200 to £28,000.
SAMPLE GRANTS The Canonbury Tower Charitable Trust (£28,000); The Francis Bacon Research Trust (£15,000); Feldon Charitable Trust (£3,500); The Grand Charity (£3,000); Monken Hadley Church Fund (£2,500); Royal British Legion (£200).
FINANCES *Financial year end* 05/04/2020 *Income* £69,200 *Total grants* £52,200 *Grants to organisations* £52,200 *Assets* £896,800
TRUSTEES Marquess of Northampton; Earl Daniel Compton.
HOW TO APPLY Contact the correspondent for further information.
CONTACT DETAILS The Trustees, 5th Floor, 8 Finsbury Circus, London EC2M 7AZ *Tel.* 020 7399 0000

■ Douglas Compton James Charitable Trust

CC NO 1091125 **ESTABLISHED** 2002
WHERE FUNDING CAN BE GIVEN The Masonic Province of Northamptonshire and Huntingdonshire.
WHO CAN BENEFIT Registered charities.
WHAT IS FUNDED General charitable purposes including: education and social welfare. Some preference is given for Masonic charities.
RANGE OF GRANTS Up to £50,000 but mostly £1,000 to £3,000.
SAMPLE GRANTS Stephen Perse Foundation (£54,000); Wellingborough School (£32,000); Grafham Water Sailability (£3,000); FareShare and Happy Days Children's Charity (£2,000 each); British Red Cross and Deafblind (£1,000 each).
FINANCES *Financial year end* 05/04/2020 *Income* £135,900 *Total grants* £136,000 *Grants to organisations* £136,000 *Assets* £5,660,000
TRUSTEES Ian Clarke; Philip Humphrey; Richard Ongley; Thomas Reed.
OTHER INFORMATION Grants were made to 36 organisations during the year.
HOW TO APPLY Contact the correspondent for further information.
CONTACT DETAILS Louise Davies, Montague House, Chancery Lane, Thrapston, Northamptonshire NN14 4LN *Tel.* 01832 732161 *Email* louise.davies@vshlaw.co.uk

■ Congregational & General Charitable Trust

CC NO 297013 **ESTABLISHED** 1987
WHERE FUNDING CAN BE GIVEN UK.
WHO CAN BENEFIT Churches; religious bodies.
WHAT IS FUNDED The overall care, upkeep and extension of churches in particular those of the United Reformed and Congregational denominations; church community projects; promotion of the Christian religion and, in particular, the United Reformed and Congregational denominations, and other churches of the Protestant tradition.
WHAT IS NOT FUNDED Running costs of the church Organ and Church bells restoration; conservation/restoration of works of art; manse works; graveyard maintenance; solar panels.
TYPE OF GRANT Capital costs; project funding.
RANGE OF GRANTS £1,000 to £25,000.
SAMPLE GRANTS St Edmund's Church Powys (£15,000); St Laurence – Catsfield (£12,000); Elstow Bunyan Christian (£7,500); Christ Church Fairwarp (£6,300); West Melton URC (£3,200); Deane URC (£2,500); Killylea Methodist (£1,000).
FINANCES *Financial year end* 31/12/2019 *Income* £543,100 *Total grants* £606,600 *Grants to organisations* £606,600 *Assets* £16,430,000
TRUSTEES Revd David Grosch-Miller; Alastair Forsyth; Susan Austin; Christopher Evans; Revd David Coote; Margaret Atkinson; Revd Richard Turnbull; Revd Pamela Ward; John Holmes; Revd Margaret Tait.
HOW TO APPLY Application forms can be downloaded from the trust's website, where upcoming deadlines are also posted, along with guidance on what to include in your application.
CONTACT DETAILS Trish Thorpe, Trust Administrator, PO Box 1111, Lincoln, Lincolnshire LN5 0WJ *Email* enquiries@candgtrust.org.uk *Website* www.candgtrust.org.uk

The Connolly Foundation

CC NO 1109135 **ESTABLISHED** 2004

WHERE FUNDING CAN BE GIVEN Bedfordshire.

WHO CAN BENEFIT Registered charities; schools.

WHAT IS FUNDED Community development; children and young people; education; older people.

SAMPLE GRANTS Bedford College (£200,000); Youthscape (£100,000); Sue Ryder Hospice (£50,000); Bedford Daycare Centre (£20,000); Harlington School (£2,500).

FINANCES *Financial year end* 31/05/2019
Income £21,706,000 *Total grants* £512,500
Grants to organisations £512,500
Assets £70,489,000

TRUSTEES Vanessa Connolly; Michael Callanan; Andrew Rowe; Shyam Ashoka; Nigel Croft.

OTHER INFORMATION The 2018/19 accounts were the latest available at the time of writing (June 2021).

HOW TO APPLY Contact the correspondent for further information.

CONTACT DETAILS The Trustees, Manor Farm Court, Lower Sundon, Luton, Bedfordshire LU3 3NZ *Email* enquiry@connollyfoundation.org.uk *Website* www.connollyfoundation.org.uk

The Ernest Cook Trust

CC NO 1146629 **ESTABLISHED** 1952

WHERE FUNDING CAN BE GIVEN UK.

WHO CAN BENEFIT State schools; registered charities; other recognised not-for-profit organisations.

WHAT IS FUNDED Education, particularly extra-curricular activities.

SAMPLE GRANTS City of Bradford YMCA and Farms for City Children (£15,000 each); The Smallpiece Trust (£11,000); Earth Trust (£10,000); Future Roots (£8,400); City and Guilds of London Art School and Salisbury Cathedral (£4,000 each).

FINANCES *Financial year end* 31/03/2020
Income £6,230,000 *Total grants* £499,400
Grants to organisations £499,400
Assets £179,310,000

TRUSTEES Andrew Christie-Miller; Harry Henderson; Simon Eliot; Sir Bertie Ross; Mary Riall; Jennifer Greenwood.

OTHER INFORMATION In 2019/20, 503 schools received £500 each. The trust awarded 536 grants in total.

HOW TO APPLY See the trust's website for information on the application processes for each funding stream.

CONTACT DETAILS Suzie Paton, Head of Grants, The Estate Office, Fairford Park, Fairford, Gloucestershire GL7 4JH *Tel.* 01285 712492 *Email* grants@ernestcooktrust.org.uk *Website* www.ernestcooktrust.org.uk

The Cooks Charity

CC NO 297913 **ESTABLISHED** 1987

WHERE FUNDING CAN BE GIVEN UK, with a preference for London.

WHO CAN BENEFIT Charitable organisations associated with the catering industry; individuals in the catering industry and their dependants.

WHAT IS FUNDED Education associated with the catering industry; skills and training associated with the catering industry.

TYPE OF GRANT Project funding; capital costs.

SAMPLE GRANTS Royal Academy of Culinary Arts (£57,900); The Clink (£40,000); Crisis Skylight Cafe (£4,500); Spitalfields Crypt Trust (£2,100); 7th St Pancras Girl Guides (£270).

FINANCES *Financial year end* 30/06/2019
Income £273,100 *Total grants* £251,000
Grants to organisations £251,000
Assets £5,510,000

TRUSTEES Graham Price; Commodore David Smith; Oliver Goodinge; Peter Wright; Bev Puxley.

OTHER INFORMATION Grants were made to 14 organisations and broken down as follows: advancement of education (£203,900); purposes connected with London (£43,000); general welfare (£4,200). The 2018/19 accounts were the latest available at the time of writing (June 2021).

HOW TO APPLY Applications should be submitted by email to the Clerk. Further information on how to apply can be found on the grant-maker's website.

CONTACT DETAILS Peter Wilkinson, Clerk, 18 Solent Drive, Warsash, Southampton, Hampshire SO31 9HB *Tel.* 07503 373606 *Email* clerk@cookslivery.org.uk *Website* www.cookslivery.org.uk

The Catherine Cookson Charitable Trust

CC NO 272895 **ESTABLISHED** 1977

WHERE FUNDING CAN BE GIVEN UK, with a preference for the North East.

WHO CAN BENEFIT Charitable organisations

WHAT IS FUNDED General charitable purposes, including: education and training; health; children and young people; religious activities; animal welfare; disability; art and culture.

RANGE OF GRANTS £250 to £100,000.

SAMPLE GRANTS Durham School's Bursary Campaign (£250,000); Evelina Children's Hospital (£50,000); Alzheimer's Research Trust (£25,000); Ellingham Village Hall (£20,0000); Children's Respite Trust (£10,000); Strathmore Road Methodist Church (£4,000); Tall Ships Youth Trust (£2,000); The Country Trust (£1,000); Dogs Trust (£500); Action for Sick Children (£250).

FINANCES *Financial year end* 05/04/2020
Income £1,160,000 *Total grants* £1,320,000
Grants to organisations £1,320,000
Assets £28,090,000

TRUSTEES Peter Magnay; David Hawkins; Hugh Marshall; Daniel Sallows.

OTHER INFORMATION Grants were awarded to 277 organisations and were broken down as follows: education and training (£354,500); medical, health and sickness (£299,100); arts and culture (£296,200); other charities/voluntary bodies (£169,800); disability (£99,600); religious activities (£69,600); children and young people (£26,900); animal welfare (£5,000).

HOW TO APPLY There is no standard application form but written applications, enclosing an sae should be sent to the correspondence address provided. There is no set format or time limit for applications, which enables many groups to apply for a grant. Charities interested in applying should complete the short online form which is available on the trust's website.

CONTACT DETAILS The Trustees, c/o Thomas Magnay and Co., 8 St Mary's Green, Whickham, Newcastle upon Tyne, Tyne and Wear NE16 4DN *Tel.* 0191 488 7459 *Email* enquiries@thomasmagnay.co.uk *Website* catherinecookson.com/trust

■ The Keith Coombs Trust

CC NO 1149791 **ESTABLISHED** 2012

WHERE FUNDING CAN BE GIVEN UK, with a preference for the West Midlands.

WHO CAN BENEFIT Registered charities.

WHAT IS FUNDED General charitable purposes; children and young people; health; education.

SAMPLE GRANTS A list of beneficiaries was not included in the annual report and accounts.

FINANCES *Financial year end* 12/09/2020 *Income* £98,600 *Total grants* £100,600 *Grants to organisations* £100,600 *Assets* £4,500

TRUSTEES Anthony Coombs; Graham Coombs; Demetrios Markou; Christine Ingram; Chris Redford; Manjeet Bhogal.

HOW TO APPLY Contact the correspondent for further information.

CONTACT DETAILS Christine Ingram, Trustee, c/o S and U plc, 2 Stratford Court, Cranmore Boulevard, Solihull, West Midlands B90 4QT *Tel.* 0121 705 7777 *Email* christineingram@suplc.co.uk

■ Mabel Cooper Charity

CC NO 264621 **ESTABLISHED** 1972

WHERE FUNDING CAN BE GIVEN UK, with a preference for south Devon.

WHO CAN BENEFIT Registered charities.

WHAT IS FUNDED General charitable purposes. Preference is given to projects with low overheads.

WHAT IS NOT FUNDED Individuals.

SAMPLE GRANTS Devon Air Ambulance (£10,000); Alzheimer's Research UK, Crisis, Cancer Research, Macmillan Cancer Support, St Luke's Hospice and St Peter's Hospice (£5,000 each); Rowcroft House Foundation, Salvation Army and Shelter (£2,500 each); Clic Sargent and Future Trees Trust (£1,000 each).

FINANCES *Financial year end* 30/06/2019 *Income* £208,000 *Total grants* £69,000 *Grants to organisations* £69,000 *Assets* £5,790,000

TRUSTEES Alison Barrett; Ian Harbottle; David Harbottle.

OTHER INFORMATION The 2018/19 accounts were the latest available at the time of writing (May 2021).

HOW TO APPLY Contact the correspondent for further information.

CONTACT DETAILS The Trustees, Middle Manor, Lascot Hill, Wedmore, Somerset BS28 4AF *Tel.* 01934 712102

■ The Alice Ellen Cooper Dean Charitable Foundation

CC NO 273298 **ESTABLISHED** 1977

WHERE FUNDING CAN BE GIVEN UK, with a preference for Dorset and West Hampshire; occasionally overseas.

WHO CAN BENEFIT Local and national charities registered in the UK, including (on occasion) those who work overseas.

WHAT IS FUNDED General charitable purposes including: education; religion; social welfare.

WHAT IS NOT FUNDED No grants are made to individuals or non UK-registered charitable entities.

TYPE OF GRANT Project funding.

RANGE OF GRANTS Generally, up to £30,000.

SAMPLE GRANTS Dorset County Hospital Charity (£100,000); Poole Communities Trust (£30,000); Lantern Trust (£20,000); Spinal Injuries Association (£10,000); Hope and Homes for Children, Huntingdon's Disease Association, Sports Forum for the Disabled and Wessex Heritage Trust (£5,000 each); Purbeck Arts Week Festival (£2,000).

FINANCES *Financial year end* 31/03/2020 *Income* £1,370,000 *Total grants* £1,120,000 *Grants to organisations* £1,120,000 *Assets* £33,280,000

TRUSTEES Linda Bowditch; Douglas Neville-Jones; Emma Blackburn; John Bowditch; Alastair Cowen; Richard Wedgwood; Richard King.

OTHER INFORMATION Grants were awarded to 142 organisations during the year.

HOW TO APPLY Apply in writing to the correspondent. The foundation considers applications for funding of projects and appeals from local and national charitable bodies registered with the Charity Commission. Applicants are asked to provide a summary of the project together with costings, financial accounts and details of fundraising activities.

CONTACT DETAILS The Trustees, c/o Edwards and Keeping, Unity Chambers, 34 High East Street, Dorchester, Dorset DT1 1HA *Tel.* 01305 251333 *Email* marygodding@edwardsandkeeping.co.uk

■ Co-operative Community Investment Foundation

CC NO 1093028 **ESTABLISHED** 2000

WHERE FUNDING CAN BE GIVEN UK.

WHO CAN BENEFIT Registered charities and community groups.

WHAT IS FUNDED Disadvantaged communities; youth loneliness; community enterprise.

RANGE OF GRANTS Generally up to £50,000.

SAMPLE GRANTS Envision (£132,500); The Children's Society (£69,800); Women's Technology Centre (£50,000); White Rock Neighbourhood Ventures (£40,000); Changing Our Lives (£35,000); Scotswood Garden (£21,200); UK Youth (£20,000).

FINANCES *Financial year end* 31/12/2019 *Income* £4,340,000 *Total grants* £3,050,000 *Grants to organisations* £3,050,000 *Assets* £22,730,000

TRUSTEES Shelia Malley; Sarah Woodcock; Saleem Chowdhery; Daniel Crowe; Jamie Ward-Smith; Sharon Jones; Lois McClure.

OTHER INFORMATION Grants were broken down as follows: youth loneliness (£1.37 million); community spaces; (£1.28 million); strategic development (£337,200); digital capacity building (£66,900). Only organisations receiving grants of over £20,000 were listed as beneficiaries in the charity's accounts. Grants of under £20,000 totalled £732,800.

HOW TO APPLY Funding rounds for specific programmes open periodically during the year and will be advertised on the foundation's website.

CONTACT DETAILS Louise Snelders, Funding and Contracts Manager, 9th floor, 1 Angel Square, Manchester M60 0AG *Tel.* 0161 692 1877 *Email* foundation@coop.co.uk *Website* https://www.coopfoundation.org.uk

Marjorie Coote Animal Charity Trust

CC NO 208493 **ESTABLISHED** 1954

WHERE FUNDING CAN BE GIVEN Worldwide, in practice England; Northern Ireland; Scotland.

WHO CAN BENEFIT Registered charities.

WHAT IS FUNDED The care and protection of horses, dogs, other animals and birds.

WHAT IS NOT FUNDED Individuals.

TYPE OF GRANT Capital costs; project costs.

RANGE OF GRANTS £500 to £20,000.

SAMPLE GRANTS Animal Health Trust (£20,000); RSPCA Sheffield (£14,600); Support Dogs (£10,000); Environmental Investigation Agency (£4,000); Sea Life Trust (£3,000); Rainforest Concern (£2,000); Orangutan Appeal UK (£1,000); All Creatures Great and Small (£500).

FINANCES *Financial year end* 05/04/2020 *Income* £169,200 *Total grants* £180,700 *Grants to organisations* £180,700 *Assets* £3,250,000

TRUSTEES Jill Holah; Lady Neill; Mrs S. Browne; Nicola Baguley; Sarah Neill.

OTHER INFORMATION The trust deed names five registered charities as the original beneficiaries; however, this has expanded and the trust now supports other charities as well. During the year, the trustees provided ongoing financial support totalling £93,100 to 19 organisations and made 51 one-off grants totalling £87,600.

HOW TO APPLY Contact the correspondent for further information. Applications should reach the correspondent during September for consideration in October/November. Appeals received at other times of the year are deferred until the following autumn unless they require consideration for an urgent 'one-off' grant for a specific project.

CONTACT DETAILS Jill Holah, Trustee, End Cottage, Terrington, York, North Yorkshire YO60 6PU *Tel.* 01653 648847 *Email* j.holah@mcacharity.org.uk

The Helen Jean Cope Charity

CC NO 1125937 **ESTABLISHED** 1998

WHERE FUNDING CAN BE GIVEN East Midlands, with a particular preference for Leicestershire.

WHO CAN BENEFIT Registered charities.

WHAT IS FUNDED General charitable purposes.

WHAT IS NOT FUNDED Individuals; unregistered charities.

TYPE OF GRANT Generally single projects; capital costs.

RANGE OF GRANTS £500 to £5,000.

SAMPLE GRANTS Fearon Community Association (£5,000); Leicestershire Search and Rescue (£2,500); Nottingham Nightstop (£2,000); Asthma Relief Leicestershire and Hospice Hope (£1,500 each); National Deaf Children's Society and St Jude's Church Nottingham (£1,000 each); Shepshed Toy Library (£500).

FINANCES *Financial year end* 31/12/2019 *Income* £135,800 *Total grants* £95,000 *Grants to organisations* £95,000 *Assets* £4,240,000

TRUSTEES Malcolm Carrington; Lindsay Brydson; Matthew Freckelton; Alan Roberts; Graham Freckelton; Anthony Benskin.

OTHER INFORMATION Grants were awarded to 67 charities during the year.

HOW TO APPLY Apply by post to the correspondent including the following: the full name and address of the charity to which correspondence should be sent and cheques made payable in the event of a grant being made; your charity number; a brief description of your charity and its activities if this is a first application; what the grant is for; who will benefit; how much any specific items will cost; other fundraising activities being carried out and the amount raised so far; a set of audited accounts where available; a copy of your reserves policy. The trustees meet about five times a year.

CONTACT DETAILS Mr J. Carrington, Secretary, 1 Woodgate, Loughborough, Leicestershire LE11 2TY *Tel.* 01509 218298 *Email* info@thehelenjeancopecharity.co.uk *Website* www.thehelenjeancopecharity.co.uk

The J. Reginald Corah Foundation Fund

CC NO 220792 **ESTABLISHED** 1953

WHERE FUNDING CAN BE GIVEN Leicester, Leicestershire and Rutland.

WHO CAN BENEFIT Charitable organisations. However, particular favour is given organisations benefitting employees, ex-employees and their dependants of the hosiery firms in Leicester and Rutland.

WHAT IS FUNDED Children; disability; education; community; medical causes; social welfare.

WHAT IS NOT FUNDED Applications from individuals are not considered unless made by, or supported by, a recognised charitable organisation.

RANGE OF GRANTS Typically up to £3,000.

SAMPLE GRANTS Leicester Children's Holiday Association (£3,000); Leicester Combat Academy (£2,200); LOROS Hospice (£2,000); CF Dream Holidays (£1,600); Giving World and Warning Zone (£1,300 each).

FINANCES *Financial year end* 31/03/2020 *Income* £126,700 *Total grants* £103,400 *Grants to organisations* £103,400 *Assets* £5,990,000

TRUSTEES David Corah; Roger Bowder; Jonathan Pears.

HOW TO APPLY Contact the correspondent for further information.

CONTACT DETAILS The Trustees, 20 Welby Road, Asfordby Hill, Melton Mowbray, Leicestershire LE14 3RB *Tel.* 07771 542099 *Email* jrcfoundationfund@gmail.com

The Worshipful Company of Cordwainers Charitable Trusts (Minges Gift)

CC NO 266073 **ESTABLISHED** 1972

WHERE FUNDING CAN BE GIVEN UK, with some preference for the City of London.

WHO CAN BENEFIT Registered charities; schools and colleges; universities; places of worship; individuals.

WHAT IS FUNDED Young people and disadvantaged groups; education; people who are blind or partially sighted; support for those working in the footwear industry; medicine; churches; armed forces charities; older people; people who are deaf; social welfare; music.

TYPE OF GRANT Project funding; capital costs; development funding.

RANGE OF GRANTS £100 to £30,000.

SAMPLE GRANTS De Montfort University (£30,000); University of Northampton (£22,000); Guildhall School of Music (£12,500); Footwear Friends (£8,000); Royal Marsden Cancer Charity (£5,000); Lord Mayor's Fund (£2,000); Guildhall Library (£250).

FINANCES *Financial year end* 31/07/2020 *Income* £246,300 *Total grants* £174,100 *Grants to organisations* £174,100 *Assets* £4,460,000

TRUSTEES John Peal; Sir Roger Gifford; Peter Lamble.

OTHER INFORMATION The charity is comprised of Minge's Gift (Charity Commission no. 266073), the Common Investment Fund – Pooled Trusts (Charity Commission no. 261891) and the Emily Jackson Bequest (Charity Commission no. 220442). During 2019/20, grants to organisations totalled £154,700. A further £19,400 was awarded to the designated Cordwainer Charity of the Year which was Harry's Giant Pledge in aid of the Royal Marsden Cancer Charity.

HOW TO APPLY Our previous research indicates that the charity identifies organisations to support; unsolicited applications are not accepted.

CONTACT DETAILS The Trustees, The Cordwainers Company, Clothworkers Hall, Dunster Court, Mincing Lane, London EC3R 7AH *Tel.* 020 7929 1121 *Email* charity@cordwainers.org *Website* www.cordwainers.org

■ The Gershon Coren Charitable Foundation (also known as The Muriel and Gus Coren Charitable Foundation)

CC NO 257615 **ESTABLISHED** 1968

WHERE FUNDING CAN BE GIVEN UK, Israel and financially developing countries.

WHO CAN BENEFIT Charitable organisations, particularly Jewish organisations.

WHAT IS FUNDED General charitable purposes; social welfare; Jewish causes.

RANGE OF GRANTS Grants mostly up to £12,000, although a few larger grants are often donated each year.

SAMPLE GRANTS JNF Charitable Trust (£105,200); Gategi Village Self Help Group (£90,000); Foundation for Jewish Heritage (£40,000); Manna UK and Smart Giving (£30,000 each); Centre for Jewish Life and Prostate Cancer (£3,000 each).

FINANCES *Financial year end* 05/04/2020 *Income* £31,970,000 *Total grants* £425,200 *Grants to organisations* £425,200 *Assets* £30,090,000

TRUSTEES Walter Stanton; Anthony Coren.

OTHER INFORMATION In 2019/20 the foundation awarded grants to 42 organisations.

HOW TO APPLY Contact the correspondent for further information.

CONTACT DETAILS Graham Weinberg, 5 Golders Park Close, London NW11 7QR *Tel.* 020 7429 4100 *Email* graham.weinberg@mhllp.co.uk

■ Michael Cornish Charitable Trust

CC NO 1107890 **ESTABLISHED** 2005

WHERE FUNDING CAN BE GIVEN Worldwide with a preference for Lincolnshire.

WHO CAN BENEFIT Charities and not-for-profit organisations; schools.

WHAT IS FUNDED Overseas aid and general charitable purposes, including: children and young people, people with disabilities, economic and community development, amateur sport and health.

TYPE OF GRANT Project funding.

RANGE OF GRANTS Up to £5,000 but mostly £250 to £1,000.

SAMPLE GRANTS Salvation Army (£5,000); RNLI (£4,000); KidsOut UK, Skillforce and Think Children (£1,000 each); Save the Children (£250).

FINANCES *Financial year end* 31/12/2019 *Income* £226,100 *Total grants* £122,800 *Grants to organisations* £122,800 *Assets* £18,360,000

TRUSTEES Michael Cornish; Harriet Cornish; Richard Vigar; Susan Cornish; Stephen Cornish.

HOW TO APPLY Applications can be made through the trust's website. The website states: 'Applications are reviewed quarterly in March, June, September and December. Once you submit an application you will receive an email confirming the date your application will be reviewed. We will confirm the outcome of your application within 30 days of the given review date.'

CONTACT DETAILS Phillipa Cridland, Trust Administrator, c/o Wright Vigar Ltd, 15 Newland, Lincoln, Lincolnshire LN1 1XG *Tel.* 01522 531341 *Website* www.michaelcornishcharity.org.uk

■ The Evan Cornish Foundation

CC NO 1112703 **ESTABLISHED** 2005

WHERE FUNDING CAN BE GIVEN UK, with a preference for northern England; overseas.

WHO CAN BENEFIT Registered charities; not-for-profit organisations; CICs.

WHAT IS FUNDED Human rights; social and economic inequality; education; health; criminal justice system; older people; refugees and asylum seekers; homelessness. International projects which promote tolerance and equality for women or combat human rights violations. International applicants must have a registered UK office.

WHAT IS NOT FUNDED Building work or repairs; political activities; animal welfare; academic research; medical research; individuals/gap year students; holiday club providers; flight costs. Religious organisations – the trustees will not consider applications: for projects that promote or evangelise any particular faith; from organisations whose goals include the promotion of their faith; from organisations which discriminate internally or externally based on faith. The trustees will consider applications from organisations that grew from a religious basis but now have a multi-faith and secular approach.

TYPE OF GRANT Project funding.

RANGE OF GRANTS £1,000 to £50,000. First time applicants should not apply for more than £5,000.

SAMPLE GRANTS Lincolnshire Community Foundation (£50,000); Project Football (£25,000); Christian Aid (£10,000); Afghan Connection (£8,000); South Sinai Foundation and War Child (£5,000 each); Jeevika Trust (£3,000).

FINANCES *Financial year end* 05/04/2020 *Income* £234,700 *Total grants* £682,200 *Grants to organisations* £682,200 *Assets* £8,870,000

TRUSTEES Rachel Cornish; Barbara Ward; Sally Cornish.

OTHER INFORMATION Organisations with projects in other areas of England or the UK (i.e. not based in the north of England) may still apply if its project is: unique in the UK; involves advocacy/policy work; or affects people in the UK prison system. In 2019/20 grants were awarded to 76 organisations.

HOW TO APPLY Applications must be made through the foundation's website. Applicants should submit: a copy of your most recent accounts; a copy of your project budget; details of an independent, UK-based referee, not affiliated to your organisation; supporting information about your project. The trustees meet three times per years. Check the website for application deadlines.

CONTACT DETAILS Nat Loftus, Charity Administrator, The Innovation Centre, 217 Portobello, Sheffield, South Yorkshire S1 4DP *Tel.* 0114 224 2230 *Email* contactus@evancornishfoundation.org.uk *Website* www.evancornishfoundation.org.uk

■ Cornwall Community Foundation

CC NO 1099977 **ESTABLISHED** 2003

WHERE FUNDING CAN BE GIVEN Cornwall and the Isles of Scilly.

WHO CAN BENEFIT Registered charities; voluntary or community groups; social enterprises; individuals.

WHAT IS FUNDED General charitable purposes including: disadvantage; exclusion; welfare; disability; community spaces.

TYPE OF GRANT Project costs; core/revenue costs; capital costs.

SAMPLE GRANTS A list of beneficiaries was not included in the annual report and accounts.

FINANCES *Financial year end* 31/12/2019 *Income* £2,720,000 *Total grants* £734,900 *Grants to organisations* £734,900 *Assets* £8,300,000

TRUSTEES Daphne Skinnard; Timothy Smith; John Ede; Thomas Oss; Jane Trahair; Kim Conchie; James Williams; Natercia Hughes; Emma Mantle; Nicola Marquid; Jane Marquis; Jane Hartley; Stamford Galsworthy; The Hon. Evelyn Boscawen; Bishop Philip Mounstephen; Jonathan Cunliffe; Toby Ashworth; Deborah Hinton.

OTHER INFORMATION This is one of the 46 UK community foundations, which distribute funding for a wide range of purposes. As with all community foundations, there are a number of donor-advised funds managed on behalf of individuals, families and charitable trusts. Grant schemes tend to change frequently; consult the foundation's website for details of current programmes and up-to-date deadlines.

HOW TO APPLY Potential applicants are advised to visit the community foundation's website or contact its grants team to find the most suitable funding stream.

CONTACT DETAILS The Grants Team, Suite 1, Sheers Barton, Lawhitton, Launceston, Cornwall PL15 9NJ *Tel.* 01566 779333 *Email* office@cornwallfoundation.com *Website* https://www.cornwallcommunityfoundation.com

■ The Duke of Cornwall's Benevolent Fund

CC NO 269183 **ESTABLISHED** 1975

WHERE FUNDING CAN BE GIVEN UK, with a preference for Cornwall.

WHO CAN BENEFIT Charitable organisations.

WHAT IS FUNDED Social welfare; provision of almshouses, hospitals and hospices; education and training; arts and culture; religion; heritage and historic buildings.

RANGE OF GRANTS Up to £100,000 but generally £1,000 to £5,000.

SAMPLE GRANTS Cornwall Community Foundation (£100,000); Plantlife (£75,000); Cornwall Historic Churches Trust (£35,000); Bosence Farm and Urban Diversity CIC (£5,000 each); Friends of Bude Sea Pool (£1,000).

FINANCES *Financial year end* 30/06/2020 *Income* £124,900 *Total grants* £303,200 *Grants to organisations* £303,200 *Assets* £5,630,000

TRUSTEES Col Edward Bolitho; Sir James Leigh-Pemberton; Alastair Martin; Catherine Mead.

HOW TO APPLY Contact the correspondent for further information.

CONTACT DETAILS Terry Cotter, Secretary, Duchy of Cornwall, 10 Buckingham Gate, London SW1E 6LA *Tel.* 020 7834 7346

■ The Cornwell Charitable Trust

CC NO 1012467 **ESTABLISHED** 1992

WHERE FUNDING CAN BE GIVEN UK; overseas.

WHO CAN BENEFIT Registered charitable organisations; individuals.

WHAT IS FUNDED General charitable purposes.

SAMPLE GRANTS Médecins Sans Frontières (£50,000); Lincoln College Oxford (£45,000); Trussell Trust (£10,000); Crisis UK and Pancreatic Cancer Scotland (£5,000 each).

FINANCES *Financial year end* 05/04/2020 *Income* £52,300 *Total grants* £172,000 *Grants to organisations* £172,000 *Assets* £990,000

TRUSTEES Valerie Cornwell; Matthew Bennett; Mark Bailey.

HOW TO APPLY Contact the correspondent for further information.

CONTACT DETAILS The Trustees, Devonshire House, 1 Devonshire Street, London W1W 5DR *Tel.* 020 7304 2000 *Email* cw@citroenwells.co.uk

■ The Corporation of Trinity House of Deptford Strond

CC NO 211869 **ESTABLISHED** 1514

WHERE FUNDING CAN BE GIVEN UK.

WHO CAN BENEFIT Charitable organisations related to seafarers.

WHAT IS FUNDED The education, safety, support and welfare of seafarers and their dependants.

TYPE OF GRANT Capital costs; project funding; strategic funding; development funding.

RANGE OF GRANTS £5,500 to £120,000 for major grants.

SAMPLE GRANTS Shipwrecked Fishermen and Mariners' Royal Benevolent Society (£110,000); Royal Alfred Seafarers' Society (£100,000); Seafarers UK (£30,000); Care for Veterans (£10,000).

FINANCES *Financial year end* 31/03/2020 *Income* £9,910,000 *Total grants* £1,670,000 *Grants to organisations* £1,670,000 *Assets* £279,230,000

TRUSTEES Capt. Nigel Palmer; Capt. Nigel Hope; Capt. Roger Barker; Cdre. Robert Dorey; Capt. Ian McNaught; Commodore Ian McNaught; Commodore William Walworth; Richard Sadler; Capt. Stephen Gobbi; Malcolm Glaister; Rear Admiral David Snelson.

HOW TO APPLY Full information on how to apply for a grant can be found on the charity's website.

CONTACT DETAILS Vikki Muir, Grants Manager, Trinity House, Tower Hill, London EC3N 4DH *Tel.* 020 7481 6903 *Email* Victoria.Muir@trinityhouse.co.uk *Website* https://www.trinityhouse.co.uk/supporting-seafarers/maritime-charity

■ Corra Foundation

OSCR NO SC009481 **ESTABLISHED** 1986
WHERE FUNDING CAN BE GIVEN Scotland; Zambia; Rwanda; Malawi; Pakistan.
WHO CAN BENEFIT Charitable organisations.
WHAT IS FUNDED Social welfare; children and young people; homelessness; families affected by substance abuse; international development (Zambia, Rwanda, Malawi and Pakistan).
WHAT IS NOT FUNDED Exclusion criteria differs between grant programmes. See the website for further details.
TYPE OF GRANT Core costs; salaries; project funding.
SAMPLE GRANTS A list of beneficiaries was not included in the annual report and accounts.
FINANCES *Financial year end* 31/12/2019
Income £22,150,000
Total grants £20,430,000
Grants to organisations £20,430,000
Assets £27,650,000
TRUSTEES Trevor Civval; Luke McCullough; Joy Barlow; Elizabeth Y. Carmichael; Claire Gibson; David Johnson; Richard Martin; Elaine McKean; Fiona Sanford; Judith Turbyne; Christine McLaughlin; Mildred Zimunya; Michaela Collins; H. Charles Abram.
OTHER INFORMATION The foundation is one of four Lloyds Banking Group charities, covering England and Wales, Scotland, Northern Ireland and the Channel Islands. The foundation delivered 12 different funding programmes in 2019, some of which were delivered on behalf of the Scottish government. Grants were broken down as follows: CYPFEIF and ALEC Fund (£13.9 million); Housing First Scotland Fund and Partnership Drugs Initiative (£1.3 million each); International grants (£1 million) Henry Duncan Awards (£981,000); Substance Misuse Challenge Fund (£924,000); #Shiftthepower Comic Relief Fund (£702,000); Listening Fund (£169,000); Family Recovery Initiative Fund and the Place-based Programme (£30,000 each).
HOW TO APPLY Applications can be made via the foundation's website.
CONTACT DETAILS Grants Team, Riverside House, 502 Gorgie Road, Edinburgh EH11 3AF *Tel.* 0131 444 4020 *Email* hello@corra.scot *Website* https://www.corra.scot

■ The Costa Family Charitable Trust

CC NO 221604 **ESTABLISHED** 1964
WHERE FUNDING CAN BE GIVEN UK.
WHO CAN BENEFIT Christian organisations; individuals.
WHAT IS FUNDED Christian causes.
RANGE OF GRANTS Mostly under £10,000.
SAMPLE GRANTS 24/7 Prayer (£174,200); Alpha International (£29,500); Love Your Neighbour (£1,000); Change Academy and Philo Trust (£500 each).
FINANCES *Financial year end* 05/04/2020
Income £338,800 *Total grants* £285,100
Grants to organisations £276,000
Assets £60,700
TRUSTEES Kenneth Costa; Ann Costa.
OTHER INFORMATION Grants were awarded to 20 organisations. Grants to 14 individuals totalled £9,100.
HOW TO APPLY The trust's Charity Commission record states that: 'No funding requests are solicited or acknowledged.'
CONTACT DETAILS The Trustees, 35 Tite Street, London SW3 4JP *Tel.* 07785 467441

■ The Cotswold Primrose Charitable Trust

CC NO 1162291 **ESTABLISHED** 2015
WHERE FUNDING CAN BE GIVEN UK, with a preference for Gloucestershire.
WHO CAN BENEFIT Registered charities.
WHAT IS FUNDED Education and training; employability; sport and physical activities.
SAMPLE GRANTS The Door (£22,000); Allsorts (£13,400 in two grants); GL11 Community Hub (£12,000); Living Paintings (£5,200).
FINANCES *Financial year end* 05/04/2020
Income £38,400 *Total grants* £81,900
Grants to organisations £81,900
Assets £329,400
TRUSTEES Vivien Styles; Paul Styles; Kate Gregg; Sarah Ives.
OTHER INFORMATION Grants were made to nine organisations during the year.
HOW TO APPLY Apply in writing to the correspondent. Applications should be accompanied by a set of the organisations latest report and full financial statement.
CONTACT DETAILS The Trustees, c/o New Quadrant Partners Ltd, 4th Floor, 5 Chancery Lane, London WC2A 1LG *Tel.* 020 7430 7157

■ Council for World Mission (UK)

CC NO 1097842 **ESTABLISHED** 2003
WHERE FUNDING CAN BE GIVEN Worldwide.
WHO CAN BENEFIT Christians; missionaries; churches. Grants are awarded to the 32 member churches of Council for World Mission Ltd and associated individuals.
WHAT IS FUNDED The advancement of Christianity; strengthening the missionary work of Council for World Mission and its members; providing resources for churches; strategic training and capacity building for churches.
TYPE OF GRANT One-off; recurring; capacity building; pro bono support; scholarships.
SAMPLE GRANTS A list of the member churches can be seen in the 2019 annual report.
FINANCES *Financial year end* 31/12/2019
Income £3,520,000 *Total grants* £8,080,000
Grants to organisations £8,080,000
Assets £168,000,000
TRUSTEES Rose Wedderburn; Revd Kudzani; Giron Lyttan; Revd Hemen Halder; Sarah Yiran; Lindsey Brown.
OTHER INFORMATION The distribution of grants to organisations and individuals was not available. Details of the charity's funding programmes are available in the 2019 annual report and on the website. The charity also runs conferences and training programmes for church leaders and missionaries, with some focus on encouraging young people and women into missionary work.
HOW TO APPLY The charity makes grants to its member churches. To find out more information about becoming a member, contact the correspondent. Details of current open programmes, including training programmes for individuals, can be found on the charity's website.
CONTACT DETAILS The Trustees, 11 St George's Circus, London SE1 8EH *Tel.* 020 7222 4214 *Email* council.uk@cwmission.org or wayne@cwmeurope.org *Website* www.cwmission.org

The County Council of Dyfed Welsh Church Fund

CC NO 506583 **ESTABLISHED** 1977

WHERE FUNDING CAN BE GIVEN Carmarthenshire, Ceredigion and Pembrokeshire.

WHO CAN BENEFIT Churches and chapels; charitable organisations benefitting people in the local area; individuals.

WHAT IS FUNDED Maintenance of places of worship; advancement of education; arts and culture; social welfare; advancement of religion; general charitable purposes that benefit the local community.

TYPE OF GRANT Project funding; capital costs; core costs.

RANGE OF GRANTS Up to £10,000; mostly £1,000 to £3,000.

SAMPLE GRANTS Bethel Church – Carmarthen (£10,000); Carmarthen and District Youth Opera and Gosen Chapel (£3,000 each); Ray Ceredigion (£2,500); Aberporth Community Council (£1,300).

FINANCES *Financial year end* 31/03/2020
Income £107,000 *Total grants* £121,100
Grants to organisations £121,100
Assets £4,820,000

TRUSTEES Chris Moore, Jonathan Haswell; Stephen Johnson.

OTHER INFORMATION A breakdown of grants awarded throughout the year by region is as follows: Carmarthenshire (£84,500); Ceredigion (£19,900); Pembrokeshire (£16,700).

HOW TO APPLY Contact the correspondent for further information.

CONTACT DETAILS The Trustees, Corporate Services, County Hall, Carmarthen, Carmarthenshire SA31 1JP *Tel.* 01267 224180 *Email* AParnell@carmarthenshire.gov.uk

Countypier Ltd

CC NO 295399 **ESTABLISHED** 1985

WHERE FUNDING CAN BE GIVEN UK.

WHO CAN BENEFIT Mainly Jewish charitable organisation.

WHAT IS FUNDED Promotion of the Orthodox Jewish faith; social welfare.

TYPE OF GRANT Unrestricted funding.

RANGE OF GRANTS £12,000 to £515,000.

SAMPLE GRANTS Friends of Sanz Institutions (£243,000); Notzar Chesed (£85,000); One Heart Lev Echad (£38,500); Lehachzikom (£16,000); ABC Trust Ltd (£12,500).

FINANCES *Financial year end* 31/03/2020
Income £815,600 *Total grants* £945,700
Grants to organisations £945,700
Assets £6,240,000

TRUSTEES Ahron Halpern; Esther Halpern; Chana Klein.

HOW TO APPLY Contact the correspondent for further information.

CONTACT DETAILS The Trustees, Greenwood Student House, 29–31 Station Road, London N22 6UX *Tel.* 020 8881 3080

Coutts Charitable Foundation

CC NO 1150784 **ESTABLISHED** 2013

WHERE FUNDING CAN BE GIVEN UK.

WHO CAN BENEFIT Charitable organisations.

WHAT IS FUNDED The prevention of poverty (particularly focused on women and girls in the UK).

RANGE OF GRANTS Up to £150,000.

SAMPLE GRANTS Stockport Women's Centre and The Nelson Trust (£150,000 each); End Violence Against Women Coalition (£135,000); Southall Black Sisters Trust (£120,000); The Fairlight Trust Anawim and Women for Refugee Women (£90,000 each); Working Chance (£75,000).

FINANCES *Financial year end* 01/04/2019
Income £94,300 *Total grants* £810,000
Grants to organisations £810,000
Assets £4,210,000

TRUSTEES Francesca Barnes; Judith McNeill; Dr Linda Yueh, Lord Walgrave of North Hill; Alison Rose Slade; Thomas Kenrick; Rachel Harrington; Peter Flavel; Camilla Stowell; Laura Lines.

OTHER INFORMATION Grants were made to seven organisations throughout the year. The 2018/19 accounts were the latest available at the time of writing (January 2021).

HOW TO APPLY The foundation does not accept unsolicited applications. However, if you wish to bring your organisation to the foundation's attention there is a information submission form which can be downloaded from the website and emailed or posted to the correspondent. The foundation will then be in touch if it wishes to learn more about your organisation. Refer to the foundation's helpful website for more details.

CONTACT DETAILS The Trustees, c/o Coutts & Co., 440 Strand, London WC2R 0QS *Tel.* 020 7753 1000 *Email* coutts.foundation@coutts.com *Website* https://www.coutts.com/coutts-foundation.html

Coventry Building Society Charitable Foundation

CC NO 1072244 **ESTABLISHED** 1998

WHERE FUNDING CAN BE GIVEN Areas within the building society's branch network – Coventry and Warwickshire; Birmingham and Black Country; Gloucestershire; Oxfordshire; Bristol; Wiltshire and Swindon; Leicestershire and Rutland; Northamptonshire; Somerset; Milton Keynes; Nottinghamshire; Staffordshire; South Yorkshire; Wales.

WHO CAN BENEFIT Registered charities and community groups with an income under £250,000.

WHAT IS FUNDED General charitable purposes. Priority is given to groups or activities aimed at improving the quality of life and opportunities in communities affected by disadvantage, deprivation and social exclusion.

RANGE OF GRANTS Small grants of up to £2,000.

SAMPLE GRANTS Heart of England Community Foundation (£23,800); Birmingham and Black Country Community Foundation (£8,900); Quartet Community Foundation (£5,000); Northamptonshire Community Foundation (£1,800); Somerset Community Foundation (£1,200).

FINANCES *Financial year end* 31/12/2019
Income £70,000 *Total grants* £70,000
Grants to organisations £70,000
Assets £5,360,000

TRUSTEES Darin Landon; Thomas Crane; Tina Jones.

OTHER INFORMATION This is the charitable foundation of Coventry Building Society. Grants are awarded to community foundations which distribute grants of up to £2,000 to charities and community groups on behalf of the foundation. During the year, grants were awarded to 14 community foundations.

HOW TO APPLY Applications can be made online through the community foundation for your area. In order to do this choose the area closest to where your charity operates from the table at the bottom of the Coventry Building Society Charitable Foundation website and click on the relevant link. This will take you to the community foundation website for your area. The foundation asks: 'If you have any queries about the application process contact your local Community Foundation directly.'

CONTACT DETAILS Contact the relevant Community Foundation, Coventry Building Society, Oak Tree Court, Harry Weston Road, Coventry, Warwickshire CV3 2UN *Tel.* 0800 121 8899 *Website* https://www.coventrybuildingsociety.co.uk/consumer/who-we-are/charities/charitable-foundation.html

The Noel Coward Foundation

CC NO 1178029 **ESTABLISHED** 2000

WHERE FUNDING CAN BE GIVEN UK.

WHO CAN BENEFIT Arts organisations.

WHAT IS FUNDED The arts.

WHAT IS NOT FUNDED Production costs; individuals.

TYPE OF GRANT Single grants for specific projects.

SAMPLE GRANTS A list of beneficiaries was not included in the annual report and accounts.

FINANCES *Financial year end* 31/03/2020 *Income* £189,800 *Total grants* £191,400 *Grants to organisations* £191,400 *Assets* £526,300

TRUSTEES Robert Lee; Alan Brodie; Peter Kyle.

OTHER INFORMATION Priority is given to organisations with a strong educational element and those with particular but not exclusive emphasis on supporting people entering or in the early stages of a career in the arts. Grants were distributed as follows: workshops (£69,200); education (£68,400); theatre (£39,300); other (£14,500).

HOW TO APPLY Application forms can be downloaded from the foundation's website where application deadlines can also be found. The foundation encourages interested organisations to get in touch before submitting an application to discuss suitability and ensure all the required information is provided.

CONTACT DETAILS The Grants Committee, Paddock Suite, The Courtyard, 55 Charterhouse Street, London EC1M 6HA *Email* ncf@alanbrodie.com *Website* https://www.noelcoward.org

The Sir Tom Cowie Charitable Trust

CC NO 1096936 **ESTABLISHED** 2003

WHERE FUNDING CAN BE GIVEN City of Sunderland and County Durham.

WHO CAN BENEFIT Registered charities.

WHAT IS FUNDED General charitable purposes including the natural environment; heritage; social welfare; the environment; children and young people.

WHAT IS NOT FUNDED Individuals; national and international charities seeking partial funding for large projects.

TYPE OF GRANT Capital costs; project funding.

RANGE OF GRANTS Usually up to £20,000.

SAMPLE GRANTS Woodshed Workshop (£22,500); East Durham Community Development Trust (£10,000); Sunderland Community Soup Kitchen (£2,500); Durham Association of Boys and Girls Clubs (£1,500).

FINANCES *Financial year end* 31/08/2020 *Income* £104,000 *Total grants* £108,800 *Grants to organisations* £108,800 *Assets* £5,490,000

TRUSTEES Peter Blackett; David Gray; Lady Diana Cowie.

HOW TO APPLY Application forms can be completed and submitted on the trust's website, or downloaded and returned to the mailing address.

CONTACT DETAILS Emma Gray, Grants Administrator, Estate Office, Broadwood Hall, Lanchester, Durham, County Durham DH7 0TN *Tel.* 01207 529663 *Email* ecg@graysllp.co.uk *Website* www.stcct.co.uk

Dudley and Geoffrey Cox Charitable Trust

CC NO 277761 **ESTABLISHED** 1979

WHERE FUNDING CAN BE GIVEN UK, with a preference for London and the South East.

WHO CAN BENEFIT Registered charities; hospices; schools; universities.

WHAT IS FUNDED Medical research; young people; social welfare; education.

SAMPLE GRANTS Merchant Taylors' School (£54,000); Engineering Development Trust (£13,100); Breast Cancer Now (£7,000); Pace Centre (£8,400); Alzheimer's Society (£5,000); West London Action for Children (£4,000); Anglia Ruskin University (£500).

FINANCES *Financial year end* 31/12/2019 *Income* £254,200 *Total grants* £299,100 *Grants to organisations* £299,100 *Assets* £9,250,000

TRUSTEES Ian Ferres; Peter Watkins; John Wosner; Peter Magill; Michael Boyle.

HOW TO APPLY Unsolicited applications are not accepted.

CONTACT DETAILS Charities Officer, Merchant Taylors' Company, 30 Threadneedle Street, London EC2R 8JB *Tel.* 020 7450 4440 *Email* charities@merchant-taylors.co.uk

The Sir William Coxen Trust Fund

CC NO 206936 **ESTABLISHED** 1940

WHERE FUNDING CAN BE GIVEN England.

WHO CAN BENEFIT Hospitals or charitable institutions carrying out orthopaedic work.

WHAT IS FUNDED Orthopaedic work.

WHAT IS NOT FUNDED Individuals; non-charitable institutions.

RANGE OF GRANTS £5,000 to £60,000.

SAMPLE GRANTS University of East Anglia (£60,000); Strongbones Children's Charitable Trust (£20,000); Great Ormond Street Hospital Children's Charity (£10,000); Action Medical Research, Spinal Injuries Association and Versus Arthritis (£5,000 each).

FINANCES *Financial year end* 31/03/2020 *Income* £17,700 *Total grants* £105,000 *Grants to organisations* £105,000 *Assets* £211,000

TRUSTEES Alderman Sir Roger Gifford; Alderman Sir Alan Yarrow; Alderman Prem Goyal; Alderman Ian Luder; Alderman Robert Howard.

HOW TO APPLY Apply in writing to the correspondent.

CONTACT DETAILS Lorraine Brook, Town Clerk, The Town Clerk's Office, Corporation of London, PO Box 270, Guildhall, London EC2P 2EJ *Tel.* 020 7332 1409 *Email* lorraine.brook@cityoflondon.gov.uk

The Lord Cozens-Hardy Trust

CC NO 264237 **ESTABLISHED** 1972
WHERE FUNDING CAN BE GIVEN UK, with a preference for Norfolk.
WHO CAN BENEFIT Registered charities.
WHAT IS FUNDED General charitable purposes; medicine; health; social welfare; education.
WHAT IS NOT FUNDED Individuals.
TYPE OF GRANT Capital costs; core/revenue costs.
RANGE OF GRANTS Mostly for smaller amounts of £3,000 or less.
SAMPLE GRANTS Huntington's Disease Association (£20,000); Meningitis Now (£5,000); Age Concern and Assist Trust (£3,000 each); Guide Dog's for the Blind (£2,000); Liverpool School of Tropical Medicine, Read for Good and Shelter (£1,000 each).
FINANCES *Financial year end* 05/04/2020 *Income* £110,400 *Total grants* £100,000 *Grants to organisations* £100,000 *Assets* £2,960,000
TRUSTEES John Vandeleur Phelps; Linda Phelps; Benjamin Vandeleur Phelps; Justin Ripman.
OTHER INFORMATION Grants of less than £1,000 totalled £12,000.
HOW TO APPLY Apply in writing to the correspondent. Applications are reviewed annually, usually in January, therefore applications should be made between October and December.
CONTACT DETAILS The Trustees, PO Box 28, Holt, Norfolk NR25 7WH *Tel.* 01603 693303

The CPF Trust

CC NO 262468 **ESTABLISHED** 1971
WHERE FUNDING CAN BE GIVEN Mainly in the UK, occasionally overseas.
WHO CAN BENEFIT Charitable organisations.
WHAT IS FUNDED General charitable purposes.
RANGE OF GRANTS Up to £27,500 but mostly £500 to £3,000.
SAMPLE GRANTS Eton College (£27,500); Carers Trust (£3,000); Parkinson's Disease (£2,000); Support Dogs (£1,000); Friends of National Libraries (£250).
FINANCES *Financial year end* 06/04/2020 *Income* £124,200 *Total grants* £81,500 *Grants to organisations* £81,500 *Assets* £1,790,000
TRUSTEES Sir Matthew Farrer; Nicola Guthrie; Dr Isobel Pinder; Jenett Farrer.
HOW TO APPLY Contact the correspondent for further information.
CONTACT DETAILS The Trustees, 6 Priory Avenue, London W4 1TX *Tel.* 020 8994 6052 *Email* jcfarrer@gmail.com

The Craignish Trust

OSCR NO SC016882 **ESTABLISHED** 1961
WHERE FUNDING CAN BE GIVEN UK, with a preference for Scotland.
WHO CAN BENEFIT Registered charities.
WHAT IS FUNDED General charitable purposes; the environment; human rights.
TYPE OF GRANT Capital costs; core/revenue costs; seed funding/start-up funding; project funding; unrestricted funding.
RANGE OF GRANTS Up to £10,000.
SAMPLE GRANTS Sustainable Inshore Fisheries Trust (£10,000); Scottish Environmental Link (£5,000); Butterfly Conservation Scotland (£2,500); Bikes for Refugees and John Muir Trust (£2,000 each).
FINANCES *Financial year end* 05/04/2020 *Income* £144,700 *Total grants* £80,000 *Grants to organisations* £80,000 *Assets* £6,330,000
OTHER INFORMATION Grants were awarded to 26 organisations during the year.
HOW TO APPLY Apply in writing to the correspondent. Details of the project should be included together with a copy of the most recent audited accounts.
CONTACT DETAILS The Trustees, c/o Geoghegans Chartered Accountants, 6 St Colme Street, Edinburgh EH3 6AD

The Craps Charitable Trust

CC NO 271492 **ESTABLISHED** 1976
WHERE FUNDING CAN BE GIVEN UK, Israel.
WHO CAN BENEFIT Charitable organisations; universities.
WHAT IS FUNDED General charitable purposes, particularly Jewish causes and organisations.
RANGE OF GRANTS Up to £25,000.
SAMPLE GRANTS British Technion Society (£25,000); Jewish Care (£20,000); Nightingale Home for Aged Jews and The Friends of the Jerusalem Botanical Gardens (£16,000 each); Friends of the Hebrew University (£14,000); Ben-Gurion University Foundation and Norwood Ravenswood (£4,000 each); Save the Children (£2,000); Amnesty International, National Theatre and Shelter (£1,000 each).
FINANCES *Financial year end* 05/04/2019 *Income* £225,100 *Total grants* £185,500 *Grants to organisations* £185,500 *Assets* £4,740,000
TRUSTEES Caroline Dent; Jonathan Dent; Louisa Dent.
OTHER INFORMATION Grants were awarded to 29 organisations during the year. The 2018/19 accounts were the latest available at the time of writing (January 2021).
HOW TO APPLY Contact the correspondent for further information.
CONTACT DETAILS The Trustees, Grant Thornton, Victoria House, 4th Floor, 199 Avebury Boulevard, Milton Keynes MK9 1AU *Tel.* 01908 359674 *Email* julie.l.masterson@uk.gt.com

CRASH

CC NO 1054107 **ESTABLISHED** 1996
WHERE FUNDING CAN BE GIVEN UK.
WHO CAN BENEFIT UK-registered charities; hospices.
WHAT IS FUNDED Homeless charities and hospices' building projects.
WHAT IS NOT FUNDED A detailed list of exclusions can be found on the charity's website.
TYPE OF GRANT Capital costs.
RANGE OF GRANTS Up to £40,000.
SAMPLE GRANTS Greenwich and Bexley Community Hospice (£40,000); Blythe House Hospice – Derbyshire (£30,000); Emmaus Community South Lambeth and Surrey (£20,000); Digartref Cyf – Anglesey (£12,000); Halton Haven Hospice – Runcorn (£10,000); Emmaus Community Greenwich (£6,500); Helen and Douglas House Children's Hospice – Oxford (£600).
FINANCES *Financial year end* 31/03/2020 *Income* £1,510,000 *Total grants* £243,800 *Grants to organisations* £243,800 *Assets* £833,000
TRUSTEES Alan Brookes; Anthony Giddings; Kevin Corbett; Fiona Duncombe; Ian Bolster; Fracois

Morrow; Matthew Pullen; John O'Grady; James Wimpenny.
OTHER INFORMATION The charity provides grants, pro bono consultancy services and free-of-charge or discounted building materials. Grants were awarded to 14 organisations and gifts in kind totalled £672,300.
HOW TO APPLY Applications can be made through the charity's website.
CONTACT DETAILS Projects Manager, The Gatehouse, 2 Devonhurst Place, Heathfield Terrace, London W4 4JD *Tel.* 020 8742 0717 *Email* froberts@crash.org.uk *Website* www.crash.org.uk

■ Michael Crawford Children's Charity

CC NO 1042211 **ESTABLISHED** 1994
WHERE FUNDING CAN BE GIVEN Throughout England and Wales.
WHO CAN BENEFIT Registered charities.
WHAT IS FUNDED Children and young people; social welfare; health.
SAMPLE GRANTS The Sick Children's Trust (£25,000).
FINANCES *Financial year end* 31/10/2019 *Income* £146,500 *Total grants* £55,300 *Grants to organisations* £55,300 *Assets* £6,260,000
TRUSTEES Alan Clark; Michael Crawford; Kenneth Dias; Natasha Macaller.
OTHER INFORMATION The 2018/19 accounts were the latest available at the time of writing (June 2021).
HOW TO APPLY Contact the correspondent for further information.
CONTACT DETAILS The Trustees, Regina House, 124 Finchley Road, London NW3 5JS *Tel.* 020 7433 2400

■ The Cray Trust

OSCR NO SC005592 **ESTABLISHED** 1976
WHERE FUNDING CAN BE GIVEN Scotland; Midlothian.
WHO CAN BENEFIT Registered charities.
WHAT IS FUNDED General charitable purposes.
WHAT IS NOT FUNDED Previous research suggests the trust does not make grants to political appeals, large UK or international charities, or individuals.
RANGE OF GRANTS £50 to £5,000.
SAMPLE GRANTS Macmillan Cancer Support (£9,800); Maggie's Centre (£8,200); Carers of West Lothian (£6,700); Friends of Hilary Storm School, Glenisla Church and Project Trust (£5,000 each); Dundee Carers Centre (£2,000).
FINANCES *Financial year end* 05/04/2020 *Income* £49,500 *Total grants* £52,100 *Grants to organisations* £52,100 *Assets* £891,200
OTHER INFORMATION In 2019/20 the trust awarded 75 grants.
HOW TO APPLY Contact the correspondent for further information.
CONTACT DETAILS The Trustees, c/o Azets, Exchange Place 3, Semple Street, Edinburgh EH3 8BL

■ The Elizabeth Creak Charitable Trust

CC NO 286838 **ESTABLISHED** 1983
WHERE FUNDING CAN BE GIVEN UK, with a preference for Warwickshire.
WHO CAN BENEFIT Charities; training bodies; universities.
WHAT IS FUNDED Agricultural education and support; life sciences education.
SAMPLE GRANTS Grants of £25,000 and over included: Studley College (£30,000); Harper Adams University and Newcastle University (£25,000 each).
FINANCES *Financial year end* 31/03/2020 *Income* £1,190,000 *Total grants* £1,150,000 *Grants to organisations* £1,150,000 *Assets* £25,890,000
TRUSTEES John Hulse; Nicholas Quilter Abell; Johnathan May.
OTHER INFORMATION Grants were broken down as follows: life sciences education (£919,200); agricultural national support (£203,000); other local projects (£24,000). Grants of under £25,000 totalled £177,600. Each year the trust awards approximately £200,000 to UK universities for student scholarships. The trust also funds four university chairs.
HOW TO APPLY The trustees usually meet every two months to consider grant applications. Apply in writing to the correspondent.
CONTACT DETAILS John Hulse, Trustee, 27 Widney Road, Knowle, Solihull, West Midlands B93 9DX *Tel.* 01564 773951 *Email* creakcharity@hotmail.com

■ Creative Scotland

ESTABLISHED 2010
WHERE FUNDING CAN BE GIVEN Scotland.
WHO CAN BENEFIT Organisations; individuals.
WHAT IS FUNDED Creative Scotland is a public body that distributes funding from the Scottish government and The National Lottery. It supports the arts, screen and creative industries across the whole of Scotland.
WHAT IS NOT FUNDED Most programmes have their own specific exclusions, details of which are available on the Creative Scotland website.
TYPE OF GRANT Project funding; core costs.
SAMPLE GRANTS A list of beneficiaries was not included in the annual report and accounts.
FINANCES *Financial year end* 31/03/2020 *Income* £34,750,000 *Total grants* £77,220,000 *Grants to organisations* £77,220,000 *Assets* £7,620,000
TRUSTEES Robert Wilson; Ewan Angus; David Brew; Elizabeth Partyka; David Strachan; Duncan Cockburn; Philip Long; Stephanie Fraser; Sarah Munro.
OTHER INFORMATION The grant total represents the net grants issued taken from Creative Scotland's consolidated report. The report shows the financial position of both Creative Scotland (CS) and the Creative Scotland National Lottery Distribution Fund (CS NLDF).
HOW TO APPLY For information on the various funding programmes available, visit the Creative Scotland website.
CONTACT DETAILS Enquiries Service, Waverely Gate, 2–4 Waterloo Place, Edinburgh EH1 3EG *Tel.* 0345 603 6000 *Email* enquiries@creativescotland.com *Website* www.creativescotland.com

■ Credit Suisse EMEA Foundation

CC NO 1122472 **ESTABLISHED** 2007
WHERE FUNDING CAN BE GIVEN UK; Europe; the Middle East; Africa.
WHO CAN BENEFIT Registered charities; early-stage organisations and initiatives.
WHAT IS FUNDED The education and training of children and young people.
WHAT IS NOT FUNDED Proposals that: directly replace or subsidise statutory funding or for activities that are the responsibility of statutory bodies; administration and costs not directly associated with the application; individuals; promotion of religious or political causes; holidays; retrospective expenditure; general appeals; animal welfare; festivals, sports and leisure activities.
TYPE OF GRANT Project funding; multi-year partnerships (one to five years); development funding; salaries; core costs.
RANGE OF GRANTS Typically up to £250,000.
SAMPLE GRANTS Ambition Institute (£296,000); Fair Education Alliance (£268,400); ThinkForward (£210,000); The Difference (£160,000); Franklin Scholars and Royal National Children's SpringBoard Foundation (£35,000 each); Age UK (£29,000).
FINANCES *Financial year end* 31/12/2019 *Income* £1,420,000 *Total grants* £1,500,000 *Grants to organisations* £1,500,000 *Assets* £1,870,000
TRUSTEES Michelle Mendelsson; Aneta Kocemba-Muchowicz; Colin Hely-Hutchinson; Mark Ellis; Marisa Drew; Marc Pereira-Mendoza; Guy Varney; Natalia Nicolaidis; Sean Alleyne; Karen Newton; Caroline Waddington; Matthew Weston; Ian Hale; Katarzyna Jozefowicz; Nicola Kane.
OTHER INFORMATION The foundation's core grant-making programme funds registered charities that fulfil its mission in Europe, the Middle East and Africa, and its UK Small Grants Programme funds early-stage innovative organisations in the UK. Grants were made to 14 organisations during the year, some of which formed part of multi-year commitments.
HOW TO APPLY Contact your local Credit Suisse office for further information.
CONTACT DETAILS Corporate Citizenship Team, Credit Suisse, 1 Cabot Square, London E14 4QJ *Tel.* 020 7888 8888 *Email* emea.corporatecitizenship@credit-suisse.com *Website* https://www.credit-suisse.com/about-us/en/our-company/corporate-responsibility/economy-society/emea.html

■ The Crerar Trust

CC NO 221335 **ESTABLISHED** 1903
WHERE FUNDING CAN BE GIVEN Areas where Crerar Hotels are based (mainly Scotland).
WHO CAN BENEFIT Charitable organisations.
WHAT IS FUNDED General charitable purposes; social welfare.
TYPE OF GRANT Capital costs; project funding.
RANGE OF GRANTS £1,000 to £25,000.
SAMPLE GRANTS HIT Scotland (£25,000); Charlie House (£10,000); Canine Concern Scotland Trust (£5,000); Care for Carers (£3,000); Centre for the Moving Image (£1,600).
FINANCES *Financial year end* 05/04/2020 *Income* £345,800 *Total grants* £226,100 *Grants to organisations* £226,100 *Assets* £10,190,000
TRUSTEES Patrick Crerar; James Barrack; Jeanette Crerar; Sheila Crerar.
HOW TO APPLY See the trust's website for application information.
CONTACT DETAILS Claire Smith, General Secretary, Newmains, Stenton, Dunbar, East Lothian EH42 1TQ *Tel.* 01620 822051 *Email* clerk@crerartrust.com *Website* https://www.crerarhotels.com/crerar-trust

■ The Crescent Trust

CC NO 327644 **ESTABLISHED** 1987
WHERE FUNDING CAN BE GIVEN UK.
WHO CAN BENEFIT Charitable organisations; museums; galleries.
WHAT IS FUNDED General charitable purposes, particularly: encouragement and protection of nature; gardens; arts and culture.
SAMPLE GRANTS Previous beneficiaries have included: The Attingham Trust (£11,000); Chalke Valley History Trust (£7,500); The Garden Museum, Team Domenica (£5,000 each); Public Monuments and Sculpture Association (£4,500); Watts Gallery (£2,500).
FINANCES *Financial year end* 05/04/2020 *Income* £125,400 *Total grants* £53,700 *Grants to organisations* £53,700 *Assets* £1,160,000
TRUSTEES John Tham; Richard Lascelles.
HOW TO APPLY Contact the correspondent for further information.
CONTACT DETAILS The Trustees, 7–12 Sloane Square, London SW1W 8EG *Tel.* 020 7730 5420

■ CRH Charitable Trust

CC NO 213579 **ESTABLISHED** 2006
WHERE FUNDING CAN BE GIVEN Cheshire East; Cheshire West and Chester; Lancashire; Greater Manchester; Cumbria.
WHO CAN BENEFIT Charitable organisations.
WHAT IS FUNDED Mental health; health; people with disabilities; children and young people; social welfare; medical research.
SAMPLE GRANTS Sue Ryder (£44,000); Stockport Women's Centre (£23,100); Youth Federation (£15,000); Northwich Multisports (£10,000); Time Out Group (£8,000); Back on Track (£5,000).
FINANCES *Financial year end* 31/03/2020 *Income* £761,300 *Total grants* £290,700 *Grants to organisations* £290,700 *Assets* £8,236,000
TRUSTEES Keith Hyde; Robert Race; Michael Seal; Peter Stafford; Hugh Rylands; Diana Colquhoun.
OTHER INFORMATION There is a detailed list of the projects funded by the trust on page three of its annual report.
HOW TO APPLY Apply in writing to the correspondent including a summary of your proposal.
CONTACT DETAILS Mr B. Peak, Secretary, 22 Ashworth Park, Knutsford, WA16 9DE *Tel.* 01565 651086 *Email* crhct@btinternet.com

■ Cripplegate Foundation

CC NO 207499 **ESTABLISHED** 1891
WHERE FUNDING CAN BE GIVEN London Borough of Islington and part of the City of London.
WHO CAN BENEFIT Registered charities; unregistered charities; CICs; social enterprises.
WHAT IS FUNDED Community work for disadvantaged residents including: advice and access to services; financial inclusion and capability; investing in young people; mental health and

well-being; reaching isolated people; family support.
WHAT IS NOT FUNDED Political parties; political lobbying; churches or other religious bodies where the monies will be used for religious purposes/promotion of religion; work which does not benefit Islington residents; individuals (except through identified partners); medical or academic research; expenses that have already been incurred, projects that have already taken place; residential care services or residential facilities; general appeals; trips/outings (unless part of a bigger project); debts.
TYPE OF GRANT Core/revenue costs; project funding.
RANGE OF GRANTS £1,700 to £300,000.
SAMPLE GRANTS Islington Law Centre (£115,000); The Parent House (£62,000); Grandparents Plus (£40,000); The Brandon Centre and The Claremont Project (£30,000 each); Islington Giving (£26,400); Talk for Health (£20,000); Federation of Iraqi Refugees (£9,000); Asmara Football Club and Artbox London (£5,000 each); Friends Of Copenhagen Primary School (£2,500); Highbury Walkers (£880).
FINANCES *Financial year end* 31/12/2019
Income £2,350,000 *Total grants* £1,555,000
Grants to organisations £1,500,000
Assets £44,460,000
TRUSTEES Governors: Edmund Brandt; Frances Carter; Nezahat Cihan; Anne-Marie Ellis; Alderman David Graves; Rob Hull; Tom Jupp; Cllr Jenny Kay; James Kempton; Sarah Lee; Susan Pearson; Kate Rodgers; Amir Rizwan; Revd Katherine Rumens; Gillian Tong; Manny Wiafe.
OTHER INFORMATION Grants to individuals totalled £55,000. Grants to organisations were made through three different programmes, some in partnership with Islington Giving and Islington Council.
HOW TO APPLY Funding programmes open at different times of the year. Application forms and guidance documents are made available on the foundation's website when programmes open. See the foundation's 'Support and Funding' webpage for more information.
CONTACT DETAILS Programme Team, 13 Elliott's Place, Islington, London N1 8HX *Tel.* 020 7288 6940 *Email* grants@cripplegate.org.uk *Website* www.cripplegate.org

■ Crisis UK

CC NO 1082947 **ESTABLISHED** 1967
WHERE FUNDING CAN BE GIVEN England, Scotland and Wales.
WHO CAN BENEFIT Registered charities; housing associations; individuals.
WHAT IS FUNDED Homelessness and housing.
RANGE OF GRANTS Typically up to £50,000 but programme dependent.
SAMPLE GRANTS Only the beneficiaries of the Tackling Multiple Disadvantage programme were named in the accounts: City and Hackney Mind; St Mungo's; Thames Reach.
FINANCES *Financial year end* 30/06/2019
Income £53,540,000 *Total grants* £434,000
Grants to organisations £352,000
Assets £26,920,000
TRUSTEES Tristia Harrison; Rob Perrins; Tamsin Stirling; Martin Cheeseman; Julia Goldsworthy; Alison Wallace; Terrie Alafat; Ann McLvor; Damien Regent; Geetha Rabindrakumar; Robert Weston; Victoria Fox.
OTHER INFORMATION Grants to organisations were broken down as follows: Tackling Multiple Disadvantage programme (three grants totalling £149,000); European Union Settlement Scheme (eight grants totalling £123,000); Tackling homelessness for women survivors of modern day slavery (two grants totalling £55,000); other (£25,000). Grants were made to 64 individuals through the Crisis Changing Lives programme with a combined total of £82,000. The 2018/19 accounts were the latest available at the time of writing (January 2021).
HOW TO APPLY Refer to the website for application forms and deadlines for any current grant schemes.
CONTACT DETAILS The Trustees, 66 Commercial Street, London E1 6LT *Tel.* 0300 636 1967 *Email* enquiries@crisis.org.uk *Website* www.crisis.org.uk

■ The Cross Trust

CC NO 1127046 **ESTABLISHED** 2008
WHERE FUNDING CAN BE GIVEN UK and overseas.
WHO CAN BENEFIT Registered charities; unregistered charities; schools; religious bodies/institutions; individuals.
WHAT IS FUNDED Social welfare; advancement of religious and secular education; the advancement of the Christian faith in the UK and overseas.
SAMPLE GRANTS The Cross Trust (£500,000); London City Mission (£150,000); Soulmates Academy (£50,000); Tyndale House (£30,000); Anglian Communion (£1,000).
FINANCES *Financial year end* 05/04/2020
Income £4,000,000 *Total grants* £1,217,000
Grants to organisations £1,180,000
Assets £2,980,000
TRUSTEES David Lilley; Jenny Farmer; Douglas Olsen; The Lord Michael Farmer.
OTHER INFORMATION Grants to individuals totalled £36,800.
HOW TO APPLY Apply in writing to the correspondent.
CONTACT DETAILS The Lord Michael Farmer, Trustee, Cansdales, Bourbon Court, Nightingales Corner, Amersham, Buckinghamshire HP7 9QS *Tel.* 01494 765428 *Email* mailto@cansdales.co.uk

■ The Croydon Relief in Need Charities

CC NO 810114 **ESTABLISHED** 1962
WHERE FUNDING CAN BE GIVEN The borough of Croydon.
WHO CAN BENEFIT Local charities; individuals.
WHAT IS FUNDED Health; social welfare.
TYPE OF GRANT One-off project grants; core costs.
SAMPLE GRANTS Youth Zone (£75,000); Croydon Vision (£33,300); Age UK (£20,000); National Autistic Society (£2,400); PDSA (£1,000).
FINANCES *Financial year end* 31/12/2019
Income £218,800 *Total grants* £352,600
Grants to organisations £352,600
Assets £96,900
TRUSTEE Croydon Almshouse Charities Trustee Company Ltd.
HOW TO APPLY Application forms are available from the charity's website. Completed forms can be returned by email or post. The grants committee meets quarterly.
CONTACT DETAILS Hayley James, Elis David Almshouses, Duppas Hill Terrace, Croydon CR0 4BT *Tel.* 020 8688 2649 *Email* HayleyJames@croydonalmshouses.org.uk *Website* www.croydonalmshouses.org.uk

The Peter Cruddas Foundation

CC NO 1117323 **ESTABLISHED** 2006

WHERE FUNDING CAN BE GIVEN England and Wales, with some preference for London.

WHO CAN BENEFIT Charities registered with the Charity Commission.

WHAT IS FUNDED Projects supporting disadvantaged and disengaged young people (aged 16 to 30) with pathways to education, training and employment, including work experience/skills projects and youth work in London, especially evening work.

WHAT IS NOT FUNDED CICs; social enterprises; capital appeals; individuals; Scottish and Irish charities.

RANGE OF GRANTS Mostly up to £10,000.

SAMPLE GRANTS Community Security Trust (£36,500); Greenhouse Sport (£25,000); Hackney Quest (£12,000); Bounce Back Foundation (£10,000); Making the Leap (£9,000); Young Vic Theatre (£5,000); Tall Ship Youth Trust (£3,500); Weizman UK (£1,000); The Cure Parkinson's Trust (£500).

FINANCES *Financial year end* 31/03/2020 *Income* £80 *Total grants* £287,800 *Grants to organisations* £287,800

TRUSTEES Rt Hon. Lord Young of Graffham; Peter Cruddas; Martin Paisner.

OTHER INFORMATION Full accounts were not available to view on the Charity Commission's website due to the foundation's low income. We have therefore estimated the grant total based on its total expenditure.

HOW TO APPLY Application forms are available to download from the foundation's website and should be returned via email. Further guidance can be found on the foundation's website.

CONTACT DETAILS Stephen Cox, Company Secretary and Foundation Administrator, 133 Houndsditch, London EC3A 7BX *Tel.* 020 3003 8360 *Email* s.cox@petercruddasfoundation.org.uk *Website* www.petercruddasfoundation.org.uk

Cruden Foundation Ltd

OSCR NO SC004987 **ESTABLISHED** 1956

WHERE FUNDING CAN BE GIVEN Scotland.

WHO CAN BENEFIT Registered charities.

WHAT IS FUNDED Social welfare; health; the arts; education; heritage and conservation.

TYPE OF GRANT Capital costs; core/revenue costs; project funding.

RANGE OF GRANTS Up to £25,000.

SAMPLE GRANTS Edinburgh International Festival (£25,000); Pitlochry Festival Theatre (£15,000); Capital Theatres, Edinburgh Headway Group and The Edinburgh Clothing Store (£10,000 each); Horatio's Garden, Scottish Opera and St Columba's Hospice (£5,000 each); George Watson's Family Foundation and Scottish Seabird Centre (£3,000 each); Bobath Scotland, Edinburgh International Science Festival and NSPCC Scotland (£2,500 each).

FINANCES *Financial year end* 31/07/2020 *Income* £380,900 *Total grants* £323,900 *Grants to organisations* £323,900 *Assets* £11,360,000

TRUSTEES J. Rafferty; K. Reid; Mrs A. Paul; Dr J. Campbell.

OTHER INFORMATION Grants were made to 164 organisations during the year. Grants were broken down as follows: social welfare (£102,000); medical causes (£98,900); arts (£98,000); heritage conservation and education (£12,500 each). Only organisations receiving grants of over £2,500 were listed as beneficiaries in the charity's accounts. Grants of less than £2,500 totalled £142,800.

HOW TO APPLY Apply in writing to the correspondent, accompanied by most recent accounts.

CONTACT DETAILS The Trustees, 16 Walker Street, Edinburgh EH3 7LP *Website* https://www.cruden-ltd.co.uk/group/about-us/corporate-and-social-responsibility

CSIS Charity Fund

CC NO 1121671 **ESTABLISHED** 2007

WHERE FUNDING CAN BE GIVEN UK.

WHO CAN BENEFIT Charitable organisations.

WHAT IS FUNDED Grants are made to UK organisations that assist civil and public servants and their families with social welfare or health needs.

TYPE OF GRANT Unrestricted; core costs; pump-priming.

RANGE OF GRANTS Up to £250,000.

SAMPLE GRANTS The Charity for Civil Servants (£250,000); BT Benevolent Fund (£60,000); Rowland Hill Fund (£50,000); Civil Service Retirement Fellowship (£35,000); NHS Retirement Fellowship and Social Workers Benevolent Fund (£20,000 each); National Federation of Occupational Pensioner (£10,000); Chilterns MS Centre (£5,000); The Lee Rigby Foundation (£500).

FINANCES *Financial year end* 31/12/2019 *Income* £575,500 *Total grants* £821,100 *Grants to organisations* £798,500 *Assets* £2,100,000

TRUSTEES Angleos Pampos; Sun-Hee Park; Gaby Glasener-Cipollone; Colin Birch; Michael Duggan; Mary Jeffrey; Deborah Terry; Sally Bundock; Charles Cochrane; Ian Albert; Ray Flanigan; Tunde Ojetola; Rebecca Gooch.

OTHER INFORMATION Grants were made to 30 organisations during the year. Grants to individuals totalled £22,600.

HOW TO APPLY Contact the correspondent for further information. The trustees meet in February and March of each year to make decisions on grants.

CONTACT DETAILS Kevin Holliday, Secretary, 7 Colman House, King Street, Maidstone, Kent ME14 1DD *Tel.* 07843 342889 *Email* secretary@csischarityfund.org *Website* www.csischarityfund.org

Cumbria Community Foundation

CC NO 1075120 **ESTABLISHED** 1999

WHERE FUNDING CAN BE GIVEN Cumbria.

WHO CAN BENEFIT Registered and non-registered charities; CICs; social enterprises; PTAs; hospices; individuals.

WHAT IS FUNDED Social welfare; education and training; children and families; older people; health and well-being; community development; access to arts, sport, culture, heritage and the environment.

WHAT IS NOT FUNDED See the website for programme-specific exclusions.

TYPE OF GRANT Capital costs; core/revenue costs; project funding; seed funding/start-up funding.

RANGE OF GRANTS Mostly up to £20,000.

SAMPLE GRANTS Together We CIC (£100,000); Age UK – West Cumbria (£45,200); Dignity in Dementia (£20,000); The Farmer Network Ltd (£15,000); Cumbria Family Support (£10,000); Cumbria Action for Sustainability (£7,800); Barrow Celtic Football Club (£6,000); Carlisle

Society for the Blind and Kirkby Stephen Methodist Church (£5,000 each).

FINANCES *Financial year end* 31/03/2020 *Income* £8,470,000 *Total grants* £1,943,200 *Grants to organisations* £1,790,000 *Assets* £24,350,000

TRUSTEES Lucy Cavendish; David Moore; Anthony Keen; Adam Hearden; Marcia Fotheringham; Valerie Young; Jim Johnson; Colonel Chris Sanderson; Francis Scott; Kevin Walsh; Michael Ditchburn; Alison Johnston; Richard Roberts; Timothy Cartmell; Glenys Marriott; Susan Howorth; John Wilson; David Beeby.

OTHER INFORMATION This is one of the 46 UK community foundations, which distribute funding for a wide range of purposes. As with all community foundations, there are a number of donor-advised funds managed on behalf of individuals, families and charitable trusts. Grant schemes tend to change frequently; consult the foundation's website for details of current programmes and up-to-date deadlines. A total of 378 grants were made to organisations during the year. In addition, 180 grants were made to individuals totalling £153,200. Only beneficiaries of grants of £5,000 or more were listed in the accounts.

HOW TO APPLY Potential applicants are advised to visit the community foundation's website or contact its grants team to find the most suitable funding stream.

CONTACT DETAILS The Trustees, Dovenby Hall, Dovenby, Cockermouth, Cumbria CA13 0PN *Tel.* 01900 825760 *Email* enquiries@cumbriafoundation.org *Website* www.cumbriafoundation.org

■ The Cunningham Trust

OSCR NO SC013499 **ESTABLISHED** 1984

WHERE FUNDING CAN BE GIVEN Scotland.

WHO CAN BENEFIT Universities; research institutions.

WHAT IS FUNDED Biomedical research.

TYPE OF GRANT Project funding; research.

SAMPLE GRANTS University of Dundee (£87,500); University of St Andrews (£87,300); University of Glasgow (£86,900).

FINANCES *Financial year end* 05/04/2020 *Income* £349,700 *Total grants* £261,700 *Grants to organisations* £261,700 *Assets* £8,920,000

HOW TO APPLY The trust's website states: 'There is an annual competition for funding, open to staff in all universities. Details will be announced on this site, usually around May from which you will be able to apply for application forms.'

CONTACT DETAILS Prof. David Harrison, Scientific Advisor, Kinburn Castle, St Andrews, Fife KY16 9DR *Email* cunninghamtrust@st-andrews.ac.uk *Website* www.cunninghamtrust.org.uk

■ The Dennis Curry Charitable Trust

CC NO 263952 **ESTABLISHED** 1971

WHERE FUNDING CAN BE GIVEN UK and international.

WHO CAN BENEFIT Charitable organisations.

WHAT IS FUNDED General charitable purposes. It appears to have a particular interest in environmental causes.

RANGE OF GRANTS Mostly under £5,000.

SAMPLE GRANTS Royal Botanic Gardens (£20,000); Blue Ventures Conservation (£10,000); Cancerwise (£5,000); Alpuldram Centre (£2,000); Médecins Sans Frontières (£1,000).

FINANCES *Financial year end* 05/04/2020 *Income* £102,800 *Total grants* £94,500 *Grants to organisations* £94,500 *Assets* £4,140,000

TRUSTEES Anabel Curry; Margaret Curry-Jones; Patricia Edmond; Mr P. A. Curry.

HOW TO APPLY Contact the correspondent for further information.

CONTACT DETAILS The Trustees, Alliotts Accountants, Imperial House, 15 Kingsway, London WC2B 6UN *Tel.* 020 7240 9971 *Email* denniscurryscharity@alliotts.com

■ Itzchok Meyer Cymerman Trust Ltd

CC NO 265090 **ESTABLISHED** 1972

WHERE FUNDING CAN BE GIVEN UK and Israel.

WHO CAN BENEFIT Registered charities.

WHAT IS FUNDED The advancement of the Orthodox Jewish faith; education; social welfare; the relief of sickness; general charitable purposes. Occasionally, grants to individuals in need are also made. Many grants are given to the same organisations each year.

RANGE OF GRANTS Up to £200,000.

SAMPLE GRANTS MD and S Charitable Trust (£170,000); Ichud Mosdos Gur Ltd (£146,000); Russian Immigrant Aid Fund Ltd (£131,000); Friends of Gur Foundation Israel (£50,000); Dencommon Ltd (£36,000); Colel Polen Kupath Ramban Ltd (£34,000).

FINANCES *Financial year end* 31/03/2020 *Income* £1,390,000 *Total grants* £799,500 *Grants to organisations* £799,500 *Assets* £16,990,000

TRUSTEES Mrs H. F. Bondi; Sylvia Cymerman; Sara Heitner; Ian Heitner; Michael Cymerman; Leonard Bondi; Bernard Hoffman.

OTHER INFORMATION Grants were distributed in the following categories: education (£288,800); advancement of religion (£255,900); relief of poverty (£215,800); medical causes (£39,000). Awards of less than £30,000 totalled 202,500.

HOW TO APPLY The trustees tend to select the organisations to be supported based on their personal knowledge of the organisation's work. Although applications are not actively invited, the 2019/20 annual report states that the trustees 'are always prepared to accept any application which will be carefully considered and help given according to circumstances and funds then available'.

CONTACT DETAILS Mrs H. F. Bondi, Secretary, 497 Holloway Road, London N7 6LE *Tel.* 020 7272 2255

■ The D. G. Charitable Settlement

CC NO 1040778 **ESTABLISHED** 1994
WHERE FUNDING CAN BE GIVEN UK.
WHO CAN BENEFIT Registered charities.
WHAT IS FUNDED General charitable purposes including: homelessness; older people; human rights; cancer; the environment; overseas aid; health and well-being.
RANGE OF GRANTS Up to £200,000.
SAMPLE GRANTS Client Earth (£13.18 million); Oxfam (£100,000); Crisis (£40,000); Shelter (£25,000); Liberty Choir (£15,000); Women for Refugee Women (£10,000); Freedom from Torture (£5,000); Horsham District Scout Council (£1,000); Medical Aid for Palestinians (£500).
FINANCES *Financial year end* 30/06/2019
Income £13,800,000
Total grants £13,450,000
Grants to organisations £13,450,000
Assets £1,600
TRUSTEES David Gilmour; Polly Samson.
OTHER INFORMATION The grant total includes a £13.18 million grant to Client Earth. During the two previous financial years the grant totals were between £250,000 and £300,000. Grants were awarded to 21 organisations and broken down as follows: environment (£13.18 million); poverty overseas (£133,000); homeless (£65,000); other (£32,000); other medical causes (£15,000); human rights (£10,000) cancer (£5,000); older people (£5,000). The 2018/19 accounts were the latest available at the time of writing (February 2021).
HOW TO APPLY Contact the correspondent for further information.
CONTACT DETAILS The Trustees, Basement Flat, 7 Medina Terrace, Hove, East Sussex BN3 2WL *Tel.* 01273 780245 *Email* nicola@gilmour-dj.co.uk

■ D. M. H. Educational Trust Ltd

CC NO 271437 **ESTABLISHED** 1976
WHERE FUNDING CAN BE GIVEN England and Wales.
WHO CAN BENEFIT Jewish charitable organisations.
WHAT IS FUNDED Orthodox Jewish causes; social welfare.
RANGE OF GRANTS Typically up to £30,000.
SAMPLE GRANTS Keren Chochmas Shlomo Trust (£125,000); Rise and Shine (£43,000); British Friends of Rinat Aharon (£30,000); Edupoor Ltd (£20,000); Bais Rizhin Trust (£18,000).
FINANCES *Financial year end* 31/03/2019
Income £212,000 *Total grants* £323,600
Grants to organisations £323,600
Assets £2,240,000
TRUSTEES Samuel Jacob Halpern; Sidney Halpern; Relly Halpern; David Halpern.
OTHER INFORMATION Only organisations receiving grants of over £18,000 were listed as beneficiaries in the charity's accounts. Sundry grants totalled £46,700. The 2018/19 accounts were the latest available at the time of writing (January 2021).
HOW TO APPLY Contact the correspondent for further information.
CONTACT DETAILS David Halpern, Trustee, 31A The Park, London NW11 7ST *Tel.* 020 8731 0777 *Email* dh@dominionltd.net

■ The D'Oyly Carte Charitable Trust

CC NO 1112457 **ESTABLISHED** 1972
WHERE FUNDING CAN BE GIVEN UK.
WHO CAN BENEFIT Registered charities.
WHAT IS FUNDED The arts; health; social welfare; environmental protection or improvement.
WHAT IS NOT FUNDED A full list of exclusions can be found on the trust's helpful website.
TYPE OF GRANT Project funding and core costs. Matched funding is also considered. The majority of the trust's grants are single grants over a one-year period. Occasionally longer-term grants (usually up to three years) are agreed by the trustees when deemed to have particular merit.
SAMPLE GRANTS City and Guilds of London Art School (£10,000); Down's Syndrome Association (£4,500); Brain Charity (£4,300); Autism Bedfordshire (£3,000); Barnsley Hospice (£2,000); Reach South Sheffield (£1,300).
FINANCES *Financial year end* 31/03/2020
Income £1,660,000 *Total grants* £1,490,000
Grants to organisations £1,490,000
Assets £53,670,000
TRUSTEES Andrew Wimble; Nina Camilleri; Dr Michael O'Brien; Henry Barch; Andrew Jackson; Amelia Beringer; Julia Sibley.
OTHER INFORMATION A total of 466 grants were made during the year and distributed as follows: the arts (£785,000); medical welfare (£496,500); the environment (£209,000).
HOW TO APPLY Apply online via the trust's website. The trust's website lists the relevant submission dates and has detailed guidelines on how to apply. The trustees usually consider applications three times a year in March, July and November.
CONTACT DETAILS Grants Administrator, 6 Trull Farm Buildings, Tetbury, Gloucestershire GL8 8SQ *Tel.* 020 3637 3003 *Email* info@doylycartecharitabletrust.org *Website* www.doylycartecharitabletrust.org

■ The Daiwa Anglo-Japanese Foundation

CC NO 299955 **ESTABLISHED** 1988
WHERE FUNDING CAN BE GIVEN UK and Japan.
WHO CAN BENEFIT Schools; universities; individuals.
WHAT IS FUNDED Advancement of the UK and Japan in each other's institutions, culture, history, etc.; scholarships or maintenance allowances to allow students and academics to travel to the UK/Japan to pursue their education; charitable purposes in the UK which promote for public benefit education in the UK or Japan; charitable purposes in the UK which conduct research into cultural, historical, medical and scientific subjects and the publication of all such research.
WHAT IS NOT FUNDED See the foundation's website for detailed exclusions for each grant programme.
TYPE OF GRANT Project funding.
RANGE OF GRANTS £2,000 to £15,000.
SAMPLE GRANTS The Coronet Theatre (£6,000); Ashmolean Museum of Art and Archaeology, University of Oxford and University of Wolverhampton (£3,000 each); Glasgow School

of Art (£2,300); Compton Verney House Trust (£2,000).

FINANCES *Financial year end* 31/03/2020 *Income* £467,900 *Total grants* £282,900 *Grants to organisations* £247,200 *Assets* £37,040,000

TRUSTEES Takashi Hibino; Stephen Barber; Prof. Richard Bowring; Paul Dimond; Yoko Dochi; James Harding; Sir Tim Hitchens; Jessie Turnbull; Yusuke Kawamura; Prof. Sachiko Kusukawa; Masaki Orita; Prof. Hirotaka Takeuchi.

OTHER INFORMATION Grants were made to 85 organisations. Grants to 14 individuals totalled £35,700. The foundation also awarded £588,500 in scholarships, which has not been included in the grant totals.

HOW TO APPLY Application forms are available to download from the foundation's website where you can also find details of deadlines, further guidance and eligibility criteria.

CONTACT DETAILS The Trustees, Daiwa Foundation Japan House, 13/14 Cornwall Terrace (Outer Circle), London NW1 4QP *Email* grants@dajf.org.uk *Website* www.dajf.org.uk

■ Oizer Dalim Trust

CC NO 1045296 **ESTABLISHED** 1994

WHERE FUNDING CAN BE GIVEN UK and overseas.

WHO CAN BENEFIT Registered charities.

WHAT IS FUNDED The alleviation of poverty and furtherance of education within the Orthodox Jewish community.

SAMPLE GRANTS A list of beneficiaries was not included in the annual report and accounts.

FINANCES *Financial year end* 30/06/2020 *Income* £267,000 *Total grants* £72,400 *Grants to organisations* £72,400 *Assets* £775,300

TRUSTEES Mordechai Cik; Maurice Fruend; Moshe Cohen.

HOW TO APPLY Contact the correspondent for further information.

CONTACT DETAILS The Trustees, 68 Osbaldeston Road, London N16 7DR *Tel.* 020 8806 9111

■ The Daniell Trust

CC NO 1176166 **ESTABLISHED** 2017

WHERE FUNDING CAN BE GIVEN England; Wales; Scotland.

WHO CAN BENEFIT Charitable organisations.

WHAT IS FUNDED The care and education of children; people with learning disabilities; environmental conservation.

SAMPLE GRANTS A list of beneficiaries was not available.

FINANCES *Financial year end* 05/04/2020 *Income* £755,200 *Total grants* £54,000 *Grants to organisations* £54,000 *Assets* £71,700

TRUSTEES Katie Edwards; Keith Bennett; Odette Murray; William Prestwood; Carmen Cullis.

OTHER INFORMATION The trustees try to chose smaller or locally based projects and organisations in preference to larger national ones.

HOW TO APPLY Application forms can be downloaded from the trust's website. The trustees normally meet once a year in November to agree funding. Applications should be received before 30 September.

CONTACT DETAILS The Trustees, c/o Dyke Yaxley Ltd, 1 Brassey Road, Shrewsbury SY3 7FA *Email* Contact form on website *Website* https://www.thedanielltrust.org.uk

■ The Dashlight Foundation

CC NO 1184873 **ESTABLISHED** 2019

WHERE FUNDING CAN BE GIVEN UK, with a preference for Yorkshire; Africa.

WHO CAN BENEFIT Charitable organisations.

WHAT IS FUNDED Mental health; wildlife conservation; general charitable purposes in Yorkshire; poverty relief and education in Africa; support for refugees.

SAMPLE GRANTS Lighthouse Relief (£29,700); Oceana UK and WildAid UK (£25,000 each); Wetherby and District Foodbank (£14,500).

FINANCES *Financial year end* 31/03/2020 *Income* £1,810,000 *Total grants* £95,200 *Grants to organisations* £95,200 *Assets* £1,710,000

TRUSTEES Bethany Clarke; Jacqueline Clark; Owen Clarke; Dominic Clarke.

OTHER INFORMATION Grants were distributed as follows: wildlife conservation (£50,000); relief of poverty (£29,700); charities in Yorkshire (£14,500); relief of sickness and mental health (£1,000).

HOW TO APPLY Applications should be sent by email and be no longer than four pages. Unsuccessful applicants are not informed.

CONTACT DETAILS The Trustees, Flat G, 49 Wellington Street, London WC2E 7BN *Tel.* 01937 588826 *Email* dashlight.fdn@gmail.com

■ Baron Davenport's Charity

CC NO 217307 **ESTABLISHED** 1930

WHERE FUNDING CAN BE GIVEN Birmingham and the West Midlands counties. Applicants must be within 60 miles of Birmingham Town Hall.

WHO CAN BENEFIT Registered charities; unregistered charities; CICs; social enterprises; hospices; religious bodies/institutions; individuals.

WHAT IS FUNDED Almshouses; hospices; residential homes for older people; children and young people (under 25 years old); older people.

WHAT IS NOT FUNDED Statutory services; universities and further education colleges; nurseries and preschools; parent teacher associations; start-up organisations; retrospective expenditure; capital appeals for places of worship (unless for community use); medical research.

TYPE OF GRANT Capital costs; core/revenue costs; project funding.

RANGE OF GRANTS Up to £12,000.

SAMPLE GRANTS Broadening Choices for Older People (£12,900); Age UK Birmingham and Myton Hospices (£12,000 each); Compton Care, Mary Stevens Hospice, Stonehouse Gang and Zoë's Place Trust (£10,000 each).

FINANCES *Financial year end* 31/12/2019 *Income* £1,030,000 *Total grants* £908,300 *Grants to organisations* £549,900 *Assets* £36,460,000

TRUSTEES William Colacicchi; Sue Ayres; Lisa Bryan; Peter Horton; Alec Jones; Victoria Milligan; Lynn Clark Redwood; Victoria Smith; Mohammed Sajid.

OTHER INFORMATION Only organisations receiving grants of over £10,000 were listed as beneficiaries in the charity's accounts. Grants of under £10,000 totalled £381,000 and were awarded to 370 organisations.

HOW TO APPLY Applications can be made through the charity's website.

CONTACT DETAILS Kate Slater, Charity Administrator, Portman House, 5–7 Temple Row West, Birmingham, West Midlands B2 5NY *Tel.* 0121 236 8004 *Email* enquiries@barondavenportscharity.org *Website* www.barondavenportscharity.org

■ The Manny and Brigitta Davidson Charitable Foundation

CC NO 1175058 **ESTABLISHED** 2017

WHERE FUNDING CAN BE GIVEN UK; Israel.

WHO CAN BENEFIT Registered charities.

WHAT IS FUNDED Purchasing, holding, maintaining and exhibiting works of art; capital and infrastructure projects; social welfare.

TYPE OF GRANT Capital costs; collection and acquisition.

SAMPLE GRANTS The Noam Primary School Ltd (£350,000); The National Gallery (£100,000); Noah's Ark (£50,000); The London Academy of Music and Dramatic Art (£25,000); The Royal College of Music (£11,500).

FINANCES *Financial year end* 31/03/2020 *Income* £575,000 *Total grants* £595,500 *Grants to organisations* £595,500 *Assets* £57,300

TRUSTEES Ilan Rappaport; Richard Denton; Brigitta Davidson; Gerard Cohen; Lord Jonathan Kestenbaum; Jeremy Sandelson; Emanual Davidson.

HOW TO APPLY Contact the correspondent for further information.

CONTACT DETAILS The Trustees, OGR Stock Denton LLP, 2nd Floor, Winston House, 2 Dollis Park, London N3 1HF *Tel.* 020 8349 5500

■ The Davidson Family Charitable Trust

CC NO 262937 **ESTABLISHED** 1971

WHERE FUNDING CAN BE GIVEN England and Wales.

WHO CAN BENEFIT Mainly Jewish organisations.

WHAT IS FUNDED Education; health; religious organisations; the arts; welfare.

TYPE OF GRANT Grants are made towards larger capital projects.

SAMPLE GRANTS The Jerusalem Foundation (£800,000); Jewish Care (£30,000); Community Security Trust (£12,000); Fine Giving and Victoria and Albert Museum (£5,000 each); Rays of Sunshine and The Chicken Soup Shelter (£1,000 each); Epilepsy Action (£500).

FINANCES *Financial year end* 05/04/2020 *Income* £1,010,000 *Total grants* £871,000 *Grants to organisations* £871,000 *Assets* £181,800

TRUSTEES Gerald Davidson; Maxine Davidson.

OTHER INFORMATION Grants were awarded to 13 organisations.

HOW TO APPLY Contact the correspondent for further information.

CONTACT DETAILS Gerald Davidson, Trustee, 58 Queen Anne Street, London W1G 8HW *Tel.* 020 7224 1030

■ Michael Davies Charitable Settlement

CC NO 1000574 **ESTABLISHED** 1990

WHERE FUNDING CAN BE GIVEN UK.

WHO CAN BENEFIT Charitable organisations.

WHAT IS FUNDED General charitable purposes.

SAMPLE GRANTS Previous beneficiaries have included: Architectural Association Foundation, Camden Arts Centre, Crisis, Ebony Horse Club, Marie Curie Hospice, North London Hospice, Royal National Orthopaedic Hospital Trust and University of Sunderland Development Trust.

FINANCES *Financial year end* 05/04/2020 *Income* £3,300 *Total grants* £84,800 *Grants to organisations* £84,800

TRUSTEES Michael Davies; Kenneth Hawkins.

OTHER INFORMATION Full accounts were not available to view on the Charity Commission's website due to the charity's low income. We have therefore estimated the grant total based on the charity's total expenditure.

HOW TO APPLY Contact the correspondent for further information.

CONTACT DETAILS The Trustees, HW Lee Associates, New Derwent House, 69/73 Theobalds Road, London WC1X 8TA *Tel.* 020 7025 4600

■ Margaret Davies Charity

CC NO 235589 **ESTABLISHED** 1934

WHERE FUNDING CAN BE GIVEN Wales.

WHO CAN BENEFIT Registered charities; Welsh organisations; schools; universities; PTAs; amateur sports clubs.

WHAT IS FUNDED General charitable purposes including: visual and performing arts; education; health; social welfare; provision for young people.

TYPE OF GRANT Capital costs.

RANGE OF GRANTS Mainly under £10,000.

SAMPLE GRANTS The Gregynog Trust (£512,500); David Davies Memorial Institute (£15,000); Gregynog Festival (£10,000); Hearing Dog's for Deaf People and Welsh National Opera (£5,000 each); Tall Ships Youth Trust (£3,000); Young Women's Trust (£2,500); Nightingale House Hospice (£1,800); Bike to the Future (£1,000).

FINANCES *Financial year end* 05/04/2020 *Income* £310,200 *Total grants* £897,100 *Grants to organisations* £897,100 *Assets* £6,860,000

TRUSTEES Daniel Davies; Dr Denis Balsom; Dr Janet Lewis; Thomas Williams; Elinor Gilbey.

HOW TO APPLY Apply in writing to the correspondent. The trustees meet quarterly to consider new applications.

CONTACT DETAILS The Trustees, Plas Dolerw, Milford Road, Newtown, Powys SY16 2EH *Tel.* 01686 625228 *Email* daviescharities@gmail.com

■ The Crispin Davis Family Trust

CC NO 1150637 **ESTABLISHED** 2013

WHERE FUNDING CAN BE GIVEN Worldwide.

WHO CAN BENEFIT Registered charities; schools.

WHAT IS FUNDED Children and young people across the world who are in need of help as a result of poverty, lack of education or illness.

SAMPLE GRANTS Optimus Foundation (£300,000); Justice and Care (£50,000) Tushinde Children's Trust (£35,000); Cavoequiva (£10,000).

FINANCES *Financial year end* 05/04/2020 *Income* £238,200 *Total grants* £565,000 *Grants to organisations* £565,000 *Assets* £6,540,000

TRUSTEES Lady Jean Davis; Caroline King; Cripps Trust Corporation Ltd; Angela Spaid; Sir Crispin Davis; Julia Davis.

HOW TO APPLY Contact the correspondent for further information.

CONTACT DETAILS The Trustees, Heartwood Wealth Management, 77 Mount Ephraim, Tunbridge

Wells, Kent TN4 8BS *Tel.* 01892 701801
Email info@heartwoodgroup.co.uk

■ The Davis Foundation

CC NO 1152998 **ESTABLISHED** 2013
WHERE FUNDING CAN BE GIVEN England, South Africa and Israel.
WHO CAN BENEFIT Charitable organisations.
WHAT IS FUNDED Jewish causes; young people; older people; disability; the arts; horticulture; religious harmony; religious education; citizenship.
SAMPLE GRANTS A list of beneficiaries was not included in the annual report and accounts.
FINANCES *Financial year end* 05/04/2020
Income £4,400 *Total grants* £1,700,000
Grants to organisations £1,700,000
TRUSTEES Sir Michael Davis; Lady Barbara Davis; Sarah Davis.
OTHER INFORMATION Full accounts were not available to view on the Charity Commission's website due to the foundation's low income. We have therefore estimated the grant total based on the foundation's total expenditure.
HOW TO APPLY Contact the correspondent for further information.
CONTACT DETAILS The Trustees, 3 Beechworth Close, London NW3 7UT *Tel.* 020 7389 9512
Email applications@thedavisfoundation.com

■ The Henry and Suzanne Davis Foundation

CC NO 1153199 **ESTABLISHED** 2013
WHERE FUNDING CAN BE GIVEN England, Wales and Israel.
WHO CAN BENEFIT Charitable organisations.
WHAT IS FUNDED General charitable purposes; education and training; arts and culture; human rights.
SAMPLE GRANTS A list of beneficiaries was not included in the annual report and accounts.
FINANCES *Financial year end* 27/06/2020
Income £112,500 *Total grants* £105,500
Grants to organisations £105,500
Assets £287,900
TRUSTEES Robert Craig; Henry Davis; Suzanne Davis.
HOW TO APPLY The 2019/20 accounts state: 'The trustees have clear ideas what charities and charitable purposes they wish to support, and speculative applications for funding are unlikely to be successful.'
CONTACT DETAILS Robert Craig, Trustee, c/o Howard Kennedy LLP, No. 1 London Bridge, London SE1 9BG *Tel.* 020 3755 5421 *Email* robert.craig@howardkennedy.com

■ Dawat-E-Hadiyah Trust (United Kingdom)

CC NO 294807 **ESTABLISHED** 1986
WHERE FUNDING CAN BE GIVEN UK and overseas.
WHO CAN BENEFIT Registered charities; individuals.
WHAT IS FUNDED The advancement of the Islamic religion; education; social welfare; medical aid.
RANGE OF GRANTS Mainly under £50,000.
SAMPLE GRANTS Saifee Burhani Upliftment Trust (£1.01 million); Al Jameah Al-Sayfiyah Trust (£20,000); Anjuman-e-Saifee – Leicester (£16,900); Anjuman-e-Hamidi – Manchester (£3,000); Anjuman-e-Zaini – Croydon (£2,900); Anjuman-e-Badri – Birmingham (£1,500); Anjuman-e-Jamali – Bradford (£800).
FINANCES *Financial year end* 31/12/2018
Income £10,420,000 *Total grants* £1,102,800
Grants to organisations £1,090,000
Assets £8,870,000
TRUSTEE The 53rd Dai Al-Mutlaq, His Holiness Syedna Mufaddal Saifuddin.
OTHER INFORMATION The 2018 accounts were the latest available at the time of writing (May 2021). Grants were distributed as follows: UK-registered charities (£57,500); overseas charities (£21,400). The grant total includes a substantial grant of £1.01 million to the Saifee Burhani Upliftment Trust.
HOW TO APPLY Apply in writing to the correspondent.
CONTACT DETAILS The Trustees, 6 Mohammedi Park Complex, Rowdell Road, Northolt, Middlesex UB5 6AG *Tel.* 020 8839 0750 *Email* farazdaq@dawatuk.org

■ The De Brye Charitable Trust

CC NO 326226 **ESTABLISHED** 1982
WHERE FUNDING CAN BE GIVEN England and Wales.
WHO CAN BENEFIT Charitable organisations.
WHAT IS FUNDED General charitable purposes, preference may be given to projects for orphans, neglected children and children with physical disabilities, older people and people who are blind.
RANGE OF GRANTS Mostly under £5,000.
SAMPLE GRANTS Salisbury Cathedral (£10,000); Action Medical Research for Children (£5,000); Diabetes UK (£3,000); British Wireless For The Blind (£2,000); Clowns in the Sky (£1,500); London's Air Ambulance Charity (£1,000).
FINANCES *Financial year end* 05/04/2020
Income £114,700 *Total grants* £104,300
Grants to organisations £104,300
Assets £2,550,000
TRUSTEES Alexander de Brye; Edward Reed; Phillip Sykes.
OTHER INFORMATION Grants were broken down as follows: care and support (£23,000); overseas support (£23,000); medical causes (£22,000); children (£15,400); others (£11,000); disabled (£10,000).
HOW TO APPLY Contact the correspondent for further information.
CONTACT DETAILS The Trustees, Mercer and Hole, 72 London Road, St Albans, Hertfordshire AL1 1NS *Tel.* 01727 869141

■ The Roger De Haan Charitable Trust

CC NO 276274 **ESTABLISHED** 1978
WHERE FUNDING CAN BE GIVEN Folkestone.
WHO CAN BENEFIT Registered charities; schools; community organisations; churches; CICs.
WHAT IS FUNDED Arts and culture; education; health and welfare of older people; sports; community development, heritage and regeneration in Folkestone; social welfare; the environment.
WHAT IS NOT FUNDED See the trust's website for a full list of exclusions.
TYPE OF GRANT Capital costs; project funding; development funding.
SAMPLE GRANTS Shepway Sports Trust (£2.63 million); Kent Community Foundation (£180,000); Creative Folkestone (£82,000); Glass Door (£25,000); St Mary and St Eanswythe Parish Church PCC (£10,000); People United (£8,300); Rotary Club of the Channel (£3,000); Broadstairs Folk Week

(£2,000); Changeling Theatre Company (£1,200); Folkestone School for Girls (£100).

FINANCES *Financial year end* 05/04/2020 *Income* £1,670,000 *Total grants* £3,510,000 *Grants to organisations* £3,510,000 *Assets* £17,900,000

TRUSTEES Sir Roger De Haan; Joshua De Haan; Lady De Haan; Benjamin De Haan.

OTHER INFORMATION Grants were awarded as follows: sport (£2.68 million); health and welfare (£327,000); arts (£316,000); community development (£102,000); education (£48,000); other sectors (£35,000). Of the £3.51 million grants made 96% was granted to charitable causes in Folkestone and the surrounding area.

HOW TO APPLY Applications can be made through the trust's website. Alternatively applicants may download or print the form available on the website for completion and return to the trust by post. The trustees meet five times a year to consider grants and deadlines for the meetings can be found on the trust's website.

CONTACT DETAILS Sir Roger De Haan, Trustee, Strand House, Pilgrims Way, Monks Horton, Ashford, Kent TN25 6DR *Email* Contact form on website. *Website* www.rdhct.org.uk

■ The De Laszlo Foundation

CC NO 327383 **ESTABLISHED** 1978

WHERE FUNDING CAN BE GIVEN UK and worldwide.

WHO CAN BENEFIT Registered charities; universities; hospices.

WHAT IS FUNDED Promotion of the arts; general charitable purposes.

TYPE OF GRANT Research, project and capital costs; collections and acquisitions; scholarships and prizes.

SAMPLE GRANTS Cambridge University; City and Guilds of London Art School; Durham University; English National Ballet; Game and Wildlife Conservation Trust; The de Laszlo Archive Trust.

FINANCES *Financial year end* 05/04/2020 *Income* £770,400 *Total grants* £676,000 *Grants to organisations* £676,000 *Assets* £2,900,000

TRUSTEES Damon de Laszlo; Lucy Birkbeck; Robert de Laszlo; William de Laszlo.

OTHER INFORMATION The foundation was set up to promote the advancement and promotion of education and interest in the visual arts with special reference to encouraging knowledge of the works of contemporary painters, in particular those of the late Philip de Laszlo. In the 2019/20 accounts grants were broken down as follows: Archive Trust (£245,000); education (£131,800); medicine (£119,500); arts (£105,800); science (£30,400); other charities (£16,400); economics (£16,400); scholarships and grants (£10,500).

HOW TO APPLY Apply in writing to the correspondent.

CONTACT DETAILS The Trustees, 5 Albany Courtyard, Piccadilly, London W1J 0HF *Tel.* 020 7437 1982

■ William Dean Countryside and Educational Trust

CC NO 1044567 **ESTABLISHED** 1994

WHERE FUNDING CAN BE GIVEN UK, with a preference for Cheshire, Derbyshire, Lancashire, Staffordshire and the Wirral.

WHO CAN BENEFIT Charitable organisations; individuals.

WHAT IS FUNDED Education in natural history, ecology and the conservation of the natural environment.

RANGE OF GRANTS £150 to £16,000.

SAMPLE GRANTS Cheshire Wildlife Trust (£16,000); Astbury Mere Trust (£6,000); Congleton Building Preservation Trust (£3,500); Ruskin Mill Trust (£1,500); The Rossendale Trust (£750); Harper Asprey Wildlife Rescue (£550); Royal Forestry Society (£500); Freshfields Animal Rescue (£250); Marlfields Primary School (£150).

FINANCES *Financial year end* 31/12/2019 *Income* £104,400 *Total grants* £78,100 *Grants to organisations* £78,100 *Assets* £2,150,000

TRUSTEES John Ward; Andrew Pear; David Crawford; Rebecca Franklin; Patricia Pinto.

OTHER INFORMATION Most grants are for less than £1,000. The trust's 2019 accounts provide a comprehensive list of grantees, around half of which received grants in the previous year.

HOW TO APPLY Contact the correspondent for information. The trustees meet four times each year in March, June, September and December when applications for grants are considered.

CONTACT DETAILS Clare Amare, Co-ordinator, 51 Moss Road, Congleton CW12 3BN *Tel.* 01260 276970 *Email* williamdeantrust@gmail.com

■ Debmar Benevolent Trust Ltd

CC NO 283065 **ESTABLISHED** 1979

WHERE FUNDING CAN BE GIVEN UK and Israel.

WHO CAN BENEFIT Charitable organisations.

WHAT IS FUNDED Orthodox Jewish causes.

RANGE OF GRANTS From £10,000 to £35,000.

SAMPLE GRANTS Ohel Torah (£35,000); Kupas Rashbi (£25,200); MW (GK) Foundation and MW (CL) Foundation (£25,000 each); MW (HO) Foundation (£22,500); MW (RH) Foundation and Kolyom Trust Ltd (£20,000 each); Choimel Dalim (£10,000).

FINANCES *Financial year end* 30/06/2019 *Income* £703,200 *Total grants* £182,700 *Grants to organisations* £182,700 *Assets* £5,400,000

TRUSTEES David Olsberg; Jacob Halpern.

OTHER INFORMATION The 2018/19 accounts were the latest available at the time of writing (June 2021).

HOW TO APPLY Contact the correspondent for further information.

CONTACT DETAILS The Trustees, 16 Stanley Road, Salford, Greater Manchester M7 4RW *Tel.* 0161 798 1660

■ The Delves Charitable Trust

CC NO 231860 **ESTABLISHED** 1922

WHERE FUNDING CAN BE GIVEN UK; overseas.

WHO CAN BENEFIT Registered charities and CICs.

WHAT IS FUNDED Medical research; medical care; self-sustaining communities and economic independence; the environment; social responsibility.

TYPE OF GRANT Capital costs and project funding.

SAMPLE GRANTS Tree Aid (£11,000); Samaritans (£10,000); Action Medical Research (£8,000); Crisis (£5,500); Plantlife (£4,000); Place2Be (£500).

FINANCES *Financial year end* 05/04/2020 *Income* £284,800 *Total grants* £219,000 *Grants to organisations* £219,000 *Assets* £9,290,000

TRUSTEES Mark Breeze; George Breeze; Dr Elizabeth Breeze; Dr Charles Breeze; John Breeze; William Breeze.

HOW TO APPLY The trust does not accept unsolicited applications for funding.

CONTACT DETAILS The Trust Administrator, c/o Luminary Finance LLP, PO Box 135, Longfield, Kent DA3 8WF *Tel.* 01732 822114

■ The Demigryphon Trust

CC NO 275821 **ESTABLISHED** 1978

WHERE FUNDING CAN BE GIVEN UK.

WHO CAN BENEFIT Registered charities only.

WHAT IS FUNDED General charitable purposes including: social welfare; education; religion; health; community development; social justice; the environment; animal welfare; armed forces and emergency services.

RANGE OF GRANTS Mostly under £5,000.

SAMPLE GRANTS Christ Church College (£25,000); Adam Smith Institute and The Black Stork Charity (£10,000 each); Game and Wildlife Conservation Trust and Winston's Wish (£5,000 each).

FINANCES *Financial year end* 05/04/2020
Income £37,200 *Total grants* £60,600
Grants to organisations £60,600
Assets £2,880,000

TRUSTEE The Cowdray Trust Ltd.

OTHER INFORMATION Grants of £5,000 or more were awarded to four organisations. Grants of under £5,000 totalled £21,200.

HOW TO APPLY Contact the correspondent for further information.

CONTACT DETAILS The Trustees, 4th Floor, 10 Bruton Street, London W1J 6PX *Tel.* 020 7907 2100 *Email* charity@mfs.co.uk

■ Denman Charitable Trust

CC NO 326532 **ESTABLISHED** 1983

WHERE FUNDING CAN BE GIVEN Bristol; North East Somerset; South Gloucestershire.

WHO CAN BENEFIT Registered charities.

WHAT IS FUNDED General charitable purposes.

TYPE OF GRANT Project funding; pump-priming.

RANGE OF GRANTS Up to £20,000. Usually between £500 and £5,000.

SAMPLE GRANTS A list of beneficiaries was not included in the 2019/20 annual report and accounts.

FINANCES *Financial year end* 05/04/2020
Income £86,900 *Total grants* £84,700
Grants to organisations £84,700
Assets £33,900

TRUSTEES Arnold Denman; Dorothy Denman; Sue Blatchford; Joanna Denman; Matthew Lee.

HOW TO APPLY Apply in writing by post or email. Details of what should be included in an application can be found on the trust's website. The trustees meet to consider applications four times a year in March, June, September and December.

CONTACT DETAILS The Trustees, PO Box 1881, Old Sodbury, Bristol BS37 6WS *Email* enquiries@denmancharitabletrust.org.uk *Website* www.denmancharitabletrust.org.uk/index.html

■ Dentons UKMEA LLP Charitable Trust

CC NO 1041204 **ESTABLISHED** 1994

WHERE FUNDING CAN BE GIVEN UK.

WHO CAN BENEFIT Registered charities; hospices; community organisations.

WHAT IS FUNDED General charitable purposes.

RANGE OF GRANTS Mostly £500 to £3,000.

SAMPLE GRANTS Whitechapel Mission (£7,000); National Emergencies Trust (£5,000); Milton Keynes SNAP (£2,000); Marylebone Project and Shelter (£1,000 each); Mind (£500); Alzheimer Scotland (£200).

FINANCES *Financial year end* 30/04/2020
Income £167,200 *Total grants* £130,300
Grants to organisations £130,300
Assets £163,400

TRUSTEES Daniel Bodle; Alexis Graham; Lisa Sewell; David Payton.

OTHER INFORMATION Preference is given to charities with a connection with Dentons UK and Middle East LLP or those that are local to its offices.

HOW TO APPLY Contact the correspondent for further information.

CONTACT DETAILS The Trustees, One Fleet Place, London EC4M 7WS *Tel.* 020 7246 4843 *Email* bernadette.osullivan@dentons.com

■ Foundation Derbyshire

CC NO 1039485 **ESTABLISHED** 1996

WHERE FUNDING CAN BE GIVEN Derbyshire and the city of Derby.

WHO CAN BENEFIT Charitable organisations.

WHAT IS FUNDED General charitable purposes including: community safety; social welfare; volunteer development; homelessness; children and young people; the arts.

TYPE OF GRANT Capital costs; core/revenue costs; project funding.

RANGE OF GRANTS Mostly up to £2,000.

SAMPLE GRANTS A list of beneficiaries was not included in the annual report and accounts.

FINANCES *Financial year end* 31/03/2020
Income £543,000 *Total grants* £351,500
Grants to organisations £317,200
Assets £7,130,000

TRUSTEES Philip Bloxham; Andrew Cochrane; David Palmer; Sheila Taylor; Oliver Stephenson; Nick Hodgson; Alison Williams; Jane Gerrard-Pearse; Paul Broadhead; Louise Pinder; William Kerr; Peter Pimm.

OTHER INFORMATION This is one of the 46 UK community foundations, which distribute funding for a wide range of purposes. As with all community foundations, there are a number of donor-advised funds managed on behalf of individuals, families and charitable trusts. Grant schemes tend to change frequently – consult the foundation's website for details of current programmes and up-to-date deadlines. Grants were made to 189 organisations during the year.

HOW TO APPLY Potential applicants are advised to visit the community foundation's website or contact its grants team to find the most suitable funding stream.

CONTACT DETAILS The Grants Team, Unit 2, Heritage Business Centre, Belper, Derbyshire DE56 1SW *Tel.* 01773 525860 *Email* hello@foundationderbyshire.org *Website* www.foundationderbyshire.org

Provincial Grand Charity of the Province of Derbyshire

CC NO 701963 **ESTABLISHED** 1989

WHERE FUNDING CAN BE GIVEN Derbyshire.

WHO CAN BENEFIT Charitable organisations; Masons and their dependants; hospices; individuals.

WHAT IS FUNDED General charitable purposes including: health; disability; community; amateur sport; arts, culture and heritage; vulnerable people; young people.

SAMPLE GRANTS A list of beneficiaries was not included in the annual report and accounts.

FINANCES *Financial year end* 30/06/2020 *Income* £100,000 *Total grants* £94,800 *Grants to organisations* £91,900 *Assets* £1,400,000

TRUSTEES John Acton; Graham Sisson; Arthur Varley.

OTHER INFORMATION During the year, grants awarded to non-Masonic causes totalled £86,300. Grants awarded to 'brethren' totalled £2,900.

HOW TO APPLY Contact the correspondent for further information.

CONTACT DETAILS Secretary, Derby Masonic Hall, 457 Burton Road, Littleover, Derby, Derbyshire DE23 6XX *Tel.* 01332 272202 *Email* secretary@derbyshiremason.org *Website* www.derbyshiremason.org

The J. N. Derbyshire Trust

CC NO 231907 **ESTABLISHED** 1944

WHERE FUNDING CAN BE GIVEN UK with a strong preference for Nottingham and Nottinghamshire.

WHO CAN BENEFIT Charitable organisations.

WHAT IS FUNDED General charitable purposes including: social welfare; education; physical health; people with disabilities; children and young people; older people; women.

WHAT IS NOT FUNDED Individuals.

RANGE OF GRANTS £500 to £7,000.

SAMPLE GRANTS Jericho Road Project (£7,000); FareShare East Midlands (£6,000); PCC of St Saviour's Nottingham (£5,000); Elizabeth Finn Care Fund (£4,900); Ravenshead Community Project (£4,000); Nottinghamshire Clubs for Young People and Nottinghamshire Royal Society for the Blind (£3,300 each).

FINANCES *Financial year end* 05/04/2020 *Income* £223,500 *Total grants* £176,500 *Grants to organisations* £176,500 *Assets* £5,510,000

TRUSTEES Peter Moore; Charles George; Andrew Little; Rose Whittle; Georgina Cowan; William Carver.

OTHER INFORMATION Grants were made to 72 organisations during the year. Grants were broken down as follows: relief of poverty (£51,900); miscellaneous (£30,400); health and disability (£30,200); youth organisations (£26,200); welfare of women and children (£20,500); education (£13,000); older people (£4,300). Only beneficiaries of grants over £3,000 were listed in the accounts.

HOW TO APPLY A link to an online application form can be requested from the correspondent. Applications can be made at any time but trustees usually only meet twice a year.

CONTACT DETAILS Emma Hanson, Secretary, c/o RSM UK, 7th Floor, Suite A, City Gate East, Tollhouse Hill, Nottingham, Nottinghamshire NG1 5FS *Tel.* 0115 964 4450 *Email* emma.hanson@rsmuk.com

The Desmond Foundation

CC NO 1014352 **ESTABLISHED** 1992

WHERE FUNDING CAN BE GIVEN UK and overseas.

WHO CAN BENEFIT Charitable organisations.

WHAT IS FUNDED General charitable purposes.

RANGE OF GRANTS Mostly under £10,000.

SAMPLE GRANTS Noah's Ark Children's Hospice (£500,000); Imperial War Museum (£333,000); Greenhouse Sports (£333, 000 in two grants); Barnet Youth Zone (£100,000); Jewish Blind and Disabled (£10,000); The Chicken Soup Shelter (£1,000).

FINANCES *Financial year end* 31/12/2019 *Income* £2,650,000 *Total grants* £1,540,000 *Grants to organisations* £1,540,000 *Assets* £1,130,000

TRUSTEES Richard Desmond; Northern & Shell Services Ltd; Northern & Shell Media Group Ltd.

OTHER INFORMATION Grants were awarded to 35 organisations during the year.

HOW TO APPLY Contact the correspondent for further information.

CONTACT DETAILS The Trustees, The Northern & Shell Building, 10 Lower Thames Street, London EC3R 6EN *Tel.* 020 8612 7760 *Email* allison.racher@express.co.uk

Devon Community Foundation

CC NO 1057923 **ESTABLISHED** 1996

WHERE FUNDING CAN BE GIVEN Devon, Plymouth and Torbay.

WHO CAN BENEFIT Not-for-profit voluntary or community groups; registered charities; social enterprises; schools; individuals.

WHAT IS FUNDED General charitable purposes.

WHAT IS NOT FUNDED Applications from individuals, grant-making organisations, sole traders; alcohol or medication; building works or large-scale refurbishment; capital purchases over £1,000; consultancy or feasibility studies; large projects where the link between a grant awarded and overall project outcomes are not clear; loss of income; organisations or activities that primarily support animal welfare; overseas travel; projects or activity that promote political or religious beliefs; retrospective expenditure; sponsorship or fundraising activities.

TYPE OF GRANT Core costs; project costs.

RANGE OF GRANTS Mainly between £1,000 and £5,000.

SAMPLE GRANTS Previous beneficiaries have included: Westbank Community Health and Care (£276,300); Oakford Village Hall (£15,000); Family Compass (£4,000); LandWorks (£3,500); Magic Carpet (£1,500); Friends2SmileWith (£1,000).

FINANCES *Financial year end* 31/03/2020 *Income* £2,270,000 *Total grants* £1,224,100 *Grants to organisations* £1,200,000 *Assets* £8,830,000

TRUSTEES Edward Burnand; The Right Revd Robert Atwell; Peter Holden; Caroline Harlow; Ann Holman; Sally Wace; Dinah Cox; Revd Prof. Georgina Radford; Graham Howe.

OTHER INFORMATION This is one of the 46 UK community foundations, which distribute funding for a wide range of purposes. As with all community foundations, there are a number of donor-advised funds managed on behalf of individuals, families and charitable trusts. Grant schemes tend to change frequently; consult the foundation's website for details of current programmes and up-to-date deadlines. During 2019/20, grants were awarded to 156 organisations totalling £1.2 million and 16 individuals totalling £24,100.

HOW TO APPLY Potential applicants are advised to visit the community foundation's website or contact its grants team to find the most suitable funding stream.

CONTACT DETAILS The Grants Team, The Factory, Leat Street, Tiverton, Devon EX16 5LL *Tel.* 01884 235887 *Email* grants@devoncf.com *Website* www.devoncf.com

■ The Devon Historic Churches

CC NO 265594 **ESTABLISHED** 1973

WHERE FUNDING CAN BE GIVEN Devon; Exeter.

WHO CAN BENEFIT Churches.

WHAT IS FUNDED The historic fabric of churches; emergency repairs to churches.

WHAT IS NOT FUNDED The charity's guidelines state: 'We tend to direct our funds to the historic fabric, so that we do not normally assist the installation of plumbing, sound amplification and lighting, nor the work which public buildings perceive to be necessary to conform with ever changing legal requirements for safety or disability access.'

TYPE OF GRANT Capital costs; project funding.

RANGE OF GRANTS £300 to £5,000.

SAMPLE GRANTS Exeter Cathedral (£20,000); St Peter's Church – Ugborough (£5,000); Bovery Tracey Methodist Church (£2,000); St Peter's Church – Oakford (£500).

FINANCES *Financial year end* 31/03/2019
Income £95,400 *Total grants* £90,300
Grants to organisations £90,300
Assets £1,170,000

TRUSTEES Jon Mills; Carol Plumstead; Lady Anne Boles; Lady Burnell-Nugent; The Revd Dr David Keep; The Ven. John Rawlings; Judith Kauntze; Eleanor Stead; Lee Martin; Hendrik Vollers; Hugh Harrison; Lt Col James Michie; Lt Cdr Christopher Tuke; Charlie Hutchings; Philip Tuckett.

OTHER INFORMATION The 2018/19 accounts were the latest available at the time of writing (April 2021).

HOW TO APPLY Application forms and guidelines can be downloaded from the charity's website.

CONTACT DETAILS John Mills, Hon. Secretary, The Old Farmhouse, Hele Farm, Hennock Road, Bovey Tracey TQ13 9PP *Tel.* 01297 553666 *Email* contact@devonhistoricchurches.co.uk *Website* www.devonhistoricchurches.co.uk

■ The Duke of Devonshire's Charitable Trust

CC NO 213519 **ESTABLISHED** 1949

WHERE FUNDING CAN BE GIVEN Projects in areas which are local or relevant to Chatsworth, Bolton Abbey and the other Devonshire Group estates (Lismore Castle and Careysville Fishery in the Republic of Ireland).

WHO CAN BENEFIT UK-registered charities only.

WHAT IS FUNDED General charitable purposes.

WHAT IS NOT FUNDED Request made within 12 months of the outcome of a previously unsuccessful application; individuals or for individual research or study; projects outside the UK; multi-year funding; organisations which cannot demonstrate significant progress with fundraising.

RANGE OF GRANTS Typically £250 to £10,000.

SAMPLE GRANTS Bolton Abbey Rectory (£37,400); Derby Museums (£20,000); Tower Art Gallery (£10,000); Burbage Primary School (£2,000); Derby City Mission (£1,000).

FINANCES *Financial year end* 05/04/2020
Income £343,300 *Total grants* £307,900
Grants to organisations £307,900
Assets £13,190,000

TRUSTEES Duke of Devonshire; Duchess of Devonshire; Oliver Stephenson; William Cavendish.

HOW TO APPLY Application forms and deadlines can be found on the trust's website.

CONTACT DETAILS Mollie Moseley, Chatsworth, Bakewell, Derbyshire DE45 1PP *Email* mollie.moseley@chatsworth.org *Website* www.ddct.org.uk

■ The Laduma Dhamecha Charitable Trust

CC NO 328678 **ESTABLISHED** 1990

WHERE FUNDING CAN BE GIVEN UK and overseas.

WHO CAN BENEFIT Charitable organisations.

WHAT IS FUNDED Health; education; general charitable purposes.

SAMPLE GRANTS A list of beneficiaries was not included in the annual report and accounts.

FINANCES *Financial year end* 31/03/2020
Income £779,900 *Total grants* £1,250,000
Grants to organisations £1,250,000
Assets £2,780,000

TRUSTEES Pradip Dhamecha; Shantilal Dhamecha; Manish Dhamecha.

OTHER INFORMATION During 2019/20, grants to organisations in the UK totalled £1.16 million and grants to overseas organisations totalled £90,300.

HOW TO APPLY Contact the correspondent for further information.

CONTACT DETAILS Pradip Dhamecha, Trustee, c/o The Dhamecha Group, 2 Hathaway Close, Stanmore, Middlesex HA7 3NR *Tel.* 020 8903 8181 *Email* info@dhamecha.com

■ Diabetes UK

CC NO 215199 **ESTABLISHED** 1934

WHERE FUNDING CAN BE GIVEN UK.

WHO CAN BENEFIT Research institutions; universities.

WHAT IS FUNDED To promote and fund research into the causes, treatment and alleviation of the effects of diabetes.

TYPE OF GRANT Equipment; fellowships; research grants; small grants; studentships.

RANGE OF GRANTS Generally up to £500,000.

SAMPLE GRANTS Imperial College (£747,000); University of Exeter (£517,000); Cardiff University (£385,000); University of Leeds (£289,000); University of York (£185,000); Imperial College London (£136,000); Brunel University (£102,000).

FINANCES *Financial year end* 31/12/2019
Income £38,840,000 *Total grants* £6,630,000
Grants to organisations £6,630,000
Assets £17,370,000

TRUSTEES Sir Peter Dixon; Dr Robert Young; Helen McCallum; Gareth Hoskin; Janice Watson; Prof. Mohamed Hanif; Robin Swindell; Ian King; Rosie Thomas; Dr Wendy Thomson; Melanie Gray; Henry Burns.

OTHER INFORMATION Only organisations receiving grants of over £100,000 were listed as beneficiaries in the charity's accounts. Grants of under £100,000 totalled £896,000.

HOW TO APPLY Potential applicants are first advised to read the 'General guidelines for research grant applicants' on the charity's website. Information on the application process and deadlines for each specific scheme is also available on the website.

CONTACT DETAILS Research Department, Wells Lawrence House, 126 Back Church Lane, London E1 1FH *Tel.* 01345 123 239 *Email* research@diabetes.org.uk *Website* www.diabetes.org.uk

The Dibden Allotments Fund

CC NO 255778 **ESTABLISHED** 1995

WHERE FUNDING CAN BE GIVEN Hythe; Fawley; Marchwood; Dibden.

WHO CAN BENEFIT Individuals; charitable organisations; schools and colleges; amateur sports clubs; hospitals and hospices.

WHAT IS FUNDED The charity distributes grants under the following areas of work: disability; schools/colleges; children and young people; community and medical welfare.

WHAT IS NOT FUNDED Grants will not be awarded to a church or other religious group to promote religion, fund religious activities or to support activities which are only available to members of the church or religious group.

TYPE OF GRANT It should be noted that the charity aims to pump prime rather than commit to ongoing support and therefore would not normally provide ongoing support for longer than three years.

RANGE OF GRANTS Up to £23,000.

SAMPLE GRANTS Handy Trust (£21,000); Marchwood Scout and Guide Building Project (£20,000); Home-Start Hampshire (£4,000); Noadswood School (£1,000); Go South Coast Ltd (£100).

FINANCES *Financial year end* 31/03/2020 *Income* £428,600 *Total grants* £289,100 *Grants to organisations* £117,500 *Assets* £9,470,000

TRUSTEES Alan Alvey; Sean Cullen; Declan English; Jill Tomlin; Stephanie Osbourne; Judith Saxby; Pat Hedges; Christina James; Melody Roberts.

OTHER INFORMATION Grants were broken down as follows: community (£73,300); youth (£27,600); schools and colleges (£11,600); medical causes (£5,000).

HOW TO APPLY Application forms, criteria and guidelines are available to download from the from the charity's website.

CONTACT DETAILS The Trustees, 7 Drummond Court, Prospect Place, Hythe, Hampshire SO45 6HD *Tel.* 023 8084 1305 *Email* dibdenallotments@btconnect.com *Website* www.daf-hythe.org.uk

The Gillian Dickinson Trust

CC NO 1094362 **ESTABLISHED** 2002

WHERE FUNDING CAN BE GIVEN County Durham, Northumberland and Tyne and Wear.

WHO CAN BENEFIT Registered charities; museums; arts and theatre groups; CICs.

WHAT IS FUNDED The promotion of creativity in young people from disadvantaged backgrounds.

TYPE OF GRANT Capital grants.

RANGE OF GRANTS Grants up to £75,000.

SAMPLE GRANTS The Samling Foundation (£75,000); National Youth Theatre (£15,000); Birkheads Wild (£10,000); Hexham Abbey Heritage (£3,000); Cheeseburn Sculpture (£2,000); Enter CIC (£1,500); Baliffgate Museum (£1,200).

FINANCES *Financial year end* 05/04/2020 *Income* £53,800 *Total grants* £108,500 *Grants to organisations* £108,500 *Assets* £1,190,000

TRUSTEES Alexander Dickinson; Piers Dickinson; Adrian Gifford; James Ramsbotham.

OTHER INFORMATION Grants were made to seven organisations in 2019/20.

HOW TO APPLY Applications can be made using the trust's online application form, available at its website, where criteria and guidelines are also posted.

CONTACT DETAILS The Trustees, c/o Womble Bond Dickinson, One Trinity, Broad Chare, Newcastle upon Tyne, Tyne and Wear NE1 2HF *Tel.* 0191 279 9000 *Email* grants@gilliandickinsontrust.org.uk *Website* www.gilliandickinsontrust.org.uk

Didymus

CC NO 1152432 **ESTABLISHED** 2013

WHERE FUNDING CAN BE GIVEN England; Wales; Africa; Central America; South America.

WHO CAN BENEFIT Registered charities.

WHAT IS FUNDED Social inclusion; education; the arts; equality and diversity; religious understanding.

WHAT IS NOT FUNDED Large national charities (those with an annual income in excess of £2 million); charities dedicated to issues deemed well-funded by the trustees; statutory authorities.

RANGE OF GRANTS Up to £5,000.

SAMPLE GRANTS Drunken Chorus (£10,000); Cecily's Fund and Prisoners' Advice Service (£5,000 each); Team Kenya (£4,700); Bees for Development (£4,400); Tools for Self Reliance (£4,000); Flute Theatre (£3,000); Pembrokeshire People First (£2,000).

FINANCES *Financial year end* 01/12/2019 *Income* £329,300 *Total grants* £228,500 *Grants to organisations* £228,500 *Assets* £2,480,000

TRUSTEES Alan Wall; Caroline Cummins; Revd Dr Daphne Green; Helen Wall; Olivia Houlihan; William Corbett.

OTHER INFORMATION The 2018/19 accounts were the latest available at the time of writing (January 2021).

HOW TO APPLY Applications can be made via the charity's website. Applications for funding may be made at any time. Applications received within six weeks of a trustees' meeting will be considered at the following meeting.

CONTACT DETAILS Sheila Powell, Cresswell Crabtree and Sons, 12 Market Street, Hebden Bridge, West Yorkshire HX7 6AD *Tel.* 01422 842431 *Email* info@didymus-charity.org.uk *Website* www.didymus-charity.org.uk

Digital Xtra Fund

OSCR NO SC047272 **ESTABLISHED** 2017

WHERE FUNDING CAN BE GIVEN Scotland.

WHO CAN BENEFIT Charitable organisations; schools; universities.

WHAT IS FUNDED Developing the digital skills of children and young people.

TYPE OF GRANT Project funding.

SAMPLE GRANTS Civic Digits CIC (£5,000); University of the Highlands and Islands (£4,500); King's Park Primary School (£2,700); Bun Sgoil Bhreascleit (£1,100).

FINANCES *Financial year end* 31/03/2020 *Income* £152,700 *Total grants* £99,700 *Grants to organisations* £99,700 *Assets* £40,300

HOW TO APPLY Apply via the fund's website where application deadlines can also be found.

CONTACT DETAILS The Trustees, c/o ScotlandIS, Oracle Campus, Blackness Road, Springfield,

Edinburgh EH49 7LR *Tel.* 01506 472200 *Email* info@digitalxtrafund.scot *Website* https://www.digitalxtrafund.scot

■ Dinwoodie Charitable Company

CC NO 1151139 **ESTABLISHED** 1968

WHERE FUNDING CAN BE GIVEN UK.

WHO CAN BENEFIT Research fellowships; postgraduate medical centres.

WHAT IS FUNDED The provision of medical and healthcare education and training.

WHAT IS NOT FUNDED Basic scientific research unless related to medical education; the 'on-costs' of infrastructure projects (maintenance, refurbishment, replacement and salaries other than for directly relating to project management); undergraduate education (although consideration might be given to innovative proposals from new medical schools); projects in vulnerable institutions unless these are part of an agreed turn-around process.

TYPE OF GRANT Project funding; research.

RANGE OF GRANTS Up to £1 million.

SAMPLE GRANTS Royal College of Physicians (£250,000); Faculty of Medical Leadership and Management (£165,000); Christies (£125,000); Royal College of Surgeons-Oxford University (£58,400); ICENI (£50,000); World Cancer Research Fund (£27,500); Royal College of Psychiatrists (£20,000).

FINANCES *Financial year end* 31/03/2020 *Income* £815,300 *Total grants* £715,300 *Grants to organisations* £715,300 *Assets* £4,320,000

TRUSTEES John Black; Dr Patrick Cadigan; Richard Arkle; Ian Goalen; John Pears.

OTHER INFORMATION Grants were awarded to eight organisations. Grants were broken down as follows: postgraduate medical centres (£465,300) and research fellowships (£270,000).

HOW TO APPLY Contact the correspondent for further information.

CONTACT DETAILS Ian Goalen, Managing Trustee, 4 Tytherington Green, Macclesfield, Cheshire SK10 2FA *Tel.* 01625 610549 *Email* dinwoodie@irwinmitchell.com

■ The Dischma Charitable Trust

CC NO 1077501 **ESTABLISHED** 1999

WHERE FUNDING CAN BE GIVEN Worldwide, with a strong preference for London and Hampshire.

WHO CAN BENEFIT Charitable organisations.

WHAT IS FUNDED General charitable purposes, with a preference for: education; arts and culture; conservation; human and animal welfare.

WHAT IS NOT FUNDED Medical research charities.

RANGE OF GRANTS £200 to £20,000.

SAMPLE GRANTS Passage (£20,000); Breast Cancer Haven, Glass Door and Royal Trinity Hospice (£10,000 each); Compassion In World Farming International and The Ralph Bates Pancreatic Cancer Centre (£5,000 each); WWF UK (£4,000); Women's Aid and Sentebale (£3,000 each); Prisoners' Advice Service and SPANA (£2,500 each); The Big Issue Foundation and Ro-ro Sailing Project (£1,000 each); Tall Ships (£500); Finding Rhythms (£200).

FINANCES *Financial year end* 31/12/2019 *Income* £1,250,000 *Total grants* £147,800 *Grants to organisations* £147,800 *Assets* £6,700,000

TRUSTEES Simon Robertson; Edward Robertson; Lorna Robertson Timmis; Virginia Robertson; Selina Robertson; Arabella Brooke.

OTHER INFORMATION Grants were awarded to 59 organisations and distributed as follows; children and welfare (£33,000), general medical/mental health and disability (£29,300), general (£21,000), animal welfare and homelessness (£14,000 each), the arts (£11,000), elderly welfare (£10,500), wildlife and conservation (£6,000), education and the relief of poverty (£4,500 each).

HOW TO APPLY Apply in writing to the correspondent. The trustees meet half-yearly to review applications for funding. Only successful applicants are notified of the trustees' decision.

CONTACT DETAILS Linda Cousins, Secretary, Rathbones, 8 Finsbury Circus, London EC2M 7AZ *Tel.* 020 7399 0820 *Email* linda.cousins@rathbones.com

■ The Djanogly Foundation

CC NO 280500 **ESTABLISHED** 1980

WHERE FUNDING CAN BE GIVEN UK and Israel.

WHO CAN BENEFIT Registered charities; schools and universities.

WHAT IS FUNDED Jewish causes; arts and culture.

TYPE OF GRANT Project funding, particularly projects that are new and may require a number of years to establish.

RANGE OF GRANTS Mostly under £3,000.

SAMPLE GRANTS University of Nottingham (£40,000); The Kessler Foundation UK (£25,000); National Gallery (£10,000); Royal Drawing School (£530); Bromley House Library (£120).

FINANCES *Financial year end* 05/04/2020 *Income* £115,700 *Total grants* £223,800 *Grants to organisations* £223,800 *Assets* £3,410,000

TRUSTEES Sir Harry Djanogly; Michael Djanogly; Jonathan Djanogly.

OTHER INFORMATION The foundation awarded grants to 37 organisations during the year.

HOW TO APPLY Contact the correspondent for further information.

CONTACT DETAILS The Trustees, 3 Angel Court, London SW1Y 6QF *Tel.* 020 7930 9845

■ The DLM Charitable Trust

CC NO 328520 **ESTABLISHED** 1990

WHERE FUNDING CAN BE GIVEN UK, with a preference for Oxford.

WHO CAN BENEFIT Charitable organisations.

WHAT IS FUNDED General charitable purposes.

WHAT IS NOT FUNDED Grants are not awarded for individuals.

RANGE OF GRANTS Mostly under £3,000.

SAMPLE GRANTS Flourishing Families Leeds (£15,000); Aspire Oxford (£5,000); Bookfeast and Deafblind UK (£3,000 each); St Luke's Hospital (£2,000).

FINANCES *Financial year end* 05/04/2020 *Income* £187,800 *Total grants* £104,000 *Grants to organisations* £104,000 *Assets* £7,050,000

TRUSTEES Jeffrey Cloke; Jennifer Pyper; Philippa Sawyer.

OTHER INFORMATION Grants were made to 24 organisations during the year.

HOW TO APPLY Contact the correspondent for further information.

CONTACT DETAILS The Trustees, Water Eaton Manor, Water Eaton, Oxford, Oxfordshire OX2 8HE *Tel.* 01865 515753 *Email* pippasawyer@watereaton.clara.co.uk

■ William and Frances Dobie Charitable Foundation

CC NO 1172795 **ESTABLISHED** 2017
WHERE FUNDING CAN BE GIVEN England and Wales.
WHO CAN BENEFIT Charitable organisations.
WHAT IS FUNDED General charitable purposes; education/training; the advancement of health or saving of lives; religious activities.
SAMPLE GRANTS A list of beneficiaries was not included in the annual report and accounts.
FINANCES *Financial year end* 05/04/2020
Income £50,100 *Total grants* £55,300
Grants to organisations £55,300
Assets £1,770,000
TRUSTEES Carl McColgan; Jonathan Parkin; Philip Byrne.
HOW TO APPLY Contact the correspondent for further information.
CONTACT DETAILS Carl McColgan, Trustee, 62 Bridge Lane, Bramhall, Stockport SK7 3AW *Tel.* 0161 834 0440

■ The Ken Dodd Charitable Foundation

CC NO 1179779 **ESTABLISHED** 2013
WHERE FUNDING CAN BE GIVEN UK, with a preference for Merseyside.
WHO CAN BENEFIT Charitable organisations.
WHAT IS FUNDED Performing arts; social welfare.
SAMPLE GRANTS Combat Stress and Shakespeare North Playhouse Trust (£250,000 each); St John the Evangelist Church – Knotty Ash (£120,000); The Liverpool Heart and Chest Hospital Charity (£25,000); Liverpool and Merseyside Theatres Trust Ltd and The Salvation Army – Strawberry Field (£20,000 each); Lyndale Knowsley Cancer Support Centre Ltd (£5,000).
FINANCES *Financial year end* 31/03/2020
Income £12,890,000 *Total grants* £810,000
Grants to organisations £810,000
Assets £10,240,000
TRUSTEES Lady Sybilanne Dodd; Peter Vaines; John Lewis.
HOW TO APPLY Contact the correspondent for further information.
CONTACT DETAILS The Trustees, Barristers Chambers, 3 Field Court, London WC1R 5EP *Tel.* 020 3693 3700

■ The Derek and Eileen Dodgson Foundation

CC NO 1018776 **ESTABLISHED** 1993
WHERE FUNDING CAN BE GIVEN Brighton and Hove; East Sussex; West Sussex.
WHO CAN BENEFIT Individuals and organisations.
WHAT IS FUNDED Welfare of older people.
SAMPLE GRANTS City Mission (£11,500); FareShare (£7,500); Friends First (£6,500); Spiral (£3,000); Freshstart (£2,800).
FINANCES *Financial year end* 31/03/2019
Income £134,900 *Total grants* £103,700
Grants to organisations £103,700
Assets £2,560,000
TRUSTEES Peter Goldsmith; Christopher Butler; Christopher Wellings; David Standing; Georgina Reed; Robert Griffiths.
OTHER INFORMATION The 2018/19 accounts were the latest available at the time of writing (June 2021). Grants of under £2,500 totalled £29,100.
HOW TO APPLY Apply in writing to the correspondent. The trustees meet quarterly, or more frequently if necessary to assess grant applications.
CONTACT DETAILS Gerry Wicks, Chief Executive Officer, Flat 5, 61 Wilbury Road, Hove, East Sussex BN33PB *Tel.* 01273 749576 or 07941 947161 *Email* gerald.wicks@btinternet.com

■ Dollond Charitable Trust

CC NO 293459 **ESTABLISHED** 1986
WHERE FUNDING CAN BE GIVEN UK and Israel.
WHO CAN BENEFIT Jewish organisations.
WHAT IS FUNDED Jewish causes.
SAMPLE GRANTS A list of beneficiaries was not included in the annual report and accounts.
FINANCES *Financial year end* 31/03/2020
Income £1,860,000 *Total grants* £2,400,000
Grants to organisations £2,400,000
Assets £48,380,000
TRUSTEES Adrian Dollond; Jeffrey Milston; Melissa Dollond; Brian Dollond; Rina Dollond.
OTHER INFORMATION Although the constitution of the charity is broadly based, the trustees have adopted a policy of principally assisting the Jewish communities in Britain and Israel. Grants to 192 organisations were distributed as follows: education and training (£930,000); religious education (£500,000); health and medical causes (£275,000); disability (£320,000); relief of poverty (£340,000); other religious activities (£40,000).
HOW TO APPLY Contact the correspondent for further information.
CONTACT DETAILS Brian Dollond, Trustee and Secretary, 3rd Floor, Hathaway House, Popes Drive, Finchley, London N3 1QF *Tel.* 020 8346 6446

■ Donibristle Trust

CCNI NO NIC101313 **ESTABLISHED** 2015
WHERE FUNDING CAN BE GIVEN Worldwide.
WHO CAN BENEFIT Christian organisations; predominantly organisations in financially developing countries.
WHAT IS FUNDED Advancement of Christianity; education; health; relief of hardship and disadvantage; community development; overseas aid.
TYPE OF GRANT Projects; strategic and development funding.
SAMPLE GRANTS A list of beneficiaries was not included in the annual report and accounts.
FINANCES *Financial year end* 30/04/2019
Income £340,800 *Total grants* £232,500
Grants to organisations £232,500
Assets £412,000
TRUSTEES Ian Maccorkell; Heather Maccorkell; Cheryl Jenkins; Colin Maccorkell; Jonathan Patton.
OTHER INFORMATION During the year, a significant amount of funding was to Christian organisations working in Kosovo and the Balkans, Africa and Asia, with a small number of grants made to local charitable projects in Northern Ireland and the UK. The 2018/19 accounts were the latest available at the time of writing (January 2021).

HOW TO APPLY Apply in writing to the correspondent.
CONTACT DETAILS Ian Maccorkell, Trustee, Unit 4 Garvey Studios, 8–10 Longstone Street, Lisburn, County Antrim BT28 1TP *Tel.* 028 9266 9555 *Email* donibristletrust@gmail.com

■ The Dorfman Foundation

CC NO 1120714 **ESTABLISHED** 2007
WHERE FUNDING CAN BE GIVEN Worldwide.
WHO CAN BENEFIT Registered charities.
WHAT IS FUNDED General charitable purposes including Jewish causes and the arts.
RANGE OF GRANTS Mostly up to £50,000.
SAMPLE GRANTS Nightingale Hammerson (£670,000); Imperial War Museum (£250,000); Dalaid (£15,000); Worl Avenue (£10,000); English National Ballet (£8,7000).
FINANCES *Financial year end* 05/04/2020 *Income* £194,500 *Total grants* £2,220,000 *Grants to organisations* £2,220,000 *Assets* £5,590,000
TRUSTEES Amy Lux; Sophie Dorfman; Sir Lloyd Dorfman; Anthony Wagerman; Lloyd Dorfman; Sarah Dorfman; Peter Leach; Charles Dorfman.
OTHER INFORMATION Grants of £5,000 or less totalled £34,400.
HOW TO APPLY Contact the correspondent for further information.
CONTACT DETAILS The Trustees, 22 Manchester Square, London W1U 3PT *Tel.* 020 7725 1221 *Email* charity.correspondence@bdo.co.uk

■ Dorset Community Foundation

CC NO 1122113 **ESTABLISHED** 2007
WHERE FUNDING CAN BE GIVEN Dorset, particularly Bournemouth and Poole.
WHO CAN BENEFIT Voluntary and community organisations; charities; CICs; individuals.
WHAT IS FUNDED General charitable purposes including: children and young people; community services and development; older people; mental health; women; community cohesion.
WHAT IS NOT FUNDED A full list of exclusions can be found on the foundation's website.
TYPE OF GRANT Project funding; core/revenue funding; capital funding; strategic funding.
RANGE OF GRANTS Mostly up to £5,000.
SAMPLE GRANTS Samee (£14,000); DEED (£10,200); Dorset Rape Crisis (£6,000); Dorset Adult Asperger's Support and Wheels for Freedom (£5,000 each).
FINANCES *Financial year end* 31/03/2019 *Income* £763,500 *Total grants* £305,620 *Grants to organisations* £209,120 *Assets* £2,930,000
TRUSTEES William Ansell; Simon Young; Paul Sizeland; Geoffrey Trobridge; Jeremy Mills; Frank Guinn; Nick Fernyhough; Jonathan Greenwood; Michelle Scanlan; Martin Davidson.
OTHER INFORMATION This is one of the 46 UK community foundations, which distribute funding for a wide range of purposes. Potential applicants are advised to visit the community foundation's website or contact its grants team to find the most suitable funding stream. The 2018/19 accounts were the latest available at the time of writing (January 2021). Only organisations receiving grants of over £10,000 were listed as beneficiaries in the charity's accounts. Grants of under £5,000 totalled £96,500.
HOW TO APPLY Applications can be made online through the foundation's website.
CONTACT DETAILS The Trustees, The Spire, High Street, Poole, Dorset BH15 1DF *Tel.* 01202 670815 *Email* grants@dorsetcf.org *Website* www.dorsetcommunityfoundation.org

■ The Dorset Historic Churches Trust

CC NO 282790 **ESTABLISHED** 1960
WHERE FUNDING CAN BE GIVEN Dorset.
WHO CAN BENEFIT Christian churches and chapels in Dorset.
WHAT IS FUNDED The restoration or preservation of churches.
WHAT IS NOT FUNDED Routine maintenance and decoration; works in the churchyard; heating and electrical maintenance; new buildings or extensions; new furniture or fittings; new bells or new bell frames; replacement or repair of organs; clocks or sound-systems.
RANGE OF GRANTS From £1,000 to £12,000.
FINANCES *Financial year end* 31/12/2019 *Income* £202,000 *Total grants* £86,500 *Grants to organisations* £86,500 *Assets* £630,700
TRUSTEES David Grant; Giles Sturdy; Robert Fox; Philippa Francis; Michael Warren; James Smith; MG John Stokoe; Steven Norman; Sally-Anne Stanbury; Susan Bruce-Payne; Susan Smith; Liz Ashmead; Thomas Wickson; Revd Andrew Rowland; Dr Timothy Connor; Col Jeremy Aylwin Selfe; Capt. Thimbleby; Roger Blaber.
OTHER INFORMATION Grants were awarded to 16 churches in 2019.
HOW TO APPLY Applications are to be made to the deanery representative of the trust in the area in which the church is located, on a form available to download, together with criteria and guidelines, from the website.
CONTACT DETAILS Grants Secretary, The Old Forge, Frome St Quintin, Dorchester, Dorset DT2 0HG *Tel.* 01935 83548 *Email* grantssecretary@dhct.org.uk *Website* www.dorsethistoricchurchestrust.co.uk

■ The Double 'O' Charity Ltd

CC NO 271681 **ESTABLISHED** 1976
WHERE FUNDING CAN BE GIVEN UK and overseas.
WHO CAN BENEFIT Registered charities and individuals.
WHAT IS FUNDED General charitable purposes with a preference for social welfare, health and education.
WHAT IS NOT FUNDED No grants to individuals towards education or for their involvement in overseas charity work.
RANGE OF GRANTS £1,000 to £116,000.
SAMPLE GRANTS Barbuda Relief Fund (£116,200); White Horse Productions (£20,000); Shriners Hospital for Children (£17,000); The Ridgeway (£10,000); The Vineyard Project (£5,000); Willow Animal Sanctuary (£1,000).
FINANCES *Financial year end* 31/05/2020 *Income* £211,900 *Total grants* £155,200 *Grants to organisations* £140,000 *Assets* £66,400
TRUSTEES Peter Townshend; Rachel Fuller.
HOW TO APPLY Contact the correspondent for further information.
CONTACT DETAILS The Trustees, c/o 4 Friars Lane, Richmond, Surrey TW9 1NL *Tel.* 020 8940 8171

The Doughty Charity Trust

CC NO 274977 **ESTABLISHED** 1977

WHERE FUNDING CAN BE GIVEN England and Israel.

WHO CAN BENEFIT Jewish charitable organisations.

WHAT IS FUNDED Orthodox Jewish religious education, relief of poverty.

RANGE OF GRANTS Less than £50,000.

SAMPLE GRANTS A list of beneficiaries was not included in the annual report and accounts.

FINANCES *Financial year end* 31/12/2019 *Income* £451,500 *Total grants* £547,100 *Grants to organisations* £547,100 *Assets* £626,200

TRUSTEES Mr G. Halibard; Mrs M. Halibard.

HOW TO APPLY The trust has stated that its funds are fully committed and therefore it does not accept unsolicited applications.

CONTACT DETAILS The Trustees, 22 Ravenscroft Avenue, London NW11 0RY *Tel.* 020 8209 0500

Drapers' Charitable Fund

CC NO 251403 **ESTABLISHED** 1959

WHERE FUNDING CAN BE GIVEN England and Wales, with a strong preference for 'areas of deprivation' in Greater London.

WHO CAN BENEFIT Registered or exempt charities; schools and universities.

WHAT IS FUNDED Social welfare including homelessness, prisoners, ex-service personnel, general welfare and disability; education and young people; textiles and heritage.

WHAT IS NOT FUNDED A comprehensive list of exclusions can be found on the charity's website.

TYPE OF GRANT Core costs (including salaries); project costs. Most grants are one-off payments but occasionally multi-year grants are awarded.

RANGE OF GRANTS Generally up to £15,000.

SAMPLE GRANTS Drapers' Multi Academy Trust (£170,000); Bangor University (£40,000); RL Glasspool Charity Trust (£25,000); Access Project (£20,000); London Youth Choir and Prison Advice 8: Care Trust (£15,000 each).

FINANCES *Financial year end* 31/07/2019 *Income* £7,930,000 *Total grants* £1,900,000 *Grants to organisations* £1,900,000 *Assets* £74,090,000

TRUSTEE The Drapers' Company.

OTHER INFORMATION The 2018/19 accounts were the latest available at the time of writing (January 2021).

HOW TO APPLY Applications can be submitted by email. In order to apply you will need to send a detailed proposal document explaining what your organisation does, how you intend to spend the money, and your most recent financial accounts and trustees' report, together with a completed application summary sheet, which can be found on the charity's website alongside guidelines on how to apply.

CONTACT DETAILS Head of Charities, The Drapers' Company, Drapers' Hall, Throgmorton Avenue, London EC2N 2DQ *Tel.* 020 7588 5001 *Email* charities@thedrapers.co.uk *Website* https://www.thedrapers.co.uk/Charities/Grant-making-trusts/The-Drapers-Charitable-Fund.aspx

Dromintee Trust

CC NO 1053956 **ESTABLISHED** 1996

WHERE FUNDING CAN BE GIVEN UK and overseas with a preference for Leicestershire.

WHO CAN BENEFIT Charitable organisations.

WHAT IS FUNDED Social welfare; children and young people; health and health education, medical research.

SAMPLE GRANTS Leicester Hospitals Charity (£100,000); The Good Council Network (£50,000); Consolata Fathers (£30,000); Intercare (£20,000); The Little Sisters of the Poor at St Anne's Home (£10,000); Leicester Outdoor Pursuits Centre (£5,000).

FINANCES *Financial year end* 31/03/2020 *Income* £487,600 *Total grants* £417,000 *Grants to organisations* £417,000 *Assets* £3,310,000

TRUSTEES Robert Smith; Hugh Murphy; Margaret Murphy; Paul Tiernan; Mary Middleton; Patrick Murphy; Joseph Murphy.

OTHER INFORMATION Grants were made to 16 organisations during the year.

HOW TO APPLY Apply in writing to the correspondent.

CONTACT DETAILS Hugh Murphy, Trustee, 1 Westmoreland Avenue, Thurmaston, Leicester, Leicestershire LE4 8PH *Tel.* 0116 260 3877 *Email* drominteetrust@gmail.com

The Anne Duchess of Westminster's Charity

CC NO 245177 **ESTABLISHED** 1965

WHERE FUNDING CAN BE GIVEN Cheshire (within a 25 mile radius of Chester) and the Highlands (priority given to Sutherland); UK.

WHO CAN BENEFIT Registered charities; unregistered charities; CICs; hospices.

WHAT IS FUNDED In Cheshire and the Highlands the charity supports: mental health, carers, younger and older people, social and rural isolation and loneliness, those in and leaving care, food poverty, community projects in disadvantaged areas, alleviation of socio-economic deprivation, education and learning, ill-health and disability. National equine and horse racing charities are also supported.

WHAT IS NOT FUNDED A comprehensive list of exclusions can be found on the charity's website.

TYPE OF GRANT Core/revenue costs; project funding.

RANGE OF GRANTS Small grants of up to £5,000; large grants of £5,000 to £25,000.

SAMPLE GRANTS Priority Youth Project (£5,000); Animal Health Trust (£2,500); Listening Books (£1,400); Horatio's Garden (£1,000).

FINANCES *Financial year end* 31/03/2020 *Income* £124,600 *Total grants* £258,300 *Grants to organisations* £258,300 *Assets* £6,610,000

TRUSTEES Lucy Blow; Lady Daresbury; Mark Ridley; Richard Henniker-Wilson; Annabel James.

OTHER INFORMATION There were 60 grants made during the year.

HOW TO APPLY Applications can be made through the charity's website.

CONTACT DETAILS The Trustees, Eaton Estate Office, Eaton Hall, Eaton Park, Chester, Cheshire CH4 9E *Tel.* 01244 684433 *Email* Contact form on website *Website* www.adwc.org.uk

■ Duchy Health Charity Ltd

CC NO 271957 **ESTABLISHED** 1976

WHERE FUNDING CAN BE GIVEN Cornwall.

WHO CAN BENEFIT Registered charities; other healthcare organisations.

WHAT IS FUNDED Health; well-being; the provision of healthcare.

TYPE OF GRANT Project costs; capital and revenue expenditure; equipment and services.

SAMPLE GRANTS NHS Kernow Clinical Commissioning Group (£34,000); Sowenna Appeal (£24,000); Bosence Farm Community (£18,500); Helford River Children's Sailing Trust (£11,000); Southerly Point Multi Academy Trust (£5,000); Connecting Lives (£900).

FINANCES *Financial year end* 31/03/2020 *Income* £235,100 *Total grants* £158,300 *Grants to organisations* £158,300 *Assets* £4,710,000

TRUSTEES Graham Murdoch; Mary Vyvyan; Antoinette McLean; Dr Tamsyn Anderson; Sally-jane Coode; Aldyth Hambly-Staite; Dr John Evers; Scott Bennett; Tim Guy; Dr Barbara Vann; Jonathon Croggon; Mark Williams; Tracie North; James Robinson; Carol O'Brien.

OTHER INFORMATION Grants were made to ten organisations during the year.

HOW TO APPLY The charity has an online application process, see the website for more information.

CONTACT DETAILS Mark Williams, Secretary, Robinson Reed Layton, Peat House, Newham Road, Truro, Cornwall TR1 2DP *Tel.* 01872 276116 *Email* mark.williams@rrlcornwall.co.uk *Website* www.duchyhealthcharity.org

■ The Dulverton Trust

CC NO 1146484 **ESTABLISHED** 1949

WHERE FUNDING CAN BE GIVEN The UK (excluding Greater London and Northern Ireland), Kenya; Uganda.

WHO CAN BENEFIT Registered charities; CIOs. Particularly medium-sized charities (income of £200,000 to £3 million).

WHAT IS FUNDED Youth opportunities; general welfare; conservation; heritage; peace and humanitarian support; community development and conservation in Kenya and Uganda.

TYPE OF GRANT Capital costs; core/revenue costs; seed funding/start-up funding; project funding; unrestricted funding. Single and multi-year grants are awarded.

RANGE OF GRANTS Typically £25,000 to £35,000.

SAMPLE GRANTS Adoption UK (£150,700); Action for Conservation (£105,000); MapAction (£35,000); The Orchard Project (£32,000); Endeavour (£25,000); The Not Forgotten (£12,000); The Rugby Football Foundation (£5,000).

FINANCES *Financial year end* 31/03/2020 *Income* £2,880,000 *Total grants* £3,970,000 *Grants to organisations* £3,970,000 *Assets* £89,540,000

TRUSTEES The Earl of Gowrie; The Lord Dulverton; Christopher Wills; The Lord Hemphill; Richard Howard; Dame Mary Richardson; Tara Douglas-Home; Sir Malcolm Rifkind; Robert Wills; Dr Catherine Wills.

OTHER INFORMATION The trust awarded 77 grants during the year. Grants were distributed as follows: youth opportunities (£1.41 million); general welfare (£1.14 million); community foundations (£485,000); conservation (£272,000); preservation (£220,000); peace and humanitarian support (£179,400); Africa (£125,900); trustee exception (£80,000); local appeals (£49,000).

HOW TO APPLY Apply online via the trust's website. Applications are accepted all year but trustees make decisions in February, June and October.

CONTACT DETAILS The Trustees, 5 St James's Place, London SW1A 1NP *Tel.* 020 7495 7852 *Email* grants@dulverton.org *Website* www.dulverton.org

■ Dumbreck Charity

CC NO 273070 **ESTABLISHED** 1976

WHERE FUNDING CAN BE GIVEN West Midlands; Warwickshire; Worcestershire.

WHO CAN BENEFIT Charitable organisations.

WHAT IS FUNDED General charitable purposes including: animal welfare; children's welfare; older people; people with disabilities; health; social welfare; arts and culture.

RANGE OF GRANTS Mostly £500 to £2,000.

SAMPLE GRANTS Shipston Home Nursing (£3,000); Acorns and The British Horse Society (£2,000 each); Straight Talking and Birmingham Hippodrome Theatre Trust (£1,000 each); Pershore Civic Society (£750); YMCA Sutton Coldfield and Dog Assistance in Disability (£500 each).

FINANCES *Financial year end* 05/04/2020 *Income* £171,000 *Total grants* £153,200 *Grants to organisations* £153,200 *Assets* £3,870,000

TRUSTEES Chris Hordern; Hugh Carslake; Jane Uloth; Judith Melling.

HOW TO APPLY Contact the correspondent for further information.

CONTACT DETAILS The Trustees, c/o PS Accounting, 41 Sycamore Drive, Hollywood, Birmingham B47 5QX *Email* psaccounting@hotmail.co.uk

■ Dumfriesshire East Community Benefit Group SCIO

OSCR NO SC047593 **ESTABLISHED** 2017

WHERE FUNDING CAN BE GIVEN East Dumfriesshire.

WHO CAN BENEFIT Charities and community groups.

WHAT IS FUNDED Education; citizenship and community development; arts, science, heritage and culture; recreational facilities; the environment.

SAMPLE GRANTS Waterbeck Public Hall (£24,500); RH Youth Organisation (£5,000); Kirtle and Eaglesfield Community Council (£4,500).

FINANCES *Financial year end* 31/07/2020 *Income* £297,300 *Total grants* £304,300 *Grants to organisations* £304,300 *Assets* £244,900

HOW TO APPLY See the charity's website for information on the application process.

CONTACT DETAILS See website for relevant contact, c/o Southern Uplands Partnership, Studio 2 Lindean Mill, Galashiels, TD1 3PE *Website* https://www.decbg.org.uk

■ Dunard Fund

OSCR NO SC046889 **ESTABLISHED** 2016

WHERE FUNDING CAN BE GIVEN UK, mainly Scotland.

WHO CAN BENEFIT Registered charities.

WHAT IS FUNDED Classical music; architecture; visual arts; environmental and humanitarian projects.

TYPE OF GRANT The trustees prefer to engage with recipients to enable long-term development of projects and initiatives which have major and lasting significance.

SAMPLE GRANTS IMPACT (£2.94 million); Royal Academy of Arts (£932,900); Royal Opera House (£500,000); Scottish Chamber Orchestra (£300,000); Yorkshire Sculpture Park (£150,000); Royal Drawing School (£25,000); Abbey Church of Dunfermline (£15,000); Music in Lanark (£2,500).

FINANCES *Financial year end* 31/03/2020
Income £9,920,000 *Total grants* £8,900,000
Grants to organisations £8,900,000
Assets £73,210,000

TRUSTEES Carol Grigor; Colin Liddell; Catherine Hogel; Erik Hogel; Peter Thierfeldt; Elisabeth Lenz.

OTHER INFORMATION The fund has close links with Dunard Ltd and has previously received donations from the company.

HOW TO APPLY Contact the correspondent for further information.

CONTACT DETAILS The Trustees, c/o J. and H. Mitchell W.S., 51 Atholl Road, Pitlochry, Perthshire PH16 5BU

■ The Nine Incorporated Trades of Dundee General Fund Charity

OSCR NO SC047218 **ESTABLISHED** 1891

WHERE FUNDING CAN BE GIVEN Dundee.

WHO CAN BENEFIT Charities; community groups; schools.

WHAT IS FUNDED The advancement of the arts, heritage, culture or science to include support appropriate to the nine trades (see the website for more information about the nine different trades); citizenship and community development; social welfare; education; health; the advancement of religion; health.

SAMPLE GRANTS Dundee Design Ltd (£30,000); Abertay University (£21,000); Unicorn Preservation Society (£4,100); Hear Me (£3,000); Friends of Dundee Archives (£750).

FINANCES *Financial year end* 30/04/2019
Income £351,500 *Total grants* £188,200
Grants to organisations £188,200
Assets £1,340,000

OTHER INFORMATION The 2018/19 accounts were the latest available at the time of writing (April 2021).

HOW TO APPLY Apply via the charity's website.

CONTACT DETAILS John Fyffe, Charities Convener, 11 South Tay Street, Dundee DD1 1NY *Email* charities.convener@ninetradesofdundee.co.uk *Website* https://www.ninetradesofdundee.co.uk/funding

■ The Dunhill Medical Trust

CC NO 1140372 **ESTABLISHED** 1951

WHERE FUNDING CAN BE GIVEN UK.

WHO CAN BENEFIT Registered charities; CICs; social enterprises; universities; hospitals.

WHAT IS FUNDED Research into improving the quality of life, functional capacity and well-being for older people.

TYPE OF GRANT Capital costs; project funding; research; capacity building and development funding.

RANGE OF GRANTS Typically less than £30,000.

SAMPLE GRANTS University of Cambridge (£281,000); Timebanking UK (£39,000); Alnwick Playhouse (£22,000); British Geriatrics Society (£4,000); The Cranfield Trust (£2,000).

FINANCES *Financial year end* 31/03/2020
Income £4,140,000 *Total grants* £5,160,000
Grants to organisations £5,160,000
Assets £128,710,000

TRUSTEES Dominic Jones; Keith Shepherd; Prof. Alison Petch; Prof. Thomas Kirkwood; Deborah Walters; Michael Bellamy; James Lorigan; Prof. Stuart Parker; Prof. Bernard Conway; Eren Osman.

OTHER INFORMATION Grants were distributed as follows: academic and clinical researchers (£3.89 million); community organisations (£898,000); Older People's Care Improvement initiative (£363,400); travel bursaries (£5,300).

HOW TO APPLY Applications can be made through the trust's online grants portal.

CONTACT DETAILS The Trustees, Fifth Floor, 6 New Bridge Street, London EC4V 6AB *Tel.* 020 7403 3299 *Email* info@dunhillmedical.org.uk *Website* www.dunhillmedical.org.uk

■ Dunlossit and Islay Community Trust

OSCR NO SC047979 **ESTABLISHED** 2017

WHERE FUNDING CAN BE GIVEN Scotland with a preference for Islay.

WHO CAN BENEFIT Charitable organisations.

WHAT IS FUNDED General charitable purposes including: health, welfare; older people; children and young people; community development; citizenship; education, art, culture and heritage; the environment.

RANGE OF GRANTS Up to £50,000.

SAMPLE GRANTS Scotland's Charity Air Ambulance (£50,000); Glasgow Centre for Inclusive Living and Includem (£10,000 each); Scottish Families (£5,000).

FINANCES *Financial year end* 31/10/2019
Income £100,000 *Total grants* £75,000
Grants to organisations £75,000
Assets £1,690,000

OTHER INFORMATION The 2018/19 accounts were the latest available at the time of writing (April 2021).

HOW TO APPLY Contact the trust via the enquiries form on its website.

CONTACT DETAILS The Trustees, Turcan Connell, Princes Exchange, 1 Earl Grey Street, Edinburgh EH3 9EE *Email* Contact form on website *Website* https://www.dunlossit.org

■ The Dunn Family Charitable Trust

CC NO 297389 **ESTABLISHED** 1987

WHERE FUNDING CAN BE GIVEN UK, with a strong preference for Nottinghamshire.

WHO CAN BENEFIT Charitable organisations.

WHAT IS FUNDED General charitable purposes including health and social welfare.

SAMPLE GRANTS Oakes Trust (£4,500); Support Dogs (£3,000); Nottinghamshire Hospice (£2,000); Rainbow Children's Hospice (£1,500); Tearfund (£500).

FINANCES *Financial year end* 31/03/2020
Income £76,000 *Total grants* £57,300
Grants to organisations £57,300
Assets £2,030,000

TRUSTEES Nigel Dunn; Richard Dunn; Lisa Dunn; Graham Dunn; Jacky Dunn; Peter Dunn.

OTHER INFORMATION Grants were awarded to 29 organisations during the year.

HOW TO APPLY Contact the correspondent for further information.

CONTACT DETAILS The Trustees, Rushcliffe Estates Ltd, Tudor House, 13–15 Rectory Road, West Bridgford, Nottingham, Nottinghamshire NG2 6BE *Tel.* 0115 945 5300 *Email* contact@rushcliffe.co.uk

■ The Charles Dunstone Charitable Trust

CC NO 1085955 **ESTABLISHED** 2001

WHERE FUNDING CAN BE GIVEN UK.

WHO CAN BENEFIT Registered charities.

WHAT IS FUNDED General charitable purposes including: arts and culture; children and young people; community care; education and training; health and disability; social welfare; heritage and restoration.

SAMPLE GRANTS Brighton Belle (£500,000); The Prince's Trust (£150,300); Royal Museum Greenwich (£100,000); Make A Wish (£20,000); Lady Garden (£18,000); Comic Relief (£5,000); The Fulwood Academy (£2,200).

FINANCES *Financial year end* 05/04/2020 *Income* £653,300 *Total grants* £916,900 *Grants to organisations* £916,900 *Assets* £327,400

TRUSTEES Denis Dunstone; Adrian Bott; John Gordon; Robert Clarkson.

OTHER INFORMATION Grants were broken down as follows: heritage and restoration (£500,000); children and youth (£251,800); arts and culture (£100,000); education and training (£36,600); social welfare (£25,000); community care and ethnic organisations (£3,500).

HOW TO APPLY The 2019/20 annual report states: 'The Trust is currently fully committed and does not plan to make any new grants for the foreseeable future. Existing beneficiaries of the Trust will be notified of any change to this situation. The trustees strongly advise against submitting any unsolicited applications to the Trust.'

CONTACT DETAILS The Trustees, H. W. Fisher and Company, Acre House, 11–15 William Road, London NW1 3ER *Tel.* 020 7388 7000 *Email* jtrent@hwfisher.co.uk

■ County Durham Community Foundation

CC NO 1047625 **ESTABLISHED** 1995

WHERE FUNDING CAN BE GIVEN County Durham.

WHO CAN BENEFIT Registered charities; unregistered charities; CICs; social enterprises; PTAs; individuals.

WHAT IS FUNDED General charitable purposes.

WHAT IS NOT FUNDED Programme-specific exclusions can be found on the foundation's website.

TYPE OF GRANT Capital costs; core/revenue costs; project funding; seed funding/start-up funding.

RANGE OF GRANTS Programme dependent. In 2019/20 the average grant size was £5,100.

SAMPLE GRANTS A list of beneficiaries was not included in the annual report and accounts.

FINANCES *Financial year end* 31/03/2020 *Income* £3,850,000 *Total grants* £2,890,000 *Grants to organisations* £2,890,000 *Assets* £19,460,000

TRUSTEES Paul Chandler; Rebecca Armstrong; Duncan Barrie; Prof. Ray Hudson; James Fenwick; Stephen Hall; Ann Dolphin; Emily Burns; Colin Proudfoot.

OTHER INFORMATION This is one of the 46 UK community foundations, which distribute funding for a wide range of purposes. As with all community foundations, there are a number of donor-advised funds managed on behalf of individuals, families and charitable trusts. Grant schemes tend to change frequently; consult the foundation's website for details of current programmes and up-to-date deadlines.

HOW TO APPLY Potential applicants are advised to visit the community foundation's website or contact its grants team to find the most suitable funding stream.

CONTACT DETAILS The Grants Team, Victoria House, Whitfield Court, St John's Road, Meadowfield Industrial Estate, Durham, County Durham DH7 8XL *Tel.* 0191 378 6340 *Email* info@cdcf.org.uk *Website* www.cdcf.org.uk

■ Dushinsky Trust Ltd

CC NO 1020301 **ESTABLISHED** 1992

WHERE FUNDING CAN BE GIVEN UK and Israel.

WHO CAN BENEFIT Jewish charitable organisations.

WHAT IS FUNDED Social welfare; furtherance of Orthodox Jewish education abroad.

SAMPLE GRANTS A list of beneficiaries was not included in the annual report and accounts.

FINANCES *Financial year end* 31/03/2020 *Income* £901,900 *Total grants* £991,800 *Grants to organisations* £991,800 *Assets* £3,900

TRUSTEES Simon Reisner; Zvi Levine; Mosche Schischa.

HOW TO APPLY The trust does not accept unsolicited applications.

CONTACT DETAILS Simon Reisner, Secretary, 23 Braydon Road, London N16 6QL *Tel.* 020 8802 7144

■ The Mildred Duveen Charitable Trust

CC NO 1059355 **ESTABLISHED** 1996

WHERE FUNDING CAN BE GIVEN UK and overseas.

WHO CAN BENEFIT Charitable organisations; universities, hospices and hospitals.

WHAT IS FUNDED General charitable purposes, including animal welfare; children and young people; health and disability; education; social welfare; the environment.

WHAT IS NOT FUNDED Individuals.

RANGE OF GRANTS £500 to £10,000.

SAMPLE GRANTS Previous beneficiaries have included: Almeida Theatre (£10,000); Sparkles (£5,000); Bletchingly Skills Centre (£4,000); Palestine Trauma Centre (£2,000); National Advertising Benevolent Society (£1,500); ABF The Soldiers' Charity and Dogs Trust (£1,000 each); Canine Partners and Multiple Sclerosis Trust (£500 each).

FINANCES *Financial year end* 05/04/2020 *Income* £22,900 *Total grants* £65,100 *Grants to organisations* £65,100

TRUSTEES Peter Holgate; Adrian Houstoun; Peter Loose; David Goepel.

OTHER INFORMATION Full accounts were not available to view on the Charity Commission's website due to the trust's low income. We have therefore estimated the trust's grant total based on its total expenditure.

HOW TO APPLY Contact the correspondent for further information.

CONTACT DETAILS Peter Holgate, Trustee, Devonshire House, 60 Goswell Road, London EC1M 7AD *Tel.* 020 7566 4000 *Email* pholgate@kingstonsmith.co.uk

■ The DWF Charitable Foundation

CC NO 1157229 **ESTABLISHED** 2014

WHERE FUNDING CAN BE GIVEN UK and overseas, in countries where DWP offices are located.

WHO CAN BENEFIT Registered charities.

WHAT IS FUNDED Homelessness; health and well-being; employability; education; the environment and sustainability.

WHAT IS NOT FUNDED Academic research; activities for which a statutory body is responsible; activity taking place in school time that is a statutory responsibility; animal welfare; evaluation projects which are not related to the funded work; every day running costs and core salaries; general fundraising appeals; individuals; loans or business finance; other grant-making bodies; salaries of professional fundraisers or bid writers; professional qualifications; recurrent funding; redundancy payments; religious and political causes; sponsorship/marketing appeals/fundraising costs; start-up costs for new organisations; the advancement of religion; universities/HE facilities; vehicles and minibuses; work that has already taken place.

TYPE OF GRANT Project funding.

RANGE OF GRANTS Mostly under £5,000.

SAMPLE GRANTS Previous beneficiaries have included: Scottish Families Affected by Alcohol and Drugs (£3,800); In2Charge (£3,500); Ghazali Trust (£3,000); Katherine House Hospice (£2,500); Blackburne House, Level Trust and Manchester Cares (£2,000 each); St Anne's Hostel (£500).

FINANCES *Financial year end* 31/03/2020 *Income* £336,700 *Total grants* £127,300 *Grants to organisations* £127,300 *Assets* £1,850,000

TRUSTEES Keiran Walshe; Alex Morgan; Jewels Chamberlain; Sir Duncan Nichol; Lisa Smith; James Davies; Anthony Bayliss; Lindsay Ogunyemi; Lesley Hall; Mark Stanbury.

OTHER INFORMATION The foundation was established by DWF LLP, a multinational law firm based in Manchester. A list of the company's office locations can be found on its website.

HOW TO APPLY Applications can be submitted using an online form on the foundation's website.

CONTACT DETAILS Clare Bevan, Foundation Manager, 5 St Paul's Square, Old Hall Street, Liverpool L3 9AE *Tel.* 07736 121046 *Email* clare.beavan@dwf.law *Website* https://www.dwf.law/About-us/DWF-Foundation

■ The Dyers' Company Charitable Trust

CC NO 289547 **ESTABLISHED** 1984

WHERE FUNDING CAN BE GIVEN UK.

WHO CAN BENEFIT Registered charities; schools; universities.

WHAT IS FUNDED Education; children and young people; health; social welfare; the armed forces; the arts; the dyeing industry.

WHAT IS NOT FUNDED Individuals; international charities.

SAMPLE GRANTS University of Leeds (£21,800); Trussell Trust (£15,000); HMS Vanguard and Young Bristol (£2,000 each); Blind in Business and Prayer Book Society (£1,000 each); Axminster Heritage (£500).

FINANCES *Financial year end* 31/10/2020 *Income* £1,340,000 *Total grants* £681,900 *Grants to organisations* £681,900 *Assets* £19,700,000

TRUSTEE The Dyers Company.

OTHER INFORMATION During the year, 137 organisations were awarded grants. More than half of the trust's grants went to educational establishments.

HOW TO APPLY The trust does not accept unsolicited applications, but members of the company can nominate charities for support.

CONTACT DETAILS Assistant Clerk, Dyer's Hall, 11–13 Dowgate Hill, London EC4R 2ST *Tel.* 020 7236 7197 *Email* clerk@dyerscompany.com *Website* www.dyerscompany.co.uk

■ The James Dyson Foundation

CC NO 1099709 **ESTABLISHED** 2002

WHERE FUNDING CAN BE GIVEN Worldwide with a preference for the UK and in particular the local area around the Dyson company's UK headquarters in Malmesbury, Wiltshire.

WHO CAN BENEFIT Registered charities and educational organisations.

WHAT IS FUNDED Engineering education; medical research; scientific research; social and community welfare.

WHAT IS NOT FUNDED Animal welfare; loans or funding for individuals or companies; sports team sponsorship.

TYPE OF GRANT Project funding; research.

SAMPLE GRANTS Medical Research Grants Fund (£505,900); Japan Education Programme (£118,000); Outreach Programmes (£51,000); US Education Programme (£50,200); Alzheimer's Research UK (£40,500); Malaysia and Singapore Education Programme (£40,200); Local Community and Education Fund (£21,300); Philippines Education Programme (£9,000).

FINANCES *Financial year end* 31/12/2019 *Income* £1,120,000 *Total grants* £1,220,000 *Grants to organisations* £1,220,000 *Assets* £174,600

TRUSTEES Sir James Dyson; Lady Deirdre Dyson; Valerie West.

OTHER INFORMATION In 2019 grants were distributed under the following categories: science and medical research (£624,700); education and training (£566,700); social and community welfare (£25,600). Grants of under £1,000 totalled £14,200.

HOW TO APPLY To apply, complete the online contact form on the foundation's website. The foundation aims to respond within two weeks.

CONTACT DETAILS The Trustees, Tetbury Hill, Malmesbury, Wiltshire SN16 0RP *Tel.* 01666 746802 *Email* info@jamesdysonfoundation.com *Website* www.jamesdysonfoundation.com

■ Audrey Earle Charitable Trust

CC NO 290028 **ESTABLISHED** 1984

WHERE FUNDING CAN BE GIVEN UK.

WHO CAN BENEFIT Registered charities.

WHAT IS FUNDED General charitable purposes, with some preference for animal welfare and conservation charities.

RANGE OF GRANTS Generally up to £6,000.

SAMPLE GRANTS Animal Health Trust, British Red Cross Society, OXFAM, RNLI, Royal Star and Garter Home, Shire Horse Society and St Clements Burnham Overy PCC (£6,000 each).

FINANCES *Financial year end* 05/04/2019 *Income* £140,300 *Total grants* £132,000 *Grants to organisations* £132,000 *Assets* £6,690,000

TRUSTEES Paul Andrew Sheils; Richard Fleetwood Fuller; Peter Turner.

OTHER INFORMATION The 2018/19 accounts were the latest available at the time of writing (January 2021). Grants were made to 22 organisations in 2018/19.

HOW TO APPLY Apply in writing to the correspondent; however, the trust tends to support the same beneficiaries year after year and, therefore, it appears unlikely that new applications will receive support.

CONTACT DETAILS The Trustees, Bedford House, 21A John Street, London WC1N 2BF *Tel.* 020 7400 7770 *Email* info@moonbeever.com

■ The Earley Charity

CC NO 244823 **ESTABLISHED** 1820

WHERE FUNDING CAN BE GIVEN The Ancient Liberty of Earley (i.e. the central eastern and southern part of Reading, Earley and Lower Earley, northern Shinfield, Winnersh, Sonning and Lower Caversham).

WHO CAN BENEFIT Individuals; charitable and community organisations.

WHAT IS FUNDED General charitable purposes with a preference for social welfare, education, disability and community recreational facilities.

WHAT IS NOT FUNDED Postgraduate education; general running/living costs; core costs; open-ended salaries; general appeals; religious activities, national organisations operating in the area of benefit without a local office; general public sector appeals (apart from in a few very exceptional cases); applications from outside the area of benefit; individuals who are planning to move out of the area of benefit; individuals who have been awarded a grant within the last two years; individuals who have received three grants in the past.

TYPE OF GRANT Project funding; capital funding.

RANGE OF GRANTS £500 to £5,000.

SAMPLE GRANTS Earley CResCent Community Association (£96,800); Berkshire Women's Aid (£34,000); Reading Rockets (£12,000); Graft Thames Valley (£10,000); Citizens Advice Reading (£6,500); Berkshire Autistic Society (£5,000); Red Balloon Learner Centre Reading (£3,000); Reading Museum (£1,400); Churches in Reading Drop-in Centre (£600).

FINANCES *Financial year end* 31/12/2019 *Income* £1,750,000 *Total grants* £716,500 *Grants to organisations* £710,300 *Assets* £12,970,000

TRUSTEES Robert Ames; David Sutton; Philip Hooper; Dr Deborah Jenkins; Mary Waite; Tahir Maher; Elizabeth Ann Terry.

OTHER INFORMATION The charity awarded 27 grants to individuals during the 2019 totalling £6,500. Grants totalling £183,300 were awarded through the Earley Charity Workers scheme which covers the salary of a voluntary sector worker for up to three years.

HOW TO APPLY Application forms can be requested via email or by completing the online enquiry form. Application forms and supporting documents should be returned to the charity by post. Check the charity's website for application deadlines.

CONTACT DETAILS Jane Wittig, Clerk to the Trustees, St Nicolas Centre, Sutcliffe, Earley, Reading RG6 7JN *Tel.* 0118 926 1068 *Email* ec@earleycharity.org.uk *Website* www.earleycharity.org.uk

■ East End Community Foundation

CC NO 1147789 **ESTABLISHED** 1990

WHERE FUNDING CAN BE GIVEN The London boroughs of Tower Hamlets, Hackney, Newham and the City of London.

WHO CAN BENEFIT Registered charities; unregistered charities; CICs; social enterprises; schools.

WHAT IS FUNDED Community development and cohesion; children and young people; employability skills; education.

TYPE OF GRANT Project funding; core/revenue costs.

RANGE OF GRANTS Mostly up to £10,000.

SAMPLE GRANTS J-Go (£136,600); Bromley by Bow Centre (£46,100); Fit For What Project (£20,300); Toyhouse Libraries (£12,500); Fight for Peace (£10,000); It's Your Life (£7,000); Immediate Theatre (£5,000); Tower Hamlets Youth Sport Foundation (£3,000); Docklands Sailing and Watersports Centre (£1,500); Isle of Dogs Bangladeshi Association and Culture Centre (£250).

FINANCES *Financial year end* 31/03/2020 *Income* £2,500,000 *Total grants* £1,600,000 *Grants to organisations* £1,600,000 *Assets* £23,270,000

TRUSTEES Sahidur Rahman; Jim MacHale; Ashley Mullins; Howard Dawber; Rick Watson; Mary Frost; Victoria Clark; Katherine Webster; Cllr Guy Nicholson; Revd Jeremy Fraser; James Wright.

OTHER INFORMATION This is one of the 46 UK community foundations, which distribute funding for a wide range of purposes. As with all community foundations, there are a number of donor-advised funds managed on behalf of individuals, families and charitable trusts. Grant schemes tend to change frequently; consult the foundation's website for details of current programmes and up-to-date deadlines. The foundation awarded 195 grants during the year.

HOW TO APPLY Potential applicants are advised to visit the community foundation's website or contact its grants team to find the most suitable funding stream.

CONTACT DETAILS Grants Team, Jack Dash House, 2 Lawn House Close, London E14 9YQ *Tel.* 020 7345 4444 *Email* admin@eastendcf.org *Website* www.eastendcf.org

■ Eastern Counties Educational Trust Ltd

CC NO 310038 **ESTABLISHED** 1922
WHERE FUNDING CAN BE GIVEN Essex; Suffolk; Norfolk; Cambridgeshire; Hertfordshire.
WHO CAN BENEFIT Charitable organisations; educational institutions.
WHAT IS FUNDED Support for those with special educational needs, particularly those under 25 who have emotional and behavioural difficulties.
SAMPLE GRANTS Previous beneficiaries have included: Eden-Rose Coppice Trust (£6,000); Childhood First (£4,000); Grove Cottage (£3,000); Frozen Light Theatre (£2,500); Friends of Castiedon School (£2,000); KIDS (£1,000).
FINANCES *Financial year end* 31/03/2020 *Income* £133,100 *Total grants* £105,800 *Grants to organisations* £105,800 *Assets* £4,210,000
TRUSTEES David Boyle; Moira Usher; Robert Colwin; Ben Salmon; Harry Anderson; Deborah Hollister; Deborah Reed.
HOW TO APPLY Contact the correspondent for further information.
CONTACT DETAILS Verity Barclay, Secretary, 22 Brook Street, Coggeshall, Colchester CO6 1SH *Tel.* 01376 564025 *Email* ecet.secretary@yahoo.co.uk

■ Sir John Eastwood Foundation

CC NO 235389 **ESTABLISHED** 1964
WHERE FUNDING CAN BE GIVEN Nottinghamshire.
WHO CAN BENEFIT Local charitable organisations.
WHAT IS FUNDED General charitable purposes.
WHAT IS NOT FUNDED Individuals.
RANGE OF GRANTS Generally from £500 to £10,000.
SAMPLE GRANTS Nottinghamshire Hospice (£24,000); Warspo Youth Club (£20,000); Newark and Nottinghamshire Agricultural Society and Woodside Farm Stables (£10,000 each); Children's Air Ambulance, John Eastwood Hospice Trust and Macmillan Cancer Support (£5,000 each).
FINANCES *Financial year end* 31/03/2020 *Income* £297,500 *Total grants* £335,300 *Grants to organisations* £335,300 *Assets* £9,050,000
TRUSTEES Valerie Hardingham; David Marriott; John Mudford; Victoria Cottingham.
OTHER INFORMATION Grants were awarded to 153 organisations. Only organisations receiving grants of over £5,000 were listed in the charity's accounts. Grants of under £5,000 totalled £226,300 and were awarded to 140 organisations.
HOW TO APPLY Contact the correspondent for further information.
CONTACT DETAILS The Trustees, PO Box 9803, Handley Arcade, Leeming Street, Mansfield, Nottinghamshire NG18 9FT *Tel.* 07970 438740 *Email* sirjohneastwoodfoundation@talktalk.net

■ EBM Charitable Trust

CC NO 326186 **ESTABLISHED** 1982
WHERE FUNDING CAN BE GIVEN UK.
WHO CAN BENEFIT Charitable organisations; hospices; hospitals; educational organisations.
WHAT IS FUNDED General charitable purposes; animal welfare and research; youth development; social welfare.
TYPE OF GRANT Project funding; occasionally research.
RANGE OF GRANTS £5,000 to £200,000.
SAMPLE GRANTS British Racing School (£120,000); Animal Care Trust (£100,000); Amy Winehouse Foundation (£50,000); Camp Mohawk (£15,000); Chartwell Cancer Trust (£10,000); Lake District Calvert Trust (£7,500); Animal Health Trust (£3,000).
FINANCES *Financial year end* 30/06/2020 *Income* £1,400,000 *Total grants* £1,370,000 *Grants to organisations* £1,370,000 *Assets* £57,400,000
TRUSTEES Richard Moore; Michael Macfadyen; Stephen Hogg; Francis Moore; Lucy Forsyth.
OTHER INFORMATION The trust manages two funds, the main fund and Fitz' fund. Fitz' fund is a designated fund for animal charities. During 2019/20, £1.36 million was awarded through the main fund and £10,000 was awarded through Fitz' Fund.
HOW TO APPLY Unsolicited applications are not accepted.
CONTACT DETAILS The Trustees, Moore Family Office Ltd, 42 Berkeley Square, London W1J 5AW *Tel.* 020 7318 0845 *Email* Lynne.Webster@moorefamilyofficegroup.com

■ The Ecology Trust

CC NO 1099222 **ESTABLISHED** 2003
WHERE FUNDING CAN BE GIVEN UK and overseas.
WHO CAN BENEFIT Charitable organisations.
WHAT IS FUNDED The principal aim of the trust is to support ecological and environmental initiatives, particularly around the issues of agriculture, tropical forests and climate change. The trust also intends to help local community groups working on environmental issues in the UK and overseas, so as to empower people to contribute to policy development and to participate in planning and decision-making at the local level.
WHAT IS NOT FUNDED Retrospective work; part of general appeals or circulars; outward-bound courses, expeditions and overseas travel; capital projects (i.e. buildings and refurbishment costs); conservation of already well-supported species or of non-native species; recycling projects.
TYPE OF GRANT Project and core costs, including running costs such as salaries and overheads.
RANGE OF GRANTS £1,800 to £54,100.
SAMPLE GRANTS Fundación para la Conservación de Ibiza y Formentera (£54,100); Corporate Europe Observatory and Transnational Institute (£50,000); Seahorse Environmental (£39,900); Zoological Society of London (£38,000); Yorkshire Wildlife Trust (£5,000); New Economy Organisers Network (£4,000); Action for Conservation (£1,800).
FINANCES *Financial year end* 31/03/2020 *Income* £624,300 *Total grants* £195,400 *Grants to organisations* £195,400 *Assets* £476,800
TRUSTEES Benjamin Goldsmith; Charles Filmer; Alexander Goldsmith; Charlotte Colbert.
OTHER INFORMATION Grants were awarded to seven organisations during the year.
HOW TO APPLY Contact the correspondent for further information. The trust rarely makes grants to unsolicited applications.
CONTACT DETAILS Jon Cracknell, Secretary, 48 Kidmore Road, Caversham, Reading, Berkshire RG4 7LU *Tel.* 0118 377 9085 *Email* info@jmgfoundation.org *Website* https://www.ecologytrust.org

■ The Economist Charitable Trust

CC NO 293709 **ESTABLISHED** 1986
WHERE FUNDING CAN BE GIVEN UK; overseas.
WHO CAN BENEFIT Charitable organisations.
WHAT IS FUNDED Education; literacy and re-training; communication.
TYPE OF GRANT Project funding.
RANGE OF GRANTS The average grant size was £860 in 2019/20.
SAMPLE GRANTS Indigo Children's Fund (£13,000); Breadwinners, Global Kids, HELP, Kisharon, Kuma Cambodia and St George's Society of New York (£5,000 each).
FINANCES *Financial year end* 31/03/2020 *Income* £104,000 *Total grants* £95,500 *Grants to organisations* £95,500 *Assets* £9,500
TRUSTEES Ada Simkins; Kiran Malik; Susan Clark; Jamie Credland; Ursula Esling.
OTHER INFORMATION The trust is the corporate charity of The Economist Newspaper Ltd.
HOW TO APPLY The trust does not accept unsolicited applications.
CONTACT DETAILS The Trustees, The Adelphi, 1–11 John Adam Street, London, WC2N 6HT *Tel.* 020 7576 8000

■ The Gilbert and Eileen Edgar Foundation

CC NO 241736 **ESTABLISHED** 1965
WHERE FUNDING CAN BE GIVEN UK.
WHO CAN BENEFIT Charitable organisations.
WHAT IS FUNDED General charitable purposes with preference towards medical research, care and support; fine arts; education in the fine arts; academic education; religion; recreation.
TYPE OF GRANT Full project funding; scholarships.
RANGE OF GRANTS Grants typically range from £500 to £9,000.
SAMPLE GRANTS Not Forgotten Association (£50,000); Royal College of Music (£9,000); Royal Academy of Arts (£6,000); Royal Academy of Dramatic Art (£5,000); Alzheimer's Research UK and Marylebone Project (£1,000 each); Brainwave (£500).
FINANCES *Financial year end* 05/04/2020 *Income* £90,700 *Total grants* £114,500 *Grants to organisations* £114,500 *Assets* £1,430,000
TRUSTEES Simon Gentilli; Adam Gentilli.
OTHER INFORMATION Grants were awarded to 78 organisations in 2019/20.
HOW TO APPLY Apply in writing to the correspondent. According to the foundation's 2019/20 accounts: 'For a large number of years the trustees have concentrated on making annual grants to a range of charities. The trustees review the beneficiaries and from time to time amendments are made to the list. When funds allow the trustees occasionally make one-off grants.'
CONTACT DETAILS The Trustees, Greville Mount, Milcote, Stratford-upon-Avon, Warwickshire CV37 8AB *Tel.* 01491 639318 *Email* trustee@milcote.uk

■ The Edge Foundation

CC NO 286621 **ESTABLISHED** 1982
WHERE FUNDING CAN BE GIVEN UK.
WHO CAN BENEFIT Educational institutions; charitable organisations.
WHAT IS FUNDED Education and learning. The foundation adapts its grant schemes to address topical problems – see the website for more information.
TYPE OF GRANT Project funding.
SAMPLE GRANTS Middlesex University (£99,000); Eden Project (£95,000); XP School Doncaster (£91,000); Derby College (£80,000); University of Essex (£65,000); Barbican (£39,000).
FINANCES *Financial year end* 31/12/2019 *Income* £824,000 *Total grants* £902,000 *Grants to organisations* £902,000 *Assets* £26,710,000
TRUSTEES Prof. Colin Riordan; Neil Bates; Pauline Daniyan; Tobias Peyton-Jones; Andrew Stevens; Stephen Gray; Elaine Lilley; Michael Butler; Prof. Ann-Marie Bathmaker.
HOW TO APPLY Check the foundation's website for funding round dates and deadlines.
CONTACT DETAILS The Trustees, 44 Whitfield Street, London W1T 2RH *Tel.* 020 7960 1540 *Email* enquiry@edge.co.uk *Website* www.edge.co.uk

■ Edinburgh Children's Holiday Fund

OSCR NO SC010312 **ESTABLISHED** 1912
WHERE FUNDING CAN BE GIVEN Edinburgh and Lothian.
WHO CAN BENEFIT Charitable organisations; schools; local Councils.
WHAT IS FUNDED Children's welfare and holidays for children who are disadvantaged.
TYPE OF GRANT One-off grants.
RANGE OF GRANTS Mainly under £10,000.
SAMPLE GRANTS Children 1st (£17,500); City of Edinburgh Council (£16,000); Hopscotch (£3,500); The Roses Charitable Trust (£3,000); The Yard (£2,500); HomeLink (£2,000); Citadel Youth Centre (£1,500); St Andrew's Fox Covert Primary School (£1,200); Hearts and Minds (£1,000).
FINANCES *Financial year end* 31/10/2019 *Income* £77,500 *Total grants* £71,600 *Grants to organisations* £71,600 *Assets* £1,760,000
OTHER INFORMATION The 2018/19 accounts were the latest available at the time of writing (June 2021). During the year, grants to organisations totalled £71,600. Within this, £28,000 was awarded to four local councils to be distributed to individuals.
HOW TO APPLY Contact the correspondent for more information. Our previous research indicates that applications should be made on a form obtained from the correspondent and should be submitted in mid-December and mid-April.
CONTACT DETAILS The Trustees, c/o Bryce Wilson and Co., Hill Street Business Centre, 13 Hill Street, Edinburgh EH2 3JP

■ Edinburgh Trust No. 2 Account

CC NO 227897 **ESTABLISHED** 1959
WHERE FUNDING CAN BE GIVEN UK and overseas.
WHO CAN BENEFIT Registered charities.
WHAT IS FUNDED General charitable purposes; armed services; education.
RANGE OF GRANTS £1,000 to £2,500.
SAMPLE GRANTS St Paul's Anglican Cathedral – Valletta (£6,300); Edwina Mountbatten Trust (£3,300); National Maritime Museum (£2,100); Intelligence Corps Association (£1,500); Army Cadet Force Association (£1,300).

FINANCES *Financial year end* 05/04/2020
Income £104,200 *Total grants* £129,000
Grants to organisations £129,000
Assets £3,100,000

TRUSTEES Matthew Moss; Brig. Archie Miller-Bakewell; George Hewson.

HOW TO APPLY Contact the correspondent for further information.

CONTACT DETAILS The Trustees, The Duke of Edinburgh's Household, Buckingham Palace, London SW1A 1AA *Tel.* 020 7024 4087

■ Edupoor Ltd

CC NO 1113785 **ESTABLISHED** 2005

WHERE FUNDING CAN BE GIVEN UK and overseas.

WHO CAN BENEFIT Charitable organisations.

WHAT IS FUNDED Education and training; the relief of poverty; older people; physical and mental health; disability; general charitable purposes.

SAMPLE GRANTS A list of beneficiaries was not included in the annual report and accounts.

FINANCES *Financial year end* 30/06/2020
Income £988,200 *Total grants* £930,900
Grants to organisations £930,900
Assets £98,600

TRUSTEES Alan Shelton; Michael Shelton; Benjamin Levy.

HOW TO APPLY Contact the correspondent for further information.

CONTACT DETAILS The Trustees, Flat 10, 125 Clapton Common, Stamford Hill, London E5 9AB *Tel.* 07947 249515

■ Dr Edwards Bishop King's Fulham Endowment Fund

CC NO 1113490 **ESTABLISHED** 1981

WHERE FUNDING CAN BE GIVEN The old Metropolitan Borough of Fulham.

WHO CAN BENEFIT Individuals; registered charities and community organisations. Applications from small, emerging and minority ethnic organisations are welcomed.

WHAT IS FUNDED Social welfare; support for people on low incomes.

TYPE OF GRANT Core costs; project funding; capital costs.

RANGE OF GRANTS Generally up to £5,000 but higher awards would be considered.

SAMPLE GRANTS A list of beneficiaries was not included in the annual report and accounts.

FINANCES *Financial year end* 31/03/2020
Income £514,200 *Total grants* £478,300
Grants to organisations £301,800
Assets £7,380,000

TRUSTEES Michael Clein; Allen Smith; Ron Lawrence; Susan O'Neill; Carol Bailey; Ted Townsend; Sheila Thomas; Zahra Beg; Helen Fagan; Matthew Uberoi; Robert Fryer; Cllr Iain Cassidy.

OTHER INFORMATION Grants were given to 46 organisations (including summer schemes) in 2019/20. Grants are also made to individuals in need.

HOW TO APPLY Application forms are available to download from the charity's website and can be returned to the office by hand, by post, or by email . The trustees meet every two months.

CONTACT DETAILS Jonathan Martin, Clerk to the Trustees, Percy Barton House, 33–35 Dawes Road, Fulham, London SW6 7DT *Tel.* 020 7386 9387 *Email* clerk@debk.org.uk *Website* www.debk.org.uk

■ W. G. Edwards Charitable Foundation

CC NO 293312 **ESTABLISHED** 1985

WHERE FUNDING CAN BE GIVEN UK.

WHO CAN BENEFIT Registered charities.

WHAT IS FUNDED Care for older people; improvement of well-being.

WHAT IS NOT FUNDED Buying or leasing transport; salaries; general campaigns; revenue funding; building projects in the planning stages; IT which is for the use of administration; retrospective items; rent; individuals.

TYPE OF GRANT Capital costs; project funding; innovative schemes for ongoing care.

RANGE OF GRANTS £1,000 to £3,000 (average grant size is £1,400).

SAMPLE GRANTS Wigan and Leigh Hospice (£3,800); Bridge Care (£3,500); Alive and Kicking and Cycling Without Age (£2,000 each); Independent Arts (£1,700); Wakefield Hospice (£1,400); Voluntary Action Shetland (£1,000); Healthy Generations (£1,500); Age UK Westminster (£550).

FINANCES *Financial year end* 05/04/2020
Income £169,200 *Total grants* £135,100
Grants to organisations £135,100
Assets £3,030,000

TRUSTEES Prof. Wendy Savage; William Mackie, Lucy Polling; Sara Seymour-Savage.

OTHER INFORMATION During 2019/20, grants were made to 97 organisations.

HOW TO APPLY Detailed information outlining what should be included in grant applications and how applications should be structured is available from the foundation's website. Applications should be a maximum of four A4 pages and sent to the correspondent by email or post. There are four application deadlines each year.

CONTACT DETAILS The Trustees, 14 Windsor Terrace, South Gosforth, Newcastle upon Tyne, Tyne and Wear NE3 1YL *Tel.* 0191 284 3612 *Email* wgedwardscharity@icloud.com *Website* www.wgedwardscharitablefoundation.org.uk

■ The Eight Foundation

CC NO 1174600 **ESTABLISHED** 2017

WHERE FUNDING CAN BE GIVEN Dorset; Hampshire; Surrey; West Berkshire; West Sussex; Wiltshire.

WHO CAN BENEFIT Individuals; registered charities.

WHAT IS FUNDED Education; health; medical equipment; relief of poverty.

WHAT IS NOT FUNDED Non-registered charities; charities outside the area of benefit or charitable focus; charities with an annual income in excess of £250,000 or with over £500,000 of assets; applicants with no connection or association with Eight Wealth Management; purposes for which the government has a statutory responsibility to provide for.

RANGE OF GRANTS Up to £5,000.

SAMPLE GRANTS A list of beneficiaries was not included in the annual report and accounts.

FINANCES *Financial year end* 30/06/2019
Income £165,400 *Total grants* £73,300
Grants to organisations £73,300
Assets £80,300

TRUSTEES Storm Shepherd-Riggs; Ian Riggs; Nathaniel Geddes.

OTHER INFORMATION The 2018/19 accounts were the latest available at the time of writing (June 2021). In addition to grants totalling £73,300, the value of donated items totalled £21,600.

HOW TO APPLY Applicants must be able to demonstrate their connection or association with Eight Wealth Management, or be referred by someone within the organisation. An application form can be completed online. Applications are considered between 1 September and 1 December each year, but can be submitted at any time.

CONTACT DETAILS Storm Shepherd-Riggs, Trustee, 1460 Parkway, Whiteley, Fareham, Hampshire PO15 7AF *Tel.* 01489 555180 *Email* info@eightfoundation.co.uk *Website* https://www.eightfoundation.co.uk

■ The Eighteen Fund

CC NO 1135961 **ESTABLISHED** 2010

WHERE FUNDING CAN BE GIVEN The London Borough of Barnet.

WHO CAN BENEFIT Charitable organisations.

WHAT IS FUNDED General charitable purposes.

SAMPLE GRANTS A list of beneficiaries was not included in the annual report and accounts.

FINANCES *Financial year end* 31/03/2020 *Income* £208,300 *Total grants* £264,400 *Grants to organisations* £264,400 *Assets* £14,800

TRUSTEES Jacqueline Rashbass; Andrew Rashbass; Elie Rashbass.

OTHER INFORMATION In 2019/20 grants were made for the following causes: relief of poverty (£169,700); advancement of religion (£67,900); advancement of education (£18,800); relief of those in need (£5,300); advancement of health or the saving of lives (£2,400); other charitable purposes (£230). The grant total includes grants to organisations and individuals.

HOW TO APPLY Contact the correspondent for further information.

CONTACT DETAILS Jacqueline Rashbass, Trustee, 17 Wykeham Road, London NW4 2TB *Tel.* 07974 151494 *Email* jacqueline@rashbass.com

■ The Eighty Eight Foundation

CC NO 1149797 **ESTABLISHED** 2012

WHERE FUNDING CAN BE GIVEN UK, Ireland and South Africa.

WHO CAN BENEFIT Registered charities; unregistered charitable projects; individuals.

WHAT IS FUNDED Education and training; cancer and dementia research and care; social welfare; older people; disadvantaged artists and photographers.

SAMPLE GRANTS The Sutton Trust (£220,000); The Cares Family Ltd (£150,000); The Integrated Education Fund and The Silver Line (£100,000 each); World Vision (£53,500); Reach Academy (£44,000); Butler Gallery (£8,500).

FINANCES *Financial year end* 31/03/2020 *Income* £3,940,000 *Total grants* £681,600 *Grants to organisations* £681,600 *Assets* £14,680,000

TRUSTEES Stuart Walker; Ann Fitzmaurice; Claude Slatner; Neelish Heredia; Edward Fitzmurice; Barry Fine.

OTHER INFORMATION Grants were awarded to 14 organisations during 2019/20.

HOW TO APPLY The 2019/20 accounts state: 'The charity identifies worthy causes through its own research, the use of specialist research companies like NPC or the philanthropy units of UBS and Barclays. Once the potential charities are selected to progress to discussion by the trustees they need to submit a written proposal, showing how the grant will be spent, the phasing of the funds and the frequency and type of reporting. These proposals will then be discussed at meetings between the Board of Trustees with formal minutes being held.' Contact the correspondent for further information.

CONTACT DETAILS The Trustees, c/o Rawlinson and Hunter, Eighth Floor, 6 New Street Square, New Fetter Lane, London EC4A 3AQ *Tel.* 020 7842 2000 *Email* eighty.eight@rawlinson-hunter.com

■ Elanore Ltd

CC NO 281047 **ESTABLISHED** 1980

WHERE FUNDING CAN BE GIVEN UK.

WHO CAN BENEFIT Charitable organisations.

WHAT IS FUNDED Social welfare and education within the Orthodox Jewish community.

SAMPLE GRANTS A list of beneficiaries was not included in the annual report and accounts.

FINANCES *Financial year end* 31/03/2020 *Income* £69,800 *Total grants* £79,600 *Grants to organisations* £79,600 *Assets* £854,700

TRUSTEES Danielle Beck; Yael Tesler; Michal Beck.

HOW TO APPLY Contact the correspondent for further information.

CONTACT DETAILS Danielle Beck, Trustee, 25 Highfield Gardens, London NW11 9HD *Tel.* 020 8455 6789

■ The George Elias Charitable Trust

CC NO 273993 **ESTABLISHED** 1977

WHERE FUNDING CAN BE GIVEN UK and overseas.

WHO CAN BENEFIT Jewish organisations; registered charities.

WHAT IS FUNDED Education; relief of poverty; promotion of the Jewish faith.

TYPE OF GRANT Project funding; core costs.

SAMPLE GRANTS A list of beneficiaries was not included in the annual report and accounts.

FINANCES *Financial year end* 05/04/2019 *Income* £934,000 *Total grants* £362,000 *Grants to organisations* £362,000 *Assets* £1,320,000

TRUSTEES Ernest Elias; Stephen Elias.

OTHER INFORMATION The 2018/19 accounts were the latest available at the time of writing (June 2021).

HOW TO APPLY Contact the correspondent for information regarding the application process.

CONTACT DETAILS Stephen Elias, Trustee, Shaws Fabrics Ltd, 1 Ashley Road, Altrincham, Cheshire WA14 2DT *Tel.* 0161 928 7171 *Email* textiles@kshaw.com

■ The Elie Trust

OSCR NO SC046848 **ESTABLISHED** 2016

WHERE FUNDING CAN BE GIVEN UK and overseas.

WHO CAN BENEFIT Registered charities; hospitals; hospices; orphanages; places of worship.

WHAT IS FUNDED Health and welfare; education; Christian causes.

RANGE OF GRANTS Grants range from £1,200 to £12,400.

SAMPLE GRANTS Moshi Christian Children's Centre Ministries (£12,400); Scottish Bible Society (£6,000); For Life Trust, Hope for Glasgow (£4,800 each); Christians Against Poverty

(£3,000); Scripture Union Scotland (£1,800); Flame Trust (£1,200).

FINANCES *Financial year end* 31/08/2020
Income £54,000 *Total grants* £59,800
Grants to organisations £58,600
Assets £668,100

OTHER INFORMATION Grants to individuals totalled £1,200.

HOW TO APPLY Contact the correspondent for further information.

CONTACT DETAILS The Trustees, 72 Westermains Avenue, Kirkintilloch, East Dunbartonshire G66 1EH

■ The Marian Elizabeth Trust

CC NO 1166932 **ESTABLISHED** 2016

WHERE FUNDING CAN BE GIVEN UK.

WHO CAN BENEFIT Charitable organisations; hospices.

WHAT IS FUNDED Children with disabilities.

TYPE OF GRANT Development funding; core costs; capital costs.

RANGE OF GRANTS Grants ranged from £39,000 to £885,000.

SAMPLE GRANTS Previous beneficiaries have included: Acorn Children's Hospice (£885,000); Rainbows Hospice (£600,000); Newlife Centre (£100,000); Rutland Rotaract Family Support Centre (£39,000).

FINANCES *Financial year end* 31/03/2020
Income £11,900 *Total grants* £1,790,000
Grants to organisations £1,790,000

TRUSTEES Robert Rowley; Maureen Edwards; Michael Edwards; Rosemary Edwards.

OTHER INFORMATION Full accounts were not available to view on the Charity Commission's website due to the trust's low income. We have therefore estimated the grant total based on the trust's total expenditure.

HOW TO APPLY Contact the correspondent for further information.

CONTACT DETAILS The Trustees, The Enterprise Centre, Priors Hall, Corby NN17 5EU *Tel.* 01536 560394 *Email* info@themarianelizabethtrust.org

■ The Wilfred and Elsie Elkes Charity Fund

CC NO 326573 **ESTABLISHED** 1984

WHERE FUNDING CAN BE GIVEN Staffordshire.

WHO CAN BENEFIT Charitable organisations.

WHAT IS FUNDED General charitable purposes including: children and young people; older people; health; disability; older people.

SAMPLE GRANTS Previous beneficiaries have included: Braille Chess Association; Brainwave; Caudwell Children; Children's Air Ambulance; Lupus UK; Missing People; Seafarers UK; The Mary Sevens Hospice; Willow; Young and Inspired.

FINANCES *Financial year end* 10/08/2019
Income £116,400 *Total grants* £90,900
Grants to organisations £90,900
Assets £50,100

TRUSTEE Ludlow Trustee Company.

OTHER INFORMATION Full accounts were not available to view on the Charity Commission's website. We have therefore estimated the grant total based on the charity's total expenditure. The 2018/19 financial information was the latest available at the time of writing (June 2021).

HOW TO APPLY Contact the correspondent for further information.

CONTACT DETAILS The Trustees, 1st Floor Tower Wharf, Cheese Lane, Bristol BS2 0JJ *Tel.* 0117 313 8200 *Email* charitabletrusts@ludlowtrust.com

■ The Maud Elkington Charitable Trust

CC NO 263929 **ESTABLISHED** 1972

WHERE FUNDING CAN BE GIVEN Mainly in Desborough and the county of Northampton.

WHO CAN BENEFIT Small registered charities.

WHAT IS FUNDED General charitable purposes; social welfare.

WHAT IS NOT FUNDED Only in exceptional circumstances do the trustees make grants to individuals.

TYPE OF GRANT Project funding.

RANGE OF GRANTS £500 to £5,000. Occasionally the trust makes larger grants.

SAMPLE GRANTS Previous beneficiaries have included: Bromford Housing Association, Cancer Research UK, CARE Shangton, Charity Link – Northampton, Cynthia Spencer Hospice, Elizabeth Finn Care, Launde Abbey, Loughborough University, Multiple Sclerosis Society, Phoenix Furniture, Voluntary Action Northamptonshire.

FINANCES *Financial year end* 31/03/2020
Income £639,300 *Total grants* £646,100
Grants to organisations £646,100
Assets £27,470,000

TRUSTEES Roger Bowder; Michael Jones; Katherine Hall.

OTHER INFORMATION The trust is committed to funding one pupil at Leicester Grammar School and two pupils at Leicester High School for Girls for the period of their education. Grants of less than £5,000 were awarded to 235 institutions and grants above £5,000 were awarded to 13 institutions.

HOW TO APPLY Apply in writing to the correspondent. The trust meets bi-monthly or more if necessary to consider applications.

CONTACT DETAILS Helen Pole, Administrator, c/o Shakespeare Martineau, Two Colton Square, Leicester, Leicestershire LE1 1QH *Tel.* 0116 257 4462 *Email* helen.pole@shma.co.uk

■ The Ellerdale Trust

CC NO 1073376 **ESTABLISHED** 1998

WHERE FUNDING CAN BE GIVEN UK, with a preference for Norfolk.

WHO CAN BENEFIT Registered charities. A small proportion of grants are made to overseas charities.

WHAT IS FUNDED Children; families; disability and ill health; social welfare; holidays or breaks for carers and children from inner cities.

WHAT IS NOT FUNDED Individuals.

RANGE OF GRANTS £500 to £20,000.

SAMPLE GRANTS NSPCC (£20,000); MIND (£17,000); Gr8 As U R (£9,000); The Prince's Trust (£5,000); Action for Kids (£4,000); Eating Matters and NANSA Family Centre (£3,000 each); Swan Youth Project (£2,000); Total Ensemble Theatre Co. (£1,000); New Routes (£500).

FINANCES *Financial year end* 05/04/2020
Income £190,800 *Total grants* £172,300
Grants to organisations £172,300
Assets £6,270,000

TRUSTEES Alistair Macfarlane; Paul Kurthausen; Simon Moores; Clare Cairnes; John Elliott; Samuel Moores.

OTHER INFORMATION Grants were made to 39 organisations in 2019/20. Grant-making is mainly directed towards supporting children who have suffered abuse or bullying, who are terminally ill or require mobility equipment because of illness, who have mental illness or brain damage, or who live in deprived areas.

HOW TO APPLY Contact the correspondent for further information.

CONTACT DETAILS Mary Adlard, Director of Grant-Making, The Parlour, The High Street, Ketteringham, Wymondham, Norfolk NR18 9RU *Tel.* 01603 813340 *Email* maryadlard7@gmail.com

■ John Ellerman Foundation

CC NO 263207 **ESTABLISHED** 1971

WHERE FUNDING CAN BE GIVEN UK; UK Overseas Territories (environmental work only).

WHO CAN BENEFIT Registered charities; museums; galleries.

WHAT IS FUNDED Performing arts; museums and galleries outside London; the environment; social action.

WHAT IS NOT FUNDED Individuals, including student grants or bursaries; general and round-robin appeals; capital developments and individual items of equipment; promotion of religion or places of worship; arts organisations and projects whose main focus is supporting and developing an individual, rather than when new work is part of an artistic programme; learning and participation in the arts, where this is the primary focus of the application; leisure or individual holiday schemes; sport, where this is the core of the organisation's activities; boxing; education, such as initiatives linked to the curriculum, arts or environmental educational projects; animal welfare, captive breeding and animal rescue centres; medical research or treatment, including drug and alcohol rehabilitation services; prisons and offenders; individual campaigns; one-off events, such as conferences, trips, seminars, master classes, summer schools, single commissions, productions or festivals.

TYPE OF GRANT Core/revenue costs; project funding.

SAMPLE GRANTS Hull Maritime Museum (£170,000); Institute for Public Policy Research (£100,000); Ancient Tree Forum (£90,000); Headlong (£60,000); Sheila McKechnie Foundation (£5,000).

FINANCES *Financial year end* 31/03/2020
Income £3,820,000 *Total grants* £5,500,000
Grants to organisations £5,500,000
Assets £128,850,000

TRUSTEES Hugh Raven; Keith Shepherd; Geraldine Blake; Gary Steinberg; Peter Kyle; Tyfyal Choudhury; Annika Small; Becca Bunce.

OTHER INFORMATION Grants were broken down as follows: social action (£1.9 million); the environment (£1.44 million); arts (£1.28 million) museums and galleries (£730,000); other (£240,000).

HOW TO APPLY Apply via the foundation's website.

CONTACT DETAILS Dorothée Irving, Head of Grants, Aria House, 23 Craven Street, London WC2N 5NS *Tel.* 020 7930 8566 *Email* enquiries@ellerman.org.uk *Website* www.ellerman.org.uk

■ The Ellinson Foundation Ltd

CC NO 252018 **ESTABLISHED** 1967

WHERE FUNDING CAN BE GIVEN London; the North East; overseas.

WHO CAN BENEFIT Jewish organisations.

WHAT IS FUNDED Jewish causes including education; welfare; advancement of religion.

RANGE OF GRANTS Up to £108,000.

SAMPLE GRANTS Kesser Yehoshua (£108,000); Kesser Yeshua RP (Israel) (£75,000); Yeshivat Bney Reme (£21,400); Three Pillars (£20,000); Kollel Ohel Torah (Jerusalem) (£9,000).

FINANCES *Financial year end* 31/03/2020
Income £330,600 *Total grants* £272,700
Grants to organisations £272,700
Assets £5,780,000

TRUSTEES Alexander Ellinson; Uri Ellinson.

HOW TO APPLY Contact the correspondent for further information.

CONTACT DETAILS Uri Ellinson, Company Secretary/Trustee, First Floor, Winston House, 349 Regents Park Road, London N3 1DH *Tel.* 020 3411 2001 *Email* u.ellinson@gmail.com

■ The Elmley Foundation

CC NO 1004043 **ESTABLISHED** 1991

WHERE FUNDING CAN BE GIVEN Herefordshire and Worcestershire.

WHO CAN BENEFIT Constituted organisations and groups; individual artists from Herefordshire and Worcestershire; other individual artists whose proposals have been planned in conjunction with an organisation or body in Herefordshire or Worcestershire; students born and schooled in the two counties who are enrolled on nationally-recognised specialist arts courses.

WHAT IS FUNDED A wide variety of projects and causes within the arts (including dance, film and media, literature, music, project development, theatre and visual arts and crafts); art events; art equipment.

WHAT IS NOT FUNDED Non-arts projects; projects not involving professional artists; arts events outside the beneficial area; arts events intended to raise funds for non-arts causes; general appeals; applications for retrospective funding.

TYPE OF GRANT Capital and core costs; start-up arts events; sponsorship. Funding of up to, and over, three years will be considered. The foundation rarely covers full project costs, therefore it partners with local authorities, businesses and arts development agencies. Many of its grants are used as matching money for Arts Council, Lottery and local authority schemes.

RANGE OF GRANTS £250 to £25,000; rarely more than £2,000 for unsolicited applications.

SAMPLE GRANTS 2Faced Dance Company (£19,000); Ledbury Poetry Festival (£15,000); Borderlines Film Festival (£10,000); Open Sky Productions (£6,000); Hereford College of Arts (£4,200); Worcester Arts Workshop (£2,000); Shakespeare School (£1,000); Alloy – Hereford Jewellers Group (£500).

FINANCES *Financial year end* 05/04/2020
Income £420,900 *Total grants* £266,300
Grants to organisations £230,000
Assets £3,740,000

TRUSTEES Diana Johnson; Sally Luton; Hugh Carslake.

OTHER INFORMATION The foundation has two funding schemes: the Main Programme supports proposals which promote the appreciation, knowledge and study of the arts and of artistic achievement in Herefordshire and

Worcestershire; and the Small Grants Scheme (administered by Community First) which has two funds – one for arts events and activities and the other for arts equipment. During the year, 68 grants were given under the Main Programme and 17 under the Small Grants scheme. Grants totalling £36,300 were awarded directly to art students.

HOW TO APPLY Applicants to the Main Programme are advised to contact the foundation before making a formal application. There is an application form available to download from the website or, alternatively, applicants can send a letter including details of: what the money is needed for; an estimate of the income and expenditure for the project/programme being planned; and, in particular, who will be benefitting from the project/programme. Applications can be made at any time. Application forms and guidance notes for the Small Grants Scheme are available from the website. Questions regarding eligibility for the scheme can be directed to Emma Buckingham at Community First on 001684 312751, or email grants@comfirst.org.uk.

CONTACT DETAILS The Trustees, West Aish, Morchard Bishop, Crediton, Devon EX17 6RX *Tel.* 01363 877433 *Email* foundation@elmley.org.uk *Website* www.elmley.org.uk

The Vernon N. Ely Charitable Trust

CC NO 230033 **ESTABLISHED** 1962

WHERE FUNDING CAN BE GIVEN The London Borough of Merton.

WHO CAN BENEFIT Charitable organisations.

WHAT IS FUNDED General charitable purposes; sport.

SAMPLE GRANTS A list of beneficiaries was not included in the annual report and accounts.

FINANCES *Financial year end* 05/04/2020 *Income* £74,000 *Total grants* £73,800 *Grants to organisations* £73,800 *Assets* £1,480,000

TRUSTEES Derek Howorth; John Moyle; Richard Main.

HOW TO APPLY Contact the correspondent for further information.

CONTACT DETAILS Derek Howorth, Trustee, c/o BGM Helmores Ltd, 114A Cromwell Road, London SW7 4AG *Tel.* 020 7402 7444 *Email* Derekhoworth@bgm.co.uk

The Emerald Foundation

CC NO 1127093 **ESTABLISHED** 2008

WHERE FUNDING CAN BE GIVEN West Riding of Yorkshire.

WHO CAN BENEFIT Registered charities; schools and universities; places of worship; theatres.

WHAT IS FUNDED The performing arts; sport; animal welfare.

RANGE OF GRANTS Mostly under £15,000.

SAMPLE GRANTS Opera North (£600,000); Northern Ballet (£300,000); Leeds Playhouse (£240,000); Leeds Rugby Foundation (£150,000); Bradford Grammar School (£35,000); Bradford Cathedral (£12,500); Guide Dogs Puppy Centre Appeal (£5,000); Caring for Life (£2,000); Leeds Vocal Movement (£1,000).

FINANCES *Financial year end* 31/12/2019 *Income* £1,800,000 *Total grants* £2,230,000 *Grants to organisations* £2,230,000 *Assets* (£781,900)

TRUSTEES Peter Meredith; Karen Fojt; Dr Keith Howard; Melissa Fojt; Martin Hasyn; Emma Tregenza.

OTHER INFORMATION Grants were awarded to 45 organisations during the year and were broken down as follows: performing arts (£1.66 million); sport (£361,000); animals (£210,000).

HOW TO APPLY Applications should be made in writing or via email to the correspondent. Applications are considered twice a year.

CONTACT DETAILS Sylvia Hall, Secretary, Howard House, Wagon Lane, Bingley BD16 1WA *Tel.* 01274 777700 *Email* shall@emeraldgroup.com *Website* https://careers.emeraldpublishing.com/community/the-emerald-foundation

The Emerton-Christie Charity

CC NO 262837 **ESTABLISHED** 1971

WHERE FUNDING CAN BE GIVEN UK.

WHO CAN BENEFIT Registered charities.

WHAT IS FUNDED Health, including mental health; disability; the arts; the environment; education.

WHAT IS NOT FUNDED Individuals.

RANGE OF GRANTS Usually up to £3,000.

SAMPLE GRANTS Previous beneficiaries have included: Trinity Laban (£10,000); Comfrey Project (£5,000); Fishermen's Mission and Life Centre (£3,000 each); Carers Trust, Chance, Headway and Magpie Dance (£2,000 each); London Music Masters (£1,000); British Disabled (£500); Caresco (£300).

FINANCES *Financial year end* 05/04/2019 *Income* £87,700 *Total grants* £77,700 *Grants to organisations* £77,700

TRUSTEES Lt Col. William Niekirk; Dr Claire Mera-Nelson; Sally Walker; Joanna Jeeves.

OTHER INFORMATION The 2017/18 accounts were the latest available at the time of writing (May 2021), therefore, the grant total has been estimated using the financial information available on the Charity Commission's website. Beneficiaries have included organisations working with disadvantaged groups such as refugees and asylum seekers, victims of human trafficking and prisoners.

HOW TO APPLY Contact the correspondent for further information.

CONTACT DETAILS The Trustees, Kelswyn House, Bowness-on-Solway, Wigton, Cumbria CA7 5AG *Tel.* 07791 168778 *Email* joannajeeves@gmail.com

The Endrick Trust

OSCR NO SC012043 **ESTABLISHED** 1984

WHERE FUNDING CAN BE GIVEN Glasgow postcode area.

WHO CAN BENEFIT Registered charities.

WHAT IS FUNDED Social welfare; citizenship and community development.

WHAT IS NOT FUNDED Individuals; animals; medical research; charities with an income of more than £2 million. Repeat applications within two years are less likely to be successful.

TYPE OF GRANT Core funding; project funding.

RANGE OF GRANTS Typically £1,000 to £3,000. Larger grants of up to £50,000 are made to exceptional projects.

SAMPLE GRANTS SACRO (£50,000); Glasgow Disabled Scouts (£5,000); Boost Employability, LEAP Sports Scotland, Refuge Survival Trust and Village Storytelling Centre (£3,000 each); Tea in the Pot (£2,000); Park Villa Football Development (£1,400).

FINANCES *Financial year end* 05/04/2020 *Income* £138,100 *Total grants* £145,400 *Grants to organisations* £145,400 *Assets* £3,900,000

OTHER INFORMATION Grants were awarded to 33 organisations during the year. The trust is supporting SACRO's Garden Project with grants of £50,000 per year for three years.

HOW TO APPLY Application forms are available to download from the trust's website and should be returned via email to the correspondent.

CONTACT DETAILS Alison Hempsey, Partner, c/o T. C. Young Solicitors, 7 West George Street, Glasgow G2 1BA *Tel.* 0141 225 2573 *Email* amh@tcyoung.co.uk *Website* www.tcyoung.co.uk/info/endrick-trust

■ England and Wales Cricket Trust

CC NO 1112540 **ESTABLISHED** 2005

WHERE FUNDING CAN BE GIVEN England; Wales.

WHO CAN BENEFIT Cricket clubs; county cricket boards; cricket-based charitable organisations.

WHAT IS FUNDED Encouragement of increased participation of amateur cricket (particularly among young people; supporting other charitable organisations associated with cricket.

TYPE OF GRANT Project funding; capital costs; core costs; development funding.

SAMPLE GRANTS A list of beneficiaries was not included in the annual report and accounts.

FINANCES *Financial year end* 31/01/2020 *Income* £16,820,000 *Total grants* £11,890,000 *Grants to organisations* £11,890,000 *Assets* £38,280,000

TRUSTEES Scott Smith; James Wood; Ebony Rainford-Brent; Tom Harrison; Ian Lovett.

OTHER INFORMATION At the time of writing (January 2021) the trust's funding was mainly focused on providing grants and loans to clubs and boards affected by the COVID-19 pandemic.

HOW TO APPLY Visit the charity's website for further information.

CONTACT DETAILS The Trustees, Lord's Cricket Ground, London NW8 8QZ *Tel.* 020 7432 1200 *Email* kate.hailstone@ecb.co.uk *Website* www.ecb.co.uk

■ The Englefield Charitable Trust

CC NO 258123 **ESTABLISHED** 1968

WHERE FUNDING CAN BE GIVEN Mainly the Berkshire area; parts of Hackney and Inverness-shire which are connected with the Englefield Estate.

WHO CAN BENEFIT Mainly registered charities; some local schools and churches are supported; individuals.

WHAT IS FUNDED General charitable purposes, including: churches and religion, agriculture and conservation, heritage and arts, young people, education and community, sport, social welfare, overseas projects, medical research, armed forces charities and work overseas.

WHAT IS NOT FUNDED Applications from individuals are considered but are subject to a limit of £350 and full details are requested of what the money is needed for and confirmation that all other relevant avenues have been explored. Recipients of grants within the previous 12 months are advised not to re-apply.

TYPE OF GRANT Capital grants are preferred but revenue grants will be considered. Grants are generally one-off.

RANGE OF GRANTS Generally between £500 and £5,000.

SAMPLE GRANTS A list of beneficiaries was not included in the annual report and accounts.

FINANCES *Financial year end* 31/03/2020 *Income* £436,300 *Total grants* £896,200 *Grants to organisations* £894,400 *Assets* £14,530,000

TRUSTEES Catherine Haig; Lady Elizabeth Benyon; Richard Benyon; Zoe Benyon; Melissa Owston; Richard Bampfylde; Richard Griffiths.

OTHER INFORMATION In 2019/20 the trust received 649 applications for funding and awarded 157 grants (to organisations and individuals). Grants were made across seven categories: youth/education/community (£663,500); medical research/support (£63,600); social and welfare/support (£49,200); conservation/heritage/arts (£45,900); church/religion (£44,900); HM Forces (£16,000); overseas (£13,000).

HOW TO APPLY Apply in writing to the correspondent enclosing your organisation's latest set of accounts, your charity's registration number and the purpose for which the money is to be used. Alternatively, applications can be submitted through the online fundraising platform The Good Exchange (www.thegoodexchange.com). Applications are considered in March and October. Only applications going before the trustees will be acknowledged. More information is available on the trust's helpful website.

CONTACT DETAILS The Trustees, Englefield Estate Office, Englefield Road, Theale, Reading, Berkshire RG7 5DU *Tel.* 07880 701138 *Email* charity@englefield.co.uk *Website* https://www.englefieldestate.co.uk/community/englefield-charitable-trust

■ The Enkalon Foundation

CCNI NO NIC103528 **ESTABLISHED** 1985

WHERE FUNDING CAN BE GIVEN Northern Ireland, particularly in the Antrim area.

WHO CAN BENEFIT Charities, community groups and organisations working to improve the quality of life for people in Northern Ireland.

WHAT IS FUNDED Social welfare; animal welfare; arts, culture, heritage or science; amateur sport; health; education; citizenship and community development; healthcare equipment for ex-employees of British Enkalon, Antrim and their families.

WHAT IS NOT FUNDED Individuals (other than ex-British Enkalon employees); playgroups, PTAs, senior citizens' groups or sporting groups outside the former Antrim Borough area; medical research; travel outside Northern Ireland; projects outside Northern Ireland.

TYPE OF GRANT Core costs; running costs; project costs; healthcare equipment.

RANGE OF GRANTS Usually up to £6,000 maximum, with the average grant being £1,000.

SAMPLE GRANTS Lightwork NI – Antrim (£12,400); Riverside School Antrim (£10,000); Oasis Caring in Action (£6,000); Young Enterprise – Antrim (£4,500); Macmillan Cancer Unit Derry and National Autistic Society – Northern Ireland (£2,000 each); Dogs Trust – Northern Ireland (£1,000); Home-Start Omagh (£500); Lisnaskea Historical Society (£340).

FINANCES *Financial year end* 05/04/2020 *Income* £266,900 *Total grants* £270,700 *Grants to organisations* £195,000 *Assets* £5,870,000

TRUSTEES Peter Dalton; John Wallace; Mark Patterson; Stephen Montgomery; Karen McWhinney.

OTHER INFORMATION The foundation received 249 applications during the year and made 246 grants in total, of which 148 (£180,400) were made within the former Antrim borough area and 98 (£90,300) were made within the rest of Northern Ireland. Grants to individual ex-employees of British Enkalon, Antrim and/or their families totalled £75,700.

HOW TO APPLY The trustees meet quarterly in March, June, September and December. Applications should be submitted via the website along with supporting documentation (see details on the website).

CONTACT DETAILS Claire Cawley, Administrator, Unit 9, The Junction, County Antrim BT41 9DF *Tel.* 028 9447 7131 *Email* info@enkelonfoundation.org *Website* www.enkalonfoundation.org

Entindale Ltd

CC NO 277052 **ESTABLISHED** 1978

WHERE FUNDING CAN BE GIVEN UK and Israel.

WHO CAN BENEFIT Orthodox Jewish organisations.

WHAT IS FUNDED Advancement of the Orthodox Jewish religion; education; the relief of poverty.

RANGE OF GRANTS In 2019/20, most grants were of under £70,000.

SAMPLE GRANTS Tchabe Kollel Ltd (£85,000); Friends of Eida Chareidis Orthodox Council of Jerusalem (£72,000); Shir Chesed Beis Yisroel (£71,500).

FINANCES *Financial year end* 30/06/2020 *Income* £1,350,000 *Total grants* £2,240,000 *Grants to organisations* £2,240,000 *Assets* £17,150,000

TRUSTEES Allan Becker; Barbara Peters; Joseph Pearlman.

OTHER INFORMATION Grants of £70,000 or less totalled £2 million.

HOW TO APPLY Apply in writing to the correspondent. Contact the correspondent for further information.

CONTACT DETAILS Joseph Pearlman, Chair, 8 Highfield Gardens, London NW11 9HB *Tel.* 020 8458 9266

Epilepsy Research UK

CC NO 1100394 **ESTABLISHED** 2007

WHERE FUNDING CAN BE GIVEN UK.

WHO CAN BENEFIT Hospitals; universities; other academic institutions.

WHAT IS FUNDED Scientific research investigating the causes, diagnosis and clinical management of epilepsy and associated conditions.

TYPE OF GRANT Project funding.

RANGE OF GRANTS Ranges vary according to the grant programme.

SAMPLE GRANTS University of Birmingham (£299,000); Institute of Child Health (£128,600); University of Liverpool (£28,800); Newcastle University (£20,000).

FINANCES *Financial year end* 31/03/2020 *Income* £2,260,000 *Total grants* £1,340,000 *Grants to organisations* £1,340,000 *Assets* £2,490,000

TRUSTEES Prof. Matthew Walker; Dr Graeme Sills; Barrie Akin; The Rt Hon. David Cameron; Prof. Bruno Frenguelli; Mary Gavigan; Yvonne Hart; Dr John Hirst; Simon Lanyon; Prof. Mark Rees; Prof. Mark Richardson; Harry Salmon; Judith Spencer-Gregson.

OTHER INFORMATION The charity offers three programmes: project grants (up to £200,000 to support a research project lasting a maximum of three years); fellowship awards (up to £300,000 over four years to support fellowships); pilot studies (up to £30,000 to support pilot or start-up studies lasting no more than two years). Further information on the grant programmes offered can be found on the charity's website.

HOW TO APPLY Application forms, together with criteria, guidelines and application deadlines are available to download from the charity's website.

CONTACT DETAILS Caoimhe Bennett, Research Manager, Can Mezzanine, 7–14 Great Dover Street, London SE1 4YR *Tel.* 020 3096 7887 *Email* caoimhe@eruk.org.uk *Website* www.epilepsyresearch.org.uk

The EQ Foundation

CC NO 1161209 **ESTABLISHED** 2015

WHERE FUNDING CAN BE GIVEN Worldwide with a preference for the UK.

WHO CAN BENEFIT Charitable organisations.

WHAT IS FUNDED Projects that improve social mobility and support disadvantaged people.

TYPE OF GRANT Research; project funding.

SAMPLE GRANTS Big Give (£105,000); Advent of Change (£35,000); Access Project (£25,000); Beam (£20,000) Surfers Against Sewage (£15,200); Bike Project (£10,000) Resurgo Spear (£7,500).

FINANCES *Financial year end* 30/04/2020 *Income* £438,700 *Total grants* £322,700 *Grants to organisations* £322,700 *Assets* £833,600

TRUSTEES Mark Kenner; Jeannie Boyle; John Spiers.

OTHER INFORMATION Grants were awarded to 13 organisations during the year.

HOW TO APPLY Contact the correspondent for further information.

CONTACT DETAILS John Spiers, Trustee, Centennium House, 100 Lower Thames Street, London EC3R 6DL *Tel.* 020 7488 7110 *Email* info@eqfoundation.org.uk *Website* https://eqfoundation.org.uk

Equity Charitable Trust

CC NO 328103 **ESTABLISHED** 1989

WHERE FUNDING CAN BE GIVEN UK.

WHO CAN BENEFIT Theatres, theatre companies and professional theatre performers, with special reference to members, past and present, of the union Equity.

WHAT IS FUNDED Professional performing arts projects.

WHAT IS NOT FUNDED Non-professional performers, drama students, non-professional theatre companies, multi-arts venues, community projects or projects with no connection to the professional theatre.

RANGE OF GRANTS From £2,500 to £45,000.

SAMPLE GRANTS Dancers' Career Development (£45,000); Interact (£15,000); Queens Theatre Hornchurch; Exeter Northcote and Graeae Theatre (£5,000 each); Benjamin Gould (£2,500).

FINANCES *Financial year end* 31/03/2020 *Income* £565,500 *Total grants* £331,800 *Grants to organisations* £81,000 *Assets* £10,600,000

TRUSTEES David John; Bryn Evans; Christine Payne; Harry Landis; Stephen Ross; Stephen Gilchrist; Dr Oliver Davies; Jean Rogers; Barbara Hyslop;

Ian Barritt; William Cummings Thompson; Annie Bright; Robin Browne; Martin Brown; Ian Talbot; Malcolm Sinclair; Carille Hudson.

OTHER INFORMATION In 2019/20, £165,000 was given to 170 individuals for welfare and education.

HOW TO APPLY In the first instance, contact the correspondent to discuss your application and when the next grants committee meeting is taking place. Applications should be submitted in writing two weeks before the next meeting.

CONTACT DETAILS Kaethe Cherney, Administrator, Plouviez House, 19–20 Hatton Place, London EC1N 8RU *Tel.* 020 7831 1926 *Email* kaethe@equitycharitabletrust.org.uk *Website* www.equitycharitabletrust.org.uk

■ Esher House Charitable Trust

CC NO 276183 **ESTABLISHED** 1978

WHERE FUNDING CAN BE GIVEN England and Wales.

WHO CAN BENEFIT Registered charities.

WHAT IS FUNDED Jewish causes; health; welfare; arts and culture; children and young people; education; community.

RANGE OF GRANTS Mostly less than £1,000.

SAMPLE GRANTS A list of beneficiaries was not included in the annual report and accounts.

FINANCES *Financial year end* 30/06/2020 *Income* £167,900 *Total grants* £100,300 *Grants to organisations* £100,300 *Assets* £2,100,000

TRUSTEES Michael Conn; Hadassa Conn; Douglas Conn.

OTHER INFORMATION Grants were distributed as follows: community (£84,700); health and welfare (£12,400); children and young people (£3,000); education (£200).

HOW TO APPLY Contact the correspondent for further information.

CONTACT DETAILS Michael Conn, Trustee, 845 Finchley Road, London NW11 8NA *Tel.* 020 8455 1111 *Email* michael@1stpolicy.co.uk

■ The Essex and Southend Sports Trust

CC NO 1092238 **ESTABLISHED** 2002

WHERE FUNDING CAN BE GIVEN Essex and areas of East London traditionally attached to Essex.

WHO CAN BENEFIT Registered charities; CICs; schools; amateur sports clubs; individuals.

WHAT IS FUNDED Sports; sports equipment; sports facilities; individuals; sports projects; coaching; training; education; children and young people; community projects; disability; older people.

TYPE OF GRANT Capital costs; seed funding/start-up funding.

RANGE OF GRANTS Up to £50,000.

SAMPLE GRANTS Previous beneficiaries have included: Southend United Community and Educational Trust (£25,000); Hadleigh and Thundersley Cricket Club (£8,000); Essex County Cricket Board and Harlow Cricket Club (£5,000 each); The Prince's Trust and Southend Rugby Club (£3,000 each); South East Essex District Cricket Board (£2,500); Giffords Primary School (£2,000); Richardson-Trek Cycling team (£1,500); RSPB (£1,200).

FINANCES *Financial year end* 30/06/2020 *Income* £556,600 *Total grants* £184,800 *Grants to organisations* £184,800 *Assets* £5,620,000

TRUSTEES Joseph Sims; Linley Butler; Peter Butler; Rachel Pearse.

OTHER INFORMATION The trust's joint venture with Essex Community Foundation (the Essex and Southend Sports Charitable Fund, ESSCF) supports sporting activities for individuals. The trust made grants totalling £184,800 to ten organisations. This included £25,000 which was given to the trust's fund which is administered by Essex Community Foundation. A list of other beneficiaries was not provided.

HOW TO APPLY Contact the correspondent for further information.

CONTACT DETAILS Joe Sims, Trustee, Red House, Larks Lane, Great Waltham, Chelmsford CM3 1AD *Tel.* 01245 360385 *Email* mail@easst.org.uk *Website* www.easst.org.uk

■ Friends of Essex Churches Trust

CC NO 236033 **ESTABLISHED** 1951

WHERE FUNDING CAN BE GIVEN Essex (including Thurrock and Southend) and the five London boroughs formerly part of the county (Barking and Dagenham, Havering, Newham, Redbridge and Waltham Forest).

WHO CAN BENEFIT Christian churches.

WHAT IS FUNDED The preservation, repair, maintenance and improvement of Christian places of worship.

WHAT IS NOT FUNDED Electrical work (unless there is a written report by a qualified electrician stating that electrical installations are a fire hazard); general lighting; redecoration (unless needed as part of a scheme of eligible repairs); reseating; liturgical reordering; the introduction of other furnishings and fittings.

TYPE OF GRANT One-off repair and improvement grants.

SAMPLE GRANTS A list of beneficiaries was not included in the annual report and accounts.

FINANCES *Financial year end* 31/12/2020 *Income* £145,700 *Total grants* £151,600 *Grants to organisations* £151,600 *Assets* £305,800

TRUSTEES Catherine Leeder; Gail Jones; Jeremy Beale; John Pickthorn; Martin Stuchfield; Dr James Bettley; Rachel Grainger; Joanna Pimblett; Cannon H. Marsh.

HOW TO APPLY Application forms can be downloaded from the charity's website.

CONTACT DETAILS John Bloomfield, Secretary of the Grants Committee, 39 Lake Rise, Romford, Essex RM1 4DZ *Tel.* 01708 745273 *Email* john.bloomfield@btinternet.com *Website* www.foect.org.uk

■ Essex Community Foundation

CC NO 1052061 **ESTABLISHED** 1995

WHERE FUNDING CAN BE GIVEN Essex, Southend; Thurrock.

WHO CAN BENEFIT Voluntary and community organisations and other not-for-profit organisations, with an interest in small grassroots organisations. Individuals can also be supported.

WHAT IS FUNDED General charitable purposes.

TYPE OF GRANT Core costs/revenue costs; new or continuing projects; one-off initiatives; capital costs.

RANGE OF GRANTS Mostly £250 to £10,000. The average grant is £6,400.

SAMPLE GRANTS Home-Start Essex (£217,100); Firstsite (£106,500); Teen Talk (£39,300); Colchester Gateway Clubs (£30,000); Autism Anglia (£22,000); Southend Association of Voluntary Services (£20,800).

FINANCES *Financial year end* 30/06/2020
Income £6,340,000 *Total grants* £4,810,000
Grants to organisations £4,810,000
Assets £44,570,000

TRUSTEES Simon Hall; Peter Martin; Vivienne Wiggins; Lee Blissett; Clare Ball; Charles Cryer; Claire Read; Nicholas Alston; Russell Edey; Sandra Hollis; Joanna Wells; Charles Bishop.

OTHER INFORMATION This is one of the 46 UK community foundations, which distribute funding for a wide range of purposes. As with all community foundations, there are a number of donor-advised funds managed on behalf of individuals, families and charitable trusts. Grant schemes tend to change frequently – consult the foundation's website for details of current programmes and up-to-date deadlines. The grant total includes grants to individuals.

HOW TO APPLY Apply online via the foundation's website.

CONTACT DETAILS Grants Team, 121 New London Road, Chelmsford, Essex CM2 0QT *Tel.* 01245 356018 *Email* hello@essexcf.org.uk *Website* www.essexcommunityfoundation.org.uk

■ The Essex Heritage Trust

CC NO 802317 **ESTABLISHED** 1989

WHERE FUNDING CAN BE GIVEN Essex.

WHO CAN BENEFIT Charitable organisations; individuals.

WHAT IS FUNDED Publications about or the preservation of Essex history and restoration of monuments, significant structures, artefacts and church decorations and equipment.

WHAT IS NOT FUNDED Private properties.

TYPE OF GRANT Mostly one-off grants for revenue and capital costs.

RANGE OF GRANTS £100 to £10,000.

SAMPLE GRANTS Copped Hall Trust (£10,000); St Mary's Church – Newport (£5,000); St Michael's Church – Braintree (£4,000), Colchester Arts Centre (£3,000); Boxted Airfield Historical Group (£1,500); Pleshey Oral History Group (£900); St Nicholas' Church – Harwich (£400).

FINANCES *Financial year end* 31/03/2020
Income £76,000 *Total grants* £56,100
Grants to organisations £56,100
Assets £1,300,000

TRUSTEES Jonathan Douglas-Hughes; Jennifer Tolhurst; Lord Petre; Brian Moody; Peter Mamelok; Richard Wollaston; Mark Pertwee; Susan Brice; Dr James Bettley; Kay Twitchen; Cllr John Jowers.

OTHER INFORMATION Grants were awarded to 17 organisations.

HOW TO APPLY To apply for funding, complete the expression of interest form on the trust's website. They will then contact you with further instructions. The trustees meet three times a year to assess applications, in March, July and November and the dates of the meetings are posted on the website.

CONTACT DETAILS The Trustees, Cressing Temple, Witham Road, Braintree, Essex CM77 8PD *Tel.* 01376 585794 *Email* mail@essexheritagetrust.co.uk *Website* www.essexheritagetrust.co.uk

■ The Essex Youth Trust

CC NO 225768 **ESTABLISHED** 1963

WHERE FUNDING CAN BE GIVEN UK.

WHO CAN BENEFIT Organisations, including youth clubs.

WHAT IS FUNDED Education; social welfare; people under the age of 25, particularly looked-after children. The trust's website explains that it awards grants 'which favour beneficiaries that develop young people's physical, mental and spiritual capacities through active participation in sports and indoor and outdoor activities'.

WHAT IS NOT FUNDED Individuals.

TYPE OF GRANT Core costs; running costs; capital expenditure; project funding; salaries.

RANGE OF GRANTS Typically under £10,000.

SAMPLE GRANTS Essex Boys' and Girls' Clubs (£66,000); Cirdan Sailing Trust (£50,000); Stubbers Adventure Centre (£45,000); North Adventure Youth Centre (£16,300); Sea Change Projects Ltd (£14,000); Chain Reaction Theatre Company (£13,000).

FINANCES *Financial year end* 31/03/2020
Income £427,000 *Total grants* £332,900
Grants to organisations £332,900
Assets £7,600,000

TRUSTEES Julien Courtauld; The Ven. Duncan Green; Claire Cottrell; William Robson; Lady Julia Denison-Smith; Michael Dyer; Michael Biegel; Julie Rogers; Jonathan McEachern.

OTHER INFORMATION Only organisations receiving grants of over £10,000 were listed as beneficiaries in the charity's accounts. Grants of under £10,000 totalled £117,600 and were awarded to 42 organisations.

HOW TO APPLY The trust's website has a downloadable application form, which should be emailed to the correspondent. Grant applications are considered by the trustees quarterly in February, May, August and November. Applications made before the first day of the month in which a meeting is held will be considered at that meeting.

CONTACT DETAILS Jonathan Douglas-Hughes, Clerk, c/o Gepp and Sons, 58 New London Road, Chelmsford, Essex CM2 0PA *Tel.* 01245 493939 *Email* douglas-hughesj@gepp.co.uk *Website* https://sites.google.com/site/essexyouthtrust

■ The Estelle Trust

CC NO 1101299 **ESTABLISHED** 2003

WHERE FUNDING CAN BE GIVEN UK and Zambia.

WHO CAN BENEFIT Charitable organisations.

WHAT IS FUNDED The trust supports community and educational projects in Zambia, as well as making smaller grants to arts, educational and social development charities in the UK.

TYPE OF GRANT Start-up funding; project funding; development funding.

RANGE OF GRANTS Mostly up to £5,000.

SAMPLE GRANTS Bana Tandizo Foundation (£105,100); Corporate Education Trust (£7,900); University for Creative Arts (£5,000); Pallant House Gallery and Queens College Cambridge (£2,000 each); Disasters Emergency Committee Malawi Floods (£1,000); Breaking Ground Heritage (£500).

FINANCES *Financial year end* 31/03/2020
Income £81,600 *Total grants* £123,500
Grants to organisations £123,500
Assets £2,030,000

TRUSTEES Nigel Farrow; Gerald Ornstein; Darren Wise; Rachel Lynch; Katherine Farrow; Imogen Abed; Sarah Davies; William Ham.

OTHER INFORMATION In 2015/16 the trust established the Bana Tandizo Foundation to fund projects in Zambia.

HOW TO APPLY The trust do not accept unsolicited applications.

CONTACT DETAILS Will Ham, Fundraising and Projects Manager (UK), Office 3 Book House, 261A City Road, London EC1V 1JX *Tel.* 07970 518275 *Email* will@estelletrust.org *Website* www.estelletrust.org

■ The Ethos Foundation

CC NO 1166697 **ESTABLISHED** 2016
WHERE FUNDING CAN BE GIVEN UK.
WHO CAN BENEFIT Registered charities.
WHAT IS FUNDED General charitable purposes; community development.
SAMPLE GRANTS Beacon Fellowship; Dogs Trust; Jubilee Sailing Trust; Opera Holland Park; The Childhood Trust; The Foundling Museum.
FINANCES *Financial year end* 30/09/2020 *Income* £1,000,000 *Total grants* £1,030,000 *Grants to organisations* £1,030,000 *Assets* £563,400
TRUSTEES Grant Gordon; Brigitte Gordon; Lucy Blythe.
OTHER INFORMATION The foundation was previously called The Reekimlane Foundation. The mission of the foundation is 'to support local communities and UK society in general'.
HOW TO APPLY Unsolicited applications are not accepted.
CONTACT DETAILS The Trustees, 18 Buckingham Palace Road, London SW1W 0QP *Tel.* 07802 208276 *Email* ethosfoundation.uk@gmail.com *Website* https://www.reekimlanefoundation.org

■ Joseph Ettedgui Charitable Foundation

CC NO 1139615 **ESTABLISHED** 2010
WHERE FUNDING CAN BE GIVEN UK and overseas.
WHO CAN BENEFIT Registered charities.
WHAT IS FUNDED General charitable purposes.
RANGE OF GRANTS Up to £40,000 but mostly £5,000 to £10,000.
SAMPLE GRANTS Action Against Cancer (£40,000); The Prince's Foundation (£22,000); Crisis (£10,000); Emmaus UK (£5,000).
FINANCES *Financial year end* 31/03/2020 *Income* £55,900 *Total grants* £122,000 *Grants to organisations* £122,000 *Assets* £3,860,000
TRUSTEES Isabel Ettedgui; Peter Ettedgui; Paul Ettedgui; Genevieve Ettedgui; Matilda Ettedgui; Coutts & Co.
OTHER INFORMATION Grants were made to nine organisations.
HOW TO APPLY Unsolicited applications are not accepted.
CONTACT DETAILS The Trustees, Coutts & Co. Trustee Department, 1st Floor, Trinity Quay 1, Avon Street, Bristol BS2 0PT *Tel.* 0345 304 2424

■ The Evelyn Trust

CC NO 232891 **ESTABLISHED** 1920
WHERE FUNDING CAN BE GIVEN Cambridgeshire.
WHO CAN BENEFIT Research organisations; registered charities; not-for-profit organisations.
WHAT IS FUNDED Medical research; health and well-being.
WHAT IS NOT FUNDED Each grants programme has different eligibility criteria; refer to the relevant funding guidelines on the trust's website for full details.
TYPE OF GRANT Research; project funding; pilot studies; capital costs; strategic costs.
RANGE OF GRANTS Small grants: £4,000 to £10,000; large grants: up to £250,000.
SAMPLE GRANTS The University of Cambridge (£721,600 in seven grants); Defence Medical Welfare Service (£50,000); Addenbrooke's Charitable Trust (£40,000); CPSL Mind (£29,700); Peterborough Citizens Advice (£10,000); Cambridge and District Citizens Advice and Disability Huntingdonshire (£5,000 each).
FINANCES *Financial year end* 31/03/2020 *Income* £1,000,000 *Total grants* £982,200 *Grants to organisations* £982,200 *Assets* £23,530,000
TRUSTEES Julia Squier; Adrian Frost; Jeremy Newsum; Amy Agnew; Catherine Thomas; Prof. Rebecca Fitzgerald; Jeremy Pemberton; Will Dawkins; Bill Pike; Dr Trevor Baglin.
OTHER INFORMATION In 2019/20, the trust funded eight projects from 31 medical research applications.
HOW TO APPLY Visit the trust's helpful website for full details regarding the grant application process.
CONTACT DETAILS Rebecca Wood, Charity Director, PO Box 223, Saffron Walden, Essex CB10 9BP *Tel.* 01799 542708 *Email* office@evelyntrust.com *Website* www.evelyntrust.com

■ The Eventhall Family Charitable Trust

CC NO 803178 **ESTABLISHED** 1989
WHERE FUNDING CAN BE GIVEN UK, with a preference for the North West.
WHO CAN BENEFIT Registered charities; hospitals; religious bodies/institutions.
WHAT IS FUNDED General charitable purposes; Jewish causes.
TYPE OF GRANT Capital costs; project funding.
SAMPLE GRANTS A list of beneficiaries was not included in the annual report and accounts.
FINANCES *Financial year end* 05/04/2020 *Income* £86,400 *Total grants* £173,500 *Grants to organisations* £173,500 *Assets* £2,370,000
TRUSTEES Julia Eventhall; David Eventhall.
HOW TO APPLY Contact the correspondent for further information.
CONTACT DETAILS The Trustees, PO Box 490, Altrincham, Cheshire WA14 2ZT *Tel.* 01282 478200 *Email* efct@rectella.com

■ The Everard Foundation

CC NO 272248 **ESTABLISHED** 1976
WHERE FUNDING CAN BE GIVEN UK, with a preference for Leicestershire.
WHO CAN BENEFIT Registered charities.
WHAT IS FUNDED General charitable purposes, including: community development; education; social welfare; people with disabilities; the armed forces; the environment; health.
RANGE OF GRANTS Grants range from £150 to £20,000.
SAMPLE GRANTS Age Concern – Leicestershire and Rutland (£50,000); Action on Hearing Loss (£20,000); Tennis Leicester Charitable Trust (£16,000); British Heart Foundation (£5,000); All Saints Church, Rotherby (£2,500); Duke of Edinburgh Award (£1,000); Young Leicestershire (£500).

FINANCES *Financial year end* 05/04/2020 *Income* £129,000 *Total grants* £108,200 *Grants to organisations* £108,200 *Assets* £16,960,000

TRUSTEES Richard Everard; Serena Richards; Simon Aitkinson; Charlotte Everard.

OTHER INFORMATION During the year, grants were awarded to organisations working in the following areas: relief of those in need (£52,000); health (£29,400); community development (£19,900); the armed forces (£3,300); religion (£2,800); education (£1,000).

HOW TO APPLY Contact the correspondent for further information.

CONTACT DETAILS Richard Everard, Trustee, Everards Brewery Ltd, Unit C, Devana Avenue, Optimus Point, Glenfield, Leicester, Leicestershire LE3 8JS *Tel.* 0116 201 4307

■ Eversheds Sutherland (International) Charitable Trust

CC NO 1083594 **ESTABLISHED** 2000

WHERE FUNDING CAN BE GIVEN Charities local to the firm's UK offices.

WHO CAN BENEFIT Registered charities.

WHAT IS FUNDED General charitable purposes.

SAMPLE GRANTS Centrepoint Soho (£87,500); WaterAid (£53,000); The Hebe Foundation (£10,000); Whitechapel Mission (£5,900); MIND (£2,700); Railway Children (£2,000); Movember (£1,700).

FINANCES *Financial year end* 30/04/2020 *Income* £410,800 *Total grants* £348,400 *Grants to organisations* £348,400 *Assets* £801,400

TRUSTEES Jonathan Bowley; Clare Whitaker; Peter Scurlock; Michael Thompson; David Beswick; Kathryn Roberts; Mark Fletcher; Naeema Choudry.

OTHER INFORMATION The trust is the corporate charity of Eversheds Sutherland LLP, an international law firm. It receives its income from donations from the firm's partners and dormant client balances.

HOW TO APPLY The firm's website states: 'Each year the partners donate funds to the Eversheds Sutherland Business Lawyers Charitable Trust to create a significant pot of cash, the majority of which is allocated by reference to the number of people in each of our offices to support the various local charities chosen by each office.'

CONTACT DETAILS Kath Pring, Eversheds, 1 Callaghan Square, Cardiff CF10 5BT *Tel.* 0845 498 7156 *Email* kathpring@eversheds.com *Website* https://www.eversheds-sutherland.com/global/en/where/europe/uk/overview/csr/charitable-giving.page

■ The Eveson Charitable Trust

CC NO 1032204 **ESTABLISHED** 1993

WHERE FUNDING CAN BE GIVEN Herefordshire, Worcestershire and the county of West Midlands (covering Birmingham, Coventry, Dudley, Sandwell, Solihull, Walsall and Wolverhampton).

WHO CAN BENEFIT Mainly registered charities; however, some support is given, directly or indirectly, to statutory bodies for projects for which no statutory funding is available.

WHAT IS FUNDED People with disabilities; mental health; children in need; older people; homeless people; hospitals; hospices; medical research (being carried out wholly or mainly in the geographic area of benefit and into conditions associated with any of the foregoing groups). For statutory bodies, the trustees prefer to give support for the enhancement of services rather than the provision of what they consider to be basic needs.

WHAT IS NOT FUNDED Individuals; retrospective expenditure.

TYPE OF GRANT Capital and core/running costs; development costs.

SAMPLE GRANTS Good Shepherd Services (£275,000); National Star College (£200,000); Birmingham St Mary's Hospice (£71,200; Megan Baker House (£65,000); HVOSS (£30,000); Young People First (£12,000); The Myriad Centre Ltd (£7,000).

FINANCES *Financial year end* 31/03/2020 *Income* £1,890,000 *Total grants* £2,900,000 *Grants to organisations* £2,900,000 *Assets* £91,830,000

TRUSTEES David Pearson; Martin Davies; Louise Woodhead; Bill Wiggin; Richard Mainwaring; Judith Millward; Vivien Cockerill; Tasmin Clive; Mark Taylor; The Rt Revd Richard Jackson.

OTHER INFORMATION In 2019/20, grants were made to 289 organisations. There were 158 grants of £5,000 or less. Grants were broken down as follows: social care and development (£1 million); healthcare (£1.4 million); accommodation (£659,200).

HOW TO APPLY Application forms are available to download from the trust's website along with full guidance notes. The application form should be submitted along with: a copy of the charity's most recent report and accounts; a copy of the safeguarding policy; a project budget and any other relevant information; and a report on any previous grants (if applicable).

CONTACT DETAILS Claire Bowry, Chief Executive, 3 Sansome Place, Worcester WR11UQ *Tel.* 01905 905085 or 07394 655478 *Email* grants@eveson.org.uk *Website* https://www.eveson.org.uk

■ The Beryl Evetts and Robert Luff Animal Welfare Trust Ltd

CC NO 283944 **ESTABLISHED** 1981

WHERE FUNDING CAN BE GIVEN UK, some overseas.

WHO CAN BENEFIT Registered animal charities.

WHAT IS FUNDED Veterinary research and the care and welfare of animals.

RANGE OF GRANTS £500 to £75,000.

SAMPLE GRANTS Animal Health Trust (£75,000); Royal Veterinary College (£50,000); Animal Samaritans Midland Trust and Tenterden Cats Protection (£3,000 each); The Moreland Mouse Trust, Oak Tree Animal Charity and Cuan Wildlife Rescue (£2,500 each); Tiggywinkles (£1,500); The Calvert Trust (£1,000); Island Farm Donkey Sanctuary, ISOF (£500).

FINANCES *Financial year end* 31/08/2019 *Income* £191,700 *Total grants* £188,500 *Grants to organisations* £188,500 *Assets* £5,220,000

TRUSTEES Richard Price; Brian Nicholson; Rev Matthew Tomlinson; Melanie Condon; Sir Paul Coleridge; Lady Ruth Bodey; Dr Helen Hughes.

OTHER INFORMATION The trust awarded 30 grants to organisations during the year. The 2018/19 accounts were the latest available at the time of writing (June 2021).

HOW TO APPLY Contact the correspondent for further information.

CONTACT DETAILS Richard Price, Trustee, Waters Edge, Ferry Lane, Moulsford, Wallingford, Oxfordshire OX10 9JF *Tel.* 01491 652204 *Email* rpjprice@gmail.com

■ The Exilarch's Foundation

CC NO 275919 **ESTABLISHED** 1978

WHERE FUNDING CAN BE GIVEN Worldwide with a preference for the UK, Israel, USA and Iraq.

WHO CAN BENEFIT Charitable organisations, including Jewish organisations; hospitals; universities; schools.

WHAT IS FUNDED General charitable purposes including: social welfare; education; community development; hospitals, medical education and research; ethics.

RANGE OF GRANTS £5,000 to £1.5 million.

SAMPLE GRANTS University College London Hospital (£1.59 million); Women's Interfaith Network (£283,700); Westminster Academy (£248,400); Dangoor Education (£116,700); Jewish Leadership Council (£100,000); Jewish Lads' and Girls' Brigade (£50,000); Veteran Games (£25,000); Global Leadership Foundation (£5,000).

FINANCES *Financial year end* 31/12/2019 *Income* £13,160,000 *Total grants* £3,460,000 *Grants to organisations* £3,460,000 *Assets* £98,030,000

TRUSTEES David Dangoor; Elie Dangoor; Robert Dangoor; Michael Dangoor.

OTHER INFORMATION The foundation is the sponsor of Westminster Academy. Grants during the year were split between education (£808,700) and social welfare (£2.6 million).

HOW TO APPLY Contact the correspondent for further information.

CONTACT DETAILS The Trustees, 4 Carlos Place, Mayfair, London W1K 3AW *Tel.* 020 7399 0850

■ The ExPat Foundation

CC NO 1094041 **ESTABLISHED** 2002

WHERE FUNDING CAN BE GIVEN UK and Africa.

WHO CAN BENEFIT Registered charities.

WHAT IS FUNDED Improving the quality of life and well-being of elderly people; improving well-being and life chances of young people; in Africa there is a focus on supporting long-term initiatives.

WHAT IS NOT FUNDED Religious charities; animal welfare.

TYPE OF GRANT Core/revenue costs; unrestricted funding.

RANGE OF GRANTS Grants up to £50,000.

SAMPLE GRANTS Build It International (£58,500); Leap Confronting Conflict (£50,000); Home-Start – Hampshire (£29,400); Open Age (£25,000); Queen Elizabeth Foundation (£20,000); Fulham Good Neighbour Service (£9,500); Children Ahead (£3,500).

FINANCES *Financial year end* 05/04/2020 *Income* £1,160 *Total grants* £548,200 *Grants to organisations* £548,200

TRUSTEES Jan Knight; Janet Cummins; Caroline Coombs; Malcolm Stevens.

OTHER INFORMATION Full accounts were not available to view on the Charity Commission's website due to the foundation's low income. We have therefore estimated the grant total based on the foundation's total expenditure.

HOW TO APPLY Contact the correspondent for further information.

CONTACT DETAILS Janet Cummins, Trustee and Administration, 127 Ellesmere Road, London NW10 1LG *Tel.* 020 3609 2105 *Email* expatfdn@gmail.com *Website* https://expatfoundation.org

■ Extonglen Ltd

CC NO 286230 **ESTABLISHED** 1982

WHERE FUNDING CAN BE GIVEN UK and Israel.

WHO CAN BENEFIT Orthodox Jewish charities.

WHAT IS FUNDED The advancement of the Orthodox Jewish religion; education; the relief of poverty.

SAMPLE GRANTS Only one beneficiary was listed in the 2019 accounts, Kol Torah Ltd, which received £842,400. Previous beneficiaries have included: Ahavas Chesed, British Friends of Nishmat Yisrael, Children's Town Charity, Kupath Gemach Chaim Bechesed Viznitz Trust, Pikuach Nefesh.

FINANCES *Financial year end* 31/12/2019 *Income* £1,290,000 *Total grants* £874,900 *Grants to organisations* £874,900 *Assets* £16,830,000

TRUSTEES Meir Levine; Chaya Levine; Isaac Katzenberg.

HOW TO APPLY Contact the correspondent for further information.

CONTACT DETAILS The Trustees, New Burlington House, 1075 Finchley Road, London NW11 0PU *Tel.* 020 8731 0777 *Email* ml@rowdeal.com

■ G. F. Eyre Charitable Trust

CC NO 216040 **ESTABLISHED** 1960

WHERE FUNDING CAN BE GIVEN UK, with a focus on the South West.

WHO CAN BENEFIT National charities; local charities in the South West.

WHAT IS FUNDED General charitable purposes, including: medical research; social welfare; heritage.

RANGE OF GRANTS £500 to £17,000.

SAMPLE GRANTS DEBRA (£17,000); Dorset Natural History and Archaeological Society (£10,000); Teenage Cancer Trust (£9,000); Marie Curie Cancer Care (£5,000); South Wessex Organ Society (£2,000); WaterAid (£750); The Trussell Trust (£500).

FINANCES *Financial year end* 05/04/2020 *Income* £174,300 *Total grants* £123,800 *Grants to organisations* £123,800 *Assets* £469,800

TRUSTEES Carol Eyre; Rachel Young; George Eyre.

OTHER INFORMATION During 2019/20 the trust awarded 52 grants. Some organisations received more than one grant from the trust.

HOW TO APPLY Apply in writing to the correspondent. The trustees meet annually to consider applications. The 2019/20 annual report explains that 'in the interim, payments to good causes are nominated by individual Trustees'.

CONTACT DETAILS Andrew Richards, c/o Francis Clark LLP, Centenary House, Peninsula Park, Rydon Lane, Exeter, Devon EX2 7XE *Tel.* 01392 667000 *Email* andrew.richards@pkf-francisclark.co.uk

Esmée Fairbairn Foundation

CC NO 200051 **ESTABLISHED** 1961

WHERE FUNDING CAN BE GIVEN UK.

WHO CAN BENEFIT Charitable organisations.

WHAT IS FUNDED Preservation of species and habitat; freshwater; sustainable and ethical food; injustice and structural inequality; young leaders and artists; community development; local economies; art and culture.

WHAT IS NOT FUNDED Organisations with an annual turnover of less than £100,000 (as reflected in the latest set of accounts); organisations without at least three non-executive trustees or directors; grants for less than £30,000; social investments for less than £100,000 or more than £2 million; work that is not legally charitable; work that does not have a direct benefit in the UK; grants to individuals; capital costs including building work, renovations and equipment (grants only, social investments can be made for these); academic research – unless it can demonstrate real potential for practical outcomes; healthcare with a clinical basis, including medical research, hospices, counselling and therapy, arts therapy, education about and treatment for drug and alcohol misuse; work that is primarily the responsibility of statutory authorities; the promotion of religion.

TYPE OF GRANT Core costs; project grants; unrestricted funding. Most grants are for three years or more. Social investment is also available. Through the 'Grants Plus' scheme, recipients of grants and social investment are provided with a range of non-financial additional support.

SAMPLE GRANTS Tempo (£270,000); Stopwatch (£180,000); The Jo Cox Foundation (£120,000); Ashima (£90,000); Global Dialogue (£60,000); Shift Foundation (£20,000).

FINANCES *Financial year end* 31/12/2019
Income £7,850,000 *Total grants* £35,750,000
Grants to organisations £35,750,000
Assets £1,071,000,000

TRUSTEES Sir Jonathan Phillips; Stella Manzie; Dr Wanda Wyporska; Edward Carter; Prof. David Hill; Joe Docherty; John Fairbairn; Tom Chandos; Prof. Claire Alexander; Beatrice Hollond; Kate Lampard; Flora Fairbairn; Eleanor Updale.

OTHER INFORMATION The foundation has an informative website where further information, guidelines and examples of giving can be found.

HOW TO APPLY Expressions of interest can be submitted via the foundation's website.

CONTACT DETAILS The Grants Team, Kings Place, 90 York Way, London N1 9AG *Tel.* 020 7812 3700 *Email* info@esmeefairbairn.org.uk *Website* www.esmeefairbairn.org.uk

The Fairness Foundation

CC NO 1044174 **ESTABLISHED** 1994

WHERE FUNDING CAN BE GIVEN UK.

WHO CAN BENEFIT Charitable organisations.

WHAT IS FUNDED Animal welfare; bullying; children; citizenship; domestic abuse; fair society; human rights; LGBTQ+ rights; mental health and medical causes; migrants and refugees; older people; people with disabilities; prisoner support; the environment; women.

RANGE OF GRANTS Most grants are less than £20,000.

SAMPLE GRANTS Good Business Foundation and Tax Watch (£100,000 each); Hope and Homes for Children and RSPCA (£50,000 each); ASB Help and Crossroad's Women's Centre (£40,000 each); League Against Cruel Sports (£30,000); Christians Against Poverty (£25,000); Just for Kids Law (£23,500); Amnesty International (£20,000).

FINANCES *Financial year end* 30/04/2020
Income £1,860,000 *Total grants* £1,770,000
Grants to organisations £1,770,000
Assets £44,700

TRUSTEES Hanna Oppenheim; Julian Richer; David Robinson; Rosie Richer; Robert Rosenthal; Jonathan Levy; David Ward.

OTHER INFORMATION The foundation changed its name from The Persula Foundation to The Fairness Foundation in December 2020. Grants were awarded to 308 organisations in the following categories: fair society/citizenship (£689,000); animal welfare (£187,900); human rights (£183,400); prisoner support (£164,400); children (£159,900); medical causes (£133,800); migrants/refugees (£57,000); the environment (£48,000); women support (£41,000); LGBTQ+ (£30,400); disabilities (£30,100); older people (£19,100); mental health (£12,100); domestic abuse (£10,500); miscellaneous (£6,000); bullying (£3,000). Only organisations receiving grants of over £20,000 were listed as beneficiaries in the accounts.

HOW TO APPLY According to the 2019/20 annual report, the foundation considered applications from a variety of charitable organisations. Contact the correspondent for more information.

CONTACT DETAILS R. Bamforth, Secretary, Gallery Court, Hankey Place, London SE1 4BB *Tel.* 020 7551 5343 *Email* info@persula.org

The Fairstead Trust

CC NO 1096359 **ESTABLISHED** 2003

WHERE FUNDING CAN BE GIVEN Worldwide.

WHO CAN BENEFIT UK-registered charities; individuals.

WHAT IS FUNDED General charitable purposes.

RANGE OF GRANTS Grants are mostly £500 to £20,000.

SAMPLE GRANTS Previous beneficiaries have included: Royal Marsden Cancer Charity (£99,500); Rennie Grove Hospice Care (£20,000); Afghan Connection (£15,000); Change Foundation and Paul's Cancer Centre (£10,000 each); St Albans Cathedral (£9,000); REACT (Rapid Effective Assistance for Children with potentially Terminal illness) and Youth Talk (£5,000 each); Hopefield Animal Sanctuary (£1,000); Hearing Dogs (£500).

FINANCES *Financial year end* 05/04/2020
Income £2,600 *Total grants* £131,900
Grants to organisations £131,900

TRUSTEES Edward Cox; Wendy Cox; Lucinda Cox.

OTHER INFORMATION Full accounts were not available to view on the Charity Commission's website due to the trust's low income. We have therefore estimated the grant total based on the trust's total expenditure.

HOW TO APPLY Apply in writing to the correspondent including the following: the aims and objectives of your charity; the nature of your appeal; the total target (if for a specific project); contributions received against the target; your organisation's registered charity number; any other relevant factors. Applications should be accompanied by your organisation's full financial statements and latest annual report.

CONTACT DETAILS The Trustees, c/o New Quadrant Partners Ltd, 4th Floor, 5 Chancery Lane, London WC2A 1LG *Tel.* 020 7430 7161 *Email* charities@nqpltd.com

■ Family Philanthropy Ltd

CC NO 1181341 **ESTABLISHED** 2017

WHERE FUNDING CAN BE GIVEN UK and USA.

WHO CAN BENEFIT Charitable organisations; healthcare organisations, including nursing homes and hospitals; schools; art groups; museums; individuals.

WHAT IS FUNDED Art and culture; health and welfare; environmental conservation and sustainability; education.

SAMPLE GRANTS Chatham House (£100,000); National Portrait Gallery (£1,800).

FINANCES *Financial year end* 31/03/2019 *Income* £1,120,000 *Total grants* £101,800 *Grants to organisations* £101,800 *Assets* £1,010,000

TRUSTEES Susan Hayden; Richard Hayden; Spencer Hayden; Lindsay Hayden..

OTHER INFORMATION The 2018/19 accounts were the latest available at the time of writing (June 2021). Grants were awarded to two organisations during the year.

HOW TO APPLY Contact the correspondent for further information.

CONTACT DETAILS The Trustees, 17 Kensington Park Gardens, London W11 3HD *Tel.* 020 7570 1460 *Email* info@familyphilanthropy.org.uk

■ Famos Foundation Trust

CC NO 271211 **ESTABLISHED** 1976

WHERE FUNDING CAN BE GIVEN UK and Israel.

WHO CAN BENEFIT Orthodox Jewish organisations.

WHAT IS FUNDED The promotion of Orthodox Judaism; health; education; welfare.

SAMPLE GRANTS A list of beneficiaries was not included in the annual report and accounts.

FINANCES *Financial year end* 31/03/2019 *Income* £115,450 *Total grants* £97,800 *Grants to organisations* £97,800 *Assets* £1,930,000

TRUSTEES Rabbi Kupetz; Fay Kupetz; Isaac Kupetz; Joseph Kupetz.

OTHER INFORMATION The 2018/19 accounts were the latest available at the time of writing (May 2021).

HOW TO APPLY Contact the correspondent for further information.

CONTACT DETAILS Rabbi Kupetz, Trustee, 4 Hanover Gardens, Salford, Greater Manchester M7 4FQ *Tel.* 0161 740 5735

■ The Lord Faringdon Charitable Trust

CC NO 1084690 **ESTABLISHED** 2000

WHERE FUNDING CAN BE GIVEN UK, with a preference for Oxfordshire.

WHO CAN BENEFIT UK-registered national and local charities; hospitals.

WHAT IS FUNDED General charitable purposes, specifically: education; medical treatment; the purchase of antiques and artistic objects for museums and collections; older people; the arts and sciences, physical recreation and drama; relief of poverty.

WHAT IS NOT FUNDED Individuals.

TYPE OF GRANT Collections and acquisitions; project costs; scholarships; research.

RANGE OF GRANTS Generally between £1,000 and £5,000.

SAMPLE GRANTS National Trust Conservation Skills Centre Coleshill (£75,000); Royal Academy of Arts (£5,000); Oxford Churches Debt Centre (£3,000); Greyhounds in Need (£2,500); OCD Action (£2,000); Brain Tumour Charity, Dressability and Prospect Hospice (£1,000 each); European Squirrel Initiative (£500).

FINANCES *Financial year end* 05/04/2020 *Income* £314,500 *Total grants* £332,700 *Grants to organisations* £332,700 *Assets* £9,300,000

TRUSTEES The Hon. J. Henderson; Mrs S. Maitland Robinson; Bernard Cazenove; Edward Campbell Cottrell.

OTHER INFORMATION During 2019/20, grants were given to 99 organisations. The trust provides ongoing support to The Faringdon Collection Trust (Charity Commission no. 203770).

HOW TO APPLY Apply in writing to the correspondent detailing information on the specific purpose and expected beneficiaries of the grant.

CONTACT DETAILS Sharon Lander, Secretary, The Estate Office, Buscot Park, Faringdon, Oxfordshire SN7 8BU *Tel.* 01367 240786 *Email* estbuscot@aol.com

■ Samuel William Farmer Trust

CC NO 258459 **ESTABLISHED** 1928

WHERE FUNDING CAN BE GIVEN UK; primarily Wiltshire.

WHO CAN BENEFIT Registered charities; schools; amateur sports clubs; hospital; hospices.

WHAT IS FUNDED Education; health; social welfare.

TYPE OF GRANT Capital costs; seed funding/start-up funding.

RANGE OF GRANTS Generally between £1,000 and £5,000.

SAMPLE GRANTS Wiltshire Air Ambulance (£7,500); Royal Air Force Benevolent Fund (£5,000); Prospect Hospice (£3,000); Julia's House Children's Hospice (£2,600); Amber (£2,000); Hazel Hill Trust (£1,000).

FINANCES *Financial year end* 31/12/2019 *Income* £77,000 *Total grants* £64,500 *Grants to organisations* £63,300 *Assets* £2,980,000

TRUSTEES Bruce Waight; Jennifer Liddiard; Peter Fox-Andrews; Charles Brockis; Elaine Dewey.

OTHER INFORMATION Grants were awarded to 17 organisations in 2019. Grants to individuals totalled £1,200.

HOW TO APPLY Contact the correspondent for information regarding the application process. The trustees normally meet half yearly to consider applications.

CONTACT DETAILS Melanie Linden-Fermor, Secretary, 71 High Street, Market Lavington, Devizes, Wiltshire SN10 4AG *Tel.* 01380 813299

■ The Thomas Farr Charity

CC NO 328394 **ESTABLISHED** 1989

WHERE FUNDING CAN BE GIVEN Nottinghamshire.

WHO CAN BENEFIT Charitable organisations.

WHAT IS FUNDED Education; young people; health; older people; community development; social welfare; disability; homelessness.

WHAT IS NOT FUNDED Individuals; loans or business finance; campaigning work and projects that are primarily political; activities that have already taken place; general or mail shot appeals; activities that are the responsibility of local health or education authorities.

TYPE OF GRANT Project funding.

RANGE OF GRANTS Mostly £1,000 to £5,000.

SAMPLE GRANTS Reach Learning Disability (£10,000); Maggie's (£5,000); Ashfield Citizen Advice (£3,800); Macmillan Cancer Support (£3,000); Guide Dogs for the Blind and Hope Nottingham (£2,000 each); Lullaby Trust and Sensory Learning and Play (£1,000 each); Mansfield Junior Badminton (£500).

FINANCES *Financial year end* 05/04/2020 *Income* £310,100 *Total grants* £268,600 *Grants to organisations* £268,600 *Assets* £7,020,000

TRUSTEES Rathbone Trust Company Ltd; Philip Pruden; Amanda Farr; Henry Farr.

HOW TO APPLY Applications can be made via Nottinghamshire Community Foundation. The trustees meet three times a year to review applications, usually in March, July and November. For consideration in these meetings, applications must be received by 20 January, 20 May or 20 September respectively.

CONTACT DETAILS The Trustees, c/o Nottinghamshire Community Foundation, Pine House B, Ransom Wood Business Park, Southwell Road West, Mansfield, Nottinghamshire NG21 0HJ *Tel.* 01623 620202 *Email* enquiries@nottscf.org.uk *Website* https://thomasfarrcharity.com

The Farthing Trust

CC NO 268066 **ESTABLISHED** 1974

WHERE FUNDING CAN BE GIVEN UK and overseas.

WHO CAN BENEFIT Charitable organisations; individuals.

WHAT IS FUNDED General charitable purposes, with a focus on the advancement of religion, education, health, human rights and the reconciliation and promotion of religious and racial harmony, equality and diversity; social welfare.

RANGE OF GRANTS No restrictions are placed on grant applications.

SAMPLE GRANTS A list of beneficiaries was not included in the annual report and accounts.

FINANCES *Financial year end* 05/04/2020 *Income* £44,600 *Total grants* £188,500 *Grants to organisations* £173,100 *Assets* £4,140,000

TRUSTEES Mrs A. White; Mrs J. Martin; Ms E. Bell; Mr J. Martin.

OTHER INFORMATION More than 100 grants were made during the year. Grants to individuals totalled £15,400.

HOW TO APPLY Apply in writing to the correspondent. There are no financial or geographical restrictions placed on grant applications.

CONTACT DETAILS The Trustees, PO Box 276, Newmarket CB8 1GW *Tel.* 07598 565623 *Email* thefarthingtrust@gmail.com

The February Foundation

CC NO 1113064 **ESTABLISHED** 2006

WHERE FUNDING CAN BE GIVEN UK.

WHO CAN BENEFIT Registered charities.

WHAT IS FUNDED According to the annual report 2019/20, the trustees will consider grants for charities which: 'are for the benefit of people who are making an effort to improve their lives; are for the benefit of people who are no longer physically or mentally able to help themselves; have a long-term beneficial impact on the future of individuals, groups of individuals, or organisations; or protect the environment'. Grants are also given to 'small or minority charities where small grants will have a significant impact' and 'companies where the acquisition of equity would be in line with the foundation's charitable objectives'.

WHAT IS NOT FUNDED Child care; Citizens Advice branches; community centres; higher education; housing associations; individuals; medical research; minibuses; NHS trusts; non-departmental government bodies; overseas projects; primary education; uniformed groups; secondary education; single-faith organisations; special educational needs schools; amateur sports clubs, unless for people who have mental or physical disabilities; village halls; youth clubs and centres; charities which are party politically driven or have a commercial bias for a particular product or company.

TYPE OF GRANT Capital costs; core costs; project costs.

RANGE OF GRANTS The average grant is usually £5,000 per award.

SAMPLE GRANTS A list of beneficiaries was not included in the annual report and accounts.

FINANCES *Financial year end* 29/02/2020 *Income* £17,210,000 *Total grants* £12,600,000 *Grants to organisations* £12,600,000 *Assets* £122,000,000

TRUSTEES James Carleton; Mark Clarke; Michael Moody.

OTHER INFORMATION In 2019/20, 198 grants were made to 194 organisations and 23.1% of grant applications were successful. A one-off donation of £10.48 million was made to a (unnamed) UK charity.

HOW TO APPLY Apply in writing to the correspondent. The foundation's website states: 'Applications by email are given priority as the foundation aims to operate on a paperless basis. Send us the details and budget of the proposed project, how many people would benefit, how those benefits might be measured (not just financially), what the estimated cost of raising funds for the project is, and the full cost of raising voluntary income (especially if this is not detailed in your accounts). It is important to include in your email application full accounts for your most recent completed financial year.' If you are applying on behalf of a hospice, consult the foundation's website for details of additional required information. There are no application deadlines and applicants are normally informed of the trustee's decision within 12 weeks of submission.

CONTACT DETAILS Richard Pierce-Saunderson, Chief Executive, Spring Cottage, Church Street, Stradbroke, Suffolk IP21 5HT *Tel.* 01379 388200 *Email* rps@thefebruaryfoundation.org *Website* www.thefebruaryfoundation.org

The Feoffees of St Michael's Spurriergate York

CC NO 1159025 **ESTABLISHED** 2014

WHERE FUNDING CAN BE GIVEN York.

WHO CAN BENEFIT Churches and charitable organisations.

WHAT IS FUNDED The upkeep and maintenance of any Church of England church in York; general charitable purposes for the benefit of the inhabitants of the City of York.

WHAT IS NOT FUNDED Individuals; causes outside the City of York.
TYPE OF GRANT Capital costs; project costs; core/ revenue costs.
RANGE OF GRANTS Up to £100,000 but generally under £10,000.
SAMPLE GRANTS Previous beneficiaries have included: Tang Hall Community Service (£34,000); St Denly's Church (£30,000); Changing Lives (£15,000); St Luke's Church (£10,000); St Nick's Enviro Centre (£6,000); Community Furniture Store (York) Ltd (£3,000); Relate (£1,600); British Red Cross and RVS (£1,000 each); Family Matters (£250).
FINANCES *Financial year end* 31/12/2019 *Income* £90,700 *Total grants* £77,200 *Grants to organisations* £77,200 *Assets* £3,200,000
TRUSTEES Cai Mallett; Angela Anelay; David Titchener; Edward Waterson; Hannah Phillip; Laura Habgood-Joya; Stephen Hallett.
HOW TO APPLY Apply in writing or by email to the correspondent. The trustees meet four times a year. Full details outlining what is required in an application are listed on the funder's helpful website.
CONTACT DETAILS Lyn Rickatson, Clerk, c/o Grays Solicitors, Duncombe Place, York, North Yorkshire YO1 7DY *Tel.* 01904 634771 *Email* LynRickatson@grayssolicitors.co.uk *Website* https://www.feoffeesofstmichaelsspurriergate.org.uk

■ The George Fentham Birmingham Charity

CC NO 214487 **ESTABLISHED** 1906
WHERE FUNDING CAN BE GIVEN Birmingham.
WHO CAN BENEFIT Organisations providing services or facilities for people who are in need, hardship or distress; individuals who are long-term residents of Birmingham studying at a college or university.
WHAT IS FUNDED Organisational grants are given mainly in the following categories: children who are sick or who have disabilities; children's holidays and play schemes; young people's clubs and associations; adults who are sick or who have disabilities; social problems; community centres/neighbourhood groups; hospital charities; care for older people. Grants are given to individuals for educational purposes.
WHAT IS NOT FUNDED Salary costs; direct hardship grants to individuals.
TYPE OF GRANT Project funding; strategic and development funding.
RANGE OF GRANTS Grants are mostly between £1,000 and £5,000.
SAMPLE GRANTS Birmingham Settlement (£5,900); Dream Holidays (£4,800); FareShare (£3,000); CCS Birmingham and All Saints Youth Project (£2,000 each); Craftspace (£1,500); Family Acacia Support (£1,000).
FINANCES *Financial year end* 31/12/2019 *Income* £203,800 *Total grants* £131,100 *Grants to organisations* £100,200 *Assets* £7,370,000
TRUSTEES Martin Holcombe; Julie Scarratt; Nahid Saiyed; Margaret Flynn; Derek Ridgway; Alex Jarvis; Paul Tunnadine.
HOW TO APPLY Application forms are available to download from the charity's website, where criteria and guidelines are also posted. These should be returned to the secretary by email or post. As the meeting dates for general grants vary each year, applications are normally accepted up to one week prior to any scheduled meeting. Meetings are usually held three times a year.
CONTACT DETAILS Ms J. Hobday, Secretary, c/o Veale Wasbrough Vizards LLP, Second Floor, 3 Bindley Place, Birmingham, West Midlands B1 2JB *Tel.* 0121 227 3703 *Email* GeorgeFentham@vwv.co.uk *Website* www.georgefenthamcharity.org.uk

■ The A. M. Fenton Trust

CC NO 270353 **ESTABLISHED** 1975
WHERE FUNDING CAN BE GIVEN UK, with a preference for North Yorkshire.
WHO CAN BENEFIT Registered charities; places of worship; hospices.
WHAT IS FUNDED Health; people with disabilities; the environment, conservation and heritage.
WHAT IS NOT FUNDED Individuals.
RANGE OF GRANTS Up to £10,000.
SAMPLE GRANTS Harrogate Homeless Project (£25,000); RNLI (£20,000); Dewsbury League of Friendship (£6,000); Candlelighters and Wetherby in Support of the Elderly (£4,000 each); Citizens Advice and The Salvation Army (£2,500 each); War Memorials Trust (£1,000).
FINANCES *Financial year end* 31/12/2019 *Income* £323,900 *Total grants* £194,400 *Grants to organisations* £194,400 *Assets* £7,110,000
TRUSTEES Charles Fenton; Annalisa Fenton.
HOW TO APPLY Contact the correspondent for further information.
CONTACT DETAILS The Trustees, The A. M Fenton Trust, PO Box 788, Harrogate HG1 9RX *Tel.* 01423 564446

■ Allan and Nesta Ferguson Charitable Settlement

CC NO 275487 **ESTABLISHED** 1977
WHERE FUNDING CAN BE GIVEN UK and overseas.
WHO CAN BENEFIT UK-registered charities; universities and individuals.
WHAT IS FUNDED Education; international friendship and understanding; world peace and development. Gap year students can also be supported.
WHAT IS NOT FUNDED Retrospective funding.
TYPE OF GRANT Project funding.
SAMPLE GRANTS AMREF (£200,000); Royal Shakespeare Company (£100,000); Saferworld (£80,000); UNICEF (£50,000); World Vision UK (£25,000); Right to Play UK (£20,000); Glasgow School of Art and Royal National Lifeboat Association (£15,000 each); Trust for Research and Education on Arms Trade (£8,000).
FINANCES *Financial year end* 31/12/2019 *Income* £4,770,000 *Total grants* £2,380,600 *Grants to organisations* £2,310,000 *Assets* £33,210,000
TRUSTEES Elizabeth Banister; Prof. David Banister; Letitia Glaister; Eleanor Banister; Edmund Cairns.
OTHER INFORMATION The charity's website explains that grants to organisations are given on a matched funding basis 'so that if the applicant has raised 50% of their budget the Trustees will consider awarding matching funding up to a maximum of 50%. If the applicant has raised less than 50% of their budget the Trustees will only consider awarding a maximum of 30% funding.' Furthermore, 'evidence of actively

seeking funds from other sources is seen by the Trustees as being a beneficial addition to any application.'

HOW TO APPLY Applications are only accepted if they are submitted online using the correct form. Applications sent by post, email or fax will not be considered. Detailed guidance is available on the website, from where the following statement is taken: 'Do not contact us for guidance prior to making an application. All the information you require is contained here.' Applications are accepted at any time and the trustees review requests for up to £50,000 on a monthly basis. Funding requests for amounts exceeding £50,000 are considered at bi-annual trustees' meetings, which usually take place in March and September.

CONTACT DETAILS Letitia Glaister, Trustee, c/o Tees Law, John Street, Royston, Hertfordshire SG8 9BG *Tel.* 01763 295850 *Email* Letitia.glaister@teeslaw.com *Website* www.fergusontrust.co.uk

The Fermanagh Trust

CCNI NO NIC102726 **ESTABLISHED** 1995

WHERE FUNDING CAN BE GIVEN County Fermanagh.

WHO CAN BENEFIT Voluntary organisations.

WHAT IS FUNDED General charitable purposes; community development.

WHAT IS NOT FUNDED See the grant-maker's website for a full list of exclusions.

TYPE OF GRANT Dependent upon funding stream.

RANGE OF GRANTS Grants up to £3,000.

SAMPLE GRANTS A list of beneficiaries was not included in the annual report and accounts.

FINANCES *Financial year end* 05/04/2020 *Income* £668,400 *Total grants* £284,000 *Grants to organisations* £284,000 *Assets* £3,540,000

TRUSTEES David Bolton; Joanna McVey; Jim Ledwith; Aideen McGinley; Kevin Lunney; Ernie Fisher; Sue Bryson; Frank McManus; Anna Devlin.

HOW TO APPLY Each fund has its own application procedure and guidelines. Check the trust's website for details.

CONTACT DETAILS Lauri McCusker, Director, Fermanagh House, Broadmeadow Place, Enniskillen, County Fermanagh BT74 7HR *Tel.* 028 6632 0210 *Email* info@fermanaghtrust.org *Website* www.fermanaghtrust.org

The Fidelio Charitable Trust

CC NO 1112508 **ESTABLISHED** 2005

WHERE FUNDING CAN BE GIVEN UK.

WHO CAN BENEFIT Registered charities; arts organisations; individuals.

WHAT IS FUNDED The arts, particularly music, including opera, lieder, composition and dance. Grants are made to enable beneficiaries, for example, to receive special tuition or coaching; to participate in external competitions; to be supported for a specially arranged performance; to receive support for a special publication, musical composition or work of art.

WHAT IS NOT FUNDED Applications from individuals or groups seeking support for themselves or their children will not be considered. Applications are not generally considered for activities for people under the age of 21, or for course fees, capital items or retrospective expenditure.

TYPE OF GRANT Project funding.

RANGE OF GRANTS Grants range from £500 up to £5,000.

SAMPLE GRANTS Presteigne Festival of Music and the Arts Ltd (£4,000); Samling Institute and Opera Glass Works (£3,000 each); Britten Sinfonia Ltd (£2,500); Old Vic Theatre Trust (£2,000); Oxford Opera Company (£1,000); Stannary Brass Band (£500).

FINANCES *Financial year end* 31/03/2020 *Income* £7,600 *Total grants* £60,000 *Grants to organisations* £60,000 *Assets* £1,120,000

TRUSTEES Jennifer Wingate; Robert Boas; Elizabeth Rantzen; Barbara Arnold; Dr Patricia Morison.

HOW TO APPLY Application forms are available to download from the website, where guidelines can also be found. These should be completed and returned to the correspondent by email. Individuals and groups must be recommended by an appropriate institution, college, arts festival or similar organisation. The trustees usually meet three times a year and provisional closing dates for applications are detailed on the website. The trustees aim to inform successful applicants within one month of the relevant closing date.

CONTACT DETAILS The Trustees, c/o Brian Cook Associates, Marine House, 151 Western Road, Haywards Heath, West Sussex RH16 3LH *Tel.* 020 8292 9975 *Email* admin@fideliocharitabletrust.org.uk *Website* www.fideliocharitabletrust.org.uk

The Fidelity UK Foundation

CC NO 327899 **ESTABLISHED** 1988

WHERE FUNDING CAN BE GIVEN UK, with a preference for London, Kent and Surrey.

WHO CAN BENEFIT Registered charities. The website states that grants are 'generally made only to organisations with an annual operating budget in excess of £250,000 (or local currency equivalent)'.

WHAT IS FUNDED Education; health and medicine; disability; palliative care; social welfare; arts, culture and heritage; community development; the environment.

WHAT IS NOT FUNDED Individuals; start-up organisations; political or sectarian organisations; organisations which have been running for less than three years; private schools; sponsorships; scholarships; corporate membership; advertising and promotional projects; exhibitions; general running costs; the replacement of dated IT hardware, routine system upgrades or ongoing website content.

TYPE OF GRANT Strategic funding; capital costs; development funding; funding for technology projects.

RANGE OF GRANTS Usually between £25,000 and £150,000.

SAMPLE GRANTS Tommy's (£500,000); Marine Conservation Society (£290,000); The Outward Bound Trust (£250,000); Safelives (£170,000); The Royal Parks of London (£150,000); Black Country Living Museum (£75,000); Tavistock Relationships (£53,500); New Horizon Youth Centre (£10,000); English Heritage (£5,000).

FINANCES *Financial year end* 31/12/2019 *Income* £2,020,000 *Total grants* £11,020,000 *Grants to organisations* £11,020,000 *Assets* £272,460,000

TRUSTEES Anthony Bolton; John Owen; Sally Walden; Abigail Johnson; Elizabeth Johnson; Dr Malcolm Rogers; Sanjeev Gandhi; Peter Goldsborough; Edward Johnson.

OTHER INFORMATION During the year, the foundation awarded 62 grants totalling £11.02 million distributed as follows: health (14 grants totalling £3.6 million); education (14 grants totalling £2.7 million); arts, culture and heritage (16 grants totalling £2.3 million); community development (14 grants totalling £1.7 million); the environment (one grant totalling £290,400); cross-sector (one grant totalling £132,900); scholarships (two grants totalling £25,000).

HOW TO APPLY Applicants should submit an initial enquiry via the foundation's website. The review process takes six to eight weeks. If you are invited to make a full application the foundation staff will request further information and possibly a site visit. Initial enquiries can be submitted at any time. At the time of writing (April 2021) the foundation was not accepting new enquiries due to the COVID-19 pandemic but it was pro-actively identifying organisations to support. Check the foundation's website for updates.

CONTACT DETAILS Head of Foundations, Beech Gate, Millfield Lane, Lower Kingswood, Tadworth, Surrey KT20 6RP *Tel.* 01732 777364 *Email* foundation@fil.com *Website* www.fidelityukfoundation.org

■ Doris Field Charitable Trust

CC NO 328687 **ESTABLISHED** 1990

WHERE FUNDING CAN BE GIVEN UK, with a particular interest in Oxfordshire.

WHO CAN BENEFIT Charitable organisations.

WHAT IS FUNDED General charitable purposes.

RANGE OF GRANTS Mostly from £500 to £1,000.

SAMPLE GRANTS Cancer Research UK (£10,000); Oxfordshire Historic Churches Trust (£5,000); Age UK Oxfordshire (£2,500); English National Ballet and Rennie Grove Hospice Care (£1,000 each); Abingdon Concert Band and St Aloysius School PTA (£500); The Comfort Trust (£450).

FINANCES *Financial year end* 15/08/2019 *Income* £462,700 *Total grants* £255,500 *Grants to organisations* £255,500 *Assets* £11,700,000

TRUSTEES John Cole; Mr N. Harper; Wilhelmina Church; Helen Fanyinka.

OTHER INFORMATION A total of 254 grants were made to organisations. The 2018/19 accounts were the latest available at the time of writing (January 2021).

HOW TO APPLY Potential applicants can obtain an application form from the correspondent and submit with the required information. The trustees meet three times a year to consider applications but can respond to urgent appeals if necessary.

CONTACT DETAILS Emily Greig, c/o Blake Morgan LLP, Seacourt Tower, West Way, Oxford, Oxfordshire OX2 0FB *Tel.* 01865 254286 *Email* emily.greig@blakemorgan.co.uk

■ The Fieldrose Charitable Trust

CC NO 1156644 **ESTABLISHED** 2014

WHERE FUNDING CAN BE GIVEN England and Wales.

WHO CAN BENEFIT Charitable organisations.

WHAT IS FUNDED General charitable purposes including health and medical research.

SAMPLE GRANTS The Duke of Edinburgh's International Awards Foundation (£34,000); Prostate Cancer UK (£20,000); Cure Parkinson's Trust and The Woodland Trust (£10,000 each); Marie Curie (£5,000); Prostate Cancer UK (£1,000).

FINANCES *Financial year end* 05/04/2020 *Income* £6,410,000 *Total grants* £275,000 *Grants to organisations* £275,000 *Assets* £5,430,000

TRUSTEES Angela Scott; Paul Stibbard; Louise Stoten; Genevieve Kershaw.

OTHER INFORMATION Grants were made to 26 organisations during the year.

HOW TO APPLY Contact the correspondent for further information.

CONTACT DETAILS The Trustees, c/o New Quadrant Partners Ltd, 22 Chancery Lane, London WC2A 1LS *Tel.* 020 7430 7150 *Email* charities@nqpltd.com

■ The Fifty Fund

CC NO 214422 **ESTABLISHED** 1939

WHERE FUNDING CAN BE GIVEN Nottinghamshire.

WHO CAN BENEFIT Registered charities; individuals.

WHAT IS FUNDED Social welfare.

RANGE OF GRANTS Mostly between £1,000 and £3,000.

SAMPLE GRANTS Nottinghamshire Hospice (£22,000); Salvation Army (£7,000); The Shelter (£4,500); Read For Good (£3,000); Nottinghamshire Clubs for Young People (£2,750); Barnardo's, Carers UK and Headway Nottingham (£2,000 each); Deafblind UK (£1,000); Rainy Day Trust and Windmill Community Gardens (£500 each).

FINANCES *Financial year end* 31/12/2019 *Income* £345,900 *Total grants* £199,500 *Grants to organisations* £183,400 *Assets* £9,160,000

TRUSTEES Revd Amanda Cartwright; Richard Bonnello; Mark Jenkinson; Dr David Hannah.

OTHER INFORMATION Grants were made to 54 individuals and 88 charities during the year. During the year, 72 applications from individuals and charities were declined.

HOW TO APPLY Contact the correspondent for more information regarding the application process. The trustees meet quarterly to consider grant applications.

CONTACT DETAILS Craig Staten-Spencer, c/o Nelsons Solicitors, Pennine House, 8 Stanford Street, Nottingham, Nottinghamshire NG1 7BQ *Tel.* 0115 989 5251 *Email* craig.staten-spencer@nelsonslaw.co.uk

■ The Finborough Foundation

CC NO 1125130 **ESTABLISHED** 2007

WHERE FUNDING CAN BE GIVEN UK.

WHO CAN BENEFIT Registered charities.

WHAT IS FUNDED Education and training in the arts, science and medicine; the environment; homelessness.

RANGE OF GRANTS Up to £50,000.

SAMPLE GRANTS A list of beneficiaries was not included in the annual report and accounts.

FINANCES *Financial year end* 31/12/2019 *Income* £278,200 *Total grants* £136,000 *Grants to organisations* £136,000 *Assets* £8,630,000

TRUSTEES Charles Pettiward; Philip Hamilton; Josephine Pettiward.

OTHER INFORMATION Grants were awarded to 18 registered charities during the year, including one major grant to Treloar Trust, which receives annual funding.

HOW TO APPLY Contact the correspondent for more information.

CONTACT DETAILS Philip Hamilton, Trustee, 34 Ely Place, London EC1N 6TD *Tel.* 020 7353 1313 *Email* philip.hamilton@bowercotton.co.uk

■ Dixie Rose Findlay Charitable Trust

CC NO 251661 **ESTABLISHED** 1967

WHERE FUNDING CAN BE GIVEN UK.

WHO CAN BENEFIT Charitable organisations.

WHAT IS FUNDED General charitable purposes with a focus on children, illness, disability.

RANGE OF GRANTS Mostly £2,000 to £3,000

SAMPLE GRANTS Arthur Rank Hospice, Family Fund, Medina Valley Centre, Newcastle Vision Support, Studham Village Hall and Zoë's Place Baby Hospice (£2,400 each); A Child of Mine (£2,000).

FINANCES *Financial year end* 05/04/2019 *Income* £141,300 *Total grants* £117,600 *Grants to organisations* £117,600 *Assets* £5,370,000

TRUSTEE HSBC Trust Company (UK) Ltd.

OTHER INFORMATION Grants were made to 50 organisations during the year. The 2018/19 accounts were the latest available at the time of writing (January 2021).

HOW TO APPLY Contact the correspondent for further information.

CONTACT DETAILS The Trustees, HSBC Trust Company UK Ltd, Second Floor, 1 The Forum, Parkway, Whiteley, Fareham, Hampshire PO15 7PA *Tel.* 023 8072 2243

■ Fine & Country Foundation

CC NO 1160989 **ESTABLISHED** 2014

WHERE FUNDING CAN BE GIVEN UK and overseas.

WHO CAN BENEFIT Homeless charities; poverty prevention schemes; housing associations.

WHAT IS FUNDED Prevention of homelessness; care of people experiencing homelessness; long-term housing projects.

TYPE OF GRANT Project funding; core costs; capital costs.

RANGE OF GRANTS Up to £3,000.

SAMPLE GRANTS A list of beneficiaries was not included in the annual report and accounts.

FINANCES *Financial year end* 31/12/2019 *Income* £111,000 *Total grants* £58,700 *Grants to organisations* £58,700 *Assets* £74,500

TRUSTEES Malcolm Lindley; Sean Newman; Matthew Pike; David Lindley.

OTHER INFORMATION The foundation is more likely to make grants to organisations that have a Fine & Country office in their region.

HOW TO APPLY Potential applicants should first request a nomination from their nearest Fine & Country office and then complete an application form available from the website. Applications are accepted in March and October each year.

CONTACT DETAILS The Trustees, Fine & Country Foundation, 121 Park Lane, Mayfair, London W1K 7AG *Tel.* 020 3368 8221 *Email* grants@fineandcountry.com *Website* https://www.fineandcountryfoundation.com

■ The Finnis Scott Foundation

CC NO 1121475 **ESTABLISHED** 2006

WHERE FUNDING CAN BE GIVEN UK.

WHO CAN BENEFIT Registered charities; CICs; CIOs; PTAs; gardens; hospices. Preference is given to smaller charities. Grants are made to individuals by means of bursaries, traineeships or apprenticeships, but only through a sponsoring educational establishment or registered charity.

WHAT IS FUNDED Horticulture; fine art; art history; scientific plant projects; training of gardeners; restoration of gardens; permanent art projects, including the development of galleries, the conservation and framing of pictures, the purchase of works and the production of exhibition catalogues.

WHAT IS NOT FUNDED Retrospective expenditure; newly established organisations which do not yet have a track record or accounts; individual salaries; site-specific art installations; conceptual or performance art.

TYPE OF GRANT Capital and revenue costs.

RANGE OF GRANTS Up to £10,000 (larger grants may be considered in exceptional circumstances).

SAMPLE GRANTS The Courtauld Institute of Art (£50,000); Gainsborough's House (£30,000); Professional Gardeners Trust (£15,000); Fortescue Gardens and Penllergare Trust (£10,000 each); Greenfingers (£5,000); Queen Alexandra College (£3,000); Dudley Mind and Wildgoose Rural Training (£2,000 each); ActivLives (£1,000); Bankside Open Space (£500).

FINANCES *Financial year end* 31/12/2019 *Income* £360,800 *Total grants* £353,100 *Grants to organisations* £353,100 *Assets* £10,770,000

TRUSTEES Lady Kathryn Robinson; James Miller; David Laing; The Hon. Ursula Wide; Dr William Elliot; Ian Barnett; Dr Patricia Morison; Lord Charles Scott.

OTHER INFORMATION Grants were awarded to 72 organisations during the year out of 129 applications considered. The foundation has newly introduced The Botanical Art Award - a £10,000 award dedicated to British and Irish botanical art groups and organisations, in recognition of previous achievements and for the promotion of innovative ideas and projects.

HOW TO APPLY Applicants can download an application form from the foundation's helpful website and this should be sent to the Grant Administrator (by either email or post) with accompanying documents. The trustees meet quarterly to discuss grant applications. Applications need to reach the administrator four weeks before a meeting. The latest time applications will be accepted is 4pm on the cut-off date. Further information on applications and deadlines is available on the website. The deadline for applications to The Botanical Art Award is 31 January 2022. Applicants are asked to contact the secretary at botanicalartaward@finnis-scott-foundation.org.uk before making an application.

CONTACT DETAILS Angela Moon, Grant Administrator, c/o Hewitsons, Elgin House, Billing Road, Northampton, Northamptonshire NN1 5AU *Tel.* 01604 233233 *Email* angelamoon@hewitsons.com *Website* https://www.finnis-scott-foundation.org.uk

■ Sir John Fisher Foundation

CC NO 277844 **ESTABLISHED** 1979

WHERE FUNDING CAN BE GIVEN UK, with a strong preference for charities in the Furness peninsula and Cumbria.

WHO CAN BENEFIT Registered charities; CICs; community groups; museums; hospices; uniformed groups.

WHAT IS FUNDED General charitable purposes with a preference for maritime causes, medicine, people with disabilities, education, music, the arts, community projects.
WHAT IS NOT FUNDED Individuals; sponsorship; expeditions; the promotion of religion; places of worship; animal welfare; retrospective expenditure; pressure groups.
TYPE OF GRANT Capital and revenue funding. Occasionally research projects are supported.
RANGE OF GRANTS Grants are mostly under £20,000.
SAMPLE GRANTS The Lady Maria Fisher Foundation (£1.2 million); University of Cumbria (£240,600); The Neurological Research Trust (£110,000); Cumbria Community Foundation (£50,000); Hospice of St Mary's (£40,000); The Birchall Trust (£20,000); Word Market (£300).
FINANCES *Financial year end* 31/03/2020 *Income* £2,560,000 *Total grants* £3,480,000 *Grants to organisations* £3,480,000 *Assets* £99,610,000
TRUSTEES Diane Meacock; Daniel Tindall; Dr David Hart Jackson; Christopher Stafford Batten; Chris Tomlinson; Michael Shields; Thomas Meacock.
HOW TO APPLY Application forms are available from the correspondent or can be downloaded from the website, where guidelines can also be found. Applications should be made by submitting a completed application form, together with all relevant information (set out on the application form) to the Secretary by email or post. The trustees meet at the beginning of May and the beginning of November each year. The closing dates for applications are posted on the foundation's website.
CONTACT DETAILS David Dawson, Executive Officer, c/o Hart Jackson and Sons, 8–10 New Market Street, Ulverston, Cumbria LA12 7LW *Tel.* 07464 504756 *Email* executive@sirjohnfisherfoundation.org.uk *Website* www.sirjohnfisherfoundation.org.uk

■ Fishmongers' Company's Charitable Trust

CC NO 263690 **ESTABLISHED** 1972
WHERE FUNDING CAN BE GIVEN City of London and the Boroughs of Camden, Hackney, Islington, Lambeth, Southwark, Tower Hamlets, Newham and Westminster.
WHO CAN BENEFIT Registered charities; social enterprises; CICs.
WHAT IS FUNDED Education in prisons; mental health; food and nutrition.
TYPE OF GRANT There is a preference for project funding.
RANGE OF GRANTS £20,000 and £50,000 a year, for up to three years.
SAMPLE GRANTS The Gresham's Foundation (£196,000); Chefs in Schools (£50,000); Key4Life (£40,000); Beyond Food Foundation and The Listening Place (£15,000 each); Synchronicity Earth (£10,000); Manna Society (£3,000).
FINANCES *Financial year end* 31/12/2019 *Income* £1,390,000 *Total grants* £1,067,000 *Grants to organisations* £1,027,000 *Assets* £36,930,000
TRUSTEES The Worshipful Company of Fishmongers; Commodore Toby Williamson.
OTHER INFORMATION Grants were broken down as follows: education (£834,000); hardship grants (£59,000); health and well-being (£53,000); fisheries (£40,000); civic grants (£41,000).
HOW TO APPLY Potential applicants are requested to send a short description of their project and how much they would be looking to apply for, using the enquiry form on the charity's website.
CONTACT DETAILS The Grants Officer, The Fishmongers' Company, Fishmongers' Hall, London Bridge, London EC4R 9EL *Email* grants@fishmongers.org.uk *Website* https://fishmongers.org.uk/grants

■ Marc Fitch Fund

CC NO 313303 **ESTABLISHED** 1956
WHERE FUNDING CAN BE GIVEN UK and Ireland.
WHO CAN BENEFIT Organisations and individuals.
WHAT IS FUNDED The fund supports the publication of academic work on British and Irish history. Several disciplines are supported, see the website for more details.
WHAT IS NOT FUNDED Works principally concerned with the recent past (post-1945); new or revised editions of work already published; scientific or technical research; fieldwork; the costs of getting to the UK/Ireland from overseas; foreign travel or research outside the UK/Ireland (apart from in very exceptional circumstances); applications associated with vocational or educational courses (including postgraduate or doctoral research); building works, mounting or attending conferences; mounting exhibitions; general appeals.
TYPE OF GRANT Mainly publication costs and incidental research expenses. Also, special project grants and support for journal digitisation.
SAMPLE GRANTS A list of beneficiaries was not included in the annual report and accounts.
FINANCES *Financial year end* 05/04/2020 *Income* £259,500 *Total grants* £258,700 *Grants to organisations* £218,100 *Assets* £6,080,000
TRUSTEES Lindsay Allason-Jones; Prof. John Blair; Dr Helen Forde; Michael Hall; Andrew Murison; Bernard Nurse; Prof. David Palliser; Prof. Christiana Payne; David White; Roey Sweet.
OTHER INFORMATION In 2019/20 there were 28 grants awarded to organisations and individuals. Grants to individuals totalled £40,600.
HOW TO APPLY In the first instance see the website, where full guidelines are available. Prospective applicants should send a brief outline of their project to the charity by email. Applicants whose proposals fall within the criteria will be sent an application form. The Council of Management meets to consider applications in spring and autumn, and completed applications and references should be received by the charity by 1 March and 1 August, respectively. Note that the charity is described on its website as a 'last resort' for 'worthwhile projects that are at risk of failing without a grant'. For this reason, applicants are required to provide details of other funding sources from which they have tried to secure support.
CONTACT DETAILS Christopher Catling, Director, Flat 9, 13 Tavistock Place, London WC1H 9SH *Tel.* 020 7387 6580 *Email* mail2019@marcfitchfund.org.uk *Website* www.marcfitchfund.org.uk

■ The Earl Fitzwilliam Charitable Trust

CC NO 269388 **ESTABLISHED** 1975

WHERE FUNDING CAN BE GIVEN UK, with a preference for areas with historical family connections, chiefly in Cambridgeshire, Yorkshire and Denbighshire.

WHO CAN BENEFIT Charitable organisations linked to the Fitzwilliam Estates in Cambridgeshire and Yorkshire and the Naylor-Leyland Estate in Nantclywd. However, small and medium-sized charities that fall outside this criteria can also be supported.

WHAT IS FUNDED General charitable purposes.

RANGE OF GRANTS Generally between £100 and £10,000.

SAMPLE GRANTS Malton Amenity CIC (£65,000); Kirkham Henry Performing (£7,500); Bluebell Wood Children's Hospice and City and Guilds of London Art School (£2,000 each); Action for Elders and Music in Hospitals and Care (£1,000 each); Style for Soldiers (£500); Epilepsy Society (£220); Friends of Peterborough Cathedral (£50).

FINANCES *Financial year end* 31/03/2020 *Income* £233,200 *Total grants* £167,700 *Grants to organisations* £167,700 *Assets* £15,440,000

TRUSTEES Sir Philip Naylor-Leyland; Lady Isabella Naylor Leyland.

OTHER INFORMATION Grants were awarded to 79 organisations during 2019/20.

HOW TO APPLY Apply in writing to the correspondent. Applications are considered at meetings throughout the year.

CONTACT DETAILS R. W. Dalgliesh, Secretary, Estate Office, Milton Park, Peterborough, Cambridgeshire PE3 9HD *Tel.* 01733 267740 *Email* agent@miltonestate.co.uk

■ The Robert Fleming Hannay Memorial Charity

CC NO 1086811 **ESTABLISHED** 2000

WHERE FUNDING CAN BE GIVEN Scotland.

WHO CAN BENEFIT Charitable organisations.

WHAT IS FUNDED General charitable purposes, including: social welfare; education; religion; health; arts, culture heritage and science; human rights; disability; young people; older people.

RANGE OF GRANTS Mainly under £25,000.

SAMPLE GRANTS The Prince's Foundation (£75,000); Charterhouse Summer School of Music and Hullavington PCC (£25,000 each); The Royal College of Music (£20,000); Holy Trinity Church Brompton, Macmillan Cancer Support, Klosters Alpine Conceits and The Purcell School (£10,000 each).

FINANCES *Financial year end* 05/04/2020 *Income* £59,500 *Total grants* £219,000 *Grants to organisations* £219,000 *Assets* £1,960,000

TRUSTEES Christian Ward; Geoffrey Richards; Fiona Hannay.

OTHER INFORMATION Only organisations receiving grants of over £10,000 were listed as beneficiaries in the charity's accounts. Grants of under £10,000 totalled £34,000 and were awarded to eight organisations.

HOW TO APPLY The charity's 2019/20 annual report states that 'due to constraints on income, unsolicited applications can no longer be considered. Although some donations may be made to the same charities each year none shall be either promised or guaranteed.'

CONTACT DETAILS The Trustees, c/o RF Trustee Co. Ltd, 15 Suffolk Street, London SW1Y 4HG *Tel.* 020 3696 6721 *Email* charities@rftrustee.com

■ The Joyce Fletcher Charitable Trust

CC NO 297901 **ESTABLISHED** 1987

WHERE FUNDING CAN BE GIVEN UK with a strong preference for South West England.

WHO CAN BENEFIT Registered charities.

WHAT IS FUNDED Music and arts education; music in a social and therapeutic context; children and young people.

WHAT IS NOT FUNDED Individuals and students; statutory organisations; professional arts or music organisations; medical research charities.

TYPE OF GRANT Capital costs; core/revenue costs.

RANGE OF GRANTS Up to £6,000 but usually between £1,000 and £2,000.

SAMPLE GRANTS Welsh National Opera (£6,000); Wiltshire Music Centre (£4,000); Hope and Homes for Children (£2,000); Zenith Youth Theatre Co. (£1,000).

FINANCES *Financial year end* 05/04/2020 *Income* £78,000 *Total grants* £70,500 *Grants to organisations* £68,500 *Assets* £2,570,000

TRUSTEES Robert Fletcher; Stephen Fletcher; Susan Sharp; William Fletcher.

OTHER INFORMATION Grants were broken down as follows: music in a social and therapeutic context (£27,500); music and arts education (£22,000); other (£17,000); children and young people (£4,000). Grants were made to 27 organisations in the South West and to six national charities.

HOW TO APPLY Apply in writing to the correspondent before 1 November each year. New applicants are advised to write in September. Applications are considered between September and November each year, with grants made in early December. Telephone enquiries are accepted. The website notes that 'applications should include purpose for grant, indication of history and viability of the organisation, and summary of accounts.' Email addresses and applications that include an sae will receive a response.

CONTACT DETAILS Robert Fletcher, Trustee, 68 Circus Mews, Bath, Somerset BA1 2PW *Tel.* 01225 314355 *Website* www.joycefletchercharitabletrust.co.uk

■ The Follett Trust

CC NO 328638 **ESTABLISHED** 1990

WHERE FUNDING CAN BE GIVEN UK and overseas, with a preference for Stevenage.

WHO CAN BENEFIT Organisations and individuals.

WHAT IS FUNDED General charitable purposes; education; the arts; medical and health-related causes.

RANGE OF GRANTS Mostly up to £5,000, with some larger grants.

SAMPLE GRANTS Impilo (£21,200); Stevenage Community Trust (£15,500); Knebworth PCC (£7,300); Canon Collins Trust (£5,000); Home-Start Hertfordshire (£4,200); Red Kite Rape and Sexual Abuse Centre (£2,000); Headway Hertfordshire and The Prince's Trust (£1,000 each).

FINANCES *Financial year end* 30/06/2020 *Income* £130,000 *Total grants* £101,700 *Grants to organisations* £101,700 *Assets* £113,500

TRUSTEES Ken Follett; Barbara Follett; Rebecca Hart.

OTHER INFORMATION Grants were awarded to 17 organisations during the year. Only beneficiaries of grants of £1,000 and above were listed in the 2019/20 accounts. Grants below £1,000 totalled £13,000.

HOW TO APPLY Apply in writing to the correspondent. The annual report for 2019/20 notes that 'the majority of successful applications come from people and organisations known to the trustees or in which the trustees have a particular interest.' Replies are not sent to unsuccessful applicants unless they have provided an sae.

CONTACT DETAILS Rebecca Hart, Trustee, Kings Court, London Road, Stevenage, Hertfordshire SG1 2NG *Tel.* 01438 810400 *Email* follettrust@thefollettoffice.com

The Fonthill Foundation

CC NO 325071 **ESTABLISHED** 1974

WHERE FUNDING CAN BE GIVEN South East England; overseas.

WHO CAN BENEFIT Charitable organisations.

WHAT IS FUNDED The education of children and young people.

SAMPLE GRANTS A list of beneficiaries was not included in the annual report and accounts.

FINANCES *Financial year end* 31/08/2020 *Income* £163,900 *Total grants* £282,200 *Grants to organisations* £282,200 *Assets* £5,760,000

TRUSTEES Stephen Wilkins; Victoria Henley; Margaret Lloyd; Niki Cannon.

HOW TO APPLY The foundation's website states: 'We would love to hear about your organisation and the work you are doing. We're dynamic in constantly seeking out the best new partnerships, but note we don't take unsolicited applications for our UK or Overseas Programmes.' Application forms for the Small Grants Programme can be downloaded from the foundation's website.

CONTACT DETAILS The Trustees, PO Box 261, Lewes BN7 9LS *Email* enquiry@fonthill-foundation.org.uk *Website* https://fonthill-foundation.org.uk

The Football Association National Sports Centre Trust

CC NO 265132 **ESTABLISHED** 1972

WHERE FUNDING CAN BE GIVEN England.

WHO CAN BENEFIT County football associations; football clubs; sports associations.

WHAT IS FUNDED The provision, maintenance and improvement of facilities for use in recreational and leisure activities.

TYPE OF GRANT Capital costs.

RANGE OF GRANTS Up to £10,000.

SAMPLE GRANTS Golcar United FC; Middlezoy Rovers FC and Roade Football Supporters Club (£10,000 each); Eccleshall FC (£8,000); Bottesford FC and Shirehampton AFC (£5,000 each); Tintwistle Athletic FC (£4,600); Walmer Bridge FC (£3,750).

FINANCES *Financial year end* 31/12/2019 *Income* £153,000 *Total grants* £180,700 *Grants to organisations* £180,700 *Assets* £448,200

TRUSTEES Brian Adshead; Geoff Thompson; Mervyn Leggett.

OTHER INFORMATION The charity offers clubs at Steps 6 and below of the National League System grants of up to £10,000 towards the provision of new floodlights and new or improved changing facilities. A separate scheme is available to clubs at Step 3 and below of the National League System to receive a grant of up to £5,000 towards the cost of materials for ground improvement projects where the club has the relevant trade skills within its membership. Grants were awarded to 24 organisations during the year.

HOW TO APPLY Contact the correspondent for information regarding the application process.

CONTACT DETAILS Richard McDermott, Secretary to the Trustees, Wembley Stadium, PO BOX 1966, London SW1P 9EQ *Tel.* 0800 169 1863 *Email* richard.mcdermott@thefa.com

The Football Foundation

CC NO 1079309 **ESTABLISHED** 1999

WHERE FUNDING CAN BE GIVEN England and Wales.

WHO CAN BENEFIT A wide range of organisations, including: football clubs (grassroots, professional and semi-professional) and their associated community charities; multi-sport clubs; clubs, leagues and county FAs; local authorities; educational establishments; schools; registered charities; not-for-profit companies.

WHAT IS FUNDED According to its website, the foundation's current objectives are: 'to put into place a new generation of modern facilities in parks, schools, colleges and universities; to provide capital/revenue support to increase participation in community football; to strengthen the links between football and the community and to harness its potential as a force for good in society.'

WHAT IS NOT FUNDED Individuals. Each funding stream has its own specific list of exclusions; these can be found on the funder's website.

TYPE OF GRANT Dependent upon funding scheme.

RANGE OF GRANTS Dependent upon funding scheme.

SAMPLE GRANTS Sunderland City Council – Hubs programme (£14.22 million); London Borough Of Southwark Council (£2.4 million); University Of Leeds (£1.14 million); Chorley Council (£647,600); Bootle Football Club (£408,100); Whetstone Juniors FC (£100,000); South Cave Sporting Club (£61,100); Central Swindon North Parish Council (£24,000).

FINANCES *Financial year end* 31/05/2020 *Income* £72,220,000 *Total grants* £55,800,000 *Grants to organisations* £55,800,000 *Assets* £58,730,000

TRUSTEES Martin Glenn; Peter McCormick; John Pearce; Jemima Bird; Tim Hollingsworth; William Bush; Mark Bullingham; Elena Narozanski; Karen Taylor.

OTHER INFORMATION The foundation receives income from The Football Association, the Premier League and the Department of Culture, Media and Sport via Sports England. It then uses this money to deliver a programme of new and improved community sports facilities in towns and cities across the country. During the year, 3,061 grants were made, the vast majority of which (2,700) were awarded as small revenue grants. Only the 50 largest beneficiaries were listed in the foundation's 2019/20 accounts.

HOW TO APPLY See the foundation's helpful website for full details of funding streams which are currently open for applications.

CONTACT DETAILS Grant Management Team, 10 Eastbourne Terrace, London W2 6LG *Tel.* 0345 345 4555 *Email* enquiries@footballfoundation.org.uk *Website* www.footballfoundation.org.uk

■ The Forbes Charitable Foundation

CC NO 326476 **ESTABLISHED** 1983

WHERE FUNDING CAN BE GIVEN UK.

WHO CAN BENEFIT Registered or exempt charities; individuals; social enterprises. The foundation has a particular interest in supporting the development of new and innovative services or projects.

WHAT IS FUNDED Support for learning disabilities, including: residential care; supported living; day services; employment initiatives; skills training; support for informal carers; and transition services for young adults.

TYPE OF GRANT Capital costs; core/revenue costs; development funding; one-off and annual grants for up to three years.

RANGE OF GRANTS Up to £25,000.

SAMPLE GRANTS Avocet Trust, Halas Homes and Linkage Community Trust (£25,000 each); Walsingham Support (£21,000); Style Acre (£9,000); FAIR and The Rossendale Trust (£5,000 each); High Mead Farm (£2,500); Special Needs Enterprises Ltd (£1,400).

FINANCES *Financial year end* 05/04/2020 *Income* £236,300 *Total grants* £259,300 *Grants to organisations* £258,400 *Assets* £7,470,000

TRUSTEES Mark Morris; Ian Johnson; John Waite; Nicholas Townsend; Robert Bunting; Helen Johnson; Patrick Wallace; Nigel Doggett.

OTHER INFORMATION During the year, the foundation awarded 19 grants to organisations and one grant to an individual.

HOW TO APPLY The foundation does not accept unsolicited applications. However, organisations with an annual turnover between £1 million and £20 million should forward background information of their work to the correspondent. Details of the next programme will be announced in 2021 on the website.

CONTACT DETAILS J. Shepherd, Secretary to the Trustees, PO Box 6256, Nuneaton, Warwickshire CV11 9HT *Tel.* 07749 642664 *Email* info@theforbescharitablefoundation.org *Website* www.theforbescharitablefoundation.org

■ Ford Britain Trust

CC NO 269410 **ESTABLISHED** 1975

WHERE FUNDING CAN BE GIVEN Local to the areas in close proximity to Ford Motor Company Ltd's locations in the UK. These include Essex (including East London); Bridgend; Daventry; Liverpool; Manchester; Southampton.

WHO CAN BENEFIT Registered charities; unregistered charities; schools; PTAs; hospices.

WHAT IS FUNDED Community development; education and schools; people with special needs; people with disabilities.

WHAT IS NOT FUNDED Individuals; CICs; local authorities, councils, government and government departments; core/running costs; major building works; sponsorship or advertising; research; overseas projects; travel; religious projects; political projects; purchase of second-hand vehicles; third party fundraising initiatives.

TYPE OF GRANT New capital expenditure projects; refurbishment; IT equipment; contribution to vehicle purchases.

RANGE OF GRANTS Small grants of up to £250; large grants of £250 to £3,000.

SAMPLE GRANTS Coychurch Primary School and Smart Works – Greater Manchester (£3,000 each); Mermaids (£2,500); Ascension Community Trust (£2,100); Happy Kids and Orchard Infant School (£2,000 each).

FINANCES *Financial year end* 31/03/2020 *Income* £66,600 *Total grants* £148,600 *Grants to organisations* £148,600 *Assets* £227,700

TRUSTEES Lara Nicoll; David Russell; Wendy James; Dr June-Alison Sealy; Paul Bailey; Jenny Ball; Jane Skerry.

OTHER INFORMATION This is the corporate charity of Ford Motor Company Ltd. Only organisations receiving grants of over £1,000 were listed as beneficiaries in the charity's accounts. Grants of under £1,000 totalled £44,200.

HOW TO APPLY Application forms are available to download from the website, where guidance notes are also available. The trust's website states: 'The Ford Britain Trust particularly encourages applications supported by Ford employees, but is open to all, provided that the qualifying organisations meet our selection criteria.'

CONTACT DETAILS The Trustees, 15–02B D20-B, Ford Dunton Technical Centre, Laindon, Basildon, Essex SS15 6EE *Email* fbtrust@ford.com *Website* www.ford.co.uk/fbtrust

■ Oliver Ford Foundation

CC NO 1026551 **ESTABLISHED** 1993

WHERE FUNDING CAN BE GIVEN UK.

WHO CAN BENEFIT Registered charities; arts, culture and heritage organisations; students of the Victoria and Albert Museum, Royal Horticultural Society and Furniture History Society.

WHAT IS FUNDED Education, in particular interior design and landscaping; education, housing and training for people with disabilities.

TYPE OF GRANT Project funding; capital costs; salaries.

RANGE OF GRANTS Typically £1,000 to £50,000.

SAMPLE GRANTS Norfolk and Norwich Scope Association (£50,000); Scotts Project Trust (£25,000); Autism Bedfordshire, Exeter Gateway Centre and Stanley Grange Community Association (£10,000 each); Leeds Mencap (£5,200); MacIntyre (£4,100); Oak Tree Farm Rural Project (£460).

FINANCES *Financial year end* 05/04/2020 *Income* £72,400 *Total grants* £168,100 *Grants to organisations* £158,100 *Assets* £2,420,000

TRUSTEES Lady Alison Wakeham; Martin Levy; Matthew Pintus.

OTHER INFORMATION In 2019/20 the foundation made grants to 13 organisations.

HOW TO APPLY Contact the correspondent for further information.

CONTACT DETAILS The Trustees, c/o MacFarlanes LLP, 20 Cursitor Street, London EC4A 1LT *Tel.* 020 7831 9222

■ Fordeve Ltd

CC NO 1011612 **ESTABLISHED** 1992

WHERE FUNDING CAN BE GIVEN UK.

WHO CAN BENEFIT Orthodox Jewish organisations.

WHAT IS FUNDED The advancement of religion in accordance with the Orthodox Jewish faith; general charitable purposes.

SAMPLE GRANTS A list of beneficiaries was not included in the annual report and accounts.

FINANCES *Financial year end* 31/03/2020 *Income* £112,800 *Total grants* £91,700 *Grants to organisations* £91,700 *Assets* £599,000

TRUSTEES Helen Kon; Jeremy Kon.

OTHER INFORMATION A list of beneficiaries was not included in the annual report and accounts.

HOW TO APPLY Contact the correspondent for further information.

CONTACT DETAILS Helen Kon, Trustee, Hallswelle House, 1 Hallswelle Road, London NW11 0DH *Tel.* 020 8209 1535

■ Forest Hill Charitable Trust

CC NO 1050862 **ESTABLISHED** 1995

WHERE FUNDING CAN BE GIVEN UK and overseas.

WHO CAN BENEFIT Charitable organisations.

WHAT IS FUNDED People with disabilities; social welfare; emergency aid; children and young people; addiction; carers; victims of torture; health and medical services; medical research; trafficking and slavery; farming and fishing communities in the South West.

TYPE OF GRANT Core costs.

RANGE OF GRANTS Mostly between £500 and £2,500.

SAMPLE GRANTS LiNX (£20,000); Interserve and Tiny Tim (£2,000 each); Crosslinks (£1,500); Time for Families and Their Voice (£1,000 each); Care for Veterans (£500).

FINANCES *Financial year end* 05/04/2020 *Income* £156,100 *Total grants* £171,000 *Grants to organisations* £171,000 *Assets* £3,300,000

TRUSTEES Dr Horace Pile; Ronald Stanley Pile; Marianne Tapper; Michael Thomas; Patricia Pile.

OTHER INFORMATION The trust supports around 130 charities on a monthly basis.

HOW TO APPLY The 2019/20 annual report states: 'The trust has been unable to accept new requests for some time and the situation is unlikely to change for the foreseeable future.'

CONTACT DETAILS Patricia Pile, Secretary, Little Bluff, Treknow, Tintagel, Cornwall PL34 0EP *Tel.* 01840 779405 *Email* horacepilefhct@yahoo.co.uk

■ The Lady Forester Trust

CC NO 241187 **ESTABLISHED** 1979

WHERE FUNDING CAN BE GIVEN Shropshire.

WHO CAN BENEFIT Registered charities; individuals.

WHAT IS FUNDED Health and disability.

RANGE OF GRANTS Usually between £1,000 and £5,000.

SAMPLE GRANTS A recent list of beneficiaries was unavailable.

FINANCES *Financial year end* 31/12/2019 *Income* £214,000 *Total grants* £127,100 *Grants to organisations* £68,100 *Assets* £6,440,000

TRUSTEES Lady Catherine Forester; The Hon. Alice Stoker; Libby Collinson; Henry Carpenter; Lord Forester; The Lady Forester; Janette Stewart; Charles Whitaker.

OTHER INFORMATION In 2019 almost £59,000 was awarded to individuals.

HOW TO APPLY Apply in writing to the correspondent. The trustees meet on a quarterly basis to consider applications.

CONTACT DETAILS The Trustees, The Lady Forester Trust, The Estate Office, Willey, Broseley, Shropshire TF12 5JN *Tel.* 01952 884318 *Email* lft@willeyestates.co.uk

■ Forever Manchester

CC NO 1017504 **ESTABLISHED** 1993

WHERE FUNDING CAN BE GIVEN Greater Manchester.

WHO CAN BENEFIT Registered charities; unregistered charities; CICs; social enterprises; schools; PTAs.

WHAT IS FUNDED General charitable purposes including: older people; children and young people; stronger communities; the environment; health and well-being.

TYPE OF GRANT Core/revenue costs; project funding.

SAMPLE GRANTS A list of beneficiaries was not included in the annual report and accounts.

FINANCES *Financial year end* 31/03/2020 *Income* £2,630,000 *Total grants* £1,330,000 *Grants to organisations* £1,330,000 *Assets* £7,800,000

TRUSTEES Philip Hogben; Sandra Lindsay; Jonathan Woodall; Alan Mackin; Michael Warner; Samantha Booth; Claire Ebrey.

OTHER INFORMATION This is one of the 46 UK community foundations, which distribute funding for a wide range of purposes. As with all community foundations, there are a number of donor-advised funds managed on behalf of individuals, families and charitable trusts. Grant schemes tend to change frequently – consult the foundation's website for details of current programmes and up-to-date deadlines. Grants to individuals totalled £50,900.

HOW TO APPLY Potential applicants are advised to visit the charity's website or contact its grants team to find the most suitable funding stream.

CONTACT DETAILS Communities Team, Forever Manchester, 2nd Floor, 8 Hewitt Street, Manchester M15 4GB *Tel.* 0161 214 0940 *Email* awards@forevermanchester.com *Website* www.forevermanchester.com

■ The Forman Hardy Charitable Trust

CC NO 1000687 **ESTABLISHED** 1990

WHERE FUNDING CAN BE GIVEN Nottinghamshire.

WHO CAN BENEFIT Registered charities; community groups.

WHAT IS FUNDED General charitable purposes.

RANGE OF GRANTS Mostly up to £3,000.

SAMPLE GRANTS Previous beneficiaries have included: Multiple Sclerosis Society (£50,000); The University of Nottingham and The University of Sheffield (£25,000 each); Emmanuel House (£20,000); Nottingham City Parish – St Mary's Church (£10,000); Neville Holt Opera (£3,000); Aysgarth School (£2,000); Asthma UK, Scottish Game and Wildlife Conservation Trust, Southwell Cathedral Chapter and War Memorials Trust (£1,000 each).

FINANCES *Financial year end* 05/04/2020 *Income* £24,200 *Total grants* £100,600 *Grants to organisations* £100,600

TRUSTEES Nicholas Forman Hardy; Jane Forman Hardy; Dr Paul Sibley.

OTHER INFORMATION Full accounts were not available to view on the Charity Commission's website due to the trust's low income. We have therefore estimated the grant total based on the trust's total expenditure.
HOW TO APPLY Contact the correspondent for further information.
CONTACT DETAILS The Trustees, 64 St James's Street, Nottingham, Nottinghamshire NG1 6FJ *Tel.* 0115 950 8580 *Email* FHCTRequests@formanhardy.com

■ Donald Forrester Trust

CC NO 295833 **ESTABLISHED** 1986
WHERE FUNDING CAN BE GIVEN UK and overseas.
WHO CAN BENEFIT Registered charities.
WHAT IS FUNDED General charitable purposes including: animals and birds; people with disabilities; children and youth; community care and social welfare; hospices and hospitals; medical relief and welfare; medical research; older people; service and ex-service personnel; overseas aid; blind and deaf; education.
TYPE OF GRANT Capital costs; core/revenue costs; project funding; unrestricted funding.
RANGE OF GRANTS Generally up to £5,000.
SAMPLE GRANTS ClearVision Project and Children's Air Ambulance (£5,000 each); RNLI (£4,000); Country Days (£3,000); Little Hearts Matter (£2,500); Attic Theatre Company (£1,000).
FINANCES *Financial year end* 31/03/2020 *Income* £457,400 *Total grants* £300,600 *Grants to organisations* £300,600 *Assets* £6,610,000
TRUSTEES Wendy Forrester; Hilary Porter; Melissa Jones; Naomi Jones; Thomas Walker.
OTHER INFORMATION The trust is administered by and shares its trustees with the Gwyneth Forrester Trust (Charity Commission no. 1080921). Grants were made to 68 charities during the year. Grants were broken down as follows: community care and social welfare (£104,500); medical relief and welfare (£36,500); overseas (£34,100); blind and deaf (£27,000); children and youth (£25,000); hospice and hospitals (£24,000); older people (£21,000); disability (£15,500); education (£13,000).
HOW TO APPLY Applications can be made in writing by post or email. Full details of the application process can be found on the trust's website.
CONTACT DETAILS Adrian Hollands, Hon. Secretary, 11 Whitecroft Way, Beckenham, Kent BR3 3AQ *Tel.* 020 8629 0089 *Email* ah@forrestertrusts.com *Website* forrestertrusts.com/donald-forrester-trust

■ Gwyneth Forrester Trust

CC NO 1080921 **ESTABLISHED** 2000
WHERE FUNDING CAN BE GIVEN UK.
WHO CAN BENEFIT Registered charities.
WHAT IS FUNDED Refer to the trust's website for its current funding theme. Previous themes have been: homelessness (2019/20); children in crisis (2018/19); support for the elderly (2017/18); helping youths and ex-offenders into employment (2016/17); hospices (2015/16); mental health (2014/15).
TYPE OF GRANT Capital costs; core/revenue costs; general funding; project funding; unrestricted funding.
RANGE OF GRANTS Up to £25,000.
SAMPLE GRANTS The Big Issue Foundation (£30,500); St Martin-in-the-Fields Trust (£30,000); Alive and Kicking and Street Child (£10,000 each); House of Bread (£5,200); Children of Watamun (£500).
FINANCES *Financial year end* 31/03/2020 *Income* £847,900 *Total grants* £984,700 *Grants to organisations* £984,700 *Assets* £24,030,000
TRUSTEES Naomi Jones; Thomas Walker; Hilary Porter; Melissa Jones; Wendy Forrester.
OTHER INFORMATION The trust is administered by and shares its trustees with the Donald Forrester Trust (Charity Commission no. 295833).
HOW TO APPLY Application forms are available to download from the trust's website.
CONTACT DETAILS Adrian Hollands, Hon. secretary, 11 Whitecroft Way, Beckenham, Kent BR3 3AQ *Email* ah@forrestertrusts.com *Website* forrestertrusts.com/gwyneth-forrester-trust

■ The Anna Rosa Forster Charitable Trust

CC NO 1090028 **ESTABLISHED** 1997
WHERE FUNDING CAN BE GIVEN UK and overseas.
WHO CAN BENEFIT Registered charities.
WHAT IS FUNDED Medical research; animal welfare; famine relief.
RANGE OF GRANTS Grants usually between £2,500 and £3,500.
SAMPLE GRANTS A list of beneficiaries was not included in the annual report and accounts.
FINANCES *Financial year end* 05/04/2020 *Income* £87,100 *Total grants* £74,000 *Grants to organisations* £74,000 *Assets* £2,400,000
TRUSTEES Andrew Morgan; Sarah Sinclair: Jonathan Heslop.
OTHER INFORMATION The trust divides its income equally between animal welfare, famine relief and medical research.
HOW TO APPLY Contact the correspondent for further information.
CONTACT DETAILS Andrew Morgan, Trustee, 14 Bell Villas, Ponteland, Newcastle upon Tyne, Tyne and Wear NE20 9BE *Tel.* 01661 871012 *Email* amorgan@nicholsonmorgan.co.uk

■ The Fort Foundation

CC NO 1028639 **ESTABLISHED** 1993
WHERE FUNDING CAN BE GIVEN England and Wales, with a focus on Lancashire.
WHO CAN BENEFIT Charitable organisations and individuals.
WHAT IS FUNDED Health; amateur sport; education; art and culture; citizenship; community welfare; religion; environmental protection and improvement.
RANGE OF GRANTS Mostly between £5,000 and £20,000.
SAMPLE GRANTS The Outward Bound Trust (£80,000); Lancaster University Climate Change Group (£50,000); The Jubilee Sailing Trust (£20,000); Teenage Cancer Trust (£7,500); Burwain Sailing Club (£6,000); Old Hegg Turtle Sanctuary (£5,800); Marine Society and Sea Cadets (£5,000).
FINANCES *Financial year end* 29/02/2020 *Income* £626,000 *Total grants* £286,200 *Grants to organisations* £266,700 *Assets* £1,300,000
TRUSTEES Ian Wilson; Edward Drury; John Hartley; Peter Fort; Edward Fort.
OTHER INFORMATION Grants awarded to organisations during the year were broken down

as follows: education (£80,500); environmental protection and improvement (£68,600); amateur sport (£57,300); citizenship and community welfare (£33,600); health (£21,750); art and culture (£4,900). Grants to individuals totalled £19,400.

HOW TO APPLY Contact the correspondent for further information.

CONTACT DETAILS The Trustees, c/o Fort Vale Engineering Ltd, Calder Vale Park, Simonstone Lane, Simonstone, Burnley, Lancashire BB12 7ND *Tel.* 01282 440000 *Email* info@fortvale.com

■ The Forte Charitable Trust

CC NO 326038 **ESTABLISHED** 1982

WHERE FUNDING CAN BE GIVEN UK and overseas.

WHO CAN BENEFIT Charitable organisations; Christian organisations; hospitals; hospices.

WHAT IS FUNDED General charitable purposes; Roman Catholic causes; older people, humanitarian aid; health, especially dementia and Alzheimer's.

RANGE OF GRANTS Typically £1,000 to £5,000.

SAMPLE GRANTS The Passage (£25,000); University of Oxford Elizabeth Collins Hardship Fund (£5,000); St Patrick's Roman Catholic Church (£4,000); Centrepoint (£3,000); ClearVision Project, St Wilfrid's Hospice and Sudbury Neighbourhood Centre (£2,000 each); Braille Chess Association and Young Dementia UK (£1,000 each); The Royal Marsden Cancer Charity (£500).

FINANCES *Financial year end* 05/04/2020 *Income* £30,000 *Total grants* £81,000 *Grants to organisations* £81,000 *Assets* £1,790,000

TRUSTEES Sir Rocco Forte; Lowndes Trustee Ltd; The Hon. Olga Polizzi di Sorrentino.

OTHER INFORMATION Grants were awarded to 28 organisations during the year.

HOW TO APPLY Contact the correspondent for further information.

CONTACT DETAILS Judy Lewendon, c/o Rocco Forte Hotels Ltd, 70 Jermyn Street, London SW1Y 6NY *Tel.* 020 7321 2626 *Email* jlewendon@roccofortehotels.com

■ The Lord Forte Foundation

CC NO 298100 **ESTABLISHED** 1987

WHERE FUNDING CAN BE GIVEN UK; overseas.

WHO CAN BENEFIT Educational establishments and charities.

WHAT IS FUNDED Training courses and research or other projects within the field of hospitality, encompassing the hotel, catering, travel and tourism industries within the UK and overseas.

TYPE OF GRANT Project funding.

RANGE OF GRANTS Up to £60,000.

SAMPLE GRANTS The Wine Guild Charitable Trust (£60,000); Queen Margaret University, Edinburgh (£15,000); Springboard Charitable Trust (£11,000); Edinburgh Napier University and University of Plymouth (£5,000 each); Perth College Development Trust (£2,000).

FINANCES *Financial year end* 31/03/2020 *Income* £98,500 *Total grants* £120,500 *Grants to organisations* £120,500 *Assets* £2,460,000

TRUSTEES Sir Rocco Forte; Nick Scade; Andrew McKenzie; Geoff Booth; The Hon. Olga Di Sorrentino.

OTHER INFORMATION Grants were made to nine organisations throughout the year.

HOW TO APPLY Contact the correspondent for further information.

CONTACT DETAILS Judy Lewendon, Administrator, Rocco Forte Hotels Ltd, 70 Jermyn Street, London SW1Y 6NY *Email* jlewendon@roccofortehotels.com

■ Ian M. Foulerton Charitable Trust

CC NO 1164969 **ESTABLISHED** 2015

WHERE FUNDING CAN BE GIVEN England and Wales.

WHO CAN BENEFIT Buildings of historic, architectural, artistic or scientific interest.

WHAT IS FUNDED Arts and heritage, specifically: the preservation, conservation, protection and restoration of buildings, furniture, art, manuscripts and monuments of historic, architectural, artistic or scientific interest; advancement of education.

TYPE OF GRANT Maintenance; capital; bursaries and scholarships.

RANGE OF GRANTS Up to £50,000.

SAMPLE GRANTS Chichester Cathedral Trust CIO (£50,000); St Pancras Ministry Funds (£20,000); Crosthwaite Parochial Church (£5,000); Quay Theatre (£2,000); St Peters Dunchurch Organ Fund (£1,000).

FINANCES *Financial year end* 05/04/2020 *Income* £54,400 *Total grants* £78,000 *Grants to organisations* £78,000 *Assets* £1,640,000

TRUSTEES Duncan O'Kelly; John McEvoy; Thomas Eggar Trust Corporation Ltd.

OTHER INFORMATION Five grants were awarded during 2019/20.

HOW TO APPLY Contact the correspondent for details regarding the application process.

CONTACT DETAILS The Trustees, c/o Irwin Mitchell LLP, Thomas Eggar House, Friary Lane, Chichester, West Sussex PO19 1UF *Tel.* 01243 786111 *Email* foulerton@irwinmitchell.com

■ Four Acre Trust

CC NO 1053884 **ESTABLISHED** 1995

WHERE FUNDING CAN BE GIVEN Worldwide with a preference for UK.

WHO CAN BENEFIT Registered charities; organisations.

WHAT IS FUNDED Children and young people. Current programmes include support schools' extracurricular projects, early intervention work, international eye and water projects.

TYPE OF GRANT Revenue/core costs; capital projects.

RANGE OF GRANTS Mostly £10,000 to £100,000.

SAMPLE GRANTS Dulverton Trust (£400,000); Acumen (£100,000); Shakespeare Schools (£25,000); Oakleaf Enterprise (£20,000); Kith and Kids (£10,000); Hope Support Services (£3,000).

FINANCES *Financial year end* 31/03/2020 *Income* £972,800 *Total grants* £3,000,000 *Grants to organisations* £3,000,000 *Assets* £4,750,000

TRUSTEES John Bothamley; Taymour Ezzat; Mary Bothamley; Marion Baker; Robert Carruthers.

HOW TO APPLY The charity's 2019/20 accounts state: '4AT is essentially closed to new applications preferring to seek out relevant charities through thorough research. However, applications from charities that mirror our existing recipients, and meet our other policies, might be acceptable and approaches should first be made to our administrator with a very short synopsis of the support that is required.'

CONTACT DETAILS The Trustees, Treferanon, St Weonards, Hereford, Herefordshire HR2 8QF *Tel.* 01981 580002 *Email* info@fouracretrust.org.uk *Website* www.fouracretrust.org.uk

Foux Foundation

CC NO 1177520 **ESTABLISHED** 2018

WHERE FUNDING CAN BE GIVEN Worldwide.

WHO CAN BENEFIT Registered charities.

WHAT IS FUNDED Health; education; children and young people; the relief of poverty.

WHAT IS NOT FUNDED Charities with an income of over £3 million per annum.

RANGE OF GRANTS £27,400 to £130,000.

SAMPLE GRANTS The Felix Project (£130,000); Child Rescue Nepal (£56,500); The Kids Network (£33,400); Small Steps Project (£27,400).

FINANCES *Financial year end* 05/04/2020 *Income* £200,000 *Total grants* £247,400 *Grants to organisations* £247,400 *Assets* £126,300

TRUSTEES Adam Ferguson; Mika Foux; Joshua Segal; Laura Ferguson.

OTHER INFORMATION The foundation made four grants during the year.

HOW TO APPLY Submit a proposal via the foundation's website. The foundation encourages prospective applicants to email the foundation to see if the proposal is suitable for funding.

CONTACT DETAILS The Trustees, Gerald Edelman Chartered Accountant, 73 Cornhill, London EC3V 3QQ *Tel.* 07729 494910 *Email* hello@fouxfoundation.org.uk *Website* https://www.fouxfoundation.org.uk

Fowler Smith and Jones Trust

CC NO 1132249 **ESTABLISHED** 2009

WHERE FUNDING CAN BE GIVEN Essex.

WHO CAN BENEFIT Charitable organisations.

WHAT IS FUNDED Arts; churches; community; health; youth; general charitable purposes.

WHAT IS NOT FUNDED Individuals; animal charities; political activities; commercial ventures.

TYPE OF GRANT Capital costs; project funding; core/revenue costs.

SAMPLE GRANTS Chalkwell Bay Seascout Group (£30,000); Colchester Arts Centre and Roxwell Church (£20,000 each); Sport for Confidence (£10,000).

FINANCES *Financial year end* 30/09/2020 *Income* £738,500 *Total grants* £648,100 *Grants to organisations* £648,100 *Assets* £10,620,000

TRUSTEES Philip Tolhurst; Nicholas Charrington; Nicholas Jones; Richard Furlonger.

OTHER INFORMATION Grants were broken down as follows: capital (£170,000); youth (£156,700); community (£133,900); medical/health (£90,900); miscellaneous (£87,100); churches (£6,500); overseas (£3,000).

HOW TO APPLY Apply in writing to the correspondent. Details of what should be included in an application can be found on the trust's website.

CONTACT DETAILS Alix Mason, Third Floor, Marlborough House, Victoria Road South, Chelmsford, Essex CM1 1LN *Tel.* 01245 809899 *Email* amason@fsjtrust.org.uk *Website* fsjtrust.org.uk

The Foxglove Trust

CC NO 1137839 **ESTABLISHED** 2010

WHERE FUNDING CAN BE GIVEN Worldwide, with a preference for Somerset.

WHO CAN BENEFIT Charitable causes.

WHAT IS FUNDED General charitable purposes, including: international and local causes; sports; the arts.

SAMPLE GRANTS Purple Community Fund (£45,000); The Open Door (£8,500); Baby Bank Bristol (£7,500); TLC Children's Trust (£6,800).

FINANCES *Financial year end* 30/04/2020 *Income* £44,700 *Total grants* £143,700 *Grants to organisations* £143,700 *Assets* £1,260,000

TRUSTEES Ian Kelland; Kevin Austin.

HOW TO APPLY Apply in writing to the correspondent. The 2019/20 annual report states: 'Cases presented for consideration should, where possible, have concrete proposals and outcomes attached.'

CONTACT DETAILS Ian Kelland, Trustee, c/o Lentells Ltd, 17–18 Leach Road, Chard Business Park, Chard, Somerset TA20 1FA *Tel.* 01460 64441 *Email* ian.kelland@icloud.com

The Foyle Foundation

CC NO 1081766 **ESTABLISHED** 2000

WHERE FUNDING CAN BE GIVEN UK, particularly areas outside London and the South East.

WHO CAN BENEFIT Registered charities; schools; universities.

WHAT IS FUNDED Small Grants Scheme: general charitable purposes; Main Grants Scheme: arts, education; Foyle School Library Scheme: schools, with a preference for primary schools.

WHAT IS NOT FUNDED Individuals; CICs; social enterprises. See the foundation's website for funding guidelines and exclusions for each funding stream.

TYPE OF GRANT Capital costs; core/revenue costs; project funding; unrestricted funding.

RANGE OF GRANTS Dependent upon grant scheme. In 2019/20, the majority of grants awarded were below £50,000.

SAMPLE GRANTS Bristol Music Trust (£250,000); Black Country Living Museum (£175,000); The Royal Parks – London (£100,000); Manchester Jewish Museum (£75,000); National Trust – Swindon (£45,000); Ballyclare High School (£20,000); Mark Evison Foundation (£10,000); Fairview Schools – Perth (£5,000); Glasgow Action for Pensioners – Govan (£2,000); Woking Youth Theatre (£1,000).

FINANCES *Financial year end* 31/12/2019 *Income* £2,170,000 *Total grants* £8,990,000 *Grants to organisations* £8,990,000 *Assets* £72,740,000

TRUSTEES James Korner; Michael Smith; Sir Peter Duffell; Roy Amlot; Vikki Heywood.

HOW TO APPLY Guidelines and application forms for each of the foundation's grant schemes are available to download from the foundation's website. Specific contacts for each grants scheme may also be found here. Applications need to be submitted online. Applications are accepted all year round; however, applications for large capital projects (over £75,000) will only be considered in twice a year (spring and autumn). At the time of writing (April 2021), the foundation's website states that the major capital scheme is unlikely to re-open before autumn 2021 due to the COVID-19 pandemic.

CONTACT DETAILS David Hall, Chief Executive, Rugby Chambers, 2 Rugby Street, London WC1N 3QU *Tel.* 020 7430 9119 *Email* info@foylefoundation.org.uk *Website* www.foylefoundation.org.uk

■ Mrs D. M. France-Hayhurst Foundation

CC NO 1160394 **ESTABLISHED** 2015

WHERE FUNDING CAN BE GIVEN UK.

WHO CAN BENEFIT Registered charities.

WHAT IS FUNDED Animal welfare.

WHAT IS NOT FUNDED Individuals.

TYPE OF GRANT Project costs and capital expenditure.

RANGE OF GRANTS Grants up to £10,000, mostly £5,000.

SAMPLE GRANTS The David Shepherd Wildlife Trust (£10,000); Ponies Help Children, World Horse Welfare and Wild Futures (£5,000 each); Save Me Trust (£3,000); Cats Protection (£2,000).

FINANCES *Financial year end* 31/03/2020 *Income* £365,300 *Total grants* £122,100 *Grants to organisations* £122,100 *Assets* £13,530,000

TRUSTEES Christopher Henretty; Peter Hunter; Jennifer Shearer; Andrew Wright; Phillip Posnett; Penny Sanders.

HOW TO APPLY Application forms are available to download from the foundation's website. The completed application form and any supporting documentation should either be sent by post or email to the Secretary. The trustees meet quarterly.

CONTACT DETAILS Penelope Byatt, Secretary, c/o Charles Russell Speechlys LLP, Compass House, Lypiatt Road, Cheltenham GL50 2QJ *Tel.* 01242 246311 *Email* Penelope.Byatt@crsblaw.com *Website* www.francehayhurstcharitabletrust.org.uk

■ The Isaac and Freda Frankel Memorial Charitable Trust

CC NO 1003732 **ESTABLISHED** 1991

WHERE FUNDING CAN BE GIVEN UK and Israel.

WHO CAN BENEFIT Mainly organisations and institutions benefitting people of the Jewish faith.

WHAT IS FUNDED The advancement of religion in accordance with the Orthodox Jewish faith; the relief of poverty.

WHAT IS NOT FUNDED Individuals; students; expeditions; scholarships.

RANGE OF GRANTS £5,000 to £10,000.

SAMPLE GRANTS Be'er Avrohom UK Trust (£10,500); Friends of Kehillas Hagra (£8,200).

FINANCES *Financial year end* 31/01/2020 *Income* £72,700 *Total grants* £67,200 *Grants to organisations* £67,200 *Assets* £427,800

TRUSTEES Montague Frankel; Geraldine Frankel; J. Steinhaus; J. Silkin.

OTHER INFORMATION Grants awarded below £5,000 during the year accounted for £48,500.

HOW TO APPLY Contact the correspondent for further information.

CONTACT DETAILS The Trustees, 33 Welbeck Street, London W1G 8LX *Tel.* 020 7872 0023

■ The Elizabeth Frankland Moore and Star Foundation

CC NO 257711 **ESTABLISHED** 1969

WHERE FUNDING CAN BE GIVEN UK.

WHO CAN BENEFIT Registered charitable organisations.

WHAT IS FUNDED General charitable purposes.

RANGE OF GRANTS From £1,000 to £20,000.

SAMPLE GRANTS Coram (£20,000); St Mungo's (£17,500); Accord Hospice and The Not Forgotten Association (£15,000 each); Combat Stress, London Air Ambulance and Shelter (£10,000 each); Glasgow City Mission (£6,000); Fair Trials International and Kibble Education and Care Centre (£5,000 each); Sir John Soane Museum (£2,500); Kingston Foodbank (£1,000).

FINANCES *Financial year end* 05/04/2020 *Income* £388,200 *Total grants* £390,000 *Grants to organisations* £390,000 *Assets* £12,800,000

TRUSTEES R. Griffiths; Anne Ely; Dr David Spalton; Janine Cameron.

OTHER INFORMATION In 2019/20 the foundation received 538 applications from UK-registered organisations, of which 50 were accepted. Grants were broken down as follows: homelessness (£87,500); education and the arts (£65,500); vulnerable in society (£62,000); medical research (£61,000); hospices (£55,000); war veterans (£22,000); National Star College (£15,000); other (£12,000); human rights (£10,000). No grants were awarded to individuals during the year.

HOW TO APPLY Apply in writing to the correspondent. The trustees meet twice a year.

CONTACT DETAILS The Trustees, c/o Neuhoff and Co., 11 Towcester Road, Whittlebury, Towcester, Northamptonshire NN12 8XU *Tel.* 01327 858171 *Email* info@neuhoffandco.com

■ Jill Franklin Trust

CC NO 1000175 **ESTABLISHED** 1988

WHERE FUNDING CAN BE GIVEN Northumbria, Tyne and Wear, County Durham, Newcastle, Cleveland.

WHO CAN BENEFIT Charitable organisations, particularly small charities; churches.

WHAT IS FUNDED Church restoration; self-help groups to support people with a mental illness or learning difficulties and their carers; organisations helping and supporting refugees and asylum-seekers coming to or in the UK; the restoration of churches of architectural importance; local schemes to help ex-offenders to resettle; bereavement counselling.

WHAT IS NOT FUNDED Building work (apart from church restoration); replacement of statutory funding; projects overseas; religious organisations set up for welfare, education, etc. whose services are not open and used by people from all denominations; animal charities; environmental charities; students and individuals; medical research.

RANGE OF GRANTS Grants are typically of £1,000 for one to three years (apart from church restoration which are usually £500).

SAMPLE GRANTS Prisoners' Education Trust (£42,000); Beanstalk (£34,000); Migrant Offshore Aid Station (£33,000); A Way Out (£16,430); Justice First (£16,480); Camden City and Islington Bereavement Services (£6,000).

FINANCES *Financial year end* 05/04/2020 *Income* £101,200 *Total grants* £90,400 *Grants to organisations* £90,400 *Assets* £2,050,000

TRUSTEES Andrew Franklin; Dr Samuel Franklin; Thomas Franklin; Norman Franklin.

HOW TO APPLY Apply by email to jft@jill-franklin-trust.org.uk in 500 words or less, detailing your project and aims. Preference will be given to smaller organisations (less than £1 million turnover). Applications will be acknowledged and are normally considered in the last month of the quarter.

CONTACT DETAILS The Trustees, Flat 5, 17–19 Elsworthy Road, London NW3 3DS *Email* jft@jill-franklin-trust.org.uk *Website* www.jill-franklin-trust.org.uk

■ The Gordon Fraser Charitable Trust

CC NO 260869 **ESTABLISHED** 1966

WHERE FUNDING CAN BE GIVEN UK, with a preference for Scotland.

WHO CAN BENEFIT Registered charities.

WHAT IS FUNDED General charitable purposes, with a preference for: performing arts, particularly for children, young people and people with disabilities; visual arts and museums; small medical and environmental charities, including those with a focus on the built environment.

WHAT IS NOT FUNDED Individuals.

TYPE OF GRANT Capital costs; core/revenue costs; project funding; seed funding/start-up funding.

RANGE OF GRANTS Between £100 and £20,000 (mostly £1,000 to £2,000).

SAMPLE GRANTS Artlink Central Ltd (£7,000); Industrial Museums Scotland (£4,500); British Red Cross (£3,000); Scottish Chamber Orchestra (£2,000); Disability Snowsport UK (£1,600); Dundee Carers Centre, Eco Drama and Open Door Accommodation Project (£1,000 each); Edinburgh Chamber Orchestra (£500).

FINANCES *Financial year end* 31/01/2020 *Income* £143,800 *Total grants* £163,000 *Grants to organisations* £163,000 *Assets* £4,440,000

TRUSTEES Margaret Moss; Sarah Moss; Susannah Rae; Alexander Moss; Alison Priestley.

OTHER INFORMATION As well as its main grant-making, the trust also supports up to six projects per year through the Paper Conservation Fund which, according to the website, 'aims to help accredited museums in Scotland, in particular small and medium-sized independent ones, to work with conservators to undertake projects that conserve their collections of works on paper. Projects can be treatment, surveys, training courses and skills development workshops.' In 2019/20, grants were awarded to 98 organisations in total. Grants were broken down as follows: arts/theatre (£73,400); health (£37,700); other charitable causes (£23,700); youth work (£12,000); relief of poverty (£5,500); education (£4,800); animal welfare (£3,500); religion (£2,500).

HOW TO APPLY Applications can be made online on the trust's website or in writing to the correspondent. Applications are considered in January, April, July and October. For the Paper Conservation Fund, contact the correspondent by email for an application form and guidance. Applications are considered in January and July.

CONTACT DETAILS Claire Armstrong, Gaidrew Farmhouse, Drymen, Glasgow G63 0DN *Email* enquiries@gfct.org.uk *Website* https://www.gfct.org.uk

■ The Hugh Fraser Foundation

OSCR NO SC009303 **ESTABLISHED** 1960

WHERE FUNDING CAN BE GIVEN UK, with a strong preference for Scotland.

WHO CAN BENEFIT Charitable organisations, principally hospitals; schools and universities; arts organisations; social welfare organisations.

WHAT IS FUNDED Medical facilities and research; relief of poverty; education and learning; older people; personal development and training of young people; music and the arts; other general charitable purposes.

WHAT IS NOT FUNDED Grants are only awarded to individuals in exceptional circumstances.

TYPE OF GRANT Project, capital and revenue grants for up to three years, sometimes longer; start-up costs.

SAMPLE GRANTS Glasgow Science Centre (£100,000).

FINANCES *Financial year end* 31/03/2020 *Income* £2,880,000 *Total grants* £2,063,500 *Grants to organisations* £2,050,000 *Assets* £74,730,000

TRUSTEES Miss Patricia Fraser; Dr Kenneth Chrystie; Mrs Belinda A. Hanson; Andrew Harrow.

OTHER INFORMATION The website notes that the trustees 'consider that grants to large, highly-publicised national appeals are not likely to be as effective a use of funds as grants to smaller, more focused charitable appeals'. Only the largest beneficiary was listed in the annual accounts.

HOW TO APPLY Applications should be submitted in PDF format via email. Applications should include a description of the project and a budget, with a copy of your latest accounts or financial information. The trustees normally meet in March, June, September and December with the cut – off date for applications being a month before.

CONTACT DETAILS The Trustees, c/o Turcan Connell, 180 St Vincent Street, Glasgow G2 5SG *Email* hughfraserfoundation@turcanconnell.com *Website* https://www.turcanconnell.com/the-hugh-fraser-foundation

■ The Fraxinus Charitable Trust

CC NO 1175624 **ESTABLISHED** 2017

WHERE FUNDING CAN BE GIVEN England and Wales.

WHO CAN BENEFIT Charitable organisations.

WHAT IS FUNDED General charitable purposes.

RANGE OF GRANTS £35,000 to £48,000.

SAMPLE GRANTS Tropical Health and Education Trust (£48,000); Against Malaria Foundation and University of Leeds (£35,000).

FINANCES *Financial year end* 24/10/2019 *Income* £648,600 *Total grants* £118,000 *Grants to organisations* £118,000 *Assets* £145,300

TRUSTEE Justinian Ash, Victoria Ash, Coutts & Co.

OTHER INFORMATION The trust made three grants during the year. The 2018/19 accounts were the latest available at the time of writing (June 2021).

HOW TO APPLY Apply in writing to the correspondent.

CONTACT DETAILS The Trustees, Coutts & Co. Trustee Department, 1st Floor, Trinity Quay 1, Avon Street, Bristol BS2 0PT *Tel.* 0345 304 2424

The Joyce and Norman Freed Charitable Trust

CC NO 1174393 **ESTABLISHED** 2017

WHERE FUNDING CAN BE GIVEN England; Wales; Scotland.

WHO CAN BENEFIT Charitable organisations.

WHAT IS FUNDED General charitable purposes; education/training; the advancement of health or saving lives; disability.

SAMPLE GRANTS A full list of beneficiaries was not available.

FINANCES *Financial year end* 05/04/2020 *Income* £9,400 *Total grants* £574,500 *Grants to organisations* £574,500

TRUSTEES Sara Phillips; Alison Goldberg.

OTHER INFORMATION Full accounts were not available to view on the Charity Commission's website due to the trust's low income. We have therefore estimated the grant total based on the trust's total expenditure.

HOW TO APPLY Contact the correspondent for further information.

CONTACT DETAILS The Trustees, 21 Bedford Square, London WC1B 3HH *Tel.* 020 7637 4444

The Louis and Valerie Freedman Charitable Settlement

CC NO 271067 **ESTABLISHED** 1976

WHERE FUNDING CAN BE GIVEN UK, especially Burnham.

WHO CAN BENEFIT Registered charities. The trust's 2019/20 accounts state that the trustees are 'normally minded to help those with a link to the Freedman family".

WHAT IS FUNDED Medical research, health and sickness; children and young people; education.

TYPE OF GRANT Project costs; research funding.

RANGE OF GRANTS £10,000 to £40,000.

SAMPLE GRANTS Burnham Health Promotion Trust (£40,000); Charlie Waller Memorial Trust (£30,000); Elmbridge CAN, Médecins Sans Frontières, Prostate Cancer UK and Rekindle (£10,000 each).

FINANCES *Financial year end* 05/04/2020 *Income* £141,900 *Total grants* £130,000 *Grants to organisations* £130,000 *Assets* £3,750,000

TRUSTEES Francis Hughes; Michael Ferrier.

OTHER INFORMATION Grants were broken down as follows: medical research/health/sickness (£90,000); children/education (£40,000).

HOW TO APPLY Apply in writing to the correspondent. The trustees meet periodically.

CONTACT DETAILS Francis Hughes, Trustee, c/o Bridge House, 11 Creek Road, East Molesey, Surrey KT8 9BE *Tel.* 020 8941 4455 *Email* francis@hughescollett.co.uk

The Freelands Foundation Ltd

CC NO 1162648 **ESTABLISHED** 2015

WHERE FUNDING CAN BE GIVEN UK.

WHO CAN BENEFIT UK-registered charities, including: arts organisations; educational organisations.

WHAT IS FUNDED Support for artists and art organisations; increased access to visual art; art education; research exploring the value of art and culture.

WHAT IS NOT FUNDED Overseas organisations; individuals; activity that generates personal profit; building work or capital campaigns.

TYPE OF GRANT Project funding; research.

RANGE OF GRANTS Up to £135,000; often recurrent.

SAMPLE GRANTS Turner Contemporary (£150,000); South London Gallery(£104,400); Paragon Studios PS2 (£92,500); Spike Island Artspace Ltd (£75,000); Site Gallery (£67,000); Camden Arts Centre (£61,900); University of Edinburgh – Talbot Rice Gallery (£42,000); Somerset House Trust (£30,000); Nottingham Contemporary (£25,000).

FINANCES *Financial year end* 31/12/2019 *Income* £76,070,000 *Total grants* £817,300 *Grants to organisations* £817,300 *Assets* £85,450,000

TRUSTEES Elisabeth Murdoch; Mark Devereux; Sarah Altenstadt; Keith Tyson.

OTHER INFORMATION During 2019, grants were awarded under the following themes: education (£159,500); artists and art organisations (£657,800). A further £28,000 was awarded for research purposes.

HOW TO APPLY Contact the correspondent for further information.

CONTACT DETAILS The Trustees, 113 Regent's Park Road, London NW1 8UR *Tel.* 020 3598 7081 *Email* grants@freelandsfoundation.co.uk *Website* freelandsfoundation.co.uk

Charles S. French Charitable Trust

CC NO 206476 **ESTABLISHED** 1959

WHERE FUNDING CAN BE GIVEN Essex and north east London.

WHO CAN BENEFIT Registered charities; hospices.

WHAT IS FUNDED Older people; community and arts; people with disabilities; disadvantaged people; medical research; hospices; children and young people.

RANGE OF GRANTS Mostly £1,000 to £5,000 but sometimes larger grants are made for specific projects.

SAMPLE GRANTS Essex Boys' and Girls' Clubs (£24,000); Epping Forest Foodbank and Barts Charity (£10,000 each); Step by Step London (£5,000); Action for Family Carers (£3,000); Computers for the Disabled Essex and Mencap – City of Chelmsford (£1,500 each); FoodCycle (£1,000); South West Essex Choir (£500).

FINANCES *Financial year end* 31/03/2020 *Income* £395,800 *Total grants* £429,800 *Grants to organisations* £429,800 *Assets* £9,990,000

TRUSTEES Edwin Cook; William Noble; Joanna Thomas; Michael Foster; Chris Noble; Jamie Foster; Antonia McLeod.

OTHER INFORMATION Grants were broken down as follows: medical activities (£76,100); youth (£65,800); community (£76,200); education (£54,000); sports/holiday activities (£53,600); disabled/disadvantaged activities (£45,400); older people (£30,600); hospices (£28,300).

HOW TO APPLY Application forms can be downloaded from the trust's website and should be returned to trustmanager@csfct.org.uk with a copy of your latest accounts.

CONTACT DETAILS The Trustees, 169 High Road, Loughton, Essex IG10 4LF *Tel.* 020 8502 3575 *Email* office@csfct.org.uk *Website* www.csfct.org.uk

■ Anne French Memorial Trust

CC NO 254567 **ESTABLISHED** 1963

WHERE FUNDING CAN BE GIVEN Diocese of Norwich (Norfolk).

WHO CAN BENEFIT Individuals; churches; local charities.

WHAT IS FUNDED General charitable purposes; the Anglican Church and clergy.

SAMPLE GRANTS A list of beneficiaries was not included in the annual report and accounts.

FINANCES *Financial year end* 05/04/2020
Income £264,000 *Total grants* £356,300
Grants to organisations £152,700
Assets £6,740,000

TRUSTEES The Venerable Steven James Betts; John Jones, The Rt Revd Graham Usher.

OTHER INFORMATION Grants are mainly confined to the needs of the Anglican Church and clergy. The trust awarded £203,600 to individuals during the year.

HOW TO APPLY Contact the correspondent for further information.

CONTACT DETAILS Coraline Nicholls, Administrator, Bishop's House, Norwich, Norfolk NR3 6AB *Tel.* 01603 629001 *Email* coralie.nichols@dioceseofnorwich.org

■ The Freshfield Foundation

CC NO 1003316 **ESTABLISHED** 1991

WHERE FUNDING CAN BE GIVEN UK and overseas.

WHO CAN BENEFIT Registered charities.

WHAT IS FUNDED Climate change; sustainable development; health; education; homelessness; research into Motor Neurone Disease.

FINANCES *Financial year end* 05/04/2020
Income £11,910,000 *Total grants* £655,200
Grants to organisations £655,200
Assets £25,150,000

TRUSTEES Paul Kurthausen; Patrick Moores; Elizabeth Potter.

OTHER INFORMATION Grants were broken down as follows: sustainable development and climate change control (£100,000); education, health and general well-being of mankind (£555,200).

HOW TO APPLY The foundation's 2019/20 annual report states: 'The trustees proactively research and identify those organisations and projects that will best achieve the Foundation's aims and objectives and make grants accordingly.'

CONTACT DETAILS Paul Kurthausen, c/o BW Macfarlane LLP, Castle Chambers, 43 Castle Street, Liverpool, Merseyside L2 9SH *Tel.* 0151 236 1494 *Email* paul.k@bwm.co.uk

■ The Freshgate Trust Foundation

CC NO 221467 **ESTABLISHED** 1941

WHERE FUNDING CAN BE GIVEN Sheffield and South Yorkshire.

WHO CAN BENEFIT Registered charities; unregistered charities; social enterprises; CICs; schools; universities; amateur sports clubs; hospitals; hospices.

WHAT IS FUNDED Education (including travel and training); heritage, restoration and environment; music and the arts; recreation (including holidays and sport); welfare, health and social care.

WHAT IS NOT FUNDED See the foundation's website for a full list of exclusions.

TYPE OF GRANT Capital costs; core/revenue costs; seed funding/start-up funding.

RANGE OF GRANTS Typically between £100 and £2,000.

SAMPLE GRANTS A list of beneficiaries was not included in the annual report and accounts.

FINANCES *Financial year end* 31/12/2019
Income £175,900 *Total grants* £106,000
Grants to organisations £106,000
Assets £3,850,000

TRUSTEES David Stone; John Hopkins; Holly Dobson; Neil MacDonald; Liz Murray; Val Linnemann; Usha Fitch; Geoff Marston; Geraldine Russell; Matthew Sibley; Alison Gaddes.

OTHER INFORMATION In 2019 a total of 60 grants were made. Grants were distributed as follows: welfare, health and social care (£37,400); recreation (£27,300); heritage, restoration and environment (£18,500) education (£13,300) music and the arts (£9,500).

HOW TO APPLY Applications can be made online via the foundation's website, or by post. In the first instance, applicants should read the funding criteria available on the foundation's website. The trustees normally meet three times a year (the first week of March, July and November) to discuss grants. In order to be considered, applications should be submitted at least four weeks before each meeting. The trustees or secretary cannot enter into correspondence regarding grants decisions.

CONTACT DETAILS Emma Legdon, Trust Secretary, The Hart Shaw Building, Europa Link, Sheffield Business Park, Sheffield, South Yorkshire S9 1XU *Tel.* 0114 251 8850 *Email* emma.legdon@hartshaw.co.uk *Website* www.freshgate.org.uk

■ Friarsgate Trust

CC NO 220762 **ESTABLISHED** 1955

WHERE FUNDING CAN BE GIVEN UK, with a preference for West Sussex.

WHO CAN BENEFIT Registered charities.

WHAT IS FUNDED Older people; community and family services; people with disabilities; the education and training of disadvantaged young people under the age of 23.

TYPE OF GRANT Capital costs; project funding; core costs.

RANGE OF GRANTS Up to £10,000 but mostly £500 to £2,000.

SAMPLE GRANTS Scope (£10,000); Dementia Support (£5,000); Over the Wall (£1,000); Snak Shak and Asthma Relief (£500 each).

FINANCES *Financial year end* 05/04/2020
Income £117,200 *Total grants* £97,800
Grants to organisations £97,800
Assets £3,310,000

TRUSTEES Robert Newman; Sarah Bain; Gillian Livingstone; Diana Altman.

OTHER INFORMATION Grants were made to 49 organisations during the year.

HOW TO APPLY Application forms can be downloaded from the trust's website. The trustees meet four times a year and applications will normally be considered at the next meeting following submission of the application. The usual quarterly meeting dates are the second Tuesday of January, April, July and October.

CONTACT DETAILS Olga Powell, c/o Irwin Mitchell LLP, Thomas Edgar House, Friary Lane, Chichester, West Sussex PO19 1UF *Tel.* 01243 786111 *Email* friarsgate@irwinmitchell.com *Website* friarsgatetrust.org.uk

■ Friends Provident Charitable Foundation

CC NO 1087053 **ESTABLISHED** 2002

WHERE FUNDING CAN BE GIVEN UK.

WHO CAN BENEFIT Registered charities; social enterprise; organisations; community groups; universities.

WHAT IS FUNDED Projects that contribute to a more resilient, sustainable and fairer economic system. Grants have been awarded towards: communicating economic ideas; investor/corporate behaviour; community energy; local development; a fair transition to a low carbon economy; tax; community assets and convening; diversity, equity and inclusion.

WHAT IS NOT FUNDED Activity that is not based in or likely to have a tangible economic impact on the UK.

TYPE OF GRANT Core/revenue funding; project funding; development funding; research; campaigning; unrestricted.

RANGE OF GRANTS Up to £200,000.

SAMPLE GRANTS New Economics Foundation NEF (£200,000); The Landworkers' Alliance (£144,000); Energy Garden (£97,000); Fairshare Educational Foundation (£80,000); Manchester Metropolitan University (£38,000); Behavioural Insights Ltd (£10,000); Stir To Action Ltd (£2,500).

FINANCES *Financial year end* 30/09/2020
Income £574,700 *Total grants* £3,060,000
Grants to organisations £3,060,000
Assets £28,810,000

TRUSTEES Kathleen Kelly; Joanna Elson; Abraham Baldry; Ann Don Bosco; Aphra Sklair; Paul Dickinson; Stephen Muers; Stephanie Maier; Priya Lukka.

OTHER INFORMATION During 2019/20, grants totalling £3.1 million were paid and new grant commitments totalled £2.33 million. Out of 225 first stage applications, 39 were considered for funding. From these, 27 organisations were awarded grants, 12 of which had not previously received a grant from the foundation and the remaining 15 were previous grant holders.

HOW TO APPLY The foundation has a two-stage application process. First, potential applicants should submit their proposal through an outline application online. These applications are reviewed by an Expert Advisory Group. Successful proposals will then be invited to submit a full stage two application. Applications can be submitted at any time. Further information and guidance can be found on the foundation's website.

CONTACT DETAILS The Trustees, Blake House, 18 Blake Street, York YO1 8QG *Tel.* 01904 629675 (option 3) *Email* enquiries@friendsprovidentfoundation.org.uk *Website* www.friendsprovidentfoundation.org

■ Frognal Trust

CC NO 244444 **ESTABLISHED** 1964

WHERE FUNDING CAN BE GIVEN UK.

WHO CAN BENEFIT Registered charities.

WHAT IS FUNDED Older people; children; disability; blindness; medical research; environmental heritage.

SAMPLE GRANTS A list of beneficiaries was not included.

FINANCES *Financial year end* 05/04/2020
Income £101,300 *Total grants* £108,300
Grants to organisations £108,300
Assets £2,690,000

TRUSTEES Jennifer Fraser; Caroline Philipson-Stow; Matthew Bennett; Simon Fraser.

OTHER INFORMATION Grants were distributed as follows: medical research (£39,500); children (£19,800); people who are blind or have a disability (£19,000); older people (£19,000); environmental heritage (£11,000).

HOW TO APPLY Contact the correspondent for further information.

CONTACT DETAILS Joyce Salkeld, c/o Wilson Solicitors LLP, Alexandra House, St John's Street, Salisbury, Wiltshire SP1 2SB *Tel.* 01722 412412 *Email* joyce.salkeld@wilsonsllp.com

■ The Patrick and Helena Frost Foundation

CC NO 1005505 **ESTABLISHED** 1991

WHERE FUNDING CAN BE GIVEN UK.

WHO CAN BENEFIT Registered charities; small organisations.

WHAT IS FUNDED General charitable purposes; social welfare.

WHAT IS NOT FUNDED Individuals.

RANGE OF GRANTS £2,000 to £20,000.

SAMPLE GRANTS Ocean Youth Trust South and The Yard Theatre Ltd (£20,000 each); London Narrow Boat Project and WheelPower -The British Wheelchair Sports Foundation Ltd (£15,000 each); Childhood Tumour Trust and The London Children's Flower Society (£10,000 each); Action on Addiction (£7,500); Yeldall Christian Centres (£5,000); The Fforest Uchaf Horse and Pony Rehabilitation Centre Charitable Trust (£2,000).

FINANCES *Financial year end* 05/04/2020
Income £670,100 *Total grants* £552,000
Grants to organisations £552,000
Assets £18,890,000

TRUSTEES Luke Valner; Dominic Tayler; Neil Hendriksen; Mark Hendriksen; Clare Armitage.

OTHER INFORMATION Grants were awarded to 56 organisations during 2019/20.

HOW TO APPLY The trustees proactively seek and select the organisation they wish to support and therefore request that unsolicited applications are not submitted.

CONTACT DETAILS The Trustees, c/o Trowers and Hamlins LLP, 3 Bunhill Row, London EC1Y 8YZ *Tel.* 020 7423 8303 *Email* asorrell@trowers.com

■ The Fulmer Charitable Trust

CC NO 1070428 **ESTABLISHED** 1997

WHERE FUNDING CAN BE GIVEN UK and overseas.

WHO CAN BENEFIT Registered charities; charitable causes.

WHAT IS FUNDED The relief of suffering and hardship; education; religion; general charitable purposes.

TYPE OF GRANT Project funding.

RANGE OF GRANTS Up to £6,000 but mainly £2,000.

SAMPLE GRANTS Age UK (£6,000); Save the Children (£5,000); Child Soldiers International (£4,000); ABF The Soldiers' Charity, Malaria No More UK, Support Dogs, Toybox, Wiltshire Treehouse (£2,000); St Just Miners' Chapel Appeal (£500).

FINANCES *Financial year end* 31/12/2019
Income £573,300 *Total grants* £494,000
Grants to organisations £494,000
Assets £18,940,000

TRUSTEES Caroline Mytum; John Reis; Sally Reis; Revd Philip Bromiley.

HOW TO APPLY Contact the correspondent for further information.
CONTACT DETAILS The Trustees, Estate Office, Street Farm, Compton Bassett, Calne, Wiltshire SN11 8RH *Tel.* 01249 760410

■ The Funding Network

CC NO 1088315 **ESTABLISHED** 2000
WHERE FUNDING CAN BE GIVEN UK and overseas.
WHO CAN BENEFIT Registered charities; not-for-profit organisations, including: CICs; CIOs; social enterprises, grassroots organisations.
WHAT IS FUNDED General charitable purposes including human rights, health, education, livelihoods, inclusion, the environment, climate change, and crime reduction and peacebuilding.
WHAT IS NOT FUNDED Organisations that are involved in the promotion of religion or a political party; organisations with a turnover of over £1.2 million; fundraising challenges; individuals.
TYPE OF GRANT Project costs; strategic; start-up.
RANGE OF GRANTS Up to £30,000 (mostly up to £10,000).
SAMPLE GRANTS Flamingo Chicks (£30,600); Music in Detention (£15,100); Suited and Booted (£8,600); Tea Leaf Trust (£7,200); Design Club CIC (£6,100); Cecily's Fund (£4,900); Caxton Youth (£1,500); Maytree Respite Centre (£1,200); The Kid's Network (£250); Bottles of Hope (£60).
FINANCES *Financial year end* 31/03/2020 *Income* £725,500 *Total grants* £481,400 *Grants to organisations* £481,400 *Assets* £120,700
TRUSTEES Fiona Johnston; Ailis Clarke; Shantanu Sinha; Adrian Coles; Josh Babarinde; Ofovwe Aig-Imoukhuede; Kawika Solidum; Samuel Lush; Michael Chuter.
OTHER INFORMATION The charity invites non-profit organisations nominated by network members to apply for the opportunity to pitch for funds at its events. The funds raised are then passed onto the organisation by the network in the form of grants.
HOW TO APPLY To apply, organisations must first be sponsored by a Funding Network member. A selection panel will shortlist the strongest candidates and interview these candidates over the phone. Applicants are notified within 48 hours whether they have been selected or not. The charity does not share the details of its current members; however, organisations that do not know a current network member can ask somebody to become a member with a view to nominating them. This could be a trustee, volunteer or someone close to the organisation, but it cannot be somebody who is in paid employment of the organisation. Once they have signed up, new members are asked to attend and donate at a network event before being eligible to sponsor an organisation.
CONTACT DETAILS The Trustees, Toynbee Hall, 28 Commercial Street, London E1 6LS *Tel.* 020 7846 4070 *Email* info@thefundingnetwork.org.uk *Website* www.thefundingnetwork.org.uk

■ The G. D. Charitable Trust

CC NO 1096101 **ESTABLISHED** 2002

WHERE FUNDING CAN BE GIVEN UK and overseas.

WHO CAN BENEFIT Registered charities.

WHAT IS FUNDED Animal welfare; the environment; equal opportunities for people with disabilities; homelessness.

RANGE OF GRANTS Mainly under £50,000.

SAMPLE GRANTS Blue Marine Foundation (£97,000); Child Bereavement UK (£50,000); Save the Children (£25,000); Chichester Festival Theatre (£10,500); Bella Vista Project (£5,000); Petworth Youth Association (£2,000); Lorica Trust (£1,000); Chestnut Tree House and Wild Touch Wildlife Centre (£500 each).

FINANCES *Financial year end* 31/12/2020 *Income* £79,300 *Total grants* £191,500 *Grants to organisations* £191,500 *Assets* £4,630,000

TRUSTEES George Duffield; Alexander Fitzgibbons; Natasha Duffield.

OTHER INFORMATION Grants were made to nine organisations during 2020. The trust makes an annual donation to the Blue Marine Foundation, where George Duffield is also a trustee.

HOW TO APPLY Apply in writing to the correspondent. The trustees meet regularly to discuss applications.

CONTACT DETAILS The Trustees, c/o BDB Pitmans LLP, One Bartholomew Close, London EC1A 7BL *Tel.* 020 7227 7000

■ G. M. C. Trust

CC NO 288418 **ESTABLISHED** 1965

WHERE FUNDING CAN BE GIVEN West Midlands.

WHO CAN BENEFIT Registered charities.

WHAT IS FUNDED General charitable purposes; mental health.

WHAT IS NOT FUNDED Individuals.

TYPE OF GRANT Capital costs; core/revenue costs; seed funding/start-up funding; unrestricted funding.

RANGE OF GRANTS £1,000 to £25,000.

SAMPLE GRANTS Sense (£25,000); Hand in Hand International and The Life House (£10,000 each); Royal Birmingham Society of Artists (£6,000); Crisis and Help Musicians UK (£5,000 each); House on the Corner Community Project (£3,000); Ex Cathedra and Care for Veterans (£1,000 each).

FINANCES *Financial year end* 05/04/2020 *Income* £133,900 *Total grants* £106,500 *Grants to organisations* £106,500 *Assets* £3,400,000

TRUSTEES Bes Cadbury; MJ Cadbury; Mrs C. Fowler-Wright.

HOW TO APPLY Unsolicited applications are not accepted.

CONTACT DETAILS The Trustees, c/o Rodney Pitts Chartered Accountants, 4 Fairways, 1240 Warwick Road, Knowle, Solihull, West Midlands B93 9LL *Tel.* 01564 779971 *Email* mail@rodneypitts.com *Website* www.rodneypitts.com/pages/gmc_trust.html

■ The Gale Family Charity Trust

CC NO 289212 **ESTABLISHED** 1984

WHERE FUNDING CAN BE GIVEN UK, with a preference for Bedfordshire.

WHO CAN BENEFIT Registered charities; schools; amateur sports clubs; hospitals; religious bodies/institutions.

WHAT IS FUNDED General charitable purposes.

TYPE OF GRANT Project funding; unrestricted funding.

SAMPLE GRANTS A list of beneficiaries was not included in the annual report and accounts.

FINANCES *Financial year end* 05/04/2020 *Income* £319,600 *Total grants* £273,300 *Grants to organisations* £273,300 *Assets* £5,820,000

TRUSTEES John Tyley; Alistair Law; Doreen Watson; Warwick Browning; Charles Codrington; David Fletcher; Russell Beard; John Cleverley; Alison Phillipson.

HOW TO APPLY Apply in writing to the correspondent. The trustees meet every six months to award grants.

CONTACT DETAILS The Trustees, Northwood House, 138 Bromham Road, Bedford, Bedfordshire MK40 2QW *Tel.* 01234 354508 *Email* galefamilytrust@gmail.com

■ GambleAware

CC NO 1093910 **ESTABLISHED** 2002

WHERE FUNDING CAN BE GIVEN England, Scotland and Wales.

WHO CAN BENEFIT Registered charities; research organisations; NHS trusts.

WHAT IS FUNDED Education, prevention and treatment services and research aimed at minimising the impact of gambling.

TYPE OF GRANT Research.

RANGE OF GRANTS Up to £7 million.

SAMPLE GRANTS GamCare (£7.1 million); The Gordon Moody Association (£801,600); Leeds and York Partnership Trust (£678,000); CNWL NHS Foundation Trust – CNWL Problem Gambling Clinic (£461,500); Citizens Advice Scotland (£399,900); University of Wolverhampton (£300,300); University of Bournemouth (£280,500); Revealing Reality (£224,400).

FINANCES *Financial year end* 31/03/2020 *Income* £16,980,000 *Total grants* £10,430,000 *Grants to organisations* £10,430,000 *Assets* £12,290,000

TRUSTEES Michelle Highman; Prof. Marcantonio Spada; Rachel Pearce; Saffron Cordery; Prof. Sian Griffiths; Prof. Anthony Kessel; Paul Simpson; Kathryn Lampard.

OTHER INFORMATION During 2019/20, grants were awarded to ten organisations. Grants were distributed as follows: treatment (£9 million); research (£964,900); education (£467,300).

HOW TO APPLY The 2019/20 annual report states: 'GambleAware does not offer funding in response to speculative applications, but from time to time does issue open tenders when there is the opportunity to bid for funding for innovative projects within a broader field.' See the charity's website for more details.

CONTACT DETAILS The Trustees, Pennine Place, 2A Charing Cross Road, London WC2H 0HF *Tel.* 020 7287 1994 *Email* info@gambleaware.org *Website* about.gambleaware.org

Gamma Trust

OSCR NO SC004330 **ESTABLISHED** 1965

WHERE FUNDING CAN BE GIVEN UK and overseas, with a preference for Scotland.

WHO CAN BENEFIT Churches; charitable organisations; UK-registered charities; hospitals; universities; individuals.

WHAT IS FUNDED General charitable purposes; health; arts, culture and heritage; scientific and medical research; social welfare; ex-offenders.

RANGE OF GRANTS £100 to £2,500.

SAMPLE GRANTS Scotland Churches Trust (£2,200); Asthma UK, Prevent Breast Cancer and Wellbeing of Women (£1,500 each); Combat Stress and Scottish Mountain Rescue (£500 each); Ronald McDonald's House (£250); Cavell Nurses Trust and Oxfam (£100 each).

FINANCES *Financial year end* 05/04/2019 *Income* £51,900 *Total grants* £54,500 *Grants to organisations* £54,500 *Assets* £1,730,000

OTHER INFORMATION The 2018/19 accounts were the latest available at the time of writing (June 2021). Grants were awarded to 53 organisations during the period.

HOW TO APPLY Contact the correspondent for further information.

CONTACT DETAILS The Trustees, c/o Mazars CYB Services Ltd, 100 Queen Street, Glasgow G1 3DN

The Gannochy Trust

OSCR NO SC003133 **ESTABLISHED** 1937

WHERE FUNDING CAN BE GIVEN Scotland, with a strong preference for the Perth and Kinross area.

WHO CAN BENEFIT OSCR-registered charities.

WHAT IS FUNDED Community development; social welfare; employability; education; the natural and built environment.

TYPE OF GRANT Core funding; project funding; capital costs. Funding for up to three years may be awarded.

SAMPLE GRANTS The Y Centre (£877,400); MCR Pathways (£285,000); Culture Perth and Kinross Ltd (£150,000); Corbenic Camphil Community (£100,000).

FINANCES *Financial year end* 30/06/2020 *Income* £3,390,000 *Total grants* £4,890,000 *Grants to organisations* £4,890,000 *Assets* £201,530,000

TRUSTEES Dr James Kynaston; Ian Macmillan; Jane Mudd; David Gray; Stephen Hay; Bruce Renfrew; Roland Bean.

HOW TO APPLY There are a number of documents that applicants must complete, including an application form. These are available to download from the trust's informative website, where detailed guidance notes can also be found. Completed applications may be submitted by email or post. The trustees meet at least four times per year to consider applications, which may be submitted at any time.

CONTACT DETAILS The Trustees, Kincarrathie House Drive, Pitcullen Crescent, Perth, Perthshire PH2 7HX *Tel.* 01738 620653 *Email* admin@gannochytrust.org.uk *Website* www.gannochytrust.org.uk

The Ganzoni Charitable Trust

CC NO 263583 **ESTABLISHED** 1971

WHERE FUNDING CAN BE GIVEN Suffolk.

WHO CAN BENEFIT Registered charities; churches; hospices; hospitals; schools.

WHAT IS FUNDED General charitable purposes, including: relief of poverty; advancement of Christianity; education.

TYPE OF GRANT Mainly capital projects.

RANGE OF GRANTS Up to £5,000.

SAMPLE GRANTS Autistica and Whizz-Kidz (£2,000 each); Brainwave, Carers UK and SHINE (£1,000 each); Epilepsy Action (£500).

FINANCES *Financial year end* 05/04/2020 *Income* £265,200 *Total grants* £179,200 *Grants to organisations* £179,200 *Assets* £4,110,000

TRUSTEES John Pickering; The Hon. Mary Ganzoni; The Hon. Charles Boscawen; Louise Long.

OTHER INFORMATION Grants were made to 112 organisations.

HOW TO APPLY Contact the correspondent for further information.

CONTACT DETAILS The Trustees, c/o Birketts LLP, Providence House, 141–145 Princes Street, Ipswich, Suffolk IP1 1QJ *Tel.* 01473 232300 *Email* bill-white@birketts.co.uk

The Worshipful Company of Gardeners of London Charity

CC NO 222079 **ESTABLISHED** 1962

WHERE FUNDING CAN BE GIVEN UK, in particular London.

WHO CAN BENEFIT Registered charities with a link to horticulture and gardening.

WHAT IS FUNDED General charitable purposes; gardening projects; horticulture.

RANGE OF GRANTS £200 to £7,000.

SAMPLE GRANTS City and Guilds of London Institution (£14,000); London Children's Flower Society (£6,000); London in Bloom (£3,000); Metropolitan Public Gardens Association (£2,500); Sheriffs' and Recorders Fund (£1,000); Garden Classroom (£500); Providence Row (£250).

FINANCES *Financial year end* 30/06/2020 *Income* £81,100 *Total grants* £57,300 *Grants to organisations* £57,300 *Assets* £831,500

TRUSTEES Norman Chalmers; John Rochford; Trevor Faris; Peter Waine; Stephen Bernhard; John Gilbert; Dr Stephen Dowbiggin; Louise Robinson; Roger Hedgecoe; Rodney Petty; Bernard Williams; Dr Heather Barrett-Mold; Brian Porter.

OTHER INFORMATION During 2019/20, the charity awarded £58,000 in grants and £2,500 in educational prizes.

HOW TO APPLY Contact the correspondent for further information.

CONTACT DETAILS Charity Secretary, The Gardeners Company Charity Secretary, Capel Manor College, Bullsmoor Lane, Enfield, Middlesex EN1 4RQ *Email* t.faris@btinternet.com *Website* www.gardenerscompany.org.uk

Garfield Weston Foundation

CC NO 230260 **ESTABLISHED** 1958

WHERE FUNDING CAN BE GIVEN UK.

WHO CAN BENEFIT Registered charities; schools; universities; CICs; hospitals; hospices.

WHAT IS FUNDED Social welfare; the arts; young people; community; faith; the environment; education; health; museums and heritage.

WHAT IS NOT FUNDED Individuals; CICs; social enterprises without UK Charity Commission registration; sporting associations without UK Charity Commission registration; work that does not deliver a direct benefit in the UK, even if the organisation is registered with the Charity Commission; animal welfare charities; charities that spend the majority of their income outside the UK; local authorities and councils.
TYPE OF GRANT Capital costs; core/revenue costs; project funding.
SAMPLE GRANTS Royal College of Art (£5 million); National Theatre (£300,000); Spark Inside (£50,000); Chain Reaction and Woodmeadow Trust (£30,000 each); Adventure Plus, Barnabas and Braintrust (£25,000 each); Fusion Theatre (£5,000); New Radnor Baptist Church (£500).
FINANCES *Financial year end* 05/04/2020
Income £84,750,000
Total grants £88,110,000
Grants to organisations £88,110,000
Assets £7,463,030,000
TRUSTEES Kate Hobhouse; Sophia Weston; George Weston; Eliza Mitchell; Guy Weston; Jana Khayat; Melissa Murdoch; Georgie Dalglish; Alannah Weston.
OTHER INFORMATION The foundation made 2,121 grants during the year.
HOW TO APPLY Apply via the foundation's website.
CONTACT DETAILS The Trustees, Weston Centre, 10 Grosvenor Street, London W1K 4QY *Tel.* 020 7399 6565 *Email* admin@garfieldweston.org *Website* www.garfieldweston.org

■ The Garrick Charitable Trust

CC NO 1071279 **ESTABLISHED** 1998
WHERE FUNDING CAN BE GIVEN UK.
WHO CAN BENEFIT UK-registered charities.
WHAT IS FUNDED Theatre; music (including opera); dance; literature.
WHAT IS NOT FUNDED Drama, dance or music conservatoire training or academic studies; amateur productions; projects outside the UK; capital appeals.
RANGE OF GRANTS Usually £2,500 to £5,000.
SAMPLE GRANTS Almeida Theatre (£5,000); Poetry London (£3,500); Leeds Lieder (£2,500); The Lowry Centre (£2,000); Orion Orchestra (£1,500); Chinese Arts Now (£1,300).
FINANCES *Financial year end* 31/12/2019
Income £60,800 *Total grants* £205,200
Grants to organisations £205,200
Assets £7,060,000
TRUSTEES Sir Stephen Waley-Cohen; David Sigall; Joseph Seelig; John Coldstream; David Whelton; Dr Nigel Brown.
OTHER INFORMATION Grants were distributed as follows: theatre (£89,700); music (£74,600); dance (£26,200); literature (£14,800). The website explains that the trustees 'prefer to support proposals which: help professionals to develop their careers; are not capital appeals; allow our modest contribution to make a real difference'.
HOW TO APPLY Details of the trust's two-stage application process can be found on its website. There is no deadline for applications but the trustees meet quarterly, usually in early March, June, September and December and applications should be received in good time before a meeting to be considered.
CONTACT DETAILS Sarah Charles, Garrick Club, 15 Garrick Street, London WC2E 9AY *Tel.* 020 7395 4136 *Email* charitabletrust@garrickclub.co.uk *Website* https://www.garrickclub.co.uk/charitable_trust

■ Garthgwynion Charities

CC NO 229334 **ESTABLISHED** 1963
WHERE FUNDING CAN BE GIVEN Primarily the parishes of Isygarreg and Uwchygarreg at Machynlleth, Powys.
WHO CAN BENEFIT Charitable organisations; individuals.
WHAT IS FUNDED General charitable purposes.
SAMPLE GRANTS Campaign to End Loneliness; Ironbridge Gorge Museum; Machynlleth Tabernacle Trust; Machynlleth Town Council; Montgomeryshire Area Scout Council; Owain Glyndwr Institute.
FINANCES *Financial year end* 05/04/2020
Income £62,600 *Total grants* £76,000
Grants to organisations £76,000
Assets £150,100
TRUSTEES Eleanor Lambert; David Owen; Edward Owen; Diana Walters; Jane Anderson; Rosie Lochiel-Owen.
OTHER INFORMATION In 2019/20, grants totalling £76,000 were made to eight organisations and one individual.
HOW TO APPLY Contact the correspondent for further information.
CONTACT DETAILS The Trustees, 9B Matham Road, East Molesey, Surrey KT8 0SX *Tel.* 020 8941 4088 *Email* Garthgwynioncharities@gmail.com

■ The Gatsby Charitable Foundation

CC NO 251988 **ESTABLISHED** 1967
WHERE FUNDING CAN BE GIVEN Worldwide with a preference for the UK and East Africa.
WHO CAN BENEFIT Registered charities only. Many beneficiary organisations are specialist research institutes.
WHAT IS FUNDED Plant science; neuroscience; STEM education; Africa; public policy; the arts.
TYPE OF GRANT Project funding; core costs, including salaries; research.
SAMPLE GRANTS University of Cambridge (£8.33 million); The Sainsbury Laboratory (£3.49 million); Hebrew University of Jerusalem (£307,000); Chamber Orchestra of Europe (£500,000); Engineering UK (£75,000).
FINANCES *Financial year end* 05/04/2020
Income £105,200,000
Total grants £53,690,000
Grants to organisations £53,690,000
Assets £457,405,000
TRUSTEES Joseph Burns; Sir Andrew Cahn; Judith Portrait.
OTHER INFORMATION The trust is one of the Sainsbury Family Charitable Trusts which share a common administration – see www.sftc.org.uk for more information.
HOW TO APPLY The trustees take a proactive approach to grant-making; unsolicited applications are not considered.
CONTACT DETAILS The Trustees, The Peak, 5 Wilton Road, London SW1V 1AP *Tel.* 020 7410 0330 *Email* contact@gatsby.org.uk *Website* www.gatsby.org.uk

■ Gatwick Airport Community Trust

CC NO 1089683 **ESTABLISHED** 2001

WHERE FUNDING CAN BE GIVEN Parts of East and West Sussex, Surrey and Kent but particularly communities directly affected by operations at Gatwick Airport.

WHO CAN BENEFIT Registered charities; unregistered charities; social enterprises; schools; PTAs; hospices; religious bodies/institutions.

WHAT IS FUNDED Children and young people; art; sports facilities; the environment and conservation; community facilities; people with disabilities; older people; development of volunteering.

WHAT IS NOT FUNDED Projects or beneficiaries that are completely or largely outside the area of benefit; recurrent expenditure or running costs; ongoing costs maintenance or deficits; repeat annual applications for similar projects; costs that should be funded from other sources e.g. public bodies; applications from organisations that have statutory responsibilities unless it is a project that is over and above their core activities; the purchase of land or buildings; organisations that are working to make a profit for shareholders partners or sole owners; individuals; grants will not normally be made to organisations with excess 'free' reserves; salaries.

TYPE OF GRANT Capital costs; project funding; seed funding/start-up funding.

RANGE OF GRANTS Mostly up to £5,000.

SAMPLE GRANTS Crawley Open House (£20,000); Lindfield Cricket Club (£12,000); Wivelsfield Village Hall and Recreation Ground (£5,000); Southwater First Responders (£4,800); Children's Safety Education Foundation, Copthorne Youth Football Club, Happy Hours Pre-school, Penshurst Park Cricket Club, Police Community Clubs of Great Britain and Rockinghorse Children's Charity (£3,000 each).

FINANCES *Financial year end* 31/12/2019 *Income* £224,500 *Total grants* £174,700 *Grants to organisations* £174,700 *Assets* £51,700

TRUSTEES Richard Burrett; John Kendall; Julie Ayres; Alan Jones; Graham Knight; Elizabeth McDermid; Rajesh Sharma; Joanna Rettie.

OTHER INFORMATION Grants were made to 97 organisations. Only organisations receiving grants of over £3,000 were listed as beneficiaries in the charity's accounts.

HOW TO APPLY Application forms are available to download from the trust's helpful website along with more information about application guidelines.

CONTACT DETAILS Rosamund Quade, Administrator, GACT, PO Box 783, Chichester, West Sussex PO19 9TY *Tel.* 07444 737518 *Email* mail@gact.org.uk *Website* www.gact.org.uk

■ The Gaudio Family Foundation (UK) Ltd

CC NO 1157301 **ESTABLISHED** 2014

WHERE FUNDING CAN BE GIVEN England and Wales.

WHO CAN BENEFIT Registered charities.

WHAT IS FUNDED General charitable purposes including: relieving poverty, especially in urban areas; advancing and improving education, particularly for disadvantaged children.

RANGE OF GRANTS Up to £74,000.

SAMPLE GRANTS Gaudio Family Foundation (£2.36 million); Soc Des Amis National (£140,600); West London Zone (£57,700); Zene de Zene International (£15,700).

FINANCES *Financial year end* 31/12/2019 *Income* £8,180,000 *Total grants* £3,060,000 *Grants to organisations* £3,060,000 *Assets* £22,200,000

TRUSTEES Alfred Cavallaro; Belma Gaudio; Julius Gaudio.

OTHER INFORMATION Grants were awarded to 12 organisations.

HOW TO APPLY Applications can be made in writing to the foundation. Grant recipients will be required to produce project reports.

CONTACT DETAILS The Trustees, c/o Withers LLP, Third Floor, 20 Old Bailey, London EC4M 7AN *Tel.* 020 7597 6000 *Email* ac@fultonvittoria.com

■ The Robert Gavron Charitable Trust

CC NO 268535 **ESTABLISHED** 1974

WHERE FUNDING CAN BE GIVEN UK.

WHO CAN BENEFIT Registered charities.

WHAT IS FUNDED General charitable purposes, in particular: access to the arts; education; social policy and research; prison reform; human rights; disability.

RANGE OF GRANTS Up to £78,000 but mainly less than £20,000.

SAMPLE GRANTS Arab Israel Children's Tennis Charity (£78,300), BalletBoyz (£50,000); Mario Curio (£12,000); Clean Break (£10,000); Luberon Nature (£8,800); Camden Arts Centre (£5,000); Arts for All (£4,000); Imperial War Museum (£3,000).

FINANCES *Financial year end* 05/04/2020 *Income* £127,900 *Total grants* £454,700 *Grants to organisations* £454,700 *Assets* £7,320,000

TRUSTEES Sarah Gavron; Charles Corman; Jessica Gavron; Dr Kate Gavron.

OTHER INFORMATION Only organisations receiving grants of over £3,000 were listed as beneficiaries in the trust's accounts. Grants of under £3,000 totalled £15,400.

HOW TO APPLY Apply in writing to the correspondent. The trustees meet formally approximately four times a year.

CONTACT DETAILS The Trustees, 27 Maywin Drive, Hornchurch, Essex RM11 3ST *Tel.* 020 7400 4301 *Email* office@rgct.org.uk

■ Martin Geddes Charitable Trust

CC NO 1159776 **ESTABLISHED** 2014

WHERE FUNDING CAN BE GIVEN England and Wales.

WHO CAN BENEFIT Registered charities; charitable organisations.

WHAT IS FUNDED Support for people with a drug or alcohol dependency. Preference is given to those that 'apply a 12-step philosophy and treatment'.

TYPE OF GRANT Project funding.

SAMPLE GRANTS 1 North East; Create Recovery; Foundation for Change; Hebron Trust; Kenward Trust; Pushing Change; New Note Orchestra; Recovery Through Nature; The Living Room.

FINANCES *Financial year end* 27/08/2020 *Income* £125,600 *Total grants* £95,300 *Grants to organisations* £95,300 *Assets* £619,200

TRUSTEES Michael Collins; Alexander Geddes; Dr Sally Geddes; Judi Geisler; Jeremy Green; Cornelius O'Connor.

OTHER INFORMATION Grants were awarded to nine organisations during the year.

HOW TO APPLY Application forms can be downloaded from the trust's website. Completed forms should be returned to the correspondent by email.

CONTACT DETAILS The Trustees, Parkfield, Woodend, Styal, Wilmslow, Cheshire SK9 4HF *Tel.* 01625 540850 *Email* admin@martingeddescharitabletrust.org *Website* martingeddescharitabletrust.org

■ The Jacqueline and Michael Gee Charitable Trust

CC NO 1062566 **ESTABLISHED** 1997

WHERE FUNDING CAN BE GIVEN UK and overseas.

WHO CAN BENEFIT Charitable organisations; schools, universities; places of worship.

WHAT IS FUNDED General charitable purposes; health; education and training; arts and culture; overseas aid; Jewish causes.

RANGE OF GRANTS Up to £10,000, but mostly under £5,000.

SAMPLE GRANTS Royal Academy of Arts (£10,000); Jewish Book Council and StandWithUs UK (£5,000 each); Orchestra Foundation UK (£3,500); The Langdon Foundation (£3,000); Heart Cells Foundation (£1,600); Lifelites (£1,000); North London Hospice (£700); WIZO UK (£450).

FINANCES *Financial year end* 05/04/2020 *Income* £81,300 *Total grants* £79,700 *Grants to organisations* £79,700 *Assets* £51,500

TRUSTEES Michael Gee; Jacqueline Gee.

OTHER INFORMATION Only beneficiaries of grants of £1,000 and above were listed in the accounts (25 organisations). Grants of under £1,000 totalled £12,000. Overall, grants were distributed as follows: arts and culture (£33,500); health and medical causes (£16,900); general donations and overseas aid (£16,000); education and training (£13,300).

HOW TO APPLY Contact the correspondent for further information.

CONTACT DETAILS The Trustees, 274A Kentish Town Road, London NW5 2AA *Tel.* 020 7493 1904

■ Sir Robert Geffery's Almshouse Trust

CC NO 219153 **ESTABLISHED** 1988

WHERE FUNDING CAN BE GIVEN UK.

WHO CAN BENEFIT Registered charities; schools.

WHAT IS FUNDED Education of disadvantaged children and young people; ironwork projects; STEM projects engaging students with materials science.

WHAT IS NOT FUNDED Visit the trust's website for a detailed list of exclusions.

TYPE OF GRANT Project funding.

RANGE OF GRANTS Up to £10,000 for education projects.

SAMPLE GRANTS St Vincent's Family Project (£25,000); Shrewsbury Flaxmill Malting (£18,000); Young Lewisham Project (£10,000); Vamos Theatre CIO (£5,100); University of Cambridge (£5,000); Make Believe Arts (£220).

FINANCES *Financial year end* 31/03/2020 *Income* £2,770,000 *Total grants* £534,400 *Grants to organisations* £534,400 *Assets* £31,710,000

TRUSTEE The Ironmongers' Trust Company.

OTHER INFORMATION The trust has five other linked charities collectively known as the Ironmongers' Charities.

HOW TO APPLY Application forms can be downloaded from the Ironmongers' website.

CONTACT DETAILS The Trustees, Ironmongers' Hall, Barbican, London EC2Y 8AA *Website* https://www.ironmongers.org/charitable-grants

■ General Charity (Coventry)

CC NO 216235 **ESTABLISHED** 1983

WHERE FUNDING CAN BE GIVEN Within the boundary of the City of Coventry.

WHO CAN BENEFIT Charitable organisations benefitting residents of Coventry.

WHAT IS FUNDED Social care and development including services for children and young people, older people, people with disabilities and people who are homeless; education; medical research; healthcare including the prevention and treatment of specific diseases.

TYPE OF GRANT Core costs; capital costs; project funding.

SAMPLE GRANTS The David Scott's Coventry Jubilee Community Care Trust (£120,000); Coventry Boys and Girls Club (£30,000); Zoë's Place (£10,000); Coventry Cathedral (£5,000); Happy Days (£4,000); PDSA (£1,000).

FINANCES *Financial year end* 31/12/2019 *Income* £1,690,000 *Total grants* £878,300 *Grants to organisations* £852,100 *Assets* £11,590,000

TRUSTEES David Mason; Richard Smith; Michael Harris; Edna Eaves; Edward Curtis; Cllr Ram Lakha; Julia McNaney; David Evans; Terry Proctor; Cllr Joseph Clifford; Cllr Marcus Lapsa; Vivia Kershaw; Cllr Catherine Miks; Patricia Hetherton; Dr Roger Davies; Cllr Tarlochan Singh Jandu.

OTHER INFORMATION Grants were distributed as follows: social care and development (£455,500); healthcare (£215,700); medical causes (£145,900); education (£35,200).

HOW TO APPLY Apply in writing to the correspondent.

CONTACT DETAILS Susan Hanrahan, Clerk to the Trustees, Old Bablake, Hill Street, Coventry, Warwickshire CV1 4AN *Tel.* 024 7622 2769 *Email* cov.genchar@btconnect.com

■ The General Charity Fund

CC NO 234710 **ESTABLISHED** 1964

WHERE FUNDING CAN BE GIVEN Merseyside. In exceptional circumstances the fund will consider applications from organisations working internationally.

WHO CAN BENEFIT Registered charities.

WHAT IS FUNDED The arts; drug rehabilitation; welfare; medicine; the environment.

TYPE OF GRANT Core costs; capital costs; project funding. One-off grants only.

RANGE OF GRANTS Mostly £1,000 to £2,000.

SAMPLE GRANTS Previous beneficiaries have included: Addaction, Bat Conservation Trust, Criminon, Music of Life Foundation, Narconon, National ME Centre and Unity Theatre.

FINANCES *Financial year end* 30/06/2020 *Income* £59,800 *Total grants* £0 *Grants to organisations* £0 *Assets* £2,180,000

TRUSTEES Arnold Pilkington; Eleanor Ashton; Neil Jones.

OTHER INFORMATION The fund's 2019/20 accounts state: 'Due to difficulties in arranging Trustees' meetings, in part due to the COVID-19 pandemic, no grants were paid in this financial year.' In previous years the fund has distributed around £65,000 in grants.

HOW TO APPLY Apply in writing to the correspondent. Further information on what should be included in an application can be found on the fund's website. The trustees meet twice a year on 1 May and 1 October.

CONTACT DETAILS Lynsey Lewis, c/o Rathbones, Port of Liverpool Building, Pier Head, Liverpool, Merseyside L3 1NW *Tel.* 0151 236 6666 *Website* https://generalcharityfund.org.uk

■ The General Nursing Council for England and Wales Trust

CC NO 288068 **ESTABLISHED** 1983

WHERE FUNDING CAN BE GIVEN England and Wales.

WHO CAN BENEFIT Universities and other public bodies benefitting nurses.

WHAT IS FUNDED Research into matters directly affecting nursing or the nursing profession.

WHAT IS NOT FUNDED Organisational overheads; purchase of equipment; dissemination costs such as conference attendance and publications.

TYPE OF GRANT Research costs.

RANGE OF GRANTS The normal maximum award is £40,000.

SAMPLE GRANTS Florence Nightingale Foundation (£34,500); Oxford University Hospital NHS Trust (£36,400); Angela Ruskin University (£26,700).

FINANCES *Financial year end* 31/03/2020 *Income* £122,000 *Total grants* £82,300 *Grants to organisations* £82,300 *Assets* £3,090,000

TRUSTEES Prof. Kate Gerrish; Prof. Susan Proctor; Prof. Janice Sigsworth; Robert Parry; Prof. Anne Topping.

OTHER INFORMATION Each year there is a call for research grant applications with a specific focus, see the website for further information.

HOW TO APPLY Application forms can be downloaded from the trust's website.

CONTACT DETAILS Alan Haddon, Secretary, 29 Beech Way, Blackmore End, Wheathamstead, Hertsfordshire AL4 8LY *Email* gnct@btinternet.com *Website* www.gnct.org.uk

■ The Generations Foundation

CC NO 1110565 **ESTABLISHED** 2005

WHERE FUNDING CAN BE GIVEN UK, Borough of Merton and financially developing countries.

WHO CAN BENEFIT Local charitable organisations in Merton; charitable organisations working in the UK and in financially developing countries.

WHAT IS FUNDED The provision of a better quality of life for children who are disadvantaged, ill or who have disabilities; also, environmental protection and conservation projects.

TYPE OF GRANT Capital costs; project funding; development funding. Funding is often awarded for several years.

RANGE OF GRANTS £500 to £55,000.

SAMPLE GRANTS World Land Trust (£40,000); Home-Start Merton (£25,000); Salvation Army (£10,000); Dorset Mind (£2,000); MNDA (£500).

FINANCES *Financial year end* 05/04/2020 *Income* £150,200 *Total grants* £173,200 *Grants to organisations* £173,200 *Assets* £59,600

TRUSTEES Bob Finch; Stephen Finch; Rohini Finch.

OTHER INFORMATION Funding was awarded to 14 organisations during the year.

HOW TO APPLY Application forms are available to download from the website. Potential applicants should contact the foundation by email before applying to gauge whether their application is likely to be successful.

CONTACT DETAILS The Trustees, 36 Marryat Road, Wimbledon, London SW19 5BD *Tel.* 020 8946 7760 *Email* generationstrust@mail.com *Website* www.generationsct.co.uk

■ The Steven Gerrard Foundation

CC NO 1140813 **ESTABLISHED** 2011

WHERE FUNDING CAN BE GIVEN UK, with a preference for Liverpool.

WHO CAN BENEFIT Registered charities.

WHAT IS FUNDED To provide relief to children and young people in need, whether through illness, family breakdown, disability, involvement in the streets, financial or educational disadvantage.

SAMPLE GRANTS Claire House Children's Hospice (£202,400); Rays of Sunshine Children's Charity (£12,000); Spire Leeds Hospital (£10,600); Born Too Soon (£5,000).

FINANCES *Financial year end* 31/12/2019 *Income* £291,800 *Total grants* £238,500 *Grants to organisations* £238,500 *Assets* £22,300

TRUSTEES Steven Gerrard; Peter Sterling; Andrew Sterling.

HOW TO APPLY At the time of writing (May 2021) the website stated: 'We currently have no further information on future grants cycles, as soon as we do the website will be updated accordingly." See the website for updates.

CONTACT DETAILS The Trustees, PKF Cooper Parry, Sky View, Argosy Road, East Midlands Airport, Castle Donington, Derbyshire DE74 2SA *Tel.* 01332 411163 *Email* info@stevengerrardfoundation.org *Website* www.stevengerrardfoundation.org

■ The Gertner Charitable Trust

CC NO 327380 **ESTABLISHED** 1987

WHERE FUNDING CAN BE GIVEN UK and overseas.

WHO CAN BENEFIT Jewish charities and individuals.

WHAT IS FUNDED Jewish charitable purposes, including: education; health; welfare.

SAMPLE GRANTS A list of beneficiaries was not included in the annual report and accounts.

FINANCES *Financial year end* 31/03/2019 *Income* £503,000 *Total grants* £441,600 *Grants to organisations* £404,000 *Assets* £6,657,000

TRUSTEES Michael Wechsler; Michelle Gertner; Simon Jacobs; Mendi Gertner.

OTHER INFORMATION In 2018/19 £37,600 was given to individuals. The 2018/19 accounts were the latest available at the time of writing (June 2021).

HOW TO APPLY Apply in writing to the correspondent. The trustees meet quarterly.

CONTACT DETAILS The Trustees, Fordgate House, Union House, 1 Allsop Place, London NW1 5LF *Tel.* 020 7224 1234

■ The Tara Getty Foundation

CC NO 1107895 **ESTABLISHED** 2004

WHERE FUNDING CAN BE GIVEN UK and overseas.

WHO CAN BENEFIT Charitable organisations.

WHAT IS FUNDED Conservation; the environment; climate change; community development; education; health and saving lives; medical research; mental health; disaster relief; children and young people; research.

SAMPLE GRANTS Africa Foundation; Clean Slate; Garsington Opera; InterAct Stroke Support; KidsOut UK; Ocean Family Foundation; The Amber Foundation; Sentebale; The Cambridge Trust; The Nehemiah Project; The Royal Society of Literature.

FINANCES *Financial year end* 31/12/2019
Income £258,600 *Total grants* £393,100
Grants to organisations £393,100
Assets £23,900

TRUSTEES Patrick Maxwell; Tara Getty; Louise Creasey.

OTHER INFORMATION Grants were awarded to 12 organisations during the year in the following categories: education (£219,300); marine conservation (£133,300); community (£18,000); young people (£18,000); medical causes (£4,500). The individual grant amounts were not listed in the accounts. See the foundation's 2019 annual report for a detailed list of its updated objectives.

HOW TO APPLY Apply in writing to the correspondent. Shortlisted charities will be contacted for more detailed information. The foundation requests a full breakdown of the project, detailed financial statements and a breakdown of secured and projected income for the upcoming year.

CONTACT DETAILS The Trustees, 26 Curzon Street, London W1J 7TQ *Tel.* 020 7409 3900

■ The Gibbons Family Trust

CC NO 290884 **ESTABLISHED** 1984

WHERE FUNDING CAN BE GIVEN Devon, with a preference for East Devon and the Isle of Thanet in Kent.

WHO CAN BENEFIT Registered charities; not-for-profit organisations; individuals.

WHAT IS FUNDED The welfare, education, training and recreation of children and young people up to the age of 25.

WHAT IS NOT FUNDED Ongoing fees (e.g. regular payments for education); individuals taking trips overseas; retrospective expenditure.

TYPE OF GRANT Capital costs; project funding.

RANGE OF GRANTS Grants up to £6,500.

SAMPLE GRANTS Maytree Special School, Torbay (£3,000); Whizz-Kidz (£2,000); Thanet Disabled Riding Centre (£2,500); Brainwave and Exeter Phoenix Ltd (£1,500 each); Lifeworks (£1,000); Living Paintings (£500).

FINANCES *Financial year end* 31/03/2020
Income £102,300 *Total grants* £87,500
Grants to organisations £81,000
Assets £2,300,000

TRUSTEES Prof. Chris King; Dr John Frankish; Dr Miles Joyner; Elizabeth Lee; Dr Clive Stubbings.

HOW TO APPLY Applications can be made through an online form on the trust's website as well as the application criteria for each grant category. Only one application from any applicant will be considered in any financial year (April to March).

CONTACT DETAILS The Trustees, The Gibbons Trusts, 14 Fore Street, Budleigh Salterton, Devon EX9 6NG *Tel.* 07483 335759 *Email* enquiries@gibbonstrusts.org *Website* https://gibbonstrusts.org.uk

■ The David Gibbons Foundation

CC NO 1134727 **ESTABLISHED** 2010

WHERE FUNDING CAN BE GIVEN Devon.

WHO CAN BENEFIT Registered charities and community groups; individuals.

WHAT IS FUNDED Social welfare; older people; health.

WHAT IS NOT FUNDED Ongoing fees (e.g. regular payments for rent); individuals for trips overseas; organisations which have had a grant within the past 12 months.

RANGE OF GRANTS Generally up to £5,000.

SAMPLE GRANTS Budleigh Hub (£6,000); Exeter Leukaemia Fund (£4,000); TLC Palliative Care at Home CIC (£3,000); Mid Devon Mobility (£2,000); Age UK Devon (£1,000); Torbay Advice Network (£500).

FINANCES *Financial year end* 31/03/2020
Income £134,300 *Total grants* £157,900
Grants to organisations £139,000
Assets £3,010,000

TRUSTEES Dr John Frankish; Dr Miles Joyner; Prof. Chris King; Elizabeth Lee; Dr Clive Stubbings.

OTHER INFORMATION In 2019/20 a total of 98 grants were awarded. Of this amount, 28 grants were awarded to individuals totalling £18,900. The foundation is closely linked to, and shares a website with, The Gibbons Family Trust (Charity Commission No. 290884).

HOW TO APPLY To apply, use the online application form on the foundation's website, where full guidelines and deadlines are also available.

CONTACT DETAILS Cathy Houghton, Trusts Manager, The Gibbons Trusts, 14 Fore Street, Budleigh Salterton, Devon EX9 6NG *Tel.* 07483 335759 *Email* enquiries@gibbonstrusts.org *Website* https://gibbonstrusts.org.uk

■ The Gibbs Charitable Trusts

CC NO 207997 **ESTABLISHED** 1946

WHERE FUNDING CAN BE GIVEN UK, with a preference for Wales; overseas.

WHO CAN BENEFIT Registered charities; CICs.

WHAT IS FUNDED Methodist churches and organisations; health; welfare; arts and culture; education.

WHAT IS NOT FUNDED Individuals.

TYPE OF GRANT Buildings; capital and project grants.

RANGE OF GRANTS The majority of grants are between £500 and £10,000.

SAMPLE GRANTS Victoria Methodist – Bristol (£10,000); Medécins Sans Frontières (£6,000); Tree Aid (£5,000); Practical Action (£4,000); Brecknock Society and Museum Friends (£3,000); Brecon Baroque Festival (£2,500); Teacher Aid (£500).

FINANCES *Financial year end* 31/03/2020
Income £98,900 *Total grants* £99,500
Grants to organisations £99,500
Assets £2,890,000

TRUSTEES Dr James Gibbs; Dr John Gibbs; Andrew Gibbs; Celia Gibbs; Elizabeth Gibbs; Dr Jessica Gibbs; Dr John E. Gibbs; Patience Gibbs; Rebecca Gibbs; William Gibbs; Juliet Gibbs; James D. Gibbs; Timothy Gibbs.

OTHER INFORMATION In 2019/20 the trust made 49 grants. The trust's entry on the Charity Commission's website suggests that few new applicants are supported.

HOW TO APPLY Apply using the online portal available on the trust's website.

CONTACT DETAILS Dr James Gibbs, Trustee, 8 Victoria Square, Bristol BS8 4ET *Tel.* 0117 973 6615 *Email* jamesgibbs@btinternet.com *Website* www.gibbstrust.org.uk

■ The Simon Gibson Charitable Trust

CC NO 269501 **ESTABLISHED** 1975

WHERE FUNDING CAN BE GIVEN Suffolk; Norfolk; Cambridgeshire; Hertfordshire; Glamorganshire; Gwent; Powys; Carmarthenshire.

WHO CAN BENEFIT UK-registered charities and CICs. National charities are more likely to be considered if they support local causes in the areas listed above.

WHAT IS FUNDED General charitable purposes, with a preference for: organisations working with young people or older people; conservation; education; religion.

WHAT IS NOT FUNDED Individuals or organisations applying on behalf of individuals; students for educational or gap year sponsorship; conferences, seminars or workshops; overseas charities (other than those working in conservation or previously known to the trustees).

TYPE OF GRANT Core costs; specific project funding.

RANGE OF GRANTS Grants from £1,000 to £20,000, with most grants in the range of £3,000 to £5,000.

SAMPLE GRANTS Livery Company of Wales Charitable Trust (£20,000); Ely Cathedral Appeal Fund (£10,800); Army Benevolent Fund, Combat Stress (£5,000 each); Hospice UK (Help the Hospices) (£3,000); Cardiff Metropolitan University (£4,000); Brain Tumour Research (£2,000).

FINANCES *Financial year end* 05/04/2020 *Income* £1,270,000 *Total grants* £826,800 *Grants to organisations* £826,800 *Assets* £17,770,000

TRUSTEES Bryan Marsh; George Gibson; Deborah Connor; John Homfray.

HOW TO APPLY Application forms are available to download from the website and should be returned to the trust by post. Applications should be submitted between 1 January and 31 March each year.

CONTACT DETAILS Bryan Marsh, Trustee, PO Box 109, Cowbridge CF71 9EA *Tel.* 01446 775991 *Email* bryan.marsh@sgctrust.org.uk *Website* https://www.sgctrust.org.uk

■ The G. C. Gibson Charitable Trust

CC NO 258710 **ESTABLISHED** 1968

WHERE FUNDING CAN BE GIVEN Worldwide.

WHO CAN BENEFIT UK-registered charities operating anywhere in the world. Priority is given to smaller charities with an income from donations from the public and grant-making charities of up to £1 million.

WHAT IS FUNDED General charitable purposes, with grants falling within the following categories: community and other social projects; health, hospices and medical research; art, music and education; and religion. The majority of support is already committed to existing beneficiaries; however, the trust supports around ten new applicants each year. New applications are focused on a particular theme, which can vary depending on the year.

WHAT IS NOT FUNDED The fabric of Christian churches, hospices, educational farms, riding and carriage driving for people with disabilities, cancer care and research, theatres and museums.

TYPE OF GRANT Mainly recurring for core costs; capital and one-off project costs are also supported.

RANGE OF GRANTS Normally £1,000 to £10,000 – this varies depending upon the annual theme.

SAMPLE GRANTS A list of beneficiaries was not included in the annual report and accounts.

FINANCES *Financial year end* 31/03/2020 *Income* £796,700 *Total grants* £625,700 *Grants to organisations* £625,700 *Assets* £14,540,000

TRUSTEES Anna Dalrymple; Martin Gibson; Jane Gibson; Lucy Kelly; Edward Gibson; Thomas Homfray.

HOW TO APPLY If new to the trust, applications should be made using the online form on the website only. Applications open on the 1st of August and close around the end of August each year. Prospective applicants are advised to read the guidelines before applying, as these may change with each funding round. The trustees prefer short applications (maximum of one page). Applicants are usually notified of the trustees' decisions in October. The trustees can be contacted by email only; they do not respond to or acknowledge letters.

CONTACT DETAILS The Trustees, Durnsford Mill House, Mildenhall, Marlborough, Wiltshire SN8 2NG *Tel.* 07850 859824 *Email* gcgibsoncharity@gmail.com *Website* www.gcgct.org

■ The Girdlers' Company Charitable Trust

CC NO 328026 **ESTABLISHED** 1988

WHERE FUNDING CAN BE GIVEN England, with a preference for London and, in particular, Islington, Hammersmith and Peckham; New Zealand.

WHO CAN BENEFIT Registered and exempt charities; CIOs; community and amateur sports clubs.

WHAT IS FUNDED Employability through vocational training; support to carers; mental health; education; literacy; ex-offenders.

TYPE OF GRANT Grants to principal charities are for three years. One-off grants are awarded depending on available funds.

RANGE OF GRANTS Principal charities: up to £25,000 per year. One-off grants: up to £10,000.

SAMPLE GRANTS A list of beneficiaries was not included in the annual report and accounts.

FINANCES *Financial year end* 29/09/2019 *Income* £213,000 *Total grants* £771,200 *Grants to organisations* £771,200 *Assets* £5,610,000

TRUSTEE The Girdlers' Company.

OTHER INFORMATION Around half of the trust's annual grants are made to its 'principal charities', many of which it maintains longstanding and close relationships. In 2018/19 grants totalling £314,500 (representing 42% of total grants awarded) were made to the principal charities. The 2018/19 accounts were the latest available at the time of writing (April 2021).

HOW TO APPLY At the time of writing (April 2021), the website states that the trust will accept applications for one-off grants of up to £10,000 from organisations that deliver clearly defined outcomes and that support at least one of the trust's focus areas. An eligibility quiz is available on the website. The Benefactions Committee currently meets in mid-January and late June to review applications. At the next Court meeting (currently early February and early

July) applications will be considered and (if successful) approved by the Court. All applicants will be advised of the outcome, whether or not they have been successful. Applications should be made through the website. It appears that the trust does not accept unsolicited applications for its other funding streams.

CONTACT DETAILS M. Whiteside, Clerk, Girdlers Hall, Basinghall Avenue, London EC2V 5DD *Tel.* 020 7448 4851 *Email* clerk@girdlers.co.uk *Website* www.girdlers.co.uk

■ The B. and P. Glasser Charitable Trust

CC NO 326571 **ESTABLISHED** 1984

WHERE FUNDING CAN BE GIVEN UK and worldwide.

WHO CAN BENEFIT Registered charities and community organisations.

WHAT IS FUNDED General charitable purposes; health; disability; social welfare; Jewish causes.

WHAT IS NOT FUNDED Individuals, including students.

RANGE OF GRANTS £750 to £10,000.

SAMPLE GRANTS Nightingale House (£10,000); Jewish Care (£8,000); Blind Veterans UK (£3,000); Jewish Deaf Association (£2,750); ActionAid UK (£2,000); Cancer Research UK (£1,250); Samaritans – Chiltern Branch (£750).

FINANCES *Financial year end* 31/10/2019 *Income* £80,900 *Total grants* £105,000 *Grants to organisations* £105,000 *Assets* £2,760,000

TRUSTEES Michael Glasser; John Glasser.

OTHER INFORMATION The 2018/19 accounts were the latest available at the time of writing (June 2021). Grants were awarded to 28 organisations during the year.

HOW TO APPLY Apply in writing to the correspondent. In order to keep administrative costs to a minimum, the trustees are unable to reply to unsuccessful applicants.

CONTACT DETAILS The Trustees, c/o BDO LLP, 55 Baker Street, London W1U 7EU *Tel.* 020 7486 5888 *Email* nicki.fletcher@bdo.co.uk

■ The Glass-House Trust

CC NO 1144990 **ESTABLISHED** 2011

WHERE FUNDING CAN BE GIVEN UK, occasionally overseas.

WHO CAN BENEFIT Registered charities; activities with a clearly defined charitable purpose.

WHAT IS FUNDED The built environment; child development; social research/policy; the arts.

WHAT IS NOT FUNDED Individuals; education fees; expeditions.

TYPE OF GRANT Core costs; project funding; development funding; salaries; research.

RANGE OF GRANTS Up to £100,000.

SAMPLE GRANTS Glass-House Community-Led Design (£100,000); A Space (£55,000); MayDay Rooms (£50,000); Raven Row (£35,000); Money for Madagascar (£23,500); Transform Drug Policy Foundation (£15,000); Bloody Good Period and South Yorkshire's Community Foundation (£5,000 each); The Sainsbury Archive (£3,000).

FINANCES *Financial year end* 05/04/2020 *Income* £205,900 *Total grants* £291,500 *Grants to organisations* £291,500 *Assets* £9,450,000

TRUSTEES Alex Sainsbury; Judith Portrait; Elinor Sainsbury.

OTHER INFORMATION The trust is one of the Sainsbury Family Charitable Trusts which share a common administration – see www.sftc.org.uk for more information. According to the 2019/20 accounts, grants were awarded to nine organisations during the year.

HOW TO APPLY Unsolicited applications are not accepted.

CONTACT DETAILS Robert Bell, Director, The Peak, 5 Wilton Road, London SW1V 1AP *Tel.* 020 7410 0330 *Email* info@sfct.org.uk *Website* https://www.sfct.org.uk/Glass-house.html

■ The F. Glenister Woodger Trust

CC NO 802642 **ESTABLISHED** 1989

WHERE FUNDING CAN BE GIVEN West Wittering.

WHO CAN BENEFIT Registered charities; unregistered charities; social enterprises; schools; universities; PTAs; amateur sports clubs; hospitals; hospices; local authorities.

WHAT IS FUNDED General charitable purposes.

TYPE OF GRANT Capital costs; seed funding/start-up funding.

RANGE OF GRANTS Grants range from £200 up to £203,900.

SAMPLE GRANTS The Apuldram Centre (£203,900); South Downs National Park Trust (£120,000); Dementia Support/Sage House (£100,000); Lifecentre (£53,000); Stirlands Cricket Club (£15,000); Shelter (£2,000); Witterings United FC (£200).

FINANCES *Financial year end* 05/04/2020 *Income* £1,800,000 *Total grants* £755,500 *Grants to organisations* £755,500 *Assets* £39,880,000

TRUSTEES Rosamund Champ; William Craven; Stuart Dobbin; Maxine Pickup; Rosamund Gentle; Dr Adrian Gregory.

OTHER INFORMATION Grants were awarded to 27 organisations in 2019/20.

HOW TO APPLY Apply in writing to the correspondent. The trustees meet quarterly to review grant applications.

CONTACT DETAILS The Trustees, The Pavilion, Rookwood Road, West Wittering, Chichester, West Sussex PO20 8LT *Tel.* 01243 513116 *Email* office@wfgwoodgertrust.org

■ The Gloag Foundation

OSCR NO SC035799 **ESTABLISHED** 2004

WHERE FUNDING CAN BE GIVEN UK and overseas.

WHO CAN BENEFIT Charitable organisations and individuals.

WHAT IS FUNDED Health; relief of poverty; anti-exploitation and people trafficking; Christianity.

RANGE OF GRANTS Mostly up to £100,000. Larger grants in excess of £1 million are made to Freedom from Fistula Foundation.

SAMPLE GRANTS Freedom From Fistula Foundation (£1.3 million); Kenya Children's Homes – UK (£98,300); Open Doors (£87,400); Young Life (£70,300); Harmeny Trust (£50,000); Alcohol Recovery Scotland (£30,000); Kenya Children's Homes (£18,200).

FINANCES *Financial year end* 31/12/2019 *Income* £2,370,000 *Total grants* £1,836,600 *Grants to organisations* £1,770,000 *Assets* £8,440,000

OTHER INFORMATION Grants were made to support the foundation's main focuses in Kenya through its supported charities (£116,400) and in support of Freedom from Fistula Foundation (£1.31 million). New grants were also awarded to charities and were broken down as follows: relief of poverty (£117,300); anti-exploitation and people trafficking (£88,400); advancement of Christianity (£70,300); health (£57,300); others (£4,500). Grants to individuals are primarily made to support international students in further education courses in the UK.

HOW TO APPLY The foundation's website states that it 'no longer accepts unsolicited applications or requests. Applications are by invitation only.'

CONTACT DETAILS The Trustees, The Steading, Kinfauns, Perth, Perthshire PH2 7JU *Tel.* 01738 633264 *Website* www.gloagfoundation.org.uk

■ Global Charities

CC NO 1091657 **ESTABLISHED** 1978

WHERE FUNDING CAN BE GIVEN UK.

WHO CAN BENEFIT Registered charities.

WHAT IS FUNDED Mental health; domestic abuse; grief; poverty; carers; loneliness.

TYPE OF GRANT Project funding; capital costs; core costs.

SAMPLE GRANTS Previous beneficiaries have included: Alex TLC; Amy and Friends; Cam Sight; Carers Milton Keynes; Heel and Toe; Learning Through Horses; Reuben's Retreat; Skylarks; The Sickle Cell Society.

FINANCES *Financial year end* 31/03/2020 *Income* £4,490,000 *Total grants* £1,350,000 *Grants to organisations* £1,350,000 *Assets* £2,150,000

TRUSTEES Marcia Asare; Martin Allen; Jennifer Stubbs; Joanne Kenrick; Michael Connole; Jonathan Norbury; Shalni Sood; Gareth Andrewartha; Sally Cairns; Ulrika Hogberg.

OTHER INFORMATION The charity made 32 grants broken down as follows: disability (£545,500); illness (£316,000); lack of opportunity (£299,300); young carers (£72,600); mental health (£67,900); bereavement (£45,400).

HOW TO APPLY At the time of writing (January 2021) the charity was not accepting applications. Charities can join the mailing list to be notified of any changes to the grants programme.

CONTACT DETAILS The Trustees, 30 Leicester Square, London WC2H 7LA *Tel.* 0345 606 0990 *Email* grants@makesomenoise.com *Website* www.makesomenoise.com

■ County of Gloucestershire Community Foundation

CC NO 900239 **ESTABLISHED** 1989

WHERE FUNDING CAN BE GIVEN Gloucestershire.

WHO CAN BENEFIT Charities; charitable organisations, including CICs and social enterprises; individuals.

WHAT IS FUNDED General charitable purposes.

WHAT IS NOT FUNDED See the website for programme-specific exclusions.

TYPE OF GRANT Programme dependent.

RANGE OF GRANTS £1,000 to £10,000.

SAMPLE GRANTS Getting Court and The Country Food Trust (£10,000 each); Active Gloucestershire (£6,500); Cheltenham Housing Aid Centre and Shine! (£5,000 each); Fair Shares Gloucestershire (£3,000); Gloucestershire Deaf Association (£2,000); The Wiggly Worm (£1,000); Marah Trust (£500).

FINANCES *Financial year end* 31/12/2019 *Income* £290,200 *Total grants* £305,700 *Grants to organisations* £300,700 *Assets* £7,480,000

TRUSTEES Richard Ingle; Christine Ellson; Tracy Clark; Richard Stephens; Helen Lovatt; Anthony Waite; James Tabor; Norman Gardner; Jonatan Dunley.

OTHER INFORMATION This is one of the 46 UK community foundations, which distribute funding for a wide range of purposes. As with all community foundations, there are a number of donor-advised funds managed on behalf of individuals, families and charitable trusts. Grant schemes tend to change frequently; consult the foundation's website for details of current programmes and up-to-date deadlines. A total of 97 grants were awarded to organisations during the year in the following categories: children and young people (£112,200); disability and health (£63,700); families (£39,800); relief of poverty (£34,900); older people (£26,600); disadvantaged communities (£22,500); minority communities (£1,000); In addition, 19 grants were awarded to individuals totalling £5,000.

HOW TO APPLY Potential applicants are advised to visit the community foundation's website or contact its grants team to find the most suitable funding stream.

CONTACT DETAILS Talitha Nelson, Chief Executive Officer, The Manor, Boddington, Cheltenham, Gloucestershire GL51 0TJ *Tel.* 01242 851357 *Email* ceo@gloucestershirecf.org.uk *Website* www.gloucestershirecf.org.uk

■ The Gloucestershire Historic Churches Trust

CC NO 1120266 **ESTABLISHED** 1980

WHERE FUNDING CAN BE GIVEN Gloucestershire, South Gloucestershire and North Bristol.

WHO CAN BENEFIT Places of worship of all Christian denominations.

WHAT IS FUNDED Repair, maintenance and improvements to the fabric of religious buildings and their contents, as well as to their surrounding churchyards.

WHAT IS NOT FUNDED Substantial repairs unless the work has been specified by an architect or surveyor with appropriate conservation training.

TYPE OF GRANT One-off, but repeat applications may be considered; capital costs.

RANGE OF GRANTS Up to £10,000.

SAMPLE GRANTS Holy Trinity – Stapleton (£10,000); Holy Innocents – Highnam (£8,000); St James – Mangotsfield (£5,000); St Michael – Abenhall (£4,500); St Cyr – Stonehouse (£2,000); St James – Stoke Orchard (£1,500); St Mary Magdalene – Twyning (£1,000).

FINANCES *Financial year end* 31/12/2019 *Income* £163,900 *Total grants* £152,000 *Grants to organisations* £152,000 *Assets* £1,890,000

TRUSTEES David Kingsmill; Helen Whitbread; Stephen Langton; Jonathan McKechnie-Jarvis; James Drennan; Colin Senior.

OTHER INFORMATION Grants were made to 34 places of worship in 2019.

HOW TO APPLY Application forms and full guidelines can be downloaded from the trust's website. Completed applications should be returned to the Chair of the Grants Committee by post. When an application is received the trustees will arrange a meeting at your church to discuss your application and view the proposed work. The committee meets on the first Monday of June and December. Applications should be made by the end of April for the June meeting or by the end of October for the December meeting. You will normally be informed of the decision within two weeks of the meeting. The Grants Committee is likely to be more generous to applicants who support the work of the trust by an annual donation and/or by taking part in the annual sponsored Ride+Stride event. For further information on applications email jonathanmj@virginmedia.com.

CONTACT DETAILS Jonathan MacKechnie-Jarvis, Chair of the Grants Committee, 73 Forest View Road, Tuffley, Gloucester, Gloucestershire GL4 0BY *Tel.* 01452 502174 *Email* grants@ghct.org.uk *Website* www.ghct.org.uk

■ Worshipful Company of Glovers of London Charitable Trust

CC NO 269091 **ESTABLISHED** 1975

WHERE FUNDING CAN BE GIVEN UK, with a preference for London.

WHO CAN BENEFIT Charitable and educational organisations; individuals.

WHAT IS FUNDED General charitable purposes; education; social welfare; provision of gloves; prosthetics.

TYPE OF GRANT Projects; bursaries; prizes.

RANGE OF GRANTS Up to £7,700.

SAMPLE GRANTS King Edward's School – Witley (£7,700); City of London School (£5,500); gloves for homeless charities (£4,900); University of West London (£4,300); Glove Design Competition (£2,300); Church of St Margaret – Lothbury and Lord Mayor's Charities (£2,000 each).

FINANCES *Financial year end* 05/04/2020 *Income* £86,700 *Total grants* £77,900 *Grants to organisations* £54,900 *Assets* £748,400

TRUSTEE The Worshipful Company of Glovers of London.

OTHER INFORMATION In 2019/20 grants for 'gloves and glove related projects' totalled £16,800, bursaries and other charitable grants totalled £36,200, and grants to two individuals for prosthetics totalled £23,000.

HOW TO APPLY Contact the correspondent for further information.

CONTACT DETAILS Lt Col Mark Butler, Clerk, c/o Knox Cropper and Co., 65 Leadenhall Street, London EC3A 2AD *Tel.* 01747 851887 *Email* clerk@theglovierscompany.org

■ The Godinton Charitable Trust

CC NO 268321 **ESTABLISHED** 1974

WHERE FUNDING CAN BE GIVEN Kent.

WHO CAN BENEFIT The trust provides regular support for The Godinton House Preservation Trust, as well as supporting local registered charities, churches and hospices.

WHAT IS FUNDED General charitable purposes.

WHAT IS NOT FUNDED Individuals; organisations based outside Kent.

TYPE OF GRANT Capital costs; general funding.

RANGE OF GRANTS Generally £500 to £3,000.

SAMPLE GRANTS Godinton House Preservation Trust (£175,800); Great Chart Church (£3,000); Rising Sun Domestic Violence and Abuse Service (£2,000); Hothfield Church (£1,750); Charing Surgery Gardeners Group and Music at Malling (£1,000 each); Weald of Kent Preservation Society (£500).

FINANCES *Financial year end* 31/10/2019 *Income* £184,700 *Total grants* £317,200 *Grants to organisations* £317,200 *Assets* £6,540,000

TRUSTEES The Hon. Wyndham Plumptre; The Hon. John Leigh-Pemberton; Michael Jennings; Terence Bennett.

OTHER INFORMATION The 2018/19 accounts were the latest available at the time of writing (April 2021). Grants were awarded to 32 organisations in total during the year.

HOW TO APPLY Contact the correspondent for information regarding the application process.

CONTACT DETAILS The Trustees, Godinton House, Godinton Lane, Ashford, Kent TN23 3BP *Tel.* 01233 632652 *Email* office@godintonhouse.co.uk

■ Worshipful Company of Gold and Silver Wyre Drawers Second Charitable Trust Fund

CC NO 802491 **ESTABLISHED** 1969

WHERE FUNDING CAN BE GIVEN London.

WHO CAN BENEFIT Registered charities.

WHAT IS FUNDED General charitable purposes, including: medical causes; education; music; children and young people; the armed forces; the gold and silver wire trade.

RANGE OF GRANTS Up to £12,500.

SAMPLE GRANTS Previous beneficiaries have included: Tilehouse Counselling (£12,600); Royal School of Needlework Goldwork and Bursary (£6,000); Goldsmiths C&DC Jewellery Awards (£3,000); 101 Squadron Centenary (£1,100); Action for ME and Queen Alexandra's Hospital Home (£1,000 each); Bexley Heath Young Peoples Service (£200); City and Guilds of London Institute (£50).

FINANCES *Financial year end* 31/12/2019 *Income* £139,800 *Total grants* £111,700 *Grants to organisations* £111,700 *Assets* £1,550,000

TRUSTEES Michael Gunston; Revd Gordon Warren; Brian Turner; Roger Carter; Air Cdre Cynthia Fowler.

HOW TO APPLY Apply in writing to the correspondent. The trustees meet four times a year. The 2019 annual report states: 'Application for grants are considered and a review of actual and budgeted expenditure is carried out at each meeting.'

CONTACT DETAILS Cdr Mark Dickens, Clerk, Lye Green Forge, Lye Green, Crowborough, East Sussex TN6 1UU *Tel.* 07825 157866 *Email* clerk@gswd.co.uk *Website* www.gswd.co.uk

■ Sydney and Phyllis Goldberg Memorial Charitable Trust

CC NO 291835 **ESTABLISHED** 1985

WHERE FUNDING CAN BE GIVEN UK and overseas.

WHO CAN BENEFIT Charitable organisations; hospitals; overseas organisations.

WHAT IS FUNDED Medical research; social welfare; health; disability.

WHAT IS NOT FUNDED Individuals.

TYPE OF GRANT Project funding.

RANGE OF GRANTS Typically £3,000 to £15,000.

SAMPLE GRANTS Children with Special Needs Foundation, Life Centre and The British Stammering Association (£15,000 each); Nepal Earthquake Appeal (£10,000); Child Brain Injury Trust (£7,500); British Earthquake and Tsunami Support and Isaac Goldberg Charity Trust (£3,000 each).

FINANCES *Financial year end* 05/04/2020
Income £137,700 *Total grants* £130,200
Grants to organisations £130,200
Assets £3,680,000

TRUSTEES Christopher Pexton; Howard Vowles; Michael Church.

OTHER INFORMATION In 2019/20 the trust made grants to 14 organisations totalling £130,200.

HOW TO APPLY Apply in writing to the correspondent. The trustees meet once a year.

CONTACT DETAILS The Trustees, c/o Begbies, 9 Bonhill Street, London EC2A 4DJ *Tel.* 020 7628 5801

■ The Goldcrest Charitable Trust

CC NO 1147149 **ESTABLISHED** 2012

WHERE FUNDING CAN BE GIVEN UK.

WHO CAN BENEFIT Charitable organisations.

WHAT IS FUNDED General charitable purposes including health.

RANGE OF GRANTS Up to £25,000.

SAMPLE GRANTS Huntingdon's Disease Association (£25,000); MNDA (£20,000); Headway (£10,000); Step Together (£5,000); The Hamlet (£2,000).

FINANCES *Financial year end* 30/04/2020
Income £43,000 *Total grants* £154,300
Grants to organisations £154,300
Assets £1,930,000

TRUSTEES Julie Dyson; Neil Dyson; Coutts & Co.

HOW TO APPLY Apply by letter to the correspondent.

CONTACT DETAILS The Trustees, Coutts & Co. Trustee Department, 1st Floor, Trinity Quay 1, Avon Street, Bristol BS2 0PT *Tel.* 0345 304 2424

■ The Golden Bottle Trust

CC NO 327026 **ESTABLISHED** 1985

WHERE FUNDING CAN BE GIVEN Worldwide, with a preference for the UK.

WHO CAN BENEFIT Charitable organisations.

WHAT IS FUNDED General charitable purposes.

RANGE OF GRANTS £250 to £10,000, with some larger grants.

SAMPLE GRANTS The Fore (£300,000); Epic Foundation and RefuAid (£100,000 each); Henry C Hoare Charitable Trust (£60,000); Lord Mayor's Appeal (£35,000); Temple Bar Trust (£25,000); Acumen Fund (£15,000); Blue Marine Foundation and Stepping Out Foundation (£10,000 each).

FINANCES *Financial year end* 30/09/2019
Income £3,280,000 *Total grants* £2,110,000
Grants to organisations £2,110,000
Assets £18,470,000

TRUSTEE Messrs. Hoare Trustees.

OTHER INFORMATION The 2018/19 accounts were the latest available at the time of writing (May 2021). Only beneficiaries of grants of over £10,000 were listed in the accounts. The grant total does not include £201,700 given by the trust to match staff fundraising.

HOW TO APPLY The website states that the trust prefers to use trusted partners and networks to identify suitable causes to help. For this reason, unsolicited grant requests are not accepted.

CONTACT DETAILS Messrs. Hoare Trustees, c/o C. Hoare and Co., 37 Fleet Street, London EC4P 4DQ *Tel.* 020 7353 4522 *Website* https://www.hoaresbank.co.uk/golden-bottle-trust

■ The Goldman Sachs Charitable Gift Fund (UK)

CC NO 1120148 **ESTABLISHED** 2007

WHERE FUNDING CAN BE GIVEN UK and overseas.

WHO CAN BENEFIT Registered charities; schools and universities.

WHAT IS FUNDED Education; relief of poverty; arts and culture; humanitarian relief; health; community; general charitable purposes.

TYPE OF GRANT Unrestricted.

SAMPLE GRANTS Larger grants included: Columbia University (£536,600); Princeton University (£221,200); PeacePlayers International (£109,100); Lucile Packard Foundation for Children's Health (£72,800).

FINANCES *Financial year end* 30/06/2020
Income £3,860,000 *Total grants* £1,640,000
Grants to organisations £1,640,000
Assets £15,040,000

TRUSTEES Robert Katz; Graham Shaw; Peter Fahey.

OTHER INFORMATION This fund was established by Goldman Sachs International in 2007 as one of the vehicles for its charitable giving. It is also connected to Goldman Sachs Gives. The financial details were reported in the fund's accounts in USD. They were converted into GBP at the time of writing (April 2021). A total of 86 grants were made to organisations during the year. Only beneficiaries of grants above $100,000 were listed in the accounts. Grants below $100,000 totalled $863,166 (£628,000).

HOW TO APPLY The annual report for 2019/20 explains that the fund 'operates as a donor-advised fund whereby the directors establish donor accounts for individual donors to make recommendations, although the ultimate decision for the distribution of funds tests solely with the directors of the fund'.

CONTACT DETAILS The Trustees, Goldman Sachs, Peterborough Court, 133 Fleet Street, London EC4A 2BB *Tel.* 020 7774 1000

■ Goldman Sachs Gives (UK)

CC NO 1123956 **ESTABLISHED** 2008

WHERE FUNDING CAN BE GIVEN Worldwide.

WHO CAN BENEFIT Registered charities; schools; universities.

WHAT IS FUNDED Education; community; humanitarian relief; medical research; arts and culture; other charitable purposes.

TYPE OF GRANT Project costs.

RANGE OF GRANTS Typically less than £450,000.

SAMPLE GRANTS Greenhouse Sports Ltd (£854,000); Mind (£590,000); Fondation de L'assistance Publique (£518,000).

FINANCES *Financial year end* 30/06/2020
Income £23,360,000
Total grants £18,180,000
Grants to organisations £18,180,000
Assets £90,800,000

TRUSTEES Jenny Evans; Robert Katz; Graham Shaw; Peter Fahey.

OTHER INFORMATION In 2019/20, 653 grants were awarded to organisations. Grants of less than £450,000 totalled £15.4 million.

HOW TO APPLY The annual report for 2015/16 explains that the fund 'operates as a donor-advised fund whereby the directors establish donor accounts for individual donors to make recommendations, although the ultimate decision for the distribution of funds rests solely with the directors of the Fund.

CONTACT DETAILS Jenny Evans, Trustee, Goldman Sachs, Peterborough Court, 133 Fleet Street,

London EC4A 2BB *Tel.* 020 7774 1000 *Website* https://www.goldmansachs.com/citizenship/goldman-sachs-gives

■ The Goldsmiths' Company Charity

CC NO 1175593 **ESTABLISHED** 1961

WHERE FUNDING CAN BE GIVEN UK, with a preference for London.

WHO CAN BENEFIT Registered charities with a turnover of less than £5 million. National charities or charities operating in London can be supported.

WHAT IS FUNDED At the time of writing (June 2021) the focus for grant-making was prisoner resettlement and organisations working with minority communities in prison.

WHAT IS NOT FUNDED A comprehensive list of exclusions can be found on the charity's website.

RANGE OF GRANTS Up to £5,000 (small grants) or up to £30,000 (large grants).

SAMPLE GRANTS The Goldsmiths' Centre (£1.81 million); National Churches Trust (£100,000); Pan Livery – No Going Back Project (£50,000); Duke of Edinburgh's Award Scheme (£36,000); Safer London (£20,000); Arts4Dementia (£10,000); Liverpool Cares (£4,500); Alliance Dance Unit – Hounslow (£2,000); Odd Eyes Theatre – Shoreditch (£1,000); Michael Sobell Hospice (£50).

FINANCES *Financial year end* 31/03/2020 *Income* £5,090,000 *Total grants* £3,700,000 *Grants to organisations* £3,700,000 *Assets* £136,930,000

TRUSTEES Lord Mark Bridges; Timothy Schroder; Edward Harley; Rupert Hambro; Thomas Fattorini; Richard Agutter; George Macdonald; Dr Charles Mackworth-Young; William Parente; Michael Prideaux; Edward Braham; Victoria Broackes; Judith Cobham-Lowe; Richard Fox; Joanna Hardy; Arthur Drysdale; Dame Lynne Brindley; Neil Carson; Arthur Galsworthy; Jane Goad; Hector Miller; Michael Wainwright; Brig. Edward Butler; Richard Madeley.

OTHER INFORMATION In light of the COVID-19 pandemic, during 2021–22 the charity will focus its support on fewer, larger partnerships with criminal justice charities. Prior to this re-strategy, the charity awarded small grants of up to £5,000 for culture, general welfare and medical welfare/disability (the small grants programme will not run in 2021–22), and large grants of up to £30,000 for disadvantaged young people, rehabilitation/resettlement of prisoners and combatting isolation and loneliness among older people in the UK. The charity also sponsors primary and secondary level educational initiatives and awards grants in support of the goldsmithing trade and associated skills. During 2019/20, the charity made 179 grants to organisations across these areas.

HOW TO APPLY In the first instance see the charity's helpful website, where full information is available.

CONTACT DETAILS David Reddaway, Clerk, Goldsmiths' Hall, 13 Foster Lane, London EC2V 6BN *Tel.* 020 7606 7010 *Email* grants@thegoldsmiths.co.uk *Website* www.thegoldsmiths.co.uk/charities

■ The Golf Foundation Ltd

CC NO 285917 **ESTABLISHED** 1953

WHERE FUNDING CAN BE GIVEN UK.

WHO CAN BENEFIT Organisations providing formal golf tuition and informal introductory golfing experience to children and young people.

WHAT IS FUNDED The development, promotion and support of junior golf.

WHAT IS NOT FUNDED Individuals.

TYPE OF GRANT Full and part recovery of costs incurred by the provision of golf tuition.

RANGE OF GRANTS Up to £150,000.

SAMPLE GRANTS Golf Roots Centres (£173,700); Scottish Golf (£95,200); Wales Golf (£29,000); Box of Tricks (£21,300); Satellite Clubs (£17,700); HSBC Roots Plus (£14,900); Road to the Open (£4,000); Feel Inspired (£125).

FINANCES *Financial year end* 31/03/2020 *Income* £1,580,000 *Total grants* £381,800 *Grants to organisations* £381,800 *Assets* £2,650,000

TRUSTEES Nicholas Sladden; Stephen Proctor; Ian Armitage; Sally Stewart; Nick Bragg; Stephen Lewis; Kevin Barker; Jeremy Tomlinson; Evie Carter; Davinder Jhamat.

OTHER INFORMATION Grants were awarded to nine organisations during the year.

HOW TO APPLY Although the foundation states that it chooses its beneficiaries each year, unsolicited applications from organisations that share its aims and objectives may be considered. Contact the foundation's representative in your area for further details on applying for funding – details can be found on the foundation's website.

CONTACT DETAILS Mark Cooke, Head of Finance, Ambition Broxbourne Business Centre, Pindar Road, Hoddesdon, Hertfordshire EN11 0FJ *Tel.* 01992 449830 *Email* mark.cooke@golf-foundation.org *Website* www.golf-foundation.org

■ The Golsoncott Foundation

CC NO 1070885 **ESTABLISHED** 1998

WHERE FUNDING CAN BE GIVEN UK.

WHO CAN BENEFIT Arts organisations.

WHAT IS FUNDED The arts, including: performance, exhibition, artistic craft, or education; music; ballet; theatre; museums; literature; fine arts; crafts; bursary funds.

WHAT IS NOT FUNDED Individuals; organisations whose focus on the arts is part of their wider social, youth, educational, faith-based, or therapeutic work; schools; capital appeals from museums, galleries, theatres, arts complexes, or other projects (apart from by invitation).

TYPE OF GRANT Project funding; bursaries.

RANGE OF GRANTS Grants rarely exceed £3,000.

SAMPLE GRANTS Dunster Festival (£3,000); Contains Art (£2,500); National Children's Orchestra (£2,000); Poetry London (£1,500); London Youth Choir and Pleasance Theatre (£1,000 each); Delphi Trust and New Renaissance (£500 each); Soundworld (£180).

FINANCES *Financial year end* 30/06/2020 *Income* £86,400 *Total grants* £63,300 *Grants to organisations* £63,300 *Assets* £2,300,000

TRUSTEES Jo Lively; Dame Penelope Lively; Steve Wick; Dr Harriet Wood; Izzy Wick; Eliza Thompson.

OTHER INFORMATION In 2019/20 grants were awarded to 77 separate organisations or projects. The foundation sponsors the Society of Wood Engravers' Rachel Reckitt Open Prize.

HOW TO APPLY The trustees meet quarterly to consider applications, in February, May, August and November (see the website for news on the impact of the COVID-19 pandemic on meeting dates). As of January 2020, applications should be supplied in both digital and hard copy to the correspondent. Accounts and supporting information should be provided in hard copy only. Applications should be submitted a month before the next trustees' meeting. Details of the information required in the application is available on the website. According to the website, 'second or further applications will not be considered until a minimum of 12 months has elapsed since determination of the previous application, whether successful or not'.

CONTACT DETAILS Hal Bishop, Administrator, 53 St Leonard's Road, Exeter, Devon EX2 4LS *Tel.* 01392 252855 *Email* golsoncott@btinternet.com *Website* www.golsoncott.org.uk

■ Nicholas and Judith Goodison's Charitable Settlement

CC NO 1004124 **ESTABLISHED** 1991

WHERE FUNDING CAN BE GIVEN UK.

WHO CAN BENEFIT Registered charities.

WHAT IS FUNDED Arts; arts education.

WHAT IS NOT FUNDED Individuals.

TYPE OF GRANT Capital costs; arts acquisition; project costs.

RANGE OF GRANTS £250 to £11,000.

SAMPLE GRANTS Kings College Cambridge (£11,000); Handel House (£7,500); Wigmore Hall (£4,700); National Gallery, National Youth Orchestra, Tate Foundation and Woodland Trust (£3,000 each); Academy of Ancient Music and English National Opera (£2,500 each); World Monuments Fund (£350); Heritage of London Trust (£250).

FINANCES *Financial year end* 05/04/2020 *Income* £74,600 *Total grants* £74,500 *Grants to organisations* £74,500 *Assets* £1,230,000

TRUSTEES Sir Nicholas Goodison; Lady Judith Goodison; Katharine Goodison.

HOW TO APPLY Contact the correspondent for further information.

CONTACT DETAILS The Trustees, PO Box 2512, London W1A 5ZP *Tel.* 07535 408375 *Email* goodisonn2@btinternet.com

■ The Goodman Foundation

CC NO 1097231 **ESTABLISHED** 2003

WHERE FUNDING CAN BE GIVEN UK and overseas.

WHO CAN BENEFIT Charitable organisations.

WHAT IS FUNDED General charitable purposes; the relief of poverty; older people; illness and disability; children; overseas assistance and disaster relief.

SAMPLE GRANTS A list of beneficiaries was not included in the annual report and accounts.

FINANCES *Financial year end* 31/03/2020 *Income* £8,280,000 *Total grants* £600,700 *Grants to organisations* £600,700 *Assets* £69,550,000

TRUSTEES Laurence Goodman; Catherine Goodman; Philip Morgan.

OTHER INFORMATION Grants made during the year were broken down as follows: relief of poverty and support for older people and people with disabilities (12 grants totalling £319,400); children's charities (two grants totalling £188,400); other charitable causes (five grants totalling £69,300); overseas assistance and disasters (two grants totalling £23,700).

HOW TO APPLY Contact the correspondent for further information.

CONTACT DETAILS The Trustees, c/o ABP, Unit 6290, Bishops Court, Solihull Parkway, Birmingham Business Park, Birmingham B37 7YB *Tel.* 0121 717 2500

■ The Mike Gooley Trailfinders Charity

CC NO 1048993 **ESTABLISHED** 1995

WHERE FUNDING CAN BE GIVEN UK.

WHO CAN BENEFIT Charitable organisations.

WHAT IS FUNDED Medical research; youth community projects; education; the armed forces.

SAMPLE GRANTS A list of beneficiaries was not included in the annual report and accounts.

FINANCES *Financial year end* 30/06/2020 *Income* £637,100 *Total grants* £1,760,000 *Grants to organisations* £1,760,000 *Assets* £21,950,000

TRUSTEES Tristan Gooley; Michael Gooley; Bernadette Gooley; Fiona Gooley.

HOW TO APPLY Contact the correspondent for further information.

CONTACT DETAILS The Trustees, 9 Abingdon Road, London W8 6AH *Tel.* 020 7938 3143

■ The Goshen Trust

CC NO 1119064 **ESTABLISHED** 2007

WHERE FUNDING CAN BE GIVEN England and Wales, with a preference for the North East.

WHO CAN BENEFIT Christian organisations; churches; charitable organisations.

WHAT IS FUNDED Christian causes. The trust states in its 2019/20 annual report that its aims are to 'encourage and develop Christian projects which otherwise may not be able to reach an effective operational conclusion as well as supporting those that are already well established'.

TYPE OF GRANT Project costs.

RANGE OF GRANTS Mostly £1,000 to £60,000.

SAMPLE GRANTS Trans4M International (£93,700); Hope Project and Urban Saints (£60,000 each); Caring for Life (£50,000); Christian Institute (£30,000); Leading the Way (£20,000); Operation Mobilisation (£11,000); Pelton Parish Church (£5,000); Gideon International (£1,000).

FINANCES *Financial year end* 05/04/2020 *Income* £236,300 *Total grants* £648,700 *Grants to organisations* £648,700 *Assets* £8,470,000

TRUSTEES Jonathan Dicken; Alison Dicken; Pauline Dicken; Albert Dicken.

OTHER INFORMATION Only grants of £1,000 and above were listed in the 2019/20 accounts (31 grants). Grants of less than £1,000 totalled £2,300.

HOW TO APPLY Apply in writing to the correspondent. The trustees meet several times a year to consider applications. All applications are acknowledged; if applicants do not receive any further communication from the trust they should assume that they have been unsuccessful.

CONTACT DETAILS Company Secretary, PO Box 275, Stanley, County Durham DH8 1HH *Email* admin@goshentrust.org

■ The Gosling Foundation Ltd

CC NO 326840 **ESTABLISHED** 1985

WHERE FUNDING CAN BE GIVEN UK.

WHO CAN BENEFIT Charitable organisations.

WHAT IS FUNDED Education; relief of poverty; religion; general charitable purposes for community benefit.

WHAT IS NOT FUNDED Individuals.

RANGE OF GRANTS Mostly £1,000 to £10,000.

SAMPLE GRANTS Maritime Society and Sea Cadets and SSAFA (£50,000 each); Ellen Macarthur Cancer Trust (£12,000); Windsor Benefit Trust (£10,000); The Royal British Legion (£7,200); Kettering Sea Cadets and Parkinson's UK (£5,000 each); Pancreatic Cancer Research Fund (£3,000); Children's Trust (£2,000); Dogs Trust (£1,000).

FINANCES *Financial year end* 31/03/2020 *Income* £53,580,000 *Total grants* £347,500 *Grants to organisations* £347,500 *Assets* £166,740,000

TRUSTEES Hon. Capt. Adam Gosling; Peter Caplan; Nicholas Giles.

OTHER INFORMATION In 2019/20, 42 grants totalling £607,500 were committed to 45 beneficiaries for the following purposes: community (£403,300); advancement of education (£165,200); relief of poverty (£95,000). Grants paid during the year totalled £347,500.

HOW TO APPLY At the time of writing (May 2021) the foundation's website stated it was currently closed to unsolicited applications until it launches its new website in May 2021. Check the website for updates.

CONTACT DETAILS The Trustees, 2A Kempson Road, London SW6 4PU *Tel.* 020 7495 5599 *Email* Gosling.Foundation@conprop.co.uk *Website* https://www.thegoslingfoundation.com

■ The Edward Gostling Foundation

CC NO 1068617 **ESTABLISHED** 1998

WHERE FUNDING CAN BE GIVEN UK.

WHO CAN BENEFIT UK-registered charities. The trustees have a preference for small and medium-sized charities.

WHAT IS FUNDED Disability; social welfare and illness. The foundation focuses on charities that have an impact across one or more of the following four 'life themes': health and well-being; independent living at home; respite; transition. The foundation's website expands on each theme.

WHAT IS NOT FUNDED Individuals; completed projects; political or religious causes; statutory services; universities colleges or further education colleges (except where the organisation is wholly for students with additional needs; other grant-making charities or umbrella organisations; community centres and youth clubs (except those that benefit older people, people with disabilities or people with a long-term illness); overseas projects.

TYPE OF GRANT Project funding, unrestricted.

RANGE OF GRANTS Small fast-track grants of up to £5,000 and large grants over £5,000.

SAMPLE GRANTS Whizz-Kidz (£550,000); Independence at Home (£280,000); Centrestage Communities (£50,000); Buttle UK (£25,000); The Meath Epilepsy Charity (£23,500); Rivertime Boat Trust (£18,000); St Luke's Hospital Oxford (£15,000); Action4Youth and The Honeypot Children's Charity (£10,000 each).

FINANCES *Financial year end* 31/03/2020 *Income* £4,190,000 *Total grants* £4,270,000 *Grants to organisations* £4,270,000 *Assets* £97,160,000

TRUSTEES Michael Street; John O'Sullivan; Robert White; Denis Taylor; Christine Erwood; Russell Meadows; Colin Clarkson; Stephen O'Sullivan; Victoria Hoskins.

HOW TO APPLY Applicants are advised to visit the foundation's website in the first instance. The website provides detailed information on the application process and what to include in an application. The trustees meet four times a year and applications can be made at any time.

CONTACT DETAILS The Grants Manager, Suite 1, 61 Thames Street, Windsor, Berkshire SL4 1QW *Tel.* 01753 753900 *Email* info@theactfoundation.co.uk or use the contact form on the website. *Website* https://www.edwardgostlingfoundation.org.uk

■ The Gould Charitable Trust

CC NO 1035453 **ESTABLISHED** 1993

WHERE FUNDING CAN BE GIVEN UK; Israel; Philippines.

WHO CAN BENEFIT Registered charities; Jewish organisations.

WHAT IS FUNDED General charitable purposes, particularly education and training and health.

RANGE OF GRANTS Mostly up to £4,000.

SAMPLE GRANTS UJIA (£25,000); Sarratt Parent Association (£5,000); Alzheimer's Research Trust and Beit Halochem (£4,000 each); Jewish Women's Aid (£3,000); Learning Righteous (£2,000); Médecins Sans Frontières (£1,000); Friends of Hebrew University (£500); Centrepoint (£200); Medic Alert Foundation (£40).

FINANCES *Financial year end* 05/04/2019 *Income* £80,200 *Total grants* £65,500 *Grants to organisations* £65,500 *Assets* £1,260,000

TRUSTEES Simon Gould; Sidney Gould; Lawrence Gould; Matthew Gould.

OTHER INFORMATION The 2018/19 annual accounts were the most recent available on the Charity Commission's website at the time of writing (May 2021). Grants were awarded to 33 organisations during the year.

HOW TO APPLY Contact the correspondent for more information.

CONTACT DETAILS Sidney Gould, Trustee, Flat 1, Oak Lodge, 67 West Heath Road, London NW3 7AP *Tel.* 020 8868 2700 *Email* sidney.gould@gmail.com

■ Gowling WLG (UK) Charitable Trust

CC NO 803009 **ESTABLISHED** 1990

WHERE FUNDING CAN BE GIVEN UK in practice, but preference for: London; Birmingham; Coventry; Dudley; Sandwell; Solihull; Walsall.

WHO CAN BENEFIT Registered charities.

WHAT IS FUNDED General charitable purposes.

WHAT IS NOT FUNDED The trust does not usually award grants to individuals or organisations which are not charities.

RANGE OF GRANTS £100 to £7,000.

SAMPLE GRANTS The Buddy Bag Foundation (£14,000); The KEHS Trust (£7,000); University of Birmingham (£4,500); Working Families (£2,000); Hands On London and Wolverhampton Youth Zone (£1,000 each); Down's Syndrome Association (£600); Hope Coventry (£550);

Teenage Cancer Trust (£250); The Lord Mayor's Appeal (£100); Living Without Abuse (£55).

FINANCES *Financial year end* 05/04/2020 *Income* £162,600 *Total grants* £116,900 *Grants to organisations* £116,900 *Assets* £106,900

TRUSTEES Lee Nuttall; Philip Clissitt; Andreas Stylianou.

OTHER INFORMATION Grants were awarded to 131 organisations during the year. A large proportion of the grants made were under £1,000.

HOW TO APPLY Contact the correspondent for further information.

CONTACT DETAILS The Trustees, c/o Gowling WLG (UK) LLP, Two Snowhill, Snow Hill Queensway, Birmingham B4 6WR *Tel.* 0121 233 1000

■ The Hemraj Goyal Foundation

CC NO 1136483 **ESTABLISHED** 2010

WHERE FUNDING CAN BE GIVEN UK and overseas.

WHO CAN BENEFIT Charitable organisations.

WHAT IS FUNDED General charitable purposes, particularly: disadvantaged children; women's rights; education; people with disabilities.

RANGE OF GRANTS Up to £70,000.

SAMPLE GRANTS One Family UK (£84,500); iPartner India (£68,200); Child Action (£40,200); British Asian Trust and Outward Bound Trust (£25,000 each); Barnardo's (£20,000); Partition Museum (£15,000); Sense International (£10,000).

FINANCES *Financial year end* 31/12/2019 *Income* £326,100 *Total grants* £364,500 *Grants to organisations* £364,500 *Assets* £57,100

TRUSTEES Anita Goyal; Vidya Goyal; Avnish Goyal.

OTHER INFORMATION In 2019 grants were awarded to 29 organisations. This includes 20 small grants of under £10,000. Only beneficiaries of grants of £10,000 and above were listed in the accounts.

HOW TO APPLY Contact the correspondent for information regarding the application process.

CONTACT DETAILS The Trustees, Hallmark Care Homes, Kingfisher House, 2 Woodbrook Crescent, Radford Way, Billericay, Essex CM12 0EQ *Tel.* 01277 655655 *Email* info@hgf.org.uk *Website* www.hgf.org.uk

■ Grace Charitable Trust

CC NO 292984 **ESTABLISHED** 1985

WHERE FUNDING CAN BE GIVEN UK and overseas.

WHO CAN BENEFIT Registered charities; schools; hospitals; religious bodies/institutions.

WHAT IS FUNDED General charitable purposes; medical causes; Christian and church-based activities; education.

TYPE OF GRANT Capital costs; core/revenue costs; seeding funding/start-up funding.

SAMPLE GRANTS A list of beneficiaries was not included in the annual report and accounts.

FINANCES *Financial year end* 30/04/2020 *Income* £690,200 *Total grants* £631,200 *Grants to organisations* £631,200 *Assets* £2,710,000

TRUSTEES Eric Payne; Robert Quayle; Mark Mitchell; Robert Wright; Angela Payne.

OTHER INFORMATION Grants were distributed as follows: Christian-based activities (£368,300); social and medical causes (£215,600); education (£37,000); general charitable purposes (£10,400).

HOW TO APPLY Unsolicited applications are not accepted. Grants are only made to charities known to the settlors.

CONTACT DETAILS Eric Payne, Trustee, Swinford House GCT Office, Norton's Lane, Great Barrow, Chester, Cheshire CH3 7JZ *Tel.* 01928 740773 *Email* gracecharitabletrust@live.co.uk

■ The Grace Trust

CC NO 257516 **ESTABLISHED** 1967

WHERE FUNDING CAN BE GIVEN UK and overseas.

WHO CAN BENEFIT Registered charities.

WHAT IS FUNDED Education; childcare; non-statutory emergency services and medical relief; disaster relief; medical research; humanitarian aid; relief of poverty; disability support; life preservation; advancement of Christianity.

RANGE OF GRANTS Mostly £100 to £5,000, with several particularly large grants awarded each year.

SAMPLE GRANTS OneSchool Global UK (£18.3 million); Focus Learning Trust (£11 million); NAF Fond DK (£1.69 million); Balmoral Education (£120,800); Welsh Air Ambulance (£10,000); Air Ambulance Yorkshire (£5,000); Sightsavers (£3,000); Starlight Children's Foundation (£2,500); Islington People's Rights (£1,000); Experiential Christian Ministries (£500); Pump Aid (£100).

FINANCES *Financial year end* 31/12/2019 *Income* £102,690,000 *Total grants* £32,420,000 *Grants to organisations* £32,420,000 *Assets* £32,490,000

TRUSTEES Scribefort Ltd; Aller Brook Ltd.

OTHER INFORMATION Grants were awarded to 239 organisations during the year. A substantial amount of the grant total is awarded to Focus Learning Trust each year. A large donation was also made to OneSchool Global UK.

HOW TO APPLY The annual report for 2019 states: 'The trustees recognise the importance of being outward looking and of making grants to a wide range of charities in order to demonstrate public benefit. The independent Grant Making Committee is encouraged to make grants in accordance with the criteria set out [in the annual report] but also to give due consideration to any applications for grants from charities. Checks are made to ensure that charities to whom grants are made are well run, financially sound; that their fundraising and administration costs are proportionate and moderate, and who therefore maximise the percentage of funds received that are actually applied to the relevant charitable purpose.'

CONTACT DETAILS The Trustees, Chelwood House, Cox Lane, Chesington, Surrey KT9 1DN *Tel.* 020 3301 3806 *Email* enquiries@thegracetrust.org.uk *Website* www.thegracetrust.org.uk

■ The James Grace Trust

CC NO 1185450 **ESTABLISHED** 2019

WHERE FUNDING CAN BE GIVEN UK; the Middle East; Northern Africa.

WHO CAN BENEFIT Charitable organisations.

WHAT IS FUNDED Advancement of the Christian faith; social welfare; education.

SAMPLE GRANTS Vogelaar Donaties (£16,000); Fountain of Life (£13,000); Interserve GB (£7,000); Saltmine (£3,000); Leavers Coulson Trust (£1,000).

FINANCES *Financial year end* 30/06/2020 *Income* £736,800 *Total grants* £75,000 *Grants to organisations* £75,000 *Assets* £645,500

TRUSTEES Christopher Winfield; Ian Sutherland; Janet Sutherland; Jyotir Banerjee.

HOW TO APPLY It is unlikely that unsolicited applications will be successful. Almost all grants are made to organisations already known to the trustees.

CONTACT DETAILS The Trustees, 23 Mill Lane, Saffron Walden, CB10 2AS *Email* ian@sutherlandviolin.com

■ The Graham Trust

OSCR NO SC038269 **ESTABLISHED** 2007

WHERE FUNDING CAN BE GIVEN UK, with a preference for Scotland.

WHO CAN BENEFIT Registered charities; individuals.

WHAT IS FUNDED General charitable purposes, with a preference for: saving of lives; arts and heritage; relief of those in need; animal welfare.

RANGE OF GRANTS £500 to £20,000.

SAMPLE GRANTS Pancreatic Cancer Research (£22,500); RNLI and St Michael's Hospice (£15,000 each); Bethany Christian Trust (£10,000); Scotland Huntingdon Association (£5,000); Scotland's Charity Air Ambulance (£3,000); Brae Riding for the Disabled Dundee (£1,800).

FINANCES *Financial year end* 30/09/2019 *Income* £31,800 *Total grants* £122,400 *Grants to organisations* £122,400 *Assets* £1,060,000

OTHER INFORMATION The 2018/19 annual accounts were the most recent available from OSCR at the time of writing (April 2021).

HOW TO APPLY The trustees meet once a year in the autumn. Applications can be made online, via email or by post. Relevant templates are available to download from the website. Only successful applicants will be contacted.

CONTACT DETAILS Mr A. Douds, Trustee, 14 Dirac Road, Ashley Down, Bristol BS7 9LP *Email* thegrahamtrust@gmail.com *Website* thegrahamtrust.co.uk

■ Grahame Charitable Foundation Ltd

CC NO 1102332 **ESTABLISHED** 2004

WHERE FUNDING CAN BE GIVEN UK and overseas.

WHO CAN BENEFIT Mainly Jewish charities and organisations.

WHAT IS FUNDED Education; social welfare; Jewish causes.

WHAT IS NOT FUNDED Individuals.

SAMPLE GRANTS Previous beneficiaries have included: Jerusalem College of Technology and Keren Avraham Bezalel (£25,000 each); Emunah (£20,000); Partnership for Schools (£13,600); Charities Aid Foundation (£12,500); Beis Ruzhin Trust (£11,000); Yesodey Hatorah School (£10,000); Beit Almog (£6,000); Campaign Against Antisemitism and Kehilat Kadima (£5,000 each).

FINANCES *Financial year end* 31/12/2018 *Income* £190,000 *Total grants* £516,000 *Grants to organisations* £516,000 *Assets* £177,000

TRUSTEES Mr J. M. Greenwood; Alan Grahame; Joel Greenwood; Sara Shaw.

HOW TO APPLY Contact the correspondent for further information.

CONTACT DETAILS The Trustees, Unit 102, 116 Ballards Lane, Finchley, London N3 2DN *Tel.* 07710 221636

■ The Granada Foundation

CC NO 241693 **ESTABLISHED** 1965

WHERE FUNDING CAN BE GIVEN The North West.

WHO CAN BENEFIT Registered charities; not-for-profit organisations occasionally considered.

WHAT IS FUNDED The study, practice and appreciation of fine arts and science; engaging young people and adults to take an interest in science; provision of facilities for recreation or other leisure-time occupation in the interests of social welfare; education; festivals and events.

WHAT IS NOT FUNDED Salaries; long-term revenue funding; general appeals; individuals; courses of study; expeditions; overseas travel; youth clubs/community associations; the foundation will not be the sole funder of projects and applicants should not expect 100% of funding unless there are exceptional circumstances; at the time of writing (April 2021), the foundation is not accepting applications for large-scale capital projects (visit the website for up-to-date information).

TYPE OF GRANT Project funding, including new projects; capital costs.

RANGE OF GRANTS £500 to £10,000, with the average grant £2,000.

SAMPLE GRANTS Buxton Festival (£10,000); MusicLinks Ltd (£6,000); Engineering Development Trust (£4,000); Rule of Threes Arts Ltd (£3,000); Liverpool Arab Arts Festival and Streetwise Opera (£2,000 each); Manchester Literature Festival (£1,400); Grizedale Arts (£1,000).

FINANCES *Financial year end* 31/03/2020 *Income* £41,000 *Total grants* £102,400 *Grants to organisations* £102,400 *Assets* £3,030,000

TRUSTEES Philip Ramsbottom; Prof. Jennifer Latto; Virginia Tandy; Robert Scott.

OTHER INFORMATION In 2019/20 a total of 40 grants were made. Grants were broken down as follows: recreation and leisure time occupation (£45,400); appreciation of the fine arts (£34,000); promotion of education (£15,000); study and application of the sciences (£8,000).

HOW TO APPLY In the first instance, organisations wishing to apply should provide a brief outline of the project for which funding is sought by completing the short enquiry form available at the foundation's website. If the project meets the funding criteria, a full application pack will be sent out by email. Dates of upcoming Advisory Council meetings, as well as relevant deadlines for applications, are detailed on the website.

CONTACT DETAILS Irene Langford, Administrator, PO Box 3430, Chester CH1 9BZ *Tel.* 01244 661867 *Email* enquiries@granadafoundation.org *Website* www.granadafoundation.org

■ The Grand Trust CIO

CC NO 1179280 **ESTABLISHED** 2018

WHERE FUNDING CAN BE GIVEN England and Wales.

WHO CAN BENEFIT Charitable organisations.

WHAT IS FUNDED The trust makes grants in support of those who provide assistance to marginalised groups and those from disadvantaged backgrounds.

SAMPLE GRANTS A list of beneficiaries was not included in the annual report and accounts.

FINANCES *Financial year end* 30/06/2020 *Income* £1,210,000 *Total grants* £382,700 *Grants to organisations* £382,700 *Assets* £1,040,000

TRUSTEES Danielle Peet; Joanne Radcliff; Steven Appleton.
HOW TO APPLY Contact the correspondent for further information.
CONTACT DETAILS The Trustees, c/o Brabners LLP, 55 King Street, Manchester M2 4LQ *Tel.* 0161 836 8949

■ The Grange Farm Centre Trust

CC NO 285162 **ESTABLISHED** 1984
WHERE FUNDING CAN BE GIVEN The London Metropolitan Police District and Epping Forest, Essex.
WHO CAN BENEFIT Charitable organisations; amateur sports clubs; schools; churches.
WHAT IS FUNDED Recreation and leisure activities.
SAMPLE GRANTS Chigwell Lawn Tennis Club; Epping Forest Reuses; Flash Musical; Lambourne Parish Church; Lifelites; Waltham Abbey Youth; Woodford Rugby Club; Voluntary Action Epping Forest.
FINANCES *Financial year end* 05/04/2020 *Income* £620,300 *Total grants* £50,300 *Grants to organisations* £50,300 *Assets* £14,650,000
TRUSTEES Charles Scrutton; Peter Minoletti; Trevor Johnson; Robert Church; Mary Sartin; Marshall Vance; Richard Morgan; Javed Salim.
OTHER INFORMATION During the year, 21 grants were awarded.
HOW TO APPLY Contact the clerk for information regarding the application process.
CONTACT DETAILS Mr J. Worby, Clerk, c/o 181 High Street, Epping, Essex CM16 4BQ *Tel.* 01992 578642 *Email* info@grangefarmcentre.co.uk *Website* www.grangefarmcentre.co.uk

■ The Grant Foundation

CC NO 1084915 **ESTABLISHED** 2001
WHERE FUNDING CAN BE GIVEN Worldwide.
WHO CAN BENEFIT Registered charities; charitable and religious organisations; individuals.
WHAT IS FUNDED General charitable purposes; advancement of the Christian faith; education and welfare of children and young people; emergency appeals.
TYPE OF GRANT Core funding; project funding; sponsorship; capital costs.
RANGE OF GRANTS Up to £30,000.
SAMPLE GRANTS 2nd Amersham on the Hill Scout Group (two grants totalling £225,000); The Lambeth Trust (three grants totalling £40,000); Christians Against Poverty (two grants totalling £30,000); Alpha International (£20,000); Just Love (£10,000) Food for the Hungry UK (£5,800); Citizens Advice Chiltern (£5,260); Autism Bedfordshire and Safe Families For Children (£5,000).
FINANCES *Financial year end* 31/12/2019 *Income* £590,000 *Total grants* £614,500 *Grants to organisations* £614,500 *Assets* £11,500
TRUSTEES Catherine Grant; Duncan Grant; Stuart Grant; Gary Grant; Anna Warner-McLoughlin; Alastair Grant.
OTHER INFORMATION In 2019, 127 grants were made to organisations. Grants of over £5,000 were awarded to 23 organisations, some of which received multiple grants. In addition, 99 grants of less than £5,000 totalled £131,400. No grants were awarded to individuals during the year.
HOW TO APPLY Contact the correspondent for further information.
CONTACT DETAILS Anna Warner-McLoughlin, Trustee, The Entertainer, Broughton Business Park, Bell Lane, Amersham HP6 6GL *Tel.* 01494 737037 *Email* anna@thegrantfoundation.org.uk

■ The Grantham Yorke Trust

CC NO 228466 **ESTABLISHED** 1963
WHERE FUNDING CAN BE GIVEN West Midlands.
WHO CAN BENEFIT Individuals aged under 25 who are in need and organisations working with them. A wide variety of organisations are supported including charities, museums, hospices, youth clubs, CICs, educational and religious organisations.
WHAT IS FUNDED Young people; education; physical and social training; rehabilitation; recreation and leisure; financial assistance; equipment for education or profession.
TYPE OF GRANT General funding; capital costs (including school/profession equipment).
RANGE OF GRANTS £1,000 to £10,000.
SAMPLE GRANTS Severn Valley Railway Charitable Trust (£10,000); Warley Baptist Church (£7,500); The Feast Youth Project and Touchstones Child Bereavement Support (£5,000 each); Birmingham Opera Company (£3,000); Kenelm Youth Trust and Shakespeare Hospice (£2,500 each); Queen Alexandra College (£1,500); 2nd Warwick Sea Scouts (£1,000).
FINANCES *Financial year end* 05/04/2020 *Income* £298,500 *Total grants* £302,200 *Grants to organisations* £285,300 *Assets* £5,850,000
TRUSTEES Revd Matthew Thompson; Fred Rattley; Howard Belton; Philip Smiglarski; Sue Butler; Tim Clarke; Hugh Sherriffe; Ruth Burgess; Beverley Momenabadi.
OTHER INFORMATION Grants were awarded to 80 organisations and 33 individuals during the year.
HOW TO APPLY Apply in writing to the correspondent. The trustees meet quarterly.
CONTACT DETAILS Chrissy Norgrove, Clerk to the Trustees, The Estate Office, Wharf Cottage, Broombank, Newham Bridge, Tenbury Wells, Worcestershire WR15 8NY *Tel.* 07799 784019 *Email* chrissy@granthamyorketrust.org.uk

■ GrantScape

CC NO 1102249 **ESTABLISHED** 2003
WHERE FUNDING CAN BE GIVEN UK.
WHO CAN BENEFIT Registered charities; community organisations, CICs.
WHAT IS FUNDED General charitable purposes including: environment; community development; sports and recreation; social welfare.
WHAT IS NOT FUNDED Each fund is subject to its own exclusions which are listed on the website.
TYPE OF GRANT Capital costs; project funding.
RANGE OF GRANTS Up to £100,000.
SAMPLE GRANTS Bradworthy Methodist Church (£4,800); Crick Community Sports Centre (£1,800); Bacup Cricket Club (£1,500); Dean Parish Council (£1,300); Disability Support Calderdale (£900).
FINANCES *Financial year end* 31/03/2020 *Income* £3,710,000 *Total grants* £4,020,000 *Grants to organisations* £4,020,000 *Assets* £2,190,000
TRUSTEES Thomas Walker; Michael Clarke; Stuart McAleese; Philippa Lyons; Michael Singh; Anthony Cox; John Mills.

OTHER INFORMATION Grantscape administers community funds on behalf of developers, such as wind farms, landfill sites, solar farms and renewable energy plants.

HOW TO APPLY Applicants should visit the 'Grant and Project Finder' section of the charity's website to find information on all grant programmes currently available. Applications should be made online via the website.

CONTACT DETAILS Kim Wilkinson, Grant Administrator, Office E, Whitsundoles, Broughton Road, Salford, Milton Keynes, Buckinghamshire MK17 8BU *Tel.* 01908 247630 *Email* info@grantscape.org.uk *Website* www.grantscape.org.uk

■ The J. G. Graves Charitable Trust

CC NO 207481 **ESTABLISHED** 1930

WHERE FUNDING CAN BE GIVEN Sheffield.

WHO CAN BENEFIT Registered charities; charitable organisations; CICs; hospices.

WHAT IS FUNDED General charitable purposes; disadvantaged groups; community development; well-being and health; heritage; education; parks and open spaces; sports and recreation; art galleries and libraries for public use; medical research, recreational and sporting facilities; community projects connected to churches; special needs schools for non-mainstream educational expenditure.

WHAT IS NOT FUNDED Individuals; national organisations (unless the application is submitted by a local representative and the application relates specifically to Sheffield); facilities or activities which are a statutory responsibility.

TYPE OF GRANT Capital costs (preferred); seed funding; running costs. Up to three years in exceptional circumstances.

RANGE OF GRANTS Typically £500 to £3,000.

SAMPLE GRANTS Sheffield Archives (£5,000); Friends of Greenhill Library and Pitsmoor Adventure Playground (£3,000 each); Oughtibridge Chapel (£2,000); National Schizophrenia Fellowship (£1,500); Stradbrooke Ravens FC (£1,300).

FINANCES *Financial year end* 31/12/2019 *Income* £198,700 *Total grants* £144,100 *Grants to organisations* £144,100 *Assets* £5,980,000

TRUSTEES Dona Womack; John Bramah; Peter Clarkson; Dr Derek Cullen; Cllr Jackie Drayton; Cllr Peter Price; Kim Streets; Rodrick Plews; Adrian Graves.

OTHER INFORMATION Grants were awarded to 86 organisations during the year. Grants of £1,000 or less totalled £22,200.

HOW TO APPLY Applications can be made through the trust's website. The trustees meet quarterly to discuss applications. Applications should reach the secretary by one of the following dates: 31 March, 30 June, 30 September or 31 December. Applicants should receive notification of the decision about their application within four weeks of the relevant meeting.

CONTACT DETAILS Jane Marshall, Secretary, c/o BHP Chartered Accountants, 2 Rutland Park, Sheffield, South Yorkshire S10 2PD *Tel.* 0114 266 7171 *Email* jane.marshall@bhp.co.uk *Website* jggravescharitabletrust.co.uk

■ The Gray Trust

CC NO 210914 **ESTABLISHED** 1962

WHERE FUNDING CAN BE GIVEN Nottinghamshire, especially the parishes of Linby and Papplewick.

WHO CAN BENEFIT Charitable organisations.

WHAT IS FUNDED General charitable purposes, primarily for the benefit of older people, including the provision of sheltered accommodation.

TYPE OF GRANT Capital costs; revenue projects.

RANGE OF GRANTS Typically between £500 and £2,000.

SAMPLE GRANTS St Michael's and St James' – Linby cum Papplewick (£10,000); St Peter's Church Tollerton (£2,000); ABF – The Soldiers' Charity, Macmillan Cancer Relief – Nottingham Committee and Rainbows Children's Hospice (£1,000 each); Citizens Advice – Ashfield, Guide Dogs for the Blind, Scope and Windmill Community Gardens (£500 each).

FINANCES *Financial year end* 05/04/2020 *Income* £164,600 *Total grants* £234,000 *Grants to organisations* £234,000 *Assets* £5,070,000

TRUSTEES Claire Hardstaff; Bella Harlow; Richard Pannell; Revd Canon Keith Turner; Kirstin Thompson.

OTHER INFORMATION In 2019/20 the trust made grants to 39 organisations for the following purposes: churches (£18,500); medical causes (£7,000); local causes, young people and other charitable causes (£3,000 each); the armed forces (£1,500); older people (£1,300).

HOW TO APPLY Contact the correspondent for further information.

CONTACT DETAILS Charlene Truman, c/o Smith Cooper Ltd, 2 Lace Market Square, Nottingham, Nottinghamshire NG1 1PB *Tel.* 0115 945 4300 *Email* charlene.truman@smithcooper.co.uk

■ Gordon Gray Trust

CC NO 213935 **ESTABLISHED** 1960

WHERE FUNDING CAN BE GIVEN England, with a preference for Gloucestershire and Worcestershire.

WHO CAN BENEFIT Registered charities.

WHAT IS FUNDED General charitable purposes, with a preference for medical charities, the welfare of children and older people, and environmental and local organisations.

WHAT IS NOT FUNDED Individuals.

RANGE OF GRANTS Mostly £500 to £4,000.

SAMPLE GRANTS Avon Navigation Trust (£10,000); Great Oaks Dean Forest Hospice (£6,000); Diabetes UK and Marie Curie Cancer Care (£4,000 each); Royal Medical Benevolent Fund (£3,000); NSPCC (£2,000); Sense (£1,500); Tewkesbury Nature Reserve (£1,000); First Bredon Scout Group (£500); Gloucestershire Historic Churches Trust (£75).

FINANCES *Financial year end* 30/09/2020 *Income* £133,200 *Total grants* £154,200 *Grants to organisations* £154,200 *Assets* £5,910,000

TRUSTEES Dr B. Gray; Mrs M. Gray; Mr E. Roberts; Miss R. Holmes; Mrs S. Watson-Armstrong; Mr C. Wilder.

OTHER INFORMATION Grants were made to 63 organisations during the year.

HOW TO APPLY Apply in writing to the correspondent. The trust's Charity Commission record notes that 'if you do not receive a reply to a request for funding, your application has been unsuccessful.'

CONTACT DETAILS Melanie Gray, Clerk to the Trustees, Grange Farm, Main Road, Bredon, Tewkesbury, Gloucestershire GL20 7EL *Tel.* 01684 772366

■ The Great Britain Sasakawa Foundation

CC NO 290766 **ESTABLISHED** 1985

WHERE FUNDING CAN BE GIVEN UK and Japan.

WHO CAN BENEFIT Voluntary, educational and cultural organisations; registered charities benefitting citizens of UK and Japan. Emphasis on innovative projects and those involving groups of people in both countries (especially young people) rather than individuals.

WHAT IS FUNDED Activities which support mutual understanding between the Japanese and UK citizens in the following fields: arts and culture; humanities and social issues; Japanese language and Japanese studies; medicine and health; science, technology and the environment; sport; youth and education.

WHAT IS NOT FUNDED Individuals; consumables; fees; salaries; purchase of materials; capital projects such as the purchase, construction or maintenance of buildings; completed or current projects; student fees or travel for study, apart from PhD fieldwork in Japan (limited to £1,000 maximum).

TYPE OF GRANT 'Pump-priming' funding; research; up to three years.

RANGE OF GRANTS Awards average £1,500 to £2,000 and do not normally exceed £5,000 to £6,000 for larger-scale projects. Butterfield Awards: around £5,000 for up to three years.

SAMPLE GRANTS A full list of beneficiaries can be found in the foundation's annual reports, available from its helpful website.

FINANCES *Financial year end* 31/12/2019 *Income* £969,800 *Total grants* £852,400 *Grants to organisations* £850,600 *Assets* £28,810,000

TRUSTEES Ambassador Hiroaki Fujii; The Earl of St Andrews; Prof. David Cope; Tatsuya Tanami; Joanna Pitman; Prof. Yuichi Hosoya; Prof. Yoriko Kawaguchi; Prof. Janet Hunter; Prof. Ryuichi Teshima; Jeremy Scott; Prof. Izumi Kadono.

OTHER INFORMATION Grants were awarded to 196 organisations and one individual during the year. The foundation also delivers its Butterfield Awards for collaboration between qualified professionals in the fields of medical research and public health practice.

HOW TO APPLY Full application details can be found on the website. Application forms for the London office can also be downloaded here and once completed they must be sent via email to grants@gbsf.org.uk. To apply to the Tokyo office, the applicant must email tokyo@gbsf.org.uk before making an application. Trustees make the final decisions on awards at meetings held in London three times a year (normally March, May and November) and Tokyo twice a year (normally April and October). The deadline for London applicants are as follows: 15 December for a decision in March; 31 March for a decision in May; 15 September for a decision in November. The annual deadline for the Butterfield Awards is 15 December.

CONTACT DETAILS The Trustees, Lower Ground Floor, 24 Bedford Row, London WC1R 4TQ *Tel.* 020 7436 9042 *Email* grants@gbsf.org.uk *Website* www.gbsf.org.uk

■ The Great Stone Bridge Trust of Edenbridge

CC NO 224309 **ESTABLISHED** 1964

WHERE FUNDING CAN BE GIVEN Edenbridge, Kent.

WHO CAN BENEFIT Charitable organisations; clubs; societies; educational organisations; individuals.

WHAT IS FUNDED General charitable purposes including a wide range of religious, social welfare, medical research, sporting and other community support activities.

TYPE OF GRANT Project funding; start-up funding; capital costs; revenue costs.

SAMPLE GRANTS Edenbridge Primary School; West Kent Extra; Eden Valley Museum, Edenbridge Parish Church.

FINANCES *Financial year end* 31/12/2019 *Income* £163,400 *Total grants* £112,300 *Grants to organisations* £112,300 *Assets* £3,200,000

TRUSTEES Roy Cunnington; Giles Jackman; John Hodson; Clive Pearman; Ben Brownless; Julie Johnson; Robert Todd; Julie Thompsett; Alan Smart; Margot McArthur.

OTHER INFORMATION Grants were made to 40 organisations in 2019. Several beneficiaries were listed in the year's annual accounts, although the specific amount given to each organisation was not included. According to the website, grant amounts can vary from as little as £100 to thousands, dependent on funding requirements and benefit to the community.

HOW TO APPLY Application forms can be downloaded from the website and should be returned by email to the correspondent.

CONTACT DETAILS John Southworth, Clerk to the Trustees, c/o Southworth and Co. Ltd, Treasures, Bough Beech Road, Four Elms, Edenbridge, Kent TN8 6NE *Tel.* 01732 700670 *Email* clerk@gsbtrust.org *Website* https://www.gsbt.co.uk

■ The Greater Manchester High Sheriff's Police Trust

CC NO 1040579 **ESTABLISHED** 1994

WHERE FUNDING CAN BE GIVEN Greater Manchester.

WHO CAN BENEFIT Charitable organisations; amateur sports clubs.

WHAT IS FUNDED Prevention of crime; community support; community and race-related initiatives; education in all matters relating to substance abuse.

WHAT IS NOT FUNDED Individuals; vehicles; salaries; professional fees.

TYPE OF GRANT Project funding.

RANGE OF GRANTS Up to £10,400.

SAMPLE GRANTS Child Safety Media (£10,400); Crimestoppers (£10,000); Caribbean and African Health Network (£5,000); Garden House (£4,800); Seashell Trust (£4,100); Tameside Sea Cadets (£3,100); Manchester Youth Zone (£2,800); Mustard Tree (£2,500); St John's Boxing Club (£2,200)

FINANCES *Financial year end* 31/03/2020 *Income* £293,600 *Total grants* £291,200 *Grants to organisations* £291,200 *Assets* £4,630,000

TRUSTEES Paul Griffiths; Vincent A. Sweeney; Sharman Birtles; Edith Conn; S. Dixon; Christine Lee-Jones; George Almond; Michael Greenwood; Nicholas Bird; Ian Hopkins; Gerry Yeung; Lady Joy Smith; Eamonn Sean O'Neal; Mark Adlestone.

OTHER INFORMATION During 2019/20, grants of less than £2,000 totalled £147,800.

HOW TO APPLY Application forms can be downloaded from the trust's website. Once completed, these can be sent to the correspondent via email. The trustees meet four times a year to consider applications.

CONTACT DETAILS Glen Lockett, Head Of Income Generation, Neighbourhoods, Confidence and Equality Team, Openshaw Complex, Lawton Street, Openshaw, Manchester M11 2NS *Tel.* 0161 856 8977 *Email* HighSheriff.Trust@gmp.police.uk *Website* www.gmhspt.org

■ The Kenneth and Susan Green Charitable Foundation

CC NO 1147248 **ESTABLISHED** 2012

WHERE FUNDING CAN BE GIVEN UK.

WHO CAN BENEFIT Charitable organisations.

WHAT IS FUNDED General charitable purposes; social welfare; education; health; arts and culture; heritage; science.

WHAT IS NOT FUNDED Individuals.

RANGE OF GRANTS Mainly up to £50,000.

SAMPLE GRANTS Royal Opera House Covent Garden Foundation (£210,000); Royal Ballet School (£50,000); Royal National Lifeboat Institution (£25,000); Helford River Children's Sailing Trust and The Pepper Foundation (£10,000 each).

FINANCES *Financial year end* 31/12/2019 *Income* £571,200 *Total grants* £324,400 *Grants to organisations* £324,400 *Assets* £5,220,000

TRUSTEES Kenneth Green; Philip Stokes; Susan Green; Sarah Scragg; Charlotte Garlick.

OTHER INFORMATION In 2019, grants were distributed as follows: arts, culture, heritage and science (£210,100); education, health and saving lives (£113,300); relief of poverty (£1,000). Grants of under £10,000 totalled £19,400.

HOW TO APPLY Apply in writing to the correspondent. Previous research suggests that the foundation supports a few specific charities and does not seek new applications.

CONTACT DETAILS The Trustees, c/o Kenneth Green Associates, Hill House, Monument Hill, Weybridge, Surrey KT13 8RX *Tel.* 01932 827060

■ The Green Hall Foundation

CC NO 270775 **ESTABLISHED** 1976

WHERE FUNDING CAN BE GIVEN UK and overseas.

WHO CAN BENEFIT UK-registered charities only.

WHAT IS FUNDED The foundation makes grants to 'sustainably improve' the lives of older people, young people in need, people with disabilities or illnesses and people who are disadvantaged or are experiencing homelessness.

WHAT IS NOT FUNDED Individuals; general running costs; salaries.

TYPE OF GRANT Capital costs and special project funding.

RANGE OF GRANTS Typically £1,000 to £10,000.

SAMPLE GRANTS RNLI Lifeboat (£39,000); British Red Cross and Salvation Army (£10,000 each); Warwick Wheelchair Basketball Academy (£6,000); Great Ormond Street Hospital Children's Charity (£5,000); Accessible arts (£3,500); Arthur Rank Hospice (£3,000); Second Chance Animal Rescue (£2,500); Dyspraxia Foundation and Youth on The Move – London (£1,000 each).

FINANCES *Financial year end* 05/04/2020 *Income* £380,300 *Total grants* £393,700 *Grants to organisations* £393,700 *Assets* £9,510,000

TRUSTEES Margaret Hall; Sue Collinson; Nigel Hall; Peter Morgan; Charlotte Footer.

HOW TO APPLY Applications must be made online through the foundation's website. The trustees meet twice a year, in May and November. In the May meeting, applications from charities in all income brackets will be considered. In the November meeting, only applications from charities with an annual income of £250,000 or less will be considered. Only the first 100 applications received by the foundation will be taken forward to be considered by the trustees. The opening dates for application cycles are detailed on the website and the cycles close when the 100th application has been received.

CONTACT DETAILS The Trustees, 2nd Floor, International House, 41 The Parade, St Helier, Jersey JE2 3QQ *Tel.* 01534 487757 *Email* greenhallfoundation@fcmtrust.com *Website* www.greenhallfoundation.org

■ Philip and Judith Green Trust

CC NO 1109933 **ESTABLISHED** 2005

WHERE FUNDING CAN BE GIVEN UK and overseas.

WHO CAN BENEFIT Registered charities; Christian missionaries; churches; universities.

WHAT IS FUNDED Education in underprivileged communities; Christianity, in particular support for missionaries and places of worship; health.

RANGE OF GRANTS Up to £17,500.

SAMPLE GRANTS Previous beneficiaries have included: Inherit Your Rights (£17,500); Greyfriars Church (£17,200); Rinell Carey Holmquist (£6,600); Bible Society and London Business School (£5,000); Philharmonia Orchestra (£3,500); Christ Church Paarl (£2,500); Greyfriars Mission (£1,200); British and Foreign Bible Society (£400); Five Talents (£200).

FINANCES *Financial year end* 31/03/2020 *Income* £0 *Total grants* £83,500 *Grants to organisations* £83,500

TRUSTEES Philip Green; Judith Green.

OTHER INFORMATION Full accounts were not available to view on the Charity Commission's website due to the trust's low income. We have therefore estimated the grant total based on the trust's total expenditure.

HOW TO APPLY Contact the correspondent for information.

CONTACT DETAILS Philip Green, Trustee, c/o Dixon Wilson Chartered Accountants, 22 Chancery Lane, London WC2A 1LS *Tel.* 0118 984 5935 *Email* philipngreen@me.com

■ Greenham Trust Ltd

CC NO 1062762 **ESTABLISHED** 1997

WHERE FUNDING CAN BE GIVEN West Berkshire and specific ward areas of North Hampshire.

WHO CAN BENEFIT Charitable organisations; individuals.

WHAT IS FUNDED Social welfare; education; sport; health and well-being; the arts, heritage and science; community; human rights and diversity; the environment; wildlife; the armed forces and emergency services.

WHAT IS NOT FUNDED A full list of exclusions can be found on the trust's website.

TYPE OF GRANT Project funding.

SAMPLE GRANTS A list of beneficiaries was not included in the annual report and accounts.

FINANCES *Financial year end* 31/03/2020 *Income* £15,660,000 *Total grants* £1,395,000 *Grants to organisations* £1,360,000 *Assets* £81,520,000

TRUSTEES Charlie Brims; Justyn Waterworth; Malcolm Morris; Sir Peter Michael; Zoe Benyon; David Bailey; Fiona Spencer Jones; Julian Cazalet; Robert Woods; Bibby Hayward; Graham Mather.

OTHER INFORMATION Grants were broken down as follows: community (£515,300); youth (£177,900); sport (£147,100); disability (£132,600); health (£131,200); education (£129,100); arts (£72,300); elderly (£45,700); economic (£6,000); conservation (£1,000). Educational grants to individuals totalled £35,000.

HOW TO APPLY All applications should be made through The Good Exchange. A link can be found on the trust's website.

CONTACT DETAILS The Trustees, Liberty House, The Enterprise Centre, Greenham Business Park, Newbury, Berkshire RG19 6HS *Tel.* 01635 736740 *Email* grantenquiries@greenhamtrust.com *Website* https://greenhamtrust.com

■ The Greenslade Family Foundation

CC NO 1178046 **ESTABLISHED** 2017

WHERE FUNDING CAN BE GIVEN UK.

WHO CAN BENEFIT Charitable organisations.

WHAT IS FUNDED Extracurricular activities for children and young adults.

SAMPLE GRANTS Children & the Arts (£68,000); The Polka Theatre (£25,000); Action for Stammering Children (£10,000).

FINANCES *Financial year end* 05/04/2020 *Income* £5,660,000 *Total grants* £103,000 *Grants to organisations* £103,000 *Assets* £5,740,000

TRUSTEES Carolyn Greenslade; Carol Bailey; James Wilcox.

HOW TO APPLY Contact the correspondent for further information.

CONTACT DETAILS The Trustees, 33 Grosvenor Street, Mayfair, London W1K 4QU *Email* laurence.barrat@floreat.com

■ The Greggs Foundation

CC NO 296590 **ESTABLISHED** 1987

WHERE FUNDING CAN BE GIVEN UK, with a preference for the North East (Northumberland, Tyne and Wear, Durham and Teesside) and in the regional divisions of Greggs plc.

WHO CAN BENEFIT Charitable organisations; community groups; not-for-profit organisations; schools; individuals.

WHAT IS FUNDED Community support; social welfare; inequality; health and well-being; children and young people; the environment; older people; social isolation; disability; homelessness; carers; education.

WHAT IS NOT FUNDED See the grant-maker's website for a full list of exclusions.

TYPE OF GRANT Core and running costs; project costs. Funding may be given for up to three years. The type of funding is dependent on the grant programme.

RANGE OF GRANTS Dependent upon funding stream.

SAMPLE GRANTS A list of beneficiaries was not included in the annual report and accounts.

FINANCES *Financial year end* 31/12/2019 *Income* £3,620,000 *Total grants* £3,194,300 *Grants to organisations* £2,840,000 *Assets* £24,360,000

TRUSTEES Andrew Davison; Richard Hutton; Roisin Currie; Jane Hartley; Fiona Nicholson; Kate Bradley; Karen Wilkinson-Bell; Sanjay Singh; Steve Haines; Mick Thompson.

OTHER INFORMATION The foundation offers several different grant programmes, see the foundation's website for full information. During 2019, the foundation provided 428 grants to community organisations and over 3,000 hardship grants to individuals in need.

HOW TO APPLY Apply online via the foundation's website. Each grants programme has its own criteria, guidelines and application process, all of which are available to view on the website.

CONTACT DETAILS Justine Massingham, Grants Manager, Greggs House, Quorum Business Park, Newcastle upon Tyne, Tyne and Wear NE12 8BU *Tel.* 0191 212 7626 *Email* grants@greggsfoundation.org.uk *Website* www.greggsfoundation.org.uk

■ The Gretna Charitable Trust

CC NO 1020533 **ESTABLISHED** 1993

WHERE FUNDING CAN BE GIVEN UK, with a preference for Hertfordshire and London.

WHO CAN BENEFIT Registered charities; individuals.

WHAT IS FUNDED General charitable purposes.

SAMPLE GRANTS Previous beneficiaries have included: British Australia Society; Charlie Waller Memorial Trust; Garden Museum – Lambeth; Haileybury Youth Club; Mensah Recovery Support Agency; Royal Engineers Museum; The Globe Theatre; The Scout Association; World Sight Foundation.

FINANCES *Financial year end* 05/04/2020 *Income* £124,600 *Total grants* £85,500 *Grants to organisations* £85,500 *Assets* £351,300

TRUSTEES Richard Walduck; Susan Walduck; Alexander Walduck; Alison Duncan.

HOW TO APPLY Our previous research suggests that the trustees discourage unsolicited applications.

CONTACT DETAILS Alexander Walduck, Trustee, c/o Directors' Office, Imperial Hotel, 61–66 Russell Square, London WC1B 5BB *Tel.* 020 7691 2623 *Email* awalduck@imperialhotels.co.uk

■ The Grimmitt Trust

CC NO 801975 **ESTABLISHED** 1986

WHERE FUNDING CAN BE GIVEN The Birmingham, Dudley, Wolverhampton and Walsall postcode areas; overseas.

WHO CAN BENEFIT Registered charities; unregistered charities; hospitals; hospices; individuals; PTAs; universities.

WHAT IS FUNDED Community; children and youth; culture and education; health; older people; overseas aid.

WHAT IS NOT FUNDED National charities; CICs; social enterprises.

TYPE OF GRANT General funding; project funding; core/revenue costs; unrestricted funding.

RANGE OF GRANTS Mostly £2,000 or less.

SAMPLE GRANTS The Ironbridge Gorge Museum Trust (£2,500); Better Pathways, Hope Projects, John Taylor Hospice, Moseley Road Baths, Royal Shakespeare Company, Sport4Life, St Martin's Centre for Health and Healing and Tipton Food Bank (£2,000 each).

FINANCES *Financial year end* 05/04/2020 *Income* £304,000 *Total grants* £305,300 *Grants to organisations* £304,500 *Assets* £10,080,000

TRUSTEES Sue Day; David Owen; Tim Welch; Jenny Dickins; Sarah Wilkey; Phil Smith; Trevor Jones; Emma Pardoe.

OTHER INFORMATION From 318 applications received by the trust in 2019/20, grants were made to 239 organisations and individuals. Grants of less than £2,000 totalled £138,300.

HOW TO APPLY Applicants should contact the secretary, who will advise on what to include. The trustees meet three times a year to consider applications. Applicants must demonstrate that their project is in line with the trust's objectives.

CONTACT DETAILS Vanessa Welch, Secretary, 151B All Saints Road, Kings Heath, Birmingham, West Midlands B14 6AT *Tel.* 07576 195955 *Email* admin@grimmitt-trust.org.uk

■ The Grocers' Charity

CC NO 255230 **ESTABLISHED** 1968

WHERE FUNDING CAN BE GIVEN UK.

WHO CAN BENEFIT UK-registered charities only.

WHAT IS FUNDED Children and young people; disability and inclusion; older people; the environment and conservation; health; heritage; military; social welfare; the arts; medical research.

WHAT IS NOT FUNDED Support is rarely given to the following unless there is a specific or long-standing connection with the Grocers' Company: places of worship; educational establishments; hospices; charities whose beneficiaries are overseas; non-UK-registered charities; non-medical charities with a turnover of over £500,000; individuals.

TYPE OF GRANT Funding for new and existing projects; core costs; typically one-off; research.

RANGE OF GRANTS Mostly under £10,000.

SAMPLE GRANTS Oundle School (£150,000); Mossbourne Community Academy (£20,000); Cavell Nurses' Trust (£10,000); The Listening Place (£7,500); St Mary and Holy Trinity Bow (£7,000); Silverlining Brain Injury Charity (£5,000); The Country Food Trust (£2,500); Therapy Garden (£2,000).

FINANCES *Financial year end* 31/07/2020 *Income* £812,400 *Total grants* £830,000 *Grants to organisations* £830,000 *Assets* £24,640,000

TRUSTEE The Grocers' Trust Company Ltd.

OTHER INFORMATION During 2019/20, 153 grants were awarded: of these, 25 were for less than £2,000 and the remainder ranged between £2,000 and £150,000. Grants were awarded for the following purposes: education (£286,800); relief of poverty and young people (£172,800); older people and other (£107,400); health (£75,700); disability (£70,500); arts and heritage (£64,200); churches (£52,600). Only organisations receiving grants of over £2,000 were listed as beneficiaries in the charity's accounts.

HOW TO APPLY Applications can be made via the charity's website. Current application deadlines can be found on the website. The Education and Charities Committee usually meet four times a year to consider applications.

CONTACT DETAILS Michelle Molyneux, Charity Manager, Grocers' Hall, Princes Street, London EC2R 8AD *Tel.* 020 7606 3113 *Email* charity@grocershall.co.uk *Website* www.grocershall.co.uk

■ M. and R. Gross Charities Ltd

CC NO 251888 **ESTABLISHED** 1967

WHERE FUNDING CAN BE GIVEN UK and overseas.

WHO CAN BENEFIT Jewish organisations.

WHAT IS FUNDED Orthodox Jewish educational and religious activities; the relief of Jewish people who are in need.

SAMPLE GRANTS Asser Bishvil Foundation (£118,000); United Talmudical Associates Ltd (£103,800); Yetev Lev London Jerusalem Trust (£36,200); The Rehabilitation Trust (£36,000) and Beis Ruchel D'Satmar London Ltd (£35,400).

FINANCES *Financial year end* 31/03/2020 *Income* £2,730,000 *Total grants* £1,110,000 *Grants to organisations* £1,110,000 *Assets* £55,000,000

TRUSTEES Rifka Gross; Sarah Padwa; Michael Saberski; Leonard Lerner.

OTHER INFORMATION A full list of beneficiaries was not included in the annual report and accounts; however, details of four 'material' grants were provided.

HOW TO APPLY Contact the correspondent for further information. Applications are assessed regularly and many smaller grants are dealt with through a grant-making agency, United Talmudical Associates Ltd.

CONTACT DETAILS The Trustees, c/o Cohen Arnold, New Burlington House, 1075 Finchley Road, London NW11 0PU *Tel.* 020 8731 0777 *Email* mail@cohenarnold.com

■ Groundwork UK

CC NO 291558 **ESTABLISHED** 1981

WHERE FUNDING CAN BE GIVEN UK.

WHO CAN BENEFIT Registered charities and community groups.

WHAT IS FUNDED Combatting the nature and climate emergency; health and well-being; access to learning and work and opportunities; community development.

TYPE OF GRANT Capital costs; core/revenue costs; project funding.

SAMPLE GRANTS A list of beneficiaries was not included in the annual report and accounts.

FINANCES *Financial year end* 31/03/2020 *Income* £25,170,000 *Total grants* £22,120,000 *Grants to organisations* £22,120,000 *Assets* £3,420,000

TRUSTEES Graham Hartley; Wendy Golland; Faiza Amin; Andrew Thurston; Michael Omerod; Jack White; Jeff Greenidge; Anthony Nelson; Paul Roots; Geoff Howesgo; Stuart Bonham; Catherine Culverhouse; Anne-Marie Simpson; Alan Smith; Tony Berry; Mike Master.

OTHER INFORMATION Groundwork UK manages a number of grant schemes on the behalf of businesses, public sector and third sector partners.

HOW TO APPLY Check the Groundwork UK website for details of grant programmes currently being administered.

CONTACT DETAILS The Trustees, Suite B2, The Walker Building, 58 Oxford Street, Birmingham, West Midlands B5 5NR *Tel.* 0121 236 8565 *Email* info@groundwork.org.uk *Website* www.groundwork.org.uk

The N. and R. Grunbaum Charitable Trust

CC NO 1068524 **ESTABLISHED** 1998
WHERE FUNDING CAN BE GIVEN UK and Israel.
WHO CAN BENEFIT Registered charities and Jewish organisations.
WHAT IS FUNDED Relief of poverty; advancement of Jewish education and religion.
SAMPLE GRANTS A list of beneficiaries was not included in the annual report and accounts.
FINANCES *Financial year end* 31/03/2020
Income £67,100 *Total grants* £68,600
Grants to organisations £68,600
Assets £11,700
TRUSTEES Norman Grunbaum; Rosella Grunbaum; David Grunbaum.
HOW TO APPLY Apply in writing to the correspondent.
CONTACT DETAILS Norman Grunbaum, Trustee, 7 Northdene Gardens, London N15 6LX *Tel.* 020 8800 9974

The Walter Guinness Charitable Trust

CC NO 205375 **ESTABLISHED** 1968
WHERE FUNDING CAN BE GIVEN India; the UK; preference for Wiltshire.
WHO CAN BENEFIT Registered charities and community groups.
WHAT IS FUNDED Bursaries for education; medical research; projects relating to people with disabilities, older people, veterans, prisoners, children, families and young people.
RANGE OF GRANTS £1,000 to £5,000.
SAMPLE GRANTS Macmillan Cancer Support (£5,000); Countess of Brecknock Hospice Trust (£5,000); Salisbury Cathedral (£4,000); Methodist Homes for the Aged (£3,500); Home-start South Wiltshire (£2,000); Young Carers Development Trust (£1,200).
FINANCES *Financial year end* 05/04/2020
Income £179,800 *Total grants* £189,800
Grants to organisations £189,800
Assets £8,340,000
TRUSTEES Finn Guinness; Rosaleen Mulji; Catriona Guinness.
OTHER INFORMATION Of the 124 grants made, 72 were less than/up to £1,000 and 52 were more than £1,000.
HOW TO APPLY Contact the correspondent for further information.
CONTACT DETAILS The Trustees, Biddesden House, Biddesden, Andover, Hampshire SP11 9DN *Tel.* 01582 439270 *Email* WGuinnessCT@tmf-group.com

Calouste Gulbenkian Foundation – UK Branch

ESTABLISHED 1956
WHERE FUNDING CAN BE GIVEN UK and the Republic of Ireland.
WHO CAN BENEFIT Registered charities; unregistered charities; CICs; social enterprises.
WHAT IS FUNDED The foundation's UK branch focuses on three themes: Valuing the Ocean – connecting and building relationships designed to help protect the oceans; Citizen Engagement on Climate – demonstrating what effective public engagement on climate looks like and creating conditions for its scaling; The Civic Role of Arts Organisations – creating a movement of change-makers who want arts organisations to play a civic role in their communities.
TYPE OF GRANT General funding; core/revenue costs; project funding; unrestricted funding.
SAMPLE GRANTS A list of beneficiaries was not included in the annual report and accounts.
FINANCES *Financial year end* 31/12/2019
Total grants £1,510,000
Grants to organisations £1,510,000
OTHER INFORMATION The foundation, which was established in Portugal, is headquartered in Lisbon and has offices in Paris and London. It is not a UK-registered charity and therefore full accounts were not available to view. The grant total is taken from the foundation's 2019 annual review.
HOW TO APPLY Unsolicited applications are not accepted. The foundation's website states: 'Our approach to funding is that we do not accept unsolicited applications. This is because we do not fund projects or organisations reactively. We think of our approach as being "interactive" rather than "reactive" or "proactive".'
CONTACT DETAILS The Trustees, 50 Hoxton Square, London N1 6PB *Tel.* 020 7012 1400 *Email* info@gulbenkian.org.uk *Website* https://gulbenkian.pt/uk-branch

The Gunter Charitable Trust

CC NO 268346 **ESTABLISHED** 1974
WHERE FUNDING CAN BE GIVEN UK and overseas.
WHO CAN BENEFIT Charitable organisations.
WHAT IS FUNDED General charitable purposes.
RANGE OF GRANTS £400 to £6,000.
SAMPLE GRANTS WWF-UK (£6,000); Freedom From Torture (£4,800); Liverpool School of Tropical Medicine (£3,000); Health and Hope UK (£2,500); Womankind Worldwide (£1,400); Compassion in Dying (£1,000); Plantlife International (£400).
FINANCES *Financial year end* 05/04/2020
Income £86,300 *Total grants* £82,200
Grants to organisations £82,200
Assets £2,370,000
TRUSTEES James Findlay; Richard Worrall.
HOW TO APPLY Unsolicited applications are not accepted. The trust's 2019/20 accounts state that 'the Appointing Authority nominates their chosen charities to the trustees on a bi-annual basis. These are then considered by the trustees, and donations are made accordingly.'
CONTACT DETAILS The Trustees, c/o Forsters LLP, 31 Hill Street, London W1J 5LS *Tel.* 020 7863 8333

Dr Guthrie's Association

OSCR NO SC009302 **ESTABLISHED** 1986
WHERE FUNDING CAN BE GIVEN Scotland, with a preference for Edinburgh.
WHO CAN BENEFIT Not-for-profit organisations.
WHAT IS FUNDED The care and welfare of disadvantaged young people under the age of 22. Priority will be given to: organisations supporting economically and socially disadvantaged children and young people aged 10–21 years; small local organisations as opposed to national organisations; creative and outdoor pursuits for disadvantaged children and young people; organisations supporting young unemployed people.
WHAT IS NOT FUNDED Individuals; environmental or conservation projects; other grant-making or fundraising charities; endowment funds; building or restoration projects; retrospective expenditure. The application form gives further examples of what will not be supported.

RANGE OF GRANTS £250 to £2,000.
SAMPLE GRANTS Abernethy Trust (£3,000); Bethany Christian Trust (£2,000); Noonday (£1,500); Sea the Change CIC (£1,000); St Theresa's Youth Club (£750); Blue Sky Autism Project (£500).
FINANCES *Financial year end* 31/03/2020 *Income* £46,300 *Total grants* £93,700 *Grants to organisations* £93,700 *Assets* £1,730,000
HOW TO APPLY Application forms are available to download from the administrator's website.
CONTACT DETAILS The Grant Administrator, PO BOX 28838, Edinburgh EH15 2XZ. *Email* drguthrie16@gmail.com *Website* https://www.azets.co.uk/dr-guthrie-s-association

■ The Guy Foundation

CC NO 1178782 **ESTABLISHED** 2018
WHERE FUNDING CAN BE GIVEN Worldwide.
WHO CAN BENEFIT Universities; non-profit research organisations.
WHAT IS FUNDED Quantum biology research.
WHAT IS NOT FUNDED Indirect costs; overheads; salary recovery costs for staff funded full-time by the employing organisation; PhD students; fees for academic courses; equipment that is not going to be used primarily for the project; costs for capital builds or refurbishment.
TYPE OF GRANT Project funding; research.
RANGE OF GRANTS Up to £400,000.
SAMPLE GRANTS A list of beneficiaries was not included in the annual report and accounts.
FINANCES *Financial year end* 30/04/2020 *Income* £5,200 *Total grants* £452,900 *Grants to organisations* £452,900 *Assets* £723,800
TRUSTEES Eric Dixon; Richard Brass; Jonathan Laughton; Dr Geoffrey Guy; Katherine Guy.
HOW TO APPLY Contact the foundation by email to request an application form.
CONTACT DETAILS The Trustees, The Estate Office, Chedington Court, Chedington, Beaminster DT8 3HY *Email* info@theguyfoundation.org *Website* https://www.theguyfoundation.org

■ The Gynaecological Cancer Fund

CC NO 1154755 **ESTABLISHED** 2013
WHERE FUNDING CAN BE GIVEN UK, predominantly.
WHO CAN BENEFIT Charitable organisations; hospitals.
WHAT IS FUNDED Charitable organisations; hospitals.
RANGE OF GRANTS £100,000 to £200,000.
SAMPLE GRANTS The Royal Marsden (£200,000); Jenny Halpern Prince (£100,000).
FINANCES *Financial year end* 31/01/2020 *Income* £990,400 *Total grants* £300,000 *Grants to organisations* £300,000 *Assets* £639,800
TRUSTEES Jenny Prince; Jennifer Emanuel; Annalisa Jenkins; Dame Helena Morrissey.
OTHER INFORMATION Grants were awarded to two organisations during the year.
HOW TO APPLY Contact the correspondent for further information.
CONTACT DETAILS The Trustees, 17 Gresse Street, 6 Evelyn Yard, London W1T 1QL *Tel.* 020 7462 8500 *Email* info@ladygardenfoundation.com *Website* https://www.ladygardenfoundation.com

■ H. C. D. Memorial Fund

CC NO 1044956 **ESTABLISHED** 1995

WHERE FUNDING CAN BE GIVEN UK and overseas.

WHO CAN BENEFIT Charitable organisations.

WHAT IS FUNDED Education and employment; health; prisoner and refugee welfare; the environment, in particular climate change; international development and peace-keeping; community development.

TYPE OF GRANT Capital costs; core/revenue costs; seed funding/start-up funding; project funding; unrestricted funding.

RANGE OF GRANTS £10,000 to £35,000.

SAMPLE GRANTS Centre for Alternative Technology (£64,500); Health Poverty Action – Guatemala (£35,000); Feedback Global and Key 4 Life (£25,000 each); Christian Aid – Lebanon (£24,000); Children Heard Not Seen (£20,000); Womankind (£15,000); Meals Behind the Wire (£10,800); Stand Against Sexual Exploitation (£10,000).

FINANCES *Financial year end* 30/06/2020 *Income* £933,700 *Total grants* £980,200 *Grants to organisations* £980,200 *Assets* £875,400

TRUSTEES Jeremy Debenham; Bill Flinn; Nicholas Debenham; Harriet Lear; Joanna Lear; Susannah Drummond.

OTHER INFORMATION Grants totalling £424,900 were made to 20 organisations in the UK in support of health, community, the environment, and the well-being of prisoners and refugees. The remaining 25 grants (£555,300) were made to organisations overseas.

HOW TO APPLY Apply in writing to the correspondent, although our research suggests that the trustees seek out their own projects and rarely respond to unsolicited applications.

CONTACT DETAILS Susannah Drummond, Secretary, 24 Fern Avenue, Jesmond, Newcastle upon Tyne, Tyne and Wear NE2 2QT *Tel.* 0191 281 4228 *Email* hcdmemorialfund@gmail.com

■ H. C. Foundation

CC NO 1148306 **ESTABLISHED** 2012

WHERE FUNDING CAN BE GIVEN UK.

WHO CAN BENEFIT Jewish charitable organisations.

WHAT IS FUNDED Jewish causes; education; health; social welfare.

SAMPLE GRANTS Achisomoch Aid Company Ltd (£61,000); Chevras Mo'oz Ladol and Kef Kids (£10,000 each).

FINANCES *Financial year end* 31/03/2020 *Income* £51,400 *Total grants* £111,000 *Grants to organisations* £111,000 *Assets* £593,100

TRUSTEES Bernard Groszman; Shelley Groszman; Shirley March.

OTHER INFORMATION Grants were awarded to eight organisations during the year.

HOW TO APPLY Contact the correspondent for further information.

CONTACT DETAILS The Trustees, 1 Bridge Lane, 1st Floor, Suite 1A, London NW11 0EA *Tel.* 020 8458 8900

■ Hackney Parochial Charities

CC NO 219876 **ESTABLISHED** 1904

WHERE FUNDING CAN BE GIVEN The London Borough of Hackney.

WHO CAN BENEFIT Registered charities; CICs; schools; hospitals; hospices; religious bodies/ institutions; individuals.

WHAT IS FUNDED Social welfare; education; breaks for families and children; projects for advancement in life.

WHAT IS NOT FUNDED A full list of exclusions can be found on the charity's website.

TYPE OF GRANT Core/revenue costs; project funding.

RANGE OF GRANTS Up to £20,000; however, the majority of grants are for £4,000 or less.

SAMPLE GRANTS Hackney Community Law Centre (£30,000); Hackney Doorways (£20,000); Hackney Quest (£15,000); Hackney Migrant Centre and Woman's Trust (£10,000 each); Age UK – East London (£5,000); The Community Hub (£2,700).

FINANCES *Financial year end* 31/03/2019 *Income* £346,300 *Total grants* £362,800 *Grants to organisations* £283,000 *Assets* £6,690,000

TRUSTEES Cllr Chris Kennedy; Jacquie Driver; Nicola Baboneau; Irfan Malik; Rob Chapman; Cllr Sharon Patrick; Revd Alexander Gordon; Mary Cannon; Allan Hilton; Tosin Oladipo.

OTHER INFORMATION During the year, the charity made 155 hardship grants to individuals totalling £79,800. The 2018/19 accounts were the latest available at the time of writing (January 2021).

HOW TO APPLY Application forms are available to download from the charity's website. Applications can be submitted at any time. The trustees meet bi-annually to consider project applications.

CONTACT DETAILS Clerk to the Trustees, c/o 6 Trull Farm Building, Tetbury, Gloucestershire GL8 8SQ *Tel.* 020 3397 7805 *Email* hackney@thetrustpartnership.com *Website* www.hackneyparochialcharities.org.uk

■ The Hadfield Charitable Trust

CC NO 1067491 **ESTABLISHED** 1997

WHERE FUNDING CAN BE GIVEN Cumbria.

WHO CAN BENEFIT Charitable organisations.

WHAT IS FUNDED Youth and employment; social welfare; older people; the arts; the environment.

TYPE OF GRANT Mainly one-off (occasionally for two to three years); project funding: capital costs preferred; revenue costs considered.

RANGE OF GRANTS Mainly between £500 and £5,000.

SAMPLE GRANTS Growing Well (£6,800); Church in The Barn and Hospice at Home Carlisle and North Lakeland (£5,000 each); Autism Support Allerdale and Copeland and Huntington's Disease Association (£3,000 each); Dent Reading Room (£1,000); Natland and Oxenholme Table Tennis (£500).

FINANCES *Financial year end* 31/08/2020 *Income* £291,500 *Total grants* £241,800 *Grants to organisations* £241,800 *Assets* £8,550,000

TRUSTEES Roy Morris; William Rathbone; Andrew Morris; Andrew Forsyth; Caroline Addison; Duncan Bailey.

OTHER INFORMATION The trust awarded a total of 86 grants during 2019/20 and they were distributed as follows: social needs (£157,900); youth and employment (£53,900); the arts

(£16,200); the environment (£7,000); older people (£6,500); other (£380).

HOW TO APPLY Application forms are available from the trust's website. The completed application form should be sent to the administrator by post or email along with supporting documents, details of which are on the website. Application deadlines are usually 1 February, 1 June and 1 October; applications must be received by midday on these dates to be considered. Applicants are encouraged to contact the trust before applying to discuss their plans with the administrator or assistant.

CONTACT DETAILS Susan Berriman, Trust Administrator, Shoestone Cottage, Garnett Bridge, Kendal, Cumbria LA8 9AZ *Tel.* 01539 823112 *Email* admin@hadfieldtrust.org.uk *Website* www.hadfieldtrust.org.uk

The Hadley Trust

CC NO 1064823 **ESTABLISHED** 1997

WHERE FUNDING CAN BE GIVEN UK.

WHO CAN BENEFIT Registered charities; organisations with charitable purposes.

WHAT IS FUNDED Crime and justice; young people; disabilities; social investment; local causes; health; welfare reform; international; and hospices.

TYPE OF GRANT Core costs; project funding; capital costs; development funding.

SAMPLE GRANTS Centre for Crime and Justice Studies; Centre for Justice Innovation; Crest Advisory; Criminal Justice Alliance; Coram Voice; Noah's Ark Children's Hospice; Prison Reform Trust; Prisoners' Education Trust; Social Market Foundation.

FINANCES *Financial year end* 31/03/2020 *Income* £6,260,000 *Total grants* £3,610,000 *Grants to organisations* £3,610,000 *Assets* £210,170,000

TRUSTEES Sir Philip Hulme; Thomas Hulme; Katherine Prideaux; Lady Janet Hulme; Sophie Swift; Juliet Lyon.

OTHER INFORMATION In 2019/20 the trust made grants to 84 organisations. The trustees prefer to work with small to medium-sized charities and establish the trust as a reliable, long-term funding partner.

HOW TO APPLY Apply in writing to the correspondent. Although the majority of the trust's funds are already committed, new applications are still considered.

CONTACT DETAILS Carol Biggs, Gladsmuir, Hadley Common, Barnet, Hertfordshire EN5 5QE *Tel.* 020 8447 4577 *Email* carol@hadleytrust.org

Hadras Kodesh Trust

CC NO 1105885 **ESTABLISHED** 2004

WHERE FUNDING CAN BE GIVEN Overseas and the UK, with a preference for Hackney.

WHO CAN BENEFIT Jewish charitable organisations and individuals.

WHAT IS FUNDED The advancement of Orthodox Jewish religious education and the Orthodox Jewish faith throughout the world; particularly through supporting the activities of religious publishers.

SAMPLE GRANTS A list of beneficiaries was not included in the annual report and accounts.

FINANCES *Financial year end* 09/07/2020 *Income* £3,300,000 *Total grants* £3,400,000 *Grants to organisations* £3,400,000 *Assets* £290,100

TRUSTEES Pincus Mann; Yoel Fisher.

HOW TO APPLY Contact the correspondent for further information.

CONTACT DETAILS The Trustees, 52 East Bank, London N16 5PZ *Tel.* 020 8880 8941 *Email* pincus@hktrust.org

The Hadrian Trust

CC NO 272161 **ESTABLISHED** 1976

WHERE FUNDING CAN BE GIVEN Tyne and Wear, Northumberland and Durham, including Hartlepool.

WHO CAN BENEFIT Registered charities; CICs; social enterprises; PTAs; hospices.

WHAT IS FUNDED Social welfare; young people; disability; older people; women; ethnic minorities; education; the arts; the environment. There is a detailed list of areas of interest within each category on the website.

WHAT IS NOT FUNDED Capital projects for major building improvements; repair of buildings used solely for worship; animal protection charities; charities based outside the geographic area of benefit; national charities making general appeals; individuals.

TYPE OF GRANT Capital costs; project costs; part salaries; core/revenue costs; seed funding/ start-up funding.

RANGE OF GRANTS Mostly between £500 and £2,000.

SAMPLE GRANTS A list of beneficiaries was not included in the annual report and accounts.

FINANCES *Financial year end* 30/09/2020 *Income* £243,500 *Total grants* £213,500 *Grants to organisations* £213,500 *Assets* £8,230,000

TRUSTEES Pauline Dodgson; Jim Dias; Ian Brown; Colin Fitzpatrick; Catherine Wood; Dorothy Parker.

OTHER INFORMATION A total of 182 grants were made during 2019/20.

HOW TO APPLY Applications can be made online via the trust's website, or by post. The trustees meet quarterly, usually in January, April, July and October. Applications must be received three weeks before the trustees' meeting. Refer to the website for application deadlines and information on what to include.

CONTACT DETAILS The Trustees, PO Box 785, Whitley Bay, Tyne and Wear NE26 9DW *Tel.* 07815 785074 *Email* enquiries@hadriantrust.co.uk *Website* www.hadriantrust.co.uk

The Alfred Haines Charitable Trust

CC NO 327166 **ESTABLISHED** 1986

WHERE FUNDING CAN BE GIVEN Birmingham and the West Midlands.

WHO CAN BENEFIT Local organisations helping people to improve their quality of life.

WHAT IS FUNDED Children and young people (youth work/workers); family support and counselling; support for people who are homeless, unemployed or in debt; humanitarian and Christian overseas aid; support for people who are medically disadvantaged; care for people who are older or who have disabilities; holidays for disadvantaged children and teenagers.

WHAT IS NOT FUNDED See the trust's website for a full list of exclusions. Organisations that have received support from Quothquan Trust should not apply.

TYPE OF GRANT Specific projects and items rather than general running costs.
RANGE OF GRANTS £250 to £2,000.
SAMPLE GRANTS A list of beneficiaries was not included in the annual report and accounts.
FINANCES *Financial year end* 31/03/2020 *Income* £33,700 *Total grants* £72,200 *Grants to organisations* £72,200 *Assets* £1,240,000
TRUSTEES Gregor Moss; Paul Gilmour.
OTHER INFORMATION During the year, the trust awarded 71 grants to organisations, distributed as follows: family support and counselling (£27,500); children and young people (£11,700); support for the homeless, unemployed and those in debt (£10,500); care for older people and people with disabilities (£4,500); holidays for children and teenagers who are disadvantaged (£3,700); support for people who are medically disadvantaged (£2,300).
HOW TO APPLY Applications should include: a brief description of the activities of your organisation; details of the project and its overall cost; what funds have already been raised and how the remaining funds are to be raised; a copy of your latest accounts including any associated or parent organisation; and any other leaflets or supporting documentation. Applicants are advised to consider the exclusion list prior to application. Applications are not acknowledged and unsuccessful applicants are not notified. The trust shares administration with the Quothquan Trust (Charity Commission number: 1110647). Applications which are more relevant to the Quothquan Trust will be passed over, so a separate application is not necessary.
CONTACT DETAILS The Trustees, Dale Farm, Worcester Lane, Sutton Coldfield, West Midlands B75 5PR *Tel.* 0121 323 3236 *Website* www.ahct.org.uk

■ Halifax Foundation for Northern Ireland

CCNI NO NIC101763 **ESTABLISHED** 1986
WHERE FUNDING CAN BE GIVEN Northern Ireland.
WHO CAN BENEFIT Registered charities with incomes of under £1 million.
WHAT IS FUNDED Social and community needs including: community services, advice services, people with special needs; health, civic responsibility, cultural enrichment; education and training including: employment and life skills.
WHAT IS NOT FUNDED See the foundation's website for a full list of exclusions.
TYPE OF GRANT Core costs; materials and equipment; salary costs; volunteer expenses; project costs; refurbishment; activities; training; disabled access; transport costs.
RANGE OF GRANTS The average grant is currently between £3,000 and £4,000.
SAMPLE GRANTS Previous beneficiaries have included: Angel Eyes Northern Ireland – 'Pitching 4 Pounds' programme (£15,000); Ballymoney Evergreen Club and The Buddy Bear Trust (£4,000 each); Wheelworks (£3,500); Northern Ireland Rural Women's Network (£3,450).
FINANCES *Financial year end* 31/12/2019 *Income* £1,720,000 *Total grants* £1,340,000 *Grants to organisations* £1,340,000 *Assets* £3,090,000
TRUSTEES Imelda Macmillan; Paula Leathem; Áine McCoy; Gillian Boyd; Ken Simpson; Barry Connolly; John Leckey; Michael Prendergast; Melvin Slaine.
OTHER INFORMATION Grants were broken down as follows: social and community welfare (£790,800); education and training (£455,800); matched giving (£93,700).
HOW TO APPLY All applications must be made online via the foundation's website, where full guidelines, including a list of supporting documentation required, are available. The Community Grants Programme operates on a rolling basis.
CONTACT DETAILS Brenda McMullan, Company Secretary, Clifton House Heritage Centre, 2 North Queen Street, Belfast BT15 1ES *Tel.* 028 9032 3000 *Email* grants@halifaxfoundationni.org *Website* www.halifaxfoundationni.org

■ The Halsall Foundation

CC NO 1174779 **ESTABLISHED** 2017
WHERE FUNDING CAN BE GIVEN Lancashire.
WHO CAN BENEFIT Registered charities.
WHAT IS FUNDED Children, young people and families; older people; people with disabilities; people who are socially isolated.
WHAT IS NOT FUNDED Animal welfare; arts and heritage; conservation and the environment; expeditions and overseas travel; general fundraising appeals; individual and sports sponsorship; national charities and large organisations; mainstream education and mainstream sport.
TYPE OF GRANT One-off grants for capital projects; start-up and/or ongoing running costs for specific projects; multi-year revenue grants for core funding.
RANGE OF GRANTS Up to £35,000.
SAMPLE GRANTS The Boathouse Youth (£35,000); Aspired Futures and Rainbow Hub (£15,000 each); Logan's Foundation (£10,000); Mustard Seed, Outward Bound Trust and South Shore Partnership (£5,000 each).
FINANCES *Financial year end* 31/08/2020 *Income* £150,000 *Total grants* £90,000 *Grants to organisations* £90,000 *Assets* £84,000
TRUSTEES Philip Gartside; John Dean; David Halsall; Dr Richard Reed.
OTHER INFORMATION In 2019/20 grants were awarded to seven organisations.
HOW TO APPLY Applications can be made via the foundation's website.
CONTACT DETAILS The Trustees, c/o MHA Moore and Smalley, Richard House, 9 Winckley Square, Preston PR1 3HP *Tel.* 07912 993562 *Email* application@thehalsallfoundation.org *Website* https://www.thehalsallfoundation.org

■ Hamamelis Trust

CC NO 280938 **ESTABLISHED** 1980
WHERE FUNDING CAN BE GIVEN UK, but with a preference for the Godalming and Surrey areas.
WHO CAN BENEFIT Registered charities; universities.
WHAT IS FUNDED Medical research and ecological conservation.
WHAT IS NOT FUNDED Projects outside the UK.
RANGE OF GRANTS Up to £20,000 but typically of less than £3,000.
SAMPLE GRANTS Lorica Trust Ltd (£20,500); Butterfly Conservation and Surrey Drug and Alcohol Care (£5,000 each); Compassion In World Farming (£3,400); Fight Against Blindness and The Surrey Wildlife Trust (£3,000 each); Orthopaedic

Research UK (£2,500); Child Growth Trust (£2,000); Save Me Trust (£1,400).

FINANCES *Financial year end* 05/04/2020 *Income* £107,300 *Total grants* £67,400 *Grants to organisations* £67,400 *Assets* £3,360,000

TRUSTEES Laura Dadswell; Dr Adam Stone; Lucy Mirouze.

OTHER INFORMATION Grants were made to 17 organisations during the year. Each year grants are split equally between medical research and ecological conservation.

HOW TO APPLY Apply in writing to the correspondent. All applicants are asked to include a short summary of the project with estimated costings. Unsuccessful applications are not acknowledged. Medical applications are assessed by Dr Adam Stone, who is a medically qualified trustee.

CONTACT DETAILS Laura Dadswell, Trustee, c/o Penningtons Manches Cooper LLP, 31 Chertsey Street, Guildford, Surrey GU1 4HD *Tel.* 01483 791800

■ The Hamilton Davies Trust

CC NO 1106123 **ESTABLISHED** 2004

WHERE FUNDING CAN BE GIVEN Irlam; Cadishead; Rixton-with-Glazebrook.

WHO CAN BENEFIT Not-for-profit organisations with a governing body or committee, bank account and constitution (including registered charities, amateur sports clubs, parish councils, schools and colleges, CICs and voluntary/community groups); individuals.

WHAT IS FUNDED Community; education; recreation; regeneration.

TYPE OF GRANT One-off grants; capital costs.

SAMPLE GRANTS Previous beneficiaries have included: Newton-le-Willows Boys' and Girls' Club (£270,000); Manchester Technology Trust (£180,000); Manchester United Foundation (£25,000); Lady James' Hall (£8,000); St Helen's Primary School (£6,200); 2nd Irlam Scout Group (£3,500); Preston Hall (£3,000); Hollins Green Bowling Club (£900); Irlam Junior Football Club (£500).

FINANCES *Financial year end* 05/04/2020 *Income* £717,800 *Total grants* £908,400 *Grants to organisations* £905,600 *Assets* £2,570,000

TRUSTEES Neil McArthur; Graham Chisnall; Frank Cocker.

OTHER INFORMATION The trust also supports young people looking to develop practical and employability skills through the Chris Stocks Fund.

HOW TO APPLY For applications of under £150, you need to send a letter detailing: a brief outline of the project and its benefits; who will be involved; how many people will be involved; who will benefit; how many people will benefit; what area will the project benefit; the amount of financial support required; details of any other funding received or applied for. Application forms for amounts of over £150 can be downloaded from the trust's website.

CONTACT DETAILS Mandy Coleman, General Manager, Hamilton Davies House, 117C Liverpool Road, Cadishead, Manchester M44 5BG *Tel.* 0161 222 4003 *Email* hello@hamiltondavies.org.uk *Website* www.hamiltondavies.org.uk

■ Paul Hamlyn Foundation

CC NO 1102927 **ESTABLISHED** 1987

WHERE FUNDING CAN BE GIVEN UK and India.

WHO CAN BENEFIT Registered charities and organisations; NGOs.

WHAT IS FUNDED General charitable purposes; social welfare; the arts; young people.

WHAT IS NOT FUNDED See the 'Exclusions' page of the foundation's website for full details of what will not be supported.

TYPE OF GRANT The foundation administers a variety of funds, ranging from smaller one-off grants to large grants received over a few years.

RANGE OF GRANTS £10,000 to £400,000 (varies according to fund).

SAMPLE GRANTS Coventry City of Culture Trust (£500,000); Manchester International Festival (£400,000); ACTA Community Theatre (£270,000); Pentland Infant and Nursery School (£149,800); Hounslow Action for Youth (£60,000); Shishu Sarothi Centre for Rehabilitation and Training for Multiple Disability (£55,000); Centre for Contemporary Arts (£40,000); Stack Recruitment CIC (£15,100); African Prisons Project (£12,100); 42nd Street (£5,000).

FINANCES *Financial year end* 31/03/2020 *Income* £32,210,000 *Total grants* £46,850,000 *Grants to organisations* £46,070,000 *Assets* £736,440,000

TRUSTEES Claire Whitaker; Lord Anthony Hall; Jane Hamlyn; James Lingwood; Michael Hamlyn; Tom Wylie; Tim Bunting; Charles Leadbeater; Dr Janet McKenley-Simpson.

OTHER INFORMATION Grants were made to 363 organisations.

HOW TO APPLY Applications can only be submitted via the online application process. Information about available funds and grants can be found on the foundation's detailed website.

CONTACT DETAILS Grants Team, 5–11 Leeke Street, London WC1X 9HY *Tel.* 020 7812 3300 *Email* information@phf.org.uk *Website* www.phf.org.uk

■ The Helen Hamlyn Trust

CC NO 1084839 **ESTABLISHED** 2000

WHERE FUNDING CAN BE GIVEN Worldwide.

WHO CAN BENEFIT Charitable organisations, with a focus on innovative medium and long-term projects; small local and regional charities; museums; educational organisations.

WHAT IS FUNDED Medical innovation; education and welfare; arts and culture, including the professional development of musicians and performing artists; young people; young offenders; conserving heritage in India; international humanitarian affairs; older people.

TYPE OF GRANT Project funding; core costs; research; development costs.

RANGE OF GRANTS Up to £1 million; small grants of up to £10,000.

SAMPLE GRANTS University College London Institute of Education – Helen Hamlyn Centre for Pedagogy (£254,800); Royal Opera House – London (£100,000); Chartered College of Teaching (£20,000); Bronx Documentary Centre (£7,000); National Voices and V&A Museum (£4,500 each); CAPA College (£4,000).

FINANCES *Financial year end* 31/03/2020 *Income* £2,220,000 *Total grants* £1,200,000 *Grants to organisations* £1,200,000 *Assets* £5,760,000

TRUSTEES Lady Hamlyn; Dr Kate Gavron; Dr Shobita Punja; Brendan Cahill; Margaret O'Rorke; Dr Deborah Swallow; Stephen Lewin; Dame Alison Peacock; Lord Ara Darzi.

OTHER INFORMATION During the year, grants were awarded for the following purposes: education and welfare (£877,700); arts and culture (£242,300); heritage and conservation in India (£81,500); older people (£2,000); medical causes (£1,200). Grants of £3,000 and under totalled £18,300.

HOW TO APPLY The trustees have previously noted that 'their energies are focused on the initiation of projects and they do not accept unsolicited applications for major grants'. Appeals for small awards (up to £10,000) may be directed to the correspondent. The trustees meet formally twice a year and informally throughout the year.

CONTACT DETAILS John Roche, Director of Finance and Administration, Unit 1, Drayton House Court, Drayton St Leonard, Oxfordshire OX10 7BG *Tel.* 07969 811531 *Email* john.roche@helenhamlyntrust.org *Website* www.phf.org.uk/our-work-in-the-uk/helen-hamlyn-trust

Hammersmith United Charities

CC NO 205856 **ESTABLISHED** 1992

WHERE FUNDING CAN BE GIVEN The eight northern wards of Hammersmith and Fulham.

WHO CAN BENEFIT Registered charities; constituted organisations such as CICs; schools (for work which is not part of the normal curriculum and where the school can show that children experiencing some kind of disadvantage will benefit).

WHAT IS FUNDED Families and children; food and shelter; homelessness; social welfare; social mobility and inclusion; disabilities; community work.

WHAT IS NOT FUNDED Religious or political causes; animal welfare; environmental causes; work outside the beneficial area.

TYPE OF GRANT Core costs; project funding.

RANGE OF GRANTS Up to £20,000.

SAMPLE GRANTS Shepherds Bush Family Centre (£20,000); St Paul's Money Advice Centre (£15,000); For Brian CIC (£10,000); Mother and Child Welfare Organisation (£5,000); Agents of Change (£4,000); Friends of Wormholt Park (£3,000); Magic Me (£1,200); Death Café (£350).

FINANCES *Financial year end* 31/03/2020 *Income* £1,420,000 *Total grants* £398,500 *Grants to organisations* £398,500 *Assets* £32,390,000

TRUSTEE Hammersmith United Trustee Company.

OTHER INFORMATION In total, 64 grants were awarded during the year. According to the 2019/20 accounts, 45% of the grants made during the year were awarded to organisations supporting children and young people. Micro grants (up to £500) for small organisations totalled £5,000. The charity also provides affordable sheltered housing in Hammersmith.

HOW TO APPLY The charity welcomes initial grant enquiries by phone or email. The charity's website states: 'We like to meet new applicants to develop a better understanding of what they are doing and we are happy to give advice about potential projects.' Grant application forms can be downloaded from the website. The charity has three grants committee meetings each year and the dates of these and the dates by which forms must be received for each meeting are advertised on the website. Once completed, application forms must be emailed to the correspondent. The charity's helpful website provides a number of documents relating to grant-making guidelines and the type of grants which the trustees are willing to award.

CONTACT DETAILS The Trustees, Sycamore House, Sycamore Gardens, London W6 0AS *Tel.* 020 8741 4326 *Email* grants@hamunitedcharities.com *Website* www.hamunitedcharities.org.uk

Hampshire and Isle of Wight Community Foundation

CC NO 1100417 **ESTABLISHED** 2002

WHERE FUNDING CAN BE GIVEN Hampshire; Isle of Wight.

WHO CAN BENEFIT Charities; community and voluntary groups; community clubs; hospices; CICs.

WHAT IS FUNDED General charitable purposes including: poverty and disadvantage; social inclusion; health, mental health and disability; older people; children and young people; sport and recreation; community and family support; education, employment and training; counselling, advice and mentoring.

WHAT IS NOT FUNDED See the website for programme-specific exclusions.

TYPE OF GRANT Programme dependent.

RANGE OF GRANTS Up to £15,000.

SAMPLE GRANTS Hampshire and Wight Trust for Maritime Archaeology (£15,000); Citizens Advice Basingstoke (two grants totalling £12,400); City Life Church (£9,000); Safe New Futures (£6,000); Solent Mind (£5,000); 1st Sarisbury Scout Group (£4,800); Home-Start Butser (£3,300); Isle of Wight Beach Soccer (£1,000); Orchard House Residents Group (£500); Mary Rose School (£200); Rowans Hospice (£66).

FINANCES *Financial year end* 31/12/2019 *Income* £801,500 *Total grants* £693,100 *Grants to organisations* £671,600 *Assets* £13,810,000

TRUSTEES Canon Dr Hugh Mason; Jane Sandars; Cllr Dan Putty; Jo Ash; Rebecca Kennelly; Jonathan Moseley; Virginia Lovell; Adrian Rutter; James Kennedy; Cllr Andrew Joy; Krysia Butwilowska; Sukanya Sitaram; Michael Smith.

OTHER INFORMATION This is one of the 46 UK community foundations, which distribute funding for a wide range of purposes. As with all community foundations, there are a number of donor-advised funds managed on behalf of individuals, families and charitable trusts. Grant schemes tend to change frequently; consult the foundation's website for details of current programmes and up-to-date deadlines. During the year, grants to individuals totalled £21,500. A full list of beneficiaries can be downloaded from the website.

HOW TO APPLY Potential applicants should see the foundation's website for details of funds currently available or contact the foundation directly. Application criteria, procedures and deadlines vary for each of the funds. Full details and separate application forms for each fund can found on the foundation's website.

CONTACT DETAILS The Trustees, Westgate Chambers, Staple Gardens, Winchester, Hampshire SO23 8SR *Tel.* 01962 798700 (general enquiries) or 01962 798695 (grants queries) *Email* info@hiwcf.com or grantsadmin@hiwcf.com *Website* https://www.hiwcf.com

■ The Hampstead Wells and Campden Trust

CC NO 1094611 **ESTABLISHED** 1971

WHERE FUNDING CAN BE GIVEN North Camden (the area comprising the old Metropolitan Borough of Hampstead; see the trust's website for a map of the specific area).

WHO CAN BENEFIT Charitable organisations; voluntary groups; community projects; individuals.

WHAT IS FUNDED Social welfare; health.

WHAT IS NOT FUNDED Outings; trips; social events.

TYPE OF GRANT Core/revenue costs; project funding; occasionally capital costs.

RANGE OF GRANTS Mostly between £1,000 and £20,000.

SAMPLE GRANTS Citizens Advice (£50,000); Home-Start Camden (£12,000); Campden Community Law Centre, Young Campden Foundation (£10,000 each); West Hampstead Women's Centre (£7,500); Maggie's (£2,000); WAC Arts (£1,000).

FINANCES *Financial year end* 30/09/2020 *Income* £390,600 *Total grants* £239,000 *Grants to organisations* £130,500 *Assets* £16,770,000

TRUSTEES Gaynor Bassey; Geoff Berridge; Mike Bieber; Steven Bobasch; Francoise Findlay; Revd Jeremy Fletcher; Tibor Gold; Gaynor Humphreys; Christian Percy; Charles Perrin; Jenny Stevens; Simone Hensby.

OTHER INFORMATION Grants were made to 16 organisations and 783 individuals during the year.

HOW TO APPLY It is recommended that you contact the Grants and Development Officer to discuss any potential applications before starting an application. Refer to the trust's website for details of each grant category and further application guidelines, including application deadlines. Application forms can be downloaded from the website.

CONTACT DETAILS Joanna Goga, Grants and Development Officer, 62 Rosslyn Hill, London NW3 1ND *Tel.* 020 7435 1570 *Email* grant@hwct.co.uk or joanna@hwct.co.uk *Website* www.hwct.org.uk

■ Hampton Fund

CC NO 211756 **ESTABLISHED** 1811

WHERE FUNDING CAN BE GIVEN Hampton; Hampton Hill; Hampton Wick; Teddington; Twickenham; Whitton.

WHO CAN BENEFIT Charities; voluntary sector organisations; community groups; individuals.

WHAT IS FUNDED Disability; older people; children and young people; carers and mental health; as well as community activities.

WHAT IS NOT FUNDED Anything which is the responsibility of a statutory body; national general charitable appeals; animal welfare; the advancement of religion and religious groups, unless they offer a non-religious service to the community; commercial and business activities; endowment appeals; projects of a political nature; retrospective expenditure, both capital and revenue; organisations whose free reserves exceed 12 months of their running costs; non-charitable social enterprises.

RANGE OF GRANTS Up to £60,000.

SAMPLE GRANTS Age UK – Richmond upon Thames (two grants totalling £70,000); Richmond Mencap (three grants totalling £44,500); MTV Youth Hampton (£24,000); My Life Films (£15,000); Art and Soul (£9,000); Learn English at Home (£7,500); Richmond upon Thames Gateway Club (£2,000); Richmond and Kingston ME Group (£750).

FINANCES *Financial year end* 30/06/2019 *Income* £2,370,000 *Total grants* £2,069,700 *Grants to organisations* £1,340,000 *Assets* £62,100,000

TRUSTEES Kim Loxton; Sharika Sharma; Adele Kimber; Dr James Brockbank; David Meggitt; Clive Beaumont; Hilary Hart; Dr Martin Duffy; Martin Seymour; Revd Ben Lovell; Geraldine Locke.

OTHER INFORMATION Grants were made to 79 organisations during the year and were broken down as follows: disability (£252,900); community activities (£231,500); carers (£190,700); health and well-being (£162,300); children and young people (£158,600); older people (£137,600); education (£61,500); advice, advocacy and outreach (£60,000); housing and homelessness (£55,500); arts, sports and recreation (£28,400). Grants to individuals in need totalled £729,700. The 2018/19 accounts were the latest available at the time of writing (January 2021).

HOW TO APPLY Application forms and guidance notes are available to download from the charity's website.

CONTACT DETAILS The Trustees, 15 High Street, Hampton, Middlesex TW12 2SA *Tel.* 020 8941 7866 *Email* david@hfac.co.uk *Website* www.hfac.co.uk

■ The W. A. Handley Charity Trust

CC NO 230435 **ESTABLISHED** 1963

WHERE FUNDING CAN BE GIVEN Northumberland; Tyne and Wear; County Durham (including Hartlepool); Cumbria (including Carlisle).

WHO CAN BENEFIT Registered charities.

WHAT IS FUNDED General charitable purposes including: social welfare; health; older people; young people; people with disabilities; maritime and service causes; education; employment; community support; historic and religious buildings; the environment; music and the arts; volunteering and the voluntary sector.

RANGE OF GRANTS Generally between £500 and £10,000.

SAMPLE GRANTS Combat Stress (£7,500); Newcastle Centre for Unemployment and St Mungo's Church – Simonburn (£5,000 each); Percy Park Rugby Football Club (£4,000); Upper Coquetdale Film Group (£3,500); NSPCC (£2,300); Institute for Cancer Research (£1,000); Heel and Toe Children's Charity (£340).

FINANCES *Financial year end* 31/03/2020 *Income* £249,300 *Total grants* £299,100 *Grants to organisations* £299,100 *Assets* £8,150,000

TRUSTEES Bill Dryden; Tony Glenton; David Milligan.

OTHER INFORMATION In 2019/20, the trust awarded grants to 129 organisations, among which 97 were annual grants totalling £166,600 and 32 were one-off grants totalling £132,500.

HOW TO APPLY Apply in writing to the correspondent, including official charity number and full back-up information.

CONTACT DETAILS Trust Secretary, c/o Ryecroft Glenton, 32 Portland Terrace, Newcastle upon Tyne, Tyne and Wear NE2 1QP *Tel.* 0191 281 1292 *Email* davidmilligan@ryecroft-glenton.co.uk

■ The Lennox Hannay Charitable Trust

CC NO 1080198 **ESTABLISHED** 2000
WHERE FUNDING CAN BE GIVEN England, Wales and Scotland.
WHO CAN BENEFIT Registered charities.
WHAT IS FUNDED General charitable purposes; education; disability; social welfare; health; animal welfare; arts and culture; the environment; the armed forces and emergency services; community development; human rights and equality.
RANGE OF GRANTS Up to £60,000.
SAMPLE GRANTS Young Epilepsy (£60,000); East Anglia Children's Hospice (£50,000); Embrace Child Victims of Crime (£41,000); Westminster City School General Charitable Trust (£30,000); National Emergencies Trust and The Missing Salmon Alliance (£25,000).
FINANCES *Financial year end* 31/03/2020 *Income* £939,600 *Total grants* £714,000 *Grants to organisations* £714,000 *Assets* £29,290,000
TRUSTEES Caroline Wilmot-Sitwell; Tara Douglas-Home; Joanne King; RF Trustee Co. Ltd.
OTHER INFORMATION During the year, the foundation made 107 grants to UK-registered charities in support of a wide variety of causes. Only beneficiaries of grants of £25,000 and above were listed in the accounts. Grants of between £2,000 and £25,000 totalled £283,000. Grants of below £2,000 totalled £60,000.
HOW TO APPLY Apply in writing to the correspondent via post. There are no deadlines. The trustees meet twice a year to discuss applications.
CONTACT DETAILS Mrs C. E. Scott, Company Secretary, c/o RF Trustee Co. Ltd, 15 Suffolk Street, London SW1Y 4HG *Tel.* 020 3696 6721 *Email* charities@rftrustee.com

■ The Kathleen Hannay Memorial Charity

CC NO 299600 **ESTABLISHED** 1988
WHERE FUNDING CAN BE GIVEN UK and worldwide.
WHO CAN BENEFIT Registered charities.
WHAT IS FUNDED General charitable purposes; health; children and young people; the arts.
WHAT IS NOT FUNDED Individuals; non-registered charities.
RANGE OF GRANTS Up to £50,000.
SAMPLE GRANTS New English Ballet Trust (£50,000); Children's Burns Trust (£25,000); Cambridge House Opera Company (£15,000).
FINANCES *Financial year end* 05/04/2020 *Income* £227,500 *Total grants* £257,500 *Grants to organisations* £257,500 *Assets* £12,230,000
TRUSTEES Simon Weil; Christian Ward; Jonathan Weil; Laura Watkins.
OTHER INFORMATION Grants were made to 29 charities. Grants of less than £15,000 totalled £127,500.
HOW TO APPLY Unsolicited applications are not accepted.
CONTACT DETAILS Mrs H. D'Monte, Secretary to the Trustees, c/o BDB Pitmans LLP, One Bartholomew Close, London EC1A 7BL *Tel.* 020 7783 3685

■ The Happold Foundation

CC NO 1050814 **ESTABLISHED** 1995
WHERE FUNDING CAN BE GIVEN Worldwide.
WHO CAN BENEFIT UK-based organisations; students; engineers.
WHAT IS FUNDED Engineering and the built environment.
TYPE OF GRANT Research funding; project funding; scholarships; education; pilot programmes.
RANGE OF GRANTS £500 to £10,000.
SAMPLE GRANTS A list of beneficiaries was not included in the annual report and accounts.
FINANCES *Financial year end* 30/04/2020 *Income* £322,900 *Total grants* £224,900 *Grants to organisations* £224,900 *Assets* £334,100
TRUSTEES Paul Rogers; Ian Liddell; Robert Okpala; Sarah Sachs; Tom Newby; Anna Bruni; Andrew Daubney; Matthew Happold; Celia Way; Furgus Anderson; Steve Williamson; Ian Stewart; Ian Maddocks.
HOW TO APPLY Application forms may be downloaded from the foundation's website and should be completed and returned to the correspondent by email. A detailed set of guidance notes, outlining how proposals will be judged, what should be included in an application and what additional material should be submitted, can also be found on the website.
CONTACT DETAILS The Trustees, Buro Happold, 230 Lower Bristol Road, Bath, Somerset BA2 3DQ *Tel.* 020 7927 9745 *Email* info@happoldfoundation.org *Website* https://www.happoldfoundation.org

■ The Haramead Trust

CC NO 1047416 **ESTABLISHED** 1995
WHERE FUNDING CAN BE GIVEN UK and overseas with a preference for the East Midlands.
WHO CAN BENEFIT Registered charities; individuals.
WHAT IS FUNDED Children and young people; social and medical assistance; homelessness; education.
RANGE OF GRANTS Up to £60,000.
SAMPLE GRANTS Mind (£60,000); Leicestershire Cares (£51,000); ActionAid and Charity Link (£25,000 each); Women's Aid Leicester (£15,000); Farm Africa and Walkabout Foundation (£10,000 each).
FINANCES *Financial year end* 31/03/2020 *Income* £2,160,000 *Total grants* £417,000 *Grants to organisations* £417,000 *Assets* £2,750,000
TRUSTEES Robert Smith; Winifred Linnett; Victoria Duddles; Dr Mary Hanlon.
HOW TO APPLY Contact the correspondent for information regarding the application process.
CONTACT DETAILS The Trustees, Park House, Park Hill, Gaddesby, Leicestershire LE7 4WH *Tel.* 01664 840908 *Email* harameadtrust@aol.com

■ Harbinson Charitable Trust

OSCR NO SC015248 **ESTABLISHED** 1984
WHERE FUNDING CAN BE GIVEN UK and overseas.
WHO CAN BENEFIT Charitable organisations, particularly those working in international development.
WHAT IS FUNDED Social welfare; education; advancement of religion.
RANGE OF GRANTS Mostly up to £5,000.
SAMPLE GRANTS Pathway Centre for Hope (£39,200); Orcadia Creative Learning Centre

£21,000); Médecins Sans Frontières (£5,400); Greenpeace Environmental Trust (£4,600); Renewable World (£3,400); Mvule Trust – Uganda (£1,900); Global Giving UK (£1,000); Womankind Worldwide (£400); Migrant Offshore Aid Station (MOAS) (£200).

FINANCES *Financial year end* 05/04/2019
Income £152,600 *Total grants* £152,000
Grants to organisations £152,000
Assets £6,250,000

OTHER INFORMATION The 2018/19 accounts were the latest available at the time of writing (January 2021).

HOW TO APPLY Contact the correspondent for further information.

CONTACT DETAILS The Trustees, 190 St Vincent Street, Glasgow G2 5SP

■ Harborne Parish Lands Charity

CC NO 219031 **ESTABLISHED** 1576

WHERE FUNDING CAN BE GIVEN The ancient parish of Harborne, which includes parts of Harborne, Smethwick, Bearwood and Quinton (see the charity's website for a map outlining the beneficial area).

WHO CAN BENEFIT Charitable organisations; CICs; hospices; individuals.

WHAT IS FUNDED Social welfare; community causes; health; accommodation and housing. The charity has adopted the following grant priorities: provision for 16 to 24 year olds who are not in education, employment or training (NEET) or are at risk of becoming NEET; services for older people; debt and money management; food and household goods distribution.

TYPE OF GRANT Buildings and capital costs; core costs; development; projects; salaries.

RANGE OF GRANTS Grants range from £2,000 to £20,000.

SAMPLE GRANTS A list of beneficiaries was not included in the annual report and accounts.

FINANCES *Financial year end* 30/06/2020
Income £1,440,000 *Total grants* £117,900
Grants to organisations £83,200
Assets £21,270,000

TRUSTEES Rachel Silber; Frank Wayt; Nigel Thompson; Geoff Hewitt; Buddhi Chetiyawardana; David Jeffrey; Kerry Bolister; Vic Silvester; Cllr Bawa Dhallu.

OTHER INFORMATION In 2019/20, £34,700 was given to 26 individuals.

HOW TO APPLY Applications should be made on a form available from the correspondent. An exact map of the beneficial area can be obtained from the charity (or on its website) and should be consulted before an application is submitted. Details of the application process, including deadlines, are posted on the charity's website.

CONTACT DETAILS Peter Hardisty, Grants Officer, 109 Court Oak Road, Harborne, Birmingham, West Midlands B17 9AA *Tel.* 0121 426 1600 *Email* peter.hardisty@hplc.org.uk *Website* www.hplc.org.uk

■ The Harbour Charitable Trust

CC NO 234268 **ESTABLISHED** 1962

WHERE FUNDING CAN BE GIVEN London; Israel.

WHO CAN BENEFIT Registered charities; Jewish organisations.

WHAT IS FUNDED General charitable purposes; Jewish causes; education; childcare; healthcare; older people; the arts; religion.

RANGE OF GRANTS Up to £100,000 but mostly under £10,000.

SAMPLE GRANTS Yad Sarah (£100,000); The Jerusalem Foundation (£50,000); Jewish Care (£10,000); Designer Crafts Foundation (£6,000); Alzheimer's Research UK (£1,000); Wigmore Hall (£500); Save the Children (£20).

FINANCES *Financial year end* 05/04/2020
Income £187,400 *Total grants* £283,500
Grants to organisations £283,500
Assets £4,660,000

TRUSTEES Barbara Green; Elaine Knobil.

OTHER INFORMATION During the year, grants were made to 24 organisations across the following categories: religious and interfaith (£216,000); healthcare (£46,500); the arts (£20,000); other (£500); childcare (£500).

HOW TO APPLY Contact the correspondent for further information.

CONTACT DETAILS The Trustees, 11 Leadenhall Street, London EC3V 1LP *Tel.* 020 7280 0500 *Email* roberto.c@acuityprofessional.com

■ The Harbour Foundation

CC NO 264927 **ESTABLISHED** 1970

WHERE FUNDING CAN BE GIVEN Worldwide in practice, mostly in the UK and occasionally in Israel.

WHO CAN BENEFIT Registered charities; charitable organisations.

WHAT IS FUNDED Refugees; people experiencing homelessness; scientific and technical education and research; music; general charitable purposes.

RANGE OF GRANTS Up to £200,000.

SAMPLE GRANTS Ben Gurion University Foundation and British Friends of Hebrew University of Jerusalem (£200,000 each); Royal College of Music (£28,000); The Wigmore Hall Trust and Royal Society of Arts (£20,000 each); National Emergencies Trust (£8,000); FareShare (£5,000).

FINANCES *Financial year end* 31/05/2020
Income £1,904,500 *Total grants* £701,700
Grants to organisations £701,700
Assets £20,220,000

TRUSTEES Susan Harbour; Dr Daniel Harbour; Edmond Harbour; Gideon Harbour; Harry Rich; Richard Hermer.

OTHER INFORMATION In 2019/20, grants were made to 44 registered charities, in the following categories: education (£414,500); relief (£133,500); the arts (£119,200); social organisations (£21,000); medical causes (£13,500).

HOW TO APPLY Contact the correspondent for further information.

CONTACT DETAILS Mr D. Abrahams, Secretary, 1 Red Place, London W1K 6PL *Tel.* 020 7456 8180

■ The David and Claudia Harding Foundation

CC NO 1120878 **ESTABLISHED** 2007

WHERE FUNDING CAN BE GIVEN UK.

WHO CAN BENEFIT Charitable organisations; universities; schools and colleges.

WHAT IS FUNDED Music and the arts; medicine and health; children and education; general charitable purposes. The foundation's primary focus is on scientific research and education.

SAMPLE GRANTS University of Cambridge (£100 million); Universität Potsdam (£171,600); Policy Exchange (£150,000); New Venture Fund (£59,100).

FINANCES *Financial year end* 31/12/2019
Income £53,930,000
Total grants £100,410,000
Grants to organisations £100,410,000
Assets £8,870,000

TRUSTEES David Harding; Claudia Harding; Steven Lindley.

OTHER INFORMATION The grant total includes a grant of £100 million to the University of Cambridge. Only organisations that received grants of over £50,000 were listed as beneficiaries in the charity's accounts. Grants of under £50,000 totalled £24,700.

HOW TO APPLY Contact the correspondent for further information.

CONTACT DETAILS The Trustees, Grove House, 27 Hammersmith Grove, London, London W6 ONE *Tel.* 020 8576 5800

■ The Harding Trust

CC NO 328182 **ESTABLISHED** 1989

WHERE FUNDING CAN BE GIVEN Mainly Staffordshire and the surrounding areas.

WHO CAN BENEFIT Charitable organisations; theatres; hospices.

WHAT IS FUNDED The trust supports public education in and the appreciation of the art and science of music, mainly by providing sponsorship or other support for public concerts, recitals and performances by both amateur and professional organisations. Local hospices and medical charities also receive support.

TYPE OF GRANT Project funding; strategic costs. Mostly recurrent.

RANGE OF GRANTS Typically £1,000 to £7,000.

SAMPLE GRANTS Previous beneficiaries have included: Stoke-on-Trent Festival Ltd (£65,000); Malvern Theatre Trust (£10,000); Royal Philharmonic Orchestra (£6,000); Clonter Farm Music Festival (£5,500); Birmingham Piano Festival (£4,000); Midlands Air Ambulance (£2,000); Katharine House Hospice (£1,500); British Red Cross (£1,000).

FINANCES *Financial year end* 05/04/2020
Income £196,200 *Total grants* £155,200
Grants to organisations £155,200
Assets £4,710,000

TRUSTEES Geoffrey Wall; John Fowell; Michael Lloyd; Richard Platt.

OTHER INFORMATION In 2019/20 grants for musical projects totalled £143,700 and grants to other causes totalled £11,500.

HOW TO APPLY Contact the correspondent for further information.

CONTACT DETAILS Jane Fagan, Horton House, Exchange Flags, Liverpool, Merseyside L2 3YL *Tel.* 0151 600 3000 *Email* jane.fagan@brabners.com

■ Ros Harding Trust

CC NO 1087005 **ESTABLISHED** 1999

WHERE FUNDING CAN BE GIVEN Purley, Coulsdon and Godstone.

WHO CAN BENEFIT Charitable organisations; churches.

WHAT IS FUNDED Social welfare, particularly of older people; the promotion of Christianity, particularly among young people.

WHAT IS NOT FUNDED Individuals.

RANGE OF GRANTS Between £300 and £10,000.

SAMPLE GRANTS Godstone Baptist Church (£10,000); South Norwood and Woodside Community Association (£8,000); Old Lodge Lane Baptist Church (£6,800); Purley Baptist Church and Shirley Neighbourhood Care (£3,000 each); Kevoirdo's Big Love Foundation and Selsdon Centre for the Retired (£2,000); Croham Hurst Good Neighbours and Upper Norwood Association for Community Care (£1,500 each); Croydon Hearing Resource Centre (£500); RAF Association Kenley and Caterham (£300).

FINANCES *Financial year end* 31/03/2020
Income £56,800 *Total grants* £56,200
Grants to organisations £56,200
Assets £1,390,000

TRUSTEES David Colpus; John Cooper; Carol Winterburn; Revd Eilen Poore.

OTHER INFORMATION In 2019/20 the trust made grants to 22 organisations.

HOW TO APPLY Contact the correspondent for further information.

CONTACT DETAILS Mrs S. Rogers, Clerk to the Trustees, 15 Hurst View Road, South Croydon, Surrey CR2 7AJ *Tel.* 020 8660 4537 *Email* rhtrust@outlook.com

■ William Harding's Charity

CC NO 310619 **ESTABLISHED** 1978

WHERE FUNDING CAN BE GIVEN Aylesbury.

WHO CAN BENEFIT Registered charities; CICs; social enterprises; schools; amateur sports clubs; individuals.

WHAT IS FUNDED General charitable purposes, including: education and training; relief in need; provision of almshouses.

TYPE OF GRANT Core/revenue costs; seed funding/start-up funding; travel; unrestricted funding. Often recurrent.

RANGE OF GRANTS Mostly under £20,000.

SAMPLE GRANTS Mandeville School (£51,000); Aylesbury Youth Action (£15,000); Queens Park Art Centre (£14,000); Broughton Junior School (£10,000); Aylesbury Bowls Club (£6,000); Aylesbury Hindu Temple (£3,000); RSPB (£1,600); Autumn Leaf Club (£1,500); Arthritis Care (£270).

FINANCES *Financial year end* 31/12/2019
Income £1,180,000 *Total grants* £551,100
Grants to organisations £302,500
Assets £38,840,000

TRUSTEES Les Sheldon; Anne Brooker; Penni Thorne; Roger Evans; William Chapple; Ranjula Takodra; Lennard Wakelam; Susan Hewitt; Roy Collis.

OTHER INFORMATION During 2019, grants to organisations were made for the following purposes: schools and educational organisations (£154,100); relief in need (£73,400); travel for clubs/societies/groups (£45,000); youth groups (£30,000). Grants were also made to individuals towards equipment and tools for young people and individual pupil support.

HOW TO APPLY Application forms are available on request from the charity, either by collection or by sending an sae. The trustees meet on a regular basis to consider applications.

CONTACT DETAILS John Leggett, Clerk to the Trustees, 14 Bourbon Street, Aylesbury, Buckinghamshire HP20 2RS *Tel.* 01296 318501 *Email* doudjag@pandcllp.co.uk *Website* https://www.leapwithus.org.uk/funding/william-hardings-charity

■ The Harebell Centenary Fund

CC NO 1003552 **ESTABLISHED** 1991

WHERE FUNDING CAN BE GIVEN UK.

WHO CAN BENEFIT Registered charities.

WHAT IS FUNDED General charitable purposes, including the education of young people; neurological and neurosurgical research; animal welfare.

WHAT IS NOT FUNDED Individuals.

TYPE OF GRANT Capital costs; core/revenue costs; unrestricted funding.

RANGE OF GRANTS Most grants are for £10,000.

SAMPLE GRANTS Alzheimer's Research UK, Brain Tumour Support, Canine Partners and Success After Stroke (£10,000 each); Special People (£9,400); Encephalitis Society (£5,000); Crathie School (£4,000).

FINANCES *Financial year end* 31/12/2019 *Income* £284,500 *Total grants* £138,400 *Grants to organisations* £138,400 *Assets* £7,820,000

TRUSTEES Michael Goodbody; Penelope Chapman; Angela Fossick.

OTHER INFORMATION In 2019 grants were awarded to 28 organisations.

HOW TO APPLY Unsolicited applications are not accepted. The trustees prefer to make grants to charities whose work they have come across through their own research.

CONTACT DETAILS Penelope Chapman, Trustee, 50 Broadway, Westminster, London SW1H 0BL *Tel.* 020 7783 3533 *Email* PennyChapman@bdbpitmans.com

■ The Harpur Trust

CC NO 1066861 **ESTABLISHED** 1566

WHERE FUNDING CAN BE GIVEN Bedford.

WHO CAN BENEFIT Registered charities; not-for-profit organisations; social enterprises; CICs; schools.

WHAT IS FUNDED Education; social welfare; health; recreation.

WHAT IS NOT FUNDED Businesses; projects that promote a particular religion; projects which are the responsibility of the local authority or national government; projects that do not benefit the residents of the Borough of Bedford; costs already incurred; trips, except in very exceptional circumstances.

TYPE OF GRANT Capital costs; project funding for up to three years.

RANGE OF GRANTS Up to £150,000. The majority of successful applications are for up to £20,000.

SAMPLE GRANTS FACES and Link to Change (£143,800); Bedford Borough Council (£50,000); HMP Bedford (£30,000); CHUMS CIC (£20,200); YMCA Bedfordshire (£7,500); Bedford Daycare Hospice (£5,000); Wilstead Bowls Club (£1,000).

FINANCES *Financial year end* 30/06/2020 *Income* £53,870,000 *Total grants* £1,275,000 *Grants to organisations* £1,180,000 *Assets* £183,550,000

TRUSTEES John Fordham; Shirley Jackson; Abu Sultan; James Black; Clive Temple; Terrence Rigby; David Wilson; Michael Womack; Philip Wallace; William Phillimore; Susan Clark; Mark Taylor; Tina Beddoes; Prof. Stephen Mayson; Hugh Stewart; Sir Clive Loader; Dr Jennifer Till; Dr Anne Egan; Rhian Castell; Linbert Spencer; Shirley Jackson; Harriett Mather; Judit Sogan; Sarah Wheeler.

OTHER INFORMATION Grants were made to 65 organisations and 20 individuals during the year.

HOW TO APPLY Applications can be made via the trust's website. The trust's application guidance states: 'Contact us to discuss your request well before you intend to submit an application. We are happy to provide assistance at any stage during the application process.'

CONTACT DETAILS Lucy Bardner, Grants Manager, Princeton Court, The Pilgrim Centre, Brickhill Drive, Bedford, Bedfordshire MK41 7PZ *Tel.* 01234 369503 *Email* grants@harpurtrust.org.uk *Website* www.harpurtrust.org.uk

■ The Peter and Teresa Harris Charitable Trust

CC NO 1161183 **ESTABLISHED** 2010

WHERE FUNDING CAN BE GIVEN England; Wales.

WHO CAN BENEFIT Charitable organisations.

WHAT IS FUNDED General charitable purposes.

RANGE OF GRANTS Up to £31,500 but mostly from £500 to £10,000.

SAMPLE GRANTS Greenwich Performs (£31,500); Talk About Art (£7,500); KidsOut UK (£2,000); Prostate Cancer UK (£1,000); Tramshed Arts Ltd (£500).

FINANCES *Financial year end* 05/04/2020 *Income* £51,100 *Total grants* £150,400 *Grants to organisations* £150,400 *Assets* £2,560,000

TRUSTEES Duncan Rabagilati; Tim Barnes.

OTHER INFORMATION Grants were made to 42 organisations.

HOW TO APPLY Contact the correspondent for further information.

CONTACT DETAILS The Trustees, c/o Gregsons Solicitors, 19 Tabor Grove, London SW19 4EX *Tel.* 020 8946 1173 *Email* duncan@gregsons.co.uk

■ The Harris Family Charitable Trust

CC NO 1064394 **ESTABLISHED** 1997

WHERE FUNDING CAN BE GIVEN UK.

WHO CAN BENEFIT Charitable organisations.

WHAT IS FUNDED Health.

TYPE OF GRANT Project funding.

SAMPLE GRANTS A list of beneficiaries was not available.

FINANCES *Financial year end* 30/04/2020 *Income* £24,700 *Total grants* £128,500 *Grants to organisations* £128,500

TRUSTEES Ronnie Harris; Loretta Harris; Charlotte Harris; Sophie Harris; Toby Harris.

OTHER INFORMATION Full accounts were not available to view on the Charity Commission's website due to the trust's low income. We have therefore estimated the grant total based on the trust's total expenditure.

HOW TO APPLY According to the annual report for 2018/19, the trust 'invites applications for funding of projects through various sources' and 'the applications are reviewed by the trustees who ensure that they are in accordance with the charity's objectives'.

CONTACT DETAILS The Trustees, 64 New Cavendish Street, London W1G 8TB *Tel.* 020 7467 6300

■ The Edith Lilian Harrison 2000 Foundation

CC NO 1085651 **ESTABLISHED** 2000

WHERE FUNDING CAN BE GIVEN UK.

WHO CAN BENEFIT Registered charities.

WHAT IS FUNDED General charitable purposes, particularly health, disability and social welfare.

RANGE OF GRANTS Generally between £1,000 and £5,000.

SAMPLE GRANTS Salisbury Hospice (£50,000); Autistica, Clean Rivers Trust and Veterans Aid (£5,000 each); Carers UK (£4,000); Anne Robson Trust and Contact the Elderly (£2,000 each); My Life My Choice and The Neurological Alliance (£1,000 each).

FINANCES *Financial year end* 05/04/2020 *Income* £49,800 *Total grants* £312,000 *Grants to organisations* £312,000 *Assets* £1,090,000

TRUSTEES Geoffrey Peyer; Clive Andrews; Paul Bradley.

HOW TO APPLY Apply in writing to the correspondent. The trustees meet to consider application every six months, usually in May and November.

CONTACT DETAILS The Trustees, c/o TWM Solicitors LLP, 40 West Street, Reigate, Surrey RH2 9BT *Tel.* 01737 221212 *Email* paul.bradley@twmsolicitors.com

■ The Peter Harrison Foundation

CC NO 1076579 **ESTABLISHED** 1999

WHERE FUNDING CAN BE GIVEN UK, with some preference for the South East.

WHO CAN BENEFIT Registered charities; community amateur sports clubs.

WHAT IS FUNDED Access to sport for people with disabilities; care for children and young people with special needs; education.

WHAT IS NOT FUNDED Retrospective expenditure; activities that are primarily the responsibility of central or local government; individuals; CICs; overseas projects; adventure challenges or expeditions in the UK or abroad; religious projects.

TYPE OF GRANT Capital, revenue and project funding; salaries.

RANGE OF GRANTS Up to £100,000.

SAMPLE GRANTS Loughborough University (£200,000); Leatherhead and Dorking Gymnastics Club (£100,000); SportsAid Trust (£50,000); Young Epilepsy (£30,000); Elmhurst Ballet School Trust (£25,000); Highland Disability Sport (£22,500); Reigate Parish Church School (£10,000); The Children's Trust (£5,000); African Caribbean Leukaemia Trust (£1,500); Sparkles (£250).

FINANCES *Financial year end* 31/05/2020 *Income* £3,320,000 *Total grants* £1,990,000 *Grants to organisations* £1,990,000 *Assets* £48,960,000

TRUSTEES Peter Harrison; Julia Harrison-Lee; Peter Lee; Nicholas Harrison.

OTHER INFORMATION The foundation has two open grant programmes: Opportunities through Sport (53 grants totalling £1.01 million) – sporting activity or projects which provide opportunities for people with disabilities or who are otherwise disadvantaged; and Special Needs and Care for Children and Young People in the South East of England (31 grants totalling £637,100) – projects that work with or benefit disabled, chronically or terminally ill children and their parents/carers, and children or young people at risk of crime, truancy, addiction, or homelessness. The remaining grants awarded during the year were distributed at the trustees' discretion.

HOW TO APPLY There is a two-stage application process – first, complete the initial enquiry form online and if you are successful a full application form will be sent out. There is no application deadline but you may only apply to one of the programmes at any one time. The trustees meet four times a year.

CONTACT DETAILS Rachael Crooks, Grants Administrator, Foundation House, 42–48 London Road, Reigate, Surrey RH2 9QQ *Tel.* 01737 228000 *Email* enquiries@peterharrisonfoundation.org *Website* www.peterharrisonfoundation.org

■ The Harrison-Frank Family Foundation (UK) Ltd

CC NO 1155149 **ESTABLISHED** 2013

WHERE FUNDING CAN BE GIVEN UK.

WHO CAN BENEFIT Registered charities.

WHAT IS FUNDED General charitable purposes, including: health; education; poverty; people with disabilities; housing; arts, culture, heritage and science; human rights.

RANGE OF GRANTS From £2,000 to £35,000. The majority of grants are of £5,000.

SAMPLE GRANTS The New Israel Fund (£35,000); Cancer Research and Médecins Sans Frontières – UK (£10,000 each); Myeloma UK, Action for Stammering Children and Amnesty International (£5,000 each); Prisoners' Advice Trust (£2,000).

FINANCES *Financial year end* 31/12/2019 *Income* £522,700 *Total grants* £170,000 *Grants to organisations* £170,000 *Assets* £9,540,000

TRUSTEES Barbara Harrison; Fredrik Ulfsater; Richard Harrison; David Harrison; Michele Harrison; Louise Williams; Steven Marcovitch; Jeanne Harrison; Dominic Duffy.

OTHER INFORMATION In 2019 grants were awarded to 24 organisations.

HOW TO APPLY Contact the correspondent for further information.

CONTACT DETAILS The Trustees, Flat 17, 34 Seymour Place, London W1H 7NS *Tel.* 020 7724 1154 *Email* bfraharrison@hotmail.com

■ The Harry and Mary Foundation

CC NO 1148707 **ESTABLISHED** 2012

WHERE FUNDING CAN BE GIVEN West Yorkshire; Bradford.

WHO CAN BENEFIT Registered charities.

WHAT IS FUNDED The education of children and young people (under 25); health; social welfare.

SAMPLE GRANTS Bradford Hospitals (£22,200); Bradford Nightstop (£20,000); Daybreak and The Ear Project (£5,000 each); Bradford Foodbank (£750).

FINANCES *Financial year end* 31/03/2020 *Income* £352,200 *Total grants* £73,000 *Grants to organisations* £73,000 *Assets* £6,890,000

TRUSTEES Robert Walker; Robert Bastow; John Clough.

OTHER INFORMATION Grants were made to eight organisations.

HOW TO APPLY Contact the correspondent for further information.

CONTACT DETAILS The Trustees, 11 Keighley Road, Cross Hills, Keighley BD20 7DA *Tel.* 01535 630298

■ Gay and Peter Hartley's Hillards Charitable Trust

CC NO 327879 **ESTABLISHED** 1988

WHERE FUNDING CAN BE GIVEN Northern and central England – see website for a list of the 45 towns supported.

WHO CAN BENEFIT Independent, locally managed, non-profit, voluntary and community-based organisations that provide social support to the communities once served by Hillards stores.

WHAT IS FUNDED Care for older people; children's welfare; education; physical/mental health; education; church-based projects with a proven outreach factor.

WHAT IS NOT FUNDED See the trust's helpful website for a full list of exclusions.

TYPE OF GRANT Normally one-off.

RANGE OF GRANTS Up to £1,000.

SAMPLE GRANTS Cavendish Cancer Centre, REACT (Rapid Effective Assistance for Children with potentially Terminal illness), Overgate Hospice and RNLI (£1,000 each); York Air Ambulance (£750); Crisis (£500); Slaid Hill in Bloom (£50).

FINANCES *Financial year end* 31/12/2019
Income £85,500 *Total grants* £94,200
Grants to organisations £94,200
Assets £1,800,000

TRUSTEES Simon Hillard Hartley; Adam Hillard Hartley; Peter Hillard Hartley; Susan Hillard Hartley; George Hillard Hartley; Oscar Hillard Hartley.

HOW TO APPLY Applicants can apply online. The website also provides an eligibility checker and helpful guidance notes.

CONTACT DETAILS Chris Hindle, Secretary to the Trustees, Shadwell Grange, 400 Shadwell Lane, Leeds, West Yorkshire LS17 8AW
Email secretary@hillardstrust.org
Website https://www.hillardstrust.org

■ Edward Harvist Trust (The Harvist Estate)

CC NO 211970 **ESTABLISHED** 1994

WHERE FUNDING CAN BE GIVEN The London boroughs of Barnet, Brent, Camden, Harrow and the City of Westminster.

WHO CAN BENEFIT Charitable organisations.

WHAT IS FUNDED General charitable purposes including: health; social welfare; recreation and leisure; older people; education.

TYPE OF GRANT Mainly one-off awards for capital costs; project funding.

SAMPLE GRANTS Learning Through Horses (£10,000); Wembley Scout Group (£5,000); London Accordion Orchestra (£4,000); Essendine School (£3,000); Dutch Pot Lunch and Social Club (£600).

FINANCES *Financial year end* 31/03/2020
Income £351,000 *Total grants* £282,400
Grants to organisations £282,400
Assets £9,610,000

TRUSTEES Cllr Nitin Parekh; Cllr Mary Daly; Cllr Alex Prager; Cllr Angela Harvey; Cllr Heather Johnson.

HOW TO APPLY Applications must be made through the appropriate local authority, not through the correspondent. At the time of writing (January 2021) there was information about the trust (such as eligibility criteria and application procedures) available on each of the five borough councils' websites. This information could be found following a search for the trust's name using the websites' search bars. There may be different criteria and application procedures imposed by the five local authorities.

CONTACT DETAILS Hugh Peart, Honorary Secretary, London Borough of Harrow, Finance Department, PO Box 21, Civic Centre, Harrow, Middlesex HA1 2XY *Tel.* 020 8424 1450
Email treasurymanagement@harrow.gov.uk

■ The Hasluck Charitable Trust

CC NO 1115323 **ESTABLISHED** 2006

WHERE FUNDING CAN BE GIVEN UK and overseas.

WHO CAN BENEFIT Registered charities.

WHAT IS FUNDED General charitable purposes, including: health; social welfare; disability; young people; older people; overseas aid.

WHAT IS NOT FUNDED Individuals.

TYPE OF GRANT Unrestricted funding.

RANGE OF GRANTS Usually £1,000 or £2,000.

SAMPLE GRANTS Barnardo's and Macmillan Cancer Support (£9,000 each); Euan's Guide, Seafarers UK and Tom's Trust (£2,000 each); Criminon UK, Evergreen Africa, Pintsize Theatre Company and Waterloo Community Counselling (£1,000 each).

FINANCES *Financial year end* 05/04/2020
Income £209,300 *Total grants* £142,000
Grants to organisations £142,000
Assets £1,820,000

TRUSTEES Matthew Wakefield; John Billing; Mark Wheeler.

OTHER INFORMATION During the year, 62 grants were made to 54 charities. The trust makes regular payments to eight charities (Barnardo's, International Fund for Animal Welfare, Macmillan Cancer Support, Mrs R H Hotblacks Michelham Priory Endowment Fund, Riding for the Disabled Association, RNLI, RSPB and Scope), which are of particular interest to the settlor. The remainder was distributed to a wide range of charitable causes.

HOW TO APPLY Apply in writing to the correspondent. Grants are generally awarded in January and July, although consideration is given to appeals received at other times of the year. Only successful applications are acknowledged.

CONTACT DETAILS John Billing, Trustee, c/o Rathbone Trust Legal Services Ltd, 8 Finsbury Circus, London EC2M 7AZ *Tel.* 020 7399 0447
Email john.billing@rathbones.com

■ The Maurice Hatter Foundation

CC NO 298119 **ESTABLISHED** 1987

WHERE FUNDING CAN BE GIVEN UK; Israel; overseas.

WHO CAN BENEFIT Registered charities and educational bodies, particularly those with links to the Jewish community.

WHAT IS FUNDED General charitable purposes, in particular: education and technology; medical research (especially cardiology); disability; Jewish causes; social welfare and social mobility; international policy research.

TYPE OF GRANT Grants or long/short-term loans.

SAMPLE GRANTS University College London Hospitals – Hatter Cardiovascular Oncology Fellowship (£500,000); Kisharon (£250,000); University College Hospital Charity Fund – Hatter Cardiovascular Institute (£100,000); University College London Hospitals Charity (£68,100).

FINANCES *Financial year end* 05/04/2019
Income £6,210,000 *Total grants* £1,270,000
Grants to organisations £1,270,000
Assets £20,300,000

TRUSTEES Piers Barclay; Richard Hatter; Fausto Furlotti.

OTHER INFORMATION The 2018/19 accounts were the latest available at the time of writing (June

2021). Grants were awarded as follows: medical research (£568,100); social welfare (£415,900); education (£262,900); religion (£22,000); international policy research (£5,000). Only beneficiaries of grants of over £100,000 were listed in the accounts. Grants of under £100,000 totalled £269,000.

HOW TO APPLY Contact the correspondent for further information.

CONTACT DETAILS The Trustees, c/o Smith and Williamson, Onslow House, Onslow Street, Guildford, Surrey GU1 4TL *Tel.* 01483 407100

■ The Hawthorne Charitable Trust

CC NO 233921 **ESTABLISHED** 1964

WHERE FUNDING CAN BE GIVEN UK, in particular Hereford and Worcester.

WHO CAN BENEFIT Registered charities; hospices; some UK charities working overseas are supported.

WHAT IS FUNDED General charitable purposes; medical causes, health and sickness; the environment, conservation and heritage; disability; animal care; the relief of poverty.

WHAT IS NOT FUNDED Individuals.

TYPE OF GRANT Mostly recurring.

RANGE OF GRANTS Mostly between £1,000 and £3,000.

SAMPLE GRANTS Southern Thailand Elephant Foundation (£25,000); Downside Mission Trust (£5,000); ABF The Soldiers' Charity and Hospice Care Kenya (£2,500 each); Museum of Royal Worcester and The Passage (£2,000 each); Malvern Sea Cadets and Woodland Trust (£1,000 each); Prickles Hedgehog Rescue (£500).

FINANCES *Financial year end* 05/04/2020 *Income* £233,000 *Total grants* £187,500 *Grants to organisations* £187,500 *Assets* £9,720,000

TRUSTEES Alexandra Berington; Richard White; Roger Clark; Thomas Berington.

OTHER INFORMATION Grants were awarded to 77 organisations during the year in the following categories: medical, health and sickness (27 grants totalling £62,500); other charitable purposes (23 grants totalling £41,000); the environment, conservation and heritage (11 grants totalling £32,500); animal welfare (six grants totalling £31,500); care for people with disabilities (eight grants totalling £17,000); relief of poverty (two grants totalling £3,000).

HOW TO APPLY Contact the correspondent for further information.

CONTACT DETAILS Tatia Goldstone, c/o RSM UK Tax and Accounting Ltd, Marlborough House, Victoria Road South, Chelmsford CM11 1LN *Tel.* 01245 354402 *Email* tatia.goldstone@rsmuk.com

■ Hays Travel Foundation

CC NO 1161373 **ESTABLISHED** 2015

WHERE FUNDING CAN BE GIVEN England, in areas where Hayes Travel operates.

WHO CAN BENEFIT Registered charities; CICs; hospices.

WHAT IS FUNDED Support of young people in the following areas: education; prevention of poverty; health; arts; culture; sport.

WHAT IS NOT FUNDED Organisations that do not operate or have an impact in an area in which Hays Travel has a branch.

TYPE OF GRANT Project costs; capital costs; mostly one-off.

RANGE OF GRANTS Mostly up to £8,000.

SAMPLE GRANTS Artichoke (£12,000); Community by Nature and Creative Kids (£8,000 each); Leeds Mencap (£5,000); Exim Dance Company CIC (£4,500); Friends of Oak Grove College (£3,000); The Sick Children's Trust (£1,300); Dorset Children's Foundation (£150); Poole Hospital Stroke Unit and Torbay and South Devon NHS Trust (£50 each).

FINANCES *Financial year end* 31/10/2019 *Income* £335,200 *Total grants* £316,100 *Grants to organisations* £316,100 *Assets* £1,000

TRUSTEES William Fleetwood; Prof. Peter Fidler; Irene Hays; John Hays; Michael Dillon; Claire Maith; Dorothy Gregory.

OTHER INFORMATION Grants were made to 61 organisations during the year totalling £316,100, of which £36,400 was awarded in matched funding to Hays Travel Ltd branches for their fundraising activities for local charities. The 2018/19 accounts were the latest available at the time of writing (January 2021).

HOW TO APPLY Apply through the online portal on the foundation's website.

CONTACT DETAILS The Trustees, Gilbridge House, High Street West, Sunderland, Tyne and Wear SR1 3HA *Tel.* 0191 814 8094 *Email* enquiries@haystravelfoundation.co.uk *Website* https://www.haystravel.co.uk/foundation/home.phtml

■ The Charles Hayward Foundation

CC NO 1078969 **ESTABLISHED** 1961

WHERE FUNDING CAN BE GIVEN UK and Commonwealth countries in Africa.

WHO CAN BENEFIT UK-registered charities.

WHAT IS FUNDED Main grant programme: charities with an income of more than £350,000 working in the areas of social and criminal justice, and heritage and conservation. The overseas programme is for charities with an income of between £150,000 and £5 million working in the areas of clean water and sanitation, basic health programmes, and self-sustainability through training in farming skills and income generation activities. Small grant programme: charities with an income of less than £350,000 working in the areas of social and criminal justice and older people.

WHAT IS NOT FUNDED General exclusions: endowments; general appeals; grant-making charities; individuals; loans and deficits; retrospective expenditure; core costs; academic institutions. Individual programmes may have their own additional exclusions – see the programme-specific guidelines.

TYPE OF GRANT Capital costs; project funding; salaries.

RANGE OF GRANTS Up to £25,000. Projects can be funded over one to three years.

SAMPLE GRANTS Victoria and Albert Museum (£50,000); Phoenix Domestic Abuse Services (£23,000); World Medical Fund (£15,000); Community Drug and Alcohol Recovery Services (£12,000); Hope Housing, Training and Support (£10,000); Kaloko Trust (£8,000); Inspiring Grace (£4,000); Dover SmART Project (£3,000); Advice Support Knowledge Information (£2,000); Street Child (£500); Amber Trust (£200).

FINANCES *Financial year end* 31/12/2019 *Income* £5,300 *Total grants* £2,210,000 *Grants to organisations* £2,210,000 *Assets* £72,110,000

TRUSTEES Susan Heath; Julia Chamberlain; Caroline Donald; Richard Griffith; Alexander Heath; Brian Insch; Nikolas van Leuven.

OTHER INFORMATION Grants were paid to 186 organisations and distributed as follows: social and criminal justice (£1.36 million); heritage and conservation (£298,500); small grants (£249,300); overseas (£216,700); miscellaneous (£82,700).

HOW TO APPLY Details of how to apply are available on the foundation's website. Applications to the small grant programme are accepted on a rolling basis and are considered every two to three months. The main grant programme has a two-stage application process. Firstly, applications are considered by the grants committee, which recommends applications to be considered by the trustees at the second stage of the process. Trustees' meetings usually take place in February, April, July and November.

CONTACT DETAILS Dorothy Napierala, Director, Hayward House, 45 Harrington Gardens, London SW7 4JU *Tel.* 020 7370 7063 *Email* dorothy@charleshaywardfoundation.org.uk *Website* www.charleshaywardfoundation.org.uk

■ The Headley Trust

CC NO 266620 **ESTABLISHED** 1973

WHERE FUNDING CAN BE GIVEN UK; sub-Saharan anglophone Africa; Ethiopia; Central and Eastern Europe.

WHO CAN BENEFIT Registered charities; churches; museums; galleries.

WHAT IS FUNDED Arts and heritage; development projects in sub-Saharan anglophone Africa; education; health and social welfare. There is a small grant scheme to help local museums and galleries purchase objects for their collections. Small grants are also available to provide practical aids to people with disabilities (third-party referrals only).

WHAT IS NOT FUNDED Individuals; expeditions. For cathedrals/churches grants: education centres, conferences, exhibition or heritage space, organs, clocks, bells, plumbing, kitchens or heating. Note that for overseas projects priority will be given to locally led organisations employing local experts.

TYPE OF GRANT Capital and project costs; core costs; salaries; acquisitions costs; bursaries.

RANGE OF GRANTS Typically up to £50,000. Up to £2,500 for mobility equipment for people with disabilities.

SAMPLE GRANTS British Museum Development Trust (£750,000); Hackney Quest (£90,000); Age UK Cheshire (£50,000); Guildhall School of Music and Drama (£30,000); Venice in Peril Fund (£20,000); Diocese of Lichfield (six grants totalling £18,500); North Hampshire Medical Fund (£10,000); Sussex Archaeological Society (£5,000).

FINANCES *Financial year end* 05/04/2020 *Income* £2,220,000 *Total grants* £3,560,000 *Grants to organisations* £3,560,000 *Assets* £65,490,000

TRUSTEES Lady Susan Sainsbury; Judith Portrait; Timothy Sainsbury; Sir Timothy Sainsbury; Camilla Sainsbury; Amanda McCrystal.

OTHER INFORMATION The trust is one of the Sainsbury Family Charitable Trusts which share a common administration – see www.sftc.org.uk for more information. Grants approved during the year were broken down as follows: arts and heritage – UK (120 grants totalling £1.78 million); health and social welfare (115 grants totalling £596,500); financially developing countries (nine grants totalling £225,800); education (eight grants totalling £194,000); arts and heritage – overseas (five grants totalling £103,000).

HOW TO APPLY Applications can be made online, by post to The Sainsbury Family Charitable Trusts, or by email to proposals@sfct.org.uk. At the time of writing (April 2021) the trust was not accepting due to the COVID-19 pandemic. Written applications should be no longer than two sides of A4 and provide the same information as the online form. Application forms for the trust's Museums Archaeological Acquisition Fund and Aids for Disabled People Programme are separate and can be found on the website.

CONTACT DETAILS Miss S. Levander, Administrator, The Peak, 5 Wilton Road, London SW1V 1AP *Tel.* 020 7410 0330 *Email* info@sfct.org.uk *Website* https://www.sfct.org.uk/Headley.html

■ The Health Foundation

CC NO 286967 **ESTABLISHED** 1983

WHERE FUNDING CAN BE GIVEN UK.

WHO CAN BENEFIT Registered charities; unregistered charities; NHS trusts; universities; hospitals; hospices; individuals.

WHAT IS FUNDED Health care and public health research; training and development.

WHAT IS NOT FUNDED See the grant-maker's website for a full list of exclusions relevant to the grant programme being applied to.

TYPE OF GRANT Project funding; research; partnerships.

RANGE OF GRANTS Dependent upon funding stream.

SAMPLE GRANTS Local Government Association – Shaping Places Healthier Lives (£1.74 million); University College London (£300,000); Resolution Foundation (£204,900); Imperial College Healthcare Trust (£124,300); Cardiff and Vale University Health Board (£75,000); Centre for Sustainable Healthcare (£50,000); Queens Nursing Institute Scotland (£26,500); Scottish Ambulance Service (£5,000); The London Clinic (£3,500).

FINANCES *Financial year end* 31/12/2019 *Income* £16,110,000 *Total grants* £20,040,000 *Grants to organisations* £20,040,000 *Assets* £1,053,920,000

TRUSTEES Sir Hugh Taylor; Sharmila Nebhrajani; Martyn Hole; Prof. Rosalind Smyth; Melloney Poole; Sir David Dalton; Branwen Jeffreys; Eric Gregory; Loraine Hawkins; Dr Ruth Hussey; David Smart; Prof. Dawn Edge; Katherine Blacklock; Ravi Gurumurthy.

OTHER INFORMATION The foundation runs a wide variety of funding programmes, aimed at different organisations and individuals. The three main funding areas are improvement projects, research projects and fellowships. In the first instance, potential applicants should visit the funder's informative website for full details regarding grant-making activity. According to the 2019 accounts, grants paid during the year totalled £20.04 million. Funding is typically awarded for between one and four years.

HOW TO APPLY The foundation does not consider unprompted requests or proposals for funding. Programmes open for applications are advertised on the foundation's website. These are likely to change frequently and candidates are advised to visit the website for the most up-to-date information. You may sign up for a website account to receive alerts when new funding opportunities go live. Application forms are available online, together with full guidelines and specific requirements and deadlines for each of the programmes. There is also a helpful FAQ page, which should be consulted by potential applicants.

CONTACT DETAILS Programmes Team, 8 Salisbury Square, London EC4Y 8AP *Tel.* 020 7257 8000 *Email* info@health.org.uk *Website* www.health.org.uk

■ May Hearnshaw's Charity

CC NO 1008638 **ESTABLISHED** 1992

WHERE FUNDING CAN BE GIVEN South Yorkshire, north Nottinghamshire, Derbyshire, east Lancashire and Cheshire.

WHO CAN BENEFIT Charitable organisations; hospices; universities.

WHAT IS FUNDED Education; promotion of religion; health; social welfare.

RANGE OF GRANTS Up to £10,000, but mostly between £1,000 and £5,000.

SAMPLE GRANTS St Wilfrid's Centre (£10,500); Sheffield Royal Society for Blind (£5,000); Child Autism and Premier Learning (£1,000 each); Runabout (£500).

FINANCES *Financial year end* 05/04/2020 *Income* £87,500 *Total grants* £96,600 *Grants to organisations* £74,600 *Assets* £2,140,000

TRUSTEES Charles Ringrose; Michael Ward; Richard Law; William Munro.

OTHER INFORMATION A total of 33 organisations received support.

HOW TO APPLY Applications may be made in writing to the correspondent. The trustees usually meet three times a year to decide on and make major grants to charitable organisations but may decide to make grants at any time.

CONTACT DETAILS The Trustees, BHP Chartered Accountants, 2 Rutland Park, Sheffield, South Yorkshire S10 2PD *Tel.* 0114 266 7171 *Email* paul.randall@bhp.co.uk

■ Heart of England Community Foundation

CC NO 1117345 **ESTABLISHED** 1995

WHERE FUNDING CAN BE GIVEN Birmingham; Coventry; Dudley; Sandwell; Solihull; Walsall; Warwickshire; Wolverhampton.

WHO CAN BENEFIT Charitable organisations, including CICs and social enterprises; individuals.

WHAT IS FUNDED General charitable purposes; social welfare; community development; education; health.

WHAT IS NOT FUNDED Applicants should check each funding programme for exclusions.

TYPE OF GRANT Project costs; capital costs; salaries; start-up costs.

SAMPLE GRANTS A list of beneficiaries was not included in the annual report and accounts.

FINANCES *Financial year end* 31/03/2020 *Income* £6,610,000 *Total grants* £3,980,000 *Grants to organisations* £3,980,000 *Assets* £19,370,000

TRUSTEES Daniel Worthing; Lucie Byron; Russell Bailey; John Taylor; Paul Belfield; Philip Ewing; Christopher West; Amrik Bhabra; Jasmin Koasha; Jude Jennison; Michelle Vincent; Naeem Alvi; Sally Carrick; Calum Nisbet.

OTHER INFORMATION This is one of the 46 UK community foundations, which distribute funding for a wide range of purposes. As with all community foundations, there are a number of donor-advised funds managed on behalf of individuals, families and charitable trusts. Grant schemes tend to change frequently; consult the foundation's website for details of current programmes and up-to-date deadlines. A detailed breakdown of grants awarded is given in the foundation's annual grant-making report, which is available on its website.

HOW TO APPLY Potential applicants are advised to visit the community foundation's website or contact its grants team to find the most suitable funding stream.

CONTACT DETAILS Sarah Phillips, Executive Officer, c/o PSA Group, Pinley House, Sunbeam Way, Coventry, Warwickshire CV3 1ND *Tel.* 024 7688 4434 *Email* info@heartofenglandcf.co.uk *Website* www.heartofenglandcf.co.uk

■ Heart Research UK

CC NO 1044821 **ESTABLISHED** 1967

WHERE FUNDING CAN BE GIVEN UK.

WHO CAN BENEFIT Community groups; voluntary organisations; hospitals; universities; CICs.

WHAT IS FUNDED Medical research; education; health; community projects.

WHAT IS NOT FUNDED Government organisations; local authority groups.

TYPE OF GRANT Project funding (including equipment and travel); research.

RANGE OF GRANTS Up to £250,000 in medical research grants; up to £10,000 in Healthy Heart grants.

SAMPLE GRANTS Ulster University (£248,400); Imperial College Healthcare NHS Trust (£150,000); University of Bristol (£147,000); University of Glasgow (£128,900); University of Leeds (£63,400); Chelsea and Westminster Hospital (£20,000); Cardiff City FC Foundation and Wirral Multicultural Organisation (£10,000 each); The Outlook Trust (£4,200); Y Services for Young People (£3,400).

FINANCES *Financial year end* 31/12/2019 *Income* £2,630,000 *Total grants* £1,590,000 *Grants to organisations* £1,590,000 *Assets* £5,480,000

TRUSTEES Paul Rogerson; Richard Hemsley; Dr David Dickinson; Kevin Watterson; Anthony Knight; Dr Catherine Dickinson; Anthony Kilner; Paul Smith; Richard Brown; Peter Braidley; Julie Fenwick; Pierre Bouvet; Christopher Newman.

OTHER INFORMATION In total, 29 grants were awarded during the year. The charity made grants through two programmes during the year: medical research was awarded 14 grants (£1.5 million); HRUK and SUBWAY* Healthy Heart grants were awarded to 15 organisations (£101,200). More details are available on Heart Research UK's helpful website.

HOW TO APPLY Application forms, full guidelines and up-to-date deadlines for each programme can be found on the charity's website or requested from the correspondent.

CONTACT DETAILS The Trustees, Suite 12D, Joseph's Well, Hanover Walk, Leeds, West Yorkshire LS3 1AB *Tel.* 0113 234 7474 *Email* info@heartresearch.org.uk *Website* www.heartresearch.org.uk

■ The Hearth Foundation

CC NO 1165540 **ESTABLISHED** 2016

WHERE FUNDING CAN BE GIVEN England and Wales, with a preference for the north of England and the Midlands.

WHO CAN BENEFIT Charitable organisations.

WHAT IS FUNDED General charitable purposes.

SAMPLE GRANTS A list of beneficiaries was not included in the annual report and accounts.
FINANCES *Financial year end* 05/04/2020 *Income* £181,000 *Total grants* £86,500 *Grants to organisations* £86,500 *Assets* £2,520,000
TRUSTEES Chris Bosworth; Mrs H. Bosworth; Mrs J. Bosworth; Michael Bosworth; Dr S. Bosworth; Mrs V. Bosworth.
HOW TO APPLY Apply in writing to the correspondent. Applications are considered throughout the year and grants are awarded during the first calendar quarter of each year.
CONTACT DETAILS Michael Bosworth, Trustee, Monkstone, Main Street, Mowsley, Lutterworth, Leicestershire LE17 6NU *Tel.* 0116 240 2162 *Email* michael.bosworth@btopenworld.com

■ The Heathcoat Trust

CC NO 203367 **ESTABLISHED** 1945
WHERE FUNDING CAN BE GIVEN Local causes in and around Tiverton, Devon.
WHO CAN BENEFIT Local organisations to Tiverton and national charities working on projects in that area; educational bodies; individual grants to employees and pensioners (and their dependants) of the Heathcoat group of companies.
WHAT IS FUNDED Social welfare; education and training; health; local causes.
RANGE OF GRANTS Mostly up to £2,500.
SAMPLE GRANTS Cornwall Air Ambulance (£5,000); Churches Housing Action Team (two grants totalling £4,000); Exeter Deaf Academy (£3,700); Riverside Hall – Bampton (£2,800); West Exe Sports and Social Club (£2,500); Heathcoat Cricket Club (£2,000); Cullompton Family Centre and Tiverton Senior Citizens Association (£1,000 each).
FINANCES *Financial year end* 05/04/2020 *Income* £859,300 *Total grants* £731,700 *Grants to organisations* £299,100 *Assets* £23,180,000
TRUSTEES Mark Drysdale; Sir Ian Heathcoat-Amory; John Smith; Susan Westlake; Julian Morgan; Bryony Pullen.
OTHER INFORMATION During the year, £108,100 was awarded to charitable organisations and £191,000 was awarded to educational bodies. It appears that the remaining grants were awarded in support of individuals. Only charitable organisations that received grants of £1,000 and above were listed in the accounts (32 organisations, some of which received multiple grants).
HOW TO APPLY Contact the correspondent for details regarding how to apply. The trustees meet regularly to consider applications for grants.
CONTACT DETAILS Helen Isaac, Secretary to the Trustees, The Factory, West Exe, Tiverton, Devon EX16 5LL *Tel.* 01884 244296 *Email* heathcoattrust@heathcoat.co.uk

■ Heathrow Community Trust

CC NO 1058617 **ESTABLISHED** 2019
WHERE FUNDING CAN BE GIVEN The areas surrounding Heathrow Airport (Ealing, Hillingdon, Hounslow, Richmond, Runnymede, Slough, South Bucks, Spelthorne, and the Royal Borough of Windsor and Maidenhead).
WHO CAN BENEFIT Local authorities; schools and colleges; hospices; charities; community groups; social enterprises; CICs; not-for-profit companies.
WHAT IS FUNDED The environment and sustainability; social welfare; recreation; young people; education and training; bringing communities together; research and development projects.
WHAT IS NOT FUNDED Refer to the trust's website for the specific eligibility criteria and restrictions of each grant programme.
TYPE OF GRANT Restricted project-based funding of capital costs, revenue costs, direct project costs, overhead costs.
RANGE OF GRANTS Up to £25,000, but programme dependent.
SAMPLE GRANTS The Eikon Charity (£47,400); Fine Futures (£45,200); Oxfordshire Crossroads (£22,500); West London River Group (£20,900); Stanwell Village Hall (£17,000); Slough West Indian People's Enterprise (£15,000); Spark! (Hounslow Education Business Charity) (£9,400); Victoria Junior School (£5,000); The Manor Friends Charity (£2,100).
FINANCES *Financial year end* 31/12/2019 *Income* £1,060,000 *Total grants* £1,330,000 *Grants to organisations* £1,330,000 *Assets* £295,500
TRUSTEES Alison Keeley; David Cottrell; Gennie Dearman; Dr Prabhjot Basra; Andy Kerswill; Richard De Belder; Michael Murphy; Chris Johnston; Samina Hussain; Carol Hui.
OTHER INFORMATION Grants are awarded through five distinct programmes (see the website for details). In 2019, grants were broken down as follows: Communities for Tomorrow (£497,500); Communities for Youth (£435,100); Communities Together (£256,600); Heathrow Active People Initiative (£53,300); Development Fund (£39,700). Grants awarded to Heathrow Airport staff for matched funding totalled £25,400. A list of beneficiaries was not available in the year's accounts; a sample of projects funded between 2018 and 2020 has been taken from the trust's website.
HOW TO APPLY Application forms and guidance notes for each of the grant programmes are available from the trust's website, where important dates for application submissions and decision-making are also listed.
CONTACT DETAILS The Trustees, The Compass Centre, Nelson Road, London Heathrow Airport, Hounslow, London TW6 2GW *Tel.* 01895 839916 *Email* HCT@Groundwork.org.uk *Website* https://www.heathrowcommunitytrust.org

■ The Heathside Charitable Trust

CC NO 326959 **ESTABLISHED** 1985
WHERE FUNDING CAN BE GIVEN UK and overseas.
WHO CAN BENEFIT Charitable organisations. Our previous research suggests the trust has a preference for funding Jewish organisations and causes.
WHAT IS FUNDED General charitable purposes; education; welfare; healthcare.
WHAT IS NOT FUNDED Individuals.
SAMPLE GRANTS A full list of beneficiaries was not available. One beneficiary was noted in the accounts: The Portland Trust (£50,000).
FINANCES *Financial year end* 31/12/2019 *Income* £595,500 *Total grants* £422,600 *Grants to organisations* £422,600 *Assets* £4,990,000
TRUSTEES Sir Harry Solomon; Lady Judith Solomon; Geoffrey Jayson; Louise Jacobs; Daniel Solomon; Juliet Solomon; Sam Jacobs; James Jacobs.
OTHER INFORMATION A total of 78 grants were made during the year, in the following categories:

education (40%); welfare (21%); healthcare (21%); other (18%).

HOW TO APPLY Applications can be made in writing to the correspondent at any time. The 2019 annual report states that the trustees 'invite relevant applications, particularly from organisations introduced by reliable contacts of the trustees'. The trustees meet four times a year to discuss and approve existing and new grants.

CONTACT DETAILS The Trustees, 32 Hampstead High Street, London NW3 1QD *Tel.* 020 7431 7739

■ The Charlotte Heber-Percy Charitable Trust

CC NO 284387 **ESTABLISHED** 1981

WHERE FUNDING CAN BE GIVEN UK and overseas.

WHO CAN BENEFIT Charitable organisations.

WHAT IS FUNDED General charitable purposes; education and children; animal welfare; the environment; medical research; hospices; arts and museums.

WHAT IS NOT FUNDED Individuals.

RANGE OF GRANTS Up to £20,000, but mostly between £1,000 and £10,000.

SAMPLE GRANTS Horatio's Garden and The Nelson Trust (£20,000 each); Royal Ballet School (£15,000); Brooke Hospital for Animals (£10,000); The Friends of Aphrodisias Trust (£6,000); Emmaus Oxford and Trinity Sailing Foundation (£5,000 each); Chipping Campden Music Festival (£3,000); People Potential Possibilities (£1,000); St John's Church – Taynton (£200).

FINANCES *Financial year end* 05/04/2019 *Income* £333,100 *Total grants* £298,500 *Grants to organisations* £298,500 *Assets* £8,040,000

TRUSTEES Joanna Prest; Charlotte Heber-Percy.

OTHER INFORMATION The 2018/19 accounts were the latest available at the time of writing (May 2021). Grants were awarded to 47 organisations and distributed as follows: medical, cancer and hospices (£86,000); the arts and museums (£63,900); education and children (£54,000); animal welfare and the environment (£40,000); general charitable purposes (£30,000); local organisations (£17,700); international charities (£6,900).

HOW TO APPLY Applications should be made in writing to the correspondent. The trustees meet on a quarterly basis to consider applications. Only successful applicants are notified.

CONTACT DETAILS The Trustees, c/o Rathbone Trust Company Ltd, 8 Finsbury Circus, London EC2M 7AZ *Tel.* 020 7399 0820 *Email* linda.cousins@rathbones.com

■ Ernest Hecht Charitable Foundation

CC NO 1095850 **ESTABLISHED** 2002

WHERE FUNDING CAN BE GIVEN UK.

WHO CAN BENEFIT UK-registered charities.

WHAT IS FUNDED Art; healthcare; literature; music and theatre.

WHAT IS NOT FUNDED Individuals; charities whose primary area of benefit is outside the UK.

TYPE OF GRANT Project funding; core costs; capital costs.

RANGE OF GRANTS Up to £15,000 but mostly £1,000 to £5,000.

SAMPLE GRANTS Music in Hospitals and Care (£15,000); Coram Beanstalk (£12,500); Gate Theatre (£10,000); Alive and Kicking (£4,000); Blyth Star (£3,000); BLESMA (£500).

FINANCES *Financial year end* 31/12/2019 *Income* £719,900 *Total grants* £278,300 *Grants to organisations* £278,300 *Assets* £150,000

TRUSTEES Robert Ward; Barb Jungr; Ben Barkow.

OTHER INFORMATION Grants were made to 39 organisations during the year.

HOW TO APPLY Apply using the application form available to download from the foundation's website. The form should be returned along with copies of your organisation's two most recent sets of audited accounts. Only completed forms returned via email are accepted. There are no deadlines for applications.

CONTACT DETAILS The Trustees, 843 Finchley Road, London NW11 8NA *Email* info@ernesthechtcharitablefoundation.org *Website* ernesthechtcharitablefoundation.org

■ The Percy Hedley 1990 Charitable Trust

CC NO 1000033 **ESTABLISHED** 1990

WHERE FUNDING CAN BE GIVEN UK, with a preference for Northumberland and Tyne and Wear.

WHO CAN BENEFIT Registered charities.

WHAT IS FUNDED General charitable purposes.

TYPE OF GRANT Capital costs; core and revenue costs.

RANGE OF GRANTS Typically £500 to £1,000.

SAMPLE GRANTS Percy Hedley Foundation (£3,000); Newcastle Cathedral Trust (£2,000); Campaign to Protect Rural England, Samaritans of Tyneside and Surfers Against Sewage (£1,000 each); Canine Partners, Kidney Research UK, Listening Books and Wellbeing of Women (£500 each).

FINANCES *Financial year end* 20/04/2020 *Income* £63,100 *Total grants* £59,000 *Grants to organisations* £59,000 *Assets* £54,100

TRUSTEES John Armstrong; Bill Meikle; Fiona Ruffman.

OTHER INFORMATION Grants were given to 78 organisations in 2019/20.

HOW TO APPLY Apply in writing to the correspondent.

CONTACT DETAILS The Trustees, 10 Castleton Close, Newcastle upon Tyne, Tyne and Wear NE2 2HF *Tel.* 0191 281 5953 *Email* contact.phct@gmail.com

■ The Hedley Foundation

CC NO 262933 **ESTABLISHED** 1971

WHERE FUNDING CAN BE GIVEN UK.

WHO CAN BENEFIT Small to medium-sized registered charities.

WHAT IS FUNDED Supporting young people in the following areas: recreation; sport; training; health; welfare; outdoor education and adventure activities. Also, supporting young people who have disabilities or terminal illness, through funding specialist equipment and respite breaks. The foundation is particularly keen on supporting open air and adventure-type activities and young people who are at risk of offending. The foundation also supports elderly people and those receiving end-of-life care, as well as social welfare projects for carers, homeless people and ex-offenders.

WHAT IS NOT FUNDED Churches, cathedrals and museums; exclusive charities (which only help people from specific groups); applications from individuals directly; appeals for general funding, salary, deficit, core revenue or transport funding; appeals for building works or refurbishment projects.

TYPE OF GRANT Capital costs.

RANGE OF GRANTS Typically between £250 and £5,000.

SAMPLE GRANTS In2Change South Yorkshire Ltd (£25,000); Edward James Foundation (West Dean College) (£21,000); Young Musicians Symphony Orchestra (£15,000); English National Ballet School, Tapping House Hospice, Raleigh International and United World Colleges (£10,000 each).

FINANCES *Financial year end* 31/03/2020
Income £1,340,000 *Total grants* £678,400
Grants to organisations £678,400
Assets £34,800,000

TRUSTEES Lorna Stuttaford; Patrick Holcroft; Angus Fanshawe; Sir Andrew Ford; David Byam-Cook; Alexander Scully; Charles Bennett.

OTHER INFORMATION Grants were made to 273 charities during the year and were broken down as follows: young people (£276,900); disability (£225,600); other (£103,800); terminally ill people and hospices (£72,200). Only two organisations that received grants of over £10,000 were listed as beneficiaries in the charity's accounts; therefore beneficiaries from the previous year have been included. Grants of below £10,000 totalled £678,400.

HOW TO APPLY Application forms can be downloaded from the foundation's website and should be completed in typescript and returned by post. Emailed applications cannot be considered. Dates of trustees' meetings are listed on the website.

CONTACT DETAILS Lucy Janes, Appeals Secretary, Victoria House, 1–3 College Hill, London EC4R 2RA *Tel.* 020 7489 8076 *Email* ljanes@hedleyfoundation.org.uk *Website* www.hedleyfoundation.org.uk

■ The Michael Heller Charitable Foundation

CC NO 327832 **ESTABLISHED** 1988

WHERE FUNDING CAN BE GIVEN Worldwide.

WHO CAN BENEFIT Charitable organisations; research institutions; universities.

WHAT IS FUNDED Medical, scientific and educational research; humanitarian causes.

WHAT IS NOT FUNDED Individuals.

TYPE OF GRANT Funding for specific projects.

SAMPLE GRANTS A list of beneficiaries was not included in the annual report and accounts.

FINANCES *Financial year end* 31/05/2020
Income £263,000 *Total grants* £105,300
Grants to organisations £105,300
Assets £4,100,000

TRUSTEES Lady Morven Heller; Sir Michael Heller; W. S. Trustee Company Ltd.

OTHER INFORMATION Grants were broken down as follows: humanitarian (£44,800); education (£38,100); research (£22,500).

HOW TO APPLY Contact the correspondent for further information.

CONTACT DETAILS The Trustees, 24 Bruton Place, London W1J 6NE *Tel.* 020 7415 5000

■ The Simon Heller Charitable Settlement

CC NO 265405 **ESTABLISHED** 1972

WHERE FUNDING CAN BE GIVEN UK and overseas.

WHO CAN BENEFIT Charitable organisations; research institutions; universities.

WHAT IS FUNDED Medical, scientific and educational research, as well as humanitarian support. Jewish causes have also been supported.

TYPE OF GRANT Funding for specific projects.

SAMPLE GRANTS Previous beneficiaries have included: Aish Hatora; Chief Rabbinate Charitable Trust; Institute for Jewish Policy Research; Jewish Care; Scopus; Spiro Institute.

FINANCES *Financial year end* 05/04/2020
Income £454,500 *Total grants* £281,800
Grants to organisations £281,800
Assets £7,100,000

TRUSTEES Sir Michael Heller; Lady Morven Heller; W. S. Trustee Company Ltd.

OTHER INFORMATION Grants were distributed as follows: humanitarian (£183,300); education (£81,500); research (£17,000). The trustees of the charity also administer The Michael Heller Charitable Foundation (Charity Commission no. 327832), which has similar charitable purposes.

HOW TO APPLY Contact the correspondent for further information.

CONTACT DETAILS The Trustees, 24 Bruton Place, London W1J 6NE *Tel.* 020 7415 5000

■ Help for Health

CC NO 1091814 **ESTABLISHED** 2002

WHERE FUNDING CAN BE GIVEN Within the boundaries of East Yorkshire, Hull, and North and North East Lincolnshire.

WHO CAN BENEFIT Registered charities; medical and research bodies; universities.

WHAT IS FUNDED Healthcare provision (including facilities and equipment); medical research; medical education.

TYPE OF GRANT Capital costs (healthcare facilities and equipment); research; project funding.

RANGE OF GRANTS Mostly up to £25,000.

SAMPLE GRANTS Health Stars Impact Appeal (£50,000); Mires Beck Nursery (£25,000); Bodmin Road Church (£22,500); Med Equip 4 Kids (£10,000); Hull Churches Home from Hospital (£15,000); University of Hull (£9,000); Panathlon Foundation (£3,100).

FINANCES *Financial year end* 30/06/2019
Income £27,900 *Total grants* £226,400
Grants to organisations £226,400
Assets £5,370,000

TRUSTEES Andrew Milner; Prof. Peter Lee; Stuart Smith; Andrew Mould; Richard Field; Victoria Winterton; Carol Ann Hargreaves; Dr Emma Pinder; David Nuttall.

OTHER INFORMATION Only organisations that received grants of over £3,000 were listed as beneficiaries in the charity's accounts. Grants of under £3,000 totalled £11,000. The 2018/19 accounts were the latest available at the time of writing (January 2021).

HOW TO APPLY Application forms can be downloaded from the charity's website. The trustees wish to receive applications in electronic format only. Applications should be submitted at least 14 days prior to the relevant trustees' meeting date, advertised on the charity's website.

CONTACT DETAILS The Trustees, c/o RSM, 2 Humber Quays, Wellington Street West, Hull, East Yorkshire HU1 2BN *Tel.* 01482 607200 *Email* info@helphealth.org.uk *Website* www.helphealth.org.uk

Help the Homeless Ltd

CC NO 271988 **ESTABLISHED** 1975

WHERE FUNDING CAN BE GIVEN UK.

WHO CAN BENEFIT Small/medium-sized or newly registered charities with a turnover of less than £1 million a year.

WHAT IS FUNDED Homelessness – projects should assist individuals in their return to society, rather than offer shelter or other forms of sustenance.

WHAT IS NOT FUNDED Running/core costs; computers and IT equipment.

RANGE OF GRANTS Normally up to £5,000.

SAMPLE GRANTS Routes to Roots (£5,000); East Northants Faith Group and Hope House Essex (£3,000 each); Clock Tower Sanctuary (£2,500); Renewed Hope Trust and Shelter (£2,000 each); Hope 4 Barking and Dagenham (£1,500); New Start Oban (£1,000); Handcrafted (£600).

FINANCES *Financial year end* 31/03/2020 *Income* £83,600 *Total grants* £78,500 *Grants to organisations* £78,500 *Assets* £1,060,000

TRUSTEES Terry Rogers; Peter Fullerton; Francis Bergin; Stuart Holmes; Susan Conrad; Eamon McGoldrick.

OTHER INFORMATION Grants were made to 30 organisations during the year.

HOW TO APPLY Application forms can be downloaded from the charity's website. The website states that applicants should 'clearly describe the aims and structure of their organisation, their future plans and specific details of how any grant money will be spent' as well as provide the latest available audited accounts. The quarterly deadlines for applications each year are: 15 March, 15 June, 15 September and 15 December. Repeat applications can be made no earlier than two years after the receipt of a decision on the previous application. The charity no longer accepts applications by post.

CONTACT DETAILS The Trustees, 88 Gordon Road, Shoreham-by-Sea, West Sussex BN43 6WE *Tel.* 07717 004504 *Email* hth@help-the-homeless.org.uk *Website* www.help-the-homeless.org.uk

The Helping Foundation

CC NO 1104484 **ESTABLISHED** 2004

WHERE FUNDING CAN BE GIVEN UK.

WHO CAN BENEFIT Orthodox Jewish organisations; registered charities; occasionally individuals.

WHAT IS FUNDED Orthodox Jewish causes.

TYPE OF GRANT Project funding.

SAMPLE GRANTS A list of beneficiaries was not included in the annual report and accounts.

FINANCES *Financial year end* 31/12/2019 *Income* £23,700,000 *Total grants* £8,990,000 *Grants to organisations* £8,990,000 *Assets* £338,500,000

TRUSTEES Rachel Weis; Rabbi Aubrey Weis; David Neuwirth; Benny Stone; Sir Weis.

HOW TO APPLY Contact the correspondent for further information.

CONTACT DETAILS The Trustees, Flat 1, Allanadale Court, Waterpark Road, Salford, Greater Manchester M7 4JN *Tel.* 01617 40116

The Hemby Charitable Trust

CC NO 1073028 **ESTABLISHED** 1998

WHERE FUNDING CAN BE GIVEN Merseyside and Wirral.

WHO CAN BENEFIT Registered charities or organisations applying to become one.

WHAT IS FUNDED General charitable purposes; older people; the arts; social welfare; young people and employment; the environment.

WHAT IS NOT FUNDED Applicants from outside the area of benefit; sponsorship in any form; individuals; religious bodies; places of worship (unless there is significant non-worship community use); political organisations; pressure groups; feasibility studies; schools seeking specialist status; any form of memorial; repeat applicants within two years of a successful application.

TYPE OF GRANT Capital funding is preferred, although revenue requests may be considered.

RANGE OF GRANTS Mostly £500 to £3,000.

SAMPLE GRANTS Cystic Fibrosis Trust (£2,500); ADHD Foundation and Guide Dogs for the Blind (£2,000 each); National Youth Advocacy Service (£1,500); Woodlands Hospice Charitable Trust (£1,300); Live Music Now (£1,200); Target Ovarian Cancer (£1,000); The Comedy Trust (£500).

FINANCES *Financial year end* 31/01/2020 *Income* £105,000 *Total grants* £99,200 *Grants to organisations* £99,200 *Assets* £3,310,000

TRUSTEES Andrew Morris; Roy Morris; Caroline Tod; David Fairclough; Stuart Kepple.

OTHER INFORMATION In 2019/20 the trust received 88 applications and awarded 66 grants. Grants were distributed in the following categories: social welfare (£54,700); young people and employment (£24,700); the arts (£12,300); help for older people (£7,600).

HOW TO APPLY Applications can be made using a form available from the trust's website. Completed application forms should be returned to the correspondent together with a copy of your most recent accounts. Up to two additional A4 sheets can be added to the application form if space is needed. The deadlines for applications are normally on the first of February, June and October (by 12pm noon). Check the trust's website for the latest deadline dates. Applications are not acknowledged, but applicants are welcome to email or telephone the correspondent to check if their submission has been received. The website advises potential applicants to get in touch via phone if they are unsure how to complete the application form (including the size of the grant to be requested).

CONTACT DETAILS Tom Evans, Administrator, c/o Rathbone Investment Management Ltd, Port of Liverpool Building, Pier Head, Liverpool, Merseyside L3 1NW *Tel.* 07503 319182 *Email* adminathembytrust@talktalk.net *Website* hembytrust.org.uk

The Christina Mary Hendrie Trust

OSCR NO SC014514 **ESTABLISHED** 1975

WHERE FUNDING CAN BE GIVEN Scotland and Canada.

WHO CAN BENEFIT Registered charities; hospices.

WHAT IS FUNDED Young people, older people and veterans.

WHAT IS NOT FUNDED Individuals; building projects. See the trust's helpful website for more information on eligibility critieria.

TYPE OF GRANT General funding; running costs (for hospices).

RANGE OF GRANTS The average award is £7,500.
SAMPLE GRANTS The Yard (£40,000); Super Power Agency (£35,000); The St Andrew's Charitable Foundation (£25,100); Baillieston Community and Perth and Kinross Association of Voluntary Services (£16,500 each).
FINANCES *Financial year end* 31/03/2020 *Income* £137,100 *Total grants* £285,800 *Grants to organisations* £285,800 *Assets* £6,970,000
OTHER INFORMATION In response to the COVID-19 pandemic, the trust's grant-making focus for 2020/21 is on charities that it has previously supported.
HOW TO APPLY Applications can be made online via the trust's website.
CONTACT DETAILS Audrey Souness, Secretary, 1 Rutland Court, Edinburgh EH3 8EY *Tel.* 0131 270 7700 *Website* www.christinamaryhendrietrust.com

■ Henley Educational Trust

CC NO 309237 **ESTABLISHED** 1604
WHERE FUNDING CAN BE GIVEN Henley-on-Thames and the parishes of Bix and Rotherfield Greys in Oxfordshire and Remenham in Berkshire only.
WHO CAN BENEFIT State-maintained schools and colleges; youth and sports clubs, playgroups; charities; individuals under the age of 25.
WHAT IS FUNDED The education of children and young people (up to the age of 25), including related purposes such as extracurricular activities, sports, music, training, events, etc. Grants are also awarded to individuals.
TYPE OF GRANT Project funding; capital costs.
RANGE OF GRANTS Mostly up to £9,000.
SAMPLE GRANTS Gillotts Academy (£21,400); Henley College (£9,100); Henley Youth Festival (£5,000); Badgemore School (£2,200); Henley Cricket Club (£2,000); Crazies Hill School (£250).
FINANCES *Financial year end* 31/03/2020 *Income* £157,800 *Total grants* £130,700 *Grants to organisations* £111,100 *Assets* £3,660,000
TRUSTEES Susan Bishop; Kenneth Arlett; Debbie Wermann; Kellie Hinton; Revd Jeremy Taylor; Michelle Thomas; Amanda Heath; Elizabeth Hodgkin; Maureen Smith; Tristan Arnison; Isobel Morrow.
OTHER INFORMATION Grants were made to 11 organisations and 80 individuals during the year. Grants were broken down as follows: promotion of education for children and young people (£92,100); individuals in need (£19,600); provision of special benefits for schools (£19,000).
HOW TO APPLY Apply using a form available to download from the website, where criteria, guidelines and upcoming meeting dates are also posted.
CONTACT DETAILS Catherine Gosby, Clerk to the Trustees, 1A Coldharbour Close, Henley-on-Thames, Reading, Berkshire RG9 1QF *Tel.* 01491 524994 *Email* clerk@henleyeducationaltrust.com *Website* www.henleyeducationaltrust.com

■ Henley Royal Regatta Charitable Trust

CC NO 299597 **ESTABLISHED** 1988
WHERE FUNDING CAN BE GIVEN UK.
WHO CAN BENEFIT Sports clubs and related organisations; individuals.
WHAT IS FUNDED Projects associated with, or promoting, rowing.
TYPE OF GRANT Project funding; scholarships.
RANGE OF GRANTS £250 to £75,000.
SAMPLE GRANTS Rowing Foundation (£75,000); Warrington Youth Rowing (£64,800); British Rowing Scholarships (£35,200); National Junior Indoor Rowing Club (£10,000); Ball Cup Regatta (£5,200); Hinksey Sculling School (£3,500); Henley Disabled Regatta (£500); Marlow Rowing Club (£250).
FINANCES *Financial year end* 31/10/2019 *Income* £62,600 *Total grants* £201,500 *Grants to organisations* £201,500 *Assets* £7,450,000
TRUSTEES Sarah Winckless; Christopher Baillieu; Richard Lester; Sir Steve Redgrave; Richard Stanhope.
OTHER INFORMATION The trust is associated with the Henley Royal Regatta rowing event. Grants were made to nine organisations during the year, including a donation to British Rowing which funded five scholarships for individuals. The 2018/19 accounts were the latest available at the time of writing (January 2021).
HOW TO APPLY Contact the correspondent for further information.
CONTACT DETAILS Mr D. G. M. Grist, Secretary, Henley Royal Regatta Headquarters, Henley Bridge, Henley-on-Thames, Oxfordshire RG9 2LY *Tel.* 01491 572153 *Email* dgrist@regattahq.co.uk *Website* https://www.hrr.co.uk/charitable-trust

■ The Tim Henman Foundation

CC NO 1161964 **ESTABLISHED** 2015
WHERE FUNDING CAN BE GIVEN England and Wales.
WHO CAN BENEFIT Registered charities; schools and educational establishments; hospices.
WHAT IS FUNDED Children and young people's education, health and welfare.
TYPE OF GRANT Development funding; capital costs; projects; scholarships.
RANGE OF GRANTS £10,000 to £25,000.
SAMPLE GRANTS Raynes Park High School (£25,000); Naomi House and Jack's Place (£21,700); Chailey Heritage Foundation (£20,000); Ackworth School (£15,000); Chadsgrove School (£10,000).
FINANCES *Financial year end* 31/12/2019 *Income* £275,900 *Total grants* £141,300 *Grants to organisations* £141,300 *Assets* £586,000
TRUSTEES Jan Felgate; Lucy Henman; Tim Henman; Benn Shepherd; Sir David Carter; Mark Laurence; Ashley Silverton; Trevor Alldridge; Kevan Walsh; Andrew Hynard.
OTHER INFORMATION Grants were awarded to 13 organisations during the year.
HOW TO APPLY Contact the correspondent for information regarding the application process.
CONTACT DETAILS The Trustees, Ashcombe House, 5 The Crescent, Leatherhead, Surrey KT22 8DY *Tel.* 01372 849614 *Email* info@henmanfoundation.org *Website* www.henmanfoundation.org

The G. D. Herbert Charitable Trust

CC NO 295998 **ESTABLISHED** 1986

WHERE FUNDING CAN BE GIVEN UK.

WHO CAN BENEFIT Charitable organisations.

WHAT IS FUNDED General charitable purposes, particularly: medicine; health; social welfare; environmental causes.

TYPE OF GRANT Mainly recurrent, with occasional one-off awards (in the areas of health and welfare only).

RANGE OF GRANTS Up to £3,000.

SAMPLE GRANTS The Outward Bound Trust, NSPCC, PDSA, Shelter and The Woodland Trust (£3,000 each); Great Ormond Street Hospital Children's Charity and Noah's Ark Children's Hospice (£800 each).

FINANCES *Financial year end* 05/04/2020 *Income* £84,800 *Total grants* £76,400 *Grants to organisations* £76,400 *Assets* £2,090,000

TRUSTEES Michael Beaumont; Mrs J. Cuxson.

OTHER INFORMATION The trust makes grants to 25 organisations each year as well as four 'special' grants to other charities.

HOW TO APPLY The annual report for 2019/20 states that the trustees 'review donations at their annual general meeting in February/March of each year and may make some adjustments but for the most part continue the donations to the beneficiaries listed year on year'.

CONTACT DETAILS The Trustees, c/o Veale Wasbrough Vizards LLP, 24 King William Street, London EC4R 9AT *Tel.* 020 7405 1234 *Email* mbyrne@vwv.co.uk

Herefordshire Community Foundation

CC NO 1094935 **ESTABLISHED** 2002

WHERE FUNDING CAN BE GIVEN Herefordshire.

WHO CAN BENEFIT Registered charities; unregistered charities; CICs; social enterprises; schools; hospices; individuals.

WHAT IS FUNDED General charitable purposes.

WHAT IS NOT FUNDED Animal welfare; arts projects with no community or charitable element; direct replacement of statutory funding; medical research; political groups or activities promoting political beliefs; religious groups seeking to influence people's religious choices; sports projects with no community or charitable element; general appeals.

TYPE OF GRANT Capital costs; core/revenue costs; seed funding/start-up costs; project funding.

SAMPLE GRANTS Previous beneficiaries have included: Neuromuscular Centre (£7,100); Oswestry Rugby Club (£4,100); Marches Counselling Service (£2,400); Get into Reading (£900); Young Boots Football (£700); Kington Museum (£200).

FINANCES *Financial year end* 31/03/2020 *Income* £713,700 *Total grants* £513,800 *Grants to organisations* £513,800 *Assets* £4,560,000

TRUSTEES Frank Myers; William Lindesay; Philippa Spens; Karen Hall; Beata Davison; Louise Stevenson; Antony Lowther; Shelagh Wynn; Laura Hughes; Oliver Cooke; Caroline Rixon; Geoffrey Hughes.

OTHER INFORMATION This is one of the 46 UK community foundations, which distribute funding for a wide range of purposes. As with all community foundations, there are a number of donor-advised funds managed on behalf of individuals, families and charitable trusts. Grant schemes tend to change frequently; consult the foundation's website for details of current programmes and up-to-date deadlines. During 2019/20 a total of 221 grants were made to organisations and individuals. The foundation also supported a further 110 households that had been affected by Storm Dennis. The grant total includes grants to individuals.

HOW TO APPLY Potential applicants are advised to visit the community foundation's website or contact its grants team to find the most suitable funding stream.

CONTACT DETAILS Grants Administrator, The Fred Bulmer Centre, Wall Street, Hereford, Herefordshire HR4 9HP *Tel.* 01432 272550 *Email* admin@herefordshirecf.org *Website* https://www.herefordshirecf.org

The Herefordshire Historic Churches Trust

CC NO 511181 **ESTABLISHED** 1954

WHERE FUNDING CAN BE GIVEN Herefordshire.

WHO CAN BENEFIT Churches of all denominations.

WHAT IS FUNDED Church restoration, repair, maintenance and improvements.

TYPE OF GRANT One-off awards for capital and core costs (primarily for repair and maintenance); project funding; loans of up to £10,000 are also available.

RANGE OF GRANTS £1,000 to £15,000.

SAMPLE GRANTS Stoke Lacy (£15,000); Leominster (£10,000); Burghill (£5,000); Dorstone (£3,500); Cradley (£1,500); Bosbury (£1,000); Llaneynoe (£900).

FINANCES *Financial year end* 31/12/2019 *Income* £88,900 *Total grants* £90,600 *Grants to organisations* £90,600 *Assets* £954,700

TRUSTEES David Furnival; Ali Jones; Jill Gallimore; Stephen Cheetham; Lady Susanna McFarlane; John Handby; Ben Furnival; Archdeacon Derek Chedzey; Rod Barker.

OTHER INFORMATION Major grants were paid to 17 churches during 2019/20. A further £6,100 was awarded as activity grants and £610 was awarded as development grants.

HOW TO APPLY Application forms can be completed on the trust's website, where guidance notes can also be found. Potential applicants are encouraged to contact the trust at an early stage to discuss their project. Deadlines for applications are normally 15 March and 15 September for trustees' meetings in April and October. Small grants in respect of urgent repairs may be made outside these timescales – contact the correspondent for more information.

CONTACT DETAILS David Furnival, Chair, Coppice Barn, The Woodhouse Farm, Staplow, Ledbury, Herefordshire HR8 1NP *Tel.* 01531 641955 *Email* david.furnival13@gmail.com *Website* www.hhct.co.uk

Heritage Lottery Fund

ESTABLISHED 1994

WHERE FUNDING CAN BE GIVEN UK.

WHO CAN BENEFIT Charitable organisations; heritage enterprises.

WHAT IS FUNDED Heritage projects.

TYPE OF GRANT Direct project costs including capital costs, salaries, training, repairs and maintenance.

RANGE OF GRANTS £3,000 to £5 million.
SAMPLE GRANTS Canterbury Cathedral; Historic England; Hull City Council; Imperial War Museums; National Maritime Museum; The British Library.
FINANCES *Financial year end* 31/03/2020 *Income* £357,270,000 *Total grants* £251,920,000 *Grants to organisations* £251,920,000 *Assets* £322,630,000
TRUSTEES Rene Olivieri; Baroness Kay Andrews; Maria Adebowale-Schwarte; Jim Dixon; Dr Claire Feehily; Sarah Flannigan; Perdita Hunt; Ray Macfarlane; Prof. David Stocker; Mukesh Sharma.
HOW TO APPLY All applications must be submitted via the online application portal.
CONTACT DETAILS The Trustees, 7 Holbein Place, London SW1W 8NR *Tel.* 020 7591 6044 *Email* enquire@heritagefund.org.uk

■ The Heritage of London Trust Ltd

CC NO 280272 **ESTABLISHED** 1980
WHERE FUNDING CAN BE GIVEN Greater London.
WHO CAN BENEFIT Buildings or monuments which are of architectural or historic interest; community organisations; local authorities; statutory bodies.
WHAT IS FUNDED The conservation and restoration of historic buildings and monuments (or specific architectural features on historic buildings and monuments) which are in community or public use.
WHAT IS NOT FUNDED Buildings in private ownership that are not open or available for public use and enjoyment; roof replacements or repairs; restoration schemes where the work has already been completed; general maintenance or repairs.
TYPE OF GRANT Restoration grants, awarded over a period of three years.
RANGE OF GRANTS £1,000 to £15,000.
SAMPLE GRANTS Sarah Siddons statue (£12,000); Reliance Arcade (£10,000); Wren Spire (£7,000); Broomfield Park Memorial (£6,000); Nathaniel Montefiore Drinking Fountain, Richmond Green Drinking Fountain and St Mary's Islington (£5,000 each); Toynbee Hall (£4,000); Garden Museum (£2,000).
FINANCES *Financial year end* 31/03/2020 *Income* £347,600 *Total grants* £87,600 *Grants to organisations* £87,600 *Assets* £788,600
TRUSTEES Dr Patricia Morison; John Phillips; Kit Kemp; Jamie Cayzer-Colvin; Dora Dixon-Fyle; Louisa McCarthy; Jamie Ritblat; Michael Hoare.
OTHER INFORMATION Buildings do not need to be listed in order to be eligible, but must be considered of historic or architectural interest.
HOW TO APPLY In the first instance, applicants should contact the trust via phone, email or enquiry form to discuss the project. If a project is considered to be suitable for funding, the trustees will arrange a visit to discuss it further. The applicant will then be asked to complete the online application form. The trustees meet three times a year to considered applications.
CONTACT DETAILS The Trustees, 34 Grosvenor Gardens, London SW1W 0DH *Tel.* 020 7099 0559 *Email* info@heritageoflondon.com *Website* https://www.heritageoflondon.org

■ Hertfordshire Community Foundation

CC NO 1156082 **ESTABLISHED** 1988
WHERE FUNDING CAN BE GIVEN Hertfordshire.
WHO CAN BENEFIT Formally constituted community groups; charitable organisations; individuals.
WHAT IS FUNDED General charitable purposes.
WHAT IS NOT FUNDED See individual grant programmes for specific exclusions.
TYPE OF GRANT Project funding; capital costs.
SAMPLE GRANTS A list of beneficiaries was not included in the annual report and accounts.
FINANCES *Financial year end* 31/03/2020 *Income* £2,060,000 *Total grants* £982,000 *Grants to organisations* £959,100 *Assets* £11,080,000
TRUSTEES Sally Burton; William Hobhouse; John Saner; Augustus Machado; Simon Tilley; Suzana Harvey; Jill Burridge; Terence Douris; Anna Bates; Henry Hibbert; Suzanne Westlake; James Williams.
OTHER INFORMATION This is one of the 46 UK community foundations, which distribute funding for a wide range of purposes. As with all community foundations, there are a number of donor-advised funds managed on behalf of individuals, families and charitable trusts. Grant schemes tend to change frequently; consult the foundation's website for details of current programmes and up-to-date deadlines. During 2019/20, grants to individuals totalled £22,900.
HOW TO APPLY Potential applicants are advised to visit the community foundation's website or contact its grants team to find the most suitable funding stream.
CONTACT DETAILS Grants Team, Foundation House, 2–4 Forum Place, Fiddlebridge Lane, Hatfield, Hertfordshire AL10 0RN *Tel.* 01707 251351 *Email* grants@hertscf.org.uk *Website* www.hertscf.org.uk

■ HFC Help For Children UK Ltd

CC NO 1116081 **ESTABLISHED** 2006
WHERE FUNDING CAN BE GIVEN London and the South East.
WHO CAN BENEFIT Registered charities; CICs.
WHAT IS FUNDED The prevention of or treatment for child abuse.
WHAT IS NOT FUNDED Lobbying activities; annual fundraising drives; projects undertaken by individuals; multi-year grants.
TYPE OF GRANT Project funding; research.
RANGE OF GRANTS Up to £20,000.
SAMPLE GRANTS Abianda (£44,000); Safer London (£40,000); Imara CIC (£36,000); Home-Start and Marie Collins Foundation (£34,000); The Mulberry Bush School (£22,000).
FINANCES *Financial year end* 31/12/2019 *Income* £417,100 *Total grants* £210,000 *Grants to organisations* £210,000 *Assets* £236,400
TRUSTEES Robert Schultz; Philip Bland; Louise Denning; Elizabeth Buss; Robert Mirsky; Jonathan May; Jonathan Napora; Clare Walkeden; Sonia Davies; Greg Gliner; James Wellwood; Jack Edward; Melanie Pittas; Christopher Radley-Gardner; Chris Pugh; Scott Coey; Sue Petrie; Neill Ebers; Jeff Bronheim; Dan Petrovic; Damon Ambrosini.
HOW TO APPLY Applicants should first complete a Letter of Intent, which can be downloaded from the application section of the Help for Children website. After review, selected organisations will be invited to complete a full proposal. Declined

Letters of Intent are acknowledged. Visit the charity's website for current deadlines.

CONTACT DETAILS Sumudu Waas, Grants Manager, 106 W. 32nd Street, 2nd Floor, New York NY 10001 *Tel.* 212-991-9600 ext. 343 *Email* swaas@hfc.org *Website* www.hfc.org

P. and C. Hickinbotham Charitable Trust

CC NO 216432 **ESTABLISHED** 1947

WHERE FUNDING CAN BE GIVEN UK, with a preference for Leicestershire and Rutland. The trust also supports a small number of projects in North Wales and Northern Ireland.

WHO CAN BENEFIT Registered charities only.

WHAT IS FUNDED General charitable purposes; social welfare; people with disabilities; people experiencing homelessness; substance abuse; prisoners' education and rehabilitation; vulnerable groups; children and young people; the arts; the environment.

WHAT IS NOT FUNDED Individuals; large national charities (unless for a specific project); groups without charitable status; general running costs; repeat grants.

TYPE OF GRANT One-off grants, specialist equipment; premises purchase or renovation; start-up costs.

RANGE OF GRANTS Grants tend to range from £500 to £2,000, although there is no set upper limit.

SAMPLE GRANTS Leicester Charity Link (£7,500); RNLI and Age UK – Leicestershire and Rutland (£5,000 each); Dove Cottage Day Hospice (£2,500); Leicestershire Chorale, Cossington Project Group and Angels and Monsters (£2,000 each).

FINANCES *Financial year end* 05/04/2020 *Income* £94,000 *Total grants* £158,500 *Grants to organisations* £158,500 *Assets* £4,710,000

TRUSTEES Roger Hickinbotham; Anna Steiger; Rachel Hickinbotham; Charlotte Palmer; Frances Hickinbotham; Alice Hickinbotham.

OTHER INFORMATION Grants of under £2,000 totalled £95,500.

HOW TO APPLY Apply in writing to the correspondent. The trustees meet once per quarter to consider applications.

CONTACT DETAILS Roger Hickinbotham, Trustee, 9 Windmill Way, Lyddington, Oakham, Rutland LE15 9LY *Tel.* 07885 099327 *Email* rogerhick@gmail.com *Website* www.hickinbothamtrust.org.uk

The Alan Edward Higgs Charity

CC NO 509367 **ESTABLISHED** 1979

WHERE FUNDING CAN BE GIVEN Within 25 miles of the centre of Coventry.

WHO CAN BENEFIT Registered charities.

WHAT IS FUNDED Disadvantaged young people; families and children.

WHAT IS NOT FUNDED Individuals; activities outside the beneficial area; statutory bodies and anything deemed to be the responsibility of the state; nurseries, schools and colleges; hospitals and health authorities; academic research, scholarships, or bursaries; the promotion of religion; endowment appeals; restoration and conservation of buildings (unless for community use); retrospective expenditure; widely circulated appeals.

TYPE OF GRANT Capital costs; core/revenue costs; seed funding/start-up costs.

RANGE OF GRANTS Mostly between £1,000 and £20,000.

SAMPLE GRANTS Historic Coventry Trust (£640,000); Acorns Children's Hospice Trust (£30,000); Myton Hospice (£20,000); Bradby Club for Young People (£10,000); St Francis Employability (£8,000); Teenage Cancer Trust (£5,000); Lullaby Trust (£4,500); The Notables Foundation (£1,000).

FINANCES *Financial year end* 05/04/2020 *Income* £685,200 *Total grants* £855,700 *Grants to organisations* £855,700 *Assets* £16,920,000

TRUSTEES Marilyn Knatchbull-Hugessen; Rowley Higgs; Emily Barlow; Mark Franklin.

OTHER INFORMATION Grants were made to 25 organisations during 2019/20.

HOW TO APPLY Applications can be made online through the charity's website, where detailed guidelines are also available.

CONTACT DETAILS Peter Knatchbull-Hugessen, Clerk, The Ricoh Arena, Judd's Lane, Longford, Coventry, Warwickshire CV6 6GE *Tel.* 024 7622 1311 *Email* clerk@higgscharity.org.uk *Website* www.higgscharity.org.uk

The Highcroft Charitable Trust

CC NO 272684 **ESTABLISHED** 1975

WHERE FUNDING CAN BE GIVEN UK and overseas.

WHO CAN BENEFIT Jewish charitable organisations.

WHAT IS FUNDED The advancement and study of the Jewish faith and the study of the Torah; the relief of poverty and advancement of education among people of the Jewish faith.

RANGE OF GRANTS Generally, up to £25,000.

SAMPLE GRANTS Tevini Ltd (£18,000); Mesifta Talmudical College (£12,500); Academy for Talmudical Research (Kolel Harabanim) and Society of Friends of the Torah (£10,000 each); Kollel Bnei Yissochor and Kollel Rabinow (divre Shir) Foundation London (£7,500 each); Bayit Lepletot (£7,200).

FINANCES *Financial year end* 30/06/2020 *Income* £250,600 *Total grants* £99,000 *Grants to organisations* £99,000 *Assets* £1,400,000

TRUSTEES Richard Fischer; Bella Reicher; Alexander Eisner.

OTHER INFORMATION Grants of less than £4,000 totalled £26,400.

HOW TO APPLY Apply in writing to the correspondent. Contact the correspondent for further information.

CONTACT DETAILS The Trustees, 15 Highcroft Gardens, London NW11 0LY *Tel.* 020 8458 5382

Highway One Trust

CC NO 1164753 **ESTABLISHED** 2016

WHERE FUNDING CAN BE GIVEN England and Wales.

WHO CAN BENEFIT Registered charities (UK or international); not-for-profit organisations.

WHAT IS FUNDED Disfiguring medical conditions; women in need; prison and injustice; poverty; homelessness; economic regeneration; internet and mobile networks (such as cyber abuse); Christianity.

TYPE OF GRANT Multi-year funding; core costs; capital costs; project funding.

RANGE OF GRANTS £5,000 to £10,000.

SAMPLE GRANTS Bullies Out (£10,500); Changing Faces, Child Hope UK, Christian Solidarity Worldwide, Only Connect, Prison Reform Trust, Reprieve and Tearfund (£10,000 each).

FINANCES *Financial year end* 31/12/2019
Income £122,000 *Total grants* £141,100
Grants to organisations £141,100
Assets £2,210,000

TRUSTEES Jacqueline Elton; Neil Maybin; Michael Armstrong; Dr Sarah Rutherford.

HOW TO APPLY The policy of the trustees is to not award unsolicited grants; however, the website states: 'If you feel your work or project meets our criteria, you may send an email outlining the work or project in no more than fifty words to the researcher at info@highwayonetrust.com.'

CONTACT DETAILS The Trustees, 2nd Floor, Church House, 86 Tavistock Place, London WC1H 9RT *Tel.* 020 8878 0701 *Email* info@highwayonetrust.com *Website* highwayonetrust.com

■ The Hilden Charitable Fund

CC NO 232591 **ESTABLISHED** 1963

WHERE FUNDING CAN BE GIVEN UK and financially developing countries.

WHO CAN BENEFIT Registered charities; CICs; voluntary organisations; NGOs; social enterprises.

WHAT IS FUNDED In the UK: homelessness; asylum seekers and refugees; people affected by the criminal justice system; community initiatives for disadvantaged young people (aged 16 to 25). Overseas: community development; disaster relief; education; health; a preference exists for projects addressing the needs of girls and women.

WHAT IS NOT FUNDED Individuals; well-funded national charities.

TYPE OF GRANT Project funding; unrestricted core/revenue costs; multi-year.

SAMPLE GRANTS Joint Council for the Welfare of Immigrants – London (£20,000); London Football Journeys (£8,000); Barts Health NHS Trust – London (£6,900); Ecologia Youth Trust – Kenya (£6,000); Inverness Foodstuff, Kestrel Theatre Company and Springfield Domestic Abuse Support – South Lakeland (£5,000 each); Stonebridge City Farm – Nottingham (£4,700); St Vincent's Support Centre – Leeds (£2,500).

FINANCES *Financial year end* 05/04/2020
Income £437,500 *Total grants* £415,900
Grants to organisations £415,900
Assets £12,710,000

TRUSTEES Patrick Rampton; Robert Rampton; Ms E. Rodeck; Prof. D. Rampton; Prof. M. Rampton; Prof. C. Rodeck; Jonathan Branch; Elizabeth Rodeck; Emma Jenkins; Catherine Rampton; A. J. M. Rampton; Bandi Mbubi; Samia Khatun; Mr J. Rampton; Maggie Baxter.

OTHER INFORMATION During 2019/20, a total of 84 grants were awarded from 906 applications. In addition to its main grants programme, the charity has allocated a small budget to help community groups run summer play schemes for disadvantaged communities.

HOW TO APPLY Applications can be made at any time using the online application form on the charity's website. Applicants are welcome to contact the charity for advice before making an application. It typically takes between three and five months to process applications.

CONTACT DETAILS Catherine Sotto, Office Manager, 34 North End Road, London W14 0SH *Tel.* 020 7603 1525 *Email* admin@hildencharitablefund.org *Website* www.hildencharitablefund.org.uk

■ The Derek Hill Foundation

CC NO 801590 **ESTABLISHED** 1989

WHERE FUNDING CAN BE GIVEN UK.

WHO CAN BENEFIT Charitable organisations and individuals.

WHAT IS FUNDED Arts and culture; music; literature; education.

RANGE OF GRANTS Typically under £5,000.

SAMPLE GRANTS Creative Youth Network (£5,000); Crisis UK (£3,000); Opera North Ltd (£2,000); The Lennox Berkeley Society (£1,000); The Foundling Museum (£500).

FINANCES *Financial year end* 09/05/2020
Income £36,000 *Total grants* £152,200
Grants to organisations £147,500
Assets £1,300,000

TRUSTEES Ian Paterson; Earl of Gowrie; Rathbone Trust Company Ltd; Joseph Batteram.

OTHER INFORMATION Grants were distributed as follows: arts (£58,500); music (£40,000); theatre (£18,500); education (£15,400); literature (£14,000); individuals (£4,700); museums (£1,000).

HOW TO APPLY Contact the correspondent for further information.

CONTACT DETAILS The Trustees, Rathbone Trust Company Ltd, 8 Finsbury Circus, London EC2M 7AZ *Tel.* 020 7399 0835

■ The Hillier Trust

CC NO 1147629 **ESTABLISHED** 2012

WHERE FUNDING CAN BE GIVEN Worldwide.

WHO CAN BENEFIT Registered charities, mainly those which have a Christian ethos; individuals.

WHAT IS FUNDED Development and support work for disadvantaged groups; Christian causes.

RANGE OF GRANTS Typically between £500 and £4,000.

SAMPLE GRANTS The Family Trust (£200,000); Embrace the Middle East (£14,000); Heart of Kent Hospice (£13,000); Maidstone Churches Winter Shelter (£5,000); Safe Anaesthesia Worldwide (£4,000); Emanuel Hospice (£3,000); Salvation Army (£2,500); Maidstone Deanery (£1,000).

FINANCES *Financial year end* 30/06/2020
Income £69,000 *Total grants* £272,400
Grants to organisations £272,400
Assets £3,510,000

TRUSTEES Anthony Hillier; Susan Hillier; Elizabeth Jordan.

OTHER INFORMATION Grants were made to 17 organisations in 2019/20. Each year a substantial grant is made to The Family Trust.

HOW TO APPLY Apply in writing to the correspondent. The trustees communicate regularly throughout the year to consider grant applications.

CONTACT DETAILS Anthony Hillier, Trustee, Loose Court Farmhouse, Old Drive, Maidstone, Kent ME15 9SE *Tel.* 07767 775792 *Email* tonyhillier@zen.co.uk

■ R. G. Hills Charitable Trust

CC NO 1008914 **ESTABLISHED** 1982

WHERE FUNDING CAN BE GIVEN UK and overseas with a preference for Kent.

WHO CAN BENEFIT Registered charities.

WHAT IS FUNDED General charitable purposes with some preference for health, poverty and education.

RANGE OF GRANTS Grants range from £1,000 to £5,000.

SAMPLE GRANTS Catching Lives (£5,000); Dementia Support (£4,000); Kent Wildlife Trust and African Children's Fund Ltd (£3,000 each); Duchenne UK (£2,500); Fauna and Flora International (£2,000); Fort Amherst Heritage Trust (£1,000).

FINANCES *Financial year end* 31/03/2020 *Income* £159,000 *Total grants* £130,500 *Grants to organisations* £130,500 *Assets* £3,490,000

TRUSTEES Kenneth Jones; Harvey Barrett.

OTHER INFORMATION In 2019/20, grants were awarded to 64 organisations.

HOW TO APPLY Contact the correspondent for further information.

CONTACT DETAILS The Trustees, c/o Furley Page, 39–40 St Margaret's Street, Canterbury CT1 2TX *Tel.* 01227 763939

■ Hinchley Charitable Trust

CC NO 1108412 **ESTABLISHED** 1973

WHERE FUNDING CAN BE GIVEN UK and Ireland; occasionally overseas.

WHO CAN BENEFIT Registered charities.

WHAT IS FUNDED Training of Christian leaders; holistic Christian mission in communities; Christian youth organisations; Christian influence in the public sphere.

WHAT IS NOT FUNDED Individuals.

TYPE OF GRANT Project funding; strategic funding; development funding; core costs; salaries.

RANGE OF GRANTS Up to £15,000.

SAMPLE GRANTS Youthscape (£15,000); Karis Neighbourhood Scheme (£10,000); Innovista Thrive (£8,000); Parish Nursing (£7,000); Mount Merrion (£6,000); Church and Media Network and Thrive Youth Ministries (£5,000 each).

FINANCES *Financial year end* 30/06/2019 *Income* £181,900 *Total grants* £166,500 *Grants to organisations* £166,500 *Assets* £3,860,000

TRUSTEES Dr Brian Stanley; Prof. Paul Cloke; John Levick; Mark Hobbs; Roger Northcott; Rebecca Corbett.

OTHER INFORMATION The 2018/19 accounts were the latest available at the time of writing (May 2021). During the year, grants were made to 20 organisations and were distributed within the following categories: holistic mission (£61,500); young people (£56,500); public sphere (£43,500); training leaders (£5,000).

HOW TO APPLY The trust's website states: 'Our aim is to work with a select number of charity partners and therefore we do not accept unsolicited applications.'

CONTACT DETAILS The Trustees, 2 Arnold Drive, Chessington, Surrey KT9 2GD *Tel.* 020 8397 1087 *Email* info@hinchleycharitabletrust.org.uk *Website* www.hinchleycharitabletrust.org.uk

■ The Lady Hind Trust

CC NO 208877 **ESTABLISHED** 1951

WHERE FUNDING CAN BE GIVEN Nottinghamshire and Norfolk.

WHO CAN BENEFIT Registered and exempt charities; CICs; churches; uniformed groups; educational organisations; hospices; community groups and clubs.

WHAT IS FUNDED General charitable purposes, particularly social welfare and health and disability (including healthcare services, health education, personal social services and social preventive schemes); churches; education; arts and culture; the environment and heritage; accommodation.

WHAT IS NOT FUNDED Individuals; organisations working or based outside England; activities that are the responsibility of the local health authority, education authority or similar body.

RANGE OF GRANTS Mostly under £5,000.

SAMPLE GRANTS Priscilla Bacon Norfolk Hospice Care Ltd (£45,000); Maggie's Nottingham (£10,000); Framework Housing Association (£5,000); University of East Anglia (£4,000); St Peter's United Charities (£3,000); Rescue Wooden Boats (£2,500); Schoolreaders (£2,000); Spinal Muscular Atrophy UK and The Police Community Clubs of Great Britain (£1,000 each).

FINANCES *Financial year end* 31/12/2020 *Income* £424,700 *Total grants* £485,800 *Grants to organisations* £485,800 *Assets* £22,000,000

TRUSTEES Charles Barratt; Timothy Farr; Nigel Savory; John Pears.

OTHER INFORMATION During the year, over 129 organisations were supported. Grants of over £1,000 were distributed as follows: medical/disability (£155,500); welfare (£144,000); other (£44,500); churches (£41,000); education (£32,500); the environment (£19,500); the arts (£15,000); heritage (£9,500); groups/clubs (£9,000); accommodation (£6,000).

HOW TO APPLY Applications should be made in writing via post to the correspondent. Applications must be received by 20 January, 20 May or 20 September, to be considered at the trustees' meetings held in March, July and November, respectively. Applicants should also provide their latest set of accounts. Full details of what should be included in an application can be found on the trust's website. Unsuccessful applicants are not notified.

CONTACT DETAILS Trust Administrator, PO Box 10455, Nottingham, Nottinghamshire NG5 0HR *Tel.* 07710 639946 *Email* ladyhind@btinternet.com *Website* www.ladyhindtrust.org.uk

■ The Hinduja Foundation

CC NO 802756 **ESTABLISHED** 1989

WHERE FUNDING CAN BE GIVEN Worldwide.

WHO CAN BENEFIT Registered charities; educational and cultural organisations.

WHAT IS FUNDED Health and medicine; education; relief of poverty, hunger and sickness; interfaith understanding; arts and culture; social, economic and international development-related research.

TYPE OF GRANT General funding; capital costs; project funding; research.

RANGE OF GRANTS £100 to £20,000.

SAMPLE GRANTS International Society for Krishna Consciousness (£20,000); Wadham College – University of Oxford (£23,800); The British Asian Trust (£20,000); Centrepoint (£10,000); The Serpentine Trust (£2,500); Siri Guru Singh Sabha (£2,200); The Royal Opera House (£1,000); Plan International (£580); Help the Aged (£140).

FINANCES *Financial year end* 31/12/2019 *Income* £151,500 *Total grants* £97,100 *Grants to organisations* £97,100 *Assets* £15,600

TRUSTEES Srichand Hinduja; Gopichand Hinduja; Prakash Hinduja; Sanjay Hinduja; Dheeraj Hinduja.

OTHER INFORMATION During 2019, 12 organisations received grants. Grants were distributed in the following categories: relief in need (£30,700);

education (£30,700) interfaith understanding (£29,700); cultural awareness and the arts (£6,000).

HOW TO APPLY Contact the correspondent for further information.

CONTACT DETAILS Michael Urwick, New Zealand House, 80 Haymarket, London SW1Y 4TE *Tel.* 020 7839 4661 *Email* mu@sangamltd.com *Website* www.hindujafoundation.org/index.html

■ The Hinrichsen Foundation

CC NO 272389 **ESTABLISHED** 1976

WHERE FUNDING CAN BE GIVEN UK.

WHO CAN BENEFIT Charities; organisations and individuals.

WHAT IS FUNDED The performance of contemporary music, including: the commissioning of new work; non-commercial recording; publication. The website explains that the trustees will occasionally fund musicological research projects 'not being conducted under the aegis of an academic institution'.

WHAT IS NOT FUNDED The purchase of musical instruments or equipment including the electronic or computer variety; retrospective expenditure; degree courses; applications for which there are existing official schemes of help. According to its website, the foundation will not usually support 'projects with a very large over-arching budget or where the budgeting is unclear or largely speculative.'

TYPE OF GRANT One-off project funding; multi-year partnerships; research.

RANGE OF GRANTS Small grants of £500 to £2,500; larger grants of £2,000 upwards.

SAMPLE GRANTS Huddersfield 2019 (£10,000); Vale of Glamorgan Festival (£5,000); London Contemporary Music Festival (£3,000); Sound Festival 2019 (£2,000); Dartington Summer School, Two Moors Festival and Wild Plum Arts (£1,000 each); 840 series (£750).

FINANCES *Financial year end* 31/12/2019 *Income* £8,130,000 *Total grants* £72,000 *Grants to organisations* £53,000 *Assets* £4,400,000

TRUSTEES Tim Berg; Mark Bromley; Tabby Estell; Eleanor Gussman; Dr Linda Hurst; Ed McKeon; Keith Potter; Prof. Stephen Walsh.

OTHER INFORMATION In 2019 grants to 37 organisations and 16 individuals were approved.

HOW TO APPLY Application forms and guidelines can be found on the foundation's website. At the time of writing (May 2021) the foundation had temporarily closed its grants programme due to COVID-19. Check the foundation's website for the latest information.

CONTACT DETAILS The Trustees, 2–6 Baches Street, London N1 6DN *Tel.* 020 7553 4000 *Email* hinrichsen.foundation@editionpeters.com *Website* www.hinrichsenfoundation.org.uk

■ The Hintze Family Charity Foundation

CC NO 1101842 **ESTABLISHED** 2003

WHERE FUNDING CAN BE GIVEN England and Wales, particularly the Diocese of Southwark; overseas.

WHO CAN BENEFIT Registered charities; churches; museums, galleries; libraries and other cultural bodies; educational organisations.

WHAT IS FUNDED Education; the Christian faith; the armed services; health; general charitable purposes.

TYPE OF GRANT One-off or multi-year; capital and revenue funding, including salaries and core costs.

SAMPLE GRANTS Previous beneficiaries have included: Advance Charitable Fund UK, British Film Institute, British Museum, Canterbury Cathedral Trust, Institute of Economic Affairs, National Portrait Gallery, Outward Bound Trust, Southwark Diocese Clergy Support Fund Campaign, The Black Stork Charity and The Prince's Teaching Institute.

FINANCES *Financial year end* 31/12/2019 *Income* £3,390,000 *Total grants* £4,000,000 *Grants to organisations* £4,000,000 *Assets* £364,200

TRUSTEES Sir Michael Hintze; Sir Michael Peat; Duncan Baxter.

OTHER INFORMATION During 2019, the foundation awarded grants totalling £4 million, which included commitments from previous years. At the end of 2019, the foundation committed £8.2 million in grants over the next 13 years.

HOW TO APPLY The 2019 annual report explains that the foundation 'invites applications for grants from charities which further the objectives of the foundation. No specific format is required for applications. Applications and potential donations identified by the Chief Executive and the trustees are considered at trustees' meetings.'

CONTACT DETAILS Kate Rees-Doherty, Secretary, 4th Floor, One Strand, London WC2N 5HR *Tel.* 020 7201 2444 *Email* enquiries@hfcf.org.uk *Website* https://michael-hintze.com

■ The Hiscox Foundation

CC NO 327635 **ESTABLISHED** 1987

WHERE FUNDING CAN BE GIVEN Worldwide, primarily in the UK.

WHO CAN BENEFIT Registered charities.

WHAT IS FUNDED General charitable purposes; education; medical science; the arts; independent living for older, disadvantaged or vulnerable members of society.

WHAT IS NOT FUNDED Scholarships; event sponsorship; new business start-up funding; carbon offset schemes; requests from other charitable foundations.

TYPE OF GRANT Usually one-off; occasionally unrestricted; multi-year.

RANGE OF GRANTS Mostly up to £30,000.

SAMPLE GRANTS The Trussell Trust (£50,000); Dress for Success (£30,000); Ipswich Hospital Charitable Fund (£20,800); Age UK (£10,000); Sightsavers (£5,000); Autism East Midlands (£4,500); Whale and Dolphin Conservation (£1,000); ABF The Soldiers' Charity (£500); CALM – Campaign Against Living Miserably (£10).

FINANCES *Financial year end* 05/04/2020 *Income* £431,500 *Total grants* £457,200 *Grants to organisations* £457,200 *Assets* £7,520,000

TRUSTEES Rory Barker; Amanda Brown; Craig Martindale; Frances Loring; Lee Turner; Robert Childs; Nick Orton.

OTHER INFORMATION Grants were awarded to 79 charities during 2019/20.

HOW TO APPLY Applications can be made at any time using the foundation's online application form. Unsolicited applications are not accepted for multi-year grants.

CONTACT DETAILS The Trustees, Hiscox Underwriting Ltd, 1 Great St Helen's, London EC3A 6HX *Tel.* 020 7614 5299 *Email* hiscox.foundation@hiscox.com *Website* https://www.hiscoxgroup.com/hiscox-foundation-uk

■ Historic Environment Scotland

OSCR NO SC045925 **ESTABLISHED** 2015

WHERE FUNDING CAN BE GIVEN Scotland.

WHO CAN BENEFIT Individuals and organisations.

WHAT IS FUNDED The protection and promotion of the historic environment.

TYPE OF GRANT Project funding; capital costs.

SAMPLE GRANTS East Ayrshire Council (£1.12 million); Glasgow Life (£500,000); Archaeology Scotland (£30,000); Society of Antiquaries of Scotland (£3,000); Leadhills Heritage (£530).

FINANCES *Financial year end* 31/03/2020 *Income* £95,540,000 *Total grants* £13,190,000 *Grants to organisations* £13,190,000 *Assets* £12,580,000

HOW TO APPLY Apply via the charity's website. Applicants are required to submit a brief expression of interest form before making an application.

CONTACT DETAILS Grants Team, Longmore House, Salisbury Place, Edinburgh EH9 1SH *Tel.* 0131 668 8600 *Email* grants@hes.scot *Website* https://www.historicenvironment.scot

■ Historic Houses Foundation

CC NO 1111049 **ESTABLISHED** 2005

WHERE FUNDING CAN BE GIVEN England and Wales.

WHO CAN BENEFIT Organisations; building preservation trusts; private owners.

WHAT IS FUNDED The repair and conservation of rural historic buildings and structures including, where appropriate, their gardens grounds and outbuildings; the conservation, maintenance and restoration of works of art and objects of outstanding artistic, scientific or historic interest.

WHAT IS NOT FUNDED A detailed list of exclusions can be found on the foundation's website.

TYPE OF GRANT Capital costs; project funding.

RANGE OF GRANTS Up to £70,000.

SAMPLE GRANTS Highcliffe Castle (£70,000); Cobham Dairy (£50,000); Abercamlais Bridge (£30,000); Stonor Park (£24,000); Tickenham Court (£15,000); Gwydir Castle (£8,400); Sulgrave Manor (£6,000); Leighton Hall (£910).

FINANCES *Financial year end* 30/06/2020 *Income* £325,900 *Total grants* £696,800 *Grants to organisations* £696,800 *Assets* £11,420,000

TRUSTEES Nicholas Barber; Norman Hudson; Sir Andrew Jardine; Mary King; Jeremy Musson; Sir John Parsons; Oliver Pearcey; Richard Compton.

OTHER INFORMATION The Historic Houses Foundation was formerly known as The Country Houses Foundation. The foundation's website includes comprehensive case studies of previous grant-making projects.

HOW TO APPLY The foundation requires applicants to complete a pre-application form to confirm that projects fit its criteria. Pre-application forms and application forms can be downloaded from the foundation's website.

CONTACT DETAILS David Price, Secretary, Sheephouse Farm, Uley Road, Dursley, Gloucestershire GL11 5AD *Tel.* 01453 547124 *Email* info@historichousesfoundation.org.uk *Website* https://www.historichousesfoundation.org.uk

■ The Henry C. Hoare Charitable Trust

CC NO 1088669 **ESTABLISHED** 2001

WHERE FUNDING CAN BE GIVEN UK.

WHO CAN BENEFIT Registered charities.

WHAT IS FUNDED General charitable purposes, including: the environment; health; education; citizenship and community development; animal welfare; relief in need (young and older people, disability, ill health); religion; public policy; and arts, culture, heritage or science.

RANGE OF GRANTS Mostly up to £25,000.

SAMPLE GRANTS Wiltshire Wildlife Trust (£35,000); University of Cambridge and Wincanton Community Venture (£25,000 each); Royal Forestry Society (£20,000); March Foundation (£15,000); Future Trees Trust and Mindful Initiative (£10,000 each).

FINANCES *Financial year end* 30/09/2019 *Income* £189,800 *Total grants* £451,300 *Grants to organisations* £451,300 *Assets* £5,360,000

TRUSTEES Henry Hoare; Hoare Trustees.

OTHER INFORMATION The 2018/19 accounts were the most recent available from the Charity Commission at the time of writing (May 2021). Grants were made for the following purposes: environmental protection or improvement (£161,000); citizenship/community development (£73,000); education (£70,000); health and saving lives (£66,500); relief of those in need (£32,500); animal welfare (£29,800); religion (£15,500); arts, culture, heritage or science (£3,000). Only beneficiaries of grants of £10,000 and above were listed in the accounts.

HOW TO APPLY The annual report for 2018/19 states that the trustees 'seldom grant funds to unsolicited requests for donations'.

CONTACT DETAILS Hoare Trustees, c/o C. Hoare and Co., 37 Fleet Street, London EC4P 4DQ *Tel.* 020 7353 4522

■ The Hobson Charity Ltd

CC NO 326839 **ESTABLISHED** 1985

WHERE FUNDING CAN BE GIVEN UK.

WHO CAN BENEFIT Registered charities; educational organisations; cultural organisations; churches; hospices.

WHAT IS FUNDED A wide range of charitable purposes, including: social welfare; education; health; religious activities; the relief of poverty; the armed forces; arts, culture and heritage; animal welfare; the environment and conservation; community causes.

WHAT IS NOT FUNDED Unless there are exceptional circumstances, the charity will not support salaries, core costs or multi-year grants.

TYPE OF GRANT Project funding.

RANGE OF GRANTS No minimum or maximum, mostly up to £20,000.

SAMPLE GRANTS University College London Glioma Research Group (£150,000); Normandy Memorial Trust (£25,000); St Andrew's Church – Totteridge (£20,000); Helen Arkell Dyslexia Centre (£6,500); Reading Association for the Blind (£5,000); Suffolk Own Sanctuary (£2,000); London Wheelchair Rugby Club

(£1,500); Hurting to Healing (£750); Elim Life Church Kingstanding (£500).

FINANCES *Financial year end* 31/03/2020 *Income* £955,400 *Total grants* £313,000 *Grants to organisations* £313,000 *Assets* £39,480,000

TRUSTEES Deborah Hobson; Lady Patricia Hobson; Jennifer Richardson; Elizabeth Kelsall; Emma Richardson.

OTHER INFORMATION Grants were made to 160 organisations in 2019/20.

HOW TO APPLY Applicants should first read the eligibility criteria and guidance on the charity's website. Applications may then be made using the online application form.

CONTACT DETAILS The Trustees, PO Box No. 57691, London NW7 0GR *Tel.* 020 3880 6425 *Email* post@hobsoncharity.org.uk or use the contact form on the website. *Website* https://hobsoncharity.org.uk

Hockerill Educational Foundation

CC NO 311018 **ESTABLISHED** 1977

WHERE FUNDING CAN BE GIVEN UK and overseas, with a preference for the dioceses of Chelmsford and St Albans.

WHO CAN BENEFIT Registered charities; religious bodies/organisations; individuals; corporate bodies.

WHAT IS FUNDED Education and training; Christianity.

WHAT IS NOT FUNDED General appeals for funds; 'bricks and mortar' building projects; purposes that are the clear responsibility of another body.

TYPE OF GRANT Seed funding/start-up funding; research; project funding.

RANGE OF GRANTS Up to £50,000.

SAMPLE GRANTS Culham St Gabriel's 3forRE Scheme (£8,500); Rose Castle Foundation (£6,900); NATRE New2RE Scheme (£6,000); Faith in Schools and The Archbishop of York's Youth Trust (£5,000 each); St Albans Cathedral Education Trust and Sutton School Work Trust (£3,000 each); ACCT (£600).

FINANCES *Financial year end* 31/03/2020 *Income* £354,600 *Total grants* £314,900 *Grants to organisations* £270,000 *Assets* £6,560,000

TRUSTEES The Ven. Janet Mackenzie; Janet Scott; David Morton; Jonathan Longstaff; Raymond Slade; Tim Elbourne; Hannah Potter; The Ven Robin King; Colin Bird; Anthea Kenna; Revd Dr Alan Smith.

OTHER INFORMATION Grants were distributed as follows: Diocese of Chelmsford (£110,000); Diocese of St Albans (£110,000); corporate grants (£50,000).

HOW TO APPLY Application forms and further information are available on the foundation's website.

CONTACT DETAILS The Trustees, 3 The Swallows, Harlow, Essex CM17 0AR *Tel.* 01279 420855 *Email* info@hockerillfoundation.org.uk *Website* www.hockerillfoundation.org.uk

The Jane Hodge Foundation

CC NO 216053 **ESTABLISHED** 1962

WHERE FUNDING CAN BE GIVEN UK, with a preference for Wales; overseas.

WHO CAN BENEFIT Charitable organisations; hospices; educational organisations; churches.

WHAT IS FUNDED Medical care and research, in particular local hospices, children's care and research in the fields of cancer and mental health; education, including the arts and those with special educational needs; welfare, in particular supporting those who are disadvantaged; religion, in particular facilities in church buildings and inclusive activities for the community.

TYPE OF GRANT Research; project funding.

RANGE OF GRANTS Usually under £200,000.

SAMPLE GRANTS St Fagans National Museum of History (£200,000); Cardiff University (£158,200); Royal Welsh College of Music and Drama (£135,000); Welsh National Opera – Youth and Communities Programme (£100,000); Swansea University (£91,400); Arts & Business Cymru (£65,000); Huggard (£36,100).

FINANCES *Financial year end* 30/09/2020 *Income* £723,400 *Total grants* £1,080,000 *Grants to organisations* £1,080,000 *Assets* £40,970,000

TRUSTEES Ian Davies; Jonathan Hodge; Karen Hodge; Helen Molyneux.

OTHER INFORMATION In 2019/20, 54 grants were awarded to organisations in the following areas: medical research (£130,100); care and welfare (£119,000); education (£22,000); other (£2,500).

HOW TO APPLY Apply in writing via email. Full details of what should be included can be found on the foundation's website. Applications are not accepted by post.

CONTACT DETAILS The Foundation Administrator, One Central Square, Cardiff CF10 1FS *Tel.* 029 2078 7674 *Email* contact@hodgefoundation.org.uk *Website* www.hodgefoundation.org.uk

The Holbeck Charitable Trust

CC NO 1146205 **ESTABLISHED** 2006

WHERE FUNDING CAN BE GIVEN Worldwide, with a preference for London and Yorkshire.

WHO CAN BENEFIT Registered charities; charitable organisations; community and voluntary organisations; excepted charities and exempt charities; individuals.

WHAT IS FUNDED General charitable purposes, including: medical research; education, including scholarships; Christian causes; people in need; sports and recreation; relief for those affected by natural disasters; unemployment; buildings of historical importance; the arts.

WHAT IS NOT FUNDED See the website for a full list of exclusions.

TYPE OF GRANT Project costs; core funding; salaries; one-off grants to be delivered over one to three years; scholarships; research.

RANGE OF GRANTS Up to £120,000. Unsolicited applications usually receive between £500 and £5,000.

SAMPLE GRANTS Cardinal Hume Centre; Helmsley Arts Centre; National Railway Museum; The Poppy Factory Ryedale Festival Trust Ltd; Tommy's; Wilberforce Trust; Yorkshire Ballet Seminars Charitable Trust.

FINANCES *Financial year end* 05/04/2020 *Income* £110,000 *Total grants* £351,000 *Grants to organisations* £314,000 *Assets* £1,740,000

TRUSTEES Gordon Horsfield; Joshua Horsfield; Victoria Denman; Camilla Seligman; John Lane; Francesca Horsfield.

OTHER INFORMATION From 300 grant applications, 51 grants awarded were awarded during 2019/20. Grants were distributed as follows: relief to deprived areas (£115,000); education (£97,000); medical research and palliative care

(£44,000); public amenities/recreation facilities (£37,000); young people, excluding education (£21,000). Grants to individuals totalled £37,000.

HOW TO APPLY Applications should be made through the online portal available from the trust's website. In addition, a hard copy of the completed grant application form must also be signed and returned via post together with a short covering letter to the correspondent. Applications cannot be considered until the signed hard copy has been received. The trustees meet four times a year to consider applications, usually in March, June, September and December. Visit the website for further information. At the time of writing (April 2021) the trust has temporarily stopped accepting new applications to give priority to charities with existing relations during the COVID-19 pandemic. Check the website for further updates.

CONTACT DETAILS Gerry Morrison, Secretary, c/o Rollits LLP, Forsyth House, Alpha Court, Monks Cross, York, North Yorkshire YO32 9WN *Tel.* 01904 688500 *Email* gerry.morrison@rollits.com *Website* https://www.holbecktrust.com

■ The Holden Charitable Trust

CC NO 264185 **ESTABLISHED** 1972

WHERE FUNDING CAN BE GIVEN UK.

WHO CAN BENEFIT Charitable organisations, primarily within the Jewish community.

WHAT IS FUNDED Orthodox Jewish education; the advancement of the Orthodox Jewish religion; the relief of poverty.

RANGE OF GRANTS £2,000 to £43,000.

SAMPLE GRANTS Ohel Bnei Yaakov (£102,000); British Friends of Mercaz Hatorah (£43,000); TTT (£20,700); BJOF (£10,000); Sosson VeSimcha CT (£6,000); SOFT (£2,500).

FINANCES *Financial year end* 05/04/2020 *Income* £464,400 *Total grants* £392,300 *Grants to organisations* £392,300 *Assets* £638,500

TRUSTEES Michael Lopian; Daniel Lopian.

HOW TO APPLY Contact the correspondent for further information.

CONTACT DETAILS The Trustees, 1st Floor, Cloister House, Riverside, New Bailey Street, Manchester M3 5FS *Tel.* 0161 832 8721 *Email* david.lopian@lopiangb.co.uk

■ Hollick Family Foundation

CC NO 1060228 **ESTABLISHED** 1997

WHERE FUNDING CAN BE GIVEN No specific restrictions, although a preference exists for Kensington and Chelsea, Camden, East Sussex and Kent.

WHO CAN BENEFIT Registered small and medium-sized charities; community-led organisations.

WHAT IS FUNDED General charitable purposes including education and training; human rights; housing; mental health; women; young people; the arts.

TYPE OF GRANT Seed funding; one-off grants; long-term project funding.

RANGE OF GRANTS £1,000 to £15,000.

SAMPLE GRANTS A list of beneficiaries was not included in the annual report and accounts.

FINANCES *Financial year end* 05/04/2020 *Income* £5,260,000 *Total grants* £366,800 *Grants to organisations* £366,800 *Assets* £21,740,000

TRUSTEES Caroline Kemp; The Hon. Georgina Hollick; David Beech; The Hon. Abigail Benoliel; Lady Sue Woodford-Hollick; Lord Clive Hollick.

HOW TO APPLY Apply in writing to the correspondent. The trustees meet at least twice a year.

CONTACT DETAILS David Beech, Trustee, Prager Metis LLP, 5A Bear Lane, Southwark, London SE1 0UH *Tel.* 020 7632 1400 *Email* dbeech@pragermetis.com

■ The Holliday Foundation

CC NO 1089931 **ESTABLISHED** 2001

WHERE FUNDING CAN BE GIVEN Worldwide.

WHO CAN BENEFIT Charitable organisations; individuals.

WHAT IS FUNDED General charitable purposes, with particular interest in: enabling children and young people to better themselves; the arts.

TYPE OF GRANT Apprenticeships; bursaries; grants.

RANGE OF GRANTS Mostly £5,000 to £20,000.

SAMPLE GRANTS Previous beneficiaries have included: Grange Park Opera (£100,000); Syria Relief (£20,000); Children in Crisis (£15,000); East Coast Sail Trust, Electric Umbrella and Sparkes Home Sri Lanka (£10,000 each); Protect Animals Greece (£5,000).

FINANCES *Financial year end* 31/03/2020 *Income* £24,400 *Total grants* £87,500 *Grants to organisations* £87,500

TRUSTEES David Garrett; James Cave; Antony Wilson; Jane Garrett; Huw Llewellyn; Ashley Hurst; Tom Braiden.

OTHER INFORMATION Full accounts were not available to view on the Charity Commission's website due to the foundation's low income. We have therefore estimated the grant total based on the foundation's total expenditure.

HOW TO APPLY Contact the correspondent for information regarding the application process. The trustees normally meet at least four times a year and may visit applicants before deciding whether to make a payment.

CONTACT DETAILS Linda Wasfi, c/o Alvarium Investment Ltd, 10 Old Burlington Street, London W1S 3AG *Tel.* 020 7195 1400 *Email* linda.wasfi@alvariuminvestments.com

■ Dorothy Holmes Charitable Trust

CC NO 237213 **ESTABLISHED** 1964

WHERE FUNDING CAN BE GIVEN UK, with a preference for Dorset.

WHO CAN BENEFIT UK-registered charities, especially smaller organisations.

WHAT IS FUNDED General charitable purposes.

SAMPLE GRANTS A list of beneficiaries was not included in the annual report and accounts.

FINANCES *Financial year end* 05/04/2020 *Income* £5,100 *Total grants* £55,000 *Grants to organisations* £55,000

TRUSTEES Dr Susan Roberts; Margaret Cody; James Roberts.

OTHER INFORMATION Full accounts were not available to view on the Charity Commission's website due to the trust's low income. We have therefore estimated the grant total based on the trust's total expenditure.

HOW TO APPLY Contact the correspondent for further information.

CONTACT DETAILS Margaret Cody, Trustee, 5A Bear Lane, Southwark, London SE1 0UH *Tel.* 020 7632 1400 *Email* mcody@pragermetis.com

■ P. H. Holt Foundation

CC NO 1113708 **ESTABLISHED** 1955

WHERE FUNDING CAN BE GIVEN Merseyside.

WHO CAN BENEFIT Registered charities; universities.

WHAT IS FUNDED General charitable purposes in Merseyside, including: community development; social welfare; education; the arts; the environment.

WHAT IS NOT FUNDED CICs, social enterprises, or commercial endeavours; national charities and charities outside Merseyside; organisations enjoying high-profile support; activities of a statutory nature; work that has already taken place; umbrella charities that do not deliver direct services; grants to individuals and certain uniformed groups; scientific and medical research; one-off holidays, trips, sponsorship of individuals or events; religious and political causes; general charity appeals or mailshots.

TYPE OF GRANT Capital costs; seed/start-up funding; project funding.

RANGE OF GRANTS Typically between £5,000 and £10,000.

SAMPLE GRANTS Liverpool Hope University (£20,000); Deafness Resource Centre (£10,000); Brunswick Youth and Community Centre (£8,400); Granby 4 Streets (£5,000); Toxteth Women's Centre (£3,000); 20 Stories High (£1,900).

FINANCES *Financial year end* 31/03/2020 *Income* £296,000 *Total grants* £448,200 *Grants to organisations* £448,200 *Assets* £19,280,000

TRUSTEES Ian Bakewell; Elspeth Christie; Ann Crotty; Chris Evered; Mike Furniss; Amy de Joia; Ian Matthews; Lesley Martin-Wright; Ken Ravenscroft.

OTHER INFORMATION Grants were broken down as follows: community and overcoming barriers (£328,000); access to education (£65,000); engagement in the arts (£55,200).

HOW TO APPLY Application forms can be accessed on the foundation's helpful website and should be returned by email together with a copy of your latest annual report and accounts.

CONTACT DETAILS Anne Edwards, Trust Administrator, 151 Dale Street, Liverpool, Merseyside L2 2AH *Tel.* 0151 237 2663 *Email* administrator@phholtfoundation.org.uk *Website* www.phholtfoundation.org.uk

■ The Holywood Trust

OSCR NO SC009942 **ESTABLISHED** 1981

WHERE FUNDING CAN BE GIVEN Dumfries and Galloway.

WHO CAN BENEFIT Individuals; constituted charitable organisations which work with young people; voluntary organisations; statutory bodies; groups of young people within a constituted organisation.

WHAT IS FUNDED Young people, primarily those aged 15 to 25; personal development; sports; the arts; group development activities; education; health; social welfare; residential activities.

TYPE OF GRANT One-off; capital and core costs; recurring funding; salaries; project costs.

RANGE OF GRANTS Up to £100,000.

SAMPLE GRANTS Kirkcudbright Development Trust (£152,500); Aberlour Child Care Trust (£92,500); The Stove Network (£50,600); Independent Living Support (£35,000); Dumfries Table Tennis Club (£25,000); Lochside Community Association (£17,000); Chariots of Fire Equestrian Centre (£15,000); Step Forward Volunteering (£12,300); Lockerbie Academy (£10,000).

FINANCES *Financial year end* 05/04/2020 *Income* £3,190,000 *Total grants* £2,570,200 *Grants to organisations* £2,410,000 *Assets* £96,990,000

TRUSTEES Valerie McElroy; John Jencks; Ben Weatherall; Amy Agnew; Clara Weatherall.

OTHER INFORMATION During 2019/20, 166 grant awards were made to organisations from 182 applications. Grants of under £10,000 totalled £385,600.

HOW TO APPLY Applications can be made using a form available from the trust's website (criteria and guidelines can also be found here). The trustees meet quarterly to discuss applications for over £2,500; deadline dates are set prior to each meeting and advertised on the trust's website. Applications for under £2,500 or less than this amount can be submitted any time and should be processed within four to six weeks. There is no minimum or maximum amount for applicants to request. Organisations may submit their applications electronically but the trustees also require a hard signed copy with all documents before the application form can be processed.

CONTACT DETAILS Clare Hanna, Grants Officer, Hestan House, Crichton Business Park, Bankend Road, Dumfries, Dumfries and Galloway DG1 4TA *Tel.* 01387 269176 *Email* funds@holywood-trust.org.uk *Website* www.holywood-trust.org.uk

■ Homelands Charitable Trust

CC NO 214322 **ESTABLISHED** 1962

WHERE FUNDING CAN BE GIVEN UK.

WHO CAN BENEFIT Registered charities; hospices.

WHAT IS FUNDED General charitable purposes; the General Conference of the New Church; medical research; care and protection of children; hospices.

RANGE OF GRANTS Mostly £1,000 to £3,000.

SAMPLE GRANTS Previous beneficiaries have included: Anorexia and Bulimia Care, Benslow Music Trust, Broadfield Memorial Fund, Edinburgh Young Carers Project, Friends of the Earth, General Conference of New Church, Riding for the Disabled, RNLI, Sailors' Families Society, SOS Children's Villages, St Luke's Hospice and Womankind Worldwide.

FINANCES *Financial year end* 05/04/2020 *Income* £317,200 *Total grants* £321,000 *Grants to organisations* £321,000 *Assets* £7,930,000

TRUSTEES Nigel Armstrong; Revd Clifford Curry; Robert Curry; Eleanor Maquire.

OTHER INFORMATION During 2019/20, grants were distributed as follows: other charities (£110,500); church (£110,000); care and protection of children (£58,000); medical causes (£24,000) hospices (£18,500). A list of beneficiaries was not included in the annual report and accounts.

HOW TO APPLY Contact the correspondent for further information.

CONTACT DETAILS Nigel Armstrong, Trustee, 4th Floor, Imperial House, 8 Kean Street, London WC2B 4AS *Tel.* 020 7240 9971

The Mary Homfray Charitable Trust

CC NO 273564 **ESTABLISHED** 1977

WHERE FUNDING CAN BE GIVEN UK, with priority given to Wales.

WHO CAN BENEFIT Registered charities.

WHAT IS FUNDED General charitable purposes.

RANGE OF GRANTS £1,000 to £5,000.

SAMPLE GRANTS Barnardo's (£10,000); Royal Veterinary College (£5,000); Amelia Trust (£4,000); Leonard Cheshire Disability (£3,000); Duke of Edinburgh Award in Wales and Whizz-Kidz (£2,000 each); Danger Point (£1,000).

FINANCES *Financial year end* 05/04/2020
Income £163,700 *Total grants* £142,000
Grants to organisations £142,000
Assets £3,550,000

TRUSTEES Matthew Homfray; Mary Homfray; Josephine Homfray; Dr Tessa Pemberton.

HOW TO APPLY Applications should only be made via the online application form on the trust's website. Applications are considered at the trustees' annual meeting in spring.

CONTACT DETAILS The Trustees, c/o Deloitte PCS Ltd, 5 Callaghan Square, Cardiff CF10 5BT
Email apply@maryhomfrayct.org
Website https://www.maryhomfrayct.org

Sir Harold Hood's Charitable Trust

CC NO 225870 **ESTABLISHED** 1962

WHERE FUNDING CAN BE GIVEN Worldwide.

WHO CAN BENEFIT Roman Catholic registered charities and churches.

WHAT IS FUNDED Roman Catholic charitable purposes.

RANGE OF GRANTS Grants range from £500 up to £55,000.

SAMPLE GRANTS Craig Lodge Trust (£55,000); St Richard Reynolds Catholic College (£45,000); Diocese of Nottingham (£28,0000; Duchess of Leeds Foundation (£25,000); Diocese of Brentwood (£10,000); Oratory School, Reading (£5,000); Little Sisters of the Poor – Leeds (£500).

FINANCES *Financial year end* 05/04/2020
Income £816,700 *Total grants* £780,000
Grants to organisations £780,000
Assets £31,210,000

TRUSTEES Dom Hood; Lord True; Lady True; Margaret Hood; Christian Elwes.

HOW TO APPLY Contact the correspondent for further information.

CONTACT DETAILS The Trustees, c/o haysmacintyre, 10 Queens Street Place, London EC4R 1AG
Tel. 020 7969 5500
Email hoodcharitabletrust@yahoo.co.uk

Hope Trust

OSCR NO SC000987 **ESTABLISHED** 1912

WHERE FUNDING CAN BE GIVEN Worldwide, with a preference for Scotland.

WHO CAN BENEFIT Christian individuals and organisations; charitable organisations; individuals.

WHAT IS FUNDED The trust supports projects that promote temperance and the reformed tradition as well as those that work with people affected by substance abuse.

RANGE OF GRANTS Mostly £3,000 to £3,500.

SAMPLE GRANTS Postdoctoral Fellowship (£27,400); Aberdeen Centre for Protestant Theology (£3,600); Borderline, Edinburgh Young Carers, Fresh Start, Salvation Army, Scottish Alcohol Counselling and Street Connection (£3,500 each); Edinburgh Theological Seminary and John Hope Scholarship (£3,000 each).

FINANCES *Financial year end* 31/12/2019
Income £297,900 *Total grants* £234,700
Grants to organisations £234,700
Assets £7,430,000

OTHER INFORMATION Grants were made to both organisations and individuals.

HOW TO APPLY Contact the correspondent for further information.

CONTACT DETAILS The Trustees, Glenorchy House, 20 Union Street, Edinburgh EH1 3LR

The Thomas J. Horne Memorial Trust

CC NO 1010625 **ESTABLISHED** 1992

WHERE FUNDING CAN BE GIVEN UK and overseas.

WHO CAN BENEFIT Charitable organisations; hospices.

WHAT IS FUNDED Hospices, particularly children's hospices and related charities; disability; health; homelessness; self-help groups in financially developing countries.

RANGE OF GRANTS Mostly £5,000 to £10,000.

SAMPLE GRANTS World Medical Fund (£20,000); Ellenor (£10,000); Alzheimer's Society (£8,500); The Sick Children's Trust (£8,000); Corby and District Cancer Care (£7,500); St Barnabas Hospice Trust and The Smile Train UK (£6,000 each); Whitby Dog Rescue (£1,000).

FINANCES *Financial year end* 31/03/2020
Income £418,700 *Total grants* £817,500
Grants to organisations £817,500
Assets £19,660,000

TRUSTEES Jeff Horne; Jon Horne; Emma Horne.

OTHER INFORMATION During 2019/20 grants were awarded to 118 organisations.

HOW TO APPLY Our previous research indicates that unsolicited applications are not accepted; however, the trust's 2019 annual report states: 'Grant-making decisions are made at the trustees' meetings when applications received from charities will be discussed with a view to acceptance.'

CONTACT DETAILS The Trustees, Kingsdown, Warmlake Road, Chart Sutton, Maidstone, Kent ME17 3RP *Tel.* 01622 842638 *Email* cc@horne-trust.org.uk

The Horners Charity Fund

CC NO 292204 **ESTABLISHED** 1929

WHERE FUNDING CAN BE GIVEN London.

WHO CAN BENEFIT Registered charities; individuals; educational establishments.

WHAT IS FUNDED General charitable purposes; education; education related to the plastics industry; scholarships and bursaries; health.

RANGE OF GRANTS Up to £30,000.

SAMPLE GRANTS SANDS (£25,000); Design in Plastic (£12,000); Careers Advice (£10,100); British Science Association (£8,500); Blind in Business and Honeypot (£5,000 each); The Children's Literacy Charity (£2,500); Fantastic Plastic and Plastiquarian (£1,000 each).

FINANCES *Financial year end* 31/12/2019
Income £156,400 *Total grants* £154,100
Grants to organisations £123,100
Assets £3,620,000

TRUSTEES Gordon Haines; John MacCabe; David Spofforth; Michael Birrell; Dr Helen Davies; Colin Freedman; Dr David Giachardi; Hugh Moss; Martin Muirhead; David Chitty.

OTHER INFORMATION During 2019 the charity awarded £123,100 in grants to organisations. Grants were distributed as follows: general (£66,200); educational (£57,000). A further £29,600 was awarded to individuals for scholarships. Awards of up to £1,000 totalled £2,000.

HOW TO APPLY Contact the correspondent for further information.

CONTACT DETAILS R. Joyce, Clerk to the Trustees, 7 Seaton Road, Wigston, Leicestershire LE18 2BY *Tel.* 0116 288 0226 *Website* www.horners.org.uk

■ The Horse Trust

CC NO 231748 **ESTABLISHED** 1886

WHERE FUNDING CAN BE GIVEN UK.

WHO CAN BENEFIT UK veterinary schools; other universities.

WHAT IS FUNDED Horses' health and welfare.

TYPE OF GRANT Research grants; PhD and postgraduate studentships; pump-priming projects.

RANGE OF GRANTS Up to £126,000.

SAMPLE GRANTS University of Liverpool (£126,100); Moredun Research (£111,700); University of Edinburgh (£47,100); University of Bristol (£36,200); Roslin Institute (£35,300); Royal Veterinary College (£17,000); University of Glasgow (£9,600); Hartpury (£6,000).

FINANCES *Financial year end* 31/12/2019 *Income* £2,590,000 *Total grants* £417,000 *Grants to organisations* £417,000 *Assets* £26,650,000

TRUSTEES Prof. Josh Slater; Milly Soames; Rupert Neal; David Cook; Caroline Roddis; Bronwen Jones; Lord Rupert de Mauley; Prof. Peter Clegg; Dr Ian Bowen; Prof. Bruce McGorum; Christopher Marriott; Laura McGillycuddy.

HOW TO APPLY Preliminary applications can be made in October each year. Those who are successful will be invited to complete a full application. Further details can be found on the trust's website.

CONTACT DETAILS Jan Rogers, Director of Research and Policy, Speen Farm, Slad Lane, Speen, Princes Risborough, Buckinghamshire HP27 0PP *Tel.* 01494 488464 *Email* jan@horsetrust.org.uk *Website* https://www.horsetrust.org.uk

■ Horwich Shotter Charitable Trust

CC NO 1068651 **ESTABLISHED** 1998

WHERE FUNDING CAN BE GIVEN UK, with a preference for Greater Manchester.

WHO CAN BENEFIT Individuals and charitable organisations.

WHAT IS FUNDED Education and the advancement of the Jewish faith.

SAMPLE GRANTS A list of beneficiaries was not included in the annual report and accounts.

FINANCES *Financial year end* 30/11/2019 *Income* £25,100 *Total grants* £111,400 *Grants to organisations* £111,400 *Assets* £58,700

TRUSTEES Maurice Horwich; Howard Horwich; Jeffrey Horwich; Aharon Horwich.

OTHER INFORMATION The 2018/19 accounts were the latest available at the time of writing (April 2021).

HOW TO APPLY Contact the correspondent for further information.

CONTACT DETAILS The Trustees, 13 Singleton Road, Salford, Greater Manchester M7 4NN *Tel.* 0161 792 2441

■ Hospice UK

CC NO 1014851 **ESTABLISHED** 1984

WHERE FUNDING CAN BE GIVEN UK.

WHO CAN BENEFIT Hospices; other institutions related to hospices and hospice care; hospice staff.

WHAT IS FUNDED Support for hospices; projects that improve hospice care; hospice staff.

WHAT IS NOT FUNDED Exclusion criteria may vary according to the programme being applied to; see the grant-maker's website for further information.

TYPE OF GRANT Core costs; project funding; capital costs; development funding; bursaries.

RANGE OF GRANTS Up to £50,000, but programme dependent.

SAMPLE GRANTS Saint Michael's Hospice – Harrogate (£39,900); Nottinghamshire Hospice (£20,300); Princess Alice Hospice – Surrey (£20,000); Mary Stevens Hospice – Stourbridge (£14,900); St Elizabeth Hospice – Ipswich (£12,900); Great Oaks Dean Forest Hospice (£7,800).

FINANCES *Financial year end* 31/03/2020 *Income* £6,380,000 *Total grants* £1,220,000 *Grants to organisations* £1,220,000 *Assets* £6,350,000

TRUSTEES Emma Reynolds; Michelle Rollinson; Anthony Collins; Paul Jennings; David Smith; Catherine Tompkins; John Knight; Dr Michael Miller; Sonia Rees; Stephen Roberts.

OTHER INFORMATION Grants were awarded to 311 organisations during the year and were distributed as follows: grants to support family carers (£483,000); grants to develop bereavement services in hospices (£448,000); professional development grants (£172,000); grants to support regional capital projects (£44,000); other grant programmes (£43,000).

HOW TO APPLY Applications can be made via the grant-maker's website when the relevant programme is open for applications.

CONTACT DETAILS Grants Team, 34–44 Britannia Street, London WC1X 9JG *Tel.* 020 7520 8200 *Email* grants@hospiceuk.org *Website* www.hospiceuk.org

■ The Hospital of God at Greatham

CC NO 1123540 **ESTABLISHED** 2008

WHERE FUNDING CAN BE GIVEN Hartlepool, Stockton, Darlington, County Durham, Sunderland, Gateshead, South Tyneside, North Tyneside, Newcastle upon Tyne and Northumberland.

WHO CAN BENEFIT Charitable organisations; voluntary groups.

WHAT IS FUNDED Support for disadvantaged people in the following areas: asylum seekers; children; older people; victims of domestic violence and abuse; substance misuse; ex-offenders; homelessness; hospices; mental health; physical health; social welfare; community projects.

WHAT IS NOT FUNDED Capital works or money-raising appeals; statutory education and related travel or adventure projects; holidays (unless for personal or group development); national organisations (unless independently constituted and funded, delivering in the North East);

conferences and feasibility studies; medical equipment and related projects; general appeals.

TYPE OF GRANT Project funding.

RANGE OF GRANTS Up to £3,000.

SAMPLE GRANTS A list of beneficiaries was not included in the annual report and accounts.

FINANCES *Financial year end* 31/10/2019 *Income* £4,920,000 *Total grants* £99,200 *Grants to organisations* £99,200 *Assets* £43,930,000

TRUSTEES Philippa Sinclair; Rt Revd Mark Wroe; Lois Neal; Annette Nylund; Mike Taylerson; Margaret Bousfield; Col Chris Dickinson; Robert Eden.

OTHER INFORMATION The 2018/19 accounts were the latest available at the time of writing (June 2021). Grants totalling £99,200 were awarded to 71 organisations during the period. The charity also owns and manages 123 almshouses.

HOW TO APPLY Application forms can be completed online through the charity's website. Applications can be submitted twice a year to be considered by the Grants Committee. Visit the website for current deadlines.

CONTACT DETAILS Lawrence McAnelly, Director, The Estate Office, Greatham, Hartlepool, County Durham TS25 2HS *Tel.* 01429 870247 *Email* lawrence.mcanelly@hospitalofgod.org.uk *Website* www.hospitalofgod.org.uk

The Hospital Saturday Fund

CC NO 1123381 **ESTABLISHED** 1873

WHERE FUNDING CAN BE GIVEN UK and the Republic of Ireland.

WHO CAN BENEFIT Registered health charities; hospitals; hospices; clinics, medically-associated charities; welfare organisations providing health services; individuals. Organisations must be registered with the Charity Commission or the appropriate regional body (outside England and Wales).

WHAT IS FUNDED Medical causes; healthcare; research; specialist equipment, welfare needs; scholarships to individuals.

WHAT IS NOT FUNDED Unregistered organisations; organisations carrying out non-medically related activities; general fundraising appeals.

TYPE OF GRANT Medical capital projects; medical care; research; support of medical training; grants for running costs are also considered; awards are mainly one-off.

RANGE OF GRANTS Up to £10,000; mostly £2,000.

SAMPLE GRANTS Highland and Island Blood Bikes; Irish Guide Dogs; Leonard Cheshire; London Air Ambulance; The Meath Epilepsy Charity; Merchants Quay Ireland; Richard House; Teenage Cancer Trust; Wigan and Leigh Hospice.

FINANCES *Financial year end* 31/12/2019 *Income* £32,110,000 *Total grants* £1,545,800 *Grants to organisations* £1,440,000 *Assets* £30,540,000

TRUSTEES Paul Palmer; John Greenwood; Jane Dalton; John Randel; David Thomas; Mark Davies; Margaret Rogers.

OTHER INFORMATION During the year, 144 grants were awarded to individuals totalling £105,800. A further 434 grants were awarded to medical charities, hospices and hospitals including the special medical school grant. The vast majority of grants awarded were for £2,000. Grants of less than £2,000 were made to 49 organisations and 127 grants were awarded ranging from £2,000 to £10,000.

HOW TO APPLY Applications should be made using the online system on the charity's website (the charity does not accept paper applications). Additional documents to support your application may be emailed to the correspondent. The Grants Committee meets quarterly. Submission dates can be found on the website; these vary depending on the size of grant.

CONTACT DETAILS Dee Wright, Charity Co-ordinator, 24 Upper Ground, London SE1 9PD *Tel.* 020 7207 1334 *Email* charity@hsf.eu.com *Website* www.hospitalsaturdayfund.org

The Sir Joseph Hotung Charitable Settlement

CC NO 1082710 **ESTABLISHED** 2000

WHERE FUNDING CAN BE GIVEN Worldwide.

WHO CAN BENEFIT Charitable organisations.

WHAT IS FUNDED Medical causes; education; human rights.

SAMPLE GRANTS St George's University of London (£314,900); CARA (Council for At-Risk Academics) (£180,000 in two grants); Chatham House (£45,000 in two grants); Hong Kong Watch (£30,000 in two grants); Spinal Research (£1,200 in 12 grants).

FINANCES *Financial year end* 05/04/2020 *Income* £1,590,000 *Total grants* £571,000 *Grants to organisations* £571,000 *Assets* £2,760,000

TRUSTEES Sir Joseph Hotung; Prof. Sir Robert Boyd; Peter Painton; Prof. Dame Jessica Rawson.

OTHER INFORMATION In 2019/20, five organisations were supported.

HOW TO APPLY Contact the correspondent for further information.

CONTACT DETAILS Peter Painton, Trustee, c/o Penningtons Manches Cooper LLP, 125 Wood Street, London EC2V 7AW *Email* henry.painton@blueyonder.co.uk

House of Industry Estate

CC NO 257079 **ESTABLISHED** 1988

WHERE FUNDING CAN BE GIVEN Borough of Bedford.

WHO CAN BENEFIT Charitable organisations.

WHAT IS FUNDED Social welfare.

WHAT IS NOT FUNDED Capital expenditure cannot involve works to land or property.

TYPE OF GRANT Capital costs; project funding; core costs.

RANGE OF GRANTS Up to £25,000.

SAMPLE GRANTS Previous beneficiaries have included: Bedford Community Rights; Bedfordshire Garden Carers; Bedford Pilgrims Housing Association; Kempston Summer School; and King's Arms Project.

FINANCES *Financial year end* 31/03/2019 *Income* £246,400 *Total grants* £276,900 *Grants to organisations* £276,900 *Assets* £5,230,000

TRUSTEES Cllr Tim Hill; Cllr Stephen Moon; Cllr Tom Wooton; Cllr Michael Headley; Cllr Colleen Atkins; Cllr Louise Jackson; Cllr Christine McHugh.

OTHER INFORMATION The 2018/19 accounts were the latest available at the time of writing (January 2021).

HOW TO APPLY Application forms can be found on the grant-maker's website and should be submitted via email. Guidelines for grants may vary depending on what the grant is awarded for; for a full list of guidelines, see the guidelines document on the grant-maker's website. The trustees will particularly welcome applications where an award will enable the applicant to leverage additional grant funding from other grant-making bodies (e.g. matched funding).

CONTACT DETAILS Lee Phanco, Chief Officer for Customer Experience and Digital Services, Bedford Borough Council, Borough Hall, Cauldwell Street, Bedford MK42 9AP *Tel.* 01234 267422 *Email* Community.Welfare@bedford.gov.uk *Website* https://www.bedford.gov.uk/benefits-and-support/advice-and-benefits-grants/grants-for-financial-assist

■ Housing Pathways Trust

CC NO 211053 **ESTABLISHED** 1962

WHERE FUNDING CAN BE GIVEN Ealing and Brentford.

WHO CAN BENEFIT Community groups and small charities; individuals; places of learning; churches.

WHAT IS FUNDED Social welfare; health; education; homelessness; isolation; domestic abuse; counselling and support services; people with disabilities; social cohesion.

WHAT IS NOT FUNDED Exclusion criteria may vary according to the programme being applied to. See the trust's website for further information.

TYPE OF GRANT Main grants programme: project funding; start-up funding; core costs; grants of up to three years; full cost recovery is supported. See the website for types of funding awarded by other current programmes.

RANGE OF GRANTS £250 to £10,000, but programme dependent.

SAMPLE GRANTS Ealing Mediation Services and Welshore (£15,000 each); Ealing Law (£18,000); Ealing Mencap (£10,000); Mindfood CIC (£8,300); Soundbite Festival (West Ealing Neighbours) (£5,000); Christ the Saviour – Ealing and St Paul's – Ealing (£2,000 each); George's Southall (£1,200).

FINANCES *Financial year end* 31/03/2020
Income £1,490,000 *Total grants* £94,300
Grants to organisations £94,300
Assets £12,560,000

TRUSTEE Housing Pathways.

OTHER INFORMATION The main grants programme is generally limited to small organisations defined as those with an annual income of less than £100,000. During the year, nine organisations were awarded grants through the main grants programme totalling £83,300 (some of the grants were multi-year). The ecclesiastical fund, administered by the Ealing Deanery Synod, awarded £15,100 to eight organisations. The trust also owns 134 almshouse units.

HOW TO APPLY Online application forms for the main grants programme are available on the trust's website. Other current programmes are also advertised on the website. For further information, contact the correspondent.

CONTACT DETAILS The Grants Officer, Housing Pathways, Unit 33, Dean Court, Bowmans Close, London W13 9YU *Tel.* 020 8579 7411 *Email* info@yourpathways.org.uk *Website* www.yourpathways.org.uk

■ The Reta Lila Howard Foundation

CC NO 1041634 **ESTABLISHED** 1994

WHERE FUNDING CAN BE GIVEN UK and the Republic of Ireland.

WHO CAN BENEFIT Registered charities.

WHAT IS FUNDED Education and extracurricular activities for children and young people under the age of 16.

WHAT IS NOT FUNDED Individuals; organisations which are not registered charities; core costs; (sole) capital projects; annual charitable appeals; general endowment funds; budget deficits; fundraising drives or events; conferences; student aid.

TYPE OF GRANT Short-term project funding.

RANGE OF GRANTS £10,000 to £100,000.

SAMPLE GRANTS Kids Run Free (£100,000); Action for Conservation (£60,000); Tree Council (£45,000): Sense about Science (£37,000); Camden Music Trust (£30,000); Walk Through the Bible UK (£26,000); YoungMinds (£20,000); Woodland Trust (£15,300); The Bike Project (£10,000); Rose Road (£7,300).

FINANCES *Financial year end* 31/03/2020
Income £52,700 *Total grants* £725,000
Grants to organisations £725,000
Assets £17,180,000

TRUSTEES Sarah Mitchell; Melissa Murdoch; Gregg Weston; Tamara Rebanks; Pilar Bauta; Galvin Weston.

OTHER INFORMATION During the year, 22 grants were awarded.

HOW TO APPLY The foundation has previously stated that it does not accept unsolicited applications as the trustees seek out and support projects they are interested in.

CONTACT DETAILS The Trustees, Horsmonden Business Centre, The Business Centre, Green Road, Horsmonden, Tonbridge, Kent TN12 8JS *Tel.* 07852 924412 *Email* retalilahoward@gmail.com

■ James T. Howat Charitable Trust

OSCR NO SC000201 **ESTABLISHED** 1989

WHERE FUNDING CAN BE GIVEN Primarily Glasgow, but support can also be given to Scottish and UK-wide organisations.

WHO CAN BENEFIT Charitable organisations including: universities; cultural bodies; organisations caring for people who are sick; local community organisations; social groups; individuals.

WHAT IS FUNDED General charitable purposes.

WHAT IS NOT FUNDED Medical electives; second or further qualifications; payment of school fees; costs incurred at tertiary educational establishments; religious organisations seeking to grow rather than compliment existing services.

TYPE OF GRANT Core costs; projects; research; running expenditure; start-up costs; educational support to individuals.

RANGE OF GRANTS Up to £10,000, but most grants are of £500.

SAMPLE GRANTS Epilepsy Association of Scotland (£2,000 in four grants); Abercorn School Fund (£750); Bliss Scotland; Borders Forest Trust, Contact and East Glasgow Music School (£500 each); Edinburgh Fringe Society (£250).

FINANCES *Financial year end* 05/04/2020
Income £232,800 *Total grants* £239,700
Grants to organisations £232,700
Assets £5,270,000

OTHER INFORMATION In 2019/20, grants were made to 15 individuals totalling £7,000.

HOW TO APPLY Applications may be made in writing to the correspondent and should include: a summary of your request (no longer than one side of A4) backed up as necessary with schedules, a copy of your latest accounts and/ or business plan, a breakdown of costs and financial needs (where possible), information on the effect the grant will have, details of other grants applied for or awarded, evidence that the project will help its beneficiaries and that they are involved in the decision-making. Applications should demonstrate potential impact. Unsuccessful applicants are not acknowledged due to the large number of applications received. The trustees meet to consider grants in March, June, September and December; applications should be received in the preceding month.

CONTACT DETAILS The Trustees, c/o Harper Macleod LLP, The Ca'd'oro, 45 Gordon Street, Glasgow G1 3PE

■ The Hudson Foundation

CC NO 280332 **ESTABLISHED** 1980

WHERE FUNDING CAN BE GIVEN Wisbech.

WHO CAN BENEFIT Charitable organisations.

WHAT IS FUNDED General charitable purposes; relief of people who are older or infirm; community development.

TYPE OF GRANT Capital projects; revenue expenditure.

SAMPLE GRANTS Alan Hudson Day Treatment Centre (£150,000); Gorefield Primary School (£20,000); Methodist Homes for the Aged (£12,700); Rural Cambridgeshire Citizens Advice (£5,800); Cambridgeshire Deaf Association and Kinderley Primary School (£2,500 each); Guide Dogs for the Blind and Wisbech Sea Cadets (£2,000 each).

FINANCES *Financial year end* 31/07/2019 *Income* £1,610,000 *Total grants* £197,500 *Grants to organisations* £197,500 *Assets* £2,670,000

TRUSTEES David Ball; Stephen Layton; Edward Newling; Stephen Hutchinson.

OTHER INFORMATION In 2018/19 eight grants were awarded. The 2018/19 accounts were the latest available at the time of writing (April 2021).

HOW TO APPLY Contact the correspondent for further information.

CONTACT DETAILS The Trustees, 1–3 York Row, Wisbech, Cambridgeshire PE13 1EA *Tel.* 01945 461456

■ The Huggard Charitable Trust

CC NO 327501 **ESTABLISHED** 1987

WHERE FUNDING CAN BE GIVEN UK, with a preference for South Wales.

WHO CAN BENEFIT Charitable organisations.

WHAT IS FUNDED Community support; homelessness; support for people who are disadvantaged, older, ill or who have disabilities.

WHAT IS NOT FUNDED Individuals.

TYPE OF GRANT Project funding.

SAMPLE GRANTS A list of beneficiaries was not included in the annual report and accounts.

FINANCES *Financial year end* 31/03/2020 *Income* £61,100 *Total grants* £93,700 *Grants to organisations* £93,700 *Assets* £2,610,000

TRUSTEES Anne Helme; Stephen Thomas; Anne Chiplen.

OTHER INFORMATION Grants were given to 93 organisations during the year.

HOW TO APPLY The trustees are not inviting applications for funds; they support a list of charities provided by their founder.

CONTACT DETAILS The Trustees, 25 Harvey Crescent, Aberavon, Port Talbot, Neath Port Talbot SA12 6DF *Tel.* 07926 190632

■ The Hull and East Riding Charitable Trust

CC NO 516866 **ESTABLISHED** 1985

WHERE FUNDING CAN BE GIVEN Hull and the East Riding of Yorkshire.

WHO CAN BENEFIT Charitable organisations; schools.

WHAT IS FUNDED General charitable purposes.

WHAT IS NOT FUNDED Education; political purposes; religious purposes (although requests for notable buildings with a good level of community use will be evaluated).

TYPE OF GRANT Project funding; capital costs; core costs.

RANGE OF GRANTS Generally up to £5,000.

SAMPLE GRANTS CASE (£10,000); Barnardo's (£5,000); Hull Women's Centre (£3,500); Amazing Grace Chapel (£3,000); British Disabled Angling Association (£2,000); Woodcraft Folk (£1,000); Kelvin Hall School (£500).

FINANCES *Financial year end* 05/04/2020 *Income* £212,200 *Total grants* £268,900 *Grants to organisations* £268,900 *Assets* £7,260,000

TRUSTEES Adrian Horsley; Matthew Fletcher; Victoria Carver.

OTHER INFORMATION The trust awarded 121 grants during the year to a range of organisations benefitting the residents of the East Riding of Yorkshire.

HOW TO APPLY Full details of information required and how to submit an application are available from the trust's website. The trustees meet twice a year – in early May and November. Appeals should be submitted by 20 April and 20 October, respectively.

CONTACT DETAILS John Barnes, Secretary, Greenmeades, Kemp Road, Swanland, East Yorkshire HU14 3LY *Tel.* 01482 634664 *Email* john.barnes@herct.org.uk *Website* www.herct.org.uk

■ The Humanitarian Trust

CC NO 208575 **ESTABLISHED** 1946

WHERE FUNDING CAN BE GIVEN UK and Israel.

WHO CAN BENEFIT Mostly Jewish charitable organisations; individuals (via studentships).

WHAT IS FUNDED General charitable purposes.

RANGE OF GRANTS £2,000 to £10,000.

SAMPLE GRANTS Holocaust Educational Trust (£15,000); Institute for Jewish Policy Research (£10,000); Birkbeck College (£9,000); Jerusalem Foundation (£7,500); Anne Frank Trust UK (£6,000); Leo Baeck Educational Centre (£5,000); Patterns of Prejudice (£3,000).

FINANCES *Financial year end* 05/04/2020 *Income* £240,200 *Total grants* £208,500 *Grants to organisations* £196,500 *Assets* £4,950,000

TRUSTEES Jacques Gunsbourg; Pierre Halban; Emmanuelle Kasavi; Alexander Halban.

OTHER INFORMATION Grants were awarded to 22 organisations in the following categories: academic and educational (£97,000, £12,000

of which was awarded to individuals through studentships); social service (£87,000); and medical and charitable (£12,500).

HOW TO APPLY The trust does not accept unsolicited applications from organisations, although the trustees may occasionally invite charities to submit applications for consideration at board meetings.

CONTACT DETAILS The Trustees, 20 Gloucester Place, London W1U 8HA *Tel.* 020 7486 7760 *Email* humanitariantrust@prismthegiftfund.co.uk *Website* www.humanitariantrust.co.uk

■ Michael and Shirley Hunt Charitable Trust

CC NO 1063418 **ESTABLISHED** 1997

WHERE FUNDING CAN BE GIVEN UK and overseas.

WHO CAN BENEFIT Charitable organisations and individuals.

WHAT IS FUNDED People who have been in the criminal justice system or affected by it; animal welfare; general charitable purposes.

RANGE OF GRANTS Up to £10,000.

SAMPLE GRANTS Martlets Hospice (£7,000); Create (£4,300); Prison Advice and Care Trust (Pact) (£3,000); Dogs Trust (£2,000); Animals in Need (£1,500); Crisis and Wild Futures (£1,000 each).

FINANCES *Financial year end* 31/03/2020 *Income* £242,600 *Total grants* £72,400 *Grants to organisations* £68,600 *Assets* £7,400,000

TRUSTEES Wanda Baker; Chester Hunt; Shirley Hunt; Deborah Jenkins; Kathy Mayberry.

OTHER INFORMATION During the year, 45 organisations received support. Only organisations that received grants of over £1,000 were listed as beneficiaries in the charity's accounts. Grants of under £1,000 totalled £9,300 and were awarded to 16 organisations. Grants were broken down as follows: animal welfare (28 grants totalling £25,600); prisoners and their families (13 grants totalling £22,800); general charitable purposes (four grants totalling £16,400).

HOW TO APPLY All applications have to be made in writing. Applications are considered upon receipt and formal meetings are held as necessary, at least once a year.

CONTACT DETAILS Deborah Jenkins, Trustee, Ansty House, Henfield Road, Small Dole, Henfield, West Sussex BN5 9XH *Tel.* 01903 817116

■ The Albert Hunt Trust

CC NO 1180640 **ESTABLISHED** 1979

WHERE FUNDING CAN BE GIVEN UK.

WHO CAN BENEFIT Registered charities.

WHAT IS FUNDED The promotion and enhancement of physical and mental welfare. Grants are made in three categories: health and well-being; hospice appeals; and homeless appeals.

WHAT IS NOT FUNDED Animal welfare; arts/heritage; conservation/the environment; expeditions and overseas travel; individual and sports sponsorship; mainstream able-bodied sport (disabled sports projects are considered); the promotion of religion; medical research.

TYPE OF GRANT Single awards for capital projects; grants for core funding to include staff costs; ongoing running costs for specific projects.

RANGE OF GRANTS From £1,000 to £30,000, with most grants of between £1,000 and £5,000.

SAMPLE GRANTS St George's Crypt (£30,000); Milton Keynes University Hospital and YMCA Cornwall (£25,000 each); Response Organisation and Wessex Cancer Trust (£10,000 each); The Shakespeare Hospice (£7,000); Fresh Start, Positive Action in Housing and Sandwell Homeless (£5,000 each); The Manna Society (£3,000); Articulate Arts (£2,000); Afghan and Central Asian Association (£1,000).

FINANCES *Financial year end* 05/04/2020 *Income* £65,470,000 *Total grants* £2,190,000 *Grants to organisations* £2,190,000 *Assets* £53,200,000

TRUSTEES Bridget McGuire; Kate McGuire; Stephen Harvey; Ian Fleming.

OTHER INFORMATION The trust re-registered as a charitable incorporated organisation (CIO) in November 2018. All assets were transferred to the successor charity in April 2019. As such, the reporting period of the trust's most recent accounts is November 2018 to April 2020. The trust awarded 422 grants to organisations during this period. Grants were distributed as follows: hospice appeals (£898,000); health and well-being appeals (£854,500); homeless appeals (£434,400).

HOW TO APPLY Applications can be made through the trust's website. Applications are reviewed on a monthly rolling basis. Applications by post or email will not be considered. Due to the COVID-19 pandemic, applications for capital projects were not being considered at the time of writing (March 2021). This decision will be reviewed in July 2021. If you are planning to apply to the trust for a grant towards a capital project, check the trust's website from August 2021 onwards.

CONTACT DETAILS Jane Deller Ray, Operations Manager, The Hermitage, 15A Shenfield Road, Brentwood, Essex CM15 8AG *Tel.* 0330 113 7280 *Email* info@alberthunttrust.org.uk *Website* https://www.alberthunttrust.org.uk

■ The Hunter Foundation

OSCR NO SC027532 **ESTABLISHED** 1998

WHERE FUNDING CAN BE GIVEN UK; overseas.

WHO CAN BENEFIT Charitable organisations; schools; social enterprises.

WHAT IS FUNDED Education, entrepreneurship and poverty alleviation in the UK and internationally.

TYPE OF GRANT Project funding; strategic funding; development funding; start-up funding.

SAMPLE GRANTS Kiltwalk (£2.01 million); Children in Need (£1.1 million); Social Innovation Partnership (£736,400); Cambridge Conservation Initiative (£500,000); Moyo Development Company (£144,500); Founders 4 Schools (£45,000).

FINANCES *Financial year end* 31/03/2020 *Income* £53,700,000 *Total grants* £8,501,800 *Grants to organisations* £8,410,000 *Assets* £47,860,000

TRUSTEES Sir Tom Hunter; Lady Marion Hunter; Jim McMahon.

HOW TO APPLY Contact the foundation using the contact form on the website. If a project appears to be of initial interest, the trustees will contact you to discuss taking the application further.

CONTACT DETAILS The Trustees, Marathon House, Olympic Business Park, Drybridge Road, Dundonald, Ayrshire KA2 9AE *Email* info@thehunterfoundation.co.uk *Website* www.thehunterfoundation.co.uk

Miss Agnes H. Hunter's Trust

OSCR NO SC004843 **ESTABLISHED** 1954

WHERE FUNDING CAN BE GIVEN Scotland.

WHO CAN BENEFIT OSCR-registered charities.

WHAT IS FUNDED Support for people with disabilities; education and training for disadvantaged people aged 16 or over who have left school.

WHAT IS NOT FUNDED A full list of exclusions can be found on the restrictions page of the trust's website.

TYPE OF GRANT Project funding; core costs.

RANGE OF GRANTS £3,000 to £15,000. The trust notes that it reserves a degree of flexibility on award values.

SAMPLE GRANTS Citadel Youth Centre SCIO (£25,000); Lead Scotland (£20,000); Dancebase (£17,000); Community Food Initiatives North East (£12,000); Headway Glasgow (£9,800); Interest Link Borders (£6,500).

FINANCES *Financial year end* 30/06/2020 *Income* £579,300 *Total grants* £508,900 *Grants to organisations* £508,900 *Assets* £15,310,000

TRUSTEES Walter Thomson; Keith Burdon; Alison Campbell; Elaine Crichton; Norman Dunning; John Hume.

OTHER INFORMATION The trust notes that it is particularly keen to hear from the following: smaller charities with a strong local community presence; causes that do not have a strong public profile, including start-up organisations; charities developing innovative approaches, including pilot projects. Grants in 2019/20 were broken down as follows: education and training – 17 grants (£279,900); disabled people – 20 grants (£229,000).

HOW TO APPLY Applications can be made online via the trust's website when the grants programme is open.

CONTACT DETAILS Sarah Wright, Trust Manger, Davidson House, 57 Queen Charlotte Street, Edinburgh EH6 7EY *Tel.* 0131 538 5496 *Email* s.wright@agneshunter.org.uk *Website* www.agneshunter.org.uk

The Hunting Horn General Charitable Trust

CC NO 1149358 **ESTABLISHED** 2012

WHERE FUNDING CAN BE GIVEN UK.

WHO CAN BENEFIT Charitable organisations; churches.

WHAT IS FUNDED General charitable purposes.

SAMPLE GRANTS Campaign for Female Education (CAMFED) (£70,000); Trinity Church (£30,400); Mandritsara Trust (£18,000); Eden Baptist Church (£10,000); A29 OH Academy (£2,000); British Red Cross (£1,000).

FINANCES *Financial year end* 31/05/2020 *Income* £32,100 *Total grants* £159,400 *Grants to organisations* £159,400 *Assets* £5,550,000

TRUSTEES Sean Jackson; Martin Oldfield.

HOW TO APPLY Contact the correspondent for further information.

CONTACT DETAILS The Trustees, 3 Adams Road, Cambridge, Cambridgeshire CB3 9AD *Tel.* 01223 476769

The Huntingdon Foundation Ltd

CC NO 286504 **ESTABLISHED** 1984

WHERE FUNDING CAN BE GIVEN UK and Israel.

WHO CAN BENEFIT Organisations benefitting Jewish people; Jewish schools, universities and other educational organisations.

WHAT IS FUNDED Jewish causes; education and training.

RANGE OF GRANTS Up to £36,000.

SAMPLE GRANTS MGS Charitable Trust (£36,000); Beis Yaacov (£30,000); Friends of Mir (£28,600); Comet Charities (£25,000); Gateshead Talmudical College (£18,000); Achisomoch Aid Company Ltd (£15,000); Hasmonean School (£10,000); Ezra U'Marpeh (£9,000).

FINANCES *Financial year end* 31/03/2020 *Income* £732,000 *Total grants* £189,600 *Grants to organisations* £189,600 *Assets* £16,100,000

TRUSTEES Rachel Jeidel; Dr Shoshanna Perl; Jonathan Perl; Joseph Perl; Naomi Tsorotzkin; Benjamin Perl.

HOW TO APPLY Apply in writing to the correspondent. The trustees meet several times a year.

CONTACT DETAILS The Trustees, Foframe House, 35–37 Brent Street, London NW4 2EF *Tel.* 020 3411 2001

Huntingdon Freemen's Trust

CC NO 1044573 **ESTABLISHED** 1993

WHERE FUNDING CAN BE GIVEN The area covered by Huntingdon Town Council, including Oxmoor, Hartford, Sapley, Stukeley Meadows and Hinchingbrooke Park.

WHO CAN BENEFIT Registered charities; individuals; students; churches; local groups and organisations involved in sports, hobbies and the arts.

WHAT IS FUNDED Children; domestic violence; education; care for older people; health; recreation and leisure; unemployment.

TYPE OF GRANT Capital costs; project costs.

SAMPLE GRANTS A list of beneficiaries was not included in the annual report and accounts.

FINANCES *Financial year end* 30/04/2020 *Income* £538,900 *Total grants* £212,900 *Grants to organisations* £212,900 *Assets* £17,540,000

TRUSTEES John Hough; Jonathan Hampstead; Brian Bradshaw; Michael Shellens; Kate Parker; Jill Watkin-Tavener; Juliet Cole.

OTHER INFORMATION The grant total includes grants awarded to individuals.

HOW TO APPLY Application forms for organisations and individuals are available on the trust's website. Forms should be returned to the correspondent.

CONTACT DETAILS Karen Clark, Grants Officer, 37 High Street, Huntingdon, Cambridgeshire PE29 3AQ *Tel.* 01480 414909 *Email* info@huntingdonfreemen.org.uk *Website* www.huntingdonfreemen.org.uk

Hurdale Charity Ltd

CC NO 276997 **ESTABLISHED** 1978

WHERE FUNDING CAN BE GIVEN England and Wales.

WHO CAN BENEFIT Charitable organisations benefitting Jewish people and promoting the Orthodox Jewish way of life.

WHAT IS FUNDED Jewish causes.

RANGE OF GRANTS Mostly up to £100,000, with some larger grants.

SAMPLE GRANTS Moundfield Charities Ltd (£310,000); Springfield Trust Ltd (£260,000); Friends of Wiznitz (£100,000); Chevras Mo'oz Ladol (£45,000); Yeshiva Haromo (£30,000); Bayis Lepleitos (£25,000).

FINANCES *Financial year end* 31/03/2020
Income £2,150,000 *Total grants* £2,090,000
Grants to organisations £2,090,000
Assets £29,650,000

TRUSTEES David Oestreicher; Abraham Oestreicher; Jacob Oestreicher; Benjamin Oestreicher.

OTHER INFORMATION Only beneficiaries of grants of £25,000 and above were listed in the 2019/20 accounts (18 organisations). Grants of under £25,000 totalled £401,000.

HOW TO APPLY Contact the correspondent for further information.

CONTACT DETAILS Abraham Oestreicher, Trustee, 162 Osbaldeston Road, London N16 6NJ *Tel.* 020 8731 0770

■ The Hurley Partners Charitable Trust

CC NO 1179041 **ESTABLISHED** 2018

WHERE FUNDING CAN BE GIVEN UK.

WHO CAN BENEFIT Registered charities.

WHAT IS FUNDED The purchase of medical equipment.

TYPE OF GRANT Capital costs.

SAMPLE GRANTS St George's Hospital (£135,000).

FINANCES *Financial year end* 31/12/2019
Income £160,300 *Total grants* £136,400
Grants to organisations £136,400
Assets £23,900

TRUSTEES Paul Burridge; Paul Cody; Amber Dane; Anthony Hurley; Laura Stewart.

HOW TO APPLY Contact the correspondent for further information.

CONTACT DETAILS The Trustees, 12 Conduit Street, Mayfair, London W1S 2XH *Tel.* 020 8936 3970

■ The Hutchinson Charitable Trust

CC NO 1155643 **ESTABLISHED** 2012

WHERE FUNDING CAN BE GIVEN UK, with a preference for Fenland, particularly Wisbech.

WHO CAN BENEFIT Charitable organisations.

WHAT IS FUNDED General charitable purposes, mainly (but not exclusively) in the areas of: agriculture; disadvantaged people; education; Fenland charities, especially those connected with Wisbech.

SAMPLE GRANTS Royal Agricultural Benevolent Institution (£50,000); The Addington Fund (£20,000); King's Lynn Samaritans and Send a Cow (£12,500 each).

FINANCES *Financial year end* 31/12/2019
Income £297,300 *Total grants* £161,500
Grants to organisations £161,500
Assets £5,430,000

TRUSTEES David Hutchinson; Michael Hutchinson.

OTHER INFORMATION The trust awarded grants within the following categories: agriculture (£85,000); disadvantaged people (£49,500); Fenland (£15,500); education (£11,500).

HOW TO APPLY Contact the correspondent for further information.

CONTACT DETAILS The Trustees, 10 Victory Road, Wisbech, Cambridgeshire PE13 2PU *Tel.* 01945 586409

■ The Hutton Foundation

CC NO 1106521 **ESTABLISHED** 2004

WHERE FUNDING CAN BE GIVEN UK and overseas.

WHO CAN BENEFIT Charitable organisations.

WHAT IS FUNDED General charitable purposes.

SAMPLE GRANTS Forgotten People (£189,600); Theological Institute (£42,800); Cardinal Hume Centre (£10,000).

FINANCES *Financial year end* 31/12/2019
Income £42,900 *Total grants* £277,300
Grants to organisations £277,300
Assets £1,590,000

TRUSTEES Amanda Hutton; Graham Hutton; James Hutton; Richard Hutton.

HOW TO APPLY Contact the correspondent for further information.

CONTACT DETAILS Jaclyn Donnina, Secretary and Treasurer, The Old House, Bramley Road, Silchester, Reading, Berkshire RG7 2LU *Tel.* 07786 921033

■ The Nani Huyu Charitable Trust

CC NO 1082868 **ESTABLISHED** 2000

WHERE FUNDING CAN BE GIVEN UK, with a strong preference for Bristol and the surrounding areas.

WHO CAN BENEFIT Charitable organisations, with a strong preference for small local charities.

WHAT IS FUNDED Social and economic circumstances; health; young people (education, training and accommodation); older people (end-of-life medical care and assistance).

RANGE OF GRANTS £1,000 to £20,000.

SAMPLE GRANTS Womankind (£20,000); Young Carers (£16,000); Young Bristol (£14,000); Bristol Mediation (£14,000); Brain Tumour Support (£10,000); Somerset Community Foundation (£6,000); Age UK Somerset (£5,000); Cerebral Palsy Plus (£2,000); Relate (£1,000).

FINANCES *Financial year end* 31/10/2019
Income £208,700 *Total grants* £190,500
Grants to organisations £190,500
Assets £5,930,000

TRUSTEES Ben Whitmore; Charles Thatcher; Maureen Whitmore; Susan Webb; Jenny Wilson; Lucy Walford.

OTHER INFORMATION Grants were awarded to 22 organisations during the year. At the time of writing (April 2021) the 2018/19 accounts were the most recent available.

HOW TO APPLY Contact the correspondent for further information.

CONTACT DETAILS The Trustees, Rusling House, Butcombe, Bristol BS40 7XQ *Tel.* 01275 474433 *Email* maureensimonwhitmore@btinternet.com

■ Hyde Charitable Trust

CC NO 289888 **ESTABLISHED** 1984

WHERE FUNDING CAN BE GIVEN The areas in which the Hyde Group operates (London, the South East, the East of England and the East Midlands).

WHO CAN BENEFIT Community groups; individuals.

WHAT IS FUNDED Employability; young people; reducing isolation; mental health and well-being; food poverty; fuel poverty; reducing the impact of violence; community cohesion.

TYPE OF GRANT Project funding.

SAMPLE GRANTS A list of beneficiaries was not included in the annual report and accounts.

FINANCES *Financial year end* 31/03/2020 *Income* £392,000 *Total grants* £297,000 *Grants to organisations* £215,000 *Assets* £9,320,000

TRUSTEES Jonathan Prichard; Patrick Law; Brid O'Dwyer; Katherine Rodgers; Jen Wight; Geron Walker.

OTHER INFORMATION During 2019/20 grants were awarded to 24 organisations and 130 individuals.

HOW TO APPLY Contact the correspondent for further information.

CONTACT DETAILS The Trustees, Hyde Housing Association, 30 Park Street, London SE1 9EQ *Tel.* 020 3207 2782 *Email* zoe.ollerearnshaw@hyde-housing.co.uk *Website* https://www.hyde-housing.co.uk/corporate/our-social-purpose/the-hyde-charitable-trust

■ Hyde Park Place Estate Charity

CC NO 212439 **ESTABLISHED** 1914

WHERE FUNDING CAN BE GIVEN City of Westminster.

WHO CAN BENEFIT Charities and community organisations.

WHAT IS FUNDED Church maintenance; social welfare; health; education.

TYPE OF GRANT Capital costs.

RANGE OF GRANTS Mostly £1,000 to £5,000.

SAMPLE GRANTS St George's Hanover Square (£19,200); Asthma Relief, Shelter, DreamArts, St John's Hospice and Woman's Trust (£5,000 each), Listening Books (£3,000); Cardboard Citizens and Iris Theatre (£2,000 each); South Westminster Community Festival (£1,500).

FINANCES *Financial year end* 25/03/2020 *Income* £628,600 *Total grants* £273,100 *Grants to organisations* £273,100 *Assets* £13,960,000

TRUSTEES Revd Roderick Leece; Mark Hewitt; Graham Barnes.

HOW TO APPLY Apply in writing to the correspondent. The trustees meet four times a year.

CONTACT DETAILS Shirley Vaughn, Clerk to the Trustees, St George's Church, The Vestry, 2A Mill Street, London W1S 1FX *Tel.* 020 7629 0874 *Email* hppec@stgeorgeshanoversquare.org

IBM United Kingdom Trust

CC NO 290462 **ESTABLISHED** 1984

WHERE FUNDING CAN BE GIVEN UK; Europe; the Middle East; Africa.

WHO CAN BENEFIT Charitable organisations; universities, hospitals and other research organisations.

WHAT IS FUNDED Education and training in information technology (IT); research with an emphasis (but not exclusively) on IT; improving life for people with disabilities and other disadvantages through the use of IT; improving social welfare, health and the environment through the use of technology; disaster relief.

TYPE OF GRANT Capital costs; project funding; research.

RANGE OF GRANTS Up to £173,000.

SAMPLE GRANTS Stop the Traffik (£173,000); Danish Refugee Council (£161,000); FACE (£53,000); Joblinge (£52,000); Emmaus France (£47,000); Movement on the Ground (£45,000); Association Aurore (£32,000).

FINANCES *Financial year end* 31/12/2019 *Income* £197,000 *Total grants* £636,000 *Grants to organisations* £636,000 *Assets* £3,760,000

TRUSTEES Prof. Derek Bell; Anne Wolfe; Naomi Hill; Andrew Fitzgerald; Juliet Upton; Bryan Berry; Kuljit Takhar.

OTHER INFORMATION During 2019, grants were distributed in the following categories: provision of IT and other services (£494,000); promoting volunteering (£127,000); support for research (£17,000); miscellaneous (£2,000). Only organisations that received grants of over £30,000 were listed as beneficiaries in the trust's accounts. Grants of under £30,000 totalled £236,000 and were awarded to 193 organisations.

HOW TO APPLY Contact the correspondent for further information.

CONTACT DETAILS The Trustees, IBM United Kingdom Ltd, 1PG1, 76 Upper Ground, London SE1 9PZ *Tel.* 020 7202 3608 *Email* wakefim@uk.ibm.com

Ibrahim Foundation Ltd

CC NO 1149438 **ESTABLISHED** 2012

WHERE FUNDING CAN BE GIVEN UK and overseas.

WHO CAN BENEFIT Registered charities; educational organisations; community projects.

WHAT IS FUNDED General charitable purposes; community building; the environment; families; strengthening not-for-profit organisations.

WHAT IS NOT FUNDED Applications are not considered from the same organisations in successive grant cycles.

TYPE OF GRANT Capital costs; core costs; project funding; unrestricted.

RANGE OF GRANTS Up to £50,000 but usually between £500 and £10,000.

SAMPLE GRANTS A list of beneficiaries was not available.

FINANCES *Financial year end* 31/05/2020 *Income* £92,200 *Total grants* £91,600 *Grants to organisations* £91,600 *Assets* £4,000

TRUSTEES Dr Azeem Ibrahim; Adeel Ibrahim; Aadil Butt.

OTHER INFORMATION In 2019/20 grants totalling £91,600 were awarded towards community building.

HOW TO APPLY Initial contact can be made via the foundation's website.

CONTACT DETAILS The Trustees, 18 Little Street, Glasgow G3 8DQ *Tel.* 0141 416 1991 *Email* info@ibrahimfoundation.com *Website* www.ibrahimfoundation.com

The Iceland Foods Charitable Foundation

CC NO 281943 **ESTABLISHED** 1973

WHERE FUNDING CAN BE GIVEN UK.

WHO CAN BENEFIT Registered charities (often medical charities); hospices; universities.

WHAT IS FUNDED General charitable purposes.

TYPE OF GRANT Capital costs; development funding; research.

SAMPLE GRANTS Alzheimer's Research UK (£605,500); The UK Sepsis Trust (£250,000); British Lung Foundation (£100,000); Clwyd Special Riding Centre (£25,000); Surfers Against Sewage (£10,000); 1st Standstone Scout Group (£5,000); The Teenage Cancer Trust (£1,000).

FINANCES *Financial year end* 05/04/2020 *Income* £1,970,000 *Total grants* £1,570,000 *Grants to organisations* £1,570,000 *Assets* £4,560,000

TRUSTEES Tarsem Dhaliwal; Sir Malcolm Walker; Richard Walker.

OTHER INFORMATION Each year the foundation chooses one principal charity partner as well as supporting causes nominated by Iceland employees.

HOW TO APPLY Contact the correspondent for more information. At the time of writing (April 2021) the foundation's website states that funding is fully committed for the current financial year.

CONTACT DETAILS The Trustees, Second Avenue, Deeside Industrial Park, Deeside, Flintshire CH5 2NW *Tel.* 01244 842885 *Email* ifcf@Iceland.co.uk *Website* https://www.ifcf.org.uk

The Idlewild Trust

CC NO 268124 **ESTABLISHED** 1974

WHERE FUNDING CAN BE GIVEN UK.

WHO CAN BENEFIT Registered charities; museums; galleries; churches that are excepted charities.

WHAT IS FUNDED The arts, including programmes that improve opportunities for young professionals working within the arts, particularly at an early stage in their career; conservation of historic or artistically important objects and works of art in museums, galleries, places of worship, historic buildings or their grounds.

WHAT IS NOT FUNDED A full list of exclusions can be found in the funding guidelines document on the trust's website.

TYPE OF GRANT Project funding.

RANGE OF GRANTS Up to £5,000.

SAMPLE GRANTS National Youth Theatre (£5,000); NDC Wales (£4,000); Royal Museums Greenwich (£3,000); Historic Royal Palaces (£2,500); Pleasance Theatres Trust (£2,000); All Saints Church – Snodland (£600).

FINANCES *Financial year end* 31/12/2019 *Income* £208,200 *Total grants* £184,200 *Grants to organisations* £184,200 *Assets* £6,510,000

OTHER INFORMATION The trustees considered 192 appeals and awarded 47 grants in 2019.

HOW TO APPLY Applications can be made via the trust's website. Applicants should note that there are separate forms for arts and conservation applications.

CONTACT DETAILS The Director, Marshall House, 66 Newcomen Street, London SE1 1YT *Email* info@idlewildtrust.org.uk *Website* www.idlewildtrust.org.uk

■ IGO Foundation Ltd

CC NO 1148316 **ESTABLISHED** 2012

WHERE FUNDING CAN BE GIVEN Worldwide.

WHO CAN BENEFIT Charitable organisations.

WHAT IS FUNDED Jewish causes including: education; Jewish history; welfare.

RANGE OF GRANTS £4,500 to £29,000.

SAMPLE GRANTS Kollel Yeshuas Chaim (£25,000); Yishaya Adler Memorial Trust (£13,000); Keren Prasim, Keren Sholomo Trust, Mifal Hachesed Vehatzdokoh and Beis Soroh Schneirer (£10,000 each); Achisomoch Aid Company Ltd and Keren Hatzolas Doros (£5,000 each); Chaim Charitable Company Ltd (£4,500).

FINANCES *Financial year end* 30/06/2020 *Income* £156,800 *Total grants* £186,900 *Grants to organisations* £186,900 *Assets* £1,250,000

OTHER INFORMATION Eighteen grants were awarded to charitable organisations during the year.

HOW TO APPLY Contact the correspondent for further information.

CONTACT DETAILS The Trustees, 29 Grosvenor Gardens, London NW11 0HE

■ The Iliffe Family Charitable Trust

CC NO 273437 **ESTABLISHED** 1977

WHERE FUNDING CAN BE GIVEN UK.

WHO CAN BENEFIT Registered charities; hospices, hospitals.

WHAT IS FUNDED General charitable purposes; social welfare; education; Christianity; conservation; medical.

SAMPLE GRANTS Jubilee Sailing Trust (£25,000); Afghan Connection (£13,500); Mary Rose Trust (£10,000); Cystic Fibrosis Trust (£5,000); The Watermill Theatre (£3,000); Coventry City of Culture Trust (£2,000); Farm Africa (£1,000); Southern Spinal Injuries Trust (£200).

FINANCES *Financial year end* 05/04/2020 *Income* £200,800 *Total grants* £170,700 *Grants to organisations* £170,700 *Assets* £1,480,000

OTHER INFORMATION Grants were broken down as follows: welfare (12 grants totalling £61,300); education (four grants totalling £46,000); heritage (five grants totalling £22,500); medical (nine grants totalling £18,000); conservation (three grants totalling £15,000); and religion (two grants totalling £8,000).

HOW TO APPLY Contact the correspondent for further information.

CONTACT DETAILS The Trustees, Barn Close, Burnt Hill, Yattendon, Berkshire RG18 0UX *Tel.* 01635 203929 *Email* ifct@yattendon.co.uk

■ Imagine Foundation

CC NO 1152864 **ESTABLISHED** 2013

WHERE FUNDING CAN BE GIVEN UK.

WHO CAN BENEFIT Registered charities.

WHAT IS FUNDED People who are disadvantaged; community development.

TYPE OF GRANT Ongoing partnerships; project funding.

RANGE OF GRANTS Up to £21,500.

SAMPLE GRANTS LS14 Trust (£21,500); Thrive (£18,000); Handcrafted (£15,000); Luminary Bakery (£12,000); Families Outside and School of Hard Knocks (£10,000 each); Music in Detention (£8,000); Juno Project (£7,500); Bike Back (£750).

FINANCES *Financial year end* 31/12/2019 *Income* £261,200 *Total grants* £230,800 *Grants to organisations* £230,800 *Assets* £704,600

OTHER INFORMATION The foundation mainly provides grants to charities with which it has ongoing partnerships. During 2019, grants were made to 26 organisations. Grants were distributed as follows: supporting disadvantaged young people (£75,500); capacity building (£73,300); using creativity to change the story (£45,500); community development (£36,500).

HOW TO APPLY At the time of writing (January 2021) the charity had closed its application process and was taking applications by invitation only. The 2019 accounts state: 'Rather than open a funding window which generates a lot of applications for a small amount of potential new partnerships, we want to explore other ways of reaching out to new and younger charities. This may be by developing a network of partner referees who could introduce us to new projects in their area.'

CONTACT DETAILS The Trustees, Lower Farm, Oakley Road, Chinnor, Oxfordshire OX39 4HR *Tel.* 07973 675257 *Email* info@if-trust.org *Website* www.if-trust.org

■ Impact Funding Partners Ltd

OSCR NO SC035037 **ESTABLISHED** 2003

WHERE FUNDING CAN BE GIVEN Scotland.

WHO CAN BENEFIT Charitable organisations.

WHAT IS FUNDED The charity manages a number of grant programmes that aim to create 'a fair, inclusive society where communities thrive and people are engaged, connected, and able to shape their own lives'. The charity's website states that it has knowledge in a wide range of policy areas including: volunteering; loneliness and isolation; poverty, community engagement; health and well-being; violence against women and girls; and fair work and employability. Refer to the website for up-to-date information on current funds.

WHAT IS NOT FUNDED See the charity's website for details of any exclusions for each fund.

TYPE OF GRANT Dependent upon grant programme.

RANGE OF GRANTS Up to £455,000; mostly up to £100,000.

SAMPLE GRANTS South Lanarkshire and East Renfrewshire Women's Aid (£455,800); East and Midlothian Women's Aid (£372,900); Angus Women's Aid (£224,900); Barnardo's Scotland

(£191,700); Children 1st (£125,700); Scottish Borders Council (£106,300); City of Edinburgh Council (£101,100); Dumfriesshire and Stewartry Women's Aid (£100,700).

FINANCES *Financial year end* 31/03/2020 *Income* £13,300,000 *Total grants* £12,080,000 *Grants to organisations* £12,080,000 *Assets* £1,060,000

TRUSTEES Pervin Ahmad; Dalvir Johal; Graham Leydon; Joanna McLaughlin; Jim Nicol; Iqbal Bedi; Daphne Biliouri-Grant.

OTHER INFORMATION Grants of less than £100,000 totalled £7.16 million in 2019/20.

HOW TO APPLY Application forms and guidance notes for open programmes are available on the charity's website. Grant programmes may open and close so applicants should check the website for the most recent updates.

CONTACT DETAILS The Trustees, Robertson House, 152 Bath Street, Glasgow G2 4TB *Tel.* 01383 620780 *Email* info@impactfundingpartners.com *Website* https://www.impactfundingpartners.com

■ Impetus

CC NO 1152262 **ESTABLISHED** 2013

WHERE FUNDING CAN BE GIVEN UK.

WHO CAN BENEFIT Registered charities.

WHAT IS FUNDED Disadvantaged people aged 11 to 24.

TYPE OF GRANT Core funding; development and strategic funding along with management and pro bono support.

RANGE OF GRANTS £50,000 to £630,000.

SAMPLE GRANTS City Gateway (£632,200); Action Tutoring (£440,500); IntoUniversity (£375,000); Dallaglio Rugby Works (£272,200); Football Beyond Borders and Tutor Trust (£100,000 each); Voice 21 (£75,000); ThinkForward (£66,000).

FINANCES *Financial year end* 31/12/2019 *Income* £7,310,000 *Total grants* £3,680,000 *Grants to organisations* £3,680,000 *Assets* £6,380,000

TRUSTEES Charles Edwards; Vanessa Maydon; Lisa Stone; Rohan Haldea; Hanneke Smits; Simon Turner; Robert Ramsauer; Louis Elson; Natasha Porter; Filippo Cardini; Shani Zindel; Bill Benjamin.

OTHER INFORMATION The charity was formed from the merger of the Impetus Trust and Private Equity Foundation.

HOW TO APPLY The charity's website states that it does not accept unsolicited applications.

CONTACT DETAILS The Trustees, 10 Queen Street Place, London EC4R 1AG *Tel.* 07414 405029 *Email* info@impetus.org.uk *Website* www.impetus.org.uk

■ The Indigo Trust

CC NO 1075920 **ESTABLISHED** 1999

WHERE FUNDING CAN BE GIVEN UK and sub-Saharan Africa, with a preference for Uganda, Kenya, Nigeria, South Africa and Ghana.

WHO CAN BENEFIT Registered charities.

WHAT IS FUNDED Technology-driven projects for social change in sub-Saharan Africa which focus on transparency, accountability or public service delivery and which use mobile and/or web technologies as a core part of the project.

WHAT IS NOT FUNDED Individuals; educational fees; expeditions.

TYPE OF GRANT Core and revenue costs; seed funding; start-up funding; project funding; unrestricted funding.

RANGE OF GRANTS Initially £10,000 to £20,000. Larger grants are available for organisations the trustees have prior knowledge of.

SAMPLE GRANTS Trussell Trust and National Emergencies Trust (£1 million each); Oxfordshire Community Foundation (£500,000); African Legal Information Institute (£180,000); 360Giving (£150,000); medConfidential (£20,000); Ten Years' Time Enterprises Ltd (£10,000); mySociety (£5,300); The Rainbow Project (£2,000).

FINANCES *Financial year end* 05/04/2020 *Income* £4,340,000 *Total grants* £4,010,000 *Grants to organisations* £4,010,000 *Assets* £9,920,000

TRUSTEES Dominic Flynn; Francesca Perrin; William Perrin.

OTHER INFORMATION The trust is one of the Sainsbury Family Charitable Trusts which share a common administration – see www.sftc.org.uk for more information. The trust made grants to 38 organisations during the year, including some larger COVID-19 emergency grants.

HOW TO APPLY The trust's website states the following: 'Indigo is not currently accepting unsolicited proposals. Experience has taught us that an open application process is burdensome for both sides and rarely results in new grants being awarded.'

CONTACT DETAILS Robert Bell, Director, The Peak, 5 Wilton Road, London SW1V 1AP *Tel.* 020 7410 0330 *Email* indigo@sfct.org.uk *Website* https://indigotrust.org.uk

■ The Inflexion Foundation

CC NO 1179624 **ESTABLISHED** 2018

WHERE FUNDING CAN BE GIVEN England and Wales.

WHO CAN BENEFIT Registered charities.

WHAT IS FUNDED Social isolation and loneliness; health; environmental conservation.

SAMPLE GRANTS A list of beneficiaries was not included in the annual report and accounts.

FINANCES *Financial year end* 31/03/2020 *Income* £250,200 *Total grants* £159,000 *Grants to organisations* £159,000 *Assets* £114,500

TRUSTEES James Goold; John Hartz; Simon Turner.

HOW TO APPLY Contact the correspondent for further information.

CONTACT DETAILS The Trustees, 47 Queen Anne Street, London WIG 9JG *Tel.* 020 7487 9827 *Email* manager@inflexionfoundation.com

■ The Ingram Trust

CC NO 1040194 **ESTABLISHED** 1994

WHERE FUNDING CAN BE GIVEN UK and overseas, with a preference for Surrey.

WHO CAN BENEFIT Registered charities.

WHAT IS FUNDED General charitable purposes.

WHAT IS NOT FUNDED Non-registered charities; individuals; charities specialising in overseas aid unless they are dedicated to encouraging self-help and providing more permanent solutions to problems; animal charities except those concerned with wildlife conservation.

TYPE OF GRANT Project funding; capital costs.

SAMPLE GRANTS WWF – UK (£60,000); The Royal National Theatre (£50,000); Shelter (£30,000); Alzheimer's Society (£20,000); Outward Bound Trust (£15,000); Princess Alice Hospice

(£10,000); Cherry Trees – Respite Care (£5,000).

FINANCES *Financial year end* 05/04/2020 *Income* £227,800 *Total grants* £628,000 *Grants to organisations* £628,000 *Assets* £9,330,000

TRUSTEES Janet Ingram; Clare Maurice; Sally Ingram; Jonathan Ingram; Christopher Ingram.

OTHER INFORMATION The majority of grants will be made for periods of three to four years at a time in order for the trustees to better assess grant applications and monitor progress. Grants were made to 29 organisations during the year.

HOW TO APPLY Contact the correspondent for further information.

CONTACT DETAILS The Trustees, 8th Floor, 6 New Street Square, London EC4A 3AQ *Tel.* 020 7842 2000 *Email* theingramtrust@rawlinson-hunter.com

■ The Inlight Trust

CC NO 236782 **ESTABLISHED** 1957

WHERE FUNDING CAN BE GIVEN UK.

WHO CAN BENEFIT Registered charities.

WHAT IS FUNDED Religious and spiritual development, healing and growth.

WHAT IS NOT FUNDED Individuals, including students; organisations which are not registered charities; general appeals from large national organisations; church buildings.

TYPE OF GRANT Usually one-off for a specific project or part of a project. Bursary schemes are eligible. Core funding and/or salaries are rarely considered.

SAMPLE GRANTS St Wilfrid's Hospice (£30,000); The Meditation Centre (£21,000); Christian Education Movement (£15,000); The Interfaith Network (£10,000); Outworks Trust (£5,000); Kadampa Buddhist Centre (£2,000); Bibles For Children (£1,000).

FINANCES *Financial year end* 31/03/2020 *Income* £345,300 *Total grants* £333,000 *Grants to organisations* £333,000 *Assets* £6,910,000

TRUSTEES Judy Hayward; Sharon Knight; Jane Dunham; Dr David Panton; Shirley Vening; Stephen Collins.

HOW TO APPLY Previous research has shown that applications should be made in writing to the correspondent, including details of the need, the intended project to meet it, an outline of budget, your most recent available annual accounts, and a copy of your trust deed or your entry on the Charity Commission register. Only applications from eligible bodies are acknowledged and only successful applicants are informed.

CONTACT DETAILS Clare Pegden, Administrator, PO Box 2, Liss, Hampshire GU33 6YP *Tel.* 07970 540015 *Email* inlight.trust01@ntlworld.com

■ The Inman Charity

CC NO 261366 **ESTABLISHED** 1970

WHERE FUNDING CAN BE GIVEN UK.

WHO CAN BENEFIT Charitable organisations.

WHAT IS FUNDED General charitable purposes, with a particular interest in: medical research; care of older people; social welfare; hospices; physical and mental disability including deafness and blindness; the armed forces.

WHAT IS NOT FUNDED Individuals; young children and infants; maintenance of buildings at a local level (e.g. churches and village halls); animal welfare; wildlife and environmental conservation; religious charities.

RANGE OF GRANTS Generally £2,000 to £5,000.

SAMPLE GRANTS Inman Charity Medical Research Fund – King's College London (£14,000); Hospice UK (£10,000); Roy Castle Lung Cancer Foundation (£6,000); Carers Network (£5,000); In Kind Direct (£3,000); Musical Connections (£2,000).

FINANCES *Financial year end* 31/12/2019 *Income* £182,300 *Total grants* £326,000 *Grants to organisations* £326,000 *Assets* £5,960,000

TRUSTEES A. Walker; Belinda Strother; Michael Matthews; John Langdon; Inman Charity Trustees.

OTHER INFORMATION The charity also awards a regular grant of £25,000 to the Victor Inman Bursary Fund.

HOW TO APPLY Applications should be made in writing to the correspondent. Full details of the application process can be found on the charity's website.

CONTACT DETAILS The Trustees, BM Box 2831, London WC1N 3XX *Tel.* 020 7465 4300 *Website* www.inmancharity.org

■ Inner London Magistrates Court Poor Box and Feeder Charity

CC NO 1046214 **ESTABLISHED** 1995

WHERE FUNDING CAN BE GIVEN Inner London.

WHO CAN BENEFIT Individuals; courts; probation services; organisations which provide relief of hardships faced by people who come into contact with the courts.

WHAT IS FUNDED Relief of need, hardship and distress of people concerned, directly or indirectly, in any proceedings at magistrates courts in the London region, including family and youth courts.

WHAT IS NOT FUNDED It was previously understood that the charity will not fund the direct relief of rates, taxes or other public funds.

RANGE OF GRANTS £2,000 to £16,000.

SAMPLE GRANTS Prisoners' Family and Friends (£16,000); Circle Community, Prisoner's Education Trust and St Mungo's (£10,000 each); Personal Support Unit (£6,000); Centrepoint, The Big Issue and The Margins Project (£5,000 each); Marylebone Project (£3,000).

FINANCES *Financial year end* 31/03/2019 *Income* £182,100 *Total grants* £135,000 *Grants to organisations* £135,000 *Assets* £4,560,000

TRUSTEES Jane Richardson; Richard Kozak; The Lady Emma Arbuthnot; Louise Moloney; Sam Gooze; Tanweer Ikram.

OTHER INFORMATION Grants were made to 19 organisations during the year. The 2018/19 accounts were the latest available at the time of writing (January 2021).

HOW TO APPLY Apply in writing to the correspondent. The following was taken from the annual report for 2018/19: 'The trustees invite applications for grants from the courts themselves, the probation services and organisations involved in identifying and relieving need and hardship suffered in prison. The trustees are also aware that the needs and hardship of those who come into contact with the courts are often associated with homelessness, substance misuse, domestic violence and poverty and applications are invited from organisations which provide relief in those areas specifically to beneficiaries in the London region. The trustees do not commit to repeat or renew a relief grant on any occasion.'

CONTACT DETAILS The Trustees, Ealing Magistrates' Court, 448 High Road, Green Man Lane, London W13 0SD *Tel.* 07901 822125 *Email* ilmcpbf@btinternet.com

■ The Innocent Foundation

CC NO 1104289 **ESTABLISHED** 2004

WHERE FUNDING CAN BE GIVEN Worldwide.

WHO CAN BENEFIT Community-based projects and non-government organisations in financially developing countries where the Innocent Drinks company sources fruit. Generally, organisations must be UK-registered or have UK representation to receive funds.

WHAT IS FUNDED Food poverty. The foundation has two goals: 1) stop children dying of hunger – funding for projects which diagnose and treat children facing severe hunger and for cutting-edge research in this area; 2) help low-income families feed themselves – funding for agricultural projects.

WHAT IS NOT FUNDED Seed funding; individuals; religious or political causes; general appeals or circulars; events or conferences; seed funding is not given for core costs alone (but these can be included as overheads pro-rated to the project); major capital costs, such as buildings or machinery.

TYPE OF GRANT Most funds are allocated in multi-year partnerships; some one-off projects. Development funding; project funding; research.

RANGE OF GRANTS Mostly up to £90,000.

SAMPLE GRANTS The Alliance for International Medical Action (£249,700); Washington University (£197,600); Concern Worldwide and Oxfam (£90,000 each); Aga Khan Foundation (£44,700); Renewable World (£36,500); Practical Action (£25,000); Blue Ventures (£15,500); Ace Africa (£12,700).

FINANCES *Financial year end* 30/06/2020 *Income* £1,000,000 *Total grants* £1,280,000 *Grants to organisations* £1,280,000 *Assets* £3,000,000

TRUSTEES Adam Balon; Jonathan Wright; Richard Reed; Christina Archer; Douglas Lamont; Sarah-Jane Norman; Camilla Knox-Clarke.

OTHER INFORMATION The Innocent Foundation was set up by Innocent Drinks in 2004. Each year the company gives at least 10% of its profits to charity. During the year, grants were distributed to 19 projects (including four COVID-19 emergency relief donations).

HOW TO APPLY According to the 2019/20 annual report, the foundation has an annual application cycle for its second goal. Contact the foundation for more information.

CONTACT DETAILS Kate Franks, Foundation Director, The Innocent Foundation, 342 Ladbroke Grove, London W10 5BU *Tel.* 020 3235 0352 *Email* hello@innocentfoundation.org *Website* www.innocentfoundation.org

■ The Institute for Policy Research

CC NO 285143 **ESTABLISHED** 1982

WHERE FUNDING CAN BE GIVEN UK.

WHO CAN BENEFIT Non-charitable organisations; universities; other research institutions.

WHAT IS FUNDED Specific policy studies, conferences and lectures to enhance public discussion of issues normally in the economic, industrial, social and foreign policy fields.

TYPE OF GRANT Project funding.

SAMPLE GRANTS TaxPayers' Alliance (£117,500); Centre for Policy Studies (£50,000); Open Europe and Politeia (£40,000); The Bruges Group (£2,000).

FINANCES *Financial year end* 30/09/2020 *Income* £317,500 *Total grants* £249,500 *Grants to organisations* £249,500 *Assets* £454,200

TRUSTEES Simon Webley; Eric Koops; Anthony Speaight; Jennifer Nicholson.

OTHER INFORMATION Grants were broken down as follows: research projects (£224,500); conferences, seminars and publications (£25,000).

HOW TO APPLY Contact the correspondent for further information.

CONTACT DETAILS The Trustees, Flat 38, Charleston Court, 61 West Cliff Road, Broadstairs, Kent CT10 1RY *Tel.* 07815 502279 *Email* peter.orbelljones@yahoo.com

■ Integrated Education Fund

CCNI NO NIC104886 **ESTABLISHED** 1992

WHERE FUNDING CAN BE GIVEN Northern Ireland.

WHO CAN BENEFIT Schools undergoing or exploring the integration of pupils from both the Catholic and Protestant communities; existing integrated schools; community/parent groups exploring integrated education for their area.

WHAT IS FUNDED Integrated education. Full eligibility criteria and further details for each category are given on the website.

TYPE OF GRANT Research; evaluation; start-up costs; projects; development costs; training; salaries; capital costs.

SAMPLE GRANTS Previous beneficiaries have included: Atlantic Philanthropies (£209,500); Parental Engagement Campaign (£56,500); Turnaround Foundation (£32,000).

FINANCES *Financial year end* 31/03/2020 *Income* £900,800 *Total grants* £652,100 *Grants to organisations* £652,100 *Assets* £1,790,000

TRUSTEES David Cooke; Grainne Clarke; Roderick Downer; Michael McKernan; Ellen McVea; Richard Lemon; Mary Roulston; Barbara McAtamney; Christopher Lynas; Kathleen O'Hare; Peter Osborne; Jane Morrice; Brandon McMaster; Patricia Murtagh.

HOW TO APPLY Application forms are available to download from the website, where detailed guidance is also provided.

CONTACT DETAILS Claire Carlin, Grants Officer, Forestview, Purdy's Lane, Belfast BT8 7AR *Tel.* 028 9069 4099 *Email* info@ief.org.uk or Claire@ief.org.uk *Website* www.ief.org.uk

■ The International Bankers Charitable Trust

CC NO 1087630 **ESTABLISHED** 2001

WHERE FUNDING CAN BE GIVEN UK, with a preference for London.

WHO CAN BENEFIT Registered charities; schools; universities.

WHAT IS FUNDED Charities working with young people in education, financial literacy, employability, raising aspirations for education and employability; disadvantaged individuals for a clear purpose and measurable impact; City of

London and financial services-linked charitable initiatives.

TYPE OF GRANT Project funding; strategic funding.

RANGE OF GRANTS Typically up to £1,000 for new applicants, but larger awards may be considered.

SAMPLE GRANTS The Brokerage Citylink (£44,000); School Home Support (£8,200); Mansion House Scholarship Scheme (£5,000); The Business School -City University (£4,300); Grandparent Plus (£1,500); The Sheriffs' and Recorder's Fund (£250).

FINANCES *Financial year end* 30/09/2019 *Income* £179,900 *Total grants* £92,600 *Grants to organisations* £92,600 *Assets* £1,070,000

TRUSTEE The Worshipful Company of International Bankers.

OTHER INFORMATION The 2018/19 accounts were the latest available at the time of writing (June 2021).

HOW TO APPLY Applications can be made online via the charity's website.

CONTACT DETAILS The Trustees, 3rd Floor, 12 Austin Friars, London EC2N 2HE *Tel.* 020 7374 0212 *Email* clerk@internationalbankers.co.uk *Website* internationalbankers.org.uk/charity-education/charity-applications

■ International Bible Students Association

CC NO 216647 **ESTABLISHED** 1964

WHERE FUNDING CAN BE GIVEN Worldwide.

WHO CAN BENEFIT Christian (Jehovah's Witnesses) organisations and individuals.

WHAT IS FUNDED Promotion of the Christian religion as practised by Jehovah's Witnesses; supporting the spiritual and mental welfare of Jehovah's Witnesses; hosting conventions for Bible education; the purchase and distribution of religious literature; care for members of the Order; disaster relief.

TYPE OF GRANT Capital costs; emergency aid.

SAMPLE GRANTS The Kingdom Hall Trust (£320,000).

FINANCES *Financial year end* 31/08/2019 *Income* £27,500,000 *Total grants* £370,700 *Grants to organisations* £370,700 *Assets* £161,210,000

TRUSTEES Stephen Papps; Karl Snaith; Ivor Darby; Jonathan Manley; Stephen Symonds.

OTHER INFORMATION The 2018/19 accounts were the latest available at the time of writing (May 2021). Grants were distributed as follows: Europe (£365,000); North America (£5,000); Africa (£700). Note that the grant total in 2018/19 was considerably lower than those in previous years.

HOW TO APPLY Contact the correspondent for further information.

CONTACT DETAILS The Trustees, 1 Kingdom Way, West Hanningfield, Chelmsford CM2 8FW *Tel.* 020 8906 2211

■ The Inverforth Charitable Trust

CC NO 274132 **ESTABLISHED** 1977

WHERE FUNDING CAN BE GIVEN UK.

WHO CAN BENEFIT Charitable organisations.

WHAT IS FUNDED General charitable purposes including: health; hospices; young people and education; the armed forces; the arts; community.

RANGE OF GRANTS Up to £10,000.

SAMPLE GRANTS Alzheimer's Society (£10,000); Art Fund, Childhood First and Royal Trinity Hospice (£7,000 each); Royal Marsden Cancer Charity (£5,000); Rennie Grove Hospice Care (£1,000); Supporting Wounded Veterans (£500); Oscar India (£300).

FINANCES *Financial year end* 31/12/2019 *Income* £38,400 *Total grants* £68,800 *Grants to organisations* £68,800 *Assets* £6,810,000

TRUSTEES Rt Hon. Elizabeth Lady Inverforth; Rt Hon. Andrew Lord Inverforth; Jonathan Kane.

OTHER INFORMATION The trust categorised the awards made during the year as: physical and mental health (four grants); hospices (three grants); youth and education (two grants); military and international (two grants); the arts (one grant); community (one grant). The trust supports UK and international charities, but tends to support the same charities annually. In 2019 the trust made grants to six charities it had not supported previously.

HOW TO APPLY Contact the correspondent for further information.

CONTACT DETAILS The Hon. Clarinda Kane, Secretary and Treasurer, 58A Flood Street, London SW3 5TE *Tel.* 020 7680 8100 *Email* clarindakane@btopenworld.com

■ The Investindustrial Foundation

CC NO 1169179 **ESTABLISHED** 2011

WHERE FUNDING CAN BE GIVEN England; Wales; Italy; Spain; Switzerland; USA.

WHO CAN BENEFIT Charitable organisations.

WHAT IS FUNDED Education; diversity; environmental protection and conservation; arts, culture, heritage and science.

TYPE OF GRANT Project funding.

SAMPLE GRANTS A list of beneficiaries was not included in the annual report and accounts.

FINANCES *Financial year end* 31/03/2020 *Income* £1,140,000 *Total grants* £1,100,000 *Grants to organisations* £1,100,000 *Assets* £36,200

TRUSTEES Emanuele Bonomi; Rohan Maxwell; Natalie Ramsden; Oliver Dunn.

OTHER INFORMATION Grants were broken down as follows: development of higher education (£535,300); medical support (£341,900); sustainability studies (£215,100). Financial information has been converted from Euros using the exchange rate at the time of writing (June 2021).

HOW TO APPLY Contact the correspondent for further information.

CONTACT DETAILS The Trustees, 16 Palace Street, London SW1E 5JD *Tel.* 020 7664 2121 *Website* https://www.investindustrial.com/social-responsibility/our-foundation.html

■ Investream Charitable Trust

CC NO 1097052 **ESTABLISHED** 2003

WHERE FUNDING CAN BE GIVEN Worldwide with a preference for the UK and Israel.

WHO CAN BENEFIT Registered charities; educational establishments.

WHAT IS FUNDED Jewish causes; general charitable purposes, with a focus on education, community, care for older people and medical causes.

SAMPLE GRANTS A list of beneficiaries was not included in the annual report and accounts.

FINANCES *Financial year end* 30/04/2019
Income £110,700 *Total grants* £892,200
Grants to organisations £892,200
Assets £1,570,000

TRUSTEES Mark Morris; Graham Morris.

OTHER INFORMATION The 2018/19 accounts were the latest available at the time of writing (June 2021). A list of beneficiaries was not included in the annual report and accounts.

HOW TO APPLY Contact the correspondent for further information.

CONTACT DETAILS The Trustees, Investream Ltd, 1 Portland Place, London W1B 1PN *Tel.* 020 7486 2800

■ The Invigorate Charitable Trust

CC NO 1162752 **ESTABLISHED** 2015

WHERE FUNDING CAN BE GIVEN UK and overseas.

WHO CAN BENEFIT Charitable organisations.

WHAT IS FUNDED General charitable purposes.

WHAT IS NOT FUNDED Health or saving lives; amateur sport; environmental protection or improvement; animal welfare; the armed forces and emergency services.

RANGE OF GRANTS £2,000 to £25,000.

SAMPLE GRANTS A list of beneficiaries was not included in the annual report and accounts.

FINANCES *Financial year end* 05/04/2020
Income £202,700 *Total grants* £240,400
Grants to organisations £240,400
Assets £201,900

TRUSTEES Timothy Parr; Kate Aitchison.

OTHER INFORMATION During the year, grants were awarded to 18 organisations, across the following categories: relief of young people (UK and overseas) (£67,000); relief of illness or disability (£65,000); advancement of Christianity (UK and overseas) (£58,400); advancement of citizenship/community development (£35,000); prevention or relief of poverty (£15,000).

HOW TO APPLY Contact the correspondent for more information regarding the application process.

CONTACT DETAILS Kate Aitchison, Trustee, 5th Floor, Central Square, 29 Wellington Street, Leeds, West Yorkshire LS1 4DL *Tel.* 0113 285 5000 *Email* kate.aitchison@rsmuk.com

■ The Ireland Fund of Great Britain

CC NO 327889 **ESTABLISHED** 1976

WHERE FUNDING CAN BE GIVEN UK, with a preference for Northern Ireland; Ireland.

WHO CAN BENEFIT Charities; community groups; voluntary groups.

WHAT IS FUNDED Education; community development; relief of poverty; the arts and culture; mental and physical health; older people; young people; peace and reconciliation.

TYPE OF GRANT Project funding.

RANGE OF GRANTS Mostly up to £20,000.

SAMPLE GRANTS Blackrock College Development (£283,000); Irish Sailing Foundation (£41,300); Integrated Education Fund (£21,300); Royal Academy of Music (£14,300); Glenstal Abbey (£10,000); St Patrick's Roof Appeal (£5,300); AslAm (£1,000); Southwark Irish Pensioners Project (£400).

FINANCES *Financial year end* 31/03/2020
Income £784,400 *Total grants* £456,300
Grants to organisations £456,300
Assets £272,000

TRUSTEES Seamus McGarry; Ruairi Conneely; Zach Webb; Rory Godson; Garrett Hayes; Eoin Bastible; Emily Bohill; Rachel Naughton; Declan Tiernan; Brian Dickie; Emer Finnan; Conor Hillery; John Feeney; Evelyn Bourke.

OTHER INFORMATION The Ireland Fund of Great Britain (IFGB) is one of 12 chapters of The Irish Funds. The IFBG makes grants through a donor-advised grants programme and an annual grant round. During 2019/20, grants were awarded to 15 organisations in the following areas: education (£411,200); community development/the relief of poverty (£25,900); sharing and developing Irish arts and culture (£19,300). The Irish Funds also has its own grant programmes for organisations in the Republic of Ireland and Northern Ireland, details of which can be found on the website.

HOW TO APPLY Guidelines, exclusions and full information on the application process are announced on the website when the relevant programme opens.

CONTACT DETAILS Katie Jemmett, Director, Level 17, Dashwood House, 69 Old Broad Street, London EC2M 1QS *Tel.* 07597 665646 *Email* ifgb@irelandfunds.org *Website* https://irelandfunds.org/chapters/worldwide/great-britain

■ Irish Youth Foundation (UK) Ltd (incorporating The Lawlor Foundation)

CC NO 328265 **ESTABLISHED** 1989

WHERE FUNDING CAN BE GIVEN UK.

WHO CAN BENEFIT Charities and community organisations.

WHAT IS FUNDED Projects benefitting young Irish people or enhancing their personal and social development, especially if they are disadvantaged or in need. A wide range of projects is supported which include: training/counselling; mental and physical health; substance and alcohol abuse rehabilitation; advice/advocacy; youth work; family support; homelessness; educational, cultural and social activities; cross-community initiatives; Irish Travellers; disability.

WHAT IS NOT FUNDED Projects for people over 25 (in Northern Ireland) and over 30 (in England, Scotland and Wales); general appeals; large/national charities; academic research; alleviating deficits already incurred; individuals (except for university students applying under the Lawlor Foundation education programme); capital bids; overseas travel; multiple applications from a single organisation.

TYPE OF GRANT Programme development grants; seed funding; core costs and salaries; awards to upgrade premises and/or equipment. One year only.

RANGE OF GRANTS In Northern Ireland: up to £10,000. In England, Scotland and Wales: small grants of up to £2,500; standard grants ranging from £2,500 to £10,000.

SAMPLE GRANTS Previous beneficiaries have included: New Horizon Youth Centre – London (£9,500); Solace Women's Aid – London (£9,000); Brent Centre for Young People (£4,000); Birmingham Irish Association and The Brandon Centre – London (£3,000 each); Birmingham TradFest (£2,000); Conradh na Gaeilge Glaschu – Glasgow and Irish Arts Foundation – Leeds (£1,000 each).

FINANCES *Financial year end* 31/12/2019
Income £358,800 *Total grants* £191,400
Grants to organisations £191,400
Assets £2,880,000

TRUSTEES Alan Byrne; Mark Gough; Geraldine O'Callaghan; June Trimble; Richard Corrigan; John Dwyer; Ciara Brett; Virginia Lawlor.

OTHER INFORMATION Irish Youth Foundation (UK) Ltd merged with the Lawlor Foundation in 2005.

HOW TO APPLY Application forms become available during the annual funding round. Check the website for current deadlines and detailed guidelines. Unsolicited applications at other times during the year are not accepted.

CONTACT DETAILS Linda Tanner, Company Secretary and Head of Operations, Irish Cultural Centre, 5 Blacks Road, Hammersmith, London W6 9DT *Tel.* 020 8748 9640 *Email* linda@iyf.org.uk *Website* www.iyf.org.uk

■ The Charles Irving Charitable Trust

CC NO 297712 **ESTABLISHED** 1987

WHERE FUNDING CAN BE GIVEN Gloucestershire, in particular Cheltenham.

WHO CAN BENEFIT Charitable organisations; individuals.

WHAT IS FUNDED General charitable purposes; social welfare; disadvantaged people; local community projects; disability; homelessness; mental health; respite and holidays; older people; resettlement of offenders.

WHAT IS NOT FUNDED Ongoing grants; research; expeditions; computers or other equipment (unless benefitting people with disabilities); causes outside the county of Gloucester except for a few organisations.

TYPE OF GRANT One-off; mainly capital projects; project costs.

RANGE OF GRANTS Mostly up to £2,500, with some larger grants.

SAMPLE GRANTS Gloucestershire Eye Therapy Trust (£150,000); Cheltenham Silver Band (£50,000); The Butterfly Garden (£41,500); Sue Ryder Leckhampton (£8,900); St Thomas More Nursery School (£4,000); Tall Ships (£3,000).

FINANCES *Financial year end* 30/09/2019 *Income* £18,600 *Total grants* £420,000 *Grants to organisations* £420,000 *Assets* £413,600

TRUSTEES Tony Hilder; Mrs J. Lane; Mr D. Oldham; Peter Shephard.

OTHER INFORMATION At the time of writing (May 2021) the 2018/19 accounts were the latest available to view on the Charity Commission's website. During the year, 103 grants were made to organisations in the following categories: local community projects (£270,500); disability (£56,200); homelessness (£39,100); mental health (£38,600); resettlement of offenders (£7,500); older people (£4,600); respite care and holidays (£2,500); victim support (£1,000). Only beneficiaries of grants of £5,000 and above were listed in the accounts.

HOW TO APPLY The 2018/19 annual report states: 'The Trustees welcome applications by letter, giving details of the proposed project, its total cost and the amount if any already raised or promised from other sources. Other information such as a budget and details of the number of people expected to benefit will also be helpful.'

CONTACT DETAILS The Trustees, PO Box 868, Cheltenham GL53 9WZ *Tel.* 01242 234848

■ The Irving Memorial Trust

CC NO 1173441 **ESTABLISHED** 2017

WHERE FUNDING CAN BE GIVEN UK.

WHO CAN BENEFIT Charitable organisations.

WHAT IS FUNDED General charitable purposes.

RANGE OF GRANTS £60 to £20,000.

SAMPLE GRANTS London Symphony Orchestra (£20,000); Family First (£10,000); Cystic Fibrosis Trust (£5,000); DEMAND and The Brain Tumour Charity (£3,000 each); Homeland and The Linda Tremble Foundation (£1,000 each); Winterbourne Medieval Barn Trust (£250); Food Lifeline (£60).

FINANCES *Financial year end* 19/04/2020 *Income* £24,000 *Total grants* £367,900 *Grants to organisations* £367,900 *Assets* £1,060,000

TRUSTEES Pamela Huntingford; Andrew Huntingford; Ludlow.

OTHER INFORMATION Grants were awarded to 183 organisations during the year.

HOW TO APPLY Contact the correspondent for further information.

CONTACT DETAILS The Trustees, 1st Floor, Tower Wharf, Cheese Lane, Bristol BS2 0JJ *Tel.* 0117 313 8200 *Email* charitabletrusts@ludlowtrust.com

■ The Isla Foundation

ESTABLISHED 2013

WHERE FUNDING CAN BE GIVEN UK.

WHO CAN BENEFIT Charitable organisations with an income of under £10 million.

WHAT IS FUNDED Social welfare.

WHAT IS NOT FUNDED Fundraising events; repayment of debt; redundancy costs; contribution to reserves; religious events.

TYPE OF GRANT Project funding; staff costs; capital costs; core costs.

SAMPLE GRANTS Southall Black Sisters (£85,000); End Violence Against Women (£51,800); Citizens UK (£30,000); Nurses United (£20,000); The Felix Project (£5,000); Hackney Food Bank and Newham Community Renewal Programme (£2,500 each).

FINANCES *Total grants* £199,300 *Grants to organisations* £199,300

OTHER INFORMATION The foundation's accounts were not available to view. The grant total and beneficiaries have been taken from the foundation's website. The foundation continually assesses where the greatest need for funding lies and awards grants accordingly. Since 2013 grants have been made in the following areas: violence against women and girls, rights and equality (51%) homelessness, food security, housing (19%); community projects (11%); campaigning and advocacy (6%); the environment (6%); social justice (4%); criminal justice (1%).

HOW TO APPLY Apply online via the foundation's website, where information on new funding calls can also be found.

CONTACT DETAILS Grants Team, Coppergate House, Unit 412, 10 White's Row, London E1 7NF *Email* info@islafoundation.com *Website* https://islafoundation.com

The Isle of Anglesey Charitable Trust

CC NO 1000818 **ESTABLISHED** 1990

WHERE FUNDING CAN BE GIVEN Isle of Anglesey.

WHO CAN BENEFIT Charitable and community organisations; village halls; sports facilities.

WHAT IS FUNDED General charitable purposes; education; health; arts and culture; conservation; the environment; community development.

WHAT IS NOT FUNDED Individuals.

TYPE OF GRANT Capital costs; core/revenue costs.

RANGE OF GRANTS Large grants (upwards of £8,000); small grants (up to £8,000).

SAMPLE GRANTS Oriel Ynys Môn (£430,000); Menter Môn Leader Scheme (£132,100); Urdd Gobaith Cymru (£88,000); Aberffraw Village Hall (£43,100); Cemaes Football Club (£37,200); Anglesey Food Bank (£20,000); Anglesey Column Trust (£10,000); Tudor Cyf (£6,000).

FINANCES *Financial year end* 30/09/2019 *Income* £1,080,000 *Total grants* £1,870,000 *Grants to organisations* £1,870,000 *Assets* £21,380,000

TRUSTEE Isle of Anglesey County Council.

OTHER INFORMATION The 2018/19 accounts were the latest available at the time of writing (April 2021). Grants were awarded to 103 organisations during the year.

HOW TO APPLY Application forms can be requested from the correspondent. According to the 2018/19 accounts, the trustees invite applications for funding usually once a year through advertising in local papers.

CONTACT DETAILS The Trustees, Isle of Anglesey County Council, Council Offices, Llangefni, Anglesey LL77 7TW *Tel.* 01248 752675 *Email* gjrfi@anglesey.gov.uk

Isle of Wight Foundation

CC NO 1163489 **ESTABLISHED** 2013

WHERE FUNDING CAN BE GIVEN Isle of Wight.

WHO CAN BENEFIT Registered charities; not-for-profit organisations; CICs; voluntary and community groups.

WHAT IS FUNDED Support for social exclusion; access to employment; community development; citizenship.

WHAT IS NOT FUNDED Projects or activities that do not meet any of the foundation's aims and criteria; any costs incurred when putting together a grant application; activities that happen or start before the grant is confirmed; political or religious activities; day-to-day operating costs (for example, utility bills, council tax, rent and insurance); land or building projects where the ownership or lease is not yet in place (including any planning permissions); ongoing staff costs; projects or activities that the state or a statutory body has a legal obligation to provide; projects that cannot be completed within 12 months of the date of the letter confirming the grant; individuals.

TYPE OF GRANT Projects; capital costs; salaries.

RANGE OF GRANTS £3,000 to £16,000.

SAMPLE GRANTS Ability Dogs 4 Young People, Cowes Sailability Club, Isle of Wight Search and Rescue and The Phoenix Project (£16,000 each); Wight Dash (£11,300); Wessex Cancer Trust (£5,900); Elite Soccer UK (£3,500).

FINANCES *Financial year end* 31/12/2019 *Income* £92,400 *Total grants* £84,700 *Grants to organisations* £84,700 *Assets* £13,700

TRUSTEES Philip Horton; Arnaud Judet: Robert Gillespie; Emma Scott.

HOW TO APPLY Calls for applications are usually issued in February, with the closing date for applications falling around the beginning of May. Consult the website for current deadlines and guidelines.

CONTACT DETAILS Nicola Vaughan, Foundation Supervisor, Fulcrum, 105 Piccadilly, London W1J 7NJ *Tel.* 020 3006 4700 *Email* IWFoundation@IslandRoads.com *Website* www.islandroads.com/137-iw-foundation.html

The ITF Seafarers Trust

CC NO 281936 **ESTABLISHED** 1981

WHERE FUNDING CAN BE GIVEN Worldwide.

WHO CAN BENEFIT Registered charities; educational institutions; trade unions; NGOs.

WHAT IS FUNDED Welfare, health and education of seafarers, their families and dependants.

WHAT IS NOT FUNDED Retrospective funding for completed projects; deficits which have already been incurred; projects which promote particular religious beliefs; recurring costs.

TYPE OF GRANT Capital costs; core costs; project funding; research.

RANGE OF GRANTS Small grants (£500 to £75,000); large grants (over £75,000).

SAMPLE GRANTS AMOSUP (£1.03 million); Seafarers' Rights International (£498,000); United Seamen's Service (£197,600); Mission To Seafarers (£77,800); Ship Visitor Platform (£46,500); Merchant Navy Welfare Board (£35,000); Care Ashore (£20,000); International Maritime Employers' Council (£10,700).

FINANCES *Financial year end* 31/12/2019 *Income* £2,200,000 *Total grants* £3,860,000 *Grants to organisations* £3,860,000 *Assets* £48,080,000

TRUSTEES Paddy Crumlin; Dave Heindel; Stephen Cotton; Brian Orrell; Abdulgani Serang; Jacqueline Smith.

OTHER INFORMATION Grants were awarded to around 50 organisations during the year. Grants were broken down as follows: operational support (£2.4 million); vehicles (£729,700); training (£430,900); research into seafarers' welfare (£346,900); raising awareness of seafarers' rights (£107,400); other (£47,000); buildings, internet, computers and telecommunications (£10,700); health (£2,700).

HOW TO APPLY All applications must be made online. Refer to the funder's website for further information.

CONTACT DETAILS The Trustees, ITF House, 49–60 Borough Road, London SE1 1DR *Tel.* 020 7403 2733 *Email* info@seafarerstrust.org *Website* www.seafarerstrust.org

■ The J. and J. Benevolent Foundation

CC NO 1146602 **ESTABLISHED** 2012

WHERE FUNDING CAN BE GIVEN England.

WHO CAN BENEFIT Charitable organisations; individuals.

WHAT IS FUNDED Orthodox Jewish religious causes; education; social welfare.

RANGE OF GRANTS Up to £60,000.

SAMPLE GRANTS Achisomoch Aid Company Ltd (£60,000); Emuno Educational Centre Ltd (£22,900); Menorah High School Foundation Trust (£17,000); Friends of Mercaz Hatorah Belz Macnivka (£16,200).

FINANCES *Financial year end* 31/03/2020 *Income* £85,100 *Total grants* £157,600 *Grants to organisations* £157,600 *Assets* £59,900

TRUSTEES Joseph Adler; Judi Adler.

OTHER INFORMATION During the year, grants of over £10,000 were made to five organisations. Grants of less than £10,000 totalled £41,600. No grants were made to individuals.

HOW TO APPLY Apply to the trustees in writing. The trustees consider all requests which they receive and make grants based on the level of funds available.

CONTACT DETAILS The Trustees, c/o Cohen Arnold, New Burlington House, 1075 Finchley Road, London NW11 0PU *Tel.* 020 8731 0777 *Email* mail@cohenarnold.com

■ The J. A. R. Charitable Trust

CC NO 248418 **ESTABLISHED** 1966

WHERE FUNDING CAN BE GIVEN Worldwide.

WHO CAN BENEFIT Registered charities; places of worship.

WHAT IS FUNDED Advancement of the Roman Catholic Church; provision of education for people under 30; relief in need for people over 55.

WHAT IS NOT FUNDED Individuals.

RANGE OF GRANTS £500 to £5,000.

SAMPLE GRANTS JMB Educational Fund (£5,500) Ordinariate of Our Lady of Walsingham (£5,000); St Joseph's Pastoral Centre, The Passage and Eastbourne College (£4,000 each); Archdiocese of Liverpool and Catholic Children's Society Brentwood (£3,000 each); Tongabezi School Trust (£2,500); Walsingham Trust (£2,000); Ministry of Stories (£1,000); Audio Active (£500).

FINANCES *Financial year end* 05/04/2020 *Income* £123,300 *Total grants* £88,000 *Grants to organisations* £88,000 *Assets* £3,820,000

TRUSTEES Revd William Young; Revd Paschal Ryan; Benedict Noble.

OTHER INFORMATION Grants were awarded to 29 organisations during the year.

HOW TO APPLY The trustees identify projects and organizations they wish to support; they do not accept unsolicited applications.

CONTACT DETAILS The Trustees, c/o Hunters Solicitors, 9 New Square, London WC2A 3QN *Tel.* 020 7412 0050 *Email* wilfrid.vernormiles@hunterslaw.com

■ The J. J. Charitable Trust

CC NO 1015792 **ESTABLISHED** 1989

WHERE FUNDING CAN BE GIVEN UK and overseas.

WHO CAN BENEFIT UK-registered charities.

WHAT IS FUNDED Literacy; sustainable lifestyles; environmental projects in the UK and Africa; innovative projects.

WHAT IS NOT FUNDED Individuals; educational fees; expeditions.

TYPE OF GRANT Seed funding; development funding; project funding; core costs.

RANGE OF GRANTS Mostly up to £60,000.

SAMPLE GRANTS Makerversity (£79,000); Friends of the Earth Charitable Trust (£53,600); Platform (£40,000); The Circle of Women (£20,000); British Ceramics Federation (£12,500); Salisbury Cathedral School (£3,900); Royal Geographical Society (£500).

FINANCES *Financial year end* 05/04/2020 *Income* £1,100,000 *Total grants* £781,800 *Grants to organisations* £781,800 *Assets* £39,480,000

TRUSTEES John Sainsbury; Mark Sainsbury; Lucy Guard.

OTHER INFORMATION The trust is one of the Sainsbury Family Charitable Trusts which share a common administration – see www.sftc.org.uk for more information. During the year, grants were made for the following purposes: the environment – UK (£699,900); general charitable purposes (£41,900); the environment – overseas (£40,000). No grants were made in support of literacy during the year. The list of beneficiaries relates to grants approved (rather than paid) during the year, some of which are payable over multiple years.

HOW TO APPLY Funding enquiries can be submitted online. Generally applications should be sent by post to The Sainsbury Family Charitable Trusts, or by email to proposals@sfct.org.uk. Details of what to include can be found on the website. The website stresses that the vast majority of applications are unsuccessful. If your proposal is a candidate for support you will hear from the trust within eight weeks of the acknowledgement.

CONTACT DETAILS Robert Bell, Director, The Peak, 5 Wilton Road, London SW1V 1AP *Tel.* 020 7410 0330 *Email* info@sfct.org.uk *Website* www.sfct.org.uk

■ The Jabbs Foundation

CC NO 1128402 **ESTABLISHED** 2009

WHERE FUNDING CAN BE GIVEN UK, with a preference for the West Midlands, particularly Birmingham.

WHO CAN BENEFIT Registered charities; universities; educational and research institutions; women's centres.

WHAT IS FUNDED Medical research; education (including educational activities by arts organisations); family and community relationships in West Midlands; supporting vulnerable members of society, the prevention of people entering the criminal justice system; research into the health of trees and forests; encouraging the planting of new trees for educational opportunities.

TYPE OF GRANT Research; capital costs; core costs; salaries.

SAMPLE GRANTS University of Birmingham (£2.08 million); City of Birmingham Symphony Orchestra – Commonwealth Games and Heart of England Community Foundation (£100,000 each); Springboard (£26,000); Lapal Canal Trust (£10,000); Smart Works Birmingham (£7,500).

FINANCES *Financial year end* 31/08/2019 *Income* £2,320,000 *Total grants* £2,480,000 *Grants to organisations* £2,480,000 *Assets* £1,410,000

TRUSTEES Robin Daniels; Alexander Wright; Ruth Keighley.

OTHER INFORMATION The 2018/19 accounts were the latest available at the time of writing (May 2021). Grants to organisations were broken down as follows: tree/forest research and tree planting (£2.07 million); social welfare and crime prevention (£177,600); education (£142,000); medical research (£58,000); family and community relationships in the West Midlands (£28,400). Grants of £50,000 and under totalled £195,900.

HOW TO APPLY The foundation's 2018/19 accounts state: 'The JABBS Foundation does not encourage speculative grant requests, but the trustees read all applications that are received and consider these against the five priority areas.

CONTACT DETAILS The Trustees, PO Box 16067, Birmingham, West Midlands B32 9GP *Tel.* 0121 428 2593 *Email* office@harborneoffice.co.uk

■ The Sir Barry Jackson County Fund

CC NO 517306 **ESTABLISHED** 1985

WHERE FUNDING CAN BE GIVEN Birmingham, Coventry, Dudley, Sandwell, Solihull, Walsall and Wolverhampton.

WHO CAN BENEFIT Registered charities; theatres; CICs; touring companies.

WHAT IS FUNDED Small-scale, touring and educational theatre projects. There are three different funds available: The County Fund, which funds productions of plays suitable for urban audiences with little or no previous theatre experience; The Hornton Fund, which develops talent (including acting and writing) in children and young people under the age of 25; and The Sir Barry Jackson Trust Fund, which commissions new work and supports Birmingham Repertory Theatre.

WHAT IS NOT FUNDED Individuals.

TYPE OF GRANT Project funding; capital costs.

RANGE OF GRANTS Typically up to £5,000.

SAMPLE GRANTS Birmingham Repertory Theatre-Community Tour (£60,000); Birmingham Repertory Theatre-Writers' Commission (£5,000); Vamos Theatre (£3,000); The Bone Ensemble (£2,500); Mercurial Arts (£2,000); Birmingham Back to Backs (£1,700); BE Festival CIC (£1,400).

FINANCES *Financial year end* 05/04/2020 *Income* £105,000 *Total grants* £93,600 *Grants to organisations* £93,600 *Assets* £1,740,000

TRUSTEES David Burman Edgar; Roger Burman; Anthony Chorley; Graham Winteringham; Ian King; Deborah Shaw; Barry Bowles; Prof. Claire Cochrane; Linda Morgan; Graham Saunders; Amelia Ladbrook.

HOW TO APPLY Application and contact details forms are available from the Hon. Secretary or to download from the website. Applications are usually considered twice a year, in January and June, and should be submitted no later than 1 December and 1 May, respectively. Further information and guidance on how to apply, the funds available and application stipulations can be found at www.birmingham-rep.co.uk/we-are-the-rep/the-sir-barry-jackson-trust.html.

CONTACT DETAILS Stephen Gill, Hon. Secretary, c/o Birmingham Repertory Theatre Ltd, Centenary Square, Broad Street, Birmingham, West Midlands B1 2EP *Tel.* 01983 617842 *Email* sbjt@outlook.com *Website* www.sirbarryjacksoncountyfund.org.uk

■ The Frank Jackson Foundation

CC NO 1007600 **ESTABLISHED** 1992

WHERE FUNDING CAN BE GIVEN South Africa and the UK, with a preference for Suffolk.

WHO CAN BENEFIT Schools; colleges; universities; charitable organisations.

WHAT IS FUNDED Education; teacher training; environmental research.

TYPE OF GRANT Research; unrestricted.

RANGE OF GRANTS Up to £87,500.

SAMPLE GRANTS Clifton Preparatory Nottingham Road (£87,100); Oriel College Development Trust (£82,800); VULA Programme (£56,300); Island Trust (£35,000); Physics Partners (£25,000); Aldeburgh Cinema (£15,000); Winston Churchill Memorial Trust (£10,000).

FINANCES *Financial year end* 05/04/2020 *Income* £498,100 *Total grants* £895,500 *Grants to organisations* £895,500 *Assets* £22,960,000

TRUSTEES Amanda Taylor; Leila Brown; Timothy Seymour; David Tennant; Thomas Sheldon; Mary-Anne Gribbon.

OTHER INFORMATION Grants were made to 40 organisations during the year, of which nine were categorised as 'smaller grants'. Only beneficiaries of grants of £10,000 and above were listed in the 2019/20 accounts. Grants of less than £10,000 totalled £71,200.

HOW TO APPLY The foundation's website states that it does not accept unsolicited applications. The trustees 'prefer to actively seek out good causes which meet the foundation's aims'. However, the foundation does welcome enquiries if an organisation believes they meet the criteria. In this case, a short enquiry that summarises in a paragraph how your work meets the criteria should be emailed to the correspondent.

CONTACT DETAILS Lisa Mills, Administrator, 24 Taylor Way, Great Baddow, Chelmsford, Essex CM2 8ZG *Email* frankjacksonfoundation@live.co.uk *Website* www.frankjacksonfoundation.org.uk

■ The Jagclif Charitable Trust

CC NO 1163459 **ESTABLISHED** 2015

WHERE FUNDING CAN BE GIVEN UK and overseas.

WHO CAN BENEFIT Charitable organisations.

WHAT IS FUNDED General charitable purposes.

SAMPLE GRANTS ARK (£10.45 million); War Child (£750,000); Fly Navy Heritage Trust (£300,000); Save the Children (£20,000); Walk the Walk (£1,000).

FINANCES *Financial year end* 30/06/2019 *Income* £12,520,000 *Total grants* £12,130,000 *Grants to organisations* £12,130,000 *Assets* £15,990,000

TRUSTEES Duncan Eriksen; Ernesto Fragomeni; Claudia Wace; Ian Wace.

OTHER INFORMATION The 2018/19 accounts were the latest available at the time of writing (June 2021).

HOW TO APPLY Contact the correspondent for further information.

CONTACT DETAILS The Trustees, Marshall Wace Asset Management, George House, 131 Sloane

Street, London, SW1X 9AT *Tel.* 020 7925 7723 *Email* jagclif@mwam.com

■ John James Bristol Foundation

CC NO 288417 **ESTABLISHED** 1983

WHERE FUNDING CAN BE GIVEN Bristol.

WHO CAN BENEFIT Registered charities; exempt charities; social enterprises; CICs.

WHAT IS FUNDED Education; health; older people; general charitable purposes.

WHAT IS NOT FUNDED Individuals.

TYPE OF GRANT Capital costs; seed funding/start-up funding; unrestricted funding.

RANGE OF GRANTS Up to £300,000, but generally below £5,000.

SAMPLE GRANTS We The Curious (£205,000); Caring In Bristol (£58,500); Badminton School (£30,000); Mothers for Mothers (£5,000); Avon Community Association (£3,500).

FINANCES *Financial year end* 30/09/2020 *Income* £2,110,000 *Total grants* £2,340,000 *Grants to organisations* £2,340,000 *Assets* £80,700,000

TRUSTEES David Johnson; John Evans; Joan Johnson; Peter Goodwin; Nicola Parker; Andrew Webley; Andrew Jardine; Elizabeth Cambers; Julia Norton; Dr John Haworth.

OTHER INFORMATION Grants were broken down as follows: health (£1.31 million); education (£792,300); older people (£165,400); general (£71,000)

HOW TO APPLY Apply in writing via post or email. Full information on what should be included in an application can be found on the foundation's website.

CONTACT DETAILS Louise O'Donnell, Chief Executive, 7 Clyde Road, Redland, Bristol BS6 6RG *Tel.* 0117 923 9444 *Email* info@johnjames.org.uk *Website* www.johnjames.org.uk

■ Lady Eda Jardine Charitable Trust

OSCR NO SC011599 **ESTABLISHED** 1960

WHERE FUNDING CAN BE GIVEN Scotland.

WHO CAN BENEFIT Charitable organisations; hospices; churches; universities.

WHAT IS FUNDED In addition to supporting a number of specific organisations (The Heriot-Watt College, University of Edinburgh, The Edinburgh Festival of Music and Drama and The National Trust in Scotland), the trustees select a different charitable sector to support each year. The trustees elected to support health and disability in 2018/19, children and young people in 2019/20, and heritage, conservation, the environment, gardens and the arts in 2020/21 (year to 5 April 2021).

RANGE OF GRANTS Mostly £1,000 to £3,000.

SAMPLE GRANTS University of Edinburgh Development Trust (£6,000); National Trust for Scotland (£4,000); Children's Music Foundation in Scotland and Sandpiper Trust (£3,000 each); Riding for the Disabled (£2,500); Homelink Family Support (£2,000); Special Needs Adventure Playground (£1,500); Scottish Autism (£1,000).

FINANCES *Financial year end* 05/04/2020 *Income* £73,700 *Total grants* £58,000 *Grants to organisations* £58,000 *Assets* £1,760,000

OTHER INFORMATION Grants were made to 26 organisations during the year.

HOW TO APPLY Contact the correspondent regarding the funding focus for the year. Applications should be made in writing to the correspondent.

CONTACT DETAILS The Trustees, c/o Anderson Strathern LLP, 1 Rutland Court, Edinburgh EH3 8EY

■ John Jarrold Trust Ltd

CC NO 242029 **ESTABLISHED** 1965

WHERE FUNDING CAN BE GIVEN Norfolk, with a current focus on the Norwich, Wymondham and Cromer areas; financially developing countries.

WHO CAN BENEFIT Registered charities; unregistered charities; social enterprises; schools; universities; hospices; PTAs; hospitals; CICs; religious bodies/institutions.

WHAT IS FUNDED Social welfare and community; the arts; education; medical research; churches and historic buildings; the environment; support in financially developing countries. Special attention is given to education and research in the natural sciences.

WHAT IS NOT FUNDED Individual education programmes or needs; gap year type projects are not currently assisted; applications from individual churches. The trust has long-standing relationships with several charities which operate overseas and does not accept applications from new charities unless there is some specific connection to Norwich and Norfolk.

TYPE OF GRANT Project funding; capital costs; core/revenue costs.

RANGE OF GRANTS £200 to £5,000, with the majority of grants being under £1,000.

SAMPLE GRANTS Norfolk Community Sports Foundation (£10,000); The Prince's Trust and YMCA Norfolk (£5,000 each); Norfolk Churches Trust (£2,000); Norwich Theatre Royal (£1,000); Meningitis Now (£600); Coleman Schools PTA (£500); Combat Stress (£250); Wymondham College (£25).

FINANCES *Financial year end* 05/04/2020 *Income* £69,200 *Total grants* £65,600 *Grants to organisations* £65,600 *Assets* £2,470,000

TRUSTEES Caroline Jarrold; Antony Jarrold; Waltraud Jarrold; Charles Jarrold; Susan Jarrold; Julian Jarrold.

OTHER INFORMATION During the year, grants were awarded to 56 organisations in the following categories: social and welfare (£39,200); education (£9,500); the arts (£9,300); churches, historic buildings and heritage (£4,300); overseas (£3,000); the environment (£500). The trust supports the Norfolk Churches Trust on a regular basis.

HOW TO APPLY At the time of writing (May 2021) the website stated: 'COVID-19 is likely to have a significant negative impact on the income of the Trust for the next period and the Trustees do not have any Grant Giving Meetings scheduled at present. Potential applicants are asked not to make submissions until invited to do so. Further updates will be posted as more information becomes available.' The trustees would typically meet twice a year to consider applications.

CONTACT DETAILS Caroline Jarrold, Secretary, c/o Jarrold and Sons Ltd, St James Works, 12–20 Whitefriars, Norwich, Norfolk NR3 1SH *Tel.* 01603 677360 *Email* caroline.jarrold@jarrold.com *Website* www.johnjarroldtrust.org.uk

JD Foundation

CC NO 1167090 **ESTABLISHED** 2015

WHERE FUNDING CAN BE GIVEN UK.

WHO CAN BENEFIT Registered charities.

WHAT IS FUNDED Disadvantaged children and young people including mental health and homelessness charities.

SAMPLE GRANTS Charity partners included: Bolton Wanderers; Buddies of the Birches; Cardiac Risk in the Young; Kidscape; Manchester Youth Zone; Mountain Rescue England and Wales; Papyrus; Scottish Mountain Rescue; Smiling Families; YoungMinds.

FINANCES *Financial year end* 31/01/2020 *Income* £464,700 *Total grants* £438,300 *Grants to organisations* £438,300 *Assets* £52,800

TRUSTEES Daniel Finley; Siobhan Mawdsley; Traci Corrie; Julie Blomley; Nigel Keen; Neil Greenhalgh.

HOW TO APPLY Support is awarded to charity partners. Contact the foundation for further information.

CONTACT DETAILS Siobhan Mawdsley, Secretary, JD Sports Fashion, Edinburgh House, Hollins Brook Way, Bury BL9 8RR *Tel.* 0161 767 1000 *Email* thejdfoundation@jdplc.com *Website* https://www.jdplc.com/jd-foundation

The Roger and Jean Jefcoate Trust

CC NO 1096211 **ESTABLISHED** 1983

WHERE FUNDING CAN BE GIVEN Milton Keynes, Buckinghamshire and adjacent counties.

WHO CAN BENEFIT Local, regional and small national disability and healthcare charities.

WHAT IS FUNDED Health and well-being, especially advice and practical help for people with hidden disabilities such as dementia or mental health conditions; older people; carers.

TYPE OF GRANT Running costs; general funding; capital projects; project costs.

RANGE OF GRANTS Typically £3,000 to £10,000.

SAMPLE GRANTS Scannappeal – Stoke Mandeville Hospital (£20,000); Nerve Tumours UK – London (£10,000); British False Memory Society – Bath (£8,000); Young Dementia UK – Witney (£6,000); Bedford MS Therapy Centre and Stoke Mandeville Spinal Research (£5,000 each); My Life My Choice – Oxford (£3,000); Freedom from Torture – London (£2,000).

FINANCES *Financial year end* 31/10/2020 *Income* £248,500 *Total grants* £189,000 *Grants to organisations* £189,000 *Assets* £3,640,000

TRUSTEES Roger Jefcoate; Rosemary McCloskey; Vivien Dinning; Carol Wemyss; Alistair Wemyss; Kathryn Hobbs.

OTHER INFORMATION During 2019/20, grants were awarded to 27 charities, among which five organisations received funding in response to the COVID-19 pandemic, totalling £94,000.

HOW TO APPLY Apply in writing to the correspondent. The trustees meet at least twice annually to discuss applications.

CONTACT DETAILS The Trustees, 2 Copse Gate, Winslow, Buckingham, Buckinghamshire MK18 3HX *Tel.* 01296 715466

Jeffrey Charitable Trust

OSCR NO SC015990 **ESTABLISHED** 1972

WHERE FUNDING CAN BE GIVEN Scotland and elsewhere.

WHO CAN BENEFIT Registered charities; hospices; hospitals; schools and colleges.

WHAT IS FUNDED Medical research; carers.

WHAT IS NOT FUNDED Animal-related charities, medical electives and projects eligible for statutory support are not considered.

TYPE OF GRANT Capital costs; project costs; core costs; research; start-up costs. Funding is available for up to three years.

RANGE OF GRANTS Grants range from £3,000 to £28,400; typically awards are of £3,000 to £5,000.

SAMPLE GRANTS Tenovus Scotland (£28,400); Glasgow City Mission (£5,000); Troon Coastal Rowing Club (£4,000); Glasgow Gorillas, The National Youth Board of Scotland, Sailors' Children's Society and St Columba's Hospice (£3,000 each).

FINANCES *Financial year end* 05/04/2020 *Income* £60,100 *Total grants* £58,400 *Grants to organisations* £58,400 *Assets* £1,600,000

HOW TO APPLY Applications can be made in writing to the correspondent, although due to continuing support to long-term projects and anticipated repeat grants to other organisations, new requests for assistance are unlikely to be successful.

CONTACT DETAILS The Trustees, c/o Mitchells Roberton Law Firm, George House, 36 North Hanover Street, Glasgow G1 2AD

Rees Jeffreys Road Fund

CC NO 217771 **ESTABLISHED** 1950

WHERE FUNDING CAN BE GIVEN UK.

WHO CAN BENEFIT Registered charities; unregistered charities; CICs; universities; individuals.

WHAT IS FUNDED Education and research in transport; projects that improve the roadside environment for motorists and other road users.

TYPE OF GRANT Capital costs; project funding.

RANGE OF GRANTS £5,000 to £25,000.

SAMPLE GRANTS Hainaker Windmill Rest Area (£30,000); ADEPT Highway Trees Study (£25,000); Heybridge Basin Access (£8,000); CIRIA – Gully Pots (£7,500); Backroads Active Travel (£7,100).

FINANCES *Financial year end* 31/12/2020 *Income* £152,400 *Total grants* £108,300 *Grants to organisations* £98,300 *Assets* £7,090,000

TRUSTEES David Tarrant; Ginny Clarke; Prof. Glenn Lyons; Steve Gooding; Leon Daniels; Hilary Chipping; Prof. Glenn Lyons.

OTHER INFORMATION Grants were broken down as follows: research and other projects (£53,200); roadside rests and land adjoining (£45,100); educational bursaries and support (£10,000). It is worth noting that the charity paused new applications for both organisations and the bursary scheme in 2020 due to the COVID-19 pandemic, so the grant total is slightly lower than usual.

HOW TO APPLY Visit the charity's website for full details regarding the application process.

CONTACT DETAILS Ruth Bravery, Secretary, Flat 22, Jetty Court, Old Bellgate Place, London E14 3SX *Tel.* 05603 849370 *Email* secretary@reesjeffreys.co.uk *Website* www.reesjeffreys.co.uk

The Jenour Foundation

CC NO 256637 **ESTABLISHED** 1968

WHERE FUNDING CAN BE GIVEN UK, with a special interest in Wales.

WHO CAN BENEFIT Registered charities only.

WHAT IS FUNDED General charitable purposes including: health causes; medical research; young people; arts and culture; animal welfare.

TYPE OF GRANT Capital projects.

RANGE OF GRANTS Grants range from £1,000 to £6,000.

SAMPLE GRANTS Cancer Research Wales, Macmillan Cancer Support (£6,000 each); Welsh National Opera, The Army Benevolent Fund (£5,000 each); Ty Hafan (£3,000); Samaritans (£2,000); National Deaf Children's Society (£1,000).

FINANCES *Financial year end* 05/04/2020 *Income* £125,700 *Total grants* £116,800 *Grants to organisations* £116,800 *Assets* £3,730,000

TRUSTEES Sir Peter Phillips; James Zorab; Christopher Davies; Greer Hooper.

OTHER INFORMATION Grants were awarded to 43 organisations during the year.

HOW TO APPLY The trustees request that written applications are submitted to the registered office.

CONTACT DETAILS The Trustees, c/o Azets, Ty Derw, Lime Tree Court, Mulberry Drive, Cardiff Gate Business Park, Cardiff CF23 8AB *Tel.* 029 2054 9939 *Email* claire.thompson@azets.co.uk

The Jephcott Charitable Trust

CC NO 240915 **ESTABLISHED** 1965

WHERE FUNDING CAN BE GIVEN Worldwide.

WHO CAN BENEFIT Charitable organisations.

WHAT IS FUNDED Health; education; the natural environment; population control.

WHAT IS NOT FUNDED Organisations whose administrative expenses form more than 15% of their annual income; individuals; animal welfare; heritage.

TYPE OF GRANT Capital costs; project funding.

RANGE OF GRANTS Grants range from £2,000 to £10,000 and in exceptional cases up to £20,000.

SAMPLE GRANTS Kids Aid Tanzania (£10,000); Shine Trust (£8,000); Sports Forum for the Disabled (£6,000); Stay at School and Grow Peace (£5,000 each); Child Action Nepal (£1,700).

FINANCES *Financial year end* 30/06/2020 *Income* £49,800 *Total grants* £130,300 *Grants to organisations* £130,300 *Assets* £7,210,000

TRUSTEES Mark Jephcott; Lady Mary Jephcott; Stephen Lamdin; Keith Morgan; Dr David Thomas; James Parker; Christopher Parker.

OTHER INFORMATION Grants were made to 19 organisations during the year.

HOW TO APPLY Full and detailed guidelines and application forms can be downloaded from the trust's website. Applications are considered at trustees' meetings which are held in April and October.

CONTACT DETAILS The Secretary, The Threshing Barn, Ford, Kingsbridge, Devon TQ7 2LN *Tel.* 07941 102509 *Website* www.jephcottcharitabletrust.org.uk

The Jerusalem Trust

CC NO 285696 **ESTABLISHED** 1982

WHERE FUNDING CAN BE GIVEN Worldwide.

WHO CAN BENEFIT Registered charities.

WHAT IS FUNDED Christian evangelism and relief work overseas; Christian media and education; evangelism and Christian mission in the UK. The trust also runs a small grants programme to commission new art work for churches.

WHAT IS NOT FUNDED Building or repair work for churches; individuals.

TYPE OF GRANT Core costs; salaries; project funding; capacity building.

RANGE OF GRANTS Grants range from £33,500 up to £190,000.

SAMPLE GRANTS Tearfund (£190,000); CAFOD and Safe Families for Children (£100,000 each); Coventry Cathedral (£60,000); Fegans (£50,000); Religious Education Council (£40,000); Liverpool Hope University (£33,500).

FINANCES *Financial year end* 05/04/2020 *Income* £3,020,000 *Total grants* £2,940,000 *Grants to organisations* £2,940,000 *Assets* £96,610,000

TRUSTEES Lady Susan Sainsbury; The Rt Hon. Sir Timothy Sainsbury; Prof. Peter Frankopan; Melanie Townsend; David Wright; Mark Browning; Colin Harbidge.

OTHER INFORMATION The trust is one of the Sainsbury Family Charitable Trusts which share a common administration – see www.sftc.org.uk for more information. In 2019/20, the trustees committed 30% of their budget to Christian education, 15% to Christian evangelism and relief work overseas, 13% to Christian media, 39% to evangelism and Christian missions in the UK, and 3% to Christian art.

HOW TO APPLY Apply using the online application form on the trust's website which includes details of what to include. Alternatively you may submit a funding enquiry by post to The Sainsbury Family Charitable Trusts. Your enquiry should be no longer than two sides of A4 and provide the same information as the form.

CONTACT DETAILS Robert Bell, Director, The Peak, 5 Wilton Road, London SW1V 1AP *Tel.* 020 7410 0330 *Email* info@sfct.org.uk or proposals@sfct.org.uk *Website* www.sfct.org.uk

Jesus Hospital Charity

CC NO 1075889 **ESTABLISHED** 1679

WHERE FUNDING CAN BE GIVEN Barnet.

WHO CAN BENEFIT Charitable organisations and individuals.

WHAT IS FUNDED Social welfare.

RANGE OF GRANTS Mostly £1,000 to £5,000.

SAMPLE GRANTS Noah's Ark (£7,000); Sense (£3,000); Spring Chicken (£1,300); Rainbow Transport (£470).

FINANCES *Financial year end* 31/12/2019 *Income* £769,500 *Total grants* £62,400 *Grants to organisations* £56,300 *Assets* £15,020,000

TRUSTEES Lady Janet Hulme; Catherine Cavanagh; Steven Sowerby; Brian Salinger; William Carrington; Brenda Sanford; Barbara Taylor; Neil Anthony; Malcom Bye; Margaret McPeake; Peter Hobday; Michael Crisp.

OTHER INFORMATION Grants to individuals totalled £6,100.

HOW TO APPLY Application forms are available to download from the charity's website.

CONTACT DETAILS The Trustees, Ravenscroft Lodge, 37 Union Street, Barnet, Hertfordshire EN5 4HY *Tel.* 020 8440 4374 *Email* info@jesushospitalcharity.org.uk *Website* www.jesushospitalcharity.org.uk

■ Jewish Child's Day (JCD)

CC NO 209266 **ESTABLISHED** 1947

WHERE FUNDING CAN BE GIVEN Worldwide with a preference for Israel and the UK.

WHO CAN BENEFIT Registered charities providing equipment or services of direct benefit to Jewish children (up to the age of 18).

WHAT IS FUNDED Jewish children.

TYPE OF GRANT Items of equipment; project funding.

RANGE OF GRANTS Generally £1,000 to £5,000, with occasional larger grants.

SAMPLE GRANTS Arugot (£25,400); One Heart (£5,000); Akim Haifa (£4,000); Dolev Homes (£2,500); Bayis Sheli (£1,000).

FINANCES *Financial year end* 30/06/2020 *Income* £1,450,000 *Total grants* £765,000 *Grants to organisations* £765,000 *Assets* £1,920,000

TRUSTEES Melvyn Orton; David Collins; Charles Spungin; Gary Cohen; Virginia Campus; Joy Moss; Stephen Moss; Gaby Lazarus; Susie Olins; Frankie Epstein.

OTHER INFORMATION Grants were distributed as follows: Israel (£255,400); UK (£126,700); rest of the world (£27,800).

HOW TO APPLY Contact the correspondent for further information on applying for a grant.

CONTACT DETAILS Adele Busse, First Floor, Elscot House, Arcadia Avenue, London N3 2JU *Tel.* 020 8446 8804 *Email* adele.busse@jcd.uk.com *Website* jcd.uk.com/projects-grants

■ The Jewish Youth Fund

CC NO 251902 **ESTABLISHED** 1937

WHERE FUNDING CAN BE GIVEN UK.

WHO CAN BENEFIT Jewish organisations.

WHAT IS FUNDED Jewish youth work projects, equipment.

TYPE OF GRANT Projects and equipment. Loans may be offered towards the cost of building. The charity can provide start-up costs as well as subsequent funding.

RANGE OF GRANTS Usually £1,000 to £50,000.

SAMPLE GRANTS Previous beneficiaries have included: Chaverim Winter Camp, Friends of Bnei Akiva, Jewish Women's Aid, Kisharon, Maccabi GB, Noam, Skeet Hill House and Step by Step.

FINANCES *Financial year end* 30/09/2020 *Income* £75,800 *Total grants* £194,200 *Grants to organisations* £194,200 *Assets* £3,020,000

TRUSTEES Philippa Strauss; Adam Rose; Lady Ruth Morris of Kenwood; Lord Jonathan Morris; David Goldberg; Elliot Simberg; Stephen Spitz; Esmond Rosen; Simon Cutner; Joseph Woolf; Philip Goldstein.

HOW TO APPLY Applications can be made on a form available online. Applicants should enclose a copy of their latest accounts and annual report. For the most up-to-date submission deadline, consult the charity's website.

CONTACT DETAILS Julia Samuel, Secretary, 35 Ballards Lane, London N3 1XW *Email* info@jyf.org.uk *Website* www.jyf.org.uk

■ Joffe Charitable Trust

CC NO 1180520 **ESTABLISHED** 1968

WHERE FUNDING CAN BE GIVEN Worldwide/lower income countries.

WHO CAN BENEFIT Registered charities.

WHAT IS FUNDED Corruption and the promotion of tax justice; building stronger not-for-profit organisations.

WHAT IS NOT FUNDED Emergency relief; individuals; physical infrastructure; the arts; work that only benefits UK communities.

TYPE OF GRANT Grants for up to three years; development funding; project costs; core costs; unrestricted; start-up funding.

RANGE OF GRANTS The trust normally makes grants in the range of £5,000 to £30,000 per year for up to three years.

SAMPLE GRANTS People and Planet (£43,400); ActionAid (£30,000); Omega Research Foundation (£20,000); Tax Watch Ltd (£15,000).

FINANCES *Financial year end* 31/12/2019 *Income* £10,670,000 *Total grants* £452,600 *Grants to organisations* £452,600 *Assets* £10,810,000

TRUSTEES Vanetta Joffe; Deb Joffe; Myles Wickstead; Barbara Frost.

HOW TO APPLY The charity is a relatively small charitable trust and can only make a few new grants each year. Most of the initiatives it funds come through its existing networks. However, the trust welcomes enquiries from applicants whose work is in line with the trust's objectives. Full details of how to approach the charity can be found on its website.

CONTACT DETAILS Carin Lake, Trust Manager, 4th Floor, Invicta House, 108–114 Golden Lane, London EC1Y 0TL *Email* carin@joffetrust.org *Website* https://joffetrust.org

■ The Elton John Aids Foundation (EJAF)

CC NO 1017336 **ESTABLISHED** 1993

WHERE FUNDING CAN BE GIVEN Worldwide.

WHO CAN BENEFIT Registered charities; community-based organisations.

WHAT IS FUNDED HIV/AIDS welfare and prevention; health and the saving of lives; the prevention or relief of poverty; overseas aid; LGBTQ+ rights; health advice and addiction; advocacy and campaigning.

WHAT IS NOT FUNDED Exclusions vary for each programme. Check the foundation's website for full details.

TYPE OF GRANT Programme dependent.

RANGE OF GRANTS Up to £4 million.

SAMPLE GRANTS Scanad Kenya (£3.92 million); Population Services International (£2.17 million); Lambeth Borough Council (£547,700); India HIV/AIDS Alliance (£416,500); Alliance for Public Health (£234,800); National AIDS Trust (£120,000); Humanitarian Action (£70,000).

FINANCES *Financial year end* 31/12/2019 *Income* £15,830,000 *Total grants* £8,490,000 *Grants to organisations* £8,490,000 *Assets* £15,000,000

TRUSTEES David Furnish; John Bergius; Dr Mark Dybul; Tracy Blackwell; Ilana Kloss; Ajaz Ahmed; Dr Eric Goosby.

HOW TO APPLY See the foundation's website for more information on its open funding programmes, eligibility criteria and details of how to make an application.

CONTACT DETAILS The Trustees, 1 Blythe Road, London W14 0HG *Tel.* 020 7603 9996 *Email* admin@eltonjohnaidsfoundation.org *Website* london.ejaf.org/grants

■ Lillie Johnson Charitable Trust

CC NO 326761 **ESTABLISHED** 1984

WHERE FUNDING CAN BE GIVEN UK, with a preference for the West Midlands.

WHO CAN BENEFIT Charitable organisations; hospices; hospitals.

WHAT IS FUNDED General charitable purposes, particularly health, disability, and children and young people.

WHAT IS NOT FUNDED In practice, individuals are not supported.

RANGE OF GRANTS Up to £45,000; the vast majority of grants are of £1,000 or less.

SAMPLE GRANTS LEC Worcester (£45,000); Birmingham Youth Theatre (£5,100); The Prince's Trust (£4,000); Hearts of England Association (£2,500); Birmingham Children's Hospital, Brain Tumour Support and Solihull Samaritans (£2,000 each); Harborne Carnival (£1,500); Breast Cancer Haven, Family Care Trust, Living Paintings, Macmillan Nurses, Sight Concern and West Midlands Tennis Foundation (£1,000 each).

FINANCES *Financial year end* 05/04/2020 *Income* £207,800 *Total grants* £185,000 *Grants to organisations* £185,000 *Assets* £6,530,000

TRUSTEES Victor Lyttle; John Desmond; Verena Adams; Lynn Brookes; Daniel Adams; Alastair Lyttle.

OTHER INFORMATION A total of 193 organisations were supported in 2019/20. Grants of less than £1,000 totalled £86,000 and were distributed between 156 organisations.

HOW TO APPLY Apply in writing to the correspondent. Contact the correspondent for further information before making an application.

CONTACT DETAILS John Desmond, Trustee, 39 Rodbourne Road, Harborne, Birmingham, West Midlands B17 0PN *Tel.* 07854 175530 *Email* john.w.desmond@googlemail.com

■ The Johnson Foundation

CC NO 518660 **ESTABLISHED** 1987

WHERE FUNDING CAN BE GIVEN Liverpool and the Merseyside area.

WHO CAN BENEFIT Registered charities; community care organisations; educational bodies. The 2019/20 annual report states that: 'While the Foundation is always prepared to help large charities, it tends to specialise in helping the smaller charities unable to afford professional fund raisers.'

WHAT IS FUNDED General charitable purposes; education; health; the relief of poverty and sickness.

WHAT IS NOT FUNDED Individuals.

TYPE OF GRANT One-off or for up to two years; recurrent costs; project funding; research funding.

RANGE OF GRANTS Up to £150,000.

SAMPLE GRANTS Pacific Road Enterprise Hub (£150,000); Feeding Birkenhead (£90,000); Liverpool Heart and Chest Hospital (£80,000); Wirral Hospice St Johns (£7,500); North West Cancer Research (£5,500); MedEquip 4 Kids (£4,300); Hoylake Community Centre (£3,100); Claire House Children's Hospice (£2,000); Amy and Friends (£1,500); Mayor's Special Charity (£1,000).

FINANCES *Financial year end* 31/03/2020 *Income* £153,000 *Total grants* £551,500 *Grants to organisations* £551,500 *Assets* £2,700,000

TRUSTEES Christopher Johnson; Peter Johnson; Katherine Eugeni; Charlotte Johnson; Susan Stevenson.

HOW TO APPLY Applications can be made in writing to the correspondent. The trustees meet monthly to discuss applications.

CONTACT DETAILS Kate Eugeni, Trust Administrator, G6, Pacific Road Business Hub, 1 Pacific Road, Birkenhead, Merseyside CH41 1LJ *Tel.* 0151 650 6987 *Email* kate@johnsonfoundation.co.uk

■ Johnnie Johnson Trust

CC NO 200351 **ESTABLISHED** 1961

WHERE FUNDING CAN BE GIVEN UK, with a preference for the Midlands.

WHO CAN BENEFIT Charitable organisations which provide activities for children and young people, particularly those who are disadvantaged or who have disabilities.

WHAT IS FUNDED The trust supports activities which promote the development of individuals by being either physically and/or mentally challenging. Sailing and water sports for young people in the Midlands are a priority.

TYPE OF GRANT Usually one-off, for equipment or for specific purposes.

RANGE OF GRANTS Up to £19,000 but mostly from £1,000 to £5,000.

SAMPLE GRANTS Outward Bound Trust (£19,100); UK Windsurfing Association (£7,600); Off the Record (£2,500); Kinship Care Northern Ireland Ltd (£1,100).

FINANCES *Financial year end* 31/12/2019 *Income* £132,100 *Total grants* £120,700 *Grants to organisations* £120,700 *Assets* £5,610,000

TRUSTEES Jane Fordham; Peter Johnson; Katherine Cross; Christopher Johnson; Alice Johnson.

HOW TO APPLY Contact the correspondent for further information.

CONTACT DETAILS The Trustees, The Trust Partnership Ltd, 6 Trull Farm Buildings, Tetbury, Gloucestershire GL8 8SQ *Tel.* 01285 841900

■ The Christopher and Kirsty Johnston Charitable Trust

CC NO 1159433 **ESTABLISHED** 2014

WHERE FUNDING CAN BE GIVEN UK and overseas.

WHO CAN BENEFIT Charitable organisations.

WHAT IS FUNDED General charitable purposes.

RANGE OF GRANTS Up to £70,000.

SAMPLE GRANTS Mission to Seafarers (£70,000); All Saints Chiang Mai Mission (£46,000); Willen Hospice (£25,000); Dementia UK (£5,000); Support Dogs and Puzzle Centre (£1,000 each).

FINANCES *Financial year end* 30/06/2020 *Income* £256,300 *Total grants* £220,000 *Grants to organisations* £220,000 *Assets* £77,600

TRUSTEES Dr John Barber; Christopher Johnston; Kirsty Johnston.

OTHER INFORMATION Grants were made to 11 organisations during the year.

HOW TO APPLY Apply in writing to the correspondent. Note that the trust has limited sources of income.

CONTACT DETAILS The Trustees, 24 Tudor Gardens, Stony Stratford, Milton Keynes, Buckinghamshire MK11 1HX *Tel.* 01908 562113 *Email* candkjct@gmail.com

■ The Joicey Trust

CC NO 244679 **ESTABLISHED** 1965

WHERE FUNDING CAN BE GIVEN Northumberland; Tyne and Wear; the Scottish Borders.

WHO CAN BENEFIT Registered charities; unregistered charities; CICs; places of worship.

WHAT IS FUNDED General charitable purposes.

WHAT IS NOT FUNDED Research and research costs within core funding applications; charities not registered within the beneficiary area or with gross incoming resources exceeding £1 million.

TYPE OF GRANT Capital costs; core/revenue costs.

SAMPLE GRANTS Greggs Foundation (£15,000); Acorns – North Tyneside (£5,000); Young and Sweet (£3,000); Children's Foundation (£1,900); Gisland Village Hall (£400).

FINANCES *Financial year end* 05/04/2020 *Income* £319,900 *Total grants* £352,600 *Grants to organisations* £352,600 *Assets* £6,950,000

TRUSTEES The Hon. Andrew Joicey; Mr R. H. Dickinson; The Hon. Mrs K. J. Crosbie Dawson; The Rt Hon. Lady Joicey; The Rt Hon. The Lord Joicey.

HOW TO APPLY Applications can be obtained by completing a contact form on the trust's website. The trustees meet twice a year, usually in January/early February and late June/July. Applications should be submitted to the appeals secretary in time to allow for any queries to be resolved by 30 November or 31 May each year for consideration at the next trustees' meeting; early applications are therefore encouraged.

CONTACT DETAILS The Trustees, One Trinity, Broad Chare, Newcastle upon Tyne NE1 2HF *Tel.* 0191 279 9676 *Email* appeals@thejoiceytrust.org.uk *Website* www.thejoiceytrust.org.uk

■ The Jones 1986 Charitable Trust

CC NO 327176 **ESTABLISHED** 1986

WHERE FUNDING CAN BE GIVEN Primarily Nottinghamshire.

WHO CAN BENEFIT Charitable organisations; schools; CICs; hospices.

WHAT IS FUNDED Social welfare; health and disability; older people; children and young people.

WHAT IS NOT FUNDED Individuals; activities that are the responsibility of the local health authority, education authority or similar body.

TYPE OF GRANT Capital costs; core/revenue costs.

RANGE OF GRANTS Up to £1 million, but mostly between £1,000 and £10,000.

SAMPLE GRANTS Nottinghamshire Hospice (£1 million); Trinity Centre (£15,000); Newlife (£10,000); Wild Things (£3,00); Orchid Cancer Appeal (£2,000); Deafblind UK (£1,000).

FINANCES *Financial year end* 05/04/2020 *Income* £1,610,000 *Total grants* £1,330,000 *Grants to organisations* £1,330,000 *Assets* £43,770,000

TRUSTEES John Pears; David Lindley; Richard Stanley.

OTHER INFORMATION Grants were distributed as follows: relief of sickness and disability (£1.11 million); community benefit (£150,000); young people's welfare (£69,700); older people's welfare (£2,200).

HOW TO APPLY Application forms can be found on the funder's website.

CONTACT DETAILS David Lindley, Trustee, c/o Smith Cooper Ltd, 2 Lace Market Square, Nottingham, Nottinghamshire NG1 1PB *Tel.* 07710 639946 *Email* jonestrust86@gmail.com

■ The Marjorie and Geoffrey Jones Charitable Trust

CC NO 1051031 **ESTABLISHED** 1995

WHERE FUNDING CAN BE GIVEN Principally Torbay, Devon and the South West.

WHO CAN BENEFIT Registered charities; CICs.

WHAT IS FUNDED General charitable purposes, including health and disability, children and families, arts and culture, sport, and the environment.

WHAT IS NOT FUNDED Individuals.

SAMPLE GRANTS Previous beneficiaries have included: Babbacombe Cliff Railway CIC, Exeter Cathedral, Green Hill Arts, Living Options Devon, The Paignton Picture House Trust, Motor Neurone Disease Association, National Search and Rescue Dog Association, National Trust, Shelter, Trinity Sailing Foundation and Youth Genesis.

FINANCES *Financial year end* 25/02/2020 *Income* £21,700 *Total grants* £50,000 *Grants to organisations* £50,000

TRUSTEES Nigel Wollen; William Boughey; Philip Kay; Katrina Vollentine.

OTHER INFORMATION Full accounts were not available to view on the Charity Commission's website due to the trust's low income. We have therefore estimated the grant total based on the trust's total expenditure.

HOW TO APPLY Apply in writing to the correspondent. The trustees usually meet to consider awards between two and four times a year.

CONTACT DETAILS Lynn Young, Carlton House, 30 The Terrace, Torquay, Devon TQ1 1BS *Tel.* 01803 213251 *Email* lynn.young@wollenmichelmore.co.uk

■ The Muriel Jones Foundation

CC NO 1135107 **ESTABLISHED** 2010

WHERE FUNDING CAN BE GIVEN UK and overseas.

WHO CAN BENEFIT Charitable organisations.

WHAT IS FUNDED General charitable purposes.

RANGE OF GRANTS £200 to £200,000.

SAMPLE GRANTS Médecins Sans Frontières (£200,000); Animals Asia Foundation and World Land Trust (£100,000 each); Epatoma Foundation (seven grants totalling £70,600); FareShare (£50,000); Downside Up (two grants totalling £18,000); Downside Abbey General Trust (£2,700); Prader-Willi Syndrome Association (£1,000); Crohn's and Colitis (£200).

FINANCES *Financial year end* 28/02/2020 *Income* £126,800 *Total grants* £751,600 *Grants to organisations* £751,600 *Assets* £5,210,000

TRUSTEES Richard Brindle; Katie Brindle; Coutts & Co.

OTHER INFORMATION The foundation awarded a total of 23 grants to 15 organisations in 2019/20. Our research shows that the foundation has a preference for environmental, welfare and human rights charities.

HOW TO APPLY Apply by letter to the correspondent.

CONTACT DETAILS The Trustees, Coutts & Co. Trustee Department, 1st Floor, Trinity Quay 1,

Avon Street, Bristol BS2 0PT *Tel.* 0345 304 2424

■ The Jordan Charitable Foundation

CC NO 1051507 **ESTABLISHED** 1995

WHERE FUNDING CAN BE GIVEN UK.

WHO CAN BENEFIT Registered charities.

WHAT IS FUNDED Children and young people; education.

TYPE OF GRANT Capital costs; core/revenue costs.

RANGE OF GRANTS Mostly between £2,000 and £20,000.

SAMPLE GRANTS The Sutton Trust (£2.5 million); The Prince's Trust (£500,000); The Samaritans (£15,000); Woodlands Trust (£10,000); Plantlife (£500).

FINANCES *Financial year end* 31/12/2019 *Income* £4,780,000 *Total grants* £5,050,000 *Grants to organisations* £5,050,000 *Assets* £128,480,000

TRUSTEES Sir George Russell; Christopher Bliss; Anthony Brierley; Nicholas Fry; Snowport Ltd; Parkdove Ltd.

OTHER INFORMATION Grants were made to 59 organisations. The foundation used to support a variety of causes throughout Herefordshire but now focuses primarily on education.

HOW TO APPLY Applications may be made in writing to the correspondent. The trustees meet four times a year.

CONTACT DETAILS The Trustees, 8th Floor, 6 New Street Square, New Fetter Lane, London EC4A 3AQ *Tel.* 020 7842 2000 *Email* jordan@rawlinson-hunter.com

■ The Joron Charitable Trust

CC NO 1062547 **ESTABLISHED** 1997

WHERE FUNDING CAN BE GIVEN UK.

WHO CAN BENEFIT Registered charities; hospitals.

WHAT IS FUNDED General charitable purposes; education; medical research.

TYPE OF GRANT Project funding; core/revenue costs; capital costs; one-off.

RANGE OF GRANTS Up to £500,000.

SAMPLE GRANTS The Gem Project (£375,000); NHS Direct Together (£150,000); UNICEF (£25,000); Blind Veterans UK (£5,000); The Salvation Army (£2,500).

FINANCES *Financial year end* 31/03/2020 *Income* £853,000 *Total grants* £839,200 *Grants to organisations* £839,200 *Assets* £214,600

TRUSTEES Bruce Jarvis; John Jarvis; Sandra Jarvis; Juliet Jarvis.

OTHER INFORMATION The trust awarded 21 grants during the year.

HOW TO APPLY Apply in writing to the correspondent. There is no formal application procedure.

CONTACT DETAILS The Trustees, c/o Ravensale Ltd, New Broadway, London W5 2XA *Tel.* 020 8908 4655 *Email* info@ravensale.com

■ J. E. Joseph Charitable Fund

CC NO 209058 **ESTABLISHED** 1946

WHERE FUNDING CAN BE GIVEN London, Manchester, Israel and India.

WHO CAN BENEFIT Jewish charities.

WHAT IS FUNDED The relief of poverty and suffering; education; advancement of the Jewish religion; other charitable purposes beneficial to the Jewish community.

WHAT IS NOT FUNDED Individuals (however, individuals may receive support in exceptional cases in which the whole community may benefit); large national charities with significant income; capital projects are generally not supported.

RANGE OF GRANTS £1,200 to £7,500.

SAMPLE GRANTS University Jewish Chaplaincy Board and Jewish Choice (£7,500); S&P Synagogue Welfare Board (£5,500); Melabev (£4,500); Moishe House (£3,500); Feuerstein Institute (£3,000); AKIM Haifa (£2,500); Jaffa Institute (£2,000); Ilford Eastern Sephardi Synagogue (£1,300).

FINANCES *Financial year end* 05/04/2020 *Income* £178,300 *Total grants* £152,000 *Grants to organisations* £152,000 *Assets* £4,970,000

TRUSTEE J. E. Joseph Trustee Company Ltd.

OTHER INFORMATION Forty-five grants were awarded to organisations during the year. According to the annual report for 2019/20, 'the trustees decided to reduce or not award grants to charities with large incomes and multimillion-pound budgets. Grants were directed more towards smaller charities, where the trust's grants made a difference and were relatively important to them.'

HOW TO APPLY Applications may be made in writing to the correspondent, including a copy of the latest accounts. The trustees respond to all applications, which are first vetted by the secretary.

CONTACT DETAILS Roger Leon, Secretary, 10 Compass Close, Edgware, Middlesex HA8 8HU *Tel.* 020 8958 0126 *Email* roger.leon@btinternet.com

■ The Cyril and Eve Jumbo Charitable Trust

CC NO 1097209 **ESTABLISHED** 2003

WHERE FUNDING CAN BE GIVEN Worldwide.

WHO CAN BENEFIT Charitable organisations.

WHAT IS FUNDED General charitable purposes; overseas aid.

TYPE OF GRANT The website states that the trustees are 'less keen on capital projects'.

RANGE OF GRANTS £100 to £15,000.

SAMPLE GRANTS My Action for Kids (£33,500); World Jewish Relief (£30,000); Literacy Pirates (£22,500); Send a Cow (£11,250); Ahmadiyya Muslim Association UK (£10,000); Humanity First (£5,500); CRISIS (£2,500) Action Against Cancer (£500); Mental Health UK (£100).

FINANCES *Financial year end* 05/04/2020 *Income* £268,100 *Total grants* £303,500 *Grants to organisations* £303,500 *Assets* £2,090,000

TRUSTEES Geoffrey Margolis; Rafiq Hayat; Edward Engulu; Lorraine Margolis.

OTHER INFORMATION The trust's funding is equally divided between causes in the UK and overseas. Its website describes a preference for programmes for adolescents and post-adolescents in England and self-sufficiency projects in financially developing countries.

HOW TO APPLY The annual report states that applications can be submitted to the trustees and are considered regularly. Applications should be sent in writing and incorporate full details of the charity for which funding is requested. Acknowledgements are usually sent to unsuccessful applicants.

CONTACT DETAILS The Trustees, Mumbo Jumbo World, 48 Great Marlborough Street, London W1F 7BB *Tel.* 020 7437 0879 *Email* charity@mjw13.com *Website* www.cejct.com

■ Anton Jurgens Charitable Trust

CC NO 259885 **ESTABLISHED** 1969

WHERE FUNDING CAN BE GIVEN UK.

WHO CAN BENEFIT UK-registered charities.

WHAT IS FUNDED People who are socially disadvantaged and/or have mental and/or physical disabilities.

WHAT IS NOT FUNDED Religious promotion; arts and culture (unless used for therapeutic purposes).

TYPE OF GRANT Generally one-off; project funding.

RANGE OF GRANTS £2,000 to £5,000.

SAMPLE GRANTS The Ulysses Trust (£7,000); Crisis (£4,000); Animal Antiks and Wintercomfort (£3,000 each); Bath City Farm and Life Education (£2,000 each); Siblings Together (£1,500).

FINANCES *Financial year end* 05/04/2020 *Income* £275,300 *Total grants* £277,300 *Grants to organisations* £277,300 *Assets* £7,363,000

TRUSTEES Hans Veraart; Maria Edge-Jurgens; Frans Tilman; Frans Jurgens; Paul Beek.

OTHER INFORMATION Grants were made to more than 50 organisations during the year.

HOW TO APPLY Applications can be made via the trust's website.

CONTACT DETAILS Vivienne Jurgens, Kellas Estate, Mains of Kellas, Kellas, Moray IV30 8TS *Email* grants@ajct.org.uk *Website* https://www.antonjurgensfonds.nl/en/applications/ajct

■ The Jusaca Charitable Trust

CC NO 1012966 **ESTABLISHED** 1992

WHERE FUNDING CAN BE GIVEN UK and overseas, particularly Israel.

WHO CAN BENEFIT Registered charities; schools; universities; hospices; religious bodies/institutions.

WHAT IS FUNDED General charitable purposes; Jewish causes; the relief of poverty; health; education; the arts; research; housing.

TYPE OF GRANT Capital costs; core and revenue costs; seed funding; start-up funding.

RANGE OF GRANTS Typically £1,000 to £5,000.

SAMPLE GRANTS World Jewish Relief (£40,100); Jewish Care (£20,000); Israel Free Loan Association (£18,600).

FINANCES *Financial year end* 31/03/2020 *Income* £198,000 *Total grants* £334,800 *Grants to organisations* £334,800 *Assets* £3,430,000

TRUSTEES Dr Donald Franklin; Miriam Emanuel; Maurice Emanuel; Jacob Emanuel; Mrs D. Franklin; Rachel Paul; Sara Emanuel; Ms C. Emanuel.

HOW TO APPLY Contact the correspondent for further information.

CONTACT DETAILS The Trustees, 17 Ashburnham Grove, London SE10 8UH *Tel.* 020 8692 2467

■ Kantor Charitable Foundation

CC NO 1173550 **ESTABLISHED** 2017

WHERE FUNDING CAN BE GIVEN UK.

WHO CAN BENEFIT Charitable organisations.

WHAT IS FUNDED General charitable purposes; the arts; health; education; Jewish religion and culture.

RANGE OF GRANTS £9,000 and above, with some exceptional larger grants.

SAMPLE GRANTS Previous beneficiaries have included: King Edward VII's Hospital (£9 million); Anna Freud Centre (£1.5 million); University College School (£200,000); Jewish Leadership Council (£150,000); The Board of Deputies of British Jews (£72,000); Jewish Care (£10,000); Maggie Keswick Jencks Cancer Trust and Royal Marines charity (£9,000 each).

FINANCES *Financial year end* 31/12/2019 *Income* £9,300 *Total grants* £2,630,000 *Grants to organisations* £2,630,000

TRUSTEE Kantor Trustees.

OTHER INFORMATION Full accounts were not available to view on the Charity Commission's website due to the foundation's low income. We have therefore estimated the grant total based on the foundation's total expenditure.

HOW TO APPLY The foundation does not invite unsolicited applications.

CONTACT DETAILS Dr Kantor, Chair of the Board, c/o Withers LLP, Third Floor, 20 Old Bailey, London EC4M 7AN *Tel.* 020 7507 6000

■ The Boris Karloff Charitable Foundation

CC NO 326898 **ESTABLISHED** 1985

WHERE FUNDING CAN BE GIVEN UK.

WHO CAN BENEFIT Charitable organisations; performing arts organisations.

WHAT IS FUNDED Performing arts; the promotion of cricket; young cricketers.

RANGE OF GRANTS Mostly £500 to £6,000.

SAMPLE GRANTS The Young Vic Company (£12,600); The London Academy of Music and Dramatic Art (£6,000); Arundel Castle Cricket Foundation (£5,000); Irish Theatre Company and Scene and Heard (£2,000 each); The Performing Arts Children's Charity and Young Urban Arts Foundation (£1,000 each); Edinburgh International Festival (£500).

FINANCES *Financial year end* 05/04/2020 *Income* £86,500 *Total grants* £66,200 *Grants to organisations* £66,200 *Assets* £2,560,000

TRUSTEES James Fairclough; Owen Lewis; Carole Fairclough.

OTHER INFORMATION During the year, the foundation awarded 37 grants to organisations.

HOW TO APPLY Contact the correspondent for further information.

CONTACT DETAILS The Trustees, c/o Russell Cooke Solicitors, 2 Putney Hill, London SW15 6AB *Tel.* 020 8394 6488

■ The Karlsson Jativa Charitable Foundation

CC NO 1168787 **ESTABLISHED** 2016

WHERE FUNDING CAN BE GIVEN UK; Sweden; Peru; Bolivia; Ecuador; Colombia.

WHO CAN BENEFIT Registered charities; music schools; conservatories; orchestras; choirs; or other music establishments, with preference given to well-established charities.

WHAT IS FUNDED Music, including increasing access to music education; health; education; the relief of poverty.

SAMPLE GRANTS Latin American Children's Trust (£1 million); Signatur Foundation Sweden (£533,600); Birmingham Conservatoire (£100,000); Aurora Orchestra and London Music Masters (£50,000 each).

FINANCES *Financial year end* 31/12/2019 *Income* £629,600 *Total grants* £1,730,000 *Grants to organisations* £1,730,000 *Assets* £30,170,000

TRUSTEES Erland Karlsson; Rose Karlsson; Martin Andersson; Jeremy Arnold; Annika Magnusson.

OTHER INFORMATION Through its Signatur programmes in the UK and Sweden, the foundation awards grants to promote the advancement of music, particularly among young people. The foundation also supports poverty, health and education in Latin America through an annual donation to Latin American Children's Trust, a UK-registered charity. Grants were awarded to five organisations during the year, for poverty, health and education (£1 million) and music (£733,600).

HOW TO APPLY The trustees identify projects to be funded. Contact the foundation for further information.

CONTACT DETAILS Claire Miller, 2nd Floor, 23 King Street, London SW1Y 6QY *Tel.* 020 3931 5210 *Email* info@kjcf.org.uk *Website* https://kjcf.org.uk

■ The Ian Karten Charitable Trust

CC NO 281721 **ESTABLISHED** 1980

WHERE FUNDING CAN BE GIVEN UK; the Republic of Ireland; Israel.

WHO CAN BENEFIT Current Karten Centres; individuals wishing to enter and complete higher and postgraduate education.

WHAT IS FUNDED Improving the quality of life and independence of people with severe physical, sensory or cognitive disabilities or mental health problems by providing Karten Centres, where people are supported to use technology and assistive technology in learning, working or residential contexts; study and research at universities in the UK and Israel, particularly the provision of access funding for students in challenging personal circumstances to study at Southampton and Warwick Universities; awareness and education of Jewish/non-Jewish relations.

TYPE OF GRANT Project funding; capital costs.

RANGE OF GRANTS Generally up to £25,000.

SAMPLE GRANTS Parkes Institute Southampton University (£69,900); Natspec TechAbility (£24,900); Aspire (£25,000); ROC College (£16,500); The University of Southampton (£250); The Grange (£2,083); The Anne Frank Educational Trust (£500).

FINANCES *Financial year end* 30/09/2019 *Income* £534,200 *Total grants* £491,400 *Grants to organisations* £491,400 *Assets* £14,640,000

TRUSTEES Anthony Davis; Sally Cooke; Alexandra Moran; Edward Copisarow.

OTHER INFORMATION The 2018/19 accounts were the latest available at the time of writing (April 2021). The trust awarded £98,100 in scholarships and bursaries, as well as £393,300 to Karten Centres and other grants throughout the year.

HOW TO APPLY Our previous research indicates that the trustees only consider grants to charities supported in the past. Grants are no longer being made for new Karten Centres; however, existing centres may be able to apply for additional or upgraded equipment – check the trust's website for the next application deadline. The trustees meet every six months to review the accounts and to discuss any proposed donations, scholarships and bursaries.

CONTACT DETAILS The Trustees, International House, 64 Nile Street, London SO41 1BD *Tel.* 07720 931477 *Email* ines@iankartencharitabletrust.org.uk *Website* www.karten-network.org.uk

■ The Kasner Charitable Trust

CC NO 267510 **ESTABLISHED** 1973

WHERE FUNDING CAN BE GIVEN UK and overseas, with a preference for Manchester, London and Israel.

WHO CAN BENEFIT Charitable organisations; educational establishments; medical institutions; places of worship.

WHAT IS FUNDED Jewish causes, particularly the relief of poverty, the advancement of education and the furtherance of the Jewish faith. Organisations supported during 2019/20 were involved in maintaining places of religious services, providing Jewish education at primary and secondary school level, providing advanced study and higher education, helping children with special educational needs, providing medical advocacy, assisting couples experiencing infertility and supporting communities in 'immigrant' towns in Israel.

RANGE OF GRANTS Up to £5 million.

SAMPLE GRANTS UK Toremet Ltd (£5.29 million); Friends of the United Institutions of Arad (£584,000); Friends of Gur Foundation Israel (£470,000); KKL Charity Accounts (£250,000); Dignity Organisation (£144,000); Gitter Foundation (£50,000); Yesodey Hatorah Schools (£49,000); March of the Living (UK) Ltd (£46,000).

FINANCES *Financial year end* 31/03/2020 *Income* £11,470,000 *Total grants* £8,270,000 *Grants to organisations* £8,270,000 *Assets* £5,550,000

TRUSTEES Baruch Erlich; Judith Erlich; David Winegarten.

OTHER INFORMATION Grants were broken down as follows: the advancement of education (£3.89 million); general charitable purposes (£1.81 million); 'development of the Land of Israel and its citizens' (£1.33 million); relief of poverty (£623,700); the furtherance of religion (£482,700); medical advocacy and equipment (£131,200). Note: grants covering more than one category were classified under general charitable purposes. Grants of less than £45,000 totalled 270,000.

HOW TO APPLY Apply in writing to the correspondent. Most applications are successful. Certain organisations are investigated personally by the trustees and may receive larger grants.

CONTACT DETAILS Baruch Erlich, Trustee, 1A Gresham Gardens, London NW11 8NX *Tel.* 020 3637 2868

■ The Michael and Ilse Katz Foundation

CC NO 263726 **ESTABLISHED** 1971

WHERE FUNDING CAN BE GIVEN UK and overseas.

WHO CAN BENEFIT International and UK schemes and organisations benefitting Jewish people; at-risk groups or people who are disadvantaged by poverty or socially isolated.

WHAT IS FUNDED General charitable purposes, particularly Jewish causes and health/disability and social welfare.

RANGE OF GRANTS Up to £15,000.

SAMPLE GRANTS University College London Institute of Ophthalmology (£15,000); Jewish Care (£10,000); Bournemouth Symphony Orchestra and Nightingale Hammerson (£8,000 each); Beth Shalom (The Holocaust Centre); OHEL Sarah; Royal National Institute for the Blind and Starlight Children's Foundation (£5,000 each); Whizz-Kidz and Yad Vashem UK Foundation (£2,000 each).

FINANCES *Financial year end* 05/04/2019 *Income* £116,800 *Total grants* £85,000 *Grants to organisations* £85,000 *Assets* £2,882,400

TRUSTEES Norris Gilbert; Osman Azis; Lord Rupert Nathan; Jonathan Azis.

OTHER INFORMATION The 2018/19 accounts were the latest available at the time of writing (June 2021).

HOW TO APPLY Applications may be made in writing to the correspondent.

CONTACT DETAILS The Trustees, Counting House, Trelill, Bodmin PL30 3HZ *Tel.* 01208 851814 *Email* osmanazis@btconnect.com

■ C. S. Kaufman Charitable Trust

CC NO 253194 **ESTABLISHED** 1967

WHERE FUNDING CAN BE GIVEN UK.

WHO CAN BENEFIT Organisations benefitting Jewish people.

WHAT IS FUNDED Jewish causes; the promotion of the Jewish faith and education.

RANGE OF GRANTS Between £400 and £25,000 per grant.

SAMPLE GRANTS Keren Gemillas Chesed Fund (£110,000); Inspiration, Hadras Kodesh Trust and Craven Walk Beth Hamedrash Trust (£25,000 each); Kollel Sharei Shlomor (£5,000); SOFT (£1,000); Gateshead Hebrew Congregation (£432).

FINANCES *Financial year end* 05/04/2019 *Income* £97,800 *Total grants* £357,900 *Grants to organisations* £357,900 *Assets* £1,130,000

TRUSTEES Israel Kaufman; Simon Kaufman; Mr J. Kaufman; Mrs L. Kaufman.

OTHER INFORMATION The 2018/19 accounts were the latest available at the time of writing (January 2021). There were 31 awards made during the year, with some organisations receiving more than one grant.

HOW TO APPLY Contact the correspondent for further information.

CONTACT DETAILS The Trustees, c/o Ernst & Young LLP, Citygate, St James Boulevard, Newcastle upon Tyne, Tyne and Wear NE1 4JD *Tel.* 0191 247 2500

The Emmanuel Kaye Foundation

CC NO 280281 **ESTABLISHED** 1980

WHERE FUNDING CAN BE GIVEN UK, with a preference for north-east Hampshire.

WHO CAN BENEFIT Registered charities; charitable organisations.

WHAT IS FUNDED General charitable purposes, including the following: medical research; penal reform; education; music; performing arts; the prevention of sexual exploitation; social welfare; community development.

RANGE OF GRANTS £5,000 to £30,000.

SAMPLE GRANTS Parkinson's UK (£150,000); Lyric Hammersmith (£32,000); Rosa Fund (£30,000); Against Violence and Abuse (£25,000); Awards for Young Musicians (£20,000); Prison Reform Trust (£10,000); The Cure Parkinson's Trust (£5,000).

FINANCES *Financial year end* 31/07/2020 *Income* £970,300 *Total grants* £724,000 *Grants to organisations* £724,000 *Assets* £4,470,000

TRUSTEES John Forster; Eleanor Kaye; Louise Kaye; Madeleine Hawes; Anton Sternberg.

OTHER INFORMATION Grants were awarded to 31 organisations during the year in the following categories: medical research; penal reform; education; music for young people; performing arts; prevention of sexual exploitation; other.

HOW TO APPLY The charity's 2019/20 accounts state: 'The foundation does not accept unsolicited requests for grants or donations, focusing its support for registered charities principally, but not exclusively, where a relationship with trustees has been established.'

CONTACT DETAILS John Forster, Trustee, PO Box 1579, Woking, Surrey GU21 9DS *Tel.* 07585 341626 *Email* john@ekf.org.uk

The Kelly Family Charitable Trust

CC NO 1102440 **ESTABLISHED** 2004

WHERE FUNDING CAN BE GIVEN UK.

WHO CAN BENEFIT Registered charities; CICs.

WHAT IS FUNDED Family support, in particular practical support, relationship counselling and mediation; families of offenders and ex-offenders; families suffering from the effects of sexual, physical, domestic or substance abuse.

WHAT IS NOT FUNDED Non-registered charities; individuals; national charities (only regional projects will be considered); general appeals; organisations with specific religious or political agendas.

TYPE OF GRANT Core/revenue costs; capital costs.

RANGE OF GRANTS Up to £5,000, but higher amounts may be considered.

SAMPLE GRANTS Acacia; Carefree Kids; Dadswork; Family Intervention Counselling; Parents Against Child Exploitation; Play Therapy Base; Public Initiative for Prevention of Suicide and Self Harm, Relate; Women's Work Derbyshire.

FINANCES *Financial year end* 31/03/2020 *Income* £111,000 *Total grants* £71,000 *Grants to organisations* £71,000 *Assets* £2,430,000

TRUSTEES Annie Kelly; Brian Mattingley; Jenny Kelly; Sheldon Cordell; Michael Field.

OTHER INFORMATION The trustees prefer to support charities whose income is below £500,000. However, larger charities with pioneering pilot projects will be considered.

HOW TO APPLY Application forms can be downloaded from the trust's website. Grants are awarded twice a year and appeals must be submitted by 1 March or 1 September.

CONTACT DETAILS Stuart Armstrong, Grants Administrator, 8 Mansfield Place, Edinburgh EH3 6NB *Email* mail@kfct.org *Website* www.kfct.org.uk

The Kay Kendall Leukaemia Fund

CC NO 290772 **ESTABLISHED** 1984

WHERE FUNDING CAN BE GIVEN UK.

WHO CAN BENEFIT Organisations and institutions conducting research into leukaemia or related diseases; patient care and support centres.

WHAT IS FUNDED Medical research into and treatment of leukaemia or related diseases. The charity particularly welcomes proposals relating to the prevention, diagnosis or therapy of leukaemia.

WHAT IS NOT FUNDED Project grant applications submitted simultaneously to other funding bodies will not be accepted.

TYPE OF GRANT Research funding; capital costs; equipment; clinical support; fellowships; project grants for up to three years.

SAMPLE GRANTS Cambridge Institute for Medical Research (£293,700); Institute of Cancer Research (£100,000); CRUK Manchester Institute (£70,800); Bloodwise (£50,000); Hope for Tomorrow (£25,000).

FINANCES *Financial year end* 05/04/2020 *Income* £169,000 *Total grants* £2,361,500 *Grants to organisations* £2,340,000 *Assets* £10,750,000

TRUSTEES Judith Portrait; Timothy Sainsbury; Charles Metcalfe.

OTHER INFORMATION The charity is one of the Sainsbury Family Charitable Trusts which share a common administration – see www.sftc.org.uk for more information. The trustees have agreed to spend out the charity's capital. The last year of grant-making will be 2021/22.

HOW TO APPLY Application forms are available from the charity's office; application guidelines can be found on the charity's website.

CONTACT DETAILS The Trustees, The Peak, 5 Wilton Road, London SW1V 1AP *Tel.* 020 7410 0330 *Email* info@kklf.org.uk *Website* www.kklf.org.uk

William Kendall's Charity (Wax Chandlers' Company)

CC NO 228361 **ESTABLISHED** 1559

WHERE FUNDING CAN BE GIVEN Greater London and the London Borough of Bexley.

WHO CAN BENEFIT Registered charities; educational organisations.

WHAT IS FUNDED General charitable purposes; the relief of those in need, particularly inhabitants of Greater London and members of the company and their dependants; young people; education.

WHAT IS NOT FUNDED Individuals.

RANGE OF GRANTS Up to £15,000.

SAMPLE GRANTS Stepney City Farm and JustB (£15,000); London Youth (£11,000); Outward Bound Trust (£10,000); City of London School for Girls and Guildhall School of Music and Drama (£5,300 each); Bexley Women's Aid and St Paul's Cathedral Chorister (£2,000 each).

FINANCES *Financial year end* 31/03/2020 *Income* £191,400 *Total grants* £91,100 *Grants to organisations* £91,100 *Assets* £4,380,000

TRUSTEES John Sleeman; Jon Simpson; Lynda Marston-Weston; Dr Jonathan Munday; Joan Beavington; Susan Green; Lt Col John Chambers; Dame Fiona Woolf; Andrew Cooper; Ian Appleton; Peter Tompkins; Arthur Davey; Robert Holland; Anthony Bickmore; Margaret Ginman; Timothy Maile; Heather Hawker.

OTHER INFORMATION During 2019/20, grants totalling £91,100 were distributed through the following grant programmes: Greater London Fund (£51,000); Bexley Fund (£27,600); Persons in Need Fund (£12,500).

HOW TO APPLY The Bexley Small Grants Scheme is administered by the Bexley Voluntary Services Council – applicants may call 020 8304 0911 for more details. The Greater London Fund and Persons in Need Fund are operated on a commissioning basis and unsolicited applications are not accepted.

CONTACT DETAILS Richard Moule, Clerk, Wax Chandlers' Hall, 6 Gresham Street, London EC2V 7AD *Tel.* 020 7606 3591 *Email* clerk@waxchandlers.org.uk *Website* www.waxchandlers.org.uk/charity/index.php

■ The Kennedy Charitable Foundation

CC NO 1052001 **ESTABLISHED** 1995

WHERE FUNDING CAN BE GIVEN UK, USA and Ireland, with a preference for County Mayo and Sligo.

WHO CAN BENEFIT Registered charities; hospices; religious organisations; schools.

WHAT IS FUNDED General charitable purposes; religion, mainly Roman Catholic causes.

RANGE OF GRANTS Mostly under £3,000.

SAMPLE GRANTS Previous beneficiaries have included: Diocese of Shrewsbury (£20,500); Hope Houser (£10,600); Little Sisters of the Poor (£3,000); Archdiocese of Cardiff (£2,800); Easkey Community Council (£1,800); Children's Adventure Farm Trust (£1,000); Neuro Muscular Centre (£500); Irish Hospice Foundation (£175).

FINANCES *Financial year end* 05/04/2019 *Income* £63,600 *Total grants* £69,500 *Grants to organisations* £69,500 *Assets* £185,200

TRUSTEES John Kennedy; Kathleen Kennedy; Joe Kennedy; Patrick Kennedy; Anna Kelly.

OTHER INFORMATION The 2018/19 accounts were the latest available at the time of writing (June 2021).

HOW TO APPLY Contact the correspondent for further information.

CONTACT DETAILS The Trustees, 3 Woodvale, Langham Road, Bowdon, Altrincham WA14 2HT *Tel.* 0161 929 7556 *Email* amk@kennedycharitablefoundation.org.uk

■ The Kennedy Trust for Rheumatology Research

CC NO 260059 **ESTABLISHED** 1969

WHERE FUNDING CAN BE GIVEN England.

WHO CAN BENEFIT Registered charities; universities; research projects; hospitals.

WHAT IS FUNDED Basic and translational research into rheumatic and related musculoskeletal, immunological and inflammatory diseases.

TYPE OF GRANT Research.

SAMPLE GRANTS The Kennedy Institute at Oxford (£3.93 million); University of Birmingham (£2.39 million); University of Edinburgh (£1.98 million); King's College London (£100,000) University of Manchester (£85,000).

FINANCES *Financial year end* 30/09/2020 *Income* £8,800,000 *Total grants* £8,490,000 *Grants to organisations* £8,490,000 *Assets* £276,280,000

TRUSTEES Prof. Hill Gaston; Prof. Stephen Holgate; David Paterson; Victoria White; Rodney Hornstein; Edmund Buckley; Margaret Frost; Mark Dighero; Prof. Andrew Cope; Jennifer Johnson.

OTHER INFORMATION The trust provides long-term funding to The Kennedy Institute.

HOW TO APPLY Visit the trust's website for information on current funding initiatives. The website states: 'We consider informal approaches from, and offer support to, institutions only; we do not consider personal applications.'

CONTACT DETAILS Zoe Montanaro, Grants and Office Manager, One Lyric Square, Hammersmith, London W6 0NB *Tel.* 020 8834 1562 *Email* z.montanaro@kennedytrust.org *Website* www.kennedytrust.org

■ The Kennel Club Charitable Trust

CC NO 327802 **ESTABLISHED** 1988

WHERE FUNDING CAN BE GIVEN UK.

WHO CAN BENEFIT Charitable organisations; re-homing organisations; universities and other research bodies.

WHAT IS FUNDED Research into canine diseases; canine welfare.

WHAT IS NOT FUNDED Individuals; political organisations; applications purely for building costs; requests from organisations which are not primarily focused on dogs (e.g. general animal shelters).

TYPE OF GRANT One-off and recurring grants; capital, core and project costs; research.

RANGE OF GRANTS £100 to 103,500.

SAMPLE GRANTS Animal Health Trust – KC Genetics Centre (£103,500); Royal Veterinary College (£92,200); Roslin Institute (£47,500); Friends for Life (£9,000); Rushton Dog Rescue (£5,000); Wageningen Livestock Research (£4,300); Oak Tree Animal Charity (£2,700); Dog Photographer of the Year (£1,000); Wilmington (£120).

FINANCES *Financial year end* 31/12/2019 *Income* £297,000 *Total grants* £624,800 *Grants to organisations* £624,800 *Assets* £2,320,000

TRUSTEES Michael Herrtage; Revd William King; Dr Andrew Higgins; Jennifer Millard; Graham Hill; Rosemary Smart.

HOW TO APPLY Apply in writing to the correspondent, providing your organisation's latest accounts (and registered charity number, if applicable) and clearly stating the details of the costs for which you are requesting funding, for what purpose and over what period of time. For scientific project proposals, apply using the application form on the trust's website. The trustees meet four times a year. Further guidance is given on the trust's website.

CONTACT DETAILS The Administrator, 10 Clarges Street, Piccadilly, London W1J 8AB *Tel.* 020 7518 6874 *Email* kcct@thekennelclub.org.uk *Website* https://www.thekennelclub.org.uk/our-resources/the-kennel-club-charitable-trust

The Kensington and Chelsea Foundation

CC NO 1125940 **ESTABLISHED** 2009

WHERE FUNDING CAN BE GIVEN Kensington and Chelsea.

WHO CAN BENEFIT Charities; community groups; organisations working within the borough; individuals.

WHAT IS FUNDED Children and young people; skills and employment; isolation and loneliness; vulnerable older people living in fuel poverty.

TYPE OF GRANT Project costs.

RANGE OF GRANTS Up to £50,000.

SAMPLE GRANTS SOS Project (£50,000); Latimer Community Art Therapy (£30,000); Age UK Kensington and Chelsea (£20,800); ACAVA – Association for Cultural Advancement through Visual Art (£15,600); North Kensington Women's Textile Workshop (£2,800); New Horizons (£850); Rugby Portobello Trust (£80).

FINANCES *Financial year end* 31/03/2020 *Income* £1,130,000 *Total grants* £1,137,600 *Grants to organisations* £1,120,000 *Assets* £1,640,000

TRUSTEES Cynthia Dize; Jerome Raphaely; Clare Ferguson; Lucinda Stafford-Deitsch; Richard Briance; Jennifer Greenbury; Martin Morgan; William Crone; Esma Dukali; Abdi Aden; Peter Winslow; Abdurahman Sayed.

OTHER INFORMATION The foundation made grants totalling £619,600 to 47 local charities and community groups through its grant programme. An additional £515,300 was awarded to 59 organisations through the Grenfell Community Development Fund. The foundation also distributed £17,600 through its 'Winter Warmth Campaign' to vulnerable older people in the borough towards winter fuel bills.

HOW TO APPLY In the first instance, applicants should consult the foundation's website, which details what funding is currently available.

CONTACT DETAILS The Trustees, 111–117 Lancaster Road, Ladbroke Grove, London W11 1QT *Tel.* 020 7229 5499 *Email* team@thekandcfoundation.com *Website* https://thekandcfoundation.com

The Friends of Kent Churches

CC NO 207021 **ESTABLISHED** 1949

WHERE FUNDING CAN BE GIVEN Kent.

WHO CAN BENEFIT Churches.

WHAT IS FUNDED Churches undertaking repairs to their fabric; church maintenance; church facilities; roof alarms.

WHAT IS NOT FUNDED Work that has already started; reordering; redecorating (except where required for other eligible work); major new facilities; bells; clocks; organs; churchyards and churchyard walls (except for monuments of special importance).

TYPE OF GRANT Capital grants.

RANGE OF GRANTS £500 to £20,000.

SAMPLE GRANTS St Margaret – High Halstow (£20,000); St Mary – Greenhythe (£15,000); All Saints – All Hallows (£11,000); St John the Baptist (£6,000); SS Peter and Paul (£5,000); Holy Cross – Hoath (£3,500); St Nicholas – Allington (£2,500); St George – Bickley (£500).

FINANCES *Financial year end* 31/12/2019 *Income* £204,600 *Total grants* £176,000 *Grants to organisations* £176,000 *Assets* £669,500

TRUSTEES Sir Paul Britton; Jane Bird; Paul Smallwood; Mary Gibbins; Lucilla Neame; Richard Latham; The Ven. Peter Lock; Margaret Williams; Leslie Smith.

OTHER INFORMATION During 2019, 30 grants were awarded.

HOW TO APPLY Application forms are available from the charity's website, along with full guidelines. The form should be returned, preferably by email, to the correspondent, along with a copy of the latest audited church accounts and the accounts of any associated bodies that have the upkeep of the church as their main objective. Applications should be sent to the correspondent by 1 May or 1 November for consideration at the trustees' meeting in July or January, respectively. Grants are valid for two years. Application forms specifically for roof alarms can be downloaded from the charity's website and should be returned to the correspondent.

CONTACT DETAILS Deb Sutch, Secretary, Parsonage Farm House, Hampstead Lane, Yalding, Maidstone, Kent ME18 6HG *Tel.* 01622 815569 *Email* debsutch@btinternet.com *Website* www.friendsofkentchurches.co.uk

Kent Community Foundation

CC NO 1084361 **ESTABLISHED** 2001

WHERE FUNDING CAN BE GIVEN The county of Kent and the borough of Medway.

WHO CAN BENEFIT Local charities, community groups and voluntary organisations; individuals.

WHAT IS FUNDED A wide range of purposes.

TYPE OF GRANT Core, capital and project expenditure; one-off and recurrent.

SAMPLE GRANTS Sparks (£500,000); The J's Hospice (£75,000); Romney Marsh Day Centre (£34,000); Gap (£21,600); Carers FIRST (£17,400); Ellenor (£15,200); Blackthorn Trust (£13,000); Age Concern Sandwich Centre and Kent Cricket Development Trust (£10,500 each); Friends of Holcot (£10,100).

FINANCES *Financial year end* 31/03/2020 *Income* £8,670,000 *Total grants* £3,277,100 *Grants to organisations* £3,240,000 *Assets* £26,360,000

TRUSTEES Hugo Fenwick; Georgina Warner; William Williams; Lord Sackville-West; Sarah Hohler; Gail Hall; Tim Bull; Melissa Murdoch; Russell Race; Dr Emilia Falcetti.

OTHER INFORMATION This is one of the 46 UK community foundations, which distribute funding for a wide range of purposes. As with all community foundations, there are a number of donor-advised funds managed on behalf of individuals, families and charitable trusts. Grant schemes tend to change frequently; consult the foundation's website for details of current programmes and up-to-date deadlines.

HOW TO APPLY Potential applicants are advised to visit the community foundation's website or contact its grants team to find the most suitable funding stream.

CONTACT DETAILS Grants Team, Evegate Park Barn, Evegate, Ashford, Kent TN25 6SX *Tel.* 01303 814500 *Email* admin@kentcf.org.uk *Website* www.kentcf.org.uk/apply

The Kentown Wizard Foundation

CC NO 1163956 **ESTABLISHED** 2015

WHERE FUNDING CAN BE GIVEN Worldwide, with a preference for the UK.

WHO CAN BENEFIT UK-registered charities.

WHAT IS FUNDED Children and young people living with life-limiting conditions and disabilities, and their families.

TYPE OF GRANT Core costs; project funding; multi-year grants.

RANGE OF GRANTS Up to £800,000.

SAMPLE GRANTS Make a Wish (£800,000); Brian House (£29,500); Kid's Cancer Charity (£22,600).

FINANCES *Financial year end* 31/03/2020 *Income* £1,140,000 *Total grants* £852,000 *Grants to organisations* £852,000 *Assets* £63,930,000

TRUSTEES David Bamber; Kenneth Townsley; Richard Ingle; Kathryn Graham.

OTHER INFORMATION During 2019/20 grants were awarded to three organisations, within the following categories; wish-granting charities (£800,000); charities providing respite care, end-of-life care and other vital support (£52,000).

HOW TO APPLY According to its website, the foundation seeks out potential charity partners and therefore does not accept unsolicited applications.

CONTACT DETAILS The Trustees, Metro House Ltd, Unit 14–17, Metropolitan Business Park, Preston New Road, Blackpool FY3 9LT *Tel.* 01253 446923 *Email* enquiries@kentownwizard.org *Website* www.kentownwizard.org

■ The Nancy Kenyon Charitable Trust

CC NO 265359 **ESTABLISHED** 1972

WHERE FUNDING CAN BE GIVEN UK and overseas.

WHO CAN BENEFIT Registered small charities; individuals.

WHAT IS FUNDED General charitable purposes; Christian causes.

RANGE OF GRANTS Up to £10,500.

SAMPLE GRANTS Nancy Oldfield Trust (£10,500); One More Child (£5,000); Aylsham Boxing Club and RISE Africa UK (£3,000 each); Gloucestershire Young Carers and St Saviour's Priory (£2,000 each); Cromer Food Bank (£1,000); Kiva (£160).

FINANCES *Financial year end* 05/04/2020 *Income* £74,500 *Total grants* £77,700 *Grants to organisations* £71,700 *Assets* £1,540,000

TRUSTEES Lucy Phipps; Sarah Kenyon; Sally Kenyon; Peter Kenyon; Kieron Kenyon; David Kenyon; Emily Kenyon.

OTHER INFORMATION Grants were made to 27 organisations during the year. Grants to individuals totalled £6,000.

HOW TO APPLY Applications can be made in writing to the correspondent at any time. Our previous research notes that applications for causes not known to the trustees are considered annually in December.

CONTACT DETAILS The Trustees, c/o Brook Financial Management Ltd, Meads Barn, Ashwell Business Park, Ashwell, Ilminster, Somerset TA19 9DX *Tel.* 01460 259852

■ E. and E. Kernkraut Charities Ltd

CC NO 275636 **ESTABLISHED** 1973

WHERE FUNDING CAN BE GIVEN UK and overseas.

WHO CAN BENEFIT Charitable organisations.

WHAT IS FUNDED The advancement of religion in accordance with the Orthodox Jewish faith; education; general charitable purposes.

RANGE OF GRANTS Generally up to around £50,000, with occasional larger grants.

SAMPLE GRANTS The ABC Trust (£56,000); Friends of Wiznitz Ltd (£50,000); United Talmudical Associates and Alte Feiga Trust (£43,000 each); Hadras Kodesh Trust (£38,800); Talmud Torah Education Ltd (£15,000).

FINANCES *Financial year end* 31/03/2020 *Income* £994,700 *Total grants* £649,100 *Grants to organisations* £649,100 *Assets* £6,980,000

TRUSTEES Eli Kernkraut; Esther Kernkraut; Joseph Kernkraut; Jacob Kernkraut.

OTHER INFORMATION Grants of under £15,000 totalled £152,300.

HOW TO APPLY Apply in writing to the correspondent. Contact the correspondent for further information. According to the annual report for 2019/20, when making grants, the trustees 'use their personal knowledge of the relevant institutions, their representatives, operational efficiency and reputation'.

CONTACT DETAILS Eli Kernkraut, Chair, The Knoll, Fountayne Road, London N16 7EA *Tel.* 020 8806 7947 *Email* mail@cohenarnold.com

■ The Peter Kershaw Trust

CC NO 268934 **ESTABLISHED** 1974

WHERE FUNDING CAN BE GIVEN Greater Manchester.

WHO CAN BENEFIT Registered charities; schools.

WHAT IS FUNDED Social welfare; medical research; youth work; school bursaries.

WHAT IS NOT FUNDED Individuals; loans; new building work (but payments for fitting out specialist premises may be made); long-term commitments (awards may be paid for up to three years); industrial and provident societies; CICs.

TYPE OF GRANT Salaries; seed funding/start-up funding; pump-priming; project funding; bursaries.

RANGE OF GRANTS Mostly between £1,000 and £3,000. Up to £50,000 over three years for the memorial bursary.

SAMPLE GRANTS N-Gage (£10,000); Cheadle Hulme School (£7,000); St Peter's Delamere PCC (£5,000); Football Beyond Borders and Mustard Tree (£3,000 each); The Anthony Seddon Fund and Young Women's Trust (£2,000 each); Read for Good (£1,000); Manchester Grammar School (£670); The Cure Parkinson's Trust (£250).

FINANCES *Financial year end* 31/03/2020 *Income* £234,100 *Total grants* £216,700 *Grants to organisations* £216,700 *Assets* £7,120,000

TRUSTEES Margaret Rushbrooke; Richard Kershaw; Rosemary Adams; Tim Page; Jane Kershaw; Bernard Lever.

OTHER INFORMATION Grants were awarded to 64 organisations in 2019/20. Support was allocated as follows: social welfare (£134,100); memorial bursary (to fund youth worker salaries/youth work) (£50,000); school bursaries (to assist parents with children at secondary school who encounter financial problems) (£32,600).

HOW TO APPLY Applications should be made in writing to the correspondent by post (email applications are not accepted) and should be accompanied by the latest financial statements. For social welfare grants, an application form can be downloaded from the website. Meeting dates and deadlines are posted on the trust's website.

CONTACT DETAILS Emma Willder, Secretary to the Trustees, Room G104, Bolton Arena, Arena Approach, Horwich, Bolton, Lancashire BL6 6LB *Tel.* 01204 414317 *Email* peterkershawtrust@gmail.com *Website* www.peterkershawtrust.org

■ The Ursula Keyes Trust

CC NO 517200 **ESTABLISHED** 1985

WHERE FUNDING CAN BE GIVEN Chester and the surrounding areas.

WHO CAN BENEFIT Charitable organisations (including national charities if there is a link to a local beneficiary); medical and social care institutions; schools; individuals.

WHAT IS FUNDED General charitable purposes, particularly health and medical causes and social care. The trust's website further explains: 'A wide range of causes are supported, including cultural and leisure projects, particularly when matched by other fundraising efforts.'

TYPE OF GRANT Capital costs.

RANGE OF GRANTS Up to £40,000 but mostly from £1,000 to £10,000.

SAMPLE GRANTS Chester FC Community Trust (£40,000); West Cheshire Athletic Club (£30,000); Hospice of the Good Shepherd (£23,800); Neuro Therapy Centre (£10,300); Space (£5,000); Vision Support (£2,000); The Garden Quarter Association (£1,000).

FINANCES *Financial year end* 31/12/2019 *Income* £351,400 *Total grants* £236,200 *Grants to organisations* £228,200 *Assets* £4,400,000

TRUSTEES Euan Elliot; Jim Kane; John Leaman; John Brimelow; Dr Ian Russell; Dr Peter Reid; John McLintock.

OTHER INFORMATION Grants to individuals totalled £8,000.

HOW TO APPLY Applications should be made in writing to the correspondent, including a copy of the form available to download from the website. Appeals are considered at the trustees' quarterly meetings, which take place at the end of January, April, July and October (see the website for exact dates); they should reach the trustees at least two weeks before any particular meeting.

CONTACT DETAILS The Trustees, c/o RSM, One City Place, Queens Road, Chester CH1 3BQ *Tel.* 01244 505100 *Email* enquiries@ursula-keyes-trust.org.uk *Website* www.ursula-keyes-trust.org.uk

■ KFC Foundation

CC NO 1163560 **ESTABLISHED** 2015

WHERE FUNDING CAN BE GIVEN UK.

WHO CAN BENEFIT Registered charities; CICs; unincorporated clubs or associations; unregistered charities. For community grants, organisations must have a turnover of less than £300,000.

WHAT IS FUNDED Projects that benefit young people aged 11 to 25 years old, particularly those in a position of social disadvantage (i.e. care leavers, those experiencing homelessness, young carers, young parents, young people at risk of or with experience of the criminal justice system).

WHAT IS NOT FUNDED For community grants: general fundraising or sponsorship appeals; political campaigns; the promotion of religion; overseas travel; curricular activities that take place during the school day; research; loan repayments; vehicle purchase; medical equipment; major capital projects; interventions which fail to demonstrate long-term impact or support; one-off events; generic youth work activities (i.e. those not tailored towards the priority groups).

TYPE OF GRANT Project funding; small capital costs.

RANGE OF GRANTS Partnerships: mostly up to £35,000; community grants: £200 to £2,000.

SAMPLE GRANTS Comic Relief (£400,000); Young Lives Foundation (£35,100); Young People First and Youth Association (£25,000 each); Kids Inspire – Essex (£23,000); Focus Charity (£19,400); Childhood Trust (£13,300); Positive Futures (£10,200).

FINANCES *Financial year end* 31/12/2019 *Income* £1,180,000 *Total grants* £699,000 *Grants to organisations* £699,000 *Assets* £538,700

TRUSTEES Alvin Owusu; Meg Farren; Akram Khan; Neil Morrison; Simon Coates; Paula MacKenzie; Nichola Newman; Jennie Wright; James Fletcher.

OTHER INFORMATION Grants were awarded to 16 organisations during the year – the foundation continued to support the charity partners that KFC restaurant teams had voted for in 2018. A grant of £400,000 was awarded to Comic Relief (57% of the total grant expenditure). The foundation also awards community grants to support grassroots organisations at the heart of its restaurants' communities – see the website for details.

HOW TO APPLY For community grants, check the website for open funding rounds and apply via the foundation's website. For charity partnerships, contact the foundation for further information.

CONTACT DETAILS Louise Norris, Secretary, Orion Gate, Guilford Road, Woking GU22 7NJ *Tel.* 07837 093381 *Email* uk-kfc-foundation@yum.com *Website* https://www.kfc.co.uk/kfc-foundation-community-grants

■ Kidney Research UK

CC NO 252892 **ESTABLISHED** 1967

WHERE FUNDING CAN BE GIVEN UK.

WHO CAN BENEFIT Recognised renal research establishments supporting medical professionals including universities and hospitals.

WHAT IS FUNDED The charity funds research with the aim of improving the understanding of kidney disease, its causes, treatment and management.

SAMPLE GRANTS A list of beneficiaries was not included in the annual report and accounts.

FINANCES *Financial year end* 31/03/2020 *Income* £9,950,000 *Total grants* £5,290,000 *Grants to organisations* £5,290,000 *Assets* £7,030,000

TRUSTEES Dr Allan Davidson; Lisa Chan; Prof. Caroline Savage; Prof. Jeremy Hughes; Prof. Sunil Bhandari; Dr David Hughes; Dr Adan Sharif; Dr Charles Thompson; Jill Norman; Prof. Elizabeth Lightstone; Adrian Akers; Ben Digby; Angel Watt; Tom Kelly; Deirdre James.

OTHER INFORMATION The website states that approximately 80% of charitable expenditure is applied to research and 20% to providing health information and raising awareness of kidney disease.

HOW TO APPLY Applications must be submitted through the online portal, which can be accessed via the charity's website.

CONTACT DETAILS Research Grants Committee, Nene Hall, Peterborough Business Park, Lynch Wood, Peterborough, Cambridgeshire PE2 6FZ *Tel.* 0300 303 1100 *Email* enquiries@kidneyresearchuk.org *Website* www.kidneyresearchuk.org

■ The Kildare Trust

CC NO 1148325 **ESTABLISHED** 2012

WHERE FUNDING CAN BE GIVEN Worcestershire.

WHO CAN BENEFIT Registered charities; hospices; churches.

WHAT IS FUNDED General charitable purposes, with a preference for music and health.

RANGE OF GRANTS Up to £20,000.

SAMPLE GRANTS Acorns Children's Hospice Trust and St Richard's Hospice (£20,000 each); Worcester Live Charitable Trust (£12,000); Macmillan Cancer Support (£10,000); St Mary's Church (£8,000); Age Concern and Happy Days (£5,000 each); PSP Association (£1,000).

FINANCES *Financial year end* 05/04/2019 *Income* £247,100 *Total grants* £233,500 *Grants to organisations* £233,500 *Assets* £1,110,000

TRUSTEES Martin Needham; Dawn Oliver; Ian Crockatt Smith; Anthony Champion; Geoffrey Probert.

OTHER INFORMATION The 2018/19 accounts were the latest available at the time of writing (May 2021). During the year, the trust awarded grants to 22 organisations.

HOW TO APPLY Contact the correspondent for further information.

CONTACT DETAILS Dawn Oliver, Trustee, c/o Harrison Clark Solicitors, 5 Deansway, Worcester, Worcestershire WR1 2JG *Tel.* 01905 744871

■ Kilpatrick Fraser Charitable Trust

OSCR NO SC046233 **ESTABLISHED** 2016

WHERE FUNDING CAN BE GIVEN UK and overseas, with a preference for Scotland.

WHO CAN BENEFIT Registered charities; community groups; medical research organisations; hospices. Primarily, Scotland-based organisations.

WHAT IS FUNDED Children and young people; medical research and support for older people and people with learning difficulties; cancer support and research; social inclusion; employability; social or economic disadvantage; community development; the arts, heritage, culture and science; sport and recreation.

TYPE OF GRANT Small-scale, targeted projects; provision of equipment; medical research.

RANGE OF GRANTS Mostly up to around £12,000.

SAMPLE GRANTS Scottish Football Partnership (£40,000); Erskine Hospital (£13,700); Cure International (£10,400); Spinal Research (£9,200); Glasgow Children's Hospital (£7,700); ChildLine (£7,600); Smile Train (£7,000); Marie Curie – Belfast (£6,600); Edinburgh Science (£6,400); Guide Dogs for the Blind and Muscular Dystrophy (£5,000 each).

FINANCES *Financial year end* 31/03/2020 *Income* £245,400 *Total grants* £248,800 *Grants to organisations* £248,800 *Assets* £434,100

OTHER INFORMATION In 2019/20, grants were awarded to 69 organisations. Grants of under £5,000 totalled £129,800.

HOW TO APPLY Contact the correspondent for further information.

CONTACT DETAILS The Trustees, c/o Brodies LLP, 110 Queen Street, Glasgow G1 3BX

■ The Kilroot Foundation

CC NO 1173150 **ESTABLISHED** 2017

WHERE FUNDING CAN BE GIVEN UK and overseas.

WHO CAN BENEFIT Registered charities.

WHAT IS FUNDED The development and support of children and young people; conservation of the natural and built environment.

RANGE OF GRANTS Capital costs; project funding; one-off and recurrent.

SAMPLE GRANTS Salmon and Trout Conservancy and The Garden Museum (£30,000 each); Rugby Portobello Trust (£5,000); Avondale Extra (£2,500); Eton College (£1,500).

FINANCES *Financial year end* 05/04/2020 *Income* £100,100 *Total grants* £155,000 *Grants to organisations* £155,000 *Assets* £3,420,000

TRUSTEES Matthew Dobbs; Denis Clough; Katherine Dobbs.

OTHER INFORMATION Grants were made to 13 organisations.

HOW TO APPLY Contact the correspondent for more information.

CONTACT DETAILS The Trustees, 13 Portland Road, London W11 4LH *Tel.* 020 7658 6973

■ The King Henry VIII Endowed Trust – Warwick

CC NO 232862 **ESTABLISHED** 1545

WHERE FUNDING CAN BE GIVEN The former borough of Warwick (the CV34 postcode area).

WHO CAN BENEFIT Registered charities; unregistered charities; schools; PTAs; amateur sports clubs; hospitals; hospices; religious bodies/institutions; local authorities; individuals.

WHAT IS FUNDED General charitable purposes. Charitable expenditure is allocated in the following proportions: 50% to the five historic Anglican churches in Warwick; 30% to the Warwick Independent Schools Foundation; and 20% to causes benefitting inhabitants of the town.

WHAT IS NOT FUNDED Projects outside the beneficial area; projects for which central or local government has a financial responsibility; retrospective grants.

TYPE OF GRANT Capital costs; core/revenue costs; seed funding/start-up funding; project funding; unrestricted funding.

RANGE OF GRANTS Up to £30,000.

SAMPLE GRANTS Warwick Apprenticing Charities (£30,000); 2nd Warwick Sea Scouts (£25,000); Myton School (£18,600); Chase Meadow Community Centre (£10,000); Aylesford Primary School (£6,600); Warwick Tennis Club (£4,200); Cruse Bereavement Care (£2,700); Dogs for Good (£1,000).

FINANCES *Financial year end* 31/12/2019 *Income* £8,580,000 *Total grants* £233,000 *Grants to organisations* £232,300 *Assets* £52,760,000

TRUSTEES Stephen Cross; Kathryn Parr; John Edwards; Ian Furlong; Stephen Copley; Revd David Brown; Neil Thurley; Michael Peachey; Marie Ashe; Susan Grinnell; Stephen Jobburn.

OTHER INFORMATION During 2019 the trust distributed a total of £1.5 million, with £786,600 being distributed to the five Anglican churches in the town and £482,000 to the Warwick Independent Schools Foundation. Grants from the Town Share were made to 37 different organisations and totalled £233,000, of which £700 was awarded to individuals. We have taken the Town Share figure as our grant total, as the other figures represent restricted funds from the trust's permanent endowment.

HOW TO APPLY Application forms are available to download from the trust's website and should be returned by post or email. Detailed grant guidelines are also available to view on the website. The trustees consider applications on a quarterly basis, usually in March, June, September and November. Check the website for current deadlines. In the case of an emergency, applications may be fast-tracked.

CONTACT DETAILS Jonathan Wassall, Clerk, 12 High Street, Warwick, Warwickshire CV34 4AP *Tel.* 01926 495533 *Email* jwassall@kinghenryviii.org.uk *Website* www.kinghenryviii.org.uk

■ The Mary Kinross Charitable Trust

CC NO 212206 **ESTABLISHED** 1957

WHERE FUNDING CAN BE GIVEN UK.

WHO CAN BENEFIT Registered charities; CICs; social enterprises; universities.

WHAT IS FUNDED Medical research; young people; penal affairs; health, including mental health; community development.

WHAT IS NOT FUNDED Individuals.

TYPE OF GRANT Capital costs; core/revenue costs; seed funding/start-up funding; project funding; unrestricted funding.

RANGE OF GRANTS Up to £100,000.

SAMPLE GRANTS Max Planck University College London Centre, University College London (£100,000); Bendrigg Trust (£65,000); Bipolar UK (£40,000); New Horizon Youth Centre (£20,000); Housing for Women (£15,000); Spitalfields Crypt Trust (£5,000); The Bach Players (£2,500); Warstock Community Centre (£1,500).

FINANCES *Financial year end* 31/03/2020 *Income* £695,400 *Total grants* £705,300 *Grants to organisations* £705,300 *Assets* £43,070,000

TRUSTEES Elizabeth Shields; Fiona Adams; Dr Neil Cross; Gordon Hague; Elizabeth Barber.

OTHER INFORMATION Grants were broken down as follows: medical research (£214,000 in three grants); young people (£172,300 in seven grants); penal affairs (£138,000 in eight grants); health (£91,500 in five grants); mental health (£78,500 in five grants); miscellaneous (£9,500 in three grants); community development (£8,000 in three grants).

HOW TO APPLY The majority of unsolicited applications are unsuccessful, as most new organisations are recommended by the trustees or the Chair. However, should an organisation wish to submit an application, it must be done in writing. Telephone calls and emails are discouraged.

CONTACT DETAILS Fiona Adams, Trustee, 36 Grove Avenue, Moseley, Birmingham, West Midlands B13 9RY *Email* marykinrossct@gmail.com

■ Laura Kinsella Foundation

CC NO 1145325 **ESTABLISHED** 2011

WHERE FUNDING CAN BE GIVEN Worldwide.

WHO CAN BENEFIT Charitable organisations; individuals.

WHAT IS FUNDED General charitable purposes, including the arts, human rights and social welfare.

RANGE OF GRANTS From £50 to £40,000.

SAMPLE GRANTS Previous beneficiaries have included: Reprieve (£36,000); Camplin Trust, Centre for Criminal Appeals and Rock the Cotswolds (£10,000 each); Centre for European Reform and Stroud Valleys Support (£5,000 each); Crisis and Footsteps (£2,000 each); Arts Emergency and Alternative Theatre (£1,000 each); Solace Women's Aid (£100).

FINANCES *Financial year end* 05/04/2020 *Income* £49,200 *Total grants* £314,300 *Grants to organisations* £314,300 *Assets* £2,650,000

TRUSTEES Stephen Kinsella; Alison Jolly; Michael Dickson.

HOW TO APPLY Apply in writing to the correspondent. Only successful applicants are notified in writing.

CONTACT DETAILS The Trustees, c/o Bates Wells and Braithwaite, 10 Queen Street Place, London EC4R 1BE *Tel.* 020 7551 7777

■ The Graham Kirkham Foundation

CC NO 1002390 **ESTABLISHED** 1991

WHERE FUNDING CAN BE GIVEN UK.

WHO CAN BENEFIT Registered charities; voluntary organisations; individuals.

WHAT IS FUNDED General charitable purposes, including the following: education; the relief of illness and poverty; medical research; the study and appreciation of literature, art, music and science; animal welfare and rescue; armed forces communities; support for substance abusers; recreational facilities for social welfare; protection and preservation of buildings and sites of historical and natural beauty.

RANGE OF GRANTS Mostly up to £20,000.

SAMPLE GRANTS The Worshipful Company of Furniture Makers Charitable Fund (£50,000); Animal Health Trust and Odyssey (£20,000 each); The Friendly Band (£10,000); Arafest and Macmillan Cancer Support (£5,000 each); Saints and Sinners (£4,000); The Prince's Trust (£500).

FINANCES *Financial year end* 31/07/2019 *Income* £88,800 *Total grants* £156,200 *Grants to organisations* £156,200 *Assets* £9,900

TRUSTEES Lord Graham Kirkham; Lady Pauline Kirkham; The Hon. Michael Kirkham.

OTHER INFORMATION The 2018/19 accounts were the latest available at the time of writing (May 2021). Grants were awarded to 14 organisations during the year in the following categories: welfare (£74,500); healthcare (£52,500); culture (£29,200).

HOW TO APPLY Contact the correspondent for information regarding the application process.

CONTACT DETAILS The Trustees, 8 Ebor Court, Redhouse Interchange, Adwick le Street, Doncaster, South Yorkshire DN6 7FE *Tel.* 01302 573301

The Kirschel Foundation

CC NO 1067672 **ESTABLISHED** 1998

WHERE FUNDING CAN BE GIVEN UK.

WHO CAN BENEFIT Registered charities; CICs; schools; PTAs; amateur sports clubs; hospitals; hospices; religious bodies/institutions.

WHAT IS FUNDED Jewish causes; health; disability; social welfare; education and training.

TYPE OF GRANT Capital costs; core/revenue costs; project funding; unrestricted funding; general funding.

RANGE OF GRANTS Up to £75,000.

SAMPLE GRANTS Aharat Shalom Charity Fund (£75,000); Gateshead Academy for Torah Studies (£25,000); Tivka UK (£11,200); United Talmudical Associates Ltd (£5,000); Chabad Lubavitch (£2,500); Children in Crisis (£1,000).

FINANCES *Financial year end* 31/07/2019 *Income* £231,000 *Total grants* £218,700 *Grants to organisations* £218,700 *Assets* £35,900

TRUSTEES Laurence Kirschel; Ivona Kirschel.

OTHER INFORMATION The 2018/19 annual report and accounts were the latest available at the time of writing (June 2021).

HOW TO APPLY Contact the correspondent for further information.

CONTACT DETAILS The Trustees, 26 Soho Square, London W1D 4NU *Tel.* 020 7437 4372

Robert Kitchin (Saddlers' Company)

CC NO 211169 **ESTABLISHED** 1891

WHERE FUNDING CAN BE GIVEN Greater London, with a preference for organisations benefitting people who are/have been resident or educated in the City of London.

WHO CAN BENEFIT Educational establishments; charitable organisations; individuals.

WHAT IS FUNDED The education of disadvantaged young people.

TYPE OF GRANT Project funding; bursaries for students.

SAMPLE GRANTS Previous beneficiaries have included: Beormund Primary School – Southwark, Capel Manor College – Enfield, City of London Academy – Islington and the XLP Project – Tower Hamlets.

FINANCES *Financial year end* 31/03/2020 *Income* £105,400 *Total grants* £105,300 *Grants to organisations* £102,800 *Assets* £3,990,000

TRUSTEE Saddlers' Company.

OTHER INFORMATION Each year, 65% of net income is restricted to City University and St Ethelburga's Centre for Reconciliation and Peace. The remaining 35% is distributed at the discretion of the trustees.

HOW TO APPLY Contact the correspondent for more information.

CONTACT DETAILS The Clerk to the Trustees, Saddlers' Company, Saddlers' Hall, 40 Gutter Lane, London EC2V 6BR *Tel.* 020 7726 8661 *Email* clerk@saddlersco.co.uk *Website* www.saddlersco.co.uk

The Ernest Kleinwort Charitable Trust

CC NO 229665 **ESTABLISHED** 1963

WHERE FUNDING CAN BE GIVEN UK, with a preference for Sussex; worldwide.

WHO CAN BENEFIT Registered charities, with a preference for those operating in Sussex across a range of fields and environmental or wildlife organisations.

WHAT IS FUNDED Wildlife and environmental conservation; family planning; care of older and young people; disability, general social welfare; hospices; medical research; other charitable causes.

WHAT IS NOT FUNDED See the trust's website for a full list of exclusions.

TYPE OF GRANT Start-up funding; core/revenue costs; project costs; capital costs; conditionally renewable grants for up to three years may be agreed on occasions.

RANGE OF GRANTS Mostly of £20,000 or less.

SAMPLE GRANTS Tusk (£168,000); St Catherine's Hospice (£130,000); Off The Fence Trust (£35,000); Galapagos Conservation Trust (£30,000); The Sara Lee Trust (£10,000); The Chaseley Trust (£15,000); Education Training Consortium Sussex (£8,000); Whizz-Kidz (£5,000); Bristol Natural History Consortium (£1,100); REACT (Rapid Effective Assistance for Children with potentially Terminal illness) (£500).

FINANCES *Financial year end* 31/03/2020 *Income* £741,600 *Total grants* £1,830,000 *Grants to organisations* £1,830,000 *Assets* £58,930,000

TRUSTEES Marina Rose Kleinwort; Sir Richard Kleinwort; Alexander Hamilton Kleinwort; Rt Hon. Edmund Christopher; Lord Chandos; Charlie Mayhew.

OTHER INFORMATION During the year, the trust awarded 198 grants, supporting 59% of applicants.

HOW TO APPLY Applicants should complete the eligibility questionnaire in the first instance. Application forms can be completed online on the trust's website. Small grant applications are accepted and considered throughout the year. Medium grant applications are accepted four times per year, during the following periods: 4 January to 11 February, 18 April to 19 May, 10 July to 20 August, and 9 October to 19 November. Large grant applications are accepted twice per year, during the following periods: 4 January to 4 March, and 10 July to 10 September. See the trust's website for further information.

CONTACT DETAILS Andrina Murrell, Administrator, EKCT, c/o Knill James, 1 Bell Lane, Lewes BN7 1JU *Tel.* 07960 057742 *Email* admin@ekct.org.uk *Website* www.ekct.org.uk

Sir James Knott Trust

CC NO 1001363 **ESTABLISHED** 1990

WHERE FUNDING CAN BE GIVEN Durham; Gateshead; Hartlepool; Newcastle upon Tyne; North Tyneside; Northumberland; South Tyneside.

WHO CAN BENEFIT Registered charities; community groups; social enterprises.

WHAT IS FUNDED General charitable purposes, with special consideration for charitable activities known to have been of particular interest to Sir James Knott, including military and maritime organisations, youth clubs, projects to help older people, and education and training. Support is also given for arts and culture, community projects, conservation and the environment, health and sport, historic buildings and heritage, and homelessness.

WHAT IS NOT FUNDED Individuals; research; activity which has already taken place or which takes place outside the trust's area of benefit.

TYPE OF GRANT Capital and core costs; salaries; start-up expenditure; matched funding.

RANGE OF GRANTS Grants range from £400 to £300,000. It is unusual for the trust to make grants in excess of £30,000.

SAMPLE GRANTS Community Foundation Tyne and Wear and Northumberland (£100,000); Newcastle United Foundation (£50,000), County Durham Community Foundation (£25,000); Gateshead Carers (£10,000); Northern Sinfonia (£7,000); Woodlands Park Association (£4,000); Weardale Museum (£2,000).

FINANCES *Financial year end* 31/03/2020
Income £1,980,000 *Total grants* £1,580,000
Grants to organisations £1,580,000
Assets £51,440,000

TRUSTEES John Cresswell; Revd Fiona Sample; Ben Speke; Sir Walter Riddell.

OTHER INFORMATION In 2019/20, 308 grants were made. Applications for awards below £1,000 (or, in exceptional circumstances, for larger amounts) can be considered between the trustees' meetings.

HOW TO APPLY Check the eligibility criteria on the trust's website before applying. Applications can be made online via the website, which also has details on how to apply, application deadlines and frequently asked questions.

CONTACT DETAILS Ms J. Curry, Trust Secretary, Suite 103, First Floor, Broadacre House, Market Street East, Newcastle, Tyne and Wear NE1 6JQ *Tel.* 0191 432 8990 *Email* info@knott-trust.co.uk *Website* www.knott-trust.co.uk

■ The Kobler Trust

CC NO 275237 **ESTABLISHED** 1963

WHERE FUNDING CAN BE GIVEN UK.

WHO CAN BENEFIT Registered charities; hospices.

WHAT IS FUNDED General charitable purposes; the arts; Jewish causes; health and disability; children and young people.

WHAT IS NOT FUNDED Grants to individuals are only given in exceptional circumstances.

RANGE OF GRANTS From £300 to £15,000, but typically less than £500.

SAMPLE GRANTS KeshetUK (£15,000); UK Jewish Film Festival (£6,000); The Marlowe Trust (£5,000); St Christopher's Hospice (£400); Starlight Children's Foundation, Together for Short Lives, Thumbs Up Club and Jewish Association for Mental Illness (£300 each).

FINANCES *Financial year end* 05/04/2020
Income £107,400 *Total grants* £66,400
Grants to organisations £66,400
Assets £2,620,000

TRUSTEES Andrew Stone; Antoine Xuereb; Joel Israelsohn; Joanne Evans.

OTHER INFORMATION During the year, 104 organisations received grants.

HOW TO APPLY Applications should be made in writing to the trustees. Applications are considered by the trustees on a regular basis, both at the trustees' meetings and between meetings. Acknowledgements are generally not sent out to unsuccessful applicants.

CONTACT DETAILS The Trustees, c/o Lewis Silkin LLP, 10 Clifford's Inn Passage, London EC4A 1BL *Tel.* 020 7074 8000 *Email* info@lewissilkin.com

■ Kollel and Co. Ltd

CC NO 1077180 **ESTABLISHED** 1999

WHERE FUNDING CAN BE GIVEN Worldwide.

WHO CAN BENEFIT Charitable organisations with a Jewish focus.

WHAT IS FUNDED Jewish causes; the relief of poverty; religious activities and education; medical needs; general charitable purposes.

TYPE OF GRANT Building, equipment and project costs.

RANGE OF GRANTS Up to £106,900.

SAMPLE GRANTS Revach Vehazole Trust (£106,900); Ezer V'Hatzalah Ltd (£83,100); Chevras Mo'oz Ladol (£39,500); Blooming Blossoms Trust (£18,300); The ABC Trust (£1,300).

FINANCES *Financial year end* 31/01/2020
Income £786,800 *Total grants* £720,500
Grants to organisations £720,500
Assets £5,520,000

TRUSTEES Simon Low; Judith Weiss; Rachel Kalish.

OTHER INFORMATION The annual report and accounts for 2019/20 list nine grants totalling £450,000 as well as grants of under £50,000 totalling £270,500.

HOW TO APPLY Contact the correspondent for further information.

CONTACT DETAILS Simon Low, Trustee, 7 Overlea Road, London E5 9BG *Tel.* 020 8806 1570

■ Kolyom Trust Ltd

CC NO 1112084 **ESTABLISHED** 2005

WHERE FUNDING CAN BE GIVEN Worldwide.

WHO CAN BENEFIT Registered charities.

WHAT IS FUNDED Jewish religion, education and welfare.

SAMPLE GRANTS A list of beneficiaries was not included in the annual report and accounts.

FINANCES *Financial year end* 31/05/2020
Income £3,460,000 *Total grants* £3,490,000
Grants to organisations £3,490,000
Assets £1,360,000

TRUSTEES Isaac Bamberger; Hyman Weiss; Victor Frankenhuis.

OTHER INFORMATION Grants were distributed as follows: relief of poverty (£2.6 million); educational grants (£711,000); religious grants (£194,300).

HOW TO APPLY According to the trust's annual report for 2019/20, it 'invites applications for funding through contacting local philanthropists to contribute towards projects that both the trustees and the philanthropists feel are appropriate for the charity's objects'.

CONTACT DETAILS The Trustees, 134 Leicester Road, Salford, Greater Manchester M7 4GB *Tel.* 0161 740 1960

■ KPE4 Charitable Trust

OSCR NO SC047599 **ESTABLISHED** 2017

WHERE FUNDING CAN BE GIVEN Edinburgh; Lothian; Fife.

WHO CAN BENEFIT Scottish charities.

WHAT IS FUNDED Social welfare; education; health; community development; citizenship; arts, culture, heritage and science; sport; recreation facilities; human rights, conflict resolution and reconciliation; racial harmony; equality and diversity; the environment; animal welfare.

SAMPLE GRANTS Friends of the City Art Centre and Museum (£154,500); Light Up Learning (£60,000); Edinburgh Science Festival (£53,500); Canongate Youth (£13,000); Bikes for Refugees (£10,000); Pilton Children's and Youth Project Gold Account (£1,500).

FINANCES *Financial year end* 05/04/2020
Income £1,510,000 *Total grants* £1,000,000
Grants to organisations £1,000,000
Assets £1,750,000

HOW TO APPLY Apply in writing to the correspondent. The trustees meet four times a year.

CONTACT DETAILS The Trustees, c/o Morton Fraser LLP, Quartermile Two, 2 Lister Square, Edinburgh EH3 9GL

■ The KPMG Foundation

CC NO 1086518 **ESTABLISHED** 2000

WHERE FUNDING CAN BE GIVEN UK.

WHO CAN BENEFIT Registered charities; social enterprises.

WHAT IS FUNDED Promoting lifelong learning and improving numeracy and literacy skills for children and young people from disadvantaged communities in the UK.

TYPE OF GRANT Project funding.

RANGE OF GRANTS Mainly under £100,000.

SAMPLE GRANTS Education Endowment Foundation (£262,000 in two grants); Frontline and Reach Foundation (£100,000 each); Family Action (£65,500); Future First (£50,000); Enabling Enterprise (£49,600); School Home Support (£25,000).

FINANCES *Financial year end* 30/09/2020
Income £914,000 *Total grants* £1,150,000
Grants to organisations £1,150,000
Assets £6,080,000

TRUSTEES Rachel Hopcroft; Robin Cartwright; Christine Gilbert; Corrine Harms; David Bartram; Antony Cates; Peter Sherratt; David Woodward.

OTHER INFORMATION The foundation is funded primarily by donations from KPMG LLP, which also 'bears 50% of all administrative costs incurred by the foundation'. During 2019/20 the foundation awarded 17 grants in support of 'children and young people in deprived families'.

HOW TO APPLY The foundation proactively identifies organisations to support and therefore does not accept unsolicited applications; however, the website states: 'if you share our purpose, priorities and approach, contact us with a brief description of your work and a link to your own website. Where there is a strong alignment, we will respond.'

CONTACT DETAILS Judith McNeill, CEO, 15 Canada Square, Canary Wharf, London E14 5GL *Tel.* 020 7311 4217 *Email* kpmgfoundation@kpmg.co.uk *Website* https://kpmgfoundation.org.uk/index.html

■ The Kreitman Foundation

CC NO 269046 **ESTABLISHED** 1975

WHERE FUNDING CAN BE GIVEN UK.

WHO CAN BENEFIT Charitable organisations.

WHAT IS FUNDED Currently, the foundation's main focus is the climate crisis. Previously, support has also been given towards supporting the rights of LGBTQ+ young people and addressing gender norms and stereotypes.

TYPE OF GRANT Project funding; one-off; multi-year.

RANGE OF GRANTS £700 to £40,000.

SAMPLE GRANTS Myeloma UK (£120,000); The Kayapó Project (£5,000); Just Like Us (£13,000); Global Dialogue (£700).

FINANCES *Financial year end* 05/04/2020
Income £297,100 *Total grants* £138,700
Grants to organisations £138,700
Assets £2,900,000

TRUSTEES Richard Luck-Hille; Emma Walker; Rowena Teall.

OTHER INFORMATION During 2019/20, four grants were made within the following categories: health and welfare (£120,000); human rights (£13,700); and conservation (£5,000). In 2013, the foundation entered into a long-term funding project with Myeloma UK, which receives quarterly payments of £30,000.

HOW TO APPLY In the first instance, potential applicants should contact the foundation via email, providing a brief introduction and their latest financials. The trustees will then make contact if they wish to explore further. The 2019 annual report states: 'The trustees receive and assess unsolicited enquiries but generally adopt a largely strategic approach to funding.'

CONTACT DETAILS The Trustees, 5th Floor, Mariner House, 62 Prince Street, Bristol BS1 4QD *Tel.* 0117 971 3445 *Email* info@kreitmanfoundation.org.uk *Website* https://www.kreitmanfoundation.org.uk

■ Kupath Gemach Chaim Bechesed Viznitz Trust

CC NO 1110323 **ESTABLISHED** 2005

WHERE FUNDING CAN BE GIVEN UK and overseas, including Israel.

WHO CAN BENEFIT Registered charities; individuals.

WHAT IS FUNDED Social welfare; the advancement of the Orthodox Jewish faith and Orthodox Jewish religious education.

TYPE OF GRANT Grants; interest-free loans.

SAMPLE GRANTS Anyei Haolam (£20,000); Servus (£10,000); Collel Ahavat Israel Wiznitz (£9,000).

FINANCES *Financial year end* 31/05/2020
Income £564,400 *Total grants* £553,300
Grants to organisations £200,300
Assets £1,200

TRUSTEES Israel Kahan; Saul Weiss; Alexander Pifko.

OTHER INFORMATION Grants were broken down as follows: education (£589,800); advancement of religion (£60,500); relief of poverty (£46,000). During the year, a further £358,000 was granted to individuals in need.

HOW TO APPLY Contact the correspondent for further information.

CONTACT DETAILS The Trustees, 171 Kyverdale Road, London N16 6PS *Tel.* 020 8442 9604

■ Kusuma Trust UK

CC NO 1126983 **ESTABLISHED** 2008

WHERE FUNDING CAN BE GIVEN India, Gibraltar; UK.

WHO CAN BENEFIT Registered charitable organisations.

WHAT IS FUNDED Health and well-being; access to opportunities; community development and the environment; research.

TYPE OF GRANT Project funding; research.

RANGE OF GRANTS Mostly up to £63,000.

SAMPLE GRANTS Chelsea and Westminster Hospital (£150,000); Trees for Cities (£15,000); The Stevens Group (£12,000); Art Against Knives (£10,000); Chefs in Schools (£10,000).

FINANCES *Financial year end* 31/12/2019
Income £4,020,000 *Total grants* £1,480,000
Grants to organisations £1,480,000
Assets £373,000,000

TRUSTEES Anurag Dikshit; Nitin Jain; Dr Soma Pujari.

HOW TO APPLY The trust's website states: 'We do not accept unsolicited applications for funding – instead we select our partnerships based on shared values and mutual interests: creating access to opportunities, improving health and well-being, and investing in our communities and environment.'

CONTACT DETAILS The Trustees, 5th Floor, 55 New Oxford Street, London WC1A 1BS *Email* info@kusumatrust.org *Website* www.kusumatrust.org

■ The Kyte Charitable Trust

CC NO 1035886 **ESTABLISHED** 1994

WHERE FUNDING CAN BE GIVEN UK.

WHO CAN BENEFIT Jewish charitable organisations.

WHAT IS FUNDED General charitable purposes; arts, culture and heritage; children and young people; community support; education; healthcare; international aid; sport; Jewish causes.

SAMPLE GRANTS Previous beneficiaries have included: Maccabi London Brady Recreational Trust (£73,500); Jewish Care and UJIA (£25,000); Jewish Community Secondary School Trust (£22,500); Community Security Trust (£20,000); Chai Cancer Care (£7,200); ORT (£500).

FINANCES *Financial year end* 05/04/2020 *Income* £100,000 *Total grants* £76,200 *Grants to organisations* £76,200 *Assets* £31,600

TRUSTEES Tracey Kyte; James Kyte; Ilana Kyte; Max Kyte; David Kyte.

HOW TO APPLY Contact the correspondent for further information.

CONTACT DETAILS The Trustees, First Floor, Nations House, 103 Wigmore Street, London W1U 1QS *Tel.* 020 7486 7700

■ The Labone Charitable Trust

CC NO 1042836 **ESTABLISHED** 1994

WHERE FUNDING CAN BE GIVEN England; Scotland; Burma; Moldova; Nigeria; Zimbabwe.

WHO CAN BENEFIT Roman Catholics and registered charities.

WHAT IS FUNDED General charitable purposes.

RANGE OF GRANTS Up to £20,000.

SAMPLE GRANTS Thecle Gambe (£20,400); Kukura Neshungu Institute (£14,100); Moldova Project (£5,200); The Lenton Centre (£5,000); African Mission Fund (£3,600); HCPT.Doncaster Group (£3,000); West Area Project (£1,600).

FINANCES *Financial year end* 31/03/2020 *Income* £72,500 *Total grants* £70,600 *Grants to organisations* £68,600 *Assets* £4,010,000

TRUSTEES Alfred Carer; Ann Carer; Christopher Young; Maria Cummins.

OTHER INFORMATION In 2019/20 grants were awarded to 11 organisations and four individuals.

HOW TO APPLY Contact the correspondent for further information.

CONTACT DETAILS The Trustees, 52 Aspley Park Drive, Nottingham, Nottinghamshire NG8 3EG *Tel.* 0115 854 7007

■ Ladbrokes Coral Trust

CC NO 1101804 **ESTABLISHED** 2003

WHERE FUNDING CAN BE GIVEN UK.

WHO CAN BENEFIT Registered charities, hospices, hospitals, community groups.

WHAT IS FUNDED Health: principally research/ treatment, hospice services and disability support; education: supporting people with disabilities or who are disdvantaged and sports services for disadvantaged people or communities; community: focusing on homelessness projects, older people and social activity projects for those at risk.

SAMPLE GRANTS A list of beneficiaries was not included in the annual report and accounts.

FINANCES *Financial year end* 31/12/2019 *Income* £273,600 *Total grants* £260,900 *Grants to organisations* £260,900 *Assets* £252,900

TRUSTEES Karen Thraves; Shaun Giblin; Simon Reynolds; Nick Batram; Jay Dossetter; Craig Watson; Simon O'Halloran.

OTHER INFORMATION Grants were broken down as follows: medical causes (£208,600); hospices and hospitals (£40,600); various (£7,300); social welfare (£4,400).

HOW TO APPLY In the first instance, the support of a local shop should be secured. The trustees meet every month to consider grant requests from shop and head office fundraisers and registered charities.

CONTACT DETAILS The Trustees, c/o GVC Holdings plc, 3rd Floor, One New Change, London EC4M 9AF *Tel.* 020 3938 0000 *Email* charity@ladbrokescoral.com

■ The K. P. Ladd Charitable Trust

CC NO 1091493 **ESTABLISHED** 2002

WHERE FUNDING CAN BE GIVEN UK and overseas.

WHO CAN BENEFIT Religious bodies; places of worship.

WHAT IS FUNDED Christian causes; missionary work; overseas aid.

TYPE OF GRANT Capital costs; core and revenue costs; seed funding; start-up funding; project funding; unrestricted funding.

RANGE OF GRANTS Typically less than £5,000.

SAMPLE GRANTS London Institute for Contemporary Christianity (£45,500); London City Mission (£8,000); Kepplewray Trust (£6,000); Church Army (£3,000); Urban Saints (£2,000).

FINANCES *Financial year end* 30/04/2020 *Income* £182,300 *Total grants* £104,000 *Grants to organisations* £104,000 *Assets* £3,000,000

TRUSTEES Rosemary Ladd; Brian Ladd; Kenneth Ladd; Ian Creswick.

HOW TO APPLY The trust has stated that it 'is fully committed and does not reply to unsolicited requests'. The trustees select charities known to them personally.

CONTACT DETAILS Brian Ladd, Trustee, 34 St Mary's Avenue, Northwood, Middlesex HA6 3AZ *Tel.* 020 7399 9563 *Email* brian.ladd@licc.org.uk

■ John Laing Charitable Trust

CC NO 236852 **ESTABLISHED** 1962

WHERE FUNDING CAN BE GIVEN UK and, occasionally, countries where John Laing Group plc operates.

WHO CAN BENEFIT Registered charities; CICs; NGOs; organisations outside the UK with a link with the John Laing Group; existing and former employees of John Laing Group plc who are in need.

WHAT IS FUNDED Education; community regeneration; disadvantaged young people; homelessness.

WHAT IS NOT FUNDED Individuals other than current or former employees of John Laing Group plc; organisations not aligned to the trust's strategic priorities; organisations whose main aim is animal welfare; sponsorships; projects that are not for public benefit.

TYPE OF GRANT Project funding; core funding; capital costs; single and multi-year funding.

SAMPLE GRANTS Historic England (£375,000); Young Enterprise (£60,000); The Silver Line (£50,000); Police Youth Citizens Club (£35,500); Arvon, Homeless Link and National Literacy Trust (£25,000 each); Alzheimer's Research UK (£10,000); Samaritans – North Hertfordshire and Stevenage (£5,000).

FINANCES *Financial year end* 31/12/2020 *Income* £2,740,000 *Total grants* £2,043,000 *Grants to organisations* £1,520,000 *Assets* £69,060,000

TRUSTEES Stewart Laing; Christopher Laing; Timothy Foster; Lynette Krige; Sir Martin Laing; Alexandra Gregory; Christopher Laing.

HOW TO APPLY At the time of writing (January 2021) the trust's website stated: 'Note that applications to the Trust are currently closed. Until further notice, we [will] only [be processing] invited applications.' Check the trust's website for further information.

CONTACT DETAILS Jenny Impey, Trust Director, 33 Bunns Lane, London NW7 2DX *Email* jenny.impey@laing.com *Website* https://johnlaingcharitabletrust.com

■ Maurice and Hilda Laing Charitable Trust

CC NO 1058109 **ESTABLISHED** 1996

WHERE FUNDING CAN BE GIVEN UK and overseas, with a preference for sub-Saharan Africa.

WHO CAN BENEFIT UK-registered charities.

WHAT IS FUNDED The advancement of the Christian faith and values; people in the UK who are disadvantaged, vulnerable and/or socially isolated such as prisoners and ex-offenders, people who are homeless, children and young people and refugees; the relief of poverty overseas, with an emphasis on street children, education, sustainable livelihoods and people with disabilities.

WHAT IS NOT FUNDED Charities registered overseas; umbrella, second-tier or grant-making organisations; state-maintained or independent schools (other than those for pupils with special educational needs); hospices (other than those with which the trust has a strong local connection); NHS hospital trusts and other establishments offering medical care; amateur sports clubs; individuals (whether for education, travel or medical purposes); animal welfare; general appeals or circulars; campaigning or lobbying activities, feasibility studies and social research; professional training (including attendance at conferences, courses, etc.); costs of staging one-off events such as festivals or conferences; gap-year projects, residential and overseas exchange programmes; summer activities for children/young people or after-school clubs; core running costs of local organisations (rent, utilities, salaries, etc.); cancer research and cancer care; national helpline running costs; church workers' salaries (children and family workers, youth workers, worship leaders, outreach workers, etc.); church restoration or repair (including church roofs, spires, organs, bells, wall paintings, etc.).

TYPE OF GRANT Project funding; capital costs.

RANGE OF GRANTS Grants typically range between £5,000 and £25,000, although the trust has the capacity to make a small number of larger grants each year.

SAMPLE GRANTS Wesley House Cambridge (£374,300); Christians Against Poverty (£35,000); Essence (£10,000); Family Support Work (£5,000).

FINANCES *Financial year end* 31/12/2019 *Income* £863,400 *Total grants* £1,560,000 *Grants to organisations* £1,560,000 *Assets* £24,660,000

TRUSTEES Charles Laing; Sir Ewan Harper; Stephen Ludlow; Andrea Currie; Simon Martle; Dr Paul Den Bosch.

OTHER INFORMATION This is one of four Laing Family Trusts. The Laing Family Trusts are run on a co-ordinated basis, which means that you do not need to make multiple applications to the individual trusts. Your application will automatically be directed to the most appropriate of the four trusts.

HOW TO APPLY Apply in writing to the correspondent by post. Applicants are asked to download and complete an application cover sheet, which is available on the completion of an eligibility quiz. Full details of what should be included in an application can be found on the trust's website.

CONTACT DETAILS Belgin Wingrove, Grants Manager, 33 Bunns Lane, Mill Hill, London NW7 2DX *Tel.* 020 8238 8890 *Email* info@laingfamilytrusts.org.uk *Website* https://www.laingfamilytrusts.org.uk

■ Christopher Laing Foundation

CC NO 278460 **ESTABLISHED** 1979

WHERE FUNDING CAN BE GIVEN UK, with a preference for Hertfordshire and Oxfordshire.

WHO CAN BENEFIT Registered charities.

WHAT IS FUNDED Young people; education; the environment; homelessness; disability.

TYPE OF GRANT Capital; core costs; project funding.

RANGE OF GRANTS Up to £100,000 but mostly from £1,000 to £50,000.

SAMPLE GRANTS The Lord's Taverners (£70,000); Duke of Edinburgh's Award (£55,000); RNLI (£30,000); The National Emergencies Trust (£20,000); Action for ME and Blossom House School (£10,000 each); RAW Workshop (£5,000); Little Green Pig (£3,000).

FINANCES *Financial year end* 05/04/2020 *Income* £451,000 *Total grants* £483,000 *Grants to organisations* £483,000 *Assets* £10,640,000

TRUSTEES Christopher Laing; Diana Laing; John Keeble; Michael Laing; Richard Haines; Carla Seale.

OTHER INFORMATION In 2019/20 grants were made to 20 organisations and were broken down as follows: social welfare (£215,000); children and young people (£143,000); culture and the environment (£65,000); Charities Aid Foundation (£60,000).

HOW TO APPLY Application forms can be downloaded from the foundation's website. Applications are considered regularly by the trustees, so the application process is always open.

CONTACT DETAILS The Trustees, TMF Global Services (UK) Ltd, 960 Capability Green, Luton, Bedfordshire LU1 3PE *Tel.* 01582 439200 *Email* claing_charity@tmf-group.com *Website* https://www.christopherlaingfoundation.com

■ The David Laing Foundation

CC NO 278462 **ESTABLISHED** 1979

WHERE FUNDING CAN BE GIVEN Mainly Hertfordshire, Oxfordshire, Leicestershire and Northamptonshire, with some UK-wide and worldwide grants.

WHO CAN BENEFIT Organisations benefitting children, including those who are adopted, fostered or in care; one-parent families; people with disabilities.

WHAT IS FUNDED General charitable purposes, with a focus on young people, disability and the arts.

WHAT IS NOT FUNDED Individuals.

TYPE OF GRANT One-off; capital costs; some charities are closely associated with the foundation and benefit frequently.

RANGE OF GRANTS Mostly under £7,000.

SAMPLE GRANTS Northamptonshire Community Foundation (£115,000); Crusade Community Boats (£30,000); Adrenaline Alley (£25,000); The Royal College of Music (£19,500); Northamptonshire Association of Youth Clubs (£12,500); National Youth Jazz (£7,000).

FINANCES *Financial year end* 05/04/2020 *Income* £200,200 *Total grants* £378,200 *Grants to organisations* £378,200 *Assets* £6,240,000

TRUSTEES David Laing; Stuart Lewis; Frances Laing; Francis Barlow.

OTHER INFORMATION Only organisations that received grants of over £7,000 were listed as beneficiaries in the charity's accounts. Grants of under £7,000 totalled £129,200. Grants were broken down as follows: arts and culture (£200,100); general charitable purposes

(£81,300); children and young people (£38,300); social welfare/sports/recreation (£31,500); disability/disadvantage/health and well-being (£15,500); religion (£6,500); overseas aid (£5,300).

HOW TO APPLY Contact the correspondent for further information.

CONTACT DETAILS The Trustees, The Manor House, Grafton Underwood, Kettering, Northamptonshire NN14 3AA *Email* david@david-laing.co.uk

■ The Kirby Laing Foundation

CC NO 264299 **ESTABLISHED** 1972

WHERE FUNDING CAN BE GIVEN UK and overseas, with a preference for Asia.

WHO CAN BENEFIT Registered charities; churches with exempt status.

WHAT IS FUNDED Christian causes; education, particularly STEM subjects and traditional crafts; medical welfare and research, particularly into dementia, stroke and other neurodegenerative diseases; opera and the performing arts; the environment; overseas development projects; children and young people; older people; people with disabilities.

WHAT IS NOT FUNDED See the website for a full list of exclusions.

TYPE OF GRANT Capital costs; programme development costs; endowment/capacity building; project costs; research; multi-year; one-off.

RANGE OF GRANTS Up to £110,000.

SAMPLE GRANTS SAT-7 Trust Ltd (£110,000); Restoration of Appearance and Function Trust (£75,000); Project Equinox (£50,000); Newcastle Cathedral (£25,000); Gurkha Welfare Trust (£10,000); The Himalayan Trust UK (£9,300); The Cricket Foundation – Chance to Shine, De Havilland Aircraft Museum and Motor Neurone Disease Association (£5,000 each).

FINANCES *Financial year end* 31/12/2019 *Income* £2,410,000 *Total grants* £1,740,000 *Grants to organisations* £1,740,000 *Assets* £63,570,000

TRUSTEES David Laing; Simon Webley; Revd Charles Burch; Dr Frederick Lewis.

OTHER INFORMATION During 2019, grants were awarded to 110 organisations, including 21 grants of between £500 and £4,000 that were made through Charities Aid Foundation, totalling £25,000.

HOW TO APPLY The Laing Family Trusts are run on a co-ordinated basis; applications are directed to the most suitable of the four trusts, so multiple applications are not necessary. Full details of how to submit an application can be found on the foundation's website.

CONTACT DETAILS Elizabeth Harley, Trust Director, 33 Bunns Lane, Mill Hill, London NW7 2DX *Tel.* 020 8238 8890 *Email* info@laingfamilytrusts.org.uk *Website* www.laingfamilytrusts.org.uk

■ The Martin Laing Foundation

CC NO 278461 **ESTABLISHED** 1979

WHERE FUNDING CAN BE GIVEN Malta; Norfolk; Essex; Hertfordshire.

WHO CAN BENEFIT Registered charities.

WHAT IS FUNDED The environment and conservation; projects benefitting disadvantaged young people or older people in Norfolk, Essex or Hertfordshire; development projects in Malta.

WHAT IS NOT FUNDED A list of exclusions can be found on the foundation's website.

TYPE OF GRANT One-off awards for capital costs or one-off/recurrent project grants.

RANGE OF GRANTS £500 to £10,000.

SAMPLE GRANTS Diocese in Europe (£50,000); The Pushkin Trust and WWF-UK (£10,000 each); Action for ME (£7,500); Ormiston Children and Families Trust (£5,000); Richmond Foundation (£4,300); The Inspire Foundation (£1,000); Kilbryde Hospice (£500).

FINANCES *Financial year end* 05/04/2020 *Income* £398,500 *Total grants* £202,500 *Grants to organisations* £202,500 *Assets* £11,426,000

TRUSTEES Edward Kirby Laing; Sir Martin Laing; Lady Laing; Nicholas Gregory; Colin Fletcher; Alexandra Gregory.

OTHER INFORMATION This is one of the Laing Family Trusts. Detailed information on this and the other Laing charities can be found on the website. There were 30 awards made in 2019/20 (including 11 through Charities Aid Foundation).

HOW TO APPLY The Laing Family Trusts are administered and co-ordinated centrally; applications are directed to the most suitable of the four trusts, so multiple applications are not necessary. Detailed guidance on how to make an application can be found online. The majority of unsolicited applications are unsuccessful. Applications for overseas projects are by invitation only.

CONTACT DETAILS Bryony Livesey, Grants Administrator, Laing Family Trusts, 33 Bunns Lane, London NW7 2DX *Tel.* 020 8238 8890 *Email* info@laingfamilytrusts.org.uk *Website* www.laingfamilytrusts.org.uk

■ The Beatrice Laing Trust

CC NO 211884 **ESTABLISHED** 1952

WHERE FUNDING CAN BE GIVEN UK and overseas.

WHO CAN BENEFIT Mainly registered charities. Christian organisations. Grants to overseas projects are normally made through a registered UK charity.

WHAT IS FUNDED The relief of poverty; the advancement of the evangelical Christian faith; social welfare; disadvantaged individuals; the education, training and development of young people; employment; older people; homelessness; people with physical, mental or learning difficulties; former armed forces personnel; ex-offenders; small-scale development projects overseas; direct health services (rather than medical research). A very small number of individuals are supported, with most being retired missionaries who are known to the founders and who receive an annual grant.

WHAT IS NOT FUNDED General appeals or circulars; campaigning or lobbying activities; umbrella, second-tier or grant-making organisations; professional associations or professional training projects; feasibility studies and social research; individual sponsorship requirements; grants to individuals for educational, medical or travel purposes including gap-year projects and overseas exchange programmes; summer activities for children/young people or after-school clubs; state-maintained or independent schools other than those for pupils with special educational needs; uniformed groups such as Scouts and Guides; costs of staging one-off events, festivals or conferences; animal welfare; core running costs of hospices, counselling projects and other local organisations; church restoration or repair (including organs and bells).

TYPE OF GRANT Mainly one-off, capital costs; one-off or recurrent project expenditure.

RANGE OF GRANTS Mostly between £500 and £30,000.

SAMPLE GRANTS Exeter Royal Academy for Deaf Education (£60,000 in two grants); Carlisle Cathedral (£30,000); Huntingdon Methodist Church (£20,000); C2C Social Action (£15,000); Church Homeless Trust (£10,000); Alvechurch Baptist Church (£500).

FINANCES *Financial year end* 05/04/2020 *Income* £2,740,000 *Total grants* £2,160,000 *Grants to organisations* £2,160,000 *Assets* £68,180,000

TRUSTEES Christopher Laing; David Laing; Sir Martin Laing; Charles Laing; Paula Blacker; Alexandra Gregory.

HOW TO APPLY This is one of the Laing Family Trusts which are administered and co-ordinated centrally; applications are directed to the most suitable of the four trusts, so multiple applications are not necessary. Detailed guidance on how to make an application can be found on the website, along with an eligibility quiz.

CONTACT DETAILS Becci McCormick, Grants Administrator, c/o Laing Family Trusts, 33 Bunns Lane, Mill Hill, London NW7 2DX *Tel.* 020 8238 8890 *Email* info@laingfamilytrusts.org.uk *Website* www.laingfamilytrusts.org.uk

The Leonard Laity Stoate Charitable Trust

CC NO 221325 **ESTABLISHED** 1950

WHERE FUNDING CAN BE GIVEN Bristol, Somerset, Cornwall, Devon and Dorset.

WHO CAN BENEFIT Registered charities; religious bodies/institutions.

WHAT IS FUNDED Methodism; general charitable purposes; social welfare; medical causes; disability; children and young people; community projects; the arts; overseas aid; the environment.

WHAT IS NOT FUNDED Individuals; non-registered charities; CICs; large projects; general appeals by national charities; running costs.

TYPE OF GRANT Capital costs; core/revenue costs; seed funding/start-up costs.

RANGE OF GRANTS £100 to £2,000.

SAMPLE GRANTS Parkway Methodist Church – Bristol (£2,400); Support Through Court – Exeter (£2,000); Champernowne Play Park – Modbury (£1,500); Bridgwater Foodbank and Tobacco Factory Theatres – Bristol (£1,000 each); Friends of St Margaret's Church – Bideford (£500); RSPCA – Horsham (£100).

FINANCES *Financial year end* 31/03/2020 *Income* £90,800 *Total grants* £79,100 *Grants to organisations* £79,100 *Assets* £1,930,000

TRUSTEES Stephen Duckworth; Philip Stoate; Dr Christopher Stoate; Dr Pam Stoate; Mark Harnden; The Revd Dr Jonathan Pye; Natasha Jones.

OTHER INFORMATION Grants were awarded to 95 organisations during the year. Due to the large number of applications the trust receives, applications from outside its geographic area of focus are unlikely to be successful.

HOW TO APPLY Applications should be made in writing to the correspondent (not by email or telephone) and should include the information specified on the trust's website. There is no dedicated application form. The majority of grants are awarded at half-yearly meetings in April/May and October/November; applications should be received at least two months prior.

CONTACT DETAILS Philip Stoate, Secretary, 41 Tower Hill, Williton, Taunton, Somerset TA4 4JR *Tel.* 07923 824313 *Email* secretary@stoate-charity.org.uk *Website* www.stoate-charity.org.uk

The Lake House Charity

CC NO 1126293 **ESTABLISHED** 2008

WHERE FUNDING CAN BE GIVEN UK.

WHO CAN BENEFIT Registered charities, with a preference for small and local charities.

WHAT IS FUNDED Support and care for sick and disadvantaged children and young people; older people.

WHAT IS NOT FUNDED Individuals; non-registered charities.

TYPE OF GRANT Project funding; core funding; one-off and repeat requests.

RANGE OF GRANTS Mostly £5,000 and under.

SAMPLE GRANTS The Big Give Christmas Challenge (£26,700); Challengers (£15,000); Amelie and Daniel Linsey Foundation (£5,000); Music in Hospitals and Care (£3,000); Action on Elder Abuse and Winston's Wish (£2,500 each); Lennox Children's Cancer Fund (£1,000); Age Exchange (£500); DEBRA (£400).

FINANCES *Financial year end* 05/04/2020 *Income* £50,000 *Total grants* £104,400 *Grants to organisations* £104,400 *Assets* £1,800

TRUSTEES Helen Perry; Timothy Perry; Sarah Mulford; Gerard Maguire; Andrew Butler-Casser; Marcus Platt; Sasha Platt.

OTHER INFORMATION Grants were made to 29 organisations during the year.

HOW TO APPLY Application forms can be downloaded from the website and should be returned via email to the correspondent. The trustees meet twice a year and applications can be sent at any time. Every application will receive a response. Full guidelines on applications can be found on the website.

CONTACT DETAILS The Trustees, PO Box 651, Weybridge, Surrey KT13 3EP *Tel.* 01932 848028 *Email* lakehouse.office@googlemail.com *Website* www.thelakehouse.org.uk

Community Foundations for Lancashire and Merseyside

CC NO 1068887 **ESTABLISHED** 1998

WHERE FUNDING CAN BE GIVEN Merseyside and Lancashire.

WHO CAN BENEFIT Registered charities; unregistered charities; social enterprises; CICs; schools.

WHAT IS FUNDED A wide range of purposes including housing, social welfare, youth opportunities, the environment, health and well-being, community services and development.

WHAT IS NOT FUNDED The advancement of religion; the advancement of political beliefs or party politics; activities understood to be the exclusive responsibility of statutory authorities; retrospective expenditure; the funding of any public or private sector compensation and/or mitigation. There may also be fund-specific exclusions.

TYPE OF GRANT Core costs; project funding; seed funding/start-up funding.

RANGE OF GRANTS In 2018/19, the average award was £4,450.
SAMPLE GRANTS Previous beneficiaries have included: dot-art Schools; Fire Support Network; Halton Voluntary Action; Jo Jo Mind and Body; Liverpool Academy of Art; Liverpool Greenbank Wheelchair Basketball Club; The Zero Centre; and Twin Vision.
FINANCES *Financial year end* 31/03/2019 *Income* £3,870,000 *Total grants* £2,650,000 *Grants to organisations* £2,650,000 *Assets* £18,000,000
TRUSTEES Arthur Roberts; Andrew Myers; Chris Bliss; Amanda Meachin; William Waring; Colin Wardale; Carmel Hall; George Mendoros; Nasima Zaman; Donna Howitt.
OTHER INFORMATION This is one of the 46 UK community foundations, which distribute funding for a wide range of purposes. As with all community foundations, there are a number of donor-advised funds managed on behalf of individuals, families and charitable trusts. Grant schemes tend to change frequently; consult the foundation's website for details of current programmes and up-to-date deadlines. Grants were distributed as follows: Merseyside (348 grants); Lancashire (193 grants); rest of the UK (50 grants). The foundation has separate websites for funding in Merseyside and funding in Lancashire. The 2018/19 accounts were the latest available at the time of writing (January 2021).
HOW TO APPLY Potential applicants are advised to visit the community foundation's website or contact its grants team to find the most suitable funding stream.
CONTACT DETAILS Grants Team, Third Floor, Stanley Building, 43 Hanover Street, Liverpool, Merseyside L1 3DN *Tel.* 0330 440 4900 *Email* applications@cflm.email *Website* www.cfmerseyside.org.uk www.lancsfoundation.org.uk

■ Lancashire Environmental Fund Ltd

CC NO 1074983 **ESTABLISHED** 1998
WHERE FUNDING CAN BE GIVEN Lancashire (excluding the unitary authority districts of Blackpool and Blackburn). Projects must be located within ten miles of a landfill site.
WHO CAN BENEFIT Any not-for-profit organisation, charity, trust, community group, or voluntary organisation.
WHAT IS FUNDED Providing and maintaining public amenities and parks to the benefit of the natural, social or built environment. The charity's website states: 'Projects to date have included improvements to community facilities, general environmental improvements, creation and management of habitats, improvements to parks, gardens, open spaces, play areas, recreational facilities, ponds, canals and rivers and natural biodiversity.'
WHAT IS NOT FUNDED For a comprehensive list of exclusions, applicants are advised to refer to the guidance notes of the specific grant programme to which they intend to apply.
TYPE OF GRANT Project costs; capital costs.
RANGE OF GRANTS Green grants of up to £1,000; small grants of up to £15,000; main grants of up to £30,000.
SAMPLE GRANTS Friends of Preesall Park (£23,900); St Joseph's Community Centre and Todmorden Angling Society (£10,000 each); Newchurch Village Community Association Garden (£540).
FINANCES *Financial year end* 31/12/2019 *Income* £1,080,000 *Total grants* £1,240,000 *Grants to organisations* £1,240,000 *Assets* £1,040,000
TRUSTEES Francis McGinty; Andrew Hughes; Albert Atkinson; John Drury.
HOW TO APPLY Detailed and helpful guidance notes and application forms for each funding strand can be found on the charity's website.
CONTACT DETAILS The Fund Manager, The Barn, Berkeley Drive, Bamber Bridge, Preston, Lancashire PR5 6BY *Tel.* 01772 317247 *Email* general@lancsenvfund.org.uk *Website* www.lancsenvfund.org.uk

■ The Lancashire Foundation

CC NO 1149184 **ESTABLISHED** 2012
WHERE FUNDING CAN BE GIVEN UK; Bermuda; worldwide.
WHO CAN BENEFIT Charitable organisations.
WHAT IS FUNDED General charitable purposes; young people; people who are disadvantaged.
TYPE OF GRANT One-off and multi-year grants.
RANGE OF GRANTS Up to £60,000.
SAMPLE GRANTS The Family Centre (£60,000); St Giles Trust (£42,300); Cancer Research UK (£25,900); Vauxhall City Farm (£20,000); London Air Ambulance (£10,000); Child Bereavement UK (£7,000); Care for Children and Medical Detection Dogs (£5,000 each); Ahoy Centre (£2,000).
FINANCES *Financial year end* 31/12/2019 *Income* £596,800 *Total grants* £376,700 *Grants to organisations* £376,700 *Assets* £2,240,000
TRUSTEES Derek Stapley; Louise Wells; Emma Grimes; Christopher Wilkinson.
OTHER INFORMATION This foundation is the corporate charity of the Lancashire group of insurance companies, which operates in Bermuda and London. The foundation receives its income through an annual donation from the group. Grants were awarded to 28 organisations during the year. Only grants of over £2,000 were listed in the accounts.
HOW TO APPLY Apply in writing to the correspondent, further guidance can be found on the foundation's website.
CONTACT DETAILS Donations Committee, Lancashire Insurance Company (UK), Level 29, 20 Fenchurch Street, London EC3M 3BY *Tel.* 020 7264 4056 *Website* www.lancashiregroup.com/en/responsibility/lancashire-foundation.html

■ Duchy of Lancaster Benevolent Fund

CC NO 1026752 **ESTABLISHED** 1993
WHERE FUNDING CAN BE GIVEN Lancashire, Greater Manchester and Merseyside; elsewhere in the country where the Duchy of Lancaster has historical links.
WHO CAN BENEFIT Charitable organisations.
WHAT IS FUNDED General charitable purposes; young people and education; people with disabilities; older people and people who are unwell; community; religious causes.
RANGE OF GRANTS Mostly up to £5,000.
SAMPLE GRANTS Independence at Home (£30,000); Read and Simonstone Village Hall (£15,000); Lancaster University Regional Heritage Unit (£9,000); Preston Muslim Forum (£5,000);

Whizz-Kidz (£4,000); Emerge (£3,000); Church Pastoral Aid Society (£2,000).

FINANCES *Financial year end* 31/03/2020 *Income* £577,900 *Total grants* £523,300 *Grants to organisations* £520,000 *Assets* £14,330,000

TRUSTEES Mark Blundell; Warren Smith; Lord Shuttleworth; Richard Snowden; Chris Adcock; Robert Miles; Sir Michael Stevens.

OTHER INFORMATION Grants were broken down as follows: community help (£204,800); youth and education (£143,100); people with disabilities and older people (£81,900); religious causes (£34,600); miscellaneous (£32,000). Only organisations that received grants of over £2,000 were listed as beneficiaries in the charity's accounts. Grants of under £2,000 totalled £141,900 and were awarded to 223 organisations.

HOW TO APPLY Contact the correspondent for further information.

CONTACT DETAILS The Secretary, 1 Lancaster Place, Strand, London WC2E 7ED *Tel.* 020 7269 1700 *Email* info@duchyoflancaster.co.uk *Website* www.duchyoflancaster.co.uk

■ Lancaster Foundation

CC NO 1066850 **ESTABLISHED** 1997

WHERE FUNDING CAN BE GIVEN UK and Africa.

WHO CAN BENEFIT Christian registered charities only.

WHAT IS FUNDED Christianity, social welfare; health; children and young people.

SAMPLE GRANTS Message Trust (£212,100); Every Life International (£120,700); Hope Together (£10,000); Tough Living Preston (£1,000).

FINANCES *Financial year end* 31/03/2020 *Income* £3,000,000 *Total grants* £2,670,000 *Grants to organisations* £2,670,000 *Assets* £58,640,000

TRUSTEES Rosemary Lancaster; Dr John Lancaster; Steven Lancaster; Julie Broadhurst.

HOW TO APPLY The foundation's annual report for 2019/20 states: 'Although many applications are received, the administrative structure of the charity does not allow for the consideration of unsolicited requests for grant funding.'

CONTACT DETAILS The Trustees, Text House, 152 Bawdlands, Clitheroe, Lancashire BB7 2LA *Tel.* 01200 444404

■ LandAid Charitable Trust (LandAid)

CC NO 295157 **ESTABLISHED** 1986

WHERE FUNDING CAN BE GIVEN UK.

WHO CAN BENEFIT Registered charitable organisations working in the UK.

WHAT IS FUNDED Youth homelessness.

TYPE OF GRANT One-off; project funding; capital costs.

SAMPLE GRANTS StreetSmart (£100,000); Harp Southend and Local Solutions (£75,000 each); New Horizon Youth Centre (£46,000); Homeless Link (£14,300).

FINANCES *Financial year end* 31/03/2020 *Income* £2,820,000 *Total grants* £689,800 *Grants to organisations* £689,800 *Assets* £1,940,000

TRUSTEES Alistair Elliot; Susan Hickey; Melanie Leech; Mark Reynolds; Gillian Bowen; Scott Parsons; Suzanne Avery; David Erwin; Michael Slade; Daniel Hughes; Claire Milton; Andrew Gulliford; Robert Bould.

HOW TO APPLY In the first instance, visit the LandAid website for full information of the charity's work. Open rounds of applications for funding are advertised online.

CONTACT DETAILS Grants Team, St Albans House, 5th Floor, 57–59 Haymarket, London SW1Y 4QX *Email* enquiries@landaid.org *Website* www.landaid.org

■ The Allen Lane Foundation

CC NO 248031 **ESTABLISHED** 1966

WHERE FUNDING CAN BE GIVEN England (excluding Greater London), Scotland, Wales and Northern Ireland. Organisations with offices in London are eligible if the people who benefit from their work are not only in London.

WHO CAN BENEFIT Registered charities; unregistered charities; CICs; social enterprises.

WHAT IS FUNDED Asylum seekers and refugees; Travellers; migrants; offenders and ex-offenders; older people; people experiencing mental health problems; people experiencing violence or abuse; social cohesion.

WHAT IS NOT FUNDED See the foundation's helpful website for a comprehensive list of exclusions.

TYPE OF GRANT Core/revenue costs; seed funding/start-up funding; unrestricted funding.

RANGE OF GRANTS The maximum grant size is £15,000 and the average grant size is around £5,000.

SAMPLE GRANTS Safer Living Foundation (£15,000); Storybook Dads (£10,000); Flower Estate Family Action (£8,000); Copeland Age and Advice Service (£6,000); Rebuild East Midlands and ToastLoveCoffee CIC (£5,000 each); Bipolar Scotland (£4,800); Sunderland Literacy Aid CIC (£2,500); Active Citizens Wirral Association (£1,000); Lansdown Friendship Club (£500).

FINANCES *Financial year end* 31/03/2020 *Income* £744,800 *Total grants* £777,600 *Grants to organisations* £777,600 *Assets* £17,320,000

TRUSTEES Zoe Teale; Juliet Walker; Fredrica Teale; Margaret Hyde; Philip Walsh; Maurice Frankel; Justine Cadbury.

OTHER INFORMATION According to the 2019/20 accounts, grants were committed to 137 organisations during the year with a combined total of £784,000. An unspecified number of grants were withdrawn; therefore, we have used the 'grants paid' figure as the foundation's grant total (£777,600). The average grant size was £5,720. The foundation's 2019/20 accounts also state that 96 grants were single-year grants, with fewer being for two or three years. From a total of 440 applications made to the foundation during the year, 303 were refused, resulting in an overall success rate of 32%. There was also a good geographical spread across the UK, with 105 grants awarded in England, 22 in Scotland, six in Wales and four in Northern Ireland. The foundation's website states: 'While recognising (and being willing to support) ongoing, tried and tested projects, we are also particularly interested in unusual, imaginative or pioneering projects which have perhaps not yet caught the public imagination.'

HOW TO APPLY The foundation has an online application system whereby applicants can take an eligibility quiz. If the potential applicant is eligible to apply, they will be directed to the foundation's online application form. Full details and guidelines for applicants are available on the foundation's helpful website.

CONTACT DETAILS Gill Aconley, Grants Officer, 90 The Mount, York, North Yorkshire YO24 1AR *Tel.* 01904 613223 *Email* info@allenlane.org.uk *Website* www.allenlane.org.uk

■ Langdale Trust

CC NO 215317 **ESTABLISHED** 1960

WHERE FUNDING CAN BE GIVEN UK, with some preference for Birmingham.

WHO CAN BENEFIT Registered charities, including those working overseas; hospices; museums and theatres.

WHAT IS FUNDED General charitable purposes, including the following: animal welfare; conservation; health; social welfare; the environment; young people and older people.

WHAT IS NOT FUNDED Individuals.

TYPE OF GRANT One-off and recurrent.

RANGE OF GRANTS £1,000 to £6,000.

SAMPLE GRANTS Future Trees Trust and Rainforest Foundation (£6,000 each); Survival International (£5,000); Oxfam (£4,000); Hearing Dogs, National Youth Music Theatre, Prisoners Abroad and Stroke Association (£3,000 each); Orangutan Appeal UK (£2,000); Headway Birmingham and Solihull and Tall Ships Youth Trust (£1,000 each).

FINANCES *Financial year end* 30/11/2019 *Income* £185,100 *Total grants* £171,000 *Grants to organisations* £171,000 *Assets* £5,540,000

TRUSTEES Timothy Wilson; Theresa Wilson; Jethro Elvin; Naomi Rieley.

OTHER INFORMATION The 2018/19 accounts were the latest available at the time of writing (June 2021). Grants were awarded to 62 organisations during the year.

HOW TO APPLY Contact the correspondent for further information.

CONTACT DETAILS The Trustees, c/o Veale Wasbrough Vizards LLP, Second Floor, 3 Brindley Place, Birmingham, West Midlands B1 2JB *Tel.* 0121 227 3705 *Email* poneill@vwv.co.uk

■ The R. J. Larg Family Trust

OSCR NO SC004946 **ESTABLISHED** 1970

WHERE FUNDING CAN BE GIVEN Scotland, particularly Dundee, Angus, Tayside and North East Fife.

WHO CAN BENEFIT Charitable organisations; hospices; uniformed groups.

WHAT IS FUNDED Social welfare; health and disability causes; medical research; the arts; music; community or citizenship development.

TYPE OF GRANT Generally one-off, some recurring.

RANGE OF GRANTS Grants range from £250 to £5,000 but are typically of around £1,000 to £2,000.

SAMPLE GRANTS High School of Dundee (Cadet Force) (£6,000); Optimistic Sound, Dundee Parish Church (St Mary's), High School of Dundee (Larg Scholarship) (£5,000 each); Scottish Wildlife Trust – Angus and Dundee (£3,000); Macmillan Cancer Support (£2,000); Brittle Bone Society (£500).

FINANCES *Financial year end* 05/04/2020 *Income* £157,500 *Total grants* £121,000 *Grants to organisations* £121,000 *Assets* £3,570,000

HOW TO APPLY Contact the correspondent for further information.

CONTACT DETAILS The Trustees, c/o Thorntons Law LLP, Whitehall House, 33 Yeaman Shore, Dundee DD1 4BJ *Tel.* 01382 229111

■ Largsmount Ltd

CC NO 280509 **ESTABLISHED** 1979

WHERE FUNDING CAN BE GIVEN UK and overseas, namely Israel.

WHO CAN BENEFIT Educational and religious institutions; organisations set up to provide for the people in need. Mainly Orthodox Jewish charities.

WHAT IS FUNDED Jewish causes; the advancement of Orthodox Jewish religion and education.

RANGE OF GRANTS £50,000 to £486,200.

SAMPLE GRANTS S K Charitable Trust (£486,200); Five K Foundation (£308,900); H P Charitable Trust (£154,200); C E K Stern Charitable Trust (£136,600); M O Charitable Trust (£96,700); J O Charitable Trust (£63,800).

FINANCES *Financial year end* 31/12/2019 *Income* £8,900 *Total grants* £770,000 *Grants to organisations* £770,000

TRUSTEES Simon Kaufman; Noemi Kaufman.

OTHER INFORMATION Full accounts were not available to view on the Charity Commission's website due to the charity's low income. We have therefore estimated the grant total based on the charity's total expenditure.

HOW TO APPLY Contact the correspondent for further information.

CONTACT DETAILS Simon Kaufman, Secretary/Trustee, 50 Keswick Street, Gateshead, Tyne and Wear NE8 1TQ *Tel.* 0191 490 0140

■ Mrs M. A. Lascelles Charitable Trust

OSCR NO SC003495 **ESTABLISHED** 1968

WHERE FUNDING CAN BE GIVEN UK, in particular Scotland.

WHO CAN BENEFIT Charitable organisations, including those working overseas.

WHAT IS FUNDED General charitable purposes.

RANGE OF GRANTS Mostly up to £2,000.

SAMPLE GRANTS Glenfarg Community Centre (£5,000); The Whitley Fund for Nature (£3,000); Concern Worldwide, Scottish Ballet and Shelter Scotland (£2,000 each); Ethiopiaid and Women and Children First UK (£1,500 each); Cancer Research UK (£1,000); St Michael and All Angels Church (£500); Canine Partners (£200).

FINANCES *Financial year end* 05/04/2020 *Income* £63,700 *Total grants* £81,200 *Grants to organisations* £81,200 *Assets* £1,940,000

OTHER INFORMATION During the year, 60 grants were awarded to 59 organisations for a broad range of causes including arts and culture, animal welfare, health, the environment and social welfare, among others.

HOW TO APPLY Contact the correspondent for further information.

CONTACT DETAILS The Trustees, c/o Thorntons Law LLP, Whitehall House, 33 Yeaman Shore, Dundee DD1 4BJ

■ Laslett's (Hinton) Charity

CC NO 233696 **ESTABLISHED** 1879

WHERE FUNDING CAN BE GIVEN Worcestershire.

WHO CAN BENEFIT Charitable organisations; churches.

WHAT IS FUNDED The repair and restoration of churches and chapels connected with the established Church of England; social welfare; older people; children and young people; housing and homelessness.

WHAT IS NOT FUNDED Individuals (other than through a qualifying organisation); overseas charities; profit based organisations.
SAMPLE GRANTS A list of beneficiaries was not included in the annual report and accounts.
FINANCES *Financial year end* 31/12/2019 *Income* £438,200 *Total grants* £211,800 *Grants to organisations* £211,800 *Assets* £18,190,000
TRUSTEES Peter Hughes; Douglas Dale; Mrs G. T. Newman; Kay Vincent; Mrs A. E. Lodge; Mr J. Panter; Mrs E. A. Pugh-Cook; Mrs M. Jones; Michael Tarver; Mr T. J. Bridges; Lorraine Preece; Colin Anstey.
HOW TO APPLY Applications can be made on a form available to download from the charity's website. Guidance notes are also provided on the charity's website. Applications are considered on a quarterly basis, in January, April, July and October. Upcoming deadlines are given on the charity's website.
CONTACT DETAILS The Trustees, Kateryn Heywood House, Berkeley Court, The Foregate, Worcester, Worcestershire WR1 3QG *Email* admin@lasletts.org.uk *Website* www.lasletts.org.uk

■ The Lauffer Family Charitable Foundation

CC NO 251115 **ESTABLISHED** 1967
WHERE FUNDING CAN BE GIVEN UK; other British Commonwealth countries; Israel; USA.
WHO CAN BENEFIT Charitable organisations; Jewish charities.
WHAT IS FUNDED Jewish causes and general charitable purposes, including education, religious activities, the environment, healthcare, social welfare, children and families, and recreation and culture.
WHAT IS NOT FUNDED Individuals.
RANGE OF GRANTS From under £1,000 to £89,000.
SAMPLE GRANTS Kehal Charedim Trust (£89,000 in seven grants); Beis Aharon Trust (£31,500 in three grants); Rimon Jewish Primary School (£19,950 in five grants); Jewish Deaf Association (£17,000); Yad Eliezer Trust (£12,000 in two grants); Kol Yerushalayim Kollel Trust and Zoological Society of London (£2,000 each); Ezer Mizion (£1,000).
FINANCES *Financial year end* 31/03/2020 *Income* £158,500 *Total grants* £436,500 *Grants to organisations* £436,500 *Assets* £3,970,000
TRUSTEES Jonathan Lauffer; Robin Lauffer; Gideon Lauffer.
OTHER INFORMATION During 2019/20, 177 grants were made, including 59 grants of less than £1,000 totalling almost £16,000. Beneficiaries of grants of under £1,000 were not listed.
HOW TO APPLY Applications may be made in writing to the correspondent. The trustees meet from time to time to consider applications.
CONTACT DETAILS Jonathan Lauffer, Trustee, 23 Hampstead Way, London NW11 7JN *Tel.* 020 7431 4200 *Email* jonathanlauffer13@gmail.com

■ Mrs F. B. Laurence Charitable Trust

CC NO 296548 **ESTABLISHED** 1976
WHERE FUNDING CAN BE GIVEN UK and overseas.
WHO CAN BENEFIT UK-registered charities, particularly organisations benefitting ex-service and service people, retired people, unemployed people and disadvantaged members of society within the UK or overseas to whom the UK owes a duty of care.
WHAT IS FUNDED General charitable purposes; social welfare; accommodation and housing; community facilities and activities; protection of the environment and wildlife; health and disability; older people; vulnerable and disadvantaged individuals; justice and human rights; service and ex-servicemen and women; special schools and special needs education and literacy.
WHAT IS NOT FUNDED Individuals are not supported.
TYPE OF GRANT Generally one-off awards for core costs, project expenses and start-up costs.
RANGE OF GRANTS Grants of up to £5,000.
SAMPLE GRANTS Halow Project (£4,000); St Nicholas School (£3,000); Plant Life, Making Space, Riding for the Disabled (£2,000 each); The Lynchmere Society, Access Sport (Brixton BMX Club) (£1,500 each).
FINANCES *Financial year end* 30/06/2020 *Income* £89,700 *Total grants* £71,700 *Grants to organisations* £71,700 *Assets* £2,700,000
TRUSTEES Caroline Fry; William Hamilton; Payne Hicks Beach Trust Corporation.
HOW TO APPLY Applications may be made in writing to the correspondent, including the latest set of accounts. Only registered charities will be considered. According to our research, applications should be no more than two sides of A4 and include the following information: who you are; what you do; what distinguishes your work from that of others in your field; where applicable, a description of the project that the money you are asking for is going towards and a business plan/budget; what funds have already been raised and how; how much you are seeking from the trust; and how you intend to measure the potential benefits of your project or work as a whole. The trustees meet at least once a year.
CONTACT DETAILS The Trustees, BM Box 2082, London WC1N 3XX *Tel.* 020 7465 4300

■ The Kathleen Laurence Trust

CC NO 296461 **ESTABLISHED** 1987
WHERE FUNDING CAN BE GIVEN UK.
WHO CAN BENEFIT Charitable organisations.
WHAT IS FUNDED General charitable purposes including the following: medical research; children and young people; animal welfare.
TYPE OF GRANT One-off and recurrent.
RANGE OF GRANTS Up to £35,000 but mostly grants of £1,000 to £1,500.
SAMPLE GRANTS Arthritis Research UK (£35,000); Battersea Cats and Dogs Home (£26,500); Young and Free (£1,500); Linkable and Tiny Tickers Ltd (£1,000 each).
FINANCES *Financial year end* 09/02/2020 *Income* £83,000 *Total grants* £260,500 *Grants to organisations* £260,500 *Assets* £2,450,000
TRUSTEE Coutts & Co.
OTHER INFORMATION The trust made 42 grants during the year.
HOW TO APPLY Apply by letter to the correspondent.
CONTACT DETAILS The Trustees, Coutts & Co. Trustee Department, 1st Floor, Trinity Quay 1, Avon Street, Bristol BS2 0PT *Tel.* 0345 304 2424

■ The Law Family Charitable Foundation

CC NO 1141997 **ESTABLISHED** 2011

WHERE FUNDING CAN BE GIVEN UK.

WHO CAN BENEFIT Registered charities; CICs; universities.

WHAT IS FUNDED General charitable purposes including education, health, disability, the arts, young people, the environment and sustainability.

RANGE OF GRANTS Mostly up to £150,000, with some exceptional larger grants.

SAMPLE GRANTS The Law Family Educational Trust (£3 million); Royal United Services Institute (£1 million); Speakers for Schools (£660,000); Maggie's at Marsden (£268,700); Pro Bono Economics (£140,000); Game and Wildlife Conservation Trust (£1,000); The Lord Mayor's Appeal (£50,000); Noah's Ark Children's Hospice (£25,000); Tavistock Youth Centre (£5,000).

FINANCES *Financial year end* 04/04/2020 *Income* £90,900 *Total grants* £5,410,000 *Grants to organisations* £5,410,000 *Assets* £27,000,000

TRUSTEES Andrew Law; Zoe Law; Roger Sadewsky.

OTHER INFORMATION Grants of more than £1,000 were made to 16 organisations during the year. Grants of under £1,000 totalled £3,800. The foundation makes annual donations to The Law Family Educational Trust (Charity Commission no. 1169320) and in 2019/20 donated £3 million to the trust. It also made a large grant of £1 million to The Royal United Services Institute.

HOW TO APPLY Contact the correspondent for further information. A contact form is available on the website.

CONTACT DETAILS The Trustees, c/o Caxton Europe Asset Management, Third Floor, 40 Berkeley Square, London W1J 5AL *Tel.* 020 7647 4057 *Website* www.lawfamilycharitablefoundation.org

■ The Betty Lawes Foundation

CC NO 274025 **ESTABLISHED** 1977

WHERE FUNDING CAN BE GIVEN UK and overseas.

WHO CAN BENEFIT Registered charities.

WHAT IS FUNDED General charitable purposes.

WHAT IS NOT FUNDED The foundation avoids awarding grants to organisations of an overtly political nature, including quasi-political secular organisations promoting a subjective opinion, or organisations which conflict with the views of Volac's client base or employees.

RANGE OF GRANTS Typically £1,000 to £30,000.

SAMPLE GRANTS Agriculture Horticulture Development Board (£1 million); Multiple Sclerosis Society (£50,000); Chester Zoo (£30,000); Red Balloon Learning Centre (£15,000); Blue Smile and Tusk Trust (£10,000 each); Addenbrooke's, Hillcrest Aids Centre Trust and RNLI (£5,000 each); Help for Heroes (£1,000).

FINANCES *Financial year end* 31/12/2018 *Income* £439,400 *Total grants* £1,560,000 *Grants to organisations* £1,560,000 *Assets* £28,330,000

TRUSTEES Margaret Lee; Patricia Neville; William Crane.

OTHER INFORMATION The grant total for 2019 was notably larger than that in the previous accounting period due to a substantial donation to the Agriculture Horticulture Development Board of £1 million. During the year, the foundation made grants to 36 organisations.

HOW TO APPLY Unsolicited applications were not being accepted at the time of writing (March 2021). Contact the correspondent for further information.

CONTACT DETAILS The Trustees, Volac International, 50 Fishers Lane, Orwell, Royston, Hertfordshire SG8 5QX *Tel.* 01223 208021

■ The Richard Lawes Foundation

CC NO 274042 **ESTABLISHED** 1977

WHERE FUNDING CAN BE GIVEN UK.

WHO CAN BENEFIT Charitable organisations, with a preference for registered charities, especially smaller charities or local branches of large charities.

WHAT IS FUNDED General charitable purposes, including medical research, bereavement support, mental health and young people.

TYPE OF GRANT Specific projects or capital costs.

SAMPLE GRANTS A list of beneficiaries was not included in the annual report and accounts.

FINANCES *Financial year end* 05/04/2020 *Income* £240,700 *Total grants* £333,900 *Grants to organisations* £333,900 *Assets* £6,890,000

TRUSTEES William Lawes; Dr Dorothea Lawes; Janet Withers; David Northcroft.

HOW TO APPLY Contact the correspondent for further information.

CONTACT DETAILS Bobby Lawes, Trustee, Longhayes, Lowerdown, Bovey Tracey, Newton Abbot, Devon TQ13 9LF *Tel.* 07850 126351 *Email* Bobbylawes@aol.com

■ The Edgar E. Lawley Foundation

CC NO 201589 **ESTABLISHED** 1961

WHERE FUNDING CAN BE GIVEN UK, with a preference for the West Midlands.

WHO CAN BENEFIT Registered charities; charitable organisations; hospitals and hospices; schools and universities.

WHAT IS FUNDED General charitable purposes; education in the arts, commerce and industry; health and disability; medical care and research; older people; children and young people; community causes.

WHAT IS NOT FUNDED Appeals from or on behalf of individuals.

TYPE OF GRANT One-off, generally unrestricted funding.

RANGE OF GRANTS About £1,500 on average.

SAMPLE GRANTS Acorns Children's Hospice; Avenues Community Association; Birmingham Vernon Sea Scouts; Coram Beanstalk; Drug Watch Foundation; Lichfield Stroke Club; Rugby Mountaineering Club; Versus Arthritis; Walsall Bereavement Support Service.

FINANCES *Financial year end* 05/04/2020 *Income* £223,700 *Total grants* £241,500 *Grants to organisations* £241,500 *Assets* £3,900,000

TRUSTEES John Cooke; Philip Cooke; Frank Jackson; Katherine Coates; Laura Cooke.

OTHER INFORMATION There were 161 awards made during 2019/20. During the year, grants were awarded in six broad areas: medical, research and other miscellaneous projects; hospices; older people; children and young people; community; and disability.

HOW TO APPLY Application rounds typically open on 1 August and close on 31 October. Application forms and full guidance are available to download from the foundation's website during this time. The website states: 'applications are made [via] the Foundation's online grant application system and no other information is required to be submitted.' The foundation receives approximately 500 applications per year for grants but in a normal year can only fund approximately 160 of them.

CONTACT DETAILS The Trustees, PO Box 456, Esher, Surrey KT10 1DP *Tel.* 01372 805760 *Email* edgarelawley@gmail.com *Website* www.edgarelawleyfoundation.org.uk

■ The Herd Lawson and Muriel Lawson Charitable Trust

CC NO 1113220 **ESTABLISHED** 2006

WHERE FUNDING CAN BE GIVEN England and Wales, with a preference for Cumbria.

WHO CAN BENEFIT Charitable organisations.

WHAT IS FUNDED This trust supports a number of named organisations each year as well as organisations benefitting older people in need, particularly those who are members of evangelical or Christian Brethren churches.

RANGE OF GRANTS £1,200 to £30,000.

SAMPLE GRANTS British Red Cross and WWF-UK (£30,000 each); Christian Workers Relief Fund (£21,600); Hospice at Home West Cumbria (£14,400); Hospice of St Mary of Furness (£9,600); Spring Mount Christian Fellowship, Ambleside Welfare Charity and Parr Street Evangelical Church (£3,600 each); Sight Advice South Lakes (£2,400); Sandhills Lane Christian Brethren Church (£1,200).

FINANCES *Financial year end* 05/04/2020 *Income* £248,300 *Total grants* £120,000 *Grants to organisations* £120,000 *Assets* £1,969,000

TRUSTEES Brian Herd; Robert Barker; Dr Jenny Barker; William Corin; Andrew Hewitt; Paul Cookson; Ian Jenkinson.

OTHER INFORMATION There were 11 awards made during the year.

HOW TO APPLY The trust receives more applications than it can deal with and does not seek further unsolicited appeals. The trust has previously informed us that 'the trustees have established a number of charities to whom they make grants each year and they very rarely make any donations to other charities.'

CONTACT DETAILS Robert Barker, Trustee, The Estate Office, 14 Church Street, Ambleside, Cumbria LA22 0BT *Tel.* 01539 434758

■ Lawson Beckman Charitable Trust

CC NO 261378 **ESTABLISHED** 1970

WHERE FUNDING CAN BE GIVEN UK.

WHO CAN BENEFIT Charitable organisations.

WHAT IS FUNDED Jewish causes; health; education; social welfare.

WHAT IS NOT FUNDED Individuals.

SAMPLE GRANTS Jewish Care (£12,500); The Jewish Leadership Council (£10,000); The Jewish Volunteering Network (£5,000); Centrepoint (£4,000).

FINANCES *Financial year end* 31/03/2020 *Income* £115,600 *Total grants* £100,000 *Grants to organisations* £100,000 *Assets* £4,170,000

TRUSTEES Melvin Lawson; Lynton Stock; Francis Katz.

OTHER INFORMATION Grants were distributed as follows: health/preservation of lives (£39,000); education/training (£31,000); religious activities (£20,000); general charitable purposes (£10,000).

HOW TO APPLY Contact the correspondent for further information.

CONTACT DETAILS The Trustees, c/o AB Group Ltd, 2nd Floor, 25 Old Burlington Street, London W1S 3AN *Email* bt@abplc.co.uk

■ The Lawson Trust CIO

CC NO 1171822 **ESTABLISHED** 1980

WHERE FUNDING CAN BE GIVEN Kent and Sussex.

WHO CAN BENEFIT Charitable organisations; registered charities, including those registered as a company limited by guarantee; CIOs. Preference is given to local organisations.

WHAT IS FUNDED The arts and heritage; education; the environment; health; social and economic disadvantage; children and young adults; older people; people with disabilities; the armed forces.

WHAT IS NOT FUNDED Individuals; non-registered charities; overseas charities; political parties; religious causes.

TYPE OF GRANT Project costs.

RANGE OF GRANTS Mostly £5,000 and under.

SAMPLE GRANTS Kent Community Foundation – matched funding (£1 million); Heart of Kent Hospice (£40,000); Little Gate Farm (£20,000); Turner Contemporary (£10,000); Macmillan Cancer Support and Turning Tides Homelessness (£5,000 each); Happy Days Children's Charity (£2,000); The David Shepherd Wildlife Foundation (£1,500); Bowel Cancer UK (£500).

FINANCES *Financial year end* 31/03/2020 *Income* £653,700 *Total grants* £1,660,000 *Grants to organisations* £1,660,000 *Assets* £18,510,000

TRUSTEES Philip Thomas; Sarah Hill; Michael Norrie; Jennifer Thomas; Robert Blundell; Antony Hooper; Sarah Payle.

OTHER INFORMATION Grants were awarded to 98 organisations during the year, of which 82 were grants of up to £10,000. During the year, the trust granted £1 million in matched funding to Kent Community Foundation.

HOW TO APPLY Applicants based in Kent seeking funding of up to £5,000 can apply to the Lawson Endowment for Kent. Further information on this fund can be found on the Kent Community Foundation website. The trust also has an endowment with Sussex Community Foundation. Applicants based in Sussex with an annual income of under £1 million can apply to the foundation for a grant via its website. National charities or charities outside the criteria for the two community foundations can apply via the trust's online application process. Applicants should first complete the eligibility checker on the trust's website. Eligible organisations will then be provided with a link to the online application form. Applications can be made at any time. The trustees meet four times per year. Check the trust's website for meeting dates.

CONTACT DETAILS The Trustees, PO Box 506, Ramsgate CT11 1DZ *Email* enquiries@lawsontrust.co.uk *Website* www.lawsontrust.org

■ The Leach Fourteenth Trust

CC NO 204844 **ESTABLISHED** 1961

WHERE FUNDING CAN BE GIVEN UK, with some preference for the South West.

WHO CAN BENEFIT Registered charities based in the UK.

WHAT IS FUNDED General charitable purposes; health; the environment; international development; the arts.

TYPE OF GRANT Project funding; one-off grants.

RANGE OF GRANTS Typically less than £3,000.

SAMPLE GRANTS Médecins Sans Frontières (£13,000); Cornwall Air Ambulance (£5,000); Durrell Wildlife Conservation Trust (£3,500); The Romney Marsh Historic Churches Trust (£2,500); Alexander Devine Children's Cancer Trust (£2,000); Afghan Connection, Canine Partners and Injured Jockeys Fund (£1,000 each).

FINANCES *Financial year end* 05/04/2020 *Income* £103,700 *Total grants* £100,500 *Grants to organisations* £100,500 *Assets* £3,240,000

TRUSTEES Roger Murray-Leach; Judith Murray Nash; John Henderson; Tamsin Murray-Leach; Grant Nash; Karen Brooking.

OTHER INFORMATION Grants were awarded to 74 organisations during the year. Only beneficiaries of grants of £1,000 and above were listed in the accounts. Grants of under £1,000 totalled £8,500.

HOW TO APPLY Contact the correspondent for further information.

CONTACT DETAILS The Trustees, c/o BHP LLP, Rievaulx House, 1 St Mary's Court, Blossom Street, York, North Yorkshire YO24 1AH *Tel.* 01904 628551

■ The David Lean Foundation

CC NO 1067074 **ESTABLISHED** 1997

WHERE FUNDING CAN BE GIVEN UK.

WHO CAN BENEFIT Charitable organisations; educational establishments; other charitable institutions whose aims are similar to those of the foundation.

WHAT IS FUNDED The promotion and advancement of education and the cultivation and improvement of public taste in the visual arts, particularly in the field of film production, including screenplay writing, film direction and editing.

WHAT IS NOT FUNDED Scholarships or grants for individuals are not awarded directly by the foundation.

SAMPLE GRANTS British Film Institute (£97,400); National Film and Television School (£97,400); British Academy of Film and Television Arts (£49,000); The Arts Fund (£3,500); Carnforth Heritage Centre and Chelsea and Westminster Hospital (£2,000 each).

FINANCES *Financial year end* 31/12/2019 *Income* £176,300 *Total grants* £251,900 *Grants to organisations* £251,900 *Assets* £509,200

TRUSTEES Anthony Reeves; Max Thowless-Reeves; Sally Beard.

HOW TO APPLY Contact the correspondent for further information.

CONTACT DETAILS The Trustees, The Bradshaws, Codsall, Staffordshire WV8 2HU *Tel.* 01902 754855 *Email* aareeves@davidleanfoundation.com

■ The Leathersellers' Company Charitable Fund

CC NO 278072 **ESTABLISHED** 1979

WHERE FUNDING CAN BE GIVEN UK, particularly London.

WHO CAN BENEFIT UK-registered charities, including CIOs; educational establishments; individuals.

WHAT IS FUNDED General charitable purposes including: education and employment; disability; health; the arts; the environment; criminal justice and rehabilitation; homelessness; domestic abuse; advice and support for vulnerable and disadvantaged members of society; the leather and hide trades and education in leather technology.

WHAT IS NOT FUNDED Medical research; capital restoration projects for the sole purpose of conservation/heritage; hospices; CICs.

TYPE OF GRANT One-off and multi-year grants (up to four years); core, unrestricted funding; project expenditure; capital costs. Student awards are for general living costs.

RANGE OF GRANTS Programme dependent, but typically under £20,000.

SAMPLE GRANTS Colfe's School (£428,000); Leathersellers' Federation of Schools (£182,000); Fitzwilliam College (£125,000); Guildhall School Trust (£25,000); Cockpit Arts (£22,000); Ebony Horse Club, Giving World, Kingston Churches Action on Homelessness and Women's Work – Derbyshire (£20,000 each).

FINANCES *Financial year end* 31/07/2020 *Income* £2,030,000 *Total grants* £3,468,000 *Grants to organisations* £3,230,000 *Assets* £62,210,000

TRUSTEES Matthew Lawrence; The Leathersellers' Company.

OTHER INFORMATION Grants were made to 87 individuals for educational purposes totalling £238,000. Only beneficiaries of grants of £20,000 and above were listed in the accounts. Grants of less than £20,000 to organisations totalled just over £2 million. Grants were distributed in the following categories: education (£1 million); recreation (£342,000); disability (£298,000); domestic and sexual abuse (£274,000); homelessness (£265,000); health (£175,000); advice (£166,000); community support (£164,000); food and essentials provision (£159,000); creative arts (£135,000); criminal justice and rehabilitation (£114,000); employability (£100,000); leather-associated causes (£86,000); services support (£22,000); heritage and the environment (£20,000).

HOW TO APPLY Applications can be made using the online form on the charity's website. At the time of writing (April 2021) the main grants programme had been suspended. A new strategy for 2021–22 (beginning September 2021) will be published on the website in due course. Applicants to the small grants programme can expect a decision within four weeks. See the website for further details and deadlines.

CONTACT DETAILS David Santa-Olalla, Clerk to the Leathersellers' Company, 7 St Helen's Place, London EC3A 6AB *Tel.* 020 7330 1444 *Email* dmsantao@leathersellers.co.uk or enquiries@leathersellers.co.uk *Website* https://leathersellers.co.uk/charitablefund

The Leche Trust

CC NO 225659 **ESTABLISHED** 1963

WHERE FUNDING CAN BE GIVEN UK.

WHO CAN BENEFIT Registered charities; exempt charities; public authorities which are subject to financial regulation.

WHAT IS FUNDED The preservation and conservation of art and architecture, churches and historic collections, with preference given to objects of the Georgian period or earlier; performing arts, particularly music, dance and drama; education.

WHAT IS NOT FUNDED CICs; schools; social welfare; environmental or wildlife projects; health and medicine; buildings and objects in private ownership. See the website for a full list of exclusions.

TYPE OF GRANT Project funding; bursaries; acquisitions.

RANGE OF GRANTS Up to £5,000.

SAMPLE GRANTS Norfolk Museums Development Trust (£16,000); University of Northumbria – bursary (£5,000); The Landmark Trust (£4,000); All Saints Church – Suffolk (£3,000); New English Ballet Theatre (£2,500); Armagh Robinson Library and Postal Heritage Trust (£2,000 each); Rifco Theatre (£1,500); Bristol International Jazz Festival (£1,000); Improbable (£880).

FINANCES *Financial year end* 31/07/2020 *Income* £139,300 *Total grants* £212,200 *Grants to organisations* £196,200 *Assets* £7,000,000

TRUSTEES Ariane Bankes; Andrew Cameron; Thomas Howard; Robin Dhar; Dr Helen Jacobsen; Diana Spiegelberg; Susan Sturrock.

OTHER INFORMATION Educational bursaries paid to individuals via the Overseas PhD Student programme totalled £16,000 during 2019/20; however, this programme has now closed. Grants were awarded to 80 organisations as follows: performing arts (£95,200); historic objects and collections (£40,600); places of worship (£26,500); education (bursaries paid to institutions) (£20,000); historic buildings (£14,000).

HOW TO APPLY There is no formal application form and requests should be made in writing to the correspondent via post or email. Full details of what should be included in written applications can be found on the trust's website. The trustees meet three times a year to review applications, normally in February, June and October. See the website for deadline dates.

CONTACT DETAILS Rosemary Ewles, Grants Director, 105 Greenway Avenue, London E17 3QL *Tel.* 020 3233 0023 *Email* info@lechetrust.org *Website* www.lechetrust.org

The Arnold Lee Charitable Trust

CC NO 264437 **ESTABLISHED** 1972

WHERE FUNDING CAN BE GIVEN UK.

WHO CAN BENEFIT Registered charities; Jewish organisations.

WHAT IS FUNDED General charitable purposes; Jewish causes.

RANGE OF GRANTS Mostly below £10,000. Larger grants are occasionally awarded.

SAMPLE GRANTS Policy Exchange (£25,000); St John Hospice (£25,000); Mesila UK (£20,000); Jewish Care (£10,000); Centre for Jewish Life (£5,000).

FINANCES *Financial year end* 05/04/2020 *Income* £124,400 *Total grants* £210,100 *Grants to organisations* £210,100 *Assets* £1,670,000

TRUSTEES Edward Lee; Alan Lee.

HOW TO APPLY Applications may be made in writing to the correspondent.

CONTACT DETAILS The Trustees, Palladium House, 1–4 Argyll Street, London W1F 7LD *Tel.* 020 7437 7666 *Email* petronellaevans@princetonplc.com

The William Leech Charity

CC NO 265491 **ESTABLISHED** 1972

WHERE FUNDING CAN BE GIVEN The North East; overseas.

WHO CAN BENEFIT UK-registered charities; CICs.

WHAT IS FUNDED General charitable purposes in the North East; support for volunteers. The charity's Lady Leech Fund also funds projects supporting children in financially developing countries.

WHAT IS NOT FUNDED Individuals; students; gap years or personal travel; the arts; expeditions; minibuses.

TYPE OF GRANT One-off and recurring grants; interest-free loans; project funding; research.

RANGE OF GRANTS Mostly £500 to £10,000.

SAMPLE GRANTS The Northern Retrieval Centre (£100,000); The Beacon Community Project (£10,000); Ghanaian Children's Trust and North East Maritime Trust (£4,000 each); HospiceCare North Northumberland (£3,000); Lifespan (£1,000); Pelton Youth Project (£500); North of England Brass Band Championships (£250).

FINANCES *Financial year end* 31/03/2020 *Income* £633,700 *Total grants* £220,700 *Grants to organisations* £220,700 *Assets* £18,270,000

TRUSTEES David Stabler; Adrian Gifford; Barry Wallace; Richard Leech; Revd Prof. David Wilkinson.

OTHER INFORMATION The 2019/20 accounts cover the period from 1 March 2019 to 31 March 2020. Grants awarded through the main fund totalled £202,000 and grants through the Lady Leech Fund totalled £18,700.

HOW TO APPLY Applications can be made online through the charity's website. The charity no longer accepts applications made by post.

CONTACT DETAILS The Trustees, c/o Robson Laidler, Fernwood House, Fernwood Road, Jesmond, Newcastle upon Tyne, Tyne and Wear NE2 1TJ *Tel.* 0191 281 8191 *Email* enquiries@williamleechcharity.org.uk or use the contact form on the website. *Website* www.williamleechcharity.org.uk

Leeds Building Society Charitable Foundation

CC NO 1074429 **ESTABLISHED** 1999

WHERE FUNDING CAN BE GIVEN UK.

WHO CAN BENEFIT UK-registered charities. The foundation will only accept applications from UK-registered charities with a turnover of less than £1 million.

WHAT IS FUNDED General charitable purposes; community projects focusing on social welfare and relief in need; vulnerable people and disadvantaged individuals.

WHAT IS NOT FUNDED Religious, military or political projects; overseas charities; individuals (including sponsorship); animal welfare projects; medical research; general running costs, such as salaries or rent; general fundraising appeals; building restoration; items for staff use.

TYPE OF GRANT Capital expenditure.

RANGE OF GRANTS The majority of donations are of under £1,000.
SAMPLE GRANTS A list of beneficiaries was not included in the annual report and accounts.
FINANCES *Financial year end* 31/12/2019 *Income* £150,200 *Total grants* £155,600 *Grants to organisations* £155,600 *Assets* £1,100
TRUSTEES Peter Chadwick; Gary Brook; Carla Marshall; Gary Hetherington; David Marsh; Deborah Walker; Timothy Steere.
OTHER INFORMATION Grants were broken down as follows: disability (£66,200); illness (£24,100); disadvantage (£23,800); homelessness (£15,700); poverty (£13,700); social inclusion (£12,100).
HOW TO APPLY Apply online through the foundation's website, where information on trustees' meeting dates can also be found.
CONTACT DETAILS The Trustees, Leeds Building Society, 105 Albion Street, Leeds, West Yorkshire LS1 5AS *Tel.* 0113 225 7518 *Email* foundation@leedsbuildingsociety.co.uk *Website* www.leedsbuildingsociety.co.uk/your-society/about-us/charitable-foundation

■ Leeds Community Foundation (LCF)

CC NO 1096892 **ESTABLISHED** 2005
WHERE FUNDING CAN BE GIVEN Leeds and Bradford.
WHO CAN BENEFIT Community and voluntary groups; registered charities; not-for-profit organisations; social enterprises.
WHAT IS FUNDED General charitable purposes.
TYPE OF GRANT Capital costs; core costs; project funding.
SAMPLE GRANTS Centrepoint Works (£36,400); Youth Community Builders (£7,500); Wonder Holidaze (£5,200); Healthy Living (£2,000).
FINANCES *Financial year end* 31/03/2020 *Income* £5,850,000 *Total grants* £3,730,000 *Grants to organisations* £3,730,000 *Assets* £23,150,000
TRUSTEES John McGhee; Anthony Cooke; Deidre Reid; Craig Burton; Corrina Lawrence; Carolyn Cooper-Black; George Fox; Cleveland Henry; Rooshi Collins; Michael Jackson; Thomas Bridges; Sharon Orr.
OTHER INFORMATION This is one of the 46 UK community foundations, which distribute funding for a wide range of purposes. As with all community foundations, there are a number of donor-advised funds managed on behalf of individuals, families and charitable trusts. Grant schemes tend to change frequently; consult the foundation's website for details of current programmes and up-to-date deadlines.
HOW TO APPLY See the foundation's website for details of open grant programmes.
CONTACT DETAILS Sam Caldwell, Head of Grants, 1st Floor, 51A St Paul's Street, Leeds, West Yorkshire LS1 2TE *Tel.* 0113 242 2426 *Email* grants@leedscf.org.uk *Website* www.leedscf.org.uk

■ The Leeward Trust

OSCR NO SC047870 **ESTABLISHED** 2017
WHERE FUNDING CAN BE GIVEN UK; India; Africa; South America.
WHO CAN BENEFIT Charitable organisations.
WHAT IS FUNDED Social welfare; education; health; citizenship and community development, arts, heritage, culture and science; recreational activities; human rights and conflict resolution; religious or racial harmony; equality and diversity; the environment; animal welfare.
SAMPLE GRANTS A list of beneficiaries was not included in the annual report and accounts.
FINANCES *Financial year end* 31/03/2020 *Income* £283,100 *Total grants* £272,500 *Grants to organisations* £272,500 *Assets* £9,100
OTHER INFORMATION Grants were distributed as follows: age, ill health, disability and financial hardship (£51,700); poverty (£49,800); the environment (£39,000); education (£27,500); human rights, conflict resolution and reconciliation (£22,500); animal welfare (£17,500); religious or racial harmony (£11,300).
HOW TO APPLY Contact the correspondent for further information.
CONTACT DETAILS The Trustees, c/o Gillespie Macandrew, 5 Atholl Crescent, Edinburgh EH3 8EJ

■ The Legal Education Foundation

CC NO 271297 **ESTABLISHED** 1962
WHERE FUNDING CAN BE GIVEN UK.
WHO CAN BENEFIT Legally constituted organisations undertaking charitable work in the UK, including charities, CICs, limited companies, private law firms and research institutions.
WHAT IS FUNDED Legal education, training and development; access to employment in the legal profession; public understanding of the law; the use of technology in legal education; research.
WHAT IS NOT FUNDED Individuals; work outside the UK; capital expenditure on buildings and vehicles. A full list of exclusions can be found on the foundation's website.
TYPE OF GRANT Core costs; salaries; project funding; modest capital expenditure directly related to the work.
RANGE OF GRANTS Programme dependent.
SAMPLE GRANTS The Baring Foundation (£600,000); Child Poverty Action Group (two grants totalling £429,000); The Access to Justice Foundation (£250,000); Human Rights Consortium (£148,000); Refugee Action (£74,000); Derbyshire Law Centre (£59,000); Unlock Democracy (£33,000); Law Centres Network (£20,000); Royal Mencap Society (£7,000).
FINANCES *Financial year end* 30/06/2020 *Income* £10,300,000 *Total grants* £5,460,000 *Grants to organisations* £5,460,000 *Assets* £245,750,000
TRUSTEES Vivek Luthra; Rupen Shah; Hetan Shah; Roger Finbow; Alison Pickup; Monica Risam; Timothy Dutton; Patricia Sloan; Ailsa Beaton; Guy Beringer; Jonathan Freeman; Rupert Baron.
OTHER INFORMATION Grants were made to 57 organisations during the year in the following categories: stronger sector – training and support for a thriving social justice legal sector (£3.6 million); advancing high-quality thinking, training and practice (£1.21 million); fairer systems (£351,000); increasing public understanding of the law (£289,000). The foundation has an excellent website with detailed information about its grant-making.
HOW TO APPLY Apply using the online application form on the foundation's website. If successful at the first stage, you will be invited to make a full application – you will be sent a personalised link to a second-stage form. A grant timetable is posted on the foundation's website, with up-to-date application deadlines.

CONTACT DETAILS Clare Johns, Foundation Accountant and Secretary, Suite 2, Ground Floor, River House, Broadford Park, Shalford, Guildford, Surrey GU4 8EP *Tel.* 020 3005 5695 *Email* clare.johns@thelef.org *Website* thelegaleducationfoundation.org

■ Leicestershire and Rutland Masonic Charity Association

CC NO 234054 **ESTABLISHED** 1964

WHERE FUNDING CAN BE GIVEN Leicestershire and Rutland.

WHO CAN BENEFIT Registered charities, with a preference for small local charities; community clubs; Freemasons and their dependants.

WHAT IS FUNDED General charitable purposes; Masonry; support of Freemasons and their families.

RANGE OF GRANTS Mostly £2,000 and under.

SAMPLE GRANTS Masonic Charitable Foundation (£19,300); Rainbows (£7,800); Prostate Cancer Fund (£3,500); Hamilton Air Cadets and The Spark Arts For Children (£2,000 each); Leicestershire Rape Crisis (£1,600); 14th Nativity Scout Group (£1,500); Coping with Cancer (£1,000); Sunflowers Suicide Support (£500); LOROS (Leicester Hospice Charity) (£200).

FINANCES *Financial year end* 31/05/2020 *Income* £116,000 *Total grants* £126,800 *Grants to organisations* £126,300 *Assets* £205,000

TRUSTEES David Sandrovitch; Dr Andrew Green; Ian Nesbitt; David Highton; Brent Goodwin; Peter Kinder; Robert Mason; Philip Caswell; Michael Molyneux; Paul Wallace; Michael Potter; Brian Carruthers; Adrian de Rodriguez Pearse.

OTHER INFORMATION During the year, grants to organisations were broken down as follows: local non-Masonic organisations (54 donations totalling £102,700); Masonic charities (one donation of £19,300); emergency grants to charities (£4,400). Emergency grants to individuals totalled £460.

HOW TO APPLY The association encourages applications for grants from local non-Masonic charities. Apply in writing to the correspondent or use the contact form available on the website. For emergency grants for individuals, the 2019/20 annual report explains that a nomination can be 'made through the Master and members of any lodge in the province by those entitled to the benefits of membership'.

CONTACT DETAILS The Trustees, Freemasons' Hall, 80 London Road, Leicester, Leicestershire LE2 0RA *Tel.* 0116 223 6998 *Email* lrmca@pglleics.co.uk *Website* https://www.pglleics.org.uk/charitable-work

■ Leicestershire, Leicester and Rutland Community Foundation

CC NO 1135322 **ESTABLISHED** 2002

WHERE FUNDING CAN BE GIVEN Leicestershire, Leicester and Rutland.

WHO CAN BENEFIT Charities and community groups, with some preference for smaller groups.

WHAT IS FUNDED General charitable purposes.

TYPE OF GRANT Running and project costs.

SAMPLE GRANTS Previous beneficiaries have included: Grimsby Town Football (£25,000); Room for Music Studios (£5,000); Sustainable Land Trust (£4,100); Leicester Stroke Club £4,000); Parish Community Hub (£3,500); Leicester City of Sanctuary (£3,000); Drum and Bass CIC (£2,500); Anstey Youth Cafe (£2,300); Ashby Arts Festival (£650).

FINANCES *Financial year end* 31/03/2020 *Income* £842,300 *Total grants* £533,200 *Grants to organisations* £533,200 *Assets* £2,960,000

TRUSTEES Dr Vijay Sharma; Ian McCormack; Stuart Dawkins; Richard Colton; Riaz Ravat; Robin Clarke; Trevor Shaw; Justine Flack.

OTHER INFORMATION This is one of the 46 UK community foundations, which distribute funding for a wide range of purposes. As with all community foundations, there are a number of donor-advised funds managed on behalf of individuals, families and charitable trusts. Grant schemes tend to change frequently; consult the foundation's website for details of current programmes and up-to-date deadlines.

HOW TO APPLY Potential applicants are advised to visit the community foundation's website or contact its grants team to find the most suitable funding stream.

CONTACT DETAILS Grants Team, 3 Wycliffe Street, Leicester, Leicestershire LE1 5LR *Email* grants@llrcommunityfoundation.org.uk *Website* www.llrcommunityfoundation.org.uk

■ The Kennedy Leigh Charitable Trust

CC NO 288293 **ESTABLISHED** 1983

WHERE FUNDING CAN BE GIVEN UK and Israel.

WHO CAN BENEFIT Registered charities.

WHAT IS FUNDED General charitable purposes; medicine and health; education; social welfare; human rights and equality; arts, culture and heritage.

WHAT IS NOT FUNDED This trust will not be accepting applications for funding from charitable organisations outside Israel for the foreseeable future. Applications from individuals will also be dismissed.

TYPE OF GRANT Capital costs; core costs; seed/start-up funding.

RANGE OF GRANTS Up to £250,000.

SAMPLE GRANTS Magen David Adom UK (£250,000); Shaare Zedek (£65,000); CHAI-Lifeline (£22,500); British Friends of the Hebrew University (£16,300); New Israel Fund (£15,000); Jewish Association for the Mentally Ill (£5,000).

FINANCES *Financial year end* 31/03/2020 *Income* £570,400 *Total grants* £519,500 *Grants to organisations* £519,500 *Assets* £21,690,000

TRUSTEES Alexander Sorkin; Angela Sorkin; Geoffrey Goldkorn; Carole Berman; Anthony Foux; Benjamin Goldkorn; Jacob Sorkin.

OTHER INFORMATION Grants were awarded to more than 27 Jewish organisations in 2019/20. Grants of less than £1,000 totalled £1,100.

HOW TO APPLY Contact the correspondent for further information.

CONTACT DETAILS The Trustees, ORT House, 126 Albert Street, London NW1 7NE *Tel.* 020 7267 6500

■ The Leigh Trust

CC NO 275372 **ESTABLISHED** 1976

WHERE FUNDING CAN BE GIVEN UK and overseas.

WHO CAN BENEFIT Registered charities.

WHAT IS FUNDED Drug and alcohol rehabilitation; criminal justice; asylum seekers; racial equality; education; young people at risk.

WHAT IS NOT FUNDED Individuals.

RANGE OF GRANTS Mostly £1,000 to £5,000.

SAMPLE GRANTS Glyndebourne Productions (£15,000); Prisoners Abroad (£10,000); Prison Choir Project (£8,000); Give a Book (£7,500); Refugee Support Network (£6,000); Refugee Survival Trust (£3,000); Young People Taking Action (£2,000); Refugee Info Bus (£1,500); Open Door Exmouth (£1,000).

FINANCES *Financial year end* 05/04/2019 *Income* £90,700 *Total grants* £230,400 *Grants to organisations* £230,400 *Assets* £3,400,000

TRUSTEES The Hon. David Bernstein; Caroline Moorehead; Jonathan Bond.

OTHER INFORMATION The 2018/19 accounts were the latest available at the time of writing (May 2021). In total, 72 grants were awarded during the year. Grants were awarded in four categories: criminal justice/young offenders (£92,500); asylum seekers and refugees (£56,900); drug and alcohol rehabilitation (£46,000); other (£35,000).

HOW TO APPLY The 2018/19 annual report states: 'Organisations applying for grants must provide their most recent audited accounts, a registered charity number and, most importantly, a cash flow statement for the next 12 months. Similarly all organisations to whom conditional commitments have been made must submit their annual report and accounts each year until these commitments have been fulfilled. All applications should have a stamped self-addressed envelope attached. The actual request for funds must be concise and preferably summarised on one side of A4 paper. The policy of the trustees is to support those organisations which they believe to be in greatest need. The trustees can only respond favourably to very few applicants.'

CONTACT DETAILS The Trustees, 9 Bonhill Street, London EC2A 4DJ *Tel.* 020 7628 5801 *Email* admin@begbiesaccountants.co.uk

■ Lempriere Pringle 2015

CC NO 1161516 **ESTABLISHED** 2015

WHERE FUNDING CAN BE GIVEN Bishop Auckland and the surrounding areas.

WHO CAN BENEFIT Registered charities; churches; individuals.

WHAT IS FUNDED Regeneration and community development.

SAMPLE GRANTS The Auckland Project (£14.5 million); SHED (£3.5 million); Stockton Project (£121,600); First Fruit (£75,000).

FINANCES *Financial year end* 31/03/2020 *Income* £21,600,000 *Total grants* £20,670,000 *Grants to organisations* £20,670,000 *Assets* £12,120,000

TRUSTEES Dr Jane Ruffer; Dr Norman Fraser; Elizabeth Booker; Jonathan Ruffer; Harriet O'Rourke; Richard Chartres; Ashe Windham.

HOW TO APPLY The 2019/20 annual accounts state: 'The organisation is proactive in identifying projects, ministries, charities and individuals whose work relates to the organisation's objectives, but who generally are pursuing their causes without resorting to funding via professional fundraisers.' Contact the correspondent for further information before making an application to the charity.

CONTACT DETAILS The Trustees, 17 Ilderton Road, Stockton-on-Tees, County Durham TS18 2SR *Email* ordhouse1@btinternet.com

■ Leng Charitable Trust

OSCR NO SC009285 **ESTABLISHED** 1989

WHERE FUNDING CAN BE GIVEN Dundee and Tayside.

WHO CAN BENEFIT Registered charities; churches; hospices; universities.

WHAT IS FUNDED General charitable purposes.

SAMPLE GRANTS Salvation Army (£35,000); RNLI (£15,000); The Archie Foundation (£20,000); Kettins Parish Hall (£10,000); British Liver Trust (£4,000); Work Place Chaplaincy Scotland (£2,000).

FINANCES *Financial year end* 31/12/2019 *Income* £321,200 *Total grants* £292,600 *Grants to organisations* £292,600 *Assets* £8,120,000

HOW TO APPLY Contact the correspondent for further information.

CONTACT DETAILS The Trustees, c/o Thorntons Law LLP, Whitehall House, 33 Yeaman Shore, Dundee DD1 4BJ

■ The Mark Leonard Trust

CC NO 1040323 **ESTABLISHED** 1994

WHERE FUNDING CAN BE GIVEN Worldwide, but mainly UK.

WHO CAN BENEFIT Registered charities.

WHAT IS FUNDED Environmental causes, particularly sustainable agriculture, food and climate change; young people, particularly those at risk of offending.

WHAT IS NOT FUNDED Individuals; educational fees; expeditions.

TYPE OF GRANT Core costs; capital costs; development funding; seed/start-up funding.

SAMPLE GRANTS In Place of War (£250,000); Greenhouse PR Ltd (£72,000); ClientEarth (£50,000); Make My Money Matter (£33,300); Oil Change International (£15,000); Centre for London (£10,000); Forest Without Frontiers (£5,000); The Clink Charity (£3,000).

FINANCES *Financial year end* 05/04/2020 *Income* £1,340,000 *Total grants* £1,000,000 *Grants to organisations* £1,000,000 *Assets* £17,750,000

TRUSTEES Zivi Sainsbury; John Sainsbury; Mark Sainsbury.

OTHER INFORMATION The trust is one of the Sainsbury Family Charitable Trusts, which share a common administration – see www.sftc.org.uk for more information. Grants were awarded to 21 organisations.

HOW TO APPLY Unsolicited applications are not accepted.

CONTACT DETAILS Robert Bell, Director, The Peak, 5 Wilton Road, London SW1V 1AP *Tel.* 020 7410 0330 *Email* info@sfct.org.uk *Website* www.sfct.org.uk

■ The Leri Charitable Trust

CC NO 1075107 **ESTABLISHED** 1999

WHERE FUNDING CAN BE GIVEN UK, with a preference for Manchester and the London Borough of Brent.

WHO CAN BENEFIT Registered charities.

WHAT IS FUNDED General charitable purposes, including: social welfare; human rights and economic justice; equality and diversity; education; the arts, culture, heritage and science; community development; health; refugees and asylum seekers; justice for Palestinians; the environment.
TYPE OF GRANT The 2019/20 annual report states that the trust gives 'one-off multiple payments to either previously supported or new charities'.
SAMPLE GRANTS A list of beneficiaries was not included in the annual report and accounts.
FINANCES *Financial year end* 02/03/2020 *Income* £274,600 *Total grants* £844,400 *Grants to organisations* £844,400 *Assets* £12,380,000
TRUSTEES Alison Broadberry; Geoffrey Hellings; Leon Rosselson; Ruth Rosselson; John Ryan.
HOW TO APPLY The trust does not accept unsolicited applications.
CONTACT DETAILS Michael Reynolds, Administrator, c/o Edwin Coe LLP, 2 Stone Buildings, London WC2A 3TH *Tel.* 020 7691 4048 *Email* michael.reynolds@edwincoe.com

■ The Leverhulme Trust

CC NO 1159154 **ESTABLISHED** 1925
WHERE FUNDING CAN BE GIVEN UK.
WHO CAN BENEFIT Educational organisations; research bodies; charities; art organisations; individuals.
WHAT IS FUNDED Scholarships, fellowships and prizes for education and research.
WHAT IS NOT FUNDED See the website for a full list of exclusions.
TYPE OF GRANT One-off; projects; research; running costs; salaries.
RANGE OF GRANTS Dependent on grant programme.
SAMPLE GRANTS University of Cambridge (£4.81 million in 49 grants); University of Birmingham (£3.02 million in 15 grants); University of Nottingham (£2.15 million in 13 grants); University of Sheffield (£1.8 million in 17 grants); Lancaster University (£987,000 in seven grants); University of Aberdeen (£600,000 in five grants); Oxford Brookes University (£513,000 in two grants).
FINANCES *Financial year end* 31/12/2019 *Income* £111,490,000 *Total grants* £88,740,000 *Grants to organisations* £88,740,000 *Assets* £3,516,490,000
TRUSTEES Niall Fitzgerald; Patrick Cescau; David Lewis; Leena Nair; Alan Jope; Christopher Saul; Doug Baillie; Steve Williams; Mhairi McEwan; Clive Butler; Rudy Markham; Prof. Keith Gull.
OTHER INFORMATION During 2019, 659 grants were awarded to individuals and organisations from a total of 3,663 applications. The grant total includes grants to both individuals and organisations.
HOW TO APPLY Each programme, scholarship or award has its own individual application deadlines and procedures. Full details and guidelines for each scheme are available from the trust directly or via its website. The trust welcomes contact from applicants who are uncertain about their eligibility. Full contact details are available on the trust's website to help applicants determine which person is the most suitable to approach. In assessing appeals, the trustees evaluate the project's originality, importance, significance and merit. Cross-disciplinary projects may be favoured.
CONTACT DETAILS Programme correspondent, 1 Pemberton Row, London EC4A 3BG *Tel.* 020 7042 9888 *Email* grants@leverhulme.ac.uk *Website* www.leverhulme.ac.uk

■ Lord Leverhulme's Charitable Trust

CC NO 212431 **ESTABLISHED** 1957
WHERE FUNDING CAN BE GIVEN UK with a strong preference for Cheshire, Merseyside and south Lancashire.
WHO CAN BENEFIT Registered and exempt charities.
WHAT IS FUNDED Health; community; education; the arts; animal welfare; the environment; places of worship.
SAMPLE GRANTS Liverpool University (£200,000); Lady Lever Art Gallery and Royal College of Surgeons (£100,000 each); Royal College of Physicians (£50,000); Liverpool School of Tropical Medicine (£35,000); Chester Cathedral (£30,000); Bolton School (£30,000); Guards Chapel (£20,000).
FINANCES *Financial year end* 05/04/2020 *Income* £695,500 *Total grants* £1,160,000 *Grants to organisations* £1,160,000 *Assets* £33,200,000
TRUSTEES Sir Algernon Heber-Percy; Anthony Hannay; Henry Wilson.
OTHER INFORMATION Grants were made for the following purposes: religious establishments (£439,000); education (£385,000); health (£190,600); community (£101,400); the arts (£22,500; animal welfare (£20,000); the environment (£3,200).
HOW TO APPLY The trust states in its 2019/20 annual report: 'Priority is given [. . .] to applications from Cheshire, Merseyside and south Lancashire and the charities supported by the settlor in his lifetime. Others who do not meet those criteria should not apply without prior invitation but should, on a single sheet, state briefly their aims and apply fully only on being asked to do so. A handful of charities have heeded this warning and telephoned our administrator but the continuing volume of applications from charities which plainly do not meet the stated criteria suggests that many applicants do not concern themselves with their target's policies.'
CONTACT DETAILS The Trustees, Leverhulme Estate Office, Hesketh Grange, Manor Road, Thornton Hough, Wirral, Merseyside CH63 1JD *Tel.* 0151 336 4828 *Email* llctadmin@leverhulme.net

■ The Ralph Levy Charitable Company Ltd

CC NO 200009 **ESTABLISHED** 1961
WHERE FUNDING CAN BE GIVEN UK and overseas.
WHO CAN BENEFIT Charitable organisations.
WHAT IS FUNDED General charitable purposes, including education, health, social welfare and the arts.
SAMPLE GRANTS A list of beneficiaries was not included in the annual report and accounts.
FINANCES *Financial year end* 05/04/2020 *Income* £456,200 *Total grants* £480,200 *Grants to organisations* £480,200 *Assets* £270,700
TRUSTEES Daniel Levy; Stuart Levy; Christopher Andrews.
OTHER INFORMATION Grants were distributed as follows: medical causes (£221,600); welfare (£156,100); education (£96,600); the arts

(£6,000). Grants were made to 70 charitable causes in the UK and five overseas charities.
HOW TO APPLY Apply in writing to the correspondent. The trustees meet monthly to discuss and approve grant applications.
CONTACT DETAILS The Trustees, 116 Piccadilly, London W1J 7BJ *Tel.* 020 7408 9333 *Email* charity@ralphtrustees.co.uk

■ Joseph Levy Foundation

CC NO 1165225 **ESTABLISHED** 1965
WHERE FUNDING CAN BE GIVEN UK and Israel.
WHO CAN BENEFIT Registered charities.
WHAT IS FUNDED From April 2021 to March 2022 the foundation will focus on two areas: youth disadvantage and cystic fibrosis.
TYPE OF GRANT Project costs; capital and core costs; research; salaries; start-up costs; up to and over three years.
SAMPLE GRANTS Cystic Fibrosis Holiday Fund (£165,700); Ambitious About Autism (£116,900); Resources for Autism (£13,400); Voicebox (£10,000).
FINANCES *Financial year end* 31/03/2020 *Income* £907,700 *Total grants* £559,800 *Grants to organisations* £559,800 *Assets* £20,230,000
TRUSTEES Melanie Levy; Jane Jason; Katie Ellison; James Jason; Claudia Giat; Mark Jason.
HOW TO APPLY Unsolicited applications are not accepted. The foundation's website states: 'Note that JLF does not usually accept unsolicited grant applications. We search proactively for opportunities where funding could make a difference.'
CONTACT DETAILS The Trustees, 1st Floor, 1 Bell Street, London NW1 5BY *Tel.* 020 7616 1200 *Email* info@jlf.org.uk *Website* www.jlf.org.uk

■ Cecil and Hilda Lewis Charitable Trust

CC NO 258763 **ESTABLISHED** 1962
WHERE FUNDING CAN BE GIVEN UK and overseas.
WHO CAN BENEFIT Charitable organisations; educational establishments; medical organisations; art institutions.
WHAT IS FUNDED General charitable purposes, including the following: social welfare; older people; education in the UK and Israel (focusing on children with disabilities); arts and culture; medical research; health; students and educational establishments; disaster relief.
TYPE OF GRANT One-year and multi-year grants.
RANGE OF GRANTS Most grants are of under £11,000.
SAMPLE GRANTS Treloar Trust and Friends of Yad Sarah (£20,000 each).
FINANCES *Financial year end* 31/12/2020 *Income* £311,200 *Total grants* £231,700 *Grants to organisations* £231,700 *Assets* £7,130,000
TRUSTEES Catherine Wills; Robert Lewis; Alan Mason; Roger Wise.
OTHER INFORMATION A total of 45 organisations were supported in 2020. Grants of less than £11,000 totalled £191,700.
HOW TO APPLY Apply in writing to the correspondent. The trustees meet regularly to review grant applications.
CONTACT DETAILS Robert Lewis, Trustee and Secretary, Rotherwood, Jumps Road, Churt, Farnham, Surrey GU10 2JZ *Tel.* 01252 792189

■ Bernard Lewis Family Charitable Trust

CC NO 1125035 **ESTABLISHED** 2008
WHERE FUNDING CAN BE GIVEN UK.
WHO CAN BENEFIT Registered charities.
WHAT IS FUNDED Child welfare; health; general charitable purposes; older people; Jewish religious support; education.
RANGE OF GRANTS Up to £900,000, but usually between £2,000 and £150,000.
SAMPLE GRANTS Place2Be (£900,000); Newlife Foundation for Disabled Children (£300,000); Compassion of Dying (£150,000); Jewish Leadership Council (£75,000); Headway and Jewish Care (£50,000 each); Magic Bus (£18,000); The Disability Foundation (£5,000); Care4Calais (£3,000); Brain Circle (£700).
FINANCES *Financial year end* 31/12/2019 *Income* £2,560,000 *Total grants* £2,280,000 *Grants to organisations* £2,280,000 *Assets* £8,080,000
TRUSTEES Clive Lewis; Bernard Lewis; Caroline Grange; Leonard Lewis.
OTHER INFORMATION Grants were broken down as follows: child and social care (£1.47 million); general charitable funding (£444,300); Jewish community support (£198,000); medical support (£120,000); older people (£50,000); education (£700). Grants were awarded to 31 organisations during the year. Grants of less than £1,000 totalled £2,100.
HOW TO APPLY The trust does not accept unsolicited applications.
CONTACT DETAILS The Trustees, c/o The Giving Department, Sky Light City Tower, 50 Basinghall Street, London EC2V 5DE *Tel.* 07730 091970

■ David and Ruth Lewis Family Charitable Trust

CC NO 259892 **ESTABLISHED** 1969
WHERE FUNDING CAN BE GIVEN UK and overseas.
WHO CAN BENEFIT Charitable bodies and research organisations.
WHAT IS FUNDED General charitable purposes; medical research; Jewish religious support; child and social care; older people; education.
TYPE OF GRANT Most grants are one-off payments but some medical research grants can run for three years.
SAMPLE GRANTS Institute of Cancer Research (£375,000); Jewish Care (£250,000); Cancer Research (£200,000).
FINANCES *Financial year end* 31/05/2020 *Income* £2,910,000 *Total grants* £1,500,000 *Grants to organisations* £1,500,000 *Assets* £21,000,000
TRUSTEES Benjamin Lewis; Simon Lewis; Rachel Lewis.
OTHER INFORMATION Grants were broken down as follows: medical research and support (£777,000); general charitable funding (£310,300); support for older people (£260,000); children and social care (£101,000); education (£50,000).
HOW TO APPLY Contact the correspondent for further information.
CONTACT DETAILS The Trustees, Chelsea House, West Gate, Ealing, London W5 1DR *Tel.* 020 8991 4502

■ John Lewis Foundation

CC NO 1118162 **ESTABLISHED** 2007

WHERE FUNDING CAN BE GIVEN UK and overseas (particularly areas that support the John Lewis business).

WHO CAN BENEFIT Registered charities; non-registered voluntary organisations; CICs; hospices.

WHAT IS FUNDED Education and training; healthcare; community development; employment; the environment.

SAMPLE GRANTS The Save the Children Fund (£125,000); British Asian Trust (£83,500); WaterAid (£50,000); The Baytree Centre (£25,000); Leonard Cheshire (£12,000); Disability Resource Centre (£10,000).

FINANCES *Financial year end* 31/01/2020 *Income* £772,000 *Total grants* £771,600 *Grants to organisations* £771,600 *Assets* £997,700

TRUSTEES Christine Kasoulis; Simon Bishop; Paul Buchanan; Sarah Gillard; Margaret Porteous.

HOW TO APPLY At the time of writing (June 2021), according to its website, the foundation was conducting a review of its giving and had therefore suspended all new funding. See the foundation's website for further information.

CONTACT DETAILS The Trustees, 171 Victoria Street, London SW1E 5NN *Tel.* 020 7592 5658 *Email* johnlewisfoundation@johnlewis.co.uk *Website* www.johnlewisfoundation.org

■ The Sir Edward Lewis Foundation

CC NO 264475 **ESTABLISHED** 1972

WHERE FUNDING CAN BE GIVEN UK and overseas.

WHO CAN BENEFIT Registered charities.

WHAT IS FUNDED General charitable purposes.

WHAT IS NOT FUNDED Individuals.

TYPE OF GRANT Capital costs; core/revenue costs.

RANGE OF GRANTS From £500 to £27,000, but mostly up to £10,000.

SAMPLE GRANTS Arnold Foundation for Rugby School (£27,000); Combat Stress (£10,000); David Shepherd Wildlife Foundation (£5,000 each); Earl Mountbatten Hospice (£4,000); Music in Hospitals (£3,000); RNIB (£2,000); Uphill Ski Club (£1,000); Aeolian Singers (£500).

FINANCES *Financial year end* 05/04/2020 *Income* £289,600 *Total grants* £240,500 *Grants to organisations* £240,500 *Assets* £8,880,000

TRUSTEES Richard Lewis; Mark Harris; Sarah Dorin; Christopher Lewis; David Lewis.

OTHER INFORMATION The trustees prefer to support charities known personally to them and those favoured by the settlor. During 2019/20, grants were awarded to 91 organisations. The foundation provides annual grants to a number of charities, but new appeals are regularly considered.

HOW TO APPLY Apply in writing to the correspondent by post. The trustees meet bi-annually, in May and December, to consider new applications.

CONTACT DETAILS The Trustees, c/o Rawlinson and Hunter, Eighth Floor, 6 New Street Square, New Fetter Lane, London EC4A 3AQ *Tel.* 020 7842 2000 *Email* lewis.foundation@rawlinson-hunter.com

■ The Charles Lewis Foundation

CC NO 1179185 **ESTABLISHED** 2018

WHERE FUNDING CAN BE GIVEN UK.

WHO CAN BENEFIT Registered charities.

WHAT IS FUNDED General charitable purposes, including children and young people and community.

TYPE OF GRANT Project funding; core costs.

SAMPLE GRANTS Taylor Made Dreams (£15,000); Buttle (£10,000); Missing People (£2,000); Family Holiday Association (£1,000).

FINANCES *Financial year end* 31/03/2020 *Income* £100,000 *Total grants* £84,600 *Grants to organisations* £84,600 *Assets* £48,300

TRUSTEES Geoffrey Lewis; Della Skeates.

OTHER INFORMATION Grants were made to 19 organisations.

HOW TO APPLY Contact the correspondent for further information.

CONTACT DETAILS The Trustees, Unit 4, The Diamond, Holland Road, Oxted RH8 9BQ *Tel.* 07876 654045 *Email* office@tclf.org.uk

■ The Light Fund Company

CC NO 1145596 **ESTABLISHED** 2004

WHERE FUNDING CAN BE GIVEN UK and Africa.

WHO CAN BENEFIT Registered charities; occasionally individuals from the licensing industry.

WHAT IS FUNDED General charitable purposes with a preference for children and young people, health and medical research.

TYPE OF GRANT Project funding; capital costs; running costs.

RANGE OF GRANTS Typically up to £5,000.

SAMPLE GRANTS Francis House Children's Hospice (£6,700); Brain Tumour Society, Read For Good and Women and Children First UK (£5,000 each); London Wheelchair Rugby Club (£4,200); Berkshire MS Therapy Centre (£3,800); Cherry Trees (£3,500); Alzheimer's Society (£1,000).

FINANCES *Financial year end* 31/01/2020 *Income* £169,900 *Total grants* £158,900 *Grants to organisations* £158,900 *Assets* £2,400

TRUSTEES Hannah Mungo; Ian Downes; Kelvyn Gardner; Katherine Ball; Trevor Jones; Ashley Holman; Paul Hodgson; Caroline High; Ian Hyder; Jacqueline Brown; Victoria Hill; Alicia Davenport; Sabrina Segalov; David Scott.

OTHER INFORMATION During 2019/20, 34 organisations were supported.

HOW TO APPLY Applications can be made through the charity's website. At the time of writing (May 2021) the foundation was not accepting applications due to the COVID-19 pandemic. Check the foundation's website for the latest information.

CONTACT DETAILS The Trustees, c/o Max Publishing, United House, North Road, London N7 9DP *Tel.* 020 7700 6740 *Email* info@lightfund.org *Website* www.lightfund.org

■ The Limbourne Trust

CC NO 1113796 **ESTABLISHED** 2006

WHERE FUNDING CAN BE GIVEN UK and overseas.

WHO CAN BENEFIT Charitable organisations; community projects.

WHAT IS FUNDED The environment and sustainability; conservation; community projects; disadvantaged people; education, in particular in literature, music, drama and dance; health; the relief of poverty; general charitable purposes.

TYPE OF GRANT Capital costs; project funding.
RANGE OF GRANTS Typically up to £10,000.
SAMPLE GRANTS Farms for City Children (£12,800); Magdalene Group and Suffolk Refugee Support (£10,000 each); Nancy Oldfield Trust and The Simon Community (£8,000 each); Cambridge Junction (£7,000); Good Chance Theatre and Snape Maltings (£5,000 each); Pear Tree Fund (£4,500); Buckingham Emergency Food Appeal (£1,000).
FINANCES *Financial year end* 05/04/2020 *Income* £106,400 *Total grants* £71,300 *Grants to organisations* £71,300 *Assets* £3,660,000
TRUSTEES Mrs E. A. Thistlethwayte; Katharine Thistlethwayte; Dr Andrew Eastaugh; Penelope Heath.
OTHER INFORMATION Grants were made to ten organisations during 2019/20.
HOW TO APPLY According to the 2019/20 annual report, 'the trustees will seek to identify those projects where the greatest and widest benefit can be attained, and usually will only consider written applications and, where necessary, make further enquiries'.
CONTACT DETAILS The Trustees, Downs Farm, Homersfield, Harleston, Norfolk IP20 0NS *Tel.* 07572 966087

■ Limoges Charitable Trust

CC NO 1016178 **ESTABLISHED** 1991
WHERE FUNDING CAN BE GIVEN UK, with a preference for Birmingham.
WHO CAN BENEFIT Registered charities; universities; hospices; churches; community organisations; individuals (occasionally).
WHAT IS FUNDED General charitable purposes, including health, the environment, arts and heritage, community purposes, children and young people and animal welfare.
RANGE OF GRANTS Mostly up to £10,000.
SAMPLE GRANTS St Peter's Church – Bickenhill (£17,000); Dudley International Piano Competition (£15,000); The Police Arboretum Memorial Trust (£10,000); Three Choirs Festival (£3,000); Portsmouth Cathedral (£2,200); Help Harry Help Others and University of Birmingham Music Scholarship (£2,000 each); A1 Petline (£1,500); Queen Alexandra College and St Mary's Hospice (£1,000 each); The Elgar Festival (£600); Samaritans Birmingham and The Donkey Sanctuary (£500 each); Scope (£300); Cramer Cat Rescue (£250).
FINANCES *Financial year end* 05/04/2020 *Income* £30,800 *Total grants* £153,300 *Grants to organisations* £151,300 *Assets* £876,000
TRUSTEES Judy Dyke; Andrew Milner; Martin Dyke.
OTHER INFORMATION In 2019/20, a total of 76 grants were made. Grants to individuals totalled £2,000.
HOW TO APPLY Apply in writing to the correspondent. The trustees usually meet four times a year to consider applications.
CONTACT DETAILS The Trustees, c/o Tyndallwoods Solicitors, 29 Woodbourne Road, Edgbaston, Birmingham, West Midlands B17 8BY *Tel.* 0121 693 2222 *Email* jdyke@tyndallwoods.co.uk

■ The Linbury Trust

CC NO 287077 **ESTABLISHED** 1983
WHERE FUNDING CAN BE GIVEN UK and overseas, particularly Palestine and the Caribbean.
WHO CAN BENEFIT Charitable organisations; museums and galleries; educational organisations.
WHAT IS FUNDED Visual and performing arts; museums and heritage; social welfare; education; the environment; medical causes; work overseas; emergency relief.
WHAT IS NOT FUNDED Our previous research suggests that support is not given for individuals, educational fees or expeditions.
TYPE OF GRANT Core and capital costs; project costs; collections and acquisitions; development funding.
SAMPLE GRANTS Courtauld Institute of Art (£1.5 million); Science Museum (£750,000); Maggie's Cancer Caring Centre – Southampton (£400,000); University of Oxford – Saïd Business School (£185,000); Octagon Theatre (£100,000); Innovation for Agriculture (£60,000); Crisis and St Paul's Cathedral Foundation (£50,000 each).
FINANCES *Financial year end* 05/04/2020 *Income* £4,750,000 *Total grants* £9,750,000 *Grants to organisations* £9,750,000 *Assets* £120,340,000
TRUSTEES Sir Martin Jacomb; Richard Adams; John Sainsbury; Sarah Butler-Sloss; Lord Sainsbury of Preston Candover; Lady Anya Sainsbury; James Barnard; The Hon. Mark Sainsbury.
OTHER INFORMATION The trust is one of the Sainsbury Family Charitable Trusts which share a common administration – see www.sftc.org.uk for more information. A total of 125 organisations were supported during the year. Grants of under £50,000 were awarded to 81 organisations, totalling £1.3 million.
HOW TO APPLY The trust's website states that it does not accept unsolicited applications but rather identifies potential organisations 'through recommendation, partnership work and research'.
CONTACT DETAILS The Trustees, The Peak, 5 Wilton Road, London SW1V 1AP *Tel.* 020 7410 0330 *Email* linbury@sfct.org.uk *Website* www.linburytrust.org.uk

■ Lincolnshire Community Foundation

CC NO 1092328 **ESTABLISHED** 2002
WHERE FUNDING CAN BE GIVEN Lincolnshire.
WHO CAN BENEFIT Registered charities; unregistered charities; hospices; uniformed groups; CICs; social enterprises; schools; PTAs; amateur sports clubs; religious bodies/institutions; individuals.
WHAT IS FUNDED General charitable purposes; education; social welfare; health; community.
TYPE OF GRANT Capital costs; core/revenue costs; seed funding/start-up funding; project funding; unrestricted funding.
SAMPLE GRANTS Citizens Advice Mid Lincolnshire; Crosby Community Association; Fusion Creative; Heart of Sleaford; Holbeach Hospital; Lincolnshire Action Trust; Responders to Warmth; St Giles Community Garden; St Luke's Community Choir.
FINANCES *Financial year end* 31/03/2020 *Income* £1,100,000 *Total grants* £793,300 *Grants to organisations* £793,300 *Assets* £5,020,000

TRUSTEES Richard Ferens; Jane Hiles; Andrew Clark; Paul Scott; Lizzie Milligan-Manby; Lynda Phillips; Paula Baumber.

OTHER INFORMATION This is one of the 46 UK community foundations, which distribute funding for a wide range of purposes. As with all community foundations, there are a number of donor-advised funds managed on behalf of individuals, families and charitable trusts. Grant schemes tend to change frequently – consult the foundation's website for details of current programmes and up-to-date deadlines.

HOW TO APPLY Visit the foundation's website for details of current grant schemes. Application forms can be downloaded from the foundation's website or requested by phone.

CONTACT DETAILS The Trustees, 4 Mill House, Moneys Yard, Carre Street, Sleaford, Lincolnshire NG34 7TW *Tel.* 01529 305825 *Email* info@lincolnshirecf.co.uk *Website* www.lincolnshirecf.co.uk

■ The Linden Charitable Trust

CC NO 326788 **ESTABLISHED** 1985

WHERE FUNDING CAN BE GIVEN UK, with a preference for North and West Yorkshire.

WHO CAN BENEFIT Registered charities; hospices; arts organisations.

WHAT IS FUNDED Cancer relief and research; the arts; children; people experiencing loneliness; general charitable purposes.

WHAT IS NOT FUNDED Individuals.

RANGE OF GRANTS £500 to £2,000.

SAMPLE GRANTS Felix's Future (£1,000); Co-Active Arts (£820); St Robert's Church (£360).

FINANCES *Financial year end* 05/04/2020 *Income* £85,700 *Total grants* £2,200 *Grants to organisations* £2,200 *Assets* £2,980,000

TRUSTEES John Swales; Robert Swales; Margaret Swales; Kathryn Swales; Karen Rutter.

OTHER INFORMATION In 2019/20 the trustees postponed grant-making due to the COVID-19 pandemic. As a result, grants to organisations during the period totalled only £2,200, which is significantly lower than in previous years (2018/19 – £108,700, 2017/18 – £104,500).

HOW TO APPLY Contact the correspondent for further information.

CONTACT DETAILS The Trustees, PO Box 826, Harrogate, North Yorkshire HG1 9XQ *Tel.* 01423 541577 *Email* lindentrust@gmail.com

■ The Linder Foundation

CC NO 267509 **ESTABLISHED** 1974

WHERE FUNDING CAN BE GIVEN UK.

WHO CAN BENEFIT UK-registered charities or exempt charities; universities and teaching hospitals; museums and arts charities.

WHAT IS FUNDED Medical research; funding for medical electives and hardship grants at selected universities; hospices and respite care; improving the mental health and development of young people, particularly teenagers, young offenders and those in care; the environment; the arts, including musical tuition and concerts.

WHAT IS NOT FUNDED Non-UK-registered charities/exempt charities.

TYPE OF GRANT Mainly one-off; project funding; seed funding; research.

RANGE OF GRANTS Generally up to £30,000.

SAMPLE GRANTS Royal College of Surgeons – Fellowships (£50,000); Victoria and Albert Museum (£33,000); Médecins Sans Frontières (£30,000); National Children's Orchestra (£25,000); DEBRA and Neuromuscular Centre (£10,000 each); Phyllis Tuckwell Hospice (£9,500); Beatrix Potter Society (£8,000).

FINANCES *Financial year end* 31/03/2020 *Income* £505,000 *Total grants* £457,500 *Grants to organisations* £457,500 *Assets* £15,340,000

TRUSTEES Jack Ladeveze; Audrey Ladeveze; Michael Butler; Carole Cook; Jonathan Fountain; Henrietta Buxton; Amanda Smith.

OTHER INFORMATION Grants were made to 16 organisations in 2019/20. The grants total includes £108,000 awarded in elective and hardship grants to seven university medical schools.

HOW TO APPLY Check the website for open funding rounds and apply using the online form on the foundation's website. The annual report for 2019/20 states: 'Unsolicited applications are accepted, but the Trustees do receive a very high number of grant applications which, in line with their grant-making policy, are mostly unsuccessful.'

CONTACT DETAILS Elizabeth Fathi, The Clerk, c/o The Trust Partnership, 6 Trull Farm Buildings, Trull, Gloucestershire GL8 8SQ *Tel.* 020 3997 4444 *Email* admin@thelinderfoundation.org.uk *Website* www.enidlinderfoundation.com

■ The Lindley Foundation (TLF)

CC NO 1152760 **ESTABLISHED** 2013

WHERE FUNDING CAN BE GIVEN England and Wales; overseas.

WHO CAN BENEFIT Registered charities.

WHAT IS FUNDED General charitable purposes.

TYPE OF GRANT One-off; recurrent.

RANGE OF GRANTS Typically under £25,000.

SAMPLE GRANTS Robert F. Kennedy Human Rights UK (£40,500); Durham University (£20,000); Sesame Workshop (£16,000); One More Child (£2,500); Chefs in Schools and Sofea (£1,000 each).

FINANCES *Financial year end* 11/06/2020 *Income* £80,830 *Total grants* £81,000 *Grants to organisations* £81,000 *Assets* £486,900

TRUSTEES Alison Lindley; Paul Lindley; Ella Lindley; Coutts & Co.

OTHER INFORMATION During 2019/20, eight grants were made to six organisations.

HOW TO APPLY Apply by letter to the correspondent.

CONTACT DETAILS The Trustees, Coutts & Co. Trustee Department, 1st Floor, Trinity Quay 1, Avon Street, Bristol BS2 0PT *Tel.* 0345 304 2424

■ The Frank Litchfield Charitable Trust

CC NO 1038943 **ESTABLISHED** 1994

WHERE FUNDING CAN BE GIVEN Cambridgeshire, Essex and Hertfordshire.

WHO CAN BENEFIT Charitable organisations and projects.

WHAT IS FUNDED General charitable purposes, in particular health, disability, social welfare and medical research.

TYPE OF GRANT Project funding; research.

RANGE OF GRANTS Mostly between £500 and £2,000.

SAMPLE GRANTS Cambridge Community Foundation (£70,300); Fluency Trust and Kings Junior

Voices (£2,000 each); Chess Homeless (£1,250); Action Medical Research for Children, County Food Trust and Dyspraxia Foundation (£1,000 each); Sutton Community Farm (£500); WellChild (£250).

FINANCES *Financial year end* 31/03/2020 *Income* £141,000 *Total grants* £151,300 *Grants to organisations* £151,300 *Assets* £10,310,000

TRUSTEES Michael Womack; David Chater; Michael Hamilton.

HOW TO APPLY Contact the correspondent for further information.

CONTACT DETAILS Michael Womack, Trustee, 12 De Freville Avenue, Cambridge, Cambridgeshire CB4 1HR *Tel.* 01223 358012 *Email* womack@btinternet.com

■ The Charles Littlewood Hill Trust

CC NO 286350 **ESTABLISHED** 1978

WHERE FUNDING CAN BE GIVEN UK, with a preference for Nottinghamshire and Norfolk.

WHO CAN BENEFIT Charitable organisations; educational establishments; churches; community organisations.

WHAT IS FUNDED General charitable causes; social welfare; health and disability; the armed forces; the environment; education; religious activities; arts and culture.

WHAT IS NOT FUNDED Individuals; activities which are the responsibility of local authorities or similar bodies.

TYPE OF GRANT In practice, unrestricted funding, including capital and core costs. Applications for starter finance are encouraged, but grants are seldom made to endowment or capital funds.

RANGE OF GRANTS Usually £5,000 or less.

SAMPLE GRANTS Priscilla Bacon Norfolk Hospice Care Ltd (£31,000); Portland College (£20,000); East Anglia's Children's Hospices (£8,000); YMCA Norfolk (£5,000); Southwell Music Festival (£2,500); Literacy Volunteers In Nottinghamshire Schools (£2,000); Asthma UK and Combat Stress (£1,000 each).

FINANCES *Financial year end* 31/12/2019 *Income* £234,300 *Total grants* £190,500 *Grants to organisations* £190,500 *Assets* £5,280,000

TRUSTEES Charles Barratt; Nigel Savory; Tim Farr; John Pears.

OTHER INFORMATION Grants of £1,000 and above were awarded to 73 organisations and were broken down as follows: medical/disability (£89,500); welfare (£44,500); education (£9,000); other (£8,000); churches (£7,500); the armed forces (£6,000); groups/clubs (£5,500); accommodation and the environment (£5,000 each); the arts (£4,500).

HOW TO APPLY Applications must be made in writing to the correspondent, including the latest set of audited accounts, at least one month before trustees' meetings in March, July and November. Unsuccessful applicants will not be notified.

CONTACT DETAILS Mr D. N. Lindley, Trust Administrator, PO Box 10454, Nottingham, Nottinghamshire NG5 0HQ *Tel.* 07710 639946 *Email* charles.hill@btinternet.com *Website* www.charleshill.org.uk

■ The Second Joseph Aaron Littman Foundation

CC NO 201892 **ESTABLISHED** 1961

WHERE FUNDING CAN BE GIVEN Worldwide.

WHO CAN BENEFIT Registered charities only.

WHAT IS FUNDED General charitable purposes; social welfare; education; Jewish causes; academic and medical research.

WHAT IS NOT FUNDED Individuals.

TYPE OF GRANT General funding; research.

RANGE OF GRANTS Usually £1,000 to £15,000.

SAMPLE GRANTS The Littman Library of Jewish Civilisation (£189,000); Westminster Synagogue (£15,000); Wolfson College (£12,500); Friends of Louis Jacobs and VISTA Education and Training (£5,000 each); Memorial Scrolls Trust (£3,000); UJIA (£2,000).

FINANCES *Financial year end* 05/04/2020 *Income* £429,100 *Total grants* £309,600 *Grants to organisations* £309,600 *Assets* £8,330,000

TRUSTEES Colette Littman; Joanna Littman; Rabbi Dr Thomas Salamon.

OTHER INFORMATION Only organisations that received grants of over £2,000 were listed as beneficiaries in the foundation's accounts. Grants of under £2,000 totalled £15,800. The foundation provides continuing substantial support to the Littman Library of Jewish Civilisation.

HOW TO APPLY Contact the correspondent for further information.

CONTACT DETAILS The Trustees, Manor Farm, Mill Lane, Charlton Mackrell, Somerton, Somerset TA11 7BQ *Tel.* 01458 223650

■ The George John and Sheilah Livanos Charitable Trust

CC NO 1002279 **ESTABLISHED** 1985

WHERE FUNDING CAN BE GIVEN UK.

WHO CAN BENEFIT Registered charities.

WHAT IS FUNDED General charitable purposes.

RANGE OF GRANTS From £2,500 to £155,000.

SAMPLE GRANTS Previous beneficiaries have included: Gainsborough House (£155,000); Bletchley Park Trust (£15,000); Ekklesia Project Fakenham (£12,000); Whoopsadaisy (£3,300); Housing the Homeless, South East Cancer Help Centre and Crackerjack's Children's Trust (£2,500 each).

FINANCES *Financial year end* 31/12/2019 *Income* £19,100 *Total grants* £94,000 *Grants to organisations* £94,000

TRUSTEES Philip Harris; Timothy Cripps.

OTHER INFORMATION Full accounts were not available to view on the Charity Commission's website due to the trust's low income. We have therefore estimated the grant total based on the trust's total expenditure.

HOW TO APPLY According to the trust's 2018 annual accounts: 'Unsolicited applications are accepted, but the trustees do receive a very high number of grant applications which, in line with the trustees' grant-making policy, are mostly unsuccessful. The trustees prefer to make donations to charities whose work they have researched and which is in accordance with the aims and objectives of the charity for the year.'

CONTACT DETAILS The Trustees, c/o Longmores, 24 Castle Street, Hertford, Hertfordshire SG14 1HP *Tel.* 01992 300333

Liverpool Charity and Voluntary Services (LCVS)

CC NO 223485 **ESTABLISHED** 1970

WHERE FUNDING CAN BE GIVEN Merseyside.

WHO CAN BENEFIT Registered charities; CICs.

WHAT IS FUNDED General charitable purposes; health; education; income stability; arts and culture.

WHAT IS NOT FUNDED Exclusions for each of the charity's grant programmes can be found on its website.

TYPE OF GRANT Capital costs; project funding; core costs (including salaries).

SAMPLE GRANTS A list of beneficiaries was not included in the annual report and accounts.

FINANCES *Financial year end* 31/03/2019 *Income* £6,560,000 *Total grants* £4,190,000 *Grants to organisations* £4,190,000 *Assets* £7,590,000

TRUSTEES Jonny Hesketh; Michael Thomas; Duncan Brookes; John Price; James Sloan; Heather Akehurst; Michael James; Kenneth Perry; Michael Salla; Dorcas Akeju; Louise Scholes; Susan Williams.

OTHER INFORMATION The charity acts in a similar manner to a community foundation, administrating the giving of much smaller charitable trusts. Comprehensive details of all of the grant programmes are available from the charity's website and details of new programmes or new funding rounds are posted as they come up. The 2018/19 accounts were the latest available at the time of writing (February 2021).

HOW TO APPLY Apply online via the charity's website.

CONTACT DETAILS Grants Team, 151 Dale Street, Liverpool, Merseyside L2 2AH *Tel.* 0151 227 5177 *Email* grants@lcvs.org.uk *Website* www.lcvs.org.uk

The Livingston Charitable Trust

CC NO 1139841 **ESTABLISHED** 2018

WHERE FUNDING CAN BE GIVEN UK; India; Pakistan; Kenya; Tanzania.

WHO CAN BENEFIT Charitable organisations.

WHAT IS FUNDED Social welfare; health; education; water, sanitation and hygiene (WASH).

SAMPLE GRANTS A list of beneficiaries was not included in the annual report and accounts.

FINANCES *Financial year end* 31/12/2019 *Income* £267,500 *Total grants* £135,200 *Grants to organisations* £135,200 *Assets* £127,400

TRUSTEES Mohammed Jumani; Jawad Jumani; Ghulam Jumani.

HOW TO APPLY Contact the correspondent for further information.

CONTACT DETAILS The Trustees, 30A Woodlands Park, Livingston EH54 8AT

Jack Livingstone Charitable Trust

CC NO 263473 **ESTABLISHED** 1971

WHERE FUNDING CAN BE GIVEN UK and worldwide, with a preference for the Manchester area.

WHO CAN BENEFIT Registered charities.

WHAT IS FUNDED General charitable purposes; Jewish causes.

RANGE OF GRANTS Up to £115,000, but generally under £10,000.

SAMPLE GRANTS Manchester Jewish Museum (£115,000); The Jerusalem Foundation (£100,000); Langford Foundation (£10,000); Community Security Trust (£8,500); Justifi (£5,000); The Lowry Centre Trust (£2,500); Hale Barns Club and Southport New Synagogue (£1,000 each).

FINANCES *Financial year end* 05/04/2020 *Income* £65,300 *Total grants* £310,900 *Grants to organisations* £310,900 *Assets* £1,820,000

TRUSTEES Janice Livingstone; Terence Livingstone; Brian White.

OTHER INFORMATION Only organisations that received grants of over £1,000 were listed as beneficiaries in the trust's accounts. Grants of under £1,000 totalled £3,900.

HOW TO APPLY Contact the correspondent for further information.

CONTACT DETAILS Janice Livingstone, Trustee, Apsley Cottage, Vale Road, Bowdon, Altrincham, Cheshire WA14 3AF *Tel.* 0161 928 0760 *Email* 2taf56@gmail.com

The Ian and Natalie Livingstone Charitable Trust

CC NO 1149025 **ESTABLISHED** 2012

WHERE FUNDING CAN BE GIVEN UK.

WHO CAN BENEFIT Registered charities.

WHAT IS FUNDED Children and young people; disadvantaged people.

WHAT IS NOT FUNDED Individuals.

TYPE OF GRANT Project funding; capital costs; core costs.

RANGE OF GRANTS Generally up to £50,000.

SAMPLE GRANTS British Academy of Film and Television Arts (£93,700); Dalaid (£50,000); Make-A-Wish Foundation (£20,000); Place2Be (£10,000); Highgate School (£5,000).

FINANCES *Financial year end* 31/03/2020 *Income* £90,500 *Total grants* £201,300 *Grants to organisations* £201,300 *Assets* £21,900

TRUSTEES Ian Livingstone; Natalie Livingstone; Mark Levitt.

OTHER INFORMATION The trustees will consider grant applications for up to £250,000.

HOW TO APPLY Contact the correspondent for further information.

CONTACT DETAILS The Trustees, Blick Rothenberg Ltd, Palladium House, 1–4 Argyll Street, London W1F 7LD *Tel.* 020 7437 7666 *Email* email@blickrothenberg.com

The Elaine and Angus Lloyd Charitable Trust

CC NO 237250 **ESTABLISHED** 1964

WHERE FUNDING CAN BE GIVEN UK, with a preference for Surrey and Kent.

WHO CAN BENEFIT Individuals; local, regional and UK-wide organisations.

WHAT IS FUNDED General charitable purposes; health; medical causes; disability; social welfare; Christianity.

TYPE OF GRANT Recurrent and one-off.

RANGE OF GRANTS Up to £20,000, but mostly around £1,000 to £3,000.

SAMPLE GRANTS Spear Brighton (£15,000); What on Earth Foundation (£14,500); Archie Lloyd Charitable Foundation (£10,000); Rhema Bible College (£5,800); Hope Garden Medical Centre (£4,000); Diabetes UK (£2,500); Pilgrims Hospices (£1,500); Oesophageal Patients Association and St Clement's Church – Sandwich (£1,000 each).

FINANCES *Financial year end* 05/04/2020 *Income* £139,600 *Total grants* £127,600 *Grants to organisations* £123,200 *Assets* £2,930,000

TRUSTEES Angus Lloyd; John Gordon; James Lloyd; Philippa Smith; Virginia Best; Christopher Lloyd; Sir Michael Craig-Cooper; The Revd Richard Lloyd.

OTHER INFORMATION Only beneficiaries of grants of above £1,000 were listed in the accounts. Grants of over £1,000 were made to 27 organisations and two individuals during the year.

HOW TO APPLY Grants are generally awarded to charities or for purposes known to one or more of the trustees, but applications may be made in writing to the correspondent. The trustees meet regularly to consider grants.

CONTACT DETAILS Ross Badger, Ground Floor, 45 Pall Mall, London SW1Y 5JG *Tel.* 020 7930 7797 *Email* ross.badger@hhLLP.co.uk

■ The W. M. and B. W. Lloyd Trust

CC NO 503384 **ESTABLISHED** 1974

WHERE FUNDING CAN BE GIVEN Darwen.

WHO CAN BENEFIT Charitable organisations, especially hospitals and hospices.

WHAT IS FUNDED General charitable purposes for the people of Darwen; the advancement of education; medical science and the provision of medical equipment; the provision and improvement of public amenities; emergency support.

TYPE OF GRANT Capital costs.

SAMPLE GRANTS A list of beneficiaries was not included in the annual report and accounts.

FINANCES *Financial year end* 05/04/2020 *Income* £131,400 *Total grants* £91,500 *Grants to organisations* £91,500 *Assets* £3,630,000

TRUSTEES John Jacklin; Jason Slack; Dorothy Parsons; Alan Slack.

OTHER INFORMATION The trust has previously stated that it has five committees: emergency, education, social amenities, medical and T. P. Davies Fund. Each committee considers requests particular to its area of remit and reports to the trustees with its recommendations. The trust also administers the T. P. Davies Fund and Darwen Probation Volunteers Fund.

HOW TO APPLY Apply in writing to the correspondent either by post or email.

CONTACT DETAILS John Jacklin, Secretary and Trustee, Gorse Barn, Rock Lane, Tockholes, Darwen, Lancashire BB3 0LX *Tel.* 01254 771367 *Email* johnjacklin@homecall.co.uk

■ The Andrew Lloyd Webber Foundation

CC NO 1015648 **ESTABLISHED** 1992

WHERE FUNDING CAN BE GIVEN England and Wales.

WHO CAN BENEFIT Registered charities; CICs.

WHAT IS FUNDED Arts; culture; heritage.

WHAT IS NOT FUNDED A full list of exclusions can be found on the foundation's website.

TYPE OF GRANT Project funding.

RANGE OF GRANTS Grants range from £1,000 to £89,900.

SAMPLE GRANTS Eton College – 6th Form Music Scholarships (£89,900); Arts Educational Schools (£45,900); Urdang Schools Ltd (£38,400); Royal Central School of Speech and Drama (£33,500); Birmingham Conservatoire (£18,500); Southwark Playhouse – Young Company (£9,800).

FINANCES *Financial year end* 31/12/2019 *Income* £450,000 *Total grants* £552,000 *Grants to organisations* £552,000 *Assets* £37,940,000

TRUSTEES Emma Marsh; Lady Madeline Lloyd Webber; Louise Fennell; Phillip Freedman; Dr Simon Thurley; Mark Wordsworth; Katherine Reardon.

OTHER INFORMATION Full details of all the foundation's current grant programmes are available on the website.

HOW TO APPLY At the time of writing (March 2021) the foundation was not accepting applications. See the foundation's website for further information.

CONTACT DETAILS Sarah Miller, Administrator, Sydmonton Court Estate, Burghclere, Newbury, Berkshire RG20 9NJ *Tel.* 01635 278594 *Email* sarah@andrewlloydwebberfoundation.com *Website* www.andrewlloydwebberfoundation.com

■ Lloyd's Charities Trust

CC NO 207232 **ESTABLISHED** 1953

WHERE FUNDING CAN BE GIVEN Worldwide; UK, with a preference for east London.

WHO CAN BENEFIT Charitable organisations.

WHAT IS FUNDED Disasters and emergencies and humanitarian work; general charitable purposes.

TYPE OF GRANT One-off; recurrent; project costs; bursaries.

SAMPLE GRANTS A list of beneficiaries was not included in the annual report and accounts.

FINANCES *Financial year end* 31/12/2019 *Income* £635,000 *Total grants* £625,800 *Grants to organisations* £625,800 *Assets* £2,990,000

TRUSTEES Mark Filder; Victoria; David Ibeson; Andrew Brooks; Oliver Ferrari; Amy Bumstead; Caroline Klein; Claire O'Meara; Elizabeth Cabrera; Hannah-Polly Williams.

OTHER INFORMATION The Lloyd's Market Charity Awards are donations to charities supported by individuals working in the Lloyd's market.

HOW TO APPLY Applications for the Lloyd's Market Charity Awards can be made via the trust's website, where guidelines and application deadlines can also be found. The trust will not be accepting any other funding or partnership requests until 2022. Details will be announced on the trust's website.

CONTACT DETAILS The Trustees, Lloyd's Building, 1 Lime Street, London EC3M 7HA *Tel.* 020 7327 1000 *Email* responsiblebusiness@lloyds.com *Website* https://www.lloyds.com/about-lloyds/responsible-business/community-involvement/lloyds-charities-trust

■ Lloyds Bank Foundation for England and Wales

CC NO 327114 **ESTABLISHED** 1986

WHERE FUNDING CAN BE GIVEN England and Wales.

WHO CAN BENEFIT Registered charities.

WHAT IS FUNDED Work related to: addiction and dependency; asylum seekers and refugees; care leavers; domestic abuse; people who are homeless or vulnerably housed; learning disabilities; mental health; offending, prison or community service; sexual abuse and exploitation; trafficking and modern slavery; young parents.

WHAT IS NOT FUNDED CICs, or any other organisations that are not charities or CIOs registered in England and Wales; infrastructure or umbrella organisations; organisations whose primary purpose is to give funds to individuals or other organisations (i.e. organisations using more than 50% of annual expenditure as grants); hospitals, health authorities or hospices; rescue services; nurseries, preschools or playgroups; schools, colleges or universities; animal charities; charities working predominantly outside England and Wales; organisations that do not have a purpose/benefit beyond the promotion of religion.
TYPE OF GRANT Unrestricted.
RANGE OF GRANTS Grants of £50,000.
SAMPLE GRANTS A list of beneficiaries was not included in the annual report and accounts.
FINANCES *Financial year end* 31/12/2019
Income £14,740,000
Total grants £25,700,000
Grants to organisations £25,700,000
Assets £40,770,000
TRUSTEES Neil Wooding; Rebecca Shaw; Kamran Mallick; Catharine Cheetham; Prof. Akwugo Emejulu; Ruth Sutherland; Darren Knight; Joanna Harris; Gareth Oakley; Dame Margaret Morgan; Baroness Irene Fritchie; Sara Weller.
OTHER INFORMATION Grants were made to 935 organisations in 2019.
HOW TO APPLY Applications can be made via the foundation's website. There is no closing date for applications. The foundation aims to give a decision within four months of receiving an application.
CONTACT DETAILS Grants Team, Pentagon House, 52–54 Southwark Street, London SE1 1UN *Tel.* 0370 411 1223 *Email* enquiries@lloydsbankfoundation.org.uk *Website* https://www.lloydsbankfoundation.org.uk

■ Lloyds Bank Foundation for the Channel Islands

CC NO 327113 **ESTABLISHED** 1986
WHERE FUNDING CAN BE GIVEN Channel Islands.
WHO CAN BENEFIT Registered charities.
WHAT IS FUNDED Work related to: people with health issues or disabilities; homelessness; alcohol or drug dependency; carers; discrimination and disadvantage; literacy; domestic violence; people leaving institutional care.
WHAT IS NOT FUNDED Organisations which are not registered charities; individual requests; sponsorship requests; international appeals; animal welfare; environmental charities; expeditions or overseas travel; the promotion of religion (charities with a religious element whose objectives demonstrate a wider benefit to people experiencing disadvantage may not be excluded); schools and colleges (except for projects that will benefit disadvantaged students and are clearly additional to statutory responsibilities); activities which are the responsibility of a statutory body or the islands' governments; activities which duplicate or overlap a service already provided; applications for salaries which would apply to the applicant; charities which have received a grant from the foundation in the previous 12 months or have received three years' continuous funding.
TYPE OF GRANT Capital costs; core/revenue costs; project funding; seed/start-up funding.
SAMPLE GRANTS Every Child Our Future LBG (£83,500); Guernsey Alcohol Advisory Service (£40,000); Mind Jersey (£30,000); Service Station (£25,000); St Peter's Church (£10,000); Triumph Over Phobia (£2,000).
FINANCES *Financial year end* 31/12/2019
Income £769,800 *Total grants* £909,600
Grants to organisations £909,600
Assets £1,840,000
TRUSTEES Kathryn Ann Le Quesne; David Hodgetts; John Henwood; Gavin Scott Ferguson; Heather MacCallum; Tracey Johnson; Neil Fellows; Brian Heath; Alasdair Gardner.
HOW TO APPLY Applications can be made via the foundation's website. Applicants are encouraged to discuss their project with the Executive Director before completing an application form.
CONTACT DETAILS Johanna Le Poidevin, Executive Director, Sarnia House, Le Truchot, St Peter Port, Guernsey GY1 4EF *Tel.* 01481 706360 *Email* jlepoidevin@lloydsbankfoundation.org.uk *Website* https://www.lloydsbankfoundationci.org.uk

■ Lloyd's Patriotic Fund

CC NO 210173 **ESTABLISHED** 1803
WHERE FUNDING CAN BE GIVEN England and Wales.
WHO CAN BENEFIT Registered charities.
WHAT IS FUNDED Support for veterans and their families after they have finished their service.
TYPE OF GRANT Project funding.
RANGE OF GRANTS Up to £200,000.
SAMPLE GRANTS Combat Stress and Regular Forces Employment Association (£110,000 each); SSAFA (£28,000); First Light Trust and Scotty's Little Soldiers (£20,000 each).
FINANCES *Financial year end* 30/06/2020
Income £441,000 *Total grants* £332,000
Grants to organisations £332,000
Assets £3,440,000
TRUSTEES Neil Maidment; Caroline Sandeman-Allen; Richard Williams; Air Commodore Wendy Rothery; Edward Butler; Bruce Carnegie Brown; Alexander Findlay; Michelle Alston; Duncan Welham; William Roscoe.
OTHER INFORMATION The charity provides long-term support to a number of partner organisations as well as smaller one-off grants.
HOW TO APPLY See the charity's website for the latest information on grants.
CONTACT DETAILS Corporate Social Responsibility Manager, Lloyd's, One Lime Street, London EC3M 7HA *Tel.* 020 7327 5484 *Email* responsiblebusiness@lloyds.com *Website* www.lloyds.com/lpf

■ Lloyd's Register Foundation

CC NO 1145988 **ESTABLISHED** 2012
WHERE FUNDING CAN BE GIVEN Worldwide.
WHO CAN BENEFIT Universities and research institutes.
WHAT IS FUNDED Improving public safety through engineering related education, training and research.
TYPE OF GRANT Research funding; project funding.
SAMPLE GRANTS University College of London (£1.16 million); University of Nottingham (£830,000); FISH Safety Foundation (£449,000); Tall Ship Youth Trust (£126,000); Museum of London Archaeology (£100,000); British Science Association (£50,000); NumberBoost (£30,000); RNLI (£4,000).
FINANCES *Financial year end* 30/06/2019
Income £10,390,000 *Total grants* £7,700,000
Grants to organisations £7,700,000
Assets £298,770,000

TRUSTEES Ishbel Macpherson; Andreas Sohmen-Pao; Rosemary Martin; Carol Sergeant; Thomas Anderson; Dame Una O'Brien; Lambros Varnavides.
OTHER INFORMATION The foundation's 2018/19 accounts were the latest available at the time of writing (June 2021).
HOW TO APPLY Applications can be made via the foundation's grants portal and are reviewed at monthly meetings.
CONTACT DETAILS Michelle Davies, Company Secretary, 71 Fenchurch Street, London EC3M 4BS *Email* michelle.davies@lr.org *Website* www.lrfoundation.org.uk

■ Local Trent Ltd

CC NO 326329 **ESTABLISHED** 1982
WHERE FUNDING CAN BE GIVEN UK, with some preference for Manchester.
WHO CAN BENEFIT Charities; educational or religious institutions.
WHAT IS FUNDED The advancement of the Orthodox Jewish faith. The trustees will consider applications from organisations concerned with Orthodox Jewish faith education and the relief of poverty in the Jewish community.
TYPE OF GRANT £5,000 to £30,000.
RANGE OF GRANTS Generally, up to around £30,000.
SAMPLE GRANTS Zoreia Zedokos (£30,000); Chasdei Yoel Charitable Trust (£27,900); Kol Yom (£13,000); Keren Habinyan D'Satmar (£10,000); Kesser Torah School (£6,300); Yeshiva Ohel Shimon (£6,000); Kollel Tchabe (£5,100).
FINANCES *Financial year end* 31/03/2020 *Income* £230,900 *Total grants* £269,000 *Grants to organisations* £269,000 *Assets* £1,100,000
TRUSTEES Hyman Weiss; Mina Weiss; Philip Weiss; Zisel Weiss; Yocheved Weiss.
OTHER INFORMATION Grants were broken down as follows: relief of hardship and poverty in the Jewish community (£122,700); the advancement of religion and the Orthodox Jewish faith (£83,200); Orthodox Jewish education and religious studies (£63,100). Awards of less than £5,000 totalled £65,900.
HOW TO APPLY Apply in writing to the correspondent. Contact the correspondent for further information.
CONTACT DETAILS The Trustees, c/o Lopian Gross Barnett and Co., 1st Floor, Cloisters House, New Bailey Street, Manchester M3 5FS *Tel.* 0161 832 8721

■ The Locker Foundation

CC NO 264180 **ESTABLISHED** 1966
WHERE FUNDING CAN BE GIVEN UK and overseas (Israel).
WHO CAN BENEFIT Jewish organisations; hospices; places of worship; schools; registered charities.
WHAT IS FUNDED General charitable purposes, with a preference for Jewish causes, health and disability, and religious education.
TYPE OF GRANT Project funding.
RANGE OF GRANTS £200 to £112,000.
SAMPLE GRANTS Magen David Adam UK (£112,100); Tikva Children's Home (£58,000); Chai Cancer Care (£50,000); Noa Girls (£25,000); Community Security Trust and Norwood Ravenswood (£20,000 each); World Jewish Relief (£15,000); Jewish Deaf Association (£9,900); Chicken Soup Shelter (£9,000); Birmingham Hebrew Congregation (£3,000); Kef Kids (£1,000); Matilda Marks Kennedy School (£500); United Synagogue (£200).
FINANCES *Financial year end* 05/04/2020 *Income* £1,010,000 *Total grants* £764,000 *Grants to organisations* £764,000 *Assets* £10,370,000
TRUSTEES Susannah Segal; Malcolm Carter.
OTHER INFORMATION Grants were made to 26 organisations during the year.
HOW TO APPLY Contact the correspondent for further information.
CONTACT DETAILS Malcolm Carter, Chair, 65 Flower Lane, Mill Hill, London NW7 2JN *Tel.* 07956 325198 *Email* thelockerfoundation@hotmail.com

■ The Lockwood Charitable Foundation

CC NO 1123272 **ESTABLISHED** 2008
WHERE FUNDING CAN BE GIVEN England and Wales.
WHO CAN BENEFIT Registered charities; educational organisations; cultural organisations.
WHAT IS FUNDED General charitable purposes including the following: health; education; culture and heritage; Christian causes.
RANGE OF GRANTS Up to £100,000.
SAMPLE GRANTS The Kensington and Chelsea Foundation (£100,000); Embrace (£75,000); Spinal Injuries Association (£50,000); Frome Medical Practice Community (£25,000); Princess Alice Hospice (£12,500); Help2Read and Missing People (£5,000 each); Bliss and National Animal Welfare (£1,000 each).
FINANCES *Financial year end* 05/04/2020 *Income* £313,200 *Total grants* £430,800 *Grants to organisations* £430,800 *Assets* £4,490,000
TRUSTEES Lesley Lockwood; Dr Rebecca Lockwood; Richard Lockwood.
OTHER INFORMATION Grants were awarded to 17 organisations during 2019/20.
HOW TO APPLY Contact the correspondent for further information.
CONTACT DETAILS Richard Lockwood, Trustee, The Tithe Barn, The Avenue, Compton, Guildford, Surrey GU3 1JW *Tel.* 01483 415480

■ Loftus Charitable Trust

CC NO 297664 **ESTABLISHED** 1987
WHERE FUNDING CAN BE GIVEN UK.
WHO CAN BENEFIT Jewish organisations; religious and educational institutions.
WHAT IS FUNDED Jewish causes, primarily social welfare, Jewish education and the advancement of Judaism.
RANGE OF GRANTS £10,000 to £580,000.
SAMPLE GRANTS Kisharon (£538,000); Neve Michael Charitable Trust (£165,000); Jewish School Network (£67,600); The Black Stork Charity (£50,000); Jewish Care (£33,500); Jewish Leadership Council (£10,000).
FINANCES *Financial year end* 05/04/2019 *Income* £1,040,000 *Total grants* £1,280,000 *Grants to organisations* £1,280,000 *Assets* £5,810,000
TRUSTEES Andrew Loftus; Anthony Loftus; Richard Loftus.
OTHER INFORMATION The 2018/19 accounts were the latest available at the time of writing (April 2021). Grants were awarded to 29 institutions during the year.
HOW TO APPLY The trustees use their own knowledge to inform grant-making decisions. They typically

invite organisations to submit a formal application. All applications must explain in detail how the funds will be used and what will be achieved.

CONTACT DETAILS The Trustees, 55 Blandford Street, Marylebone, London W1U 7HW *Tel.* 020 7604 5900 *Email* andrew@loftusfp.com

■ London Catalyst

CC NO 1066739 **ESTABLISHED** 1872

WHERE FUNDING CAN BE GIVEN Greater London, within the boundaries of the M25.

WHO CAN BENEFIT Registered charities; unregistered charities; CICs; hospices; churches.

WHAT IS FUNDED Health and well-being; social welfare.

WHAT IS NOT FUNDED Individuals; general appeals.

TYPE OF GRANT Capital costs; core/revenue costs; project funding; seed/start-up funding.

RANGE OF GRANTS Project grants range from £1,000 to £5,000.

SAMPLE GRANTS Headway West London (£5,000); Room to Heal (£3,000); Age UK Westminster (£1,500); WellCare (£1,000).

FINANCES *Financial year end* 31/12/2019 *Income* £328,700 *Total grants* £299,400 *Grants to organisations* £299,400 *Assets* £14,000,000

TRUSTEES Mark Palframan; Emma Whitby; Andrew Davidson; Joan Major; Yasmin Hussain; Dr Sarah Divall; Danny Daly; Philippe Granger; Dr Muhammad Bari.

HOW TO APPLY Full guidance, including helpful FAQs, is available to download from the charity's website. The trustees usually meet four times a year, in February, May, September and November. Completed applications must be received at least four weeks in advance of meetings.

CONTACT DETAILS The Trustees, 45 Westminster Bridge Road, London SE1 7JB *Tel.* 020 3828 4204 *Email* london.catalyst@peabody.org.uk *Website* www.londoncatalyst.org.uk

■ The London Community Foundation (LCF)

CC NO 1091263 **ESTABLISHED** 2002

WHERE FUNDING CAN BE GIVEN London.

WHO CAN BENEFIT Charities and community groups; small and medium-sized organisations; social enterprises; CICs.

WHAT IS FUNDED General charitable purposes, in particular: arts, culture and heritage; life skills, employability and enterprise; stronger communities; physical and mental health, well-being and safety; the environment.

WHAT IS NOT FUNDED Political groups; activities which promote religion (faith groups may be assisted). Specific criteria may apply for different funds – check the foundation's website for further information.

TYPE OF GRANT Capital and core costs, feasibility studies, project funding, running costs, salaries and start-up costs.

RANGE OF GRANTS In 2019/20 the average grant was £14,658.

SAMPLE GRANTS The Dwayne Simpson Foundation (£50,000); The Show Crib (£47,000); Solidarity Sports and The Clement James Centre (£45,000 each); Homeless Link (£44,400); Music Fusion (£41,600); Migration Museum Project (£40,200 in two grants).

FINANCES *Financial year end* 31/03/2020 *Income* £9,800,000 *Total grants* £9,092,000 *Grants to organisations* £9,060,000 *Assets* £24,060,000

TRUSTEES Veesh Sharma; Timothy Ingram; Edward Greenhalgh; Natalie Creary-Aninakwa; Gaynor Humphreys; Russell Prior; John Hume; Sanjay Mazumder; Genine Whitehorne; Paul Cattermull.

OTHER INFORMATION This is one of the 46 UK community foundations, which distribute funding for a wide range of purposes. As with all community foundations, there are a number of donor-advised funds managed on behalf of individuals, families and charitable trusts. Grant schemes tend to change frequently; consult the foundation's website for details of current programmes and up-to-date deadlines. During 2019/20, 765 grants were awarded, including 618 to organisations (£9.06 million) and 147 to individuals (£32,000). Only organisations that received over £40,000 were listed as beneficiaries in the accounts.

HOW TO APPLY Potential applicants are advised to visit the community foundation's website or contact its programmes team to find the most suitable funding stream.

CONTACT DETAILS Programmes Team, Unit 1.04, Piano House, 9 Brighton Terrace, London SW9 8DJ *Tel.* 020 7582 5117 *Email* info@londoncf.org.uk *Website* www.londoncf.org.uk

■ London Freemasons Charity

CC NO 1081205 **ESTABLISHED** 2000

WHERE FUNDING CAN BE GIVEN Greater London.

WHO CAN BENEFIT Charitable organisations.

WHAT IS FUNDED General charitable purposes with particular focus on: the relief of need, poverty or distress; healthcare or medical support; the advancement of education.

RANGE OF GRANTS Mostly £500 to £10,000.

SAMPLE GRANTS London Fire Brigade (£1.24 million); Oral Health Foundation (£10,000); The Albany (£4,500); Brompton Cycles (£3,000); St Johns Ambulance (£1,500).

FINANCES *Financial year end* 30/09/2020 *Income* £851,700 *Total grants* £1,420,000 *Grants to organisations* £1,420,000 *Assets* £2,160,000

TRUSTEES Marios Stylianides; Quentin Humberstone; Stratton Richey; Augustus Ullstein QC; Thomas Toumazis; Peter Jennings.

OTHER INFORMATION A significantly larger grant of £1.24 million was made to London Fire Brigade in 2019/20.

HOW TO APPLY Contact the correspondent for further information.

CONTACT DETAILS The Trustees, 60 Great Queen Street, PO Box 29055, London WC2B 5AZ *Tel.* 020 7539 2930 *Email* c.hunt@metgl.com

■ London Housing Foundation Ltd (LHF)

CC NO 270178 **ESTABLISHED** 1975

WHERE FUNDING CAN BE GIVEN London.

WHO CAN BENEFIT Voluntary bodies; charities; housing and social care organisations. Projects 'must help people who are, have been, or are at risk of becoming homeless'.

WHAT IS FUNDED Housing and homelessness and work to prevent people from becoming homeless.

TYPE OF GRANT Project funding; research.

SAMPLE GRANTS Depaul International (£104,000); PACT (£41,000); Cambridge House (£15,800); Hope Worldwide (£10,000).

FINANCES *Financial year end* 31/03/2020 *Income* £637,600 *Total grants* £309,800 *Grants to organisations* £309,800 *Assets* £14,600,000

TRUSTEES Simon Dow; Ian Brady; John Stebbing; Jeremy Swain; Nicholas Hardwick; Derek Joseph; Clare Miller; Eleanor Stringer; Victoria Rayner.

HOW TO APPLY Applicants are asked to complete a short application form on the foundation's website and wait for a response.

CONTACT DETAILS Cassandra Karanjia, Altair Ltd, Tempus Wharf, 29A Bermondsey Wall West, London SE16 4SA *Tel.* 020 7934 0177 *Email* simon.dow@lhf.org.uk *Website* lhf.org.uk/programmes-and-grants

■ London Legal Support Trust (LLST)

CC NO 1101906 **ESTABLISHED** 2004

WHERE FUNDING CAN BE GIVEN London and the home counties.

WHO CAN BENEFIT Voluntary sector legal agencies and network organisations that support such agencies.

WHAT IS FUNDED Free legal advice services.

WHAT IS NOT FUNDED Any non-charitable activity; organisations applying for general advice as opposed to specialist legal advice.

TYPE OF GRANT Core/revenue costs; capital costs; seed funding; development funding.

SAMPLE GRANTS Law Works (£13,700); AIRE Centre (£10,300); Citizens Advice Richmond (£5,100); Protect (£1,300); Rights of Women (£830); Shelter Legal (£230); DIY Law (£160).

FINANCES *Financial year end* 31/12/2019 *Income* £1,370,000 *Total grants* £929,600 *Grants to organisations* £929,600 *Assets* £314,400

TRUSTEES Amanda Illing; Katherine Pasfield; Peter Gardner; Marc Sosnow; Sarah McKeown; James Harper; Graham Huntley; Jeremy Thomas; Alistair Woodland; Richard Dyton; Joy Julien; Emma Turnbull; Rodger Pressland.

OTHER INFORMATION At the time of writing (February 2021), the trust's small grants programme had been suspended. The trust also holds fundraising events and shares its sector knowledge and experience to help improve agencies' sustainability.

HOW TO APPLY See the trust's website for details of how to apply.

CONTACT DETAILS Nezahat Cihan, Chief Executive Officer, National Pro Bono Centre, 48 Chancery Lane, London WC2A 1JF *Tel.* 020 7092 3974 *Email* info@info@llst.org.uk *Website* https://londonlegalsupporttrust.org.uk

■ The London Marathon Charitable Trust Ltd

CC NO 283813 **ESTABLISHED** 1981

WHERE FUNDING CAN BE GIVEN London.

WHO CAN BENEFIT Charities; local authorities; community and voluntary sector organisations; amateur sports clubs, parish and town councils; educational organisations.

WHAT IS FUNDED The improvement of sports and recreation facilities; access to physical activity.

WHAT IS NOT FUNDED A full list of exclusions is available on the trust's website.

TYPE OF GRANT Capital costs; core costs; project funding.

RANGE OF GRANTS Small grants of £5,000 to £50,000; major grants of £50,000 to £250,000.

SAMPLE GRANTS Transport for London (£2 million); London United Community Benefit Society (£820,000); London Borough of Croydon (£500,000); Leatherhead and Dorking Gymnastics Club (£150,000); Woodford Rugby Ground Ltd (£35,000); GoodGym (£10,000); Bagshot Cricket Club (£3,600); Restorative Justice for All (£400).

FINANCES *Financial year end* 31/12/2019 *Income* £9,280,000 *Total grants* £11,590,000 *Grants to organisations* £11,590,000 *Assets* £8,800,000

TRUSTEES Richard Henry; Alan Pascoe; Sir Rodney Walker; Dawn Austwick; Terry Duddy; Clare Shepherd; Lee Mason; Samantha Orde; Charles Johnston; John Austin; Gillian McKay; Robert Rigby.

OTHER INFORMATION The trust is funded by the surplus profits from London Marathon Events Ltd. The 2019/20 accounts covered a 15-month period. The trust currently operates two grant programmes: facilities grants (open to applications) and strategic partnership grants (invitation only). During 2019/20, grants were broken down as follows: facilities grants (£6.35 million); strategic partnership grants (£5.25 million).

HOW TO APPLY Full details of the application process can be found on the 'How to apply' page of the trust's website. At the time of writing (May 2021) the trust was not accepting any new applications to its grant programmes as a result of COVID-19. Check the website for the latest information.

CONTACT DETAILS The Trustees, Marathon House, 190 Great Dover Street, London SE1 4YB *Tel.* 020 7902 0215 *Email* info@lmct.org.uk *Website* www.lmct.org.uk

■ Longleigh Foundation

CC NO 1169016 **ESTABLISHED** 2015

WHERE FUNDING CAN BE GIVEN England.

WHO CAN BENEFIT Registered charities; not-for-profit organisations; NGOs. The foundation also runs a hardship grant scheme to support Stonewater residents (a social housing provider).

WHAT IS FUNDED The relief of people in need; the provision of housing, amenities, facilities or services; skills and training to aid employment; young people; older people; people with disabilities; domestic abuse.

TYPE OF GRANT Project grants; strategic funding; capital costs.

SAMPLE GRANTS Southampton Women's Refuge (£81,500); The Mustard Tree Foundation (£75,000); Lippy People Charitable Trust (£50,000); University of Stirling (£43,200); Justlife Foundation (£25,000); Bootcamp Project – Stonewater (£13,900).

FINANCES *Financial year end* 31/03/2020 *Income* £2,530,000 *Total grants* £1,114,700 *Grants to organisations* £845,900 *Assets* £4,930,000

TRUSTEES John Emerson; Elizabeth Morris; Ron Williamson; Anne Dokov.

OTHER INFORMATION Grants were broken down as follows: project grants (£802,700); research grants (£43,200). Only organisations that received grants of over £10,000 were listed as beneficiaries in the charity's accounts. Grants of under £10,000 totalled £30,800. Grants totalling £268,800 were also made to Stonewater Ltd residents.

HOW TO APPLY The foundation puts out calls for applications with a specific brief. Applicants will then be asked to send a short video with a response to the call for applications explaining how their approach will help meet the foundation's mission of 'enabling lives to be transformed'. Check the website for further information.

CONTACT DETAILS Charlotte Dicks, Grants Programme Manager, Stonewater Ltd, Suite C, Lancaster House, Grange Business Park, Enderby Road, Whetstone, Leicester, Leicestershire LE8 6EP *Tel.* 020 7164 6199 *Email* charlotte@longleigh.org *Website* www.longleigh.org

■ The William and Katherine Longman Trust

CC NO 800785 **ESTABLISHED** 1988

WHERE FUNDING CAN BE GIVEN UK.

WHO CAN BENEFIT Registered charities.

WHAT IS FUNDED General charitable purposes.

SAMPLE GRANTS Previous beneficiaries have included: Mizpah Trust (£125,000); The Kel Trust (£80,000); Vanessa Grant Trust (£30,000); Chelsea Arts Club Trust (£25,000); Chelsea Festival and World Child Cancer Fund (£20,000 each); Hope Education Trust and Royal Academy of Dramatic Art (RADA) (£10,000 each); Action for ME (£5,000); The Children's Society (£4,500); Age Concern – Kensington and Chelsea (£3,500); RSPCA – Harmsworth Hospital (£3,000); St Mungo's (£2,500); and Prisoners Abroad (£1,000).

FINANCES *Financial year end* 05/04/2020 *Income* £31,400 *Total grants* £600,000 *Grants to organisations* £600,000 *Assets* £981,200

TRUSTEES William Harriman; Alan Bell.

OTHER INFORMATION The trust's grants for 2019/20 are listed in a document available from the correspondent.

HOW TO APPLY Apply in writing to the correspondent. The 2019/20 annual report states: 'The trustees' current policy is to consider all written appeals received but only successful applicants are notified of the trustees' decision.'

CONTACT DETAILS Karen Wall, Administrator, 28 Julian Road, Orpington, Kent BR6 6HU *Tel.* 07711 961788 *Email* karen@walltrustsupport.co.uk

■ The Lord's Taverners

CC NO 306054 **ESTABLISHED** 1950

WHERE FUNDING CAN BE GIVEN UK.

WHO CAN BENEFIT Schools; organisations that cater for young people with disabilities under the age of 25; amateur sports clubs and organisations for young people.

WHAT IS FUNDED Sports programmes for children and young people with disabilities; specially adapted minibuses; adapted indoor and outdoor play equipment; sports wheelchairs for young people with disabilities.

WHAT IS NOT FUNDED Exclusion criteria may differ according to the grant being awarded. See the applications section of the charity's website for exclusion criteria for the relevant grant programme.

TYPE OF GRANT Capital costs; project funding.

SAMPLE GRANTS Brian Johnston Memorial Fund (£46,000).

FINANCES *Financial year end* 30/09/2019 *Income* £5,590,000 *Total grants* £1,470,000 *Grants to organisations* £1,470,000 *Assets* £7,100,000

TRUSTEES Dr David Collier; Suzy Christopher; Alistair Subba Row; Mike Gatting; Ian Martin; Tony Matharu; Dr Andrew McDonald; Angela Rippon; Caj Sohal; John Taylor; Sandra Verkuyten; Richard White.

OTHER INFORMATION Grants in 2018/19 were made for the following purposes and organisations: minibuses (£972,000); wheelchair and disability sports (£439,000); Brian Johnston Memorial Fund (£46,000). The 2018/19 accounts were the latest available at the time of writing (June 2021).

HOW TO APPLY Instructions on how to apply are available from the grant-maker's website. Applications are reviewed throughout the year.

CONTACT DETAILS The Trustees, 90 Chancery Lane, London WC2A 1EU *Tel.* 020 7025 0000 *Email* contact@lordstaverners.org *Website* www.lordstaverners.org

■ The Lower Green Foundation

CC NO 1137862 **ESTABLISHED** 2010

WHERE FUNDING CAN BE GIVEN Worldwide.

WHO CAN BENEFIT Charitable organisations.

WHAT IS FUNDED General charitable purposes. The annual report for 2019/20 indicates that future priorities include: education for young people; youth apprenticeship schemes; and medical research.

RANGE OF GRANTS Grants range from £2,000 to £974,300.

SAMPLE GRANTS The Pret Foundation (£974,300); Aldridge Foundation and Guy's and St Thomas' Charity (£50,000 each); Motivation (£40,000); First Give (£25,000); ACET UK (£20,000); Hawkley Parish Hall (£2,000).

FINANCES *Financial year end* 30/04/2020 *Income* £988,500 *Total grants* £1,240,000 *Grants to organisations* £1,240,000 *Assets* £253,300

TRUSTEES Laurence Billett; Marina Sajitz; Sinclair Beecham.

OTHER INFORMATION In 2019/20, grants were awarded to 14 organisations.

HOW TO APPLY Contact the correspondent for further information.

CONTACT DETAILS The Trustees, The Lower Green Foundation, 28 Eaton Avenue, Matrix Office Park, Buckshaw Village, Chorley, Lancashire PR7 7NA *Tel.* 01772 299888 *Email* info@lowergreen.com

■ The C. L. Loyd Charitable Trust

CC NO 265076 **ESTABLISHED** 1973

WHERE FUNDING CAN BE GIVEN UK, with a preference for local causes in Oxfordshire.

WHO CAN BENEFIT National charities and local organisations known by or associated with the trustees, benefitting at risk groups, people with disabilities, or those who are disadvantaged by poverty or socially isolated.

WHAT IS FUNDED General charitable purposes including health, welfare, the arts and heritage.

RANGE OF GRANTS Mostly under £5,000.

SAMPLE GRANTS Country Buildings Protection Trust (£55,000); Flawley PCC (£5,000); The Opera Story (£5,000); The Royal Marsden Cancer Charity (£1,000).

FINANCES *Financial year end* 05/04/2020 *Income* £90,000 *Total grants* £83,000 *Grants to organisations* £83,000 *Assets* £2,760,000

TRUSTEES Thomas Loyd; Alexandra Loyd.

OTHER INFORMATION Grants were awarded to 14 organisations during the year.

HOW TO APPLY Grants are only made to charities known to the trustees.

CONTACT DETAILS The Trustees, The Locking Estate Office, Ardington, Wantage, Oxfordshire OX12 8PP *Tel.* 020 7680 8100

■ LPW Ltd

CC NO 1148784 **ESTABLISHED** 2012

WHERE FUNDING CAN BE GIVEN UK.

WHO CAN BENEFIT Charities and community groups.

WHAT IS FUNDED The advancement of the Orthodox Jewish religion and education; the relief of poverty.

SAMPLE GRANTS Support The Charity Worker (£55,000); Kollel Viznitz London (£36,000); Edupoor Ltd (£25,000); Chasdei Aharon Ltd (£25,000); Chasdei Sholom Trust (£25,000); Care All Ltd (£25,000); Rise and Shine (£18,000).

FINANCES *Financial year end* 31/12/2019 *Income* £841,900 *Total grants* £214,000 *Grants to organisations* £214,000 *Assets* £16,630,000

TRUSTEES Daniela Rosenthal; Monica Rosenthal; Nicholas Rosenthal; Talia Cohen; Ronny Rosenthal.

OTHER INFORMATION Grants were broken down as follows: relief of poverty (£100,000); other general charitable purposes (£55,000); advancement of the Jewish religion (£36,000); advancement of education (£18,000); grants to other grant-making charities (£5,000). Only organisations that received grants of over £10,000 were listed as beneficiaries in the charity's accounts. Grants of under £10,000 totalled £5,000.

HOW TO APPLY Contact the correspondent for further information.

CONTACT DETAILS The Trustees, c/o Cohen Arnold, New Burlington House, 1075 Finchley Road, London NW11 0PU *Tel.* 020 8731 0777

■ Robert Luff Foundation Ltd

CC NO 273810 **ESTABLISHED** 1966

WHERE FUNDING CAN BE GIVEN UK.

WHO CAN BENEFIT Medical research charities and organisations, including hospices and hospitals.

WHAT IS FUNDED Medical research.

TYPE OF GRANT Research; normally recurrent.

RANGE OF GRANTS Up to £150,000.

SAMPLE GRANTS Cystic Fibrosis Trust and Rosetrees Trust (£150,000 each); ESPA Research (£80,000); Sheffield Teaching Hospital (£50,000); British Scoliosis Research Foundation and The Brain Tumour Charity (£25,000 each); Macular Society (£20,000); Royal Trinity Hospice (£10,000); Windrush Trust (£5,000).

FINANCES *Financial year end* 31/08/2019 *Income* £1,530,000 *Total grants* £1,160,000 *Grants to organisations* £1,160,000 *Assets* £37,440,000

TRUSTEES Melanie Condon; Brian Nicholson; Richard Price; Revd Matthew Tomlinson; Lady Ruth Bodey; Sir Paul Coleridge; Dr Helen Hughes.

OTHER INFORMATION The 2018/19 accounts were the latest available at the time of writing (June 2021). Only organisations that received grants of £5,000 and above were listed as beneficiaries in the foundation's accounts (36 organisations). Grants of under £5,000 totalled £10,000. Of the 36 beneficiaries listed, eight had not received a donation in the previous year.

HOW TO APPLY While the foundation tends to support the same charities on an annual basis, several new beneficiaries are funded each year. Contact the correspondent for more information regarding the application process.

CONTACT DETAILS Richard Price, Company Secretary, Waters Edge, Ferry Lane, Moulsford, Wallingford, Oxfordshire OX10 9JF *Tel.* 01491 652204 *Email* rpjprice@gmail.com

■ The Henry Lumley Charitable Trust

CC NO 1079480 **ESTABLISHED** 1997

WHERE FUNDING CAN BE GIVEN Worldwide.

WHO CAN BENEFIT Registered charities; individuals.

WHAT IS FUNDED General charitable purposes, with a preference towards medicine, education and the relief of poverty.

RANGE OF GRANTS Mostly £2,500 to £5,000.

SAMPLE GRANTS Community Foundation for Surrey (£7,500); Alzheimer's Research UK, Epilepsy Action and International Spinal Research Trust (£5,000 each); Army Benevolent Fund, Autistica, Gurkha Welfare Trust and Outward Bound Trust (£2,500 each); Royal School of Needlework (£1,000).

FINANCES *Financial year end* 31/12/2019 *Income* £77,200 *Total grants* £98,500 *Grants to organisations* £98,500 *Assets* £2,940,000

TRUSTEES Peter Lumley; Henry Lumley; James Porter; Robert Lumley.

HOW TO APPLY Contact the correspondent for further information.

CONTACT DETAILS The Trustees, Grove End, Bagshot, Surrey GU19 5HY *Tel.* 01276 458141

■ Lord and Lady Lurgan Trust

CC NO 297046 **ESTABLISHED** 1987

WHERE FUNDING CAN BE GIVEN UK (mainly London), Northern Ireland and South Africa.

WHO CAN BENEFIT Registered charities; educational establishments; hospices.

WHAT IS FUNDED UK grants tend to be London-centric and have a bias towards: music and arts education and participation; deafness and other disabilities; older people; medical relief, including hospice support and medical research. In Northern Ireland and South Africa, grants are not restricted by particular categories but rather by the trustees' perception of need.

WHAT IS NOT FUNDED Grants to individuals or for expeditions are not made. It is unlikely that the trust will be able to help with core costs and it is unable to respond to emergency appeals.

TYPE OF GRANT Generally one-off payments.

RANGE OF GRANTS Between £1,000 and £5,000.

SAMPLE GRANTS Royal College of Music (£11,500); The Cure Parkinson's Trust (£3,000); English National Opera (£2,500); Cued Speech UK (£2,000); The Pushkin Trust (£1,600); Bampton Classical Opera (£1,500); Resources for Autism (£1,000).

FINANCES *Financial year end* 31/12/2019
Income £15,300 *Total grants* £68,800
Grants to organisations £68,800
Assets £644,200

TRUSTEES Andrew Stebbings; Diana Graves; Brendan Beder.

OTHER INFORMATION Grants were broken down as follows: arts and music (£35,000); Northern Ireland (£7,600); medical causes (£6,000); deafness/blindness (£4,000); hospices (£3,700); older people (£1,000).

HOW TO APPLY Application forms can be downloaded from the trust's website and should preferably be returned by email. Applicants should read the grant policy on the website before completing the form. The trustees meet twice a year, in December and July. Deadlines are published on the website. Applications must also include: the latest signed and audited accounts; a budget for the financial year in which the project falls, separating income which relates to the project; the budget for the project; and details about any other funding received or pending.

CONTACT DETAILS The Trustees, 45 Cadogan Gardens, London SW3 2TB *Tel.* 07368 652694 *Email* info@lurgantrust.org *Website* www.lurgantrust.org

■ The Lyndal Tree Foundation

CC NO 1125024 **ESTABLISHED** 2008

WHERE FUNDING CAN BE GIVEN UK, with a preference for Yorkshire and Scotland.

WHO CAN BENEFIT Registered charities.

WHAT IS FUNDED Children and young people; health; social welfare; medical research.

TYPE OF GRANT One-off grants; regular support.

RANGE OF GRANTS Grants range from £2,000 to £20,000.

SAMPLE GRANTS Motivation All Stars (£20,000); PKAVS (£12,000); Motivation and Action for Kids (£10,000 each); Yorkshire Air Ambulance and CHAS (Children's Hospices Across Scotland) (£5,000 each); REACT (Rapid Effective Assistance for Children with potentially Terminal illness) (£3,000); Abbeyfield The Dales (£2,000).

FINANCES *Financial year end* 05/04/2020
Income £94,800 *Total grants* £101,000
Grants to organisations £101,000
Assets £1,620,000

TRUSTEES Lynda Duttine; Steven Duttine; Jennifer Brodie; Susan Fidler.

OTHER INFORMATION In 2019/20, 14 grants were awarded.

HOW TO APPLY Contact the correspondent for further information.

CONTACT DETAILS The Trustees, PO Box 330, Ilkley, West Yorkshire LS29 1GD *Tel.* 07725 900511

■ John Lyon's Charity

CC NO 237725 **ESTABLISHED** 1572

WHERE FUNDING CAN BE GIVEN The London boroughs of Barnet, Brent, Camden, City of London, City of Westminster, Ealing, Hammersmith and Fulham, Harrow, and Kensington and Chelsea.

WHO CAN BENEFIT Registered charities; schools.

WHAT IS FUNDED The education of children and young people up to the age of 25.

WHAT IS NOT FUNDED Individuals; organisations that do not have charitable status or those acting as a conduit; national charities with no track record of delivery in the charity's beneficial area; grant-making organisations; not-for-profit organisations that are not registered charities; registered social landlords; schools that have not yet been inspected by Ofsted; hospitals, hospices or clinical commissioning groups; registered charities that have applied on behalf of organisations that are not registered with the Charity Commission.

TYPE OF GRANT Capital costs; core/revenue costs; project funding; unrestricted funding; capacity building; multi-year funding.

RANGE OF GRANTS A typical grant is in the range of £20,000 to £30,000 per annum for three years.

SAMPLE GRANTS Securing Success (£45,500); Belmont School (£40,000); Arts Depot (£30,000); National Youth Theatre (£25,000); The Listening Place (£14,000).

FINANCES *Financial year end* 31/03/2020
Income £9,340,000 *Total grants* £10,770,000
Grants to organisations £10,770,000
Assets £345,400,000

TRUSTEE The Keepers and Governors of the Possessions Revenues and Goods of the Free Grammar School of John Lyon.

OTHER INFORMATION Grants were awarded in the following programme areas: bursaries (£1.87 million); arts and science (£1.48 million); education and learning (£1.43 million); youth clubs and youth activities (£1.33 million); emotional well-being (£1.03 million); children and families (£853,000); youth issues (£796,000); special needs and disability (£745,000); capacity building (£639,000); sport (£451,000); training (£93,000); other (£5,000).

HOW TO APPLY Apply online via the charity's grants portal.

CONTACT DETAILS The Trustees, Griffin Lodge, 45A Cadogan Gardens, London SW3 2TB *Tel.* 020 7259 1700 *Email* info@jlc.london *Website* www.jlc.london

■ Sylvanus Lysons Charity

CC NO 202939 **ESTABLISHED** 1980

WHERE FUNDING CAN BE GIVEN Diocese of Gloucester.

WHO CAN BENEFIT Individuals; organisations; religious bodies; widows of clergy.

WHAT IS FUNDED The religious and charitable work of the Church of England, particularly work with disadvantaged young people and adults; children and young people; community initiatives.

WHAT IS NOT FUNDED Grants are not given for the repair or maintenance or improvement of churches or other buildings, other than in very exceptional circumstances.

RANGE OF GRANTS Mostly under £10,000.

SAMPLE GRANTS Gloucester Diocese Wellbeing Counselling Service (£20,000); Wayfarers Monastery (£12,000); Cheltenham CAP Debt Centre (£5,000); Tetbury Parish Church (£2,000).

FINANCES *Financial year end* 30/09/2020
Income £35,700 *Total grants* £234,000
Grants to organisations £200,300
Assets £13,800,000

TRUSTEES Ian Templeton; The Ven. Philip Andrew; Mr G. V. Doswell; The Right Revd Robert Springett.

HOW TO APPLY Application forms can be downloaded from the charity's website and should be returned by post to Mr Andrew Holloway. Applications should be received at least three weeks before the trustees' meetings. Meeting dates are posted on the website. Queries relating to applications can be directed to Revd

Helen Sammon by email: helen.sammon@gmail.com or phone: 07554 992892.

CONTACT DETAILS Andrew Holloway, Associate Partner, c/o Tayntons Solicitors, 8–12 Clarence Street, Gloucester, Gloucestershire GL1 1DZ *Email* andrew.holloway@tayntons.co.uk *Website* https://sylvanuslysons.wordpress.com

■ M. and C. Trust

CC NO 265391 **ESTABLISHED** 1972
WHERE FUNDING CAN BE GIVEN UK.
WHO CAN BENEFIT Mainly Jewish organisations; educational establishments; health institutions.
WHAT IS FUNDED Jewish causes; social welfare.
WHAT IS NOT FUNDED Individuals.
RANGE OF GRANTS Usually between £3,000 and £10,000.
SAMPLE GRANTS Carers Trust and Holocaust Education Trust (£10,000 each); Freedom from Torture (£8,000); Become and Destitute Asylum Seekers (£5,000 each); Hot Line Meals Service (£3,000); Milly Days (£1,000).
FINANCES *Financial year end* 05/04/2020 *Income* £132,500 *Total grants* £180,000 *Grants to organisations* £180,000 *Assets* £4,040,000
TRUSTEES Rachel Lebus; Matthew Bernstein; Elizabeth Marks; Victoria Fairley.
OTHER INFORMATION Grants were broken down as follows: relief of poverty (£38,000); social care (£30,000); community (£30,000); youth work (£15,000); other (£14,000); education (£10,000).
HOW TO APPLY Applications should be made via email rather than post.
CONTACT DETAILS Helen Price, c/o Mercer and Hole Trustees Ltd, Gloucester House, 72 London Road, St Albans, Hertfordshire AL1 1NS *Tel.* 01727 869141 *Email* helenprice@mercerhole.co.uk

■ M. B. Foundation

CC NO 222104 **ESTABLISHED** 1965
WHERE FUNDING CAN BE GIVEN UK, with some preference for Greater Manchester.
WHO CAN BENEFIT Jewish organisations; individuals.
WHAT IS FUNDED Jewish causes, particularly the advancement of the Jewish faith, Jewish education and the relief of poverty in the Jewish community.
SAMPLE GRANTS KBS (£157,600); Bikur Cholim and Gemiluth Chesed Trust (£45,750).
FINANCES *Financial year end* 31/03/2019 *Income* £308,000 *Total grants* £1,150,000 *Grants to organisations* £1,150,000 *Assets* £5,720,000
TRUSTEES Solomon Bamberger; Rabbi Mordechai Bamberger.
OTHER INFORMATION The 2018/19 accounts were the latest available at the time of writing (April 2021). The grant total of £1.15 million includes educational grants (£535,400), relief of poverty grants (£107,400) and religious grants (£77,300). Grants of under £1,000 totalled £23,900. A full list of beneficiaries was not available.
HOW TO APPLY Contact the correspondent for further information.
CONTACT DETAILS Trustees, Fairways House, George Street, Prestwich, Manchester M25 9WS *Tel.* 0161 787 7898

■ The M. Y. A. Charitable Trust

CC NO 299642 **ESTABLISHED** 1987
WHERE FUNDING CAN BE GIVEN In practice, UK and Israel.
WHO CAN BENEFIT Charitable organisations and individuals.
WHAT IS FUNDED Orthodox Jewish causes, including religious education and the relief of poverty.
SAMPLE GRANTS Yesamach Levav Trust (£16,200); Ezer Bekovoid (£12,300).
FINANCES *Financial year end* 30/04/2020 *Income* £178,000 *Total grants* £117,800 *Grants to organisations* £115,300 *Assets* £2,209,000
TRUSTEES Myer Rothfeld; Eve Rothfeld; Hannah Schraiber; Joseph Pfeffer.
OTHER INFORMATION During the year, grants to individuals totalled £2,500. Grants to unspecified organisations totalled £86,900. According to the annual report for 2019/20, the trust also provides short-term interest-free loans 'to assist individuals with financial hardship or charitable institutions with educational advancement'.
HOW TO APPLY Contact the correspondent for further information.
CONTACT DETAILS The Trustees, Medcar House, 149A Stamford Hill, London N16 5LL *Tel.* 020 8800 3582

■ The R. S. Macdonald Charitable Trust

OSCR NO SC012710 **ESTABLISHED** 1978
WHERE FUNDING CAN BE GIVEN Scotland.
WHO CAN BENEFIT Registered charities operating in Scotland and universities.
WHAT IS FUNDED Neurological conditions; visual impairment; child welfare; animal welfare; medical research; RNLI lifeboats.
TYPE OF GRANT Revenue or capital costs; project funding or core funding; one-off awards; multi-year awards for up to three years; seedcorn/unrestricted funding.
SAMPLE GRANTS Previous beneficiaries have included: Scottish SPCA (£120,000); RNLI (£52,000); Family Rights Group (£47,000); Volunteering Matters (£43,000); Argyle and Bute Rape Crisis (£38,500); Deafblind Scotland (£18,000); Paws for Progress CIC (£12,000); Cetacean Research and Rescue Unit and Whizz-Kidz (£10,000); Lung Ha Theatre Company (£5,000); Borders Talking Newspapers (£2,000).
FINANCES *Financial year end* 31/03/2020 *Income* £2,070,000 *Total grants* £2,400,000 *Grants to organisations* £2,400,000 *Assets* £79,000,000
TRUSTEES Bruce Rigby; Moira Easson; Patricia Donald; Fiona Patrick; John Paterson; Robert Ross.
OTHER INFORMATION During the year, the trust awarded 87 grants.
HOW TO APPLY Applications can be made through the trust's website. Small grant applications can be submitted at any time. The main grants programme has specific deadlines for each area of work – check the website for the latest deadlines.
CONTACT DETAILS Katie Winwick, Grants and Relationships Manager, 21 Rutland Square, Edinburgh EH1 2BB *Tel.* 0131 228 4681 *Email* office@rsmacdonald.com *Website* www.rsmacdonald.com

■ The Macdonald-Buchanan Charitable Trust

CC NO 209994 **ESTABLISHED** 1952

WHERE FUNDING CAN BE GIVEN Worldwide with a preference for Northamptonshire.

WHO CAN BENEFIT Registered charities.

WHAT IS FUNDED General charitable purposes including health and disability, animal welfare, children and young people and older people.

RANGE OF GRANTS Grants range from £2,500 to £75,000.

SAMPLE GRANTS Racing Welfare (£75,000); Carriejo Charitable Trust and Orrin Charitable Trust (£25,000 each); Charities Aid Foundation (£25,000 in two grants); Macmillan Cancer Support and St Luke's Hospital (£10,000 each).

FINANCES *Financial year end* 31/12/2019 *Income* £158,700 *Total grants* £170,000 *Grants to organisations* £170,000 *Assets* £4,350,000

TRUSTEES Alastair Macdonald-Buchanan; Mary Philipson; Joanna Lascelles; Hugh Macdonald-Buchanan.

OTHER INFORMATION Grants were made for the following: general welfare (£150,000); hospices and cancer (£10,000); medical causes (£10,000).

HOW TO APPLY Apply in writing to the correspondent. The annual report for 2019 states that the trustees will 'no longer consider appeals which are directed to the charity, preferring to consider appeals that have been received by them individually'.

CONTACT DETAILS Linda Cousins, Administrator, Rathbone Trust Co. Ltd, 8 Finsbury Circus, London EC2M 7AZ *Tel.* 020 7399 0820 *Email* linda.cousins@rathbones.com

■ Mace Foundation

CC NO 1150134 **ESTABLISHED** 2012

WHERE FUNDING CAN BE GIVEN UK.

WHO CAN BENEFIT Registered charities; schools; hospitals.

WHAT IS FUNDED Education; social welfare; health; culture, heritage and sport.

WHAT IS NOT FUNDED Political parties.

TYPE OF GRANT Project funding; strategic funding; pro bono.

RANGE OF GRANTS £10,000 to £40,000.

SAMPLE GRANTS Construction Youth Trust (£40,000); Mind (£40,000); LandAid (£20,000); Youth Hostel Association (£20,000).

FINANCES *Financial year end* 31/12/2019 *Income* £586,300 *Total grants* £130,000 *Grants to organisations* £130,000 *Assets* £66,400

TRUSTEES Deborah Jane Reynolds; Isabel McAllister; Mark Reynolds; Barbara Welch; Hannah Livesey; Jason Millett; Rosario Abbate; Dr Judith Grant.

OTHER INFORMATION This is the charitable foundation of the Mace Group, a construction and consultancy firm based in London. The foundation makes grants to its strategic partner charities and matches funds raised by Mace Group employees. Overall, four grants were made to strategic partner charities in 2019.

HOW TO APPLY The foundation does not accept unsolicited applications.

CONTACT DETAILS The Trustees, Mace Group, 155 Moorgate, London EC2M 6XB *Tel.* 020 3522 3385 *Email* mace.foundation@macegroup.com *Website* https://www.macegroup.com/about-us/mace-foundation

■ The Mackay and Brewer Charitable Trust

CC NO 1072666 **ESTABLISHED** 1998

WHERE FUNDING CAN BE GIVEN UK.

WHO CAN BENEFIT Charitable organisations.

WHAT IS FUNDED General charitable purposes.

TYPE OF GRANT Recurrent.

RANGE OF GRANTS £11,300 per grant.

SAMPLE GRANTS Hampshire Association for the Care of the Blind, Macmillan Cancer Trust, Marie Curie Cancer Care, Open Doors, PDSA, St John Ambulance in Wales, The National Trust for Scotland and The Salvation Army (£11,300 each).

FINANCES *Financial year end* 05/04/2020 *Income* £83,400 *Total grants* £90,200 *Grants to organisations* £90,200 *Assets* £2,820,000

TRUSTEE HSBC Trust Company UK Ltd.

OTHER INFORMATION Grants were awarded to eight charities during the year. The trust makes grants to these charities every year.

HOW TO APPLY Contact the correspondent for further information.

CONTACT DETAILS S. D'Ambrosio, Trust Manager, HSBC Trust Company UK Ltd, Forum 1, 2nd Floor, The Forum, Parkway, Whiteley, Fareham, Hampshire PO15 7PA *Tel.* 023 8199 9231

■ The Mackintosh Foundation

CC NO 327751 **ESTABLISHED** 1988

WHERE FUNDING CAN BE GIVEN Worldwide. In practice, mainly UK.

WHO CAN BENEFIT Registered charities; educational establishments; individuals.

WHAT IS FUNDED Theatre and the performing arts; medical aid, particularly research into cancer and HIV and AIDS; homelessness; community projects; the environment; general charitable purposes.

TYPE OF GRANT Capital costs; schools' core costs; research; project costs.

RANGE OF GRANTS Up to £1 million, but mainly between £5,000 and £60,000.

SAMPLE GRANTS Mountview Academy of Theatre Arts Ltd (£1 million); Children in Need (£60,000); National Youth Arts Trust (£50,000); Pimlico Opera (£10,000); Motivation Charitable Trust (£7,500); Action on Addiction and Breast Cancer Now (£5,000 each).

FINANCES *Financial year end* 31/03/2020 *Income* £10,130,000 *Total grants* £1,684,000 *Grants to organisations* £1,680,000 *Assets* £14,330,000

TRUSTEES Nicholas Allott; Sir Cameron MacKintosh; Nicholas MacKintosh; Robert Noble; Bart Peerless; Thomas Schonberg; Richard Pappas; Alan Finch; A. Constable.

OTHER INFORMATION A total of 166 grants were made to organisations. Donations of less than £5,000 totalled £159,500.

HOW TO APPLY Applications should be made in writing to the correspondent, outlining details of the applying organisation, the project for which funding is required and a breakdown of the costs involved. Supporting documents should be kept to a minimum and an sae enclosed (if materials are to be returned).

CONTACT DETAILS Richard Knibb, General Secretary, 1 Bedford Square, London WC1B 3RB *Tel.* 020 7637 8866 *Email* info@camack.co.uk

■ The MacRobert Trust 2019

OSCR NO SC049475 **ESTABLISHED** 1943
WHERE FUNDING CAN BE GIVEN UK, mainly Scotland.
WHO CAN BENEFIT Registered charities; universities and non-fee-paying schools; libraries; uniformed groups; local and regional charitable organisations in Tarland and the nearby area.
WHAT IS FUNDED Armed forces services and seafarers; education and training; children and young people; science, engineering and technology; agriculture and horticulture.
TYPE OF GRANT Core costs; project expenditure; capital costs; buildings; research. One-off and three-year grants are available.
RANGE OF GRANTS Up to £300,000 but grants are usually of less than £44,500.
SAMPLE GRANTS Prince's Foundation (£300,000); Aboyne and Deeside Community Shed (£44,500); RAFA (£34,000); The Smallpiece Trust (£25,500); Edinburgh Science Foundation Ltd (£16,000); Scottish Veterans (£10,000); Forget Me Not Club (£100).
FINANCES *Financial year end* 05/04/2020
Income £2,990,000 *Total grants* £837,500
Grants to organisations £837,500
Assets £82,150,000
TRUSTEES Sabrina Campbell, Charles Crole; Mr J. Fowlie; Group Capt. William Gibson; Prof. Gordon Masterton; Cdre Charles Stevenson; Jamie Montgomery; Dr Rebecca McCormick.
OTHER INFORMATION Accounts were not available to view as the charity has recently been re-registered under a new OSCR number. We have therefore taken the financial information from the previous charity's (OSCR no. SC031346) 2019/20 accounts.
HOW TO APPLY See the trust's website for the latest information on applications.
CONTACT DETAILS Alison Donaldson, Charity Manager, Cromar, Tarland, Aboyne, Aberdeenshire AB34 4UD *Tel.* 01339 881444 *Email* alison@themacroberttrust.org.uk *Website* www.themacroberttrust.org.uk

■ The Mactaggart Third Fund

OSCR NO SC014285 **ESTABLISHED** 1968
WHERE FUNDING CAN BE GIVEN UK and overseas.
WHO CAN BENEFIT Registered charities.
WHAT IS FUNDED General charitable purposes.
RANGE OF GRANTS Grants range from £200 up to £81,800.
SAMPLE GRANTS Man-O-War Relief Fund (£81,800); The Banff Canmore Community Foundation (£62,400); Health Navigator Foundation (£31,300); Caribbean Anti-Poverty Relief Fund (£10,000); Islay Book Festival (£7,800); World Jewish Relief (£2,000); Trumpington Parish Church (£200).
FINANCES *Financial year end* 30/04/2020
Income £936,500 *Total grants* £541,400
Grants to organisations £541,400
Assets £19,860,000
TRUSTEES Alastair Mactaggart; Robert Gore; Fiona Mactaggart; Andrew Mactaggart; Sir John Mactaggart.
HOW TO APPLY The charity does not accept unsolicited applications.
CONTACT DETAILS The Trustees, 229 Fenwick Road, Giffnock, Glasgow G46 6JQ *Website* www.mactaggartthirdfund.org

■ The Ian Mactaggart Trust (The Mactaggart Second Fund)

OSCR NO SC012502 **ESTABLISHED** 1984
WHERE FUNDING CAN BE GIVEN UK.
WHO CAN BENEFIT Charitable organisations.
WHAT IS FUNDED General charitable purposes.
SAMPLE GRANTS Kulen Outreach (£84,900); Oxfordshire Community Foundation (£25,000); Soho Theatre (£12,500); Classics for All (£3,000); Amnesty International (£2,000); Mary's Meals (£1,000); Penny Brohn Centre (£500).
FINANCES *Financial year end* 30/04/2020
Income £884,400 *Total grants* £517,400
Grants to organisations £517,400
Assets £17,000,000
TRUSTEES Sir John Mactaggart; Robert Gore; Fiona Mactaggart; Jane Mactaggart; Philip Mactaggart; Leora Armstrong.
HOW TO APPLY The trust does not accept unsolicited applications.
CONTACT DETAILS The Trustees, 229 Fenwick Road, Giffnock, Glasgow G46 6JQ *Website* www.ianmactaggarttrust.org

■ The Magdalen and Lasher Charity (General Fund)

CC NO 211415 **ESTABLISHED** 1837
WHERE FUNDING CAN BE GIVEN Hastings.
WHO CAN BENEFIT Individuals; charitable organisations.
WHAT IS FUNDED Older people and those in need in Hastings; education; healthcare; community services; the relief of poverty.
WHAT IS NOT FUNDED Debt repayment; minibuses.
TYPE OF GRANT One-off, specific projects.
SAMPLE GRANTS Previous beneficiaries have included: 4th Hastings Guides; Amicus Horizon; Association of Carers, Broomgrove Play Scheme; Counselling Plus; Hastings Advice and Representation Centre; Salvation Army – St Andrews Square; St Clement and All Saints; Surviving Christmas; Snowflake Trust Night Shelter; White Rock Theatre.
FINANCES *Financial year end* 31/03/2020
Income £477,000 *Total grants* £122,100
Grants to organisations £85,600
Assets £13,860,000
TRUSTEES Keith Donaldson; Gareth Bendon; Ian Steel; Jenny Blackburn; Michael Foster; Clive Gilbraith; Susan Parsons; Sue Phillips; Ann Wing; Andrew Patmore; Cllr James Bacon; Dr Patricia Lock; John Bilsby.
OTHER INFORMATION The origins of the charity go back to 1294, when land was donated in support of a local leper and pest house. It merged with another charity in 1691, but the Mayor and Hastings Corporation controlled the funds. In 1837, the charity was placed under independent trusteeship and in 1877, the charity was divided into three main branches – a pensions branch, an eleemosynary (alms) branch and an education branch.
HOW TO APPLY See the charity's website for the latest information on applications.
CONTACT DETAILS Marcia Woolf, Administrator, The Magdalen and Lasher Charity, Old Hastings House, 132 High Street, Hastings, East Sussex TN34 3ET *Tel.* 01424 452646 *Email* mlc@oldhastingshouse.co.uk *Website* magdalenandlasher.co.uk

The Mageni Trust

CC NO 1070732 **ESTABLISHED** 1998

WHERE FUNDING CAN BE GIVEN UK.

WHO CAN BENEFIT Arts organisations; registered charities; hospitals and hospices.

WHAT IS FUNDED A wide range of general charitable purposes, particularly the arts.

WHAT IS NOT FUNDED Individuals.

TYPE OF GRANT One-off and recurrent.

RANGE OF GRANTS £500 to £10,000.

SAMPLE GRANTS London Philharmonic Orchestra (£10,000); You Make It (£5,500); JDRF (£3,000); National Youth Orchestra (£2,500); National Trust, RNLI and Save the Children UK (£2,000 each); London Music Masters (£1,500); Bromley Youth Music Trust and English Heritage (£1,000 each); Anthony Nolan, Cecily's Fund and Chase Africa (£500 each).

FINANCES *Financial year end* 31/05/2020 *Income* £900,000 *Total grants* £139,400 *Grants to organisations* £139,400 *Assets* £1,740,000

TRUSTEES Garfield Collins; Gillian Collins; Alex Collins; Tom Collins.

OTHER INFORMATION Grants were awarded to 91 organisations during the year.

HOW TO APPLY Unsolicited applications are not considered.

CONTACT DETAILS The Trustees, Leslie Cottage, The Promenade, Pevensey Bay, East Sussex BN24 6HE *Tel.* 01323 460770 *Email* garfcollins@gmail.com

The Mahoro Charitable Trust

CC NO 1151200 **ESTABLISHED** 2013

WHERE FUNDING CAN BE GIVEN UK.

WHO CAN BENEFIT Charitable organisations.

WHAT IS FUNDED General charitable purposes, with a preference for health and social welfare charities.

RANGE OF GRANTS Grants range from £5,000 up to £100,000.

SAMPLE GRANTS Greenhouse (£100,000); Old Vic Theatre (£75,000); Royal Marsden (£60,000); Sick Children's Trust (£50,000); London Royal Ambulance (£33,000); Arts Emergency Trust (£10,000); St Cuthbert's Centre (£5,000).

FINANCES *Financial year end* 05/04/2020 *Income* £939,600 *Total grants* £443,000 *Grants to organisations* £443,000 *Assets* £1,600,000

TRUSTEES Holly Ellis; Jenny Ellis; Luke Ellis; Rory Ellis.

OTHER INFORMATION Grants were awarded to 12 organisations during the year.

HOW TO APPLY Contact the correspondent for further information.

CONTACT DETAILS The Trustees, Flat 25, Sir John Lyon House, 8 High Timber Street, London EC4V 3PA *Tel.* 01892 701847 *Email* mahorotrust@gmail.com

Makers of Playing Cards Charity

CC NO 232876 **ESTABLISHED** 1943

WHERE FUNDING CAN BE GIVEN England and Wales.

WHO CAN BENEFIT Registered charities.

WHAT IS FUNDED Education; children and young people; causes related to the City of London; causes with which the charity has a connection; general charitable purposes. Further details are given on the charity's website.

WHAT IS NOT FUNDED Individuals.

RANGE OF GRANTS Generally up to £1,000.

SAMPLE GRANTS Aberdeen Sea Scouts; Hot Line Meals; Kids in Action; MENCAP; University of the Arts; Young Actors Theatre.

FINANCES *Financial year end* 05/04/2020 *Income* £130,600 *Total grants* £80,000 *Grants to organisations* £80,000 *Assets* £789,800

TRUSTEES Mark Winston; Dr Christopher Eaton; Nicholas Prentice; Edward Copisarow; Benjamin Madden; Barbara Jeanne; Capt. Michael Davis-Marks; Dr Paul Bostock; David Hussey; Giles Stockton.

OTHER INFORMATION According to the charity's website, grants are generally for £1,000 in the first instance. The trustees are keen to support smaller charities with an annual income of less than £300,000 per year.

HOW TO APPLY Apply to the correspondent via email. The application should: be no longer than one side of A4; set out how you would spend a grant of £1,000; explain briefly how the work for which you seek funds meets the Makers of Playing Cards Charity's charitable objects; and include a copy of your most recent annual report and accounts.

CONTACT DETAILS The Prime Almoner, 35 Ascot Way, Bicester, Oxfordshire OX26 1AG *Tel.* 020 7531 5990 *Email* charityalmoners@makersofplayingcards.co.uk *Website* www.makersofplayingcards.co.uk

Making a Difference Locally Ltd

CC NO 1123800 **ESTABLISHED** 2008

WHERE FUNDING CAN BE GIVEN UK, in areas local to Nisa Retail Ltd stores (see the store locator on the website).

WHO CAN BENEFIT Registered charities or good causes with a dedicated business bank account. Organisations should ideally be located within ten miles of a Nisa Retail store.

WHAT IS FUNDED General charitable purposes; community projects and causes spanning health and well-being, education, employment, good food and nutrition, shelter and security.

WHAT IS NOT FUNDED Individuals.

RANGE OF GRANTS Mostly up to £1,000.

SAMPLE GRANTS Batten Disease Family Association (BDFA) (£17,000); Lindsey Lodge Hospice (£15,500); Health Stars and The Dash Charity (£15,000 each); Children and Families in Grief (£12,000); Adferiad Recovery (£10,000).

FINANCES *Financial year end* 30/06/2020 *Income* £1,200,000 *Total grants* £810,100 *Grants to organisations* £810,100 *Assets* £1,590,000

TRUSTEES Stephen Leach; Scott Etherington; John McNeill; Kathryn Marsden; Andrew Barber; Christopher Taylor; David Stokes.

OTHER INFORMATION Grants were awarded to 1,724 organisations during the year as follows: retailers' nominated institutions (£622,500); local institutions (£110,400); national institutions (£77,100). Only beneficiaries of grants of £10,000 and above were listed in the accounts (six organisations). The remaining grants were for between £10 and £1,000. In October 2020, the charity launched its Heart of the Community Awards, offering grants of up to £5,000 to good causes. Nominations are accepted from Nisa partners via a dedicated website when funding rounds open – check the website for updates.

HOW TO APPLY Use the store locator on the Nisa website to contact your local store. Individual retailers can then submit a form to the Making a Difference Locally committee for approval.

Enquiries should be sent via the contact form on the website.

CONTACT DETAILS The Trustees, Waldo Way, Normanby Enterprise Park, Scunthorpe, North Lincolnshire DN15 9GE *Tel.* 01724 282028 *Email* makingadifference@nisaretail.com *Website* https://www.nisalocally.co.uk/community

The Mallinckrodt Foundation

CC NO 1058011 **ESTABLISHED** 1996

WHERE FUNDING CAN BE GIVEN UK and overseas.

WHO CAN BENEFIT Charitable organisations; universities.

WHAT IS FUNDED General charitable purposes.

RANGE OF GRANTS Up to £20,000.

SAMPLE GRANTS Harvard Kennedy School of Government – Dean's Council (£20,100); Corporation of the Hall of Arts and Scientists Royal Albert Hall (£15,000); Blackfriars Hall – Oxford and University of Oxford Development Trust (£10,000 each); Mallinckrodt Sisters (£8,200); Christian Responsibility in Public Affairs and Companions of Windsor – via the Foundation of the College of St George (£5,000 each); Marine Conservation Society (£4,000).

FINANCES *Financial year end* 05/04/2020 *Income* £186,400 *Total grants* £77,300 *Grants to organisations* £77,300 *Assets* £5,280,000

TRUSTEES Charmaine von Mallinckrodt; Claire Howard; Edward Mallinckrodt; Philip Mallinckrodt.

OTHER INFORMATION In 2019/20 grants were awarded to eight organisations.

HOW TO APPLY The 2019/20 annual report states: 'The Trustees identify projects and organisations they wish to support. The Foundation does not make grants to people or organisations that apply speculatively.' Any interest in the foundation should be addressed to the correspondent.

CONTACT DETAILS Charities Manager, 81 Rivington Street, London EC2A 3AY *Tel.* 020 3170 5793

Man Group plc Charitable Trust

CC NO 275386 **ESTABLISHED** 1978

WHERE FUNDING CAN BE GIVEN UK.

WHO CAN BENEFIT Small to medium-sized registered charities.

WHAT IS FUNDED Literacy, numeracy and programmes that support disadvantaged people to engage with education and build the necessary vital life skills to improve life chances and employment prospects.

WHAT IS NOT FUNDED Large national charities; charities which use external fundraising agencies; charities primarily devoted to promoting religious beliefs; endowment funds; requests to directly replace statutory funding; individual beneficiaries; general media campaigns or campaigning or advocacy work to influence policy debates; applicants which have been successful during the last 12 months; work which has already been completed; capital projects and appeals; sponsorship or funding towards marketing appeals or fundraising events; organisations or projects whose primary purpose is political. Furthermore, the trust will not consider charities with high administration costs relative to the services they provide.

TYPE OF GRANT Core costs, including salaries and overheads; project costs.

RANGE OF GRANTS £10,000 to £50,000.

SAMPLE GRANTS City Gateway; Refugee Support Network (£50,000); The Children's Literacy Charity (£40,000); NSPCC (£25,000); XLP (£25,000); Raise Your Hands (£20,000).

FINANCES *Financial year end* 31/12/2019 *Income* £353,900 *Total grants* £548,000 *Grants to organisations* £548,000 *Assets* £1,130,000

TRUSTEES Keith Haydon; Carol Ward; Teun Johnston; Lydia Bosworth; Antoine Forterre; Steven Desmyter; Chris Pyper.

OTHER INFORMATION Grants were made to 14 charities in 2019.

HOW TO APPLY In the first instance, see the foundation's page on the Man Group website, where a document detailing eligibility criteria and guidelines on how to apply is available. The document states that the trust has a two-stage application process. After reading the trust's eligibility criteria, principles and exclusions, a brief expression of interest that is no longer than one side of A4 should be sent via email. If your expression of interest is successful, you will be invited to submit a stage two application form for consideration by the trustees, who usually meet twice a year. Successful applicants will be notified by telephone or email. All unsuccessful applicants will be notified and will usually receive an outline explanation for the rejection.

CONTACT DETAILS The Trustees, Man Group plc, Riverbank House, 2 Swan Lane, London EC4R 3AD *Email* charitable.trust@man.com *Website* https://www.man.com/responsibility

The Manackerman Charitable Trust

CC NO 326147 **ESTABLISHED** 1982

WHERE FUNDING CAN BE GIVEN UK, with a preference for Brent, Bury, Hackney, Salford and Scotland; Israel.

WHO CAN BENEFIT Jewish organisations; educational establishments; hospitals.

WHAT IS FUNDED Jewish causes; education; health and medicine; disability; the relief of poverty.

RANGE OF GRANTS Generally up to £25,000.

SAMPLE GRANTS Federation of Great Britain and Ireland (£25,000); Laniado Hospital UK (£20,900); King David High School – Manchester (£10,000); Friends of Lubavitch Scotland (£6,000); League of Jewish Women, Leket UK, The Friends of Alyn Orthopaedic Hospital for Children – Jerusalem and UK Toremet Ltd (£5,000 each).

FINANCES *Financial year end* 31/03/2020 *Income* £50,600 *Total grants* £99,900 *Grants to organisations* £99,900 *Assets* £348,500

TRUSTEES Jonathan Marks; Vanessa Marks; Aryeh Marks.

OTHER INFORMATION Grants of less than £5,000 totalled £18,000.

HOW TO APPLY Contact the correspondent for further information.

CONTACT DETAILS Jonathan Marks, Trustee, 3 Park Lane, Salford, Greater Manchester M7 4HT *Tel.* 0161 832 3434

Manchester Airport Community Trust Fund

CC NO 1071703 **ESTABLISHED** 1997

WHERE FUNDING CAN BE GIVEN Within a ten-mile radius of Manchester airport, concentrating on the areas most exposed to aircraft noise.

WHO CAN BENEFIT Community groups, voluntary groups, self-help groups, community charities or local branches of national charities.

WHAT IS FUNDED The environment; social welfare; community development and services.

TYPE OF GRANT Anything which is tangible and long lasting (i.e. equipment).

RANGE OF GRANTS Up to £3,000.

SAMPLE GRANTS Alderley and Wilmslow Musical Theatre Company and Levenshulme Tameside District Scouts (£3,000 each); Friends of Scholes Park (£2,400); Old Library CIO (£1,500); Cheadle and Gatley JFC (£1,300); Chelford Tenants and Residents Association (£650); Grow Edgeley (£380).

FINANCES *Financial year end* 31/03/2020 *Income* £156,300 *Total grants* £111,100 *Grants to organisations* £111,100 *Assets* £44,700

TRUSTEES Paul Andrews; John Taylor; Cllr Don Stockton; Michael Whetton; Wendy Sinfield; John Twigg; Bill Fairfoull; Bob Rudd.

OTHER INFORMATION Grants were made to 55 organisations during the 2019/20 financial year.

HOW TO APPLY Apply online via the charity's website. The trustees meet four times a year – application deadlines are published on the website.

CONTACT DETAILS The Trustees, Manchester Airport plc, Olympic House, Manchester Airport, Manchester M90 1QX *Tel.* 0161 489 5833 *Email* trust.fund@manairport.co.uk *Website* www.manchesterairport.co.uk/community/working-in-our-community/community-trust-fund

The Manchester Guardian Society Charitable Trust

CC NO 515341 **ESTABLISHED** 1984

WHERE FUNDING CAN BE GIVEN Greater Manchester.

WHO CAN BENEFIT Charities; uniformed groups; arts organisations; community associations. Preference is usually shown to smaller charities and community groups in the Greater Manchester area.

WHAT IS FUNDED General charitable purposes, especially children and young people, ill health and disability, older people, disadvantaged individuals, education, the arts and community causes.

WHAT IS NOT FUNDED Individuals; substitution of statutory funding; political groups; religious groups; salaries; recurrent costs; other funding bodies; core funding for public sector services; the purchase of computer and associated equipment.

TYPE OF GRANT Primarily small, one-off awards for capital projects.

RANGE OF GRANTS Mostly up to £3,500.

SAMPLE GRANTS Previous beneficiaries have included: DEBRA Charity North West Office; Dogs for the Disabled; Freedom from Torture; Hand on Heart Charity; Greater Manchester Scouts; Manchester YMCA; New Hope Ashton; Northwood Youth Advice Service; REACT (Rapid Effective Assistance for Children with potentially Terminal illness); SENSE.

FINANCES *Financial year end* 05/04/2020 *Income* £155,200 *Total grants* £138,600 *Grants to organisations* £138,600 *Assets* £4,230,000

TRUSTEES Philip Horton; Warren Smith; Lorraine Worsley; Paul Griffiths; Vivien Carter; Diane Hawkins; Sharman Birtles; Lt Col Shauna Dixon.

OTHER INFORMATION In 2019/20 grants were awarded to 81 organisations.

HOW TO APPLY An application form can be downloaded from the charity's website along with guidelines on how to complete it. Only one application will be accepted from an organisation within a two-year period.

CONTACT DETAILS The Trustees, c/o Addleshaw Goddard LLP, One St Peter's Square, Manchester, Greater Manchester M2 3DE *Tel.* 0161 934 6190 *Email* MGSmailbox@addleshawgoddard.com *Website* www.manchesterguardiansociety.org.uk

The W. M. Mann Foundation

OSCR NO SC010111 **ESTABLISHED** 1992

WHERE FUNDING CAN BE GIVEN Mainly Scotland, but UK-wide organisations may be assisted.

WHO CAN BENEFIT Charitable organisations; universities; hospices; hospitals; uniformed groups.

WHAT IS FUNDED General charitable purposes, including the arts, education, music and medical causes.

WHAT IS NOT FUNDED Individuals.

RANGE OF GRANTS Generally between £500 and £2,000.

SAMPLE GRANTS Culture and Sport – Glasgow (£33,000); Erskine Glasgow (£10,000); Glasgow Life (£3,000); Beatson Cancer Care (£2,000); Housing Options Scotland (£1,500); Family Fund (£1,200); Friends of Camperdown (£1,000); Arbroath and Montrose District Scouts (£500); Addiction Recovery Centre (£300).

FINANCES *Financial year end* 05/04/2020 *Income* £557,200 *Total grants* £171,000 *Grants to organisations* £171,000 *Assets* £7,680,000

OTHER INFORMATION In 2019/20 grants were made to 110 organisations.

HOW TO APPLY Apply in writing to the correspondent and include your organisation's latest annual report and accounts.

CONTACT DETAILS The Trustees, 201 Bath Street, Glasgow G2 4HZ *Tel.* 0141 248 4936 *Email* mail@wmmanngroup.co.uk

R. W. Mann Trust

CC NO 1095699 **ESTABLISHED** 1959

WHERE FUNDING CAN BE GIVEN North Tyneside; south-east Northumberland and east Newcastle. In exceptional cases also Tyne and Wear, Durham and Northumberland.

WHO CAN BENEFIT Local registered charities; youth groups (uniformed and non-uniformed); schools; hospitals; CICs; social enterprises; voluntary groups.

WHAT IS FUNDED General charitable purposes, including the following: social welfare; education; health; children and young people; people with disabilities; older people.

WHAT IS NOT FUNDED Large, well-established national charities; individuals; church buildings, except those used for community groups; deficits already incurred; the replacement of statutory funding.

TYPE OF GRANT Regular annual contributions; one-off donations; grants for capital projects.
RANGE OF GRANTS £100 to £10,000 (the average grant is £1,000).
SAMPLE GRANTS CVA Blyth Valley (£5,000); Northumberland CVA (£4,000); Acorn Community Church and St Paul's Community Partnership (£2,000); Mind – Tyneside and Northumberland (£1,000); Grainger Park CIO (£750); The Jack Charlton Disabled Anglers Association (£500); Penrith and District Red Squirrel Group (£250).
FINANCES *Financial year end* 31/03/2020
Income £74,500 *Total grants* £116,200
Grants to organisations £116,200
Assets £2,000,000
TRUSTEES Judith Hamilton; Guy Javens; Monica Heath.
OTHER INFORMATION In 2019/20 the trust made a total of 122 donations to 106 organisations or groups.
HOW TO APPLY Applications should be made in writing to the correspondent – consult the trust's website for a full list of what should be included. The trustees meet regularly and applicants usually hear if their application has been successful within six weeks.
CONTACT DETAILS John Hamilton, Secretary, PO Box 119, Gosforth, Newcastle upon Tyne, Tyne and Wear NE3 4WF *Tel.* 0191 284 2158
Email john.hamilton@onyx.octacon.co.uk
Website www.rwmanntrust.org.uk

■ The Manson Family Charitable Trust

CC NO 1168888 **ESTABLISHED** 2015
WHERE FUNDING CAN BE GIVEN UK and Israel.
WHO CAN BENEFIT Established charities, especially smaller organisations in the UK and overseas.
WHAT IS FUNDED General charitable purposes, particularly educational, religious, health and social well-being organisations; Jewish causes.
RANGE OF GRANTS Mostly under £10,000.
SAMPLE GRANTS Ma'ayan Project (£35,000); Jerusalem Foundation (£19,100); The Langdon Foundation (£17,700); MGS Trust (£10,000); The Friendship Circle (£8,000); Gesher and Manchester Jewish Museum (£5,000 each); Leuka (£4,300); Community Security Trust (£3,500); Aish UK, Designability, Manchester Jewish School for Special Education and StandWithUs (£1,000 each). Grants to unspecified organisations totalled £24,400.
FINANCES *Financial year end* 31/12/2019
Income £31,800 *Total grants* £139,900
Grants to organisations £139,900
Assets £2,126,000
TRUSTEES Edward Manson; Jonathan Manson; Avril Manson; Lauren Ornstein; Hannah Peters.
OTHER INFORMATION The 2019 accounts were the latest available at the time of writing (May 2021). Grants to UK organisations account for 75% of the grant total, with the remainder available to overseas charities.
HOW TO APPLY Contact the correspondent for further information.
CONTACT DETAILS Jonathan Manson, Chair, 4 Parklands, Whitefield, Manchester M45 7WY *Tel.* 0161 245 1201

■ The Marandi Foundation

CC NO 1172282 **ESTABLISHED** 2017
WHERE FUNDING CAN BE GIVEN UK.
WHO CAN BENEFIT Registered charities.
WHAT IS FUNDED Education and training; mental health and well-being support services; arts and culture.
TYPE OF GRANT Project funding.
RANGE OF GRANTS £13,700 to £395,000.
SAMPLE GRANTS The Watercolour World (£395,000); Orphan Disease (£154,800); Sentebale (£50,000); The Serpentine Trust (£13,700).
FINANCES *Financial year end* 05/04/2020
Income £679,900 *Total grants* £613,500
Grants to organisations £613,500
Assets £67,600
TRUSTEES Narmina Marandi; Javad Marandi; Michael Lockett.
OTHER INFORMATION A total of £613,500 was awarded to four organisations during the year.
HOW TO APPLY Contact the correspondent for further information.
CONTACT DETAILS The Trustees, 103 Mount Street, London W1K 2TJ *Tel.* 07771 787730
Email info@themarandifoundation.org
Website https://www.themarandifoundation.org

■ Marbeh Torah Trust

CC NO 292491 **ESTABLISHED** 1985
WHERE FUNDING CAN BE GIVEN UK and overseas, particularly Israel.
WHO CAN BENEFIT Jewish charitable organisations, especially educational establishments; individuals.
WHAT IS FUNDED The advancement of Orthodox Jewish religious education and the relief of poverty.
RANGE OF GRANTS £3,000 to £187,000.
SAMPLE GRANTS Yeshiva Marbeh Torah (£187,900); Chazon Avraham Yitzchak (£42,300); Margenita DeAvraham (£11,600); Ohavei Torah (£10,000); Beis Dovid (£6,200); Riosan (£3,000).
FINANCES *Financial year end* 31/12/2019
Income £265,500 *Total grants* £261,000
Grants to organisations £261,000
Assets £4,800
TRUSTEES Jacob Elzas; Moishe Elzas; Simone Elzas.
OTHER INFORMATION The trustees made grants to six organisations in 2019, primarily for Jewish education.
HOW TO APPLY Contact the correspondent for further information.
CONTACT DETAILS The Trustees, 116 Castlewood Road, London N15 6BE

■ The Marchig Animal Welfare Trust

CC NO 802133 **ESTABLISHED** 1989
WHERE FUNDING CAN BE GIVEN Worldwide (excluding the USA and Canada).
WHO CAN BENEFIT Charitable organisations and veterinarians.
WHAT IS FUNDED Animal welfare.
WHAT IS NOT FUNDED Expeditions; activities that are not totally animal welfare related; educational studies or other courses; salaries; support for conferences and meetings.
TYPE OF GRANT Project funding; capital costs.
RANGE OF GRANTS Grants range from £20,800 up to £362,400.
SAMPLE GRANTS Worldwide Veterinary Service (£362,400); University of Edinburgh (£200,000); Blue Cross of India (£130,000);

Karuna Society for Animals and Nature (£30,000); Jagged Peak Films Ltd (£24,700); Humane Society International (£21,800); Help in Suffering (£20,800).

FINANCES *Financial year end* 31/12/2019 *Income* £228,800 *Total grants* £999,000 *Grants to organisations* £999,000 *Assets* £14,400,000

TRUSTEES Les Ward; Dr Jerzy Mlotkiewicz; Janice McLoughlin; Fraser Symon; Matthew Tickle.

OTHER INFORMATION A total of 43 grants were awarded during the year, of which 16 were of less than £5,000. Grants to UK organisations totalled £671,400 and overseas grants totalled £327,500.

HOW TO APPLY See the trust's website for the latest information on applications.

CONTACT DETAILS The Trustees, c/o Lindsays Solicitors, Caledonian Exchange, 19A Canning Street, Edinburgh EH3 8HE *Tel.* 01383 737084 *Email* applications@marchigtrust.org *Website* www.marchigtrust.org

■ The Stella and Alexander Margulies Charitable Trust

CC NO 220441 **ESTABLISHED** 1962

WHERE FUNDING CAN BE GIVEN UK and Israel.

WHO CAN BENEFIT Charitable organisations, particularly those benefitting Jewish people.

WHAT IS FUNDED Arts and culture; education; medical research; Jewish causes.

SAMPLE GRANTS Shaare Zedek UK (£180,000); Israel Philharmonic Orchestra Foundation (£22,700); Weizman Institute (£18,000); Tate Foundation (£6,000); Camp Simcha (£500); Torah Temimah Trust (£180).

FINANCES *Financial year end* 05/04/2020 *Income* £132,900 *Total grants* £240,200 *Grants to organisations* £240,200 *Assets* £9,140,000

TRUSTEES Marcus Marguiles; Alexander Sorkin; Martin Paisner; Leslie Michaels; Sir Stuart Lipton.

OTHER INFORMATION Grants were made to nine organisations and were broken down as follows: medical research (£180,000); relief for individuals of faith (£41,400); education (£10,000); arts and culture (£6,000); religious sites and monuments (£2,400); religious activities (£500).

HOW TO APPLY Contact the correspondent for further information.

CONTACT DETAILS The Trustees, 27 Berkeley Square, London W1J 6EL *Tel.* 020 7343 7200 *Email* jill.tyrrell@timeproducts.co.uk

■ The Michael Marks Charitable Trust

CC NO 248136 **ESTABLISHED** 1966

WHERE FUNDING CAN BE GIVEN UK and overseas.

WHO CAN BENEFIT Registered charities; galleries, museums and libraries; educational institutions.

WHAT IS FUNDED Arts and culture; the environment and conservation.

WHAT IS NOT FUNDED Registered charities only. Awards are not made to individuals or profit-making organisations.

RANGE OF GRANTS £500 to £25,000.

SAMPLE GRANTS Oxford Philharmonic Orchestra (£29,800); Jewish Community of Thessaloniki (£22,500); British Library (£15,900); Teatru Manoel (£10,000); Sea Life Trust (£5,000); Sound Waves SCIO (£3,000); Future Trees Trust (£2,000); Greek Archaeological Society of Great Britain (£500).

FINANCES *Financial year end* 31/01/2020 *Income* £183,000 *Total grants* £234,300 *Grants to organisations* £234,300 *Assets* £5,520,000

TRUSTEES Lady Marina Marks; Sir Christopher White; Noel Annesley.

OTHER INFORMATION Grants were broken down as follows: arts (£141,700); the environment (£49,200); education (£43,400).

HOW TO APPLY Applications should be made in writing to the correspondent and include audited accounts, information on other bodies approached and details of any funding obtained. The trustees meet twice a year, usually in January and July, to consider applications. Applicants will not receive a response unless they have been successful. The trustees will only accept written correspondence by regular mail.

CONTACT DETAILS Lady Marina Marks, Trustee, 5 Elm Tree Road, London NW8 9JY *Tel.* 020 7286 4633 *Email* michaelmarkscharitabletrust@hotmail.co.uk

■ The Marks Family Charitable Trust

CC NO 263776 **ESTABLISHED** 1971

WHERE FUNDING CAN BE GIVEN UK and Israel.

WHO CAN BENEFIT Registered charities.

WHAT IS FUNDED Children and young people; healthcare; education; the arts; refugees.

WHAT IS NOT FUNDED Individuals.

RANGE OF GRANTS Typically £5,000 to £20,000.

SAMPLE GRANTS Exeter College Oxford (£17,000); Refugees At Home (£15,000); Birds Life (£10,000); Anglo-Israel Association (£5,000); Walter and Liesel Schwab Charitable Trust (£4,000); Demelza House Children's Hospice (£500); National Gallery (£80).

FINANCES *Financial year end* 05/04/2020 *Income* £105,100 *Total grants* £123,300 *Grants to organisations* £123,300 *Assets* £5,280,000

TRUSTEES Lord Marks of Broughton; Lady Marks of Broughton; The Hon. Michael Marks; The Hon. Miriam Cooper.

HOW TO APPLY An online application form can be found on the trust's website along with full application guidelines.

CONTACT DETAILS The Trustees, c/o HW Fisher and Co., Acre House, 11–15 William Road, London NW1 3ER *Tel.* 020 7388 7000 *Email* office@marksfamilycharitabletrust.com *Website* https://www.marksfamilycharitabletrust.com

■ The J. P. Marland Charitable Trust

CC NO 1049350 **ESTABLISHED** 1995

WHERE FUNDING CAN BE GIVEN UK.

WHO CAN BENEFIT Registered charities and individuals.

WHAT IS FUNDED General charitable purposes, including the arts, sports, medical causes, teaching and community needs.

RANGE OF GRANTS Up to £25,000.

SAMPLE GRANTS Outdoor Trust (£12,500); Secret Spitfire (£10,000); Action on Addiction (£6,500); Pallant House Gallery and Stroke Association (£5,000 each); Royal Marsden

Hospital (£2,000); La Folia Music and Portrait Gala Silent Auction (£1,200 each).

FINANCES *Financial year end* 01/10/2019 *Income* £155,500 *Total grants* £58,800 *Grants to organisations* £58,800 *Assets* £854,800

TRUSTEES The Rt Hon. Lord Jonathan Marland; Carol Law; Marcus Marland; Hugo Marland.

OTHER INFORMATION The 2018/19 accounts were the most recent available at the time of writing (April 2021). Grants were made to 22 organisations during the year and included 12 grants of £1,000 or less. Only beneficiaries of grants of over £1,000 were listed in the accounts. Overall, grants were distributed as follows: medical causes, teaching and community (£33,900); the arts (£24,800).

HOW TO APPLY Apply via email to the correspondent.

CONTACT DETAILS Lord Jonathan Marland, Trustee, 78 Belgrave Road, London SW1V 2BJ *Tel.* 020 7752 0177 *Email* jpmarlandcharitabletrust@marland.co *Website* www.marland.co

■ Marmot Charitable Trust

CC NO 1106619 **ESTABLISHED** 2004

WHERE FUNDING CAN BE GIVEN Worldwide.

WHO CAN BENEFIT 'Green' organisations; educational institutions; environmental and peace projects.

WHAT IS FUNDED The trust's Charity Commission record states that the trustees are interested in 'funding green initiatives that are working towards a sustainable future, and peace and security [initiatives] that are seeking to reduce international conflict including by the eventual elimination of nuclear weapons'.

TYPE OF GRANT Project and core costs can be covered.

RANGE OF GRANTS £1,000 to £25,000.

SAMPLE GRANTS Plan B Earth (£25,000); British American Security Information Council (BASIC) (£22,600); Centre for Alternative Technology Zero Carbon Britain Project and ShareAction – UK Policy Programme (£20,000 each); The Poverty and Environment Trust – Community Energy Project (£12,200); Platform London (£5,000); Network for Social Change Charitable Trust and The 10:10 Foundation (£4,000 each); Earth Resources Green New Deal Project and Environmental Funders Network (£2,000 each).

FINANCES *Financial year end* 05/04/2020 *Income* £52,800 *Total grants* £143,800 *Grants to organisations* £143,800 *Assets* £3,031,300

TRUSTEES Martin Bevis Gillett; Jonathan Gillett; Jeanni Barlow.

HOW TO APPLY The trustees have informed us directly that they do not accept unsolicited applications.

CONTACT DETAILS The Trustees, c/o BM Marmot, London WC1N 3XX *Tel.* 07707 996220 *Email* marmot.trust@gmail.com

■ The Marque Foundation

CC NO 1174823 **ESTABLISHED** 2017

WHERE FUNDING CAN BE GIVEN UK.

WHO CAN BENEFIT Registered charities; Jewish organisations.

WHAT IS FUNDED The relief of poverty; education; religion; medical care.

RANGE OF GRANTS Up to £162,700.

SAMPLE GRANTS Asser Bishvil Foundation (£162,700); Yad Eliezer Trust (£114,600); Tomchei Yotzei Anglia (£10,000).

FINANCES *Financial year end* 31/03/2021 *Income* £300,000 *Total grants* £290,100 *Grants to organisations* £290,100 *Assets* £99,900

TRUSTEES Alexander Schimmel; Benjamin Schimmel; Leopold Schimmel.

OTHER INFORMATION Only beneficiaries of grants of above £5,000 were listed in the accounts. Grants of under £5,000 totalled £2,800.

HOW TO APPLY Contact the correspondent for further information.

CONTACT DETAILS The Trustees, 121 Princes Park Avenue, London NW11 0JS *Tel.* 020 8455 0100

■ The Michael Marsh Charitable Trust

CC NO 220473 **ESTABLISHED** 1958

WHERE FUNDING CAN BE GIVEN Birmingham, Staffordshire, Worcestershire, Warwickshire, Coventry, Wolverhampton and associated towns in the Black Country.

WHO CAN BENEFIT Registered charities; CICs; schools; universities; hospitals; hospices; religious bodies/institutions.

WHAT IS FUNDED General charitable purposes; education/training; disabilities; children/young people; the relief of poverty; older people.

WHAT IS NOT FUNDED Animals; entertainment charities; replacement of statutory funding; running costs; individuals.

TYPE OF GRANT Capital costs; seed funding/start-up funding; project funding.

RANGE OF GRANTS Usually between £1,000 and £5,000.

SAMPLE GRANTS S4E Ltd (£60,000); SENSE (£25,000); Trailblazers Mentoring (£6,000); Acorns Children's Hospice Trust (£5,000); St Anne's Hostel (£3,800); The Prince's Trust (£2,500); The Gap (£2,000); ABF The Soldiers' Charity (£1,500); Sudden Productions (£1,000).

FINANCES *Financial year end* 05/04/2020 *Income* £142,700 *Total grants* £265,500 *Grants to organisations* £265,500 *Assets* £2,160,000

TRUSTEES Peter Barber; Susan Bennett; Lee Nuttall.

OTHER INFORMATION Grants were broken down as follows: education and training (£81,000); people with disabilities (£66,000); children and young people (£45,000); general charitable purposes (£40,200); relief of poverty (£26,300); older people (£7,000).

HOW TO APPLY Apply in writing to the correspondent. The trustees meet around four times a year to consider applications.

CONTACT DETAILS Louise Ruane, Clerk to the Trustees, Pear Tree Cottage, Yarrington Road, Alfrick, Worcester, Worcestershire WR6 5EX *Tel.* 07812 743485 *Email* louise.ruane@michaelmarsh.org.uk

■ The Marsh Christian Trust

CC NO 284470 **ESTABLISHED** 1981

WHERE FUNDING CAN BE GIVEN UK.

WHO CAN BENEFIT Registered charities.

WHAT IS FUNDED General charitable purposes, with a preference towards the following: literature, arts and heritage; social welfare; environmental causes and animal welfare; education and training.

WHAT IS NOT FUNDED Individuals; churches; hospices or hospitals; start-up costs; project costs; sponsorship proposals.

TYPE OF GRANT Core/revenue costs; unrestricted funding.

RANGE OF GRANTS Usually £300 to £2,000.

SAMPLE GRANTS Natural History Museum (£2,500); English Speaking Union (£1,200); Different Strokes (£700); IT Schools Africa (£600); Medical Aid for Palestinians (£550); Crystal Palace Museum (£400); Kent Wildlife Trust (£360); Friends of Cathedral Music (£150); Chiswick House Friends (£30).

FINANCES *Financial year end* 05/04/2020
Income £1,480,000 *Total grants* £304,900
Grants to organisations £304,900
Assets £12,670,000

TRUSTEES Brian Marsh; Natalie Collings; Antonia Marsh; Camilla Kenyon; Charles Micklewright; Nicholas Carter.

OTHER INFORMATION Grants and awards totalling £304,900 were awarded to over 350 organisations and individuals. The trust also maintains the Marsh Awards Scheme, which recognises individual and group achievements in the charity sector. Full details are available on the website.

HOW TO APPLY Apply in writing to the correspondent – there is no standard application form. The trust requires a cover letter and a full copy of the applicant's report and accounts. There are no deadlines for applications. Further information can be found on the trust's website.

CONTACT DETAILS Annie McCarthy, Trust Manager, 4 Matthew Parker Street, London SW1H 9NP *Tel.* 020 7233 3112 *Email* mccarthy@bpmarsh.co.uk *Website* www.marshchristiantrust.org

■ Charity of John Marshall

CC NO 206780 **ESTABLISHED** 1631

WHERE FUNDING CAN BE GIVEN England and Wales (for parsonage grants); Canterbury, Guildford, Lincoln, Rochester and Southwark (for church restoration grants).

WHO CAN BENEFIT Anglican parish churches and cathedrals.

WHAT IS FUNDED Support for parsonage buildings throughout England and Wales; help with the upkeep of Anglican churches and cathedrals in Kent, Surrey and Lincolnshire (as the counties were defined in 1855), including the installation of CCTV and burglar alarms; support for the parish of Christ Church in Southwark; education.

WHAT IS NOT FUNDED Parsonage grants cannot be applied for by individual clergy or other denominations.

TYPE OF GRANT Building and other capital works.

RANGE OF GRANTS Grants to churches: usually £4,000 to £20,000; awards to parsonages: usually £2,000 to £20,000.

SAMPLE GRANTS Guildford Diocese (£52,500); Christ Church Erith – Rochester and St Luke – Woodside (£20,000 each); Coventry Diocese, St Andrew the Apostle – Lincoln and St Nicholas' Thames Ditton – Guilford (£10,000 each); St Swithun's Bicker – Lincoln and Truro Diocese (£5,000 each); Southwell Diocese (£3,100); Swansea Diocese (£500).

FINANCES *Financial year end* 31/12/2019
Income £1,380,000 *Total grants* £881,000
Grants to organisations £881,000
Assets £21,950,000

TRUSTEES Col Anthony Guthrie; Stephen Clark; William Eason; Anthea Nicholson; John Heawood; Revd Jonathan Rust; Surbhi Malhotra-Trenkel; Lesley Bosman; Eleanor Lang; Charles Ledsam; Alastair Moss; Adrian Smallwood.

OTHER INFORMATION Restoration grants were made to 34 churches during 2019, totalling £442,500, and 36 dioceses received grants for the purchase, improvement or improved security of parsonages, totalling £362,000. Funds made available to Marshall's Educational Foundation totalled £34,800 and individual grants were made to Christ Church – Southwark (£32,900) and All Saint's Church – Stamford (£8,700).

HOW TO APPLY Applications must be submitted through the charity's website. Applications for parsonages must be made through the relevant Diocesan Parsonage Board. Applications for church restoration grants must give information on the project (i.e. description, cost, timings) and the importance of the proposed works, how they will benefit the mission and ministry of the church and how the project fits with the diocese's strategic aims. The Grants Committee meets three times per year to shortlist applications for the full board of trustees to approve. The website also has a helpful page dedicated to other funding sources for church improvements.

CONTACT DETAILS Catherine de Cintra, Clerk to the Trustees, Marshall House, 66 Newcomen Street, London SE1 1YT *Tel.* 020 7407 2979 *Email* grantoffice@marshalls.org.uk *Website* www.marshalls.org.uk

■ Charlotte Marshall Charitable Trust

CC NO 211941 **ESTABLISHED** 1962

WHERE FUNDING CAN BE GIVEN UK.

WHO CAN BENEFIT Registered charities; educational institutions benefitting Roman Catholics; hospices.

WHAT IS FUNDED Two-thirds of the trust's income is allocated to support educational, religious and other charitable purposes for Roman Catholics, and the remainder is distributed at the trustees' discretion.

RANGE OF GRANTS Mostly up to £1,500.

SAMPLE GRANTS Roman Catholic activity: St Richard's Catholic College (£2,000); Bibles for Children, Cardinal Hume Centre, St Gemma's Hospice and St Chad's Cathedral (£1,000 each). Non-Roman Catholic activity: Asthma Relief, Rainbow Trust Children's Charity, St John Ambulance and Sussex Prisoners' Families CIC (£500 each).

FINANCES *Financial year end* 05/04/2020
Income £64,100 *Total grants* £60,800
Grants to organisations £60,800
Assets £400,200

TRUSTEES Joseph Cosgrave; Kevin Page; John Russell; Rachel Cosgrave.

OTHER INFORMATION Grants were made to 70 organisations in 2019/20, including 34 for non-Roman Catholic activities.

HOW TO APPLY Contact the correspondent to request an application form.

CONTACT DETAILS The Trustees, c/o C&C. Marshall Ltd, 55–65 Castleham Road, St Leonards-on-Sea, St Leonards-on-Sea, East Sussex TN38 9NU *Tel.* 01424 856655 *Email* christinac@marshall-tufflex.com

■ D. G. Marshall of Cambridge Trust

CC NO 286468 **ESTABLISHED** 1982

WHERE FUNDING CAN BE GIVEN UK, with a preference for Cambridgeshire.

WHO CAN BENEFIT Registered charities; community organisations.

WHAT IS FUNDED Aviation; children and young people; health and disability; education; community projects.

RANGE OF GRANTS Mostly £500 to £3,000, although the 2018/19 accounts state that 'there is no minimum or maximum donation'.

SAMPLE GRANTS Form the Future (£10,000); The Arthur Rank Hospice (£6,000); Air League, Cambridge United Community Trust and Parkinson's UK (£3,000 each); Ely Cathedral Restoration Trust and Mind (£1,000 each); Bobby Moore Bowel Cancer Fund (£500); Cancer Research UK (£150); Crisis (£90).

FINANCES *Financial year end* 05/04/2019 *Income* £53,800 *Total grants* £52,100 *Grants to organisations* £52,100 *Assets* £2,550,000

TRUSTEES Michael Marshall; Sarah Moynihan; Robert Marshall; Julie Ingham.

OTHER INFORMATION The 2018/19 accounts were the latest available at the time of writing (January 2021). Grants were made to 33 organisations for the following purposes: children (£15,500); health and disability (£11,000); hospitals and related organisations (£10,000); aviation (£8,000); local community (£6,300); education (£1,300).

HOW TO APPLY Contact the correspondent for further information.

CONTACT DETAILS The Trustees, Airport House, The Airport, Newmarket Road, Cambridge CB5 8RY *Tel.* 01223 373737

The Kristina Martin Charitable Trust

CC NO 249913 **ESTABLISHED** 1966

WHERE FUNDING CAN BE GIVEN UK.

WHO CAN BENEFIT Registered and exempt charities.

WHAT IS FUNDED General charitable purposes, particularly mental health, suicide prevention and care following bereavement.

TYPE OF GRANT One-off grants.

RANGE OF GRANTS Between £5,000 and £25,000.

SAMPLE GRANTS Samaritans, Suffolk Mind and Survivors of Bereavement by Suicide (£25,000 each); Air Ambulances UK, Crisis UK, Cruse Bereavement Care and Rethink Mental Illness (£15,000 each); Inkpen Memorial Playing Field (£5,000); St Benedict's Roman Catholic School (£1,600).

FINANCES *Financial year end* 05/04/2020 *Income* £301,000 *Total grants* £411,600 *Grants to organisations* £411,600 *Assets* £7,240,000

TRUSTEES Peter Tompkins; Andrew Parry.

OTHER INFORMATION During 2019/20 grants were made to 24 organisations.

HOW TO APPLY The 2019/20 annual report states that the trust is 'seldom able to make grants in response to unsolicited applications': however, applications can be made using the form on the trust's website. Grants are usually made by 31 January and 30 June each year.

CONTACT DETAILS The Trustees, c/o Irwin Mitchell LLP, Davidson House, Forbury Square, Reading, Berkshire RG1 3EU *Tel.* 07766 714420 *Email* info@kmct.org.uk *Website* https://sites.google.com/kmct.org.uk/kmct/home

The Martin Charitable Trust

OSCR NO SC028487 **ESTABLISHED** 1998

WHERE FUNDING CAN BE GIVEN UK, mainly Scotland, and particularly Glasgow and Strathclyde; overseas.

WHO CAN BENEFIT Charitable organisations.

WHAT IS FUNDED Education; health; citizenship; community development; arts and culture; heritage; sport; the provision of recreational facilities; the environment; older people; disability; animal welfare.

WHAT IS NOT FUNDED Individuals.

SAMPLE GRANTS Previous beneficiaries have included: Ardgowan Hospice (£8,000); Tenovus Scotland (£6,000); Kelvinside Academy (£5,000); Glasgow Care Foundation (£4,000); British Red Cross Society, Cancer Research UK and Christian Aid Scotland (£3,000 each); The National Trust for Scotland (£2,000); Seafarers UK and St Columba Church of Scotland (£1,000 each).

FINANCES *Financial year end* 30/11/2019 *Income* £117,000 *Total grants* £124,500 *Grants to organisations* £124,500 *Assets* £3,120,000

OTHER INFORMATION The 2018/19 accounts were the latest available at the time of writing (April 2021).

HOW TO APPLY Apply in writing to the correspondent, including up-to-date accounts.

CONTACT DETAILS The Trustees, c/o Miller Beckett and Jackson Solicitors, 190 St Vincent Street, Glasgow G2 5SP *Tel.* 0141 204 2833

Sir George Martin Trust

CC NO 223554 **ESTABLISHED** 1956

WHERE FUNDING CAN BE GIVEN West and North Yorkshire.

WHO CAN BENEFIT Registered charities; churches; educational establishments; hospices; museums.

WHAT IS FUNDED Children and young people; church appeals; the environment; hospices; mental well-being; museums and historic buildings; music and the arts; older people; physical and learning disabilities; school and university outreach; social welfare; sports for disadvantaged communities.

WHAT IS NOT FUNDED Appeals that are not focused on West and/or North Yorkshire; individuals; overseas seminars or exchange visits by individuals or groups; medical appeals of a capital or revenue nature; medical research projects; restoration schemes for church roofs, spires, etc.; playgroups.

TYPE OF GRANT Capital costs; core/revenue costs; unrestricted funding.

RANGE OF GRANTS Mostly from £1,000 to £3,000.

SAMPLE GRANTS Bradford Youth Development Project, Forget Me Not Children's Hospice and Kidz Aware (£5,000 each); Holy Rood House (£3,000); Tutti Frutti Productions (£2,000); Cardigan Centre (£1,000); HOPE (£500).

FINANCES *Financial year end* 05/04/2020 *Income* £325,300 *Total grants* £229,400 *Grants to organisations* £229,400 *Assets* £7,760,000

TRUSTEES Martin Bethel; Roger Marshall; David Coates; Marjorie Martin; Paul Taylor; Morven Whyte; Sarah Blenkinsop; Sir George Martin Trust Company Ltd.

OTHER INFORMATION Grants of £3,000 and under totalled £202,200 and were awarded to 125 organisations.

HOW TO APPLY Visit the trust's website for full details regarding the application process. Application forms can be requested via email or phone from the correspondent. The application form should be returned by post or email and include details about your organisation, your work and your current financial situation. The trustees meet in March, June, September and November each year.

CONTACT DETAILS Carla Marshall, Trust Manager, 6 Firs Avenue, Harrogate, North Yorkshire HG2 9HA *Tel.* 01423 810222 *Email* info@sirgeorgemartintrust.org.uk *Website* www.sirgeorgemartintrust.org.uk

■ The Geoffrey and Pauline Martin Trust

CC NO 1176463 **ESTABLISHED** 2017

WHERE FUNDING CAN BE GIVEN Worldwide.

WHO CAN BENEFIT Registered charities.

WHAT IS FUNDED Medical conditions; animal welfare, with a particular interest in cats.

RANGE OF GRANTS £5,000 to £20,000.

SAMPLE GRANTS University of Liverpool – Ageing and Chronic Disease (£20,000); Alder Hey, Hectors Greyhound Rescue and Wirral Animal Sanctuary (£10,000 each); Horse Sense and North Clwyd Animal Rescue (£5,000 each).

FINANCES *Financial year end* 30/06/2020
Income £130,000 *Total grants* £90,000
Grants to organisations £90,000
Assets £4,920,000

TRUSTEES Tony Bayliss; Jane Fagan; Philip Barks.

OTHER INFORMATION Nine grants were made during the year.

HOW TO APPLY Contact the correspondent for further information.

CONTACT DETAILS The Trustees, c/o DSG Chartered Accountants, Castle Chambers, 43 Castle Street, Liverpool, Merseyside L2 9TL *Tel.* 0151 243 1214

■ John Martin's Charity

CC NO 527473 **ESTABLISHED** 1714

WHERE FUNDING CAN BE GIVEN Evesham and surrounding villages only.

WHO CAN BENEFIT Individuals and charitable or voluntary organisations and schools benefitting the residents of Evesham.

WHAT IS FUNDED Religious support – to assist the vicars and PCCs within the town of Evesham; relief in need – to assist individuals and organisations within the town of Evesham who are in conditions of need, hardship and distress; the promotion of education – to promote education to those residing within the town of Evesham and to provide benefits to the schools and college within Evesham; health – to support people with chronic health problems and other related health issues.

TYPE OF GRANT One-off capital costs, general expenditure and project costs.

RANGE OF GRANTS £500 to £30,000.

SAMPLE GRANTS All Saints PCC – Evesham (£32,200); Evesham College (£5,000); Evesham Men in Sheds (£1,600); Hampton Flower Show (£150).

FINANCES *Financial year end* 31/03/2020
Income £854,000 *Total grants* £628,000
Grants to organisations £240,000
Assets £23,740,000

TRUSTEES Valerie Butler; Josephine Sandalls; Julie Westlake; Alan Booth; Janet Osbourne; John Smith; Revd Mark Binney; Stuart Allerton; Sherraden Murphy; Cyril Scorse; John Wilson; Philip Airdrie.

OTHER INFORMATION Grants were broken down as follows: religious support (£70,800); social welfare (£66,600); education (£63,800); health and other charitable purposes (£46,600).

HOW TO APPLY Application forms are available on the charity's website. Applications are considered once per quarter.

CONTACT DETAILS The Trustees, 16 Queens Road, Evesham, Worcestershire WR11 4JN *Tel.* 01386 765440 *Email* enquiries@johnmartins.org.uk *Website* www.johnmartins.org.uk

■ The Dan Maskell Tennis Trust

CC NO 1133589 **ESTABLISHED** 2009

WHERE FUNDING CAN BE GIVEN UK.

WHO CAN BENEFIT Individuals; disability groups and programmes; tennis clubs; associations; schools.

WHAT IS FUNDED The promotion of physical health, fitness and the general well-being of people with disabilities through the sport of tennis.

WHAT IS NOT FUNDED Items considered as luxury, such as electrical equipment (for example, videos), clothing or individual transport costs, are not covered. Publicity, promotions, advertising, general administration and catering at tournaments and events are not within the criteria for grant aid.

TYPE OF GRANT The purchase of wheelchairs, tennis equipment and grants for coaching.

RANGE OF GRANTS Up to £1,500 for a group, club or project and £500 for an individual.

SAMPLE GRANTS A list of beneficiaries was not included in the annual report and accounts.

FINANCES *Financial year end* 31/12/2019
Income £85,100 *Total grants* £65,000
Grants to organisations £65,000
Assets £593,100

TRUSTEES Sue Wolstenholme; Lilas Davidson; John James; Rob McCowen; Noel McShane; Robin Maskell-Charlton; Ian Peacock; Geraint Richards; Lesley Cundy.

OTHER INFORMATION Grants were made to 125 organisations and individuals in 2019.

HOW TO APPLY The trustees meet at least three times a year, usually around May, September and December. Application forms are available from the trust's website and should be submitted in advance of the meeting, the exact dates of which are specified on the website. Completed application forms can be returned by post or scanned and emailed to the correspondent. Applicants are requested to provide as much information as possible and include details of the costs for each item or facility. The guidelines also note: 'Before applying for assistance, you are advised to consult The Tennis Foundation and/or your local County Tennis Association.'

CONTACT DETAILS The Trustees, c/o Sport Wins, PO Box 238, Tadworth, Surrey KT20 5WT *Tel.* 01737 831707 *Email* info@danmaskelltennistrust.org.uk *Website* www.danmaskelltennistrust.org.uk

■ Masonic Charitable Foundation

CC NO 1164703 **ESTABLISHED** 2015

WHERE FUNDING CAN BE GIVEN England and Wales.

WHO CAN BENEFIT Registered charities; research bodies; hospices (those receiving 60% or less of their funding from the NHS).

WHAT IS FUNDED Disadvantaged children and young people; isolation in later life; medical research into degenerative diseases; hospice care; disaster relief.

WHAT IS NOT FUNDED Each grant programme has its own exclusions; consult the foundation's website for details.

TYPE OF GRANT Project costs; core costs; PhD studentships.

RANGE OF GRANTS Small grants of £1,000 to £15,000; large grants of £10,000 to £60,000.

SAMPLE GRANTS Addaction (£79,800); Blue Smile (£15,000); Yellow Submarine (£5,000); Boomerang (£1,800); Cornwall Blood Bikes (£500).

FINANCES *Financial year end* 31/03/2019
Income £88,671,000
Total grants £10,048,000
Grants to organisations £10,048,000
Assets £389,886,000

TRUSTEES Christopher Head; Alan Graham; Clive Emerson; Michael Heenan; Howard Sabin; Andrew Wauchope; David Watson; Anthony Harvey; John Boyington; Simon Duckworth; Charles Cunnington; Nigel Vaughan; Sir Paul Williams; James Newman; His Hon. Judge Richard Hone; Timothy Chapman; Howard Wilson; Sinead Brophy; Dr Simon Fellerman.

OTHER INFORMATION The foundation was established in 2015 to bring together the previous work of four national Masonic charities: The Freemasons' Grand Charity; the Royal Masonic Trust for Girls and Boys; the Masonic Samaritan Fund; and the Royal Masonic Benevolent Institution. The grant total refers to grants made to non-Masonic causes. The 2018/19 accounts were the latest available at the time of writing (February 2021).

HOW TO APPLY Applications can be made through the foundation's website. Grants for medical research and disaster relief are for invited applicants only.

CONTACT DETAILS Grants Team, Freemasons' Hall, 60 Great Queen Street, London WC2B 5AZ *Tel.* 020 3146 3337 *Website* mcf.org.uk

■ Nancie Massey Charitable Trust

OSCR NO SC008977 **ESTABLISHED** 1989

WHERE FUNDING CAN BE GIVEN Scotland, particularly the City of Edinburgh.

WHO CAN BENEFIT Registered charities.

WHAT IS FUNDED Medical research and care; the arts; education; the community.

WHAT IS NOT FUNDED Individuals.

RANGE OF GRANTS Typically £2,500 to £10,000.

SAMPLE GRANTS National Galleries of Scotland Foundation (£100,000); Hearts and Minds (£10,000); Disability Snowsport UK (£5,000); Changing Faces, REACT (Rapid Effective Assistance for Children with potentially Terminal illness) and Tall Ships Youth Trust (£3,000 each); CCLASP, Fife Young Carers, Lothian Autistic Society and Waverley Care (£2,500 each).

FINANCES *Financial year end* 05/04/2020
Income £308,800 *Total grants* £297,000
Grants to organisations £297,000
Assets £5,500,000

OTHER INFORMATION The trust made grants to 37 organisations in 2019/20.

HOW TO APPLY Contact the correspondent for further information.

CONTACT DETAILS The Trustees, c/o Chiene + Tait LLP, 61 Dublin Street, Edinburgh EH3 6NL

■ The Master Charitable Trust

CC NO 1139904 **ESTABLISHED** 2009

WHERE FUNDING CAN BE GIVEN UK and overseas.

WHO CAN BENEFIT Registered charities.

WHAT IS FUNDED Education; poverty; religion; health; community development; arts and culture; heritage; science; human rights; the environment; social welfare; animal welfare; the armed forces; children and young people; older people.

RANGE OF GRANTS Mostly £10,000 to £500,000.

SAMPLE GRANTS The Prince's Trust (£7.79 million); Chelsea and Westminster Hospital NHS Foundation Trust (£1.03 million); Action on Addiction (£735,200); Forward Trust (£470,500); Guards' Chapel Trust (£150,000); The Butterfly Tree (£87,100); Mindsong (£45,000); Yorkshire Dales Millennium Trust (£20,000); SG Foundation (£10,000).

FINANCES *Financial year end* 30/09/2019
Income £59,300,000
Total grants £25,030,000
Grants to organisations £25,030,000
Assets £135,210,000

TRUSTEE Hoare Trustees.

OTHER INFORMATION The 2018/19 accounts were the latest available at the time of writing (April 2021). Grants were awarded to 495 charities during the year.

HOW TO APPLY Apply in writing to the correspondent. Charities and organisations are usually chosen at the donor's request.

CONTACT DETAILS Hoare Trustees, 37 Fleet Street, London EC4P 4DQ *Tel.* 020 7353 4522 *Website* https://www.hoaresbank.co.uk/master-charitable-trust

■ Matchroom Sport Charitable Foundation

CC NO 1167276 **ESTABLISHED** 2016

WHERE FUNDING CAN BE GIVEN UK.

WHO CAN BENEFIT Registered charities; hospices.

WHAT IS FUNDED General charitable purposes including the following: sports and community charities; children and young people; hospices.

SAMPLE GRANTS Alexandra Park and Palace Charitable Trust, Haven House Children's Hospice and The Jessie May Trust (£50,000 each); Microphthalmia, Anophthalmia and Coloboma Support (£20,000); KEEN London (£5,000).

FINANCES *Financial year end* 30/06/2020
Income £261,400 *Total grants* £175,000
Grants to organisations £175,000
Assets £111,900

TRUSTEES Edward Lowy; Jason Ferguson; Susan Hearn; Catherine Godding; Chloe Hearn.

HOW TO APPLY The foundation's website states: 'email us an overview of your organisation along with details of your funding requirements'.

CONTACT DETAILS The Trustees, Mascalls, Mascalls Lane, Brentwood, Essex CM14 5LJ *Tel.* 01277 359917 *Email* mscf@matchroom.com *Website* www.matchroomsport.foundation

■ Material World Foundation

CC NO 266746 **ESTABLISHED** 1968

WHERE FUNDING CAN BE GIVEN UK and overseas.

WHO CAN BENEFIT Charitable organisations.

WHAT IS FUNDED The arts; people with disabilities; social welfare.

SAMPLE GRANTS The Film Foundation (£152,700); Achievable Foundation (£35,900); Waves for Water (£20,000); Crisis (£10,000).

FINANCES *Financial year end* 31/12/2019 *Income* £319,700 *Total grants* £763,400 *Grants to organisations* £763,400 *Assets* £1,550,000

TRUSTEES Linda Arias; Dhani Harrison; Deborah Owen; Leslie Boss; Ken Roberts; Olivia Harrison.

OTHER INFORMATION The foundation was established by George Harrison.

HOW TO APPLY Contact the correspondent for further information.

CONTACT DETAILS The Trustees, c/o Shipleys, 10 Orange Street, London WC2H 7DQ *Tel.* 020 7312 0000 *Email* advice@shipleys.com *Website* https://www.materialworldfoundation.com

■ The Mather Family Charitable Trust

CC NO 1180415 **ESTABLISHED** 2018

WHERE FUNDING CAN BE GIVEN England and Wales.

WHO CAN BENEFIT Registered charities; individuals.

WHAT IS FUNDED General charitable purposes.

TYPE OF GRANT One-off and recurrent.

RANGE OF GRANTS Typically £100 to £10,000.

SAMPLE GRANTS Forever Manchester (£30,000); Rossendale Trust and Space for Autism (£10,000 each); Prostate Cancer UK (£2,500); Heart Foundation (£1,000); Trussell Trust (£500); Save the Children and Children First (£100 each).

FINANCES *Financial year end* 05/04/2020 *Income* £1,750,000 *Total grants* £55,300 *Grants to organisations* £55,300 *Assets* £3,370,000

TRUSTEES Kara Mather; Aimee Mather; Harry Mather; Suzanne Mather; Trevor Mather.

OTHER INFORMATION In 2019/20 the trust made grants totalling £55,300 to ten organisations, with the majority accrued to Forever Manchester (£30,000), an ongoing recipient.

HOW TO APPLY Contact the correspondent for further information.

CONTACT DETAILS The Trustees, c/o Brightside Planning, Atlas 3, St George's Square, Bolton BL1 2HB *Tel.* 0330 223 3833 *Email* ruth@gobrightside.co.uk

■ Mathew Trust

OSCR NO SC016284 **ESTABLISHED** 1935

WHERE FUNDING CAN BE GIVEN City of Dundee; Angus; Perth and Kinross; Fife.

WHO CAN BENEFIT Registered charities; social enterprises; CICs; schools; individuals; local authorities.

WHAT IS FUNDED Adult education; vocational and professional training; the relief of poverty by providing assistance in the recruitment of people who are unemployed or who are likely to become unemployed in the near future.

TYPE OF GRANT Project funding.

SAMPLE GRANTS Showcase the Street (£30,000); Launch It (£25,000); Cambo Heritage Works (£6,000); The Circle CIC (£4,000); Enable (£1,500).

FINANCES *Financial year end* 30/04/2020 *Income* £301,200 *Total grants* £293,700 *Grants to organisations* £292,100 *Assets* £9,250,000

OTHER INFORMATION During the year, 19 grants were awarded to organisations and a further four, totalling £1,600, were awarded to individuals.

HOW TO APPLY Apply in writing to the correspondent. Appeals are generally considered every two months.

CONTACT DETAILS The Trustees, c/o Henderson Loggie, The Vision Building, 20 Greenmarket, Dundee DD1 4QB *Tel.* 01382 200055

■ The Matliwala Family Charitable Trust

CC NO 1012756 **ESTABLISHED** 1992

WHERE FUNDING CAN BE GIVEN UK and India.

WHO CAN BENEFIT Charitable organisations.

WHAT IS FUNDED The advancement of education for pupils at Matliwala School of Baruch in Gujarat, India, including assisting with the provision of equipment and facilities; the advancement of the Islamic religion; the relief of sickness and poverty; the advancement of education.

SAMPLE GRANTS A list of beneficiaries was not included in the annual report and accounts.

FINANCES *Financial year end* 24/03/2020 *Income* £532,500 *Total grants* £124,800 *Grants to organisations* £118,800 *Assets* £7,530,000

TRUSTEES Ayyub Bux; Yousuf Bux; Hasina Bux; Usman Salya; Fatima Ismail; Afzal Essa.

OTHER INFORMATION During the year, £20,000 was awarded in the UK and £104,800 was awarded overseas. Grants to individuals totalled £6,000.

HOW TO APPLY Applications may be made in writing to the correspondent. The trustees meet monthly to assess grant applications and approve awards. The annual report for 2019/20 states: 'The charity welcomes applications for grants from all quarters and these are assessed by the trustees on their individual merits. Awards are given according to the individual needs of the applicant, depending on the funds available.'

CONTACT DETAILS Ayyub Bux, Trustee, Barton Hall, Garstang Road, Broughton, Preston, Lancashire PR3 5BT *Tel.* 01772 706501

■ Maudsley Charity

CC NO 1055440 **ESTABLISHED** 1996

WHERE FUNDING CAN BE GIVEN South London.

WHO CAN BENEFIT Registered charities; unregistered charities; CICs; social enterprises; schools; universities; hospitals; hospices; religious bodies/institutions; local authorities.

WHAT IS FUNDED Mental health projects across south London.

TYPE OF GRANT Project funding.

RANGE OF GRANTS £1,000 to £1.5 million.

SAMPLE GRANTS South London and Maudsley NHS FT (£1.51 million in 34 grants); King's College London (£657,000 in ten grants); Alcohol Change (£24,000); Raw Material (£12,000); Hear Us (£8,000 in two grants); Mental Fight Club (£1,000).

FINANCES *Financial year end* 31/03/2020 *Income* £4,230,000 *Total grants* £2,900,000 *Grants to organisations* £2,900,000 *Assets* £146,020,000

OTHER INFORMATION Grants were awarded to 67 organisations during the year.

HOW TO APPLY See the charity's website for the latest information on open funding programmes.

CONTACT DETAILS Grants Team, ORTUS, 82–96 Grove Lane, London SE5 8SN *Tel.* 020 3696 9760 *Email* rebecca.gray@maudsleycharity.org *Website* https://maudsleycharity.org

■ The Violet Mauray Charitable Trust

CC NO 1001716 **ESTABLISHED** 1990

WHERE FUNDING CAN BE GIVEN UK.

WHO CAN BENEFIT Registered charities.

WHAT IS FUNDED General charitable purposes, including health and Jewish causes.

TYPE OF GRANT One-off.

RANGE OF GRANTS Mainly between £1,000 and £6,000.

SAMPLE GRANTS Jewish Care (£13,000); St Mungo's (£7,000); Combat Stress (£6,000); Moorfields Eye Charity (£5,000); Nightingale Hammerson (£3,000); Canine Partners (£2,000); Music in Hospitals and Versus Arthritis (£1,000 each).

FINANCES *Financial year end* 05/04/2020 *Income* £57,700 *Total grants* £90,000 *Grants to organisations* £90,000 *Assets* £2,140,000

OTHER INFORMATION Grants were made to 24 organisations during 2019/20.

HOW TO APPLY Apply in writing to the correspondent. The trustees meet regularly to consider applications. Grants are made on an ad hoc basis.

CONTACT DETAILS The Trustees, PO Box 76480, London N10 9FB *Tel.* 07841 048997 *Email* violetmauraytrust@gmail.com

■ Mayfair Charities Ltd

CC NO 255281 **ESTABLISHED** 1968

WHERE FUNDING CAN BE GIVEN UK and overseas (especially Israel).

WHO CAN BENEFIT Registered charities benefitting the Orthodox Jewish community, particularly children and young adults; educational institutions; religious organisations.

WHAT IS FUNDED Orthodox Jewish causes; religion; education; the relief of poverty; social welfare in the Jewish community.

TYPE OF GRANT One-off awards for capital and running costs.

RANGE OF GRANTS £12,000 to £1.6 million.

SAMPLE GRANTS Beth Jacob Grammar School for Girls Ltd (£1.6 million); Society of Friends of Israel Ltd (£136,000); Mir Yeshiva (£123,000); Kahal Chasidim Bobov (£59,000); Slabodka Yeshiva Trust (£32,000); String of Pearls (£20,000); Mercaz Hatorah Netzach Yisroel, Keren Shlomo Trust and Young and Inspired (£15,000 each); Centre for Torah Education Trust (£13,000); Ben Amram Charitable Trust (£12,000).

FINANCES *Financial year end* 31/03/2020 *Income* £4,710,000 *Total grants* £3,790,000 *Grants to organisations* £3,790,000 *Assets* £85,330,000

OTHER INFORMATION Grants were made in the following categories: the advancement of religion and education (£3.6 million) and the relief of poverty (£226,000).

HOW TO APPLY Contact the correspondent for further information.

CONTACT DETAILS The Trustees, Freshwater Group of Companies, Freshwater House, 158–162 Shaftesbury Avenue, London WC2H 8HR *Tel.* 020 7836 1555

■ The Mayfield Valley Arts Trust

CC NO 327665 **ESTABLISHED** 1987

WHERE FUNDING CAN BE GIVEN UK, with a special preference for Yorkshire.

WHO CAN BENEFIT Charitable organisations; schools.

WHAT IS FUNDED Young artists; music education; the arts and music.

WHAT IS NOT FUNDED Grants are not awarded for the education of individual students, the purchase of musical instruments for individuals, schools, organisations, or capital appeals.

TYPE OF GRANT Recurrent.

RANGE OF GRANTS £10,000 to £30,000.

SAMPLE GRANTS Live Music Now, Music in the Round and York Early Music Foundation (£30,000 each); AHT Enterprise Grants (£29,100); Prussia Cove (£15,000); Wigmore Hall (£10,000).

FINANCES *Financial year end* 05/04/2020 *Income* £122,300 *Total grants* £144,100 *Grants to organisations* £144,100 *Assets* £1,830,000

OTHER INFORMATION Grants were awarded to six organisations during the year.

HOW TO APPLY Application forms can be found on the charity's website. The trustees meet once a year, usually in autumn. Applications should be received at least three months in advance.

CONTACT DETAILS The Trustees, 14 Abbots Drive, Ballasalla, Isle of Man IM9 3EB *Tel.* 0114 266 7141 *Email* jthornton@mayfieldartstrust.org *Website* www.mayfieldartstrust.org.uk

■ Mayheights Ltd

CC NO 1112291 **ESTABLISHED** 2005

WHERE FUNDING CAN BE GIVEN Barnet, Hackney and Israel.

WHO CAN BENEFIT Registered charities; voluntary organisations; schools.

WHAT IS FUNDED The advancement of the Orthodox Jewish religion; Jewish education; the relief of poverty; medical purposes.

RANGE OF GRANTS Up to £270,000.

SAMPLE GRANTS Amudei Olam (£270,000); Mifal Torah (£237,300); Yeshivas Ateret Shlomo (£230,500); Ezer V'hatzalah Ltd (£178,200); Mifal Zedko Vchesed (£150,500); Nextgrant Ltd (£123,400); Rookwood Foundation (£80,000); Chesed Shel Emess (£65,300); Congregation Yetev Lev Synagogue (£62,000); Congregation Minchas Yehudah (£50,000).

FINANCES *Financial year end* 31/03/2020 *Income* £4,170,000 *Total grants* £2,210,000 *Grants to organisations* £2,210,000 *Assets* £18,490,000

OTHER INFORMATION Grants of under £50,000 totalled £700,600.

HOW TO APPLY Apply in writing to the correspondent. The charity's 2019/20 accounts note that while not actively inviting applications, the trustees consider all requests received.

CONTACT DETAILS The Trustees, 36 Gilda Crescent, London N16 6JP *Tel.* 020 8806 1234

■ Maypride Ltd

CC NO 289394 **ESTABLISHED** 1984

WHERE FUNDING CAN BE GIVEN UK.

WHO CAN BENEFIT Jewish organisations.

WHAT IS FUNDED The advancement of the Orthodox Jewish religion; the advancement of the education and relief of poverty of those belonging to that faith.

WHAT IS NOT FUNDED Individuals.

RANGE OF GRANTS £1,000 to £30,000.

SAMPLE GRANTS Beis Ahron Trust and Keren Hatzolas Doros Alei Siach (£31,000 each); Give and Earn (£26,000); Shaykel Esuh and Satmar Kollel (£10,000 each); British Friends Mosdos Tchernobil (£9,000); Ben Amram Charitable Trust and SOFT (£7,000 each); Youth Space (£5,000); Ohavei Torasecha (£2,000); Ruzhin Sadigura Trust (£1,700).

FINANCES *Financial year end* 31/03/2019 *Income* £56,100 *Total grants* £165,700 *Grants to organisations* £165,700 *Assets* £423,500

TRUSTEES Andre Sternlicht; Esther Sternlicht.

OTHER INFORMATION The 2018/19 annual accounts were the latest available at the time of writing (June 2021). Grants were awarded to 16 organisations during that year.

HOW TO APPLY Contact the correspondent for further information.

CONTACT DETAILS The Trustees, 5 North End Road, London NW11 7RJ *Tel.* 020 8455 6789

■ Mazars Charitable Trust

CC NO 1150459 **ESTABLISHED** 2012

WHERE FUNDING CAN BE GIVEN UK.

WHO CAN BENEFIT Registered charities; voluntary organisations; hospices; colleges and schools.

WHAT IS FUNDED General charitable purposes. Support is normally only given to projects which are nominated to the management committee by the partners and staff of Mazars LLP, a global audit, tax and advisory group.

RANGE OF GRANTS Up to £25,000.

SAMPLE GRANTS Previous beneficiaries have included: Friends of Asha (£25,000); Erskine Hospital Ltd (£14,400); Muntada Aid (£10,000); King's Arms Project Bedford (£9,000); Burning Nights CRPS Support (£5,000); The RAF Association (£2,000).

FINANCES *Financial year end* 31/03/2020 *Income* £400 *Total grants* £390,000 *Grants to organisations* £390,000

TRUSTEES Alan Edwards; David Evans; Lesley Fox; Philip Verity; Kim Hurst.

OTHER INFORMATION Full accounts were not available to view on the Charity Commission's website due to the trust's low income. We therefore estimated the trust's grant total based on its total expenditure.

HOW TO APPLY The trustees do not respond to unsolicited applications. All nominations for grants have to be proposed by staff members of Mazars LLP: no grant applications should be submitted directly to the trust.

CONTACT DETAILS The Trustees, PO Box 462, Bicester, Oxfordshire OX26 9LY *Tel.* 07756 323888 *Email* mazarscharitabletrust@gmail.com

■ MBNA General Foundation

CC NO 1065515 **ESTABLISHED** 1997

WHERE FUNDING CAN BE GIVEN Within a 30-mile radius of MBNA Ltd's Chester campus.

WHO CAN BENEFIT Charities; community groups; schools.

WHAT IS FUNDED General charitable purposes including the following: children and young people; older people; people with disabilities; schools.

SAMPLE GRANTS Tarvin Primary School (£39,100); Chester FC Trust Fund (£32,500); Hope House Hospice (£22,900); Cheshire Connect (£20,000); Penerlag County Primary School (£10,000); Llay United Youth FC (£500).

FINANCES *Financial year end* 31/12/2019 *Income* £34,900 *Total grants* £441,000 *Grants to organisations* £441,000 *Assets* £754,400

TRUSTEES Mr Stables; Ian Doherty; Sean Humphreys; Ellyn Corfield; Mark Elliot.

HOW TO APPLY Contact the correspondent for further information. The foundation considers both internal requests (those considered to have a connection to an employee of MBNA Ltd or a historic relationship/connection to MBNA Ltd) and external requests (no connection to MBNA Ltd) for funding.

CONTACT DETAILS The Trustees, Stansfield House, Chester Business Park, Chester CH4 9QQ *Tel.* 01244 672999

■ The Robert McAlpine Foundation

CC NO 226646 **ESTABLISHED** 1963

WHERE FUNDING CAN BE GIVEN UK.

WHO CAN BENEFIT Registered charities; schools; hospices; hospitals.

WHAT IS FUNDED General charitable purposes; medical research; social welfare; children with disabilities; older people; young people.

WHAT IS NOT FUNDED Fundraising activities.

TYPE OF GRANT Capital costs; running costs; project funding; research.

RANGE OF GRANTS £5,000 to £10,000.

SAMPLE GRANTS A list of beneficiaries was not included in the annual report and accounts.

FINANCES *Financial year end* 31/03/2020 *Income* £826,600 *Total grants* £632,100 *Grants to organisations* £632,100 *Assets* £15,440,000

TRUSTEES Adrian McAlpine; Cullum McAlpine; The Hon. David McAlpine; Gavin McAlpine.

HOW TO APPLY Apply in writing or via email to the correspondent. Appeals should be no more than two A4 pages and include a copy of your organisation's most recent accounts – visit the foundation's website for details on what to include. The trustees meet annually in November to approve grants – applications must be received no later than 31 August to be considered at the next meeting. The foundation is unable to accept any appeal requests by telephone.

CONTACT DETAILS Appeals Manager, Eaton Court, Maylands Avenue, Hemel Hempstead, Hertfordshire HP2 7TR *Tel.* 0333 566 2069 *Email* foundation@srm.com *Website* www.robertmcalpinefoundation.org

■ Gemma and Chris McGough Charitable Foundation CIO

CC NO 1173373 **ESTABLISHED** 2017
WHERE FUNDING CAN BE GIVEN Worldwide.
WHO CAN BENEFIT Registered charities.
WHAT IS FUNDED Education and training; health; disability; social welfare; the environment; human rights; children and young people.
TYPE OF GRANT Project funding.
SAMPLE GRANTS A full list of beneficiaries was not available.
FINANCES *Financial year end* 30/06/2020 *Income* £102,000 *Total grants* £101,700 *Grants to organisations* £101,700 *Assets* £955,100
TRUSTEES Gemma McGough; Christopher McGough; Clare Macbeth.
OTHER INFORMATION In 2019/20, the foundation awarded grants of under two categories: the environment (£67,600) and children and families (£34,100).
HOW TO APPLY Apply in writing to the correspondent. Limited consideration is given to unsolicited applications, but small grant requests may be considered.
CONTACT DETAILS Gemma McGough, Trustee, The Rosery, Ilmer, Princes Risborough, Buckinghamshire HP27 9QZ *Tel.* 07843 279792 *Email* gemmamcgough@outlook.com *Website* https://www.mcgoughfoundation.org

■ McGreevy No. 5 Settlement

CC NO 280666 **ESTABLISHED** 1979
WHERE FUNDING CAN BE GIVEN UK, with some preference for the Bristol and Bath areas.
WHO CAN BENEFIT Registered charities.
WHAT IS FUNDED General charitable purposes; children and young people; health.
RANGE OF GRANTS Up to £25,000.
SAMPLE GRANTS Helen Arkell Dyslexia Centre and NSPCC (£25,000 each); Somerset Community Foundation (£20,000); Designability Bath, Feeding Bristol, Sofa Project and Voices Bath (£5,000 each); Watlington Hospital Charitable Trust (£1,000).
FINANCES *Financial year end* 05/04/2020 *Income* £90,000 *Total grants* £51,000 *Grants to organisations* £51,000 *Assets* £2,720,000
TRUSTEES Avon Executor and Trustee Co. Ltd; Anthony McGreevy; Elise McGreevy-Harris; Katrina Paterson.
OTHER INFORMATION Grants were paid to three organisations in 2019/20, totalling £51,000. A further eight grants were committed (i.e. grants offered but cheques not cleared) totalling £51,000. The list of beneficiaries includes recipients of both grants paid and committed.
HOW TO APPLY Contact the correspondent for further information.
CONTACT DETAILS The Trustees, Yew Court, Riverview Road, Pangbourne, Reading, Berkshire RG8 7AU *Tel.* 0117 905 4000 *Email* elise139@aol.com

■ D. D. McPhail Charitable Settlement

CC NO 267588 **ESTABLISHED** 1973
WHERE FUNDING CAN BE GIVEN UK.
WHO CAN BENEFIT Mainly small and medium-sized registered charities; hospices; educational institutions and research centres.
WHAT IS FUNDED Medical research; people with disabilities, particularly children; older people.
TYPE OF GRANT Research funding; project funding.
RANGE OF GRANTS Small grants – up to £4,000; large grants – typically up to £100,000.
SAMPLE GRANTS Sign Health (£163,000); Community Links (£100,000); Devon Community Foundation (£25,000); Community Foundation for Lancashire (£20,000); The Cure Parkinson's Trust (£10,000); Bibic (£5,000); Imperial College London (£4,000); deafPLUS and East Elmbridge Foodbank (£2,000 each).
FINANCES *Financial year end* 05/04/2020 *Income* £452,800 *Total grants* £519,100 *Grants to organisations* £519,100 *Assets* £8,780,000
TRUSTEES Edward Coley; Julia Noble; Mary Meeks; Olivia Hancock; George de Courcy-Wheeler; Helene Jelman; Jane Brake.
OTHER INFORMATION Grants were made to 29 organisations during the year, of which 94% were large grants (between £5,000 and £163,000).
HOW TO APPLY The 2019/20 annual report states the following: 'Trustees identify potential projects for assessment by the Executive Director. The Trust makes no commitment to respond to unsolicited applications.'
CONTACT DETAILS Katharine Moss, Executive Director, PO Box 432, Bicester, Oxfordshire OX26 9JL *Tel.* 07523 440550 *Email* director.ddmcphail@gmail.com *Website* www.ddmcphailcharitablesettlement.co.uk

■ Medical Research Foundation

CC NO 1138223 **ESTABLISHED** 2011
WHERE FUNDING CAN BE GIVEN UK and Africa.
WHO CAN BENEFIT Universities; research institutions.
WHAT IS FUNDED Medical research.
TYPE OF GRANT Research grants; infrastructure and equipment grants; fellowships and studentships; skill-sharing and collaborations; dissemination of research results.
RANGE OF GRANTS Up to £1 million.
SAMPLE GRANTS University of Birmingham (£614,000); Imperial College London (£401,000); University of Exeter (£30,000); Francis Crick Institute (£7,000); University of Manchester (£1,000).
FINANCES *Financial year end* 31/03/2020 *Income* £9,230,000 *Total grants* £3,050,000 *Grants to organisations* £3,050,000 *Assets* £59,140,000
TRUSTEES Susan Wilkinson; Dr Lesley Sherratt; Prof. Daniel Altman; Russell Delew; Prof. Moira Whyte; Richard Lackmann; Dr Hans Haitchi; David Zahn; Prof. Calliope Farsides.
HOW TO APPLY Applications can be made via the foundation's website, where details of open programmes and application deadlines can also be found.
CONTACT DETAILS The Trustees, 49–51 East Road, London N1 0AH *Tel.* 020 7250 0210 *Email* research@medicalresearchfoundation.org.uk *Website* www.medicalresearchfoundation.org.uk

■ Medical Research Scotland

OSCR NO SC014959 **ESTABLISHED** 1953
WHERE FUNDING CAN BE GIVEN Scotland.
WHO CAN BENEFIT Universities; research institutions.
WHAT IS FUNDED Medical research.
TYPE OF GRANT PhD studentships; undergraduate scholarships; fellowships.

SAMPLE GRANTS A list of beneficiaries was not included in the annual report and accounts.

FINANCES *Financial year end* 31/03/2020 *Income* £1,780,000 *Total grants* £1,880,000 *Grants to organisations* £1,880,000 *Assets* £35,600,000

TRUSTEES Prof. Philip Winn; Prof. John Brown; Prof. Bernie Conway; Linda Duncan; Alasdair Gill; Prof. Andrea Nolan; Dr Michael Roberts; Barry Rose; Prof. Heather Wallace; Prof. Jenny Woof.

HOW TO APPLY Detailed information regarding the foundation's grant programmes, guidance notes, deadlines for applications and more is available from the charity's website.

CONTACT DETAILS The Trustees, c/o Turcan Connell, Princes Exchange, 1 Earl Grey Street, Edinburgh EH3 9EE *Tel.* 0131 659 8800 *Email* enquiries@medicalresearchscotland.org.uk *Website* www.medicalresearchscotland.org.uk

■ The Medicash Foundation

CC NO 257636 **ESTABLISHED** 1969

WHERE FUNDING CAN BE GIVEN The North West.

WHO CAN BENEFIT NHS and health-related charities.

WHAT IS FUNDED Health.

SAMPLE GRANTS Feeding Birkenhead (£27,800); Foundation for the Prevention of Blindness (£24,000); The Clatterbridge Cancer Charity (£15,000); Cyclists Fighting Cancer and Deafblind UK (£5,000 each); Crohn's and Colitis UK (£3,000); Chinese Wellbeing (£2,000); Knowsley Older People's Fun Olympics (£820); Glyndwr University (£250).

FINANCES *Financial year end* 31/12/2019 *Income* £856,000 *Total grants* £590,900 *Grants to organisations* £590,900 *Assets* £1,154,000

TRUSTEE Medicash Health Benefits Ltd.

HOW TO APPLY Application forms can be downloaded from the foundation's website.

CONTACT DETAILS The Trustees, Medicash Ltd, 1 Derby Square, Liverpool L2 1AB *Tel.* 0151 702 0202 *Email* linda.traynor@medicash.org *Website* https://www.medicash.org/charity

■ The Medlock Charitable Trust

CC NO 326927 **ESTABLISHED** 1985

WHERE FUNDING CAN BE GIVEN UK, with a preference for Bath and the borough of Boston, Lincolnshire.

WHO CAN BENEFIT Registered charities, preferably smaller charities; educational establishments; local community groups.

WHAT IS FUNDED Education; health and social care; housing; sports and recreation; arts and culture; the environment and conservation; community services; employment.

WHAT IS NOT FUNDED Individuals; animal charities; competitions; events; educational institutions where only a privileged elite will benefit.

RANGE OF GRANTS Up to £50,000 but generally from £5,000 to £15,000.

SAMPLE GRANTS The Boshier-Hinton Foundation (£180,000); Southmead Hospital Charity (£100,000); Wells Cathedral (£90,000); Avon and Bristol Law Centre (£50,000); Young Carers Development Trust (£30,000); The Butterfly Hospice Trust (£15,000); Focus Counselling (£10,000); The Gurkha Welfare Trust (£8,000); Blackhorse Primary School PTA (£7,000); Lincolnshire Community and Voluntary Service (£5,000); Hawkspring (£3,000); Bath Postal Museum (£2,000); Home-Start Bristol (£1,000); Midsomer Norton RFC Junior Section Ltd (£300).

FINANCES *Financial year end* 31/07/2019 *Income* £407,900 *Total grants* £1,880,000 *Grants to organisations* £1,880,000 *Assets* £36,440,000

TRUSTEES David Medlock; Jacqueline Medlock; Mark Goodman; Peter Medlock.

OTHER INFORMATION In 2018/19, grants were made to 174 organisations from a total of 539 applications. Of these grants, 124 were for £10,000 or less. This is in line with the trust's policy of 'supporting smaller charities with grants which mean a great deal to them'.

HOW TO APPLY Apply through the online application form available on the trust's website. The trustees meet monthly to assess applications. The website also details information on how grant applications are assessed.

CONTACT DETAILS The Trustees, St George's Lodge, 33 Oldfield Road, Bath, Somerset BA2 3NE *Tel.* 01225 946226 *Email* office@medlockcharitabletrust.org *Website* https://medlockcharitabletrust.org

■ The Meikle Foundation

OSCR NO SC009842 **ESTABLISHED** 1972

WHERE FUNDING CAN BE GIVEN Scotland, with a preference for the Fife and Aberdeen areas.

WHO CAN BENEFIT Predominately Scottish charities or charities with a Scottish connection.

WHAT IS FUNDED General charitable purposes.

WHAT IS NOT FUNDED Individuals.

RANGE OF GRANTS Generally up to £2,000.

SAMPLE GRANTS RNLI and Scottish Refugee Council (£4,000 each); Carers Trust for Scotland and Leonard Cheshire Foundation (£3,000 each); Combat Stress, Dysart St Clair Church and Scottish Ballet (£2,000 each); REACT (Rapid Effective Assistance for Children with potentially Terminal illness) and Surfers Against Sewage (£1,000 each).

FINANCES *Financial year end* 05/04/2020 *Income* £503,900 *Total grants* £343,400 *Grants to organisations* £343,400 *Assets* £8,450,000

OTHER INFORMATION The foundation has been renamed from the Martin Connell Charitable Trust to The Meikle Foundation to reflect the family name of the four sisters who set it up in 1973.

HOW TO APPLY Contact the foundation's administrator for information on the application process. The trustees meet twice a year to consider appeals.

CONTACT DETAILS Sandra Graham, Administrator, Dentons UKMEA LLP, 1 George Square, Glasgow G2 1AL *Tel.* 0330 222 1765 *Email* sandra.graham@dentons.com *Website* https://www.themeiklefoundation.com

■ Melodor Ltd

CC NO 260972 **ESTABLISHED** 1970

WHERE FUNDING CAN BE GIVEN UK and overseas.

WHO CAN BENEFIT Orthodox Jewish institutions; Jewish educational institutions and charities.

WHAT IS FUNDED General charitable purposes, especially education and religion, with a focus on Orthodox Jewish causes; the relief of poverty; health.

RANGE OF GRANTS Up to £65,000.

SAMPLE GRANTS Asser Bishvil Foundation (£65,800); Ohel Torah (£25,400); Choimel Dalim (£25,000); Ateres Yoel (£10,000); Chasdei Yoel

Charitable Trust (£8,800); Tov Vchesed (£8,000); Talmud Torah Yetev Lev Ltd (£6,500); Kollel Gaon Yaakov (£5,000).

FINANCES *Financial year end* 29/03/2020 *Income* £266,600 *Total grants* £183,200 *Grants to organisations* £183,200 *Assets* £598,000

TRUSTEES Hyman Weiss; Philip Weiss; Zisel Weiss; Pinchas Neumann; Maurice Neumann; Yocheved Weiss; Eli Neumann; Esther Henry; Henry Neumann; Janet Bleier; Miriam Friedlander; Rebecca Delange; Rivka Ollech; Rivka Rabinowitz; Pesha Kohn; Yehoshua Weiss.

OTHER INFORMATION Grants of less than £5,000 amounted to £28,800.

HOW TO APPLY Apply in writing to the correspondent. The charity's annual report for 2019/20 states: 'The governors receive many applications for grants, mainly by mail, but also verbally. Each application is considered against the criteria established by the charity. Although the charity does not advertise, it is well known within its community and there are many requests received for grants.'

CONTACT DETAILS Henry Neumann, Company Secretary, 10 Cubley Road, Salford, Greater Manchester M7 4GN *Tel.* 0161 720 6188

■ The Melow Charitable Trust

CC NO 275454 **ESTABLISHED** 1978

WHERE FUNDING CAN BE GIVEN UK and overseas.

WHO CAN BENEFIT Mainly Jewish charities.

WHAT IS FUNDED Jewish causes; the relief of poverty; the advancement of religion and religious education.

SAMPLE GRANTS Ezer V'Hatzalah Ltd (£620,000); Friends of Zichron Dovid (£61,000); Chasdei Aharon Ltd and Start Upright (£50,000 each); Inspirations and Shaarei Chesed Trust (£30,000 each).

FINANCES *Financial year end* 31/12/2019 *Income* £1,480,000 *Total grants* £1,710,000 *Grants to organisations* £1,710,000 *Assets* £12,220,000

TRUSTEES Miriam Spitz; Esther Weiser.

OTHER INFORMATION Only organisations that received grants of over £30,000 were listed as beneficiaries in the charity's accounts. Grants of under £30,000 totalled £164,000.

HOW TO APPLY Contact the correspondent for further information.

CONTACT DETAILS The Trustees, 21 Warwick Grove, London E5 9HX *Tel.* 020 8806 1549

■ Meningitis Research Foundation

CC NO 1091105 **ESTABLISHED** 2002

WHERE FUNDING CAN BE GIVEN UK.

WHO CAN BENEFIT Research organisations; universities.

WHAT IS FUNDED Research into the causes, prevention, and treatment of all forms of meningitis and associated infections.

TYPE OF GRANT Research funding.

SAMPLE GRANTS Health Protection Scotland; National Centre for Communicable Diseases – South Africa; Public Health England; University of Bristol; University of Cambridge.

FINANCES *Financial year end* 31/03/2020 *Income* £2,340,000 *Total grants* £145,000 *Grants to organisations* £145,000 *Assets* £994,400

TRUSTEES David Moed; Brian Scott; Margaret Smith; Sarah Jeffery; Dr Susan Grieve; Martin Vaggers; Dr Jane Cope; Prof. Ray Borrow; Michael Nallen; Stephen Highwood; Dr Nick Manson.

HOW TO APPLY Calls for funding proposals are periodically posted on the foundation's website.

CONTACT DETAILS Liz Rodgers, Research Projects Manager, Newminster House, 27–29 Baldwin Street, Bristol BS1 1LT *Tel.* 0333 405 6258 *Email* elizabethr@meningitis.org *Website* www.meningitis.org

■ Menuchar Ltd

CC NO 262782 **ESTABLISHED** 1971

WHERE FUNDING CAN BE GIVEN UK.

WHO CAN BENEFIT Jewish organisations and religious establishments.

WHAT IS FUNDED The advancement of religion in accordance with the Orthodox Jewish faith and the relief of people in need.

SAMPLE GRANTS There was no list of beneficiaries contained within the annual report and accounts.

FINANCES *Financial year end* 31/03/2020 *Income* £510,000 *Total grants* £557,700 *Grants to organisations* £557,700 *Assets* £340,500

TRUSTEES Gail Bude; Raphael Bude.

OTHER INFORMATION A list of beneficiaries was not included in the annual report and accounts.

HOW TO APPLY Contact the correspondent for further information.

CONTACT DETAILS Helena Bude, Secretary, Barry Flack and Co. Ltd, The Brentano Suite, Prospect House, 2 Athenaeum Road, London N20 9AE *Tel.* 020 8369 5170

■ Mercaz Torah Vechesed Ltd

CC NO 1109212 **ESTABLISHED** 2005

WHERE FUNDING CAN BE GIVEN Worldwide, with a preference for Barnet, Hackney and Israel.

WHO CAN BENEFIT Charitable organisations and individuals.

WHAT IS FUNDED Orthodox Jewish religious education; the relief of poverty and ill health among members of the Orthodox Jewish community.

SAMPLE GRANTS Ohr Haganuz Maseh Rokeach (£642,300); Parshat Mordchai (£530,400); Adnei Hakodesh (£415,500); Achozat Aharon (£152,500); Mamleches Hatorah (£128,000); Birchat Aharon (£58,900); Give N'earn (£50,000).

FINANCES *Financial year end* 31/01/2020 *Income* £2,220,000 *Total grants* £2,200,000 *Grants to organisations* £2,200,000 *Assets* £70,700

TRUSTEES Joseph Ostreicher; Mordche Rand.

OTHER INFORMATION There were no grants made to individuals directly in the 2019/20 financial year. Grants of less than £50,000 amounted to £125,008.

HOW TO APPLY Contact the correspondent for further information.

CONTACT DETAILS Joseph Ostreicher, Trustee, 28 Braydon Road, London N16 6QB *Tel.* 020 8880 5366 *Email* umarpeh@gmail.com

The Brian Mercer Charitable Trust

CC NO 1076925 **ESTABLISHED** 1999

WHERE FUNDING CAN BE GIVEN UK; Blackburn; overseas.

WHO CAN BENEFIT UK-registered charities with an annual income of under £700,000.

WHAT IS FUNDED Art in the North West; causes local to Blackburn; health and welfare (UK and overseas).

WHAT IS NOT FUNDED Charities based outside the UK and Ireland; individuals; medical research; interventions that discriminate on the grounds of gender, religion, sexual orientation, disability, race, colour or ethnicity; UK initiatives for specific local areas other than Blackburn.

TYPE OF GRANT Project funding.

SAMPLE GRANTS Drugs for Neglected Diseases (£40,000); Concern Worldwide (£28,900); Salvation Army (£20,000); Legs4Africa (£5,000); Blackburn College (£2,500).

FINANCES *Financial year end* 05/04/2020 *Income* £354,100 *Total grants* £197,100 *Grants to organisations* £197,100 *Assets* £29,740,000

TRUSTEES Roger Duckworth; John Merrill; Ann Clitheroe; Jane Clancy.

OTHER INFORMATION Within the broad objectives of the charity, grant-making is focused on the following areas: the prevention and relief of human suffering (75%), the arts (12.5%), and causes local to Blackburn (12.5%). A total of 20 grants were awarded during the year.

HOW TO APPLY Application forms and deadlines can be found on the trust's website.

CONTACT DETAILS The Trustees, c/o Beever and Struthers, Central Buildings, Richmond Terrace, Blackburn BB1 7AP *Tel.* 01254 686600 *Email* info@brianmercertrust.org *Website* https://www.brianmercertrust.org

The Mercers' Charitable Foundation

CC NO 326340 **ESTABLISHED** 1982

WHERE FUNDING CAN BE GIVEN UK, with a preference for London, Norfolk, Lincolnshire and the North East.

WHO CAN BENEFIT Registered charities; charities exempt from registration; churches.

WHAT IS FUNDED Education; children and young people; older people; housing and homelessness; refugees; community services; churches; families.

WHAT IS NOT FUNDED Retrospective costs; newly established groups; individuals or students; work overseas; capital projects.

TYPE OF GRANT Core costs; project funding; salaries.

SAMPLE GRANTS Construction Industry Trust for Youth (£143,000); University of the Arts (£90,500); Windsor Leadership Trust (£47,500); One Westminster (£40,000); Northumberland Community Bank (£30,000); Newham All Star Sports (£25,000); English National Ballet (£16,700); Durham Diocesan Board of Finance (£10,000); Guild of Mercers' Scholars (£7,000).

FINANCES *Financial year end* 31/03/2020 *Income* £4,460,000 *Total grants* £5,450,000 *Grants to organisations* £5,450,000 *Assets* £19,930,000

TRUSTEE The Mercers' Company.

OTHER INFORMATION Grants were broken down as follows: young people and education (£2.71 million in 77 grants); church and communities programme (£1.46 million in 60 grants); older people and housing programme (£1.05 million in 41 grants); other (£238,000 in 17 grants).

HOW TO APPLY More information (including guidelines and notes on exclusions) is available on the website. Only applications submitted using the application form on the website are accepted.

CONTACT DETAILS The Trustees, The Mercers' Company, 6 Frederick's Place, London EC2R 8AB *Tel.* 020 7776 7250 *Email* grants@mercers.co.uk *Website* https://www.mercers.co.uk/philanthropy

Merchant Navy Welfare Board

CC NO 212799 **ESTABLISHED** 1962

WHERE FUNDING CAN BE GIVEN The UK and its overseas territories.

WHO CAN BENEFIT Charitable organisations related to sailors and seafarers.

WHAT IS FUNDED The welfare of merchant seafarers, fishermen and their dependants.

TYPE OF GRANT Capital costs; start-up costs.

RANGE OF GRANTS Up to £5,000.

SAMPLE GRANTS Sir Gabriel Woods' Mariners' Home (£45,800); Nautilus Welfare Fund (£8,500); Mission to Seafarers – Fowey (£7,800); Care Ashore (£1,400); Merchant Navy Honours Consultative Committee (£100).

FINANCES *Financial year end* 31/12/2019 *Income* £814,400 *Total grants* £234,000 *Grants to organisations* £234,000 *Assets* £15,090,000

TRUSTEES Mark Carden; David Appleton; Alison Godfrey; Adrian Hodgson; Alexander Campbell; Timothy Springett; Justin Osmond; Mark Dickinson; Graham Lane; Ijeoma Ajibade; Andrew Cassels; Darren Procter; Catherine Spencer.

OTHER INFORMATION Grants are only made to the charity's constituent organisations.

HOW TO APPLY Application forms can be downloaded from the charity's website.

CONTACT DETAILS The Trustees, 8 Cumberland Place, Southampton, Hampshire SO15 2BH *Tel.* 023 8033 7799 *Email* enquiries@mnwb.org.uk *Website* www.mnwb.org

The Merchant Taylors' Company Charities Fund

CC NO 1069124 **ESTABLISHED** 1941

WHERE FUNDING CAN BE GIVEN UK, especially inner London and the boroughs of Lewisham, Southwark, Tower Hamlets and Hackney and their environs.

WHO CAN BENEFIT Charitable organisations; educational institutions; churches.

WHAT IS FUNDED General charitable purposes, including the relief of poverty, health and disability, education and training and religious causes.

WHAT IS NOT FUNDED Building costs; medical research; generalised appeals; very large charities; individuals; funding that will be passed on to individuals or third parties.

TYPE OF GRANT One-off grants or three-year tapering grants.

RANGE OF GRANTS Usually between £5,000 and £15,000.

SAMPLE GRANTS Bowhaven (£50,000); Magic Breakfast (£10,000); Invincible Me (£5,000); MTS Outward Bound (£4,200); Bespoke Tailors' Benevolent Association (£2,500); St Paul's

Cathedral Choir School (£1,000); St Michaels (£500).

FINANCES *Financial year end* 31/12/2019 *Income* £305,600 *Total grants* £86,200 *Grants to organisations* £86,200 *Assets* £1,450,000

TRUSTEES Rupert Bull; Richard Sullivan; Revd Ralph Godsall; David Jackson.

OTHER INFORMATION Part of the grant total is restricted to the awarding of prizes and grants to schools and churches associated with the Merchant Taylors' Company.

HOW TO APPLY According to the website, at present, awards are restricted to charities nominated by the Livery Committee. Applications may only be made with the support of a member of the Merchant Taylors' Company or by invitation.

CONTACT DETAILS The Trustees, Merchant Taylor's Hall, 30 Threadneedle Street, London EC2R 8JB *Tel.* 020 7450 4440 *Email* charities@merchant-taylors.co.uk *Website* www.merchant-taylors.co.uk/charities

The Merchant Venturers' Charity

CC NO 264302 **ESTABLISHED** 1972

WHERE FUNDING CAN BE GIVEN The greater Bristol area.

WHO CAN BENEFIT Local and regional charitable organisations; local branches of national organisations.

WHAT IS FUNDED Social welfare; children and young people; education; the environment; social enterprise; healthcare; culture and the arts; and projects that will benefit greater Bristol and its economic development.

WHAT IS NOT FUNDED Statutory organisations or the direct replacement of statutory funding; retrospective costs; activities that are intended to raise funds for other organisations. Grants are unlikely to be made towards the cost of an existing salaried position.

TYPE OF GRANT Capital equipment or ongoing revenue costs.

RANGE OF GRANTS Generally between £500 and £5,000.

SAMPLE GRANTS Cathedral Trust (£50,000); Clifton Down Charitable Trust (£15,000); Bristol Tranquiliser Project, Feeding Bristol, Genesis Trust and South Bristol Youth (£5,000 each).

FINANCES *Financial year end* 31/12/2019 *Income* £403,900 *Total grants* £245,200 *Grants to organisations* £245,200 *Assets* £8,910,000

TRUSTEE SMV Trustee Company Ltd.

OTHER INFORMATION Only organisations that received grants of over £5,000 were listed as beneficiaries in the charity's accounts. Grants of under £5,000 totalled £95,100.

HOW TO APPLY Application forms and detailed guidelines are accessible on the charity's website. Once completed, forms can be returned via email. The members of the Charity Committee meet four times a year, typically in January, April, July and October, to consider applications for funding.

CONTACT DETAILS Helen Parker, The Old Court House, Church Street, Nailsworth, Stroud, Gloucestershire GL6 0BP *Tel.* 0117 973 8058 *Email* enquiries@merchantventurers.com *Website* www.merchantventurers.com

Merchants' House of Glasgow

OSCR NO SC008900 **ESTABLISHED** 1605

WHERE FUNDING CAN BE GIVEN Glasgow and the west of Scotland.

WHO CAN BENEFIT Registered charities working in Glasgow and the west of Scotland; individuals.

WHAT IS FUNDED General charitable purposes.

TYPE OF GRANT Project funding; capital costs; core/revenue costs.

RANGE OF GRANTS Between £500 and £10,000.

SAMPLE GRANTS Royal Scottish National Orchestra (£17,600); Scottish Nautical Welfare Association (£15,000); Lodging House Mission (£11,500); Royal Liverpool Seamen's Orphan Institution (£8,000); National Youth Choir (£7,000) Deafblind (£6,000).

FINANCES *Financial year end* 31/12/2019 *Income* £1,260,000 *Total grants* £368,600 *Grants to organisations* £239,200 *Assets* £11,200,000

OTHER INFORMATION Grants were made to 55 organisations. Only organisations that received grants of over £5,000 were listed as beneficiaries in the charity's accounts. Grants of under £5,000 totalled £52,500 and were awarded to 45 organisations.

HOW TO APPLY Application forms can be accessed from the charity's website and submitted online. Applications must be accompanied by the latest copy of audited accounts and any other supporting documentation informing about the organisation's principal activities.

CONTACT DETAILS The Directors, 7 West George Street, Glasgow G2 1BA *Tel.* 0141 221 8272 *Email* info@merchantshouse.org.uk *Website* www.merchantshouse.org.uk

Mercury Phoenix Trust

CC NO 1013768 **ESTABLISHED** 1992

WHERE FUNDING CAN BE GIVEN UK and overseas.

WHO CAN BENEFIT Registered charities; HIV/AIDS-related projects.

WHAT IS FUNDED HIV and AIDS awareness, particularly when aimed at young people in and out of school; projects to help children orphaned by AIDS; relief of poverty, sickness and distress of people affected by HIV and AIDS.

WHAT IS NOT FUNDED Individuals; travel grants.

TYPE OF GRANT Project funding; strategic funding.

RANGE OF GRANTS Generally up to £10,000.

SAMPLE GRANTS Sakh'Ulutsha: Scripture Union Lifeskills Education Initiative (£30,000); AVERT (£10,500); Restless Development (£16,900); Hillcrest Aids Centre Trust (£6,100); NAM (£5,000); Zamaxulo Orphanage (£3,000); Paramedical Education Trust (£1,800).

FINANCES *Financial year end* 31/03/2020 *Income* £1,140,000 *Total grants* £581,600 *Grants to organisations* £581,600 *Assets* £2,660,000

TRUSTEES Brian May; Henry Beach; Mary Austin; Roger Taylor.

OTHER INFORMATION Grants are made across a number of countries.

HOW TO APPLY Contact the correspondent for an application form. In addition to the form, the trust also requires a budget and the applying organisation's registration certificate, most recent audited accounts and annual report, and constitution or memorandum and articles of association.

CONTACT DETAILS Janice Page, PO Box 704, Chesham, Buckinghamshire HP5 1XF *Tel.* 01494 766799 *Email* jan@idrec.com *Website* www.mercuryphoenixtrust.com

■ T. and J. Meyer Family Foundation Ltd

CC NO 1087507 **ESTABLISHED** 2000

WHERE FUNDING CAN BE GIVEN Worldwide.

WHO CAN BENEFIT Charitable organisations.

WHAT IS FUNDED Education; healthcare; conservation; membership.

TYPE OF GRANT Core costs.

RANGE OF GRANTS Grants range from £3,600 to £155,700.

SAMPLE GRANTS Cree Foundation (£155,700); Educate! (£72,100); Lwala Community Alliance (£54,100); Silverleaf Academy (£36,100); Sustainable Living Center (£12,300); Advance Charity (£9,300); Windermere Island Foundation (£3,600).

FINANCES *Financial year end* 31/12/2019 *Income* £622,700 *Total grants* £690,000 *Grants to organisations* £690,000 *Assets* £18,720,000

TRUSTEES Jane Meyer; Edwin Falkman; Dr Della Drees.

OTHER INFORMATION During the year, the foundation awarded 15 grants. The financial information has been converted from USD using the exchange rate at the time of writing (March 2021).

HOW TO APPLY The foundation does not accept unsolicited applications.

CONTACT DETAILS The Trustees, 3 Kendrick Mews, London SW7 3HG *Tel.* 020 7581 9900 *Email* info@tjmff.org

■ The Mickel Fund

OSCR NO SC003266 **ESTABLISHED** 1970

WHERE FUNDING CAN BE GIVEN UK and overseas.

WHO CAN BENEFIT Registered charities.

WHAT IS FUNDED Education; social welfare; arts, culture and heritage; sports; healthcare and medical research.

WHAT IS NOT FUNDED Events such as conferences, seminars and exhibitions; fee-charging residential homes, nurseries and care facilities; fundraising events; individuals; loans or the repayment of loans; religious promotion; replacement of statutory funds; schools, other than preschool and afterschool clubs and activities promoting parental and community involvement.

TYPE OF GRANT Capital costs; core costs; project funding.

SAMPLE GRANTS Previous beneficiaries have included: Addaction (£50,000); Social Bite (£30,000); Hearts and Minds (£10,000); Achieve More and Scottish Opera (£5,000 each); FABB Scotland (£4,000).

FINANCES *Financial year end* 05/04/2019 *Income* £176,400 *Total grants* £135,000 *Grants to organisations* £135,000

TRUSTEES Bruce Mickel; Mairi Mickel; Oliver Bassi; Alan Hartley; Finlay Mickel; Mandy Graham.

OTHER INFORMATION The 2018/19 accounts were the latest available at the time of writing (June 2021).

HOW TO APPLY Apply via the charity's website.

CONTACT DETAILS The Trustees, 1 Atlantic Quay, 1 Robertson Street, Glasgow G2 8JB *Tel.* 0141 242 7527 *Email* admin@mickelfund.org.uk *Website* www.mickelfund.org.uk

■ The Mickleham Trust

CC NO 1048337 **ESTABLISHED** 1995

WHERE FUNDING CAN BE GIVEN UK, with a preference for Norfolk.

WHO CAN BENEFIT Registered charities.

WHAT IS FUNDED Social welfare; health and disability; blind or partially sighted people; children and young people; older people.

RANGE OF GRANTS Usually between £1,000 and £5,000.

SAMPLE GRANTS Priscilla Bacon Hospice (£75,000); Livability (£23,000); East Anglian Children's Hospice (£10,000); The Matthew Project (£5,000); The Children's Society (£3,000); Whizz-Kidz (£2,000); Samaritans – Norwich (£1,000).

FINANCES *Financial year end* 31/03/2020 *Income* £321,000 *Total grants* £289,700 *Grants to organisations* £289,700 *Assets* £5,170,000

TRUSTEES Philip Norton; Revd Sheila Nunney; Anne Richardson.

OTHER INFORMATION Grants were made to 97 organisations. During the year, £274,700 was awarded to social welfare and medical charities and £15,000 was awarded in support of people living with blindness or partial sightedness.

HOW TO APPLY Contact the correspondent for further information.

CONTACT DETAILS Philip Norton, Trustee, c/o Hansells Solicitors and Financial Advisers, 13–14 The Close, Norwich, Norfolk NR1 4DS *Tel.* 01603 615731 *Email* philipnorton@hansells.co.uk

■ The Gerald Micklem Charitable Trust

CC NO 802583 **ESTABLISHED** 1988

WHERE FUNDING CAN BE GIVEN UK, with a strong preference for Hampshire and West Sussex.

WHO CAN BENEFIT UK-registered charities; hospices.

WHAT IS FUNDED Adults and children with physical and learning disabilities; carers for older people and people with disabilities, especially young carers; the environment and wildlife; hospices; medical conditions affecting both adults and children; support for older people, including those with Alzheimer's or dementia.

WHAT IS NOT FUNDED Individuals; charities that are not registered in the UK; churches; drug/alcohol abuse and counselling; disadvantaged children and young people; education/schools (except those for disabled children); homelessness and housing; local community groups; medical research; mental health; museums, galleries and heritage; overseas aid; performing arts and cultural organisations.

TYPE OF GRANT Core costs; capital projects.

RANGE OF GRANTS Typically between £3,000 and £10,000.

SAMPLE GRANTS Home Farm Trust (£71,600); The Golf Foundation (£25,000); London Air Ambulance (£10,000); The Mulberry Centre (£8,000); The Wessex Heritage Trust and Read for Good (£5,000 each); The Amber Trust (£2,500).

FINANCES *Financial year end* 31/12/2019 *Income* £501,300 *Total grants* £331,500 *Grants to organisations* £331,500 *Assets* £3,060,000

TRUSTEES Susan Shone; Joanna Scott-Dalgleish; Helen Ratcliffe.

OTHER INFORMATION During the year, 35 awards were made from 307 applications.

HOW TO APPLY There is no formal application form – applications should be made in writing to the correspondent by post (not email). Applicants must also provide a copy of their latest annual report and accounts. Enquiries prior to any application may be made by email. The trustees usually consider awards in January/February; therefore, they ask for submissions to be sent 'towards the end of a calendar year so that the information they contain is most up to date when considered', preferably as late as possible. However, appeals are not carried forward and should be with the trustees by 31 December.

CONTACT DETAILS Susan Shone, Trustee, Bolinge Hill Farm, Buriton, Petersfield, Hampshire GU31 4NN *Tel.* 01730 264207 *Email* mail@geraldmicklemct.org.uk *Website* www.geraldmicklemct.org.uk

■ The Masonic Province of Middlesex Charitable Trust (Middlesex Masonic Charity)

CC NO 1064406 **ESTABLISHED** 1997

WHERE FUNDING CAN BE GIVEN Middlesex.

WHO CAN BENEFIT Charitable organisations in Middlesex or with strong Middlesex connections, including charities (generally, registered charities), hospices, hospitals, schools, universities and scout groups. Both Masonic and non-Masonic organisations are assisted.

WHAT IS FUNDED General charitable purposes and non-Masonic charities; youth development; community projects; support for medical and care facilities; relief of poverty and educational assistance for Freemasons and their families, including higher education scholarships.

WHAT IS NOT FUNDED Day-to-day running costs.

TYPE OF GRANT One-off; capital costs; project funding.

RANGE OF GRANTS £800 to £15,000.

SAMPLE GRANTS Friends of Prince Michael of Kent Court (£15,000); City University Gordon Bourne – bursary (£10,000); 1st Northwood Scout Group (£5,000); Music in Hospitals and Care (£3,000); Brent Young Carers Service (£2,500); Michael Sobell Hospice Charity (£1,000); Harrow District Masonic Centre (£800).

FINANCES *Financial year end* 30/09/2019 *Income* £81,100 *Total grants* £63,200 *Grants to organisations* £63,200 *Assets* £2,120,000

TRUSTEES Peter Gledhill; Adrian Howorth; David Chambers; David Yeaman; Stephen Ramsay.

OTHER INFORMATION The 2018/19 accounts were the latest available at the time of writing (June 2021). Grants were awarded to 18 organisations, of which 97% were non-Masonic charities.

HOW TO APPLY It is expected that charities needing assistance will be supported by lodges, chapters or individuals, but they may also apply directly. Application forms are available on the website or can be obtained from the correspondent. The 2018/19 annual report states that applicants must provide additional information, 'including two years' audited financial statements, supporting quotations or invoices for proposed expenditure and relevant literature needed to enable the Trustees to reach a decision'. The trust will also consider applications for assistance from Freemasons in distress or their families or dependants. However, these petitions should be submitted in the first instance to the Provincial Grand Almoner, who will report with recommendations directly to the trustees.

CONTACT DETAILS David Chambers, Trustee, 175 New Haw Road, Addlestone, Surrey KT15 2DP *Tel.* 01932 821943 *Email* secretary@mpmct.org *Website* https://pglm.org.uk/our-work/charities/middlesex-masonic

■ The Mikheev Charitable Trust

CC NO 1162591 **ESTABLISHED** 2015

WHERE FUNDING CAN BE GIVEN England and Wales.

WHO CAN BENEFIT Charitable organisations; arts organisations; universities.

WHAT IS FUNDED General charitable purposes; the advancement of education, science, religion, public policy and the arts.

RANGE OF GRANTS £1,000 to £15,000.

SAMPLE GRANTS Hall School Charitable Trust (£25,000); University of Cambridge (£16,500); The Prince's Teaching Institute (£12,500); Think Forward UK (£10,000); United Youth Football Club (£3,000); Opera Holland Park (£1,000).

FINANCES *Financial year end* 05/04/2020 *Income* £433,900 *Total grants* £74,000 *Grants to organisations* £74,000 *Assets* £6,490,000

TRUSTEES Adrian Weller; Katerina Woolhouse; Lev Mikheev; Natalia Mikheev.

OTHER INFORMATION Grants were awarded to eight organisations during the year.

HOW TO APPLY Contact the correspondent for further information.

CONTACT DETAILS The Trustees, c/o Withers LLP, 20 Old Bailey, London EC4M 7AN *Tel.* 020 7597 6000

■ The Mila Charitable Organisation

CC NO 1169936 **ESTABLISHED** 2016

WHERE FUNDING CAN BE GIVEN UK and overseas.

WHO CAN BENEFIT Charitable organisations.

WHAT IS FUNDED General charitable purposes including education, the arts, culture, heritage, heritage, science and the environment.

SAMPLE GRANTS Sien Agosto (£30,000); Children's City Vienna (£18,300); Ouseburn Farm Charity (£16,000); The Comfrey Project (£15,000); Shobana Jeyasingh Dance (£5,000).

FINANCES *Financial year end* 31/12/2019 *Income* £456,700 *Total grants* £85,300 *Grants to organisations* £85,300 *Assets* £5,450,000

TRUSTEES Hamish Forsyth; Anna Nasmyth; Dr Leonard Bentley; Kate Nasmyth; Polly Phipps; Prof. Kim Ashley; Laura Nasmyth; Mark Francis.

HOW TO APPLY Contact the correspondent for further information.

CONTACT DETAILS The Trustees, 71 Queen Victoria Street, London, EC4V 4AY *Tel.* 020 7395 3000

■ The Millennium Oak Trust

CC NO 1083384 **ESTABLISHED** 2000

WHERE FUNDING CAN BE GIVEN Worldwide, mainly UK.

WHO CAN BENEFIT Charitable organisations; schools; youth organisations; hospices.

WHAT IS FUNDED General charitable purposes; the relief of those in need; health; mental health; education; the environment.

SAMPLE GRANTS Amnesty International, Caring in Bristol, Greenpeace, Hersham Youth, Knowl Hill School, Liberty International, Macmillan Nurses,

Open Spaces, Sightsavers, The Airfield Environment Trust, Whales and Dolphins Conservation, Woking Hospice.

FINANCES *Financial year end* 31/07/2020 *Income* £52,200 *Total grants* £176,500 *Grants to organisations* £176,500 *Assets* £1,880,000

TRUSTEES Norma Todd; Alexander Roads; Nicholas Roads; Richard Roads; Dawn Roads; Andrew Arminger.

OTHER INFORMATION Grants were awarded to 34 organisations during the year.

HOW TO APPLY The trustees nominate organisations for consideration. According to the trust's Charity Commission record, it does not normally accept unsolicited applications.

CONTACT DETAILS The Trustees, 26 Vicarage Road, Kingfield, Woking, Surrey GU22 9BH *Tel.* 01483 762859

■ Millennium Stadium Charitable Trust (Ymddiriedclaeth Elusennol Stadiwm y Mileniwm)

CC NO 1086596 **ESTABLISHED** 2001

WHERE FUNDING CAN BE GIVEN Wales.

WHO CAN BENEFIT Registered charities; PTAs; CICs; social enterprises.

WHAT IS FUNDED The arts, especially the performing and visual arts; community cohesion; people with disabilities; the environment and sustainability; sport.

WHAT IS NOT FUNDED Projects outside Wales; day-to-day running costs; projects that seek to redistribute grant funding for the benefit of third-party organisations; repayment of debts or overdrafts; retrospective requests; requests from individuals; payment to profit-making organisations; applications made solely in the name of a local authority.

TYPE OF GRANT Capital costs; core/revenue costs; project funding; seed funding/start-up funding.

RANGE OF GRANTS Regional grants – up to £7,500; local grants – up to £2,500.

SAMPLE GRANTS A list of beneficiaries was not included in the annual report and accounts.

FINANCES *Financial year end* 31/03/2020 *Income* £343,100 *Total grants* £454,600 *Grants to organisations* £454,600 *Assets* £133,900

TRUSTEES Ian Davies; John Lloyd-Jones; Gerallt Hughes; Russell Goodway; Andrew Walker; John Rawlins; Cllr Peter Bradbury; David Hammond; Jonathan Day; Hywel Roberts; David Young.

HOW TO APPLY The trustees meet in March to discuss local applications and in November to discuss regional applications. Deadline dates can be found on the trust's website, along with full guidelines and application forms.

CONTACT DETAILS Sarah Fox, Trust Administrator, c/o Foxse Consultancy, Suite 1, 4 Bessemer Road, Cardiff CF11 8BA *Tel.* 029 2002 2143 *Email* info@millenniumstadiumtrust.org.uk *Website* https://www.millenniumstadiumtrust.org.uk

■ Hugh and Mary Miller Bequest Trust

OSCR NO SC014950 **ESTABLISHED** 1976

WHERE FUNDING CAN BE GIVEN Scotland.

WHO CAN BENEFIT Registered charities.

WHAT IS FUNDED General charitable purposes; disability.

RANGE OF GRANTS Usually between £1,000 and £7,000.

SAMPLE GRANTS Haven Products Ltd (£14,800); Hansel Foundation and Music in Hospitals Scotland (£7,000 each); Thistle Foundation (£4,700); The Prince's Trust (£3,200); Dyslexia Scotwest and Motability (£1,200 each).

FINANCES *Financial year end* 05/04/2019 *Income* £136,000 *Total grants* £117,400 *Grants to organisations* £117,400 *Assets* £3,200,000

OTHER INFORMATION The 2018/19 accounts were the latest available at the time of writing (January 2021). Grants were awarded to 29 organisations during the year.

HOW TO APPLY Apply in writing to the Secretaries to the Trust, who administer the charity and pass on applications to the trustees for consideration at their annual meeting.

CONTACT DETAILS The Secretaries to the Trust, c/o Dentons UK and Middle East LLP, 1 George Square, Glasgow G2 1AL

■ The Ronald Miller Foundation

OSCR NO SC008798 **ESTABLISHED** 1979

WHERE FUNDING CAN BE GIVEN UK, with a preference for Scotland.

WHO CAN BENEFIT Registered charities.

WHAT IS FUNDED Animals and the environment; medical causes; education; children and young people; general charitable purposes.

WHAT IS NOT FUNDED Individuals.

SAMPLE GRANTS A list of beneficiaries was not included in the annual report and accounts.

FINANCES *Financial year end* 05/04/2020 *Income* £221,200 *Total grants* £180,800 *Grants to organisations* £180,800 *Assets* £5,250,000

OTHER INFORMATION During the year, the foundation made grants to 83 organisations for the following purposes: medical causes (£45,800); education (£40,600); general (£34,500); children (£30,000); animals, birds, etc. (£27,500); special appeals (£2,500).

HOW TO APPLY Contact the correspondent for further information.

CONTACT DETAILS The Trustees, Dentons UK and Middle East LLP, 1 George Square, Glasgow G2 1AL

■ Jean and Roger Miller's Charitable Trust

OSCR NO SC046216 **ESTABLISHED** 2015

WHERE FUNDING CAN BE GIVEN UK and overseas, with a strong preference for Scotland.

WHO CAN BENEFIT Registered charities; community groups; individuals. Principally, but not limited to, organisations or individuals based in Scotland.

WHAT IS FUNDED General charitable purposes.

TYPE OF GRANT Recurring.

RANGE OF GRANTS Usually between £1,000 and £25,000.

SAMPLE GRANTS Capital Theatres (£87,500); The National Trust for Scotland and St Andrew's and St George's West Church (£25,000 each); Edinburgh Napier University Development Trust and The Woodland Trust (£12,500 each); Wildfowl and Wetlands Trust (£6,300); Murrayfield Wanderers Rugby Trust Foundation and St John Scotland (£1,300 each).

FINANCES *Financial year end* 31/12/2019
Income £282,400 *Total grants* £258,800
Grants to organisations £258,800
Assets £818,400

OTHER INFORMATION The 16 organisations supported in 2019 were all supported in 2018. Our research suggests that organisations are often supported on a recurring basis; however, applications are considered annually by the trustees.

HOW TO APPLY Contact the correspondent for further information.

CONTACT DETAILS The Trustees, c/o Brodies LLP, 15 Atholl Crescent, Edinburgh EH3 8HA *Tel.* 0131 228 3777

■ The Millfield House Foundation (1)

CC NO 1158914 **ESTABLISHED** 1976

WHERE FUNDING CAN BE GIVEN The North East.

WHO CAN BENEFIT Registered charities; universities.

WHAT IS FUNDED Social and economic inequality projects; policy work and research.

WHAT IS NOT FUNDED Refer to the foundation's helpful website for more details.

TYPE OF GRANT One-off grants; core costs; project funding; research.

RANGE OF GRANTS Mostly up to £42,000.

SAMPLE GRANTS IPPR North (£84,000); Regional Refugee Forum North East and VONNE (£42,000 each); Youth Homelessness North East (£40,000); Newcastle Citizens Advice (£35,000).

FINANCES *Financial year end* 05/04/2020
Income £164,000 *Total grants* £286,700
Grants to organisations £285,500
Assets £5,800,000

TRUSTEES Dr Yvonne Gale; Peter Deans; Allan Brownrigg; Rhiannon Bearne; Jonathan Walker; John McCabe; Laura Seebohm.

OTHER INFORMATION Grants were paid to six organisations during the year. The foundation has a distinct focus on working with a small number of 'strategic partners'.

HOW TO APPLY The foundation funds a small number of strategic partner organisations on a regular basis. While occasional one-off grants are made at the trustees' discretion, unsolicited grant applications are not accepted.

CONTACT DETAILS Cullagh Warnock, Administrator and Trust Manager, 7 Lesbury Road, Heaton, Newcastle upon Tyne, Tyne and Wear NE6 5LB *Tel.* 07595 280401 *Email* cullagh@mhfdn.org.uk *Website* www.mhfdn.org.uk

■ The Millichope Foundation

CC NO 282357 **ESTABLISHED** 1993

WHERE FUNDING CAN BE GIVEN Worldwide, mainly the UK, with a preference for Shropshire.

WHO CAN BENEFIT Charitable organisations.

WHAT IS FUNDED The arts and culture; conservation projects and the environment; heritage; disaster relief; general charitable purposes.

WHAT IS NOT FUNDED Individuals.

RANGE OF GRANTS Mostly up to £5,000.

SAMPLE GRANTS Brazilian Atlantic Rainforest Trust (£25,000); Fauna and Flora International (£20,000); Severn Hospice, Shropshire Historic Churches Trust and University of Cambridge (£5,000 each); Shrewsbury Christian Centre (£3,000); Royal Forestry Society (£2,500); Shropshire Domestic Abuse Service (£1,000); Music in Hospitals (£750); Shrewsbury Abbey – organ restoration (£500).

FINANCES *Financial year end* 05/04/2020
Income £452,400 *Total grants* £269,400
Grants to organisations £269,400
Assets £6,850,000

TRUSTEES Bridget Marshall; Sarah Bury; Lindsay Bury; Frank Bury; Mrs H. Horne.

OTHER INFORMATION Grants were awarded to 115 organisations during the year.

HOW TO APPLY Apply in writing to the correspondent. The trustees meet several times a year to consider applications.

CONTACT DETAILS Sarah Bury, Trustee, The Old Rectory, Tugford, Craven Arms, Shropshire SY7 9HS *Tel.* 01584 841234 *Email* sarah@millichope.com

■ Millie's Watch

CC NO 1179664 **ESTABLISHED** 2018

WHERE FUNDING CAN BE GIVEN England and Wales, with a possible preference for the West Midlands.

WHO CAN BENEFIT Charitable organisations.

WHAT IS FUNDED General charitable purposes.

SAMPLE GRANTS Queen Elizabeth Hospital Birmingham Charity (£54,200 in two grants); Warwickshire Wildlife Trust (£17,000); Home from Hospital Care, The Albrighton Trust and The Royal Horticultural Society (£5,000 each); School Home Support Service UK (£2,500).

FINANCES *Financial year end* 06/08/2019
Income £3,020,000 *Total grants* £88,700
Grants to organisations £88,700
Assets £313,400

TRUSTEES Julie Stretton; Rebecca Ayres; Mary Ayres; Rachel Harrod; Coutts & Co.

OTHER INFORMATION The 2018/19 accounts were the latest available at the time of writing (February 2021).

HOW TO APPLY Apply by letter to the correspondent.

CONTACT DETAILS The Trustees, Coutts & Co. Trustee Department, 1st Floor, Trinity Quay 1, Avon Street, Bristol BS2 0PT *Tel.* 0345 304 2424

■ Mills and Reeve Charitable Trust

CC NO 326271 **ESTABLISHED** 1982

WHERE FUNDING CAN BE GIVEN UK, with a preference for charities based near the offices of Mills and Reeve LLP.

WHO CAN BENEFIT Charitable organisations; universities.

WHAT IS FUNDED General charitable purposes, with a preference for medical research and social welfare.

TYPE OF GRANT One-off and recurrent grants for research; eligible expenditure; project funding.

RANGE OF GRANTS Generally up to £2,500.

SAMPLE GRANTS Shelter (£10,000); Barnabus – Manchester (£5,400); Cambridge Rape Crisis Centre (£4,000); Tom's Trust (£2,500); Simon on the Streets (£1,300); Birmingham Citizens Advice, Molly Olly's Wishes and Parkinson's UK (£1,000) each.

FINANCES *Financial year end* 31/05/2019
Income £132,200 *Total grants* £87,400
Grants to organisations £87,400
Assets £273,800

TRUSTEES Greg Gibson; Guy Hinchley; Tom Pickthorn; Dawn Brathwaite; Justin Ripman; Sarah Seed; Alison Bull; Neil Howes; Stuart Thompson.

OTHER INFORMATION The trust is the corporate charity of Mills and Reeve LLP, which provides a substantial proportion of the trust's income, and each trustee is a member or a former member of the company. Only organisations that received grants of £1,000 and over were listed as beneficiaries in the trust's accounts. Grants of under £1,000 totalled £16,800. The 2018/19 accounts were the latest available at the time of writing (February 2021).

HOW TO APPLY According to the annual report for 2018/19, the trust makes smaller grants on an ad hoc basis and favours charities nominated by employees of Mills and Reeve LLP or based near one of the company's offices. Contact the correspondent for further information.

CONTACT DETAILS The Trustees, Botanic House, 100 Hills Road, Cambridge CB2 1PH *Tel.* 01223 222273 *Website* https://www.mills-reeve.com/about-us/making-a-positive-impact

■ The Millward Charitable Trust

CC NO 328564 **ESTABLISHED** 1990

WHERE FUNDING CAN BE GIVEN UK and overseas.

WHO CAN BENEFIT Charitable organisations; churches.

WHAT IS FUNDED Social welfare; the performing arts; religion; animal welfare; education.

RANGE OF GRANTS Typically up to £20,000.

SAMPLE GRANTS City of Birmingham Symphony Orchestra (£50,000); Music in the Round (three grants totalling £42,000); Dale Street Methodist Church (two grants totalling £30,000); Prison Reform Trust (£20,000); Leamington Music (£10,000); St Giles Church (£5,000).

FINANCES *Financial year end* 05/04/2020 *Income* £90,000 *Total grants* £247,800 *Grants to organisations* £247,800 *Assets* £1,790,000

TRUSTEES Maurice Millward; Sheila Millward; John Hulse.

OTHER INFORMATION Grants were awarded in the following categories: performing arts (six grants totalling £107,000); social welfare (seven grants totalling £75,800); religion (seven grants totalling £65,000). Only beneficiaries of grants of above £1,000 were listed in the accounts. Some beneficiaries received multiple grants.

HOW TO APPLY Apply in writing to the correspondent. The trustees meet regularly to consider applications.

CONTACT DETAILS Maurice Millward, Trustee, 23–25 Waterloo Place, Warwick Street, Leamington Spa, Warwickshire CV32 5LA *Tel.* 01926 451000 *Email* maurice@mauricemillward.co.uk

■ The Milne Family Foundation

OSCR NO SC046335 **ESTABLISHED** 2016

WHERE FUNDING CAN BE GIVEN UK, with a preference for Scotland; overseas.

WHO CAN BENEFIT Registered charities.

WHAT IS FUNDED The advancement of education and religion through the promotion of the Christian gospel; education; health; citizenship; community development; social welfare.

SAMPLE GRANTS Worldlink (£62,000); Lessons 4 Life (£36,000); Choices Aberdeen (£24,000); Bensham Gospel Hall (£18,000); Children 1st (£8,000); The Haven Kilmalcolm (£6,000).

FINANCES *Financial year end* 31/12/2019 *Income* £1,190,000 *Total grants* £1,170,000 *Grants to organisations* £1,170,000 *Assets* £31,500

OTHER INFORMATION The foundation receives the majority of its funding from Balmoral Group Holdings and its related companies.

HOW TO APPLY Contact the correspondent for further information.

CONTACT DETAILS The Trustees, Balmoral Park, Loirston, Aberdeen, AB12 3GY

■ The Clare Milne Trust

CC NO 1084733 **ESTABLISHED** 1999

WHERE FUNDING CAN BE GIVEN The south west of England, with a preference for Devon and Cornwall.

WHO CAN BENEFIT Local and regional charities.

WHAT IS FUNDED Disability projects, especially those for adults.

WHAT IS NOT FUNDED Individuals; national charities are not normally supported.

TYPE OF GRANT Generally a partial contribution towards the total cost of a project.

RANGE OF GRANTS Typically, grants range between £2,000 and £25,000.

SAMPLE GRANTS Exeter Deaf Academy (£395,000); Friends of Avalon School PTA (£50,000); Hall for Cornwall (£30,000); Devon in Sight (£20,000); Cornwall Community Foundation (£10,000); Down's Syndrome Association (£4,000).

FINANCES *Financial year end* 31/12/2019 *Income* £1,240,000 *Total grants* £1,170,000 *Grants to organisations* £1,170,000 *Assets* £40,570,000

TRUSTEES Margaret Rogers; Christine Kirk; Robert Spencer; Eavan McCafferty; Sarah Haywood.

OTHER INFORMATION Grants were made to 77 charities during the year.

HOW TO APPLY Application forms can be downloaded from the trust's website. The form should be returned to the secretary along with a covering letter (on your letterhead), details regarding your proposal (up to two sides of A4) and a budget for the project. The trustees usually meet four times a year and aim to contact applicants within two weeks from the date of the meeting. Check the trust's website for the latest information on application deadlines and detailed guidelines on how to apply.

CONTACT DETAILS Emma Houlding, Secretary, Claypitts, Ladram Road, Otterton, Devon EX9 7HT *Tel.* 01395 270418 *Email* secretary@claremilnetrust.com *Website* www.claremilnetrust.com

■ The James Milner Foundation

CC NO 1146768 **ESTABLISHED** 2011

WHERE FUNDING CAN BE GIVEN UK.

WHO CAN BENEFIT Charitable organisations.

WHAT IS FUNDED Children and young people; sport and recreation, particularly football, rugby and cricket; education; health.

TYPE OF GRANT Project costs; development funding; service provision.

RANGE OF GRANTS Up to £75,000 but mainly under £20,000.

SAMPLE GRANTS Help for Heroes and NSPCC (£75,000 each); Liverpool FC Foundation (£16,000); Leeds Rhino Foundation and Motor Neuron Disease Association (£10,000 each); Bloodwise (£5,400).

FINANCES *Financial year end* 31/12/2019 *Income* £603,300 *Total grants* £191,400 *Grants to organisations* £191,400 *Assets* £412,000

TRUSTEES Christopher Hudson; Mark Hovell; Damaris Treasure; Marie-Christine Bouchier.

OTHER INFORMATION In total, six grants were awarded during 2019. The foundation provides annual support to the NSPCC, Blood Cancer UK and Help for Heroes. At the time of writing (May 2021), the foundation's website was undergoing maintenance. Check the website for updates.

HOW TO APPLY Contact the correspondent for further information.

CONTACT DETAILS The Trustees, c/o Mills and Reeve, 1 New York Street, Manchester M1 4HD *Tel.* 0161 235 5420 *Email* mark.hovell@mills-reeve.com *Website* www.thejamesmilnerfoundation.com

■ Milton Keynes Community Foundation Ltd

CC NO 295107 **ESTABLISHED** 1987

WHERE FUNDING CAN BE GIVEN Milton Keynes unitary authority.

WHO CAN BENEFIT Registered charities; not-for-profit community groups; social enterprises; amateur sports clubs; faith groups; CICs; voluntary sector organisations.

WHAT IS FUNDED The relief of poverty, ill health, disability or disadvantage; the arts and leisure.

WHAT IS NOT FUNDED Exclusion criteria differ between funds – see the foundation's website for further information.

TYPE OF GRANT Start-up costs; project extension or development core costs; pilot projects; equipment and resources.

SAMPLE GRANTS Previous beneficiaries have included: YiS Youth Counselling Service (£120,000); Carers MK (£25,000); Enrych Buckinghamshire (£17,000); Action4Youth (£10,000); Wroughton Men in Sheds and Wriggle Dance Theatre (£5,000 each); Moribayassa African Drumming Community Group (£1,000); Youth Information Service (£535); West Bletchley District Guides (£10).

FINANCES *Financial year end* 31/03/2020 *Income* £3,750,000 *Total grants* £1,151,000 *Grants to organisations* £1,140,000 *Assets* £68,080,000

TRUSTEES Carole Baume; Kate Chadwick; Shirley Jones; Stephen Harris; Lawrence Revill; Shaun Lee; Jill Heaton; Kurshida Mirza; Elizabeth Henderson; Paul Nolan; Christopher Shaw.

OTHER INFORMATION This is one of the 46 UK community foundations, which distribute funding for a wide range of purposes. As with all community foundations, there are a number of donor-advised funds managed on behalf of individuals, families and charitable trusts. Grant schemes tend to change frequently; consult the foundation's website for details of current programmes and up-to-date deadlines.

HOW TO APPLY Potential applicants are advised to visit the community foundation's website or contact its grants/programmes team to find the most suitable funding stream.

CONTACT DETAILS The Programmes Team, Acorn House, 381 Midsummer Boulevard, Milton Keynes, Buckinghamshire MK9 3HP *Tel.* 01908 690276 *Email* applications@mkcommunityfoundation.co.uk *Website* www.mkcommunityfoundation.co.uk

■ Mind

CC NO 219830 **ESTABLISHED** 1962

WHERE FUNDING CAN BE GIVEN England and Wales.

WHO CAN BENEFIT Registered charities; local Mind organisations; universities.

WHAT IS FUNDED Mental health; improving mental health services and access; training and development opportunities for people working in mental health.

WHAT IS NOT FUNDED Exclusion criteria differ between funding programmes – see the website for details.

TYPE OF GRANT Programme dependent.

RANGE OF GRANTS Programme dependent; mostly up to £250,000 in 2019/20.

SAMPLE GRANTS Time to Change – P3 (£1.88 million); Whole School Approach (£446,000); Get Set to Go (£258,000); Mentally Healthy Universities (£210,000); Pace Setter (£144,000); Connector Fund (£99,000); Morrisons Foundation (£68,000); Covenant Fund Project (£37,000); On Your Side (£9,000); One Mind Wales Group (£3,000).

FINANCES *Financial year end* 31/03/2020 *Income* £58,280,000 *Total grants* £5,140,000 *Grants to organisations* £5,140,000 *Assets* £16,400,000

TRUSTEES Stephanie Spring; Valerie Harrison; Ian Ruddock; Emrys Elias; Alyson Scott; Anna Hughes; Joanne Theodoulou; Steve Gilbert; Alex Jensen; Christer Stoyell; Shubulade Smith; Mandeep Rupra; Philippa Gluckich; Jonathan Wilderspin.

OTHER INFORMATION Mind runs several grant programmes and in 2019/20, grants were distributed to achieve the following goals: helping people take part in society equally (£2.21 million); improving services and support (£989,000); helping people to stay well (£989,000); giving people choice (£527,000); making access to services equal for everyone (£16,000). See the website for further information on current programmes available. There are also 125 local Minds, which deliver mental health services in their local areas.

HOW TO APPLY Contact the correspondent for further information. In addition to the correspondent's address listed here, local Mind organisations have their own correspondence addresses, which can be found online.

CONTACT DETAILS The Grants Team, 15–19 Broadway, Stratford, London E15 4BQ *Tel.* 020 8519 2122 *Email* info@mind.org.uk *Website* https://www.mind.org.uk

■ The Peter Minet Trust

CC NO 259963 **ESTABLISHED** 1969

WHERE FUNDING CAN BE GIVEN Lambeth and Southwark.

WHO CAN BENEFIT UK-registered charities with offices, beneficiaries and work in Lambeth or Southwark.

WHAT IS FUNDED Community cohesion; social welfare.

WHAT IS NOT FUNDED Local branches of charities that have main offices outside Lambeth or Southwark; charities that also work with beneficiaries outside Lambeth and Southwark; individuals; nurseries, schools, colleges, higher education institutions, universities and associated charities, including PTAs; places of worship; one-off events.

TYPE OF GRANT Unrestricted funding of up to £30,000 per year for up to three years.

RANGE OF GRANTS £10,000 to £30,000.

SAMPLE GRANTS Home-Start – Southwark and Loughborough Junction Action Group (£30,000 each); Walcot Educational Foundation (£250,000); Stepping Stones Learning and Leisure (£20,000); Home-Start – Lambeth (£10,000).

FINANCES *Financial year end* 30/09/2020
Income £208,900 *Total grants* £225,000
Grants to organisations £225,000
Assets £5,220,000

TRUSTEES Tracey Fletcher; Aanchal Clare; Laura Solomons; Thomas Gayfer; Patricia Okonkwo; Anne Young.

OTHER INFORMATION Grants were broken down as follows: Open Grants Fund – multi-year grants (six grants totalling £170,000); Open Grants Fund – one-off development grants (one grant of £10,000); Strategic Fund Grants (three grants totalling £75,000). The Strategic Fund is by invitation only. The Open Grants Fund is available to charities working to support 'severe and multiple challenges' of Lambeth or Southwark residents.

HOW TO APPLY The Open Grants Fund has a three-stage application process consisting of an online 'Tell Us About You' form, an application form and an in-person meeting.

CONTACT DETAILS Rachel Oglethorpe, Director, Marshall House, 66 Newcomen Street, London SE1 1YT *Tel.* 020 8037 0300 *Email* info@peterminet.org.uk *Website* www.peterminet.org.uk

■ Minton Charitable Trust

CC NO 1112106 **ESTABLISHED** 2005

WHERE FUNDING CAN BE GIVEN UK.

WHO CAN BENEFIT Charitable organisations and individuals.

WHAT IS FUNDED Education.

TYPE OF GRANT Capital and project funding.

SAMPLE GRANTS St Giles Trust (£75,000); United Kingdom Sailing Academy (£15,000).

FINANCES *Financial year end* 05/04/2020
Income £273,000 *Total grants* £90,000
Grants to organisations £90,000
Assets £1,920,000

TRUSTEES Sir Anthony Greener; Richard Edmunds; Charles Greener; Claire Greener.

HOW TO APPLY Contact the correspondent for further information. Bear in mind that the main and sometimes only beneficiary is St Giles Trust, of which Sir Anthony Greener is also a trustee.

CONTACT DETAILS Sir Anthony Greener, Trustee, Dores Hill, North Sydmonton, Newbury, Berkshire RG20 9AF *Tel.* 07720 271183 *Email* greenera@mintontrust.com

■ The Mishcon Family Charitable Trust

CC NO 213165 **ESTABLISHED** 1961

WHERE FUNDING CAN BE GIVEN UK.

WHO CAN BENEFIT Registered charities, particularly Jewish organisations.

WHAT IS FUNDED General charitable purposes; Jewish causes; social welfare; health and disability; children and young people.

RANGE OF GRANTS £100 to £10,300.

SAMPLE GRANTS Friends of Alyn (£10,300); OneVoice Europe (£10,000); New North London Synagogue (£3,500); Ambitious About Autism (£2,400); Barts and The London Charity, and Benenden School (Kent) Ltd (£1,000 each); Age UK (£200); Albert Kennedy Trust (£150).

FINANCES *Financial year end* 05/04/2019
Income £76,980 *Total grants* £148,800
Grants to organisations £148,800
Assets £1,924,000

TRUSTEES Jane Landau; Peter Mishcon; Russell Mishcon.

OTHER INFORMATION The 2018/19 accounts were the latest available at the time of writing (June 2021). Grants were made to 73 organisations.

HOW TO APPLY Contact the correspondent for further information.

CONTACT DETAILS The Trustees, c/o Mercer and Hole, 72 London Road, St Albans, Hertfordshire AL1 1NS *Tel.* 01727 869141

■ The Brian Mitchell Charitable Settlement

CC NO 1003817 **ESTABLISHED** 1989

WHERE FUNDING CAN BE GIVEN UK.

WHO CAN BENEFIT Charitable organisations.

WHAT IS FUNDED General charitable purposes, including the arts, education, health, social welfare and disability.

RANGE OF GRANTS Up to £25,000.

SAMPLE GRANTS Shakespeare's Globe Theatre (£700,000); Glyndebourne (£450,000); Myeloma UK (£100,000); Temple Music Foundation (£10,000); World Sight Foundation (£5,000).

FINANCES *Financial year end* 31/03/2020
Income ££452,000 *Total grants* £2,210,000
Grants to organisations £2,210,000
Assets £3,100,000

TRUSTEES Andy Buss; John Andrews; Michael Conlon; Fraser Reavell; Maxine Pancaldi.

OTHER INFORMATION Grants were distributed as follows: the arts (53%); education (32%); medical projects in the UK (12%). Grants were also distributed for a variety of other activities including welfare and disability projects.

HOW TO APPLY Applications may be made in writing to the correspondent; however, note that the charity has several regular beneficiaries.

CONTACT DETAILS The Trustees, 14 Hackwood, Robertsbridge, East Sussex TN32 5ER
Tel. 07860 628597 *Email* john@aas.uk.net

■ The Esmé Mitchell Trust

CCNI NO NIC101659 **ESTABLISHED** 1965

WHERE FUNDING CAN BE GIVEN Northern Ireland.

WHO CAN BENEFIT Charitable organisations.

WHAT IS FUNDED General charitable purposes, including the arts and heritage.

WHAT IS NOT FUNDED Individuals.

RANGE OF GRANTS Typically between £1,000 and £5,000.

SAMPLE GRANTS Northern Ireland Opera (£40,000); Belfast Philharmonic Society and Ulster Architectural Heritage (£20,000 each); Ulster Orchestra (£10,000); War Memorials Trust (£4,000); Action Deaf Youth (£1,300); Me4Mental (£500).

FINANCES *Financial year end* 05/04/2020
Income £266,700 *Total grants* £243,600
Grants to organisations £243,600
Assets £7,210,000

TRUSTEE Cleaver Fulton Rankin Trustees Ltd.

OTHER INFORMATION Grants were awarded to 51 organisations during the year. The majority of grants were awarded from the charity's general fund. A total of seven grants were awarded from the charity's heritage fund.

HOW TO APPLY Contact the correspondent for further information.

CONTACT DETAILS The Trustees, c/o Cleaver Fulton Rankin Solicitors, 50 Bedford Street, Belfast BT2 7FW *Tel.* 028 9024 3141 *Email* trusts@cfrlaw.co.uk

The Mittal Foundation

CC NO 1146604 **ESTABLISHED** 2012
WHERE FUNDING CAN BE GIVEN UK, USA and India.
WHO CAN BENEFIT Registered charities; universities.
WHAT IS FUNDED General charitable purposes, especially education and training, the arts, the prevention of poverty and malnutrition, and children and young people.
SAMPLE GRANTS The British Asian Trust (£138,400); Boston Children's Hospital, Harvard University, The Prince's Trust and University of Pennsylvania (amounts unknown).
FINANCES *Financial year end* 31/12/2019 *Income* £2,020,000 *Total grants* £596,200 *Grants to organisations* £596,200 *Assets* £1,910,000
TRUSTEES Usha Mittal; Megha Mittal; Vanisha Mittal Bhatia; Aditya Mittal.
OTHER INFORMATION A number of pages of the 2019 accounts were not available to view online; therefore, we have used the 'expenditure on charitable activities' figure for the grant total. Some beneficiaries were named in the annual report, but not all grant amounts were noted.
HOW TO APPLY The foundation does not accept unsolicited applications. The trustees research and use their personal contacts to identify suitable grantees.
CONTACT DETAILS The Trustees, c/o Mittal Investments Ltd, Floor 3, Berkeley Square House, Berkeley Square, London W1J 6BU *Tel.* 020 7659 1033

Keren Mitzvah Trust

CC NO 1041948 **ESTABLISHED** 1994
WHERE FUNDING CAN BE GIVEN UK.
WHO CAN BENEFIT Registered charities, particularly Jewish organisations; individuals.
WHAT IS FUNDED General charitable purposes; Jewish causes; relief of poverty; religious activities; education; health.
TYPE OF GRANT One-off and recurrent, generally unrestricted.
RANGE OF GRANTS Up to £70,800.
SAMPLE GRANTS Achisomoch Aid Company Ltd (£70,800); Camp Simcha and Kisharon (£7,500 each).
FINANCES *Financial year end* 31/12/2019 *Income* £111,800 *Total grants* £131,100 *Grants to organisations* £131,100 *Assets* £15,900
TRUSTEES Manny Weiss; Alan McCormack; Neil Bradley.
HOW TO APPLY Apply in writing to the correspondent. The trustees have previously stated that they generally support their own personal charities.
CONTACT DETAILS The Trustees, 1 Manchester Square, London W1U 3AB *Tel.* 020 3219 2600

The Mizpah Trust

CC NO 287231 **ESTABLISHED** 1983
WHERE FUNDING CAN BE GIVEN UK and overseas.
WHO CAN BENEFIT Registered charities; schools; individuals.
WHAT IS FUNDED General charitable purposes; the relief of poverty; education; the promotion of the Christian faith; overseas aid; medical research.
RANGE OF GRANTS £1,000 to £5,000, with an exceptional grant of £60,500.
SAMPLE GRANTS A list of beneficiaries was not available; however, the main beneficiary was noted as the Vanessa Grant Girls' School.
FINANCES *Financial year end* 05/04/2020 *Income* £124,400 *Total grants* £69,500 *Grants to organisations* £69,500 *Assets* £268,500
TRUSTEES Alan Bell; Julia Bell; Anthony Bell.
OTHER INFORMATION During the year, the trust awarded grants totalling £69,500, distributed as follows: education (£60,500); promotion of the Christian faith (£5,000); relief of poverty (£3,000); medical research (£1,000).
HOW TO APPLY The trustees will not respond to unsolicited requests for donations.
CONTACT DETAILS Alan Bell, Trustee, Foresters House, Humbly Grove, South Warnborough, Hook, Hampshire RG29 1RY *Tel.* 01256 862263 *Email* alancobell@gmail.com

Mobbs Memorial Trust Ltd

CC NO 202478 **ESTABLISHED** 1963
WHERE FUNDING CAN BE GIVEN Stoke Poges and district, within a 35-mile radius of St Giles' Church.
WHO CAN BENEFIT Charitable organisations; churches; schools and colleges.
WHAT IS FUNDED St Giles' Church and other charitable purposes including sports and recreation, health, conservation and the environment, and community facilities and services.
WHAT IS NOT FUNDED The following applications are not normally supported: those from or for individuals or private companies; those from national charitable organisations unless a specific need arises within the local area; those that should be funded by national or local government; those for running costs, apart from exceptional cases within a four-mile radius of Stoke Poges.
TYPE OF GRANT One-off capital projects.
RANGE OF GRANTS Usually £500 to £10,000.
SAMPLE GRANTS Chiltern Music Therapy (£5,000); Iver Heath Infant School and Nursery (£4,000); 84th Reading Scouts Group (£3,000); Great Marlow School Boat Club (£2,000); Shopmobility – High Wycombe (£1,400); Stoke Poges Flower Fund (£300).
FINANCES *Financial year end* 31/03/2020 *Income* £108,400 *Total grants* £107,360 *Grants to organisations* £106,500 *Assets* £3,040,000
TRUSTEES Sandra Greenslade; Chris Mobbs; Dr Charles Mobbs; Alexandra Mobbs.
HOW TO APPLY Apply in writing to the correspondent via email (applications@mobbsmemorialtrust.com). The trustees meet quarterly, normally in March, June, September and December. Full guidelines are available to view on the trust's website.
CONTACT DETAILS Sarah Greenslade, Chair, Victoria House, 26 Queen Victoria Street, Reading, Berkshire RG1 1TG *Tel.* 0118 957 3238 *Email* applications@mobbsmemorialtrust.com or sandragreenslade@mobbsmemorialtrust.com *Website* www.mobbsmemorialtrust.com

The Mohn Westlake Foundation

CC NO 1170045 **ESTABLISHED** 2016
WHERE FUNDING CAN BE GIVEN England and Wales.
WHO CAN BENEFIT Organisations that support young people.
WHAT IS FUNDED Young people; education; recreation and leisure; the arts and science; research; general charitable purposes.
TYPE OF GRANT Project costs.

RANGE OF GRANTS £25,000 to £4 million.
SAMPLE GRANTS Royal Opera House Covent Garden Foundation (£4.3 million); Mental Health Innovation (£3 million); Place2Be (£700,000); Screen Academy Foundation (£555,000); Full Fact (£250,000); Tutor Trust (£25,000).
FINANCES *Financial year end* 31/12/2019 *Income* £7,260,000 *Total grants* £11,540,000 *Grants to organisations* £11,540,000 *Assets* £18,340,000
TRUSTEES Robert Westlake; Marit Mohn; Diana Gerald; Stian Westlake; Coutts & Co.
OTHER INFORMATION In 2019, £11.4 million was awarded in grants to 14 organisations.
HOW TO APPLY The foundation's website provides detailed information on how registered charities or social enterprises can apply. Applications should be made in writing and include the following: the purpose of the funding, evidence of need, outcomes, the amount sought and a set of the latest accounts. Although unsolicited applications are accepted, most funding is allocated through specific call-outs. Where appropriate, the website will carry details of this.
CONTACT DETAILS The Trustees, Coutts & Co., Trustee Department, 440 Strand, London WC2R 0QS *Tel.* 0345 304 2424 *Email* charitytrusts@coutts.com *Website* https://www.themohnwestlakefoundation.co.uk

■ Mole Charitable Trust

CC NO 281452 **ESTABLISHED** 1980
WHERE FUNDING CAN BE GIVEN UK, with a preference for Manchester.
WHO CAN BENEFIT Registered charities; schools and colleges; universities.
WHAT IS FUNDED Jewish causes; educational purposes; the relief of poverty; organisations working with children.
SAMPLE GRANTS Three Pillars Charity (£30,000); Manchester Charitable Trust (£22,000); The Roston Charitable Trust (£20,000); Aim Habonim; King David School (£10,000 each); Teshuvoh Tefilloh Tzedokoh (£2,000).
FINANCES *Financial year end* 31/03/2020 *Income* £250,400 *Total grants* £192,500 *Grants to organisations* £192,500 *Assets* £2,690,000
TRUSTEES Martin Gross; Leah Gross.
OTHER INFORMATION Grants were distributed as follows: educational institutions (£89,500); relief of poverty (£22,000); religious institutions (£16,500).
HOW TO APPLY Contact the correspondent for further information.
CONTACT DETAILS The Trustees, 2 Okeover Road, Salford, Greater Manchester M7 4JX *Tel.* 0161 832 8721 *Email* martin.gross@lopiangb.co.uk

■ The Alexander Moncur Trust

OSCR NO SC008863 **ESTABLISHED** 1946
WHERE FUNDING CAN BE GIVEN Dundee and the surrounding areas.
WHO CAN BENEFIT Registered charities.
WHAT IS FUNDED Cultural, health, educational and social projects.
TYPE OF GRANT General funding; revenue; one-off and recurrent.
RANGE OF GRANTS Generally, up to £5,000. Multi-year grants in the range of £10,000 per year for up to three years.
SAMPLE GRANTS Dundee Heritage Trust (£12,000); Maggie Keswick Jencks Cancer Centre (£7,000); Dundee Age Concern, Dundee Starter Packs and The Food Train (£5,000 each); Broughty Ferry YMCA, Kingdom Abuse Survivors Project and Tay Sail Training (£3,000 each); Hearing Dogs for Deaf People and Target Ovarian Cancer (£2,000 each).
FINANCES *Financial year end* 29/12/2019 *Income* £308,100 *Total grants* £206,000 *Grants to organisations* £205,000 *Assets* £9,260,000
OTHER INFORMATION The 2018/19 accounts were the latest available at the time of writing (February 2021). The trust awarded 79 revenue grants to organisations during the year, which had a combined total of £205,000. Grants of £1,000 and under totalled £16,000. A further two grants were awarded to individuals, totalling £1,000. In almost all circumstances only applications from registered charities will be considered. As a rough geographic guide, almost all grants are awarded to charities or their projects that fall within an area stretching around Dundee, through north Fife, Perth and Angus.
HOW TO APPLY Application forms are available to download from the trust's helpful website and should be returned to Miller Hendry Solicitors. Forms can also be requested from Miller Hendry Solicitors on 01382 200000. The application deadlines are 31 March and 30 September each year.
CONTACT DETAILS Ernest Boath, Administrator, c/o Miller Hendry Solicitors, 13 Ward Road, Dundee DD1 1LU *Tel.* 01382 200000 *Email* info@moncurtrust.org *Website* https://www.moncurtrust.org

■ The Monday Charitable Trust

CC NO 1174232 **ESTABLISHED** 2017
WHERE FUNDING CAN BE GIVEN UK.
WHO CAN BENEFIT UK-registered charities.
WHAT IS FUNDED Disadvantage, mainly in the fields of housing, education, welfare and social mobility.
SAMPLE GRANTS UK Youth (£1.28 million); Royal College of Art (£750,000); Central YMCA (£70,000); Grass Roots (£36,000); Multiple Sclerosis Society (£5,000).
FINANCES *Financial year end* 31/03/2020 *Income* £3,600,000 *Total grants* £5,560,000 *Grants to organisations* £5,560,000 *Assets* £89,870,000
TRUSTEES Douglas Blausten; Elspeth Lane; Sarah Baxter; Jonathan Brinsden; Andrew Johnston.
HOW TO APPLY Unsolicited applications are not accepted.
CONTACT DETAILS The Trustees, c/o BDB Pitmans, One Bartholomew Close, London EC1A 7BL *Tel.* 020 7783 3685

■ The Monmouthshire County Council Welsh Church Act Fund

CC NO 507094 **ESTABLISHED** 1996
WHERE FUNDING CAN BE GIVEN Blaenau Gwent, Caerphilly, Monmouthshire, Newport and Torfaen.
WHO CAN BENEFIT Organisations; religious organisations; libraries and museums; individual residents.
WHAT IS FUNDED General charitable purposes, including the following: education; religion;

social welfare; art and heritage; community benefit.

TYPE OF GRANT Capital costs; core costs.

SAMPLE GRANTS Caerphilly County Borough Council (£216,600); Monmouthshire County Council (£42,000); Torfaen County Borough Council (£38,400); Newport City Council (£33,900); Blaenau Gwent County Borough Council (£24,400).

FINANCES *Financial year end* 31/03/2019
Income £210,600 *Total grants* £355,400
Grants to organisations £315,700
Assets £5,370,000

TRUSTEE Monmouthshire County Council.

OTHER INFORMATION The 2018/19 accounts were the latest available at the time of writing (May 2021). Grants are paid to five local authorities, which administer grants to organisations and individuals on behalf of the charity (see the beneficiary list). During the year, grants to organisations were distributed as follows: religion (£163,500); community (£143,200); education (£8,700); social welfare (£250). Grants to individuals for the relief of poverty totalled £39,700.

HOW TO APPLY Applications are considered seven times a year. Application forms are available from the website. Applications from groups/ organisations will only be considered with a copy of their financial statements.

CONTACT DETAILS The Trustees, Monmouthshire County Council, County Hall, The Rhadyr, Usk, Gwent NP15 1GA *Tel.* 01633 644657 *Email* davejarrett@monmouthshire.gov.uk *Website* https://www.monmouthshire.gov.uk/ welsh-church-fund

■ Moondance Foundation

CC NO 1139224 **ESTABLISHED** 2010

WHERE FUNDING CAN BE GIVEN UK, with a strong preference for Wales; overseas.

WHO CAN BENEFIT Registered charities; constituted community groups; social enterprises; community interest organisations; CICs; other not-for-profit organisations.

WHAT IS FUNDED Children; education; older people; the environment; health; social welfare; women.

TYPE OF GRANT Project funding.

SAMPLE GRANTS Centre for Alternative Technology (£1 million); Mary's Meals (£500,000); Woodland Trust (£100,000); Aspire (£30,500); World at Play (£20,000); Community Foundation in Wales (£2,000).

FINANCES *Financial year end* 30/11/2019
Income £39,980,000
Total grants £11,650,000
Grants to organisations £11,650,000
Assets £309,710,000

TRUSTEES Louisa Scadden; Diane Briere de l'Isle-Engelhardt; Damien Engelhardt; Adrian Engelhardt; Tara Briere de l'Isle-Engelhardt; Henry Engelhardt; Shanna Briere de l'Isle-Engelhardt.

OTHER INFORMATION The 2018/19 accounts were the latest available at the time of writing (February 2021). The foundation made 134 grants from 614 applications during the year.

HOW TO APPLY Apply via the foundation's website.

CONTACT DETAILS The Trustees, c/o Azets, Ty Derw, Lime Tree Court, Cardiff Gate Business Park, Cardiff CF23 8AB *Email* moondancefoundation@ gmail.com *Website* https:// moondancefoundation.org.uk

■ The Henry Moore Foundation

CC NO 271370 **ESTABLISHED** 1977

WHERE FUNDING CAN BE GIVEN UK and overseas.

WHO CAN BENEFIT Not-for-profit institutions; arts organisations; educational bodies; individuals (research and travel grants only).

WHAT IS FUNDED Fine arts, in particular, sculpture; exhibitions; exhibition catalogues; commissions, conferences; research; postdoctoral research fellowships; publications; the development of collections through acquisitions, conservation, cataloguing and display.

WHAT IS NOT FUNDED Revenue expenditure; individuals (except research and travel grants or fellowships); retrospective expenditure; no grant (or part of any grant) may be used to pay any fee or to provide any other benefit to any individual who is a trustee of the foundation.

TYPE OF GRANT One-off and longer-term funding; publication; research; development; collections; exhibitions; fellowships; conferences and lectures.

RANGE OF GRANTS Up to £20,000, depending on grant category.

SAMPLE GRANTS Previous beneficiaries have included: Bodleian Weston Library, Frontier Publishing Norwich, Glasgow International (GI), Lady Lever Art Gallery, Museum of Modern Art Warsaw, Northern Gallery for Contemporary Art, The Public Catalogue Foundation, University of Winchester and Worcestershire County Council Archive and Archaeology Service.

FINANCES *Financial year end* 31/03/2020
Income £4,190,000 *Total grants* £500,000
Grants to organisations £500,000
Assets £108,370,000

TRUSTEES Nigel Carrington; Charles Asprey; Celia Clear; William Edgerley; Antony Griffiths; Peter Wienand; Pamela Raynor; Martin Barden.

OTHER INFORMATION During 2019/20, 92 grants were awarded in the following categories: exhibitions and new projects (£237,500); collections (£128,500); research (£44,000); fellowships (£42,000); other (£30,000); conferences, publications and workshops (£18,000). A list of previously supported projects is available on the foundation's website.

HOW TO APPLY Applications can be completed on the foundation's website. The grants committee considers applications four times a year. Check the website for further guidance and current deadlines.

CONTACT DETAILS Grants Committee, Dane Tree House, Perry Green, Much Hadham, Hertfordshire SG10 6EE *Tel.* 01279 843333 *Email* admin@henry-moore.org or use the enquiry form on the website. *Website* www. henry-moore.org

■ The George A. Moore Foundation

CC NO 262107 **ESTABLISHED** 1970

WHERE FUNDING CAN BE GIVEN North and West Yorkshire.

WHO CAN BENEFIT Registered charities.

WHAT IS FUNDED General charitable purposes.

WHAT IS NOT FUNDED Individuals; courses of study; overseas travel; holidays; purposes outside the UK.

TYPE OF GRANT Project funding.

RANGE OF GRANTS Typically £500 to £2,500; larger grants may be considered for selected projects.

SAMPLE GRANTS Henshaws – Yorkshire (£50,000); Macmillan Cancer Support (£10,000); Versus

Arthritis (£3,000); Barnardo's (£2,000); Asthma UK (£1,000).

FINANCES *Financial year end* 05/04/2020 *Income* £244,500 *Total grants* £210,200 *Grants to organisations* £210,200 *Assets* £5,810,000

TRUSTEES Richard Dawson; Jonathan Moore; Paul Turner.

OTHER INFORMATION Grants were awarded to 79 organisations, ranging from £150 to £50,000.

HOW TO APPLY Apply in writing to the correspondent. The trustees meet quarterly. Full details of what should be included in an application and application deadlines can be found on the foundation's website.

CONTACT DETAILS Angela James, Chief Administrator, 4th Floor, 10 South Parade, Leeds, West Yorkshire LS1 5QS *Tel.* 07860 701322 *Email* info@gamf.org.uk *Website* www.gamf.org.uk

John Moores Foundation

CC NO 253481 **ESTABLISHED** 1963

WHERE FUNDING CAN BE GIVEN Merseyside (including Skelmersdale, Halton and Ellesmere Port); Northern Ireland.

WHO CAN BENEFIT Registered charities; unregistered charities; social enterprises; CICs.

WHAT IS FUNDED Social welfare; mental health; BAME communities; refugees; women and girls; children and young people; discrimination; families; people who are homeless; carers; adult education.

WHAT IS NOT FUNDED Individuals; projects that are not substantially influenced by their target beneficiaries; national organisations or groups based outside the Merseyside region even if some of the service users come from the area; statutory bodies or work previously done by them; education (schools, colleges, universities and supplementary schools); faith-based projects exclusively for members of that faith, or for the promotion of religion; capital building costs; festivals, carnivals and fêtes; medicine or medical equipment; holidays and expeditions; gifts, parties, etc.; organising conferences; sport; vehicles; animal charities; the creative industries; heritage or local history projects; employability and enterprise schemes; academic or medical research; credit unions – except for the training of management committee members or the development of a new business plan; veterans; uniformed groups; sponsorship, advertising or fundraising events; counsellors not registered with the British Association for Counselling and Psychotherapy or the UK Council for Psychotherapy.

TYPE OF GRANT Running costs; capacity building; volunteer expenses; one-off projects; equipment (if part of a wider project).

SAMPLE GRANTS Previous beneficiaries have included: Granby Community Mental Health Group – Mary Seacole House (£14,000); Irish Community Care Merseyside (£10,000); Merseyside Refugee Support Network (£9,900); St Helens Carers Centre (£7,500); Knowsley Disability Concern (£5,000); Busy Bees Cross Community Playgroup (£2,000); Cruse Bereavement Care (£2,400); The Thursday Club (£1,200).

FINANCES *Financial year end* 05/04/2020 *Income* £668,500 *Total grants* £548,000 *Grants to organisations* £548,000 *Assets* £24,400,000

TRUSTEES Barnaby Moores; Kevin Moores; Nicola Eastwood; Christina Mee.

HOW TO APPLY Applicants should first check their eligibility on the foundation's website. Following this, the foundation can be contacted via email, letter or phone to obtain an application pack.

CONTACT DETAILS Phil Godfrey, Grants Director, 1st Floor, Front Office, 96 Bold Street, Liverpool, Merseyside L1 4HY *Tel.* 0151 707 6077 *Email* info@johnmooresfoundation.com *Website* www.jmf.org.uk

The Morel Charitable Trust

CC NO 268943 **ESTABLISHED** 1973

WHERE FUNDING CAN BE GIVEN Worldwide, with a preference for Bristol, Leeds, Brecon, London, Ghana, Zambia, Malawi and the Solomon Islands.

WHO CAN BENEFIT Charitable organisations.

WHAT IS FUNDED Arts and culture, particularly drama; race relations; inner-city projects; international development.

WHAT IS NOT FUNDED Individuals.

TYPE OF GRANT Project funding.

RANGE OF GRANTS Mostly £3,000 and under.

SAMPLE GRANTS Sightsavers (£6,000); OXFAM (£4,000); Christian Aid and Health Poverty Action (£3,000 each); Big House Theatre and Shakespeare Link (£2,000 each); Crickhowell District Archive Centre (£1,500); Bristol Drugs Project (£1,100); Kidz Klub Leeds (£1,000); Crickhowell Community Primary School (£600).

FINANCES *Financial year end* 31/03/2020 *Income* £59,600 *Total grants* £84,400 *Grants to organisations* £84,400 *Assets* £1,740,000

TRUSTEES Benjamin Gibbs; Dr James Gibbs; William Gibbs; Dr Emily Parry; Simon Gibbs; Dr Thomas Gibbs; Abigail Keane; Susanna Coan.

OTHER INFORMATION During the year, 42 grants were awarded to organisations. Grants were distributed as follows: international development (27 grants totalling £61,500); UK social (ten grants totalling £12,900); UK arts (five grants totalling £10,000).

HOW TO APPLY Apply in writing to the correspondent. The trustees held three meetings in 2019, in April, August and November. The annual report states that the trust 'normally grant[s] aid projects of which the trustees have personal knowledge'.

CONTACT DETAILS Simon Gibbs, Trustee, 34 Durand Gardens, London SW9 0PP *Tel.* 020 7582 6901 *Email* simoned.gibbs@yahoo.co.uk

The Morgan Charitable Foundation

CC NO 283128 **ESTABLISHED** 1981

WHERE FUNDING CAN BE GIVEN UK.

WHO CAN BENEFIT Charitable organisations.

WHAT IS FUNDED General charitable purposes; social welfare; health; overseas aid; disability; homelessness; Jewish causes.

WHAT IS NOT FUNDED Individuals.

SAMPLE GRANTS A list of beneficiaries was not available in the 2019 accounts, but a copy can be requested from the trustees.

FINANCES *Financial year end* 31/12/2019 *Income* £177,800 *Total grants* £93,300 *Grants to organisations* £93,300 *Assets* £5,860,000

TRUSTEES Carmen Gleen; Leslie Morgan; Nelly Levene; Molly Trioche; Ronnie Morgan.

OTHER INFORMATION The trustees maintain a list of charitable organisations which they regularly support and the list is reviewed half yearly at the directors' meetings.

HOW TO APPLY Applications have to be made in writing to the correspondent and include a copy of the latest annual report and accounts. The trustees meet twice a year. The foundation has previously requested not to receive telephone enquiries.

CONTACT DETAILS The Trustees, PO Box 57749, London NW11 1FD *Tel.* 07970 056111

■ The Steve Morgan Foundation

CC NO 1087056 **ESTABLISHED** 2000

WHERE FUNDING CAN BE GIVEN North Wales, Merseyside, Cheshire.

WHO CAN BENEFIT Registered charities; CICs; social enterprises; individuals.

WHAT IS FUNDED Children and young people; families; older people; health and disability; people who are socially isolated. The foundation's website states: 'All requests which would result in a positive effect on people's welfare or quality of life or improve opportunities and life choices, are considered.'

WHAT IS NOT FUNDED Application guidelines and criteria for each funding programme can be found on the foundation's website.

TYPE OF GRANT Capital costs; core costs; revenue costs.

SAMPLE GRANTS Everton in the Community (£2.46 million); Liverpool FC Foundation (£1.67 million); YMCA Crewe (£90,000); Wirral Mencap (£84,000); Same but Different (£74,000); Whitechapel Centre (£50,000); People First Merseyside (£45,000); Veterans in Sefton (£29,200).

FINANCES *Financial year end* 31/03/2020 *Income* £11,910,000 *Total grants* £9,600,000 *Grants to organisations* £9,600,000 *Assets* £251,310,000

TRUSTEES Brian Clark; Rhiannon Walker; Stephen Morgan; Vincent Fairclough; Sally Morgan; Ashley Lewis; Jonathan Masters.

OTHER INFORMATION The foundation also funds specialised equipment for people in need through its 'Enable' programme.

HOW TO APPLY For regional, major and Smiley Bus grants, applicants are requested to first check their eligibility against the criteria listed on the foundation's website. Eligible organisations are then asked submit an expression of interest via email.

CONTACT DETAILS The Trustees, PO Box 3517, Chester CH1 9ET *Email* hello@stevemorganfoundation.org.uk *Website* https://stevemorganfoundation.org.uk

■ Morgan Stanley International Foundation

CC NO 1042671 **ESTABLISHED** 1994

WHERE FUNDING CAN BE GIVEN Europe, the Middle East and Africa; local projects in Tower Hamlets and Glasgow.

WHO CAN BENEFIT Registered charities; state-funded schools.

WHAT IS FUNDED Children's health; education; welfare; disadvantaged communities across Europe, the Middle East and Africa.

WHAT IS NOT FUNDED See the foundation's website for a list of exclusions.

TYPE OF GRANT Project funding; capital costs.

RANGE OF GRANTS Up to £100,000.

SAMPLE GRANTS PEEK – Glasgow (£111,600); Bromley by Bow Centre (£77,000); PATH – London (£57,000); Integrom – Budapest (£25,000).

FINANCES *Financial year end* 31/12/2019 *Income* £1,810,000 *Total grants* £2,270,000 *Grants to organisations* £2,270,000 *Assets* £2,400,000

TRUSTEES Clare Woodman; Hanns Seibold; Maryann McMahon; Stephen Mavin; Sue Watts; Oliver Stuart; Graham Rogers; Piers Harris; Jamie Glynn; Norbert Fogarasi; Victoria Worster; Diane Hosie.

OTHER INFORMATION The foundation is the corporate charity of Morgan Stanley and Co. International plc, the financial services corporation. The foundation matches any contribution, either monetary or through volunteering, by employees, to a maximum of £500 per employee in one given year. Employees are encouraged to take on up to ten weeks' pro bono work for NGOs and charities.

HOW TO APPLY The foundation takes a proactive approach to grant-making and therefore does not accept unsolicited proposals. However, the foundation's website does state that you can make contact via email if you think your charity is a match with its funding criteria. Details of what should be included in the email can be found on the foundation's website.

CONTACT DETAILS The Trustees, Morgan Stanley and Co. International plc, 20 Bank Street, London E14 4AD *Email* communityaffairslondon@morganstanley.com *Website* https://www.morganstanley.com/pub/content/msdotcom/en/about-us/giving-back/msif-guidelines.html

■ The Miles Morland Foundation

CC NO 1150755 **ESTABLISHED** 2013

WHERE FUNDING CAN BE GIVEN UK and overseas, predominately Africa.

WHO CAN BENEFIT Charitable organisations; individuals; theatres; colleges and universities.

WHAT IS FUNDED African writing and literature; human rights; theatre and culture; literacy festivals; social welfare; work overseas.

WHAT IS NOT FUNDED Education; literacy initiatives (except for festivals); healthcare; periodicals.

TYPE OF GRANT Project funding; scholarships.

RANGE OF GRANTS Typically less than £25,000.

SAMPLE GRANTS The Royal African Society and University of East Anglia (£25,000 each); Kayd Somali Arts and Culture (£20,000); Friends of Guys Marsh Prison (£14,000); Donmar Warehouse (£6,000); Lincoln Oxford College (£10,000); UK Youth (£3,000); Reprieve (£1,200).

FINANCES *Financial year end* 31/03/2020 *Income* £532,200 *Total grants* £274,500 *Grants to organisations* £189,300 *Assets* £229,900

TRUSTEES The Hon. Alice Bragg; Cornelie Ferguson; Kate Morland; Miles Morland.

OTHER INFORMATION During the year, grants were made to ten UK organisations, totalling £122,000, and to ten overseas organisations, totalling £67,300. Four African writing scholarships were awarded to individuals, totalling £72,000. In addition, grants to UK individuals totalled £13,200. According to the website, the foundation 'supports several human rights organisations, an array of London theatres, Oxford University women's lightweight rowing, projects in Haiti and Palestine, a literacy initiative in London's Shoreditch, plus several schemes which help recovering addicts and detained prisoners in the UK'.

HOW TO APPLY The foundation's website has detailed guidance for potential applicants and an application form that should be sent via email to the correspondent. Applications not submitted online will not be considered.

CONTACT DETAILS The Trustees, 2nd Floor, Jubilee House, 2 Jubilee Place, London SW3 3TQ *Tel.* 020 7349 1245 *Email* mmf@milesmorlandfoundation.com *Website* www.milesmorlandfoundation.com

■ The Morris Charitable Trust

CC NO 802290 **ESTABLISHED** 1989

WHERE FUNDING CAN BE GIVEN UK and overseas, with a strong preference for Islington.

WHO CAN BENEFIT Registered charities; local Islington community projects. The trustees select national and international charities to support on an ad hoc basis.

WHAT IS FUNDED General charitable purposes, including education, community support and development, health and disability, with a particular emphasis on alleviating social hardship and deprivation.

WHAT IS NOT FUNDED Individuals; annual core costs (e.g. staffing, salaries or equipment hire); repeat applications within one year. Donations are generally not made to non-registered charities.

TYPE OF GRANT One-off project and capital grants for one year.

RANGE OF GRANTS Usually up to £5,000, with occasional major donations.

SAMPLE GRANTS A list of recent beneficiaries can be found on the trust's website.

FINANCES *Financial year end* 31/03/2020 *Income* £200,200 *Total grants* £142,100 *Grants to organisations* £142,100 *Assets* £309,100

TRUSTEES Paul Morris; Jack Morris; Alan Stenning; Dominic Jones; Gerald Morris; Linda Morris; Lucie Grant.

OTHER INFORMATION Grants were made to 28 organisations during the year, of which 22 were for £5,000 and under.

HOW TO APPLY Application forms are available to download from the trust's website. The trustees meet several times a year. Grants are generally not repeated within a 12-month period.

CONTACT DETAILS Linda Morris, Secretary, Business Design Centre, 52 Upper Street, Islington Green, London N1 0QH *Tel.* 020 7288 6200 *Email* info@morrischaritabletrust.com *Website* www.morrischaritabletrust.com

■ The Willie and Mabel Morris Charitable Trust

CC NO 280554 **ESTABLISHED** 1980

WHERE FUNDING CAN BE GIVEN UK.

WHO CAN BENEFIT Registered charities.

WHAT IS FUNDED General charitable purposes, with a strong preference for medical charities working in the areas of cancer, heart trouble, spasticity, arthritis and rheumatism.

WHAT IS NOT FUNDED Individuals.

RANGE OF GRANTS £100 to £10,000.

SAMPLE GRANTS Paul Strickland Scanner Centre (£10,000); Kidney Research UK (£5,000); Mental Health Foundation (£2,500); British Heart Foundation (£1,000); Friends of the Earth (£300); MS Therapy Centre – Northamptonshire (£230); Diabetes UK and Heathlands Animal Sanctuary (£100 each).

FINANCES *Financial year end* 05/04/2020 *Income* £149,700 *Total grants* £115,000 *Grants to organisations* £115,000 *Assets* £4,730,000

TRUSTEES Suzanne Marriott; Angela Tether; Andrew Tether; Alan Bryant; Verity Tether; Phoebe Tether.

OTHER INFORMATION Grants were made to 60 organisations during 2019/20.

HOW TO APPLY Apply in writing to the correspondent. The trustees meet annually to review applications. Applications made between meetings will also be considered by the trustees.

CONTACT DETAILS The Trustees, 9 The Hollies, Shefford, Bedfordshire SG17 5BX *Tel.* 01462 851897

■ The Ken and Lynne Morrison Charitable Trust

CC NO 1125586 **ESTABLISHED** 2008

WHERE FUNDING CAN BE GIVEN Yorkshire.

WHO CAN BENEFIT Registered charities; schools.

WHAT IS FUNDED Education and training; people with disabilities or special educational needs; general charitable purposes.

TYPE OF GRANT One-off grants.

RANGE OF GRANTS Up to £100,000.

SAMPLE GRANTS Barnardo's and Bradford Cathedral (£100,000 each); Yorkshire Air Ambulance (£20,000); The Bradford Toy Library (£2,000).

FINANCES *Financial year end* 05/04/2020 *Income* £495,700 *Total grants* £613,000 *Grants to organisations* £613,000 *Assets* £13,340,000

TRUSTEES Andrea Shelley; Lady Lynne Morrison.

HOW TO APPLY The trust's 2019/20 annual report states: 'The trustees identify projects and organisations they wish to support. Requests from people or organisations which apply speculatively will be considered if they are pertinent to the Trust's objectives.'

CONTACT DETAILS The Trustees, Myton Hall, Myton-on-Swale, Helperby, York, North Yorkshire YO61 2QX *Tel.* 01423 360258

■ G. M. Morrison Charitable Trust

CC NO 261380 **ESTABLISHED** 1970

WHERE FUNDING CAN BE GIVEN UK.

WHO CAN BENEFIT Registered charities operating in the UK and abroad; hospitals; hospices; universities; places of worship.

WHAT IS FUNDED General charitable purposes; medicine and health; social welfare; education and training.

WHAT IS NOT FUNDED Schemes or activities which are generally regarded as being the responsibility of statutory authorities; individuals; short-term projects; one-off capital grants (except for emergency appeals); commercial or business activities; retrospective grant applications.

TYPE OF GRANT Mostly recurrent annual awards for core/revenue costs.

RANGE OF GRANTS £1,000 to £3,000.

SAMPLE GRANTS Royal College of Surgeons (£3,000); Age UK (£2,100); Bowel and Cancer Research (£1,800); Care for the Family (£1,700); Hospice UK (£1,600); Centrepoint (£1,500); PCC of Baydon (£1,200); Seafarers UK (£1,000).

FINANCES *Financial year end* 05/04/2020 *Income* £368,000 *Total grants* £293,800 *Grants to organisations* £293,800 *Assets* £12,740,000

TRUSTEES Elizabeth Morrison; Jane Hunt; Edward Haslewood.

OTHER INFORMATION In 2019/20 the trust made 213 grants to organisations. The average grant size was £1,379. Grants were distributed as follows: medical and health (£125,300); social welfare (£88,400); others (£54,900); education and training (£25,200).

HOW TO APPLY To apply, write to the charity's address; however, note that new applications are only considered in exceptional circumstances. Applications are not acknowledged. Grants are distributed annually in January.

CONTACT DETAILS The Trustees, c/o Currey and Co. LLP, 33 Queen Anne Street, London W1G 9HY *Tel.* 020 7802 2700 *Email* gen@curreyandco.co.uk

■ The Ken and Edna Morrison Charitable Trust

CC NO 327639 **ESTABLISHED** 1987

WHERE FUNDING CAN BE GIVEN UK, with a preference for Yorkshire.

WHO CAN BENEFIT Registered charities.

WHAT IS FUNDED General charitable purposes, including the following: support for people with a disability or special educational needs; education and training.

TYPE OF GRANT One-off.

RANGE OF GRANTS £3,000 to £70,000.

SAMPLE GRANTS Age UK (£46,000); Leeds Cares (£44,000); Macmillan Cancer Support (£20,000); The Royal Agricultural Benevolent Institution (£15,000 in two grants); Bradford Nightstop and Herriot Hospice (£10,000 each).

FINANCES *Financial year end* 05/04/2020 *Income* £173,500 *Total grants* £145,000 *Grants to organisations* £145,000 *Assets* £4,570,000

TRUSTEES Eleanor Kernighan; William Morrison.

OTHER INFORMATION Grants were awarded to six organisations during the year.

HOW TO APPLY Apply in writing to the correspondent. The trust's 2019/20 accounts state: 'Future grants will include small donations (on application) to causes within the objectives and also larger donations to projects or organisations that the trustees have identified.'

CONTACT DETAILS The Trustees, c/o Progeny Private Law, Progeny House, 46 Park Place, Leeds, North Yorkshire LS1 2RY *Tel.* 0113 467 1742

■ The Morrisons Foundation

CC NO 1160224/SC045634 **ESTABLISHED** 2014

WHERE FUNDING CAN BE GIVEN Areas of company presence in England, Scotland and Wales.

WHO CAN BENEFIT Charities that have been registered for a minimum of one year.

WHAT IS FUNDED General charitable purposes; community; health; education; social welfare; the arts and culture.

WHAT IS NOT FUNDED Non-registered charities; individuals; salaries and running costs; part-funding. A full list of exclusions can be found on the foundation's website.

TYPE OF GRANT Capital costs and project funding.

RANGE OF GRANTS Up to £25,000.

SAMPLE GRANTS Ickle Pickles and The Children's Trust (£25,000 each); Dentaid (£20,000); Emmaus Oxford (£18,400); Lincolnshire Emergency Blood Bikes Service (£14,700); British Disabled Angling Association (£7,400); Pinpoint (£5,000); Disability Snowsport UK (£4,600).

FINANCES *Financial year end* 02/02/2020 *Income* £1,950,000 *Total grants* £2,810,000 *Grants to organisations* £2,810,000 *Assets* £2,030,000

TRUSTEES Kate Bratt-Farrar; Guy Mason; Jonathan Burke; David Scott; Andrew Clappen; Sarah Wilkinson; Zulfiqar Karim; Charles Jones.

OTHER INFORMATION This is the corporate charity of the supermarket chain Morrisons. In addition to its grant-making, the foundation also matches employees' fundraising efforts (£357,000 in 2019/20).

HOW TO APPLY Applications can be completed online through the foundation's website. Applications are accepted and reviewed on a continual basis. Applicants will be notified of a decision by telephone or email, even if the application is unsuccessful.

CONTACT DETAILS The Trustees, Hilmore House, Gain Lane, Bradford, West Yorkshire BD3 7DL *Tel.* 0845 611 4449 *Email* foundation.enquiries@morrisonsplc.co.uk *Website* www.morrisonsfoundation.com

■ The Morton Charitable Trust (Dundee)

OSCR NO SC004507 **ESTABLISHED** 1987

WHERE FUNDING CAN BE GIVEN UK, with a preference for Scotland.

WHO CAN BENEFIT Registered charities.

WHAT IS FUNDED General charitable purposes; education and training; health; social welfare; sports and recreation.

SAMPLE GRANTS A list of beneficiaries was not included in the annual report and accounts.

FINANCES *Financial year end* 05/04/2020 *Income* £32,600 *Total grants* £72,800 *Grants to organisations* £72,800 *Assets* £921,100

HOW TO APPLY Contact the correspondent for further information.

CONTACT DETAILS Trust Secretary, 23 Ogilvie Court, Broughty Ferry, Dundee DD5 1LR

■ The Mosawi Foundation

CC NO 1157269 **ESTABLISHED** 2014

WHERE FUNDING CAN BE GIVEN UK, with a preference for Oxfordshire; overseas.

WHO CAN BENEFIT Charitable organisations.

WHAT IS FUNDED Children and young people; community development; education; healthcare and trauma relief; social welfare.

RANGE OF GRANTS Up to £600,000.

SAMPLE GRANTS Royal Welsh College of Music and Drama (£600,000); AMAR Foundation (£50,000); Albaby Baptist Church (£16,500); St Martin-in-the-Fields (£15,000).

FINANCES *Financial year end* 05/04/2020 *Income* £675,000 *Total grants* £1,080,000 *Grants to organisations* £1,080,000 *Assets* £1,020,000

TRUSTEES Mr A. A. Mosawi; Eleanor Mosawi; Mrs E. M. Mosawi.

HOW TO APPLY Contact the foundation for further information on the application process.

CONTACT DETAILS The Trustees, PO Box 4822, Henley-on-Thames, Oxfordshire, RG9 1AY *Email* info@themosawifoundation.org *Website* https://www.themosawifoundation.org/index.php

■ The Moshal Charitable Trust

CC NO 284448 **ESTABLISHED** 1982
WHERE FUNDING CAN BE GIVEN UK.
WHO CAN BENEFIT Charitable and educational organisations.
WHAT IS FUNDED General charitable purposes; education; Jewish causes.
SAMPLE GRANTS A list of beneficiaries was not included in the annual report and accounts.
FINANCES *Financial year end* 31/03/2020 *Income* £130,700 *Total grants* £107,000 *Grants to organisations* £107,000 *Assets* £840,600
TRUSTEES David Halpern; Lea Halpern.
HOW TO APPLY Contact the correspondent for further information.
CONTACT DETAILS The Trustees, New Riverside House, 439 Lower Broughton Road, Salford M7 2FX *Tel.* 0161 792 2626

■ Vyoel Moshe Charitable Trust

CC NO 327054 **ESTABLISHED** 1986
WHERE FUNDING CAN BE GIVEN UK and overseas, including Israel, the USA and Europe.
WHO CAN BENEFIT Registered charities; religious bodies; synagogues; individuals.
WHAT IS FUNDED Education, religion and the relief of poverty, with a focus on Jewish causes. Awards made to religious bodies are given to synagogues for the preservation of cemeteries, Jewish culture and heritage.
RANGE OF GRANTS £3,000 to £25,000.
SAMPLE GRANTS Previous beneficiaries have included: Mishkanos Haroyim, Mosdos Yetyev Lev Antwerp, Talmud Torah Tuv Yerushalaim, Talmud Tora Hamekoris Remoh, Toldos Aharon, Yeshivas Kol Aryeh.
FINANCES *Financial year end* 31/03/2020 *Income* £1,400,000 *Total grants* £1,460,000 *Grants to organisations* £1,460,000 *Assets* £7,800
TRUSTEES Jacob Frankel; Berish Berger; Shulom Cik.
HOW TO APPLY Apply in writing to the correspondent. The 2019/20 annual report states that 'the trustees select the institutions to be supported according to their personal knowledge of work of the institution. Individuals are referred to the charity by local rabbis. Any application is carefully considered and help given according to circumstances and funds then available.'
CONTACT DETAILS The Trustees, 2–4 Chardmore Road, London N16 6HX *Tel.* 07975 952011

■ The Alexander Mosley Charitable Trust

CC NO 1142898 **ESTABLISHED** 2011
WHERE FUNDING CAN BE GIVEN UK and overseas.
WHO CAN BENEFIT Mainly UK-registered charities. According to the 2019/20 annual report, applications from UK-registered charities will be considered in priority to applications from unregistered charities. Beneficiaries have also included schools, colleges and universities.
WHAT IS FUNDED General charitable purposes.
WHAT IS NOT FUNDED Large national charities (i.e. those with an annual income in excess of £10 million or with over £100 million in assets); charities dedicated to issues deemed by the trustees to be already well funded within the UK; charities dedicated to purposes for which the UK government has a statutory responsibility to provide.
TYPE OF GRANT One-off; recurrent.
RANGE OF GRANTS £10,000 to £6 million (in 2019/20).
SAMPLE GRANTS University of Oxford (£6 million); St Peter's College – Oxford (£5 million); Global NCAP (£1 million); Eastern Alliance for Safe and Sustainable Transport (£500,000); Imperial College of Science Technology and Medicine (£200,000); Inside Justice (£100,000); Children's Radio Foundation (£81,000 in two grants); Willow Foundation (£10,000).
FINANCES *Financial year end* 05/04/2020 *Income* £7,980,000 *Total grants* £14,980,000 *Grants to organisations* £14,980,000 *Assets* £4,190,000
TRUSTEES Horatio Mortimer; Max Mosley; Emma Mosley; Max Mosley.
OTHER INFORMATION Grants were committed to 17 organisations during the year.
HOW TO APPLY Apply in writing to the correspondent. The trustees only reply to successful applicants.
CONTACT DETAILS The Trustees, 10 New Square, Lincoln's Inn, London WC2A 3QG *Tel.* 020 7465 4300

■ The Mosselson Charitable Trust

CC NO 266517 **ESTABLISHED** 1974
WHERE FUNDING CAN BE GIVEN UK.
WHO CAN BENEFIT Charitable organisations.
WHAT IS FUNDED Education; medicine and medical research; women and children's support and welfare; religion; social welfare.
SAMPLE GRANTS Childline; Holocaust Education Trust; Jewish Women's Week; Family Housing Association; Nightingale House; Shaare Zedek Medical Centre.
FINANCES *Financial year end* 30/09/2019 *Income* £104,200 *Total grants* £205,700 *Grants to organisations* £205,700 *Assets* £3,300,000
TRUSTEES Dr Jacqueline Mosselson; Marian Mosselson.
OTHER INFORMATION The trust's 2018/19 annual report, the latest available at the time of writing, (June 2021), states that the trustees' long-term goal is to establish a student scholarship programme at graduate level to provide financial assistance in diverse fields of study, with an emphasis on higher education. A list of beneficiaries was not available in the 2018/19 accounts; the sample given is taken from a previous year's accounts.
HOW TO APPLY Contact the correspondent for further information.
CONTACT DETAILS The Trustees, Denmoss House, 10 Greenland Street, London NW1 0ND *Tel.* 020 7428 1929

■ Moto in the Community

CC NO 1111147 **ESTABLISHED** 2005
WHERE FUNDING CAN BE GIVEN UK.
WHO CAN BENEFIT Community groups; registered charities; individuals working for Moto; schools.
WHAT IS FUNDED Conservation of the environment; road safety education; development of local communities.

WHAT IS NOT FUNDED Overseas applications; religion; politics.

RANGE OF GRANTS Grants of up to £2,000 but mostly of £500.

SAMPLE GRANTS Wessex Children's Hospice Trust (£2,000); Wellgate Primary School (£1,000); Swings and Smiles, Dover Taekwondo and Musical Connections (£500 each); Myaware Cornwall (£190).

FINANCES *Financial year end* 31/12/2019 *Income* £1,030,000 *Total grants* £812,100 *Grants to organisations* £812,100 *Assets* £333,700

TRUSTEES Daniel Horsley; Peter Mould; Louise Hughes; John Masters; Brynn Hewitt; Julie Sturgess; Stephen Rac; Gene McDonald; James Gunn; Guy Latchem; Coral Brodie.

HOW TO APPLY Visit the charity's website for further information.

CONTACT DETAILS The Trustees, Moto in the Community Trust, Moto Hospitality Ltd, Toddington Service Area, Junction 12 M1 Southbound, Toddington, Bedfordshire LU5 6HR *Tel.* 01525 878500 *Email* motocharity@moto-way.co.uk *Website* https://moto-way.com/moto-in-the-community

■ Motor Neurone Disease Association

CC NO 294354 **ESTABLISHED** 1986

WHERE FUNDING CAN BE GIVEN UK and overseas.

WHO CAN BENEFIT Universities; hospitals; other research institutions; charitable organisations associated with motor neurone disease; individuals.

WHAT IS FUNDED Research into motor neurone disease; support for individuals diagnosed with motor neurone disease.

TYPE OF GRANT Project funding; capital costs; core/revenue funding; research grants.

RANGE OF GRANTS Grants vary according to the programme.

SAMPLE GRANTS King's College London (£662,000); University of Sheffield (£308,000); Leeds Care Centre (£102,000); School of Biomedical Sciences (£82,000); MRC Mitochondrial Biology Unit (£57,000); Sussex MND Care and Research Network (£42,000).

FINANCES *Financial year end* 31/12/2019 *Income* £18,630,000 *Total grants* £5,780,000 *Grants to organisations* £4,520,000 *Assets* £10,680,000

TRUSTEES Richard Coleman; Janet Warren; Tim Kidd; Alan Graham; Siobhan Rooney; Dr Nikhil Sharma; Dr Heather Smith; Katy Styles; Vicky Paeschel; Devia Gurjar; Shaun Gee; Catherine Knight; Andrew Cawdell.

OTHER INFORMATION Research grants consist of: project grants (up to £255,000 for up to three years for biomedical or healthcare research); PhD studentships (up to £100,000 for up to three years for PhD training in motor neurone disease-related projects); small grants (varying amounts for up to four years for rapid follow-up of new findings and small pump-priming grants). The grant-maker also provides the Lady Edith Wolfson Fellowship Programme in partnership with the Medical Research Council, which offers fellowships. Further information on grant programmes is available on the grant-maker's website.

HOW TO APPLY The application process may vary according to the programme being applied to. Further information on each programme, including the application process, is available on the grant-maker's website.

CONTACT DETAILS Research Grants Team, Francis Crick House, 6 Summerhouse Road, Moulton Park, Northampton, Northamptonshire NN3 6BJ *Tel.* 01604 250505 *Email* enquiries@mndassociation.org *Website* www.mndassociation.org/research

■ The Edwina Mountbatten and Leonora Children's Foundation

CC NO 228166 **ESTABLISHED** 1960

WHERE FUNDING CAN BE GIVEN UK and overseas.

WHO CAN BENEFIT Registered charities; hospitals; hospices.

WHAT IS FUNDED Healthcare; nursing; paediatric cancer.

TYPE OF GRANT Project funding.

RANGE OF GRANTS Mostly £10,000 to £20,000.

SAMPLE GRANTS Ark Cancer Charity (£100,000); Look (£50,000); Countess Mountbatten Hospice and St John of Jerusalem Eye Hospital (£20,000 each); Gift of Sight and Health and Hope UK (£10,000 each); Intercare – Aid for Africa and The Stable Family Home Trust (£5,000 each).

FINANCES *Financial year end* 31/12/2019 *Income* £117,700 *Total grants* £245,000 *Grants to organisations* £245,000 *Assets* £6,710,000

TRUSTEES Peter Mimpriss; Myrddin Rees; Lady Mary Fagan; Lady Alexandra Knatchbull; The Hon. Countess Mountbatten of Burma.

OTHER INFORMATION Grants were made to ten organisations during the year.

HOW TO APPLY Contact the correspondent for further information.

CONTACT DETAILS Richard Jordan-Baker, Trust Secretary, The Estate Office, Broadlands, Romsey, Hampshire SO51 9ZE *Tel.* 01794 505080 *Email* sheilabrown@broadlandsestates.co.uk

■ The Mowgli Trust

CC NO 1173842 **ESTABLISHED** 2017

WHERE FUNDING CAN BE GIVEN UK.

WHO CAN BENEFIT Registered charities.

WHAT IS FUNDED General charitable purposes.

RANGE OF GRANTS £6,000 to £48,500.

SAMPLE GRANTS Tearfund (£48,500); Action Against Hunger (£33,300); The Maggie Keswick Jencks Cancer Caring Centres Trust (£24,100); The Clatterbridge Cancer Charity (£22,000); Bobath Children's Therapy Centre Wales (£9,000); Rainbows Hospice for Children and Young People (£6,400).

FINANCES *Financial year end* 31/03/2020 *Income* £340,500 *Total grants* £294,200 *Grants to organisations* £294,200 *Assets* £37,200

TRUSTEES Clare White; Jane Lake; Nisha Katona; Matthew Peck.

OTHER INFORMATION A total of 13 grants were made during the year. Charities supported are typically local to a branch of Mowgli Street Food.

HOW TO APPLY Unsolicited applications are not accepted. The trust's website states: 'Be advised that we will not accept unsolicited applications for partnerships, prizes or awards as we work only with our carefully selected charity partners.'

CONTACT DETAILS The Trustees, 69 Bold Street, Liverpool L1 4EZ *Tel.* 01517 08505 *Email* zara@mowglistreetfood.com *Website* https://mowglitrust.com

The MSE Charity

CC NO 1121320 ESTABLISHED 2008

WHERE FUNDING CAN BE GIVEN UK.

WHO CAN BENEFIT Registered charities; CICs; credit unions; non-profit organisations with a constitution.

WHAT IS FUNDED Financial literacy; debt, money and consumer issues education.

WHAT IS NOT FUNDED Individuals; statutory organisations; organisations with an annual income exceeding £500,000 and with more than six months' worth of free reserves. For a full list of exclusions, see the FAQ section of the charity's website.

TYPE OF GRANT Project costs.

RANGE OF GRANTS Up to £7,500. As of July 2020 the charity will also fund up to £500 per application for essential IT equipment for project delivery.

SAMPLE GRANTS Anybody Can Cook; Bute Advice Centre; Citizens Advice St Albans District; Deaf Connexions; Headway Portsmouth and South East Hampshire; Quaker Social Action; SOS Domestic Abuse Projects; Trinity Winchester; Urban Community Projects; Wipers; Your Own Place.

FINANCES *Financial year end* 31/03/2020 *Income* £95,600 *Total grants* £81,900 *Grants to organisations* £81,900 *Assets* £59,400

TRUSTEES Tony Tesciuba; Katie Davies; Vanessa Bissessur; Teej Dew; Clarissa Coleman; Marcus Herbert.

OTHER INFORMATION The charity provides two rounds of grants per year, focusing on four themes through a two-year cycle. The themes for 2021/22 are: raising the next generation; life-changing transitions; living with long-term challenges; building and developing resilience. A sample of previous beneficiaries has been taken from the website.

HOW TO APPLY Applicants should complete an online application form when the relevant funding round opens (in February or September – see the website for exact deadlines). Each grant round is limited to the first 40 applicants. A template which previews the questions that will need to be answered can be found on the website. An eligibility quiz is also available on the website.

CONTACT DETAILS Grants Advisory Panel, c/o Tesciuba Ltd, 72 Cavendish Road, Salford M7 4WA *Tel.* 0161 211 0205 *Email* info@msecharity.com *Website* www.msecharity.com

The Mulberry Trust

CC NO 263296 ESTABLISHED 1971

WHERE FUNDING CAN BE GIVEN UK, with a preference for Essex.

WHO CAN BENEFIT Charitable organisations; hospices; arts organisations; environmental organisations; Christian organisations.

WHAT IS FUNDED General charitable purposes, particularly parenting and family welfare; children, older people, homelessness, debt relief and counselling, community development, education and research, religious and interfaith work, health, the arts, and the environment.

WHAT IS NOT FUNDED Individuals.

RANGE OF GRANTS £1,000 to £30,000.

SAMPLE GRANTS Pioneer Sailing Trust (£30,000); Home-Start Essex (£20,000); Harlow Citizens Advice (£15,500); Maldon Citizens Advice (£10,000); St Clare Hospice (£5,000); St Francis Hospice (£3,000); Bugatti Trust (£1,000); Dr Edwin Doubleday Trust (£500).

FINANCES *Financial year end* 05/04/2020 *Income* £82,000 *Total grants* £311,700 *Grants to organisations* £311,700 *Assets* £2,410,000

TRUSTEES Ann Marks; Charles Woodhouse; Timothy Marks; Rupert Marks; William Marks; Christopher Marks; Leonie Marks; Susan Gow.

OTHER INFORMATION Grants totalling £311,700 were awarded to 44 organisations for a wide variety of causes, the vast majority of which were located in the Essex area.

HOW TO APPLY The trust does not accept unsolicited applications.

CONTACT DETAILS The Trustees, c/o Farrer and Co., 65–66 Lincoln's Inn Fields, London WC2A 3LH *Tel.* 020 3375 7000 *Email* secretarialservices@farrer.co.uk

The Mulchand Foundation

CC NO 1181826 ESTABLISHED 2019

WHERE FUNDING CAN BE GIVEN England and Wales.

WHO CAN BENEFIT Registered charities.

WHAT IS FUNDED General charitable purposes.

SAMPLE GRANTS A list of beneficiaries was not available in the annual report and accounts for 2019.

FINANCES *Financial year end* 29/02/2020 *Income* £228,700 *Total grants* £57,600 *Grants to organisations* £57,600 *Assets* £171,200

TRUSTEES Rajan Mulchand; Sanjay Mulchand; Venika Mulchand.

HOW TO APPLY Contact the correspondent for further information.

CONTACT DETAILS Sanjay Mulchand, Trustee, c/o Laltex Group, Leigh Commerce Park, Green Fold Way, Leigh, WN7 3XH *Tel.* 01942 687000 *Email* sanjay@laltex.com

The Frederick Mulder Foundation

CC NO 296019 ESTABLISHED 1986

WHERE FUNDING CAN BE GIVEN Worldwide.

WHO CAN BENEFIT Registered and non-registered charities; social enterprises.

WHAT IS FUNDED Social change philanthropy; climate change; global poverty.

TYPE OF GRANT Project funding; seed funding/start-up funding; core/revenue costs. One-off and multi-year grants.

RANGE OF GRANTS Usually £1,000 to £50,000.

SAMPLE GRANTS Climate Bonds Initiative (£50,000); Beaver Trust (£30,000); Glacier Trust (£30,000); Global Witness (£5,000); Roots and Wings Foundation – Hungary (£5,400).

FINANCES *Financial year end* 31/03/2020 *Income* £175,500 *Total grants* £502,300 *Grants to organisations* £502,300 *Assets* £5,800,000

TRUSTEES Dr Frederick Mulder; Hannah Mulder; Robin Bowman.

OTHER INFORMATION The foundation supports many small social change organisations around the world through The Funding Network, which was founded by Frederick Mulder.

HOW TO APPLY The foundation does not accept unsolicited applications.

CONTACT DETAILS Brynn Higgs, Director, 83 Belsize Park Gardens, London NW3 4NJ *Email* brynn@fredericksmulderfoundation.org.uk *Website* www.frederickmulderfoundation.org.uk

■ Multiple Sclerosis Society

CC NO 1139257 **ESTABLISHED** 2010

WHERE FUNDING CAN BE GIVEN UK.

WHO CAN BENEFIT Recognised NHS and UK academic institutions.

WHAT IS FUNDED Multiple sclerosis research.

TYPE OF GRANT Research funding; PhD studentships; project grants; individuals and their carers.

SAMPLE GRANTS University of Edinburgh (£1.03 million); University of Cambridge (£1.06 million); University College London (£459,000); International Progressive MS Alliance (£378,000); University of Glasgow (£209,000); Walton Centre NHS Trust (£126,000); University of Plymouth (£51,000).

FINANCES *Financial year end* 31/12/2019 *Income* £28,600,000 *Total grants* £5,887,000 *Grants to organisations* £4,930,000 *Assets* £17,100,000

TRUSTEES Sarah Schol; Stuart Secker; Nicholas Winser; Ceri Smith; Dr Anne Shinkwin; Marion King; Susan Crane; Anthony Upshall; Dr Shewly Khanam Choudhury; Polly Williams; Emily Revess; Nwanyieke Oluwayemi.

OTHER INFORMATION There are separate grant programmes to support individuals with multiple sclerosis and their carers. Grants made to individuals totalled £957,000.

HOW TO APPLY Applications can be made through the society's website, where details of open funding programmes and application deadlines can also be found.

CONTACT DETAILS Grants Team, MS National Centre, 372 Edgware Road, London NW2 6ND *Tel.* 0300 500 8084 *Email* research@mssociety.org.uk *Website* www.mssociety.org.uk

■ Edith Murphy Foundation

CC NO 1026062 **ESTABLISHED** 1993

WHERE FUNDING CAN BE GIVEN UK, with a preference for Leicestershire and the East Midlands.

WHO CAN BENEFIT National registered charities and organisations based in Leicestershire and the East Midlands.

WHAT IS FUNDED Social welfare; disability; older people; young people; animal welfare; research.

TYPE OF GRANT Project and research funding.

RANGE OF GRANTS The majority of grants are of under £20,000.

SAMPLE GRANTS Leicestershire Cares (£50,000); Age UK (£30,000); The Duke of Edinburgh Award – East Midlands (£25,000); Healing Little Hearts (£20,000); Whizz-Kidz (£19,300); CLIC Sargent and Northampton Saints Foundation (£15,000 each); Antibiotic Research UK and The Little Theatre – Leicester Drama Society (£10,000 each).

FINANCES *Financial year end* 31/03/2020 *Income* £739,900 *Total grants* £910,300 *Grants to organisations* £910,300 *Assets* £32,780,000

TRUSTEES David Tams; Christopher Blakesley; Richard Adkinson; Dr Charlotte Blakesley; Julian Tams; Coutts & Co.

OTHER INFORMATION During 2019/20, 146 grants were awarded to organisations. Grants were distributed as follows: welfare (£321,800); research (£169,400); children (£155,600); education (£110,000); heritage (£69,500); disability (£45,800); animals (£38,200).

HOW TO APPLY Apply in writing to the correspondent. Visit the foundation's website for information on what to include. The foundation's trustees meet four times a year to consider grant applications, usually in January, April, July and October.

CONTACT DETAILS The Trustees, c/o Ludlow Trust Company Ltd, 1st Floor, Tower Wharf, Cheese Lane, Bristol BS2 0JJ *Tel.* 0345 304 2424 *Website* www.edithmurphy.co.uk

■ Murphy-Neumann Charity Company Ltd

CC NO 229555 **ESTABLISHED** 1963

WHERE FUNDING CAN BE GIVEN UK.

WHO CAN BENEFIT Registered charities.

WHAT IS FUNDED Health; social welfare; medical research.

WHAT IS NOT FUNDED Individuals.

TYPE OF GRANT Research.

RANGE OF GRANTS £500 to £2,500.

SAMPLE GRANTS Francis House (£2,000); Youth Talk (£1,750 each); Housing the Homeless Central Fund (£1,500); National Literacy Trust and St Nicholas' Hospice Care (£1,250 each); Alzheimer's Research UK and Headway (£1,000 each); Kidney Research UK (£750); Camphill Village Trust (£500 each).

FINANCES *Financial year end* 05/04/2020 *Income* £86,800 *Total grants* £59,500 *Grants to organisations* £59,500 *Assets* £1,480,000

TRUSTEES Mark Lockett; Paula Christopher; Marcus Richman; Supamon Holmes.

OTHER INFORMATION In 2019/20, the charity made grants to 53 charities.

HOW TO APPLY Apply in writing to the correspondent, outlining the purpose of the required charitable donation. Telephone calls are not welcome. There are no application forms, guidelines or deadlines. An sae is not required. Grants are usually given in November and December. Printed grant criteria are available on request.

CONTACT DETAILS The Trustees, Hayling Cottage, Upper Street, Stratford St Mary, Colchester, Essex CO7 6JW *Tel.* 01206 323685 *Email* murphy-neumann@hayling-cottage.org.uk

■ The John R. Murray Charitable Trust

CC NO 1100199 **ESTABLISHED** 2003

WHERE FUNDING CAN BE GIVEN UK.

WHO CAN BENEFIT Registered charities.

WHAT IS FUNDED General charitable purposes including the following: arts, culture, literature and science; amateur sport; citizenship and community development; health; education; the environment; religion; social welfare.

RANGE OF GRANTS Mostly £1,000 to £50,000.

SAMPLE GRANTS University of Edinburgh Trust (£200,000); National Portrait Gallery (£110,000); CLIC Sargent (£30,000); Bronte Academy Trust (£15,000); Happy Kids (£1,000).

FINANCES *Financial year end* 31/12/2019 *Income* £566,700 *Total grants* £1,270,000 *Grants to organisations* £1,270,000 *Assets* £27,800,000

TRUSTEES John Murray; Virginia Murray; Hallam Murray; John Grey Murray; Charles Grey Murray.

OTHER INFORMATION A total of 84 grants were made in 2019. The trust's annual report for that year states that 'the scope of [the trust's] giving is determined only by the extent of [its] resources; it is not otherwise restricted either geographically or by the type of activity carried on by prospective beneficiaries or applicants.'

HOW TO APPLY The trustees will not consider unsolicited applications for grants.

CONTACT DETAILS The Trustees, 50 Albemarle Street, London W1S 4BD *Tel.* 020 7493 4361

■ Brian Murtagh Charitable Trust

CC NO 1105099 **ESTABLISHED** 2004

WHERE FUNDING CAN BE GIVEN UK and overseas.

WHO CAN BENEFIT Registered charities with an income below £350,000. Applications from individuals are considered in certain circumstances.

WHAT IS FUNDED Education, training and development for young adults and children with physical and learning disabilities; social disadvantage; poverty; sickness and trauma.

SAMPLE GRANTS A list of beneficiaries was not included in the annual report and accounts.

FINANCES *Financial year end* 31/01/2020 *Income* £384,100 *Total grants* £604,500 *Grants to organisations* £604,500 *Assets* £6,190,000

TRUSTEES Mary Noble; Brian Murtagh; Matthew Hahn; Anthony Michael Ryde; Benjamin Rencher.

HOW TO APPLY Application forms are available from the trust's website. The trustee board meets four times a year, in March, June, September and November, to consider applications.

CONTACT DETAILS The Trustees, 9 Hanson Drive, Fowey, Cornwall PL23 1ET *Tel.* 01726 832672 *Email* admin@brianmurtaghct.org.uk *Website* https://www.brianmurtaghct.org.uk

■ Music Sales Charitable Trust

CC NO 1014942 **ESTABLISHED** 1992

WHERE FUNDING CAN BE GIVEN UK, with a preference for London and Bury St Edmunds.

WHO CAN BENEFIT Registered charities.

WHAT IS FUNDED General charitable purposes, including the following: health; the arts and culture; education and training; religion; overseas aid and famine relief; disability.

WHAT IS NOT FUNDED Individuals.

RANGE OF GRANTS Mostly under £5,000.

SAMPLE GRANTS Westminster Synagogue (two grants totalling £10,000); Aldeburgh Jubilee Hall (£7,500); Osprey Wheelchair Rugby (£6,500); Bury Bach Society, Médecins Sans Frontières and St Nicholas Hospice Care (£5,000 each).

FINANCES *Financial year end* 31/12/2019 *Income* £124,200 *Total grants* £84,200 *Grants to organisations* £84,200 *Assets* £263,500

TRUSTEES Christopher Butler; Ian Morgan; Robert Wise; Mildred Wise; Mr M. Wise; Nicholas Kemp; David Stock.

OTHER INFORMATION Grants were awarded to 68 organisations in the following categories: medical, health and sickness (£38,600); education and training (£14,400); religion (£13,700); disability (£11,600); the arts and culture (£8,900); overseas aid and famine relief (£1,000). Only organisations that received grants of over £5,000 were listed as beneficiaries in the accounts. Grants of under £5,000 totalled £45,200 and were awarded to 61 organisations.

HOW TO APPLY Contact the correspondent for further information.

CONTACT DETAILS The Trustees, c/o Music Sales Ltd, 14–15 Berners Street, London W1T 3LJ *Tel.* 020 7612 7400 *Email* neville.wignall@musicsales.co.uk

■ Muslim Hands

CC NO 1105056 **ESTABLISHED** 1993

WHERE FUNDING CAN BE GIVEN Overseas and UK.

WHO CAN BENEFIT Registered charities.

WHAT IS FUNDED The relief of poverty, with a focus on the following areas: education; emergency relief; the environment; health; the relief of hunger; livelihoods; care of orphans; and the provision of clean drinking water. The majority of the foundation's work is carried out overseas; however, according to its website, the charity supports community organisations in the UK through 'funding, capacity building and forming relationships with partners to help expand their work and further benefit more members of the community'.

TYPE OF GRANT Capacity building; project funding; core/revenue costs.

SAMPLE GRANTS A full list of individual grants and funded projects is available from the charity's principal office.

FINANCES *Financial year end* 31/12/2019 *Income* £22,770,000 *Total grants* £16,220,000 *Grants to organisations* £16,220,000 *Assets* £11,900,000

TRUSTEES Dr Musharaf Hussain; Syed Lakhte Hassanain; Mohammad Amin-Ul Hasanat Shah; Saffi Ullah; Sahibzada Ghulam Jeelani; Muhammad Arshad Jamil.

HOW TO APPLY Contact the correspondent for further information.

CONTACT DETAILS The Trustees, 148–164 Gregory Boulevard, Nottingham, Nottinghamshire NG7 5JE *Tel.* 0115 911 7222 *Email* mail@muslimhands.org.uk *Website* www.muslimhands.org.uk

■ The Mutual Trust Group

CC NO 1039300 **ESTABLISHED** 1994

WHERE FUNDING CAN BE GIVEN Israel; UK; USA.

WHO CAN BENEFIT Jewish organisations.

WHAT IS FUNDED Orthodox Jewish religion and education; the relief of poverty; general charitable purposes.

TYPE OF GRANT Development funding.

RANGE OF GRANTS Up to £108,800.

SAMPLE GRANTS Yeshivas Shaar Hashamayim (£108,800); Yeshivat Kesser Hatalmud (£53,300); Mesdos Polin (£13,700); Holocaust Memorial Congregation (£10,000).

FINANCES *Financial year end* 31/12/2019 *Income* £225,400 *Total grants* £190,000 *Grants to organisations* £190,000 *Assets* £173,900

TRUSTEES Rabbi Benzion Weitz; Adrian Weisz; Michael Weitz.

OTHER INFORMATION Smaller grants towards education and the relief of poverty totalled £4,300. The 2019 accounts were the latest available at the time of writing (May 2021).

HOW TO APPLY Contact the correspondent for further information.

CONTACT DETAILS Rabbi Benzion Weitz, Chair, 12 Dunstan Road, London NW11 8AA *Tel.* 020 8458 7549

■ MW (CL) Foundation

CC NO 1134917 **ESTABLISHED** 2010
WHERE FUNDING CAN BE GIVEN Worldwide, with a preference for the UK.
WHO CAN BENEFIT Charitable organisations and education providers.
WHAT IS FUNDED Projects which promote education, the relief of poverty and the advancement of the Orthodox Jewish faith.
RANGE OF GRANTS £1,000 to £35,000.
SAMPLE GRANTS Zichron Mordechai and Devorah Weisz Foundation (£35,000), Ateres Mordechai (£21,000), Friends of Asos Chesed (£10,000), Heichal Hatorah Foundation (£9,000), Chayei Olom Yeshiva (£7,000), Hasmonean (£2,000).
FINANCES *Financial year end* 30/11/2019
Income £550,000 *Total grants* £237,000
Grants to organisations £237,000
Assets £3,340,000
TRUSTEES Hilary Olsberg; Vivienne Lewin.
OTHER INFORMATION The foundation is closely linked with the MW (RH) Foundation, MW (GK) Foundation and MW (HO) Foundation and shares the same charitable objectives. The 2018/19 accounts were the latest available at the time of writing (June 2021).
HOW TO APPLY Contact the correspondent for further information.
CONTACT DETAILS The Trustees, 38 Princes Park Avenue, London NW11 0JT *Tel.* 020 8458 2933

■ MW (GK) Foundation

CC NO 1134916 **ESTABLISHED** 2010
WHERE FUNDING CAN BE GIVEN Worldwide, with a preference for the UK.
WHO CAN BENEFIT Charitable organisations and education providers.
WHAT IS FUNDED Projects which promote education, the relief of poverty and the advancement of the Orthodox Jewish faith.
RANGE OF GRANTS From £500 to £67,000, but mostly under £10,000.
SAMPLE GRANTS One Heart Lev Echod (£67,000), Friends of Beis Chinuch Lebonos (£39,000), Debmar (£10,000), Ateres Yoel (£4,800), Tov Vochesed (£2,000), The Purim Fund (£1,000).
FINANCES *Financial year end* 30/11/2019
Income £535,000 *Total grants* £292,000
Grants to organisations £292,000
Assets £2,846,000
TRUSTEES Shlomo Klein; Gella Klein.
OTHER INFORMATION The foundation was initially known as the Weisz Children Foundation and is closely linked with the MW (CL) Foundation, MW (RH) Foundation and MW (HO) Foundation. At the time of writing (June 2021) the 2018/19 accounts were the latest accounts available. Only beneficiaries of grants of £1,000 and above were listed in the accounts (22 organisations). Grants of under £1,000 totalled £500.
HOW TO APPLY Contact the correspondent for further information.
CONTACT DETAILS The Trustees, 15 Brantwood Road, Salford, Greater Manchester M7 4EN *Tel.* 0161 792 2330

■ MW (HO) Foundation

CC NO 1134919 **ESTABLISHED** 2010
WHERE FUNDING CAN BE GIVEN Worldwide, with a preference for Manchester.
WHO CAN BENEFIT Charitable organisations and education providers.
WHAT IS FUNDED Projects which promote education, the relief of poverty and the advancement of the Orthodox Jewish faith.
SAMPLE GRANTS A list of beneficiaries was not included in the annual report and accounts.
FINANCES *Financial year end* 30/11/2019
Income £493,000 *Total grants* £406,000
Grants to organisations £406,000
Assets £2,236,500
TRUSTEES Hilary Olsberg; David Olsberg.
OTHER INFORMATION The foundation was initially known as the Meir Weisz Foundation and is closely linked with the MW (CL) Foundation, MW (GK) Foundation and MW (RH) Foundation. The 2018/19 accounts were the latest available at the time of writing (June 2021). Grants were distributed as follows: community projects (£161,300); the relief of poverty (£109,800), educational grants (£48,000), religious grants (£19,500). Other grants of under £1,000 totalled £67,200.
HOW TO APPLY Contact the correspondent for further information.
CONTACT DETAILS The Trustees, 2nd Floor Parkgates, Bury New Road, Prestwich M25 0TL *Tel.* 0161 798 1660

■ MW (RH) Foundation

CC NO 1134918 **ESTABLISHED** 2010
WHERE FUNDING CAN BE GIVEN Worldwide, with a preference for the UK.
WHO CAN BENEFIT Charitable organisations and education providers.
WHAT IS FUNDED Projects which promote education, the relief of poverty and the advancement of the Orthodox Jewish faith.
SAMPLE GRANTS A list of beneficiaries was not included in the annual report and accounts.
FINANCES *Financial year end* 30/11/2019
Income £1,376,500 *Total grants* £488,500
Grants to organisations £488,500
Assets £2,600,000
TRUSTEES Rosalind Halpern; Jacob Halpern; Abraham Halpern.
OTHER INFORMATION This foundation was initially known as the Deborah Weisz Foundation and is closely linked with the MW (CL) Foundation, MW (GK) Foundation and MW (HO) Foundation. At the time of writing (June 2021), the 2018/19 accounts were the latest available. Grants were distributed as follows: community grants (£199,300), educational grants (£186,300), the relief of poverty (£45,800), religious grants (£23,500). Grants of under £1,000 totalled £33,600.
HOW TO APPLY Contact the correspondent for further information.
CONTACT DETAILS The Trustees, 5 Park Hill, Bury Old Road, Prestwich, Greater Manchester M25 0FX *Tel.* 0161 737 7779

The Janet Nash Charitable Settlement

CC NO 326880 **ESTABLISHED** 1985

WHERE FUNDING CAN BE GIVEN UK.

WHO CAN BENEFIT Charitable organisations and individuals.

WHAT IS FUNDED Medical causes; health; social welfare.

RANGE OF GRANTS £4,000 to £60,000.

SAMPLE GRANTS The Royal Marsden NHS Foundation Trust – Surgical Research (£60,000); The Get A-Head Charitable Trust (£50,000); St Basils (£10,000); Priors Field Primary School PTA Playground fund (£5,000); Zoë's Place Baby Hospice (£4,000).

FINANCES *Financial year end* 30/04/2020 *Income* £350,000 *Total grants* £372,000 *Grants to organisations* £129,000 *Assets* £90,900

TRUSTEES Mark Jacobs; Charlotte Westall; Jacqueline Marie Dacre.

OTHER INFORMATION Grants totalling £129,000 were made to five organisations during 2019/20. Grants totalling £243,000 were made to 21 individuals.

HOW TO APPLY The charity has previously stated that it does not accept unsolicited applications.

CONTACT DETAILS The Trustees, 141 Farmer Ward Road, Kenilworth, Warwickshire CV8 2SU *Tel.* 01926 514380 *Email* JanetNashCharitableSettlement@hotmail.com

The National Churches Trust

CC NO 1119845 **ESTABLISHED** 1953

WHERE FUNDING CAN BE GIVEN UK; Channel Islands; Isle of Man; Isles of Scilly. Priority areas include the North East, Northern Ireland and Wales.

WHO CAN BENEFIT Listed and unlisted churches, chapels and meeting houses, as long as they are open for regular public worship.

WHAT IS FUNDED The repair, restoration and modernisation of Christian places of worship.

WHAT IS NOT FUNDED Ancillary buildings and structures; buildings that were not originally built as a place of worship; contents such as bells, clocks and organs (repairs and new); internal furnishings; fixtures and fittings; monument restoration; heating; lighting or reordering; the building of new places of worship.

TYPE OF GRANT Capital costs for building, renovation and modernisation.

RANGE OF GRANTS Programme dependent, ranging from £500 to £50,000.

SAMPLE GRANTS Cathedral of St Machar – Aberdeen (£40,000); Aghadowey Presbyterian Church – Derry (£20,000); St Mary and Holy Trinity – Bow, London (£10,000); Hilltop Methodist Church – Derbyshire (£5,000); St John of Beverley – East Yorkshire (£2,000); Gabalfa Baptist Church – Cardiff (£1,000); St Paternus – Cornwall (£550); St Mary – Hardwick, Cambridgeshire (£220).

FINANCES *Financial year end* 31/12/2019 *Income* £2,300,000 *Total grants* £1,300,000 *Grants to organisations* £1,300,000 *Assets* £5,760,000

TRUSTEES Sir Paul Britton; Donna McDonald; Catherine Pepinster; Luke March; Shirley Adams; Henry Julian; Richard Carr-Archer; Revd Lucy Winkett; John Drew; Dr Stephen Sklaroff.

OTHER INFORMATION Grants totalling £1.3 million were awarded to 188 projects (including 12 recommendations on behalf of other grant-making organisations). The trust has four funding programmes: Cornerstone Grants, Gateway Grants, Foundation Grants and Preventative Maintenance Micro Grants. Details of these programmes can be found on the website.

HOW TO APPLY Application forms and deadlines can be found on the trust's website. Each grant category has a unique application form. More details on selecting the correct grant category can be found on the trust's website.

CONTACT DETAILS The Trustees, 7 Tufton Street, London SW1P 3QB *Tel.* 020 7222 0605 *Email* info@nationalchurchestrust.org *Website* www.nationalchurchestrust.org/our-grants

The National Express Foundation

CC NO 1148231 **ESTABLISHED** 2012

WHERE FUNDING CAN BE GIVEN The former West Midlands county boundary and the Medway, Gravesend and Longfield areas of Kent served by Kings Ferry and Clarke's commuter coach services (postcodes ME1–12, ME14, DA3, DA11, DA12 and DA13).

WHO CAN BENEFIT Registered charities; unregistered charities; CICs; social enterprises; universities; religious bodies/institutions.

WHAT IS FUNDED Young people aged 15 to 24; education, especially bursaries for disadvantaged students; social welfare; sport; community; general charitable purposes.

WHAT IS NOT FUNDED Short-term or one-off projects; sponsorship; projects that cannot be evaluated; projects that only benefit a small number of people.

TYPE OF GRANT Project funding.

RANGE OF GRANTS Up to £20,000.

SAMPLE GRANTS EmployabilityUK and The Birmingham and Black Country Wildlife Trust (£20,000 each); University of Bath (£12,000); Coventry Youth for Christ and Halesowen College (£10,000 each); Hall Green Youth (£5,000); Essex Avenue Community Association (£3,800); Springs Church (£2,500).

FINANCES *Financial year end* 31/12/2019 *Income* £500,000 *Total grants* £483,300 *Grants to organisations* £483,300 *Assets* £25,100

TRUSTEES Ian Fraser; Madi Pilgrim; Ian Austin.

OTHER INFORMATION Grants in 2019 were broken down into two categories: community (39 grants) and educational (eight grants). This includes 12 grants paid in relation to multi-year commitments from previous years. The foundation funds student bursaries for individuals with challenging personal and financial circumstances. These grants are paid to academic partners – no grants are paid directly to individuals.

HOW TO APPLY Application forms and guidance can be downloaded from the foundation's website when funding rounds open. The website provides further information on deadlines and successful projects.

CONTACT DETAILS The Trustees, c/o National Express Ltd, National Express House, Mill Lane,

Birmingham B5 6DD *Tel.* 0121 803 5650 *Email* foundation@nationalexpress.com *Website* www.nationalexpressgroup.com/our-way/national-express-foundation

The National Garden Scheme

CC NO 1112664 **ESTABLISHED** 1927

WHERE FUNDING CAN BE GIVEN UK.

WHO CAN BENEFIT Charitable organisations.

WHAT IS FUNDED Nursing and healthcare; gardening and horticulture, including training.

WHAT IS NOT FUNDED See the relevant grant scheme on the website for exclusion criteria.

TYPE OF GRANT Project funding; development funding.

RANGE OF GRANTS Programme dependent. Larger and well-known organisations receive in the range of £20,000 to £500,000.

SAMPLE GRANTS Hospice UK, Macmillan Cancer Support and Marie Curie (£425,000 each); Carers Trust (£345,000); Parkinson's UK (£157,000); Maggie's Centres (£100,000); Horatio's Garden (£75,000); National Botanic Garden Wales (£20,000); Garden Museum (£10,000).

FINANCES *Financial year end* 31/12/2020 *Income* £1,630,000 *Total grants* £2,890,000 *Grants to organisations* £2,890,000 *Assets* £814,600

TRUSTEES Atty Beor-Roberts; Susan Copeland; Richard Barley; Rupert Tyler; Peter Clay; Alison Wright; Richard Hepworth Thompson; Susan Phipps; Arit Anderson; Andrew Ratcliffe; Maureen Kesteven; Susan Paynton; Vernon Sanderson; Mark Porter.

OTHER INFORMATION The financial information has been taken from the 2020 annual report and accounts, which are available on the charity's website. At the time of writing (April 2021), the document had not yet been published on the Charity Commission's website. Grants were awarded in three categories during the year: nursing (eight grants totalling £2.3 million); gardening and health projects (11 grants totalling £582,200); local charities nominated by garden owners (£1,900). The charity also funds training and apprenticeship schemes for gardeners and those working in gardens and horticulture. A number of the grant-maker's other schemes were not accepting new applications, including The Community Gardens Award (suspended until late 2021) and the 'guest charity' scheme (suspended until 2022). Check the website for updates.

HOW TO APPLY Contact the correspondent for further information. Each region holds an annual general meeting in late February or in March.

CONTACT DETAILS Each county has its own contact – see the website for more details. The National Garden Scheme, East Wing Hatchlands Park, East Clandon, Guildford, Surrey GU4 7RT *Tel.* 01483 211535 *Email* hello@ngs.org.uk *Website* www.ngs.org.uk

Friends of the National Libraries

CC NO 313020 **ESTABLISHED** 1932

WHERE FUNDING CAN BE GIVEN UK.

WHO CAN BENEFIT The national libraries and the libraries of national museums; record offices and archive services; university and specialist libraries; any museum, gallery or collecting institution to which the public has reasonable access and which, in the opinion of the trustees, constitutes a proper repository for the proposed acquisition.

WHAT IS FUNDED Written and printed heritage.

WHAT IS NOT FUNDED The charity will not contribute to the cost of an item already purchased, nor the costs of conservation or cataloguing.

TYPE OF GRANT Grants can be used towards the acquisition of: rare printed books; manuscripts; archives of historical, literary, artistic, architectural, musical or other interest; and fine bindings.

RANGE OF GRANTS Grants typically range from £500 to £20,000.

SAMPLE GRANTS Mitchell Library (£25,000); University of Edinburgh (£20,000); Natural History Museum (£10,000); Griffith Institute (£4,000); Brunel Museum (£5,000); Dorset History Centre (£1,000); West Sussex Record Office (£500); Wiltshire and Swindon History Centre (£190).

FINANCES *Financial year end* 31/12/2019 *Income* £638,400 *Total grants* £579,000 *Grants to organisations* £579,000 *Assets* £3,952,000

TRUSTEES Stephen Clarke; Geordie Grieg; Alexandra Sitwell; Dr Christopher Wright; Pedr ap Llwyd; Dr Jessica Gardner; Natalie Livingstone; Roland Keating; Peter Mimpriss; Christopher Whittick; Dr John Scally; Felix de Marez Oyens; Prof. Richard Ovenden; Joan Winterkorn; Dr Emma Markiewicz; Charles Sebag-Montefiore; Dr Kristian Jensen; Mark Storey.

HOW TO APPLY Full information on the application process can be found on the charity's website.

CONTACT DETAILS Nell Hoare, Secretary, PO Box 4291, Reading, Berkshire RG8 9JA *Tel.* 01491 598083 *Email* nell.hoare@fnlmail.org.uk *Website* https://www.fnl.org.uk

The National Lottery Community Fund

ESTABLISHED 2004

WHERE FUNDING CAN BE GIVEN UK.

WHO CAN BENEFIT Registered charities; CICs; social enterprises; schools; amateur sports clubs; hospices; religious bodies/institutions; local authorities.

WHAT IS FUNDED The National Lottery Community Fund runs a range of different programmes aimed at improving communities and people's lives. Some are UK-wide and others are region-specific. New programmes are introduced from time to time and others close. Potential applicants are advised to check the funder's website for up-to-date information on current and upcoming programmes.

WHAT IS NOT FUNDED There are specific and detailed conditions for each separate programme – see the funder's website for more information.

TYPE OF GRANT Capital costs; core/revenue costs; seed funding/start-up funding; project funding; unrestricted funding.

RANGE OF GRANTS Up to £10,000 through Awards for All. Larger grants are available through other funding programmes.

SAMPLE GRANTS Details of all previous grants made by the grant-maker can be found on its website or on 360Giving.

FINANCES *Financial year end* 31/03/2020 *Income* £715,990,000 *Total grants* £588,200,000 *Grants to organisations* £588,200,000 *Assets* £523,050,000

OTHER INFORMATION The grant-maker made 14,003 grants during the year. At the time of writing

(June 2021) it was focused on supporting people and communities impacted by COVID-19.

HOW TO APPLY There are different regional offices and contact details for England, Northern Ireland, Scotland and Wales (see the website for full details). All application forms and guidelines are given on the grant-maker's helpful website. If you need further guidance, you can also call the advice line on 0345 4 10 2030.

CONTACT DETAILS The Grants Team, 1 Plough Place, London EC4A 1DE *Tel.* 0345 410 2030 *Email* general.enquiries@tnlcommunityfund.org.uk *Website* https://www.tnlcommunityfund.org.uk

■ The National Manuscripts Conservation Trust

CC NO 802796 **ESTABLISHED** 1990

WHERE FUNDING CAN BE GIVEN UK.

WHO CAN BENEFIT Record offices; libraries; other publicly funded institutions including local authorities, universities and specialist record repositories; owners of manuscript material that is available to members of the public.

WHAT IS FUNDED The conservation of manuscripts, documents and archives.

WHAT IS NOT FUNDED Public records; photographic, audio-visual or printed material; capital costs; equipment; loan collections; official archives of applicant institutions. Other exclusions can be found on the trust's website.

TYPE OF GRANT Salaries; training costs; repair, binding and preservation costs; digitisation (as part of conservation).

RANGE OF GRANTS Up to £25,000, but mostly between £2,000 and £10,000.

SAMPLE GRANTS British Glass Foundation (£25,000); The Ruskin Library Museum and Research Centre (£16,800); Doncaster Archives (£10,000); Royal Welsh College of Music and Drama (£8,500); Barnsley Archives (£5,000); Croxteth Hall (£3,200); Harris Manchester College (£1,800).

FINANCES *Financial year end* 31/12/2019 *Income* £191,400 *Total grants* £155,700 *Grants to organisations* £155,700 *Assets* £2,530,000

TRUSTEES Charles Sebag-Montefiore; Prof. David McKitterick; Caroline Taylor; Dr Norman James; Caroline Checkley-Scott.

OTHER INFORMATION In 2019 grants were awarded to 19 organisations.

HOW TO APPLY Application forms are available to download from the website, along with guidance notes. Applicants are advised to contact the secretary for further advice. The deadlines are usually 1 April and 1 October – full details of how to apply are given on the charity's website.

CONTACT DETAILS Nell Hoare, Secretary, PO Box 4291, Reading, Berkshire RG8 9JA *Tel.* 01491 598083 *Email* info@nmct.org.uk *Website* www.nmct.co.uk

■ The Nationwide Foundation

CC NO 1065552 **ESTABLISHED** 1997

WHERE FUNDING CAN BE GIVEN UK.

WHO CAN BENEFIT Charitable organisations; universities; research organisations.

WHAT IS FUNDED Affordable housing; community-led housing schemes; projects working to build an understanding of life in the rented sector; homelessness; social welfare.

WHAT IS NOT FUNDED Religious or political causes; applications that do not comply with the foundation's funding criteria.

TYPE OF GRANT Project and capital costs; core costs; research; pilot projects; multi-year grants.

SAMPLE GRANTS Test and Learn Fund (£666,000); Fair Housing Futures (£113,600); New Economics Foundation (£104,100); Highlands Small Communities Housing Trust (£80,000); Zacchaeus 2000 Trust (£50,000); Tenants United – Shelter (£32,100); West Kensington Community Homes Ltd (£28,000).

FINANCES *Financial year end* 31/03/2020 *Income* £2,570,000 *Total grants* £2,750,000 *Grants to organisations* £2,750,000 *Assets* £3,740,000

TRUSTEES Baroness Usha Prashar; Antonia Bance; Judith McNeill; Robert Collins; Gill Leng; Saphie Ashtiany; Terrie Alafat; Sarah Mitchell; Sara Bennison.

OTHER INFORMATION During 2019/20, grants were made to 27 organisations.

HOW TO APPLY At the time of writing (May 2021) the foundation was focusing on current partnerships and therefore not accepting new applications. Future invitations for new applicants will be advertised on the website.

CONTACT DETAILS The Trustees, Nationwide House, Pipers Way, Swindon, Wiltshire SN38 2SN *Tel.* 01793 652002 *Email* enquiries@nationwidefoundation.org.uk *Website* www.nationwidefoundation.org.uk

■ The NDL Foundation

CC NO 1133508 **ESTABLISHED** 2009

WHERE FUNDING CAN BE GIVEN Worldwide.

WHO CAN BENEFIT UK-registered charities.

WHAT IS FUNDED General charitable purposes; education; medicine; the arts; women and children in financially developing countries.

RANGE OF GRANTS Typically up to £50,000.

SAMPLE GRANTS Previous beneficiaries have included: The Institute of Cancer Research (£145,000); Don Bosco Bangalore Girls' School Maintenance (£63,000); Women for Women International (UK) (£51,500); MyBnk (£50,000); The Friends of the French Institute (£10,000); Royal Academy of Arts (£8,300); Human Rights Watch (£3,400); The National Gallery Trust (£2,900).

FINANCES *Financial year end* 05/04/2020 *Income* £0 *Total grants* £323,800 *Grants to organisations* £323,800

TRUSTEES Claude Marion; Sylviane Destribats; Laura Destribats; Diane Destribats; Nicolas Destribats.

OTHER INFORMATION Full accounts were not available to view on the Charity Commission's website. We have therefore estimated the foundation's grant total based on its total expenditure.

HOW TO APPLY Contact the correspondent for further information.

CONTACT DETAILS The Trustees, 24 Chemin Des Moines, 1640 Rhode St Genese, Brussels, Belgium SW10 9LW *Tel.* 0322 358 1202 *Email* lucy@thendlfoundation.com

■ The Gareth Neame Foundation

CC NO 1178930 **ESTABLISHED** 2018

WHERE FUNDING CAN BE GIVEN England and Wales.

WHO CAN BENEFIT Charitable organisations.

WHAT IS FUNDED Improving the conditions and lives of people through education, advice and training.

SAMPLE GRANTS A list of beneficiaries was not included in the annual report and accounts.

FINANCES *Financial year end* 31/03/2020 *Income* £57,900 *Total grants* £67,000 *Grants to organisations* £67,000 *Assets* £397,500

TRUSTEES Brian Williams; Gareth Neame; William Townrow; Christopher Stothard.

HOW TO APPLY Apply in writing to the correspondent.

CONTACT DETAILS The Trustees, SRLV, 20–22 Great Titchfield Street, London W1W 8BE *Tel.* 020 8079 8888

■ Nemoral Ltd

CC NO 262270 **ESTABLISHED** 1971

WHERE FUNDING CAN BE GIVEN Worldwide.

WHO CAN BENEFIT Jewish organisations.

WHAT IS FUNDED The advancement of the Jewish religion and Jewish religious education; the relief of poverty in the Jewish community.

WHAT IS NOT FUNDED Individuals.

RANGE OF GRANTS £10,000 to £98,000.

SAMPLE GRANTS Asser Bishvil Foundation (£98,000); Achisomoch Aid Company Ltd (£69,000); Sharei Chesed – London (£16,000); Yetev Lev London Jerusalem Trust (£15,000); The Rehabilitation Trust (£10,000).

FINANCES *Financial year end* 30/12/2019 *Income* £75,000 *Total grants* £114,000 *Grants to organisations* £114,000 *Assets* £842,900

TRUSTEES Rivka Gross; Michael Saberski.

OTHER INFORMATION In 2018/19, the charity made grants to two organisations.

HOW TO APPLY Contact the correspondent for further information. Applications are reviewed on a regular basis.

CONTACT DETAILS The Trustees, c/o Cohen Arnold, New Burlington House, 1075 Finchley Road, London NW11 0PU *Tel.* 020 8731 0777

■ Ner Foundation

CC NO 1104866 **ESTABLISHED** 2004

WHERE FUNDING CAN BE GIVEN UK and Israel.

WHO CAN BENEFIT Orthodox Jewish organisations, community projects, schools, yeshivos and seminaries.

WHAT IS FUNDED The advancement of the Orthodox Jewish religion and education; the relief of poverty among Jewish people.

RANGE OF GRANTS Up to £103,000.

SAMPLE GRANTS Kolyom Trust (£36,300); Gefen Foundation (£21,000); Asos Chessed (£10,000).

FINANCES *Financial year end* 30/06/2020 *Income* £323,100 *Total grants* £327,400 *Grants to organisations* £327,400 *Assets* £690,800

TRUSTEES Arnold Henry; Henry Neumann; Esther Henry.

OTHER INFORMATION Grants of under £1,000 each totalled £18,500.

HOW TO APPLY Contact the correspondent for further information.

CONTACT DETAILS The Trustees, 309 Bury New Road, Salford, Manchester M7 2YN *Tel.* 0161 772 0099

■ Nesswall Ltd

CC NO 283600 **ESTABLISHED** 1981

WHERE FUNDING CAN BE GIVEN UK and overseas.

WHO CAN BENEFIT Orthodox Jewish organisations.

WHAT IS FUNDED Orthodox Jewish causes, including education and relief in need.

RANGE OF GRANTS Up to £9,000.

SAMPLE GRANTS Beth Medrash Govoha of Eretz Yisroel (£9,000); Wlodowa Charity and Rehabilitation Trust (£6,000); Keren Chochmas Shloma Trust, Yetev Lev Synagogue, Beis Rochel D'Satmar Girls' School and Shir Chesed Beis Yisroel (£5,000 each).

FINANCES *Financial year end* 31/03/2019 *Income* £67,400 *Total grants* £62,300 *Grants to organisations* £62,300 *Assets* £903,000

TRUSTEES R. Teitelbaum; H. Wahrhaftig.

OTHER INFORMATION Grants of under £4,500 totalled £7,800. The 2018/19 accounts were the latest available at the time of writing (April 2021).

HOW TO APPLY Contact the correspondent for further information.

CONTACT DETAILS The Trustees, 28 Overlea Road, London E5 9BG *Tel.* 020 8731 0777

■ Nesta

CC NO 1144091 **ESTABLISHED** 2011

WHERE FUNDING CAN BE GIVEN UK.

WHO CAN BENEFIT Registered charities; social enterprises; research institutions; universities; businesses; public organisations; CICs.

WHAT IS FUNDED The priority areas of innovation (2021–30 strategy) are: narrowing educational inequality, with a focus on early childhood and secondary education; narrowing health inequalities, with a focus on tackling food environments and loneliness; improving sustainability, with a focus on reducing household emissions and increasing productivity.

WHAT IS NOT FUNDED Each funding programme has its own exclusions; refer to the website for further information.

TYPE OF GRANT Programme dependent: project grants; research; social investment; development funding; strategic funding.

RANGE OF GRANTS Up to £350,000.

SAMPLE GRANTS Capital Credit Union Ltd and Fair For You (£350,000 each); Social Innovation Camp (£207,000); Agent Academy CIC (£150,000); Bolton College (£100,000); Open Democracy (£70,000); NatCen Social Research (£68,000); St Joseph's Hospice – Hackney (£50,000).

FINANCES *Financial year end* 31/03/2020 *Income* £43,350,000 *Total grants* £7,720,000 *Grants to organisations* £7,720,000 *Assets* £423,730,000

TRUSTEES Sarah Hunter; Christina McComb; Heider Ridha; Imran Khan; Ian Gomes; Natalie Tydeman; Moira Wallace; Jimmy Wales; Judy Gibbons; Joanna Killian; Sir John Gieve; Anthony Lilley.

OTHER INFORMATION Nesta provides financial and practical support to bring bold ideas to life in areas where society faces substantial challenges. Nesta awards funding, often in partnership with other organisations, through a mix of grants, direct investment and challenge prizes. Funding programmes open and close on a regular basis and potential applicants should refer to the website for up-to-date information. Only beneficiaries of grants of £50,000 and above were listed in the 2019/20 accounts (60 organisations). Grants of under £50,000 totalled £1.9 million (112 organisations).

HOW TO APPLY Information on current funding programmes is provided on the Nesta website, including details of how to apply.

CONTACT DETAILS The Trustees, 58, Victoria Embankment, London EC4Y ODS *Tel.* 020 7438 2500 *Email* information@nesta.org.uk *Website* www.nesta.org.uk

■ Network for Social Change Charitable Trust

CC NO 295237 **ESTABLISHED** 1986

WHERE FUNDING CAN BE GIVEN UK and overseas.

WHO CAN BENEFIT Registered charities; CICs; social enterprises.

WHAT IS FUNDED Social change; human rights and dignity; civil society; the environment and sustainability; the promotion of peace and non-violence; asylum seekers and refugees; economic justice; health and well-being; the arts and education.

WHAT IS NOT FUNDED Disaster appeals; most types of building; direct contributions to political parties. Non-charitable projects are required to use the trust's money for non-violent and legal purposes only.

TYPE OF GRANT Capital costs; core/revenue costs; seed funding/start-up funding; project funding; unrestricted funding.

RANGE OF GRANTS Mostly up to £30,000.

SAMPLE GRANTS The Green Alliance Trust (£178,400); Oxford Research Group (£48,300); The Co-operative College (£28,700); The Poverty and Environment Trust (£20,000); Open Trust (£17,000); The Mindfulness Initiative (£14,200); Aegean Solidarity Network Team UK (£10,800).

FINANCES *Financial year end* 31/08/2020 *Income* £1,320,000 *Total grants* £1,190,000 *Grants to organisations* £1,190,000 *Assets* £166,400

TRUSTEES Roger Manser; Patricia Horrocks; Mark Tucker; Annie Schiff; Gillian Howarth.

OTHER INFORMATION Two major projects were funded during the year as well as around 50 small and medium projects. Only beneficiaries of grants of £10,000 and above were listed in the accounts.

HOW TO APPLY All applications to the trust must be sponsored by a network member: unsolicited applications are not accepted. However, project summaries can be submitted on the trust's project noticeboard on its website, and if a member is interested they will get in touch. Visit the website for further information.

CONTACT DETAILS The Trustees, BM 2063, London WC1N 3XX *Tel.* 01647 61106 *Email* thenetwork@gn.apc.org *Website* thenetworkforsocialchange.org.uk

■ Newby Trust Ltd

CC NO 227151 **ESTABLISHED** 1937

WHERE FUNDING CAN BE GIVEN UK, with a preference for England.

WHO CAN BENEFIT Registered charities.

WHAT IS FUNDED Education; health; social welfare.

WHAT IS NOT FUNDED Statutory bodies; large national charities enjoying widespread support; organisations not registered with the Charity Commission; exhibitions, conferences or events; individuals volunteering overseas; the promotion of religion; work outside the UK; large capital appeals; endowment appeals.

TYPE OF GRANT Capital costs; core/revenue costs; project funding; unrestricted funding.

RANGE OF GRANTS Typically £1,000 to £30,000.

SAMPLE GRANTS Yes Futures (£30,000); Empire Fighting Chance and The Wave Project (£20,000 each); Feeding Families, St Chad's Sanctuary and The Access Project (£10,000 each); Beyond the Horizon Charity, Freedom from Torture and White City Youth Theatre (£5,000 each); Riding for the Disabled (£1,000).

FINANCES *Financial year end* 05/04/2020 *Income* £457,000 *Total grants* £398,900 *Grants to organisations* £398,900 *Assets* £19,980,000

TRUSTEES Evelyn Montgomery; Stephen Gooder; Duncan Reed; Anna Foxell; Ben Gooder; David Charlton; Antonia Gooder; Nigel Callaghan; Kate Callaghan.

OTHER INFORMATION In 2019/20, grants were distributed as follows: health (£167,500, including £67,500 in the special category); education (£114,000); welfare (£117,500). The annual special category has included support for refugees or asylum seekers and for palliative care and bereavement.

HOW TO APPLY Unsolicited applications are not accepted, but charities – particularly those associated with the annual special category – are invited to make their activities known by email to the trust.

CONTACT DETAILS Annabel Grout, Company Secretary, PO Box 87, Petworth GU28 8BH *Tel.* 01798 861459 *Email* info@newby-trust.org.uk *Website* www.newby-trust.org.uk

■ Newcomen Collett Foundation

CC NO 312804 **ESTABLISHED** 1988

WHERE FUNDING CAN BE GIVEN London Borough of Southwark.

WHO CAN BENEFIT Registered charities; unregistered charities; CICs; social enterprises; schools; PTAs; individuals.

WHAT IS FUNDED The education of young people under 25 years of age; extracurricular activities.

TYPE OF GRANT Core/revenue costs; seed funding/start-up funding; equipment.

RANGE OF GRANTS Up to £2,000.

SAMPLE GRANTS Cathedral School (£2,000); Pilgrim's Way School (£1,200); The Intrapreneurs Charity, The Young Vic and Unicorn Theatre (£1,000 each).

FINANCES *Financial year end* 30/09/2020 *Income* £137,800 *Total grants* £96,100 *Grants to organisations* £96,100 *Assets* £3,860,000

TRUSTEES Amir Eden; Alexander Leiffheidt; Janet Simpson; Neha Jain; Robin Lovell; Janet Goodhall; Revd Michael Rawson; Peter MacFarlane; Timothy McNally; Robert Ashdown.

OTHER INFORMATION The grant total includes the figures for individuals and organisations.

HOW TO APPLY Application forms are available to download, together with criteria and guidelines, from the website. The governors consider requests four times a year. The closing dates for applications are listed on the website.

CONTACT DETAILS The Governors, Marshall's House, 66 Newcomen Street, London Bridge, London SE1 1YT *Tel.* 020 7407 2967 *Email* grantoffice@newcomencollett.org.uk *Website* www.newcomencollett.org.uk

■ The Frances and Augustus Newman Foundation

CC NO 277964 **ESTABLISHED** 1978
WHERE FUNDING CAN BE GIVEN UK.
WHO CAN BENEFIT Medical colleges; academic institutions; major research centres.
WHAT IS FUNDED Medical research projects and other medical charitable causes.
TYPE OF GRANT Research core costs; salaries; buildings and equipment. Grants made can be for one to three years.
RANGE OF GRANTS Typically up to £100,000.
SAMPLE GRANTS University of Cambridge (£235,000); King's College London (£110,500); The Royal Marsden Cancer Charity (£92,100); Antibiotic Research UK (£15,000); Bloodwise (£10,000); The Row UK Foundation (£4,000).
FINANCES *Financial year end* 31/03/2020 *Income* £616,800 *Total grants* £466,600 *Grants to organisations* £466,600 *Assets* £14,320,000
TRUSTEES David Sweetnam; John Williams; Stephen Cannon; Mark Rushton.
OTHER INFORMATION Grants were awarded to six organisations during the year. Five grants were awarded for research costs. One grant relating to 'other charitable endeavours' was awarded to The Row UK Foundation.
HOW TO APPLY The annual report for 2019/20 states that the trustees 'invite applications for research grants from individuals. Applicants submit a summary of their proposals to the Trustees in a specific format; applications made in the correct format are reviewed against the research criteria established by the Trustees and the research objectives. Research posts are funded on an annual basis to undertake an agreed programme of research and continuation of the grants is subject to the annual assessment by the Trustees. The Trustees give substantial support to poor reviewed submissions from academic institutions. In respect of the limited number of other grants made, they favour projects submitted from major research centres.'
CONTACT DETAILS Ben Haines, Administrator, c/o RSM, Hartwell House, 55–61 Victoria Street, Bristol BS1 6AD *Tel.* 0117 945 2000 *Email* ben.haines@rsmuk.com

■ Newpier Charity Ltd

CC NO 293686 **ESTABLISHED** 1985
WHERE FUNDING CAN BE GIVEN UK and Israel.
WHO CAN BENEFIT Jewish organisations.
WHAT IS FUNDED The advancement of the Orthodox Jewish faith; the relief of poverty; general charitable purposes.
SAMPLE GRANTS A list of beneficiaries was not included in the annual report and accounts.
FINANCES *Financial year end* 30/06/2019 *Income* £670,000 *Total grants* £322,300 *Grants to organisations* £322,300 *Assets* £690,000
TRUSTEES Charles Margulies; Helen Knopfler; Rachel Margulies.
OTHER INFORMATION The 2018/19 accounts were the latest available at the time of writing (April 2021).
HOW TO APPLY Apply in writing to the correspondent. The trustees meet on a regular basis to consider applications.
CONTACT DETAILS The Trustees, 186 Lordship Road, London N16 5ES *Tel.* 020 8802 4449

■ Alderman Newton's Educational Foundation

CC NO 527881 **ESTABLISHED** 1983
WHERE FUNDING CAN BE GIVEN Diocese of Leicester.
WHO CAN BENEFIT Schools; individuals.
WHAT IS FUNDED Educational projects that would not normally be funded by the local education authority.
WHAT IS NOT FUNDED Equipment or costs that would normally be met from the schools budget set by the local education authority.
TYPE OF GRANT Capital costs; project funding.
SAMPLE GRANTS A list of beneficiaries was not included in the annual report and accounts.
FINANCES *Financial year end* 31/03/2020 *Income* £178,300 *Total grants* £163,300 *Grants to organisations* £163,300 *Assets* £4,400,000
TRUSTEES Suzanne Uprichard; Madan Kallow; Cllr Malcolm Unsworth; Cheryl Pharoah; Dr Richard Harries; Charles Franks; Wendy Martin; Revd Canon Philip O'Reilly; Revd Jonathan Surridge; Guy Newbury; Pauline Hinitt; Damini Vaid Hansrani.
OTHER INFORMATION The grant total includes grants to individuals and organisations.
HOW TO APPLY Application forms and guidelines are available to download from the charity's website.
CONTACT DETAILS The Clerk to the Trustees, c/o Charity Link, 20A Millstone Lane, Leicester, Leicestershire LE1 5JN *Tel.* 0116 222 2200 *Email* info@charity-link.org *Website* anef.org.uk

■ The NFU Mutual Charitable Trust

CC NO 1073064 **ESTABLISHED** 1998
WHERE FUNDING CAN BE GIVEN UK, with a preference for rural areas.
WHO CAN BENEFIT Charitable organisations; organisations with charitable aims; individuals.
WHAT IS FUNDED Agriculture; rural development; research; education; the relief of poverty in rural areas; social welfare of the inhabitants of rural communities; insurance.
WHAT IS NOT FUNDED University fees; salaries; overseas appeals; multi-year funding.
TYPE OF GRANT One-off, project funding.
RANGE OF GRANTS £1,000 to £50,000.
SAMPLE GRANTS Linking Environment and Farming (£65,000); Rural Support (£25,000); Royal Highland Educational Trust (£17,500); Young Farmers Clubs of Ulster (£11,000); Air Ambulances UK (£10,500); Farms for City Children (£8,000); Forage Aid (£5,000); Gareth Raw Rees Memorial Scholarship (£2,000).
FINANCES *Financial year end* 31/12/2019 *Income* £211,000 *Total grants* £252,500 *Grants to organisations* £252,500 *Assets* £373,000
TRUSTEES Jim McLaren; John Davies; Dr Harriet Kennedy; Andrew McCornick; Lindsay Sinclair; Minette Batters; Meurig Raymond; Ivor Ferguson.
OTHER INFORMATION Grants were made to 18 organisations during the year.
HOW TO APPLY Application forms are available from the trust's website and should be sent to the correspondent either via post or email. Details of what to include can be found on the website. The trustees meet twice a year to consider applications, currently in June and November.
CONTACT DETAILS Jim Creechan, Secretary to the Trustees, Tiddington Road, Stratford-upon-Avon,

Warwickshire CV37 7BJ *Tel.* 01789 204211 *Email* nfu_mutual_charitable_trust@nfumutual.co.uk *Website* https://www.nfumutual.co.uk/about-us/charitable-trust

■ The Nineveh Charitable Trust

CC NO 256025 **ESTABLISHED** 1968

WHERE FUNDING CAN BE GIVEN UK.

WHO CAN BENEFIT Registered charities; CICs; individual applicants (if the outcome benefits are clearly defined).

WHAT IS FUNDED The health and welfare of the general public; education, in particular agriculture, silviculture, ecology and land management; conservation of the countryside.

WHAT IS NOT FUNDED Expeditions; personal educational needs; animal sanctuaries and care; work overseas; general appeals; projects unrelated to the trust's objects.

TYPE OF GRANT Capital costs; project funding; research; development funding; salaries. Matched funding is also available.

RANGE OF GRANTS Mainly between £500 and £10,000.

SAMPLE GRANTS The Wilderness Foundation (£10,000); The Sherwood Forest Trust (£8,000); Cumbria Youth Alliance (£5,700); The Frozen Ark Project (£4,000); Happy Hill Essex (£3,500); Essex Dementia Care (£2,900); Pear Tree Special School (£1,000); Ugborough Football Club (£300).

FINANCES *Financial year end* 05/04/2020 *Income* £314,300 *Total grants* £510,000 *Grants to organisations* £510,000 *Assets* £8,390,000

TRUSTEES Robert Lewis; Dr Michael James; John MacGregor.

OTHER INFORMATION Grants were made to 161 organisations during 2019/20.

HOW TO APPLY Apply in writing to the correspondent. Three copies of the proposal should be sent to the correspondent along with an sae. Applications should be no longer than two sides. Further information on what to include in the application can be found on the trust's website.

CONTACT DETAILS The Trustees, 8 Mill Lane, Saffron Walden, Essex CB10 2AS *Tel.* 07710 998829 *Email* robert@ninevehtrust.org.uk *Website* www.ninevehtrust.org.uk

■ The Nisbet Trust

CC NO 1143496 **ESTABLISHED** 2011

WHERE FUNDING CAN BE GIVEN Bristol; North Somerset; South Gloucestershire.

WHO CAN BENEFIT Registered charities; exempt charities; not-for-profit social enterprises; CICs.

WHAT IS FUNDED Children and young people; the arts; the prevention of homelessness; community cohesion.

WHAT IS NOT FUNDED Medical research; single-condition medical charities; grants for individuals; animal welfare charities; sponsorship.

TYPE OF GRANT Project funding; capital costs; core costs.

RANGE OF GRANTS Up to £200,000. Three types of grant are available: small, medium and large.

SAMPLE GRANTS Bristol Music Trust (£200,000); The Watershed Arts Trust Ltd (£30,000); Bristol North West Food Bank (£22,000); Stand Against Racism and Inequality (£20,000); Lockleaze Neighbourhood Trust (£10,000); The Rainbow Centre for Children (£7,000); Forest of Avon Trust (£6,800); Bristol Cathedral Trust (£500).

FINANCES *Financial year end* 31/12/2019 *Income* £2,500,000 *Total grants* £1,860,000 *Grants to organisations* £1,860,000 *Assets* £1,620,000

TRUSTEES Andrew Nisbet; Anne Nisbet; Joseph Nisbet; Emily Nisbet; Zoe Joyner; Henry Bothamley.

OTHER INFORMATION During 2019, the trust awarded 94 new grants and 54 instalments of multi-year grants committed in the previous year.

HOW TO APPLY Applications can usually be made on the trust's website. At the time of writing (May 2021) the trust was not accepting new applications. Check the trust's website for the latest information.

CONTACT DETAILS Erin Porrington, Administrator, 22 Clifton Road, Bristol BS8 1AQ *Email* admin@nisbettrust.co.uk *Website* www.nisbettrust.co.uk

■ NNS Foundation

CC NO 1184159 **ESTABLISHED** 2018

WHERE FUNDING CAN BE GIVEN Worldwide, with a focus on the UK, USA and Africa.

WHO CAN BENEFIT Charitable organisations.

WHAT IS FUNDED Health; education.

SAMPLE GRANTS Swaris Foundation for Social Development (£1.2 million); Africa Mission Healthcare Foundation (£430,000).

FINANCES *Financial year end* 31/12/2019 *Income* £1,600,000 *Total grants* £1,550,000 *Grants to organisations* £1,550,000 *Assets* £10,800

TRUSTEE NNS Foundation Ltd.

OTHER INFORMATION Financial information has been converted from USD using the exchange rate at the time of writing (February 2021).

HOW TO APPLY Unsolicited applications are not accepted.

CONTACT DETAILS The Trustees, Third Floor, 20 Old Bailey, London EC4 7AN *Tel.* 020 7597 6000

■ Alice Noakes Memorial Charitable Trust

CC NO 1039663 **ESTABLISHED** 1994

WHERE FUNDING CAN BE GIVEN UK and overseas.

WHO CAN BENEFIT Registered charities; universities; individuals (including bursaries to students where the individual's area of interest furthers the objects of the charity).

WHAT IS FUNDED Research, teaching, treatment and care relating to animal welfare.

TYPE OF GRANT Project costs, capital costs, research.

RANGE OF GRANTS Usually up to £20,000, although the trustees state that they do not set a minimum or maximum level of grant.

SAMPLE GRANTS University of Cambridge – Residency (£20,000); Lake District Foundation (£3,000); Aware Trust (£2,000); Cetacean Research, Greek Cat Welfare Society and HART Wildlife Rescue (£1,000 each); Lluest Horse and Pony Trust (£600).

FINANCES *Financial year end* 31/03/2020 *Income* £95,500 *Total grants* £63,200 *Grants to organisations* £63,200 *Assets* £2,420,000

TRUSTEES Mrs J. Simpson; David Whipps; Nigel Oldacre; Jeremy Hulme; Robert Ferdinando; Stefan van Poucke.

OTHER INFORMATION Grants totalling £63,200 were made to 29 organisations during 2019/20.

HOW TO APPLY Apply in writing to the correspondent. The trustees meet twice a year.
CONTACT DETAILS The Trustees, c/o Holmes and Hills LLP, Bocking End, Braintree, Essex CM7 9AJ *Tel.* 01376 320456

■ The Nomura Charitable Trust

CC NO 1130592 **ESTABLISHED** 2009
WHERE FUNDING CAN BE GIVEN London.
WHO CAN BENEFIT Charitable organisations.
WHAT IS FUNDED The education and training of young people.
TYPE OF GRANT Grants are awarded towards specific projects and will not be increased in the event of overspending on the project.
RANGE OF GRANTS Up to £50,000.
SAMPLE GRANTS East London Business, Into University (£50,000 each); The Brokerage City (£49,400); Whizz-Kidz (£14,600).
FINANCES *Financial year end* 31/03/2020 *Income* £66,800 *Total grants* £164,000 *Grants to organisations* £164,000 *Assets* £550,300
TRUSTEES Gbolahan Ladipo; Breda Forrest; Gary Hyman; Clare Jones; Kevin Clark; Iris Hinterberger.
OTHER INFORMATION The trust awarded three grants totalling £149,400 to organisations. A further grant of £14,600 was awarded to one organisation from employee donations.
HOW TO APPLY The website states that to begin the application process, your organisation will need to be invited to apply by a member of the Community Affairs team at Nomura, following a recommendation from a Nomura employee. The trust is unable to accept unsolicited applications.
CONTACT DETAILS Samantha Barnwell, Grants Manager, 1 Angel Lane, London EC4R 3AB *Tel.* 020 7102 2005 *Email* communityaffairs@nomura.com *Website* https://www.nomuraholdings.com/csr/society/foundation/nct.html

■ The Norfolk Churches Trust Ltd

CC NO 271176 **ESTABLISHED** 1976
WHERE FUNDING CAN BE GIVEN The Diocese of Norwich and the county of Norfolk.
WHO CAN BENEFIT Churches.
WHAT IS FUNDED Church renovation and repair including; structural repairs to building fabric; the repair and restructuring of rainwater goods and drainage; window repairs – glazing and tracery; repairs to fixtures and fittings including pews, monuments, organs and ledgerstones; the conservation of wall paintings and stonework; the renewal of interior plaster; repairs to floors and pew platforms; repairs and refurbishment of bell frames; the renewal of switchgear for electrics; interior decoration when it is part of internal wall repairs and replastering.
WHAT IS NOT FUNDED Reordering projects, extensions to buildings or the installation of new facilities.
TYPE OF GRANT Buildings and feasibility studies.
RANGE OF GRANTS Grants up to £10,000.
SAMPLE GRANTS St Michael – Sutton (£10,000); St Mary – Narford (£8,800); St Mary Magdalene – Pentney (£7,000); St Peter – Wolferton and All Saints – Tilney (£5,000 each); St Francis – Heartsease, Norwich (£4,000); St Margaret – Felbrigg, (£3,000); St Nicholas – Bradwell (£300).
FINANCES *Financial year end* 31/03/2020 *Income* £349,700 *Total grants* £135,600 *Grants to organisations* £135,600 *Assets* £1,670,000
TRUSTEES Michael Sayer; Lady Egerton; Countess of Leicester; Lt Col Ian Lonsdale; Patrick Lines; Amelia Courtauld; Peter Sheppard; Dr John Madison; Charles Inglis; Holly Gold; Lauren Parker; Rosabelle Batt.
OTHER INFORMATION In 2019/20, the trust made grants to 78 churches.
HOW TO APPLY Application forms can be downloaded from the trust's website.
CONTACT DETAILS Scilla Latham, Secretary, Manor Farm House, Diss Road, Tibenham, Norwich, Norfolk NR16 1QF *Tel.* 01379 677272 *Email* secretary@norfolkchurchestrust.org.uk *Website* norfolkchurchestrust.org.uk

■ Norfolk Community Foundation

CC NO 1110817 **ESTABLISHED** 2004
WHERE FUNDING CAN BE GIVEN Norfolk.
WHO CAN BENEFIT Registered charities; local community groups; town and parish councils; CICs; social enterprises; individuals.
WHAT IS FUNDED General charitable purposes, with a preference for social welfare and community development.
SAMPLE GRANTS Sportspark (£29,300); Cambridge Science Centre (£25,500); Homes for Wells (£25,000); Access Community Trust, Dereham Town Council and Red House Youth Projects (£20,000 each).
FINANCES *Financial year end* 31/12/2019 *Income* £2,560,000 *Total grants* £2,158,000 *Grants to organisations* £2,080,000 *Assets* £24,550,000
TRUSTEES Lady Kay Fisher; Stephen Allen; Michelle Raper; Henry Cator; Jo Pearson; Michael Curnoy; Nick Pratt; Andrew Jamieson; Simon Bailey; Simon Brickles.
OTHER INFORMATION This is one of the 46 UK community foundations, which distribute funding for a wide range of purposes. As with all community foundations, there are a number of donor-advised funds managed on behalf of individuals, families and charitable trusts. Grant schemes tend to change frequently – consult the foundation's website for details of current programmes and up-to-date deadlines. Only organisations that received grants of over £20,000 were listed as beneficiaries in the charity's 2019 accounts. Grants of under £20,000 totalled £1.74 million and were awarded to 343 organisations.
HOW TO APPLY Potential applicants are advised to visit the community foundation's website or contact its grants team to find the most suitable funding stream.
CONTACT DETAILS Grants Team, St James Mill, Whitefriars, Norwich, Norfolk NR3 1TN *Tel.* 01603 623958 *Email* grants@norfolkfoundation.com *Website* www.norfolkfoundation.com

■ Educational Foundation of Alderman John Norman

CC NO 313105 **ESTABLISHED** 1962
WHERE FUNDING CAN BE GIVEN Norfolk.
WHO CAN BENEFIT Educational organisations.
WHAT IS FUNDED The education and training of children and young people, including those descended from Alderman John Norman.

RANGE OF GRANTS Up to £10,000 but mostly from £1,000 to £5,000.

SAMPLE GRANTS Priscilla Bacon Norfolk Hospice Care (£10,000); Friends of the Hewett School (£5,000); Wymondham Youth Bus (£3,000); CAST Education (£1,000).

FINANCES *Financial year end* 31/03/2020 *Income* £300,800 *Total grants* £249,700 *Grants to organisations* £113,900 *Assets* £8,670,000

TRUSTEES Roy Hughes; David Nobbs; Revd Philip Butcher; Christopher Brown; Roger Sandall; Tracey Hughes; Francis Whymark; Doc. Julia Leach; Revd Jonathan Boston; Nicholas Bevington.

OTHER INFORMATION Grants to individuals descended from Alderman John Norman totalled £95,800 and those to Old Catton residents totalled a further £40,000.

HOW TO APPLY Contact the correspondent for further information.

CONTACT DETAILS Nick Saffell, Clerk, The Atrium, St George's Street, Norwich, Norfolk NR3 1AB *Tel.* 01603 629871 *Email* nick.saffell@brown-co.com *Website* wp.normanfoundation.org.uk

■ The Norman Family Charitable Trust

CC NO 277616 **ESTABLISHED** 1979

WHERE FUNDING CAN BE GIVEN Primarily Cornwall, Devon and Somerset.

WHO CAN BENEFIT Registered charities; unregistered charities; CICs; social enterprises; schools; universities; PTAs; hospital; hospices.

WHAT IS FUNDED General charitable purposes, including the following: medical research; sport and leisure; community projects; blind, deaf and physical disabilities; children's welfare; animals, the environment and conservation; homelessness; social welfare; forces, ex-forces and emergency services; older people; mental health and learning disabilities; crime prevention, rehabilitation and addictions; employment and skills training.

WHAT IS NOT FUNDED Individuals; organisations which use live animals for experimental or research purposes; the maintenance or repair of religious buildings; national charities will only be supported for projects which will help the area of benefit.

TYPE OF GRANT Core/revenue costs; capital costs.

RANGE OF GRANTS Grants are typically of less than £5,000.

SAMPLE GRANTS Alphington Primary School (£10,000); Exmouth Community College (£8,000); St Petrock's – Exeter (£6,000); 5th Exmouth Sea Scouts, Animals in Distress (£5,000 each); Magic Breakfast (£500); Drama Express (£300).

FINANCES *Financial year end* 31/03/2020 *Income* £482,400 *Total grants* £396,200 *Grants to organisations* £396,200 *Assets* £9,610,000

TRUSTEES Catherine Houghton; Sarah Gillingham; Christopher Davis; William Tee; Liz Low; John Bain; Stephen Green.

OTHER INFORMATION Grants were made to 277 organisations during the year.

HOW TO APPLY See the trust's website for the latest information on applications.

CONTACT DETAILS Emma Le Poidevin, Grants Administrator, 14 Fore Street, Budleigh Salterton, Devon EX9 6NG *Tel.* 01395 446699 *Email* info@nfct.org *Website* www.nfct.org

■ Normanby Charitable Trust

CC NO 252102 **ESTABLISHED** 1966

WHERE FUNDING CAN BE GIVEN Mainly North Yorkshire and the North East.

WHO CAN BENEFIT Registered charities; hospices; hospitals; places of worship; PCCs; schools and colleges; universities; museums, libraries and galleries; uniformed groups.

WHAT IS FUNDED General charitable purposes, particularly arts, culture, heritage and social welfare.

WHAT IS NOT FUNDED Non-UK charities; individuals (apart from in exceptional circumstances).

RANGE OF GRANTS Up to £200,000 but mostly of £1,000.

SAMPLE GRANTS Evelyn Phipps Memorial Fund (£200,000); Caedmon College Whitby (£77,000); Hope Whitby and St Hedda's Roman Catholic Primary School (£10,000 each); Blind Veterans UK and Child Bereavement UK (£5,000 each); Crisis UK (£1,000).

FINANCES *Financial year end* 05/04/2020 *Income* £297,700 *Total grants* £365,500 *Grants to organisations* £365,500 *Assets* £10,700,000

TRUSTEES The Marquis of Normanby; Lady Lepel Kornicki; Lady Peronel Cruz; Lady Henrietta Burridge; Nicholas Buchan.

HOW TO APPLY Apply in writing to the correspondent. The trustees meet two to three times a year to award grants.

CONTACT DETAILS The Trustees, 52 Tite Street, London SW3 4JA *Tel.* 020 7352 3174 *Email* nct@normanby.org

■ North Berwick Trust

OSCR NO SC048462 **ESTABLISHED** 1975

WHERE FUNDING CAN BE GIVEN North Berwick.

WHO CAN BENEFIT Charities; community groups; individuals.

WHAT IS FUNDED Public recreation facilities and gardens; education; social welfare.

RANGE OF GRANTS Up to £30,000.

SAMPLE GRANTS North Berwick Harbour Trust Association (£30,000); Fringe by the Sea (£29,500); Law Primary School (£24,300); North Berwick in Bloom (£470).

FINANCES *Financial year end* 31/03/2020 *Income* £15,140,000 *Total grants* £236,200 *Grants to organisations* £236,200 *Assets* £13,630,000

HOW TO APPLY Application forms and deadlines can be found on the trust's website.

CONTACT DETAILS The Trustees, The Lighthouse, Heugh Road Industrial Estate, North Berwick, East Lothian, EH39 5PX *Email* info@northberwicktrust.co.uk *Website* www.northberwicktrust.co.uk

■ North East Area Miners' Social Welfare Trust Fund

CC NO 504178 **ESTABLISHED** 1977

WHERE FUNDING CAN BE GIVEN The North East.

WHO CAN BENEFIT Charitable organisations; miners' charities; miners.

WHAT IS FUNDED Miners' welfare and health; holidays and outings; recreational and social facilities.

TYPE OF GRANT Equipment; refurbishment and building costs; events sponsorship; holidays; salaries.

SAMPLE GRANTS Ashington FC; Birtley Community Centre; Easington Miners Welfare; Ferryhill Town

Band; Lynemouth Miners Welfare; Seaham Sea Angling.

FINANCES *Financial year end* 30/09/2019 *Income* £102,400 *Total grants* £93,200 *Grants to organisations* £91,500 *Assets* £2,580,000

TRUSTEES Gerrard Huitson; Ian Lavery; Alan Mardghum; David Anderson; Stephen Musgrove; John Dunn.

OTHER INFORMATION The 2018/19 accounts were the latest available at the time of writing (June 2021). Grants to individuals totalled £1,700. A full list of beneficiaries and grant amounts was not available.

HOW TO APPLY Contact the correspondent for further information. The trustees consider all applications for funding and holiday requests at their quarterly meetings or more frequently if necessary.

CONTACT DETAILS Rick O'Toole, CISWO, The Old Rectory, Rectory Drive, Whiston, Rotherham S60 4JG *Tel.* 01709 728115 *Email* rick.otoole@ciswo.org.uk *Website* www.ciswo.org.uk

■ North West Cancer Research

CC NO 519357 **ESTABLISHED** 1987

WHERE FUNDING CAN BE GIVEN The North West and North Wales.

WHO CAN BENEFIT Universities.

WHAT IS FUNDED Cancer research in the North West of England and North Wales.

WHAT IS NOT FUNDED Direct clinical care; buildings. See the website for the exclusion criteria of the relevant funding call.

TYPE OF GRANT Project funding; research; capital costs.

SAMPLE GRANTS A list of beneficiaries was not included in the annual report and accounts.

FINANCES *Financial year end* 30/09/2020 *Income* £1,540,000 *Total grants* £1,280,000 *Grants to organisations* £1,280,000 *Assets* £3,410,000

TRUSTEES Catherine Jones; Nigel Lanceley; Stephen Claus; Francis Street; Mark Haig; Catherine Bond; Hilary Atherton; Philip Robertshaw; Dr Sharvari Kothari-Short; Michael Ore; Michael FitzGerald Carter.

OTHER INFORMATION Formerly known as Clatterbridge Cancer Research (CCR), the charity in its current set-up was formed in 2012, when CCR merged with the North West Cancer Research Fund (NSCRF). The charity finances cancer research, primarily at the University of Liverpool, Lancaster University and Bangor University. Open calls for funding are advertised on the website.

HOW TO APPLY Application guidance and deadlines are made available on the website as open funding calls arise.

CONTACT DETAILS The Trustees, North West Cancer Research Centre, 200 London Road, Liverpool, Merseyside L3 9TA *Tel.* 0151 709 2919 *Email* info@nwcr.org *Website* www.nwcr.org

■ Northamptonshire Community Foundation

CC NO 1094646 **ESTABLISHED** 2001

WHERE FUNDING CAN BE GIVEN Northamptonshire.

WHO CAN BENEFIT Registered charities; unregistered charities; CICs; social enterprises; amateur sports clubs; religious bodies/institutions; individuals.

WHAT IS FUNDED General charitable purposes including the following: education and training; older people, crime prevention; sport; health; children and young people; people with disabilities; women and girls.

SAMPLE GRANTS Burton Latimer Town Council (£34,300); Moretonville Junior FC (£16,000); Northampton Door-to-Door Service (£10,000); Baby Basics Northampton (£7,000); Frontier Centre (£5,000); Empowering the Youth (£2,000); All Saints PCC (£530).

FINANCES *Financial year end* 31/03/2020 *Income* £7,100,000 *Total grants* £1,245,400 *Grants to organisations* £1,110,000 *Assets* £15,090,000

TRUSTEES Paul Southworth; David Knight; Deidre Newham; Paul Parsons; Hassan Shah; Joanna Gordon; Janine Jepson; Debra Charles; Jenny Jackson-Stops; Peter Borley-Cox.

OTHER INFORMATION This is one of the 46 UK community foundations, which distribute funding for a wide range of purposes. As with all community foundations, there are a number of donor-advised funds managed on behalf of individuals, families and charitable trusts. Grant schemes tend to change frequently – consult the foundation's website for details of current programmes and up-to-date deadlines. Grants to individuals totalled £135,400.

HOW TO APPLY Potential applicants are advised to visit the community foundation's website or contact its grants team to find the most suitable funding stream.

CONTACT DETAILS Rachel McGrath, Grants Director, 18 Albion Place, Northampton, Northamptonshire NN1 1UD *Tel.* 01604 230033 *Email* enquiries@ncf.uk.com or rachel@ncf.uk.com *Website* www.ncf.uk.com

■ Community Foundation for Northern Ireland

CCNI NO NIC105105 **ESTABLISHED** 1979

WHERE FUNDING CAN BE GIVEN Northern Ireland.

WHO CAN BENEFIT Community groups; voluntary organisations; CICs; individuals.

WHAT IS FUNDED General charitable purposes; social welfare; education and skills; civic engagement; arts, culture and heritage; community safety; the environment; health and well-being; economy and work.

WHAT IS NOT FUNDED Party political activity; the promotion of religion; trips abroad; individuals (unless an individual bursary programme); the replacement of statutory funding; projects that have already started; groups which have not complied with previous monitoring requirements.

SAMPLE GRANTS A list of beneficiaries was not included in the annual report and accounts.

FINANCES *Financial year end* 31/03/2019 *Income* £9,860,000 *Total grants* £2,020,000 *Grants to organisations* £2,020,000 *Assets* £10,610,000

TRUSTEES Maeve Monaghan; Shelley Martin; Claire McGonigle; David McCurley; Mary McKee; David Gavaghan; Dr Adrian Johnston; Jane Wilde; Ciaran Moynagh; John Gerard Gordon; Suzanne Lagan; Glenn Bradley; Dr Sophie Long.

OTHER INFORMATION This is one of the 46 UK community foundations, which distribute funding for a wide range of purposes. As with all community foundations, there are a number of donor-advised funds managed on behalf of individuals, families and charitable trusts. Grant schemes tend to change frequently; consult the foundation's website for details of current

programmes and up-to-date deadlines. The 2018/19 accounts were the latest available at the time of writing (January 2021). The foundation awarded 531 grants during the year.
HOW TO APPLY Potential applicants are advised to visit the community foundation's website or contact its grants team to find the most suitable funding stream.
CONTACT DETAILS The Grants Team, Community House, Citylink Business Park, 6A Albert Street, Belfast BT12 4HQ *Tel.* 028 9024 5927 *Email* info@communityfoundationni.org *Website* www.communityfoundationni.org

■ Northern Land Trust

CC NO 1101960 **ESTABLISHED** 2003
WHERE FUNDING CAN BE GIVEN England.
WHO CAN BENEFIT Mainly Jewish organisations.
WHAT IS FUNDED Jewish causes.
RANGE OF GRANTS From £1,000 to £173,000.
SAMPLE GRANTS Society of Friends of the Torah Ltd (£173,000); Clearwaters Trust Ltd (£140,000); Misgov Ladoch (£110,000); Kehal Yisroel D'Chasidei Gur (£37,000); The Lolev Charitable Trust (£27,500); Yeshiva Gedolah Torah Veyirah Seven Oaks Ltd (£15,000); Friends of Beis Chinuch Lebonos Trust (£5,000); Ichud Mosdos Gur Ltd (£1,000).
FINANCES *Financial year end* 28/02/2019 *Income* £26,700 *Total grants* £610,500 *Grants to organisations* £610,500 *Assets* £78,700
TRUSTEES Nathan Teitelbaum; Baruch Roitenbarg; Rafael Roitenbarg.
OTHER INFORMATION The 2018/19 accounts were the latest available at the time of writing (April 2021). Grants were made to 15 organisations during the year.
HOW TO APPLY Contact the correspondent for further information.
CONTACT DETAILS The Trustees, First Floor, Winston House, 349 Regents Park Road, London N3 1DH *Tel.* 020 3411 2001

■ Northern Pharmacies Ltd Trust Fund

CCNI NO NIC101560 **ESTABLISHED** 1977
WHERE FUNDING CAN BE GIVEN Northern Ireland.
WHO CAN BENEFIT Charitable organisations; hospices; social enterprises; individuals, in particular pharmacists and healthcare professionals.
WHAT IS FUNDED Healthcare; pharmaceutical care; the training, research and education of students and those in the pharmaceutical profession; public health.
TYPE OF GRANT Training, research and education costs; salaries; projects.
SAMPLE GRANTS Marie Curie Hospice (£31,769); Primarycare and Community Together (PACT) (£28,640).
FINANCES *Financial year end* 05/04/2020 *Income* £37,700 *Total grants* £60,400 *Grants to organisations* £60,400 *Assets* £931,600
TRUSTEES Sarah Burrows; Gerard Greene; Dr Sheelagh Hillan; Sarah Mawhinney; Michael Hamill; Dr Martin Kerr; Paul Kelly; Patrick Slevin; Dr Terry Maguire.
OTHER INFORMATION In 2019/20 the trust made three grants.
HOW TO APPLY Contact the correspondent for further information.
CONTACT DETAILS Sarah Mawhinney, Trustee, c/o 5 Annadale Avenue, Belfast BT7 3JH *Tel.* 028 9069 0444 *Email* kdouglas@communitypharmacyni.co.uk

■ The Northumbria Historic Churches Trust

CC NO 511314 **ESTABLISHED** 1980
WHERE FUNDING CAN BE GIVEN Dioceses of Durham and Newcastle.
WHO CAN BENEFIT Christian churches of any denomination within the dioceses of Durham or Newcastle.
WHAT IS FUNDED Repairs to church buildings.
WHAT IS NOT FUNDED The repair of lighting systems; bells; clocks; organs; stone cleaning; work which should be carried out as part of routine maintenance such as gutter clearing, slipped roof tile replacement and redecoration.
TYPE OF GRANT Capital costs.
RANGE OF GRANTS Grants of up to £5,000.
SAMPLE GRANTS Previous beneficiaries have included: St Giles – Birtley, St Helen's – Cornhill, St Michael and All Angels – Felton, St Mary – Middleton, Holy Cross – Ryton.
FINANCES *Financial year end* 31/01/2020 *Income* £24,400 *Total grants* £51,500 *Grants to organisations* £51,500
TRUSTEES Lt Gen. Robin Brims; Peter Ryder; Revd Canon Robert McTeer; Dr Margaret Stewart; Lawrence McLeman; Joanna Pullan; William Heslop.
OTHER INFORMATION Full accounts were not available to view on the Charity Commission's website due to the trust's low income. We have therefore estimated the grant total based on the trust's total expenditure.
HOW TO APPLY Application forms are available from the trust's website.
CONTACT DETAILS Kim Pearson, Secretary to the Trust, Coach House, Heddon House Lane, Heddon-on-the-Wall, Northumberland NE15 0JR *Tel.* 01661 852523 *Email* secretary@northumbriahct.org.uk *Website* www.northumbriahct.org.uk

■ The Northwick Trust

CC NO 285197 **ESTABLISHED** 1982
WHERE FUNDING CAN BE GIVEN UK and overseas.
WHO CAN BENEFIT Registered charities.
WHAT IS FUNDED Conservation and the natural environment; social welfare; disability; young people and citizenship.
RANGE OF GRANTS Grants range from £1,000 up to £50,000.
SAMPLE GRANTS Médecins Sans Frontières (£50,000); Global Green Grants (£25,000); Cambridgeshire Wildlife Trust and Forest School Camp (£20,000 each); Woodland Trust (£15,000); Arthur Rank Hospice (£5,000); Action for Refugees (£1,000).
FINANCES *Financial year end* 31/03/2020 *Income* £359,400 *Total grants* £450,000 *Grants to organisations* £450,000 *Assets* £10,180,000
TRUSTEES Lady Rachel Willcocks; Anne Willcocks; Mary Morgan; Kate Willcocks; Xanthe Williams; Peter McCarthy; Andrew Laurie.
OTHER INFORMATION Grants were made to 48 organisations during the year.
HOW TO APPLY Contact the correspondent for further information.

CONTACT DETAILS Peter McCarthy, Trustee, 13 Queensway, Wellingborough, Northamptonshire NN8 3RA *Tel.* 01933 222986 *Email* petermc1711@btinternet.com

■ Northwood Charitable Trust

OSCR NO SC014487 **ESTABLISHED** 1972

WHERE FUNDING CAN BE GIVEN Dundee and Tayside.

WHO CAN BENEFIT Charitable organisations; registered charities; universities; churches; CICs.

WHAT IS FUNDED General charitable purposes, particularly: the relief of poverty and inequality; advancing educational attainment; improving physical and mental health and well-being; and supporting community, heritage and cultural enrichment.

RANGE OF GRANTS Mostly up to £50,000, with some larger grants of up to £300,000.

SAMPLE GRANTS Breakthrough Dundee (£344,200); V&A – Dundee (£100,000); Children 1st (£63,500); Future Skills College (£50,000); Dundee Heritage Trust (£30,000); Insight Counselling (£20,000); University of Aberdeen (£15,000); Dundee Women's Aid (£10,000); Coldside Parish Church (£6,500); Friockheim Community Hub (£5,000).

FINANCES *Financial year end* 05/04/2019 *Income* £3,480,000 *Total grants* £3,050,000 *Grants to organisations* £3,050,000 *Assets* £100,310,000

OTHER INFORMATION The 2018/19 accounts were the latest available at the time of writing (June 2021). Grants were awarded to over 140 organisations during the year. Only beneficiaries of grants of £5,000 and above were listed in the accounts (67 organisations). Matched-funding donations to 43 organisations totalled £16,600.

HOW TO APPLY The trust's 2018/19 accounts state: 'Unsolicited applications for donations are not encouraged and will not normally be acknowledged.'

CONTACT DETAILS The Trustees, 22 Meadowside, Dundee DD1 1LN *Website* https://www.dcthomson.co.uk/partners

■ The Norton Foundation

CC NO 702638 **ESTABLISHED** 1990

WHERE FUNDING CAN BE GIVEN Birmingham, Coventry and Warwickshire.

WHO CAN BENEFIT Registered and unregistered charitable organisations; schools; community groups; individuals.

WHAT IS FUNDED Children and young people under the age of 25 who require any help with disability, drink/drug rehabilitation, medical issues, education or training, or who would benefit from counselling, holidays or social activities.

TYPE OF GRANT Project and capital grants.

RANGE OF GRANTS Grants up to £15,000.

SAMPLE GRANTS South Birmingham Young Homeless Project (£12,300); Solihull Canoe Club (£10,000); Trinity Christian Centre (£9,000); Bosnia and Herzegovina UK Network (£8,800); Sport 4 Life UK (£5,000); Shakespeare Schools Foundation (£2,500); Shrewley Parish Parents (£1,000).

FINANCES *Financial year end* 05/04/2020 *Income* £201,000 *Total grants* £208,900 *Grants to organisations* £167,800 *Assets* £4,650,000

OTHER INFORMATION During 2019/20, 47 grants were made to organisations. Grants to individuals totalled £41,100.

HOW TO APPLY Applicants should send a completed application form to the correspondent. Guidance notes are available from the foundation's website.

CONTACT DETAILS Richard Perkins, The Norton Foundation, The Paddock, Bwlch y Gwynt Road, Llysfaen, Colwyn Bay LL29 8DQ *Tel.* 01492 512079 *Email* correspondent@nortonfoundation.org *Website* www.nortonfoundation.org

■ The Norton Rose Fulbright Charitable Foundation

CC NO 1102142 **ESTABLISHED** 2004

WHERE FUNDING CAN BE GIVEN Worldwide.

WHO CAN BENEFIT Registered charities; charitable organisations.

WHAT IS FUNDED Social welfare; health; education; disaster relief; legal projects.

RANGE OF GRANTS Grants are typically of less than £15,000.

SAMPLE GRANTS Barretstown (£50,000); London Community Foundation (£30,600); Action for Children (£40,600); SWLLC (£31,500); Tower Hamlets Law Society (£25,000); Beanstalk (£20,000); Hand in Hand (£15,000).

FINANCES *Financial year end* 30/04/2020 *Income* £451,700 *Total grants* £515,200 *Grants to organisations* £515,200 *Assets* £13,300

OTHER INFORMATION Grants were made to 70 organisations in the following categories: social welfare (£430,500); medical causes (£55,700); education (£29,000). Grants of £15,000 or less totalled £197,500.

HOW TO APPLY Apply in writing to the correspondent. The foundation tends to support the same charities each year, but new charities are considered at trustees' meetings. The trustees also meet on an ad hoc basis to consider specific urgent requests, such as the support of major disaster relief appeals.

CONTACT DETAILS The Trustees, c/o Norton Rose Fullbright, 3 More London Riverside, London SE1 2AQ *Tel.* 020 7283 6000 *Website* www.nortonrosefulbright.com/corporate-responsibility

■ Norwich Town Close Estate Charity

CC NO 235678 **ESTABLISHED** 1892

WHERE FUNDING CAN BE GIVEN Within a 20-mile radius of Norwich Guildhall.

WHO CAN BENEFIT Charitable organisations; schools; nurseries; churches; statutory authorities; arts, culture and heritage organisations; hospices; museums.

WHAT IS FUNDED Education; social welfare; general charitable purposes.

TYPE OF GRANT Capital costs; project funding; capacity building.

RANGE OF GRANTS £1,000 to £100,000.

SAMPLE GRANTS Priscilla Bacon Hospice Care Ltd (£100,000); YMCA Norfolk (£90,000); St George's Theatre (£38,500); East Anglia's

Children's Hospices and The Matthew Project (£25,000 each); Museum of Norwich and Strangers' Hall (£12,500 each); BUILD Charity Ltd, GR8 AS U R and Lionwood Infant and Nursery School (£10,000 each); Norwich City Council via NORCA and SISTEMA and Total Ensemble Theatre Company (£5,000 each); National Centre for Writing and Norwich Arts Centre (£3,000 each).

FINANCES *Financial year end* 31/03/2020 *Income* £1,040,000 *Total grants* £785,200 *Grants to organisations* £640,000 *Assets* £25,620,000

TRUSTEES David Barber; Boyd Taylor; John Garside; David Fullman; Vivien Thomas; Owen Gibbs; Jacqueline Hanlon; Nigel Back; John Rushmer; Stuart Lamb; Melanie Kent; Philip Blanchflower; Cynthia Cooke; Michael Quinton; Jeanne Southgate; Elspeth Jones.

OTHER INFORMATION This charity is one of three grant-making charities comprising Norwich Charitable Trusts. In 2019/20, the charity made grants to 43 organisations.

HOW TO APPLY Contact the correspondent for further information.

CONTACT DETAILS The Trustees, 1 Woolgate Court, St Benedict's Street, Norwich, Norfolk NR2 4AP *Tel.* 01603 621023 *Email* david.hynes@norwichcharitabletrusts.org.uk *Website* https://www.norwichcharitabletrusts.org.uk

■ The Norwood and Newton Settlement

CC NO 234964 **ESTABLISHED** 1952

WHERE FUNDING CAN BE GIVEN England and Wales, with a preference for Romford in the London Borough of Havering and the surrounding area.

WHO CAN BENEFIT Methodist and other free churches; Anglican churches in Havering; small charities in Havering.

WHAT IS FUNDED The promotion of Christianity.

WHAT IS NOT FUNDED Repairs and maintenance; salaries and running costs; equipment; appeals for which lottery funding has been received or an application is being processed; churches operating a policy of closed communion table; individuals; small schemes where the cost could be covered by the church or charity; small schemes made up of individual elements that could be undertaken as and when funding is available; small schemes that are purely to comply with the Equalities Acts (e.g. ramps and toilets); schemes where building work has already been completed.

TYPE OF GRANT One-off capital building projects.

RANGE OF GRANTS Grants range from £500 to £30,000.

SAMPLE GRANTS Guildford Millmead Baptist Church – Surrey (£30,000); Tove Valley Centre – Towcester (£25,000); The Bridge Church – Hayling Island (£15,000); Harwood Methodist Church – Lancashire (£10,000); Maidstone United Reformed Church (£5,000); Soham Methodist Church – Cambridgeshire (£3,000); Elim Church – Romford (£1,000).

FINANCES *Financial year end* 31/03/2020 *Income* £418,800 *Total grants* £476,500 *Grants to organisations* £476,500 *Assets* £9,680,000

TRUSTEES Alan Gray; Stella Holland; Susan Newsom; Roger Lynch; Rodney Eborn; Trevor Marlow.

OTHER INFORMATION In 2019/20, 30 grants were awarded, ranging from £500 to £30,000.

HOW TO APPLY Apply in writing to the correspondent. In normal circumstances, applicants are sent either a refusal or an application form inviting further information within a few days. Once satisfactory information has been received, applications are considered by the trustees at quarterly meetings. Applicants are kept informed of the trustees' timescale at all times.

CONTACT DETAILS The Trustees, 5 Convent Close, Upminster, London RM14 2FA *Tel.* 01708 226618 *Email* norwoodandnewton@btinternet.com *Website* norwoodandnewton.co.uk

■ The Notgrove Trust

CC NO 278692 **ESTABLISHED** 1979

WHERE FUNDING CAN BE GIVEN Gloucestershire.

WHO CAN BENEFIT Registered charities.

WHAT IS FUNDED General charitable purposes.

WHAT IS NOT FUNDED Individuals; medical research; major national charities.

RANGE OF GRANTS Grants range from £1,000 up to £731,200.

SAMPLE GRANTS Notgrove Village Hall (£731,200); Northleach PCC (£20,000); Friends of the Cotswolds (£10,000); Great Western Air Ambulance (£5,300); Guideposts (£3,000); Guiting Music Festival (£1,200); Kempley Village Hall (£1,000).

FINANCES *Financial year end* 30/09/2019 *Income* £253,800 *Total grants* £814,400 *Grants to organisations* £814,400 *Assets* £9,170,000

TRUSTEES Elizabeth Acland; Harry Acland; Lucy Morris; Diana Acland.

OTHER INFORMATION The 2018/19 accounts were the latest available at the time of writing (June 2021). Grants were made to 27 organisations during the year.

HOW TO APPLY Apply in writing to the correspondent, including a full copy of the latest accounts. Applications are not acknowledged. If you have heard nothing within a month, you can assume that your application has been unsuccessful. Applications by email are not accepted or acknowledged. The trustees meet annually to review applications.

CONTACT DETAILS Diana Acland, Trustee, The Manor, Notgrove, Cheltenham, Gloucestershire GL54 3BT *Tel.* 01451 850239 *Email* diana@notgrove.com *Website* https://notgroveholidays.com/notgrove-estate/#trust

■ Notting Hill Genesis Community Foundation

CC NO 1109918 **ESTABLISHED** 2005

WHERE FUNDING CAN BE GIVEN Communities in London and the surrounding areas in which the Notting Hill Genesis Housing Group operates.

WHO CAN BENEFIT Charitable organisations.

WHAT IS FUNDED Financial inclusion; employment, enterprise and training; digital engagement; health and well-being; social research; volunteering.

WHAT IS NOT FUNDED National/international charities enjoying widespread support; work that has already taken place; activities that promote political or religious beliefs; the purchase of alcohol; projects that support people who live in another country; hospitals and health authorities; medical care or equipment; animal charities; military charities; academic research; capital projects; general appeals.

RANGE OF GRANTS £2,800 to £16,600 (in 2019/20).

SAMPLE GRANTS East London Advance Technology Training (£16,600); Shapelifters (£12,600); 4Front (£12,400); Place2Be (£7,500); Active Within (£6,300); Colindale Communities Trust (£5,200); London Art Therapy (£3,200); Munro Health (£2,800).

FINANCES *Financial year end* 31/03/2020 *Income* £29,000 *Total grants* £158,700 *Grants to organisations* £158,700 *Assets* £2,550,000

TRUSTEES Andrew Belton; Paul Philips; Mark Vaughan; John Hughes; Vipul Thacker; Katie Yallop, Elly Hoult; Kate Davies; Carl Byrne.

OTHER INFORMATION Grants were made to 23 organisations during the year.

HOW TO APPLY Check the website for deadlines and apply in writing to the correspondent. All applications must be supported by a Notting Hill Genesis member of staff and must show some demonstrable benefits to Notting Hill Genesis residents. If you do not have a contact at the housing association, email gwf@nhg.org.uk before sending your application. The trustees meet a minimum of two times a year to consider grant applications.

CONTACT DETAILS The Trustees, Bruce Kenrick House, 2 Killick Street, London N1 9FL *Tel.* 020 3815 0339 *Email* gteam@nhg.org.uk *Website* https://www.genesisha.org.uk/how-we-can-help-you/opportunities-you-and-your-community/genesis-wellbeing-foundation

■ Nottinghamshire Community Foundation

CC NO 1069538 **ESTABLISHED** 1998

WHERE FUNDING CAN BE GIVEN Nottinghamshire.

WHO CAN BENEFIT Registered charities; unregistered charities; CICs; social enterprises; PTAs; amateur sports clubs; hospices; individuals.

WHAT IS FUNDED General charitable purposes including the following: health; welfare; older people; children and young people; homelessness; art and music.

SAMPLE GRANTS Building a Stronger Britain (£200,900); Mohn Westlake (£40,500); Mohn Westlake (£26,500); Ashfield Community Fund (£9,000); Basil Skyers Myeloma Foundation (£2,900); 1% Matters (£2,000); Nottinghamshire Children's Welfare Fund (£600).

FINANCES *Financial year end* 31/03/2020 *Income* £983,300 *Total grants* £838,300 *Grants to organisations* £838,300 *Assets* £2,280,000

TRUSTEES Kevin Price; Lady Diana Meale; Amanda Farr; Rt Hon. Simon Tipping; Col. David Sneath; Nikki Weston; Lynn Betts; Thomas Gray; Mark Goldby; Lynn Betts.

OTHER INFORMATION This is one of the 46 UK community foundations, which distribute funding for a wide range of purposes. As with all community foundations, there are a number of donor-advised funds managed on behalf of individuals, families and charitable trusts. Grant schemes tend to change frequently – consult the foundation's website for details of current programmes and up-to-date deadlines.

HOW TO APPLY Potential applicants are advised to visit the community foundation's website or contact the foundation team to find the most suitable funding stream.

CONTACT DETAILS The Trustees, Pine House B, Southwell Road West, Rainworth, Mansfield, Nottinghamshire NG21 0HJ *Tel.* 01623 620202 *Email* enquiries@nottscf.org.uk *Website* www.nottscf.org.uk

■ The Nuffield Foundation

CC NO 206601 **ESTABLISHED** 1943

WHERE FUNDING CAN BE GIVEN Predominantly the UK.

WHO CAN BENEFIT Universities; independent research institutions; voluntary sector organisations; think tanks; primary care trusts.

WHAT IS FUNDED Science and social science research into education, justice and welfare.

WHAT IS NOT FUNDED See the foundation's website for a full list of exclusions.

TYPE OF GRANT Project funding; research funding; seed funding; strategic funding.

RANGE OF GRANTS Programme dependent – see website.

SAMPLE GRANTS University of Ulster – School of Law (£354,600); University of Edinburgh – School of Social and Political Science (£216,800); Education Policy Institute (£180,900); Full Fact (£60,000); Institute for Fiscal Studies (£32,400); University of London (£7,200); Centre for Lifelong Learning – University of Liverpool (£260).

FINANCES *Financial year end* 31/12/2019 *Income* £4,400,000 *Total grants* £9,800,000 *Grants to organisations* £9,800,000 *Assets* £411,690,000

TRUSTEES Sir Keith Burnett; Prof. Ash Amin; Prof. Ann Phoenix; Dame Colette Bowe; Prof. James Banks; The Hon, Sir Ernest Ryder; John Pullinger.

OTHER INFORMATION According to the foundation's application guidelines, all grants are awarded to organisations (host institutions) rather than individuals. In 2019 the foundation received 401 initial applications from research, development and analysis projects and considered 74 full applications. Many of the foundation's funding programmes have individual funding criteria and guidelines which are not listed here. Consult the foundation's excellent website before applying.

HOW TO APPLY Applicants should firstly read the extensive 'Guide for applicants' for the relevant funding programme. The first stage is to submit an outline application for consideration and then the proposal may be shortlisted for consideration by trustees. At this point, shortlisted applicants will be asked to submit a full application. A timetable of application deadlines can be found on the foundation's website.

CONTACT DETAILS Grants Team, 28 Bedford Square, London WC1B 3JS *Tel.* 020 7631 0566 *Email* info@nuffieldfoundation.org *Website* www.nuffieldfoundation.org

■ The Sir Peter O'Sullevan Charitable Trust

CC NO 1078889 **ESTABLISHED** 1999

WHERE FUNDING CAN BE GIVEN Worldwide.

WHO CAN BENEFIT Registered charities.

WHAT IS FUNDED Animal welfare; horses; the racing industry.

TYPE OF GRANT Capital and building costs; service delivery; project funding.

RANGE OF GRANTS Typically £10,000 to £100,000.

SAMPLE GRANTS The Jockeys' Association Trust/ Injured Jockeys Fund Hardship Grant Fund (£100,000); British Racing School (£78,700); Jamie's Farm (£36,000); Park Palace Ponies (£20,000); Lambourn RDA (£10,000); Racehorse Relief (£2,000).

FINANCES *Financial year end* 30/04/2020 *Income* £436,000 *Total grants* £1,401,800 *Grants to organisations* £1,401,800 *Assets* £4,620,000

TRUSTEES Nigel Payne; Geoffrey Hughes; Michael Dillon; John McManus; Michael Kerr-Dineen; Sir Anthony McCoy; Dierdre Flood.

OTHER INFORMATION The trust has an ongoing commitment to the following six animal welfare charities: Blue Cross, Compassion in World Farming, Racing Welfare, Brooke, British Thoroughbred Retraining Centre and World Horse Welfare. These charities receive £30,000 each per annum. The grant total includes the £180,000 distributed equally between the six charities named above as well as £903,500 to other specific projects and good causes.

HOW TO APPLY Apply in writing to the correspondent. Further guidance is available on the trust's website. Applications need to be received by the last day of November each year and will be discussed in detail by the trustees to reach a decision by the end of January.

CONTACT DETAILS Nigel Payne, Administrator, The Old School, Bolventor, Launceston, Cornwall PL15 7TS *Tel.* 01566 880292/07768 025265 *Email* nigel@earthsummit.demon.co.uk *Website* www.thevoiceofracing.com

■ The Oakdale Trust

CC NO 218827 **ESTABLISHED** 1950

WHERE FUNDING CAN BE GIVEN UK, with a preference for Wales; overseas.

WHO CAN BENEFIT Registered charities; unregistered charities; CICs.

WHAT IS FUNDED Welsh social and community projects; medical support groups in Wales; UK-based medical research projects; Welsh environmental conservation projects; the arts (where there is a Welsh connection); UK-based and registered charities working in financially developing countries; penal reform.

WHAT IS NOT FUNDED Individuals; holiday schemes; sport activities; expeditions.

TYPE OF GRANT Capital costs; core and revenue costs; seed funding/start-up funding; project funding; unrestricted funding.

RANGE OF GRANTS Grants range from £250 up to £2,000; the average grant is £1,000.

SAMPLE GRANTS The Lost ARC CIC (£15,000); Money for Madagascar (£8,000); Howard League for Penal Reform (£3,000); Amantani UK, British Red Cross and Horatio's Garden (£2,000 each); Talgarth and District Historical Society (£300).

FINANCES *Financial year end* 05/04/2020 *Income* £367,200 *Total grants* £290,700 *Grants to organisations* £290,700 *Assets* £15,200,000

TRUSTEES Rupert Cadbury; Bruce Cadbury; Olivia Tatton-Brown; Dr Rebecca Cadbury.

OTHER INFORMATION Repeat applications are not normally accepted within a two-year period.

HOW TO APPLY Apply in writing via the website or post. Full guidelines, including closing dates for applications, are published on the website. The trust states that it will accept telephone calls; however, messages should not be left on the answerphone as this is for private use only.

CONTACT DETAILS The Trustees, Tansor House, Main Street, Tansor, Peterborough, Cambridgeshire PE8 5HS *Tel.* 01832 226386 *Email* oakdale@tanh.uk *Website* www.oakdaletrust.org.uk

■ The Oakley Charitable Trust

CC NO 233041 **ESTABLISHED** 1963

WHERE FUNDING CAN BE GIVEN England, Wales and the Channel Islands, but predominantly the West Midlands.

WHO CAN BENEFIT Registered charities.

WHAT IS FUNDED Social welfare, health, education, arts, conservation and animal welfare.

WHAT IS NOT FUNDED Individuals; overseas charities; non-registered charities.

TYPE OF GRANT Core costs, project, research, recurring costs and buildings. Funding is available for one year or less.

RANGE OF GRANTS Up to £3,000, but typically less than £1,000.

SAMPLE GRANTS Loughborough Foundry Trust (£5,000); City of Birmingham Symphony Orchestra and Birmingham Hippodrome (£3,000 each); Dogs Trust and Stroke Association (£2,000 each); Seafarers UK (£1,000); Black Country Food Bank (£300).

FINANCES *Financial year end* 05/04/2020 *Income* £73,200 *Total grants* £84,200 *Grants to organisations* £84,200 *Assets* £2,280,000

TRUSTEES Christine Airey; Geoffrey Oakley; Simon Sharp.

OTHER INFORMATION Grants were made to 56 organisations during the year.

HOW TO APPLY Apply in writing to the correspondent; include the details of the project and the amount you need. You cannot apply by email. The trustees meet in March, July and November.

CONTACT DETAILS Grants Administrator, 10 St Mary's Road, Harborne, Birmingham, West Midlands B17 0HA *Tel.* 0121 427 7150 *Website* www.oakleycharitabletrust.org.uk

■ Ocean Family Foundation

CC NO 1174759 **ESTABLISHED** 2017

WHERE FUNDING CAN BE GIVEN Worldwide.

WHO CAN BENEFIT Charitable organisations; marine conservation projects.

WHAT IS FUNDED Marine conservation.

SAMPLE GRANTS The Africa Foundation (£137,200); A Plastic Free Planet Ltd (£125,000); Worldrise Onlus (£88,500); Fundación Save the Med (£42,600); Boat International Media Ltd (£35,000); Bawah Anambas Foundation (£20,300).

FINANCES *Financial year end* 29/02/2020 *Income* £577,100 *Total grants* £448,600 *Grants to organisations* £448,600 *Assets* £120,600

TRUSTEES Peter Dubens; David Till; Jessica Getty; Louise Creasey.

HOW TO APPLY Contact the foundation for further information.

CONTACT DETAILS The Trustees, 3 Cadogan Gate, London SW1X 0AS *Email* hello@oceanfamilyfoundation.org *Website* https://www.oceanfamilyfoundation.org

■ Odin Charitable Trust

CC NO 1027521 **ESTABLISHED** 1993

WHERE FUNDING CAN BE GIVEN UK.

WHO CAN BENEFIT UK-registered charities.

WHAT IS FUNDED General charitable purposes, with a preference for: the arts; care for people with disabilities; disadvantaged people; hospices; homelessness; prisoners' families; refugees; Roma and Travellers; tribes; indigenous peoples; research into false memories and dyslexia.

WHAT IS NOT FUNDED Individuals.

TYPE OF GRANT Mostly recurrent.

RANGE OF GRANTS Usually between £1,000 and £5,000, but occasionally up to £10,000.

SAMPLE GRANTS Hartlepool and District Hospice and Julian House (£10,000 each); Wiltshire Music Centre (£5,000); Cardboard Citizens, Firebird Theatre and Independent Age (£3,000 each); Asylum Welcome and FareShare (£2,000 each); Brighton and Hove Unwaged (£1,000).

FINANCES *Financial year end* 05/04/2019 *Income* £818,900 *Total grants* £234,000 *Grants to organisations* £234,000 *Assets* £9,280,000

TRUSTEES Susan Scotford; Donna Kelly; Pia Cherry; Payne Hicks Beach Trust Corporation Ltd.

OTHER INFORMATION The 2018/19 annual report and accounts were the latest available at the time of writing (June 2021). The annual report states as a guide that it is the trustees' aim to distribute £220,000 per annum. Grants were committed to around 50 organisations during the year.

HOW TO APPLY Applications should be submitted in the form of a letter or email and contain the following information: the aims and objectives of the charity, the nature of the appeal, the total target (if for a specific project), the charity's registration number, and any other relevant factors. Letters should be accompanied by a set of the charitable organisation's latest report and full accounts. Contact the correspondent for an email address.

CONTACT DETAILS Susan Scotford, Trustee, PO Box 1898, Bradford on Avon, Wiltshire BA15 1YS *Tel.* 020 7465 4300

■ The Ofenheim Charitable Trust

CC NO 286525 **ESTABLISHED** 1983

WHERE FUNDING CAN BE GIVEN Worldwide, but in practice, the UK with some preference for East Sussex.

WHO CAN BENEFIT Registered charities.

WHAT IS FUNDED General charitable purposes, particularly: older people; hospices; medical research; music; education; the arts; social welfare; wildlife preservation.

WHAT IS NOT FUNDED Individuals.

RANGE OF GRANTS Grants range from £3,500 up to £15,000.

SAMPLE GRANTS Southern Thailand Elephant Foundation (£15,000); Macmillan Cancer Support, Scope and St Mungo's (£12,000 each); National Trust (£6,500); Independent Age (£4,500); Songbird Survival (£3,500).

FINANCES *Financial year end* 31/03/2020 *Income* £515,500 *Total grants* £499,500 *Grants to organisations* £499,500 *Assets* £14,230,000

TRUSTEES Roger Clark; Rory McLeod; Dr Alexander Clark; Fiona Byrd.

OTHER INFORMATION Grants were made to 71 organisations during the year.

HOW TO APPLY Apply in writing to the correspondent. The trustees tend to support the same organisations each year and prefer to support organisations of which they have prior knowledge.

CONTACT DETAILS The Trustees, c/o RSM UK Tax and Accounting Ltd, The Pinnacle, 170 Midsummer Boulevard, Milton Keynes, Buckinghamshire MK9 1BP *Tel.* 01908 687800

■ The Ogle Christian Trust

CC NO 1061458 **ESTABLISHED** 1938

WHERE FUNDING CAN BE GIVEN Worldwide.

WHO CAN BENEFIT Registered charities.

WHAT IS FUNDED The advancement of the Christian faith; evangelism worldwide; support for missionary enterprises; Bible student training; help for retired missionary workers and famine and relief organisations.

WHAT IS NOT FUNDED Individuals; building projects; general appeals from large national organisations; salaries.

RANGE OF GRANTS From £1,000 to £25,000 but typically less than £5,000.

SAMPLE GRANTS Operation Mobilisation (£25,000); Bethany Trust (£12,000): MEM (£15,000); The Centre for Muslim-Christian Studies (£5,000); Serving in Mission and Starfish Asia (£3,000 each); Brighton and Hove City Mission (£2,000); South West Youth Missionaries (£1,000).

FINANCES *Financial year end* 31/12/2019 *Income* £102,600 *Total grants* £193,100 *Grants to organisations* £183,900 *Assets* £2,310,000

TRUSTEES Ronald Goodenough; Stephen Procter; Fiona Putley; Lynne Quanrud; Dr David Harley; Dr Carol Walker.

OTHER INFORMATION During the year, grants to individuals totalled £9,200.

HOW TO APPLY Apply in writing to the correspondent and include an sae. Our research suggests that the trustees meet in May and November but applications can be made at any time.

CONTACT DETAILS The Trustees, 43 Woolstone Road, Forest Hill, London SE23 2TR *Tel.* 07857 043212 *Email* oglectrust@rockuk.net

■ Oglesby Charitable Trust

CC NO 1026669 **ESTABLISHED** 1993

WHERE FUNDING CAN BE GIVEN Mainly the north of England.

WHO CAN BENEFIT Registered charities; CICs; hospices; galleries and theatres; churches; universities.

WHAT IS FUNDED The arts and culture; education; environmental projects; social and health inequalities; medical aid and research; building projects.

WHAT IS NOT FUNDED Non-registered charities; activities with the purpose of redistributing collected funds to other charities; animal charities; charities mainly operating outside the UK; church and all building fabric materials; charities promoting religion; conferences; fundraising costs; expeditions; general sports, unless there is an association with a disadvantaged group; holidays; individuals; routine staff training; sponsorship and marketing appeals.

TYPE OF GRANT One-off and multi-year grants for capital, core, project and research funding.

RANGE OF GRANTS Up to £350,000 but typically of less than £50,000.

SAMPLE GRANTS University of Manchester (two grants totalling £460,000); Shared Health Foundation (£350,000); Community Forest Trust (£250,000); Bloodwise (£150,000); Manchester Museum (£67,000); Centre for Social Justice (£50,000); Think Ahead (£40,000); Lifeshare (£35,000).

FINANCES *Financial year end* 30/09/2019 *Income* £10,840,000 *Total grants* £3,400,000 *Grants to organisations* £3,400,000 *Assets* £14,150,000

TRUSTEES Jean Oglesby; Katharine Vokes; Jane Oglesby; Chris Oglesby; Kathryn Graham.

OTHER INFORMATION The 2018/19 accounts were the latest available at the time of writing (June 2021). Grants were awarded to 71 organisations during the year as follows: tackling social and health inequalities (£1.18 million); artistic development (£801,000); medical aid and research (£660,000); environmental improvement (£500,200); education (£257,100). Only organisations that received grants of over £35,000 were listed as beneficiaries in the charity's accounts (38 organisations). Grants of under £35,000 totalled £616,200.

HOW TO APPLY The trust is an invitation-only funder and does not accept unsolicited applications.

CONTACT DETAILS Louise Magill, Trust Manager, Union, Albert Square, Manchester M2 6LW *Tel.* 0161 638 9200 *Email* welcome@oglesbycharitabletrust.org.uk *Website* https://oglesbycharitabletrust.org.uk

■ Oizer Charitable Trust

CC NO 1014399 **ESTABLISHED** 1992

WHERE FUNDING CAN BE GIVEN UK, with a preference for Greater Manchester.

WHO CAN BENEFIT Jewish organisations.

WHAT IS FUNDED Causes within the Jewish community, particularly the provision of Orthodox Jewish education and the advancement of religion according to the Orthodox Jewish faith.

TYPE OF GRANT Typically recurrent.

RANGE OF GRANTS Up to £84,900.

SAMPLE GRANTS Yesemach Levav Trust (£84,900); Friends of Boyan Trust (£75,000); Teshivoh Tefilloh Tzedokoh (£62,000); Bikur Cholim and Gemiluth Chesed Trust (£30,000); Chaim Charitable Trust (£28,000).

FINANCES *Financial year end* 31/03/2019 *Income* £770,000 *Total grants* £520,000 *Grants to organisations* £520,000 *Assets* £4,900,000

TRUSTEES Joshua Halpern; Cindy Halpern.

OTHER INFORMATION Additional grants of £240,000. The 2018/19 accounts were the latest available at the time of writing (April 2021).

HOW TO APPLY Contact the correspondent for further information.

CONTACT DETAILS The Trustees, 1st Floor, Cloister House, Riverside, New Bailey Street, Manchester M3 5FS *Tel.* 0161 832 8721

■ Old Possum's Practical Trust

CC NO 328558 **ESTABLISHED** 1990

WHERE FUNDING CAN BE GIVEN UK.

WHO CAN BENEFIT Registered charities; schools; arts, culture and heritage organisations; places of worship.

WHAT IS FUNDED Literary, artistic, musical and theatrical projects; historical conservation; social welfare.

TYPE OF GRANT Project funding.

RANGE OF GRANTS Typically £2,500 to £30,000.

SAMPLE GRANTS Wilton's Music Hall (£40,000); Beanstalk (£30,000); First Story and English National Ballet (£15,000 each); Arete and Real Action (£10,000); Holland Park Opera, Imperial War Museum and Roots Theatre (£5,000 each); Kingston Hospital Charity, LAMDA, Latymer Community Church and St Albans International Organ Festival (£2,500 each); Macmillan Cancer Support and Trinity Academy London (£500 each).

FINANCES *Financial year end* 31/03/2020 *Income* £262,300 *Total grants* £321,900 *Grants to organisations* £321,900 *Assets* £101,600

TRUSTEES Judith Hooper; Deirdre Simpson; Clare Reihill.

OTHER INFORMATION Grants typically last for three years. In 2019/20 the trust made grants to 41 organisations across the following areas: educational support (£103,387); the arts and historical conservation (£197,469); support for people living with disabilities or disadvantage (£21,000).

HOW TO APPLY Grant applications can only be made online, via the trust's website: applications by email, fax, letter or by telephone are no longer accepted.

CONTACT DETAILS The Trustees, c/o RSM, The Pinnacle, 170 Midsummer Boulevard, Milton Keynes, Buckinghamshire MK9 1BP *Tel.* 01908 662255 *Email* generalenquiry@old-possums-practical-trust.org.uk *Website* www.old-possums-practical-trust.org.uk

■ Henry Oldfield Trust

CC NO 1156496 **ESTABLISHED** 2014

WHERE FUNDING CAN BE GIVEN Kent and Medway.

WHO CAN BENEFIT Registered charities; galleries; museums; hospices.

WHAT IS FUNDED The promotion of entrepreneurship; people experiencing homelessness and addiction; programmes which reduce offending and re-offending; children and young people.

RANGE OF GRANTS Mostly up to £25,000.

SAMPLE GRANTS Kent and Medway Medical School (£250,000); Catch 22 Charity (£100,000); Charities Aid Foundation (£65,000); Heart of Kent Hospice (£25,000); Place2Be (£10,000); Greenwich Museum and Home-Start (£5,000 each); Duke of Edinburgh Award (£2,500); Histio UK (£500).

FINANCES *Financial year end* 31/03/2020 *Income* £337,200 *Total grants* £1,270,000 *Grants to organisations* £1,270,000 *Assets* £11,410,000

TRUSTEES Richard Oldfield; Leonora Philipps; Amicia Oldfield; Christopher Oldfield; Edward Oldfield: Baroness Jenkin.

OTHER INFORMATION During the year, grants were awarded to 62 organisations.

HOW TO APPLY Contact the correspondent for further information.

CONTACT DETAILS The Trustees, Doddington Place, Church Lane, Doddington, Sittingbourne, Kent ME9 0BB *Tel.* 01795 886385

■ The Olwyn Foundation

CC NO 1179306 **ESTABLISHED** 2018

WHERE FUNDING CAN BE GIVEN UK and overseas.

WHO CAN BENEFIT Registered charities.

WHAT IS FUNDED The empowerment, education and protection of women and girls in the UK and overseas.

TYPE OF GRANT Project funding; campaign funding; core/revenue costs; salaries. One-off and recurrent funding.

SAMPLE GRANTS A breakdown of grants was not available. Beneficiaries included: ActionAid, Child's i Foundation – Uganda, The Orchid Project and Women for Women International.

FINANCES *Financial year end* 31/12/2019 *Income* £150,000 *Total grants* £126,400 *Grants to organisations* £126,400 *Assets* £18,500

TRUSTEES Antonia Deeson; Patricia Green; Samantha Rowe-Beddoe; Samantha Merry.

OTHER INFORMATION In 2019 the foundation made grants totalling £126,400 to four charities registered in the UK. The foundation has committed up to £60,000 to the Child's i Foundation in Uganda for salaries in 2019 and 2020.

HOW TO APPLY Contact the correspondent for further information.

CONTACT DETAILS Antonia Deeson, Trustee, 38 Market Place, Folkingham, Sleaford, NG34 0SF *Tel.* 07778 792750 *Email* antonia@olwynfoundation.org *Website* https://www.olwynfoundation.com

■ One Community Foundation Ltd

CC NO 1135258 **ESTABLISHED** 2009

WHERE FUNDING CAN BE GIVEN Kirklees.

WHO CAN BENEFIT Registered charities; unregistered charities; CICs; schools; PTAs; amateur sports clubs; individuals.

WHAT IS FUNDED General charitable purposes; community development; the environment; sports; arts and social welfare.

WHAT IS NOT FUNDED Political activity; the promotion of religion; replacement of statutory funding; projects that have already started; groups which have not complied with previous monitoring requirements; animal welfare organisations.

TYPE OF GRANT Capital costs; core/revenue costs; project funding; unrestricted funding.

RANGE OF GRANTS Generally £350 to £5,000.

SAMPLE GRANTS Previous beneficiaries have included: The Batley Methodist Church (£5,000); Borough of Kirklees Swimming Squad (£4,000); Linthwaite Luncheon Club (£3,000); 1st Holme Valley Scouts (£2,500); Friends of Hade Edge School and Thongsbridge Tennis and Fitness Club (£2,000 each); Batley Smile CIC and Marsden Jazz Festival (£1,000 each); Huddersfield Town Disabled Supporters Club (£500); Oakes Community Cafe (£350).

FINANCES *Financial year end* 31/03/2020 *Income* £501,500 *Total grants* £306,400 *Grants to organisations* £306,400 *Assets* £3,360,000

TRUSTEES Tom Taylor; Judith Charlesworth; Jeremy Garside; Eric Firth; Jonathan Thornton; Dr Alan Bewsher; Ian Brierley; Sir John Harman; Joanne Bell.

OTHER INFORMATION This is one of the 46 UK community foundations, which distribute funding for a wide range of purposes. As with all community foundations, there are a number of donor-advised funds managed on behalf of individuals, families and charitable trusts. Grant schemes tend to change frequently – consult the foundation's website for details of current programmes and up-to-date deadlines. During 2019/20, 251 grants were awarded, typically in the range of £350 to £5,000. The grant total figure also includes a small number of grants to individuals (63), a separate figure for which is not recorded in the charity's accounts. The average grant size was £1,200.

HOW TO APPLY Potential applicants are advised to visit the community foundation's website or contact its grants team to find the most suitable funding stream.

CONTACT DETAILS Grants Team, c/o Chadwick Lawrence Solicitors, 13 Railway Street, Huddersfield, West Yorkshire HD1 1JS *Tel.* 01484 468397 *Email* info@one-community.org.uk *Website* www.one-community.org.uk

■ Orange Tree Trust

CC NO 1183882 **ESTABLISHED** 2018

WHERE FUNDING CAN BE GIVEN UK and overseas.

WHO CAN BENEFIT Charitable organisations.

WHAT IS FUNDED Community development; refugees; homelessness; mental health; medical research; academic study and research in the arts, humanities and social sciences.

TYPE OF GRANT Capital projects; core costs; project funding.

SAMPLE GRANTS Ahliyyah School for Girls (£54,800); University of Bristol (£30,100); The British Red Cross (£10,000); The English Stage Theatre Company (£8,600); SE1 Productions (£2,000).

FINANCES *Financial year end* 31/07/2020 *Income* £85,000 *Total grants* £105,500 *Grants to organisations* £105,500 *Assets* £8,800

TRUSTEES David Charles Freeman; Ghalia Al-Qattan; Omar Abdel Muhsen Al-Qattan.

HOW TO APPLY Apply via the trust's website. Board meetings are held quarterly from January.

CONTACT DETAILS The Trustees, 1 Edwards Street, London W8 6HE *Email* info@orangetreetrust.org *Website* https://orangetreetrust.org

■ The Orrin Charitable Trust

CC NO 274599 **ESTABLISHED** 1977

WHERE FUNDING CAN BE GIVEN Scotland; the rest of the UK; occasionally overseas.

WHO CAN BENEFIT Registered charities.

WHAT IS FUNDED General charitable purposes.

WHAT IS NOT FUNDED Individuals.

RANGE OF GRANTS From £1,000 to £7,000, but typically up to £5,000.

SAMPLE GRANTS Atlantic Salmon Trust (£7,000); The National Playing Fields Association and King Edward VII's Hospital (£5,000 each); Young Musicians Symphony Orchestra and Fishmongers' Company Charitable Trust (£4,000 each); Scots Guards Association (£3,000); The Wheelyboat Trust and Project Malawi (£2,000 each); Church of the Most Holy Redeemer (£1,000).

FINANCES *Financial year end* 05/04/2020 *Income* £53,200 *Total grants* £55,000 *Grants to organisations* £55,000 *Assets* £637,500

TRUSTEES Hugh Macdonald-Buchanan; Elizabeth Macdonald-Buchanan.

OTHER INFORMATION Grants were made to 15 organisations in 2019/20.

HOW TO APPLY Contact the correspondent for further information.

CONTACT DETAILS The Trustees of The Orrin Charitable Trust, The Hedley Foundation, Victoria House, 1–3 College Hill, London EC4R 2RA *Tel.* 020 7489 8076

■ Orthopaedic Research UK

CC NO 1111657 **ESTABLISHED** 1989

WHERE FUNDING CAN BE GIVEN UK.

WHO CAN BENEFIT Universities; medical research organisations; NHS trusts; start-ups.

WHAT IS FUNDED Medical research, in particular orthopaedic research; education and training; publishing; start-ups.

TYPE OF GRANT Research, including PhD, postdoctoral and start-up funding; project funding; seed funding/start-up funding.

RANGE OF GRANTS Typically around £75,000.

SAMPLE GRANTS University of Edinburgh (£75,000); Newcastle University (£49,800).

FINANCES *Financial year end* 30/04/2020 *Income* £1,240,000 *Total grants* £142,700 *Grants to organisations* £142,700 *Assets* £25,280,000

TRUSTEES Keith Tucker; Sarah Harkness; Prof. Neil Rushton; Peter Harrison; Prof. Matteo Santin; Adrian Downing; Dr Catherine Ball.

OTHER INFORMATION In 2019/20 the funder made grants to two organisations.

HOW TO APPLY The application process, deadlines and eligibility vary for research grants, research fellowships (RCS/ORUK Research Fellowship and RAEng/ORUK Research Fellowship) and start-up funding. Pre-submission enquiries are welcomed. Visit the funder's website for full details.

CONTACT DETAILS Dr Arash Angadji, Chief Executive, Furlong House, 10A Chandos Street, London W1G 9DQ *Tel.* 020 7637 5789 *Email* info@oruk.org *Website* www.oruk.org

■ Ostro Fayre Share Foundation

CC NO 1090985 **ESTABLISHED** 2000

WHERE FUNDING CAN BE GIVEN UK and overseas, in particular Myanmar.

WHO CAN BENEFIT Registered charities.

WHAT IS FUNDED Philanthropy and voluntary sector collaboration; interfaith relations; conflict resolution.

TYPE OF GRANT Project funding.

SAMPLE GRANTS A list of beneficiaries was not available.

FINANCES *Financial year end* 31/12/2019 *Income* £824,200 *Total grants* £1,100,000 *Grants to organisations* £1,100,000 *Assets* £1,050,000

TRUSTEES Hetty Maher; Katy Ostro; Lyddon Simon; Maurice Ostro.

OTHER INFORMATION In 2019 grants were distributed across the following areas: strengthening faith institutions (£779,900); religious and interfaith (£218,600); 'Entrepreneurial Giving' scheme (£58,200); educational (£18,000); community and older people (£12,200); children's welfare (£4,700); Myanmar project (£3,200).

HOW TO APPLY The foundation does not accept unsolicited requests for funding. However, it may consider offers of partnership in its key priority areas of philanthropy, collaboration, interfaith relations and conflict resolution.

CONTACT DETAILS The Trustees, 62 Grosvenor Street, London W1K 3JF *Tel.* 020 7569 9093 *Email* info@fayresharefoundation.org *Website* www.ostro.com/foundation

■ The O'Sullivan Family Charitable Trust

CC NO 1123757 **ESTABLISHED** 2008

WHERE FUNDING CAN BE GIVEN UK.

WHO CAN BENEFIT Registered charities.

WHAT IS FUNDED The care of people who have disabilities, especially children and young people; genetic research.

TYPE OF GRANT Research; project funding.

RANGE OF GRANTS Grants range from £2,000 to £94,100.

SAMPLE GRANTS The Playhouse Foundation (£94,100); Room to Read UK Ltd (£30,000); The Brickworks (£25,000); DEBRA (£15,000); Shepherds Down School Fund (£10,000); Whizz-Kidz (£5,000); Seenaryo (£2,000).

FINANCES *Financial year end* 30/06/2020 *Income* £238,500 *Total grants* £288,100 *Grants to organisations* £288,100 *Assets* £4,980,000

TRUSTEES Diana O'Sullivan; Finian O'Sullivan; Emily O'Sullivan; Sophie O'Sullivan; Tessa Cartwright.

HOW TO APPLY Contact the correspondent for further information.

CONTACT DETAILS The Trustees, 36 Edge Street, London W8 7PN *Tel.* 020 7131 4000

■ Otsar Trust

OSCR NO SC046456 **ESTABLISHED** 2016

WHERE FUNDING CAN BE GIVEN UK and overseas.

WHO CAN BENEFIT Charitable organisations.

WHAT IS FUNDED The advancement of the Christian faith; social welfare.

SAMPLE GRANTS A list of beneficiaries was not included in the annual report and accounts.

FINANCES *Financial year end* 30/04/2020 *Income* £202,300 *Total grants* £159,000 *Grants to organisations* £159,000 *Assets* £531,500

HOW TO APPLY Contact the correspondent for further information.

CONTACT DETAILS The Trustees, Kirkside, Kirkton of Tealing, Dundee, Angus DD4 0RD

■ The Ouseley Church Music Trust

CC NO 527519 **ESTABLISHED** 1989

WHERE FUNDING CAN BE GIVEN England, Wales and Ireland.

WHO CAN BENEFIT Registered charities; unregistered charities; schools; religious bodies/institutions.

WHAT IS FUNDED Projects that promote and maintain to a high standard the choral services and choir schools of the Church of England, the Church in Wales or the Church of Ireland.

WHAT IS NOT FUNDED Building projects; the making of recordings; the purchase of furniture or liturgical objects; organ repair; the purchase of pianos and other instruments; the design or acquisition of robes; tours or visits.

TYPE OF GRANT Capital costs; seed funding/start-up funding.

RANGE OF GRANTS Up to £50,000; for fees, £5,000 maximum.

SAMPLE GRANTS Manchester Cathedral (£10,700); Oundle for Organists Summer School (£10,000); Newcastle Cathedral (£6,000); Halifax Minster (£5,000); Royal School of Church Music (£4,000); Exeter Cathedral School (£3,000); St Giles' – Oxford (£1,200).
FINANCES *Financial year end* 31/12/2019
Income £181,000 *Total grants* £159,600
Grants to organisations £149,100
Assets £5,690,000
TRUSTEES Dr Christopher Robinson; Canon Richard White; Canon Dr Stephen Darlington; The Very Revd Mark Boyling; Dr John Rutter; Gillian Perkins; Canon Paul Mason; Timothy Byram-Wigfield; Dr Jo Spreadbury; Simon Hirtzel; David Lowe; Samantha Bradburne.
OTHER INFORMATION During 2019, the trustees considered 73 applications and authorised 51 grants totalling £149,100 to organisations. Grants totalling £10,500 were authorised for individuals. The annual report states that the majority of applications were rejected because the request was for an inappropriate course of study.
HOW TO APPLY Applications must be submitted using the trust's official application form, which is available from the correspondent, by an organisation (not an individual). The trust advises potential applicants to consider the application questions and guidelines sections listed on its website before a form is requested. Applications by fax or email will not be accepted.
CONTACT DETAILS Martin Williams, Clerk to the Trustees, PO Box 281, Stamford, Lincolnshire PE9 9BU *Tel.* 01780 752266
Email ouseleytrust@btinternet.com
Website www.ouseleytrust.org.uk

■ Ovingdean Hall Foundation

CC NO 1052478 **ESTABLISHED** 2012
WHERE FUNDING CAN BE GIVEN UK.
WHO CAN BENEFIT Registered charities; non-profit organisations; universities.
WHAT IS FUNDED Supporting the education of children and young people with a hearing impairment.
WHAT IS NOT FUNDED Overseas charities or projects; other grant-making charities; charities that use external fundraising agencies; projects the reinforce negative stereotypes of children and young people with disabilities; activities or projects which a statutory authority is responsible for.
TYPE OF GRANT Project funding; salaries; research; capital costs; scholarships for individuals.
RANGE OF GRANTS Up to £35,000.
SAMPLE GRANTS British Association of Teachers of the Deaf – Con Powell Scholarships (£71,800); Ewing Foundation (£35,000); Panathlon (£25,000); St John's School (£17,100); Signhealth (£15,000); Mousetrap (£10,000); Elizabeth Foundation (£9,100); NatSIP – The National Sensory Impairment Partnership (£2,500).
FINANCES *Financial year end* 31/03/2020
Income £78,700 *Total grants* £189,000
Grants to organisations £189,000
Assets £1,580,000
TRUSTEES Edward Moore; Hamish McAlpine; Lindsey Rousseau; John Hughes; Ian Johnson; Pauline Hughes.
OTHER INFORMATION Grants were made to nine organisations, including grants totalling £75,300 to two organisations to fund bursaries for individuals training as teachers of the deaf.
HOW TO APPLY Applications are accepted from UK-registered charities and not-for-profit organisations. The trustees meet three times a year to discuss applications. The trust is supporting organisations affected by COVID-19 but welcomes contact to discuss potential applications.
CONTACT DETAILS The Trustees, c/o Ovingdean Hall Foundation, 15 Great College Street, London SW1P 3RX *Tel.* 01273 301929 *Email* info@ovingdeanhall.org.uk *Website* www.ovingdeanhall.org

■ The Ovo Charitable Foundation

CC NO 1155954 **ESTABLISHED** 2014
WHERE FUNDING CAN BE GIVEN Worldwide.
WHO CAN BENEFIT Registered charities.
WHAT IS FUNDED Access to energy; youth poverty and homelessness; education; the environment.
TYPE OF GRANT Project funding.
RANGE OF GRANTS Mainly under £50,000.
SAMPLE GRANTS Energy 4 Impact (£1.56 million); The Benjamin Foundation (£94,600); Doorstep Library (£40,000); British Lung Foundation and Cleaning up Bristol Harbour (£20,000 each); End Youth Homelessness (£13,100); Bristol City Council (£6,400); Rock Trust (£5,200).
FINANCES *Financial year end* 31/12/2019
Income £1,010,000 *Total grants* £2,050,000
Grants to organisations £2,050,000
Assets £1,470,000
TRUSTEES Samuel Kasumu; Phillip Kerry; Gina Cicerone; Katherine Goldsmith; Raman Bhatia.
OTHER INFORMATION The foundation is the corporate charity of Ovo Energy. During 2019, grants were made to 17 organisations. Support is also given through the foundation's 'Ovo Gives Back' programme, through which local charitable causes are supported with funding and volunteering.
HOW TO APPLY The foundation largely carries out its own research to identify projects to support. According to the website, although the foundation is not currently accepting applications for grants, this might change, so check the website for any updates. 'Ovo Gives Back' grants are nominated and voted for by Ovo employees.
CONTACT DETAILS Gabi Sethi, Head of Foundation, 1 Rivergate, Bristol BS1 6ED *Tel.* 0800 599 9440 *Email* hello@ovofoundation.org.uk *Website* https://www.ovofoundation.org.uk

■ The Owen Family Trust

CC NO 251975 **ESTABLISHED** 1967
WHERE FUNDING CAN BE GIVEN UK, with a strong preference for the West Midlands.
WHO CAN BENEFIT Registered charities; schools (independent and church); Christian youth centres; churches; museums; community associations.
WHAT IS FUNDED General charitable purposes, including education and training, health and medicine, religious activities, arts, culture, heritage, and economic and community development.
WHAT IS NOT FUNDED Individuals.
RANGE OF GRANTS Mainly up to £5,000.
SAMPLE GRANTS Black Country Living Museum (£10,000); Lichfield Cathedral, Seven Valley Railway Charitable Trust, Shrewsbury Abbey and The Ironbridge Gorge Museum (£5,000 each); Bournville BookFest (£2,500); Birmingham Royal

Ballet (£2,000); Serbian Orthodox Church (£1,000).

FINANCES *Financial year end* 05/04/2020 *Income* £58,500 *Total grants* £64,500 *Grants to organisations* £64,500 *Assets* £1,030,000

TRUSTEES David Owen; Ethne Owen.

OTHER INFORMATION During 2019/20, grants were awarded to 19 organisations. Grants of under £1,500 totalled £7,500 and were awarded to seven organisations.

HOW TO APPLY Apply in writing to the correspondent. Our previous research suggests that applications should include an annual report, a project budget, general information regarding the application and an sae. The trustees meet quarterly.

CONTACT DETAILS David Owen, Trustee, Mill Dam House, Mill Lane, Aldridge, Walsall WS9 0NB *Tel.* 0121 353 1221 *Email* owenmdh@btinternet.com

■ Oxfordshire Community Foundation

CC NO 1151621 **ESTABLISHED** 2013

WHERE FUNDING CAN BE GIVEN Oxfordshire.

WHO CAN BENEFIT Community-based non-profit organisations based in Oxfordshire.

WHAT IS FUNDED General charitable purposes; social welfare.

SAMPLE GRANTS Previous beneficiaries have included: South Oxfordshire Food and Education Alliance (£45,500); Oxford Hub (£35,000); Oxfordshire Youth (£25,000); Blackbird Leys Neighbourhood Support Scheme (£10,000); Community Album (£4,000); Action for Carers Oxfordshire (£3,250); Museum of Oxford Development Trust (£3,180); Digital for Good (£2,000); Oxfordshire Bengali Cultural Society (£1,000); Hinksey Park Football Club (£500).

FINANCES *Financial year end* 31/03/2020 *Income* £2,260,000 *Total grants* £1,230,000 *Grants to organisations* £1,230,000 *Assets* £7,900,000

TRUSTEES Glyn Benson; Anne Davies; Nick Case; Laura Chapman; Neil Preddy; Kate Fyson; David Rossington; Paul Donovan.

OTHER INFORMATION This is one of the 46 UK community foundations, which distribute funding for a wide range of purposes. As with all community foundations, there are a number of donor-advised funds managed on behalf of individuals, families and charitable trusts. Grant schemes tend to change frequently; consult the foundation's website for details of current programmes and up-to-date deadlines.

HOW TO APPLY Potential applicants are advised to visit the community foundation's website or contact its grants team to find the most suitable funding stream.

CONTACT DETAILS Oxfordshire Community Foundation, 3 Woodin's Way, Oxford, Oxfordshire OX1 1HD *Tel.* 01865 798666 *Email* ocf@oxfordshire.org *Website* www.oxfordshire.org

■ Oxfordshire Historic Churches Trust (2016)

CC NO 1168567 **ESTABLISHED** 2016

WHERE FUNDING CAN BE GIVEN Oxfordshire.

WHO CAN BENEFIT Religious bodies/institutions.

WHAT IS FUNDED Churches and chapels; repairs to the fixtures, fittings and structure of churches, chapels or meeting houses used as places of public worship; new work, such as the installation of toilets and kitchens, disabled access, security systems and electrics.

WHAT IS NOT FUNDED Routine maintenance; the removal or replacement of pews; liturgical reordering; church or parish halls; car parks; buildings of less than 50 years old; work that has already started.

TYPE OF GRANT Capital costs.

RANGE OF GRANTS £1,500 to £20,000.

SAMPLE GRANTS All Saints – Spelsbury, St Mary – Swerford and St James – Bix (£20,000 each); St Mary's – Cogges (£12,000); St Andrew's – Chinnor (£10,000); Charlbury Methodist Church (£5,000); Methodist Church – Chipping Norton (£1,500).

FINANCES *Financial year end* 31/03/2020 *Income* £361,000 *Total grants* £253,000 *Grants to organisations* £253,000 *Assets* £1,820,000

TRUSTEES Richard Hughes; Prof. Malcolm Airs; Giles Dessain; Cynthia Robinson; Hilary Hall; Michael Sibly; Dr Stephen Goss; Dr Imogen Coldstream; Stephen Slack.

OTHER INFORMATION The trust awarded 24 grants to churches during the year and additionally supported the installation of 12 roof alarms.

HOW TO APPLY Applications can be made by downloading an application form from the trust's helpful website and returning it to the grants officer. The trust advises that you contact the area representative before applying.

CONTACT DETAILS The Secretary, 4 Haslemere Gardens, Oxford, Oxfordshire OX2 8EL *Tel.* 01865 559305 *Email* secretary@ohct.org.uk *Website* ohct.org.uk

■ P. F. Charitable Trust

CC NO 220124 **ESTABLISHED** 1951
WHERE FUNDING CAN BE GIVEN England, Wales and Scotland.
WHO CAN BENEFIT Charitable organisations.
WHAT IS FUNDED General charitable purposes; health; the arts, culture, heritage or science; education; community development; the advancement of religion; the armed forces and emergency services; animal welfare; human rights.
WHAT IS NOT FUNDED Individuals; non-registered charities; salaries of staff members.
TYPE OF GRANT One-off and recurring costs; buildings; core costs; project costs; research; running costs.
RANGE OF GRANTS Up to £100,000 but mostly under £30,000.
SAMPLE GRANTS Games and Wildlife Conservation Trust (£100,000); Foundation Scotland (£56,000); Alzheimer's Research UK, Helpforce, Institute of Cancer Research and University of Dundee (£50,000 each); Marie Curie (£30,000).
FINANCES *Financial year end* 31/03/2020 *Income* £3,590,000 *Total grants* £2,440,000 *Grants to organisations* £2,440,000 *Assets* £107,550,000
TRUSTEES Philip Fleming; Rory Fleming; Matthew Fleming.
OTHER INFORMATION During the year, grants were made to 397 organisations. Grants of less than £30,000 each totalled £1.92 million.
HOW TO APPLY Apply in writing to the correspondent. The trustees usually meet monthly to consider applications and approve grants.
CONTACT DETAILS The Secretary, c/o RF Trustee Co. Ltd, 15 Suffolk Street, London SW1Y 4HG *Tel.* 020 3696 6721 *Email* charities@rftrustee.com

■ The P27 Trust

CC NO 1182660 **ESTABLISHED** 2019
WHERE FUNDING CAN BE GIVEN UK and overseas.
WHO CAN BENEFIT Christian charities.
WHAT IS FUNDED The advancement of the Christian faith.
SAMPLE GRANTS Stewardship Services (UKET) Ltd (£2.5 million); Mercy Ministries (£600,000); Life Church UK (£500,000); Rwanda Aid (£30,000); Sports Chaplaincy UK (£5,000).
FINANCES *Financial year end* 31/03/2020 *Income* £4,840,000 *Total grants* £4,240,000 *Grants to organisations* £4,240,000 *Assets* £574,200
TRUSTEES Timothy Nelson; Suzanne Patrick; Kathleen Wielkopolska; Angus Wielkopolski.
HOW TO APPLY Contact the correspondent for further information.
CONTACT DETAILS The Trustees, The Farm Offices, St Helens Farm, Seaton Ross, York YO42 4NP *Email* admin@thep27trust.org.uk

■ The Doris Pacey Charitable Foundation

CC NO 1101724 **ESTABLISHED** 2003
WHERE FUNDING CAN BE GIVEN UK.
WHO CAN BENEFIT Charitable organisations.
WHAT IS FUNDED Jewish causes.
SAMPLE GRANTS World Jewish Relief (£549,500); Magen David Adom (£135,000); Jewish Women's Aid (£120,000); Jewish Care Scotland (£30,800).
FINANCES *Financial year end* 05/04/2020 *Income* £98,200 *Total grants* £1,150,000 *Grants to organisations* £1,150,000 *Assets* £3,180,000
TRUSTEES Ray Locke; Leslie Powell; Linda Courtney.
OTHER INFORMATION Grants were made to eight organisations during the year.
HOW TO APPLY Contact the correspondent for further information.
CONTACT DETAILS The Trustees, c/o Charities Aid Foundation, 25 Kings Hill Avenue, Kings Hill, West Malling, Kent ME19 4TA *Tel.* 0300 012 3187 *Email* paceyandbrynbergfoundations@cafonline.org

■ The Paget Charitable Trust

CC NO 327402 **ESTABLISHED** 1986
WHERE FUNDING CAN BE GIVEN UK and overseas.
WHO CAN BENEFIT Registered charities; hospices.
WHAT IS FUNDED General charitable purposes. Previously, support has been given towards international aid and development, disadvantaged children, education, older people, animal welfare and environmental projects.
WHAT IS NOT FUNDED Our previous research indicates that support is not given to individuals, people with mental disabilities, medical research or AIDS/HIV projects.
TYPE OF GRANT Capital costs; core/revenue costs; unrestricted funding.
SAMPLE GRANTS Previous beneficiaries have included: Second Chance (£15,000); Tibet Relief Fund of the United Kingdom (£7,300); Animals Asia Foundation and Farming Community Network (£5,000 each); Childhood First and Freedom from Torture (£4,000 each); Butterfly Hospice, Oxfam, Quaker Social Action and Southwark Community Education Council (£2,000 each); Contact the Elderly and Students' Education Trust (£1,000 each); and Headway – Leicestershire and Rutland, Hospice of Hope Romania and St Andrew's Evangelical Mission (£500 each).
FINANCES *Financial year end* 05/04/2020 *Income* £207,400 *Total grants* £157,500 *Grants to organisations* £157,500 *Assets* £12,090,000
TRUSTEES Joanna Herbert-Stepney; Vivienne Matravers; Laura Woodhead.
OTHER INFORMATION The trust is also known as The Joanna Herbert-Stepney Charitable Settlement. During 2019/20, grants were made to 94 organisations. Grants to UK-based organisations totalled £26,000 and grants to organisations working overseas totalled £131,500. In previous years, the total of grants to UK-based organisations has been significantly higher (e.g. 2018/19 – £179,500).
HOW TO APPLY Apply in writing to the correspondent. According to our previous research, the trustees have requested that applications state clearly what is required. The 2019/20 annual report states: 'The trustees consider each application from other charities on their individual merits

and research each one to ensure they are for public benefit before making any donation.'
CONTACT DETAILS The Trustees, The Old Village Stores, Dippenhall Street, Crondall, Farnham, Surrey GU10 5NZ *Tel.* 01252 850253

■ The Gerald Palmer Eling Trust Company

CC NO 1100869 **ESTABLISHED** 2003
WHERE FUNDING CAN BE GIVEN UK, with a preference for Berkshire. A small amount may be available for causes overseas.
WHO CAN BENEFIT Registered charities.
WHAT IS FUNDED Christianity, particularly the Orthodox Church; medical research and the study of medicine; the relief of sickness and poverty; supporting local charities.
RANGE OF GRANTS Grants of up to £25,000.
SAMPLE GRANTS Pelican Cancer Care (£25,000); Recovery in Mind (£15,000); Cancer Research, Priors Court (£10,000 each).
FINANCES *Financial year end* 31/03/2020 *Income* £1,720,000 *Total grants* £285,700 *Grants to organisations* £285,700 *Assets* £87,140,000
TRUSTEES Desmond Harrison; Robin Broadhurst; James Gardiner; Kenneth McDiarmid; Angela Cropley.
OTHER INFORMATION The grant sample listed includes all organisations which received a grant of over £5,000 in 2019/20. These grants made up 19% of the total donations made by the charity during the year.
HOW TO APPLY Contact the correspondent for further information.
CONTACT DETAILS D. J. Hill, Company Secretary, Eling Estate Office, Wellhouse, Hermitage, Thatcham, Berkshire RG18 9UF *Tel.* 01635 200268 *Email* charities@elingestate.co.uk

■ The Panacea Charitable Trust

CC NO 227530 **ESTABLISHED** 1926
WHERE FUNDING CAN BE GIVEN UK, with a strong preference for Bedford and its immediate region.
WHO CAN BENEFIT Christian organisations; universities; registered charities; PhD projects.
WHAT IS FUNDED Research, scholarships and conferences in the field of historical theology. Social welfare grants are made through the Bedfordshire and Luton Community Foundation and Community and Voluntary Services Bedfordshire.
WHAT IS NOT FUNDED Political parties or political lobbying; pressure groups; commercial ventures; non-charitable activities; the replacement of statutory funding.
TYPE OF GRANT Project costs.
RANGE OF GRANTS £5,000 to £100,000.
SAMPLE GRANTS Poverty, sickness and health grants programme (£109,000); Bristol University (PhD Research Project) (£18,400); Bunyan Meeting Curator (£5,000).
FINANCES *Financial year end* 31/12/2019 *Income* £764,000 *Total grants* £137,500 *Grants to organisations* £137,500 *Assets* £36,210,000
TRUSTEES Charles Monsell; Dr Justin Meggitt; Dr Naomi Hilton; Evan Jones; Sarah Cowls; Dr Phillip Lockley.
OTHER INFORMATION Grants were awarded to institutions and PhD candidates during the year.
HOW TO APPLY Apply in writing to the correspondent for grants towards funding research, publications, or academic work on historical theology. Consult the Bedfordshire and Luton Community Foundation for the most up-to-date information on social welfare grants.
CONTACT DETAILS David McLynn, Executive Officer, 14 Albany Road, Bedford, Bedfordshire MK40 3PH *Tel.* 01234 359737 *Email* admin@panaceatrust.org *Website* panaceatrust.org

■ The Pantheon Charitable Trust

CC NO 1174839 **ESTABLISHED** 2017
WHERE FUNDING CAN BE GIVEN England and Wales.
WHO CAN BENEFIT Charitable organisations.
WHAT IS FUNDED General charitable purposes.
RANGE OF GRANTS Grants range from £1,000 up to £30,900.
SAMPLE GRANTS dZi Foundation UK (£30,900); World Land Trust and Carneys Community (£20,000 each); Blue Ventures Conservation (£10,000); The Literacy Pirates and Action for ME (£5,000 each); CHICKS (£1,000).
FINANCES *Financial year end* 05/04/2020 *Income* £521,100 *Total grants* £114,900 *Grants to organisations* £114,900 *Assets* £669,400
TRUSTEES Alexander Thomas; Jemma Potter; Jocelyn Thomas; Paul Thomas; Ludlow.
OTHER INFORMATION Grants were awarded to 13 organisations in 2019/20.
HOW TO APPLY Contact the correspondent for further information.
CONTACT DETAILS The Trustees, 1st Floor, Tower Wharf, Cheese Lane, Bristol BS2 0JJ *Tel.* 0117 313 8200 *Email* charitabletrusts@ludlowtrust.com

■ The James Pantyfedwen Foundation (Ymddiriedolaeth James Pantyfedwen)

CC NO 1069598 **ESTABLISHED** 1998
WHERE FUNDING CAN BE GIVEN Wales.
WHO CAN BENEFIT Registered charities; unregistered charities; religious bodies/institutions; individuals.
WHAT IS FUNDED The advancement of religion; education; the arts; agriculture; other charitable purposes. Support is given in three main areas: to individual churches for the improvement and repair of fabric; to local and national eisteddfodau; and to postgraduate students.
WHAT IS NOT FUNDED Exclusions vary according to the type of grant being applied for. See the appropriate guideline document on the website for details.
TYPE OF GRANT Unrestricted funding.
RANGE OF GRANTS Up to £18,000.
SAMPLE GRANTS National Eisteddfod of Wales (£18,000); International Music Eisteddfod (£10,000); Aenon Baptist Church – Morriston (£8,000); St David's Church – Tonyrefail (£4,000); New Life Church – Cardigan (£3,000); Salem Chapel – Caernarfon (£2,000); Bro Aled – Llansannan (£500); Felinfach (£250); Llanarth (£80).
FINANCES *Financial year end* 31/03/2020 *Income* £709,100 *Total grants* £465,400 *Grants to organisations* £156,800 *Assets* £14,310,000
TRUSTEES Ken Richards; Gwerfyl Jones; Alun Charles; Sian Jones; Dr Rhidian Griffiths; Dr Eryn White; Wyn Jones; Prof. Jane Aaron; Revd Alun

Evans; Geraint Jones; Prof. Derec Morgan; David Lewis.

OTHER INFORMATION During 2019/20, grants totalling £308,600 were awarded to individuals.

HOW TO APPLY Guidelines and application forms for students, local eisteddfodau and churches can be found on the website. The trustees meet three times a year to consider applications.

CONTACT DETAILS Gwenan Creunant, Executive Secretary, Pantyfedwen, 9 Market Street, Aberystwyth, Ceredigion SY23 1DL *Tel.* 01970 612806 *Email* post@jamespantyfedwen.cymru *Website* www.jamespantyfedwenfoundation.org.uk

■ The Paphitis Charitable Trust

CC NO 1112721 **ESTABLISHED** 2005

WHERE FUNDING CAN BE GIVEN UK, occasionally overseas.

WHO CAN BENEFIT Registered charities.

WHAT IS FUNDED Education and sport; the relief of poverty; care in the community; general charitable purposes. There is a particular interest in children's and medical charities.

RANGE OF GRANTS Typically of less than £1,000.

SAMPLE GRANTS Previous beneficiaries have included: Children with Cancer UK (£11,000); Radiomarathon (£1,800); Grenfell Tower Appeal (£1,000 in two grants); Dementia Adventure and Ludgvan Lions Junior FC (£250 each); NSPCC (£200); St Luke's Hospice (£120); Douglas Macmillan (£100).

FINANCES *Financial year end* 30/06/2020
Income £12,800 *Total grants* £71,800
Grants to organisations £71,800

TRUSTEES Malcolm Cooke; Richard Towner; Kypros Kyprianou; Ann Mantz; Ian Childs.

OTHER INFORMATION The trust was established by entrepreneur and Dragon's Den panellist Theo Paphitis. It is funded by Theo's TV appearances, speeches and book sales. Full accounts were not available to view on the Charity Commission's website due to the trust's low income. We have therefore estimated the trust's grant total based on its total expenditure.

HOW TO APPLY Contact the correspondent for further information.

CONTACT DETAILS The Trustees, 1 St George's Road, Wimbledon, London SW19 4DR *Tel.* 020 3640 7839 *Email* charitabletrust@tprg.com *Website* https://www.theopaphitis.com/charity-patronages

■ Parabola Foundation

CC NO 1156008 **ESTABLISHED** 2013

WHERE FUNDING CAN BE GIVEN England.

WHO CAN BENEFIT Registered charities; universities.

WHAT IS FUNDED General charitable purposes with a preference for social welfare, the arts, culture and music.

TYPE OF GRANT One-off and recurrent project costs.

SAMPLE GRANTS Kings Place Music Foundation, Friends of Hawthorn School, Music in Detention Orchestra of the Age of Enlightenment, Poverty Relief Foundation, Ruwenzori Sculpture Foundation and Wayne McGregor.

FINANCES *Financial year end* 31/03/2020
Income £613,000 *Total grants* £869,300
Grants to organisations £869,300
Assets (£920,100)

TRUSTEES Deborah Jude; Anne Millican; Peter Millican.

OTHER INFORMATION Grants were broken down as follows: creative arts (£838,300); other (£31,000).

HOW TO APPLY Contact the correspondent for further information.

CONTACT DETAILS The Trustees, Broadgate Tower, 20 Primrose Street, London EC2A 2EW *Tel.* 0191 500 8571

■ The Paragon Trust

CC NO 278348 **ESTABLISHED** 1979

WHERE FUNDING CAN BE GIVEN UK and overseas.

WHO CAN BENEFIT Registered charities; individuals; hospices; hospitals; places of worship.

WHAT IS FUNDED General charitable purposes.

RANGE OF GRANTS £500 to £5,000.

SAMPLE GRANTS National Emergencies Trust (£20,000); Rainforest Foundation UK (£5,000); Nourish Community Food Bank (£2,000); Cambridge Churches Homeless Project, The Book Bus Foundation and Willen Hospice (£1,000 each); The Children's Family Trust and Wellbeing of Women (£500 each).

FINANCES *Financial year end* 22/08/2020
Income £104,600 *Total grants* £157,500
Grants to organisations £157,500
Assets £1,920,000

TRUSTEES Lucy Whistler; Philip Cunningham; Dr Fiona Cornish; Patricia Russell; Kathleen Larter.

OTHER INFORMATION During 2019/20, grants totalled £157,500, which included £39,000 in standing orders.

HOW TO APPLY The trust does not accept or acknowledge unsolicited applications.

CONTACT DETAILS The Trustees, c/o Thomson Snell and Passmore LLP, Heathervale House, 2–4 Vale Avenue, Tunbridge Wells, Kent TN1 1DJ *Tel.* 01892 510000

■ The Pargiter Trust

CC NO 1157779 **ESTABLISHED** 2005

WHERE FUNDING CAN BE GIVEN England and Guernsey.

WHO CAN BENEFIT Registered charities; grassroots projects.

WHAT IS FUNDED Older people.

SAMPLE GRANTS Community Foundation for Surrey, Kent Community Foundation and Suffolk Community Foundation (£80,000 each); University of Surrey (£77,700); Wiltshire Community Foundation (£50,000); St Mungo's City Lodge (£40,500); Age UK – Exeter (£25,000); London HIV Chaplaincy (£7,200).

FINANCES *Financial year end* 31/12/2019
Income £743,900 *Total grants* £500,500
Grants to organisations £500,500
Assets £13,610,000

TRUSTEES Suzanne Gardiner; Martyn Mogford; Victoria Westhorp; Mike Starkey; Louise Cook; Paul Metcalfe.

OTHER INFORMATION The trust also makes grants through six community foundations, in Surrey, Suffolk, Berkshire, Kent, Wiltshire and Guernsey. In 2019, the community foundations received between £30,000 and £80,000 each.

HOW TO APPLY Apply in writing to the correspondent. Most applications are received through the six community foundations with which the trust has partnerships.

CONTACT DETAILS David McManus, The Secretary, c/o AC Mole & Sons, Stafford House, Blackbrook Park Avenue, Taunton, Somerset TA1 2PX *Tel.* 07980 932716 *Email* admin@pargitertrust.org.uk *Website* https://pargitertrust.org.uk

■ The Samuel and Freda Parkinson Charitable Trust

CC NO 327749 **ESTABLISHED** 1987

WHERE FUNDING CAN BE GIVEN UK, with a preference for Cumbria.

WHO CAN BENEFIT Registered charities specified by the founder of the trust.

WHAT IS FUNDED General charitable purposes.

RANGE OF GRANTS £7,500 to £30,000.

SAMPLE GRANTS The Leonard Cheshire Foundation (£30,000); RNLI (£20,000); The Salvation Army (£14,000); Animal Concern Cumbria, Church Army and RSPCA (£10,000 each); Animal Rescue Cumbria (£7,500).

FINANCES *Financial year end* 02/11/2020 *Income* £105,200 *Total grants* £111,500 *Grants to organisations* £111,500 *Assets* £3,540,000

TRUSTEES John Crompton; Michael Fletcher; William Waterhouse.

OTHER INFORMATION Grants were awarded to eight organisations during the year. The organisations were based mostly in the north Lancashire region.

HOW TO APPLY The trust's 2019/20 accounts state: 'Each year the Trustees approach potential beneficiaries, especially in the north Lancashire and Cumbria areas, in order to ascertain their current financial position and enquire whether any of them are considering any specific projects. With these facts to hand, distributions are made, bearing in mind the Trust's investment position.'

CONTACT DETAILS The Trustees, c/o Thomson Hayton Winkley, Regent House, 25 Crescent Road, Windermere, Cumbria LA23 1BJ *Tel.* 01539 446585 *Email* info@thwlegal.co.uk

■ Parkinson's UK

CC NO 258197 **ESTABLISHED** 1969

WHERE FUNDING CAN BE GIVEN Mainly UK; occasionally, the USA.

WHO CAN BENEFIT UK universities; NHS trusts; statutory social care organisations or other research institutions.

WHAT IS FUNDED Research into Parkinson's disease.

TYPE OF GRANT Research funding.

SAMPLE GRANTS University College London (£1.38 million); Selcia Ltd (£1.24 million); NRG Therapeutics (£1 million); University of Oxford (£803,000); Imperial College London (£377,000); University of Liverpool (£225,000); Bradford Teaching Hospitals NHS Foundation (£106,000); NHS Orkney (£47,000).

FINANCES *Financial year end* 31/12/2019 *Income* £47,360,000 *Total grants* £6,641,600 *Grants to organisations* £6,580,000 *Assets* £33,810,000

TRUSTEES Tim Tamblyn; Margaret Chamberlain; Gary Shaughnessy; Peter Miller; Paul Warner; Kyle Alexander; Matthew Durdy; Paresh Thakrar; Dr Andrew Cavey; David Allan; Helen Burston; Katrina Green; Elaine Evans.

OTHER INFORMATION Grants to individuals for costs such as specialist equipment and home adaptations totalled £61,600.

HOW TO APPLY Each grant programme has its own specific deadlines and application process. See the website for more information.

CONTACT DETAILS The Trustees, 215 Vauxhall Bridge Road, London SW1V 1EJ *Tel.* 020 7932 1327 *Email* researchapplications@parkinsons.org.uk *Website* www.parkinsons.org.uk

■ Partners Global Foundation

CC NO 1177721 **ESTABLISHED** 2018

WHERE FUNDING CAN BE GIVEN England and Wales; USA; Brazil.

WHO CAN BENEFIT Registered charities.

WHAT IS FUNDED General charitable purposes; education and training; health; arts, culture, heritage and science; economic and community development and employment.

RANGE OF GRANTS £3,900 to £29,500.

SAMPLE GRANTS Artists Space – New York (£29,500); Tate Art Gallery – London (£25,000); Royal Drawing School (£15,000); Project Destined for Kids – Bronx, New York (£7,700); National Portrait Gallery of London (£7,500); King Baudouin Foundation – Germany (£3,900).

FINANCES *Financial year end* 31/12/2019 *Income* £751,400 *Total grants* £88,600 *Grants to organisations* £88,600 *Assets* £1,660,000

TRUSTEES Lonti Ebers; James Flatt; Ian Flatt.

OTHER INFORMATION Six grants were awarded in 2019.

HOW TO APPLY Contact the correspondent for further information.

CONTACT DETAILS The Trustees, 15 Wimpole Street, London W1G 9SU *Tel.* 020 7408 8496

■ The Pastoral Care Trust – The St Nicholas Care Fund

OSCR NO SC029832 **ESTABLISHED** 1993

WHERE FUNDING CAN BE GIVEN City of Glasgow and the districts of East and West Dunbartonshire; North and South Lanarkshire; Renfrewshire, East Renfrewshire and Inverclyde; the western part of Argyll and Bute around Helensburgh and the Gareloch.

WHO CAN BENEFIT Community groups; voluntary organisations; charities.

WHAT IS FUNDED Social welfare; children and young people; older people; people with disabilities; unemployment; asylum seekers and refugees; homelessness; mental health; discrimination.

WHAT IS NOT FUNDED Individuals; salaries; budget shortfalls; political campaigning; national charities.

TYPE OF GRANT Project costs; capital costs.

RANGE OF GRANTS Up to £15,000.

SAMPLE GRANTS St Vincent's Hospice Ltd (£10,000); St Andrews Soup Run (£5,000); Lourdes Theatre Group and Inclusive Holiday Club (£3,000 each); Lourdes Secondary School (£2,800); The Hope Project (£2,000); Alive and Kicking (£1,100); OLR Primary School (£175).

FINANCES *Financial year end* 30/09/2019 *Income* £103,400 *Total grants* £65,500 *Grants to organisations* £65,500 *Assets* £565,700

OTHER INFORMATION The 2018/19 financial information was the latest available at the time of writing (June 2021); however, no full accounts were available to view. We have therefore estimated the trust's 2018/19 grant total based on its total expenditure. The sample beneficiaries have been taken from the trust's website and represent grants made in 2020.

HOW TO APPLY Application forms and guidelines are available from the trust's website. Applications may be sent by post or email.

CONTACT DETAILS The Trustees, Archdiocese of Glasgow, Curial Offices, 196 Clyde Street, Glasgow G1 4JY *Tel.* 0141 226 5898 *Email* pct@rcag.org.uk *Website* www.rcag.org.uk/index.php/the-archdiocese/st-nicholas-care-fund

■ Miss M. E. S. Paterson's Charitable Trust

OSCR NO SC004835 **ESTABLISHED** 1989

WHERE FUNDING CAN BE GIVEN Scotland.

WHO CAN BENEFIT Charitable organisations and the Church of Scotland.

WHAT IS FUNDED Support to the Church of Scotland and other Christian groups for the maintenance of church buildings; general charitable purposes; older people; young people; mental and physical health; sports; the arts.

WHAT IS NOT FUNDED Individuals; students.

TYPE OF GRANT Capital costs for churches; project funding for all other organisations.

SAMPLE GRANTS Ferniehill Evangelical Church (£10,000); Bethesda Christian Fellowship (£5,000); Fresh Start (£4,000); Kindred Advocacy (£3,000); Canine Concern Scotland Trust (£2,000); St Vincent's Hospice (£1,500); Douglas Bader Foundation (£1,000).

FINANCES *Financial year end* 05/04/2020 *Income* £46,100 *Total grants* £156,100 *Grants to organisations* £156,100 *Assets* £954,000

OTHER INFORMATION Grants were made to 70 organisations in 2019/20.

HOW TO APPLY Applications can be submitted through the trust's online application form. The trustees meet twice a year, usually in June and November, to consider applications. See the website for the date of the next meeting and the deadline date for applications.

CONTACT DETAILS The Trustees, c/o Lindsays, Caledonian Exchange, 19A Canning Street, Edinburgh EH3 8HE *Tel.* 0131 656 5670 *Email* mail@swintonpatersontrust.org.uk *Website* www.swintonpatersontrust.org.uk

■ The Patrick Trust

CC NO 213849 **ESTABLISHED** 1962

WHERE FUNDING CAN BE GIVEN The West Midlands and Cornwall.

WHO CAN BENEFIT Charitable organisations.

WHAT IS FUNDED Helping young people; helping older people; a wide range of cultural and pastoral activities in the West Midlands.

WHAT IS NOT FUNDED Individuals; projects based outside the beneficial area.

TYPE OF GRANT Project and capital costs; core costs; development funding; the purchase of art.

RANGE OF GRANTS From £200 to £40,000, but usually below £10,000.

SAMPLE GRANTS Muscular Dystrophy Group of Great Britain and Northern Ireland (£37,500); The Hall for Cornwall Trust (£25,000); Birmingham Royal Ballet (£11,000); British Disabled Angling Association (£1,200); Safeline and The Prince's Trust (£1,000 each); ecobirmingham (£500); National Children's Orchestra of Great Britain (£200).

FINANCES *Financial year end* 05/04/2020 *Income* £228,600 *Total grants* £262,400 *Grants to organisations* £262,400 *Assets* £7,520,000

TRUSTEES Heather Cole; William Bond-Williams; Graham Wem; Laura Pritchard; Amanda Pillinger; Julian Pritchard.

HOW TO APPLY Organisations that feel they might meet the criteria should contact the trust. Note the following information from the website: 'Please be advised that although all applications are considered, it is no longer possible to reply to unsuccessful applicants due to the sheer volume of funding requests.'

CONTACT DETAILS The Trustees, The Lakeside Centre, 180 Lifford Lane, Birmingham, West Midlands B30 3NU *Tel.* 0121 486 3399 *Email* Use the contact form on the website *Website* https://www.thepatricktrust.org.uk

■ The Jack Patston Charitable Trust

CC NO 701658 **ESTABLISHED** 1989

WHERE FUNDING CAN BE GIVEN Leicestershire and Cambridgeshire.

WHO CAN BENEFIT Registered charities; unregistered charities; hospices; religious bodies/institutions.

WHAT IS FUNDED The preservation of wildlife and the environment; the advancement of religion; the preservation of rural church fabric.

WHAT IS NOT FUNDED Individuals.

TYPE OF GRANT Capital costs (church fabric); general funding.

RANGE OF GRANTS £1,000 to £4,000.

SAMPLE GRANTS Norton Juxta Twycross CC (£4,000); Mountsorrel Baptist Church (£3,000); Plant Heritage and Valley Christian Fellowship (£2,500 each); Bumblebee Conservation Trust and Rainbows Hospice (£2,000 each); Royal Forestry Society (£1,500); Leicester Hedgehog Rescue (£1,000).

FINANCES *Financial year end* 05/04/2020 *Income* £122,700 *Total grants* £120,500 *Grants to organisations* £120,500 *Assets* £5,080,000

TRUSTEES Charles Applegate; Stephen Knipe.

OTHER INFORMATION Grants were made to 46 organisations during the year.

HOW TO APPLY Contact the correspondent for further information.

CONTACT DETAILS The Trustees, Buckles Solicitors LLP, Grant House, 101 Bourges Boulevard, Peterborough, Cambridgeshire PE1 1NG *Tel.* 01733 888888 *Email* deborah.lewsley@buckles-law.co.uk

■ The JGW Patterson Foundation

CC NO 1094086 **ESTABLISHED** 2002

WHERE FUNDING CAN BE GIVEN Tyne and Wear, Northumberland, Durham and Cumbria.

WHO CAN BENEFIT Universities; medical research institutions; hospices.

WHAT IS FUNDED Education and research.

TYPE OF GRANT Project funding; research.

RANGE OF GRANTS Mostly from £1,000 to £35,000.

SAMPLE GRANTS Newcastle University (£664,000 in 18 grants); Newcastle University and Leeds University (£51,700); Northumbria University (£47,000); Durham University (£30,900); Great North Children's Hospital and Royal Manchester Children's Hospital (£25,700); Tynedale Hospice at Home (£15,000); Willow Burn – Derwentside Hospice Care Foundation (£5,300).

FINANCES *Financial year end* 31/03/2020 *Income* £1,060,000 *Total grants* £865,600 *Grants to organisations* £865,600 *Assets* £18,630,000

TRUSTEES David Gold; James Dias; Prof. Alan Craft; Prof. Tim Cawston; Stephen Gilroy; Prof. David Young; Prof. Steven Clifford.

OTHER INFORMATION A total of 28 grants were awarded in 2019/20. Of those grants, 18 were awarded to Newcastle University.

HOW TO APPLY Applications can be made through the foundation's website. The trustees meet quarterly, in February, May, September and

November. Completed applications for funding must be received at least one month prior to a quarterly meeting. Applications are usually then sent out for peer review and discussed again at the subsequent quarterly meeting of the trustees.

CONTACT DETAILS Pippa Aitken, Secretary, c/o Sintons LLP, The Cube, Arngrove Court, Barrack Road, Newcastle upon Tyne, Tyne and Wear NE4 6DB *Tel.* 0191 226 7878 *Email* info@jgwpattersonfoundation.co.uk *Website* jgwpattersonfoundation.co.uk

■ Payne-Gallwey 1989 Charitable Trust

CC NO 1016286 **ESTABLISHED** 1987

WHERE FUNDING CAN BE GIVEN Berkshire.

WHO CAN BENEFIT Charitable organisations, with priority given to charities with a connection to Berkshire, especially Newbury; horse racing; the services; enabling young people from deprived backgrounds; medical research; the Church of England; hospices and the care of people with terminal illnesses; people who are deaf or blind.

WHAT IS FUNDED General charitable purposes; relief of poverty; education; religion; health and well-being.

WHAT IS NOT FUNDED Any appeal with a target of over £10 million; capital projects, schools, hospitals, community centres or church restorations outside Berkshire; any charity primarily administered or funded by the government, a local authority or a quango; charities whose policies conflict with the interests of The National Farmers Union or The Country Land Business Group; any charity that campaigns against field sports.

RANGE OF GRANTS £100 to £15,000 (normally no less than £2,000).

SAMPLE GRANTS Thirkleby PCC (£15,000); Mary Hare Foundation (£10,000); Clockwork Tower (£7,500); Music in Hospitals and Care (£5,000); Hunt Servants' Fund (£4,000); Sebastian's Action Trust and Wessex Children's Hospice Trust (£3,000 each).

FINANCES *Financial year end* 05/04/2020 *Income* £203,200 *Total grants* £159,900 *Grants to organisations* £159,900 *Assets* £7,270,000

TRUSTEES Emma Nutt; Caroline Todhunter; John Ritchie; Charles Leigh-Pemberton; Edward Leigh-Pemberton.

OTHER INFORMATION Only organisations that received grants of over £3,000 are listed as beneficiaries in the charity's 2019/20 accounts. Grants of under £3,000 totalled £28,800.

HOW TO APPLY Applicants should complete an application form, which can be found on the trust's website. The trust does not have an email address and does not deal with telephone requests.

CONTACT DETAILS The Trustees, c/o Estate Office, Manor Farm, Little Coxwell, Faringdon, Oxfordshire SN7 7LW *Website* www.pgct.co.uk

■ Peacock Charitable Trust

CC NO 257655 **ESTABLISHED** 1968

WHERE FUNDING CAN BE GIVEN UK.

WHO CAN BENEFIT Registered charities.

WHAT IS FUNDED General charitable purposes, with a preference for: the education of young people; poverty relief; augmenting the income of other charities.

WHAT IS NOT FUNDED Individuals.

TYPE OF GRANT Mostly recurring.

RANGE OF GRANTS Mostly £3,500 to £35,000, with some larger grants.

SAMPLE GRANTS The Jubilee Sailing Trust (£150,000); Cancer Research UK (£95,000); National Council of YMCAs (£35,000); The Mental Health Foundation (£27,000); Helpforce (£25,000); Samaritans (£16,000); Crimestoppers Trust (£11,000); The National Trust (£5,000); Cutnall Green Primary School (£3,500).

FINANCES *Financial year end* 05/04/2019 *Income* £244,200 *Total grants* £1,420,000 *Grants to organisations* £1,420,000 *Assets* £44,400,000

TRUSTEES Charles Peacock; Bettine Bond; Dr Clare Sellors.

OTHER INFORMATION The 2018/19 accounts were the latest available at the time of writing (June 2021). Of the 83 grants awarded during the year, only seven (totalling £89,500) were made to charities that had not been supported in the previous year.

HOW TO APPLY Apply in writing to the correspondent. The trustees meet three times a year with representatives from the Charities Aid Foundation to decide on the grants to be made.

CONTACT DETAILS The Trustees, c/o Charities Aid Foundation, 25 Kings Hill Avenue, Kingshill, West Malling, Kent ME19 4TA *Tel.* 0300 012 3334 *Email* IBarnard@cafonline.org

■ Susanna Peake Charitable Trust

CC NO 283462 **ESTABLISHED** 1981

WHERE FUNDING CAN BE GIVEN Worldwide, with a preference for the South West, particularly Gloucestershire.

WHO CAN BENEFIT Registered charities.

WHAT IS FUNDED General charitable purposes, with a preference for: education; children and young people; local causes; medical and health causes; older people; people with disabilities; work outside the UK; animal welfare; the environment; the armed forces.

WHAT IS NOT FUNDED Individuals.

RANGE OF GRANTS £500 to £20,000.

SAMPLE GRANTS Cotswold Friends (£20,000); Bourton on The Hill – Retreat for the Aged (£10,000); Shelter Box (£6,000); Deafblind UK, Longborough Primary School and Trussell Trust (£5,000 each); Longfield Hospice (£4,000); Listening Book (£3,000); Prickles Hedgehog Rescue (£2,000); Action for Stammering Children (£1,000).

FINANCES *Financial year end* 05/04/2020 *Income* £200,000 *Total grants* £229,000 *Grants to organisations* £229,000 *Assets* £7,550,000

TRUSTEES Susanna Peake; Katharine Loyd.

OTHER INFORMATION In 2019/20 grants were broken down as follows: general charities (£74,500); medical causes and hospices (£48,500); older people and people with disabilities (£28,000); education and children (£27,500); international (£25,500); local charitable organisations (£18,500); animals and the environment (£5,500); the armed forces (£1,000).

HOW TO APPLY Apply in writing to the correspondent. The trustees meet on a frequent, ad hoc basis to consider applications.

CONTACT DETAILS The Trustees, Rathbone Trust Company Ltd, 8 Finsbury Circus, London EC2M 7AZ *Tel.* 020 7399 0820 *Email* linda.cousins@rathbones.com

■ David Pearlman Charitable Foundation

CC NO 287009 **ESTABLISHED** 1983

WHERE FUNDING CAN BE GIVEN UK.

WHO CAN BENEFIT Charitable organisations; Jewish organisations.

WHAT IS FUNDED Social welfare; education; health; arts, culture and heritage; citizenship and community development; Jewish causes; general charitable purposes.

RANGE OF GRANTS Up to £74,600 but mostly under £20,000.

SAMPLE GRANTS The National Youth Theatre (£74,600); The English Heritage Trust (£51,100); Care All Ltd and One Heart – Lev Echod (£35,000 each); New Entrepreneurs Foundation and Chaim Bechesed Trust (£20,000 each); Wlodowa Charity and Rehabilitation Trust (£15,000); Community Security Trust and Support the Charity Worker (£10,000 each).

FINANCES *Financial year end* 30/09/2019 *Income* £632,300 *Total grants* £686,600 *Grants to organisations* £686,600 *Assets* £6,020,000

TRUSTEES Michael Goldberger; Stuart Appleman; David Pearlman; Jonathan Hager; Mr H. A. Pearlman.

OTHER INFORMATION The 2018/19 accounts were the latest available at the time of writing (June 2021).

HOW TO APPLY Contact the correspondent for further information.

CONTACT DETAILS Michael Goldberger, Secretary, New Burlington House, 1075 Finchley Road, London NW11 0PU *Tel.* 020 8731 0777

■ The Pears Family Charitable Foundation

CC NO 1009195 **ESTABLISHED** 1991

WHERE FUNDING CAN BE GIVEN UK and overseas.

WHO CAN BENEFIT Charitable organisations; educational organisations; youth organisations.

WHAT IS FUNDED Jewish causes; community and young people; education and training; philanthropy; international development; youth social action; special educational needs and disability; palliative care; research; community health services.

TYPE OF GRANT Core costs; project funding; capital costs; research; seed funding; strategic funding; unrestricted funding.

RANGE OF GRANTS Mostly from £50,000 to £1 million, with some larger grants.

SAMPLE GRANTS Maudsley Charity (£5.5 million); University of Kent (£2 million); Hebrew University of Jerusalem (£1 million); Ambitious about Autism (£400,000); Marie Curie (£200,000); Olive Tree Initiative (£100,000); YoungMinds (£80,000); Horatio's Garden (£50,000); The Royal Society of the Arts (£7,200); Dorset County Hospital Charity (£5,000).

FINANCES *Financial year end* 31/03/2020 *Income* £22,610,000 *Total grants* £20,900,000 *Grants to organisations* £20,900,000 *Assets* £27,760,000

TRUSTEES Sir Trevor Pears; Mark Pears; David Pears.

OTHER INFORMATION During the year, funding was awarded for core and capital costs, #iWill grants (see the website for details) and towards the professional development of grantees. Due to the COVID-19 pandemic, the foundation will focus on core funding in the 2020/21 financial year. Only beneficiaries of grants of over £50,000 were listed in the accounts (except for #iWill grants, which started from £5,000).

HOW TO APPLY Unsolicited applications are not accepted. COVID-19 funding is for existing partners only.

CONTACT DETAILS Ian Shaw, Finance Director, 2 Old Brewery Mews, London NW3 1PZ *Tel.* 020 7433 3333 *Email* contact@pearsfoundation.org.uk *Website* www.pearsfoundation.org.uk

■ Rosanna Pearson's 1987 Charity Trust

CC NO 297210 **ESTABLISHED** 1987

WHERE FUNDING CAN BE GIVEN England and Wales.

WHO CAN BENEFIT Charitable organisations.

WHAT IS FUNDED General charitable purposes; education and training; the promotion of health; overseas aid; the environment; economic and community development.

SAMPLE GRANTS A list of beneficiaries was not included in the annual report and accounts.

FINANCES *Financial year end* 05/04/2020 *Income* £9,900 *Total grants* £80,000 *Grants to organisations* £80,000

TRUSTEE The Cowdray Trust Ltd.

OTHER INFORMATION Full accounts were not available to view on the Charity Commission's website due to the trust's low income. We have therefore estimated the grant total based on the trust's total expenditure.

HOW TO APPLY Contact the correspondent for more information.

CONTACT DETAILS The Trustees, 4th Floor, 10 Bruton Street, London W1J 6PX *Tel.* 020 7907 2100 *Email* charity@mfs.co.uk

■ The Pebbles Trust

CC NO 1129132 **ESTABLISHED** 2009

WHERE FUNDING CAN BE GIVEN Brighton and Hove.

WHO CAN BENEFIT UK-registered charities; CICs; individuals.

WHAT IS FUNDED General charitable purposes; support for young people with talent (in sport, music, performing arts and academia); community.

TYPE OF GRANT Project funding; capital costs; bursaries; recurrent and one-off.

RANGE OF GRANTS Mostly up to £5,000.

SAMPLE GRANTS Charities Aid Foundation (£50,500); Brighton Festival Fringe (£37,500); Martlet's Hospice (£25,000); FareShare Sussex (£5,000); Extratime (£3,000); Band of Brothers and Speak Out (£2,500 each); Bevendean Community Garden (£1,000); Waterloo Street Community Children (£300).

FINANCES *Financial year end* 31/03/2020 *Income* £124,800 *Total grants* £252,000 *Grants to organisations* £228,600 *Assets* £140,200

TRUSTEES James Arnell; Louise Arnell; Louise Stoten.

OTHER INFORMATION Grants were awarded to 24 organisations during the year. Talent grants and prizes were awarded to over 50 young people totalling £23,400. No individual person received a grant exceeding £500. The trust also partners Brighton Fringe; the trust provides core funding and bursaries (up to £300) for local young performers.

HOW TO APPLY At the time of writing (April 2021), the trust appeared to only be accepting applications for talent grants (for individuals but paid to a school, college or other organisation). Application forms can be downloaded from the website. Check the website for application deadlines.

CONTACT DETAILS James Arnell, Secretary, c/o New Quadrant Partners Ltd, 4th Floor, 5 Chancery Lane, London WC2A 1LG *Tel.* 020 7430 7159 *Email* charities@nqpltd.com *Website* https://www.pebbletrust.org

■ The Dowager Countess Eleanor Peel Trust

CC NO 214684 **ESTABLISHED** 1951

WHERE FUNDING CAN BE GIVEN UK (medical grants); Lancashire; Cumbria, Greater Manchester, Cheshire and Merseyside (general grants).

WHO CAN BENEFIT Small and medium-sized UK-registered charities; universities.

WHAT IS FUNDED Medical research; older people; social welfare.

WHAT IS NOT FUNDED Charities primarily devoted to children; charities under the control of central or local government.

TYPE OF GRANT Capital costs and project funding (general grants); pilot studies and equipment (medical research); fellowships.

SAMPLE GRANTS University of Manchester (£79,600); Cancer Community Hub (£45,000); Action on Elder Abuse (£15,000); Grit Street Aid (£2,500); East Meon PCC (£360).

FINANCES *Financial year end* 31/03/2020 *Income* £686,900 *Total grants* £691,800 *Grants to organisations* £691,800 *Assets* £16,880,000

TRUSTEES Prof. Richard Ramsden; Julius Manduell; Michael Parkinson; John Parkinson; Prof. Margaret Pearson; Prof. Peter Sibley.

OTHER INFORMATION Grants were broken down as follows: medical charities, including medical research (£266,400); social welfare (£247,100); other charitable purposes (£79,700); older people (£30,700).

HOW TO APPLY Apply via the trust's website.

CONTACT DETAILS The Secretary, c/o Hill Dickinson LLP, 50 Fountain Street, Manchester M2 2AS *Tel.* 0161 838 4977 *Email* secretary@peeltrust.com *Website* www.peeltrust.com

■ The Pell Charitable Trust

CC NO 1135398 **ESTABLISHED** 2010

WHERE FUNDING CAN BE GIVEN UK, with a preference for the south of England.

WHO CAN BENEFIT Charitable organisations.

WHAT IS FUNDED The performing arts, particularly music.

RANGE OF GRANTS £500 to £25,000.

SAMPLE GRANTS Welsh National Opera (£25,000); Royal Opera House (£23,700); Garsington Opera (£10,000); Donmar Warehouse Projects (£2,400); Woodburn Singers (£500).

FINANCES *Financial year end* 31/01/2020 *Income* £201,000 *Total grants* £85,800 *Grants to organisations* £85,800 *Assets* £756,300

TRUSTEES Marian Pell; Gordon Pell; Victoria Pell; Coutts & Co.; Oliver Pell.

OTHER INFORMATION Grants were made to 12 organisations during the year.

HOW TO APPLY Apply by letter to the correspondent.

CONTACT DETAILS The Trustees, Coutts & Co. Trustee Department, 1st Floor, Trinity Quay 1, Avon Street, Bristol BS2 0PT *Tel.* 0345 304 2424

■ The Pennycress Trust

CC NO 261536 **ESTABLISHED** 1970

WHERE FUNDING CAN BE GIVEN UK, with a preference for Cheshire and Norfolk.

WHO CAN BENEFIT Smaller charities.

WHAT IS FUNDED General charitable purposes.

WHAT IS NOT FUNDED Individuals.

RANGE OF GRANTS Typically £100 to £500.

SAMPLE GRANTS A list of beneficiaries was not available in the latest accounts.

FINANCES *Financial year end* 05/04/2019 *Income* £78,000 *Total grants* £52,700 *Grants to organisations* £52,700 *Assets* £2,490,000

TRUSTEES Rose Cholmondeley; Charles Cholmondeley; Lady Margot Huston; Priscilla Dicketts.

OTHER INFORMATION Grants were made to 144 organisations. The 2018/19 accounts were the latest available at the time of writing (April 2021).

HOW TO APPLY Apply in writing to the correspondent. The trust does not have an application form and a simple letter is sufficient. Telephone applications are not accepted.

CONTACT DETAILS Doreen Howells, 28 Clare Court, Judd Street, London WC1H 9QW *Tel.* 020 7833 0236 *Email* howellsdoreen@gmail.com

■ People's Health Trust

CC NO 1125537 **ESTABLISHED** 2008

WHERE FUNDING CAN BE GIVEN Great Britain.

WHO CAN BENEFIT Registered charities; CICs; community groups; constituted groups or voluntary organisations with a social/charitable purpose.

WHAT IS FUNDED Health and well-being; communities; social welfare; tackling inequality.

WHAT IS NOT FUNDED See the grant-maker's website for full eligibility criteria.

TYPE OF GRANT Capital costs; project funding; strategic funding.

RANGE OF GRANTS £5,000 to £40,000.

SAMPLE GRANTS Major grants recipients included: Merstham Community Trust (£110,200); Community Renewal Trust (£107,000); Youth Sport Trust (£60,000); Food and Education CIC (£38,500); Reform Radio (£33,200); Pakistan Association Huddersfield (£20,600).

FINANCES *Financial year end* 30/09/2019 *Income* £7,550,000 *Total grants* £5,610,000 *Grants to organisations* £5,610,000 *Assets* £8,290,000

TRUSTEES Barbara Simmonds; Nigel Turner; Alan Francis; Sue Cohen; Paul Ballantyne; Prof. Elizabeth Dowler; Duncan Stephenson; Thomas McIlravey; Leandra Box; Jacqueline Lodge; Dr Eva Elliot.

OTHER INFORMATION The 2018/19 accounts were the latest available at the time of writing (February 2021). During the year, the trust made grants to 179 organisations. Grants were broken down as follows: active communities (£3.52 million); local conversations (£1.39 million); local people (£683,400); strategic funding (£28,300).

HOW TO APPLY Applications can be submitted online. The trust funds organisations nationwide, in areas in which the Health Lottery operates.

However, grant rounds are divided into regional schemes. Check the website to see if a grant scheme is open in your area. Schemes open and close throughout the year.

CONTACT DETAILS Grants Team, 64 Great Eastern Street, London EC2A 3QR *Tel.* 020 7749 9119 *Email* enquiries@peopleshealthtrust.org.uk *Website* www.peopleshealthtrust.org.uk

■ People's Postcode Trust

OSCR NO SC040387 **ESTABLISHED** 2009

WHERE FUNDING CAN BE GIVEN Scotland.

WHO CAN BENEFIT Registered charities; CICs; social enterprises.

WHAT IS FUNDED Improving mental well-being; enabling community participation in the arts; preventing or reducing the impact of poverty; supporting marginalised groups and promoting equality; improving biodiversity and green spaces; enabling participation in physical activity; responding to the climate emergency and promoting sustainability; increasing community access to outdoor space.

WHAT IS NOT FUNDED Consult the trust's funding guide for a comprehensive list of organisations it does not fund.

TYPE OF GRANT Project funding; capital costs; core/revenue costs; seed funding/start-up funding.

RANGE OF GRANTS £500 to £20,000.

SAMPLE GRANTS St Ann's Advice Group (£18,800); Crossroads Derbyshire (£17,400); Safehands for Mothers (£10,000).

FINANCES *Financial year end* 31/12/2019 *Income* £8,810,000 *Total grants* £2,880,000 *Grants to organisations* £2,880,000 *Assets* £255,400

TRUSTEES Aidan Connolly; Mike Pratt; Judy Hills; Rob Flett.

OTHER INFORMATION Organisations wishing to apply for funding of more than £2,000 must be a registered charity. In 2019, 233 grants were made (England: 178, Wales: 29, Scotland: 26).

HOW TO APPLY Apply via the online application form. More details, including guidance notes and deadlines, are available from the trust's website.

CONTACT DETAILS The Trustees, 28 Charlotte Square, Edinburgh EH2 4ET *Tel.* 0131 322 9377 *Email* info@postcodetrust.org.uk *Website* www.postcodetrust.org.uk

■ Dina Perelman Trust Ltd

CC NO 274165 **ESTABLISHED** 1977

WHERE FUNDING CAN BE GIVEN UK and overseas.

WHO CAN BENEFIT Orthodox Jewish institutions.

WHAT IS FUNDED The Orthodox Jewish faith; general charitable purposes; social welfare; Jewish education and places of worship for the Jewish community.

RANGE OF GRANTS £10,000 to £300,000.

SAMPLE GRANTS The Friends of Alexander Institutions Trust (£300,000); Society of Friends of the Torah (£200,000); Chevras Mo'oz Ladol (£80,000); British Friends of Mishan L'choleh (£70,000); Mercaz Hatorah Belz Machnowka (£45,000); Yesmach Levav (£30,000); Zedoko Vochessed (£20,000).

FINANCES *Financial year end* 31/03/2020 *Income* £1,100,000 *Total grants* £905,500 *Grants to organisations* £905,500 *Assets* £9,700,000

TRUSTEES Asher Perelman; Jonah Perelman; Sara Perelman.

HOW TO APPLY Apply in writing to correspondent.

CONTACT DETAILS The Trustees, 39 Overlea Road, London E5 9BG *Tel.* 020 8809 2345

■ The Performing Right Society Foundation

CC NO 1080837 **ESTABLISHED** 2000

WHERE FUNDING CAN BE GIVEN UK.

WHO CAN BENEFIT Organisations, with a preference for not-for-profit organisations (the foundation's definition of an 'organisation' also includes projects led by promoters, talent development organisations, festivals, venues, curators and large performance groups); individuals.

WHAT IS FUNDED The creation and performance of outstanding new music in any genre and the development of artists and audiences.

WHAT IS NOT FUNDED See the relevant funding programme on the website for exclusion criteria.

TYPE OF GRANT Project funding.

RANGE OF GRANTS Programme dependent.

SAMPLE GRANTS Apples and Snakes; Birmingham Contemporary Music Group; Chamber Music Scotland; Horniman Museum and Gardens; Kings Place Music Foundation; Presteigne Festival; Stroud Valleys Artspace; The Cumnock Tryst; Unity Theatre Liverpool.

FINANCES *Financial year end* 31/12/2019 *Income* £4,120,000 *Total grants* £3,282,700 *Grants to organisations* £2,310,000 *Assets* £1,060,000

TRUSTEES Nitin Sawhney; Ameet Shah; John Reid; Richard King; Mark Poole; Caroline Norbury; Chris Butler; Lorna Clarke; Michelle Escoffery; Christine Geissmar; Susannah Simons.

OTHER INFORMATION According to the 2019 accounts, grants totalling £2.31 million were awarded to 275 organisations. Of note, £1.04 million was distributed in grants from the foundation's Open Fund programme. Grants were made to 226 individuals during the year, totalling £972,700. A list of beneficiaries for the year was not available; however, details of previous beneficiaries are available on the foundation's website.

HOW TO APPLY Apply via the foundation's website, where full guidelines for each programme are available. Deadlines for applications vary from programme to programme. The website notes that the foundation is unable to offer specific telephone or email support prior to stage one applications due to the high number of applicants. Organisations can only apply to the Open Fund once per calendar year.

CONTACT DETAILS Fiona Harvey, Secretary, 2 Pancras Square, London N1C 4AG *Tel.* 020 3741 4233 *Email* info@prsformusicfoundation.com *Website* www.prsfoundation.com

■ B. E. Perl Charitable Trust

CC NO 282847 **ESTABLISHED** 1981

WHERE FUNDING CAN BE GIVEN Barnet; Brent; Hackney; Hertfordshire.

WHO CAN BENEFIT Orthodox Jewish organisations, particularly schools and higher education institutions.

WHAT IS FUNDED Orthodox Jewish faith and education; general charitable purposes.

SAMPLE GRANTS Achisomoch Aid Company Ltd (£95,200); MGS Charitable Trust (£36,000); BFO Igud Hakolelim (£25,000); Bnos Beis Yaakov and Art Therapies (£10,000 each).

FINANCES *Financial year end* 31/03/2019
Income £1,260,000 *Total grants* £405,600
Grants to organisations £405,600
Assets £24,310,000

TRUSTEES Benjamin Perl; Joseph Perl; Rachel Jeidel; Dr Shoshanna Perl; Naomi Tsorotzkin; Mr J. Perl.

OTHER INFORMATION The 2018/19 accounts were the latest available at the time of writing (January 2021). Only organisations that received grants of over £10,000 were listed as beneficiaries in the charity's accounts. Grants of under £10,000 totalled £103,300. Grants were broken down as follows: advancement of religion (£211,100); education (£102,300); relief of poverty and illness (£64,100); general purposes (£28,100).

HOW TO APPLY Contact the correspondent for further information.

CONTACT DETAILS The Trustees, Foframe House, 35/37 Brent Street, Hendon, London NW4 2EF *Tel.* 020 3411 2001

■ The Persimmon Charitable Foundation

CC NO 1163608 **ESTABLISHED** 2015

WHERE FUNDING CAN BE GIVEN Areas of company presence in England, Scotland and Wales.

WHO CAN BENEFIT Charitable organisations.

WHAT IS FUNDED General charitable purposes, including the following: community and economic development; sustainable development; education; the arts; the environment; youth work; sport; health; social welfare.

TYPE OF GRANT Project costs; matched funding; capital costs.

RANGE OF GRANTS Building Futures programme: £1,000 to £100,000. Community Champions programme: up to £1,000. In 2019 some general grants of up to £400,000 were also made.

SAMPLE GRANTS Crisis UK (£400,000); SASH (£200,000); Portsmouth Down Syndrome Association and The Young People's Counselling Service (£100,000 each); Leeds Rowing Club and UK Astronomy (£50,000 each); Doncaster Flood Victims (£10,000); Allstars Netball Club and Redditch District Scouts (£1,000 each); Relay for Life (£500).

FINANCES *Financial year end* 31/12/2019
Income £1,100,000 *Total grants* £2,480,000
Grants to organisations £2,480,000
Assets £137,600

TRUSTEES Mike Killoran; Richard Stenhouse; Joanna Place; Roger Devlin; Dean Finch.

OTHER INFORMATION This foundation is the corporate charity of Persimmon plc, a property development company. There are currently two programmes, the Community Champions campaign, which supports small local charities and community groups with matched funding, and the Building Futures campaign, which supports children's health, sport, education and the arts with prizes of £1,000, £5,000, £20,000, £50,000 and £100,000. During the year, the foundation made grants to around 900 charities and community groups through these two programmes, as well as though numerous donations aimed at relieving poverty, ill health, disability and other disadvantage, the largest of which was £400,000 donated to Crisis UK.

HOW TO APPLY Applicants need to complete the relevant online form. Check the website for the Building Futures programme deadlines. For the Community Champions programme, the foundation needs to know how much you have already raised and how much money you need. Applications are accepted each month and charities and groups that were previously unsuccessful can apply again. The trustees prefer to support local charities. Go to https://www.persimmonhomes.com/contact to find your nearest Persimmon office.

CONTACT DETAILS The Trustees, Persimmon plc, Persimmon House, Fulford, York, North Yorkshire YO19 4FE *Tel.* 01904 642199 *Email* contact@persimmonhomes.com *Website* https://www.persimmonhomes.com/charity

■ Personal Assurance Charitable Trust

CC NO 1023274 **ESTABLISHED** 1993

WHERE FUNDING CAN BE GIVEN Worldwide.

WHO CAN BENEFIT Registered charities; support is restricted to organisations recommended by policyholders of Personal Assurance plc, their employers and employees of Personal Group Holdings plc.

WHAT IS FUNDED General charitable purposes; social welfare; health.

WHAT IS NOT FUNDED Grants are rarely made to individuals.

RANGE OF GRANTS Typically £1,000 to £5,000.

SAMPLE GRANTS Memusi Foundation (£63,000); Keech Hospice (£5,300); The Stroke Association (£4,200); Children in Need (£3,700); Foodbank Milton Keynes (£2,500); Martin House (£1,100); Samworth Charity (£1,000).

FINANCES *Financial year end* 31/12/2019
Income £75,600 *Total grants* £87,800
Grants to organisations £87,800
Assets £122,800

TRUSTEES Sarah Mace; Justine Woolf; Rebekah Tapping.

OTHER INFORMATION In 2019 the trust made a large grant to the Memusi Foundation, representing 72% of the grant total. Only organisations that received grants of over £1,000 are listed in the year's annual report and accounts; grants of under £1,000 totalled £7,000. No grants were made to individuals in 2019.

HOW TO APPLY Contact the correspondent for further information.

CONTACT DETAILS The Trustees, c/o Personal Group Holdings plc, John Ormond House, 899 Silbury Boulevard, Milton Keynes, Buckinghamshire MK9 3XL *Tel.* 01908 605000 *Email* hayley.wheatley@personalgroup.com

■ The Jack Petchey Foundation

CC NO 1076886 **ESTABLISHED** 1999

WHERE FUNDING CAN BE GIVEN London and Essex.

WHO CAN BENEFIT Registered charities; state schools and colleges; local authority youth clubs; other charitable organisations; individuals.

WHAT IS FUNDED Support for young people aged between 11 and 25 through various programmes.

WHAT IS NOT FUNDED Profit-making companies; statutory bodies (except for local authority youth clubs); private schools; political or religious activities.

TYPE OF GRANT Project funding. The foundation also funds internships, award schemes and educational visits for small groups.

RANGE OF GRANTS Programme dependent.

SAMPLE GRANTS Speakers Trust Ltd (£624,400); Royal Academy of Dance (£548,000) Table Tennis England (£181,200); Institution of Engineering and Technology (£90,500); London Youth (£61,900); UK Wallball (£36,800); Penstripe (£25,000); Young Women's Trust (£16,400); Harlow College (£10,500); Thurrock Swimming Club (£4,800); Hatfield Peverel Football Club (£1,500).

FINANCES *Financial year end* 31/12/2019 *Income* £9,670,000 *Total grants* £7,393,300 *Grants to organisations* £7,260,000 *Assets* £2,510,000

TRUSTEES Raymond Rantell; Lewis Hooper; Matthew Rantell; Ronald Mills; Robert McArthur; Sonia Sinclair.

OTHER INFORMATION As well as making grants to organisations, the foundation also provides grants of up to £400 to individuals to help them get involved in volunteering projects in the UK and overseas. In 2019 the foundation received 3,657 requests for funding. Grants were awarded to 2,657 organisations and 520 individuals.

HOW TO APPLY Applications can be made via the foundation's website. See the website for the eligibility criteria of the relevant programme. At the time of writing (April 2021), the foundation was not accepting applications for its Individual Grants for Volunteering and Educational Visits grant programmes due to the COVID-19 pandemic; check the website for updates.

CONTACT DETAILS Grants Team, Dockmaster's House, 1 Hertsmere Road, London E14 8JJ *Tel.* 020 8252 8000 *Email* mail@jackpetcheyfoundation.org.uk *Website* www.jackpetcheyfoundation.org.uk

■ Potplan Charitable Trust

CC NO 1032907 **ESTABLISHED** 1994

WHERE FUNDING CAN BE GIVEN UK and overseas.

WHO CAN BENEFIT Registered animal charities; research organisations.

WHAT IS FUNDED The promotion and improvement of the welfare of animals (dogs, cats, horses or rabbits) and the relief of their suffering; veterinary research and education.

WHAT IS NOT FUNDED Individuals; non-registered charities; studies involving experimental or invasive surgery; funding for overheads.

TYPE OF GRANT Project funding; capital costs; animal housing and repairs; research, including pump-priming/pilot grants.

RANGE OF GRANTS Scientific grants: up to £150,000 (unless for pump-priming, for which the maximum is £10,000); welfare grants: up to £20,000; special grants: up to £25,000.

SAMPLE GRANTS Animal Health Trust (11 grants totalling £478,000); Royal Veterinary College (six grants totalling £316,800); University of Nottingham (three grants totalling £151,100); StreetVet (£75,000); Worldwide Veterinary Services (£25,000); Cats Protection (£10,000); Paws for Kids (£6,000); Friends of Dartmoor Hill (£1,000).

FINANCES *Financial year end* 31/12/2019 *Income* £1,650,000 *Total grants* £1,030,000 *Grants to organisations* £1,030,000 *Assets* £926,600

TRUSTEES John Bower; Clarissa Baldwin; David Simpson; Ted Chandler; Peter Laurie; Kathryn Willis; Jamie Crittall; Gary Davess; Prof. The Lord Trees; Alan Farkas.

OTHER INFORMATION Grants were awarded to 72 organisations during the year, some of which received multiple grants. Grants were broken down as follows: scientific grants (£643,700); welfare and educational grants (£221,800); special grants (£162,400). Welfare grants can include items such as neutering, kennelling and veterinary costs, and animal housing and repairs. There are two types of scientific grants: 1) pump-priming grants of up to £10,000 for initial, one-year research projects; 2) full grants for research projects up to three years. Grant amounts are determined by the trustees. Special grants are made at the discretion of the trustees and are not open to applications.

HOW TO APPLY Application forms, eligibility criteria, full terms and conditions, and the dates for application rounds for each grant programme are available from the trust's website.

CONTACT DETAILS Catherine Bourg, Trust Administrator, Great West House (GW2), Great West Road, Brentford, Middlesex TW8 9EG *Tel.* 020 8580 8013 *Email* info@petplancharitabletrust.org.uk *Website* https://petplancharitabletrust.org.uk

■ The Pets at Home Foundation

CC NO 1104152 **ESTABLISHED** 2004

WHERE FUNDING CAN BE GIVEN UK.

WHO CAN BENEFIT Registered charities; unregistered charities; CICs.

WHAT IS FUNDED Activities which improve the welfare of UK domestic pets in rescue or reduce the number of domestic pets in rescue.

WHAT IS NOT FUNDED Individuals.

TYPE OF GRANT Capital costs; core/revenue costs; project funding.

RANGE OF GRANTS Typically up to £10,000 but a number of donations exceed this.

SAMPLE GRANTS Woodlands Animal Sanctuary (£176,400); RSPCA Hull and East Riding Branch (£100,000); Freshfields Animal Rescue (£85,300); Appledown Rescue and Rehoming Kennels (£36,500); Animals in Need, Hugs Foundation and Yorkshire Cat Rescue (£20,000 each); Friends of Ferals and Scottish SPCA (£15,000 each); Happy Staffie Rescue and Team Poundie (£10,000).

FINANCES *Financial year end* 28/03/2020 *Income* £5,060,000 *Total grants* £2,690,000 *Grants to organisations* £2,690,000 *Assets* £3,410,000

TRUSTEES Louise Stonier; George Lingwood; Dan Laurence; Adrian Bates; Andrew Bickerton; Claire Gavin; Dr Catriona Curtis; Jill Shields.

OTHER INFORMATION Grants of less than £10,000 were not listed in the annual report and accounts but totalled £1.4 million.

HOW TO APPLY Prospective applicants should first check the grant criteria to confirm their eligibility, and if eligible, complete the online request for an application form and provide the required supporting documentation. The charity's website notes that a virtual visit to the rescue to learn more about your organisation may be requested.

CONTACT DETAILS The Charity Team, c/o Pets At Home, Chester House, Epsom Avenue, Stanley Green Trading Estate, Handforth, Cheshire SK9 3DF *Tel.* 0161 486 6688 *Email* info@petsathomefoundation.co.uk *Website* www.petsathomefoundation.co.uk

The Pharsalia Charitable Trust

CC NO 1120402 **ESTABLISHED** 2007

WHERE FUNDING CAN BE GIVEN UK and overseas, with a preference for the Oxford region.

WHO CAN BENEFIT Charitable organisations.

WHAT IS FUNDED In the Oxford region: healthcare and social welfare. Nationally: medical research, higher education and health. Internationally: disaster relief.

RANGE OF GRANTS Mostly £500 to £2,000, with some larger grants.

SAMPLE GRANTS Oxford Hospital Charity (£36,000); Abingdon Bridge (£25,000); Age UK Oxfordshire (£10,000); Marie Curie and Young Dementia UK (£2,000 each); Earth Trust and Salvation Army (£1,000 each); Asthma Relief Work in Oxfordshire (£750); Crisis (£500).

FINANCES *Financial year end* 31/03/2020
Income £68,000 *Total grants* £97,200
Grants to organisations £97,200
Assets £1,240,000

TRUSTEES Nigel Stirling Blackwell; Nigel Roots; Trudy Sainsbury.

OTHER INFORMATION Grants were awarded to 30 organisations during the year, with a significant number of them being located in Oxford.

HOW TO APPLY Contact the correspondent for further information.

CONTACT DETAILS The Trustees, The Ham, Ickleton Road, Wantage, Oxfordshire OX12 9JA
Tel. 01235 426524

The Phillips and Rubens Charitable Trust

CC NO 260378 **ESTABLISHED** 1970

WHERE FUNDING CAN BE GIVEN UK.

WHO CAN BENEFIT Charitable organisations, including schools and places of worship.

WHAT IS FUNDED General charitable causes; medical research and other medical causes, including ancillary services; social welfare; education; disability; older people; providing sheltered accommodation; the arts; Jewish causes.

WHAT IS NOT FUNDED Individuals.

RANGE OF GRANTS Mostly up to £15,000, with some larger grants awarded.

SAMPLE GRANTS The Phillips Family Charitable Trust (£100,000); KKL Charity (£50,000); UJIA (£25,000); Holocaust Educational Trust (£15,000); Jewish Community Secondary School (£10,000); Community Security Trust (£5,000); Charities Aid Foundation (£4,000); RAF Museum (£2,500).

FINANCES *Financial year end* 05/04/2020
Income £476,500 *Total grants* £250,200
Grants to organisations £250,200
Assets £11,030,000

TRUSTEES Michael Phillips; Ruth Phillips; Martin Paisner; Paul Phillips; Gary Phillips; Carolyn Mishon.

OTHER INFORMATION Only beneficiaries of grants of £2,500 and above were listed in the 2019/20 accounts (14 organisations). Grants of below £2,500 totalled £12,300. A large proportion of the grants were awarded to Jewish organisations.

HOW TO APPLY Contact the correspondent for further information.

CONTACT DETAILS The Trustees, 67–69 George Street, London W1U 8LT *Tel.* 020 7487 5757
Email psphillips@aol.com

Betty Phillips Charitable Trust

CC NO 1158964 **ESTABLISHED** 2014

WHERE FUNDING CAN BE GIVEN UK.

WHO CAN BENEFIT Registered charities.

WHAT IS FUNDED Animal welfare.

SAMPLE GRANTS A list of beneficiaries was not included in the annual report and accounts.

FINANCES *Financial year end* 31/12/2019
Income £115,100 *Total grants* £88,000
Grants to organisations £88,000
Assets £3,920,000

TRUSTEES Andrew Holloway; Andrew Jones; Michael Vines; Helen Wayman; Miss H. L. Mansfield.

HOW TO APPLY Contact the correspondent for further information.

CONTACT DETAILS The Trustees, 8–12 Clarence Street, Gloucester, Gloucestershire GL1 1DZ
Tel. 01452 522047

The Phillips Charitable Trust

CC NO 1057019 **ESTABLISHED** 1995

WHERE FUNDING CAN BE GIVEN UK and Ireland.

WHO CAN BENEFIT Registered charities and individuals.

WHAT IS FUNDED Seafarers' welfare; animal care and welfare; smaller one-off national or local projects.

RANGE OF GRANTS Mostly £1,000 to £2,000.

SAMPLE GRANTS The Hope Centre (£15,000); SportsAid Eastern (£12,000); Excelsior Trust (£2,500); Animals in Need, Asthma Relief and Seafarers UK (£2,000 each); Age Concern (£1,700); Children's Aid Team and Vine Community Trust (£1,000 each).

FINANCES *Financial year end* 05/04/2020
Income £66,400 *Total grants* £51,200
Grants to organisations £51,200
Assets £2,370,000

TRUSTEES John Ford; Michael Percival; Philip Saunderson; Philippa Schanschieff; Anne Marrum.

OTHER INFORMATION A total of 16 grants were awarded in 2019/20. The trust notes that it has continued its support for SportsAid Eastern, an organisation which helps young men and women to pursue a sporting career.

HOW TO APPLY Contact the correspondent for further information.

CONTACT DETAILS Anne Henman, Clerk to the Trustees, 1 Church Lane, Brafield-on-the-Green, Northampton, Northamptonshire NN7 1BA
Tel. 01604 890748 *Email* anne@rydalchurchlane.plus.com

The Phillips Family Charitable Trust

CC NO 279120 **ESTABLISHED** 1979

WHERE FUNDING CAN BE GIVEN UK.

WHO CAN BENEFIT Registered charities; Jewish organisations.

WHAT IS FUNDED General charitable purposes, with a preference for Jewish causes.

RANGE OF GRANTS Mostly up to £5,000.

SAMPLE GRANTS London School of Jewish Studies (£10,000); United Synagogue (£6,300); Lubavitch of Edgware (£4,000); Technion UK (£3,000); March of the Living UK and The Prince's Teaching Institute (£2,000 each); MS Society (£1,000).

FINANCES *Financial year end* 05/04/2020
Income £100,000 *Total grants* £101,900
Grants to organisations £101,900
Assets £22,500

TRUSTEES Michael Phillips; Ruth Phillips; Martin Paisner; Paul Phillips; Gary Phillips.
OTHER INFORMATION During the year, 72 grants were awarded to mostly Jewish organisations. Only beneficiaries of grants of £1,000 and above were listed in the accounts. Thirty-two grants of less than £1,000 were awarded.
HOW TO APPLY Contact the correspondent for further information.
CONTACT DETAILS Paul Phillips, Trustee, 67–69 George Street, London W1U 8LT *Tel.* 020 7487 5757 *Email* psphillipsbsh@aol.com

■ The Pickwell Foundation

CC NO 1149424 **ESTABLISHED** 2012
WHERE FUNDING CAN BE GIVEN UK and overseas.
WHO CAN BENEFIT Registered charities and community groups.
WHAT IS FUNDED Displaced people; climate change.
TYPE OF GRANT Unrestricted funding; core costs; project funding.
RANGE OF GRANTS Typically £1,000 to £25,000.
SAMPLE GRANTS Client Earth (£25,000); Coram (£9,200); Amos Trust (£8,000); Protect Our Winters and Nurdle Coasts CIC (£5,000 each); Edukid (£2,800); Plough Arts Centre (£1,200).
FINANCES *Financial year end* 05/04/2021 *Income* £52,300 *Total grants* £212,400 *Grants to organisations* £212,400 *Assets* £12,900
TRUSTEES Richard Elliott; Tracey Elliott; Stephen Baker; Susannah Baker.
OTHER INFORMATION The foundation also supports Community Sponsorship in north Devon, a programme which helps resettle refugees in local communities.
HOW TO APPLY Unsolicited applications are not accepted. The foundation makes invitations to apply for funding.
CONTACT DETAILS The Trustees, Pickwell Manor, Georgeham, Braunton, Devon EX33 1LA *Tel.* 07795 109981 *Email* Contact form on website *Website* https://www.thepickwellfoundation.org.uk

■ Bernard Piggott Charitable Trust

CC NO 1154724 **ESTABLISHED** 1970
WHERE FUNDING CAN BE GIVEN North Wales and Birmingham.
WHO CAN BENEFIT Registered charities, mainly in the city of Birmingham and North Wales; also, some national charities with projects in these areas.
WHAT IS FUNDED General charitable purposes; young people and children; older people; Church of England; medicine; the armed forces.
WHAT IS NOT FUNDED Individuals.
TYPE OF GRANT One-off.
SAMPLE GRANTS Previous beneficiaries have included: Birmingham Contemporary Music Group, Dyffryn Parish Church, Kingsbury Training Centre, Montgomeryshire Youth Theatre, Northfield Eco Centre, Resources for Autism, St Mary's Church – Caerhun, Sunfield Children's Homes and Stroke Association.
FINANCES *Financial year end* 30/09/2019 *Income* £123,400 *Total grants* £61,800 *Grants to organisations* £61,800 *Assets* £1,940,000
TRUSTEES Richard Easton; Nigel Lister; Mark Painter; Geoffrey Hall; Archdeacon of Bangor.
OTHER INFORMATION At the time of writing (June 2021), the trust's 2018/19 accounts were the latest available to view.
HOW TO APPLY Apply in writing to the correspondent. The trustees' general policy is to not consider any further grant to the same organisation within the next two and a half years.
CONTACT DETAILS Jenny Whitworth, Secretary, 4 Streetsbrook Road, Shirley, Solihull, West Midlands B90 3PL *Tel.* 0121 744 1695 *Email* jenny@whitworth4.plus.com

■ The Pilgrim Trust

CC NO 206602 **ESTABLISHED** 1930
WHERE FUNDING CAN BE GIVEN UK.
WHO CAN BENEFIT UK-registered charities; organisations exempt from registration; recognised public bodies; registered friendly societies.
WHAT IS FUNDED The preservation of architecturally or historically important buildings; the preservation of historically significant artefacts or documents; social welfare; vulnerable women and girls.
WHAT IS NOT FUNDED There is an extensive list of exclusions, which can be found in the funding guidelines document. The funding guidelines document is available from the trust's website.
TYPE OF GRANT Revenue costs; salaries; project funding; capital costs; development funding; research.
RANGE OF GRANTS Mostly £3,300 to £60,000, with some outlying grants of much higher values. The trust's small grant programme is reserved for requests of £5,000 or less.
SAMPLE GRANTS Association of Independent Museums (£405,000); The Archbishops' Council (£185,000); National Churches Trust (£60,000); David Parr House CIO (£45,000); Queen Elizabeth Scholarship Trust (£20,000); Giving Life Opportunities to Women (£15,000); Azad Kashmir Welfare Association (£7,000); Pembrokeshire County Council (£5,000); Hull Minster (£3,300).
FINANCES *Financial year end* 31/12/2019 *Income* £2,160,000 *Total grants* £3,480,000 *Grants to organisations* £3,480,000 *Assets* £75,660,000
TRUSTEES Sir Mark Jones; The Hon. Lady Sarah Riddell; Sarah Staniforth; Kevin Pakenham; Caroline Butler; David Barrie; Joan Winterkorn; Atulkumar Patel; Marie Staunton; Alexander Sturgis.
OTHER INFORMATION Grants fall into two categories: preservation and scholarship grants (typically 60% of annual expenditure) and social welfare grants (typically 40% of annual expenditure). Preservation and scholarship grants are further split into: historic buildings; care of collections; training and research. During the year, the trust's social welfare grants were awarded with the aim of improving the life chances of vulnerable women and girls with early intervention projects. At the time of writing (May 2021) the social welfare programme was under review and applications were not being accepted – check the website for updates.
HOW TO APPLY Applications can be made via the trust's website using a two-stage online application form. Applicants should read the funding guidelines document prior to making an application. There are no deadlines; applications are considered at quarterly trustees' meetings.
CONTACT DETAILS The Trustees, 3rd Floor, Ebury Gate, 23 Lower Belgrave Street, London SW1W 0NR *Tel.* 020 7834 6510 *Email* info@thepilgrimtrust.org.uk *Website* www.thepilgrimtrust.org.uk

■ Elise Pilkington Charitable Trust

CC NO 1170847 **ESTABLISHED** 2016

WHERE FUNDING CAN BE GIVEN UK.

WHO CAN BENEFIT Registered charities; hospices.

WHAT IS FUNDED Older people; equine welfare.

TYPE OF GRANT Project funding; salaries; capital costs.

SAMPLE GRANTS The Brooke (£90,000 in three grants); Brendoncare (£10,000); RSPCA (£7,200); Linking Lives UK (£8,000); St Peter and St James Hospice (£5,000); Thornberry Animal Sanctuary (£4,500); Anne Robson Trust (£4,000); Dolphin Society (£3,000).

FINANCES *Financial year end* 20/04/2020 *Income* £80,400 *Total grants* £297,000 *Grants to organisations* £297,000 *Assets* £2,480,000

TRUSTEES Gemma Walpole; Claire Gordon; Revd Robert Merchant; Ruth Tarry; Helen Timpany; Dr David Shipway.

OTHER INFORMATION Grants were distributed as follows: equine grants (£236,200); older people (£48,200); hospice grants (£12,500). Equine welfare grants are normally only considered from charities that are members of the National Equine Welfare Council (NEWC) or charities that are proactively working towards NEWC membership.

HOW TO APPLY Application forms can be downloaded from the trust's website.

CONTACT DETAILS The Trust Administrator, Ridgecot, Lewes Road, Horsted Keynes, Haywards Heath, RH17 7DY *Website* https://elisepilkingtontrust.org.uk

■ Cecil Pilkington Charitable Trust

CC NO 249997 **ESTABLISHED** 1966

WHERE FUNDING CAN BE GIVEN UK.

WHO CAN BENEFIT Charitable organisations; individuals.

WHAT IS FUNDED General charitable purposes including the following: the environment; medical causes; the arts; education; welfare.

RANGE OF GRANTS Mainly £5,000 or less.

SAMPLE GRANTS King's College Parkinson's Research (£40,000); Willowbrook Hospice (£10,000); Art Against Knives, Arthritis Care, National Museums Liverpool, SANE and Soil Association (£5,000 each).

FINANCES *Financial year end* 05/10/2019 *Income* £341,400 *Total grants* £290,000 *Grants to organisations* £290,000 *Assets* £23,490,000

TRUSTEES Arnold Pilkington; Mark Feeny; Vanessa Pilkington; Heloise Pilkington.

OTHER INFORMATION The 2018/19 accounts were the latest available at the time of writing (May 2021). Only organisations that received grants of over £4,000 were listed as beneficiaries in the trust's accounts. Grants of under £4,000 totalled £105,000.

HOW TO APPLY Contact the correspondent for further information.

CONTACT DETAILS The Trustees, Duncan Sheard Glass, Castle Chambers, 43 Castle Street, Liverpool, Merseyside L2 9TL *Tel.* 0151 243 1200

■ Pilkington Charities Fund

CC NO 225911 **ESTABLISHED** 1950

WHERE FUNDING CAN BE GIVEN UK, with a strong preference for Merseyside.

WHO CAN BENEFIT Registered charities. CICs and social enterprises will be considered if they are registered charities.

WHAT IS FUNDED Helping people affected by poverty, old age or ill health.

WHAT IS NOT FUNDED Non-profit organisations, social enterprises and CICs that are not registered charities; individuals.

TYPE OF GRANT Capital costs; core costs; project funding; funding for two or three years will be considered in exceptional circumstances.

RANGE OF GRANTS Typically between £1,000 and £6,000, but occasionally larger.

SAMPLE GRANTS C&A Pilkington Trust Fund (£70,000); Macmillan Cancer Support (£15,000); Barnardo's and Wellbeing of Women (£10,000 each); Child Brain Injury Trust (£5,000); Combat Stress and Respite Association (£3,000 each); Spinal Injuries Association (£2,000); Fallen Angels Dance Theatre (£1,000).

FINANCES *Financial year end* 30/06/2020 *Income* £644,200 *Total grants* £365,500 *Grants to organisations* £365,500 *Assets* £23,590,000

TRUSTEES Neil Jones; Philip Pilkington; Eleanor Jones.

OTHER INFORMATION Grants were made to 65 organisations during the year. Large donations were made to the C&A Pilkington Trust Fund (£17,500 each quarter, totalling £70,000 for the year).

HOW TO APPLY Applications can be made in writing or by email to the correspondent. Deadlines fall on 1 May and 1 October, although urgent applications may be considered at other times. Clear instructions detailing what to include are available from the charity's helpful website.

CONTACT DETAILS Lynsey Lewis, Administrator, Rathbones, Port of Liverpool Building, Pier Head, Liverpool, Merseyside L3 1NW *Tel.* 0151 236 6666 *Email* john.duffy@rathbones.com *Website* pilkingtoncharitiesfund.org.uk

■ The Austin and Hope Pilkington Trust

CC NO 255274 **ESTABLISHED** 1967

WHERE FUNDING CAN BE GIVEN UK.

WHO CAN BENEFIT UK-registered charities only.

WHAT IS FUNDED The trust focuses on supporting a different funding priority each year. In 2021, it will be supporting homelessness, refugees and asylum seekers. In 2022, it will be supporting young people and BAME communities within the arts.

WHAT IS NOT FUNDED Capital appeals, including equipment; charities involved with religion; animal charities; holidays; individual hospices (but national organisations can apply); individuals; minibuses and vehicles; overseas projects; schools including activities; Scouts, Cubs, Guides and Brownies; Sea Cadets; Shopmobility; students; village halls.

TYPE OF GRANT Project funding.

RANGE OF GRANTS Up to £5,000.

SAMPLE GRANTS Body and Soul and Inspire (£5,000 each); National Youth Advocacy Service (£4,000); Kazzum, Kids Inspire and Young at Art (£1,000 each).

FINANCES *Financial year end* 31/12/2019
Income £338,200 *Total grants* £385,600
Grants to organisations £385,600
Assets £11,460,000

TRUSTEES Debbie Nelson; Penny Badowska; Eleanor Stride.

HOW TO APPLY Apply via the trust's website.

CONTACT DETAILS Karen Frank, Administrator, Rathbones, Port of Liverpool Building, Pier Head, Liverpool, Merseyside L3 1NW *Email* admin@austin-hope-pilkington.org.uk *Website* www.austin-hope-pilkington.org.uk

■ The Sir Harry Pilkington Trust Fund

CC NO 206740 **ESTABLISHED** 1962

WHERE FUNDING CAN BE GIVEN Merseyside.

WHO CAN BENEFIT Charitable organisations.

WHAT IS FUNDED General charitable purposes, with a preference for arts and culture, youth work and health and social welfare.

RANGE OF GRANTS Grants of up to £10,000.

SAMPLE GRANTS Merseyside Play Action Council (£10,000); LCVS – Positive About Play (£5,000); Walton Youth Project and Knowsley CVS (£3,000 each); Stanley Park Liverpool CIC (£2,000); Lister Residents Association and Tiber (£1,000 each).

FINANCES *Financial year end* 30/06/2019
Income £193,200 *Total grants* £198,200
Grants to organisations £198,200
Assets £7,620,000

TRUSTEE Liverpool Charity and Voluntary Services.

OTHER INFORMATION The 2018/19 accounts were the latest available at the time of writing (June 2021).

HOW TO APPLY Apply in writing to the correspondent. Our research indicates that an initial phone call to discuss the proposal is welcomed.

CONTACT DETAILS The Trustees, Liverpool Charity and Voluntary Services, 151 Dale Street, Liverpool, Merseyside L2 2AH *Tel.* 0151 227 5177

■ Miss A. M. Pilkington's Charitable Trust

OSCR NO SC000282 **ESTABLISHED** 1972

WHERE FUNDING CAN BE GIVEN UK, with a preference for Scotland.

WHO CAN BENEFIT Registered charities.

WHAT IS FUNDED General charitable purposes.

WHAT IS NOT FUNDED Grants are not given to overseas projects or political appeals.

RANGE OF GRANTS Almost all grants are for £1,000.

SAMPLE GRANTS ActionAid, Ark Housing, Army Cadet Force, Asthma UK, Barnardo's, Bible Society, British Lung Foundation, Brooke Hospital for Animals, Canine Partners, Deaf Action, Fife Young Carers, Levenmouth Foodbank, Scottish Huntington's Foundation, Sightsavers International and World Horse Welfare (£1,000 each).

FINANCES *Financial year end* 05/04/2020
Income £115,300 *Total grants* £99,000
Grants to organisations £99,000
Assets £3,410,000

HOW TO APPLY Contact the correspondent for further information.

CONTACT DETAILS The Trustees, EQ Chartered Accountants, 58 Bonnygate, Saltire Centre, Cupar, Fife KY15 4LD *Tel.* 01334 654044

■ PIMCO Foundation Europe

CC NO 1139109 **ESTABLISHED** 2010

WHERE FUNDING CAN BE GIVEN London.

WHO CAN BENEFIT Registered charities.

WHAT IS FUNDED Education; homelessness; overseas aid; the environment; children; arts, culture and heritage; disability.

SAMPLE GRANTS MyBnk (£123,900); British Red Cross (£90,000); House of St Barnabas (£89,600); FareShare (£75,000); EM Power and The Passage (£70,000 each); Malakia Kids and Voluntary Service Overseas (£40,000 each).

FINANCES *Financial year end* 31/12/2019
Income £1,020,000 *Total grants* £674,400
Grants to organisations £674,400
Assets £5,360,000

TRUSTEES Thomas Rice; Vishalakshi Ananthanarayanan; Ryan Blute; Craig Dawson; Ketishweran Pothalingam.

OTHER INFORMATION Grants to eight organisations represented 88% of the total grants made.

HOW TO APPLY Contact the correspondent for further information.

CONTACT DETAILS Carolina Leite, Senior Associate, 11 Baker Street, London W1U 3AH *Tel.* 020 7872 1300 *Email* carolina.leite@uk.pimco.com *Website* https://www.pimco.co.uk/en-gb/our-firm/purpose/foundation

■ Pink Ribbon Foundation

CC NO 1080839 **ESTABLISHED** 2000

WHERE FUNDING CAN BE GIVEN UK and overseas.

WHO CAN BENEFIT UK-registered charities; hospitals; hospices.

WHAT IS FUNDED Relief for people who are suffering from or have been affected by breast cancer; work to advance the understanding of breast cancer and its early detection and treatment.

WHAT IS NOT FUNDED Individuals.

TYPE OF GRANT Capital costs; research; core/revenue costs; seed funding/start-up funding; project funding; unrestricted funding.

RANGE OF GRANTS £1,000 to £5,000.

SAMPLE GRANTS Coppafeel and Prevent Breast Cancer (£5,000 each); Cancer Support Centre and Lady McAdden Trust (£4,000 each); Wigs for Heroes (£3,000); Cancer Research UK (£2,500); Cancer Help (Preston) Ltd (£2,000); Scannappeal (£1,300); Fishing for Life (£500).

FINANCES *Financial year end* 30/09/2020
Income £361,200 *Total grants* £202,600
Grants to organisations £202,600
Assets £431,900

TRUSTEES Angela Brignall; Errol McBean; Jonathan Prince.

OTHER INFORMATION Grants were awarded to 56 organisations during the year.

HOW TO APPLY Application forms can be downloaded from the foundation's website or requested by email or phone. Grant applications must be sent to the correspondent as a hard copy, along with a set of your organisation's most current accounts. The annual deadline is late May, with grants being awarded in July; check the website for exact dates. If applying from a general cancer charity, the grant must be specifically for those with or affected by breast cancer.

CONTACT DETAILS Jonathan Prince, Chair, Crofton House, 5 Morley Close, Orpington, Kent BR6 8JR *Tel.* 01689 858877 *Email* enquiries@pinkribbonfoundation.org.uk *Website* https://www.pinkribbonfoundation.org.uk

The Pitt-Rivers Charitable Trust

CC NO 283839 **ESTABLISHED** 1981

WHERE FUNDING CAN BE GIVEN UK, with a strong preference for Dorset.

WHO CAN BENEFIT Registered charities; voluntary groups; museums; individuals.

WHAT IS FUNDED General charitable purposes, with a focus on the arts, culture and the humanities.

RANGE OF GRANTS Mostly up to £3,000.

SAMPLE GRANTS Pitt-Rivers Museum Oxford (£10,000); British Museum (£4,300); Salisbury Museum (£3,000); The Grange Festival (£2,500); British Red Cross – Syria Appeal (£1,500); Dorset Historic Churches Trust and Safewise (£1,000 each).

FINANCES *Financial year end* 05/04/2020 *Income* £45,500 *Total grants* £54,300 *Grants to organisations* £54,300 *Assets* £216,800

TRUSTEES George Pitt-Rivers; Valerie Pitt-Rivers.

OTHER INFORMATION A total of 52 grants were made to organisations in 2019/20, 32 of which did not exceed £500. Most of the grants made were to organisations based in Dorset. Overall grants were distributed as follows: arts, culture and humanities (£30,300); health and human services (£8,500 each); animals (£2,500); overseas (£1,500); community development, education and religion (£1,000 each).

HOW TO APPLY Contact the correspondent for further information.

CONTACT DETAILS The Trustees, Estate Office, Hinton St Mary, Sturminster Newton, Dorset DT10 1NA *Tel.* 01258 472623

The Pixel Fund

CC NO 1191052 **ESTABLISHED** 2011

WHERE FUNDING CAN BE GIVEN UK.

WHO CAN BENEFIT Registered charities. The trustees have a strong preference for organisations with an annual income of under £10 million.

WHAT IS FUNDED The mental health and well-being of children and young people.

WHAT IS NOT FUNDED Individuals; non-UK-registered charities; projects/services delivered overseas; projects not related to mental health matters; independent schools (other than those supporting children with special educational needs); religious organisations.

TYPE OF GRANT Project funding.

RANGE OF GRANTS £500 to £5,000 for first grants, with an option for follow-on grants for existing grantees that have delivered on commitments.

SAMPLE GRANTS CHUMS Trauma Service; Clear Sky Children's Charity; Freedom from Torture; Gloucestershire Counselling Service; Meningitis Now; Rainbow Trust Children's Charity; Support Dogs; The Guild of Psychotherapists; The Listening Place; York Mind.

FINANCES *Financial year end* 05/04/2020 *Income* £189,900 *Total grants* £87,900 *Grants to organisations* £87,900

TRUSTEES James Hitch; Katherine Ferrie; Sandra Thomson.

OTHER INFORMATION As the charity was re-registered as a CIO in October 2020, its accounts were not available to download from the Charity Commission. Therefore, the grant total has been estimated based off previous years' expenditure. The trustees wish to target grant applications for specific projects. No single grant is ever more than 5% of the organisation's annual income.

HOW TO APPLY Potential applicants are first advised to familiarise themselves with the charity's application checklist, which includes details of eligibility criteria. If you are eligible, contact the charity using the online contact form with a brief outline of your organisation, what you do and your reason for requesting a grant. The charity is paperless and does not accept postal correspondence. If successful, you will be invited to submit a stage one application form. It will be considered at the next trustees' meeting and if successful, you will be invited to complete the stage two application process.

CONTACT DETAILS The Trustees, 9 Southlands Road, Bromley, Kent BR2 9QR *Tel.* 07756 629245 *Email* Use the contact form on the website. *Website* www.pixelfund.org.uk

Thomas Pocklington Trust

CC NO 1113729 **ESTABLISHED** 2005

WHERE FUNDING CAN BE GIVEN UK.

WHO CAN BENEFIT Charitable organisations.

WHAT IS FUNDED Research into sight loss; support for people with sight loss.

TYPE OF GRANT Research, project and development funding.

RANGE OF GRANTS £1,000 to £719,000.

SAMPLE GRANTS London Vision (£719,000); Visionary (£401,000); Birmingham Vision (£202,000); Wiltshire Sight (£200,000); Metro Blind Sports (£165,000); MyBnk (£40,000); Macular Society (£10,000); Vision UK (£2,000); Service (£1,000).

FINANCES *Financial year end* 31/03/2020 *Income* £5,240,000 *Total grants* £2,120,000 *Grants to organisations* £2,120,000 *Assets* £167,300,000

TRUSTEES Jenny Pearce; Mervyn Williamson; Alastair Chapman; Philip Longworth; Graham Findlay; Matt Wadsworth; Rashmikant Mehta; Judith Potts.

OTHER INFORMATION Grants were awarded to 24 organisations during the year.

HOW TO APPLY Grant application forms are available on the trust's website. Applicants should first send an email to research@pocklington-trust.org.uk, detailing their project goals and how they will achieve them in two or three brief paragraphs. A draft proposal may be requested either in short or in full.

CONTACT DETAILS The Trustees, Tavistock House South (Entrance D), Tavistock Square, London WC1H 9LG *Tel.* 020 8995 0880 *Email* info@pocklington-trust.org.uk *Website* www.pocklington-trust.org.uk

The Points Family Trust

CC NO 1174432 **ESTABLISHED** 2017

WHERE FUNDING CAN BE GIVEN England and Wales.

WHO CAN BENEFIT Charitable organisations.

WHAT IS FUNDED General charitable purposes.

RANGE OF GRANTS Grants range from £2,000 up to £15,000.

SAMPLE GRANTS Medical Foundation for the Care of Victims of Torture (£15,000); The Whitley Fund for Nature (£12,500); Save the Elephants (£10,300); Crosslight and UK Friends of the TMF (£4,000 each); Baynards Zambia Trust (£3,000); The East End Community Foundation (£2,000).

FINANCES *Financial year end* 05/04/2020 *Income* £11,900 *Total grants* £50,800 *Grants to organisations* £50,800 *Assets* £805,900

TRUSTEES Jonathan Points; Natalie Yong; Francis Sullivan.

OTHER INFORMATION Grants were awarded to seven organisations in 2019/20.

HOW TO APPLY Contact the correspondent for further information.

CONTACT DETAILS Jonathan Points, Trustee, 28 Portland Road, London W11 4LG *Tel.* 020 7792 9261

■ Polden-Puckham Charitable Foundation

CC NO 1003024 **ESTABLISHED** 1991

WHERE FUNDING CAN BE GIVEN UK and overseas.

WHO CAN BENEFIT Registered charities; non-governmental organisations.

WHAT IS FUNDED Peace and security; environmental sustainability.

WHAT IS NOT FUNDED Consult the foundation's website for a detailed list of grant exclusions.

TYPE OF GRANT Core/revenue costs; seed funding/start-up funding; project funding; unrestricted funding.

RANGE OF GRANTS Typically £5,000 to £20,000 per year, for up to three years.

SAMPLE GRANTS COP26 Coalition (received by War on Want) (£50,000); Sustainable Soil Alliance (£20,000); Bioregional Learning Centre, Finance for the Future and Positive Money (£15,000 each); Hope for the Future, Pesticides Action Network and Power for People (£10,000 each); Climate Outreach (£5,000); Glimpse and UK Student Climate Network (£2,500 each); UK Youth Climate Coalition (£2,000).

FINANCES *Financial year end* 05/04/2020
Income £322,000 *Total grants* £577,600
Grants to organisations £577,600
Assets £14,140,000

TRUSTEES Stephen Pittam; Angela Seay; Jonathan Gillett; Dorothy Ball; Simon Fisher.

OTHER INFORMATION In 2019/20, the charity made 42 grants to charitable organisations: 27 under environmental sustainability (£403,600) and 15 under peace and security (£173,900).

HOW TO APPLY Deadlines, application forms, guidance notes and an eligibility test can be accessed on the charity's website; formal submissions should be made via the online application form.

CONTACT DETAILS C. Oliver, Trust Secretary, BM PPCF, London, Greater London WC1N 3XX *Tel.* 020 7193 7364 *Email* ppcf@polden-puckham.org.uk *Website* www.polden-puckham.org.uk

■ The George and Esme Pollitzer Charitable Settlement

CC NO 212631 **ESTABLISHED** 1960

WHERE FUNDING CAN BE GIVEN UK.

WHO CAN BENEFIT Registered charities.

WHAT IS FUNDED Parenting, the family and children's work; the armed forces; people with disabilities and older people; the community and environment; Jewish faith; health and medical research.

RANGE OF GRANTS Typically £5,000.

SAMPLE GRANTS AbilityNet (£10,000); All Stars Youth Club, Better Lives Foundation, Felix Fund and Thames River Trust (£5,000 each); Bag Books (£4,000).

FINANCES *Financial year end* 05/04/2020
Income £144,100 *Total grants* £109,000
Grants to organisations £109,000
Assets £414,000

TRUSTEES Richard Pollitzer; Catherine Charles; Joseph Pollitzer; Frances Pollitzer.

HOW TO APPLY Contact the correspondent for further information.

CONTACT DETAILS The Trustees, Saffery Champness, St Catherine's Court, Berkeley Place, Clifton, Bristol BS8 1BQ *Tel.* 0117 915 1617

■ The Polonsky Foundation

CC NO 291143 **ESTABLISHED** 1985

WHERE FUNDING CAN BE GIVEN UK; Israel; USA; France; Italy.

WHO CAN BENEFIT Universities; arts and cultural institutions.

WHAT IS FUNDED Cultural heritage and digitisation (at major libraries and museums); education and research in the humanities and social sciences; innovation and excellence in the (performing) arts.

RANGE OF GRANTS Up to £784,000.

SAMPLE GRANTS Friends of Bezalel Academy of Arts (£784,100); The Van Leer Jerusalem Institute (£599,100); University of Oxford (£104,000); Aspen Music Festival and School (£60,900); Oxford Centre of Hebrew and Jewish Studies (£39,900); Consortium of European Research Libraries (£15,300).

FINANCES *Financial year end* 31/03/2020
Income £442,000 *Total grants* £3,420,000
Grants to organisations £3,420,000
Assets £15,200,000

TRUSTEES Dr Leonard Polonsky; Dr Georgette Bennett; Marc Polonsky; Hannah Whitney; Joshua-Marc Tanenbaum.

OTHER INFORMATION In 2019/20, 16 grants of £15,300 or more were awarded. Other grants to institutions totalled £317,700.

HOW TO APPLY The foundation does not accept unsolicited applications.

CONTACT DETAILS The Trustees, 8 Park Crescent, London W1B 1PG *Tel.* 020 7436 1997 *Website* https://polonskyfoundation.org

■ The Porta Pia 2012 Foundation

CC NO 1152582 **ESTABLISHED** 2013

WHERE FUNDING CAN BE GIVEN UK.

WHO CAN BENEFIT Registered charities.

WHAT IS FUNDED General charitable purposes; poverty relief; economic and community development and employment; recreation.

RANGE OF GRANTS Up to £22,500.

SAMPLE GRANTS Streetchild (£22,500); The Hope Foundation (£15,000); Carers Trust, Crisis and The Passage (£10,000 each); The Fostering Network and Why me? UK (£5,000 each).

FINANCES *Financial year end* 31/12/2019
Income £97,100 *Total grants* £148,000
Grants to organisations £148,000
Assets £3,080,000

TRUSTEES Helen O'Shea; James O'Shea; Joanne Sennitt.

OTHER INFORMATION Grants were awarded to 29 organisations during the year, of which 16 were of £3,000 or less. Grants were awarded for a wide range of causes.

HOW TO APPLY The 2019 accounts state that unsolicited applications to the foundation are considered at the trustees' quarterly meetings; however, 'most grants made are to a variety of charities of which the Trustees have prior and personal knowledge.' Contact the correspondent for further information.

CONTACT DETAILS The Trustees, c/o Investment Quorum Ltd, Guild Hall House, 85 Gresham Street, London EC2V 7NQ *Tel.* 020 7337 1390

■ The Portal Trust

CC NO 312425 **ESTABLISHED** 1748

WHERE FUNDING CAN BE GIVEN Camden, Greenwich, Hackney, Hammersmith and Fulham, Islington, Kensington and Chelsea, Lambeth, Lewisham, Newham, Southwark, Tower Hamlets, Wandsworth, Westminster and the City of London.

WHO CAN BENEFIT Charitable organisations; schools; individuals.

WHAT IS FUNDED Education. The trust's focus areas are: widening participation in further and higher education; truancy, exclusion and behaviour management; prisoners' education; new initiatives. Funding applications should benefit children and young people under the age of 25 who are residents of the named inner London boroughs and from a low-income or disadvantaged background.

WHAT IS NOT FUNDED Projects that do not meet a trust priority; supplementary schools or mother-tongue teaching; youth and community groups, or projects taking place in these settings; general fundraising campaigns or appeals; costs for equipment or salaries that are the statutory responsibility of education authorities; costs to substitute the withdrawal or reduction of statutory funding; costs for work or activities that have already taken place prior to the grant application; costs already covered by core funding or other grants; capital costs that are exclusively for the purchase, repair or furnishing of buildings, or the purchase of vehicles, computers, sports equipment or improvements to school grounds.

TYPE OF GRANT Project funding, capital costs, development funding, running programmes/ workshops, maintenance, core costs for schools. Funding may be available for up to three years.

RANGE OF GRANTS Generally up to £50,000.

SAMPLE GRANTS London College of Fashion (£200,000); St Mary's University (£100,000); Tutu Foundation (£50,000); British Exploring Society (£40,000); Film London (£34,300); East End Community Foundation (£20,000); Chelsea Academy Foundation (£15,000); Cripplegate Foundation (£10,000); London Music Fund (£6,000); Southbank Sinfonia (£3,000).

FINANCES *Financial year end* 31/03/2020 *Income* £7,260,000 *Total grants* £1,867,000 *Grants to organisations* £1,840,000 *Assets* £179,870,000

TRUSTEES Cllr Denise Jones; John Hall; David Hogben; Hon. Brian Barker; Paul Bloomfield; Revd Trevor Critchlow; Revd Laura Jorgensen; Jenny Moseley; Sophie Fernandes; Helen Folorunso.

OTHER INFORMATION In 2021 the foundation changed its name from the Sir John Cass's Foundation to The Portal Trust due to Sir John Cass's links with the slave trade.

HOW TO APPLY The trust operates a two-stage application process – an initial enquiry and a full application stage. At the time of writing (March 2021) the trust was not accepting any applications due to the COVID-19 pandemic – see the website for the current application process.

CONTACT DETAILS Megan Falck, Grants Manager, 31 Jewry Street, London EC3N 2EY *Tel.* 020 7480 5884 *Email* contactus@sirjohncass.org *Website* sirjohncassfoundation.com

■ The Portishead Nautical Trust

CC NO 228876 **ESTABLISHED** 1986

WHERE FUNDING CAN BE GIVEN Portishead, Bristol, North Somerset, South Gloucestershire and the South West.

WHO CAN BENEFIT Charitable organisations; individuals.

WHAT IS FUNDED Projects and activities to assist young people (under the age of 25) who need help due to deprivation, poverty, financial hardship, parental neglect, lack of control, or other misfortune.

WHAT IS NOT FUNDED The trust only considers applications that will benefit young people under the age of 25.

RANGE OF GRANTS Mostly £1,000 to £3,000.

SAMPLE GRANTS Portishead Youth Centre (£15,000); Carers Support Centre and Wheels Project (£3,000 each); Wellspring Counselling (£2,500); Bristol Old Vic Trust and Cruse Bereavement Care (£2,000 each); Self Injury Support Ltd (£1,500); Whizz-Kidz (£1,000).

FINANCES *Financial year end* 31/03/2020 *Income* £92,700 *Total grants* £83,500 *Grants to organisations* £75,300 *Assets* £1,990,000

TRUSTEES Martyn Cruse; Susan Haysom; Colin Crossman; Patricia Margerison; Peter Dingley-Brown; Anne McPherson; Conrad Woodhead.

OTHER INFORMATION Grants were awarded to 30 organisations during the year and grants totalling £8,200 were awarded to individuals. According to the 2019/20 accounts, The Portishead Youth Centre continued to be the trust's major beneficiary during the year.

HOW TO APPLY Applications can be made by email or by post. Application forms can be found on the trust's website. The trustees usually meet four times per annum.

CONTACT DETAILS Mrs E. Knight, Secretary, 108 High Street, Portishead, Bristol BS20 6AJ *Tel.* 01275 847463 *Email* portisheadnauticaltrust@gmail.com

■ The Portrack Charitable Trust

CC NO 266120 **ESTABLISHED** 1973

WHERE FUNDING CAN BE GIVEN England, Wales and Scotland.

WHO CAN BENEFIT Registered charitable organisations.

WHAT IS FUNDED Health; disability; the prevention and relief of poverty; overseas aid; the arts, culture, heritage and science; the environment; young people; older people.

WHAT IS NOT FUNDED Individuals; non-UK-registered charities.

RANGE OF GRANTS Mostly £1,000 to £10,000, with some larger grants.

SAMPLE GRANTS The Trussell Trust (£500,000); The Film and TV Charity and University College London Development Fund (£100,000 each); The Fishmongers' Company Charity and Medical Aid for Palestinians (£10,000 each); Community Law Advice Network (£5,000); Re-Cycle Bikes to Africa (£2,000); Scottish Autism (£1,000).

FINANCES *Financial year end* 05/04/2020 *Income* £9,300,000 *Total grants* £924,000 *Grants to organisations* £924,000 *Assets* £13,110,000

TRUSTEES John Jencks; Lily Jencks; Louisa Jencks.

OTHER INFORMATION Grants were made to 25 organisations during the year for a range of causes.

HOW TO APPLY At the time of writing (May 2021), the trust was not accepting new applications. Its Charity Commission record stated: 'May 2021: We have a backlog of applications to review and are not accepting any new ones. All correspondence by email please.'

CONTACT DETAILS Lucy Dare, Administrator, The Old Stable, 15A Huntingdon Street, London N1 1BU *Email* portrackcharitabletrust@gmail.com

■ Postcode Community Trust

OSCR NO SC044772 **ESTABLISHED** 2014

WHERE FUNDING CAN BE GIVEN Wales.

WHO CAN BENEFIT Registered charities; constituted community organisations such as CICs or CIOs; social enterprises; not-for-profit organisations.

WHAT IS FUNDED Mental well-being; participation in arts and sports; social welfare; supporting disadvantaged people; biodiversity and green space; the climate emergency and sustainability; access to the outdoors.

WHAT IS NOT FUNDED A comprehensive list of exclusions can be found on the trust's website and includes: individuals; statutory activities; nurseries, schools, colleges or universities; organisations with an annual income over £1 million.

TYPE OF GRANT Project funding; capital costs. Both for 12 months.

RANGE OF GRANTS From £250 to £20,000. Grants of more than £2,000 are for registered charities only.

SAMPLE GRANTS Venture Scotland (£20,000); Tintwistle Athletic FC (£2,000); Hornets Community Boxing Club (£1,300).

FINANCES *Financial year end* 31/12/2019 *Income* £8,700,000 *Total grants* £2,740,000 *Grants to organisations* £2,740,000 *Assets* £351,100

TRUSTEES Aidan Connolly; Michael Pratt; Judith Hills; Robert Flett; Elizabeth Tait.

OTHER INFORMATION During 2019, under the Community Grants Programme, 218 grants totalling £2.19 million were awarded across the following categories: community health and well-being (£1.05 million); reducing isolation (£628,800); arts and physical recreation (£512,800). A further £550,000 was awarded through the Magic Little Grants scheme through the Local Giving Foundation.

HOW TO APPLY There are several funding rounds each year, with deadlines detailed on the trust's website alongside guidance and tips for submissions. Applications can be made using the trust's online form.

CONTACT DETAILS The Trustees, 28 Charlotte Square, Edinburgh EH2 4ET *Tel.* 0131 322 9399 *Email* info@postcodecommunitytrust.org.uk *Website* www.postcodecommunitytrust.org.uk

■ Postcode Local Trust

OSCR NO SC045504 **ESTABLISHED** 2015

WHERE FUNDING CAN BE GIVEN The west of England.

WHO CAN BENEFIT Registered charities; constituted voluntary or community groups; CICs; CIOs; not-for-profit organisations; social enterprises.

WHAT IS FUNDED Mental well-being; participation in arts and sports; social welfare; supporting disadvantaged people; biodiversity and green space; the climate emergency and sustainability; access to the outdoors.

WHAT IS NOT FUNDED A comprehensive list of exclusions can be found on the trust's website and includes: individuals; statutory activities; colleges or universities; organisations with annual income over £1 million.

TYPE OF GRANT Project funding; capital costs. Both for 12 months.

RANGE OF GRANTS From £250 to £20,000. Grants of more than £2,000 are for registered charities only.

SAMPLE GRANTS The Barlow Institute (£20,000); Wimbledon and Putney Commons Conservators (£3,000); Make It Happen Birkenhead Ltd (£1,720).

FINANCES *Financial year end* 31/12/2019 *Income* £8,720,000 *Total grants* £2,930,000 *Grants to organisations* £2,930,000 *Assets* £260,500

TRUSTEES Aidan Connolly; Michael Pratt; Judith Hills; Robert Flett; Elizabeth Tait.

OTHER INFORMATION During 2019, under the Community Grants Programme, 213 grants totalling £2.22 million were awarded across the following categories: community access to green space (£1.42 million); biodiversity and green spaces (£499,700); climate change and sustainability (£301,200). A further £562,000 was awarded to 489 schools through the Local Schools Nature Grants scheme.

HOW TO APPLY There are several funding rounds each year, with deadlines detailed on the trust's website alongside guidance and tips for submissions. Applications are made using the trust's online form.

CONTACT DETAILS The Trustees, 28 Charlotte Square, Edinburgh EH2 4ET *Tel.* 0131 322 9388 *Email* info@postcodelocaltrust.org.uk *Website* www.postcodelocaltrust.org.uk

■ Postcode Society Trust (formerly Postcode Dream Trust)

OSCR NO SC044911 **ESTABLISHED** 2014

WHERE FUNDING CAN BE GIVEN The south of England.

WHO CAN BENEFIT Registered charities; constituted community organisations such as CICs or CIOs; social enterprises; not-for-profit organisations.

WHAT IS FUNDED Mental well-being; participation in arts and sports; social welfare; supporting disadvantaged people; biodiversity and green space; the climate emergency and sustainability; access to the outdoors.

WHAT IS NOT FUNDED A comprehensive list of exclusions can be found on the trust's website and includes: individuals; statutory activities; nurseries, schools, colleges or universities; organisations with annual income over £1 million.

TYPE OF GRANT Project funding; core costs.

RANGE OF GRANTS £500 to £20,000.

SAMPLE GRANTS Ellen MacArthur Foundation, London Wildlife Trust and The Wildlife Trust BCN (£1 million each).

FINANCES *Financial year end* 31/12/2019 *Income* £9,100,000 *Total grants* £3,000,000 *Grants to organisations* £3,000,000 *Assets* £4,180,000

TRUSTEES Aidan Connolly; Michael Pratt; Judith Hills; Robert Flett; Elizabeth Tait.

OTHER INFORMATION In 2019, under the previous grant-making policy, the trust awarded grants of £1 million each to three organisations working in the area of environmental conservation and protection.

HOW TO APPLY There are several funding rounds each year, with deadlines detailed on the trust's website alongside guidance and tips for submissions. Applications are made using the trust's online form.

CONTACT DETAILS The Trustees, 28 Charlotte Square, Edinburgh EH2 4ET *Tel.* 0131 322 9430 *Email* info@postcodesocietytrust.org.uk *Website* https://www.postcodesocietytrust.org.uk

■ The Mary Potter Convent Hospital Trust

CC NO 1078525 **ESTABLISHED** 1999

WHERE FUNDING CAN BE GIVEN Nottinghamshire.

WHO CAN BENEFIT Charitable organisations; CICs; social enterprises; schools; universities; hospitals; hospices; PTAs; religious bodies/institutions; local authorities; individuals.

WHAT IS FUNDED Medical causes and healthcare.

TYPE OF GRANT Capital costs; core and revenue costs; seed funding; start-up funding; project funding.

RANGE OF GRANTS Up to £10,000.

SAMPLE GRANTS Portland College (£10,000); The Friary (£7,000); Rainbows Hospice (£5,500); CLIC Sergeant, Macmillan Cancer and University of Nottingham (£5,000 each).

FINANCES *Financial year end* 30/06/2020 *Income* £144,500 *Total grants* £184,300 *Grants to organisations* £158,000 *Assets* £3,460,000

TRUSTEES Chris Bain; Sister Jeanette Connell; Sister Anne Haugh; Mervyn Jones; Martin Witherspoon; Shaun Finn; Aidan Goulding; Godfrey Archer; Simon Clunie; Margaret Hollingworth.

OTHER INFORMATION During 2019/20, the trust supported 16 organisations. Only organisations that received grants of over £5,000 were listed as beneficiaries in the charity's accounts. Grants of under £5,000 totalled £18,000 and were awarded to six organisations.

HOW TO APPLY Apply in writing to the correspondent. Unsuccessful applicants will not be notified.

CONTACT DETAILS Martin Witherspoon, Trustee, c/o Massers Solicitors, Rossell House, Tudor Square, West Bridgford, Nottingham, Nottinghamshire NG2 6BT *Tel.* 0115 851 1603 *Email* martinw@massers.co.uk

■ David and Elaine Potter Foundation

CC NO 1078217 **ESTABLISHED** 1999

WHERE FUNDING CAN BE GIVEN UK and overseas, particularly South Africa.

WHO CAN BENEFIT Registered charities; educational organisations.

WHAT IS FUNDED Education and training; human rights; civil society; the arts; general charitable purposes.

WHAT IS NOT FUNDED Individuals; CICs; retrospective costs; full economic costs for universities; political organisations; clinical trials; religious organisations that work only for the benefit of members of their own religion; building or rebuilding schools; individual schools or school projects; school equipment or scaling up projects; civic education/citizenship education programmes.

TYPE OF GRANT Core/revenue costs; project funding; unrestricted funding.

RANGE OF GRANTS £5,000 to £150,000.

SAMPLE GRANTS Trust for the Bureau of Investigative Journalism (£150,000); University of Cape Town (£129,000); Numeric – Bluestream Education Trust (£74,900); Philharmonia Orchestra (£50,000); Transparency International UK (£45,000); Performa (£30,000); Stuart Hall Foundation (£20,000); One to One Children's Fund (£10,000); Royal Court Theatre (£5,000).

FINANCES *Financial year end* 31/12/2019 *Income* £526,400 *Total grants* £1,010,000 *Grants to organisations* £1,010,000 *Assets* £17,480,000

TRUSTEES Dr David Potter; Dr Elaine Potter; Michael Polonsky; Michael Langley; Samuel Potter.

OTHER INFORMATION In 2019 the foundation awarded 24 grants, totalling £1.01 million.

HOW TO APPLY Applications are by invitation only: unsolicited applications are not accepted. The website notes that organisations that believe their work may align with the foundation's focuses should contact the foundation by email to discuss their potential eligibility.

CONTACT DETAILS The Trustees, 5 Welbeck Street, London W1G 9YQ *Tel.* 020 3915 9283 *Email* info@potterfoundation.com *Website* www.potterfoundation.com

■ Poundland Foundation

CC NO 1194291 **ESTABLISHED** 2021

WHERE FUNDING CAN BE GIVEN UK.

WHO CAN BENEFIT Registered charities; constituted groups or clubs; CICs.

WHAT IS FUNDED Community services and development; children's sports.

SAMPLE GRANTS A list of beneficiaries was not included in the annual report and accounts.

FINANCES *Total grants* £825,000 *Grants to organisations* £825,000

TRUSTEES Simon Wells; Mark Hanton; Olivia McLoughlin; Mark Pym; Roger Wendt; Adrian Holder; Sharon Jackson; Laura Yonish; Emma Pearson; Ben Jenner.

OTHER INFORMATION The foundation was registered with the Charity Commission in April 2021; therefore, full financial information was not available. At the time of writing (June 2021) the foundation's website stated that it planned to distribute £825,000 in cash grants over the next year. The foundation's first grant scheme provided equipment grants of up to £750 for sports clubs/organisations supporting children up to the age of 18.

HOW TO APPLY Apply via the foundation's website.

CONTACT DETAILS The Trustees, Poundland CSC, Midland Road, Walsall WS1 3TX *Tel.* 0121 568 7000 *Email* foundation@poundland.co.uk or use the contact form on the website. *Website* https://poundlandfoundation.org.uk

■ Power to Change Trust

CC NO 1159982 **ESTABLISHED** 2015

WHERE FUNDING CAN BE GIVEN England.

WHO CAN BENEFIT Community businesses.

WHAT IS FUNDED Supporting people to start and grow community businesses to revive local assets, protect services and address local needs.

TYPE OF GRANT Capital costs; project costs; salaries; professional fees; seed funding; community shares.

RANGE OF GRANTS Typically up to £10,000.

SAMPLE GRANTS Previous beneficiaries have included: Jubilee Pool Penzance (£300,000); ASH Yorkshire CIC (£297,000); Sutton Community Farm (£66,000); Impact Hub Brixton

(£32,500); University of Liverpool (£29,500); Litherland REMYCA F.C. (£14,700); Salford Hope (£10,000); Incredible Aquagarden Todmorden (£5,000); Garibaldi Pub – Redhill and Hildersham Community Pub (£2,500 each).

FINANCES *Financial year end* 31/12/2019 *Income* £1,600,000 *Total grants* £20,940,000 *Grants to organisations* £20,940,000 *Assets* £67,620,000

TRUSTEE Power to Change Trustee Ltd.

OTHER INFORMATION In 2019 the trust made grants totalling £20.94 million, allocated across several funding programmes. Consult the website for up-to-date information on current funding programmes.

HOW TO APPLY Consult the trust's helpful website for information about each specific grant programme.

CONTACT DETAILS The Grants Team, The Clarence Centre, 6 St George's Circus, London SE1 6FE *Tel.* 020 3857 7270 *Email* info@thepowertochange.org.uk *Website* www.thepowertochange.org.uk

■ Premierquote Ltd

CC NO 801957 **ESTABLISHED** 1985

WHERE FUNDING CAN BE GIVEN UK.

WHO CAN BENEFIT Jewish organisations and schools.

WHAT IS FUNDED The advancement of the Orthodox Jewish faith; the relief of poverty.

SAMPLE GRANTS A list of grant recipients is detailed in a separate publication available from the charity's registered office address (PO Box 7010, 2nd Floor, 38 Warren Street, London, W1A 2EA).

FINANCES *Financial year end* 30/09/2019 *Income* £1,109,000 *Total grants* £602,400 *Grants to organisations* £602,400 *Assets* £10,153,000

TRUSTEES Henry Last; Leah Last; Morris Wiesenfield.

OTHER INFORMATION The 2018/19 accounts were the most recent available from the Charity Commission at the time of writing (May 2021).

HOW TO APPLY Contact the correspondent for further information.

CONTACT DETAILS Henry Last, Trustee, 18 Green Walk, London NW4 2AJ *Tel.* 020 8203 0665

■ Premishlaner Charitable Trust

CC NO 1046945 **ESTABLISHED** 1995

WHERE FUNDING CAN BE GIVEN UK; Israel.

WHO CAN BENEFIT Jewish organisations.

WHAT IS FUNDED The advancement of Orthodox Jewish education and faith.

RANGE OF GRANTS Up to £26,000.

SAMPLE GRANTS J and R Charitable Trust (£26,000); B F O Rinas Hachesed (£25,000); Amud Hatzokah (£18,000); Asser Bishvil Foundation (£12,000); A Time and Friends of Ediah Charedies (£5,000 each).

FINANCES *Financial year end* 30/06/2020 *Income* £183,600 *Total grants* £191,800 *Grants to organisations* £191,800 *Assets* £357,500

TRUSTEES C. Freudenberger; C. Margulies.

OTHER INFORMATION Only beneficiaries of grants of £5,000 and above were listed in the accounts (nine organisations). Grants of less than £5,000 totalled £65,800.

HOW TO APPLY Contact the correspondent for information regarding the application process.

CONTACT DETAILS The Trustees, 186 Lordship Road, London N16 5ES *Tel.* 020 8802 4449

■ The Pret Foundation

CC NO 1050195 **ESTABLISHED** 1995

WHERE FUNDING CAN BE GIVEN UK, in communities local to Pret A Manger shops.

WHO CAN BENEFIT Registered charities.

WHAT IS FUNDED Homelessness; social welfare; food poverty; education, training and employment.

TYPE OF GRANT Project costs; pay for support workers, rent, course supplies, counselling and drop-in centres.

RANGE OF GRANTS Up to £20,000.

SAMPLE GRANTS The 999 Club (£20,000); London City Mission (£13,100); Bethany Christian Trust (£10,000); Breaking Barriers (£7,500); Action Homeless – Leicester (£6,300); Peterborough Soup Kitchen (£5,200); The People's Kitchen (£5,000).

FINANCES *Financial year end* 31/12/2018 *Income* £2,160,000 *Total grants* £662,800 *Grants to organisations* £662,800 *Assets* £491,700

TRUSTEES Clive Schlee; Andrea Wareham; Valerie Cuminet; Pano Christou; Dilys Winterkorn; Dulcie McDermott.

OTHER INFORMATION The 2018 accounts were the latest available at the time of writing (June 2021). Grants were awarded to 201 organisations during the year, of which 147 were for under £5,000. Only beneficiaries of grants of £5,000 and above were listed in the accounts. In addition to grants, food donations totalled £29,400 and equipment donations totalled £55,100.

HOW TO APPLY Contact the correspondent for further information.

CONTACT DETAILS The Trustees, 10 Bressenden Place, London SW1E 5DH *Tel.* 07584 213354 *Email* pretfoundation.donations@pret.com *Website* https://www.pret.co.uk/en-GB/the-pret-foundation

■ Price Parry Charitable Trust

CC NO 1178567 **ESTABLISHED** 2018

WHERE FUNDING CAN BE GIVEN Merseyside, with a preference for the Wirral.

WHO CAN BENEFIT Registered charities.

WHAT IS FUNDED General charitable purposes. Preference is given towards: social welfare; the alleviation of poverty; the support of various medical fields; older people; the environment; supporting disadvantaged people through community projects; and disaster relief (worldwide).

RANGE OF GRANTS £500 to £5,000.

SAMPLE GRANTS Claire House and Sefton Children (£5,000 each); Age UK Wirral (£3,000); Birkenhead Development Trust (£2,500); Bluecoat Display Centre and Breckfield Centre (£2,000 each); Neuromuscular Centre (£1,000); Birkenhead YMCA (£470).

FINANCES *Financial year end* 30/09/2019 *Income* £59,700 *Total grants* £65,300 *Grants to organisations* £65,300 *Assets* £1,590,000

TRUSTEES Roy Morris; Barbara Pedersen; Bernard Kenny.

OTHER INFORMATION The 2018/19 accounts were the latest available at the time of writing (June 2021). Grants were awarded to 22 organisations during the year.

HOW TO APPLY Application forms can be downloaded from the Community Action Wirral website. The trustees meet twice a year to review grant applications; however, they will consider applications prior to such meetings if they receive urgent requests for funding.

CONTACT DETAILS Elaine Clayton, Administrator, Rathbone Investment Management, Port of Liverpool Building, Pier Head, Liverpool L3 1NW *Tel.* 0151 236 6666 *Email* elaine.clayton@rathbones.com *Website* https://communityactionwirral.org.uk/the-price-parry-charitable-trust/application-form-price-parry-charitable-trust

■ Sir John Priestman Charity Trust

CC NO 209397 **ESTABLISHED** 1931

WHERE FUNDING CAN BE GIVEN Sunderland; County Durham; churches in the county of York.

WHO CAN BENEFIT Charitable organisations; churches; schools.

WHAT IS FUNDED Social welfare; older people; education; hospitals and convalescent homes; nurses; social welfare; upkeep of Church of England institutions, including the purchase of organs.

TYPE OF GRANT Project costs; equipment and building costs.

RANGE OF GRANTS Up to £15,000.

SAMPLE GRANTS Outward Bound (£12,200); Riccall PCC Fabric Fund (£10,000); The Sunderland Orphanage and Educational Foundation (£8,500); St Michael's Heighington PCC (£6,000); Motor Neurone Disease Association (£4,000); Lambton Street Youth Centre (£3,300); The Children Charity (£1,500); St Andrew's Sea Scout Group (£750).

FINANCES *Financial year end* 31/12/2019 *Income* £556,200 *Total grants* £430,800 *Grants to organisations* £430,800 *Assets* £14,900,000

TRUSTEES Peter Taylor; Timothy Norton; Thomas Greenwell; Jean Majer.

OTHER INFORMATION Only in special circumstances are grants awarded outside the specified geographical area or to individuals. A number of charities are supported by way of annual grants.

HOW TO APPLY Contact the correspondent for details on how to apply. The trustees meet on a quarterly basis to consider applications and award grants.

CONTACT DETAILS The Trustees, 19 John Street, Sunderland, Tyne and Wear SR1 1JG *Tel.* 0191 567 4857

■ The Primrose Trust

CC NO 800049 **ESTABLISHED** 1986

WHERE FUNDING CAN BE GIVEN UK.

WHO CAN BENEFIT Registered charities.

WHAT IS FUNDED General charitable purposes, with a strong preference for animal welfare.

TYPE OF GRANT Core costs; capital costs; project funding.

RANGE OF GRANTS £5,000 to £45,000.

SAMPLE GRANTS Animals Asia (£45,000); Langford Trust for Animal Health and Welfare (£30,000); Free the Bears (£25,000); Animal Health Trust and Coppershell Farm Animal Sanctuary (£20,000 each); British Hen Welfare Trust and UK Boston Terrier Rescue (£10,000 each); Badger Trust – Sussex and Goatacre Farm for Animal Health and Welfare (£5,000 each).

FINANCES *Financial year end* 05/04/2020 *Income* £159,000 *Total grants* £170,000 *Grants to organisations* £170,000 *Assets* £3,900,000

TRUSTEES Malcolm Clark; Susan Boyes-Korkis.

HOW TO APPLY The trustees request written applications, to be submitted to the registered office. The trustees meet annually to consider applications.

CONTACT DETAILS The Trustees, c/o Deloitte LLP, 5 Callaghan Square, Cardiff CF10 5BT *Tel.* 029 2026 4257 *Email* lham@deloitte.co.uk

■ The Prince of Wales's Charitable Foundation

CC NO 1127255 **ESTABLISHED** 1979

WHERE FUNDING CAN BE GIVEN UK.

WHO CAN BENEFIT UK-registered not-for-profit organisations that have been active for at least two years.

WHAT IS FUNDED Heritage and conservation; education; health and well-being; social inclusion; the environment; the countryside; the arts; religion; animal welfare; social welfare; older people; disaster relief.

WHAT IS NOT FUNDED Individuals; public bodies; organisations that mainly distribute grants to other organisations; organisations that are looking to support similar projects delivered by any of The Prince's of Wales's charities; organisations with an income of more than £1 million; organisations with political associations or interests; projects that require capital expenditure, with the exception of community-based, religion-related and heritage restoration projects.

TYPE OF GRANT Core costs; project funding; strategic funding.

RANGE OF GRANTS Small grants of up to £5,000 and major grants of over £5,000.

SAMPLE GRANTS Rare Breeds Survival Trust (£128,400); Bumblebee Conservation Trust (£105,000); City Hospice Growing Together Project (£1,500).

FINANCES *Financial year end* 31/03/2020 *Income* £13,910,000 *Total grants* £5,920,000 *Grants to organisations* £5,920,000 *Assets* £9,770,000

TRUSTEES Sir Ian Cheshire; Clive Alderton; Dame Julie Moore; Dame Louise Casey; Kristin Rechberger; The Hon. Sarah Jane Butler-Sloss.

OTHER INFORMATION During 2019/20, grants totalling £5.92 million were awarded to 252 charities. At the time of writing (June 2021) the foundation had temporarily closed its small grant programme; however, the website stated that it would be reopening in the summer. Check the foundation's website for the latest information. The foundation only listed a small number of beneficiaries in its 2019/20 annual report, but a full list of projects supported is available on the foundation's website.

HOW TO APPLY For the small grants programme, an online application form and further guidance are available from the foundation's website. The programme is rolling, so applications can be made at any time; however, it is stated that applications submitted one month before the Small Grant Committee meeting will be considered at the next meeting. The committee meets four times a year, usually in February, May, July and October. The major grants programme is not open to unsolicited applications.

CONTACT DETAILS Small Grant Committee, Clarence House, St James's, London SW1A 1BA *Tel.* 020 7930 4832 *Email* Use the contact form on the foundation's website. *Website* https://www.pwcf.org.uk

■ The Prince's Countryside Fund

CC NO 1136077 **ESTABLISHED** 2010

WHERE FUNDING CAN BE GIVEN UK.

WHO CAN BENEFIT Community organisations; charities; CIC's; community benefit societies; not-for-profit organisations; companies limited by guarantee; social enterprises; unincorporated associations.

WHAT IS FUNDED Projects that support the sustainability of British farming rural communities and the countryside. The three goals of the fund are: to improve the prospects of viability for family farm businesses; to support aid delivery in emergencies and build resilience; and to sustain rural communities and drive economic vibrancy.

WHAT IS NOT FUNDED The charity will not support: individuals; private businesses; statutory bodies; for-profit businesses; religious bodies where the funding will be used for religious purposes; political organisations where the funding will be used for political purposes; projects where planning permission has not be granted at the time of applying; retrospective costs; the purchase of buildings or land; planning permission, surveys or feasibility studies; care farms; projects that displace existing government funding streams; projects which do not demonstrate sufficient public benefit.

TYPE OF GRANT Project and resource funding; capital costs (equipment); core costs.

RANGE OF GRANTS Up to £50,000.

SAMPLE GRANTS Plunkett Foundation (£40,000); Young Farmers Club of Ulster (£30,000); Citizens Advice County Durham and Just Farmers (£20,000 each); Yorkshire Rural Support Network (£10,000); Lincolnshire Rural Support (£3,800); Barnard Castle Farmers Market (£2,000); KPT Development Trust (£1,000).

FINANCES *Financial year end* 31/03/2020
Income £1,510,000 *Total grants* £567,600
Grants to organisations £567,600
Assets £1,160,000

TRUSTEES Lord Curry of Kirkharle; Mark Duddridge; Sara Bennison; David Fursdon; Rob Collins; Lord Jamie Lindsay; Steve McLean; John Wilkinson; Elizabeth Buchanan; Janet McCollum; Baroness Kate Rock; Heather Hancock; Edwin Booth; Meurig Raymond.

OTHER INFORMATION During 2019/20, 31 grants were awarded. Emergency funding totalling £59,000 was provided in response to flooding during the year. The charity will consider matched funding.

HOW TO APPLY Applications should be made online through the charity's website. Check the website for updates on when the next funding round will open.

CONTACT DETAILS Beverly Davies, Grants Manager, 137 Shepherdess Walk, London N1 7RQ *Tel.* 020 7566 6672 *Email* bdavies@countrysidefund.org.uk *Website* www.princescountrysidefund.org.uk

■ The Princess Anne's Charities

CC NO 277814 **ESTABLISHED** 1979

WHERE FUNDING CAN BE GIVEN UK.

WHO CAN BENEFIT Registered charities.

WHAT IS FUNDED Social welfare; medical causes; the armed forces; children and young people; the environment and wildlife.

WHAT IS NOT FUNDED Individuals.

SAMPLE GRANTS Previous beneficiaries have included: Butler Trust, the Canal Museum Trust Cranfield Trust, Dogs Trust, Dorothy House Foundation, Durrell Wildlife Conservation Trust, the Evelina Children's Hospital Appeal, Farms for City Children, Farrer and Co. Charitable Trust, Fire Services National Benevolent Fund, the Home Farm Trust, Intensive Care Society and International League for the Protection of Horses.

FINANCES *Financial year end* 05/04/2020
Income £235,100 *Total grants* £189,300
Grants to organisations £189,300
Assets £6,600,000

TRUSTEES Vice Admiral Sir Tim Laurence; Sally Tennant; Christopher Morgan; Julian Vaughan Smith.

OTHER INFORMATION Grants were made to 34 organisations during 2019/20. Grants were distributed within the following categories: social welfare (£79,000); children and young people (£44,000); the armed forces (£28,000); medical causes (£24,300); the environment and wildlife (£14,000).

HOW TO APPLY Apply in writing to the correspondent. Applications are considered by the trustees at their meetings.

CONTACT DETAILS The Trustees, c/o Farrer and Co. LLP, 66 Lincoln's Inn Fields, London WC2A 3LH *Tel.* 020 7024 4199 *Email* charles.davies@royal.uk

■ The Priory Foundation

CC NO 295919 **ESTABLISHED** 1986

WHERE FUNDING CAN BE GIVEN UK and overseas. In the UK, preference is given to Essex and Hertfordshire.

WHO CAN BENEFIT Registered charities; individuals; schools; amateur sports clubs.

WHAT IS FUNDED General charitable purposes, in particular: sport; mental health; education; overseas relief.

RANGE OF GRANTS Up to £95,000.

SAMPLE GRANTS Saracens Sport Foundation (£95,500); Saracens Multi Academy Trust (£30,000); Saracens Hertfordshire Cricket League (£20,300); Big Yellow Think Project and Joining Jack (£10,000 each); Theo Walker Fund (£2,600); Mandy Fisher Foundation (£2,300); Sherborne Storm Swimming Club (£2,000); Mill Hill Bowling Club (£1,100).

FINANCES *Financial year end* 31/12/2019
Income £218,600 *Total grants* £197,400
Grants to organisations £173,700
Assets £3,270,000

TRUSTEES David Poutney; Nigel Wray; Lucy Mercey; Gordon Banks.

OTHER INFORMATION During 2019, grants were awarded within the following areas: sport; mental health; education; overseas poverty relief. Grants were made to nine organisations, totalling £173,700 and to three individuals, totalling £23,700.

HOW TO APPLY Apply in writing to the correspondent. Details of the eligibility criteria can be obtained by contacting the foundation.

CONTACT DETAILS The Trustees, Flat 3, Grace Court, Totteridge Green, London N20 8PY *Tel.* 020 8445 7012

■ Prison Service Charity Fund

CC NO 801678 **ESTABLISHED** 1989

WHERE FUNDING CAN BE GIVEN UK.

WHO CAN BENEFIT Charitable organisations; individuals. Applications must be sponsored by Prison Service staff who are also fundraising for the cause.

WHAT IS FUNDED Medical treatment and equipment.

WHAT IS NOT FUNDED Organisations or individuals outside the UK.

TYPE OF GRANT One-off donations.

RANGE OF GRANTS Typically up to £2,000.

SAMPLE GRANTS Hannah Martin Appeal (£2,000); Tree of Hope (£1,500); Lincs and Notts Air Ambulance, Lymphoma Action and Teenage Cancer Trust (£1,000 each); Contact the Elderly, Macmillan Cancer Support, Scope and Weymouth Veterans Hub (£500 each); Alder Hey Children's Charity (£250); Royal British Legion (£100); Zoë's Place (£50); Alzheimer's Association (£16).

FINANCES *Financial year end* 31/12/2019 *Income* £98,700 *Total grants* £98,700 *Grants to organisations* £98,700 *Assets* £972,700

TRUSTEES Bob Howard; Nevill Joseph; Kenneth Wingfield; John White; Michael Flynn; Denise Bolton; Paul Blinstone.

OTHER INFORMATION In 2019, 131 funding appeals were received from a total of 49 organisations.

HOW TO APPLY Applications are only accepted from members of the Prison Service staff. Application forms are available from the charity's website.

CONTACT DETAILS Bob Howard, Secretary, 8 The Lynxway, Liverpool, Merseyside L12 3HR *Tel.* 0151 228 7462 *Email* bob@pscf.co.uk *Website* www.prisonservicecharityfund.co.uk

■ The Privy Purse Charitable Trust

CC NO 296079 **ESTABLISHED** 1987

WHERE FUNDING CAN BE GIVEN UK and overseas.

WHO CAN BENEFIT Charities of which the Queen is a patron; ecclesiastical organisations associated with the Queen; national and international disaster relief.

WHAT IS FUNDED General charitable purposes; ecclesiastical causes; national and international disasters.

TYPE OF GRANT Core costs.

RANGE OF GRANTS Up to £65,000.

SAMPLE GRANTS St James's Palace Chapel Royal Choir (£123,000); Sandringham Group of Parishes (£65,100); Hampton Court Palace (£52,700); Windsor Great Park (£46,700); St James's Place (£25,700); Australian Red Cross – bushfires (£25,000).

FINANCES *Financial year end* 31/03/2020 *Income* £795,800 *Total grants* £600,700 *Grants to organisations* £600,700 *Assets* £4,600,000

TRUSTEES Sir Michael Stevens; Sir Edward Young; Jane Graham.

OTHER INFORMATION The trust awarded grants to organisations within the following categories: ecclesiastical (£217,300); education (£126,000); other (£257,400). Only organisations that received grants of over £20,000 were listed as beneficiaries in the trust's accounts. The trust awards an annual grant to St James's Palace Chapel Royal Choir.

HOW TO APPLY The trust does not accept unsolicited applications and only awards grants to charities of which the Queen is a patron.

CONTACT DETAILS The Trustees, Privy Purse Office, Buckingham Palace, London SW1A 1AA *Tel.* 020 7930 4832 *Email* mike.stevens@royal.uk

■ The Professional Footballers' Association Charity

CC NO 1150458 **ESTABLISHED** 2013

WHERE FUNDING CAN BE GIVEN UK.

WHO CAN BENEFIT Registered charities; sports organisations; individuals.

WHAT IS FUNDED Education on the development and social impact of football; sport, recreation and leisure facilities; equality and the elimination of discrimination; physical health; social welfare. Funding is also given towards the education, health and welfare of professional footballers, former professional footballers and young people training to become professional footballers.

TYPE OF GRANT Capital costs; development funding; project funding; strategic funding.

RANGE OF GRANTS Grants to organisations range from £5,000 to £3 million.

SAMPLE GRANTS Football Scholarship Funding (£1.64 million); Football Conference Community (£1.2 million); NHS Charities Together (£1 million); Sporting Chance and The Premier League PFA Community Fund (£400,000 each); Fairplay Awards (£15,000); People's History Museum (£5,000).

FINANCES *Financial year end* 30/06/2020 *Income* £20,460,000 *Total grants* £11,010,000 *Grants to organisations* £8,080,000 *Assets* £61,900,000

TRUSTEES Gordon Taylor; Darren Wilson; Brendon Batson; Garth Crooks; Gareth Griffiths; Jacqueline Ann Dishman; Monica Shafaq.

OTHER INFORMATION During 2019/20, grants to organisations totalled £8.08 million. Grants were also awarded to 737 individuals, totalling £1.07 million, and grants totalling £1.86 million were made on behalf of individuals to third-party organisations.

HOW TO APPLY Apply in writing to the correspondent. The Professional Football Association's website states: 'Our corporate social responsibility goals focus heavily on using football to improve wider society, so the organisations we choose are usually sport-related. However, we are passionate about many good causes, and look to support organisations that resonate with our values as often as possible.'

CONTACT DETAILS The Trustees, 20 Oxford Court, Bishopsgate, Manchester M2 3WQ *Tel.* 0161 236 0575 *Email* info@thepfa.co.uk or community@thepfa.com *Website* https://www.thepfa.com

■ The Progress Foundation

CC NO 1123219 **ESTABLISHED** 2008

WHERE FUNDING CAN BE GIVEN UK, with a strong preference for Greater London.

WHO CAN BENEFIT Registered charities; voluntary organisations; social enterprises.

WHAT IS FUNDED Young people (normally those aged 14 to 21) who are not in employment, education or training (NEET), or who are at risk of becoming so.

WHAT IS NOT FUNDED Individuals; organisations that promote a particular religious belief, unless the work is not for religious purposes and meets the foundation's funding guidelines; medical organisations; replacing or subsidising statutory funding.

TYPE OF GRANT Project funding; core costs; development funding.

RANGE OF GRANTS Up to £25,000 but typically between £10,000 and £15,000. Larger grants may be made; however, these grants are not open to applications.

SAMPLE GRANTS Jamie's Farm and Resurgo (£60,000 each); Body and Soul, Redthread and Refugee Council (£20,000 each); Mosaic Clubhouse Brixton (£18,000); Social Enterprise Academy (£17,500); ReachOut (£15,000); Vauxhall City Farm (£10,000).

FINANCES *Financial year end* 31/03/2020 *Income* £168,700 *Total grants* £332,900 *Grants to organisations* £332,900 *Assets* £2,350,000

TRUSTEES Roger Pilgrim; Nadine Majaro; Nigel Hamway.

OTHER INFORMATION The foundation states that it typically supports up to five new projects or organisations each year. During 2019/20, grants were made to 12 organisations. A total of £132,900 was awarded through the main grants programme, £80,000 was awarded through the core grants programme and £120,000 was awarded through the emergency grants programme towards the COVID-19 response.

HOW TO APPLY Application forms and details of application deadlines are available on the foundation's website. The trustees meet three times a year to consider grants, usually in March, May and September. Applications made outside the set times will not be accepted.

CONTACT DETAILS The Trustees, c/o Trust Department, NQP Ltd, 22 Chancery Lane, London WC2A 1LS *Email* Use the contact form on the foundation's website. *Website* www.progressuk.org

■ Prostate Cancer UK

CC NO 1005541 **ESTABLISHED** 1991

WHERE FUNDING CAN BE GIVEN UK.

WHO CAN BENEFIT Universities; NHS sites; research institutions.

WHAT IS FUNDED Prostate cancer research; education; training; campaigning.

TYPE OF GRANT Research; project funding.

RANGE OF GRANTS Typically up to £1.5 million.

SAMPLE GRANTS University of Oxford (£1.42 million); The Institute of Cancer Research (£1.22 million); University of Strathclyde (£553,000); Imperial College London (£405,000); Royal Marsden Hospital (£341,000); University of Ulster (£208,000).

FINANCES *Financial year end* 31/03/2020 *Income* £35,860,000 *Total grants* £6,480,000 *Grants to organisations* £6,480,000 *Assets* £31,190,000

TRUSTEES Prof. Jonathan Waxman; Lynne Robb; Andrew Mitchell; Prof. David Neal; Prof. Martin Roland; Charles Packshaw; Michael Tye; Prof. Sara Faithful; Simon Hammett; Marion Leslie; Simon Peck; Henry Obi; Kenneth Towle; Samia al Qadhi.

OTHER INFORMATION In 2019/20, grants totalling £6.48 million were awarded to 12 organisations, mainly universities. The charity's updated research strategy focuses on three key areas: better treatment, better diagnosis and smarter data.

HOW TO APPLY Grants are announced on the charity's website and its Twitter account for prostate cancer professionals. Each grant-making programme has specific guidelines and deadline dates; check the charity's website for further information.

CONTACT DETAILS The Research Team, Fourth Floor, The Counting House, 53 Tooley Street, London SE1 2QN *Tel.* 020 3310 7000 *Email* info@prostatecanceruk.org *Website* www.prostatecanceruk.org

■ The Puebla Charitable Trust

CC NO 290055 **ESTABLISHED** 1984

WHERE FUNDING CAN BE GIVEN Worldwide.

WHO CAN BENEFIT Charitable organisations.

WHAT IS FUNDED Community development initiatives; social welfare.

WHAT IS NOT FUNDED Individuals.

TYPE OF GRANT Up to three years.

RANGE OF GRANTS Up to £30,000.

SAMPLE GRANTS Survivors Fund (£30,000); ADD International and South West London Law Centres (£20,000 each); Hamlin Fistula (£7,500).

FINANCES *Financial year end* 05/04/2020 *Income* £90,800 *Total grants* £77,500 *Grants to organisations* £77,500 *Assets* £2,580,000

TRUSTEES Justin Phipps; Martin Penrose; John Moore.

OTHER INFORMATION During 2019/20 grants were awarded to four organisations. Funding commitments are often made for a period of three years.

HOW TO APPLY Apply in writing to the correspondent. The trustees are unable to acknowledge applications.

CONTACT DETAILS John Moore, Trustee, 18 Hyde Gardens, Cardinal House, Eastbourne, East Sussex BN21 4PT *Tel.* 01323 431200 *Email* Puebla@p-p.uk

■ The Purey Cust Trust CIO

CC NO 1159079 **ESTABLISHED** 1950

WHERE FUNDING CAN BE GIVEN York.

WHO CAN BENEFIT Registered charities; organisations; individuals (only through third-party organisations); Beneficiaries must be located in or around the city of York.

WHAT IS FUNDED Health; disability; mental health and well-being; health education; medical equipment.

WHAT IS NOT FUNDED Core costs; building projects.

TYPE OF GRANT One-off; equipment; service provision.

RANGE OF GRANTS Up to £10,000.

SAMPLE GRANTS Home-Start York (£10,000); Children's Heart Surgery Fund (£10,000); Accessible Arts and Media (£7,500); Action for Elders (£5,000); Guide Dogs (£3,300); York Sharks Wheelchair Basketball Club (£2,500); Carr Infant School (£680); TOGETHER (£100).

FINANCES *Financial year end* 05/04/2020 *Income* £85,500 *Total grants* £83,300 *Grants to organisations* £71,800 *Assets* £2,490,000

TRUSTEES Nigel Shaw; Phil Bodmer; Maggie Browne; Geraldine Casswell; Dr John Hamilton; Dr David Heseltine; Michael Green; Marcella Sykes.

HOW TO APPLY Application forms can be downloaded from the trust's website. Completed applications should be submitted by email or post. Applications are considered at regular meetings throughout the year. In urgent cases, the trustees can consider applications for amounts of under £250 outside meetings.

CONTACT DETAILS Kathryn Hodges, Trust Secretary, c/o Garbutt and Elliott, Triune Court, Monks Cross, York, North Yorkshire YO32 9GZ *Tel.* 01904 702384 *Email* pureycusttrust@btinternet.com *Website* www.pureycusttrust.org.uk

■ Catkin Pussywillow Charitable Trust

CC NO 1100036 **ESTABLISHED** 2003

WHERE FUNDING CAN BE GIVEN UK.

WHO CAN BENEFIT Charitable organisations.

WHAT IS FUNDED Health; welfare; education; general charitable purposes.

RANGE OF GRANTS Up to £100,000 but mostly from £2,000 to £40,000.

SAMPLE GRANTS Hampstead Theatre (£100,000); Friends of UCLA (£40,300); University of California Trust UK (£38,800); 486 J Foundation (£30,000); London Symphony Orchestra and Royal Collection Trust (£20,000 each); Anglo Israel Association (£5,000).

FINANCES *Financial year end* 05/04/2020 *Income* £161,500 *Total grants* £284,500 *Grants to organisations* £284,500 *Assets* £66,100

TRUSTEES Barry Gold; Raymond Harris; Celia Atkin.

OTHER INFORMATION Only organisations that received grants of over £3,000 were listed as beneficiaries in the trust's accounts. Grants of under £3,000 totalled £5,500.

HOW TO APPLY Contact the correspondent for further information.

CONTACT DETAILS The Trustees, c/o Adler Shine LLP, Aston House, Cornwall Ave, Church End, London N3 1LF *Tel.* 020 8371 3000

■ The PwC Foundation

CC NO 1144124 **ESTABLISHED** 2011

WHERE FUNDING CAN BE GIVEN UK.

WHO CAN BENEFIT Registered charities; CICs; social enterprises.

WHAT IS FUNDED Social inclusion through employability and education; mental health and healthcare; the environment; general charitable purposes.

WHAT IS NOT FUNDED Political organisations; lobbying groups; animal rights groups; religious bodies.

RANGE OF GRANTS Up to £136,000.

SAMPLE GRANTS Wellbeing of Women (£136,400); School for Social Entrepreneurs (£104,500); Samaritans (£97,000); The World's Big Sleep Out Trust (£54,000); Teach First (£36,000); National Literacy Trust (£14,900); Mind (£6,200); Barnardo's Northern Ireland (£40).

FINANCES *Financial year end* 30/06/2020 *Income* £1,760,000 *Total grants* £1,260,000 *Grants to organisations* £1,260,000 *Assets* £860,900

TRUSTEES Kevin Ellis; David Adair; Zelf Hussain; Kalee Talvitie-Brown; David Walters; Emma Cox.

OTHER INFORMATION The PwC Foundation is the corporate charity of PricewaterhouseCoopers LLP (PwC). As well as grants, it also provides matched funding to support the charitable activities of PwC employees.

HOW TO APPLY The foundation's 2019/20 accounts state: 'There is no current requirement for a formal open grant application process. The Steering Committee and trustees can independently identify recipients for funding who meet the charitable objectives of the Foundation. Recipients are approved by the trustees.'

CONTACT DETAILS Community Engagement Team, PricewaterhouseCoopers, 1 Embankment Place, London WC2N 6RH *Tel.* 07764 902846 *Email* uk_pwcfoundation@pwc.com *Website* www.pwc.co.uk/corporate-sustainability/the-pwc-foundation.jhtml

■ The Pye Foundation

CC NO 267851 **ESTABLISHED** 1974

WHERE FUNDING CAN BE GIVEN Cambridgeshire and the immediate surrounding area.

WHO CAN BENEFIT Registered charities and retired employees of the former Pye/Phillips group of companies.

WHAT IS FUNDED General charitable purposes, including the following: education; social welfare; older people; support for people in need.

RANGE OF GRANTS Mostly £1,000 to £6,000.

SAMPLE GRANTS The PYE Association (£30,000); Winter Comfort (£6,000); Lifecraft (£4,000); Refuge and STARs Bereavement (£3,000 each); Home-Start (£2,500); Connections Bus Project and Rotary Club of Lowestoft (£2,000 each); Mayor's Day Out (£1,000).

FINANCES *Financial year end* 31/03/2020 *Income* £117,100 *Total grants* £207,600 *Grants to organisations* £195,700 *Assets* £2,830,000

TRUSTEES Bob Bates; Roger Crabtree; Ashish Dasgupta; Rachel Hayden; Dr Anil Chhabra; Joy Childs; Richard McMullan; Dr Michael Wassall; Rick Mitchell; Hilary Seaward; Douglas Irish; John Hemming.

OTHER INFORMATION During 2019/20, grants were broken down as follows: annual grants (£170,300); one-off grants (£17,400); special project donations – Pye History Trust (£8,000). Only recipients of annual grants were listed in the foundation's accounts. The foundation also provides funding and equipment to individuals in need.

HOW TO APPLY Apply in writing to the correspondent. The trustees meet regularly to consider applications.

CONTACT DETAILS The Trustees, 70 Bishops Road, Trumpington, Cambridge, Cambridgeshire CB2 9NH *Tel.* 07768 045544 *Email* pyefoundationcamb@gmail.com

■ Mr and Mrs J. A. Pye's Charitable Settlement

CC NO 242677 **ESTABLISHED** 1965

WHERE FUNDING CAN BE GIVEN UK, with a strong preference for Oxfordshire.

WHO CAN BENEFIT Registered charities.

WHAT IS FUNDED General charitable purposes including, but not limited to, the environment, health and care, youth organisations, education, heritage and the arts.

WHAT IS NOT FUNDED Individuals; non-recognised charities; animal welfare; the promotion of religion.

RANGE OF GRANTS Generally up to £10,000.

SAMPLE GRANTS Music at Oxford (£80,000); Magdalen College School (£30,000); Association for Post-Natal Illness (£20,000 each); CLIC and See Saw (£10,000 each); Oxford Lieder Festival (£8,000); Art Fusion (£5,000); Southwold Primary School (£4,000);

Sunrise Multicultural Project (£2,000); Sue Ryder Hospice (£1,000).

FINANCES *Financial year end* 31/12/2019
Income £666,100 *Total grants* £579,800
Grants to organisations £579,800
Assets £14,380,000

TRUSTEES Patrick Mulcare; Graham Flint; Valerie Buzzard.

OTHER INFORMATION Grants were made to 134 organisations. Only organisations that received grants of over £501 were listed as beneficiaries in the charity's accounts. Grants of under £501 totalled £10,000 and were awarded to 20 organisations.

HOW TO APPLY Applications are preferred by email with Word documents attached. The grant-maker does not have an application form, but details on the information required is available on the website.

CONTACT DETAILS Lucy McCallum-Toppin, Grants Manager, Springfield, Farringdon Road, Southmoor, Oxfordshire OX13 5BG *Tel.* 01865 721269 *Email* pyecharitablesettlement@gmail.com *Website* www.pyecharitablesettlement.org

■ QBE European Operations Foundation

CC NO 1143828 **ESTABLISHED** 2011

WHERE FUNDING CAN BE GIVEN UK and Europe.

WHO CAN BENEFIT Registered charities.

WHAT IS FUNDED Healthcare; education and community-based projects.

WHAT IS NOT FUNDED See the foundation's website for exclusions.

TYPE OF GRANT Project funding; one-year funding.

SAMPLE GRANTS Alzheimer's Society (£113,400); Lucy Air Ambulance for Children (£50,000); Helen Rollason Cancer Charity (£21,500); EACH and Missing People (£10,000 each); Centrepoint (£4,000); Katherine House Hospice (£300).

FINANCES *Financial year end* 31/12/2019
Income £853,700 *Total grants* £909,000
Grants to organisations £909,000
Assets £21,000

TRUSTEES Alexandra Smith; Grant Clemence; Robert Nias; Beth McLeod; Benjamin McBean.

OTHER INFORMATION Grants were broken down as follows: non-matching grants (£693,400); grants made to match employee donations (£183,600); grants made to match employee payroll donations (£32,000).

HOW TO APPLY At the time of writing (February 2021), the foundation was not accepting grant applications. See the foundation's website for the latest information.

CONTACT DETAILS Sophie Wraith-Lee, Foundation Adviser, QBE European Operations, 1 Coval Wells, Chelmsford, Essex CM1 1WZ *Tel.* 01245 343253 *Email* QBEFoundationEO@uk.qbe.com *Website* https://qbeeurope.com/community/the-qbe-foundation

■ Quadstar Charitable Foundation

CC NO 1173951 **ESTABLISHED** 2017

WHERE FUNDING CAN BE GIVEN UK; Cambodia; Nepal; Myanmar.

WHO CAN BENEFIT Schools and colleges; individuals.

WHAT IS FUNDED Support for UK students from disadvantaged backgrounds.

TYPE OF GRANT Project funding; capital costs.

RANGE OF GRANTS £20,000 to £30,000.

SAMPLE GRANTS Atlantic College (£30,000); United World Schools (£22,400); Dulwich College (£20,000).

FINANCES *Financial year end* 31/03/2020
Income £174,000 *Total grants* £72,400
Grants to organisations £72,400
Assets £28,100

TRUSTEES Wendy Bayliss; Nick Butcher; Suzanne Smith.

OTHER INFORMATION Three grants were awarded during the year.

HOW TO APPLY Applicants are encouraged to make applications via the email address listed on the foundation's website.

CONTACT DETAILS Suzanne Smith, Trustee, Quadstar Charitable Foundation, PO Box 1260, Yateley, GU47 7GH *Tel.* 01252 845988 *Email* suzanne@quadstar.org *Website* quadstar.org

■ Quartet Community Foundation

CC NO 1080418 **ESTABLISHED** 1987

WHERE FUNDING CAN BE GIVEN Bristol, North Somerset, South Gloucestershire, Bath and North East Somerset.

WHO CAN BENEFIT Registered charities; unregistered charities; CICs; social enterprises; schools; PTAs; amateur sports clubs; hospices.

WHAT IS FUNDED General charitable purposes; community development; safety; homelessness; health; learning and education; arts, culture and heritage; the environment.

WHAT IS NOT FUNDED Animal welfare; arts or sports projects with no community or charitable element; direct replacement of statutory funding; medical research; political groups or activities promoting political beliefs; religious groups seeking to influence people's religious choices; general appeals.

TYPE OF GRANT Capital costs; core/revenue costs; seed funding/start-up costs; project funding.

RANGE OF GRANTS Grants range from £50 to £68,500.

SAMPLE GRANTS Knowle West Media Centre (£35,000); Bluebell Care Trust (£30,000 in two grants); NAOS Therapy (£15,000); WECIL Ltd (£10,000); Young Bristol's Got Talent and Age UK – Enfield (£5,000 each).

FINANCES *Financial year end* 31/03/2020
Income £13,960,000 *Total grants* £3,930,000
Grants to organisations £3,930,000
Assets £42,800,000

TRUSTEES Bina Shah; Nicholas Lee; Raj Kakar-Clayton; Julian Telling; Jonathon Baker; Merlyn Ipinson-Fleming; Annie Kilvington; Pat Meehan; Christopher Johnson; Joanna Turner; Susan Blatchford, Susan Mountstevens; Ben Silvey.

OTHER INFORMATION This is one of the 46 UK community foundations, which distribute funding for a wide range of purposes. As with all community foundations, there are a number of donor-advised funds managed on behalf of individuals, families and charitable trusts. Grant schemes tend to change frequently – consult the foundation's website for details of current programmes and up-to-date deadlines. In 2019/20, grants were made to 984 organisations, to the benefit of more than 200,000 people.

HOW TO APPLY Applicants should refer to the foundation's website for details on how to apply to each grant programme.

CONTACT DETAILS Grants Team, Royal Oak House, Royal Oak Avenue, Bristol BS1 4GB *Tel.* 0117 989 7700 *Email* info@quartetcf.org.uk *Website* www.quartetcf.org.uk

■ The Queen Anne's Gate Foundation

CC NO 1108903 **ESTABLISHED** 2005

WHERE FUNDING CAN BE GIVEN UK and Asia.

WHO CAN BENEFIT Registered charities.

WHAT IS FUNDED Education; health; rehabilitation. The trustees prefer to support rehabilitative charities and those that work with underprivileged areas of society. There is some preference for Christian organisations and those working with children and young people.

TYPE OF GRANT Multi-year grants for projects and service delivery.

RANGE OF GRANTS £5,000 to £25,000.

SAMPLE GRANTS Previous beneficiaries have included: English National Opera, Exeter Deaf Academy and Families for Children (£25,000 each); Horatio's Garden and Safelives (£20,000

each); The Two Moors Festival (£15,000); Christian Friends of Korea (£14,500); Churches Housing Action Trust and City of Exeter YMCA Community Projects (£10,000 each); Aanchal Women's Aid (£5,000).

FINANCES *Financial year end* 30/04/2020 *Income* £11,500 *Total grants* £222,400 *Grants to organisations* £222,400

TRUSTEES Nicholas Allan; Jonathan Boyer; Deborah Fisher.

OTHER INFORMATION Full accounts were not available to view on the Charity Commission's website due to the foundation's low income. We have therefore estimated the grant total based on the foundation's total expenditure.

HOW TO APPLY Apply in writing to the correspondent. The trustees meet twice a year.

CONTACT DETAILS Deborah Fisher, Trustee, Unit 4 Hill Farm, Kirby Road, Kirby Bedon, Norwich, Norfolk NR14 7DU *Tel.* 01508 480100 *Email* info@fisherlegal.co.uk

■ Queen Mary's Roehampton Trust

CC NO 211715 **ESTABLISHED** 1972

WHERE FUNDING CAN BE GIVEN UK.

WHO CAN BENEFIT Charitable organisations.

WHAT IS FUNDED The reception, accommodation, treatment or aftercare of ex-service people who acquired disabilities during their service, their dependants, and medical or surgical research associated with this group.

TYPE OF GRANT Recurring and one-off; capital; core costs; maintenance; project funding.

RANGE OF GRANTS Grants range from £2,000 to £35,000.

SAMPLE GRANTS Royal British Legion Industries (£35,000); Erskine Hospital (£30,000); Veterans Aid (£25,000); Gurkha Welfare Trust (£15,000); Spinal Injuries Association (£10,000); National Gulf Veterans and Families Association (£8,000); Association of Jewish Ex-Service Men and Women (£2,000).

FINANCES *Financial year end* 31/03/2020 *Income* £579,700 *Total grants* £564,500 *Grants to organisations* £564,500 *Assets* £12,510,000

TRUSTEES James Macnamara; Miranda Thompson-Schwab; Heather Betts; Col. Paul Cummings; Colin Green; Sir Barry Thornton; Anne Child; Dr Rakesh Bhabutta; Harvey Tilley; Alison Wyman; Ed Tytherleigh; Ian Nicoll; Air Cdre Barbara Cooper.

OTHER INFORMATION There is no minimum or maximum grant – the amount awarded is considered on a case-by-case basis.

HOW TO APPLY Contact the correspondent for further information.

CONTACT DETAILS Col S. Rowland-Jones, Clerk to the Trustees, 2 Sovereign Close, Quidhampton, Salisbury, Wiltshire SP2 9ES *Tel.* 01722 501413 *Email* qmrt@hotmail.co.uk

■ The Quilter Foundation

CC NO 1175555 **ESTABLISHED** 2018

WHERE FUNDING CAN BE GIVEN UK and the Isle of Man.

WHO CAN BENEFIT Registered charities; not-for-profit organisations.

WHAT IS FUNDED Young people, in areas including financial education and empowerment, sustainable employment, and health and well-being for young carers.

WHAT IS NOT FUNDED Political, religious or profit-making organisations.

RANGE OF GRANTS Up to £225,000.

SAMPLE GRANTS Carers Trust (£225,000); Safe New Futures (£153,500); School of Hard Knocks (£148,300); Street League (£146,300); MyBnk (£78,300); Crossroads Care (£37,000); Kickstart – Financial Futures Fund (£20,000); Disasters Emergency Committee (£11,900).

FINANCES *Financial year end* 31/12/2019 *Income* £1,070,000 *Total grants* £836,000 *Grants to organisations* £836,000 *Assets* £8,400,000

TRUSTEES Timothy Childe; Philippa Foster Back; Jane Goodland; Matthew Burton; Paul Feeney.

OTHER INFORMATION In 2019 the foundation made grants to eight charity partners (£820,000) and matched funds raised for various small charities by Quilter plc employees (£16,000).

HOW TO APPLY The foundation makes grants to selected charity partners. Contact the correspondent for further information.

CONTACT DETAILS The Trustees, c/o Quilter plc, Senator House, 85 Queen Victoria Street, London EC4V 4AB *Tel.* 020 7778 9614 *Email* responsiblebusiness@quilter.com *Website* https://www.quilter.com/responsible-business/the-quilter-foundation

■ Quintessentially Foundation

CC NO 1144584 **ESTABLISHED** 2008

WHERE FUNDING CAN BE GIVEN Worldwide.

WHO CAN BENEFIT UK-registered charities.

WHAT IS FUNDED The education, health and welfare of disadvantaged children; healthcare; conservation causes worldwide.

WHAT IS NOT FUNDED Applicants must be registered in the UK and independent of the state, political parties and religion.

TYPE OF GRANT Project funding.

RANGE OF GRANTS Grants range from £20,700 to £444,800.

SAMPLE GRANTS The Felix Project (£444,800); The Churchill Foundation (£124,000); Dimbleby Cancer Care (£118,400); Sentebale (£28,500); Royal Parks Foundations (£20,700).

FINANCES *Financial year end* 31/12/2019 *Income* £1,110,000 *Total grants* £737,300 *Grants to organisations* £737,300 *Assets* £56,300

TRUSTEES Rory Brooks; Dr Peter Crowther; Benjamin Elliot; Sebastian Lee; Emma McCarthy; Andrew Crawley.

OTHER INFORMATION In 2019 substantial grants were awarded to five organisations. The foundation partners with three to five charities per year, hosting events solely for their benefit. Often, these events are run in collaboration with the charity partner and the proceeds are awarded to the charity as a grant.

HOW TO APPLY Refer to the foundation's website for up-to-date information and guidance regarding the application process.

CONTACT DETAILS The Trustees, 29 Portland Place, London W1B 1QB *Tel.* 0845 388 7985 *Email* info@quintessentiallyfoundation.org *Website* www.quintessentiallyfoundation.org

■ Quothquan Trust

CC NO 1110647 **ESTABLISHED** 2004

WHERE FUNDING CAN BE GIVEN Birmingham and the surrounding area.

WHO CAN BENEFIT Christian organisations and individuals.

WHAT IS FUNDED Promotion of the Christian faith through specific projects and initiatives aimed at relieving poverty and sickness, and assisting people who are older, ill, or socially or economically disadvantaged; the advancement of religious education; general charitable purposes.

WHAT IS NOT FUNDED Consult the trust's website for a full list of organisations/projects that it does not support.

TYPE OF GRANT Grants are generally made on a one-off basis.

RANGE OF GRANTS £50 to £300.

SAMPLE GRANTS A list of beneficiaries was not included in the annual report and accounts.

FINANCES *Financial year end* 31/12/2019
Income £113,100 *Total grants* £319,100
Grants to organisations £151,000
Assets £1,420,000

TRUSTEES Susan Robinson; Janet Gilmour.

OTHER INFORMATION In 2019 grants totalling £168,100 were made to 39 individuals, with the rest of the grant total going to 17 organisations.

HOW TO APPLY Apply in writing to the correspondent. See the trust's website for full guidelines and criteria. Applications by email are not accepted.

CONTACT DETAILS Grant Applications Team, Dale Farm, Worcester Lane, Sutton Coldfield, West Midlands B75 5PR *Tel.* 0121 323 3236 *Website* www.quothquantrust.org.uk

R. S. Charitable Trust

CC NO 1053660 **ESTABLISHED** 1996
WHERE FUNDING CAN BE GIVEN UK and overseas.
WHO CAN BENEFIT Registered Jewish charities.
WHAT IS FUNDED Jewish causes, especially education and the relief of poverty.
RANGE OF GRANTS Up to around £50,000.
SAMPLE GRANTS The latest available accounts did not include a list of beneficiaries. Previous beneficiaries have included Beis Aharon Trust, Friends of Toldos Avrohom Yitzchok, Keren Hatzola Doros Alei Siach, the SOFT.
FINANCES *Financial year end* 05/04/2019 *Income* £294,600 *Total grants* £90,900 *Grants to organisations* £90,900 *Assets* £2,947,000
TRUSTEES Harvey Freudenberger; Michelle Freudenberger; Stuart Freudenberger; Max Freudenberger; Charles Margulies.
OTHER INFORMATION The 2018/19 accounts were the latest available at the time of writing (May 2021).
HOW TO APPLY Contact the correspondent for details on how to apply for funding.
CONTACT DETAILS The Trustees, 138 Stamford Hill, London, Greater London N16 6QT *Tel.* 020 8455 6789

The Monica Rabagliati Charitable Trust

CC NO 1086368 **ESTABLISHED** 1997
WHERE FUNDING CAN BE GIVEN UK.
WHO CAN BENEFIT Small and medium-sized organisations.
WHAT IS FUNDED Children and young people; social welfare; medical care; education; general charitable purposes.
RANGE OF GRANTS £500 to £5,000.
SAMPLE GRANTS Royal National Lifeboat Institution (£15,000); Clapton Common Boys Club and Outward Bound Trust (£5,000 each); Open Homes (£3,600); Solent Youth Zone (£2,500); Barrier Breakers (£2,000); Educate for Life (£1,000); Wessex Children (£500).
FINANCES *Financial year end* 05/04/2020 *Income* £154,700 *Total grants* £155,300 *Grants to organisations* £155,300 *Assets* £3,060,000
TRUSTEES SG Hambros Trust Company Ltd; Robert McLean.
OTHER INFORMATION Grants were made to 51 organisations in the following categories: other (£48,000), children's projects (£43,900), young people (£33,000); education (£22,800); medical causes (£7,000).
HOW TO APPLY Application forms are available to download from the website and should be completed and returned to the correspondence address. Applications are considered twice per year.
CONTACT DETAILS The Administrator, c/o SG Kleinwort Hambros Trust Company Ltd, 5th Floor, 8 St James's Square, London SW1Y 4JU *Tel.* 020 7597 3065 *Website* www.rabagliati.org.uk

Rachel Charitable Trust

CC NO 276441 **ESTABLISHED** 1978
WHERE FUNDING CAN BE GIVEN Worldwide.
WHO CAN BENEFIT Charitable organisations. Our research suggests that the trust primarily funds Jewish organisations.
WHAT IS FUNDED General charitable purposes; the advancement of religion and religious education; the relief of poverty.
SAMPLE GRANTS Kidum Miktzoee Haredi (£1.21 million); Jewish Care (£661,300); Kisharon (£629,600); Nightingale Hammerson (£300,000); United Joint Israel Appeal (£289,400); Avot Kedoshim (£240,000).
FINANCES *Financial year end* 30/06/2020 *Income* £7,630,000 *Total grants* £5,660,000 *Grants to organisations* £5,660,000 *Assets* £18,840,000
TRUSTEES Leo Noe; Susan Noe; Simon Kanter.
OTHER INFORMATION Only organisations that received grants of over £230,000 were listed as beneficiaries in the charity's accounts. Grants of under £230,000 totalled £2.32 million.
HOW TO APPLY Contact the correspondent for further information.
CONTACT DETAILS Robert Chalk, Charity Secretary, 30 Market Place, London W1W 8AP *Tel.* 020 7846 3036

The Racing Foundation

CC NO 1145297 **ESTABLISHED** 2011
WHERE FUNDING CAN BE GIVEN UK.
WHO CAN BENEFIT Charities associated with the UK horseracing and thoroughbred breeding industry. The foundation's website states that organisations that do not work exclusively within the horseracing and thoroughbred breeding industry may be supported if their work is 'of exceptional quality and can be shown to directly impact industry participants'.
WHAT IS FUNDED The welfare of members of the horseracing industry; education and training connected with the horseracing industry; racehorse welfare; equine science research.
WHAT IS NOT FUNDED Work that does not benefit the horseracing and thoroughbred breeding industry in the UK; religious causes; fundraising costs or salaries; individuals or causes which will benefit only one person; gambling addiction work (unless it specifically focuses on participants within the horseracing and thoroughbred industry; retrospective expenditure; work that is not legally charitable.
TYPE OF GRANT Project costs; core costs; capital projects; research grants. Support may include funding for overheads and salaries. Multi-year grants, usually up to three years, are considered.
RANGE OF GRANTS Grants range from £9,000 up to £2.23 million.
SAMPLE GRANTS The Professional Jockeys Association/Jockeys Education and Training Scheme/The Injured Jockeys Fund (£2.23 million); Thoroughbred Breeders Association (£570,000); Diversity in Racing (£275,000); National Horseracing College (£243,000); Scottish Racing (£120,000); British Racing School (£10,000); Horseback UK (£9,000).
FINANCES *Financial year end* 31/12/2019 *Income* £2,300,000 *Total grants* £4,910,000 *Grants to organisations* £4,910,000 *Assets* £89,670,000

HOW TO APPLY For all grant applications, apart from those for equine science research, there is a three-stage process. You should submit a first-stage application using the online form, providing basic details about your organisation. Guidelines, along with dates of application deadlines, are available from the website. The foundation operates a three-month application process, three times a year. For equine science research applications, the website requests you register as a user of the Horserace Betting Levy Board's equine grants system. Once registered, you will be able to build and submit a grant application form. To ensure that your application is considered for Racing Foundation funding, you will need to mark the relevant box on the application summary. A link for the online application system along with application deadline dates and further guidance can be found on the website. For further information on equine science research grants, contact Annie Dodd, Grants Manager at the Horserace Betting Levy Board on 020 7333 0043 ext. 873 or email equine.grants@hblb.org.uk.

CONTACT DETAILS Tansy Challis, Grants Manager, 75 High Holborn, London WC1V 6LS *Email* tansy.challis@racingfoundation.co.uk *Website* www.racingfoundation.co.uk

■ The Radcliffe Trust

CC NO 209212 **ESTABLISHED** 1714

WHERE FUNDING CAN BE GIVEN UK.

WHO CAN BENEFIT Registered or exempt charities; organisations and projects benefitting musicians and those involved in the crafts.

WHAT IS FUNDED Classical music performance and training especially chamber music, composition and music education. Particular interests within music education are music for children and adults with special needs, youth orchestras and projects at secondary and higher levels, including academic research. Heritage and crafts are also supported, especially the development of the skills, knowledge and experience that underpin the UK's traditional cultural heritage and crafts sectors.

WHAT IS NOT FUNDED Generally, individuals, retrospective grants, general appeals, endowment funds and mainstream schools. See the trust's website for scheme-specific exclusions.

TYPE OF GRANT Project funding, for up to three years.

RANGE OF GRANTS Grants generally range between £2,500 and £7,500.

SAMPLE GRANTS Queen Elizabeth Scholarship Trust (£12,000); Strawberry Hill Trust and Royal Northern College of Music (£10,000 each); Adopt a Potter (£7,500); Watts Gallery Trust (£4,000); High Mead Farm CIC (£2,000); St Barts (£600).

FINANCES *Financial year end* 31/03/2020 *Income* £649,000 *Total grants* £406,400 *Grants to organisations* £406,400 *Assets* £19,490,000

OTHER INFORMATION In 2019/20, grants were made for the following purposes: heritage and crafts (£197,200); music (£177,100); tercentenary (£30,000); miscellaneous (£2,100).

HOW TO APPLY Applications can only be submitted via the online application form. See the trust's website for further details of its schemes. The trustees meet twice yearly to oversee the charity's activities and to make decisions on grants. For both the Music and Heritage and Crafts schemes, the deadlines are 31 January and 31 July, for consideration by the trustees in June and in December, respectively. Visit the trust's website for further details of its schemes.

CONTACT DETAILS Administrator, 6 Trull Farm Buildings, Trull, Tetbury, Gloucestershire GL8 8SQ *Tel.* 01285 841900 *Email* radcliffe@thetrustpartnership.com *Website* www.theradcliffetrust.org

■ Richard Radcliffe Trust

CC NO 1068930 **ESTABLISHED** 1998

WHERE FUNDING CAN BE GIVEN UK.

WHO CAN BENEFIT Charitable organisations; hospices; theatres.

WHAT IS FUNDED General charitable purposes, including the following: education; health; citizenship; social welfare; disability; young people; nature conservation.

TYPE OF GRANT Mainly recurrent.

RANGE OF GRANTS £1,000 to £4,000.

SAMPLE GRANTS Demand (Design and Manufacture for Disability), Royal Court Theatre and Wildlife Trust (£4,000 each); Charley Heritage Foundation, St Peter and St James Hospice and YC2 Young Carers Youth Club (£3,000 each); Future Trees and Wheelpower (£2,000 each); Horatio's Garden and St Mungo's (£1,000 each).

FINANCES *Financial year end* 31/08/2019 *Income* £62,600 *Total grants* £90,000 *Grants to organisations* £90,000 *Assets* £2,250,000

OTHER INFORMATION In 2019 the trust awarded grants to 35 organisations, totalling £90,000, for the following purposes: welfare (£72,000) and conservation of the countryside (£18,000). The 2018/19 accounts were the latest available at the time of writing (February 2021).

HOW TO APPLY Contact the correspondent for more information.

CONTACT DETAILS The Trustees, 77 Moreton Road, Buckingham MK18 1JZ *Tel.* 01280 813352

■ The Bishop Radford Trust

CC NO 1113562 **ESTABLISHED** 2006

WHERE FUNDING CAN BE GIVEN UK and overseas.

WHO CAN BENEFIT Registered charities; religious bodies/institutions.

WHAT IS FUNDED Church-related projects; the education of priests, future priests and church workers; support of church ministry.

WHAT IS NOT FUNDED Non-UK-registered charities; building or capital projects; individuals; core funding; campaigns or lobbying; research; retrospective expenditure.

TYPE OF GRANT Project funding.

RANGE OF GRANTS Typically under £10,000.

SAMPLE GRANTS Anglican Communion Fund (£130,000); Bible Reading Fellowship (£50,000); Transforming Lives for Good (£15,000); Cinnamon Network (£5,000); Community Money Advice, Home for Good and The KEYS Project (£2,000 each); Emerge and

Youthscape (£1,000 each); Evangelical Alliance (£250).

FINANCES *Financial year end* 31/03/2020 *Income* £1,110,000 *Total grants* £466,800 *Grants to organisations* £466,800 *Assets* £16,340,000

TRUSTEES Lord Stephen Green; Lady Janian Green; Suzannah O'Brien; Dr Ruth Dare.

OTHER INFORMATION In 2019/20 the trust awarded grants to 53 organisations. Awards were distributed as follows: church-related projects – UK (£75,000); church-related projects – overseas (£180,000); support of church ministry – UK (£131,300); support of church ministry – overseas (£80,500).

HOW TO APPLY Applicants must check their eligibility online before making an application through the online form.

CONTACT DETAILS Suzannah O'Brien, Trustee, Devonshire House, 1 Devonshire Street, London W1W 5DR *Tel.* 020 7304 2000 *Email* enquiries@bishopradfordtrust.org.uk *Website* bishopradfordtrust.org.uk

■ The Raindance Charitable Trust

CC NO 1172166 **ESTABLISHED** 2016

WHERE FUNDING CAN BE GIVEN England, Wales and Africa (particularly Uganda).

WHO CAN BENEFIT Charitable organisations.

WHAT IS FUNDED General charitable purposes; social welfare; homelessness; children and young people; charitable work in Africa.

RANGE OF GRANTS £3,000 to £6,000.

SAMPLE GRANTS The Whitechapel Centre (£6,000); Chase Africa, FareShare South West, Microloan Foundation and Serendip Children's Home (£5,000 each); West Berkshire Homeless Response (£3,000).

FINANCES *Financial year end* 31/12/2019 *Income* £75,000 *Total grants* £70,000 *Grants to organisations* £70,000 *Assets* £26,700

TRUSTEES Alastair Young; Anthony Watson; Alisha Watson; Amelia Watson; Rukshana Watson.

OTHER INFORMATION Grants were awarded to 14 organisations during the year.

HOW TO APPLY Contact the correspondent for further information.

CONTACT DETAILS The Trustees, c/o Thrings LLP, 2 Queen Square, Bath, Somerset BA1 2HQ *Tel.* 01225 340093

■ The Rainford Trust

CC NO 266157 **ESTABLISHED** 1973

WHERE FUNDING CAN BE GIVEN Worldwide, with a preference for areas in which Pilkington plc has works or offices, especially St Helens and Merseyside.

WHO CAN BENEFIT Charitable and voluntary organisations; individuals.

WHAT IS FUNDED General charitable purposes; social welfare; health; education; the environment; the arts, particularly the performing arts.

WHAT IS NOT FUNDED Previous research suggests that funding for the arts is restricted to St Helens only. Applications from individuals for grants for educational purposes will be considered only from applicants who are normally resident in St Helens.

TYPE OF GRANT Capital costs; project funding.

RANGE OF GRANTS Typically £500 to £5,000.

SAMPLE GRANTS The World of Glass (£25,000); Whizz-Kidz (£7,000); Chora Chori and Katie Piper Foundation (£5,000 each); Traidcraft Exchange (£3,000); The Sequal Trust (£2,000); Sands (£500).

FINANCES *Financial year end* 31/07/2020 *Income* £233,900 *Total grants* £148,300 *Grants to organisations* £147,700 *Assets* £11,620,000

TRUSTEES Pilkington Family Trust Kirsty Pilkington; Annabel Moseley; David Pilkington; Simon Pilkington; Louisa Walker; Dr Clarissa Pilkington; John Pilkington; Andrew Pilkington; David Bricknell.

OTHER INFORMATION During the year, 68 grants were made to organisations and one grant was made to an individual.

HOW TO APPLY Apply on a form available from the correspondent. Applications should be accompanied by a copy of your latest accounts and cost data on the project for which funding is sought. Applicants may apply at any time. The trustees normally meet in November, March and July. A sub-appeals committee meets about 10 times a year and can either refuse, grant or pass on an application to the trustees.

CONTACT DETAILS The Trustees, c/o Brabners LLP, Horton House, Exchange Flags, Liverpool L2 3YL *Tel.* 0151 600 3362 *Email* shirley.robinson@brabners.com

■ The Randal Charitable Foundation

CC NO 1176129 **ESTABLISHED** 2017

WHERE FUNDING CAN BE GIVEN UK and overseas.

WHO CAN BENEFIT UK-registered charities.

WHAT IS FUNDED Health; mental health; social disadvantage; addiction; education.

TYPE OF GRANT One-off and recurrent.

SAMPLE GRANTS British Asian Trust (£501,000); Leicester Charity Link (£101,000); Centre for Social Justice (£40,000); CHASE Africa (£15,300); Cerebral Palsy (£3,000).

FINANCES *Financial year end* 31/12/2020 *Income* £2,050,000 *Total grants* £1,060,000 *Grants to organisations* £1,060,000 *Assets* £7,570,000

TRUSTEES Michael Hollis; Yanyan Huang; Dr Nik Kotecha; Moni Kotecha.

HOW TO APPLY Apply via the foundation's website where full details of the application process can be found.

CONTACT DETAILS The Trustees, 5 Pavilion Way, Loughborough, Leicestershire LE11 5GW *Email* grants@randalfoundation.org.uk *Website* https://www.randalfoundation.org.uk

■ The Joseph and Lena Randall Charitable Trust

CC NO 255035 **ESTABLISHED** 1967

WHERE FUNDING CAN BE GIVEN UK and France.

WHO CAN BENEFIT Registered charities; schools.

WHAT IS FUNDED General charitable purposes, including health/medical and social welfare.

WHAT IS NOT FUNDED Individuals.

RANGE OF GRANTS Up to £11,000 but mostly £1,000 to £2,000.

SAMPLE GRANTS Community Security Trust (£11,000); Royal Opera House (£7,500); RNIB (£2,500); Chain of Hope (£2,000); Listening Books (£1,000).

FINANCES *Financial year end* 05/04/2020 *Income* £96,200 *Total grants* £88,100 *Grants to organisations* £88,100 *Assets* £1,900,000

TRUSTEE Rofrano Trustee Services Ltd.

HOW TO APPLY Contact the correspondent for further information.
CONTACT DETAILS The Trustees, Europa Residence, Place des Moulins, Monte Carlo, Monaco MC98 000 *Tel.* +377 93 50 03 82 *Email* rofrano.jlrct@hotmail.fr

■ Randeree Charitable Trust

CC NO 1171689 **ESTABLISHED** 2013
WHERE FUNDING CAN BE GIVEN UK.
WHO CAN BENEFIT Charitable organisations.
WHAT IS FUNDED Education; inclusion and empowerment of disadvantaged young people; community cohesion through interfaith dialogue and research; amateur sports.
SAMPLE GRANTS Cambridge Muslim College (£44,400); Faith Belief Forum (£15,000); City University (£10,200); Blueprint Trust (£10,000).
FINANCES *Financial year end* 31/12/2019
Income £246,500 *Total grants* £95,600
Grants to organisations £95,600
Assets £3,880,000
TRUSTEES Shireen Randeree; Zaid Randeree; Simon Mitchell; Faisal Randeree; Norman Waller.
HOW TO APPLY Contact the correspondent for further information.
CONTACT DETAILS The Trustees, 90 Long Acre, London WC2E 9RA

■ The Rank Foundation Ltd

CC NO 276976 **ESTABLISHED** 1953
WHERE FUNDING CAN BE GIVEN UK.
WHO CAN BENEFIT Registered charities with an annual income of less than £500,000; churches.
WHAT IS FUNDED Christian communication; young people; education; older people; general charitable purposes.
WHAT IS NOT FUNDED Projects that are for the benefit of only one ethnic or religious group; causes supported elsewhere by the Rank Foundation (including hospices, mainstream schools, specific individuals and film-making); areas that are under the provision of state aid, such as medical requirements.
SAMPLE GRANTS Previous beneficiaries have included: Help the Hospices (£100,000); Winston Churchill Memorial Trust (£82,000); Youth Work in Sport (£66,000); City Year London (£50,000); Oban Youth Cafe (£36,500); Banbury Youth Housing (£31,000); Mersey Youth Support Trust, Royal British Legion Industries and Women's Aid – Berks and Bucks (£30,000 each); Belfast Activity Centre (£28,500); Wellingborough Youth Project (£28,000); Deaf Hill Ward, Greenbank Community Church and Prisoners Abroad (£25,000 each).
FINANCES *Financial year end* 31/12/2019
Income £4,650,000 *Total grants* £7,180,000
Grants to organisations £7,180,000
Assets £253,250,000
TRUSTEES Joey Newton; Stuart Cowen; Johanna Ropner; Deputy Assistant Commissioner Rose Fitzpatrick; Daniel Simon; Nicholas Buxton; Jason Chaffer; William Wyatt; Andrew Fleming; Lindsey Clay; Joel Davis.
OTHER INFORMATION The grant total includes a substantial grant of £2.31 million given to CTVC, an independent production company producing content that raises important ethical and moral issues which was established by Lord and Lady Rank.
HOW TO APPLY At the time of writing (May 2021) the Pebble grants programme was closed. Check the foundation's website for the latest information.
CONTACT DETAILS The Trustees, 12 Warwick Square, London SW1V 2AA *Email* contactus@rankfoundation.com *Website* www.rankfoundation.com

■ The Joseph Rank Trust

CC NO 1093844 **ESTABLISHED** 1929
WHERE FUNDING CAN BE GIVEN UK.
WHO CAN BENEFIT Registered charities; places of worship.
WHAT IS FUNDED Improvement of church properties; Christian causes supporting the educational and practical needs of people of all ages.
WHAT IS NOT FUNDED A full list of exclusions can be found on the trust's website.
TYPE OF GRANT One-off grants for capital expenditure; three year grants for core costs or project funding.
RANGE OF GRANTS £10,000 to £50,000.
SAMPLE GRANTS Joanna Project – Leeds (£45,000); Cinnamon Network (£40,000); Huntingdon Methodist Church (£30,000); Sydenham Methodist Church (£10,000).
FINANCES *Financial year end* 31/12/2019
Income £2,810,000 *Total grants* £2,790,000
Grants to organisations £2,790,000
Assets £82,720,000
TRUSTEES Sue Warner; Revd Darren Holland; James Rank; Joseph Jennings; Colin Rank; Revd Carole Holmes; Revd John Irvine; Gay Moon; Tony Reddall.
HOW TO APPLY Refer to the funder's website for information on how to make an application.
CONTACT DETAILS Dr John Higgs, Secretary, Worth Corner, Turners Hill Road, Crawley, West Sussex RH10 7SL *Tel.* 01293 873947
Email secretary@ranktrust.org *Website* www.ranktrust.org

■ The Ranworth Trust

CC NO 292633 **ESTABLISHED** 1985
WHERE FUNDING CAN BE GIVEN Worldwide with a preference for the UK, especially East Norfolk.
WHO CAN BENEFIT Registered charities.
WHAT IS FUNDED Social welfare; overseas aid; health, including medical research; education; the environment; churches and historic buildings; the arts.
WHAT IS NOT FUNDED Individuals.
TYPE OF GRANT Loans and grants are available.
RANGE OF GRANTS Grants range from £1,000 to £10,000.
SAMPLE GRANTS Cancer Research UK and Alzheimer's Research Trust (£10,000 each); Ormiston (£6,000); Marie Curie Cancer Care and Norfolk Wildlife Trust (£5,000 each); Coeliac Society (£2,000); Save the Rhino (£1,000).
FINANCES *Financial year end* 05/04/2020
Income £178,000 *Total grants* £145,700
Grants to organisations £145,700
Assets £4,700,000
TRUSTEES The Hon. Jacquetta Cator; Mark Cator; Jane Cator.
OTHER INFORMATION In 2010 a grant of £350,000 was given to Norfolk Community Foundation to establish 'The Ranworth Grassroots Fund'. The aim of the fund is to support a wide range of charitable, voluntary and community activities

across Norfolk. Applications can be made through the community foundation's website.

HOW TO APPLY Contact the correspondent for further information.

CONTACT DETAILS Mark Cator, Clerk, Reedside, Farm Lane, Ranworth, Norwich, Norfolk NR13 6HY *Tel.* 01603 663300 *Website* www.ranworthtrust.org.uk

■ The Ratcliff Foundation

CC NO 222441 **ESTABLISHED** 1959

WHERE FUNDING CAN BE GIVEN UK, with a preference for local charities in the Midlands and North Wales.

WHO CAN BENEFIT Charitable organisations.

WHAT IS FUNDED General charitable purposes.

WHAT IS NOT FUNDED Individuals.

RANGE OF GRANTS Grants range between £2,500 and £7,000.

SAMPLE GRANTS Read for Good and Castel Froma Neuro Care (£7,000 each); St Richard's Hospice Foundation (£5,000); ecobirmingham (£4,000); Katherine House Hospice and Vetlife (£3,000 each); Bumblebee Conservation Trust (£2,500).

FINANCES *Financial year end* 05/04/2020 *Income* £225,400 *Total grants* £216,000 *Grants to organisations* £216,000 *Assets* £3,400,000

TRUSTEES David Ratcliff; Carolyn Ratcliff; Gillian Thorpe; Christopher Gupwell; Pauline Key.

OTHER INFORMATION Grants were made to 65 organisations during the year, of which 21 were for less than £2,500.

HOW TO APPLY Contact the correspondent for further information.

CONTACT DETAILS Christopher Gupwell, Secretary, Woodlands, Earls Common Road, Stock Green, Redditch, Worcestershire B96 6TB *Tel.* 01386 792116 *Email* chris.gupwell@btinternet.com

■ The Rathbone Brothers Foundation

CC NO 1150432 **ESTABLISHED** 2012

WHERE FUNDING CAN BE GIVEN Areas where Rathbone Brothers plc has an office.

WHO CAN BENEFIT Charitable organisations.

WHAT IS FUNDED The main objective of the foundation is to help disadvantaged young people in the areas in which the company has a presence.

TYPE OF GRANT Capital, development and project funding.

RANGE OF GRANTS Grants are mostly of less than £9,000.

SAMPLE GRANTS Garden Classroom (£9,000); Project 28 (£8,000); St Peter and St James Hospice and Team Oasis (£5,000 each); Brathay Trust and Their Voice (£3,000 each); Andover Baptist Church (£2,000).

FINANCES *Financial year end* 31/12/2020 *Income* £239,600 *Total grants* £93,900 *Grants to organisations* £93,900 *Assets* £1,150,000

TRUSTEES Geoffrey Powell; Paul Stockton; Rathbone Trust Company Ltd; Richard Lanyon; Stuart Furzer.

HOW TO APPLY Apply in writing to your local Rathbones office or directly to the trustees.

CONTACT DETAILS Sophie Boyd-Willis, Rathbone Brothers plc, 8 Finsbury Circus, London EC2M 7AZ *Tel.* 020 7399 0000 *Email* rathbonefoundation@rathbones.com

■ The Eleanor Rathbone Charitable Trust

CC NO 233241 **ESTABLISHED** 1947

WHERE FUNDING CAN BE GIVEN UK, with the major allocation to Merseyside; international projects (sub-Saharan Africa, the Indian subcontinent, Afghanistan and Palestine).

WHO CAN BENEFIT Registered charities; unregistered charities; CICs; social enterprises.

WHAT IS FUNDED Women and girls; orphaned children; young people and families who are economically deprived and/or socially excluded; unpopular and neglected causes; human rights; refugee support; education; social inclusion; holidays and outings provided by charities helping disadvantaged children and adults from Merseyside; overseas humanitarian aid.

WHAT IS NOT FUNDED Activities which are the responsibility of a statutory body; individuals; medical research; gap-year projects; lobbying or campaigning organisations; organisations that primarily exist to promote a religion, church or sect; local charities based outside Merseyside.

TYPE OF GRANT Core/revenue costs; seed funding/start-up funding; project funding; unrestricted funding. Most grants are for one year, although requests for two and three year grants will be considered.

RANGE OF GRANTS From £1,000 to £3,000 for national and international grants and up to £5,000 for Merseyside grants. In exceptional cases grants may be higher.

SAMPLE GRANTS Independence Initiative Ltd and Merseyside Holiday Service (£5,000 each); Sefton Women's and Children's Aid and West Everton Community Council (£4,000 each); Wirral Advisory Centre (£3,000); Family Action and Young Women's Trust (£2,000 each); Build Africa and Serve Afghanistan (£1,000 each); Merseyside Caribbean Centre (£300).

FINANCES *Financial year end* 05/04/2020 *Income* £381,500 *Total grants* £331,900 *Grants to organisations* £331,900 *Assets* £9,470,000

TRUSTEES William Rathbone; Jenny Rathbone; Andrew Rathbone; Lady Angela Morgan; Mark Rathbone; Joan Bonenfant.

OTHER INFORMATION Grants were awarded to 159 organisations during the year and were distributed as follows: Merseyside (£205,100); international (£67,000); national (£55,000); holidays – Merseyside (£12,300).

HOW TO APPLY Apply using the online form available on the website. In addition, supporting documents (listed on the website) must be sent as an email attachment. Applications are accepted at any time and are considered at trustees' meetings held three times a year.

CONTACT DETAILS The Trustees, 546 Warrington Road, Rainhill, Prescot, Merseyside L35 4LZ *Tel.* 07837 656314 *Email* eleanorrathbonetrust@gmail.com *Website* www.eleanorrathbonetrust.org.uk

■ Elizabeth Rathbone Charity

CC NO 233240 **ESTABLISHED** 1921

WHERE FUNDING CAN BE GIVEN Merseyside.

WHO CAN BENEFIT Registered charities; community organisations.

WHAT IS FUNDED General charitable purposes, with a strong focus on projects which support disadvantaged women, young people and communities in Merseyside. The charity prioritises organisations which support the following: socially and/or economically disadvantaged children or adults; women; young people; homeless people; people with disabilities or chronic health problems; refugees. Projects that alleviate poverty through education or support the arts and certain medical fields will also be considered.

WHAT IS NOT FUNDED Individuals; sponsorship; political organisations; pressure groups; feasibility studies; annual applications.

RANGE OF GRANTS Mostly £1,000 to £3,000.

SAMPLE GRANTS Sheila Kay Fund (£5,000); Congolese Association of Merseyside and Sefton Opera (£3,000 each); Henshaws Society for Blind People (£2,300); Pain Relief Foundation (£2,000); Zoë's Place Baby Hospice (£1,500); West Everton Community Council (£1,000).

FINANCES *Financial year end* 05/04/2020
Income £88,800 *Total grants* £92,400
Grants to organisations £92,400
Assets £2,200,000

TRUSTEES Susan Rathbone; Caroline Rathbone; Richard Rathbone; Megan Rathbone.

OTHER INFORMATION Grants were made to 41 organisations during the year in the following categories: health, well-being and disability (£41,100); social welfare and community (£33,400); children and young people (£17,900).

HOW TO APPLY Applicants will first need to complete the online registration form on the website. An application form, which is available to download from the website, will then need to be completed and returned by email in Word format along with a copy of your organisation's most recent financial accounts. The trustees meet twice a year, usually in spring and autumn, to consider and discuss applications.

CONTACT DETAILS Liese van Alwon, Administrator, 546 Warrington Road, Rainhill, Prescot, Merseyside L35 4LZ *Tel.* 07837 656314 *Email* elrathbonetrust@gmail.com *Website* www.elizabethrathbonetrust.org

The Sigrid Rausing Trust

CC NO 1046769 **ESTABLISHED** 1995

WHERE FUNDING CAN BE GIVEN Worldwide.

WHO CAN BENEFIT Charitable or voluntary organisations.

WHAT IS FUNDED The trust runs ten programmes: advocacy, research and litigation; detention, torture and the death penalty; defending civic space; transitional justice; women's rights; LGBTQ+ rights; xenophobia and intolerance; transparency and accountability; the arts; and conservation.

TYPE OF GRANT Core costs; project funding.

RANGE OF GRANTS No minimum or maximum grant.

SAMPLE GRANTS Previous beneficiaries have included: Fundación de Antropología Forense de Guatemala (£100,000); Women's Legal Aid Centre (£90,000); Civitas Maxima (£75,000); Safe Passage (£70,000); Campaign Against Homophobia – KPH (£50,000); Above Ground (£45,000); René Cassin (£30,000); Team Domenica (£25,000); Caine Prize for African Writing (£10,000).

FINANCES *Financial year end* 31/12/2019
Income £57,530,000
Total grants £53,170,000
Grants to organisations £53,170,000
Assets £2,900,000

TRUSTEES Sigrid Rausing; Sir Jeffrey Jowell; Andrew Puddephatt; Chris Stone; Geoffrey Budlender; Mabel van Oranje; Hosh Ibrahim; Ruth Rogers; Joshua Mailman.

HOW TO APPLY The trust does not accept unsolicited applications for funding but rather invites applications from organisations that it has proactively identified. If you wish to let the trust know about your work, you may send an email describing your organisation to research@srtrust.org. Programme officers review such emails on a regular basis. If your organisation is of interest to the trust, they will make contact.

CONTACT DETAILS Sheetal Patel, Major Grants Administrator and Finance Officer, 12 Penzance Place, London W11 4PA *Tel.* 020 7313 7727 *Email* info@srtrust.org *Website* www.sigrid-rausing-trust.org

The Ravensdale Trust

CC NO 265165 **ESTABLISHED** 1973

WHERE FUNDING CAN BE GIVEN Merseyside, particularly St Helens.

WHO CAN BENEFIT Registered charities.

WHAT IS FUNDED General charitable purposes, particularly young people, older people and disadvantaged groups.

TYPE OF GRANT Core costs; project funding.

RANGE OF GRANTS Grants range from £700 up to £5,000.

SAMPLE GRANTS Previous beneficiaries have included: Willowbrook Hospice (£20,000); So the Child May Learn (£5,000); Age Concern Mid Mersey, Derbyshire Hill Family and Community Association, Halton Autistic Family Support Group, Home-Start St Helens, Mersey Regional Epilepsy Association, National Museums Liverpool and Newfield School (£1,000 each).

FINANCES *Financial year end* 05/04/2020
Income £17,800 *Total grants* £113,000
Grants to organisations £113,000

TRUSTEES Jane Fagan; Mark Feeny; Karen Toseland.

OTHER INFORMATION Full accounts were not available to view on the Charity Commission's website due to the trust's low income. We have therefore estimated the grant total based on the trust's total expenditure.

HOW TO APPLY Contact the correspondent for further information.

CONTACT DETAILS Jane Fagan, Trustee, c/o Brabners, Horton House, Exchange Flags, Liverpool, Merseyside L2 3YL *Tel.* 0151 600 3000 *Email* jane.fagan@brabners.com

The Roger Raymond Charitable Trust

CC NO 262217 **ESTABLISHED** 1971

WHERE FUNDING CAN BE GIVEN UK.

WHO CAN BENEFIT Registered charities.

WHAT IS FUNDED General charitable purposes.

WHAT IS NOT FUNDED Individuals.

RANGE OF GRANTS Typically less than £1,200.

SAMPLE GRANTS Bloxham School (£112,400); Smallpiece Trust (£4,400).

FINANCES *Financial year end* 05/04/2020
Income £564,300 *Total grants* £139,300
Grants to organisations £139,300
Assets £18,390,000

TRUSTEES Russell Pullen; Michael Raymond; Alisdair Kruger Thomson.

OTHER INFORMATION Bloxham School receives the majority of the grant total each year. Only organisations that received grants of over £1,200 were listed as beneficiaries in the charity's accounts. Grants of under £1,200 totalled £22,500.

HOW TO APPLY Apply in writing to the correspondent. The trust has stated that applications are considered throughout the year, although funds are not always available.

CONTACT DETAILS Russell Pullen, Trustee, 17 The South Border, Purley, Surrey CR8 3LL *Tel.* 020 8660 9133 *Email* russell@pullen.cix.co.uk

■ The Rayne Foundation

CC NO 1179912 **ESTABLISHED** 1962

WHERE FUNDING CAN BE GIVEN UK.

WHO CAN BENEFIT Small and medium-sized registered charities; not-for-profit organisations.

WHAT IS FUNDED Health; education; social welfare; the arts; mental health, specifically for young people; carers; older people; social change.

WHAT IS NOT FUNDED Medical research (including cancer research); retrospective expenditure; capital appeals; campaigning and lobbying work; endowments; one-off events (including performances, festivals, conferences, holidays, respite breaks and residential trips); community transport schemes and vehicle purchases; church halls and community centres; running costs of local organisations; feasibility studies or scoping work; individuals; organisations working or based outside the UK; brand new organisations; organisations which have applied and been rejected within the last 12 months; charities supporting servicemen and women.

TYPE OF GRANT Salaries and all types of project costs plus a reasonable contribution to overheads (there is no fixed percentage); general running or core costs (normally for a maximum of three years); capital costs of buildings and equipment (unless specifically stated in certain sectors); 'seed corn' projects which are likely to attract other funding, if successful; social investment loans.

RANGE OF GRANTS Typically between £10,000 and £20,000 for up to three years.

SAMPLE GRANTS Nightingale Hammerson (£124,500); Off the Record – Bristol (£90,000); The Forward Trust (£75,000): Breaking Barriers (£60,000); Bluebell Care Trust (£40,000); Wales Millennium Centre (£10,000); Student Hubs (£5,000).

FINANCES *Financial year end* 30/11/2019 *Income* £1,980,000 *Total grants* £1,990,000 *Grants to organisations* £1,990,000 *Assets* £112,760,000

TRUSTEES Lady Jane Rayne; The Hon. Robert Rayne; Prof. Sir Anthony Newman Taylor; Sir Emyr Parry; Lady Hilary Browne-Wilkinson; The Hon. Natasha Rayne; The Hon. Nicholas Rayne; Rabbi Baroness Julia Neuberger.

OTHER INFORMATION The 2018/19 accounts were the latest available at the time of writing (June 2021).

HOW TO APPLY Application forms and guidelines can be downloaded from the foundation's website.

CONTACT DETAILS Morin Carew, Grants Administrator, 3 Bromley Place, London W1T 6DB *Tel.* 020 7487 9656 *Email* info@raynefoundation.org.uk *Website* www.raynefoundation.org.uk

■ The Rayne Trust

CC NO 207392 **ESTABLISHED** 1958

WHERE FUNDING CAN BE GIVEN UK and Israel.

WHO CAN BENEFIT Registered charities, NGOs and not-for-profit organisations.

WHAT IS FUNDED Jewish organisations; mental health; disadvantaged people; the arts; education; understanding between cultures (in particular strengthening relationships between Jews and Arabs); social cohesion.

WHAT IS NOT FUNDED Individuals; retrospective costs; repayment of debts; general appeals; contributions to endowments; repeat funding; one-off events; feasibility studies or research; awareness raising campaigns and lobbying; organisations whose levels of free reserves are higher than 75% of their annual expenditure.

TYPE OF GRANT Salaries; project costs (including a reasonable contribution to overheads or on-costs); seedcorn and development funding.

RANGE OF GRANTS £10,000 to £20,000 per annum for up to three years.

SAMPLE GRANTS Israel Centre for Education Innovation (£100,000); Israel Trauma Coalition (£50,000); International Health Partners UK and UK Homes 4 Heroes (£20,000 each); Chickenshed Theatre Trust (£8,000); Cancer United and Jewish Museum London (£5,000 each).

FINANCES *Financial year end* 31/03/2020 *Income* £788,500 *Total grants* £576,800 *Grants to organisations* £576,800 *Assets* £33,260,000

TRUSTEES Lady Jane Rayne; The Hon. Robert Rayne; The Hon. Tamara Wood; Damian Rayne.

OTHER INFORMATION Grants payable during the year amounted to £95,200 in the UK and £497,400 in Israel. Only beneficiaries of grants of £5,000 and above were listed in the accounts. Grants of under £5,000 totalled £24,500.

HOW TO APPLY Stage one application forms can be downloaded from the trust's website and should be returned to israelapplications@raynetrust.org. If successful, in stage two you will have an opportunity to offer a fully developed and formal proposal.

CONTACT DETAILS The Trustees, 3 Bromley Place, London W1T 6DB *Tel.* 020 7487 9650 *Email* info@raynefoundation.org.uk *Website* https://www.raynefoundation.org.uk/grants/isr/current/guidelines

■ The John Rayner Charitable Trust

CC NO 802363 **ESTABLISHED** 1989

WHERE FUNDING CAN BE GIVEN UK.

WHO CAN BENEFIT Registered charities.

WHAT IS FUNDED Children and young people; carers and older people; health; people with disabilities; sport; the arts.

TYPE OF GRANT Core costs; project funding.

RANGE OF GRANTS £1,000 to £5,000.

SAMPLE GRANTS The Anti-Slavery Collective (£10,000); The Brain Tumour Charity (£4,000); Independent Age (£3,000); Project Food (£2,000).

FINANCES *Financial year end* 05/04/2020 *Income* £40,500 *Total grants* £55,000 *Grants to organisations* £55,000 *Assets* £781,600

TRUSTEES Juliet Wilkinson; Dr Jonathan Rayner; Louise McNeilage.

OTHER INFORMATION Grants were made to 16 organisations in 2019/20.

HOW TO APPLY Apply via the trust's website.

CONTACT DETAILS The Trustees, Scarwood, Mildenhall, Marlborough SN8 2NG *Tel.* 07771 631722 *Email* info@raynertrust.co.uk *Website* https://www.raynertrust.co.uk

■ The Sir James Reckitt Charity

CC NO 225356 **ESTABLISHED** 1921

WHERE FUNDING CAN BE GIVEN Hull and the East Riding of Yorkshire and UK. Geographical restrictions do not apply to Quaker causes.

WHO CAN BENEFIT Community organisations; Quaker organisations; national and regional charities; CICs; uniformed groups; schools.

WHAT IS FUNDED General charitable purposes, focusing on: children and young people; education; older people; the environment; medical causes; social work; Quaker causes.

TYPE OF GRANT Start-up and core costs; purchase of equipment and materials; building improvements; training costs; project development costs.

RANGE OF GRANTS Generally up to £10,000, although larger applications may be considered.

SAMPLE GRANTS The Retreat-York (£30,000); Sidcot School (£25,000); North Humberside Hospice Project (£20,000); Hymers College (£13,000); The Brain Tumour Charity (£10,000); Stroke Association (£5,000); DEBRA (£2,000).

FINANCES *Financial year end* 31/12/2019 *Income* £1,540,000 *Total grants* £1,348,300 *Grants to organisations* £1,240,000 *Assets* £49,770,000

TRUSTEES William Upton; James Holt; Robert Gibson; Ondine Upton; Caroline Jennings; Philip Holt; Robin Upton; Sarah Craven; Charles Maxted; Simon James Upton; Simon Edward Upton; Edward Upton; Rebecca Holt; Andrew Palfreman; James Atherton; Oliver Jennings.

OTHER INFORMATION In 2019, 386 grants were made to individuals totalling £105,100 for social welfare purposes. During the year, 59 grants of less than £2,000 were made totalling £59,900.

HOW TO APPLY Applications should be made by letter or email and sent to the Administrator at their postal address. Further information and guidelines can be found on the charity's website. Applications are measured against the charity's guidelines and decisions are taken at twice-yearly trustees' meetings in May and November.

CONTACT DETAILS The Administrator, 7 Derrymore Road, Willerby, Hull, East Yorkshire HU10 6ES *Tel.* 01482 655861 *Email* charity@thesirjamesreckittcharity.org.uk *Website* www.thesirjamesreckittcharity.org.uk

■ Red Hill Charitable Trust

CC NO 307891 **ESTABLISHED** 1948

WHERE FUNDING CAN BE GIVEN East Anglia, London and the home counties (west of Hampshire).

WHO CAN BENEFIT Charitable organisations.

WHAT IS FUNDED The promotion of education, including social and physical training and access to education, of young people under the age of 25 who have emotional or behavioural difficulties.

WHAT IS NOT FUNDED Individuals.

TYPE OF GRANT Project funding, primarily for capital costs. Grants can only be made for one year at a time.

RANGE OF GRANTS £1,000 to £5,000.

SAMPLE GRANTS Children's House Montessori (£8,300); Media Community (£5,000); The Gifted Organisation (£4,000); Chickenshed (£3,000); Oarsome Choice (£2,500); Goldwyn School (£1,500); Mill Rythe Infant School (£1,100).

FINANCES *Financial year end* 31/08/2019 *Income* £75,000 *Total grants* £78,600 *Grants to organisations* £78,600 *Assets* £3,150,000

TRUSTEES Antony Bunting; Michael Startup; Roger Barton; Bob Law; John Moore; Pam Jones; Kevin Moule; Allan Adams; Shellina Prendergast; Nicola Clark.

OTHER INFORMATION Grants were awarded to 23 organisations in 2018/19. The 2018/19 accounts were the latest available at the time of writing (February 2021).

HOW TO APPLY Application forms may be downloaded from the trust's website and, once completed, must be returned to the correspondent by email as a Word-processed document. Supporting materials may be sent electronically or as a hard copy. The trustees hold meetings twice yearly, in March and October. Applications for these meetings should reach the correspondent by 15 February and 15 September, respectively.

CONTACT DETAILS The Clerk to the Trustees, 3 Thurnham Oast, Aldington Lane, Thurnham, Kent ME14 3LL *Tel.* 01622 213707 *Email* clerk@redhilltrust.org *Website* www.redhilltrust.org

■ C. A. Redfern Charitable Foundation

CC NO 299918 **ESTABLISHED** 1988

WHERE FUNDING CAN BE GIVEN UK.

WHO CAN BENEFIT Registered charities; hospices.

WHAT IS FUNDED General charitable purposes; health and medical care and research; social welfare.

RANGE OF GRANTS Generally between £1,000 and £10,000.

SAMPLE GRANTS South Bucks Riding for the Disabled (£30,000); Saints and Sinners and White Ensign (£10,000 each); St Michael's Hospice, Canine Partners for Independence and St Luke's Primary School (£5,000 each); Blesma (£4,000); Youth Sport and Epilepsy Research UK (£3,000 each); The Rainbow Trust and Oracle Cancer Trust (£2,000 each); Turtle Key Arts (£1,000).

FINANCES *Financial year end* 05/04/2019 *Income* £176,700 *Total grants* £201,000 *Grants to organisations* £201,000 *Assets* £5,800,000

TRUSTEES William Maclaren; David Redfern; Simon Ward; Julian Heslop.

OTHER INFORMATION The 2018/19 accounts were the latest available at the time of writing (January 2021). Grants were made to 54 organisations during the year.

HOW TO APPLY Unsolicited applications are not accepted.

CONTACT DETAILS The Trustees, c/o PricewaterhouseCoopers, 3 Forbury Place, 23 Forbury Road, Reading, Berkshire RG1 3JH *Tel.* 0118 938 3128

■ The Reece Foundation

CC NO 1121325 **ESTABLISHED** 2007

WHERE FUNDING CAN BE GIVEN UK, with a strong preference for the North East, including Northumberland, Tyne and Wear and County Durham.

WHO CAN BENEFIT Registered charities; schools; universities.

WHAT IS FUNDED The development of maths, science and engineering skills; STEM employment opportunities.

WHAT IS NOT FUNDED Repeat applications within 12 months; sponsorship of any kind.
RANGE OF GRANTS No minimum or maximum threshold.
SAMPLE GRANTS Newcastle United Foundation (£307,000); Maggie's Centre – Freeman Hospital (£100,000); Beamish Museum (£50,000); Success4All (£40,000); Greenpower (£37,000); St Cuthbert's School (£21,000); Cambridge University Eco Racing (£20,000).
FINANCES *Financial year end* 31/12/2019 *Income* £1,560,000 *Total grants* £1,210,000 *Grants to organisations* £1,210,000 *Assets* £28,250,000
TRUSTEES Eric Morgan; Simon Gilroy; John Reece; Anne Reece; David Sandbach.
OTHER INFORMATION Only the beneficiaries of grants above £20,000 were listed in the 2019 accounts (14 organisations). Grants of below £20,000 totalled £185,600.
HOW TO APPLY Application forms are available to download from the foundation's website. Forms should be returned by post or email (applications@reece-foundation.org). Applications can be made at any time and are considered at quarterly meetings. Decisions may take up to six months.
CONTACT DETAILS The Trustees, Armstrong Works, Scotswood Road, Newcastle upon Tyne, Tyne and Wear NE15 6UX *Tel.* 0191 234 8700 *Email* enquiries@reece-foundation.org *Website* https://www.reece-foundation.org

■ Richard Reeve's Foundation

CC NO 1136337 **ESTABLISHED** 2010
WHERE FUNDING CAN BE GIVEN Camden, the City of London and Islington.
WHO CAN BENEFIT Registered charities; unregistered charities; CICs; social enterprises; schools; local authorities.
WHAT IS FUNDED Education and training for children and young people (up to the age of 25). The current focuses of the foundation are: support for projects focused on raising literacy and numeracy; progression into work; music education; maintenance grants.
WHAT IS NOT FUNDED Individuals.
TYPE OF GRANT Capital costs; project funding; unrestricted funding.
RANGE OF GRANTS £5,000 to £156,000.
SAMPLE GRANTS New North Academy (£156,600); Pakeman Primary School (£151,500); London Borough of Islington (two grants totalling £116,500); EGA School (£55,000); Action Tutoring (£36,000); London Borough of Camden (£17,900); Rotherfield Primary School (£7,700); Hegarty Maths (£4,800).
FINANCES *Financial year end* 30/06/2020 *Income* £1,340,000 *Total grants* £875,800 *Grants to organisations* £816,800 *Assets* £46,210,000
TRUSTEES Michael Hudson; Mark Jessett; Gerald Rothwell; Charlotte Hilton; Jo Emmerson; Benjamin Monaghan; Alistair Wilson; Tracey Shackle; Elizabeth Gallagher.
OTHER INFORMATION Grants to organisations were broken down as follows: literacy and numeracy (10 grants totalling £537,200); progression into work (12 grants totalling £228,600); heritage (a grant of £39,000); music (a grant of £11,800). Grants to individuals for educational purposes totalled £50,000.
HOW TO APPLY The charity's website states: 'Contact us with an outline of any proposed project and discuss it with the clerk in the first instance. We will advise of the application process at that stage.' Check the website for up-to-date information on applications.
CONTACT DETAILS Suzanna Nagle, Clerk and Company Secretary, 20–22 Wenlock Road, London N1 7GU *Tel.* 020 8323 2662 *Email* clerk@richardreevesfoundation.org.uk *Website* www.richardreevesfoundation.org.uk

■ Rentrust Foundation Ltd

CC NO 1163817 **ESTABLISHED** 2014
WHERE FUNDING CAN BE GIVEN UK.
WHO CAN BENEFIT Charitable organisations; religious educational (Jewish) institutions.
WHAT IS FUNDED Education; poverty relief; welfare; Jewish causes.
TYPE OF GRANT One-off and multi-year.
RANGE OF GRANTS Up to £100,000 (larger in the case of recurring grants).
SAMPLE GRANTS Mars Org. Ltd (£101,500); United Talmudical Associates Ltd (£100,000); Toldos Ahron Trust Ltd (£40,000); The ZSV Trust (£30,400); Sharei Chesed – London (£25,700).
FINANCES *Financial year end* 31/07/2020 *Income* £478,000 *Total grants* £371,500 *Grants to organisations* £371,500 *Assets* £1,900
TRUSTEES Esther Wosner; Pessi Eisenbach; Chavi Simon.
OTHER INFORMATION Only beneficiaries of grants over £10,000 were listed in the accounts. Grants of under £10,000 totalled £74,000.
HOW TO APPLY Contact the correspondent for information on the application process.
CONTACT DETAILS The Trustees, 5 Windus Road, London N16 6UT *Tel.* 020 3137 9885 *Email* cf@nuenterprise.co.uk

■ The Reso Charitable Foundation

CC NO 1163282 **ESTABLISHED** 2015
WHERE FUNDING CAN BE GIVEN UK; USA; South Africa.
WHO CAN BENEFIT Charitable organisations.
WHAT IS FUNDED General charitable purposes.
RANGE OF GRANTS £4,000 to £70,000.
SAMPLE GRANTS Previous beneficiaries have included: Tricycle Theatre Company (£70,000); Freedom from Torture (£50,000); Kensington and Chelsea Foundation (£25,000); Child Autism UK, Falconer School, Migrant and Refugee Communities Forum and Saffron Walden Cricket Club (£10,000 each); Brooke Donkey Sanctuary and Rhino Conservation Botswana (£5,000 each); St Cuthbert's Centre (£4,200).
FINANCES *Financial year end* 31/12/2019 *Income* £0 *Total grants* £335,300 *Grants to organisations* £335,300
TRUSTEES Andrew Stafford-Deitsch; Tony Tabatznik; Gordon Grender.
OTHER INFORMATION Full accounts were not available to view on the Charity Commission's website due to the foundation's low income. We have therefore estimated the foundation's grant total based on its total expenditure.
HOW TO APPLY Contact the correspondent for further information.
CONTACT DETAILS Andrew Stafford-Deitsch, Trustee, Blue Rock Services Ltd, 7 Cavendish Square, London W1G 0PE *Tel.* 020 7491 2262 *Email* theresocharitablefoundation@bluerockservices.co.uk

■ The Resolution Trust

CC NO 1123128 **ESTABLISHED** 2007

WHERE FUNDING CAN BE GIVEN UK.

WHO CAN BENEFIT Charitable organisations.

WHAT IS FUNDED Research/education in economic and social sciences with a particular focus on the causes, prevention or relief of poverty.

TYPE OF GRANT Project funding; research.

SAMPLE GRANTS Resolution Foundation (£6.95 million); Prospect Magazine (£1.52 million); BGV (£101,100); The Old Vic (£100,000); Labour Xchange (£15,000); Citizens UK (£10,000); Life Beat (£5,000).

FINANCES *Financial year end* 30/09/2019 *Income* £962,300 *Total grants* £8,700,000 *Grants to organisations* £8,700,000 *Assets* £43,490,000

TRUSTEE The Resolution Trust (Trustee) Ltd.

OTHER INFORMATION The 2018/19 accounts were the latest available at the time of writing (May 2021). The trust made grants to seven organisations. A large proportion of the grant total was awarded to the Resolution Foundation.

HOW TO APPLY Contact the correspondent for further information. Funding is primarily given to the trust's existing partners.

CONTACT DETAILS The Trustees, 2 Queen Annes Gate, London SW1H 9AA *Tel.* 020 3372 2960 *Email* info@resolutiontrust.org *Website* resolutiontrust.org

■ The Rest-Harrow Trust

CC NO 238042 **ESTABLISHED** 1964

WHERE FUNDING CAN BE GIVEN UK.

WHO CAN BENEFIT Registered charities.

WHAT IS FUNDED General charitable purposes, particularly medical causes and social welfare. There is some preference for Jewish organisations.

WHAT IS NOT FUNDED Non-registered charities; individuals.

TYPE OF GRANT Project funding; capital costs.

RANGE OF GRANTS From £100 to £2,000. The majority of grants are of under £500.

SAMPLE GRANTS British Friends of the Hebrew University (£2,000); Jewish Care (£1,000); Alzheimer's Society (£700); Chai Cancer Care and Motor Neurone Disease Association (£500 each); Nightingale House Hospice (£200); Blue Watch Youth Centre, Citizens Advice Mid Lincolnshire and Contact the Elderly (£100 each).

FINANCES *Financial year end* 05/04/2020 *Income* £90,100 *Total grants* £67,900 *Grants to organisations* £67,900 *Assets* £906,000

TRUSTEES Janet Bloch; Dominic Flynn; Judith Portrait.

OTHER INFORMATION Grants are usually made to national bodies rather than local branches or local groups. Grants were awarded to 298 organisations during 2019/20.

HOW TO APPLY Apply in writing to the correspondent. Only submissions from eligible bodies are acknowledged.

CONTACT DETAILS The Trustees, 21 Whitefriars Street, London EC4Y 8JJ *Tel.* 020 7092 6990

■ Reuben Foundation

CC NO 1094130 **ESTABLISHED** 2002

WHERE FUNDING CAN BE GIVEN UK and overseas (particularly Israel).

WHO CAN BENEFIT Charitable organisations, including universities and Jewish organisations; individuals.

WHAT IS FUNDED Healthcare; education; general charitable purposes.

RANGE OF GRANTS Typically £500 to £25,000. Several large grants of over £100,000 are made per year.

SAMPLE GRANTS Illuminated River Foundation (£1.5 million); Royal Marsden Cancer Charity (£1 million); British Academy of Film and Television Arts (£500,000); Community Security Trust (£225,000); ARK Schools (£125,000); Centrepoint (£80,200); Great Ormond Street Hospital Children's Charity (£33,400); Jewish Care (£10,000); The Racehorse Sanctuary (£5,000).

FINANCES *Financial year end* 31/12/2019 *Income* £5,590,000 *Total grants* £5,143,400 *Grants to organisations* £5,070,000 *Assets* £88,760,000

TRUSTEES Simon Reuben; Malcolm Turner; James Reuben; Dana Reuben; Richard Stone; Eileen Sawyer; Reuben Reuben.

OTHER INFORMATION Grants to individuals totalled £73,400 in 2019. The foundation supports a number of scholarship initiatives including the Reuben Scholarship programme alongside the University of Oxford, University College London, ARK Schools and the University of Cambridge.

HOW TO APPLY The foundation's website states that applications for grants are made by invitation only.

CONTACT DETAILS The Trustees, 4th Floor, Millbank Tower, 21–24 Millbank, London SW1P 4PQ *Tel.* 020 7802 5014 *Email* contact@reubenfoundation.com *Website* www.reubenfoundation.com

■ The Revere Charitable Trust

CC NO 1117369 **ESTABLISHED** 2006

WHERE FUNDING CAN BE GIVEN UK.

WHO CAN BENEFIT Registered charities; hospices.

WHAT IS FUNDED Medical research, in particular research into asthma and cancer; the environment; arts and culture; animal welfare; children and young people; people with disabilities.

RANGE OF GRANTS £2,500 to £105,000.

SAMPLE GRANTS Alzheimer's Research UK (£105,000); Royal Marsden Cancer Charity (£75,000); Médecins Sans Frontières (£45,000); Essex and Herts Air Ambulance (£25,000); Action for the River Kennet (£15,000); Brain Tumour Support (£10,000); Royal Horticultural Society (£5,000); LINK (£2,500).

FINANCES *Financial year end* 05/04/2020 *Income* £856,600 *Total grants* £722,700 *Grants to organisations* £722,700 *Assets* £6,530,000

TRUSTEES John Saner; Peter Willmott; Richard Willmott; Teifion Evans.

OTHER INFORMATION During 2019/20, 32 organisations received grants.

HOW TO APPLY Contact the correspondent for further information.

CONTACT DETAILS Teifion Evans, Trustee, 9 Hillside Close, Heddington, Calne, Wiltshire SN11 0PZ *Tel.* 01380 859198 *Email* teifion@tevans.plus.com

■ RG Foundation

CC NO 1180097 **ESTABLISHED** 2018

WHERE FUNDING CAN BE GIVEN Worldwide.

WHO CAN BENEFIT Registered charities.

WHAT IS FUNDED Health and well-being; education; improving access to employment.

RANGE OF GRANTS £8,000 to £40,000.

SAMPLE GRANTS Radical Recruit (£39,700); Hope for Justice (£20,000); End of Homelessness (£18,000); Centre of Youth Services (£11,900); Doc Wayne (£8,400).

FINANCES *Financial year end* 31/08/2020 *Income* £124,100 *Total grants* £146,000 *Grants to organisations* £146,000 *Assets* £23,300

TRUSTEES Stella Donoghue; Glenn Elliot; Debra Corey; Graham Simmonds; Louise Rogers.

OTHER INFORMATION This is the charitable arm of Reward Gateway, an employee engagement platform. Grants were awarded to eight organisations during the year.

HOW TO APPLY To submit a grant application, an organisation or project must be nominated by a Reward Gateway employee or a trustee of the RG Foundation, although the foundation invites invite enquiries about its grant application process via email.

CONTACT DETAILS The Trustees, 265 Tottenham Court Road, London, W1T 7RQ *Tel.* 07495 082472 *Website* rg-foundation.org

■ Rhodi Charitable Trust

CC NO 1082915 **ESTABLISHED** 2000

WHERE FUNDING CAN BE GIVEN UK and overseas, with a preference for Preston and India.

WHO CAN BENEFIT Charitable organisations; individuals.

WHAT IS FUNDED Poverty relief; social welfare; the advancement of religion; education; health.

SAMPLE GRANTS A list of beneficiaries was not included in the annual report and accounts.

FINANCES *Financial year end* 31/12/2019 *Income* £181,400 *Total grants* £115,200 *Grants to organisations* £115,200 *Assets* £1,330,000

TRUSTEES Hamida Bux; Ibrahim Bux.

OTHER INFORMATION According to its 2019 accounts, the charity operates and finances five multi-faith facilities at motorway service stations across the UK.

HOW TO APPLY Contact the correspondent for further information.

CONTACT DETAILS The Trustees, 1 Fishwick Park, Mercer Street, Preston, Lancashire PR1 4LZ *Tel.* 01772 562288

■ The Rhododendron Trust

CC NO 267192 **ESTABLISHED** 1974

WHERE FUNDING CAN BE GIVEN UK and overseas.

WHO CAN BENEFIT Registered charities.

WHAT IS FUNDED Overseas aid; disability; mental health; prisoners and ex-offenders; homelessness; older people; disadvantaged children; the arts and culture; the environment.

WHAT IS NOT FUNDED Individuals, for example on gap-year projects with another charity; local branches of national societies; medical or academic research; missionary charities.

TYPE OF GRANT Project costs.

RANGE OF GRANTS £500 to £1,500.

SAMPLE GRANTS Previous beneficiaries have included: African Revival, Book Aid International, Hardman Trust, Minority Rights Group and Womankind Worldwide (£1,000 each); Build IT International, English Touring Opera, Historic Chapels Trust, Prison Me No Way and Solar Aid (£500 each).

FINANCES *Financial year end* 05/04/2020 *Income* £146,500 *Total grants* £62,000 *Grants to organisations* £62,000 *Assets* £2,160,000

TRUSTEES Sarah Ray; Sarah Oliver; Elizabeth Baldwin; Wendy Anderson.

OTHER INFORMATION Around 50% of grants are given to overseas charities, 40% are awarded to UK charities for social welfare purposes and 10% are given to UK charities to support the arts and the environment.

HOW TO APPLY Apply in writing to the correspondent. Guidelines are available on the website. Grants are awarded once a year, typically in February or March after the trustees' meeting in January. Applicants will be informed within about a month if they have been unsuccessful.

CONTACT DETAILS The Grants Officer, 6 Bridge Street, Richmond, North Yorkshire DL10 4RW *Tel.* 07495 752060 *Email* mail@rhododendron-trust.org.uk *Website* www.rhododendron-trust.org.uk

■ Riada Trust

OSCR NO SC028314 **ESTABLISHED** 1998

WHERE FUNDING CAN BE GIVEN UK and overseas.

WHO CAN BENEFIT Charitable organisations; registered charities; hospices; hospitals.

WHAT IS FUNDED General charitable purposes, including: health; Christianity; the armed forces; sport and recreation; disability; young people.

WHAT IS NOT FUNDED Individuals.

TYPE OF GRANT Capital costs.

RANGE OF GRANTS Typically £1,000 to £5,000.

SAMPLE GRANTS Euan's Guide (£12,500); Children's Hospice Association Scotland, DEBRA and Scottish Love in Action (£5,000 each); Cricket Scotland Development Trust and Gurkha Welfare Trust (£2,000 each); Bethany Christian Trust and RAF Benevolent Fund (£1,000 each).

FINANCES *Financial year end* 31/12/2019 *Income* £48,800 *Total grants* £50,000 *Grants to organisations* £50,000 *Assets* £1,360,000

OTHER INFORMATION Grants tend to be recurring: 13 of the 14 charities that received funding in 2018 were also funded in 2019. A total of 15 organisations received funding in 2019.

HOW TO APPLY Contact the correspondent for further information.

CONTACT DETAILS The Trustees, 15 Blackford Road, Edinburgh EH9 2DT

■ Daisie Rich Trust

CC NO 236706 **ESTABLISHED** 1964

WHERE FUNDING CAN BE GIVEN Isle of Wight.

WHO CAN BENEFIT Charitable and community organisations and individuals (particularly former employees, or their spouses, of Upward and Rich Ltd).

WHAT IS FUNDED General charitable purposes; social welfare; community; youth; health; arts, culture and environment.

TYPE OF GRANT Running costs; project funding.

RANGE OF GRANTS Typically between £250 and £5,000.

SAMPLE GRANTS Brading Community Partnership (£10,000); Aspire Ryde and Barton Primary School (£5,000 each); Isle of Wight Citizens Advice (£4,000); Footprint Trust and Greater

Ryde Benevolent Trust (£3,000 each); Fair Haven Housing Trust (£1,500); Combat Stress and Isle of Wight Prostate Cancer Support Group (£1,000 each); YMCA – Young Carers Project (£700); 1st East Cowes Sea Scouts Group (£250).

FINANCES *Financial year end* 05/04/2020 *Income* £164,300 *Total grants* £140,700 *Grants to organisations* £115,100 *Assets* £3,370,000

TRUSTEES Adrian Medley; Ann Medley; Maurice Flux; David Longford; James Attrill; Claire Locke.

OTHER INFORMATION Grants were made to 61 organisations during the year. Grants to organisations and individuals (not including grants made to ex-employees of Upward and Rich Ltd – £24,100) were broken down as follows: welfare (£29,300); community (£26,800); youth (£25,400); health (£24,700); arts, culture and environment (£10,500).

HOW TO APPLY Application forms are available on the trust's website. The trustees hold regular meetings to decide on grant applications and are assisted by information gathered by the administrator. Each application is considered on its own merits and the amounts granted vary.

CONTACT DETAILS Lyn Mitchell, Administrator, The Hawthorns, Main Road, Arreton, Newport, Isle of Wight PO30 3AD *Tel.* 07866 449855 *Email* info@daisierichtrust.org.uk *Website* www.daisierichtrust.org.uk

■ The Sir Cliff Richard Charitable Trust

CC NO 1096412 **ESTABLISHED** 1969

WHERE FUNDING CAN BE GIVEN UK.

WHO CAN BENEFIT Registered charities.

WHAT IS FUNDED General charitable purposes that reflect the support, Christian commitment and interests of Sir Cliff Richard.

RANGE OF GRANTS Grants up to £2,000.

SAMPLE GRANTS A list of beneficiaries was not included in the annual report and accounts.

FINANCES *Financial year end* 30/04/2020 *Income* £150,800 *Total grants* £60,000 *Grants to organisations* £60,000 *Assets* £192,500

TRUSTEES Sir Cliff Richard; William Latham; Malcolm Smith; Tania Hogan.

HOW TO APPLY Contact the correspondent for further information.

CONTACT DETAILS William Latham, Trustee, PO Box 423, Leatherhead, Surrey KT22 2HJ *Tel.* 01372 467752 *Email* general@cliffrichard.org

■ The Clive and Sylvia Richards Charity Ltd

CC NO 327155 **ESTABLISHED** 1986

WHERE FUNDING CAN BE GIVEN Mainly UK, with some preference for Herefordshire.

WHO CAN BENEFIT Registered charities; individuals; religious bodies/institutions; hospitals; hospices; schools.

WHAT IS FUNDED General charitable purposes, but there is a preference for education, community, healthcare, heritage, the arts and religious institutions.

WHAT IS NOT FUNDED The charity does not usually fund the following: national charities; operating costs; salaries; activities that are/were the responsibility of a statutory organisation are not eligible. Overseas applications must have a UK sponsor, preferably one that is known to the trustees.

TYPE OF GRANT Capital costs; seed funding/start-up funding.

SAMPLE GRANTS Three Counties Medical School – Worcester University (£250,000); Cobalt Health (£225,000); Queen Elizabeth High School (£150,000); Sir Thomas Rich's School (£70,000); Bristol Aero Collection Trust (£50,000).

FINANCES *Financial year end* 31/03/2020 *Income* £1,810,000 *Total grants* £1,000,000 *Grants to organisations* £1,000,000 *Assets* £1,160,000

TRUSTEES Peter Henry; Sylvia Richards; Peter Dines; Peregrine Banbury; David Iddon; Gareth Davies; Liz Deutsch.

OTHER INFORMATION The 2019/20 annual report provides the following breakdown of grants awarded: healthcare and medical causes (£469,700); education (£295,900); religious (£50,700); community and other (£55,400); the arts and culture (£84,900). Grants of less than £50,000 totalled £352,700.

HOW TO APPLY Visit the charity's website for information on how to apply, application deadlines and the 'Guidance for Applicants' document.

CONTACT DETAILS Caren Administrator, Lower Hope Estate, Ullingswick, Hereford, Herefordshire HR1 3JF *Tel.* 01432 820557 *Email* admin@csrcharity.com *Website* csrcharity.com

■ Humphrey Richardson Taylor Charitable Trust

CC NO 1062836 **ESTABLISHED** 1997

WHERE FUNDING CAN BE GIVEN Surrey.

WHO CAN BENEFIT Schools; amateur music organisations; individuals.

WHAT IS FUNDED Music and music education. A list of typical purposes for which support may be given is provided on the trust's website.

WHAT IS NOT FUNDED It is rare for the trust to give funding to schools for transport costs, concert tickets or accommodation.

TYPE OF GRANT Capital projects or items (instruments, sheet music, music computers, etc.); one-off grants; scholarships; music tuition; concerts and events; sponsorship.

RANGE OF GRANTS Up to £50,000 but typically between £1,000 and £5,000.

SAMPLE GRANTS Reigate School (£50,000); Royal College of Music (£35,000); Glenthorne High School (£20,000); University of Surrey (£18,000); Southbank Sinfonia (£8,700); Guildford Opera (£5,000); Dorking Chamber Orchestra and Surrey Philharmonic Society (£2,000 each); Thames Philharmonia (£1,000); Beacon School (£450).

FINANCES *Financial year end* 31/12/2019 *Income* £624,500 *Total grants* £470,000 *Grants to organisations* £419,000 *Assets* £15,550,000

TRUSTEES Rowena Cox; William Malings; Stephen Oliver; Colin Edgerton; Ian Catling; Michael Wood; Brian Bennett.

OTHER INFORMATION During the year, grants were awarded to schools (£255,700), societies (£163,200) and individuals (£51,000). Grants were awarded to organisations for the following purposes: tuition fees and scholarships (£144,300); instrument and equipment purchases (£133,700); concerts and sponsorship (£92,000); capital projects (£48,700).

HOW TO APPLY Applications should be made by email to the correspondent. The trustees meet five times a year to consider applications. Applications should be no longer than four to six pages of A4 when printed. Specific application criteria and guidelines for schools, musical societies and individuals are available to view on the website.

CONTACT DETAILS Kate Perry, Administrator, 32 Chipstead Station Parade, Chipstead, Coulsdon, Surrey CR5 3TF *Tel.* 01737 557680 *Email* hrtaylortrust@btconnect.com *Website* www.hrtaylortrust.org.uk

■ Richmond Parish Lands Charity

CC NO 200069 **ESTABLISHED** 1786

WHERE FUNDING CAN BE GIVEN Richmond, Ham, Sheen, Mortlake and Barnes (the SW13, SW14, TW9 and TW10 postcode areas).

WHO CAN BENEFIT Registered charities; not-for-profit organisations; CICs and CIOs; sports associations; social enterprises; schools; places of worship; individuals.

WHAT IS FUNDED General charitable purposes, including the following: education; sport and recreation; health; community services; younger and older people; social welfare.

WHAT IS NOT FUNDED Private companies.

TYPE OF GRANT Both one-off and recurring grants; core costs; project funding; salaries; capital costs; seed funding/start-up funding.

RANGE OF GRANTS Typically £400 to £60,000.

SAMPLE GRANTS Richmond Carers Centre (£69,900); Citizens Advice (£65,100); Off the Record (£46,700); TAG Youth Club (£29,200); Friends of Kew (£18,000); Mortlake Community Association (£11,000); oneRichmond (£10,400); Resources for Autism (£5,000); Healthwatch (£1,500); Museum of Richmond (£1,000); Richmond Synagogue (£730); Christmas Day Dinner (£400).

FINANCES *Financial year end* 30/06/2020 *Income* £2,740,000 *Total grants* £1,758,300 *Grants to organisations* £1,550,000 *Assets* £107,620,000

TRUSTEES Paul Velluet; Gill Moffett; Owen Carew-Jones; Paul Lawrence; Jerome Misso; Carol Fletcher; Joanna Nakielny; Chris Phillips; Cllr Richard Pyne; Ruth Scott; Claire O'Donnell; Peter Buckwell; Duncan Richford.

OTHER INFORMATION In 2019/20, within the foundation's standard funding programmes, grants to organisations totalled £1.18 million, split across the following categories: projects (£485,000); regularly funded organisations (£347,100); education (£261,000). In total, £1.55 million was awarded to 92 organisations and 22 schools. Grants to individuals totalled £208,300.

HOW TO APPLY There are separate application forms and guidelines for the various types of grants, all of which can be found on the foundation's helpful website. The foundation welcomes enquiries to discuss ideas for applications. The trustees consider applications at quarterly meetings.

CONTACT DETAILS Sharon La Ronde, Grants Director, Vestry House, 21 Paradise Road, Richmond, Surrey TW9 1SA *Tel.* 020 8948 5701 *Email* grants@rplc.org.uk *Website* www.rplc.org.uk

■ Ridgesave Ltd

CC NO 288020 **ESTABLISHED** 1983

WHERE FUNDING CAN BE GIVEN UK and overseas.

WHO CAN BENEFIT Charitable organisations.

WHAT IS FUNDED The advancement of the Jewish religion; education; social welfare.

RANGE OF GRANTS Typically up to £200,000.

SAMPLE GRANTS Kolel Belz Machnovkeh (£263,000); Beis Aharon Trust (£167,000); Achisomoch Aid Company Ltd (£113,000); Keren Ezra Mimtzika (£83,000); Friends of Mercaz Hatorah Belz Macnivka (£31,000).

FINANCES *Financial year end* 31/03/2020 *Income* £899,300 *Total grants* £974,400 *Grants to organisations* £974,400 *Assets* £979,900

TRUSTEES Zelda Weiss; Joseph Weiss; Mr E. Englander; Aaron Hoffman; Menachem Reichman.

HOW TO APPLY Contact the correspondent for information.

CONTACT DETAILS The Trustees, 141B Upper Clapton Road, London E5 9DB *Tel.* 020 8806 4271 *Email* mail@cohenarnold.com

■ Rigby Foundation

CC NO 1011259 **ESTABLISHED** 1992

WHERE FUNDING CAN BE GIVEN UK.

WHO CAN BENEFIT Registered charities; individuals; hospitals; theatres.

WHAT IS FUNDED General charitable purposes; health and the saving of lives; education; arts, culture and heritage; social welfare; the armed forces.

RANGE OF GRANTS Typically up to £30,000.

SAMPLE GRANTS South Warwickshire NHS Foundation Trust (£150,000); The Prince's Trust (£100,000); Place2Be (£83,200); Coventry City of Culture Trust and The Shakespeare Hospice (£20,000 each); Coventry Cathedral, 84 Squadron and Teach First (£10,000 each); Smiling Faces (£1,000); Coventry Cyrenians (£500); SSAFA (£200).

FINANCES *Financial year end* 05/04/2020 *Income* £42,400 *Total grants* £493,200 *Grants to organisations* £493,200 *Assets* £3,350,000

TRUSTEES Sir Peter Rigby; Patricia Rigby; Steven Rigby; James Rigby.

OTHER INFORMATION In 2019/20 approximately 68% (£333,000) of the grant total (£493,200) was distributed in three larger grants to three organisations. No grants were made to individuals. A minority of grants are recurring.

HOW TO APPLY Contact the correspondent for further information.

CONTACT DETAILS The Trustees, Bridgeway House, Bridgeway, Stratford-upon-Avon, Warwickshire CV37 6YX *Tel.* 01789 610000

■ The Sir John Ritblat Family Foundation

CC NO 262463 **ESTABLISHED** 1971

WHERE FUNDING CAN BE GIVEN UK.

WHO CAN BENEFIT Charitable organisations.

WHAT IS FUNDED General charitable causes, with some preference for the arts and culture.

WHAT IS NOT FUNDED Individuals.

RANGE OF GRANTS Grants range from £130 up to £21,000.

SAMPLE GRANTS National Trust (£21,000); British Ski and Snowboard National Foundation (£10,500); Royal Institute of Great Britain (£7,600); British Friends of the Art Museums of

Israel (£6,000); The Design Museum (£4,600); CST (£1,000); Winston's Wish (£130).
FINANCES *Financial year end* 05/04/2020
Income £55,700 *Total grants* £83,500
Grants to organisations £83,500
Assets £2,470,000
TRUSTEES Mr N. Ritblat; Mr C. Wagman; Mr J. Ritblat.
OTHER INFORMATION Grants were made to 35 organisations during the year.
HOW TO APPLY Contact the correspondent for further information.
CONTACT DETAILS The Trustees, c/o Delancey Group plc, Lansdowne House, 57 Berkeley Square, London W1J 6ER *Tel.* 020 7448 1956

■ The River Farm Foundation

CC NO 1113109 **ESTABLISHED** 2006
WHERE FUNDING CAN BE GIVEN UK and overseas.
WHO CAN BENEFIT Charitable organisations.
WHAT IS FUNDED General charitable purposes, in particular: health and well-being; education; community development; children; homelessness; disadvantaged groups.
RANGE OF GRANTS Mostly under £50,000.
SAMPLE GRANTS St Edmund Hall – Tutorial Fellowship (£697,700); Busoga Trust (£330,000); The King's School Worcester – Bursary Funds (£157,500); COESA (£24,500); Acorns Children's Hospice Trust (£20,000); NSPCC (£17,000); Shelter (£16,000); Royal British Legion (£6,000).
FINANCES *Financial year end* 05/04/2020
Income £196,200 *Total grants* £1,380,000
Grants to organisations £1,380,000
Assets £45,480,000
TRUSTEES Mark Haworth; Nigel Langstaff; Deborah Fisher.
OTHER INFORMATION During 2019/20, grants were made to 12 organisations. Grants were distributed in the following categories: education (£905,200); community development (£354,500); health and welfare (£102,000); the environment and heritage (£15,000).
HOW TO APPLY Contact the correspondent for further information.
CONTACT DETAILS Deborah Fisher, Trustee, Unit 4 Hill Farm, Kirby Road, Kirby Bedon, Norwich, Norfolk NR14 7DU *Tel.* 01508 480100 *Email* info@fisherlegal.co.uk

■ The River Trust

CC NO 275843 **ESTABLISHED** 1977
WHERE FUNDING CAN BE GIVEN UK, with a preference for Sussex.
WHO CAN BENEFIT Charitable organisations; missionaries.
WHAT IS FUNDED Evangelical Christian causes.
WHAT IS NOT FUNDED Individuals; repairs of church fabric; funding towards capital expenditure.
RANGE OF GRANTS £300 to £15,000.
SAMPLE GRANTS St Peter's – Brighton (£15,000); Stewardship (£9,500); Care for the Family (£5,300); Chestnut Tree House and Innovista International (£2,000 each); Soldiers and Airmen and St Luke's Healthcare (£1,000 each); Cress (£300).
FINANCES *Financial year end* 31/10/2019
Income £87,700 *Total grants* £128,000
Grants to organisations £128,000
Assets £509,300
TRUSTEES SG Kleinwort Hambros Trust Company (UK) Ltd; Davina Irwin-Clark.
OTHER INFORMATION The 2018/19 accounts were the latest available at the time of writing (May 2021). During the year, 47 grants were awarded within the following categories: the advancement of the Christian faith (£43,400); miscellaneous (£28,800); religious welfare work (£20,200); religious education (£20,100); church funds (£10,500); missionary work (£5,000).
HOW TO APPLY Apply in writing to the correspondent. Only successful applicants are notified of the trustees' decision. The 2018/19 annual report states: 'Donations are decided periodically, and it is unusual for the trustees to respond favourably to unsolicited appeals.'
CONTACT DETAILS Scott Rice, Administrator, SG Kleinwort Hambros Trust Company (UK) Ltd, 5th Floor, 8 St James's Square, London SW1Y 4JU *Tel.* 020 3207 7041 *Email* scott.rice@kleinworthambros.com

■ Rivers Foundation

CC NO 1078545 **ESTABLISHED** 1999
WHERE FUNDING CAN BE GIVEN UK and overseas.
WHO CAN BENEFIT Charitable organisations, with a preference for small charities.
WHAT IS FUNDED General charitable purposes; support for children and young adults; projects involving the education, social development and medical well-being of young people.
TYPE OF GRANT Project costs; capital costs; educational fees; overseas trips.
SAMPLE GRANTS UK grants: Centrepoint, Crisis, Dogs on the Street, Grenfell Athletics Football Club, London Philharmonic Orchestra, Music Masters, Parkinson's UK, Safe and Sound, The Longford Trust and Youth Music. Overseas grants: Chance for Nepal, Hua Hin Charity, Jungle Aid, Love Support United and Operation Smile.
FINANCES *Financial year end* 31/03/2020
Income £87,000 *Total grants* £134,300
Grants to organisations £134,300
Assets £640,000
TRUSTEES Alan Rivers; Keith Constable; Christine Bolton; Cass Farrar; Susan Rivers; Euan Macmillan.
OTHER INFORMATION The charity's accounts for 2019/20 list 23 organisations it supported during the year, of which 14 were based in the UK. The amount each beneficiary received was not specified.
HOW TO APPLY Contact the correspondent for further information on the application process.
CONTACT DETAILS The Trustees, 190 Campden Hill Road, London W8 7TH *Tel.* 020 7792 1234 *Email* ajrultra@btinternet.com

■ Riverside Charitable Trust Ltd

CC NO 264015 **ESTABLISHED** 1972
WHERE FUNDING CAN BE GIVEN England and Wales, with a strong preference for Rossendale in Lancashire.
WHO CAN BENEFIT Charitable organisations; individuals.
WHAT IS FUNDED Education; relief of sickness for older people; relief of poverty for people employed or formerly employed in the shoe trade; general charitable purposes.
SAMPLE GRANTS A list of beneficiaries was not included in the annual report and accounts.
FINANCES *Financial year end* 05/04/2020
Income £42,900 *Total grants* £107,000
Grants to organisations £107,000
Assets £1,620,000

TRUSTEES Barry Lynch; Harry Francis; Ian Dearing; Brian Terry; Angela O'Gorman; Mark Butterworth; Nicholas Green.
OTHER INFORMATION During 2019/20, 148 grants were made for the following purposes: general charitable purposes (£69,00 in 121 grants); the relief of sickness, infirmity and older people (£18,100 in 15 grants); retired employees (£6,400 in 94 grants); death grants (£6,000 in 12 grants).
HOW TO APPLY Contact the correspondent for further information.
CONTACT DETAILS Mark Butterworth, Trustee/ Secretary, c/o E. Sutton and Son Ltd, PO Box 2, Bacup, Lancashire OL13 0DT *Tel.* 01706 874961 *Email* jennifer.dixon@esutton.co.uk

■ Rix Thompson Rothenberg Foundation

CC NO 285368 **ESTABLISHED** 1982
WHERE FUNDING CAN BE GIVEN UK.
WHO CAN BENEFIT Registered charities; CICs; museums; theatres; arts organisations.
WHAT IS FUNDED People with learning disabilities and their carers, particularly projects involving the arts and that will enhance social interaction.
WHAT IS NOT FUNDED Applications for specific learning details are not supported.
RANGE OF GRANTS £1,000 to £7,000.
SAMPLE GRANTS MK SNAP (£7,000); Open University (£6,800); Advocacy Alliance, Polka Theatre and City of Birmingham Symphony Orchestra (£5,000 each); Drake Music Scotland (£4,000); Halle Concerts Society and Welsh National Opera (£3,000 each); Centre for Studies on Inclusive Education (£1,500).
FINANCES *Financial year end* 31/12/2019 *Income* £161,000 *Total grants* £146,300 *Grants to organisations* £140,600 *Assets* £1,720,000
TRUSTEES Barrie Davis; Bob Rothenberg; Fred Heddell; Prof. Jonathan Rix; Suzanne Marriott; Prof. Andy Minnion; Simon Fox; Rory Kinnear.
OTHER INFORMATION In 2019 the foundation made grants to 31 organisations totalling £140,600 and to four individuals totalling £5,700. None of the grant recipients had received funding in 2018.
HOW TO APPLY Applicants must discuss the proposed work (either by telephone, email or letter) with the correspondent at least four months before a board meeting, which occur twice per annum (June and December). An application form must be accompanied by a copy of the organisation's latest audited accounts. Requests received without going through the correct process will not be acknowledged or considered.
CONTACT DETAILS The Administrator, c/o Pamis, University of Dundee, 15/16 Springfield, Dundee DD1 4JE *Tel.* 07532 320138 *Email* rtrfoundation@gmail.com

■ RJM Charity Trust

CC NO 288336 **ESTABLISHED** 1983
WHERE FUNDING CAN BE GIVEN Throughout England and Wales.
WHO CAN BENEFIT Charitable organisations.
WHAT IS FUNDED General charitable purposes.
SAMPLE GRANTS A list of beneficiaries was not included in the annual report and accounts.
FINANCES *Financial year end* 05/04/2020 *Income* £931,900 *Total grants* £329,600 *Grants to organisations* £329,600 *Assets* £758,000
TRUSTEES Joshua Rowe; Michelle Rowe.
HOW TO APPLY Contact the correspondent for further information.
CONTACT DETAILS The Trustees, Boulton House, 17–21 Chorlton Street, Manchester M1 3HY *Tel.* 0161 720 8787 *Email* JR@broomwell.com

■ RNID (The Royal National Institute for Deaf People)

CC NO 207720 **ESTABLISHED** 1962
WHERE FUNDING CAN BE GIVEN UK.
WHO CAN BENEFIT Research institutions; universities; hospitals.
WHAT IS FUNDED Research into hearing loss and tinnitus.
TYPE OF GRANT Research funding; fellowships; studentships.
RANGE OF GRANTS Up to £25,000.
SAMPLE GRANTS University College London (£344,000 in 20 grants); King's College London (£198,000 in 11 grants); University of Sussex (£99,000 in two grants); MRC Institute of Hearing Research (£53,000 in two grants); University of Strathclyde (£25,000 in two grants); Oxford University (£12,000); Cardiff University (£12,000); Radboudumc (£10,000).
FINANCES *Financial year end* 31/03/2020 *Income* £42,700,000 *Total grants* £1,260,000 *Grants to organisations* £1,260,000 *Assets* £3,530,000
TRUSTEES Richard Jones; Jacqueline Press; John Morgan; Dr Brian Caul; Ingrid Gallen; Gideon Hoffman; Thomas McCarthy; Lindsay Foster; Claire Bailey.
OTHER INFORMATION In 2019/20, the charity awarded 47 grants to 27 organisations.
HOW TO APPLY Details on current grant programmes, along with application opening/closing dates, can be found on the website. Alternatively, you can email research@rnid.org.uk to be notified of new grant calls.
CONTACT DETAILS The Trustees, Brightfield Business Hub, Bakewell Road, Orton Southgate, Peterborough PE2 6XU *Tel.* 0808 808 0123 *Email* research@rnid.org.uk *Website* https://rnid.org.uk

■ The Roan Charitable Trust

CC NO 1122851 **ESTABLISHED** 2008
WHERE FUNDING CAN BE GIVEN UK and overseas.
WHO CAN BENEFIT Registered charities.
WHAT IS FUNDED General charitable purposes including the following: social welfare; medical research; overseas aid; education.
RANGE OF GRANTS Up to £100,000. Mainly under £35,000.
SAMPLE GRANTS Cancer Research UK (£100,000); The Royal National Institute of Blind People (£75,000); REACT (Rapid Effective Assistance for Children with potentially Terminal illness) (£35,000); I CAN Charity (£21,100); Volunteering Matters (£15,000); Ebony Horse Club and Women's Interfaith Network (£10,000 each); The Cayo Foundation (£5,000); The Chickenshed Theatre Trust (£1,000).
FINANCES *Financial year end* 31/03/2020 *Income* £283,900 *Total grants* £497,100 *Grants to organisations* £497,100 *Assets* £7,450,000

TRUSTEES Amelia Harris; Susan Swete; Lady Margaret Jarvis; Trevor Swete.
OTHER INFORMATION Grants were awarded to 25 organisations during 2019/20.
HOW TO APPLY Apply in writing to the correspondent. The trust's 2019/20 accounts state: 'There is no formal grant application procedure. The trustees retain the services of a charitable grants advisor and take account of the advice when deciding on grants.'
CONTACT DETAILS The Trustees, c/o Solid Management Ltd, PO Box 2696, Woodford Green, London IG8 1UF *Tel.* 07771 711188 *Email* jeff@solidmanagement.co.uk

■ Robertson Hall Trust

CC NO 1073473 **ESTABLISHED** 1989
WHERE FUNDING CAN BE GIVEN Ecclesiastical Parish of Brighton.
WHO CAN BENEFIT Anglican churches.
WHAT IS FUNDED Anglican churches.
WHAT IS NOT FUNDED Individuals.
TYPE OF GRANT Revenue/core costs; capital costs; salaries.
RANGE OF GRANTS Typically £2,500 to £10,000.
SAMPLE GRANTS Chapel Royal – Brighton (£54,000); St Luke's Advice Service (£10,000); St Nicholas – Brighton (£5,000); St Mary's Rock Gardens and Books Alive (£2,500).
FINANCES *Financial year end* 31/12/2019 *Income* £93,600 *Total grants* £79,000 *Grants to organisations* £79,000 *Assets* £1,460,000
TRUSTEES Revd David Biggs; Revd Julie Newson; Revd Martin Lloyd-Williams.
OTHER INFORMATION Of the nine organisations supported in 2018, seven were also funded in 2019. A substantial donation of £54,000 was made to Brighton Parish Chapel Royal in 2018 and 2019.
HOW TO APPLY Contact the correspondent for further information.
CONTACT DETAILS The Trustees, Chapel Royal Parish Church Office, North Street, Brighton BN1 1EA *Tel.* 01273 554464

■ The Robertson Trust

OSCR NO SC002970 **ESTABLISHED** 1961
WHERE FUNDING CAN BE GIVEN Scotland.
WHO CAN BENEFIT Registered charities; constituted community groups.
WHAT IS FUNDED The trust has three funding strands aimed at alleviating poverty and trauma: financial well-being; emotional well-being and relationships; and educational and work pathways. Within these there are main priority areas – see the website for details.
WHAT IS NOT FUNDED Funding is aimed at organisations with an annual income of under £2 million. However, each of the grant types has its own eligibility criteria specifying the type and annual income levels of organisations that can apply. Consult the trust's website for full exclusion criteria.
TYPE OF GRANT Capital funding; revenue funding (unrestricted and restricted); project costs; salaries; capacity building; one-off and recurrent grants (up to five years).
RANGE OF GRANTS Dependent on grant type – see the website for full details.
SAMPLE GRANTS The trust publishes a full list of grants it has awarded to organisations on its website.
FINANCES *Financial year end* 31/03/2020 *Income* £24,000,000 *Total grants* £19,420,000 *Grants to organisations* £17,260,000 *Assets* £761,190,000
TRUSTEES Shonaig Macpherson; Heather Lamont; Judy Cromarty; Andrew Walls; Mark Batho; Garry Coutts; Prof. Lorne Crerar; Gerry McLaughlin; Edel Harris; Campbell Robb; Ligia Teixeira; Donald Workman.
OTHER INFORMATION During the year, the trust awarded grants to organisations totalling £17.26 million. Grants to individuals totalled £2.16 million. The trust's strategy for 2020–30 is to provide funding to help people in communities in Scotland who are living with poverty and trauma. At the time of writing (May 2021) the grants available included: Wee Grants, Small Grants, Large Grants, Community Vehicle Grants and Community Building Grants. See the website for the respective grant sizes, types and detailed eligibility criteria.
HOW TO APPLY Applications can be made through the trust's website, where open funds are advertised. The website features a 'funding checker' with which you can check your eligibility.
CONTACT DETAILS Jo Cook, Finance Director and Company Secretary, Robertson House, 152 Bath Street, Glasgow G2 4TB *Tel.* 0141 353 7300 *Email* funding@therobertsontrust.org.uk *Website* www.therobertsontrust.org.uk

■ The Dezna Robins Jones Charitable Foundation

CC NO 1104252 **ESTABLISHED** 2004
WHERE FUNDING CAN BE GIVEN England and Wales.
WHO CAN BENEFIT Local charitable organisations, hospitals, hospices and educational institutions.
WHAT IS FUNDED Mainly medical and educational causes, with some support given to other local charitable causes.
RANGE OF GRANTS £200 to £62,000.
SAMPLE GRANTS Previous beneficiaries have included: ActionAid, Breast Cancer Campaign, Cerebra, Kids Cancer Charity, Macmillan Cancer, Mid Rhondda Band, Neil Boobyer Rugby Solutions Ltd, Sporting Marvels and Velindre Hospital.
FINANCES *Financial year end* 31/03/2019 *Income* £35,700 *Total grants* £61,600 *Grants to organisations* £61,600 *Assets* £1,480,000
TRUSTEES Louise Boobyer; Alexia Cooke.
OTHER INFORMATION The 2018/19 annual report notes: 'The Trustees are continuing to move their focus to support more Rhondda Valley-based causes.' A recent list of beneficiaries was not included. The 2018/19 accounts were the latest available at the time of writing (June 2021).
HOW TO APPLY Apply in writing to the correspondent. The trustees meet at least twice a year.
CONTACT DETAILS The Trustees, Greenacres, Laleston, Bridgend CF32 0HN *Tel.* 01656 768584 *Email* alexia.cooke@yahoo.co.uk

■ Robyn Charitable Trust

CC NO 327745 **ESTABLISHED** 1988
WHERE FUNDING CAN BE GIVEN UK and overseas.
WHO CAN BENEFIT Charitable organisations.
WHAT IS FUNDED General charitable purposes, in particular the welfare of children.

WHAT IS NOT FUNDED Individuals.
RANGE OF GRANTS Up to £30,000.
SAMPLE GRANTS A list of beneficiaries was not included in the annual report and accounts. Previous beneficiaries have included: All Hallows Cranmore Hall School Trust Ltd (£28,500); Friends of the HSC and MSF UK Charity (£20,000 each); The H. and T. Clients' Charitable Trust (£2,000); Garrick Christmas Fund (£500); Cancer Research (£100).
FINANCES *Financial year end* 05/04/2020 *Income* £1,250,000 *Total grants* £37,400 *Grants to organisations* £37,400 *Assets* £1,990,000
TRUSTEES Chris Hutchinson; Mark Knopfler; Ronnie Harris.
OTHER INFORMATION In 2019/19 the grant total (£37,400) was significantly lower than in the previous year (£206,000).
HOW TO APPLY Contact the correspondent for further information.
CONTACT DETAILS The Trustees, 64 New Cavendish Street, London W1G 8TB *Tel.* 020 7467 6300

■ Rockcliffe Charitable Trust

CC NO 274117 **ESTABLISHED** 1977
WHERE FUNDING CAN BE GIVEN UK.
WHO CAN BENEFIT Registered charities; universities.
WHAT IS FUNDED General charitable purposes, in particular: health and health research; education; social welfare, particularly that of children; arts, culture and heritage.
WHAT IS NOT FUNDED Individuals.
RANGE OF GRANTS Typically up to £25,000.
SAMPLE GRANTS Imperial College London (£75,000); Kate's Home Nursing (£25,000); Chances for Children UK (£20,000); Age UK (£10,000); Alzheimer's UK Research Education and Care, Pallant House Gallery, Spinal Injuries Association and University of the West of England Bristol (£5,000 each); Life Education (£3,000); Cotswold Riding for the Disabled, Fine Cell Work and Royal College of Surgeons of England (£1,000 each); Dementia UK (£500); The David Nott Foundation (£100).
FINANCES *Financial year end* 05/04/2020 *Income* £362,900 *Total grants* £258,400 *Grants to organisations* £258,400 *Assets* £12,550,000
TRUSTEES Emma Keswick; Simon Keswick; Nicholas Goodson.
HOW TO APPLY Apply in writing to the correspondent. Grant applications are regularly reviewed by the trustees.
CONTACT DETAILS The Trustees, c/o Matheson and Co. Ltd, Scottish Provident Building, 3 Lombard Street, London EC3V 9AQ *Tel.* 020 7816 8137

■ The Rockspring Charitable Trust

CC NO 1175442 **ESTABLISHED** 2017
WHERE FUNDING CAN BE GIVEN England and Wales.
WHO CAN BENEFIT Charitable organisations.
WHAT IS FUNDED General charitable purposes; education/training; the advancement of health or saving of lives; the arts, culture, heritage and science.
RANGE OF GRANTS Grants range from £8,000 up to £26,000.
SAMPLE GRANTS The Guild of Handicraft Trust (£26,000); Nucleo Project (£15,000); Resurgo (£12,500); Norwich-Dedza Partnership (£11,700); West London Action for Children (£8,000).
FINANCES *Financial year end* 31/12/2019 *Income* £440,700 *Total grants* £73,200 *Grants to organisations* £73,200 *Assets* £4,450,000
TRUSTEES Fiona Plummer; Graham Carter; Richard Plummer; Susan Floyd.
OTHER INFORMATION Grants were awarded to five organisations in 2019.
HOW TO APPLY Contact the correspondent for further information.
CONTACT DETAILS Susan Floyd, Trustee, Wright Hassall, Olympus Avenue, Tachbrook Park, Warwick CV34 6BF *Tel.* 01926 883016 *Email* susan.floyd@wrighthassall.co.uk

■ The Roddick Foundation

CC NO 1061372 **ESTABLISHED** 1997
WHERE FUNDING CAN BE GIVEN UK and overseas.
WHO CAN BENEFIT Charitable and non-charitable organisations.
WHAT IS FUNDED Arts and culture; the environment; human rights; health/medical causes; social justice; education; the media; humanitarian aid.
WHAT IS NOT FUNDED Sport projects; fundraising events or conferences; sponsorship of any kind.
TYPE OF GRANT Project costs; core costs; capital costs.
RANGE OF GRANTS Up to £150,000.
SAMPLE GRANTS Help Refugees (£150,000); Miscarriages of Justice (£98,900); Direct Relief (£78,600); Global Legal Action Network (£55,000); British Inspiration Trust (£35,000); Shine Literacy (£28,000); Switchback (£25,000); Community Environmental Council (£17,000); First Ask (£8,400).
FINANCES *Financial year end* 31/03/2020 *Income* £2,390,000 *Total grants* £1,400,000 *Grants to organisations* £1,400,000 *Assets* £16,790,000
TRUSTEES Justine Roddick; Samantha Roddick; Gordon Roddick; Tina Schlieske.
OTHER INFORMATION The foundation made 60 grants to organisations during the year. Grants were distributed as follows: human rights (£489,300); the environment (£293,700); poverty/social justice (£258,300); medical and health (£185,000); arts and culture (£133,300); education and media (£45,800).
HOW TO APPLY The foundation does not accept unsolicited applications.
CONTACT DETAILS Karen Smith, Unit H, The Old Bakery, Golden Square, Petworth, West Sussex GU28 0AP *Tel.* 01798 344362 *Email* karen@theroddickfoundation.org *Website* www.theroddickfoundation.org

■ The Rofeh Trust

CC NO 1077682 **ESTABLISHED** 1999
WHERE FUNDING CAN BE GIVEN UK and Israel.
WHO CAN BENEFIT Charitable organisations.
WHAT IS FUNDED General charitable purposes; religious activities, with a possible preference for Jewish causes.
SAMPLE GRANTS A list of beneficiaries was not included in the annual report and accounts.
FINANCES *Financial year end* 31/03/2020 *Income* £99,100 *Total grants* £94,800 *Grants to organisations* £94,800 *Assets* £1,350,000
TRUSTEES Martin Dunitz; Ruth Dunitz; Vivian Wineman; Sir Henry Eder.
HOW TO APPLY Contact the correspondent for further information.

CONTACT DETAILS The Trustees, 44 Southway, London NW11 6SA *Tel.* 020 8458 7832

■ The Sir James Roll Charitable Trust

CC NO 1064963 **ESTABLISHED** 1997

WHERE FUNDING CAN BE GIVEN UK.

WHO CAN BENEFIT Registered charities; individuals.

WHAT IS FUNDED General charitable purposes; interfaith understanding; IT education; research into specific learning disorders; children and young people.

RANGE OF GRANTS All grants awarded in 2019/20 were of £1,000, except for two grants of £10,000 each.

SAMPLE GRANTS Crisis and Disasters Emergency Committee – Cyclone Idai Appeal (£10,000 each); Action for Kids, British Liver Trust, Dyspraxia Foundation, Target Ovarian Cancer and Rainbow Trust Children's Charity (£1,000 each).

FINANCES *Financial year end* 31/03/2020 *Income* £246,800 *Total grants* £203,000 *Grants to organisations* £203,000 *Assets* £4,000,000

TRUSTEES Nicholas Wharton; Brian Elvy; Jonathan Liddiard.

HOW TO APPLY Applications should be made in writing to the correspondent. The trustees usually meet around four times a year to assess grant applications.

CONTACT DETAILS The Trustees, Downs Farm, Pilgrims Way, Wouldham, Rochester, Kent ME1 3RB *Tel.* 01634 668167 *Email* nicholaswharton@btconnect.com

■ The Helen Roll Charity

CC NO 299108 **ESTABLISHED** 1988

WHERE FUNDING CAN BE GIVEN UK.

WHO CAN BENEFIT Registered (or exempt) charities.

WHAT IS FUNDED General charitable purposes. One of the trustees' aims is to support work for which charities find it difficult or impossible to obtain funds from other sources.

WHAT IS NOT FUNDED Individuals.

TYPE OF GRANT Project funding, often on a start-up basis; most charities receive long-term support.

RANGE OF GRANTS £1,000 to £10,000.

SAMPLE GRANTS West Oxfordshire Citizens Advice Bureau (£10,000); Trinity Laban Conservatoire of Music and Dance (£6,000); Canine Partners (£5,000); Oxfordshire Association for the Blind (£4,000); Compassionate Friends and REACT (Rapid Effective Assistance for Children with potentially Terminal illness) (£2,000 each); Dream Holidays (£1,000).

FINANCES *Financial year end* 30/09/2020 *Income* £40,300 *Total grants* £94,000 *Grants to organisations* £94,000 *Assets* £2,340,000

TRUSTEES Christine Reid; Patrick Stopford; Paul Strang; Frank Williamson; Jennifer Williamson; Stephen Williamson; Fiona Weiss; Jessica Mannix.

OTHER INFORMATION The charity aims to distribute about £100,000 each year to around 30 charities. The trustees work with the charities and often continue to make grants over a longer period of time. Because of this, there is limited capacity for new grants recipients each year. In 2019/20, 25 charities were awarded grants, of which nine had not been funded in the previous year.

HOW TO APPLY Apply in writing to the correspondent by email or post. Applications are accepted from 1 December to 15 February.

CONTACT DETAILS The Trustees, c/o Wenn Townsend Accountants, 30 St Giles, Oxford, Oxfordshire OX1 3LE *Tel.* 01865 559900 *Email* helen.roll@aol.co.uk

■ The Romney Marsh Historic Churches Trust

CC NO 284909 **ESTABLISHED** 1982

WHERE FUNDING CAN BE GIVEN Kent and East Sussex.

WHO CAN BENEFIT Churches.

WHAT IS FUNDED The preservation and maintenance of the fabric of churches.

TYPE OF GRANT Mainly one-off grants, but occasional interest-free loans.

SAMPLE GRANTS St Clement – Old Romney (£17,000); St Augustine – Snave (£10,000); St George – Ivychurch (£6,200); All Saints – Lydd (£2,100); All Saints – Burmarsh (£240).

FINANCES *Financial year end* 31/12/2020 *Income* £114,200 *Total grants* £60,600 *Grants to organisations* £60,600 *Assets* £849,700

TRUSTEES William Barham; Revd Patricia Fogden; Elizabeth Marshall; Ian Hamilton; John Hendy; Celia Heritage; Dr Nicholas Hudd; Judge Graham Maple; Joanna Thompson; Georgia Small; George Staple; David Hanbury; Peter Anwyl-Harris.

OTHER INFORMATION In 2020, nine churches received grants.

HOW TO APPLY Contact the correspondent for further information.

CONTACT DETAILS Secretary to the Trustees, Ring Cottage, Bethersden, Ashford, Kent TN26 3EW *Tel.* 01233 822010 *Email* secretary@romneychurches.org.uk *Website* https://romneymarshchurches.org.uk

■ The Gerald and Gail Ronson Family Foundation

CC NO 1111728 **ESTABLISHED** 2005

WHERE FUNDING CAN BE GIVEN UK and overseas, especially Israel.

WHO CAN BENEFIT Registered charities.

WHAT IS FUNDED General charitable purposes with particular interests in: Jewish causes; education; arts and culture; community; medical work; welfare; security.

TYPE OF GRANT Capital projects; research.

RANGE OF GRANTS Grants range from £300 up to £1 million.

SAMPLE GRANTS North London Hospice (£1 million); Roundhouse (£250,000); Community Security Trust (£160,500); Camp Simcha (£75,000); Overcoming MS (£10,000); Depaul International (£3,000); Norwood Ravenswood (£300).

FINANCES *Financial year end* 31/12/2019 *Income* £50,350,000 *Total grants* £3,530,000 *Grants to organisations* £3,530,000 *Assets* £211,720,000

TRUSTEES Gerald Ronson; Dame Gail Ronson; Alan Goldman; Jonathan Goldstein; Nicole Allalouf; Jeffery Shear; Marc Zilkha; Ian Rosenblatt; Amanda Ronson; Hayley Ronson; Lisa Althasen.

OTHER INFORMATION In 2019 the foundation received a donation of £27 million from Gerald Ronson as well as a gift of shares from Ronson Capital Ltd, valued at £22.31 million.

HOW TO APPLY Applications for funding can be made through the foundation's website. According to the foundation's 2019 accounts, 'the foundation makes grants on a monthly basis. All requests for donations are approved by the trustees via email. The trustees meet quarterly to discuss new applications which have been previously reviewed and shortlisted once the foundation's criteria have been met.'

CONTACT DETAILS Jeremy Trent, Secretary, c/o HW Fisher and Company, Acre House, 11–15 William Road, London NW1 3ER *Tel.* 020 7388 7000 *Email* jtrent@hwfisher.co.uk *Website* https://ronsonfoundation.org

■ Mrs L. D. Rope's Third Charitable Settlement

CC NO 290533 **ESTABLISHED** 1984

WHERE FUNDING CAN BE GIVEN UK and overseas, with a particular interest in East Suffolk.

WHO CAN BENEFIT Small registered charities that have a large volunteer force. Most grants are awarded to organisations in South East England.

WHAT IS FUNDED The relief of poverty; homelessness; families; people with disabilities; education for young people; the Roman Catholic religion and ecumenical work; international aid; general charitable purposes.

WHAT IS NOT FUNDED Overseas projects; national charities; buildings; medical research/healthcare (outside the beneficial area); schools (outside the beneficial area); environmental charities and animal welfare; the arts; matched funding; repayment of debts for individuals.

TYPE OF GRANT For unsolicited requests, grants are usually one-off and small scale.

SAMPLE GRANTS Major grants included: Ipswich Citizens Advice (£30,000); Age UK Suffolk (£24,000); The Mix (£15,000); Beyond Words and Samathpheap Chun Pikar – Cambodia (£10,000 each).

FINANCES *Financial year end* 05/04/2020 *Income* £1,740,000 *Total grants* £1,200,600 *Grants to organisations* £457,900 *Assets* £59,220,000

TRUSTEES Crispin Rope; Jeremy Winteringham Heal; Ellen Jolly; Catherine Scott.

OTHER INFORMATION The charity has a very informative annual report and accounts providing detailed guidance on what the trustees will fund.

HOW TO APPLY Send a concise letter (preferably one side of A4) explaining the main details of your request and include your most recent accounts and a budgeted breakdown of the sum you are looking to raise. The charity will also need to know whether you have applied to other funding sources and whether you have been successful elsewhere. Your application should say who your trustees are and include a daytime telephone number.

CONTACT DETAILS The Trustees, Lucy House, St William Court, Kesgrave, Ipswich, Suffolk IP5 2QP *Tel.* 01473 333288 *Email* ropetrust@lucyhouse.org.uk

■ Rosa Fund

CC NO 1124856 **ESTABLISHED** 2008

WHERE FUNDING CAN BE GIVEN UK.

WHO CAN BENEFIT Charitable organisations.

WHAT IS FUNDED Women's organisations and projects supporting women; women's safety; economic justice; health and well-being; representation in society.

WHAT IS NOT FUNDED Applicants should consult the guidance document on each funding programme's web page for a detailed list of funding exclusions.

TYPE OF GRANT Grant types are programme dependent but include: unrestricted funding; project funding; core/revenue costs.

RANGE OF GRANTS Up to £40,000.

SAMPLE GRANTS Fawcett Society (£69,600); Agenda and Welsh Women's Aid (£40,000 each); Centre for Women's Justice (£14,600); Deaf Ethnic Women's Association, Girls Friendly Society and Women's Budget Group (£5,000 each); Devon Rape Crisis and Sexual Abuse Services (£3,100).

FINANCES *Financial year end* 31/03/2020 *Income* £2,030,000 *Total grants* £596,500 *Grants to organisations* £596,500 *Assets* £948,000

TRUSTEES David Aeron-Thomas; Prof. Ruth Pearson; Sheila Malley; Dr Linda McDowell; Kay Ali; Catherine Dovey; Gillian Green; Beverley Huie; Sarah Barber; Sarah Jackson; Lisa Raftery; Reetu Sood.

OTHER INFORMATION In 2019/20, 38 grants totalling £596,500 were awarded across the following programmes: UK Justice and Equality Programme (£421,851); Voices from the Front Line (£129,610); Cummins Foundation (£45,000). Grant expenditure was notably lower than in 2018/19 (£1.98 million).

HOW TO APPLY Consult the charity's website for information on open programmes. Applications can be made through the charity's online application form before the specific deadline for each programme.

CONTACT DETAILS Rebecca Gill, Executive Director, 4th Floor, United House, North Road, London N7 9DP *Tel.* 020 7697 3466 *Email* info@rosauk.org *Website* https://rosauk.org

■ Rosca Trust

CC NO 259907 **ESTABLISHED** 1966

WHERE FUNDING CAN BE GIVEN The Southend-on-Sea, Castle Point and Rochford local authority areas.

WHO CAN BENEFIT Registered charities; CICs; voluntary and community groups; churches; hospices. The trust has a stated preference for small, grassroots organisations.

WHAT IS FUNDED Social welfare; community development; older people; people with disabilities; minority ethnic groups; asylum seekers and refugees; young people.

WHAT IS NOT FUNDED Grants are not given outside the beneficial area or to individuals.

TYPE OF GRANT One-off; capital costs; project funding; requests for administration and salary costs are considered low priority.

RANGE OF GRANTS Typically £500 to £5,000.

SAMPLE GRANTS Lifelites and Southend Against Modern Slavery (SAMS) (£5,000 each); Drugline Information and Look Good Feel Better (£3,000 each); Thorpe Bay Methodist Church and Volunteering Matters (£2,000 each); KAOS Youth Club (£1,000); Trust Links (£800).

FINANCES *Financial year end* 31/03/2020 *Income* £136,700 *Total grants* £124,400 *Grants to organisations* £124,400 *Assets* £712,300

TRUSTEES Nigel Gayner; Gary Hodson; Christine Sternshine; Judith Bailey; Anthony Quinn.

HOW TO APPLY Apply in writing to the correspondent, detailing the project and the amount requested, and include your organisation's latest accounts, bank account details and contact details. Only one application is considered per organisation

in any 12-month period. The trustees meet in January, May and September – applications must be submitted before the end of the previous month.
CONTACT DETAILS The Trustees, 1 Moat End, Thorpe Bay, Southend-on-Sea, Essex SS1 3QA *Tel.* 07768 870316 *Email* roscatrust@gmail.com *Website* https://www.roscatrust.org.uk

■ The Rose Animal Welfare Trust CIO

CC NO 1169516 **ESTABLISHED** 2016
WHERE FUNDING CAN BE GIVEN UK, with a preference for Yorkshire and the Humber.
WHO CAN BENEFIT Registered charities.
WHAT IS FUNDED Animal welfare.
RANGE OF GRANTS Mostly £5,000 or £10,000.
SAMPLE GRANTS Hull Animal Welfare Trust (£15,000); Battersea Dogs and Cats Home, Blue Cross for Pets and Cats Protection (£10,000 each); Four Paws (£5,000); Good Life Dog Rescue (£3,000).
FINANCES *Financial year end* 31/10/2020 *Income* £18,600 *Total grants* £303,000 *Grants to organisations* £303,000 *Assets* £636,600
TRUSTEES Antoinette Tomkinson; Nigel Shaw; Elizabeth Webb.
HOW TO APPLY Apply in writing to the correspondent. Grants are made each year in May and November.
CONTACT DETAILS Nigel Shaw, Trustee, 2B Westmoor Avenue, Baildon, Shipley, West Yorkshire BD17 5HE *Tel.* 01274 593779 *Email* npshaw63@gmail.com

■ The Rose Foundation

CC NO 1167144 **ESTABLISHED** 1978
WHERE FUNDING CAN BE GIVEN London.
WHO CAN BENEFIT Registered charities; exempt bodies; museums; theatres; educational institutions; community groups.
WHAT IS FUNDED Building projects where the cost is of less than £200,000. This could be a general refurbishment or a specific project.
WHAT IS NOT FUNDED The purchase of equipment; the purchase of a building or site; seed money required to draw up plans; fees.
TYPE OF GRANT Part-funding of building projects.
RANGE OF GRANTS Typically between £5,000 and £10,000.
SAMPLE GRANTS St John Ambulance (£706,800); New Amsterdam Charitable Foundation (£83,000); Royal National Theatre (£10,000); Zoological Society of London (£7,500); Centrepoint, Paddington Arts, St Paul's Church Community Project and The English Heritage Trust (£5,000 each); West London Mission (£2,500); Cystic Fibrosis Trust (£1,200).
FINANCES *Financial year end* 31/10/2019 *Income* £1,220,000 *Total grants* £1,140,000 *Grants to organisations* £1,140,000 *Assets* £30,330,000
TRUSTEES Martin Rose; Alan Rose; John Rose; Paul Rose.
OTHER INFORMATION At the time of writing (May 2021) the foundation's 2018/19 accounts were the latest available. The foundation made grants to 67 organisations during the year.
HOW TO APPLY Applications should be made in writing to the correspondent including details of the organisation and the registered charity number, together with the nature and probable approximate cost of the scheme and its anticipated start and completion dates. Applications can be submitted any time between 1 July and 31 March the following year. The trustees hope to inform applicants of their decision by the second week in July. Further information can be found on the foundation's website.
CONTACT DETAILS Martin Rose, Trustee, 28 Crawford Street, London W1H 1LN *Tel.* 020 7262 1155 *Email* martin@rosefoundation.co.uk *Website* www.rosefoundation.co.uk

■ The Cecil Rosen Foundation

CC NO 247425 **ESTABLISHED** 1966
WHERE FUNDING CAN BE GIVEN UK and Israel.
WHO CAN BENEFIT Registered charities; universities; religious bodies/institutions.
WHAT IS FUNDED Jewish causes; people with disabilities, including people who are blind; health; education; medical research; social welfare; international disaster appeals.
WHAT IS NOT FUNDED Individuals.
TYPE OF GRANT Capital costs.
SAMPLE GRANTS Alma Primary School, British Heart Foundation, Cancer Research UK, Great Ormond Street Hospital Children's Charity, Heart Cells Foundation, Jewish Deaf Society, National Institute for the Blind and Yesodeh Hatorah Primary School.
FINANCES *Financial year end* 05/04/2020 *Income* £554,800 *Total grants* £407,800 *Grants to organisations* £407,800 *Assets* £6,690,000
TRUSTEES Malcolm Ozin; John Hart; Peter Silverman; Silver Lever.
HOW TO APPLY The annual report for 2019/20 states: 'The trustees consider all applications received and give special attention to those which were originally chosen by the Settlor, Cecil Rosen.'
CONTACT DETAILS The Trustees, 35 Langstone Way, Mill Hill East, London NW7 1GT *Tel.* 020 8346 8940 *Email* contact@cecilrosenfoundation.org

■ Rosetrees Trust

CC NO 298582 **ESTABLISHED** 1988
WHERE FUNDING CAN BE GIVEN UK.
WHO CAN BENEFIT Medical research institutions.
WHAT IS FUNDED Medical research.
WHAT IS NOT FUNDED Detailed eligibility criteria for each funding programme can be found on the trust's website.
TYPE OF GRANT Project and research funding; seed funding for preliminary studies; PhD, postdoctoral and fellowship funding; salaries and consumables.
RANGE OF GRANTS Between £10,000 and £100,000 per annum, depending on the grant programme.
SAMPLE GRANTS University College London and Royal Free (£1.79 million); University of Cambridge (£624,000); University of Southampton (£534,000); King's College London (£365,400); University of Oxford (£148,900); Barts and Queen Mary (£79,500); The Royal College of Surgeons (£55,600).
FINANCES *Financial year end* 31/03/2020 *Income* £4,800,000 *Total grants* £5,980,000 *Grants to organisations* £5,980,000 *Assets* £30,630,000
TRUSTEES Richard Ross; Clive Winkler; Sam Howard; Lee Mesnick; Debra Fox; Jonathan Zenios; Hayley Katz.

OTHER INFORMATION In 2019/20, the trust made grants to ten named institutions totalling £2.74 million and grants to unspecified institutions totalling £3.24 million.

HOW TO APPLY Application forms and guidelines for each grant programme are available to download from the website. Refer to the website for the dates of application rounds.

CONTACT DETAILS Ann Berger, Chief Executive, c/o Regents Mead Group, Russell House, 140 High Street, Edgware, Middlesex HA8 7LW *Tel.* 020 8952 1414 *Email* info@rosetreestrust.co.uk *Website* www.rosetreestrust.co.uk

■ The David Ross Foundation

CC NO 1121871 **ESTABLISHED** 2007

WHERE FUNDING CAN BE GIVEN UK.

WHO CAN BENEFIT Registered charities.

WHAT IS FUNDED The foundation's main focus is young people. Areas of work include education, sport, heritage and the arts.

TYPE OF GRANT One-off.

SAMPLE GRANTS Nottingham University (£300,000); British Paralympic Association (£50,000); Action on Addiction (£5,000); National Youth Orchestra (£250); Cancer Research UK (£100).

FINANCES *Financial year end* 31/03/2020
Income £2,590,000 *Total grants* £704,800
Grants to organisations £704,800
Assets £11,680,000

TRUSTEES Mark Bolland; Ottilie Windsor; Anita Bott; Lady Caroline Ryder; David Ross; Marcia Mercer.

HOW TO APPLY Apply in writing to the correspondent. The foundation's website states: 'In assessing applications we are looking for: An outline of your project – its purpose and activities Financials – total budget, fundraising strategy and the level of funding you are seeking from DRF. Who will benefit? Community support Sustainability and legacy of your project.'

CONTACT DETAILS Joanne Hoareau, 10 St James's Place, London SW1A 1NP *Tel.* 020 7534 1551 *Email* joanne@davidrossfoundation.com *Website* www.davidrossfoundation.co.uk

■ The Rothermere Foundation

CC NO 314125 **ESTABLISHED** 1956

WHERE FUNDING CAN BE GIVEN UK.

WHO CAN BENEFIT Registered charities; individual graduates of the Memorial University of Newfoundland.

WHAT IS FUNDED General charitable purposes, including education, children's charities, the arts, sport, medical research and religious organisations.

RANGE OF GRANTS Mostly up to £10,000.

SAMPLE GRANTS Imperial War Museum Foundation (£1 million); St Peter's College Oxford (£100,000); Atlantic Salmon Trust (£20,000); The Royal Marsden (£10,000); The Chickenshed Theatre Trust and World Horse Welfare (£5,000 each); Dorset and Somerset Air Ambulance (£4,000); Wellbeing of Women (£1,000); British Heart Foundation (£500).

FINANCES *Financial year end* 30/09/2019
Income £2,430,000 *Total grants* £1,299,000
Grants to organisations £1,180,000
Assets £45,300,000

TRUSTEES Rt Hon. Viscount Jonathan Rothermere; The Viscountess Claudia Rothermere; Vyvyan Harmsworth.

OTHER INFORMATION The 2018/19 accounts were the latest available at the time of writing (May 2021). Grants totalling £119,000 were made to support three Rothermere Fellows during the year. Grants to organisations were made for the following purposes: general charitable purposes (£1.09 million); educational and children's charities (£186,300); the arts and sport (£20,000); medical research (£11,500); religious organisations (£250).

HOW TO APPLY Contact the correspondent for further information. The trustees meet twice a year to consider grant applications.

CONTACT DETAILS Vyvyan Harmsworth, Trustee, Beech Court, Canterbury Road, Challock, Ashford, Kent TN25 4DJ *Tel.* 01233 740641

■ The Rothley Trust

CC NO 219849 **ESTABLISHED** 1959

WHERE FUNDING CAN BE GIVEN Northumberland; Tyne and Wear; Durham; Cleveland.

WHO CAN BENEFIT Registered charities; CICs; voluntary groups (these must be properly constituted and must find a registered charity to act as a cheque handler).

WHAT IS FUNDED General charitable purposes, with a preference for: children and young people; disability; community projects; education; energy saving projects; ex-service people; medical causes; humanitarian aid.

WHAT IS NOT FUNDED Further education; the repair of buildings solely used for worship; religious purposes; arts, heritage or science; amateur sport; human rights, conflict resolution or reconciliation (except family mediation); environmental protection or improvement; animal welfare; residents associations; parish councils; University of the Third Age.

TYPE OF GRANT Mainly one-off donations towards specific projects. Buildings, equipment, website start-up/development costs, resources and capital grants will also be considered.

RANGE OF GRANTS Typically £2,000 and under, with some larger grants.

SAMPLE GRANTS Westfield School (£12,500); Durham Association of Boys and Girls Clubs (£6,000); Citizens Advice County Durham (£5,000); Combat Stress (£4,000); Greggs Foundation Hardship Fund (£3,000); Community Action Northumberland and HospiceCare North Northumberland (£2,000 each).

FINANCES *Financial year end* 31/03/2020
Income £239,000 *Total grants* £236,700
Grants to organisations £230,700
Assets £7,340,000

TRUSTEES Alice Brunton; Julia Brown; Anne Galbraith; Gerard Salvin; David Holborn; Donna Anderson.

OTHER INFORMATION Grants were made to 202 organisations during the year. Grants of less than £2,000 totalled £177,700 and a further £6,000 was given in grants to individuals. Grants to organisations were awarded in the following categories: community (£77,400); children and young people (£64,800); disability (£44,000); medical causes (£23,600); energy (£10,200); education (£6,000); humanitarian aid (£3,100); older people (£2,800). Only beneficiaries of grants of £2,000 and above were listed in the accounts.

HOW TO APPLY The trust prefers to receive applications by email, although it will also accept applications by post. Full details can be found on the trust's website, where criteria, guidelines and closing dates for applications are posted.

CONTACT DETAILS Gillian Allsopp, Trust Secretary, Rothley Trust, PO Box 224, Bedlington,

Northumberland NE63 3FJ *Tel.* 0191 580 5350 *Email* gilliana@rothleytrust.co.uk *Website* www.rothleytrust.org.uk

■ The Rothschild Foundation

CC NO 1138145 **ESTABLISHED** 2010

WHERE FUNDING CAN BE GIVEN UK, with a preference for causes within ten miles of the Waddesdon Estate in Buckinghamshire.

WHO CAN BENEFIT Charitable organisations; registered charities; CICs which are limited by guarantee may apply following confirmation from the Grants Manager.

WHAT IS FUNDED The arts and humanities; heritage; education; the environment; social welfare.

WHAT IS NOT FUNDED Individuals; major capital projects; medical equipment and research; academic research and bursaries; animal charities; projects outside the UK; projects promoting religion; overseas travel; charities and organisations without charitable status.

TYPE OF GRANT Project and core costs.

RANGE OF GRANTS Mostly up to £150,000.

SAMPLE GRANTS Illuminated River Foundation (£4 million); Resource Productions (£220,000); Forward Trust (£150,000); Empower to Cook (£140,000); University of Oxford (£100,000); National Criminal Justice Arts Alliance (£50,000).

FINANCES *Financial year end* 29/02/2020 *Income* £46,340,000 *Total grants* £6,330,000 *Grants to organisations* £6,330,000 *Assets* £688,120,000

TRUSTEES Lord Rothschild; The Hon. Emily Freeman-Attwood; Peter Troughton; The Hon. Janet De Botton; The Hon. Hannah Rothschild; Lord David Ogilvy; Francesco Goedhuis; S.J.P. Trust Corporation Ltd.

OTHER INFORMATION Grants were made to 125 organisations during the year. Grants were distributed as follows: arts and humanities (£5.03 million); education and social welfare (£807,000); energy and the environment (£428,000); grants to Illuminated River charitable events (£58,000). Check the website for open funding programmes. The foundation also maintains and promotes the Waddesdon Manor, its collection and estate.

HOW TO APPLY Application processes may vary depending on the programme being applied to. Check the website for open programmes and relevant application details.

CONTACT DETAILS Ellie Stout, Head of Grants, Windmill Hill, Silk Street, Waddesdon, Aylesbury Vale HP18 0JZ *Tel.* 01296 653208 *Email* grants@rothschildfoundation.org.uk or info@rothschildfoundation.org.uk *Website* https://rothschildfoundation.org.uk

■ The Eranda Rothschild Foundation

CC NO 255650 **ESTABLISHED** 1967

WHERE FUNDING CAN BE GIVEN UK and overseas. For charities working locally, priority is given to those in Buckinghamshire and Bedfordshire.

WHO CAN BENEFIT Registered charities.

WHAT IS FUNDED Medical research; education; the arts; social welfare (especially work known to the trustees).

WHAT IS NOT FUNDED Individuals; organisations which are not registered charities; capital appeals (unless of personal significance to the trustees).

SAMPLE GRANTS Previous beneficiaries have included: Alzheimer's Society; Dyslexia Scotland; Elton John AIDs Foundation; Give a Book; Jewish Care; Pace Centre; Lowry Centre Trust; Philharmonic Orchestra; Teach First.

FINANCES *Financial year end* 05/04/2020 *Income* £4,810,000 *Total grants* £3,790,000 *Grants to organisations* £3,790,000 *Assets* £118,240,000

TRUSTEES Sir Evelyn de Rothschild; Lady Lynn Forester de Rothschild; Anthony de Rothschild; Jessica de Rothschild; Sir John Peace; Ben Elliot.

OTHER INFORMATION Grants were broken down as follows: health, welfare and medical research (£2.31 million in 22 grants); education (£918,500 in 30 grants); the arts (£371,800 in 20 grants).

HOW TO APPLY The trustees prefer applications to be made using the online form on the foundation's website. Applications are considered at meetings held three times a year, usually in February/March, June/July and October/November. Charities should make only one application per year. Online applications are acknowledged automatically and every applicant will be notified of the trustees' decision (this may take several months). The foundation's website notes that it always receives more applications than it is able to fund.

CONTACT DETAILS The Secretary, PO Box 6226, Leighton Buzzard, Bedfordshire LU7 0XF *Tel.* 01296 689157 *Email* secretary@erandarothschild.org *Website* www.erandarothschild.org

■ Rothschild Foundation (Hanadiv) Europe

CC NO 1083262 **ESTABLISHED** 2000

WHERE FUNDING CAN BE GIVEN Europe and Israel.

WHO CAN BENEFIT Registered charities; universities; individuals.

WHAT IS FUNDED Jewish causes; religious education; scholarship and research; culture and heritage.

WHAT IS NOT FUNDED Ongoing costs of schools, synagogues or welfare organisations; the building of new museums or communal institutions; artistic projects in the fine arts, the performing arts, film production and creative writing; book publication; individuals (except for early career scholars); organisations based outside Europe. See the website for programme-specific exclusions.

TYPE OF GRANT Core/revenue costs; project funding; unrestricted funding.

RANGE OF GRANTS Typically up to £150,000.

SAMPLE GRANTS Gesher L'Europa (£390,000); Jewish Museum in Prague (£150,000); The Jewish Community of Stockholm (£105,800); Union of Jewish Students of the UK and Ireland (£90,000); University of Wroclaw (£80,600); Blavatnik Archive Foundation (£75,000); National Library of Israel (£60,000); National Archives of Finland (£50,000).

FINANCES *Financial year end* 31/12/2019 *Income* £57,500 *Total grants* £5,350,000 *Grants to organisations* £5,350,000 *Assets* £127,380,000

TRUSTEES Dr David Landau; Sir Victor Blank; Lord Rothschild; Beatrice Rosenberg; Adam Cohen; Hon. Beth Rothschild; Nicola Cobbold; Nicola Loftus; Bradley Fried.

OTHER INFORMATION Grants of less than £50,000 totalled £2.91 million.

HOW TO APPLY Applications must be submitted via the online application process. Refer to the website for application forms, deadlines and guidance for each programme.

CONTACT DETAILS Grant Programmes Manager, Rothschild Foundation (Hanadiv), 27 St James's Place, London SW1A 1NR *Tel.* 01296 658778 *Email* info@rothschildfoundation.eu *Website* www.rothschildfoundation.eu

■ The Roughley Charitable Trust

CC NO 264037 **ESTABLISHED** 1972

WHERE FUNDING CAN BE GIVEN Birmingham and overseas.

WHO CAN BENEFIT Registered charities.

WHAT IS FUNDED Community work (including church-based projects); social welfare for children and young people, older people, people with disabilities, offenders, people with addiction and other marginalised groups; homelessness; health and well-being; education; arts and leisure; heritage; the environment (particularly environmental improvement and green projects).

WHAT IS NOT FUNDED Birmingham-based medical charities; church fabric appeals; CICs; social enterprises; church-based projects which are essentially about the teaching of religion; animal charities; projects outside the city boundary of Birmingham.

TYPE OF GRANT Core and revenue costs; seed funding; start-up funding.

RANGE OF GRANTS Mostly £1,000 to £3,000. Larger grants are made to projects where trustees have special knowledge.

SAMPLE GRANTS Hope Projects West Midlands (£39,000); Appropriate Technology Asia (£25,000); The Wildlife Trust for Birmingham and the Black Country (£20,000); Hope Well Being (£10,000); Restore Birmingham Churches Together (£5,000); Peacemakers (£3,000); Home-Start Birmingham (£2,000); Big Brum Theatre and Birmingham Opera Company (£1,000 each).

FINANCES *Financial year end* 05/04/2020 *Income* £317,800 *Total grants* £261,200 *Grants to organisations* £261,000 *Assets* £6,270,000

TRUSTEES John Smith; Martin Smith; Verity Owen; Victor Thomas; Rachel Richards; Benjamin Newton; Camilla Newton; Caroline Ward.

OTHER INFORMATION Grants were made to 39 organisations during the year. Priority is given to small and medium-sized organisations in the city of Birmingham. The trust awards small and large grants to Birmingham charities and regular support is given to a small number of development charities working overseas. The trust does not accept unsolicited applications from overseas charities.

HOW TO APPLY Applications should be made using the form available to download on the trust's website, where the trust's eligibility criteria, guidelines and key dates are also available. Application forms should be returned to the trust by email, along with a signed letter on headed paper, two or three photographs which give a good idea of what the project is about, and any other supporting material. Accounts should only be sent if they are not available to view on the Charity Commission's website.

CONTACT DETAILS J.R.L. Smith, 90 Somerset Road, Edgbaston, Birmingham, West Midlands B15 2PP *Tel.* 0121 454 4508 *Email* correspondent@roughleytrust.org.uk *Website* www.roughleytrust.org.uk

■ The Row Fogo Charitable Trust

OSCR NO SC009685 **ESTABLISHED** 1970

WHERE FUNDING CAN BE GIVEN Edinburgh.

WHO CAN BENEFIT Registered charities; local charitable groups.

WHAT IS FUNDED Medical research projects; local projects; care of older people.

RANGE OF GRANTS Mostly £1,000 to £5,000.

SAMPLE GRANTS RNLI (£8,000); Erskine Hospital (£6,000); Age Scotland (£5,000); Scottish Autism (£3,000); Open Door Edinburgh (£2,000); Royal Voluntary Service (£1,000).

FINANCES *Financial year end* 05/04/2020 *Income* £174,900 *Total grants* £67,000 *Grants to organisations* £67,000 *Assets* £4,560,000

HOW TO APPLY Contact the correspondent for further information.

CONTACT DETAILS The Trustees, c/o Brodies LLP Solicitors, 15 Atholl Crescent, Edinburgh EH3 8HA

■ Rowanville Ltd

CC NO 267278 **ESTABLISHED** 1973

WHERE FUNDING CAN BE GIVEN UK, Israel and overseas.

WHO CAN BENEFIT Charitable organisations; Jewish religious and educational organisations.

WHAT IS FUNDED The advancement of the Orthodox Jewish faith.

RANGE OF GRANTS Up to £50,000.

SAMPLE GRANTS Ader Charitable Trust and Mercaz Chasidei Wiznitz Trust (£50,000 each); Friends of Eidah Chareidis Orthodox Council of Jerusalem (£44,000); Friends of Nachalas Bnei Shimon and Start Upright (£40,000 each).

FINANCES *Financial year end* 30/06/2020 *Income* £1,210,000 *Total grants* £970,000 *Grants to organisations* £970,000 *Assets* £10,620,000

TRUSTEES Joseph Pearlman; Ruth Pearlman; Allan Becker.

OTHER INFORMATION In 2019/20, grants of under £40,000 totalled £746,000.

HOW TO APPLY Contact the correspondent for further information.

CONTACT DETAILS Ruth Pearlman, Trustee, 8 Highfield Gardens, London NW11 9HB *Tel.* 020 8458 9266

■ The Rowlands Trust

CC NO 1062148 **ESTABLISHED** 1996

WHERE FUNDING CAN BE GIVEN Primarily the West Midlands and South Midlands, including Birmingham, Gloucestershire, Herefordshire, Shropshire, Warwickshire and Worcestershire.

WHO CAN BENEFIT Registered charities; CICs; museums; hospices; schools; Anglican churches; universities; uniformed groups; community groups.

WHAT IS FUNDED General charitable purposes, with a preference for: medical and scientific research; the services; health; social welfare; older people; people with disabilities; music; the arts; the environment; the maintenance and restoration of Anglican church buildings.

WHAT IS NOT FUNDED Individuals; animal charities; annual running costs; projects eligible for state funding.

TYPE OF GRANT Capital expenditure including buildings, projects and research.

RANGE OF GRANTS Mostly up to £7,000, occasionally larger.

SAMPLE GRANTS University of Birmingham (£55,400); Malvern Theatres Trust Ltd (£20,000); Worcester Cathedral (£15,000); Severn Valley Railway Charitable Trust (£7,000); The Mary Stevens Hospice (£5,000); Music in Hospitals (£3,000); Criminon UK (£2,000); Walking with the Wounded (£1,000); Heart of England Forest (£500).

FINANCES *Financial year end* 31/12/2019 *Income* £114,600 *Total grants* £478,300 *Grants to organisations* £478,300 *Assets* £2,810,000

TRUSTEES Gary Barber; Diana Crabtree; Ian Crockatt Smith; Patrick Wrixon; Rebecca Widdowson.

OTHER INFORMATION During the year, the trust awarded 142 grants to organisations in the following categories: social welfare, disability and older people (£226,000); research, education and training (£107,800); music and the arts (£85,800); church buildings (£43,600); the environment (£14,000); the services (£1,000).

HOW TO APPLY Application forms are available from the correspondent. The trustees meet to consider grants four times a year.

CONTACT DETAILS Louise Ruane, Administrator, c/o Bishop Fleming LLP, 1–3 College Yard, Worcester, Worcestershire WR1 2LB *Tel.* 07812 743485 *Email* louise.ruane@therowlandstrust.org.uk

■ The Joseph Rowntree Charitable Trust

CC NO 210037 **ESTABLISHED** 1904

WHERE FUNDING CAN BE GIVEN UK and overseas.

WHO CAN BENEFIT Registered charities; unregistered charities; CICs; social enterprises; universities; religious bodies/institutions; individuals.

WHAT IS FUNDED Peace and security; power and accountability; rights and justice; sustainable future; Northern Ireland.

WHAT IS NOT FUNDED A full list of exclusions can be found on the trust's website.

TYPE OF GRANT Core/revenue costs; seed funding/start-up funding; project funding; unrestricted funding.

RANGE OF GRANTS Up to £300,000.

SAMPLE GRANTS The Legal Education Foundation (£300,000); Gaslight Media Trust (£189,200); War Child (£51,000); Global Dialogue (£50,000); Upper Space CIC (£26,500); Nuclear Education Trust (£5,500).

FINANCES *Financial year end* 31/12/2019 *Income* £292,000 *Total grants* £11,170,000 *Grants to organisations* £11,170,000 *Assets* £267,370,000

TRUSTEES Susan Seymour; Jennifer Amery; Nicholas Burton; John Fitzgerald; Janet Slade; David Newton; Huw Davies; Helen Carmichael; Linda Batten; Hannah Torkington.

HOW TO APPLY Apply via the trust's website, where application deadlines can also be found.

CONTACT DETAILS The Trustees, The Garden House, Water End, York, North Yorkshire YO30 6WQ *Tel.* 01904 627810 *Email* enquiries@jrct.org.uk *Website* www.jrct.org.uk

■ The Joseph Rowntree Foundation

CC NO 1184957 **ESTABLISHED** 1904

WHERE FUNDING CAN BE GIVEN UK.

WHO CAN BENEFIT Registered charities; CICs; social enterprises; universities.

WHAT IS FUNDED Research and policy work related to solving poverty.

WHAT IS NOT FUNDED See the website for a full list of exclusions.

TYPE OF GRANT Project funding; research.

RANGE OF GRANTS Up to £315,000.

SAMPLE GRANTS Heriot-Watt University (£319,000); Citizens UK (£174,000); Involve (£120,000); The Runnymede Trust (£71,000); Bright Blue (£34,000); Faith in Community Scotland (£25,000).

FINANCES *Financial year end* 31/12/2019 *Income* £7,930,000 *Total grants* £5,840,000 *Grants to organisations* £5,840,000 *Assets* £427,830,000

TRUSTEES Zeinab Elahi; Helen Evans; David Lunts; Lesley Russell; William Haire; Kenechukwu Umeasiegbu; Prof. Carol Tannahill; Paul Jenkins; Hilary Cottam; Dr Saphie Ashtiany; Maureen Loffill; Deborah Cadman.

OTHER INFORMATION Grants of under £25,000 totalled £386,000.

HOW TO APPLY The foundation's website states: 'We are not a traditional grant-funder so we do not generally respond to speculative proposals, however if you would like a conversation about working with us on one or more of our outcome areas contact: info@jrf.org.uk.'

CONTACT DETAILS The Trustees, The Homestead, 40 Water End, York, North Yorkshire YO30 6WP *Tel.* 01904 629241 *Email* info@jrf.org.uk *Website* www.jrf.org.uk

■ Royal Artillery Charitable Fund

CC NO 210202 **ESTABLISHED** 1964

WHERE FUNDING CAN BE GIVEN UK.

WHO CAN BENEFIT Service charities; regiments; individuals.

WHAT IS FUNDED The welfare, relief and assistance of any past or present members of the Royal Artillery, their dependants and families, who are in need.

TYPE OF GRANT Grants to individuals through almonising organisations; capital costs.

RANGE OF GRANTS Typically £1,000 to £65,000. Grants to individuals average £700.

SAMPLE GRANTS Army Benevolent Fund (£65,000); Gunner Magazine (£20,000); King Edward VII Hospital and Veterans Aid (£3,000 each); Not Forgotten Association (£1,000).

FINANCES *Financial year end* 31/12/2019 *Income* £1,310,000 *Total grants* £1,496,800 *Grants to organisations* £809,400 *Assets* £35,450,000

TRUSTEES Mr C. Fletcher-Wood; Maj. Andrew Dines; Col Christopher Comport; Brig. Mark Pountain; Col. Robert Murphy; Maj. General David Cullen; Maj. James Leighton; Col. William Prior; Col Michael Relph; Col Anthony Phillips; Col Craig Palmer.

OTHER INFORMATION Grants to institutions tend to be given on a recurrent basis.

HOW TO APPLY Contact the correspondent for more information. Applications for funding on behalf of individuals can be made through the charity's online application form.

CONTACT DETAILS The Trustees, RHQRA, Artillery House, Royal Artillery Barracks, Larkhill, Salisbury, Wiltshire SP4 8QT *Tel.* 01980 845233 *Email* RAA-Asstsec@artycen.ra.mod.uk *Website* https://www.thegunners.org.uk

■ The Royal British Legion

CC NO 219279 **ESTABLISHED** 1921

WHERE FUNDING CAN BE GIVEN UK.

WHO CAN BENEFIT Charitable organisations.

WHAT IS FUNDED Projects and services benefitting serving and ex-service personnel and/or their families not already provided by the Royal British Legion and in line with its funding priorities (see the website for up-to-date information).

WHAT IS NOT FUNDED See the website for up-to-date information on exclusions.

TYPE OF GRANT Core costs; capital costs; project funding; capacity building.

RANGE OF GRANTS Mostly up to £1.5 million.

SAMPLE GRANTS The Officers' Association (£6.7 million); Combat Stress (£1.55 million); Unforgotten Forces (£1.38 million); National Memorial Arboretum (£1.19 million); Help for Heroes (£600,000); Citizens Advice Scotland (£551,000); Personnel Recovery Centres (£204,000).

FINANCES *Financial year end* 30/09/2019
Income £175,880,000
Total grants £28,590,000
Grants to organisations £12,690,000
Assets £328,910,000

TRUSTEES Lynda Atkins; Helen Owen; Heather Spence; Maj. General David Jolliffe; Rob Bedford; Debbie Sorkin; Philip Moore; Lt Col Joe Falzon; Jason Coward; Paul Harris; Tony Goodwin; David Whimpenny; Monica Risam; Una Cleminson; Elizabeth Butler; Anny Reid.

OTHER INFORMATION Grant-making is one of many charitable activities the Royal British Legion undertakes. The 2018/19 accounts were the latest available at the time of writing (May 2021). In total, 42 other organisations were awarded grants by the Royal British Legion during the year. Grants were also awarded by Poppyscotland (13 grants totalling £2.63 million) and Royal British Legion Republic of Ireland (four grants totalling £57,000) as part of the same charitable group. Individuals were awarded a total of £15.9 million.

HOW TO APPLY At the time of writing (May 2021), the External Grants programme was not accepting new applications due to the COVID-19 pandemic. Please see the charity's website for up-to-date information.

CONTACT DETAILS The Trustees, 199 Borough High Street, London SE1 1AA *Tel.* 0808 802 8080 *Email* info@britishlegion.org.uk *Website* www.britishlegion.org.uk

■ Royal Docks Trust (London)

CC NO 1045057 **ESTABLISHED** 1995

WHERE FUNDING CAN BE GIVEN The area of the London Borough of Newham that lies between the A13 trunk road (Newham Way) and the River Thames.

WHO CAN BENEFIT Registered charities; not-for-profit organisations; voluntary organisations; religious institutions carrying out charitable work.

WHAT IS FUNDED Community development; social welfare; education and training; recreation and leisure; housing; the arts; disability; heritage; religious charitable work; the environment.

WHAT IS NOT FUNDED Individuals; general appeals; revenue, top-up or retrospective funding is not given through the minor grants programme.

TYPE OF GRANT Project funding, with a preference for matched funding; start-up/seed funding; capital costs.

RANGE OF GRANTS Typically £10,000 to £30,000.

SAMPLE GRANTS Royal Docks Learning and Activity Centre (£35,000); Ascension Community Trust (£29,000); Community Food Enterprise (£25,100); Newham All Stars Sports Academy (£15,000); Caritas Anchor House (£10,000); Drop In Bereavement Centre (£4,500).

FINANCES *Financial year end* 31/03/2020
Income £323,800 *Total grants* £218,900
Grants to organisations £218,900
Assets £8,660,000

TRUSTEES Eric Sorensen; Stephen Nicholas; Sid Keys; Amanda Williams; Katie Carter; James Kenworth; Belinda Vecchio; Gary Quashie; Giovanna Grandoni; Shani Thomas; Sandra Erskine.

OTHER INFORMATION In 2019/20 the trust made grants to 11 charitable organisations totalling £218,900. There is a preference for applications which access other resources, offer the possibility of matched funding, complement regeneration initiatives and support the provision of services and resources locally through an active community and voluntary sector. Specific projects are funded for a maximum of three years.

HOW TO APPLY Application forms, along with guidance information and an outline of the schedule for submitting applications, are available from the trust's website.

CONTACT DETAILS John Johnson, Grants Development, Olive Cottage, Station Road, St Margaret's-at-Cliffe, Dover, Kent CT15 6AY *Tel.* 020 7277 8667 *Email* john.d.johnson@btinternet.com *Website* www.royaldockstrust.org.uk

■ The Royal Foundation of the Duke and Duchess of Cambridge

CC NO 1132048 **ESTABLISHED** 2009

WHERE FUNDING CAN BE GIVEN UK and overseas.

WHO CAN BENEFIT Registered charities.

WHAT IS FUNDED Conservation; early years; mental health; the emergency responders community; (in the short term) COVID-19 relief.

TYPE OF GRANT Seed funding; capital funding; project funding.

RANGE OF GRANTS Mostly £10,000 to £140,000.

SAMPLE GRANTS Zoological Society of London (£485,500); Al Manaar – The Muslim Cultural Heritage Trust (£179,700); Basel Institute on Governance (£140,000); Save the Rhino International (£107,500); Middlesbrough FC Foundation (£58,500); Mission Motorsport (£30,000); Help for Heroes (£16,300); Fauna and Flora International (£10,000); Soldiers' Arts Academy (£5,000).

FINANCES *Financial year end* 31/12/2019
Income £6,680,000 *Total grants* £4,100,000
Grants to organisations £4,100,000
Assets £5,470,000

TRUSTEES Alice Webb; Lady Demetra Pinsent; Lord Hague of Richmond, William Hague; Claire Wills; Charles Mindenhall; Simon Patterson; Zeinab Badawi-Malik; Hannah Cockburn-Logie; Jean-Christophe Gray.

OTHER INFORMATION During the year, grants were awarded to 51 organisation in the following categories: conservation (£1.55 million); mental health (£1.2 million); young people (£573,700); the armed forces (£435,900); empowering communities (£179,700). In addition, the 2019 annual report states that 'following the decision of The Duke and Duchess of Sussex to leave the Royal Foundation to set up their own charitable organisation, an unrestricted grant of

£145,000 was awarded to Sussex Royal to facilitate the set-up of the new charity'. See the website for initiatives and campaigns within the foundation's current focus areas.

HOW TO APPLY Contact the foundation for further information.

CONTACT DETAILS The Trustees, c/o Kensington Palace, Palace Green, London W8 4PU *Tel.* 020 7101 2963 *Email* reception@royalfoundation.com *Website* www.royalfoundation.com

■ Royal Masonic Trust for Girls and Boys

CC NO 1170336 **ESTABLISHED** 2016

WHERE FUNDING CAN BE GIVEN England and Wales.

WHO CAN BENEFIT Registered charities (at least one year of published accounts); hospices; individual children/grandchildren of Freemasons.

WHAT IS FUNDED Children and young people; relief of poverty; education and training; primarily, the trust supports children of Freemasons but also makes grants to non-Masonic registered charities.

WHAT IS NOT FUNDED See the 'Grants to charities' section of the Masonic Charitable Foundation's helpful website for full details of eligibility requirements and exclusions with respect to activities and types of organisation.

TYPE OF GRANT Core/revenue costs; project funding; salaries; activities and materials; small grants are unrestricted.

RANGE OF GRANTS Typically £1,000 to £60,000 for registered charities and £400 to £1,500 for hospices.

SAMPLE GRANTS Contact (£149,800); Centre for Action on Rape and Abuse (£72,000); Ambitious about Autism, Child Brain Injury Trust and Family Gateway (£60,000 each); Bromley Mencap (£27,600); Blue Smile, Haven House Project and Youth Talk (£15,000 each); Balloons and The Mary Dolly Foundation (£10,000 each); The Windfall Centre (£6,000); Chestnut Tree House Children's Hospice and Martin House Children's Hospice (£1,500 each); 1st Cheshunt Scout Group (£200).

FINANCES *Financial year end* 31/03/2020
Income £5,520,000 *Total grants* £2,210,000
Grants to organisations £2,210,000
Assets £137,950,000

TRUSTEES James Newman; Masonic Charitable Foundation.

OTHER INFORMATION During 2019/20, non-Masonic donations amounted to £2.2 million (128 grants), alongside Masonic donations totalling £5.2 million (2,516 grants). Non-Masonic funding was given for the following purposes: early interventions – children and families (£2,153,000); hospice care (£53,750); other charitable purposes (£7,500); arts, culture and sport (£700). Grants are awarded in large and small categories for a period of one to three years.

HOW TO APPLY Applications are made online through the Masonic Charitable Foundation's website, where application guidelines, eligibility criteria and deadlines are available for each grant programme.

CONTACT DETAILS The Trustees, Freemasons' Hall, 60 Great Queen Street, London WC2B 5AZ *Tel.* 020 3146 3333 *Email* info@mcf.org.uk *Website* www.mcf.org.uk

■ The Royal Navy and Royal Marines Charity

CC NO 1117794 **ESTABLISHED** 2007

WHERE FUNDING CAN BE GIVEN UK.

WHO CAN BENEFIT Registered charities; CICs; social enterprises; individuals.

WHAT IS FUNDED Organisations supporting serving or ex-serving personnel from the Royal Navy and the Royal Marines, and their dependants.

WHAT IS NOT FUNDED Organisational fundraising activities; retrospective expenditure; trading ventures; research; projects that could be funded by the service, the state or other public bodies.

TYPE OF GRANT Capital costs; core and revenue costs; seed funding; start-up funding; project funding.

RANGE OF GRANTS Mostly up to £100,000.

SAMPLE GRANTS The Kings Foundation (£315,300); Drumfork Community Centre (£291,900); Portsmouth Military Alliance (£117,700); Relate (£98,700); Care for Veterans (£50,000); Horseback UK (£30,000); Naval Families Federation (£25,000); Reading Force (£15,000); Salute My Job (£10,000).

FINANCES *Financial year end* 31/12/2019
Income £16,350,000
Total grants £10,620,000
Grants to organisations £8,370,000
Assets £60,250,000

TRUSTEES Michael Tanner; James Parkin; James Crichton Pitt; Mark Lewthwaite; Lieutenant Harriet Delbridge; Gary Nicolson; Katheryn Phipps-Wiltshire; Simon Black; Andrew Jameson; Roderic Birkett; William Thomas; Andrew Robinson; Michelle Westwood; Carl Steedman; Katherine Beadle; Dr Brian Gilvary.

OTHER INFORMATION Grants to organisations were distributed as follows: Through Life Pathway (£3.2 million); Quality of Life Pathway (£2.33 million); commissioned programmes (£1.8 million); Fit for Life Pathway (£1.02 million). The charity also made grants to individuals totalling £1.25 million. Beneficiaries of grants of under £10,000 were not listed.

HOW TO APPLY Organisations should email mygrant@rnrmc.org.uk requesting a stage-one application; you will be sent a link to the online application portal. Guidelines and deadlines can be found on the website.

CONTACT DETAILS The Trustees, Building 37, HMS Excellent, Whale Island, Portsmouth, Hampshire PO2 8ER *Tel.* 023 9387 1520 *Email* theteam@rnrmc.org.uk or mygrant@rnrmc.org.uk *Website* www.rnrmc.org.uk

■ Royal Society of Wildlife Trusts

CC NO 207238 **ESTABLISHED** 1962

WHERE FUNDING CAN BE GIVEN UK.

WHO CAN BENEFIT Registered charities; community organisations; CIOs; churches.

WHAT IS FUNDED Conservation; heritage and the environment; youth and community development.

WHAT IS NOT FUNDED Individuals.

TYPE OF GRANT Project funding; campaigning.

RANGE OF GRANTS Dependent upon grants programme.

SAMPLE GRANTS Nottinghamshire Wildlife Trust (£750,000); Association of Independent Museums (£667,000); The Woodland Trust (£250,000); Down to Earth Project (£174,000); Clifford Village Hall, Staffordshire Wildlife Trust and St Paul's – Winchester (£75,000 each); Newton Hall Community Partnership (£30,000);

RNIB (£10,000); Durham Wildlife Trust (£2,000).

FINANCES *Financial year end* 31/03/2020
Income £19,860,000
Total grants £12,280,000
Grants to organisations £12,280,000
Assets £10,470,000

TRUSTEES Genevieve Landricombe; Joanna Simons; Peta Foxall; Ruth Sutherland; Sir Graham Fry; David Jordan; Joanna Pike; Stephen Aston; Steve Garland; Rob Pickford; Julian Woolford; Stewart Goshawk.

OTHER INFORMATION The charity is an umbrella organisation for 46 wildlife trusts across the UK. In 2019/20 grants were awarded across the following funding programmes: Our Bright Future (£5.38 million); Biffa Award (£3.49 million); The Wildlife Trust Grants (£2.46 million); Nature Friendly Schools (£612,000); Red Squirrels United (£343,000).

HOW TO APPLY Contact the correspondent for more information regarding the application process. For the Biffa Award Scheme, visit www.biffa-award.org for full details of how to apply.

CONTACT DETAILS The Trustees, The Kiln, Waterside, Mather Road, Newark, Nottinghamshire NG24 1WT *Tel.* 01636 677711 *Email* info@wildlifetrusts.org *Website* www.wildlifetrusts.org

■ RSM UK Foundation

CC NO 1179349 **ESTABLISHED** 2018

WHERE FUNDING CAN BE GIVEN UK and overseas.

WHO CAN BENEFIT Registered charities.

WHAT IS FUNDED The environment; citizenship and community development; the advancement of education and relief of poverty in the context of access to employment.

WHAT IS NOT FUNDED Grants are not normally made to individuals, nor for projects in countries in which another RSM Group corporate foundation is based.

SAMPLE GRANTS The Duke of Edinburgh Award (£201,000); Anthony Nolan (£91,000); Trees for Cities (£15,000); Leadership Through Sport and Business (£7,000).

FINANCES *Financial year end* 31/03/2020
Income £391,900 *Total grants* £364,600
Grants to organisations £364,600
Assets £177,400

TRUSTEES Stephen Berger; David Gwilliam; Martin Rogers; Nicholas Sladden; Kelly Adams; John Taylor.

OTHER INFORMATION The foundation supports its four core charities each year but also accepts applications from other organisations.

HOW TO APPLY Apply by email to the correspondent. Application deadlines can be found on the foundation's website.

CONTACT DETAILS The Trustees, 6th Floor, 25 Farringdon Street, London EC4A 4AB *Email* info@rsmukfoundation.com *Website* https://www.rsmukfoundation.com

■ The Rubin Foundation Charitable Trust

CC NO 327062 **ESTABLISHED** 1986

WHERE FUNDING CAN BE GIVEN UK.

WHO CAN BENEFIT Registered charities; universities; Jewish organisations.

WHAT IS FUNDED General charitable purposes.

RANGE OF GRANTS Up to £100,000.

SAMPLE GRANTS Lancaster University (£125,000); Jewish Care and UJIA (£100,000 each); University College London Development Fund (£52,600); National Emergencies Trust (£60,000); Chai Lifeline Cancer Care, Médecins Sans Frontières and The Prince's Trust (£50,000 each).

FINANCES *Financial year end* 05/04/2020
Income £3,000,000 *Total grants* £899,400
Grants to organisations £899,400
Assets £6,460,000

TRUSTEES Alison Mosheim; Angela Rubin; Robert Rubin; Andrew Rubin; Carolyn Rubin.

OTHER INFORMATION Only beneficiaries of grants of £50,000 and above were listed in the accounts. Grants of under £50,000 totalled £211,800.

HOW TO APPLY Contact the correspondent for more information. According to previous research, the foundation gives grants to charities known to members of the Rubin family and those associated with Pentland Group Ltd; therefore, unsolicited applications are unlikely to succeed.

CONTACT DETAILS The Trustees, The Pentland Centre, Lakeside House, Squires Lane, Finchley, London N3 2QL *Tel.* 020 8346 2600 *Email* amcmillan@pentland.com

■ The Ruddock Foundation for the Arts

CC NO 1134994 **ESTABLISHED** 2010

WHERE FUNDING CAN BE GIVEN UK.

WHO CAN BENEFIT Registered charities; museums, libraries and galleries; independent theatre groups; individuals.

WHAT IS FUNDED The conservation of and research into pre-1800 performing, literary and decorative arts.

TYPE OF GRANT Collections and acquisitions; project funding; research.

SAMPLE GRANTS Afrikids (£105,000); Ashmolean Museum, British Museum and Courtauld Institute (£50,000 each); Royal Academy of Arts (£25,000).

FINANCES *Financial year end* 05/04/2020
Income £899,500 *Total grants* £798,300
Grants to organisations £795,300
Assets £18,450,000

TRUSTEES Sir Paul Ruddock; Lady Jill Ruddock; Michael Fullerlove; Sophie Ruddock; Isabella Ruddock.

OTHER INFORMATION Grants were made for the following purposes: research and curatorial support (£305,000); other charitable purposes (£200,200); cultural exhibitions (£172,100); museum and gallery projects (£101,100); museum acquisitions (£20,000). The grant total includes one grant made to an individual (£3,000).

HOW TO APPLY Apply in writing to the correspondent. The trustees meet twice a year to discuss applications.

CONTACT DETAILS Sir Paul Ruddock, Trustee, 10 Colville Mews, London W11 2DA *Tel.* 020 7313 9350 *Email* nikita@ruddockfamily.com

■ The Rugby Group Benevolent Fund Ltd

CC NO 265669 **ESTABLISHED** 1955

WHERE FUNDING CAN BE GIVEN Barrington (Cambridgeshire); Chinnor (Oxfordshire); Kensworth (Bedfordshire); Lewes (Sussex); Rochester (Kent); Rugby and Southam (Warwickshire); South Ferriby (North Lincolnshire); Tilbury (Essex).

WHO CAN BENEFIT Registered charities; schools; uniformed groups; community groups; amateur sports clubs.

WHAT IS FUNDED Community projects.

WHAT IS NOT FUNDED Organisations operating outside the areas of benefit; support is not normally given for day-to-day revenue costs.

TYPE OF GRANT Capital costs for specific projects.

RANGE OF GRANTS Up to £30,000.

SAMPLE GRANTS The Bradby Club (£67,500); Rugby Gymnastics Club (£30,000); East Anglia Air Ambulance (£10,000); Hill Street Youth and Community Centre (£6,000); Cobham Bowls Club (£5,000); Aspire in Arts (£3,000); Rotary Club of Rugby (£2,000); Cancer Research UK (£1,000).

FINANCES *Financial year end* 31/12/2019 *Income* £58,900 *Total grants* £360,700 *Grants to organisations* £354,200 *Assets* £1,440,000

TRUSTEES Graeme Fuller; Norman Jones; Ian Southcott; Geoff Thomas; Nigel Appleyard; John Brooks; David Holton; Kevin Murch.

OTHER INFORMATION This fund was established in 1955 with the aim of supporting employees and former employees of Rugby Group Ltd and their dependants. The Rugby Group is now a part of CEMEX UK, a global cement manufacturer but the fund has kept its independence and is managed by a group of employees and former employees. During 2019, 53 grants were made to organisations, of which eight grants, amounting to £2,400, were for less than £1,000. In addition, grants totalling £6,500 were made to nine former employees and their dependants.

HOW TO APPLY Potential applicants must first complete an expression of interest form, available to download from the fund's website. Applicants must be able to demonstrate that the project has been properly costed and that any other support funding is in place or in prospect. Evidence of self-help is important. The trustees meet several times a year to consider applications.

CONTACT DETAILS The Trustees, Cemex UK, Cemex House, Evreux Way, Rugby, Warwickshire CV21 2DT *Tel.* 01788 517000 *Email* info@rugbygroupbenevolentfund.org.uk *Website* www.rugbygroupbenevolentfund.org.uk

■ The Russell Trust

OSCR NO SC004424 **ESTABLISHED** 1985

WHERE FUNDING CAN BE GIVEN UK, especially Scotland and primarily Fife.

WHO CAN BENEFIT Charitable organisations and voluntary bodies.

WHAT IS FUNDED General charitable purposes including the following: education; health; community development; the arts, heritage, culture and science; sport; the environment; relief of those in need.

WHAT IS NOT FUNDED Individuals.

TYPE OF GRANT Often one-off. Preference is given to new, local projects that require initial funding.

RANGE OF GRANTS Mostly up to £2,000. Several larger grants (£4,000 to £30,000) are awarded each year.

SAMPLE GRANTS University of St Andrews (£20,000); The Adam Smith Foundation (£15,000); Iona Renewables (£6,000); Stoa School (£5,000); The Phaeo and Para Cancer Charity (£4,000); Collydean Community Centre, NSPCC Scotland, Ocean Youth Trust Scotland and Visual Arts Scotland (£2,000 each).

FINANCES *Financial year end* 05/04/2020 *Income* £297,300 *Total grants* £173,400 *Grants to organisations* £173,400 *Assets* £5,670,000

OTHER INFORMATION Only the beneficiaries of grants of £2,000 and above were listed in the 2019/20 accounts (32 organisations). Grants of under £2,000 totalled £39,700.

HOW TO APPLY Contact the correspondent for further information.

CONTACT DETAILS The Secretary, 2.19, 2nd Floor, Block B, 1 Summerhall, Edinburgh EH9 1PL

■ The RVW Trust

CC NO 1066977 **ESTABLISHED** 1956

WHERE FUNDING CAN BE GIVEN UK.

WHO CAN BENEFIT Charitable organisations; CICs; social enterprises; individuals.

WHAT IS FUNDED Professional British composers who have not yet achieved a broad national or international reputation; assistance towards the performance and recording of music by neglected or currently unfashionable 20th and 21st century British composers; support for national organisations which promote public knowledge and appreciation of 20th and 21st century British music; postgraduate students of composition taking first master's degrees at British institutions.

WHAT IS NOT FUNDED A list of exclusions can be found on the trust's website under the grant-making policy.

TYPE OF GRANT Project funding.

RANGE OF GRANTS Usually between £500 and £3,000.

SAMPLE GRANTS Presteigne Festival (£7,000); Huddersfield Contemporary Music Festival (£5,000); City of Birmingham Symphony Orchestra (£2,500); Bangor Music Festival and National Youth Choir of Great Britain (£2,000 each); Three Choirs Festival and Ty Cerrd (£1,500 each); Manchester Collective and Sacconi Quartet (£1,000 each).

FINANCES *Financial year end* 31/12/2019 *Income* £505,500 *Total grants* £192,500 *Grants to organisations* £144,000 *Assets* £3,050,000

TRUSTEES Hugh Cobbe; Anthony Burton; Andrew Hunter Johnston; Helen Faulkner; Prof. Nicola LeFanu; Sally Groves; Richard Causton; Musicians Benevolent Fund.

OTHER INFORMATION Due to the COVID-19 pandemic, the trust will prioritise applications where the primary intention is live performance. The trustees expect that the pandemic will also impact their income (which derives from the royalties of Ralph Vaughan Williams's work), and as such, grant giving will be reduced to a degree. Grants were awarded to 70 organisations in 2019 and grants to individuals totalled £48,500.

HOW TO APPLY See the trust's website for detailed guidance on how to apply.

CONTACT DETAILS Rosie Johnson, Secretary and Administrator, 13 Calico Row, Plantation Wharf, London SW11 3YH *Tel.* 020 7223 3385 *Email* info@rvwtrust.org.uk *Website* www.rvwtrust.org.uk

■ S. and R. Charitable Trust

CC NO 1098326 **ESTABLISHED** 2003
WHERE FUNDING CAN BE GIVEN England.
WHO CAN BENEFIT Registered charities; individuals.
WHAT IS FUNDED General charitable purposes; health; poverty relief.
RANGE OF GRANTS Generally up to £10,000.
SAMPLE GRANTS Camp Simcha (£20,100); Chabad Lubavitch UK (£14,000); Hospice UK (£12,500); Chai-Lifeline Cancer Care (£7,500); Jewish Care (£4,300); Yad Halevi Charitable Trust (£2,500); The E Trust (£1,600).
FINANCES *Financial year end* 31/03/2020 *Income* £91,000 *Total grants* £113,300 *Grants to organisations* £102,000 *Assets* £180,100
TRUSTEES Rochelle Davis; Stephen Davis; Lee Rhodes.
OTHER INFORMATION The trust also made grants to individuals totalling £11,300. Only organisations that received grants of over £2,000 were listed as beneficiaries in the charity's accounts. Grants of under £2,000 totalled £9,800.
HOW TO APPLY Contact the correspondent for further information.
CONTACT DETAILS The Trustees, 14 Deacons Hill Road, Elstree, Borehamwood, Hertfordshire WD6 3LH *Tel.* 020 8953 5226

■ The Jeremy and John Sacher Charitable Trust

CC NO 206321 **ESTABLISHED** 1957
WHERE FUNDING CAN BE GIVEN UK and Israel.
WHO CAN BENEFIT Registered charities.
WHAT IS FUNDED General charitable purposes, with a preference for the following: arts and culture; education, science and technology; community and welfare; children and youth; health and disability; Jewish organisations and causes.
WHAT IS NOT FUNDED Grants are not made to individuals.
RANGE OF GRANTS Grants range from £500 to £44,000.
SAMPLE GRANTS The London Symphony Orchestra Ltd (£44,000); Community Security Trust (£20,000); The Notting Hill Prep Foundation, Ataxia UK (£15,000); Royal Opera House Covent Garden Foundation (£7,100); Level Water (£800); Macmillan Cancer Support (£500).
FINANCES *Financial year end* 31/01/2020 *Income* £168,000 *Total grants* £168,000 *Grants to organisations* £168,000 *Assets* £7,790,000
TRUSTEES Jeremy Sacher; Rosalind Sacher; Elisabeth Sacher.
OTHER INFORMATION This charity's working name is The Jeremy and John Sacher Charitable Trust.
HOW TO APPLY Contact the correspondent for further information.
CONTACT DETAILS The Trustees, c/o HW Fisher and Company, Acre House, 11–15 William Road, London NW1 3ER *Tel.* 020 7388 7000 *Email* info@hwfisher.co.uk

■ The Michael and Nicola Sacher Charitable Trust

CC NO 288973 **ESTABLISHED** 1984
WHERE FUNDING CAN BE GIVEN UK.
WHO CAN BENEFIT Registered charities.
WHAT IS FUNDED General charitable purposes with a preference for arts, education, animal welfare, Jewish causes, health and social welfare.
WHAT IS NOT FUNDED Individuals; organisations which are not registered charities.
RANGE OF GRANTS Generally up to £10,000.
SAMPLE GRANTS New College (£17,000), National Railway Museum (£10,000); Natural History Museum (£5,000); Jewish Care (£3,000); The Zoological Society of London (£2,500); PSPA Richard Polo (£1,000); United Synagogue (£490).
FINANCES *Financial year end* 29/02/2020 *Income* £55,500 *Total grants* £73,900 *Grants to organisations* £73,900 *Assets* £2,980,000
TRUSTEES Nicola Sacher; Michael Sacher.
OTHER INFORMATION Grants were made to 15 organisations during the year.
HOW TO APPLY Contact the correspondent for further information.
CONTACT DETAILS The Trustees, c/o HW Fisher and Company, Acre House, 11–15 William Road, London NW1 3ER *Tel.* 020 7388 7000 *Email* info@hwfisher.co.uk

■ The Dr Mortimer and Theresa Sackler Foundation

CC NO 1128926 **ESTABLISHED** 2009
WHERE FUNDING CAN BE GIVEN England; Wales; USA; overseas.
WHO CAN BENEFIT Registered charities and universities.
WHAT IS FUNDED Research; medical research; education; the arts; science.
SAMPLE GRANTS Expert Impact (£150,000); Bletchley Park (£100,000); Margaret S. Mahler Foundation (£75,900); World Monuments Fund (£67,300).
FINANCES *Financial year end* 31/12/2019 *Income* £429,900 *Total grants* £484,700 *Grants to organisations* £484,700 *Assets* £28,690,000
TRUSTEES Mrs I. Sackler Lefcourt; Dame Theresa Sackler; Dr Kathe Sackler; Marissa Sackler; Sophie Dalrymple; Mortimer Sackler; Anthony Collins; Samantha Hunt; Michael Sackler.
OTHER INFORMATION Grants were made to ten organisations in 2019.
HOW TO APPLY Contact the correspondent for further information.
CONTACT DETAILS The Trustees, 9th Floor, New Zealand House, 80 Haymarket, London SW1Y 4TQ *Tel.* 020 7930 4944

■ The Saddlers' Company Charitable Fund

CC NO 261962 **ESTABLISHED** 1970
WHERE FUNDING CAN BE GIVEN UK, with a preference for the City of London.
WHO CAN BENEFIT Registered charities; educational organisations; religious organisations; individuals.
WHAT IS FUNDED General charitable purposes; education; equestrian charities; disadvantaged young people; disability; the armed forces;

music; religious activities and churches; saddlery and leathercraft.

TYPE OF GRANT Project funding; capital costs.

SAMPLE GRANTS A list of beneficiaries was not included in the annual report and accounts.

FINANCES *Financial year end* 31/03/2020 *Income* £336,600 *Total grants* £335,000 *Grants to organisations* £305,100 *Assets* £10,990,000

TRUSTEE Saddlers' Company.

OTHER INFORMATION During 2019/20 grants to organisations totalled £305,100 and grants totalling £29,900 were awarded to 211 individuals.

HOW TO APPLY Potential applicants should register their interest by way of an introductory email to the Charities Administrator (tc@saddlersco.co.uk), who will advise whether the bid will be taken forward. The trustees will not respond to unsolicited brochures or appeal letters.

CONTACT DETAILS Charities Administrator, Saddlers' Company, Saddlers' Hall, 40 Gutter Lane, London EC2V 6BR *Tel.* 020 7726 8661 *Email* tc@saddlersco.co.uk *Website* www.saddlersco.co.uk

■ The Jean Sainsbury Animal Welfare Trust

CC NO 326358 **ESTABLISHED** 1982

WHERE FUNDING CAN BE GIVEN UK and overseas.

WHO CAN BENEFIT UK-registered national and international animal welfare charities.

WHAT IS FUNDED Animal welfare and wildlife.

WHAT IS NOT FUNDED The trust's website provides a full list of exclusions, which includes individuals.

TYPE OF GRANT Core costs; capital costs; project funding.

RANGE OF GRANTS Up to £35,000.

SAMPLE GRANTS RSPCA Hull and East Riding (£35,000); Carla Lane Animals in Need (£15,000); Cavaliers in Need (£10,000); World Parrot Trust (£7,000); British Divers Marine Life Rescue (£6,000); Bristol and Wales Cat Rescue (£5,000); BARRK – Banff and Aberdeenshire Rescue and Rehoming (£4,000); Keighley Cat Care (£3,000); Yorkshire Animal Shelter (£1,000).

FINANCES *Financial year end* 31/12/2019 *Income* £809,900 *Total grants* £441,000 *Grants to organisations* £441,000 *Assets* £26,580,000

TRUSTEES Jacqui Sharp; Madeleine Orchard; James Keliher; Mark Spurdens; Valerie Pike; Michelle Allen; Jill Inglis.

OTHER INFORMATION In 2019 charities working in the UK were awarded £353,000 and charities working overseas were awarded £88,000.

HOW TO APPLY Application forms can be downloaded from the trust's website. The trustees meet three times a year to consider applications. Applications should be received by 15 January, 1 May and 1 September. More details are available on the trust's website.

CONTACT DETAILS Barbara Georgiou, Administrator, PO Box 469, London W14 8PJ *Tel.* 020 7602 7948 *Email* jsawt7@gmail.com *Website* jeansainsburyanimalwelfare.org.uk

■ The Alan and Babette Sainsbury Charitable Fund

CC NO 292930 **ESTABLISHED** 1953

WHERE FUNDING CAN BE GIVEN UK, with some preference for Southwark; Africa.

WHO CAN BENEFIT Registered charities; theatres; community organisations; universities; research institutes.

WHAT IS FUNDED Arts and education projects for young people in Southwark, London; civil liberties and human rights charities in the UK; educational and employment opportunities for young people overseas, especially Africa; scientific and medical research on Type 1 diabetes.

WHAT IS NOT FUNDED Individuals; educational fees; expeditions.

TYPE OF GRANT Research; core/revenue costs; project funding; occasionally capital costs.

RANGE OF GRANTS Typically £5,000 to £20,000.

SAMPLE GRANTS Oxford Centre for Diabetes Endocrinology and Metabolism (£78,000); Juvenile Diabetes Research Foundation (£24,000); Blue Elephant Theatre and National Holocaust Centre (£15,000 each); Shakespeare's Globe and Student Action for Refugees (£10,000 each); Council of Christian Jews (£5,000); The Sainsbury Archive (£1,500); Refugee and Migrant Centre (£430).

FINANCES *Financial year end* 05/04/2020 *Income* £577,000 *Total grants* £518,300 *Grants to organisations* £518,300 *Assets* £13,860,000

TRUSTEES Judith Portrait; Jessica Sainsbury; John Sainsbury; Lindsey Anderson.

OTHER INFORMATION The trust is one of the Sainsbury Family Charitable Trusts which share a common administration – see www.sftc.org.uk for more information. In 2019/20 the trust made grants to 43 organisations totalling £518,300, distributed as follows: youth work (£141,000); scientific and medical research (£124,000); civil liberties and community relations (£98,500); Jewish and Israeli causes (£97,800); overseas (£44,000); general charitable purposes (£12,900).

HOW TO APPLY Applications should be submitted using the Sainsbury Family Charitable Trusts' online form or made in writing (maximum two sides of A4) to the correspondent, using the online application form as a template. Funding enquiries via email are not considered. The website stresses that most applications are unsuccessful. All applicants receive a standard acknowledgement letter.

CONTACT DETAILS Robert Bell, Director, The Peak, 5 Wilton Road, London SW1V 1AP *Tel.* 020 7410 0330 *Email* proposals@sfct.org.uk *Website* www.sfct.org.uk

■ Saint Sarkis Charity Trust

CC NO 215352 **ESTABLISHED** 1954

WHERE FUNDING CAN BE GIVEN UK and overseas.

WHO CAN BENEFIT Registered charities.

WHAT IS FUNDED Primarily, charitable causes within the Armenian community; charities developing innovative projects to support prisoners in the UK. The trust funds the Armenian Church of Saint Sarkis in London and the Gulbenkian Library at the Armenian Patriarchate in Jerusalem on an annual basis.

TYPE OF GRANT Often recurrent.

SAMPLE GRANTS Barrow Cadbury Trust (£58,000); PRIME (£29,900); Jerusalem Library (£27,500); Armenian Church of St Sarkis (£13,400);

London Armenian Poor Relief (£9,000); Armenian Church Trust (£8,200); Armenian Institute (£5,500); Armenian Diocese (£3,500).

FINANCES *Financial year end* 31/03/2020 *Income* £193,500 *Total grants* £155,000 *Grants to organisations* £155,000 *Assets* £9,390,000

TRUSTEES Martin Essayan; Rita Vartoukian; Alec D'Janoeff; Teni Shahiean.

OTHER INFORMATION In 2019/20, the trust made eight grants to organisations, including £58,000 to the Barrow Cadbury Trust, which, on behalf of the trust, recommends and administers a small number of projects connected with reducing prisoner re-offending. The trust is no longer accepting unsolicited applications for prisoner support projects.

HOW TO APPLY Apply in writing to the correspondent. There is no standard application form, so applicants should write a brief covering letter including an explanation of the exact purpose of the grant, how much is needed, with details of how the budget has been arrived at, details of any other sources of income (firm commitments and those still being explored), the charity's registration number, the latest annual report and audited accounts, and any plans for monitoring and evaluating the work.

CONTACT DETAILS Isabel Vasconcelos, Secretary to the Trustees, 50 Hoxton Square, London N1 6PB *Tel.* 020 7012 1400 *Email* info@saintsarkis.org.uk *Website* www.saintsarkis.org.uk

■ The Saintbury Trust

CC NO 326790 **ESTABLISHED** 1985

WHERE FUNDING CAN BE GIVEN West Midlands, Warwickshire, Worcestershire and North Gloucestershire (Postcodes: B, CV, DY, GL, WR, WS and WV).

WHO CAN BENEFIT Registered charities.

WHAT IS FUNDED General charitable purposes, including the following: arts, culture, heritage and science; the environment; disability; social welfare; education; health; children and young people; older people; community development; homelessness.

WHAT IS NOT FUNDED Individuals; animal charities; religious charities; unregistered charities; national charities; uniformed groups; village halls; local churches; repair, maintenance, improvement; general running costs; start-up costs. Note: neither Shropshire (including Telford and Wrekin), Staffordshire nor Herefordshire are eligible.

RANGE OF GRANTS Typically between £1,000 and £5,000.

SAMPLE GRANTS Performances Birmingham Ltd (£65,000); Alzheimer's Research UK (£20,000); National Youth Orchestra of Great Britain (£7,000); Birmingham People's Centre (£5,000); Children's University Trust (£4,000); The Jericho Foundation, Wildfowl and Wetlands Trust and Women and Families Resource Centre (£2,000 each).

FINANCES *Financial year end* 31/12/2019 *Income* £2,340,000 *Total grants* £526,000 *Grants to organisations* £526,000 *Assets* £14,010,000

TRUSTEES Victoria Houghton; Anita Bhalla; Anne Thomas; Harry Forrester; Amanda Atkinson-Willes; Jane Lewis; Cerian Brogan; Benjamin Atkinson-Willes.

OTHER INFORMATION Grants were awarded to 92 organisations during 2019/20. The trust does not respond to telephone enquiries – all correspondence should be by email or post.

HOW TO APPLY Guidance and application forms are available from the trust's website. At the time of writing (May 2021) the trust was only accepting applications from charities that have applied previously (since 2010), whether successfully or unsuccessfully. Check the foundation's website for the latest information.

CONTACT DETAILS The Trustees, PO Box 464, Abinger Hammer, Dorking, Surrey RH4 9AF *Tel.* 01223 460222 *Email* saintburytrust@btinternet.com *Website* www.thesaintburytrust.co.uk

■ The Saints and Sinners Trust Ltd

CC NO 200536 **ESTABLISHED** 1961

WHERE FUNDING CAN BE GIVEN UK.

WHO CAN BENEFIT Registered charities.

WHAT IS FUNDED General charitable purposes, mainly welfare and medical causes. Priority is given to requests for grants sponsored by members of Saints and Sinners.

WHAT IS NOT FUNDED Individuals; non-registered charities.

RANGE OF GRANTS £500 to £5,000.

SAMPLE GRANTS South Bucks RDA, RSC Next Generation ACT and Mind (£5,000 each); Reform Foundation Trust (£3,000); Honeypot Children's Charity, Injured Jockeys Fund and Institute of Hepatology (£2,500 each); Dementia UK and Smile Train (£1,500 each); ABF Golf Day (£500).

FINANCES *Financial year end* 31/10/2019 *Income* £76,600 *Total grants* £100,500 *Grants to organisations* £100,500 *Assets* £57,500

TRUSTEES Neil Benson; Sir Anthony Jolliffe; David Edwards; Sir Timothy Laurence.

OTHER INFORMATION The 2018/19 accounts were the latest available at the time of writing (June 2021). Grants were awarded to 56 organisations during the year.

HOW TO APPLY Applications are not considered unless nominated by members of the club.

CONTACT DETAILS David Edwards, Trustee, Lewis Golden LLP, 40 Queen Anne Street, London W1G 9EL *Tel.* 020 7580 7313 *Email* Charity@LewisGolden.com

■ The Salamander Charitable Trust

CC NO 273657 **ESTABLISHED** 1977

WHERE FUNDING CAN BE GIVEN UK.

WHO CAN BENEFIT Registered charities.

WHAT IS FUNDED General charitable purposes including the following: education and training; the promotion of health; social welfare; overseas aid; Christianity; arts and culture; medical research.

WHAT IS NOT FUNDED Individuals.

SAMPLE GRANTS Previous beneficiaries have included: All Nations Christian College, All Saints – Branksome Park, Birmingham Christian College, Christian Aid, Churches Commission on Overseas Students, FEBA Radio, International Christian College, London Bible College, Middle East Media, Moorland College, St James PCC – Poole, SAMS, SAT-7 UK, Trinity College and Wycliffe Bible Translators.

FINANCES *Financial year end* 05/04/2020 *Income* £61,800 *Total grants* £94,000 *Grants to organisations* £94,000 *Assets* £1,660,000

TRUSTEES Catherine Douglas; Alison Hardwick; Robert Douglas.
HOW TO APPLY The trust's income is fully allocated each year, mainly to regular beneficiaries. The trustees do not wish to receive any new requests.
CONTACT DETAILS Catharine Douglas, The Old Rectory, 5 Stamford Road, South Luffenham, Oakham, Rutland LE15 8NT *Tel.* 01782 847952 *Email* salamanderct@btinternet.com

■ Salisbury Pool Charity

CC NO 272626 **ESTABLISHED** 1976
WHERE FUNDING CAN BE GIVEN Dorset and Hertfordshire with a preference for Hatfield and Cranborne.
WHO CAN BENEFIT Registered charities; churches; schools; museums; libraries; local organisations.
WHAT IS FUNDED General charitable purposes, with a preference for heritage and conservation, social welfare and agricultural and scientific education.
RANGE OF GRANTS Typically less than £5,000.
SAMPLE GRANTS University of Hertfordshire (£25,000); Eton College (£16,700); Westminster Abbey (£10,500); Create Streets (£3,000); Cranborne Church PCC (£1,800); Normandy Memorial Trust (£1,000); Family Lives (£500); Dorset Citizens Advice (£250).
FINANCES *Financial year end* 05/04/2020 *Income* £78,300 *Total grants* £81,000 *Grants to organisations* £81,000 *Assets* £1,630,000
TRUSTEES The Most Honorable The Marquess Of Salisbury; Viscount Cranborne.
OTHER INFORMATION Grants were made to 21 organisations during the year for the following purposes: education (£52,500 in nine grants); churches (£14,700 in six grants); social welfare (£12,500 in nine grants); museums and memorials (£1,500 in two grants); other (£100 in one grant).
HOW TO APPLY Contact the correspondent for further information.
CONTACT DETAILS The Trustees, The Estate Office, Hatfield Park, Hatfield, Hertfordshire AL9 5NB *Tel.* 01707 287000 *Email* j.green@gascoyneholdings.co.uk

■ Salters' Charitable Foundation

CC NO 328258 **ESTABLISHED** 1989
WHERE FUNDING CAN BE GIVEN UK; Greater London.
WHO CAN BENEFIT Charitable organisations with an established connection to the foundation or to the City of London.
WHAT IS FUNDED General charitable purposes; London citizenship and community development; science education at school and university level; health and medicine; the armed forces.
TYPE OF GRANT Project funding; one-off donations; long-term core support.
RANGE OF GRANTS £75 to £19,000.
SAMPLE GRANTS City of London School for Girls (£19,200); The Guildhall School Trust (£17,500); Christ's Hospital (£11,000); London Community Response Fund and Doorstep Library (£10,000 each); Arkwright Scholarships Trust (£4,400); The Lord Todd Memorial Bursary – Christ's College (£3,300); Mansion House Scholarship Scheme (£2,000); Cure Parkinson's Trust (£1,000); RAFT (£500); Age UK London (£250); Royal British Legion (£150); Kilronan School (£75).
FINANCES *Financial year end* 30/06/2020 *Income* £249,100 *Total grants* £134,100 *Grants to organisations* £134,100 *Assets* £2,060,000
TRUSTEE The Salters' Company.
OTHER INFORMATION The foundation made 46 grants in 2019/20 totalling £134,100, which were distributed as follows: bursaries and education (£67,400); response to the COVID-19 pandemic (£31,300); community (£21,000); city (£11,000); military and Cadet affiliations (£6,800); Masters' Discretionary Fund (£3,000); other donations (£2,700); medical causes (£2,500).
HOW TO APPLY The foundation does not accept unsolicited applications.
CONTACT DETAILS The Trustees, The Salters' Company, Salters' Hall, 4 London Wall Place, London EC2Y 5DE *Tel.* 020 7588 5216 ext. 235 *Email* charities@salters.co.uk *Website* www.salters.co.uk

■ Samjo Ltd

CC NO 1094397 **ESTABLISHED** 2002
WHERE FUNDING CAN BE GIVEN Greater Manchester.
WHO CAN BENEFIT Jewish organisations. The charity appears to support the same core group of beneficiaries each year, but it also makes grants to other organisations. Individuals with disabilities or experiencing poverty may also be supported.
WHAT IS FUNDED Jewish charitable causes, including the following: the advancement of the Orthodox Jewish faith; education; health and disability; social welfare; older people, vulnerable individuals and children.
RANGE OF GRANTS Larger grants have ranged up to £1 million, but most are of less than £300,000.
SAMPLE GRANTS Oizer Charitable Trust and Shemtov Charitable Trust (£290,000 each); Teshivoh Tefilloh Tzedokoh (£183,100); Friends of Boyan Trust (£143,400); Bikur Cholim and Gemiluth Chesed Trust (£76,000); Chortkov Trust (£53,000); Kolyom Trust Ltd (£5,000); Asser Bishvil Foundation (£2,500).
FINANCES *Financial year end* 31/03/2020 *Income* £2,040,000 *Total grants* £1,140,000 *Grants to organisations* £1,140,000 *Assets* £16,730,000
TRUSTEES Rabbi Yisroel Friedman; Joshua Halpern; Samuel Halpern.
OTHER INFORMATION Grants to unspecified beneficiaries totalled £102,300.
HOW TO APPLY Contact the correspondent for further information.
CONTACT DETAILS The Trustees, c/o Lopian Gross Barnett and Co., 1st Floor, Cloister House, New Bailey Street, Manchester M3 5FS *Tel.* 0161 832 8721 *Email* D.Stewart@prestburymanagement.co.uk

■ The Basil Samuel Charitable Trust

CC NO 206579 **ESTABLISHED** 1959
WHERE FUNDING CAN BE GIVEN UK.
WHO CAN BENEFIT Registered charities; schools; universities; hospitals; hospices; religious bodies/institutions; local authorities.
WHAT IS FUNDED General charitable purposes, including health, social welfare, education and culture.
WHAT IS NOT FUNDED Registered charities only.

SAMPLE GRANTS A list of beneficiaries was not included in the annual report and accounts.
FINANCES *Financial year end* 05/04/2020
Income £41,300 *Total grants* £555,500
Grants to organisations £555,500
Assets £6,940,000
TRUSTEES Richard Peskin; William Furber.
HOW TO APPLY Contact the correspondent for further information.
CONTACT DETAILS The Trustees, c/o Smith and Williamson, 25 Moorgate, London EC2R 6AY *Tel.* 020 7131 4376

■ The M. J. Samuel Charitable Trust

CC NO 327013 **ESTABLISHED** 1985
WHERE FUNDING CAN BE GIVEN UK and overseas.
WHO CAN BENEFIT Charitable organisations.
WHAT IS FUNDED General charitable purposes with a preference for health, environmental causes, the arts and overseas aid.
RANGE OF GRANTS Grants up to £167,000.
SAMPLE GRANTS Prospect Burma (£167,000); Royal Marsden (£82,500); University College London Development Fund (£45,000); King's College London (£25,000): The Anna Freud Centre (£15,000); Spey Foundation (£7,200); Country Food Trust (£1,000).
FINANCES *Financial year end* 05/04/2020
Income £96,200 *Total grants* £445,400
Grants to organisations £445,400
Assets £3,140,000
TRUSTEES Hon. Michael Samuel; Hon. Julia Samuel; Lord Bearsted.
OTHER INFORMATION In 2019/20, the trust made 26 grants to organisations, including eight donations of less than £1,000 each totalling £1,500.
HOW TO APPLY Contact the correspondent for further information.
CONTACT DETAILS The Trustees, Mells Park, Mells, Frome, Somerset BA11 3QB *Tel.* 020 7402 0602 *Email* claire@mellspark.com

■ The Peter Samuel Charitable Trust

CC NO 269065 **ESTABLISHED** 1975
WHERE FUNDING CAN BE GIVEN UK, with some preference for local organisations in South Berkshire, the Scottish Highlands and East Somerset.
WHO CAN BENEFIT Charitable organisations.
WHAT IS FUNDED General charitable purposes, in particular: medical sciences; people's quality of life in the local areas; heritage and forestry/land restoration; Jewish causes.
RANGE OF GRANTS Mostly £500 to £7,000, with some larger grants.
SAMPLE GRANTS Civic Ltd (£60,000); King's College London (£30,000); Anna Freud Centre (£25,000); Child Bereavement Trust (£7,000); Game and Wildlife Conservation Trust (£6,000); Jewish Care (£3,500); Prostate Cancer UK (£1,500); Woodland Heritage (£1,000); Police Rehabilitation Trust (£500).
FINANCES *Financial year end* 31/03/2020
Income £132,400 *Total grants* £190,500
Grants to organisations £190,500
Assets £5,120,000
TRUSTEES Rt Hon. T. Viscount Bearsted; The Hon. Michael Samuel.
OTHER INFORMATION Grants were awarded to 30 organisations during the year.
HOW TO APPLY Contact the correspondent for further information.
CONTACT DETAILS The Trustees, The Estate Office – Farley Estate, Farley Hall, Castle Road, Farley Hill, Reading, Berkshire RG7 1UL *Tel.* 0118 973 0047 *Email* pa@farleyfarms.co.uk

■ The Samworth Foundation

CC NO 265647 **ESTABLISHED** 1973
WHERE FUNDING CAN BE GIVEN Worldwide. In the UK, there is a preference for the East Midlands.
WHO CAN BENEFIT Registered charities.
WHAT IS FUNDED Sexual exploitation, child trafficking and anti-slavery causes in the UK and Africa; the environment. Occasionally the foundation operates specific special interest grant programmes.
RANGE OF GRANTS Typically less than £50,000.
SAMPLE GRANTS Leicester Cathedral Charitable Trust (£250,000); Tearfund (£129,900); Parents Against Child Exploitation (£58,100); International Justice Mission UK (£50,000); Prisoners' Education Trust and Rainforest Foundation UK (£35,000 each); The Woodland Trust and WWF UK (£10,000 each).
FINANCES *Financial year end* 05/04/2020
Income £776,700 *Total grants* £2,850,250
Grants to organisations £2,850,000
Assets £59,840,000
TRUSTEES Prof. Neil Gorman; Mark Samworth; Susan Ralphs.
OTHER INFORMATION Grants were awarded to 106 organisations. Only organisations that received grants of over £10,000 were listed as beneficiaries in the foundation's accounts. Donations of under £10,000 totalled £56,200 and were awarded to 50 organisations. Grants were broken down as follows: UK core grants (£1.63 million); family and exceptional donations (£737,200); international core grants (£479,700).
HOW TO APPLY Causes are researched and identified by the trustees and organisations that meet the foundation's criteria are invited to apply. The foundation does not accept unsolicited applications.
CONTACT DETAILS The Trustees, Chetwode House, 1 Samworth Way, Melton Mowbray, Leicestershire LE13 1GA *Tel.* 01664 414500 *Email* admin@samworthfoundation.org.uk *Website* https://samworthfoundation.org.uk

■ The Sanderson Foundation

CC NO 1155744 **ESTABLISHED** 2014
WHERE FUNDING CAN BE GIVEN England and Wales.
WHO CAN BENEFIT Charitable organisation.
WHAT IS FUNDED General charitable purposes, including education.
RANGE OF GRANTS Up to £90,000.
SAMPLE GRANTS University of Oxford (£90,000); Watts Gallery (£50,000); Chalke Valley History Festival (£40,000); The London Library (£5,000); Balsam Centre (£2,000).
FINANCES *Financial year end* 31/03/2020
Income £277,800 *Total grants* £374,000
Grants to organisations £374,000
Assets £71,900
TRUSTEES Jonathan Azis; Damaris Sanderson; Timothy Sanderson.
OTHER INFORMATION Trustee Timothy Sanderson is Chair and Chief Investment Officer of Sanderson Asset Management. Grants were made to 21 organisations during the year.

HOW TO APPLY Contact the correspondent for further information.

CONTACT DETAILS Jonathan Azis, Trustee, Westwood Manor, Lower Westwood, Bradford on Avon, Wiltshire BA15 2AF *Tel.* 01225 863374 *Email* jonathanazis@parkepartnership.com

■ The Sandhu Charitable Foundation

CC NO 1114236 **ESTABLISHED** 2006

WHERE FUNDING CAN BE GIVEN Worldwide.

WHO CAN BENEFIT UK-registered charities.

WHAT IS FUNDED General charitable purposes, with a preference for: education and training; the promotion of health; social welfare; overseas aid; children and young people; people with disabilities.

TYPE OF GRANT Unrestricted funding.

RANGE OF GRANTS Grants range from £1,000 up to £80,000.

SAMPLE GRANTS Ehlers-Danlos Support UK (£80,000); Variety, The Children's Charity (£35,000); Anne Frank Trust UK (£34,000); Warwick University (£10,000); Orbis UK (£7,000); Harrow Aphasia Self Help (£5,000); Mayor's Music Fund (£1,000).

FINANCES *Financial year end* 31/03/2020 *Income* £359,100 *Total grants* £334,000 *Grants to organisations* £334,000 *Assets* £3,310,000

TRUSTEES Bimaljit Sandhu; Pardeep Sandhu.

OTHER INFORMATION In 2019/20, grants were made to 24 organisations.

HOW TO APPLY The charity supports individual charities or charitable causes, often on a single-donation basis, which the trustees identify.

CONTACT DETAILS N. Steele, Administrator and Secretary to the Trustees, First Floor, Santon House, 53–55 Uxbridge Road, Ealing, London W5 5SA *Tel.* 020 3478 3900 *Email* nsteele@thesantongroup.com *Website* https://www.thesantongroup.com/charity/the-sandhu-charitable-foundation

■ Sandra Charitable Trust

CC NO 327492 **ESTABLISHED** 1987

WHERE FUNDING CAN BE GIVEN UK, with a slight preference for the South East.

WHO CAN BENEFIT Charitable organisations; nurses.

WHAT IS FUNDED Animal welfare and research; environmental protection; the relief of poverty; youth development. Grants are also made to nurses and those studying to be nurses.

RANGE OF GRANTS Up to £50,000, but mostly up to £10,000.

SAMPLE GRANTS Kids (£50,000); Arundel Castle Cricket Foundation (£28,000); The Florence Nightingale Foundation (£17,200); Lullaby Trust (£6,000); New English Ballet Theatre (£4,000); Salisbury Cathedral (£2,000); Raleigh International (£1,000).

FINANCES *Financial year end* 30/06/2019 *Income* £828,700 *Total grants* £468,500 *Grants to organisations* £370,100 *Assets* £24,060,000

TRUSTEES Richard Moore; Michael Macfadyen; Lucy Forsyth; Francis Moore.

OTHER INFORMATION Grants were made to 91 organisations. Only organisations that received grants of over £1,000 were listed as beneficiaries in the charity's accounts. Grants of under £1,000 totalled £2,000 and were awarded to four organisations. Grants totalling £98,400 were made to 115 individuals. The 2018/19 accounts were the latest available at the time of writing (February 2021).

HOW TO APPLY The trust's 2018/19 annual report states: 'Unsolicited applications are not requested as the trustees prefer to support charities whose work they have researched and which is in accordance with the wishes of the Settlor. The trustees receive a very high number of grant applications which are mostly unsuccessful.' Applications may be considered from nurses and those training as nurses.

CONTACT DETAILS Lynne Webster, c/o Moore Family Office Ltd, 42 Berkeley Square, London W1J 5AW *Tel.* 020 7318 0845 *Email* Lynne.Webster@moorefamilyofficegroup.com

■ The Sands Family Trust

CC NO 1136909 **ESTABLISHED** 2010

WHERE FUNDING CAN BE GIVEN UK and overseas.

WHO CAN BENEFIT Charitable organisations; individuals.

WHAT IS FUNDED General charitable purposes, with a preference for education, health and the performing arts.

SAMPLE GRANTS United World Colleges (£65,700); Kay Mason Foundation (£15,000); Hackney Food Bank (£2,000).

FINANCES *Financial year end* 05/04/2020 *Income* £14,400 *Total grants* £82,700 *Grants to organisations* £82,700 *Assets* £839,900

TRUSTEES Betsy Tobin; Peter Sands; Jacqui Moseley.

OTHER INFORMATION Grants were made to two organisations during the year.

HOW TO APPLY Contact the correspondent for further information.

CONTACT DETAILS The Trustees, c/o Handelsbanken Wealth Management, 77 Mount Ephraim, Tunbridge Wells, Kent TN4 8BS *Tel.* 01892 701801 *Email* charities@heartwoodgroup.co.uk

■ Santander UK Foundation Ltd

CC NO 803655 **ESTABLISHED** 1990

WHERE FUNDING CAN BE GIVEN UK, Guernsey, Jersey and the Isle of Man.

WHO CAN BENEFIT Registered charities; CICs; not-for-profit organisations.

WHAT IS FUNDED Financial and digital skills.

WHAT IS NOT FUNDED Charities principally benefitting a single religious or ethnic group; lobbying or political causes; causes outside the UK.

TYPE OF GRANT Project funding; matched fundraising for employees.

RANGE OF GRANTS Up to £5,000.

SAMPLE GRANTS Alzheimer's Society (£193,100); Macmillan Cancer Support (£29,600); Barnardo's (£23,800); Age UK (£23,700); Cancer Research UK (£20,400); Marie Curie Cancer Care (£12,100); Action Cancer (£10,800); Children in Need (£10,600); HCPT – Hosanna House and Children's Pilgrimage Trust (£10,500).

FINANCES *Financial year end* 31/12/2019 *Income* £3,490,000 *Total grants* £1,990,000 *Grants to organisations* £1,990,000 *Assets* £18,180,000

TRUSTEES Sue Willis; Judith Moran; Christopher Fallis; John Collins; Danny Jones; Christopher Anderson.

OTHER INFORMATION Only beneficiaries that received over £10,000 were listed in the accounts. At the time of writing (June 2021) the foundation was focusing its funding to support charities through the COVID-19 crisis. Prior to this, the foundation underwent a review of its funding strategy. At the time of writing the foundation's website stated: 'We'll launch a new grants programme in 2021 to support organisations delivering skills to help people become [digitally and financially] empowered.'

HOW TO APPLY Visit the foundation's website for the most up-to-date information regarding open grant programmes.

CONTACT DETAILS The Trustees, Santander UK plc, Santander House, 201 Grafton Gate East, Milton Keynes, Buckinghamshire MK9 1AN *Email* grants@santander.co.uk *Website* www.santanderfoundation.org.uk

■ Sarum St Michael Educational Charity

CC NO 309456 **ESTABLISHED** 1980

WHERE FUNDING CAN BE GIVEN Salisbury; Devon; Dorset; Hampshire; Oxfordshire; Somerset; Wiltshire.

WHO CAN BENEFIT Schools; universities; individuals.

WHAT IS FUNDED The advancement of religious education in accordance with the principles of the Church of England, including funding for: schools; parishes and associated groups; individuals in further, higher and postgraduate education; training of teachers.

WHAT IS NOT FUNDED Maintenance costs, unless they are an integral part of a residential course; grants for buildings, fixtures or fittings; retrospective grants; contributions to the general funds of any organisation.

SAMPLE GRANTS The largest grants made in 2019 were: Salisbury Diocesan Board of Education (£65,000); Diocese of Bristol (£10,000); National Association of Teachers of RE (£7,000); Bridge Youth Project (£5,000).

FINANCES *Financial year end* 31/12/2019 *Income* £192,100 *Total grants* £208,900 *Grants to organisations* £102,700 *Assets* £6,330,000

TRUSTEES The Very Revd Alec Knight; Jennifer Pitcher; Rt Revd Nicholas Holtam; John Cox; Revd Jane Dunlop; Mrs J. Tubbs; Revd Ann Keating; Mrs J. Molnar; Prof. Elizabeth Stuart; David Pain; Robert Sykes; Revd Nicholas Papadopulos; Jonathan Leigh.

OTHER INFORMATION Ten grants were awarded to organisations in 2019. These were distributed between: teaching resources (£94,700); chapel and chaplaincy (£8,000). Grants totalling £106,200 were also awarded to 76 individuals.

HOW TO APPLY Application forms for each funding stream are available from the charity's website. Completed application forms should be emailed to the correspondent. The trustees meet four or five times a year to determine grants.

CONTACT DETAILS The Trustees, First Floor, 27A Castle Street, Salisbury, Wiltshire SP1 1TT *Tel.* 01722 422296 *Email* clerk@sarumstmichael.org *Website* www.sarumstmichael.org

■ Savannah Wisdom

CC NO 1141619 **ESTABLISHED** 2011

WHERE FUNDING CAN BE GIVEN India and the UK.

WHO CAN BENEFIT Registered charities; not-for-profit organisations; individuals.

WHAT IS FUNDED Social inequality; corruption; healthcare; gender rights; community work.

TYPE OF GRANT Project funding; capital costs; core/revenue costs; salaries.

SAMPLE GRANTS Previous beneficiaries have included: Transparency International (£24,000); British Asia Trust; Karuna Trust; Network for Social Change; The Edelgive Foundation.

FINANCES *Financial year end* 30/04/2020 *Income* £11,500 *Total grants* £280,000 *Grants to organisations* £280,000

TRUSTEES Simon Arora; Shalni Arora; Bobby Arora.

OTHER INFORMATION Full accounts were not available to view on the Charity Commission's website due to the charity's low income. We have therefore estimated the grant total based on the charity's total expenditure.

HOW TO APPLY The charity does not accept unsolicited applications.

CONTACT DETAILS The Trustees, Suite 2, Ground Floor, Torr Vale Mills, Tore Vale Road, New Mills, High Peak, Derbyshire SK22 3HS *Tel.* 0151 728 5997 *Email* admin@savannahwisdom.org *Website* https://savannahwisdom.org

■ The Savoy Educational Trust

CC NO 1161014 **ESTABLISHED** 2015

WHERE FUNDING CAN BE GIVEN UK.

WHO CAN BENEFIT Educational establishments; hospitality associations; charitable organisations/social enterprises; individuals.

WHAT IS FUNDED Hospitality-related projects and education.

TYPE OF GRANT Equipment; capital projects; project funding.

RANGE OF GRANTS Grants range from £200 up to £100,000.

SAMPLE GRANTS NPTC Group of Colleges (£100,000); La Salle Hotel School Liverpool CIC (£50,000); Roundwood Park School (£45,000); Exeter College (£8,000); Bethany School (£1,400); Framingham Earl High School (£900); CIEH (£200).

FINANCES *Financial year end* 31/03/2020 *Income* £1,660,000 *Total grants* £1,110,000 *Grants to organisations* £1,110,000 *Assets* £58,190,000

TRUSTEES Ramon Pajares; Roberts Davis; Howard Field; Dr Sally Messenger; David Taylor.

HOW TO APPLY See the trust's website for the latest information on how to apply including what to write before making an application, details on what to include in the application and application deadlines.

CONTACT DETAILS Margaret Georgiou, Administrator and Secretary to the Trustees, Room 160, 90 Long Acre, Covent Garden, London WC2E 9RZ *Tel.* 020 7849 3001 *Email* info@savoyeducationaltrust.org.uk *Website* www.savoyeducationaltrust.org.uk

■ The Scarfe Charitable Trust

CC NO 275535 **ESTABLISHED** 1978

WHERE FUNDING CAN BE GIVEN UK, mainly Suffolk.

WHO CAN BENEFIT Churches; charitable organisations.

WHAT IS FUNDED Restoration of churches; the arts and music; the environment.

TYPE OF GRANT Projects; capital costs; core costs. Funding is normally for one year or less.

RANGE OF GRANTS Grants range from £200 up to £9,500. Many grants are under £1,000.

SAMPLE GRANTS Aldeburgh Music (£9,500); INK Festival (£3,000); Revitalise, East Anglia's Children's Hospices (£2,000 each); High Tide

(£800); Uproar Theatre (£300); Music at Thornham (£200).

FINANCES *Financial year end* 31/03/2020 *Income* £67,000 *Total grants* £78,300 *Grants to organisations* £74,200 *Assets* £1,720,000

TRUSTEES Sean McTernan; Eric Maule; John McCarthy; Fraser Thomas; Sam Denny-Hodson.

OTHER INFORMATION Grant totalling £4,100 were awarded to six individuals.

HOW TO APPLY Apply in writing to the correspondent by letter or email. The trustees meet quarterly to consider applications and will not respond to correspondence unless it relates to grants it has agreed to make, or to the trust's general management.

CONTACT DETAILS Sean McTernan, Trustee, 2 The Clubhouse, Melton Park, Melton, Woodbridge, Suffolk IP12 1SY *Tel.* 01394 386192 *Email* scarfetrust@gmail.com

■ Schass Foundation

CC NO 280513 **ESTABLISHED** 1980

WHERE FUNDING CAN BE GIVEN UK, with a preference for Lancashire, Greater Manchester and London.

WHO CAN BENEFIT Jewish organisations.

WHAT IS FUNDED General charitable causes; education; poverty relief; Jewish causes.

RANGE OF GRANTS Generally up to £10,000.

SAMPLE GRANTS Broom Foundation (£12,500); Asser Bishvil Foundation (£10,000); Manchester Hachnosas Kallo Society (£7,600); Toimchei Shabbos Manchester (£3,000); B F of Shuvu (£1,000).

FINANCES *Financial year end* 31/03/2020 *Income* £60,900 *Total grants* £98,500 *Grants to organisations* £98,500 *Assets* £616,500

TRUSTEES Shulamith Bamberger; Simon Bamberger.

OTHER INFORMATION Only organisations that received grants of over £1,000 were listed as beneficiaries in the charity's accounts. Grants of under £1,000 totalled £600.

HOW TO APPLY Contact the correspondent for further information.

CONTACT DETAILS The Trustees, 30 Waterpark Road, Salford, Greater Manchester M7 4ET *Tel.* 0161 740 1112

■ The Annie Schiff Charitable Trust

CC NO 265401 **ESTABLISHED** 1973

WHERE FUNDING CAN BE GIVEN UK and overseas.

WHO CAN BENEFIT Charitable organisations.

WHAT IS FUNDED Social welfare; education; health and Jewish causes.

RANGE OF GRANTS £500 to £15,000.

SAMPLE GRANTS Previous beneficiaries have included: Friends of Beis Yisrael Trust and Menorah Grammar School Trust (£15,000 each); Elanore Ltd (£10,000); WST Charity Ltd (£8,000); Friends of Ohel Moshe (£6,000); Tifres High School, EMET and Yesamech Levav Trust (£5,000 each); North West Separdish Synagogue (£3,000); British Friends of Nadvorne (£1,500); Golders Charitable Trust (£1,100); Beth Jacob Grammar School for Girls Ltd (£1,000); Ezra U'Marpeh (£500).

FINANCES *Financial year end* 05/04/2020 *Income* £39,100 *Total grants* £92,400 *Grants to organisations* £92,400 *Assets* £68,400

TRUSTEES Joseph Pearlman; Ruth Pearlman; Zehava Danksy.

OTHER INFORMATION A list of beneficiaries was not available for 2019/20.

HOW TO APPLY Contact the correspondent for further information.

CONTACT DETAILS The Trustees, 8 Highfield Gardens, London NW11 9HB *Tel.* 020 8458 9266

■ The Anthony Scholefield Foundation

CC NO 1150446 **ESTABLISHED** 2013

WHERE FUNDING CAN BE GIVEN Worldwide, in practice UK.

WHO CAN BENEFIT Registered charities.

WHAT IS FUNDED General charitable purposes.

TYPE OF GRANT Recurrent.

RANGE OF GRANTS £2,500 to £10,000.

SAMPLE GRANTS Combat Stress and Head2Head (£10,000 each); ABF The Soldiers' Charity, Cerebral Palsy Plus, Royal British Legion, Salvation Army, St Catherine's Hospice and Samaritans (£5,000 each); Apostleship of the Sea (£2,500).

FINANCES *Financial year end* 01/11/2019 *Income* £94,600 *Total grants* £92,500 *Grants to organisations* £92,500 *Assets* £112,500

TRUSTEES Anthony Scholefield; Coutts & Co.

OTHER INFORMATION The 2018/19 accounts were the latest available at the time of writing (June 2021). Grants were awarded to 17 organisations during the year.

HOW TO APPLY Apply by letter to the correspondent.

CONTACT DETAILS The Trustees, Coutts & Co. Trustee Department, 1st Floor, Trinity Quay 1, Avon Street, Bristol BS2 0PT *Tel.* 0345 304 2424

■ O and G Schreiber Charitable Trust

CC NO 1073263 **ESTABLISHED** 1998

WHERE FUNDING CAN BE GIVEN England and Wales.

WHO CAN BENEFIT Registered charities, with a preference for Orthodox Jewish charities.

WHAT IS FUNDED Orthodox Jewish causes; education; relief of poverty among the Jewish community.

RANGE OF GRANTS Up to £50,000.

SAMPLE GRANTS Ezer V'Hatzalah Ltd (£49,460); Sharei Chesed – London (£38,020); Hadras Kodesh Trust (£25,000); Blooming Blossoms Trust (£22,500); Young and Inspired Ltd (£21,700); Friends of Zichron Dovid (£14,000); Yeitev Lev Eretz Israel Ltd (£10,580).

FINANCES *Financial year end* 31/12/2019 *Income* £110,000 *Total grants* £276,000 *Grants to organisations* £276,000 *Assets* £3,700

TRUSTEES Osias Schreiber; Gyta Schreiber.

OTHER INFORMATION In 2019 the trust made grants to seven listed organisations and an unknown number of other grants (under £10,000).

HOW TO APPLY Apply in writing to the correspondent. The charity accepts applications for grants from representatives of Orthodox Jewish charities, which are reviewed by the trustees on a regular basis.

CONTACT DETAILS Osias Schreiber, Trustee, 34 Jessam Avenue, London E5 9DU *Tel.* 020 8806 1842

■ Schroder Charity Trust

CC NO 214050 **ESTABLISHED** 1946

WHERE FUNDING CAN BE GIVEN UK and overseas.

WHO CAN BENEFIT UK-registered charities.

WHAT IS FUNDED General charitable purposes; education; health; arts, culture and heritage; community work; the armed forces; the environment; international development.

WHAT IS NOT FUNDED Individuals; animal welfare organisations; political organisations; major capital appeals.

TYPE OF GRANT Project funding; core/revenue costs.

RANGE OF GRANTS Generally up to £5,000.

SAMPLE GRANTS The Welfare Association (£10,000); Grand Bahama Disaster Relief (£7,500); Childhood Eye Cancer Trust (£5,000); Dulwich Picture Gallery (£4,000); The Norfolk Hospice (£3,000); Disability Sports Coach (£2,500); LUPUS UK (£1,000); Royal Chapel Windsor (£400).

FINANCES *Financial year end* 31/03/2020 *Income* £534,600 *Total grants* £418,200 *Grants to organisations* £418,200 *Assets* £11,650,000

TRUSTEES Mr T. Schroder; Charmaine von Mallinckrodt; Claire Howard; Leonie Schroder; John Schroder.

OTHER INFORMATION In 2019/20, grants were made to 98 charities from 486 applications.

HOW TO APPLY Applications should be made online using a form on the website. There is a short eligibility quiz that must be completed before applying for a grant. Applications can be made at any time as decisions are generally made bi-annually, around June and November. Applicants will be notified of the decision within nine months of submitting an application.

CONTACT DETAILS The Trustees, 81 Rivington Street, London EC2A 3AY *Tel.* 020 3170 5793 *Email* info@schrodercharitytrust.org *Website* www.schrodercharitytrust.org

■ The Schroder Foundation

CC NO 1107479 **ESTABLISHED** 2005

WHERE FUNDING CAN BE GIVEN Worldwide, but mainly the UK.

WHO CAN BENEFIT Registered charities.

WHAT IS FUNDED General charitable purposes, mainly within the following areas: the environment; education; arts, culture and heritage; social welfare; community; international aid. There is a separate grant programme for charities and community groups in Islay and Jura.

RANGE OF GRANTS Grants range from £200 up to £100,000.

SAMPLE GRANTS Cancer Research UK (£100,000); The Green Alliance Trust (£35,000); University of Cambridge (£20,000); Queen Elizabeth's Foundation (£10,000); Islay and Jura Community Enterprise Ltd (£6,000); Kilmeny Community Playing Fields (£700); Museum of Islay Life (£500).

FINANCES *Financial year end* 05/04/2020 *Income* £535,700 *Total grants* £1,350,000 *Grants to organisations* £1,350,000 *Assets* £10,510,000

TRUSTEES Charmaine Mallinckrodt; Leonie Schroder; Claire Howard; Michael May; Richard Robinson; Philip Mallinckrodt.

OTHER INFORMATION The foundation shares a common administration with Schroder Charity Trust. In 2019/20, the foundation awarded 62 grants. Of the grant total, £51,600 was awarded by the Islay and Jura sub-committee to organisations/causes on the islands.

HOW TO APPLY The trust does not respond to unsolicited applications.

CONTACT DETAILS The Trustees, 81 Rivington Street, London EC2A 3AY *Tel.* 020 3170 5793

■ Foundation Scotland

OSCR NO SC022910 **ESTABLISHED** 1995

WHERE FUNDING CAN BE GIVEN Scotland.

WHO CAN BENEFIT Charitable organisations.

WHAT IS FUNDED General charitable purposes including the following: health and well-being; art, culture and heritage; life skills, employability and education; community cohesion; social welfare; access to transport; the environment.

TYPE OF GRANT Capital, revenue and project funding.

RANGE OF GRANTS Usually between £250 and £5,000, but occasionally larger.

SAMPLE GRANTS Soul Soup (£10,000); Stand Easy (£7,900); LEAP Sports Scotland (£5,000); Broomhouse Centre (£3,500); Nairn Costal Rowing Club (£2,800); Glenfarg Old Folks Social Committee (£500).

FINANCES *Financial year end* 31/03/2020 *Income* £13,250,000 *Total grants* £10,000,000 *Grants to organisations* £10,000,000 *Assets* £63,560,000

TRUSTEES Barry Sillers; Toby Anstruther; Ian Marr; Samantha Fiander; Sharon Fairweather; Angus Tulloch; Sarah Whitley; James Hilder; Stephen Connelly.

OTHER INFORMATION This is one of the 46 UK community foundations, which distribute funding for a wide range of purposes. As with all community foundations, there are a number of donor-advised funds managed on behalf of individuals, families and charitable trusts. Grant schemes tend to change frequently – consult the foundation's website for details of current programmes and up-to-date deadlines.

HOW TO APPLY Potential applicants are advised to visit the community foundation's website or contact its grants team to find the most suitable funding stream.

CONTACT DETAILS Grants Team, 15 Calton Road, Edinburgh EH8 8DL *Email* enquiries@foundationscotland.org.uk *Website* www.foundationscotland.org.uk

■ Scott (Eredine) Charitable Trust

CC NO 1002267 **ESTABLISHED** 1990

WHERE FUNDING CAN BE GIVEN England and Wales.

WHO CAN BENEFIT Registered charities.

WHAT IS FUNDED General charitable purposes; armed forces/emergency service charities; people with disabilities.

TYPE OF GRANT Capital costs; project funding.

RANGE OF GRANTS Generally under £10,000.

SAMPLE GRANTS Previous beneficiaries have included: Alzheimer's Research UK (£40,000); Mental Health Research UK (£20,000); Combined Services Disabled Ski Team (£10,000); Army Benevolent Fund (£6,000); The Gurkha Welfare Trust (£5,000); RNLI (£3,500); Send a Cow (£3,000); IT Schools Africa (£2,800); Woodworks Project (£1,000).

FINANCES *Financial year end* 31/12/2019 *Income* £466,900 *Total grants* £6,730,000 *Grants to organisations* £6,730,000 *Assets* £10,740,000

TRUSTEES Keith Bruce-Smith; Amanda Scott; Col. Nick Wills; Lucy Gibson.

OTHER INFORMATION Grants were made to 90 organisations during the year. Grants paid includes £6,270,000 in respect of a transfer of shares and associated dividend income to Fieldrose Charitable Trust.

HOW TO APPLY Contact the correspondent for further information.

CONTACT DETAILS Amanda Scott, Trustee, Wise's Farm House, Ampney St Mary, Ampney St Mary, Gloucestershire GL7 5SN *Email* mandajscott@gmail.com

■ Francis C. Scott Charitable Trust

CC NO 232131 **ESTABLISHED** 1963

WHERE FUNDING CAN BE GIVEN Cumbria (excluding the South Lakeland District Council area and the old Westmorland County boundary); North Lancashire (the Lancaster district to the west of the M6 and north of Galgate).

WHO CAN BENEFIT Registered charities; organisations which are pursuing charitable objectives and have not-for-profit aims/a constitution may be considered. A preference exists for small to medium-sized organisations (turnover less than £1 million).

WHAT IS FUNDED Organisations working with children and young people (up to 24 years old) in the following areas: victims/survivors of abuse and exploitation; homelessness and its causes; those suffering from mental health problems; those leaving care or the criminal justice system; isolation in rural areas; enterprising solutions to job creation; targeted, issue-based youth work; those living in poverty.

WHAT IS NOT FUNDED Individuals; statutory organisations; national charities without a local base/project; charities with substantial unrestricted reserves; medical/health establishments; schools/educational establishments; infrastructure organisations/second-tier bodies; projects principally benefitting people outside Cumbria/north Lancashire; retrospective expenditure; expeditions or overseas travel; promotion of religion; animal welfare.

TYPE OF GRANT Capital costs; project funding; core/revenue funding; start-up costs. The majority of grants are multi-year revenue grants for core costs.

RANGE OF GRANTS Most up to £20,000.

SAMPLE GRANTS Cancer Care (£46,000); Wise Up Workshops (£42,000); Wigton Youth Station (£7,900); Dogs for Development CIC (£2,300).

FINANCES *Financial year end* 31/12/2019
Income £668,700 *Total grants* £1,260,000
Grants to organisations £1,260,000
Assets £34,310,000

TRUSTEES Joanna Plumptre; Alexander Scott; Madeleine Scott; Peter Redhead; Melanie Wotherspoon; Christine Knipe; John McGovern; Malcolm Tillyer; Carol Ostermyer.

OTHER INFORMATION Grants were made to 46 organisations and broken down as follows: other (£545,600); youth work (£425,700); mental health (£172,100); job support (£38,500); abuse survivors (£29,000); poverty (£25,400).

HOW TO APPLY Applicants are advised to contact the correspondent for an informal discussion before submitting an application for funding. Application forms are available to download from the trust's website or can be requested by phone, email or post. Applications should be completed and returned with the latest set of accounts via email or post. Applications for over £4,000 should be submitted at least five weeks before the trustees' meetings in March, July and November (contact the trust for exact dates). Applications for grants of less than £4,000 will be considered at small grants meetings every 3–4 weeks. Applicants should refer to the trust's website, which is very comprehensive and covers all aspects of the grant-making process.

CONTACT DETAILS Helen Carter, Director, Stricklandgate House, 92 Stricklandgate, Kendal, Cumbria LA9 4PU *Tel.* 01539 742608 *Email* info@fcsct.org.uk *Website* www.fcsct.org.uk

■ The Frieda Scott Charitable Trust

CC NO 221593 **ESTABLISHED** 1974

WHERE FUNDING CAN BE GIVEN Cumbria, specifically the old county of Westmorland and the area covered by South Lakeland District Council.

WHO CAN BENEFIT Voluntary or charitable organisations.

WHAT IS FUNDED General charitable purposes, particularly: projects supporting the disadvantaged and vulnerable; older people; people with disabilities, mental health problems and/or learning difficulties; children and young people; family support work; people who have experienced abuse; people recovering from substance misuse; carers; village halls; community centres; access to services for rural communities; information and advice services for charities; community arts and music; amateur sports clubs; uniformed youth groups.

WHAT IS NOT FUNDED Retrospective expenditure; statutory bodies (including health and education); promotion of religion or places of worship; individuals; animal welfare, the environment or heritage causes; museums and art galleries; national charities (apart from local branches).

TYPE OF GRANT Project funding; revenue or capital costs; occasional larger grants; possible multi-year grants where required.

RANGE OF GRANTS £200 to £20,000. Most grants are below £10,000.

SAMPLE GRANTS Manna House – Kendal (£35,000); Carer Support South Lakes (£13,000); The Bee Team – Heron Hill School (£10,000); Kendal Dementia Action Alliance and Ulverston Mind (£5,000 each); Long Marion Village Institute (£3,500); Cumbria Youth Alliance (£2,000); Appleby Emergency Response Group (£1,500); Friends of Artspace (£500).

FINANCES *Financial year end* 31/03/2020
Income £294,900 *Total grants* £242,600
Grants to organisations £242,600
Assets £9,080,000

TRUSTEES Stuart Fairclough; Richard Brownson; Vanda Lambton; Samantha Scott; Hugo Pring; Laura Southern; Alison Alger; Simon Kirby; Samuel Rayner.

OTHER INFORMATION In 2019/20, 38 organisations were awarded grants from a total of 48 applications. The average grant size was £6,400.

HOW TO APPLY Application forms can be requested from the correspondent either by post, email or phone. Alternatively, they can be downloaded from the trust's website. Applicants are welcome to contact the Trust Secretary for an informal discussion before applying. Applications are considered at meetings in March, June, September and December and should be sent at least five weeks in advance. Grants of less than £3,500 are considered by the Small Grants Committee, which meets between the main trustees' meetings. Charities should not apply to this trust and the Francis C. Scott Charitable Trust at the same time.

CONTACT DETAILS Celia Forsyth, Trust Secretary, Stricklandgate House, 92 Stricklandgate, Kendal, Cumbria LA9 4PU *Tel.* 01539 742608 *Email* info@fcsct.org.uk *Website* www.friedascott.org.uk

■ Sir Samuel Scott of Yews Trust

CC NO 220878 **ESTABLISHED** 1951

WHERE FUNDING CAN BE GIVEN UK.

WHO CAN BENEFIT Research institutions.

WHAT IS FUNDED Medical research.

RANGE OF GRANTS Typically £1,000 to £15,000.

SAMPLE GRANTS University of Oxford (£41,800); Asthma UK (£10,000); Stoke Association (£5,000); Bloodwise and Retina UK (£3,000 each); Action Medical Research (£2,000); Brain Research UK (£1,000).

FINANCES *Financial year end* 05/04/2020
Income £140,700 *Total grants* £177,800
Grants to organisations £177,800
Assets £6,920,000

TRUSTEES Edward Perks; Hermione Stanford; Camilla Withington.

OTHER INFORMATION Grants were made to 30 organisations in 2019/20.

HOW TO APPLY Contact the correspondent for more information. The trustees meet twice each year to consider grant applications.

CONTACT DETAILS The Trustees, c/o Currey and Co. LLP, 33 Queen Anne Street, London W1G 9HY *Tel.* 020 7802 2700 *Email* sirsamuelscottofyewstrust@curreyandco.co.uk

■ The Ina Scott Sutherland Charitable Foundation

OSCR NO SC046561 **ESTABLISHED** 2016

WHERE FUNDING CAN BE GIVEN Scotland, with a strong preference for Aberdeen and Aberdeenshire.

WHO CAN BENEFIT Charitable organisations, especially those with which Ina Scott Sutherland had a connection.

WHAT IS FUNDED General charitable purposes.

SAMPLE GRANTS VSA Aberdeen (£20,000); The Robert Nicol Trust (£15,000); ARC Hippotherapy, Instant Neighbour and Marie Curie (£5,000 each); Crossroads Caring Scotland (£3,500); Lomond Mountain Rescue Team (£2,000); Meningitis Now (£2,000).

FINANCES *Financial year end* 30/06/2019
Income £262,400 *Total grants* £141,800
Grants to organisations £141,800
Assets £7,460,000

OTHER INFORMATION The 2018/19 accounts were the latest available at the time of writing (May 2021). During the year, grants were made to 17 organisations.

HOW TO APPLY Contact the correspondent for further information.

CONTACT DETAILS The Trustees, c/o Peterkins Solicitors, 100 Union Street, Aberdeen, Aberdeenshire AB10 1QR

■ The John Scott Trust Fund

OSCR NO SC003297 **ESTABLISHED** 1984

WHERE FUNDING CAN BE GIVEN Scotland.

WHO CAN BENEFIT Registered charities.

WHAT IS FUNDED General charitable purposes including the following: health; social welfare; disability; children and young people.

WHAT IS NOT FUNDED Individuals.

RANGE OF GRANTS Up to £30,000.

SAMPLE GRANTS Ayrshire Hospice (£30,000); Combat Stress (£10,000); Boswell Book Festival (£5,000); Cancer Research UK (£3,000); Vics in the Community (£500).

FINANCES *Financial year end* 30/04/2020
Income £75,800 *Total grants* £241,500
Grants to organisations £241,500
Assets £2,040,000

HOW TO APPLY Contact the correspondent for further information.

CONTACT DETAILS The Trustees, Kilpatrick and Walker Solicitors, 4 Wellington Square, Ayr, Ayrshire KA7 1EN

■ Scottish Coal Industry Special Welfare Fund

OSCR NO SC001200 **ESTABLISHED** 1973

WHERE FUNDING CAN BE GIVEN Scotland.

WHO CAN BENEFIT People who are or have been employed in the mining industry and their families.

WHAT IS FUNDED The welfare of those who are or have been employed in the mining industry and their families. Support is also given for individuals in need, recreational facilities, youth clubs, holidays and courses.

SAMPLE GRANTS A list of beneficiaries was not included in the annual report and accounts.

FINANCES *Financial year end* 31/03/2020
Income £28,000 *Total grants* £119,900
Grants to organisations £119,900
Assets £487,300

HOW TO APPLY Contact the correspondent for further information.

CONTACT DETAILS The Trustees, c/o Scottish Mining Convalescent Trust, Blair Castle, Culross, Fife KY12 8JW

■ The Scottish Power Foundation

OSCR NO SC043862 **ESTABLISHED** 2013

WHERE FUNDING CAN BE GIVEN UK.

WHO CAN BENEFIT Registered charities.

WHAT IS FUNDED General charitable purposes; education; the environment; arts. heritage. culture and science; poverty relief; community development.

TYPE OF GRANT Project funding; capital costs.

RANGE OF GRANTS £10,000 to £150,000.

SAMPLE GRANTS National Museums of Scotland (£100,000); Bangor University (£73,000); Size of Wales (£60,000); CLWYD Theatre and Music in Hospitals Scotland (£50,000 each); Dumfries House (£30,000); Community First (£28,500).

FINANCES *Financial year end* 31/12/2019
Income £1,170,000 *Total grants* £1,250,000
Grants to organisations £1,250,000
Assets £228,600

TRUSTEES Mike Thornton; Melanie Hill; Sarah Mistry; Keith Anderson; Elaine Bowker; Anita Longley.

HOW TO APPLY Check the website for updates on opening dates for grant programmes..

CONTACT DETAILS Rebecca Fairley, Secretary, 320 St Vincent Street, Glasgow G2 5AD *Email* scottishpowerfoundation@scottishpower.

com *Website* www.scottishpower.com/pages/about_the_scottishpower_foundation

■ Scottish Property Industry Festival of Christmas (SPIFOX)

OSCR NO SC020660 **ESTABLISHED** 1983

WHERE FUNDING CAN BE GIVEN Scotland.

WHO CAN BENEFIT Registered charities.

WHAT IS FUNDED Financial assistance to charitable organisations providing relief to children and young people in need.

WHAT IS NOT FUNDED The charity's website states: 'It is not generally our policy to contribute to revenue or administrative needs, this having become our established practice from when our Charity was set up in 1983.'

TYPE OF GRANT Specific capital projects.

RANGE OF GRANTS Up to £50,000.

SAMPLE GRANTS Children 1st (£40,000); Friends of Seaview (£32,000); Ronald McDonald House (£25,000); Riverbase School (£15,000); Scottish Book Trust (£4,400); Youth Vision (£6,800); Deaf Connection (£3,200); Wandered Kneaded (£1,400).

FINANCES *Financial year end* 30/06/2019 *Income* £655,500 *Total grants* £360,100 *Grants to organisations* £360,100 *Assets* £138,500

TRUSTEES Christian Bruce; Alasdair Carlyle; Andy Clark; Ross Clephane; Bill Colville; Penny Hearn; Alasdair MacConnell; David Mackenzie; Kenneth McDowell; Brian McGhee; Jeremy Milliken; Danny O'Neill; Frances Sim; Ronnie Urquhart; Alan Watt.

OTHER INFORMATION All grants are awarded to allow charities to purchase equipment or improve facilities. The 2018/19 accounts were the latest available at the time of writing (February 2021).

HOW TO APPLY Contact the correspondent, or any of the trustees known to you, for an initial discussion. After this, the charity will seek further information on the project/cause to be supported, which will then be considered at the next Beneficiaries Sub-committee meeting. The charity responds to initial applications within a few weeks.

CONTACT DETAILS Alasdair Carlyle, Chair of Beneficiaries Committee, c/o Saffrey Champness LLP, Edinburgh Quay, 133 Fountainbridge, Edinburgh EH3 9BA *Email* alasdair@spifox.co.uk *Website* www.spifox.co.uk

■ Scouloudi Foundation

CC NO 205685 **ESTABLISHED** 1962

WHERE FUNDING CAN BE GIVEN UK and overseas.

WHO CAN BENEFIT UK-registered charities.

WHAT IS FUNDED Historical research; the environment; social welfare; disability; the armed forces and sailors; children and young people; health; overseas aid.

WHAT IS NOT FUNDED Individuals; welfare activities of a purely local nature; loans.

TYPE OF GRANT Research and fellowships; recurrent; one-off.

RANGE OF GRANTS Typically £1,000 to £5,000.

SAMPLE GRANTS Institute of Historical Research – University of London (£60,300); Disaster Emergencies Committee (£7,000); British Red Cross Disaster Fund, Together for Shorter Lives and Vision Aid Overseas (£5,000 each); Centrepoint, Mental Health Foundation and Royal Sailor's Rests (£3,000 each).

FINANCES *Financial year end* 07/02/2020 *Income* £200,200 *Total grants* £168,800 *Grants to organisations* £168,800 *Assets* £8,780,000

TRUSTEES Sarah Baxter; David Marnham; James Sewell.

OTHER INFORMATION The foundation awards an annual grant to the Institute of Historical Research at the University of London for fellowships, research and publications. During 2019/20, grants were made to 33 organisations. Grants were broken down as follows: the environment and humanities (£76,800); welfare (£21,000); disability (£19,000); medicine, health and hospices (£19,000); overseas aid (£17,000); children and youth (£13,000); welfare of the armed forces and sailors (£3,000).

HOW TO APPLY Applications are only open for Historical Grants fellowships. Copies of the regulations and application forms for 'Historical Awards' can be obtained from The Scouloudi Foundation Historical Awards Committee, c/o Institute of Historical Research, University of London, Senate House, Malet Street, London WC1E 7HU. The trustees meet annually to consider recommendations for grants.

CONTACT DETAILS The Trustees, c/o haysmacintyre, Thames Exchange, 10 Queen Street Place, London EC4R 1AG *Tel.* 020 7969 5500 *Email* pholden@haysmacintyre.com

■ The Screwfix Foundation

CC NO 1151375 **ESTABLISHED** 2013

WHERE FUNDING CAN BE GIVEN UK.

WHO CAN BENEFIT Registered charities and not-for-profit organisations, particularly those local to Screwfix stores.

WHAT IS FUNDED The repair, maintenance, improvement or construction of homes, community facilities or other buildings for those in need.

TYPE OF GRANT Capital costs.

RANGE OF GRANTS Up to £5,000. The average grant during 2019/20 was £4,100.

SAMPLE GRANTS A list of beneficiaries was not included in the annual report and accounts.

FINANCES *Financial year end* 31/01/2020 *Income* £1,270,000 *Total grants* £1,120,000 *Grants to organisations* £1,120,000 *Assets* £490,000

TRUSTEES Jonathan Mewett; Claire Flory; Lindsay Haselhurst; Kim McDonald; Elizabeth Bell; Stephen Dunston; Caroline Welsh; Darren Worth.

OTHER INFORMATION The foundation was established in 2013 by Screwfix Ltd, a supplier of trade tools, plumbing, electrical, bathrooms and kitchens. During 2019/20, donations totalling £1.08 million were made to 264 local charities and a further £44,000 was awarded to Macmillan and Barnardo's in support of their community build projects.

HOW TO APPLY Applications can be made via the foundation's website. Applications are reviewed quarterly, usually in March, June, September and December. All successful applicants will be contacted by post, email or phone to arrange the next step. Unsuccessful applicants will be contacted within one month of the review meeting.

CONTACT DETAILS The Trustees, Trade House, Mead Avenue, Houndstone Business Park, Yeovil,

Somerset BA22 8RT *Tel.* 01935 414100
Email foundation@screwfix.com
Website https://www.screwfix.com/help/screwfixfoundation

The SDL Foundation

CC NO 1127138 **ESTABLISHED** 2008
WHERE FUNDING CAN BE GIVEN Worldwide.
WHO CAN BENEFIT Charitable organisations.
WHAT IS FUNDED Disadvantaged communities; the relief of poverty and social welfare; sustainable economic growth and regeneration.
WHAT IS NOT FUNDED No grants will be given to causes where trustees or SDL employees would directly benefit. The foundation will also not support political or discriminatory activities or those appeals that are recognised as being large or well known.
TYPE OF GRANT Mostly multi-year grants.
RANGE OF GRANTS Up to £100,000.
SAMPLE GRANTS Microloan Foundation (Malawi) (£51,000); Bead for Life (Uganda) (£42,100); Brighter Children (USA) (£19,400); PACT (UK) (£1,300); Sportsable (UK) (£950); Alzheimer's Research UK and YoungMinds Trust (UK) (£520 each); Blythswood (Romania) (£120).
FINANCES *Financial year end* 31/12/2019
Income £206,300 *Total grants* £166,800
Grants to organisations £166,800
Assets £80,100
TRUSTEES Maria Schnell; Azad Ootam; Adrian Gocan; Roddy Temperley; Kate Bushby; Christopher Batterham; Carolina Arias.
OTHER INFORMATION The SDL Foundation is the corporate charity of SDL plc, which provides software for language translation and interpretation services. The foundation prefers to support projects where SDL employees can complement support with their own fundraising initiatives.
HOW TO APPLY Only causes supported and sponsored by SDL employees will be considered by the SDL Foundation. Contact the foundation by email for further information on how to request the support of staff and application procedures.
CONTACT DETAILS The Trustees, SDL plc, New Globe House, Vanwall Road, Maidenhead SL6 4UB *Email* kbushby@sdl.com *Website* https://www.sdl.com/about/environmental-social-governance/foundation

Seafarers UK (King George's Fund for Sailors)

CC NO 226446 **ESTABLISHED** 1917
WHERE FUNDING CAN BE GIVEN UK and Commonwealth.
WHO CAN BENEFIT Registered charities; unregistered charities; CICs.
WHAT IS FUNDED The welfare of seafarers and their families and dependants; education and training of people for service at sea; social welfare; health; the armed forces.
TYPE OF GRANT Capital costs; core/revenue costs; seed funding/start-up funding; project funding; unrestricted funding.
SAMPLE GRANTS Fisherman's Mission (£170,000); Apostleship of the Sea (£70,000); Human Rights at Sea (£25,000); International Seafarers' Welfare and Assistance (£20,000); Marine Conservation Society (£10,000); Officers' Association (£5,000).
FINANCES *Financial year end* 31/12/2019
Income £2,360,000 *Total grants* £2,200,000
Grants to organisations £2,200,000
Assets £41,720,000
TRUSTEES Mark Carden; Gerald Kidd; Lord Mountevans; Mark Dickinson; Capt. Roger Barker; Dyan Sterling; Cmdre Peter Buxton; Jeremy Monroe; Duncan Bain; Natalie Shaw; Peter Tomlin; Paul Butterworth; William Lawes; Robert Greenwood; Peter French; William Reid.
OTHER INFORMATION In 2019, £2.2 million was awarded to 43 organisations.
HOW TO APPLY Applications can be made through the charity's website.
CONTACT DETAILS Grants Team, 8 Hatherley Street, London SW1P 2QT *Tel.* 020 7932 0000 *Email* grants@seafarers.uk *Website* https://www.seafarers.uk

The Searchlight Electric Charitable Trust

CC NO 801644 **ESTABLISHED** 1988
WHERE FUNDING CAN BE GIVEN UK, with a preference for Manchester and the surrounding areas.
WHO CAN BENEFIT Registered charities.
WHAT IS FUNDED Teaching and understanding of the Jewish faith; social welfare and care of older people and those in ill health and their dependants.
WHAT IS NOT FUNDED Individuals.
SAMPLE GRANTS Previous beneficiaries have included: Bnei a Kivah Sefer Torah; Chabad Vilna; CST (Community Security Trust); Guide Dogs for the Blind; Heathlands; Langdon College; Lubavitch Manchester; Manchester Eruv Committee; Nightingales; Reshet and the Purim Fund; Sense; The Federation; UJIA (United Jewish Israel Appeal); Young Israel Synagogue.
FINANCES *Financial year end* 05/04/2020
Income £57,700 *Total grants* £96,700
Grants to organisations £96,700
Assets £1,420,000
TRUSTEES Morris Hamburger; David Hamburger; Herzl Hamburger; Daniel Hamburger.
HOW TO APPLY Contact the correspondent for further information.
CONTACT DETAILS Daniel Hamburger, Trustee, 21 Brantwood Road, Salford, Greater Manchester M7 4EN *Tel.* 0161 203 3300

Sam and Bella Sebba Charitable Trust

CC NO 253351 **ESTABLISHED** 1967
WHERE FUNDING CAN BE GIVEN UK; Israel; USA.
WHO CAN BENEFIT Registered charities; places of worship and Jewish organisations; universities; schools; hospices; social enterprises.
WHAT IS FUNDED Palliative and end-of-life care; refugees; homelessness; human rights; assistive technology.
TYPE OF GRANT Capital costs; core/revenue costs; project funding; strategic funding; development funding; capacity building; research.
RANGE OF GRANTS Mostly up to £50,000.
SAMPLE GRANTS University of Cambridge (£412,500); Together for Short Lives (£220,000); Association for Civil Rights in Israel (£63,000); Refugee Women Connect (£40,000); Body and Soul (£35,000); Hotline for Refugees and Migrants (£25,200); Anti Trafficking and Labour Exploitation Unit (£15,000); Difficult Conversations (£10,000).

FINANCES *Financial year end* 31/12/2019 *Income* £1,350,000 *Total grants* £3,680,000 *Grants to organisations* £3,680,000 *Assets* £60,080,000

TRUSTEES Judy Sebba; Tamsin Doyle; Tali Emodi; Yoav Tangir; Brian Parkinson; Odelia Sebba; Ronit Armoni; Ray Shostak.

OTHER INFORMATION The trust also awards grants in the USA (homelessness, with a focus on Seattle) and Israel (the environment, at-risk young people, human rights, disability, social justice and shared society). Only organisations that received grants of over £10,000 were listed as beneficiaries in the charity's accounts. Grants of under £10,000 totalled £67,700 and were awarded to 12 organisations.

HOW TO APPLY The website states: 'Note the Trust undertakes its own research, in line with its current priorities, and does not accept unsolicited applications and will not acknowledge them.'

CONTACT DETAILS Amy Horne, UK Grants Manager, Office 19, 5th Floor, 63–66 Hatton Garden, London EC1N 8LE *Tel.* 020 7723 6028 *Email* admin@sebbatrust.org *Website* https://samandbellasebbacharitabletrust.com

■ Seedfield Trust

CC NO 283463 **ESTABLISHED** 1981

WHERE FUNDING CAN BE GIVEN Worldwide.

WHO CAN BENEFIT Registered charities.

WHAT IS FUNDED Christian causes; disaster relief; social welfare.

WHAT IS NOT FUNDED Individuals; applications for multi-year, core funding and salaries are less likely to be successful.

TYPE OF GRANT One-off project funding.

RANGE OF GRANTS £100 to £10,000.

SAMPLE GRANTS Friends of Julius and Dora Children's Centre – Kenya (£10,000); Keswick Convention Trust and Safe Families for Children (£5,000 each); Christian Restoration Ministries Int (£3,000); Street Child (£2,000); Crosslinks and Kidz Club Leeds (£1,000 each); Borrowdale School (£500).

FINANCES *Financial year end* 31/12/2019 *Income* £107,800 *Total grants* £110,200 *Grants to organisations* £110,200 *Assets* £3,410,000

TRUSTEES David Ryan; Paul Vipond; Eric Proudfoot; Mervyn Hull; Linda Rigg.

OTHER INFORMATION Grants were made to 49 organisations during 2019.

HOW TO APPLY Application forms are available from the trust's website. The trustees meet twice each year, usually in March and November, to consider applications. Each section of the application should be completed so that it stands alone and does not refer to other documents. Additional information in relation to the project may be submitted if necessary.

CONTACT DETAILS The Trustees, PO Box 135, Keswick, Cumbria CA12 9AS *Email* seedfieldtrust@yahoo.co.uk *Website* https://seedfieldtrust.wordpress.com

■ The Segelman Trust

CC NO 1079151 **ESTABLISHED** 1992

WHERE FUNDING CAN BE GIVEN UK, occasionally overseas.

WHO CAN BENEFIT UK-registered charities.

WHAT IS FUNDED Vulnerable and disadvantaged children and families.

WHAT IS NOT FUNDED Individuals.

TYPE OF GRANT Core costs; project and development costs; start-up funding; multi-year; one-off.

RANGE OF GRANTS Up to £120,000. In 2019 the average grant was £90,000.

SAMPLE GRANTS Acumen Academy UK (£120,000); Drive Forward Foundation (£105,000); Coram Voice for the New Belongings Programme (£100,000); Love Barrow Families and WILD Young Parents Project (£90,000 each); Zone West (£50,000); Lighthouse (£30,000); The Big House (£25,000).

FINANCES *Financial year end* 31/12/2019 *Income* £1,320,000 *Total grants* £960,000 *Grants to organisations* £960,000 *Assets* £52,510,000

TRUSTEES Christopher Graves; Wilson Cotton; Rebecca Eastmond; Timothy White.

OTHER INFORMATION During 2019, the trust made grants to 28 organisations which included multi-year grants. New grants were awarded to 13 organisations.

HOW TO APPLY The trustees do not consider unsolicited applications but instead identify projects and organisations they wish to support.

CONTACT DETAILS Grants Administrator, c/o White and Co., 190 Clarence Gate Gardens, Glentworth Street, London NW1 6AD *Tel.* 020 7759 1129

■ The Selfridges Group Foundation

CC NO 1167260 **ESTABLISHED** 2015

WHERE FUNDING CAN BE GIVEN UK; Canada; Netherlands; the Republic of Ireland.

WHO CAN BENEFIT Medical research institutions; universities.

WHAT IS FUNDED Medical research.

WHAT IS NOT FUNDED The foundation's objects are restricted specifically to the advancement of such charitable purposes as the trustees see fit, provided that they do not include the promotion of any religion.

TYPE OF GRANT Research funding.

RANGE OF GRANTS £9,800 to £254,500.

SAMPLE GRANTS VU University Medical Centre (£280,000); University of Oxford (£254,500); University College London (£171,000); Stichting Katholieke Universiteit (£73,700); The University of Edinburgh (£57,500); The German Centre for Neurodegenerative Diseases (£15,000); University of Groningen (£9,800).

FINANCES *Financial year end* 31/12/2019 *Income* £1,310,000 *Total grants* £998,500 *Grants to organisations* £998,500 *Assets* £837,700

TRUSTEES Anthony Edwards; Paul Kelly; Alannah Cochrane; Adam Batty; Alexandria Forbes.

OTHER INFORMATION A total of 20 grants were made to nine organisations in 2019.

HOW TO APPLY Applications can be made via the Weston Brain Institute. A link is available on the foundation's website.

CONTACT DETAILS The Trustees, Selfridges Group, Nations House, 103 Wigmore Street, London W1U 1QS *Tel.* 020 7318 2318 *Website* https://selfridgesgroup.com/selfridges-group-foundation

■ Leslie Sell Charitable Trust

CC NO 258699 **ESTABLISHED** 1969

WHERE FUNDING CAN BE GIVEN UK.

WHO CAN BENEFIT Scout and Guide associations and individuals.

WHAT IS FUNDED The trust makes small grants to groups to help with the cost of making repairs, or purchasing sundry items of equipment. It also gives assistance to groups and individuals when they make trips in the UK or overseas.

WHAT IS NOT FUNDED The project or trip must be part of the Scouting or Guiding movement. The trust cannot award grants within three months of an event date or the date of departure for a trip.

TYPE OF GRANT Capital costs.

SAMPLE GRANTS A list of beneficiaries was not included in the annual report and accounts.

FINANCES *Financial year end* 05/04/2020 *Income* £147,100 *Total grants* £157,400 *Grants to organisations* £157,400 *Assets* £4,490,000

TRUSTEES Mary Wiltshire; Adrian Sell; Nicola Coggins.

HOW TO APPLY Application forms can be downloaded from the trust's website.

CONTACT DETAILS The Secretary, 1st Floor, 8–10 Upper Marlborough Road, St Albans, Hertfordshire AL1 3UR *Tel.* 01727 843603 *Email* admin@lesliesellct.org.uk *Website* www.lesliesellct.org.uk

■ Sellata Ltd

CC NO 285429 **ESTABLISHED** 1980

WHERE FUNDING CAN BE GIVEN UK and Israel.

WHO CAN BENEFIT Charitable organisations; individuals.

WHAT IS FUNDED Advancement of the Orthodox Jewish faith; relief of poverty.

SAMPLE GRANTS A list of beneficiaries was not included in the annual report and accounts.

FINANCES *Financial year end* 31/03/2019 *Income* £190,500 *Total grants* £198,200 *Grants to organisations* £198,200 *Assets* £921,500

TRUSTEES Joseph Stern; Eliezer Benedikt; Aron Oberlander.

OTHER INFORMATION The 2018/19 accounts were the latest available at the time of writing (February 2021).

HOW TO APPLY Contact the correspondent for more information.

CONTACT DETAILS The Trustees, 29 Fountayne Road, London N16 7EA *Tel.* 020 8809 5051 *Email* management@abarisltd.co.uk

■ The Selwood Charitable Trust

CC NO 265974 **ESTABLISHED** 1973

WHERE FUNDING CAN BE GIVEN Hampshire.

WHO CAN BENEFIT Individuals and organisations.

WHAT IS FUNDED General charitable purposes.

SAMPLE GRANTS A list of beneficiaries was not included in the annual report and accounts.

FINANCES *Financial year end* 05/04/2020 *Income* £178,300 *Total grants* £192,000 *Grants to organisations* £192,000 *Assets* £4,750,000

TRUSTEES Lorna Selwood; Kim Lazarou; Peter Stone; Simon Selwood; Timothy Selwood.

OTHER INFORMATION Grants were distributed as follows: Minstead Trust (£115,700); other (£76,300).

HOW TO APPLY Contact the correspondent for further information.

CONTACT DETAILS The Trustees, Stone Osmond Ltd, 75 Bournemouth Road, Chandler's Ford, Eastleigh, Hampshire SO53 3AP *Tel.* 023 8057 8000

■ The Cyril Shack Trust

CC NO 264270 **ESTABLISHED** 1972

WHERE FUNDING CAN BE GIVEN England.

WHO CAN BENEFIT Charitable organisations.

WHAT IS FUNDED General charitable purposes; Jewish causes.

SAMPLE GRANTS A list of beneficiaries was not included in the annual report and accounts.

FINANCES *Financial year end* 28/09/2020 *Income* £44,800 *Total grants* £132,500 *Grants to organisations* £132,500 *Assets* £636,400

TRUSTEE Cyril Shack.

HOW TO APPLY Contact the correspondent for further information.

CONTACT DETAILS Cyril Shack, Trustee, c/o Lubbock Fine Chartered Accountants, Paternoster House, 65 St Paul's Churchyard, London EC4M 8AB *Tel.* 020 7490 7766

■ Shaftoe Educational Foundation

CC NO 528101 **ESTABLISHED** 1685

WHERE FUNDING CAN BE GIVEN Parish of Haydon, Northumberland.

WHO CAN BENEFIT Groups working in Haydon with an educational initiative; students needing educational support; apprenticeships.

WHAT IS FUNDED Education and training.

TYPE OF GRANT Revenue support; development costs; capital costs.

RANGE OF GRANTS Grants range from £250 up to £23,000.

SAMPLE GRANTS Shaftoe Wise Academies (£23,000 in eight grants); Haydon Bridge Playgroup and Tiny Tots (£2,000); Almshouse Charity of John Shaftoe (£1,700); Hexham Junior Netball Club (£1,000); Haydon Bridge Scout Group (£780); Haydon Bridge High School (£630); Shaftoe Singers (£250).

FINANCES *Financial year end* 31/03/2020 *Income* £196,500 *Total grants* £71,000 *Grants to organisations* £50,600 *Assets* £8,660,000

TRUSTEES Benedict Bates; John Wardle; Doris Wardle; Paula Collis; Edward Brown; Esmond Faulks; John Drydon; Laura Gilhespy; Kelly Richardson.

OTHER INFORMATION In 2019/20, nine organisations and 30 individuals were awarded grants.

HOW TO APPLY According to the trust's website: 'Applications for grants for local groups should be submitted in writing to the Clerk stating: The initiative or activity, and its educational purpose; the cost, and if it is not for a 'one-off' grant then over what period the grant is requested, broken down into years or periods.' The trustees meet three times a year (normally on the second Thursday of March, July and November) to consider applications.

CONTACT DETAILS Peter Fletcher, Clerk, The Office, Shaftoe Terrace, Haydon Bridge, Northumberland NE47 6BW *Tel.* 01434 684239 *Email* clerkshaftoecharities@outlook.com *Website* www.shaftoecharities.org.uk

■ The Jean Shanks Foundation

CC NO 293108 **ESTABLISHED** 1985

WHERE FUNDING CAN BE GIVEN UK.

WHO CAN BENEFIT Medical research institutions (i.e. medical schools), medical Royal Colleges and similar bodies; medical students.

WHAT IS FUNDED Medical research, education and training; grants for medical students.

WHAT IS NOT FUNDED The foundation's website states: 'No grants will be made for financial hardship or any project not having a significant pathology research content.'

TYPE OF GRANT Scholarships and research funding, for up to three years.

RANGE OF GRANTS From £14,700 to £146,700.

SAMPLE GRANTS University of Cambridge (£146,700); University College London (£123,600); Pathological Society of Great Britain and Ireland (£118,400); University of Southampton (£105,200); University of Leeds (£50,000); Academy of Medical Science (£25,000); University College London (£14,700).

FINANCES *Financial year end* 31/03/2020 *Income* £604,100 *Total grants* £583,600 *Grants to organisations* £583,600 *Assets* £21,910,000

TRUSTEES Eric Rothbarth; Alistair Jones; Dr Julian Axe; Prof. Adrienne Flanagan; Prof. James Underwood; Prof. Nicholas Wright; Prof. Mark Arends.

OTHER INFORMATION Grants were made to seven organisations in 2019/20.

HOW TO APPLY Application forms can be requested from the correspondent. Full grant guidelines are available on the foundation's website.

CONTACT DETAILS Eric Rothbarth, Chair, Peppard Cottage, Peppard Common, Henley-on-Thames, Oxfordshire RG9 5LB *Tel.* 01491 628232 *Email* administrator@jeanshanksfoundation.org *Website* www.jeanshanksfoundation.org

■ The Shanly Foundation

CC NO 1065044/1182155 **ESTABLISHED** 1997

WHERE FUNDING CAN BE GIVEN Worldwide with a preference for Berkshire, Buckinghamshire, Hampshire, Hertfordshire, North London, Oxfordshire, Surrey and West Sussex.

WHO CAN BENEFIT Registered charities; sports and social groups; community organisations; scout and guide groups; schools; woodland and environmental conservation organisations; outdoor activity centres for young people.

WHAT IS FUNDED General charitable purposes; local community benefit; social and community events.

WHAT IS NOT FUNDED Individuals; research; core costs; military charities; single-faith charities; animal welfare charities; organisations that have not been in existence for at least 12 months; organisations delivering services outside the area of benefit.

TYPE OF GRANT Generally project and capital costs; usually one-off but some organisations are supported on a long-term basis.

RANGE OF GRANTS Mostly under £5,000.

SAMPLE GRANTS Beech Lodge School (£81,300); Jumbulance Trust (£11,900); Citizens Advice Windsor and Maidenhead (£10,000); Westminster City Council (£5,400); Cardiac Risk; Farms for City Children; Me2Club; Read for Good; Spinal Injuries Association.

FINANCES *Financial year end* 31/12/2019 *Income* £3,470,000 *Total grants* £513,600 *Grants to organisations* £513,600 *Assets* £2,940,000

TRUSTEES Michael Shanly; Tamra Booth; Timothy Potter; Donald Tucker; Nicholas Young.

OTHER INFORMATION The 2018/19 accounts were the latest available at the time of writing (June 2021). Grants were broken down as follows: education (£174,200); community (£170,600); health and welfare (£93,500); disability (£73,300); wildlife and conservation (£2,000). Only beneficiaries of grants of over £5,400 were listed in the accounts; therefore, some recent beneficiaries have been taken from the website. Smaller grants totalled £375,400.

HOW TO APPLY Applications should be made through the online portal on the foundation's website. The questions can be previewed before registration. General enquiries can be submitted via the online contact form.

CONTACT DETAILS Maria Mindak, Sorbon, 24–26 Aylesbury End, Beaconsfield, Buckinghamshire HP9 1LW *Tel.* 01494 683800 *Email* maria.mindak@shanlyfoundation.com *Website* www.shanlyfoundation.com

■ ShareGift (The Orr Mackintosh Foundation)

CC NO 1052686 **ESTABLISHED** 1995

WHERE FUNDING CAN BE GIVEN UK.

WHO CAN BENEFIT UK-registered charities; individuals.

WHAT IS FUNDED Charitable purposes, guided by the wishes of the donors of shares, from where the charity's income derives.

WHAT IS NOT FUNDED Grants are not given to non-UK-registered charities.

TYPE OF GRANT Unrestricted funding; core costs.

RANGE OF GRANTS Mostly £10,000 up to £375,000.

SAMPLE GRANTS St Michael's Church Centre (£375.000); Cancer Research UK (£325,000); British Heart Foundation (£80,000); IntoUniversity (£65,000); Médecins Sans Frontières and The Royal Horticultural Society (£45,000 each); Onside Youth Zones (£10,000).

FINANCES *Financial year end* 31/03/2020 *Income* £3,240,000 *Total grants* £2,720,000 *Grants to organisations* £2,720,000 *Assets* £2,370,000

TRUSTEES Alan Scott; Paul Killik; John Roundhill; Susan Swabey; Gillian Budd.

OTHER INFORMATION In 2019/20, the total number of grants awarded was 405. Individuals are also supported.

HOW TO APPLY Applications for funding are not accepted and no response will be given to charities that send unsolicited applications. ShareGift supports a wide range of charities based on the value of shares donated and the number of suggestions it receives for a charity. Charities wishing to receive funding should encourage their supporters to donate unwanted shares to ShareGift. Further information is available on the website.

CONTACT DETAILS The Trustees, 4th Floor, 67–68 Jermyn Street, London SW1Y 6NY *Tel.* 020 7930 3737 *Email* help@sharegift.org *Website* www.sharegift.org

■ The Sharp Foundation

CC NO 1168241 **ESTABLISHED** 2016

WHERE FUNDING CAN BE GIVEN UK.

WHO CAN BENEFIT Charitable organisations.

WHAT IS FUNDED General charitable purposes, including the arts.

RANGE OF GRANTS Up to £50,000.

SAMPLE GRANTS Royal Academy of Arts (£53,200); Rainbow Trust (£50,000); Royal National Theatre (£29,400); China Tang (£20,000).

FINANCES *Financial year end* 31/10/2019 *Income* £81,900 *Total grants* £210,700 *Grants to organisations* £210,700 *Assets* £336,900

TRUSTEES Richard Sharp; Caroline Sharp.

OTHER INFORMATION The 2018/19 accounts were the latest available at the time of writing (April 2021).

HOW TO APPLY Contact the correspondent for further information.

CONTACT DETAILS The Trustees, 20 Guilford Road, Tunbridge Wells, Kent TN1 1SW *Tel.* 020 3003 5370

The Shears Foundation

CC NO 1049907 **ESTABLISHED** 1994

WHERE FUNDING CAN BE GIVEN Worldwide, with a preference for Greater Manchester, Northumberland, North and West Yorkshire and Tyne and Wear.

WHO CAN BENEFIT Registered charities only.

WHAT IS FUNDED Community development, the environment, sustainable development, health and medicine, social welfare, education (adult and/or children), culture and the arts – all with a focus on education and raising awareness.

WHAT IS NOT FUNDED Capital projects; individuals; religious or political causes; single-identity groups where there is no evidence of integration; preschool groups and playgroups; domestic pets.

TYPE OF GRANT Core and revenue costs; salaries; project funding.

RANGE OF GRANTS The average value of grants was £11,800 in 2019/20. First-time applicants can apply for a maximum of £10,000.

SAMPLE GRANTS Community Foundation Linden Fund (£80,000); Bradford Grammar School and Whitley Fund for Nature (£50,000 each); Samling Foundation (£45,000); Alnwick Garden (£35,000); Haemochromatosis (£25,000).

FINANCES *Financial year end* 31/03/2020 *Income* £659,000 *Total grants* £697,200 *Grants to organisations* £697,200 *Assets* £14,350,000

TRUSTEES Mr G. Lyall; Mrs L. Shears; Mr P. Shears; Patricia Shears; Bruce Warnes; Mark Horner; Richard Shears; Louise Warnes; Georgie Shears.

OTHER INFORMATION Grants were made to 59 organisations during the year. Grants for less than £25,000 were awarded to 53 organisations and totalled £412,200. Only beneficiaries of grants of £25,000 and above were listed in the accounts.

HOW TO APPLY In the first instance, consult the foundation's website, which provides clear details on the application process and when to make an application. At the time of writing (May 2021), the website stated: 'Applications where we have not had a conversation prior to application will not be considered by our trustees. Give us a call on 07544 380316. We normally work on Monday and Tuesday each week.'

CONTACT DETAILS Bruce Warnes, Trustee, c/o The Community Foundation, Philanthropy House, Woodbine Road, Gosforth, Newcastle upon Tyne, Tyne and Wear NE3 1DD *Tel.* 07544 380316 *Email* bruce@shearsfoundation.org *Website* https://www.shearsfoundation.org

The Sheepdrove Trust

CC NO 328369 **ESTABLISHED** 1989

WHERE FUNDING CAN BE GIVEN UK, with a possible preference for north Lambeth, London.

WHO CAN BENEFIT Registered charities; schools and universities; individuals.

WHAT IS FUNDED General charitable purposes, particularly the following: sustainability; biodiversity; organic farming and nutrition; health and medical research; education and research; spiritual care; arts and culture.

SAMPLE GRANTS Previous beneficiaries have included: Coastal Grains (£30,000); Soil Association (£27,300); GM Watch (£25,000); University of Arts London (£23,800); The Prison Phoenix Trust (£20,000); Newcastle University (£16,700).

FINANCES *Financial year end* 31/12/2019 *Income* £11,800 *Total grants* £401,500 *Grants to organisations* £356,000

TRUSTEES Barnabas Kindersley; Juliet Kindersley; Peter Kindersley; Harriet Treuille; Anabel Kindersley.

OTHER INFORMATION Full accounts were not available to view on the Charity Commission's website due to the trust's low income. We have therefore estimated the grant total based on the trust's total expenditure.

HOW TO APPLY Contact the correspondent for further information.

CONTACT DETAILS The Trustees, Drove Farm, Sheepdrove, Lambourn, Hungerford, Berkshire RG17 7UN *Tel.* 01488 674726 *Email* helen.cravenjones@sheepdrove.com

The Sheffield Town Trust

CC NO 223760 **ESTABLISHED** 1297

WHERE FUNDING CAN BE GIVEN Sheffield.

WHO CAN BENEFIT Mainly local charities; national organisations will be supported if it can be demonstrated that the grants will be used exclusively for the benefit of Sheffield or its inhabitants; CICs; uniformed groups; schools; not-for-profit organisations.

WHAT IS FUNDED General charitable purposes in the Sheffield area.

WHAT IS NOT FUNDED Individuals; organisations that do not benefit Sheffield or its inhabitants; animal charities; political organisations; religious groups. The trustees will consider support for church buildings as long as those buildings will be used by the local community.

TYPE OF GRANT Recurrent and one-off; project funding.

RANGE OF GRANTS Mainly under £5,000.

SAMPLE GRANTS Christ Church – Heeley (£10,000); Age UK Sheffield (£4,300); Cathedral Archer Project and St Wilfrid's Centre (£4,000 each); Heeley Trust (£3,000); Music in Hospitals and Care (£2,500); Nerve Tumours UK (£2,000); Target Housing (£1,000); Graves Park Health Walks (£300).

FINANCES *Financial year end* 31/12/2019 *Income* £477,200 *Total grants* £341,800 *Grants to organisations* £341,800 *Assets* £9,200,000

TRUSTEES Nicholas Hutton; Adrian Staniforth; Jonathan Brayshaw; Penelope Jewitt; Jason Heath; Jane Ferretti; James Fulton; Marian Rae; Prof. Sarah Thomas; Oliver Stephenson; Zahid Hamid; Dr Julie MacDonald; Mark Swales.

OTHER INFORMATION Grants are made to 34 organisations on a recurrent basis. Non-recurrent grants were awarded to 113 organisations during 2019, of which 110 were for amounts of £5,000 or less.

HOW TO APPLY Application forms can be completed on the trust's website and need to be submitted with any supporting documents. Applicants are advised to draft their answers and documents before starting an application as the form must be completed in one go. The trustees meet four times a year in mid-February, mid-May, mid-August and mid-November. Applications should be submitted by the 15th of the preceding month.

CONTACT DETAILS George Connell, Law Clerk, c/o Keebles LLP, Commercial House, 14 Commercial Street, Sheffield, South Yorkshire S1 2AT *Tel.* 0114 276 5555 *Email* sheffieldtowntrust@keebles.com *Website* www.sheffieldtowntrust.org.uk

■ The Sheldon Trust

CC NO 242328 **ESTABLISHED** 1965

WHERE FUNDING CAN BE GIVEN UK, with a preference for the West Midlands and Greater London.

WHO CAN BENEFIT Registered charities; CICs; uniformed groups; schools.

WHAT IS FUNDED Community projects in the West Midlands (mainly volunteer-led); support for special needs groups in the West Midlands (i.e. those facing disadvantage due to age, health or disability); supporting 16 to 25 year olds nationally, especially those not in education, employment or training; holidays for people who are disadvantaged living in the West Midlands or Greater London.

WHAT IS NOT FUNDED Costs of purchasing buildings or vehicles; charities with an annual income of over £1 million and/or free unrestricted reserves to the value of more than six months of their annual expenditure.

TYPE OF GRANT Projects; salaries; equipment; furnishings; refurbishments; and running costs. Multi-year grants are available up to three years.

RANGE OF GRANTS Generally up to £10,000.

SAMPLE GRANTS Entraide (Mutual Aid) (£30,000); Southwick Neighbourhood Youth Project (£10,000); The Spring Playgroup and Pre-school (£9,000); The Women and Families Resource Centre (£6,600); Only Connect (£5,000); New Heights Warren Farm Community Project (£1,800); Farms for City Children (£650).

FINANCES *Financial year end* 05/04/2020 *Income* £267,300 *Total grants* £171,100 *Grants to organisations* £171,100 *Assets* £5,230,000

TRUSTEES Andrew Bidnell; John England; Rachel Beatton; Ruth Gibbins; Paul England.

OTHER INFORMATION Grants were made to 25 organisations during the year in the following categories: special needs groups (£105,300); youth development (£42,300); community projects (£16,800); holiday fund (£6,700).

HOW TO APPLY Applications should be submitted online, via the website, where further information and guidance is also provided. There is a separate application form for holidays. The trustees usually meet to consider applications in April and October. Queries should be emailed to the correspondent.

CONTACT DETAILS The Trustees, c/o Pothecary Witham Weld Solicitors, The Office Group, Thomas House, 84 Eccleston Square, London SW1V 1PX *Tel.* 020 7821 8211 *Email* charities@pwwsolicitors.co.uk *Website* https://www.pwwsolicitors.co.uk/charity-grants/8-the-sheldon-trust

■ The Patricia and Donald Shepherd Charitable Trust

CC NO 272948 **ESTABLISHED** 1973

WHERE FUNDING CAN BE GIVEN UK, with a preference for northern England, particularly York.

WHO CAN BENEFIT Charitable organisations.

WHAT IS FUNDED General charitable purposes; young people.

WHAT IS NOT FUNDED Individuals; local authorities.

RANGE OF GRANTS Up to £50,000.

SAMPLE GRANTS St Leonard's Hospice (£100,000); Special Boat Service Association (£50,000); Antibiotic Research UK (£25,000); Shepherd Group Brass Band (£24,000); York Early Music Centre (£4,200); Joseph Rowntree Housing Trust (£3,500); York Music Hub and York Trinity Micklegate plc (£2,000 each).

FINANCES *Financial year end* 05/04/2020 *Income* £226,800 *Total grants* £312,700 *Grants to organisations* £312,700 *Assets* £19,110,000

TRUSTEES Christine Shepherd; Iain Robertson; Jane Robertson; Michael Shepherd; Patrick Shepherd; Joseph Shepherd; Rory Robertson; Annabel Robertson; Carly Robertson.

OTHER INFORMATION During 2019/20, the trust made 16 donations to 14 charities for a wide range of causes.

HOW TO APPLY Contact the correspondent for further information.

CONTACT DETAILS The Trustees, West Mount, 129 The Mount, York, North Yorkshire YO24 1DU

■ The Sylvia and Colin Shepherd Charitable Trust

CC NO 272788 **ESTABLISHED** 1973

WHERE FUNDING CAN BE GIVEN North Yorkshire within a 25-mile radius of York.

WHO CAN BENEFIT Charitable organisations.

WHAT IS FUNDED General charitable purposes, particularly: health; social welfare; disability; older people; children and young people; the environment and conservation; heritage; the arts, science and culture.

WHAT IS NOT FUNDED Individuals.

TYPE OF GRANT Project funding.

RANGE OF GRANTS Mostly £1,000 and under, with some larger grants up to £21,000.

SAMPLE GRANTS The Franciscan Friars of the Renewal (£21,000); Magic Future Foundation (£10,000); The Ludgrove School Foundation (£5,000); York Arc Light (£4,000); Fight Bladder Cancer (£2,000); Alzheimer's Society, Restore York, The Children's Trust, The Fire Fighters Charity and York Childcare Ltd (£1,000 each).

FINANCES *Financial year end* 05/04/2020 *Income* £224,100 *Total grants* £204,900 *Grants to organisations* £204,900 *Assets* £2,690,000

TRUSTEES Sara Dickson; David Dickson; Lucy Dickson; Sophie Dickson; Harry Dickson.

OTHER INFORMATION During the year, grants of £1,000 or more were paid to 51 organisations and grants of under £1,000 were paid to 120 organisations. Grants for less than £1,000 totalled £59,600.

HOW TO APPLY Applications should be made in writing and should set out the purpose for which the funds would be used, the total amount required and other sources of finance available.

CONTACT DETAILS The Trustees, PO Box 730, York, North Yorkshire YO1 0HT *Tel.* 01904 702384 *Email* admin@scsctrust.co.uk

■ The Sherling Charitable Trust

CC NO 1079651 **ESTABLISHED** 1999

WHERE FUNDING CAN BE GIVEN UK, with a preference for Buckinghamshire and Dorset.

WHO CAN BENEFIT Charitable organisations.

WHAT IS FUNDED General charitable purposes, particularly education, sports, the arts and health.

TYPE OF GRANT Often recurrent.

RANGE OF GRANTS Grants range from £1,000 to £150,000.

SAMPLE GRANTS Scanappeal (£150,000); Chiltern MS Centre (£137,500); Centrepoint (£25,000); National Theatre, Woodrow High House (£20,000 each); Hospice of St Francis (£6,900); Deafblind (£1,000).

FINANCES *Financial year end* 31/03/2020 *Income* £431,400 *Total grants* £431,400 *Grants to organisations* £431,400 *Assets* £2,790,000

TRUSTEES Clive Sherling; Sally Sherling; Adrian Sherling; William Sherling.

OTHER INFORMATION Grants were made to 16 organisations during 2019/20, five of which had not been supported in the previous year.

HOW TO APPLY Contact the correspondent for further information.

CONTACT DETAILS Clive Sherling, Chair of the Trustees, Lincoln House, Woodside Hill, Chalfont St Peter, Gerrards Cross, Buckinghamshire SL9 9TF *Tel.* 01753 887454

■ The Archie Sherman Charitable Trust

CC NO 256893 **ESTABLISHED** 1967

WHERE FUNDING CAN BE GIVEN UK and overseas.

WHO CAN BENEFIT Charitable organisations.

WHAT IS FUNDED General charitable purposes including the following: education and training; Jewish causes; overseas aid; arts and culture; health.

TYPE OF GRANT Capital and buildings; project costs.

RANGE OF GRANTS Small and large grants, ranging from £2,000 to £81,300.

SAMPLE GRANTS The Diana and Allan Morgenthau Charitable Trust (£81,300); The Israel Children's Centers (£30,800); Royal Opera House Covent Garden Foundation and The Royal National Theatre (£25,000 each); Community Security Trust (£15,000); Shaare Zedek UK (£6,800); Israel Guide Dog Centre for the Blind (£2,000).

FINANCES *Financial year end* 05/04/2020 *Income* £1,631,000 *Total grants* £518,400 *Grants to organisations* £518,400 *Assets* £17,700,000

TRUSTEES Michael Gee; Eric Charles; Allan Morgenthau; Rhona Freedman.

OTHER INFORMATION During the year, 22 grants to organisations were awarded by the trust. The trust's annual report for 2019/20 states that the trustees review all commitments on a forward five-year basis.

HOW TO APPLY Contact the correspondent for further information.

CONTACT DETAILS The Trustees, 274A Kentish Town Road, London NW5 2AA *Tel.* 020 7493 1904 *Email* trust@sherman.co.uk

■ Shetland Charitable Trust

OSCR NO SC027025 **ESTABLISHED** 1976

WHERE FUNDING CAN BE GIVEN Shetland.

WHO CAN BENEFIT Charitable and voluntary organisations benefitting the community in Shetland.

WHAT IS FUNDED Arts projects for under 18s; activities for older people; social welfare; community development.

WHAT IS NOT FUNDED Exclusions can be found in the guidance notes on the trust's website.

TYPE OF GRANT Project costs; capital and building maintenance costs; running and recurring costs.

SAMPLE GRANTS Shetland Recreational Trust (£2.7 million); Support to Rural Care Model (£1.9 million); Shetland Amenity Trust (£1.9 million); Shetland Arts Development Agency (£603,500); Voluntary Action Shetland (£144,400); Shetland Befriending Service (£54,400); Festival Grants (£15,000).

FINANCES *Financial year end* 31/03/2020 *Income* £7,230,000 *Total grants* £7,320,000 *Grants to organisations* £7,320,000 *Assets* £315,690,000

TRUSTEES Andrew Cooper; Jolene Garriock; Yvette Hopkins; Ian Napier; Margaret Roberts; Ken Harrison; Robbie Leask; Robert Leask; Ryan Leith; Emma Miller; Alan Ockendon.

HOW TO APPLY Application forms are available to download from the trust's website.

CONTACT DETAILS Dr Ann Black, Chief Executive, 22–24 North Road, Lerwick, Shetland ZE1 0NQ *Tel.* 01595 744994 *Email* mail@shetlandcharitabletrust.co.uk *Website* www.shetlandcharitabletrust.co.uk

■ SHINE (Support and Help in Education)

CC NO 1082777 **ESTABLISHED** 1999

WHERE FUNDING CAN BE GIVEN Northern England.

WHO CAN BENEFIT Registered charities; schools; CICs.

WHAT IS FUNDED Educational projects helping children and young people aged between 4 and 14 years who are disadvantaged to fulfil their academic potential. Programmes fall under the following categories: ready for school; bridging the gap; flying high.

WHAT IS NOT FUNDED Programmes that take place outside northern England; short-term or one-off projects; bursaries or any kind of student fees; direct replacement of statutory funding; capital build programmes for schools or other education institutions.

TYPE OF GRANT Project funding; seed funding/start-up funding; core/revenue costs.

RANGE OF GRANTS Grants range from £1,400 up to £410,000 depending on the grant category.

SAMPLE GRANTS Right to Succeed (£266,800); St Edmund's Nursery (£96,000); Monteney Primary School (£80,000); HegartyMaths – H & A Learning Ltd (£60,000); Pakeman School (£15,000); Centre for Effective Philanthropy (£1,400).

FINANCES *Financial year end* 31/08/2019 *Income* £1,400,000 *Total grants* £1,880,000 *Grants to organisations* £1,880,000 *Assets* £4,370,000

TRUSTEES Lord Jim O'Neill; Cameron Ogden; Stephen Shields; Ann Mroz; Mark Heffernan; Sarah Loftus; Samantha Twiselton; Raksha Pattni; Lorna Fitzsimons; Kavita Gupta.

OTHER INFORMATION In 2017/18 the charity switched its geographical focus from London to northern England (the North West, the North

East and Yorkshire and Humberside). The 2018/19 accounts were the latest available at the time of writing (February 2021).

HOW TO APPLY Applicants should use the enquiry form, available from the charity's website, outlining the following points in no more than three or four paragraphs: an overview of the project and its aims, specifically related to academic attainment in maths, literacy or science; how it would meet SHINE's core priorities; the number of beneficiaries and schools it would reach; the overall project budget and the size of the request to SHINE.

CONTACT DETAILS The Trustees, SHINE Trust, Princes Exchange, 2 Princes Square, Leeds, West Yorkshire LS1 4HY *Tel.* 0113 280 5872 *Email* info@shinetrust.org.uk *Website* www.shinetrust.org.uk

■ The Bassil Shippam and Alsford Trust

CC NO 256996 **ESTABLISHED** 1967

WHERE FUNDING CAN BE GIVEN UK, with a preference for West Sussex.

WHO CAN BENEFIT Charitable organisations.

WHAT IS FUNDED Social welfare; young people; older people; health and medical research; education; Christian causes; arts.

RANGE OF GRANTS Grants range from £100 up to £50,000.

SAMPLE GRANTS Life Centre (£50,000); Dementia Support (£10,000); Chichester Lunch Club (£6,000); Resolute (CYE) (£5,000); West Dean College Scholarship (£3,000); Josh Amesbury Trust (£800).

FINANCES *Financial year end* 05/04/2020 *Income* £140,000 *Total grants* £98,200 *Grants to organisations* £95,100 *Assets* £3,730,000

TRUSTEES Christopher Doman; John Shippam; Molly Hanwell; Susan Trayler; Richard Tayler; Stanley Young; Janet Bailey; Simon MacFarlane; Alison Swan; Iain Macleod.

OTHER INFORMATION Grants to individuals during the year totalled £3,100.

HOW TO APPLY Contact the correspondent for further information.

CONTACT DETAILS The Trustees, Thomas Eggar House, Friary Lane, Chichester, West Sussex PO19 1UF *Tel.* 01243 786111 *Email* shippam@irwinmitchell.com

■ The Shipwrights' Charitable Fund

CC NO 262043 **ESTABLISHED** 1971

WHERE FUNDING CAN BE GIVEN UK, with a preference for the City of London.

WHO CAN BENEFIT Registered charities; unregistered charities; schools; universities; amateur sports clubs; individuals.

WHAT IS FUNDED Maritime training and education, seafarers' welfare; maritime heritage; young people.

WHAT IS NOT FUNDED Applications without a clear maritime connection.

TYPE OF GRANT Capital costs; core and revenue costs; seed funding; start-up funding; project funding.

RANGE OF GRANTS Programme dependent.

SAMPLE GRANTS Tall Ships Youth Trust (£20,000); University of Newcastle (£7,000); Sea Scouts (£4,000); George Green's School (£3,000); Ocean Youth Trust (£2,000); Southend Coastwatch (£1,000); Sailing Tectona CIC (£750); Britannia Sailing Trust (£450); Guildhall Library (£300).

FINANCES *Financial year end* 30/04/2020 *Income* £467,500 *Total grants* £221,200 *Grants to organisations* £193,400 *Assets* £5,880,000

TRUSTEES Richard Moore; Archibald Smith; Richard Close-Smith; Anthony Vlasto; John Denholm; Simon Beale; Laura Bugden; The Worshipful Company of Shipwrights; Nicholas Shaw; James Wilson.

OTHER INFORMATION Grants to individuals for educational purposes totalled £27,800. Grants to organisations were made up of general charitable donations, including both regular beneficiaries and 'responsive' grants and restricted donations.

HOW TO APPLY Applications can be submitted using the relevant online application form. Applications for responsive grants must be accompanied by a covering letter or email addressed to the clerk. Applications from organisations should, if possible, be accompanied by the latest accounts and annual report. Further guidelines on each of the trust's funding programmes are available from the website. Applications are considered in February, June and November.

CONTACT DETAILS The Clerk, Ironmongers' Hall, 1 Shaftesbury Place, Barbican, London EC2Y 8AA *Tel.* 020 7606 2376 *Email* clerk@shipwrights.co.uk *Website* www.shipwrights.co.uk

■ Shlomo Memorial Fund Ltd

CC NO 278973 **ESTABLISHED** 1978

WHERE FUNDING CAN BE GIVEN Worldwide, with a preference for the UK, Israel and USA.

WHO CAN BENEFIT Jewish organisations.

WHAT IS FUNDED Education; Jewish causes; the relief of poverty; general charitable purposes.

RANGE OF GRANTS Up to £180,000.

SAMPLE GRANTS Yad Tomechet LeNizkak Batzafon (£181,200); Layesharim Tehilla (£160,000); British Friends of Rinat Aharon (£132,500); Beer Ha'olam (£108,100); Igud Hakollelim (£52,000); Bnei Hayeshivot (£38,000); Matan Bseser (£20,000); Match Aharon (£15,000); Dorshi Tzion Beitar Elit (£11,000).

FINANCES *Financial year end* 30/09/2019 *Income* £9,970,000 *Total grants* £1,910,000 *Grants to organisations* £1,910,000 *Assets* £66,870,000

TRUSTEES Amichai Toporowitz; Hezkel Toporowitz; Eliyah Kleinerman; Channe Lopian; Chaim Kaufman; Meir Sullam; Esther Hoffner.

OTHER INFORMATION The 2019/20 accounts were the most recent available at the time of writing (June 2021).

HOW TO APPLY Contact the correspondent for more information.

CONTACT DETAILS Channe Lopian, Secretary, c/o Cohen Arnold, New Burlington House, 1075 Finchley Road, London NW11 0PU *Tel.* 0161 772 0444 *Email* info@olnato.com

■ The Shoe Zone Trust

CC NO 1112972 **ESTABLISHED** 2005

WHERE FUNDING CAN BE GIVEN The trustees prefer to support causes in Leicestershire and Rutland, as well as certain charities in the Philippines and other countries.

WHO CAN BENEFIT Charitable organisations.

WHAT IS FUNDED Education and training; social welfare; children and young people.
SAMPLE GRANTS Shepherd of the Hills – Philippines (£66,000 in two grants); Ministries Without Borders (£14,200); Amantani UK (£13,100); 500 Miles (£12,500); Cord Global, Global Care and Rotary Charity (£10,000 each).
FINANCES *Financial year end* 31/12/2019 *Income* £169,700 *Total grants* £169,400 *Grants to organisations* £169,400 *Assets* £304,300
TRUSTEES Anthony Smith; John Smith.
HOW TO APPLY Contact the correspondent for further information.
CONTACT DETAILS The Trustees, c/o Shoe Zone, Haramead Business Centre, Humberstone Road, Leicester, Leicestershire LE1 2LH *Tel.* 0116 222 3000 *Website* https://www.shoezone.com/OurCharities

■ Shulem B. Association Ltd

CC NO 313654 **ESTABLISHED** 1961
WHERE FUNDING CAN BE GIVEN UK and overseas.
WHO CAN BENEFIT Jewish organisations.
WHAT IS FUNDED Jewish religion and education; general charitable purposes.
TYPE OF GRANT Capital and revenue costs.
SAMPLE GRANTS United Talmudical Associates Ltd (£2,511,000); Rookwood Foundation Ltd (£300,000); Centurian Charities Ltd (£250,000); Chevras Mo'oz Ladol (£220,000); M and R Gross Charities (£75,000); Yesamach Levav (£65,000); Palmcourt Ltd (£50,000); CMZ Ltd (£40,000).
FINANCES *Financial year end* 30/09/2019 *Income* £6,300,000 *Total grants* £4,990,000 *Grants to organisations* £4,990,000 *Assets* £54,160,000
TRUSTEES Samuel Berger; Zelda Sternlicht; Sarah Klein.
OTHER INFORMATION The 2018/19 accounts were the latest available at the time of writing (April 2021). Grants were awarded to more than 24 institutions during the year.
HOW TO APPLY Contact the correspondent for further information.
CONTACT DETAILS The Trustees, New Burlington House, 1075 Finchley Road, London NW11 0PU *Tel.* 020 8731 0777

■ The Florence Shute Millennium Trust

CC NO 1085358 **ESTABLISHED** 2001
WHERE FUNDING CAN BE GIVEN Chepstow, Monmouthshire and the Forest of Dean.
WHO CAN BENEFIT Charitable organisations, particularly health-related organisations.
WHAT IS FUNDED Health; local causes; general charitable purposes.
TYPE OF GRANT Generally one-off funding.
RANGE OF GRANTS £1,000 to £5,000.
SAMPLE GRANTS Great Oaks Hospice (£25,000); British Scoliosis Research (£10,000); Forest of Dean Citizens Advice and Forest Pulse (£5,000 each); James Hopkins Trust (£4,000); Home-Start Monmouthshire and Teenage Cancer Trust (£3,000 each); The Nelson Trust (£2,000); The Rainbow Centre (£1,000).
FINANCES *Financial year end* 05/04/2019 *Income* £93,700 *Total grants* £94,500 *Grants to organisations* £94,500 *Assets* £2,550,000
TRUSTEES Ursula Williams; James Zorab; Richard O'Sullivan; Dr James Allison.
OTHER INFORMATION The 2018/19 accounts were the most recent available at the time of writing (May 2021). Grants were awarded to 23 organisations during the year.
HOW TO APPLY Contact the correspondent for information regarding the application process.
CONTACT DETAILS The Trustees, St Maur Beaufort Square, Chepstow NP16 5EP *Tel.* 01291 622237 *Email* vickyc@francisandco.wales

■ The Simmons & Simmons Charitable Foundation

CC NO 1129643 **ESTABLISHED** 2009
WHERE FUNDING CAN BE GIVEN Worldwide, in areas local to Simmons & Simmons' offices.
WHO CAN BENEFIT Registered charities – with a preference for smaller charities.
WHAT IS FUNDED Social welfare; education and training; access to justice and legal aid; social inclusion; human rights.
RANGE OF GRANTS Grants range from £5,000 up to £36,000.
SAMPLE GRANTS Battersea Legal Advice Centre (£36,000); The Big Issue Foundation (£25,000); Wuhan Doctors, Working Families (£20,000 each); Justice Without Borders (£15,000); Royal Voluntary Service (£10,000); Envision (£5,000).
FINANCES *Financial year end* 30/04/2020 *Income* £226,200 *Total grants* £292,300 *Grants to organisations* £292,300 *Assets* £206,200
TRUSTEES Richard Dyton; Fiona Loughrey; Colin Passmore; Devarshi Saksena; Stefania Bergia.
OTHER INFORMATION This is the corporate charity of Simmons & Simmons LLP. The foundation prioritises charities where the firm's employees can have some involvement. Grants of less than £5,000 totalled £63,000.
HOW TO APPLY Apply in writing to the correspondent by email.
CONTACT DETAILS The Trustees, Citypoint, 1 Ropemaker Street, London EC2Y 9SS *Tel.* 020 7628 2020 *Email* responsible.business@simmons-simmons.com *Website* https://www.simmons-simmons.com/en/about-us/responsible-business

■ The Singer Foundation

CC NO 277364 **ESTABLISHED** 1979
WHERE FUNDING CAN BE GIVEN UK, with a preference for the area within the Birmingham-Bristol-Reading triangle.
WHO CAN BENEFIT UK-registered charities.
WHAT IS FUNDED Supporting individuals through enterprise, employment and education.
SAMPLE GRANTS A list of beneficiaries was not included in the annual report and accounts.
FINANCES *Financial year end* 05/04/2020 *Income* £801,000 *Total grants* £97,300 *Grants to organisations* £97,300 *Assets* £3,660,000
TRUSTEES Roger Carter; Susan Carrdus; Christopher Powell; Denise Lucas; Janis Langdon; Peter Hartley; Geoffrey Taylor.
OTHER INFORMATION Grants were made to 20 organisations in 2019/20.
HOW TO APPLY Contact the foundation to request an application form.

CONTACT DETAILS Mr D. E. Jones, Administrator, Hillcrest, Ragnal Lane, Nailsworth, Stroud GL6 0RU *Tel.* 07979 860136 *Email* admin@singer.foundation

■ The Sino-British Fellowship Trust

CC NO 1174487 **ESTABLISHED** 1948
WHERE FUNDING CAN BE GIVEN UK and China.
WHO CAN BENEFIT Universities, researchers and educational institutions.
WHAT IS FUNDED Education of teachers and researchers in China; grants to enable Chinese academics or students to carry out research or study in the UK; grants to enable UK academics to undertake research with Chinese colleagues; funding for academics to enhance their knowledge of Chinese languages.
TYPE OF GRANT Scholarships and grants for research and training.
RANGE OF GRANTS Grants range from £1,000 up to £47,300.
SAMPLE GRANTS Great Britain China Educational Trust (£47,300); Royal Society (£37,500); Universities China Committee London (£29,800); British Academy (£26,000); Chinese University of Hong Kong (£20,000); Needham Research Institute (£3,900); Hong Kong University (£1,000).
FINANCES *Financial year end* 31/12/2019 *Income* £533,200 *Total grants* £500,100 *Grants to organisations* £437,000 *Assets* £13,310,000
TRUSTEES Anne Ely; Peter Ely; Frances Wood; Prof. Rosemary Foot; Prof. Hugh Baker; Ling Thompson; Prof. Wayne Ceng; Sir Christopher Hum.
OTHER INFORMATION In 2019 grants to individuals totalled £63,100.
HOW TO APPLY Contact the correspondent for further information.
CONTACT DETAILS Anne Ely, Trustee, Flat 23, Bede House, Manor Fields, London SW15 3LT *Tel.* 020 8788 6252

■ Sirius Minerals Foundation

CC NO 1163127 **ESTABLISHED** 2013
WHERE FUNDING CAN BE GIVEN North York Moors National Park; Scarborough; Redcar and Cleveland.
WHO CAN BENEFIT Charitable organisations.
WHAT IS FUNDED Community services and development; education and training; the environment; social welfare; recreation facilities.
TYPE OF GRANT Dependent upon funding programme.
RANGE OF GRANTS Dependent upon funding programme.
SAMPLE GRANTS A list of beneficiaries was not included in the annual report and accounts.
FINANCES *Financial year end* 31/05/2020 *Income* £1,010,000 *Total grants* £318,100 *Grants to organisations* £318,100 *Assets* £2,080,000
TRUSTEES Neil Irving; Jacqueline Flynn; Ian Swales; William Woods; Jonathan Samuel; Dr Elizabeth Walmsley; Sir Martin Narey.
OTHER INFORMATION The charity has different funding priorities each year.
HOW TO APPLY Visit the foundation's website for updates regarding the year's funding priorities.
CONTACT DETAILS The Trustees, Resolution House, Lake View, Scarborough, YO11 3ZB *Email* info@siriusmineralsfoundation.co.uk *Website* https://www.siriusmineralsfoundation.co.uk

■ The Thomas Sivewright Catto Charitable Settlement

CC NO 279549 **ESTABLISHED** 1979
WHERE FUNDING CAN BE GIVEN UK and overseas.
WHO CAN BENEFIT Registered charities.
WHAT IS FUNDED General charitable purposes.
TYPE OF GRANT Unrestricted funding.
RANGE OF GRANTS Typically between £500 and £5,000. Occasionally larger grants are awarded.
SAMPLE GRANTS Parkinson's UK (£58,000); Haddo Arts (£3,000); Families Outside and Rochester Cathedral (£1,000 each); Anne Frank Trust UK (£750); Gingerbread, Kidney Research UK and Zoological Society of London (£500 each).
FINANCES *Financial year end* 05/04/2020 *Income* £428,400 *Total grants* £313,100 *Grants to organisations* £313,100 *Assets* £8,070,000
TRUSTEES Lord Catto; Olivia Marchant; Zoe Richmond-Watson.
HOW TO APPLY Apply in writing to the correspondent. The trustees meet quarterly to consider applications and distribute funding.
CONTACT DETAILS The Trustees, PO Box 47408, London N21 1YW *Tel.* 020 7370 0058 *Email* office@tscatto.org.uk

■ The Skelton Bounty

CC NO 219370 **ESTABLISHED** 1934
WHERE FUNDING CAN BE GIVEN Lancashire (as it existed in 1934).
WHO CAN BENEFIT Registered charities.
WHAT IS FUNDED Social welfare, with an emphasis on older people; people with disabilities; young people; holidays for disadvantaged children and carers.
WHAT IS NOT FUNDED Large building appeals; revenue expenditure; individuals. Applications from charities in successive years are not viewed favourably.
TYPE OF GRANT Preference for small specific capital projects (particularly equipment) rather than general expenditure.
RANGE OF GRANTS £1,000 to £4,000.
SAMPLE GRANTS St Ann's Hospice (£4,000); Blackpool Boys and Girls Club (£3,500); Vauxhall Community Law and Information Centre and Sefton Children's Trust (£2,000 each); Liverpool Cares, Manchester Jewish Community Care and Rochdale Connections Trust (£1,000 each).
FINANCES *Financial year end* 05/04/2020 *Income* £118,500 *Total grants* £101,300 *Grants to organisations* £101,300 *Assets* £2,670,000
TRUSTEES Sir Mark Hedley; Roger Morris; Kamruddin Kothia; Edith Conn; Robert Hough; Gail Stanley; S. Comas; C. Hankinson.
OTHER INFORMATION Grants were awarded to 54 organisations during the year.
HOW TO APPLY Application forms are available from the correspondent or may be found on the Liverpool Charity and Voluntary Services website when the fund is open to applications (usually around springtime). Applications are considered at the trustees' meeting in July. For more information, contact grants@lcvs.org.uk.
CONTACT DETAILS The Trustees, c/o Liverpool Charity and Voluntary Services, 151 Dale street, Liverpool, Merseyside L2 2AH *Tel.* 0151 227 5177 *Email* grants@lcvs.org.uk *Website* https://www.lcvs.org.uk

■ The Skerritt Trust

CC NO 1016701 **ESTABLISHED** 1992

WHERE FUNDING CAN BE GIVEN Within a ten-mile radius of Nottingham Market Square.

WHO CAN BENEFIT Registered charities.

WHAT IS FUNDED Housing for older people.

TYPE OF GRANT Capital costs.

SAMPLE GRANTS A list of organisations which received grants during 2019/20 was not available.

FINANCES *Financial year end* 05/04/2020 *Income* £133,100 *Total grants* £106,900 *Grants to organisations* £106,900 *Assets* £2,250,000

TRUSTEES Roy Taylor; Roy Costa; Sandra Warzynska; David Lowe; Alma Davies; Theresa Clayton.

HOW TO APPLY Apply in writing to the correspondent, including annual accounts and details of the costs of the items or facilities required. The trustees consider applications at their quarterly meetings.

CONTACT DETAILS Anna Chandler, Cumberland Court, 80 Mount Street, Nottingham, Nottinghamshire NG1 6HH *Tel.* 0115 901 5558 *Email* anna.chandler@freeths.co.uk

■ The Charles Skey Charitable Trust

CC NO 277697 **ESTABLISHED** 1979

WHERE FUNDING CAN BE GIVEN UK, with a preference for Devon, Cornwall and Somerset.

WHO CAN BENEFIT Registered charities.

WHAT IS FUNDED General charitable purposes, including the following: social welfare; education; Christianity; health; citizenship/community development; arts, culture, heritage and science; amateur sport; people in need; the armed forces and emergency services.

TYPE OF GRANT Capital costs, core/revenue costs, seed funding/start-up costs.

RANGE OF GRANTS Mostly under £20,000.

SAMPLE GRANTS War Memorials Trust (£25,000); London City Mission, On Course Foundation and Royal Museums Greenwich (£20,000 each); Brasenose College – Oxford (£15,000); British Film Institute and World Sight Foundation (£10,000 each); St Andrew's Church – Kendray (£7,500); Fusiliers London Fund (£2,500).

FINANCES *Financial year end* 05/04/2020 *Income* £456,900 *Total grants* £295,000 *Grants to organisations* £295,000 *Assets* £12,300,000

TRUSTEES Christopher Berkeley; John Leggett; Revd James Leggett; David Berkeley; Edward Berkeley.

OTHER INFORMATION A total of 22 grants were awarded during the year. Grants were broken down as follows: arts, culture, heritage or science (£85,000); education (£47,500); citizenship or community development (£40,000); health and saving lives (£35,000); amateur sport (£30,000); the armed forces and emergency services (£27,500); social welfare (£22,500); religion (£7,500).

HOW TO APPLY Contact the correspondent for further information.

CONTACT DETAILS The Trustees, Flint House, Park Homer Road, Colehill, Wimborne, Dorset BH21 2SP *Tel.* 01202 883778

■ Skipton Building Society Charitable Foundation

CC NO 1079538 **ESTABLISHED** 2000

WHERE FUNDING CAN BE GIVEN UK, with a preference for areas near Skipton Building Society's principal office or one of its branches.

WHO CAN BENEFIT Registered charities, with a focus on smaller, local organisations.

WHAT IS FUNDED The welfare and education of children (under 16 years old); youth schemes and projects supporting those in their late teens and early 20s in socially deprived areas with literacy, numeracy and employment; supporting older people by reducing isolation and helping to reduce the effects of dementia and Alzheimer's.

WHAT IS NOT FUNDED Applications for general ongoing funding, running costs, rent, utility costs medical research, sponsorship, payment of salaries, counselling or expenses; requests for administration equipment, such as telephones, security systems or computers, for a charity's own use; the restoration and upkeep of buildings or maintenance of vehicles; causes serving only a specific sector of the community selected on the basis of ethnic, racial, political or religious grounds/advancement; overseas travel, expeditions or educational expenses, including causes that would otherwise qualify for support but require funds for activities outside the UK; non-registered charities, individuals or large national charities; support for activities which fall within an existing statutorily funded budget or are the responsibility of central or local government, even if the budget is insufficient to fund the activity applied for.

TYPE OF GRANT Specific items or activities.

RANGE OF GRANTS Up to £3,000.

SAMPLE GRANTS St Kentigern Hospice (£3,000); me & dee charity (£2,200); The Dash Charity (£1,500); Ilkley Community Enterprise (£1,000); Friends of Pelican Park (£800); Drama Expressions for Children (£250).

FINANCES *Financial year end* 29/02/2020 *Income* £155,600 *Total grants* £160,300 *Grants to organisations* £160,300 *Assets* £85,000

TRUSTEES Amelia Vyvyan; Alison Davies; Debra Ewing; Richard Robinson; Kitty North; John Watson; The Revd and Rt Hon. Lord Hope of Thornes.

HOW TO APPLY Applications can be made using the form available to download on the foundation's website, which should be sent to the correspondent by email or post along with two years' financial accounts. The trustees usually meet quarterly to consider funding requests.

CONTACT DETAILS The Trustees, The Bailey, Skipton, North Yorkshire BD23 1DN *Email* charitablefoundation@skipton.co.uk *Website* www.skiptoncharitablefoundation.co.uk

■ The John Slater Foundation

CC NO 231145 **ESTABLISHED** 1963

WHERE FUNDING CAN BE GIVEN UK.

WHO CAN BENEFIT Registered charities.

WHAT IS FUNDED General charitable purposes, including animal welfare, education and social welfare.

WHAT IS NOT FUNDED Individuals.

RANGE OF GRANTS £750 to £50,000.

SAMPLE GRANTS Manchester High School for Girls (£12,000 in two grants); Kidz Club – Leeds (£4,000 in two grants); ABF The Soldiers' Charity (£2,500); Cheshire Autism (£1,500); Farspace Animal Rescue (£1,000).

FINANCES *Financial year end* 05/04/2020 *Income* £164,900 *Total grants* £122,200 *Grants to organisations* £122,200 *Assets* £4,030,000

TRUSTEE HSBC Trust Company (UK) Ltd.

OTHER INFORMATION During the year, 48 grants were made to 32 organisations.

HOW TO APPLY At the time of writing (April 2021) the foundation's website stated: 'The foundation is presently fully committed to its programme of giving and unfortunately is not able to receive any further new requests of any nature at this time. Should this situation change an appropriate announcement will be made on [the foundation's] website.'

CONTACT DETAILS Richard Thompson, Trust Manager, c/o HSBC Trust Company UK Ltd, Second Floor, 1 The Forum, Parkway, Whiteley, Fareham, Hampshire PO15 7PA *Tel.* 023 8072 2225 *Website* johnslaterfoundation.org.uk

■ The Slaughter and May Charitable Trust

CC NO 1082765 **ESTABLISHED** 2000

WHERE FUNDING CAN BE GIVEN UK and occasionally other parts of the world.

WHO CAN BENEFIT Charitable organisations.

WHAT IS FUNDED Legal advice, education and training, health, social welfare, children and young people and older people.

SAMPLE GRANTS National Literacy Trust (£51,000); Islington Law Centre (£45,000); Action for Kids (£30,000); St Luke's Parochial Trust (£25,000); Internews and Social Mobility Business Partnership (£15,000 each); East London Business Alliance (£12,000); London Symphony Orchestra and Moreland Primary School (£10,000 each).

FINANCES *Financial year end* 05/04/2020 *Income* £425,100 *Total grants* £372,600 *Grants to organisations* £372,600 *Assets* £10

TRUSTEES D. E. Robertson; C. A. Connolly; I. A. M. Taylor; J. S. Nevin; R. A. Byk.

OTHER INFORMATION Grants were awarded to 18 organisations during the year.

HOW TO APPLY The trust's 2019/20 annual report states that it 'makes annual grants at its discretion to a small number of specific charitable causes and does not generally accept unsolicited funding applications'.

CONTACT DETAILS The Trustees, Slaughter and May (Trust Ltd), 2 Lambs Passage, London EC1Y 8BB *Tel.* 020 7090 3433 *Email* corporateresponsibility@slaughterandmay.com *Website* www.slaughterandmay.com

■ Sloane Robinson Foundation

CC NO 1068286 **ESTABLISHED** 1998

WHERE FUNDING CAN BE GIVEN England and Wales.

WHO CAN BENEFIT Universities; school; individuals.

WHAT IS FUNDED The advancement of education, particularly scholarships and bursaries to enable overseas students to study in the UK, or to enable UK students to study abroad, as well as to 'generally provide educational opportunities to students that would otherwise not be available to them'.

TYPE OF GRANT Grants to institutions on an ongoing basis; grants to individuals.

RANGE OF GRANTS £10,000 to £150,000.

SAMPLE GRANTS Lincoln College – Oxford (£70,000); Karta Initiative (£40,000); Royal Brompton and Harefield Hospital Charity (£25,000); Prospero World (£11,000); Keble Astrophysics Scholarship (£7,500).

FINANCES *Financial year end* 29/02/2020 *Income* £193,300 *Total grants* £292,700 *Grants to organisations* £292,700 *Assets* £17,270,000

TRUSTEES Hugh Sloane; George Robinson; Deborah Fisher.

HOW TO APPLY Apply in writing to the correspondent. The foundation is very selective in its grant-making; therefore, to avoid increased administrative costs, only successful candidates will be notified of the outcome of their application.

CONTACT DETAILS The Trustees, c/o FisherLegal LLP, Unit 4 Hill Farm, Kirby Road, Kirby Bedon, Norwich, Norfolk NR17 7DU *Tel.* 01508 480100 *Email* info@fisherlegal.co.uk

■ Rita and David Slowe Charitable Trust

CC NO 1048209 **ESTABLISHED** 1995

WHERE FUNDING CAN BE GIVEN UK and overseas, especially Africa.

WHO CAN BENEFIT Registered charities.

WHAT IS FUNDED General charitable purposes, in particular the following: homelessness; human trafficking; people who are disadvantaged overseas and overseas development, particularly in Africa.

WHAT IS NOT FUNDED Individuals.

RANGE OF GRANTS Usually £17,500, typically recurring.

SAMPLE GRANTS Big Issue Foundation, Campaign against Living Miserably (CALM), Crisis, Excellent Development, Microloan Foundation, Re-Cycle, Shelter and Wiener Library (£17,500 each).

FINANCES *Financial year end* 05/04/2020 *Income* £79,800 *Total grants* £140,000 *Grants to organisations* £140,000 *Assets* £2,300,000

TRUSTEES Elizabeth Slowe; Graham Weinberg; Jonathan Slowe; Lilian Slowe; Robert Slowe.

OTHER INFORMATION In 2019/20 the charity awarded eight grants of £17,500 each, totalling £140,000. Seven of the eight grants in 2019/20 were to beneficiaries that received funds in 2018/19.

HOW TO APPLY Contact the correspondent for more information.

CONTACT DETAILS The Trustees, 32 Hampstead High Street, London NW3 1JQ *Tel.* 020 7435 7800

■ Smallwood Trust

CC NO 205798 **ESTABLISHED** 1886

WHERE FUNDING CAN BE GIVEN UK.

WHO CAN BENEFIT Registered charities; social enterprises; not-for-profit organisations; individuals.

WHAT IS FUNDED Projects which enable women on low incomes to access new skills, training, confidence-building and employment opportunities; research and policy work relating to disadvantaged women.

TYPE OF GRANT Project funding.

RANGE OF GRANTS Dependent upon the funding programme.

SAMPLE GRANTS New Economics Foundation (£163,800); Surviving Economic Abuse (£30,000); A Way Out (£10,000); Coventry Haven (£8,500).

FINANCES *Financial year end* 31/12/2019
Income £1,440,000 *Total grants* £1,430,000
Grants to organisations £677,400
Assets £36,610,000

TRUSTEES Maureen Margie; D'Arcy Myers; Maria Toman; Catherine Hine; Rachael Bailey.

HOW TO APPLY The application process depends on the grants programme. Interested applicants should check the funder's website regularly for up-to-date information.

CONTACT DETAILS The Trustees, Lancaster House, 25 Hornyold Road, Malvern, Worcestershire WR14 1QQ *Tel.* 0300 365 1886 *Email* info@smallwoodtrust.org.uk *Website* www.smallwoodtrust.org.uk

■ Ruth Smart Foundation

CC NO 1080021 **ESTABLISHED** 2000

WHERE FUNDING CAN BE GIVEN Worldwide, but mainly in the UK and USA.

WHO CAN BENEFIT Registered charities and charitable organisations.

WHAT IS FUNDED Animal welfare and conservation.

TYPE OF GRANT Normally recurrent.

RANGE OF GRANTS Up to £25,000.

SAMPLE GRANTS Trees for Cities (£25,000); San Francisco Zoo (£15,700); Mauritian Wildlife Foundation (£12,000); Wildlife Conservation Society (£6,300); Royal Veterinary College (£3,000); Wildfowl and Wetlands Trust (£2,000); Belize Zoo (£1,600).

FINANCES *Financial year end* 31/12/2019
Income £149,000 *Total grants* £159,800
Grants to organisations £159,800
Assets £6,120,000

TRUSTEES Wilfrid Vernor-Miles; John Vernor-Miles.

OTHER INFORMATION Many of the beneficiaries are supported year after year, particularly where trustees are informed of the benefits of the foundation's funding from previous grants. Of the 22 organisations awarded donations in 2019, 20 were also funded the previous year.

HOW TO APPLY Contact the correspondent for further information.

CONTACT DETAILS Wilfrid Vernor-Miles, Chair to the Board of Trustees, c/o Hunters, 9 New Square, Lincoln's Inn, London WC2A 3QN *Tel.* 020 7412 0050

■ The SMB Trust

CC NO 263814 **ESTABLISHED** 1962

WHERE FUNDING CAN BE GIVEN UK and overseas.

WHO CAN BENEFIT Charitable organisations.

WHAT IS FUNDED Christian faith; social and medical care in the UK and abroad; famine relief and emergency aid; the environment and wildlife; education; medical research.

WHAT IS NOT FUNDED Individuals.

RANGE OF GRANTS Generally between £1,000 and £2,000.

SAMPLE GRANTS Previous beneficiaries have included: Disasters Emergency Committee (£6,000); Pilgrim Friends Society (£4,000); Oasis UK (£2,500); Zimbabwe Educational Trust (£1,200); Save the Children (£2,000); Designability, Toxteth Women's Centre and Woodland Christian Trust (£1,000 each); Rye Street Pastors (£500); Freedom from Torture (£50).

FINANCES *Financial year end* 31/03/2020
Income £559,700 *Total grants* £337,500
Grants to organisations £337,500
Assets £11,510,100

TRUSTEES Jeremy Anstead; Barbara O'Driscoll; Ian Wilson.

OTHER INFORMATION Grants were awarded to 180 organisations for the following purposes: social and medical welfare (£100,100); religion (£91,300); relief of poverty (£62,500); education and research (£38,900); famine relief and emergency aid (£35,800); the environment and wildlife (£9,000).

HOW TO APPLY Apply in writing to the correspondent, including the aims and principal activities of the applicant, the current financial position and details of any special projects for which funding is sought. There are no application forms. The trustees normally meet four times a year to consider applications. Because of the volume of appeals received, unsuccessful applicants will only receive a reply if they enclose an sae. Unsuccessful applicants are welcome to re-apply.

CONTACT DETAILS The Trustees, 15 Wilman Road, Tunbridge Wells, Kent TN4 9AJ *Tel.* 01892 537301 *Email* smbcharitabletrust@googlemail.com

■ The Mrs Smith and Mount Trust

CC NO 1009718 **ESTABLISHED** 1992

WHERE FUNDING CAN BE GIVEN Norfolk; Suffolk; Cambridgeshire; Hertfordshire; Essex; Kent; Surrey; London.

WHO CAN BENEFIT Registered charities.

WHAT IS FUNDED The trust offers two grant programmes. The Mount Fund focuses on mental health, homelessness and health in the community. The Mrs Smith Fund awards hardship funding for individuals via block grants to registered charities for a variety of circumstances which are noted on the website. Further information on each of the grant schemes is available on the website.

WHAT IS NOT FUNDED Exclusion criteria may vary between The Mount Fund and The Mrs Smith Fund. The Mount Fund will only consider appeals from national organisations at branch level where the branch is able to provide separate accounts and is responsible for its own finances. The Mount Fund will not consider applications for general counselling or from charities with an income of over £1 million, or £500,000 if the application relates to the trust's health in the community category.

TYPE OF GRANT Core costs; project funding; capital costs; development funding.

RANGE OF GRANTS Generally up to £5,000 unless the applicant meets the specific criteria for larger grants.

SAMPLE GRANTS Become (£30,000); The Magdalene Group (£12,000); Waltham Forest Churches Night Shelter (£10,000); Assist Trust and The Therapy Garden (£6,000 each); Bereavement Care (£5,000); Peterborough Citizens Advice (£4,000); Refugee Action Kingston (£3,000); Southend Mencap (£2,500).

FINANCES *Financial year end* 31/01/2020
Income £192,400 *Total grants* £415,800
Grants to organisations £415,800
Assets £8,470,000

TRUSTEES Timothy Warren; Sean Shepley; Gill Gorell Barnes; Alexander Winter; Hannah Whitehead.

OTHER INFORMATION The Mount Fund gave 64 grants totalling £373,300. The Mrs Smith Fund gave two grants totalling £12,500. The Spanoghe Grants Programme (now closed) provided one grant of £30,000.

HOW TO APPLY Applications for The Mount Fund can be made online on the trust's website. The trustees meet three times per year, in March, July and November, and applications and supporting documents must be submitted at least six weeks in advance of a meeting or by the date specified. For applications to The Mrs Smith Fund, email a one-page document providing initial details about your work to the correspondent. An application form will then be sent to you if there is an opportunity for funding.

CONTACT DETAILS The Trustees, 6 Trull Farm Buildings, Tetbury, Gloucestershire GL8 8SQ *Tel.* 020 3325 2590 *Email* admin@mrssmithandmounttrust.org *Website* mrssmithandmounttrust.org

■ Smith Bradbeer Charitable Trust

CC NO 1060418 **ESTABLISHED** 1997

WHERE FUNDING CAN BE GIVEN Worldwide, with a preference for Dorset and Hampshire.

WHO CAN BENEFIT There is no list of beneficiaries in the accounts, but the trustees state that they made 50 donations to various missionary societies and evangelists at home and abroad who have achieved their aim of spreading the word of the gospel to the various people around the world. The trust's website states that recipients generally have local contact with churches in the Hampshire area or with existing trustees, enabling the trust to receive regular updates on the progress of projects and individuals being supported.

WHAT IS FUNDED The advancement of the Christian religion; the advancement of religion based on Christian principles; welfare; general charitable purposes.

SAMPLE GRANTS Previous beneficiaries have included: Care and Relief of the Young; Cinnamon Network; Junction Church Eastleigh; Missionary Aviation Fellowship; Operation Mobilisation; Southampton Asian Christian Fellowship; Wycliffe Bible Translators.

FINANCES *Financial year end* 31/03/2020 *Income* £161,900 *Total grants* £73,900 *Grants to organisations* £73,900 *Assets* £677,100

TRUSTEES Anthony Davies; Peter Davies; Gregory Davies; Trevor Davies; Sarah Robinson.

HOW TO APPLY The trust's website states: 'If you would like to apply for a grant, contact charity@bradbeers.com.'

CONTACT DETAILS The Trustees, Smith Bradbeer and Co. Ltd, 14–20 Bell Street, Romsey, Hampshire S051 8ZE *Email* charity@bradbeers.com *Website* https://www.bradbeers.com/charitable-trust

■ The DS Smith Charitable Foundation

CC NO 1142817 **ESTABLISHED** 2011

WHERE FUNDING CAN BE GIVEN England and Wales.

WHO CAN BENEFIT Registered charities and voluntary organisations.

WHAT IS FUNDED Education and training; environmental conservation.

RANGE OF GRANTS A combination of small (of less than £1,000) and larger donations each year. The foundation welcomes opportunities to develop multi-year partnerships with key selected charities.

SAMPLE GRANTS Ellen MacArthur Foundation (£150,000); UNICEF (£42,600); The Royal Institute (£10,000); Litter Angels (£6,000); Earth Restoration (£2,000).

FINANCES *Financial year end* 30/04/2020 *Income* £34,800 *Total grants* £280,900 *Grants to organisations* £280,900 *Assets* £1,280,000

TRUSTEES Rachel Stevens; Emma Ciechan; Mark Reeve; Catriona O'Grady; Peter Clayson.

OTHER INFORMATION Grants were distributed as follows: environment (£185,800); education (£88,600); other (£6,500).

HOW TO APPLY Application forms are available from the foundation's website.

CONTACT DETAILS The Trustees, 7th Floor, 350 Euston Road, London NW1 3AX *Tel.* 020 7756 1823 *Email* charitablefoundation@dssmith.com *Website* https://www.dssmith.com/sustainability/building-strong-foundations/looking-after-people-and-our-communities/responsible-neighbour/charitable-foundation

■ The N. Smith Charitable Settlement

CC NO 276660 **ESTABLISHED** 1978

WHERE FUNDING CAN BE GIVEN UK.

WHO CAN BENEFIT Charitable organisations.

WHAT IS FUNDED General charitable purposes.

WHAT IS NOT FUNDED Individuals.

SAMPLE GRANTS A list of beneficiaries was not included in the annual report and accounts.

FINANCES *Financial year end* 05/04/2020 *Income* £182,700 *Total grants* £128,100 *Grants to organisations* £128,100 *Assets* £4,330,000

TRUSTEES Janet Adam; Susan Darlington; Anne Gregory; Christine Yates.

OTHER INFORMATION Grants awarded during 2019/20 totalled £128,100.

HOW TO APPLY Contact the correspondent for further information. The trustees hold two or three meetings each year. In 2019/20 the trustees met in July, November and March.

CONTACT DETAILS Charlotte Keating, c/o Linder Myers, Sale Point, 126–150 Washway Road, Sale, Greater Manchester M33 6AG *Tel.* 0161 832 6972 *Email* charlotte.keating@lindermyers.co.uk

■ The Peter Smith Charitable Trust for Nature

CC NO 328458 **ESTABLISHED** 1989

WHERE FUNDING CAN BE GIVEN UK.

WHO CAN BENEFIT Charitable organisations.

WHAT IS FUNDED Support of wildlife.

SAMPLE GRANTS A list of beneficiaries was not included in the annual report and accounts.

FINANCES *Financial year end* 31/12/2020 *Income* £125,000 *Total grants* £176,800 *Grants to organisations* £176,800 *Assets* £989,600

TRUSTEES Peter Smith; Sandra Smith; Paul Brittlebank; John Cowlishaw.

HOW TO APPLY Contact the correspondent for further information.

CONTACT DETAILS The Trustees, The Old Rectory, Hills End, Eversholt, Milton Keynes, Buckinghamshire MK17 9DR *Tel.* 01525 280848

The Henry Smith Charity

CC NO 230102 **ESTABLISHED** 1628

WHERE FUNDING CAN BE GIVEN UK.

WHO CAN BENEFIT Registered charities (primarily small and medium sized); not-for-profit organisations; community-based organisations; social enterprises; schools; Christian organisations.

WHAT IS FUNDED Social welfare; community services and development; Christian projects.

WHAT IS NOT FUNDED See the grant-maker's website for a full list of exclusions regarding each grant programme.

TYPE OF GRANT Running costs; salaries; project costs.

RANGE OF GRANTS Dependent upon grant programme.

SAMPLE GRANTS Befriending Scheme (£180,000); Home-Start – Arun, Worthing and Adur (£165,000); Cambridge Women's Resources Centre (£90,000); Lawrence Weston Community Farm (£74,000); Footprints Project (£20,000); Grange Park Centre (£10,000); Manchester Deaf Centre (£2,400); Broadfield Primary School (£880).

FINANCES *Financial year end* 31/12/2019 *Income* £12,040,000 *Total grants* £32,020,000 *Grants to organisations* £30,650,000 *Assets* £1,092,230,000

TRUSTEES Noel Manns; Emily Bolton; Jonathan Asquith; Ben Kernighan; Lady Bella Colgrain; Emir Feisal; Piers Feilden; Paul Hackwood; Mark Granger; Heider Ridha; James Hordern; Vivienne Dews; Emma Davies.

OTHER INFORMATION A full list of grants awarded is available to view on the charity's website. Support is given to individuals descended from the family of Henry Smith through its Kindred grants. In 2019 grants to individuals totalled £1.37 million.

HOW TO APPLY Application processes vary between grant programmes. Application details for a specific grant scheme, along with guidance, are available on the website.

CONTACT DETAILS The Trustees, 6th Floor, 65–68 Leadenhall Street, London EC3A 2AD *Tel.* 020 7264 4970 or the use the call back form on the website. *Website* www.henrysmithcharity.org.uk

Arabella and Julian Smith Family Trust

CC NO 1174447 **ESTABLISHED** 2017

WHERE FUNDING CAN BE GIVEN England and Wales.

WHO CAN BENEFIT Registered charities.

WHAT IS FUNDED General charitable purposes; education; health; social welfare; animal welfare.

WHAT IS NOT FUNDED Individuals.

TYPE OF GRANT Project funding; research.

RANGE OF GRANTS Typically £3,000 to £20,000.

SAMPLE GRANTS Community Foundation for Surrey (£50,000); Action Medical Research (£18,600); Oasis Childcare Centre (£10,000); Guide Dogs for the Blind (£5,000); Music in Hospitals and Care (£3,000).

FINANCES *Financial year end* 31/08/2019 *Income* £45,900 *Total grants* £102,100 *Grants to organisations* £102,100 *Assets* £1,110,000

TRUSTEES Alexander Smith; Arabella Smith; Julian Smith; Juliet Smith.

OTHER INFORMATION The 2018/19 accounts were the latest available at the time of writing (June 2021). In 2018/19 the trust made grants totalling £102,100 to seven organisations.

HOW TO APPLY Contact the correspondent for further information.

CONTACT DETAILS The Trustees, c/o Maris Interiors LLP, 65 Southwark Street, London SE1 0HR *Tel.* 020 7902 1760

The Martin Smith Foundation

CC NO 1150753 **ESTABLISHED** 2012

WHERE FUNDING CAN BE GIVEN UK.

WHO CAN BENEFIT Registered charities.

WHAT IS FUNDED General charitable purposes, in particular: the performing arts; education; ecology and the environment; recreational sport; the relief of poverty; and religion.

SAMPLE GRANTS Garsington Opera Ltd (£50,000); Science Museum Foundation (£24,000); Royal Academy of Music (£18,000); ClientEarth (£15,000); University of Oxford Development Trust Fund (£5,000); The Wigmore Hall Trust (£2,200); St Mary the Virgin Church (£1,000); Gloucestershire Wildlife Trust (£500); Alliance to Protect Nantucket Sound (£400).

FINANCES *Financial year end* 31/12/2019 *Income* £36,600 *Total grants* £340,100 *Grants to organisations* £340,100 *Assets* £1,520,000

TRUSTEES Lady Smith; Sir Martin Smith; Jeremy Smith; Katherine Wake; Elizabeth Buchanan; Bartholomew Peerless.

HOW TO APPLY The foundation does not accept unsolicited applications.

CONTACT DETAILS The Trustees, 5 Park Town, Oxford, Oxfordshire OX2 6SN *Tel.* 01865 554554

The Leslie Smith Foundation

CC NO 250030 **ESTABLISHED** 1964

WHERE FUNDING CAN BE GIVEN UK.

WHO CAN BENEFIT Registered charities; schools, specifically special needs schools based in the UK; hospices.

WHAT IS FUNDED General charitable purposes, particularly: children in the UK with life-changing illnesses; orphans; education and special needs schools; tree preservation.

WHAT IS NOT FUNDED Individuals.

TYPE OF GRANT Capital costs and project funding.

RANGE OF GRANTS Up to £10,000.

SAMPLE GRANTS Hope House Children's Hospice and Somerset Trust for Arts and Recreation (£10,000 each); Cancer Research UK (£5,500); Action for Children, Lucy Air Ambulance for Children, Moor Trees, Shakespeare Globe Education Trust and Tickwood Care Farm (£5,000 each); Kidney Research UK (£100).

FINANCES *Financial year end* 05/04/2020 *Income* £88,100 *Total grants* £96,000 *Grants to organisations* £96,000 *Assets* £3,520,000

TRUSTEES Deborah Fisher; Alice Rutherford Hayles; Curtis Rutherford Hayles; Emma Rutherford Hayles; Matthew Rutherford Hayles.

OTHER INFORMATION During 2019/29, 18 organisations received grants within the following categories: health (£61,000); general welfare (£15,000); welfare through the arts (£10,000); education (£5,000); tree preservation (£5,000).

HOW TO APPLY Apply in writing to the correspondent, including a summary of the project. Only successful applications are acknowledged. The trustees meet at least twice a year.

CONTACT DETAILS The Trustees, c/o Fisher Legal LLP, Unit 4 Hill Farm, Kirby Road, Kirby Bedon, Norwich, Norfolk NR14 7DU *Tel.* 01508 480100 *Email* info@fisherlegal.co.uk

■ The W. H. Smith Group Charitable Trust

CC NO 1013782 **ESTABLISHED** 1992

WHERE FUNDING CAN BE GIVEN UK.

WHO CAN BENEFIT Charitable organisations and schools.

WHAT IS FUNDED General charitable purposes; community services and development.

TYPE OF GRANT Project funding.

RANGE OF GRANTS Grants range from £900 up to £92,000.

SAMPLE GRANTS Young Readers Programme 2019–20 (£92,000); WHSmith High Street Ltd – World Book Day (£25,000); Brighter Futures (£1,700); Cancer Research UK (£1,200); Papyrus Prevention of Young Suicide and Teesside Hospice (£1,000 each); Middlesbrough Football Club Foundation (£900).

FINANCES *Financial year end* 31/12/2019 *Income* £304,600 *Total grants* £258,400 *Grants to organisations* £258,400 *Assets* £224,600

TRUSTEES Faye Sherman; Natalie Davidson; Sharon Appleton; Clare O'Grady; Nicki Woodhead; Lisa Barrett; Mitchell Hunt; Paul Johnson; Wendy Stroud; John Pouton; Danielle Richards.

HOW TO APPLY Contact the correspondent for further information.

CONTACT DETAILS The Trustees, WHSmith Ltd, Greenbridge Road, Swindon, Wiltshire SN3 3JE *Tel.* 01793 616161 *Email* corporate.responsibility@whsmith.co.uk *Website* www.whsmithplc.co.uk/corporate_responsibility/whsmith_trust

■ Stanley Smith UK Horticultural Trust

CC NO 261925 **ESTABLISHED** 1970

WHERE FUNDING CAN BE GIVEN UK and overseas.

WHO CAN BENEFIT Charitable organisations; individuals.

WHAT IS FUNDED Horticulture, gardening and botany; the promotion of biodiversity; creation, development and maintenance of gardens accessible to the public; horticultural education, training, research and publications.

WHAT IS NOT FUNDED Projects relating to commercial agriculture initiatives, commercial crop production, or forestry; wages or salaries; training or tuition fees (except traineeships paid to organisations); pure gap year travel; modern slabbing, construction materials or equipment; social welfare, socio-economic development or physical or mental welfare (except legitimate horticultural therapy projects).

TYPE OF GRANT Project costs; research and publication costs; restoration costs.

RANGE OF GRANTS Typically £500 to £4,000.

SAMPLE GRANTS International Commission for the Nomenclature of Cultivated Plants (£10,000); Research on Ellen Willmott's archives (£4,000); Royal Caledonian Horticultural Society (£3,500); Catherine Street Play Park and Community Garden and Clean Rivers Trust (£2,000 each); Amicus Trust (£500).

FINANCES *Financial year end* 05/04/2020 *Income* £165,900 *Total grants* £87,900 *Grants to organisations* £80,300 *Assets* £3,570,000

TRUSTEES Alexander De Byre; Christopher Brickell; Lady Jane Renfrew; John Simmons; Phillip Sykes; Edward Reed; Dr John David.

OTHER INFORMATION In 2019/20, the trust made 30 grants totalling £87,900: 12 concerning restoration and development of gardens, five concerning plant collecting and fieldwork trips, six concerning publications, and one concerning research and conservation. None of the organisations (or individuals) in receipt of grants in 2019/20 received grants in 2018/19.

HOW TO APPLY Applications should be submitted either via email or post to the correspondent. There is no application form; however, detailed guidance notes are available to download from the relevant section of the following website: https://www.horticulture.org.uk/careers/bursaries-and-grants. Grants are usually made in April and October.

CONTACT DETAILS Dr David Rae, Director, Royal Botanic Garden, 20A Inverleith Row, Edinburgh EH3 5LR *Tel.* 0131 248 2844 *Email* d.rae@rbge.org.uk *Website* https://www.horticulture.org.uk/careers/bursaries-and-grants

■ Philip Smith's Charitable Trust

CC NO 1003751 **ESTABLISHED** 1991

WHERE FUNDING CAN BE GIVEN UK, with a preference for Gloucestershire.

WHO CAN BENEFIT Registered charities; arts, culture and heritage organisations; hospices.

WHAT IS FUNDED General charitable purposes; the environment; older people; social welfare; the armed forces.

WHAT IS NOT FUNDED Individuals.

RANGE OF GRANTS £1,000 to £25,000.

SAMPLE GRANTS Previous beneficiaries have included: NSPCC (£25,000); Game and Wildlife Conservation Trust (£13,000); Royal Forestry Society, Salmon and Trout Conservation and Soldiers of Shropshire Museum (£5,000 each); Friends of the Connection at St Martin-in-the-Fields and Salvation Army (£2,500 each); Campden Home Nursing, Highland Hospice and Samaritans (£1,250 each).

FINANCES *Financial year end* 05/04/2020 *Income* £7,300 *Total grants* £85,100 *Grants to organisations* £85,100

TRUSTEES Hon. Philip Smith; Mary Smith.

OTHER INFORMATION Full accounts were not available to view on the Charity Commission's website due to the trust's low income. We have therefore estimated the grant total based on the trust's total expenditure.

HOW TO APPLY Apply in writing to the correspondent. The trustees meet at least twice a year to consider all requests.

CONTACT DETAILS The Trustees, c/o BDB Pitmans, One Bartholomew Close, London EC1A 7BL *Tel.* 020 7783 3685

■ The R. C. Snelling Charitable Trust

CC NO 1074776 **ESTABLISHED** 1999

WHERE FUNDING CAN BE GIVEN Within a 30-mile radius of the village of Blofield in Norfolk.

WHO CAN BENEFIT Registered charities; community groups; individuals.

WHAT IS FUNDED Medical causes; education; Christianity; social welfare; the environment.

WHAT IS NOT FUNDED Salaries; sponsorship for more than one year; general appeals where the need could be met several times over by grantors; national appeals; continued assistance with running costs.

TYPE OF GRANT Equipment; capital appeals; specific projects; local projects; assistance with running costs; seed funding; fundraising events.

RANGE OF GRANTS Up to £10,000.

SAMPLE GRANTS Norfolk Community Foundation (£10,000); Cromwell House (£7,500); Soul Foundation (£6,000); Star Throwers (£3,500); Age Concern North Norfolk and Musical Keys (£2,000 each); Norwich Puppet Theatre (£1,000); Asthma Relief (£500); Mulbarton Gymnastics Club (£250).

FINANCES *Financial year end* 30/04/2020 *Income* £12,790,000 *Total grants* £122,800 *Grants to organisations* £122,800 *Assets* £11,770,000

TRUSTEES Philip Buttinger; Rowland Cogman; Toby Wise; Colin Jacobs; Samuel Barratt; Nigel Savory; Stephan Phillips.

OTHER INFORMATION Grants were made to 74 organisations during 2019/20.

HOW TO APPLY An online application form can be completed on the trust's website.

CONTACT DETAILS The Trustees, R. C. Snelling Ltd, Laundry Lane, Blofield Heath, Norwich, Norfolk NR13 4SQ *Tel.* 01603 712202 *Email* trustee@rcsnellingcharitabletrust.org *Website* www.rcsnellingcharitabletrust.org

■ The Sobell Foundation

CC NO 274369 **ESTABLISHED** 1977

WHERE FUNDING CAN BE GIVEN Unrestricted, in practice, England and Wales, Israel, and the Commonwealth of Independent States.

WHO CAN BENEFIT Small national or local registered or exempt charities. Overseas charities must be able to provide the details of a UK-registered charity through which funding can be channelled on their behalf.

WHAT IS FUNDED The foundation's website states that the trustees aim 'to achieve a reasonable spread' between Jewish and non-Jewish charities working in the following areas: medical care and treatment, including respite care and hospices; care and education and training for adults and children who have physical or learning disabilities; care and support of older people and of children; homelessness.

WHAT IS NOT FUNDED Individuals; charities which have never received a grant from the foundation; medical research, general medical care and hospital equipment; hospices; animal welfare; mainstream education or sport; the environment; politics and campaigning; criminal justice.

TYPE OF GRANT Capital projects; core funding and projects.

RANGE OF GRANTS Grants range from £900 up to £200,000.

SAMPLE GRANTS Jewish Care (£200,000); Keshet Association for the Aged (£125,000); Desert Stars (£100,000); Royal Brompton and Harefield NHS Trust (£77,000); World Jewish Relief (£70,000).

FINANCES *Financial year end* 05/04/2020 *Income* £1,370,000 *Total grants* £5,510,000 *Grants to organisations* £5,510,000 *Assets* £54,980,000

TRUSTEES Susan Lacroix; Andrea Scouller; Julian Lee; Karis Lacroix; Jerome Lacroix; Sebastian Lee; Deborah Sobel.

OTHER INFORMATION During the year, 536 grants were awarded. Of the grants paid in the year, 98 were of amounts ranging from £20,000 to £50,000 and 5 grants were in excess of £50,000. Approximately 69% of grants paid were made to UK charities and 31% to Jewish charities in Israel and the UK. This allocation is within the ranges set by the trustees for grant allocation.

HOW TO APPLY Applicants are invited to first read the guidelines to see if they are eligible to apply. If eligible, applicants can apply online through the website. The foundation is only accepting applications from charities which have received a grant from it in the last five years. Applicants, successful or otherwise, may only re-apply to the foundation after one year. Applicants are likely to be informed of the outcome in around three months due to the volume of appeals.

CONTACT DETAILS Penny Newton, Administrator, PO Box 5402, Wincanton, Somerset BA9 0BH *Tel.* 020 8922 9097 *Email* pennynewton@sobellfoundation.org.uk *Website* www.sobellfoundation.org.uk

■ Social Business Trust

CC NO 1136151 **ESTABLISHED** 2010

WHERE FUNDING CAN BE GIVEN Undefined, in practice UK.

WHO CAN BENEFIT Social enterprises. Applicants must be registered charities or have a clear charitable purposes (e.g. CICs) and have an annual revenue of more than £1 million.

WHAT IS FUNDED General charitable purposes. The trust outlines its unique approach on its website: '[The trust's] mission is to support high growth potential social enterprises to scale-up their impact. We do that by investing cash grants and professional support from our world-class corporate partners in a carefully selected portfolio of social enterprises.'

TYPE OF GRANT A package of cash grants and in-kind services. Support is usually provided in instalments, each being conditional upon achievement of certain milestones.

SAMPLE GRANTS Challenge Partners (£775,100); The Brilliant Club (£475,400); Brightside (£253,200); Moneyline (£3,600); The Reader Organisation (£680).

FINANCES *Financial year end* 31/05/2020 *Income* £3,350,000 *Total grants* £251,500 *Grants to organisations* £251,500 *Assets* £533,400

TRUSTEES Paul Armstrong; Simon Milton; Guy Davies; Larissa Joy; Michael Crossan; Harry Nicholson; Madeleine Hale; Jan-Coos Geesink; James Hadley.

OTHER INFORMATION The grant total listed accounts for cash grants only. In total, during 2019/20, the trust contributed £2.93 million to organisations, £2.78 million of which was through the provision of in-kind services. The amounts given alongside the listed beneficiaries are the combined totals of both cash grants and in-kind services.

HOW TO APPLY The website states that eligible organisations should contact the trust about getting involved.

CONTACT DETAILS Investment Committee, BWB Charity Hub, 10 Queen Street Place, London EC4R 1BE *Tel.* 020 3096 8021 *Email* info@socialbusinesstrust.org *Website* www.socialbusinesstrust.org

Social Investment Business Foundation

CC NO 1117185 **ESTABLISHED** 2006

WHERE FUNDING CAN BE GIVEN UK.

WHO CAN BENEFIT Registered charities and social enterprises.

WHAT IS FUNDED General charitable purposes. The charity has a number of different funds; refer to the website for information on what is currently available. Funds often focus on enabling organisations to prepare for social investment or competing for contracts, or grow their scale or social impact.

WHAT IS NOT FUNDED Refer to the website for exclusions from each specific fund.

TYPE OF GRANT Grants, loans and other forms of social investment, as well as strategic support and advice.

RANGE OF GRANTS Dependent upon the grant programme.

SAMPLE GRANTS A list of beneficiaries was not included in the annual report and accounts.

FINANCES *Financial year end* 31/03/2020 *Income* £7,500,000 *Total grants* £4,190,000 *Grants to organisations* £4,190,000 *Assets* £31,170,000

TRUSTEES James Rice; Hugh Rolo; Hazel Blears; Jagjit Dosanjh-Elton; Jenny North; Sonali Siriwardena; Richard Pelly; Robert Hewitt.

HOW TO APPLY Applications can be made via the charity's website. Each fund has specific contact details to permit potential applicants to discuss the application process – full details can be found on the funder's website.

CONTACT DETAILS The Trustees, CAN Mezzanine Borough, 7–14 Great Dover Street, London SE1 4YR *Tel.* 020 3096 7900 *Email* enquiries@sibgroup.org.uk *Website* www.sibgroup.org.uk

Social Tech Trust

CC NO 1125735 **ESTABLISHED** 2008

WHERE FUNDING CAN BE GIVEN Undefined, in practice UK.

WHO CAN BENEFIT Registered charities; CICs; social enterprises; universities; local authorities.

WHAT IS FUNDED Digital technology to address social issues in the UK, with a preference for the following: health; young people; poverty relief; education about digital technology, for example how to stay safe online; older people.

TYPE OF GRANT Project funding.

RANGE OF GRANTS Up to £200,000.

SAMPLE GRANTS Previous beneficiaries have included: Beam Up Ltd, Bronze Software Labs Ltd, Carefreebreaks, Feebris, On Our Radar, The Future Fox Ltd and Twelve Two Ltd.

FINANCES *Financial year end* 31/03/2020 *Income* £99,000 *Total grants* £0 *Grants to organisations* £0 *Assets* £4,610,000

TRUSTEES Bill Liao; Sebastien Lahtinen; Elizabeth Murray; Hannah Keartland; Nicolas Temple; Russell Johnstone; Sunil Suri; Robert Tashima; Nicholas Wise; Anisah Britton.

OTHER INFORMATION The 2019/20 accounts state that no grants were made by the trust during the year because it 'distributed funds on behalf of other organisations rather than distributing [its] own funds in the period'.

HOW TO APPLY See the website for updates on open grant schemes as well as detailed guidelines and deadlines. Alternatively, prospective applicants may wish to sign up to the trust's newsletter, or follow the trust on Twitter and LinkedIn, to be the first to hear about new opportunities.

CONTACT DETAILS The Trustees, Social Tech Trust, Oxford Centre for Innovation, New Road, Oxford OX1 1BY *Tel.* 01865 334000 *Email* hello@socialtechtrust.org *Website* https://socialtechtrust.org

Societe Generale UK Foundation

CC NO 1039013 **ESTABLISHED** 1994

WHERE FUNDING CAN BE GIVEN UK and overseas.

WHO CAN BENEFIT UK-registered charities working in the UK or overseas; charitable organisations including schools, hospitals and social enterprises.

WHAT IS FUNDED Inclusion through education and employability; general charitable purposes. The foundation also supports 'SHAKE Climate Change', a programme established to support entrepreneurs combatting climate change in agriculture and food production.

WHAT IS NOT FUNDED Organisations which work outside the scope of education and employment, including religious, political, research, drugs or animal welfare activities; non-UK-registered charities; organisations whose work could damage the reputation of the Société Générale Group; requests for sponsorship, advertising, fees, gifts, prizes and personal appeals.

TYPE OF GRANT Matched funding for charitable organisations supported by Societe Generale employees; project funding – one-off and rolling donations.

RANGE OF GRANTS Up to £167,600 in 2019.

SAMPLE GRANTS CLIC Sargent (£167,600); East End Community Foundation (£130,000); East London Business Alliance (£22,000); Canon Barnett Primary School (£12,100); St Peter's Primary School (£9,800); Cancer Research UK (£2,000).

FINANCES *Financial year end* 31/12/2019 *Income* £478,700 *Total grants* £356,400 *Grants to organisations* £356,400 *Assets* £8,330,800

TRUSTEES Jasvant Singh; Ben Higgins; John Oberman; Elise Sabran; Jonathan Moxon.

OTHER INFORMATION A grant of £167,600 was awarded to the Charity of the Year, CLIC Sargent. Other grants were awarded in the form of matched funding to charities supported by staff of Société Générale. Only beneficiaries of grants over £2,000 were listed. During the year, a grant of £1.21 million was committed to Shake Climate Change, a new nine-year programme established by Rothamsted Research to support entrepreneurs combatting climate change in agriculture and food production.

HOW TO APPLY The foundation does not accept unsolicited applications.

CONTACT DETAILS Rachel Iles, 1 Bank Street, London E14 4SG *Tel.* 020 7597 3065 *Email* rachel.iles@sghambros.com

Sodexo Stop Hunger Foundation

CC NO 1110266 **ESTABLISHED** 2005

WHERE FUNDING CAN BE GIVEN UK and Ireland.

WHO CAN BENEFIT Charitable organisations.

WHAT IS FUNDED Health, nutrition and well-being; relief of poverty; social welfare; disadvantaged communities; general charitable purposes. According to the 2018/19 annual report, the Stop Hunger campaign aims to 'tackle poor nutrition in local communities, promote good nutrition and healthy lifestyles, promote basic life skills such as cooking'.

SAMPLE GRANTS Trussell Trust (£95,000); FareShare (£84,000); SSAFA Forces Help (£50,000); Community Foundation of Ireland (£20,600); Magic Breakfast (£6,900); Incredible Edible (£6,300); Edinburgh Food Social (£4,000).

FINANCES *Financial year end* 31/08/2019
Income £323,188 *Total grants* £323,200
Grants to organisations £323,200
Assets £158,500

TRUSTEES David Mulchay; Gareth John; Patrick Forbes; Sean Haley; Simon McCluskey; Nicholas Byrom; Laura Brimacombe; Stuart Winters; Samantha Scott.

OTHER INFORMATION The Sodexo Stop Hunger Foundation is the corporate charity of the food services and facilities management company, Sodexo Ltd. The 2018/19 accounts were the latest available at the time of writing (February 2021). Grants were made to 11 organisations during the year.

HOW TO APPLY Contact the foundation using the contact form available on its website.

CONTACT DETAILS The Trustees, Sodexo, 1 Southampton Row, London WC1B 5HA *Tel.* 020 7404 0110 *Email* stophunger@sodexo.com *Website* uk.stop-hunger.org/home.html

■ Sofronie Foundation

CC NO 1118621 **ESTABLISHED** 2008

WHERE FUNDING CAN BE GIVEN UK, France and the Netherlands.

WHO CAN BENEFIT Registered charities; non-profit organisations.

WHAT IS FUNDED Projects that offer young people from disadvantaged backgrounds, or who are themselves disadvantaged or struggling, opportunities to acquire skills for higher education or training for work.

TYPE OF GRANT Project funding; core costs.

RANGE OF GRANTS Typically £10,000 to £50,000.

SAMPLE GRANTS Codam (£2.5 million); Academic Musicale Philippe Jaroussky (£60,000); IntoUniversity and Social Mobility Foundation (£50,000 each); Kids Run Free and Myotubular Trust (£10,000 each).

FINANCES *Financial year end* 31/12/2019
Income £2,230,000 *Total grants* £2,440,000
Grants to organisations £2,440,000
Assets £4,880,000

TRUSTEES Harold Goddijn; Corinne Goddijn-Vigreux; Robert Wilne; Ajay Soni; Boris Walbaum.

OTHER INFORMATION In 2019 the foundation funded 16 charities, three of which had previously been supported. Four of the funded charities were UK registered.

HOW TO APPLY Applications can be made at any time through the foundation's website.

CONTACT DETAILS The Trustees, 10 Great Queen Street, London WC2B 5DH *Tel.* 020 7421 3330 *Email* enquiries@sofronie.org *Website* www.sofronie.org

■ David Solomons Charitable Trust

CC NO 297275 **ESTABLISHED** 1986

WHERE FUNDING CAN BE GIVEN UK.

WHO CAN BENEFIT Registered charities.

WHAT IS FUNDED Support for people with learning disabilities.

WHAT IS NOT FUNDED Individuals.

TYPE OF GRANT One-off grants.

RANGE OF GRANTS Generally between £500 and £2,000.

SAMPLE GRANTS Down's Syndrome Association (£10,000); Services for Education (£2,000); My Life My Choice (£1,500); The Peter Pan Centre for Children with Special Needs, Thumbs Up Club and Yellow Submarine Holidays (£1,000 each); Dressability (£750); Bradford Toy Library and Resource Centre (£500).

FINANCES *Financial year end* 05/04/2020
Income £111,800 *Total grants* £71,800
Grants to organisations £71,800
Assets £2,530,000

TRUSTEES Andrew Penny; Dr Richard Solomons; Carol Boys; Diana Huntingford; Jeremy Rutter.

OTHER INFORMATION During 2019/20 the trust awarded 60 grants. An annual grant is awarded to the Down's Syndrome Association.

HOW TO APPLY Apply in writing to the correspondent. The trustees hold three meetings a year to consider grant applications.

CONTACT DETAILS The Trustees, 2 Highfield Road, Collier Row, Romford, Essex RM5 3RA
Tel. 01708 502488
Email davidsolomonscharitabletrust@gmail.com

■ Somerset Community Foundation

CC NO 1094446 **ESTABLISHED** 2002

WHERE FUNDING CAN BE GIVEN Somerset.

WHO CAN BENEFIT Registered charities; unregistered charities; CICs; social enterprises; PTAs; amateur sports clubs; hospitals; hospices; individuals.

WHAT IS FUNDED General charitable purposes.

TYPE OF GRANT Capital costs; core/revenue costs; seed funding/start-up funding; project funding; unrestricted funding.

RANGE OF GRANTS Dependent upon grant programme. Generally up to £10,000.

SAMPLE GRANTS Minehead EYE CIC (£148,800); Bridgwater Unit 517 of the Sea Cadet Corps (£84,900); Community Council for Somerset (£59,500); Red Brick Building (£45,100); Orchard Vale Trust (£15,700); Frome Medical Practice CIC (£5,000); Art Care Education (£4,200); Engage Voluntary Sector Development (£2,500); Men in Sheds Taunton (£2,000).

FINANCES *Financial year end* 31/03/2020
Income £3,930,000 *Total grants* £2,180,000
Grants to organisations £2,180,000
Assets £9,730,000

TRUSTEES Timothy Walker; Jan Ross; Jane Barrie; Martin Kitchen; Sarah Wakefield; Lucilla Nelson; Chris Bishop; John Lyon; Bruce McIntosh; David Taylor; Michelle Ferris.

OTHER INFORMATION This is one of the 46 UK community foundations, which distribute funding for a wide range of purposes. As with all community foundations, there are a number of donor-advised funds managed on behalf of individuals, families and charitable trusts. Grant schemes tend to change frequently – consult the foundation's website for details of current programmes and up-to-date deadlines. Only organisations that received grants of over £2,000 were listed as beneficiaries in the charity's accounts. Grants of under £2,000 totalled £131,000.

HOW TO APPLY Potential applicants are advised to visit the community foundation's website or contact its grants team to find the most suitable funding stream.

CONTACT DETAILS The Trustees, Somerset Community Foundation, Yeoman House, The

Bath and West Showground, Shepton Mallet, Somerset BA4 6QN *Tel.* 01749 344949 *Email* info@somersetcf.org.uk *Website* www.somersetcf.org.uk

■ The E. C. Sosnow Charitable Trust

CC NO 273578 **ESTABLISHED** 1977

WHERE FUNDING CAN BE GIVEN UK and overseas.

WHO CAN BENEFIT Charitable organisations.

WHAT IS FUNDED Education; the arts; social welfare; health; Jewish causes.

SAMPLE GRANTS Jerusalem Foundation and The Victoria and Albert Museum (£5,000 each); Chickenshed and Holocaust Educational Trust (£3,000 each); Marie Curie (£2,000).

FINANCES *Financial year end* 05/04/2020 *Income* £81,600 *Total grants* £71,000 *Grants to organisations* £71,000 *Assets* £1,890,000

TRUSTEES Elias Fattal; Fiona Fattal; Alexandra Fattal; Richard Fattal.

OTHER INFORMATION Grants were made to 17 organisations during the year.

HOW TO APPLY Contact the correspondent for further information.

CONTACT DETAILS The Trustees, c/o Bourner Bullock, Sovereign House, 212–224 Shaftesbury Avenue, London WC2H 8HQ *Tel.* 020 7240 5821

■ The Souter Charitable Trust

OSCR NO SC029998 **ESTABLISHED** 1992

WHERE FUNDING CAN BE GIVEN UK, with a preference for Scotland; overseas.

WHO CAN BENEFIT UK-registered charities.

WHAT IS FUNDED The relief of human suffering, particularly projects with a Christian emphasis; addiction; social action; spiritual welfare; medical research.

WHAT IS NOT FUNDED Capital projects and renovation works; individuals; organisations that are not UK-registered charities.

TYPE OF GRANT Core/revenue costs; project costs; one-off and multi-year.

RANGE OF GRANTS Up to £500,000 but the majority of grants are under £15,000.

SAMPLE GRANTS Mail Force (£500,000); Hope for Justice (£379,200); Tearfund (£293,300); Venture Trust (£150,000); Bethany Christian Trust (£66,700); Destiny Church (£50,000); Social Bite (£20,000); Lunchbowl Network (£15,000).

FINANCES *Financial year end* 30/06/2020 *Income* £113,130,000 *Total grants* £9,260,000 *Grants to organisations* £9,260,000 *Assets* £90,120,000

OTHER INFORMATION In total, 1,506 grants were awarded during 2019/20. Only organisations that received grants of over £15,000 were listed as beneficiaries in the charity's accounts. Grants of under £15,000 totalled £3.84 million and were awarded to 1,413 organisations. Grants were distributed as follows: social action (£7.23 million); spiritual welfare (£1.81 million); drug and alcohol abuse (£162,300); medical research (£58,000).

HOW TO APPLY Apply in writing to the correspondent via post or email. The trustees generally meet once a month and all applications whether successful or not will be acknowledged. Check the trust's website for further information on what to include and current deadlines.

CONTACT DETAILS The Trustees, PO Box 7412, Perth, Perthshire PH1 5YX *Tel.* 01738 450408 *Email* application@soutercharitabletrust.org.uk *Website* www.soutercharitabletrust.org.uk

■ The South Yorkshire Community Foundation

CC NO 1140947 **ESTABLISHED** 1986

WHERE FUNDING CAN BE GIVEN South Yorkshire, particularly Barnsley, Doncaster, Rotherham and Sheffield.

WHO CAN BENEFIT Community and voluntary organisations; CICs.

WHAT IS FUNDED General charitable purposes.

WHAT IS NOT FUNDED See individual grant programmes for specific exclusions.

TYPE OF GRANT Capital costs, core costs, project costs, salaries.

RANGE OF GRANTS Grants vary for each funding programme.

SAMPLE GRANTS South Yorkshire Futures (£27,100); FareShare Yorkshire (£10,000); St Wilfrid's Centre (£7,000); Baby Basics and Little Miracles (£5,000 each); Age UK Barnsley (£4,800); Austerfield Study Centre (£3,900); Sheffield Japanese Play Group and Study Club (£300); Harthill with Woodall Memories and History Society (£120).

FINANCES *Financial year end* 30/09/2019 *Income* £1,700,000 *Total grants* £1,020,000 *Grants to organisations* £1,020,000 *Assets* £13,870,000

TRUSTEES Michele Wightman; Melvyn Lunn; Dr Nicholas Kitchen; Shahida Siddique; Martin Ross; Zaidah Ahmed; John Holt; Yiannis Koursis; Alex Pettifer; John Pickering; The Earl of Scarbrough; Dr Julie MacDonald; James Newman; Paul Benington; Craig McKay; Roderick Plews.

OTHER INFORMATION This is one of the 46 UK community foundations, which distribute funding for a wide range of purposes. As with all community foundations, there are a number of donor-advised funds managed on behalf of individuals, families and charitable trusts. Grant schemes tend to change frequently; consult the foundation's website for details of current programmes and up-to-date deadlines. The 2018/19 accounts were the latest available at the time of writing (June 2021).

HOW TO APPLY Potential applicants are advised to visit the community foundation's website or contact its grants team to find the most suitable funding stream.

CONTACT DETAILS Sue Wragg, Fund Manager, Unit 9–12, Jessop's Riverside, 800 Brightside Lane, Sheffield, South Yorkshire S9 2RX *Tel.* 0114 242 4857 *Email* grants@sycf.org.uk *Website* www.sycf.org.uk

■ The Stephen R. and Philippa H. Southall Charitable Trust

CC NO 223190 **ESTABLISHED** 1967

WHERE FUNDING CAN BE GIVEN UK, with a preference for Herefordshire.

WHO CAN BENEFIT Charitable organisations; hospices; museums; CIOs.

WHAT IS FUNDED General charitable purposes, in particular: education; conservation of the natural environment; cultural heritage.

RANGE OF GRANTS Typically £4,000 to £8,000.

SAMPLE GRANTS Waterworks Museum (£10,000); Prison Reform Trust (£8,000); Worcester Citizens Advice (£4,500); Crohn's and Colitis UK, Hereford Historic Churches Trust, Herefordshire Samaritans and St Michael's Hospice (£4,000 each); Macmillan Cancer Support and The Royal British Legion (£100 each).

FINANCES *Financial year end* 05/04/2020 *Income* £110,500 *Total grants* £70,700 *Grants to organisations* £70,700 *Assets* £4,710,000

TRUSTEES Candia Compton; Anna Southall; Benjamin Compton; Timothy Compton; Henry Serle; Jack Serle.

OTHER INFORMATION Out of the 17 recipients of grants in 2019/20, 16 also received grants in 2018/19. A significant proportion of the trust's grants are made in Herefordshire.

HOW TO APPLY Our previous research suggests that the trust does not consider unsolicited applications.

CONTACT DETAILS The Trustees, Beech Hill, Clifford, Hereford, Herefordshire HR3 5HE *Tel.* 01497 831765 *Email* beechhill48@gmail.com

■ W. F. Southall Trust

CC NO 218371 **ESTABLISHED** 1937

WHERE FUNDING CAN BE GIVEN UK and overseas.

WHO CAN BENEFIT Registered charities.

WHAT IS FUNDED Quaker work and witness; peace-making and conflict resolution; environmental action and sustainability; social action.

WHAT IS NOT FUNDED See the trust's website for a full list of exclusions.

TYPE OF GRANT Capital costs; core/revenue costs; seed funding/start-up funding.

RANGE OF GRANTS Mainly under £5,000.

SAMPLE GRANTS Woodbrooke Quaker Study Centre (£25,000); Second Sight (£10,000); Glenthorne Quaker Centre and Sunnyside Rural Trust (£5,000 each); Peasholme Centre York (£4,500); Hope at Home (£4,300); Peace Brigades International and Tuppenny Barn Education (£3,000 each).

FINANCES *Financial year end* 05/04/2020 *Income* £295,800 *Total grants* £353,100 *Grants to organisations* £353,100 *Assets* £10,340,000

TRUSTEES Annette Wallis; Donald Southall; Joanna Engelkamp; Mark Holtom; Richard Maw; Hannah Engelkamp; Andrew Southall; Philip Coventry.

OTHER INFORMATION During 2019/20, grants were made to 113 organisations and were distributed in the following categories: social action (£271,800); environmental action and sustainability (£32,400); quaker work and witness (£31,000); peace and reconciliation (£17,900). Only organisations that received grants of over £3,000 were listed as beneficiaries in the trust's accounts. Grants of under £3,000 totalled £80,300 and were awarded to 40 organisations.

HOW TO APPLY Applicants should first complete the trust's online eligibility checker; applicants that meet the criteria will then be provided with a link to the downloadable application form. The trustees do not accept postal applications. Any correspondence with the trust should be by phone or email (a contact form can be accessed on the trust's website).

CONTACT DETAILS Wil Berdinner, Trust Secretary, School House, Mytholm Bank, Hebden Bridge, West Yorkshire HX7 6DL *Tel.* 0300 111 1937 *Email* Use the contact form on the website. *Website* https://southalltrust.org

■ Southover Manor General Education Trust Ltd

CC NO 299593 **ESTABLISHED** 1988

WHERE FUNDING CAN BE GIVEN Sussex, Brighton and Hove.

WHO CAN BENEFIT Schools, colleges, nurseries, play groups, youth groups and any other educational organisations working with individuals under the age of 25; occasionally individuals are supported.

WHAT IS FUNDED Education of young people under the age of 25, for purposes such as the development of buildings or facilities, new learning resources, outdoor equipment, etc. The trust's website explains that priority is given to projects which 'widen educational access and opportunity and enhance achievement'.

WHAT IS NOT FUNDED Salaries; transport costs; educational visits or attendance at conferences, expeditions or overseas travel; tuition fees, subsistence expenses, endowments or scholarships; retrospective expenditure; projects with the sole purpose of promoting a particular religion or faith (although applications from faith-based organisations are accepted where there is no faith restriction in the project or the educational objectives).

TYPE OF GRANT Capital and project costs.

RANGE OF GRANTS Up to £25,000.

SAMPLE GRANTS A full list of beneficiaries was not included in the annual report and accounts. The largest grant was for £8,000 to Benfield Primary School.

FINANCES *Financial year end* 31/03/2020 *Income* £119,000 *Total grants* £116,000 *Grants to organisations* £116,000 *Assets* £3,310,000

TRUSTEES Clare Duffield; John Wakely; John Farmer; Wenda Bradley; Ian Jungius; Claire Pool; Charles Davies-Gilbert; Marcus Hanbury; Susan Winn; Dr Caroline Brand; Sophie Hepworth.

OTHER INFORMATION Grants were made to 32 organisations during the year.

HOW TO APPLY Application forms are available to download from the trust's website, where further guidance is also given. The trustees meet in May and November, and applications should be received by 31 March and 30 September, respectively.

CONTACT DETAILS The Secretary to the Trust, Woodmans Farmhouse, Ashington, Pulborough, West Sussex RH20 3AU *Tel.* 01903 893374 *Email* appn@southovermanortrust.org.uk *Website* southovermanortrust.org.uk

■ Peter Sowerby Foundation

CC NO 1151978 **ESTABLISHED** 2013

WHERE FUNDING CAN BE GIVEN UK, with some preference for North Yorkshire.

WHO CAN BENEFIT Registered or exempt charities; CICs; universities; registered social and healthcare providers.

WHAT IS FUNDED Medical research; health and social care; education and learning; community; the environment and conservation; the arts; 'innovative and catalytic' projects.

TYPE OF GRANT Mostly multi-year grants for project funding, research, development funding and capital costs.

RANGE OF GRANTS Mostly up to £93,000, with some exceptionally larger grants.

SAMPLE GRANTS University of Strathclyde (£496,100); Target Ovarian Cancer (£338,300); Yorkshire Aboretum (£200,000); National Youth Jazz Orchestra (£93,000); Bradford Literature

Festival (£87,400); Crohn's and Colitis UK (£38,200); National Youth Choirs of Great Britain (£24,500); Wild Rumpus (£23,400).

FINANCES *Financial year end* 30/09/2019
Income £1,420,000 *Total grants* £1,630,000
Grants to organisations £1,630,000
Assets £38,490,000

TRUSTEES David Aspinall; Sara Poulios; Prof. Carole Longson; Dr David Stables; Aspinalls Fiduciary Ltd.

OTHER INFORMATION The 2018/19 accounts were the latest available at the time of writing (June 2021). Grants were awarded to 13 organisations during the year.

HOW TO APPLY The foundation does not seek unsolicited applications. However, if you believe that your idea is closely aligned with the foundation's aims, you may fill in an online form on the charity's website, outlining your project, budget and proposed timeline. Occasionally, open calls for funding for health and social care projects are advertised on the website – sign up to the mailing list for updates.

CONTACT DETAILS David Aspinall, Chair of Trustees, 29 St John's Lane, Clerkenwell, London EC1M 4NA *Tel.* 0300 030 1151 *Email* info@petersowerbyfoundation.org.uk *Website* https://petersowerbyfoundation.org.uk

■ Spar Charitable Fund

CC NO 236252 **ESTABLISHED** 1964

WHERE FUNDING CAN BE GIVEN UK.

WHO CAN BENEFIT Registered charities, mostly well-known national organisations.

WHAT IS FUNDED General charitable purposes; emergency appeals.

SAMPLE GRANTS Previous beneficiaries have included: Marie Curie (£310,200); Grocery Aid (£33,900); Drink Aware (£23,700); Retail Trust (£14,600); Stillbirth and Neonatal Death Society (£8,700); NSPCC (£7,100); SPAR Inspire (£6,800).

FINANCES *Financial year end* 28/04/2020
Income £8,100 *Total grants* £74,000
Grants to organisations £74,000

TRUSTEES Peter Dodding; Patrick Doody; Dominic Hall; Mohammed Sadiq; Paul Stone; Justin Taylor; Geoffrey Hallam; Peter McBride; Mike Boardman; Julian Green; Mark Cleary; Michael Leonard; Louis Drake; Rodney Tucker.

OTHER INFORMATION Full accounts were not available to view on the Charity Commission's website due to the charity's low income. We have therefore estimated the grant total based on the charity's total expenditure.

HOW TO APPLY Contact the correspondent for further information.

CONTACT DETAILS The Trustees, Spar (UK) Ltd, Hygeia Building, 66–68 College Road, Harrow, Middlesex HA1 1BE *Tel.* 020 8426 3670 *Email* michelle.geraghty@spar.co.uk

■ Sparks Charity

CC NO 1003825 **ESTABLISHED** 1991

WHERE FUNDING CAN BE GIVEN UK.

WHO CAN BENEFIT Those conducting research at UK hospitals and universities.

WHAT IS FUNDED Medical research into conditions that affect children, babies and pregnant women.

WHAT IS NOT FUNDED See individual funding calls on the charity's the website for details of exclusions applicable to research projects.

TYPE OF GRANT Project grants; innovation grants; PhD studentships; clinical research training fellowships; programme grants.

SAMPLE GRANTS University College London (£125,000); University of Cambridge (£97,000); Brunel University (£48,000); Oxford University (£36,000); Oxford Brookes University (£26,000); Great Ormond Street Hospital Children's Charity (£2,000).

FINANCES *Financial year end* 31/03/2020
Income £1,340,000 *Total grants* £384,000
Grants to organisations £384,000
Assets £895,000

TRUSTEES Mark Sartori; Prof. Stephen Holgate.

HOW TO APPLY Refer to the charity's website for details regarding open funding rounds.

CONTACT DETAILS The Trustees, 40 Bernard Street, London WC1N 1LE *Tel.* 020 7091 7750 *Email* info@sparks.org.uk *Website* www.sparks.org.uk

■ Sparquote Ltd

CC NO 286232 **ESTABLISHED** 1982

WHERE FUNDING CAN BE GIVEN UK and overseas.

WHO CAN BENEFIT Charitable organisations.

WHAT IS FUNDED General charitable purposes; the relief of poverty; Jewish education; support for places of worship for the Jewish community.

RANGE OF GRANTS £6,000 to £212,000.

SAMPLE GRANTS Achisomoch Aid Company Ltd (£212,300); Beis Aharon Trust (£50,000); The Rehabilitation Trust (£20,000); Friends of Ganei Geula Jerusalem Ltd (£6,400).

FINANCES *Financial year end* 31/03/2020
Income £1,500,000 *Total grants* £296,400
Grants to organisations £296,400
Assets £17,700,000

TRUSTEES David Reichmann; Dov Reichmann; Anne-Mette Reichmann.

OTHER INFORMATION In 2019/20 grants were awarded to five organisations.

HOW TO APPLY Contact the correspondent for further information.

CONTACT DETAILS The Trustees, Cavendish House, 369 Burnt Oak Broadway, Edgware, London HA8 5AW *Tel.* 020 8731 0777

■ The Spear Charitable Trust

CC NO 1041568 **ESTABLISHED** 1962

WHERE FUNDING CAN BE GIVEN Mainly UK.

WHO CAN BENEFIT Registered charities; individuals.

WHAT IS FUNDED The welfare of employees and former employees of J. W. Spear and Sons plc, their families and dependants; also, general charitable purposes, with some preference for animal welfare, the environment, disability and health.

WHAT IS NOT FUNDED Appeals from individuals, other than former employees of J. W. Spear and Sons plc and their dependants, are not considered.

RANGE OF GRANTS Up to £20,000, with an exceptional grant of £75,000.

SAMPLE GRANTS Soil Association (£75,000); Royal Philatelic Society London (£20,000); St Helena's Hospice (£10,000); Suffolk Owl Sanctuary (£5,000); Interactive Stroke Support and London Air Ambulance (£2,500 each); MIND and Vier Pfoten (£1,000 each).

FINANCES *Financial year end* 31/12/2019
Income £155,800 *Total grants* £415,300
Grants to organisations £389,900
Assets £4,570,000

TRUSTEES Philip Harris; Francis Spear; Hazel Spear; Nigel Gooch.

OTHER INFORMATION Grants were made to 84 organisations and to ten individuals (former employees of J. W. Spear and Sons plc and their families and dependants).

HOW TO APPLY Apply in writing to the correspondent. The trustees state in their 2019 annual report that they will make grants without a formal application, but they encourage organisations to provide feedback on how grants are used. Feedback will be used for monitoring the quality of grants and will form the basis of assessment for any further applications.

CONTACT DETAILS Flora Gaughan, Administrator, Roughground House, Old Hall Green, Ware, Hertfordshire SG11 1HB *Tel.* 01920 823071

■ The Michael and Sarah Spencer Foundation

CC NO 1184658 **ESTABLISHED** 2019

WHERE FUNDING CAN BE GIVEN Worldwide, with a preference for the UK.

WHO CAN BENEFIT Charitable organisations; education institutions.

WHAT IS FUNDED Health; social welfare; education; the environment.

SAMPLE GRANTS Worth Abbey School Development (£6.25 million); Corpus Christi College (£5 million).

FINANCES *Financial year end* 31/03/2020 *Income* £12,510,000 *Total grants* £12,410,000 *Grants to organisations* £12,410,000 *Assets* £88,300

TRUSTEES Marina Ritossa; Michael Spencer; Sarah Spencer.

HOW TO APPLY Apply in writing the correspondent. Applications are discussed quarterly.

CONTACT DETAILS The Trustees, 3rd Floor, 39 Sloane Street, London SW1X 9LP *Tel.* 020 7448 0377 *Email* michelle.mooney@ipgl.london

■ The Jessie Spencer Trust

CC NO 219289 **ESTABLISHED** 1962

WHERE FUNDING CAN BE GIVEN UK, with some preference for the East Midlands.

WHO CAN BENEFIT Registered charities or CICs, with a preference for organisations that have significant volunteer support; hospices; churches.

WHAT IS FUNDED General charitable purposes.

WHAT IS NOT FUNDED Grants are rarely made for: individuals; organisations that are not registered charities or CICs; endowment appeals; loans or business finance; sponsorship, marketing appeals or fundraising events; campaigning or projects that are primarily political; activities that are the responsibility of the local health or education authority or similar body; retrospective expenditure; general or mail shot appeals.

TYPE OF GRANT Grants are made towards both capital and revenue expenditure. They can be recurrent for up to ten years.

RANGE OF GRANTS Grants are generally between £500 and £5,000.

SAMPLE GRANTS Nottingham Hospitals Charity (£25,000); Nottinghamshire Historic Churches Trust (£7,500); Literacy Volunteers (£5,000); Combat Stress and Beaumond House Community Hospice (£1,000 each); Listening Books (£800); RSPB Midlands Regional Office (£500).

FINANCES *Financial year end* 05/04/2020 *Income* £157,800 *Total grants* £141,500 *Grants to organisations* £140,700 *Assets* £4,340,000

TRUSTEES Bethan Mitchell; David Wild; Andrew Tiplady; Helen Lee.

HOW TO APPLY Apply in writing to the correspondent. Guidance on what to include is provided on the trust's website. Applications should be received by 20 January, 20 April, 20 July or 20 October each year for consideration at trustees' meetings in March, June, September and December, respectively. To limit costs, only successful applicants are notified.

CONTACT DETAILS John Thompson, Trust Administrator, c/o 4 Walsingham Drive, Corby Glen, Grantham, Lincolnshire NG33 4TA *Tel.* 01476 552083 *Email* jessiespencer@btinternet.com *Website* www.jessiespencertrust.org.uk

■ Spielman Charitable Trust

CC NO 278306 **ESTABLISHED** 1979

WHERE FUNDING CAN BE GIVEN Bristol and the South West.

WHO CAN BENEFIT Registered charities; individuals.

WHAT IS FUNDED General charitable purposes; social welfare; disadvantaged children and young people; health; disability; education; the arts; older people, communities.

RANGE OF GRANTS Typically £2,000 to £5,000, but occasionally larger.

SAMPLE GRANTS Tobacco Factory (£60,000); Royal Welsh College of Music and Drama (£20,000); Young Bristol (£10,000); Bristol Oncology (£7,000); Brook Clinic (£5,000); Whizz-Kidz (£3,000); FareShare (£2,000); Cerebral Palsy Plus (£1,000).

FINANCES *Financial year end* 05/04/2019 *Income* £262,300 *Total grants* £278,700 *Grants to organisations* £278,700 *Assets* £6,010,000

TRUSTEES Mr C. Moorsom; Karen Hann; Mr P. Cooper; Amelia Hann; Anna MacCarthy.

OTHER INFORMATION In 2018/19 grants were broken down as follows: children who are disadvantaged (£127,000); arts and theatre (£98,400); children with disabilities or serious illnesses (£28,000); community projects (£19,300); older people or people with disabilities (£4,000); schools (£2,000). The 2018/19 accounts were the latest available at the time of writing (February 2021).

HOW TO APPLY Contact the correspondent for further information.

CONTACT DETAILS The Trustees, Hollywood Estate, Hollywood Lane, Bristol BS10 7TW *Tel.* 0117 929 1929 *Email* junetanderson@btinternet.com

■ The Spoore, Merry and Rixman Foundation

CC NO 309040 **ESTABLISHED** 1958

WHERE FUNDING CAN BE GIVEN Maidenhead and Bray, covering the postcode area SL6 1–9 (see the map on the website).

WHO CAN BENEFIT Charitable organisations; schools; youth clubs and community organisations; individuals.

WHAT IS FUNDED Education and training; children and young people. Grants are also made to individuals for educational purposes (e.g. schools uniforms, trips, extracurricular activities).

TYPE OF GRANT Capital costs; project costs.
SAMPLE GRANTS A list of beneficiaries was not included in the annual report and accounts.
FINANCES *Financial year end* 31/12/2019 *Income* £409,000 *Total grants* £676,300 *Grants to organisations* £430,100 *Assets* £12,190,000
TRUSTEES Tony Hill; Grahame Fisher; Ian Thomas; Mayor John Story; David Coppinger; Cllr Gerry Clark; Cllr Donna Stimson; Philip Love; Ann Redgrave; Barbara Wielechowski.
OTHER INFORMATION According to the foundation's website, some of the grants made recently have included funding towards school buses, laptops for schools and individuals, new school library books and school uniform funding. Grants to individuals totalled £246,200 during the year.
HOW TO APPLY Applications can be made online or via post. See the foundation's website for details on how to apply, as application forms differ depending on the purpose of the funding. The foundation asks that applications made by post are not sent via recorded or registered post.
CONTACT DETAILS Clerk to the Trustees, PO Box 4787, Maidenhead, Berkshire SL60 1JA *Tel.* 01628 683800 *Email* clerk@smrfmaidenhead.org *Website* www.smrfmaidenhead.org.uk

■ Rosalyn and Nicholas Springer Charitable Trust

CC NO 1062239 **ESTABLISHED** 1997
WHERE FUNDING CAN BE GIVEN UK and overseas.
WHO CAN BENEFIT Charitable organisations; individuals.
WHAT IS FUNDED Grants are made in the following categories: health; education and training; arts and culture; religious activities; social welfare; general charitable purposes. There is a preference for Jewish causes.
RANGE OF GRANTS Typically £250 to £5,000.
SAMPLE GRANTS Previous beneficiaries have included: Holocaust Education Trust, Jewish Blind and Disabled, Jewish Community Secondary School, Jewish Museum, Macmillan Cancer, Maggie's, National Theatre, Purcell School of Music, WAC Arts, West London Synagogue and Wigmore Hall Trust.
FINANCES *Financial year end* 05/04/2020 *Income* £81,300 *Total grants* £99,800 *Grants to organisations* £99,800 *Assets* £37,500
TRUSTEES Rosalyn Springer; Nicholas Springer.
OTHER INFORMATION A full list of beneficiaries was not published in the charity's accounts for 2019/20, but previous accounts suggest the trust awards approximately 50 grants per year. In 2018/19 grants were made for the following purposes: medical, health and sickness (£32,000); art and culture (£16,400); general charitable purposes (£12,200); education and training (£8,000); religious activities (£7,200); relief of poverty (£4,000).
HOW TO APPLY Contact the correspondent for more information.
CONTACT DETAILS The Trustees, 274A Kentish Town Road, London NW5 2AA *Tel.* 020 7253 7272

■ The Spurrell Charitable Trust

CC NO 267287 **ESTABLISHED** 1960
WHERE FUNDING CAN BE GIVEN UK, with some preference for Norfolk.
WHO CAN BENEFIT UK-registered charities.
WHAT IS FUNDED General charitable purposes.
WHAT IS NOT FUNDED Individuals; CICs; not-for-profit organisations.
RANGE OF GRANTS Up to £10,000, on average around £1,000.
SAMPLE GRANTS East Anglia Children's Hospital (£10,000); Cure Parkinson's (£5,000); Big C Appeal (£2,000); Norfolk Wildlife Trust (£1,500); Caister Volunteer Lifeboat Service and St Mary's Church – Culworth (£1,000 each); Spixworth Youth FC (£700); Sheringham Salvation Army Band (£300).
FINANCES *Financial year end* 05/04/2020 *Income* £63,800 *Total grants* £71,200 *Grants to organisations* £71,200 *Assets* £2,500,000
TRUSTEES Ingeburg Spurrell; Martyn Spurrell; Christopher Spurrell.
OTHER INFORMATION Grants were made to 45 organisations during 2019/20.
HOW TO APPLY Apply in writing to the correspondent. The trustees meet annually to consider grants.
CONTACT DETAILS The Trustees, Harefields, Winslow Road, Little Horwood, Buckinghamshire MK17 0PD *Tel.* 01296 420113 *Email* spurrelltrust@icloud.com

■ The Geoff and Fiona Squire Foundation

CC NO 1085553 **ESTABLISHED** 2001
WHERE FUNDING CAN BE GIVEN UK.
WHO CAN BENEFIT Registered charities.
WHAT IS FUNDED General charitable purposes, particularly the following: medicine; education; disability; welfare and healthcare of children.
WHAT IS NOT FUNDED Large national charities (with an income of over £10 million or assets of more than £100 million); charities dedicated to issues that the trustees deem to be already well funded in the UK.
TYPE OF GRANT Mostly one-off donations.
RANGE OF GRANTS £500 to £150,000.
SAMPLE GRANTS The Lord's Taverners (£124,200); Horatio's Garden (£47,500); Southampton Hospital Charity (£25,000); Deafblind UK (£2,000); Dressability (£500).
FINANCES *Financial year end* 31/03/2020 *Income* £185,500 *Total grants* £844,500 *Grants to organisations* £844,500 *Assets* £8,030,000
TRUSTEES Geoff Squire; Fiona Squire; Bartholomew Peerless.
OTHER INFORMATION Grants were made to 38 charities during the year. The 2019/20 annual report states that the foundation 'will willingly work in partnership with other organisations to fund initiatives beyond the financial scope of a single organisation'.
HOW TO APPLY Contact the correspondent for further information.
CONTACT DETAILS The Trustees, 18 Henry Moore Court, Manresa Road, London SW3 6AS *Tel.* 07759 636799

■ The Vichai Srivaddhanaprabha Foundation

CC NO 1144791 **ESTABLISHED** 2011

WHERE FUNDING CAN BE GIVEN East Midlands.

WHO CAN BENEFIT Charities; charitable organisations; community groups.

WHAT IS FUNDED General charitable purposes.

WHAT IS NOT FUNDED Requests from outside the East Midlands area.

RANGE OF GRANTS Up to £800,000.

SAMPLE GRANTS Leicester Cathedral (£800,000); Gift of a Wish (£600,100); Age UK, Leicester Hospitals and Leicester Partner (£150,000 each); British Legion (£26,500); Canine Partners (£1,500); War Widows (£1,000).

FINANCES *Financial year end* 31/05/2020
Income £159,000 *Total grants* £1,880,000
Grants to organisations £1,880,000
Assets £550,800

TRUSTEES Simon Capper; Susan Whelan; Tony Lander; Alan Birchenall.

OTHER INFORMATION This foundation is the corporate charity of Leicester City Football Club. During 2019/20 grants were made to eight organisations.

HOW TO APPLY Application forms can be downloaded from the foundation's website and should be submitted by post to the correspondent when completed. Requests made by phone call will not be considered.

CONTACT DETAILS The Trustees, Charity Department, King Power Stadium, Filbert Way, Leicester, LE2 7FL *Tel.* 0116 229 4737
Email VSFoundation@lcfc.co.uk
Website https://www.lcfc.com/fans-community/foundation/foundation-overview

■ The St Hilda's Trust

CC NO 500962 **ESTABLISHED** 1904

WHERE FUNDING CAN BE GIVEN The diocese of Newcastle (Newcastle upon Tyne, North Tyneside and Northumberland).

WHO CAN BENEFIT Organisations with charitable purposes (not exclusively registered charities); churches; community projects.

WHAT IS FUNDED Disadvantaged children and young people. Particular consideration is given to projects with a degree of church involvement.

TYPE OF GRANT Project funding.

SAMPLE GRANTS A list of beneficiaries was not included in the annual report and accounts.

FINANCES *Financial year end* 31/12/2020
Income £78,400 *Total grants* £92,500
Grants to organisations £92,500
Assets £2,560,000

TRUSTEES David Littlefield; Revd Christine Brown; Roger Styring; Revd Christine Brown; Helen Cooper; Dr Margaret Wilkinson; Julian Brown.

HOW TO APPLY Application forms can be obtained from the correspondent. The trustees meet at least three times a year to consider grant applications, usually in March, June, September and December. Contact the correspondent for current deadlines.

CONTACT DETAILS Ruth O'Hagan, Secretary, Church House, St John's Terrace, North Shields, Tyne and Wear NE29 6HS *Tel.* 0191 270 4100
Email r.o'hagan@newcastle.anglican.org
Website https://www.newcastle.anglican.org/st-hildas-trust

■ The St James's Trust Settlement

CC NO 280455 **ESTABLISHED** 1980

WHERE FUNDING CAN BE GIVEN UK and USA.

WHO CAN BENEFIT Registered charities.

WHAT IS FUNDED The trust's areas of support in the UK are health, education and social justice. In the USA, it supports education, community arts projects and awareness-raising about crimes against humanity.

TYPE OF GRANT Capital costs; project funding.

RANGE OF GRANTS Mostly between £3,000 and £40,000.

SAMPLE GRANTS Three Generations (£115,800); Highbury Vale Blackstock Trust (£30,000); Caris Islington (£20,000); Living Archives (£19,700); S.A.M. (£3,900); Four Way Books (£7,900); United B Association (£790).

FINANCES *Financial year end* 05/04/2020
Income £67,600 *Total grants* £212,300
Grants to organisations £212,300
Assets £2,760,000

TRUSTEES Jane Wells; Cathy Ingram.

OTHER INFORMATION During 2019/20, three grants were made to UK organisations totalling £50,000 and 14 grants were made to organisations in the USA totalling £162,300.

HOW TO APPLY The trustees state in the 2019/20 annual report that they '[do] not seek unsolicited applications for grants and, without paid staff, are unable to respond to such applications'. The trustees identify potential beneficiaries proactively.

CONTACT DETAILS The Trustees, c/o Begbies Chartered Accountants, 9 Bonhill Street, London EC2A 4DJ *Tel.* 020 7628 5801 *Email* admin@begbiesaccountants.co.uk

■ St James's Place Charitable Foundation

CC NO 1144606 **ESTABLISHED** 1992

WHERE FUNDING CAN BE GIVEN UK and overseas.

WHO CAN BENEFIT Predominantly UK-registered charities and special needs schools. The small grants programme targets charities with an annual income of less than £1 million.

WHAT IS FUNDED The foundation's main themes are: supporting disadvantaged young people; combating cancer; supporting hospices; mental health.

WHAT IS NOT FUNDED Charities with reserves of over 50% of income; administrative costs; activities which are the responsibility of statutory providers or replacement of statutory funding; research; events; advertising; holidays; sponsorship; contributions to large capital appeals; single-faith charities; charities that are fundraising on behalf of another charity.

TYPE OF GRANT Capital items; core/revenue grants including salaries; project funding.

RANGE OF GRANTS Small grants: up to £10,000.

SAMPLE GRANTS Panathlon Foundation (£375,000); Onside Youth Zones (£250,000); The Music Works (£100,000); The Benjamin Foundation (£60,000); Meningitis Now and The Trussell Trust (£50,000 each); Young Gloucestershire (£20,000); Mustard Seed Project (£14,900); Heart N Soul (£7,000).

FINANCES *Financial year end* 31/12/2019
Income £12,850,000
Total grants £13,900,000
Grants to organisations £13,900,000
Assets £5,900,000

TRUSTEES Sir Mark Weinberg; Ian Gascoigne; Malcolm Cooper-Smith; Andrew Croft; Andrew

Humphries; Sonia Gravestock; Robert Medwyn Edwards.

OTHER INFORMATION Over 1,000 UK-registered charities were supported in 2019. A list of beneficiaries was not published in the year's annual accounts; therefore, a sample of recent beneficiaries has been taken from the foundation's website.

HOW TO APPLY Applications for the small grants scheme should be made using the form on the foundation's website. Guidelines for each of the foundation's themes are also available to download on the website. There are no deadlines for the small grants scheme and applications are considered throughout the year, although the process can take between four and six months.

CONTACT DETAILS The Trustees, St James's Place plc, St James's Place House, 1 Tetbury Road, Cirencester, Gloucestershire GL7 1FP *Tel.* 01285 878354 *Email* sjp.foundation@sjp.co.uk *Website* www.sjpfoundation.co.uk

■ Sir Walter St John's Educational Charity

CC NO 312690 **ESTABLISHED** 1992

WHERE FUNDING CAN BE GIVEN The boroughs of Wandsworth or Lambeth, with a preference for Battersea.

WHO CAN BENEFIT Registered charities; CICs; social enterprises; PTAs; individuals; local community groups.

WHAT IS FUNDED The education and training of children and young people. The Small Education Grants scheme focuses on the following groups of local children and young people: those living in areas of particular social disadvantage; refugees and asylum seekers; carers; people with disabilities; looked after children and care leavers. The Strategic Grants scheme focuses on: refugees of secondary school age, particularly unaccompanied minors and those with little previous formal education; young carers; young people who are low achieving or at risk of dropping out of education.

TYPE OF GRANT Capital costs; project funding; start-up funding.

RANGE OF GRANTS Up to £1,500 for educational grants. Up to £30,000 per year for strategic grants.

SAMPLE GRANTS Carers Hub Lambeth (£9,900); Kids (£6,500); Free to Be Kids and Regenerate (£1,500 each); The Baytree Centre (£1,000).

FINANCES *Financial year end* 05/04/2020 *Income* £231,400 *Total grants* £176,600 *Grants to organisations* £175,100 *Assets* £4,820,400

TRUSTEES Cllr Barry Fairbank; Rosemary Summerfield; Kerry Briscoe; Sarah Rackham; Christopher Wellbelove; Dave Wagner; Cllr Linda Bray; Wendy Speck; Michael Bates; The Revd Canon Simon Butler; Col Julian Radcliffe; Godfrey Allen; Sheldon Wilkie; Daphne Daytes; Col Stratton.

HOW TO APPLY Application forms, eligibility criteria and application deadlines can be found on the charity's website.

CONTACT DETAILS Susan Perry, Manager, c/o St Mary's Primary School, 7 St Joseph's Street, London SW8 4EN *Tel.* 020 7498 8878 *Email* manager@swsjcharity.org.uk *Website* www.swsjcharity.org.uk

■ St John's Foundation Est. 1174

CC NO 201476 **ESTABLISHED** 1174

WHERE FUNDING CAN BE GIVEN Bath and North East Somerset.

WHO CAN BENEFIT Charitable organisations.

WHAT IS FUNDED Child poverty; educational attainment.

SAMPLE GRANTS Sporting Family Change (£89,200); Off the Record (£40,000); Anorexia and Bulimia Care and FareShare South West (£30,000 each); Bath Area Play Project and St John's Church (£20,000 each); The Wheels Project (£15,000).

FINANCES *Financial year end* 31/12/2019 *Income* £5,880,000 *Total grants* £2,206,000 *Grants to organisations* £1,850,000 *Assets* £131,670,000

TRUSTEE St John's Hospital Trustee Ltd.

OTHER INFORMATION At the time of writing (March 2021) the foundation was changing its direction with an ambition to 'significantly reduce the educational attainment gap'. In 2019 only organisations that received grants of over £15,000 were listed as beneficiaries in the charity's accounts.

HOW TO APPLY At the time of writing (March 2021) the foundation was changing its direction, so there was no information available on the application process. See the website for up-to-date application details.

CONTACT DETAILS John Thornfield, Funding and Impact Officer, St John's Hospital, 4–5 Chapel Court, Bath BA1 1SQ *Tel.* 01225 486427 *Email* david.hobdey@stjohnsbath.org.uk *Website* https://www.stjohnsbath.org.uk/funding-support

■ St Luke's College Foundation

CC NO 306606 **ESTABLISHED** 1977

WHERE FUNDING CAN BE GIVEN UK, with a preference for the South West.

WHO CAN BENEFIT Universities, colleges and other institutions operating at university level; individuals.

WHAT IS FUNDED Theology and religious education. Corporate awards are made to universities and similar institutions to enable them to develop or enhance their provision in these fields.

WHAT IS NOT FUNDED Funding is not available for building work or to provide bursaries for institutions to administer. Schools are not supported directly (although support is given to teachers who are taking eligible studies). Grants are not normally made for periods in excess of three years. The foundation no longer makes awards to PGCE religious education students.

TYPE OF GRANT Grants can be made for periods of up to three years. Priority is given to pump-priming initiatives.

SAMPLE GRANTS South West Ministry Training Course (£33,100); Diocese of Exeter (£13,300); Anglican Consultative Council (£2,000).

FINANCES *Financial year end* 31/07/2020 *Income* £226,700 *Total grants* £108,700 *Grants to organisations* £50,400 *Assets* £7,200,000

TRUSTEES Giles Frampton; Prof. Grace Davie; The Very Revd Jonathan Greener; Revd Trevor Jones; Dr Michael Wykes; Dick Powell; Revd Dr David Rake; John Searson; Rt Revd Robert Atwell; Prof. Wendy Robinson; Katherine Freeman.

OTHER INFORMATION Grants were broken down as follows: personal (£58,300); major corporate (£46,400); small corporate (£4,000). Of the four awards given to organisations, one was for a new project that had not previously been supported.

HOW TO APPLY From 1 January each year, applicants can request an application pack by emailing the correspondent. Requests should include brief details about yourself and your plans, as well as a postal address. Applications are considered once a year and should be received by 1 May for grants starting in September. Successful applicants will be notified by 30 June.

CONTACT DETAILS David Benzie, Director, 15 St Maryhaye, Tavistock, Devon PL19 8LR *Tel.* 01822 613143 *Email* director@st-lukes-foundation.org.uk *Website* www.st-lukes-foundation.org.uk

St Monica Trust

CC NO 202151 **ESTABLISHED** 1925

WHERE FUNDING CAN BE GIVEN Bristol and the surrounding area.

WHO CAN BENEFIT Organisations; individuals and families.

WHAT IS FUNDED Support for people who have physical disabilities or long-term physical health problems; support for older people.

TYPE OF GRANT Capital items; running costs.

SAMPLE GRANTS Previous beneficiaries have included: Citizens Advice (£9,800); St Peter's Hospice, Headway Bristol and Motor Neurone Disease Association (£7,500 each); IT Help@Home (£5,000); The New Place (£3,900); Bristol and Avon Chinese Women's Group (£2,000); Bath Institute of Medical Engineering (£1,500); Western Active Stroke Group (£1,000).

FINANCES *Financial year end* 31/12/2019 *Income* £41,130,000 *Total grants* £457,500 *Grants to organisations* £296,400 *Assets* £304,100,000

TRUSTEE St Monica Trustee Company Ltd.

OTHER INFORMATION The trust runs retirement villages in Bristol and North Somerset which offer sheltered accommodation, nursing homes and dementia care homes to older people. It makes grants in support of the local community through the Community Fund. Grants are made to individuals in the form of one-off grants for emergency items as well as short-term monthly payments. During 2019, 35 organisations were supported.

HOW TO APPLY An application form can be found on the trust's website. The correspondent can be contacted for further information.

CONTACT DETAILS Community Fund Team, Cote Lane, Bristol BS9 3UN *Tel.* 0117 949 4003 *Email* community.fund@stmonicatrust.org.uk *Website* www.stmonicatrust.org.uk

St Olave's and St Saviour's Schools Foundation

CC NO 1181857 **ESTABLISHED** 1968

WHERE FUNDING CAN BE GIVEN The London Borough of Southwark.

WHO CAN BENEFIT Schools, youth groups and other organisations working with young people under the age of 25 in Southwark.

WHAT IS FUNDED Educational and extracurricular activities for children and young people (under 25 years old).

TYPE OF GRANT Project funding.

RANGE OF GRANTS Typically less than £3,000.

SAMPLE GRANTS Bede House Association (£6,500); Bridge the Gap Studios (£4,000); Colombo Street Community and Sports Centre and Flute Theatre (£3,000 each); Oliver Goldsmith Primary School (£2,000); 20th Bermondsey Scouts (£1,600); Afro-Brazilian Arts and Cultural Exchange and Resources for Autism (£1,000 each).

FINANCES *Financial year end* 31/03/2020 *Income* £1,028,000 *Total grants* £762,400 *Grants to organisations* £738,900 *Assets* £25,809,000

TRUSTEES Dr Emma Sanderson-Nash; Edwin Langdown; The Very Rev'd Andrew Nunn; Stephen Parry; Elizabeth Edwards; Cllr Stephen Wells; Laurence Johnstone; Cllr Robert Evans; Ven. Dr Paul Wright; Robert Highmore; Dr David Ryall; John Major; Natalie Bell; James Rothwell.

OTHER INFORMATION Grants to organisations in 2019/20 included two large, recurrent grants totalling £649,700 to the two schools, St Olave's Grammar School and St Saviour's School. The foundation also makes an annual grant to Southwark Cathedral's choirs, which totalled £11,800 in 2019/20. Foundation Fund grants totalled £120,600. Grants to 32 individuals totalled £31,600.

HOW TO APPLY Applications should be made on a form available to download from the foundation's website.

CONTACT DETAILS The Trustees, Foundation Centre, Europoint Centre, 5–11 Lavington Street, London SE1 0NZ *Tel.* 020 7401 2871 *Email* grants@stolavesfoundation.co.uk *Website* www.stolavesfoundationfund.org.uk

St Peter's Saltley Trust

CC NO 528915 **ESTABLISHED** 1980

WHERE FUNDING CAN BE GIVEN The dioceses of Worcester, Hereford, Lichfield, Birmingham and Coventry.

WHO CAN BENEFIT Charitable organisations, schools, colleges, individuals.

WHAT IS FUNDED Christianity; theological and religious education.

WHAT IS NOT FUNDED Grants to cover fees and personal study/research; core costs; salaries; capital projects (e.g. building repairs and maintenance); subsidies for work that churches, schools, colleges and other organisations should be doing.

TYPE OF GRANT Project funding and development funding. Mostly one-off grants.

RANGE OF GRANTS Up to £10,000.

SAMPLE GRANTS West Midlands Regional FE Chaplaincy Development (£29,400); Newbigin School of Urban Leadership (£10,000); Innervation Trust (£9,600); RE Matters (£3,000); Saltmine Trust (£1,000); Culham St Gabriel's (£6,000); Bewdley YFC (£990).

FINANCES *Financial year end* 31/03/2020 *Income* £180,300 *Total grants* £90,000 *Grants to organisations* £90,000 *Assets* £4,010,000

TRUSTEES Gordon Thornhill; Dr Peter Kent; Michael Hastilow; Revd Naomi Nixon; Revd Canon Dr Jonathan Kimber; Dr Lindsay Hall; Revd Canon Dr Mark Pryce; David Owen; Julia Ipgrave; Daniel Martin.

OTHER INFORMATION Grants were awarded to 16 projects in 2019/20.

HOW TO APPLY Full criteria and guidelines for each fund are available on the trust's helpful website. The trust asks that in the first instance you contact the correspondent to help determine if your proposal is suitable for a full application.

CONTACT DETAILS Ian Jones, Director, Gray's Court, 3 Nursery Road, Edgbaston, Birmingham, West

Midlands B15 3JX *Tel.* 0121 427 6800 *Email* director@saltleytrust.org.uk *Website* www.saltleytrust.org.uk

■ Stadium Charitable Trust

CC NO 328522 **ESTABLISHED** 1989

WHERE FUNDING CAN BE GIVEN UK.

WHO CAN BENEFIT Charitable organisations.

WHAT IS FUNDED General charitable purposes, including health, sport and recreation.

SAMPLE GRANTS Previous beneficiaries have included: Fundacion Alpe (£121,000); Dove House Hospice (£100,000); RNIB Sight Loss Appeal (£30,000); Brough Primary School (£10,000); Sailors Children's Society (£6,500); Special Smiles (£4,000); Pocklington Imagination Library (£1,000); RNLI (£800).

FINANCES *Financial year end* 05/04/2020 *Income* £3,800 *Total grants* £385,000 *Grants to organisations* £385,000

TRUSTEES Edwin Healey; Anne Rozenbroek; Andrew Fish.

OTHER INFORMATION Full accounts were not available to view on the Charity Commission's website due to the trust's low income. We have therefore estimated the grant total based on its total expenditure.

HOW TO APPLY Contact the correspondent for further information.

CONTACT DETAILS The Trustees, The Stadium Group, Welton Grange, Cowgate, Welton, East Yorkshire HU15 1NB *Tel.* 01482 667149 *Email* info@stadiumcity.co.uk

■ The Stafford Trust

OSCR NO SC018079 **ESTABLISHED** 1991

WHERE FUNDING CAN BE GIVEN UK, with a preference for Scotland.

WHO CAN BENEFIT UK-registered charities.

WHAT IS FUNDED General charitable purposes, including the following: social welfare; medical research; animal welfare; children and young people; community projects; sea rescue; welfare of armed services personnel; overseas aid.

WHAT IS NOT FUNDED Religious organisations; political organisations; retrospective grants; student travel or expeditions; general appeals or mail shots.

TYPE OF GRANT Capital projects; core costs; salaries.

RANGE OF GRANTS Mostly between £500 and £5,000.

SAMPLE GRANTS Befrienders Highland Ltd, Scottish Youth Theatre and Sunshine Wishes Children's Charity (£5,000 each); Wood Green – The Animals Charity (£4,500); Glasgow Tool Library and Wellbeing Scotland (£4,000 each); Asthma Relief (£1,900); Banchory Day Centre (£1,000).

FINANCES *Financial year end* 05/04/2020 *Income* £538,800 *Total grants* £437,800 *Grants to organisations* £437,800 *Assets* £20,310,000

TRUSTEES Gordon Wylie; Ian Ferguson; Robert Hogg; Fiona Gillespie.

OTHER INFORMATION Grants were awarded to 105 organisations during 2019/20. The average grant during the year was £4,169.

HOW TO APPLY An application form can be downloaded from the trust's website and should include the information specified on the website. The trustees usually meet twice a year in spring and autumn to review applications. Deadlines are posted on the website. Unsuccessful applicants should wait at least one year before reapplying.

CONTACT DETAILS Billy Russell, Trust Administrator, c/o Dickson Middleton CA, PO Box 14, 20 Barnton Street, Stirling, Stirlingshire FK8 1NE *Tel.* 01786 474718 *Email* staffordtrust@dicksonmiddleton.co.uk *Website* www.staffordtrust.org.uk

■ The Community Foundation for Staffordshire

CC NO 1091628 **ESTABLISHED** 2001

WHERE FUNDING CAN BE GIVEN Staffordshire.

WHO CAN BENEFIT Registered charities, community groups, CICs, individuals.

WHAT IS FUNDED General charitable purposes; social welfare; education and training; health.

WHAT IS NOT FUNDED Each funding stream has its own set of exclusions – refer to the website for details.

TYPE OF GRANT Mainly project funding but some streams also give for core costs.

RANGE OF GRANTS Dependent upon funding stream.

SAMPLE GRANTS Beat the Cold (£26,500); VAST (£12,000); Claymills Pumping (£10,000); Burton and District Mind (£9,900; Community Recycling Consortium CIC, Guy Hilton Asthma Trust, Staffordshire Council of Voluntary Youth Services and Sporting Communities CIC (£5,000 each).

FINANCES *Financial year end* 31/03/2020 *Income* £1,330,000 *Total grants* £751,300 *Grants to organisations* £751,300 *Assets* £6,300,000

TRUSTEES Adele Cope; Jeremy Lefroy; Amanda Harris; Roger Lewis; Ashley Brough; Charlotte Almond; Lorraine Green; Simon Price; Prakash Samani; Jonathan Andrew; Judy Moncrieff; Terry Walsh.

OTHER INFORMATION This is one of the 46 UK community foundations, which distribute funding for a wide range of purposes. As with all community foundations, there are a number of donor-advised funds managed on behalf of individuals, families and charitable trusts. Grant schemes tend to change frequently – consult the foundation's website for details of current programmes and up-to-date deadlines.

HOW TO APPLY Potential applicants are advised to visit the community foundation's website or contact its grants team to find the most suitable funding stream.

CONTACT DETAILS The Grants Team, Communications House, University Court, Staffordshire Technology Park, Stafford, Staffordshire ST18 0ES *Tel.* 01785 339540 *Email* office@staffsfoundation.org.uk *Website* www.staffsfoundation.org.uk

■ Standard Life Aberdeen Charitable Foundation

OSCR NO SC042597 **ESTABLISHED** 2011

WHERE FUNDING CAN BE GIVEN UK and overseas where the company has a presence.

WHO CAN BENEFIT Registered charities only.

WHAT IS FUNDED General charitable purposes. The foundation will consider most charitable donations. Beneficiaries should be located in a community close to one of Standard Life Aberdeen's offices.

WHAT IS NOT FUNDED The foundation's local community funding does not support: projects/organisations that promote religious or political views, or discriminate against protected characteristics such as sexual orientation or gender; applications from crowdfunding initiatives or individuals; projects with capital build costs; projects that do not align with the foundation's 'building connection' aim or which do not support at least one of the UN Sustainable Development Goals.

TYPE OF GRANT Project costs.

RANGE OF GRANTS Between £5,000 and £25,000. Larger grants can be requested.

SAMPLE GRANTS A list of beneficiaries was not included in the annual report and accounts.

FINANCES *Financial year end* 31/12/2019 *Income* £858,100 *Total grants* £854,600 *Grants to organisations* £854,600 *Assets* £154,700

TRUSTEES Tamsin Balfour; Paul Aggett; Sarah Anderson; Bev Hendry; Sandy MacDonald; Michael Tumilty; Sam Walker; Lynn Warren; Amanda Young.

OTHER INFORMATION The foundation also develops partnerships with charities tackling the educational needs of disadvantaged young people in emerging market countries. Grants were distributed as follows: local community support (£706,800); emerging markets projects (£147,800).

HOW TO APPLY Application forms are available from the foundation's website and should be emailed with the most recent audited accounts. Contact the foundation if you wish to discuss a larger grant or a multi-year opportunity.

CONTACT DETAILS The Trustees, 10 Queen's Terrace, Aberdeen, Aberdeenshire AB10 1XL *Email* sla.foundation@aberdeenstandard.com *Website* https://www.standardlifeaberdeen.com/en/corporate-sustainability/charitable-giving

■ Standard Life Foundation

OSCR NO SC040877 **ESTABLISHED** 2009

WHERE FUNDING CAN BE GIVEN UK, with a preference for Scotland.

WHO CAN BENEFIT Registered charities; voluntary organisations; think tanks; campaigning groups; research bodies; universities.

WHAT IS FUNDED Research, policy and campaigning on structural and individual issues relating to financial well-being.

WHAT IS NOT FUNDED See the online funding guide for a comprehensive list of exclusions, which includes individuals.

TYPE OF GRANT Project funding; core costs.

RANGE OF GRANTS Typically £30,000 to £200,000.

SAMPLE GRANTS Resolution Foundation (£190,000); IPPR Scotland (£150,000); Child Poverty Action Group (£133,000); Loughborough University's Centre for Research in Social Policy (£104,000); Fabian Society (£74,000); High Pay Centre (£62,000); Refuge (£37,000).

FINANCES *Financial year end* 31/12/2019 *Income* £683,600 *Total grants* £423,000 *Grants to organisations* £423,000 *Assets* £87,670,000

TRUSTEES Alistair Darling; James Daunt; Naomi Eisenstadt; Prof. David Hall; Lucy Heller; Prof. Elaine Kempson; Prof. Wendy Loretto; Graeme McEwan; Keith Skeoch; Euan Stirling.

OTHER INFORMATION In 2019 the foundation made grants to 13 organisations, with eight grants relating to research, three relating to policy work and two relating to campaigning.

HOW TO APPLY The foundation has two annual deadlines (in February and June). Use the foundation's template application and submit it via email to applications@standardlifefoundation.org.uk. The foundation invites potential applicants to discuss their ideas via telephone.

CONTACT DETAILS The Trustees, Level 5, 6 St Andrew Square, Edinburgh EH2 2AH *Tel.* 020 7618 1626 *Email* enquiries@standardlifefoundation.org.uk *Website* https://www.standardlifefoundation.org.uk/home

■ Stanley Foundation Ltd

CC NO 206866 **ESTABLISHED** 1960

WHERE FUNDING CAN BE GIVEN UK.

WHO CAN BENEFIT Registered charities.

WHAT IS FUNDED General charitable purposes, including the following: education and training; arts, culture and heritage; medical care and research; community development; famine and disaster relief.

WHAT IS NOT FUNDED Individuals.

RANGE OF GRANTS Typically up to £10,000.

SAMPLE GRANTS Centre for London (£15,000); Puzzle Centre (£12,000); Multiple Sclerosis and Sarah Greene Breakthrough Tribute Fund (£10,000); King's College, London Symphony Orchestra and South Bank Centre (£5,000 each)

FINANCES *Financial year end* 31/03/2020 *Income* £74,300 *Total grants* £108,000 *Grants to organisations* £108,000 *Assets* £2,050,000

TRUSTEES Elodie Stanley; Nicholas Stanley; Shaun Stanley; John Raymond; Patrick Hall; Georgina Stanley; Stephen Hall; Charles Stanley.

OTHER INFORMATION Three of the nine listed grant recipients in 2019/20 received grants in 2018/19.

HOW TO APPLY Contact the correspondent for more information. The foundation prioritises applications that enable it to maximise impact and build on previous successful funding relationships.

CONTACT DETAILS Nicholas Stanley, Trustee, c/o N. C. Morris and Co., 1 Montpelier Street, London SW7 1EX *Tel.* 07768 232986 *Email* nick@meristan.com

■ Staples Trust

CC NO 1010656 **ESTABLISHED** 1992

WHERE FUNDING CAN BE GIVEN UK and overseas, with a preference for Oxfordshire.

WHO CAN BENEFIT Registered charities; universities; CICs; museums.

WHAT IS FUNDED Gender issues (domestic violence, women's rights and gender studies); overseas projects which support the rights of indigenous people; charities defending human rights and civil liberties. The trust also administers The Frankopan Fund, which makes small grants to Croatian students. The trustees also have an interest in supporting local charities in Oxfordshire.

WHAT IS NOT FUNDED Individuals.

TYPE OF GRANT Core costs; project funding; capital costs.

RANGE OF GRANTS Mostly £500 to £25,000.

SAMPLE GRANTS University of Cambridge (£525,000); The Prince's Trust (£25,000); Pitt Rivers Museum (£20,000); Child Bereavement UK and Rainforest Concern (£10,000 each); The Felix Trust (£5,000); Museum of Anthropology and Archaeology (£3,800); Oxford Food Bank (£3,000); University of Utrecht (£500).

FINANCES *Financial year end* 05/04/2020 *Income* £423,700 *Total grants* £582,300 *Grants to organisations* £582,300 *Assets* £12,480,000

TRUSTEES Judith Portrait; Timothy Sainsbury; Jessica Sainsbury; Prof. Peter Frankopan.

OTHER INFORMATION The trust is one of the Sainsbury Family Charitable Trusts which share a common administration – see www.sftc.org.uk for more information. During the year, grants to organisations were made for the following purposes: indigenous peoples (£348,800); general charitable purposes (£128,500); gender (£58,800); the environment (£17,500); local causes (£3,000). In addition, educational grants totalling £25,800 were made through The Frankopan Fund. The list of beneficiaries includes grants paid and committed.

HOW TO APPLY Unsolicited applications are not accepted.

CONTACT DETAILS Robert Bell, Director, The Peak, 5 Wilton Road, London SW1V 1AP *Tel.* 020 7410 0330 *Email* info@sfct.org.uk *Website* www.sfct.org.uk

■ Starlow Charities Ltd

CC NO 1081386 **ESTABLISHED** 2000

WHERE FUNDING CAN BE GIVEN Worldwide.

WHO CAN BENEFIT Jewish organisations.

WHAT IS FUNDED Causes affecting the Orthodox Jewish community, including the relief of poverty, religion and religious education; general charitable purposes.

RANGE OF GRANTS £50,000 to £300,000.

SAMPLE GRANTS Ezer Bekovoid Ltd (£299,500); Ezer Bekovoid Ltd (£240,200); Beis Ruchel D'Satmar (£212,500); Hadras Kodesh Trust (£125,800); Yeitev Lev Eretz Israel Ltd (£65,000); United Talmudical Association Ltd (£50,000).

FINANCES *Financial year end* 31/07/2019 *Income* £4,370,000 *Total grants* £1,790,000 *Grants to organisations* £1,790,000 *Assets* £9,350,000

TRUSTEES Abraham Low; Avraham Shwarts; Eve Low; Isaac Hochhauser; Benzion Rudzinski.

OTHER INFORMATION Grants of less than £50,000 amounted to £331,700. The 2018/19 accounts were the latest available at the time of writing (June 2021).

HOW TO APPLY Contact the correspondent for further information.

CONTACT DETAILS The Trustees, 9 Craven Walk, London N16 6BS *Tel.* 020 8802 9517 *Email* mail@cohenarnold.com

■ The Peter Stebbings Memorial Charity

CC NO 274862 **ESTABLISHED** 1978

WHERE FUNDING CAN BE GIVEN UK and overseas, with a preference for London and financially developing countries.

WHO CAN BENEFIT UK-registered charities. Generally grants go to charities where the trustees can see how the money is being used. The trustees prefer small to medium-sized charities with annual incomes of up to £5 million.

WHAT IS FUNDED UK charities are supported in the following areas: medical research and care; social welfare; homelessness; hospices; mental health/counselling; drug and alcohol therapeutic support; community regeneration; vulnerable families, women and children. Overseas charities are supported in the following areas: education; basic skills and tools; health; sanitation, irrigation, hygiene and access to clean water; women; help for marginalised communities.

WHAT IS NOT FUNDED Individuals; large national or international charities; animal welfare; publications and journals (unless as part of a supported project); general appeals; any charity whose beneficiaries are restricted to particular faiths; educational institutions (unless there is a particular project the trustees wish to support); arts organisations (unless there is a strong social welfare focus to the work).

TYPE OF GRANT Project funding, although core costs will be considered for charities known to the trustees.

RANGE OF GRANTS Mostly between £3,000 and £10,000, with some larger grants made up to £50,000.

SAMPLE GRANTS Royal Marsden Hospital Charity (£50,000); Savannah Education Trust (£20,000); Target Ovarian Cancer (£15,000); Hackney Doorways (£10,000); The Personal Support Unit and St Mungo's (£5,000 each); Chifundo UK (£3,000); Footsteps International (£1,700).

FINANCES *Financial year end* 31/03/2020 *Income* £204,600 *Total grants* £472,600 *Grants to organisations* £472,600 *Assets* £7,020,000

TRUSTEES Andrew Stebbings; Nicholas Cosin; Jennifer Clifford.

OTHER INFORMATION Grants were awarded to 59 charities during the year.

HOW TO APPLY Application forms can be filled in on the charity's website. The trustees meet twice a year to allocate grants. Upcoming meeting dates and deadlines can be found on the charity's website.

CONTACT DETAILS Marie-Louise O'Connor, Grants Administrator (Cripps Pemberton Greenish LLP), 45 Cadogan Gardens, London SW3 2AQ *Tel.* 020 7591 3333 *Email* info@peterstebbingsmemorialcharity.org *Website* peterstebbingsmemorialcharity.org

■ The Steel Charitable Trust

CC NO 272384 **ESTABLISHED** 1976

WHERE FUNDING CAN BE GIVEN UK; Luton and Bedfordshire.

WHO CAN BENEFIT UK-registered charities; exempt charities; CICs.

WHAT IS FUNDED Arts and heritage; education; the environment; health; social or economic disadvantage.

WHAT IS NOT FUNDED Charities not registered in the UK; individuals; political parties.

TYPE OF GRANT Capital costs; project funding; research programmes; core costs.

RANGE OF GRANTS £2,500 to £25,000.

SAMPLE GRANTS Previous beneficiaries have included: Two Moors Festival Ltd (£50,000); Prostate Cancer UK (£25,000); Cheltenham Festivals and International Centre for Eye Health (£20,000 each); Birmingham Opera Company, Lutonian Cricket Club and The Royal Society for Blind Children (£10,000 each); Art Against Knives (£5,000).

FINANCES *Financial year end* 31/01/2020 *Income* £1,400,000 *Total grants* £1,150,000 *Grants to organisations* £1,150,000 *Assets* £36,200,000

TRUSTEES Peter Day; Philip Lawford; Wendy Bailey; Vanessa Fox; Nicholas Wright; Dr Mary Briggs.

OTHER INFORMATION Grants were broken down as follows: health (41.1%); arts and heritage

(18.7%); social or economic disadvantage (14.3%); education (13.5%); the environment (11.7%).
HOW TO APPLY Applicants must be made online using the form on the trust's website. The trustees meet quarterly (in March, June, September and December) to consider grant applications. See the trust's website for application deadlines.
CONTACT DETAILS Trust Manager, Suite 411, Jansel House, Hitchin Road, Stopsley, Luton, Bedfordshire LU2 7XH *Email* info@steelcharitabletrust.org.uk *Website* www.steelcharitabletrust.org.uk

■ The Steinberg Family Charitable Trust

CC NO 1045231 **ESTABLISHED** 1995
WHERE FUNDING CAN BE GIVEN The North West; Israel.
WHO CAN BENEFIT Registered charities.
WHAT IS FUNDED Jewish causes; medical care and treatment, including respite care and hospices; education and care of people with disabilities; older people; children and young people.
WHAT IS NOT FUNDED Individuals.
SAMPLE GRANTS Previous beneficiaries have included: Aish (£75,000); Fed, Hathaway Trust, United Jewish Israel Appeal and World Jewish Relief (£50,000 each); Integrated Education Fund (£25,000); SEED (£22,000); Hale Adult Hebrew Education Trust (£20,000); Centre for Social Justice and Policy Exchange (£15,000); Ascent, Ezer Layeled, Imperial War Museum, MDA Israel, Menachim Begin Heritage Foundation and Yeshiva Bais Yisroel (£10,000 each); Chai Cancer Care and Holocaust Centre (£7,500 each); Hamayon and Hazon Yeshaya (£5,000 each); Henshaw's Society, Jewish Education in Manchester, NATA and Rainbow Trust (£2,500 each); Prostate Cancer Charity (£1,000).
FINANCES *Financial year end* 05/04/2020 *Income* £2,590,000 *Total grants* £1,540,000 *Grants to organisations* £1,540,000 *Assets* £27,100,000
TRUSTEES Lady Beryl Steinberg; Jonathan Steinberg; Lynne Steinberg.
OTHER INFORMATION Grants were broken down as follows: Torah (£613,100); welfare (£532,800); miscellaneous (£125,800); education (£76,700); community (£72,100).
HOW TO APPLY Applications can be made via the trust's website.
CONTACT DETAILS The Trust Secretary, Lime Tree Cottage, 16 Bollinway, Hale, Altrincham, Cheshire WA15 0NZ *Tel.* 0161 903 8854 *Email* admin@sfct.co.uk *Website* https://www.sfct.co.uk

■ The Hugh Stenhouse Foundation

OSCR NO SC015074 **ESTABLISHED** 1968
WHERE FUNDING CAN BE GIVEN Mainly Scotland, with a preference for the west of Scotland.
WHO CAN BENEFIT Charitable organisations – there is a preference for local causes in which local communities are active participants rather than national organisations.
WHAT IS FUNDED General charitable purposes.
TYPE OF GRANT Project funding; core costs.
RANGE OF GRANTS Generally up to £5,000.
SAMPLE GRANTS Maxwelton Chapel Trust (£30,000); Sir Thomas Lipton Foundation (£4,800); CCLASP (£3,000); Braes Shorehouse Foodbank, Pregnancy Care and Counselling and Scottish Mountain Rescue (£1,800 each).
FINANCES *Financial year end* 31/03/2019 *Income* £77,700 *Total grants* £58,600 *Grants to organisations* £58,600 *Assets* £2,190,000
OTHER INFORMATION The foundation categorises its grant giving as: relief of poverty; youth; medical causes; religion; sundries. The 2018/19 accounts were the latest available at the time of writing (April 2021).
HOW TO APPLY Contact the correspondent for further information.
CONTACT DETAILS The Trustees, c/o Bell Ingram Ltd, Durn, Isla Road, Perth, Perthshire PH2 7HF

■ C. E. K. Stern Charitable Trust

CC NO 1049157 **ESTABLISHED** 1992
WHERE FUNDING CAN BE GIVEN UK and overseas, particularly Israel.
WHO CAN BENEFIT Orthodox Jewish charities and religious organisations.
WHAT IS FUNDED Orthodox Jewish religion and education; the relief of poverty.
RANGE OF GRANTS Up to £77,000, but mostly below £25,000.
SAMPLE GRANTS Friends of Beis Soroh Schneirer (£77,000); Friends of Mercaz Hatorah Belz Macnivka (£27,000); Dushinsky Trust Ltd (£25,000); Mifal Hachesed Vehatzedokoh (£24,000); One Heart – Lev Echod (£17,500); Beis Chinuch Lebonos Ltd (£13,000).
FINANCES *Financial year end* 05/04/2019 *Income* £1,920,000 *Total grants* £199,500 *Grants to organisations* £199,500 *Assets* £2,460,000
TRUSTEES Chaya Stern; Zvi Stern.
OTHER INFORMATION The 2018/19 accounts were the latest available at the time of writing (May 2021). Only organisations that received grants of over £3,500 were listed as beneficiaries in the charity's accounts. Grants of under £3,500 totalled £17,900.
HOW TO APPLY Apply in writing to the correspondent. The trust's 2018/19 accounts note: 'The Charity accepts applications for grants from representatives of Orthodox Jewish Charities, which are reviewed by the trustees on a regular basis. The trustees consider requests received and make donations based on level of funds available.'
CONTACT DETAILS Zvi Stern, Trustee, 92 Whitehall Road, Gateshead, Tyne and Wear NE8 4ET *Tel.* 0191 490 1241

■ The Sir Sigmund Sternberg Charitable Foundation

CC NO 257950 **ESTABLISHED** 1968
WHERE FUNDING CAN BE GIVEN Worldwide.
WHO CAN BENEFIT Registered charities.
WHAT IS FUNDED The foundation supports 'interfaith activities to promote racial and religious harmony'. There is a particular focus on the Christian, Jewish and Muslim faiths, and the education in, and understanding of, their fundamental tenets and beliefs.
RANGE OF GRANTS Grants range from £1,000 up to £175,300.
SAMPLE GRANTS The Faith and Belief Forum (£198,400 in two grants); Woolf Institute and Alexander Haus (£10,000 each); New Israel Fund (£5,000); Other (£4,800); Royal College of

Speech and Language Therapists and Asylum Seeker Project (£1,000 each).

FINANCES *Financial year end* 05/04/2020 *Income* £268,200 *Total grants* £233,800 *Grants to organisations* £233,800 *Assets* £4,030,000

TRUSTEES Martin Paisner; Michael Sternberg; Martin Slowe; Revd Dr Marcus Braybrooke; Noam Tamir.

HOW TO APPLY Contact the correspondent for further information.

CONTACT DETAILS The Trustees, c/o HW Fisher LLP, Acre House, 11–15 William Road, London NW1 3ER *Tel.* 020 7388 7000

■ The Sterry Family Foundation

CC NO 1143953 **ESTABLISHED** 2011

WHERE FUNDING CAN BE GIVEN UK; South Africa; Botswana; Zimbabwe; Mozambique; Zambia; Tanzania; Rwanda; Burundi; Malawi; Uganda; Kenya.

WHO CAN BENEFIT Registered charities and institutional applicants.

WHAT IS FUNDED Projects that involve education, amateur sports, health, and arts and culture.

RANGE OF GRANTS £600 to £8,000.

SAMPLE GRANTS Children's Trust (£8,000); Northern Ballet (£6,000); Malakia Kids (£4,000); Joshua Orphanage Community (£3,000); African Revival (£1,000).

FINANCES *Financial year end* 05/04/2020 *Income* £80,700 *Total grants* £90,500 *Grants to organisations* £89,300 *Assets* £3,350,000

TRUSTEES David Sterry; James Sterry; Nicola Clatworthy; Wendy Sterry.

OTHER INFORMATION Grants were awarded to 32 organisations and eight individuals during the year.

HOW TO APPLY Apply in writing to the correspondent. The foundation's 2019/20 annual report states: 'The trust invites applications for charitable donations from other registered charities. Institutional applicants submit a summary of their proposals to the trustees in a specific format, together with outline appeals. Applications made in the correct format are reviewed against the Trust Deed and its objectives.'

CONTACT DETAILS The Trustees, Rathbone Trust Company Ltd, 8 Finsbury Circus, London EC2M 7AZ *Tel.* 020 7399 0000

■ Stervon Ltd

CC NO 280958 **ESTABLISHED** 1980

WHERE FUNDING CAN BE GIVEN UK.

WHO CAN BENEFIT Charitable organisations, particularly Jewish organisations.

WHAT IS FUNDED Relief of poverty; relief of ill health and disability; advancement of Orthodox Jewish religious education.

RANGE OF GRANTS Up to £27,000.

SAMPLE GRANTS The Machzikei Hadass Communities (£27,000); Bienfaisance Pavee (£23,000); Bemosh Ltd (£15,000); Stonewhite Ltd (£12,500); The New Light Trust Ltd (£10,000).

FINANCES *Financial year end* 31/12/2019 *Income* £256,000 *Total grants* £206,000 *Grants to organisations* £206,000 *Assets* £278,000

TRUSTEES Akiva Reich; Gabriel Rothbart.

OTHER INFORMATION In 2019 grants of under £10,000 totalled £97,300.

HOW TO APPLY Contact the correspondent for more information.

CONTACT DETAILS The Trustees, 109 St Anns Road, Prestwich, Manchester M25 9GE *Tel.* 0161 737 5000 *Email* charities@haffhoff.co.uk

■ The Stevenage Community Trust

CC NO 1000762 **ESTABLISHED** 1990

WHERE FUNDING CAN BE GIVEN The borough of Stevenage and the surrounding villages of Aston, Benington, Cromer, Datchworth, Graveley, Knebworth, Little Wymondley, Old Knebworth, Walkern, Watton-at-Stone, Weston and Woolmer Green.

WHO CAN BENEFIT Charitable organisations; community groups; individuals; schools; amateur sports clubs.

WHAT IS FUNDED General charitable purposes.

WHAT IS NOT FUNDED Charities pursuing political objectives; religious evangelism; pursuing trade union objectives save for the welfare functions of trade unions; animal welfare; any other purpose inconsistent with the trust's charitable objectives; retrospective grants (items or services already purchased); the supply and fitting of flooring materials, except in exceptional circumstances.

TYPE OF GRANT Capital costs; project costs.

SAMPLE GRANTS Previous beneficiaries have included: Age Concern; Corey's Mill Lions Club; Great Ashby Youth Club; Headway Hertfordshire; Herts Area Rape Crisis Centre; Link Up Lunch Club; Phoenix Group for Deaf Children; Shaftesbury Court Sheltered Housing; St Nicholas School; Stevenage Arts Guild; Track Autism.

FINANCES *Financial year end* 31/03/2020 *Income* £195,100 *Total grants* £138,800 *Grants to organisations* £138,800 *Assets* £500,800

TRUSTEES Robert Stewart; Mike Phoenix; Ken Follett; Robert Case; Sharon Brown; Jeannette Thomas; Darren Isted; Claire Austin; Alexander Lang.

OTHER INFORMATION The grant total includes grants given to both individuals and organisations; no breakdown was given in the 2019/20 accounts.

HOW TO APPLY Application forms can be downloaded from the trust's website.

CONTACT DETAILS Caroline Haskins, Manager, Stewart House, Primmett Road, Stevenage, Hertfordshire SG1 3EE *Tel.* 01438 525390 *Email* enquiries@stevenagecommunitytrust.org *Website* www.stevenagecommunitytrust.org

■ Stevenson Family's Charitable Trust

CC NO 327148 **ESTABLISHED** 1986

WHERE FUNDING CAN BE GIVEN UK.

WHO CAN BENEFIT Registered charities; universities; hospices; theatres; museums; libraries; galleries.

WHAT IS FUNDED General charitable purposes, in particular: education and training; health and medicine; arts and culture; overseas aid; heritage and conservation; the environment.

WHAT IS NOT FUNDED Individuals.

TYPE OF GRANT One-off and recurrent grants.

RANGE OF GRANTS Typically £250 to £20,000.

SAMPLE GRANTS St Hilda's College, Oxford University (£150,000); Berkshire Community Foundation (£41,000); National Trust for Scotland and Macmillan Cancer Support (£20,000 each); The

British Museum and The National Gallery Trust (£10,000 each); Friends of the National Libraries and Windsor Festival Society Ltd (£5,000 each); National Portrait Gallery and Pimlico Opera (£1,000 each); The Children's Society (£100).

FINANCES *Financial year end* 05/04/2020 *Income* £390,600 *Total grants* £481,000 *Grants to organisations* £481,000 *Assets* £1,640,000

TRUSTEES Lady Catherine Stevenson; Sir Hugh Stevenson; Joseph Stevenson.

OTHER INFORMATION In 2019/20 the trust made grants to 45 organisations totalling £481,000. Grants were distributed across the following areas of work: education and training (£259,250); general charitable purposes (£76,050); culture and arts (£74,339); conservation and heritage (£50,315); health and medicine (£21,000).

HOW TO APPLY Unsolicited applications are not considered.

CONTACT DETAILS Sir Hugh Stevenson, Chair, Old Waterfield, Winkfield Road, Ascot, Berkshire SL5 7LJ *Tel.* 01344 620170 *Email* hugh.stevenson@oldwaterfield.com

■ Stewards Company Ltd

CC NO 234558 **ESTABLISHED** 1965

WHERE FUNDING CAN BE GIVEN UK and overseas.

WHO CAN BENEFIT Organisations involved with training people in religious education; Christian ministries; individuals. About one-third of the charity's funds are given for work overseas.

WHAT IS FUNDED Advancement of the Christian religion for charitable purposes. Substantial funds are also transferred to the Beatrice Laing Trust each year (see separate entry).

RANGE OF GRANTS Typically below £25,000, but up to £500,000.

SAMPLE GRANTS Counties (£472,000); Strategic Resource Group (£395,000); Retired Missionary Aid Fund (£240,000); Beatrice Laing Trust (£126,000); Gospel Literature Outreach (£100,000).

FINANCES *Financial year end* 31/12/2019 *Income* £3,990,000 *Total grants* £6,407,200 *Grants to organisations* £6,360,000 *Assets* £146,630,000

TRUSTEES Ian Childs; Keigh Bintley; Andrew Griffiths; Jennifer Michael; Huw Iley; Mr J. Aitken; Paul Young; Dr Joshua Fitzhugh; Simon Tomlinson; David Bingham; David Roberts; Dr John Burness; Michelangelo Leto; Philip Symons; Andrew Mayo; John Gamble; Alexander McIlhinney; Glyn Davies.

OTHER INFORMATION In 2019 the charity's grants to UK organisations totalled £3.8 million and to overseas causes totalled £2.57 million. Grants were broken down as follows: over £100,000 (£2.24 million); £25,000 to £99,000 (£1.86 million); under £25,000 (£2.26 million). Only organisations that received grants of over £100,000 were listed as beneficiaries in the charity's accounts. A total of 44 grants were made to individuals.

HOW TO APPLY Contact the correspondent for more information.

CONTACT DETAILS Andrew Griffiths, Secretary and Director of Operations, 124 Wells Road, Bath, Somerset BA2 3AH *Tel.* 01225 427236 *Email* stewardsco@stewards.co.uk

■ Sir Halley Stewart Trust

CC NO 208491 **ESTABLISHED** 1924

WHERE FUNDING CAN BE GIVEN UK and overseas.

WHO CAN BENEFIT UK charitable organisations.

WHAT IS FUNDED Prevention of human suffering; education in priority areas: medical, social, religious projects.

WHAT IS NOT FUNDED Individuals; general appeals; purchase, erection or conversion of buildings; capital costs; university overhead charges. Visit the funder's website for further details regarding applications that are not usually considered.

TYPE OF GRANT Project grants; salaries; feasibility studies; research; start-up funding. Funding may be given for up to three years.

RANGE OF GRANTS Main grants: up to £60,000; small grants: up to £5,000.

SAMPLE GRANTS University of Stirling (£119,000); University of Bath (£67,000); Church Action on Poverty (£63,000); Adfam, Imperial College London (£60,000 each); Vision Care for Homeless People (£20,000); University of Chester (£10,000).

FINANCES *Financial year end* 31/03/2020 *Income* £1,300,000 *Total grants* £1,130,000 *Grants to organisations* £1,130,000 *Assets* £32,380,000

TRUSTEES Prof. John Wyatt; Dr Duncan Stewart; Prof. Philip Whitfield; Gordon Wilcock; Theresa Bartlett; Andrew Wauchope; Dr James Bunn; Louisa Elder; Amy Holcroft; Jane Gillard; Celia Atherton; Andrew Graystone; Revd David Wilkinson; Hugh Richardson.

OTHER INFORMATION Grants of less than £10,000 totalled £46,000 during 2019/20.

HOW TO APPLY Applications can be made on the trust's website, but the trust recommends contacting the secretary first to discuss the suitability of a project before applying. Further guidelines are provided on the trust's website, where the dates of the next trustees' meetings and deadlines are also provided.

CONTACT DETAILS Annie Vickers, Administrator, BM Sir Halley Stewart Trust, London WC1N 3XX *Tel.* 020 8144 0375 *Email* email@sirhalleystewart.org.uk *Website* www.sirhalleystewart.org.uk

■ The Stewarts Law Foundation

CC NO 1136714 **ESTABLISHED** 2010

WHERE FUNDING CAN BE GIVEN UK.

WHO CAN BENEFIT Charitable organisations.

WHAT IS FUNDED Alleviating poverty; access to justice; disability; providing educational opportunity.

RANGE OF GRANTS Up to £50,000.

SAMPLE GRANTS Access to Justice Foundation (£300,000); Centrepoint, Spinal Injuries Association and St George's Crypt (£50,000 each); The Royal Marsden and Wheelpower (£30,000 each); Shooting Star Children's Hospice (£25,000); Feast! (£15,000); Free Periods (£5,000); Brainbox (£3,000).

FINANCES *Financial year end* 30/04/2020 *Income* £680,000 *Total grants* £853,300 *Grants to organisations* £853,300 *Assets* £61,100

TRUSTEES Stephen Foster; Keith Milbourne Thomas; David Hughes; Emma Hatley; Ian Gatt; Clive Zietman; Stuart Dench; Julian Chamerlayne; Katheryn Pollock; Daniel Herman; Mohan Bhaskaran; Philip Studd; David Pickstone; James Price; Debbie Chism; John Cahill; Paul Paxton; Sean Upson.

OTHER INFORMATION Only organisations that received grants of over £3,000 were listed as beneficiaries in the foundation's accounts (20 organisations). Grants of under £3,000 totalled £8,300. The foundation has a partnership with the Access to Justice Foundation, to which it awards a large grant each year. In addition, employees of Stewarts Law are given the opportunity to vote for a charity to be supported each year.

HOW TO APPLY The annual report states that 'it is not the policy of the trustees to accept direct applications for funds.'

CONTACT DETAILS John Cahill, Trustee, 5 New Street Square, London EC4A 3BF *Tel.* 020 7822 8000 *Website* https://www.stewartslaw.com/about/social-impact/the-stewarts-foundation

■ The Stobart Newlands Charitable Trust

CC NO 328464 **ESTABLISHED** 1989

WHERE FUNDING CAN BE GIVEN Worldwide.

WHO CAN BENEFIT Registered charities; missionary organisations.

WHAT IS FUNDED Christian and missionary causes.

SAMPLE GRANTS World Vision (£270,000); Tearfund (£31,500); London City Mission (£25,200); Logos Ministries (£18,000); Bible Society (£10,500).

FINANCES *Financial year end* 31/12/2019 *Income* £1,020,000 *Total grants* £988,900 *Grants to organisations* £988,900 *Assets* £93,100

TRUSTEES Ronnie Stobart; Linda Rigg; Peter Stobart; Richard Stobart.

OTHER INFORMATION Grants of less than £10,000 totalled £165,000 during the year.

HOW TO APPLY Unsolicited applications are unlikely to be successful.

CONTACT DETAILS The Trustees, Millcroft, Newlands, Hesket Newmarket, Wigton, Cumbria CA7 8HP *Tel.* 01697 478631

■ Mark Stolkin Foundation

CC NO 1138476 **ESTABLISHED** 2007

WHERE FUNDING CAN BE GIVEN England; Wales; South Africa.

WHO CAN BENEFIT Registered charities; churches; hospitals; schools and colleges; universities.

WHAT IS FUNDED Public education in the performing and visual arts; health and welfare; education; the furtherance of the Christian faith; architectural heritage.

SAMPLE GRANTS The PCC of the Ecclesiastical Parish of Holy Trinity with St Paul's – Onslow Square and St Augustine's – South Kensington (£258,100); The Francis Holland Schools Trust (£45,000); The British and Foreign Bible Society (£21,000); CLIC Sargent Cancer Care for Children (£10,000); Give Us Time (£5,000); Crisis UK (£1,000); The Felix Project (£500).

FINANCES *Financial year end* 05/04/2020 *Income* £209,800 *Total grants* £523,300 *Grants to organisations* £523,300 *Assets* £1,950,000

TRUSTEES Margeaux Stolkin; Mark Stolkin; Renate Lubert.

HOW TO APPLY Contact the correspondent for further information.

CONTACT DETAILS The Trustees, 14–16 Egerton Gardens Mews, London SW3 2EH *Tel.* 020 7589 0899

■ The Stoller Charitable Trust

CC NO 285415 **ESTABLISHED** 1982

WHERE FUNDING CAN BE GIVEN The North West with a preference for Manchester.

WHO CAN BENEFIT Charitable organisations.

WHAT IS FUNDED General charitable purposes including the following: children and young people; healthcare research and cancer relief.

WHAT IS NOT FUNDED Individuals.

SAMPLE GRANTS Previous beneficiaries have included: Bauern helfen Bauern; Cancer Research UK; Central Manchester Children's Hospitals; Imperial War Museum North; Live Music Now; Mines Advisory Group; National Memorial Arboretum; Oldham Liaison of Ex-Services Associations; Onside North West; Salvation Army; Windermere Air Show.

FINANCES *Financial year end* 05/04/2020 *Income* £694,300 *Total grants* £5,030,000 *Grants to organisations* £5,030,000 *Assets* £9,720,000

TRUSTEES Roger Gould; KSL Trustees Ltd; Sir Norman Stoller; Lady Stoller; Andrew Dixon.

HOW TO APPLY Apply in writing to the correspondent. The trustees meet regularly to review applications.

CONTACT DETAILS The Trustees, 24 Low Crompton Road, Royton, Oldham, Lancashire OL2 6YR *Tel.* 07902 857648 *Email* enquiries@stollercharitabletrust.co.uk

■ The Stone Family Foundation

CC NO 1164682 **ESTABLISHED** 2005

WHERE FUNDING CAN BE GIVEN UK and overseas.

WHO CAN BENEFIT Charitable organisations.

WHAT IS FUNDED Mental health and disadvantaged young people in the UK; water and sanitation in the financially developing world.

TYPE OF GRANT Core costs; development funding; project funding.

RANGE OF GRANTS Up to £75,000 for UK-based organisations focused on mental health and disadvantaged young people. Up to £750,000 for international organisations focused on water and sanitation.

SAMPLE GRANTS 1001Fontaines (£540,000); Safe Water Network (£462,700); Tutor Trust (£110,000); National Mind (£100,000); Youth Moves (£64,000); Aguaconsult (£10,400).

FINANCES *Financial year end* 31/12/2019 *Income* £528,400 *Total grants* £6,390,000 *Grants to organisations* £6,390,000 *Assets* £49,030,000

TRUSTEES John Stone; Charles Edwards; David Steinegger.

HOW TO APPLY The foundation does not accept unsolicited applications. The website states: 'We are a small, family foundation with limited resources and as a result we do not accept unsolicited proposals. If you have any questions, feel free to email: SFF@thinkNPC.org. Note, this email inbox is only monitored periodically.'

CONTACT DETAILS The Trustees, 201 Borough High Street, London SE1 1JA *Email* SFF@thinkNPC.org *Website* www.thesff.com

■ The Stoneygate Trust

CC NO 1119976 **ESTABLISHED** 2007

WHERE FUNDING CAN BE GIVEN England and Wales.

WHO CAN BENEFIT Charities; universities; medical research institutions.

WHAT IS FUNDED Medical research, health, social welfare and education.
SAMPLE GRANTS Kidney Research UK (£422,700); The Bridge Homelessness to Hope (£18,300); University of Oxford (£15,000); The Sam White Legacy (£5,000); Lutterworth Foodbank (£1,500).
FINANCES *Financial year end* 05/04/2020 *Income* £3,680,000 *Total grants* £3,290,000 *Grants to organisations* £3,290,000 *Assets* £5,250,000
TRUSTEES Nadine Adderley; Andrew Walden; William Adderley; Timothy Slade.
HOW TO APPLY Contact the correspondent for further information.
CONTACT DETAILS The Trustees, Two Marlborough Court, Watermead Business Park, Syston, Leicestershire LE7 1AD *Tel.* 0116 296 2323 *Email* info@stoneygatetrust.org

■ The Samuel Storey Family Charitable Trust

CC NO 267684 **ESTABLISHED** 1974
WHERE FUNDING CAN BE GIVEN UK.
WHO CAN BENEFIT Charitable organisations.
WHAT IS FUNDED General charitable purposes.
WHAT IS NOT FUNDED Individuals.
RANGE OF GRANTS Typically less than £1,000. Grants ranged from £42 to £12,500 in 2019/20.
SAMPLE GRANTS Normandy Memorial Trust (£12,500); Winchester College (£8,000); Cardiac Risk in the Young (£3,000); York Minster Fund (£2,200); St Laurence Education Trust (£1,000); ABF The Soldiers' Charity (£630); Mental Health Foundation (£200); Royal Botanic Garden Edinburgh (£40).
FINANCES *Financial year end* 05/04/2020 *Income* £247,200 *Total grants* £145,400 *Grants to organisations* £145,400 *Assets* £6,000,000
TRUSTEES Sir Richard Storey; Wren Hoskyns-Abrahall; Kenelm Storey; Elisabeth Critchley.
HOW TO APPLY Contact the correspondent for further information.
CONTACT DETAILS The Trustees, c/o 33 Queen Anne Street, London W1G 9HY *Tel.* 020 7802 2700

■ Peter Stormonth Darling Charitable Trust

CC NO 1049946 **ESTABLISHED** 1995
WHERE FUNDING CAN BE GIVEN UK and overseas.
WHO CAN BENEFIT National and local charitable organisations.
WHAT IS FUNDED General charitable purposes, mainly in the following areas: education; healthcare; heritage; sports facilities.
WHAT IS NOT FUNDED Individuals.
RANGE OF GRANTS Mostly £1,000 to £10,000, with some larger grants.
SAMPLE GRANTS Imperial College Research (£50,000); Royal Hospital for Neuro-Disability (£20,000); Cure Parkinson's Trust (£10,000); Bath Festivals (£6,000); Canine Partners (£5,000); Longlands Care Farm (£3,000); Royal Opera House (£2,000); Holburne Museum Trust (£1,000).
FINANCES *Financial year end* 31/12/2019 *Income* £72,400 *Total grants* £249,700 *Grants to organisations* £249,700 *Assets* £5,140,000
TRUSTEES John Rodwell; Dr Elizabeth Cobb; Oliver Cobb; Christa Taylor; Angus Darling; Frederick Rosier.
OTHER INFORMATION During the year, 15 grants were awarded for healthcare and sporting facilities, 12 grants were awarded for heritage and 8 grants were given for education (35 grants in total).
HOW TO APPLY The trustees have stated that they do not respond to unsolicited applications.
CONTACT DETAILS Satvinder Maan, c/o Soditic Ltd, 22 Long Acre, Covent Garden, London WC2E 9LY *Tel.* 020 7872 7042 *Email* satvinder.maan@soditic.co.uk

■ Peter Storrs Trust

CC NO 313804 **ESTABLISHED** 1970
WHERE FUNDING CAN BE GIVEN UK.
WHO CAN BENEFIT Registered charities.
WHAT IS FUNDED General charitable purposes; the advancement of education.
WHAT IS NOT FUNDED Individuals.
SAMPLE GRANTS A list of beneficiaries was not included in the annual report and accounts.
FINANCES *Financial year end* 05/04/2019 *Income* £155,100 *Total grants* £147,000 *Grants to organisations* £147,000 *Assets* £3,180,000
TRUSTEES Arthur Curtis; Caroline Blake; Harriet Curtis.
OTHER INFORMATION The 2018/19 accounts were the latest available at the time of writing (June 2021). Grants to organisations totalled £147,000.
HOW TO APPLY The trust invites applications for grants from registered charities. Apply in writing to the correspondent. The trustees meet half yearly to consider grant-making.
CONTACT DETAILS The Trustees, Suite 1, Unit 2, Stansted Courtyard, Parsonage Road, Takeley, Essex CM22 6PU *Tel.* 020 7253 3757

■ Strand Parishes Trust

CC NO 1121754 **ESTABLISHED** 2007
WHERE FUNDING CAN BE GIVEN City of Westminster.
WHO CAN BENEFIT Community organisations.
WHAT IS FUNDED Social welfare; education; young people; religious work.
WHAT IS NOT FUNDED For a full list of exclusions, consult the trust's website.
TYPE OF GRANT Project funding; capital costs; core/revenue costs; matched funding.
RANGE OF GRANTS Typically £2,500 to £5,000. Larger grants may be made in exceptional circumstances.
SAMPLE GRANTS All Souls Clubhouse (£8,500); Crisis (£7,500); FareShare (£6,000); Avenues Youth Project, Groundswell, Marie Curie Hospice and Zacchaeus 2000 (£5,000 each); St Matthew's Primary School (£2,700); Revitalise (£1,910).
FINANCES *Financial year end* 31/12/2019 *Income* £242,800 *Total grants* £194,300 *Grants to organisations* £184,200 *Assets* £7,820,000
TRUSTEES Julie Thomas; Margery Roberts; Akua Kyei-Mensah; Charles Spanton; Peter Maplestone; Jane Ker-Reid; Jean Rymer; Mary Foster; John Maycock; Revd Peter Babington.
OTHER INFORMATION In 2019 the trust made grants to 45 organisations totalling £184,200. Grants were awarded for the following purposes: relief in need (£112,800); advancement in life (£63,800); other (£10,000). The trust also makes grants to individuals.
HOW TO APPLY Application forms can be downloaded from the trust's website. A copy of your

organisation's latest annual report and accounts and budget for the current year are requested as supporting information. Applications will be considered at the following trust board meeting (the trust's website states that the board meets in March, July and November). Following submission, representatives may meet with applicants for more in-depth discussion of the proposal.

CONTACT DETAILS Roy Sully, Clerk to the Trustees, 169 Strand, London WC2R 2LS *Tel.* 020 7848 4275 *Email* sptwestminster@aol.com *Website* https://www.strandparishestrust.org.uk/home.html

■ The Strangward Trust

CC NO 1036494 **ESTABLISHED** 1993

WHERE FUNDING CAN BE GIVEN East Anglia with a preference for Bedfordshire, Cambridgeshire and Northamptonshire.

WHO CAN BENEFIT Charitable organisations.

WHAT IS FUNDED The care and treatment of people with physical or mental disabilities.

RANGE OF GRANTS Mostly under £5,000.

SAMPLE GRANTS Addenbrooke's Charitable Trust (£7,000); Assist Trust (£5,000); Autism Bedfordshire (£3,000); Deafblind UK (£2,000); Limbless Association (£1,000); Spring Common Academy (£150).

FINANCES *Financial year end* 05/04/2020 *Income* £227,800 *Total grants* £129,900 *Grants to organisations* £129,900 *Assets* £10,570,000

TRUSTEES Anne Allured; Ross Jones; Paul Goakes; Clare O'Callaghan.

HOW TO APPLY Application forms are available from the correspondent. A copy of your latest accounts (if relevant) and any other supporting documentation (e.g. copy estimates, medical reports, etc.) should also be included. The trustees meet twice a year (March and September) to decide upon donations. Applications should be submitted by the end of February and August. The trustees will consider every application submitted to them that meets the criteria of the trust. It is important that applications on behalf of national charities identify a specific need for funding in the geographic area referred to above.

CONTACT DETAILS The Trustees, Glebe House, Catworth, Huntingdon, Cambridgeshire PE28 0PA *Tel.* 01832 710230 *Email* strangwardtrust@aol.com

■ Stratford-upon-Avon Town Trust

CC NO 1088521 **ESTABLISHED** 2001

WHERE FUNDING CAN BE GIVEN Stratford-upon-Avon.

WHO CAN BENEFIT Registered charities; unregistered charities; CICs; social enterprises; schools; amateur sports clubs; hospitals; hospices; religious bodies/institutions; individuals.

WHAT IS FUNDED Reducing isolation; health and well-being; activities for young people; support during crisis; community development.

TYPE OF GRANT Capital costs; core/revenue costs; project funding.

RANGE OF GRANTS Up to £50,000. Through the Fast Track scheme, grants of up to £1,000 are made, with a decision within ten working days.

SAMPLE GRANTS King Edward VI School (£632,200, non-discretionary); Citizens Advice South Warwickshire (£182,800); ReBuild project (£65,300); The Shakespeare Hospice at Home (£50,000); Heart of England Mencap and Stratford-upon-Avon Foodbank (£30,000 each); Welcombe Hills School (£25,000); Refuge (£20,000); Stratford in Bloom (£15,000); Stratford Sharks ASC Swimming Club (£5,200); Warwickshire Police Safer Neighbourhood (£1,500).

FINANCES *Financial year end* 31/12/2019 *Income* £3,600,000 *Total grants* £1,960,100 *Grants to organisations* £1,950,000 *Assets* £60,610,000

TRUSTEES Mathew Macdonald; Tony Jackson; Elizabeth Coles; Quentin Wilson; David Taylor; Gillian Cleeve; Stephen Parker; Timothy Bailey; Clive Snowdon; Josephine Stevens; Prof. Lindsay MacDonald.

OTHER INFORMATION Discretionary grants, which totalled £1.1 million in 2019, were distributed as follows: social welfare (£565,000); recreation and leisure (£211,900); education (£209,000); other charitable purposes (£33,000); civic pride (£18,600); citizenship and community (£17,000); advancement of the Christian religion (£520).

HOW TO APPLY Application forms and guidance for each grant programme are available on the trust's website. Questions regarding applications can be directed to the trust's Grants Manager.

CONTACT DETAILS James McHugh, Grants Manager, 14 Rother Street, Stratford-upon-Avon, Warwickshire CV32 6LU *Tel.* 01789 207111 *Email* james.mchugh@stratfordtowntrust.co.uk *Website* www.stratfordtowntrust.co.uk

■ Strathnairn Community Benefit Fund Ltd

OSCR NO SC036807 **ESTABLISHED** 2005

WHERE FUNDING CAN BE GIVEN Strathnairn.

WHO CAN BENEFIT Community groups; individuals.

WHAT IS FUNDED General charitable purposes, including the following: urban or rural regeneration; social welfare; education; community development.

WHAT IS NOT FUNDED Charitable activity that is not solely to benefit the residents of Strathnairn; religious or political charitable organisations.

TYPE OF GRANT Project funding; capital costs; seed funding/start-up funding; core costs.

RANGE OF GRANTS Up to £24,000.

SAMPLE GRANTS Farr Primary and Nursery Parent Council (£24,000); Strathnairn Music Initiative (£17,000); Strathnairn News (£12,300); Care in Strathnairn (£10,000); Strathnairn Hall (£3,750); Farr Junior Football and Athletics Club (£2,350); SCATA (£500); Farr Baby and Toddler Group (£200); Strathnairn.org (£150).

FINANCES *Financial year end* 31/08/2020 *Income* £267,600 *Total grants* £809,600 *Grants to organisations* £711,600 *Assets* £898,900

TRUSTEES Ian Hunt; Darren Read; Michael Read; Alannah Haldane; Ewen Hardie; Roy McLennan; Paul MacBeth; Mark Bessell; Jayne Brinkworth.

OTHER INFORMATION In 2019/20 the trust awarded grants totalling £711,600 to organisations (through the general grants programme) and £97,100 to individuals (the vast majority of which was through the energy grants programme).

HOW TO APPLY Application forms can be downloaded from the charity's website and should be submitted via email or by post. See the charity's website for details of application deadlines.

CONTACT DETAILS Company Secretary, Farr Community Hall, Inverarnie Park, Inverarnie,

Inverness, Highlands IV2 6AX *Email* cosec@strathnairncbf.com *Website* www.strathnairncbf.com

■ The WO Street Charitable Foundation

CC NO 267127 **ESTABLISHED** 1973

WHERE FUNDING CAN BE GIVEN UK, with a preference for Lancashire and Jersey.

WHO CAN BENEFIT For the WO Street Transformation Funds: constituted groups (including community groups, voluntary organisations, charities, CICs and socal enterprises) with an annual income under £250,000.

WHAT IS FUNDED Education; relief of poverty; social and family welfare; illness and disability (particularly blindness); older people; children and young people; projects that can demonstrate engagement of the wider community.

WHAT IS NOT FUNDED Individuals. See the website for exclusion criteria of the WO Street Transformation Funds.

TYPE OF GRANT Development funding; project funding

RANGE OF GRANTS Mostly up to £5,000.

SAMPLE GRANTS WO Street Jersey Charitable Trust – Jersey (£40,000); Emmott Foundation (£30,000); Parity for Disability and Rainbow Trust Children's Charity (£5,000 each); 4Sight Vision Support (£4,000); The Silver Line Helpline (£3,500); Samaritans of Blackburn (£3,000); Butterflies Children's Charity (£2,000); Epilepsy Action (£1,000).

FINANCES *Financial year end* 31/12/2019 *Income* £567,200 *Total grants* £439,500 *Grants to organisations* £439,500 *Assets* £20,570,000

TRUSTEES Chris Priestley; Zedra Trust Company (UK) Ltd.

OTHER INFORMATION Grants were made to 114 organisations during the year, including a grant of £40,000 to the WO Street Jersey Charitable Trust, to support the foundation's objectives in Jersey. Educational bursaries totalled £61,200. In 2011 the foundation established three WO Street Transformation Funds, which are administered by Forever Manchester (for Greater Manchester grants), the Community Foundation for Lancashire (for Lancashire grants) and the Community Foundation for Merseyside (for Merseyside grants). See the relevant website for the grant amounts available.

HOW TO APPLY Application forms are available from the correspondent. The foundation's 2019 accounts state: 'Applications are invited to Zedra Trust Company (UK) Ltd and an application form will be furnished for completion and subsequent consideration by the Trustees.' Applications to the WO Street Transformation Fund can be made via the Community Foundation for Lancashire website or the Community Foundation for Merseyside website.

CONTACT DETAILS The Trustees, c/o Zedra UK Trusts, Booths Hall, Booths Park 3, Chelford Road, Knutsford WA16 8GS *Tel.* 01565 748787 *Email* charities@zedra.com *Website* https://lancsfoundation.org.uk/funds/the-wo-street-transformation-fund or https://cfmerseyside.org.uk/funds/wo-street-transformation-fund

■ The Street Foundation

CC NO 1045229 **ESTABLISHED** 1995

WHERE FUNDING CAN BE GIVEN Worldwide.

WHO CAN BENEFIT Registered charities; not-for-profit organisations.

WHAT IS FUNDED Children and young people with disabilities; social welfare; education; community development; human rights; advancement of religion.

SAMPLE GRANTS Oxford University Museum of Natural History (£57,800); The Centre for Social Justice (£40,000); The Global Warming Policy Foundation (£12,000); The Natural History Museum (£6,800).

FINANCES *Financial year end* 31/03/2020 *Income* £230,000 *Total grants* £173,900 *Grants to organisations* £173,900 *Assets* £61,900

TRUSTEES Lucinda Sharp-Smith; Richard Smith; Sarah Sharp-Smith; Susan Smith.

OTHER INFORMATION Grants were broken down as follows: education (£101,500); human rights (£40,000); community (£14,700); disability (£12,500); poverty (£5,000).

HOW TO APPLY Contact the correspondent for further information.

CONTACT DETAILS The Trustees, Kingsland House, Kingsland, Leominster, Herefordshire HR6 9SG *Tel.* 01568 708744

■ StreetSmart – Action for the Homeless

CC NO 1071657 **ESTABLISHED** 1998

WHERE FUNDING CAN BE GIVEN UK. Grants are made to charities in the cities in which the StreetSmart campaign runs. A list is available on the charity's website.

WHO CAN BENEFIT Registered UK charities.

WHAT IS FUNDED Homelessness, employability, mental health and well-being. Projects that are aimed at getting people off the streets and 'onto their feet again'.

WHAT IS NOT FUNDED The charity will not fund soup kitchens unless they form part of a drop-in centre linked into other services.

TYPE OF GRANT Project funding; capital costs.

SAMPLE GRANTS The Felix Project (£220,000); Centrepoint (£50,000); House of St Barnabas (£25,000); The Mayor's Homelessness Fund (£27,000); Running Charity, New Horizon and Cardinal Hume (£20,000 each); Ace of Clubs (£15,000); Connection at St Martin-in-the-Fields (£10,000); Aquilia Way (£7,000); Caravan (£6,000); Framework Housing Association (£3,000); Only A Pavement Away (£2,000); Llamau (£500).

FINANCES *Financial year end* 31/05/2019 *Income* £943,600 *Total grants* £738,500 *Grants to organisations* £738,500 *Assets* £313,100

TRUSTEES William Sieghart; Rocio Boycott; Mary Sturridge; Nick Emley.

OTHER INFORMATION The 2018/19 accounts were the latest available at the time of writing (June 2021). Grants were awarded to 50 organisations during the year.

HOW TO APPLY Applicants must submit their applications in writing during December.

CONTACT DETAILS Glenn Pougnet, Director, 1 St John's Lane, London EC1M 4BL *Tel.* 020 7292 5615 *Email* glenn.pougnet@streetsmart.org.uk *Website* www.streetsmart.org.uk

■ The Joseph Strong Frazer Trust

CC NO 235311 **ESTABLISHED** 1940

WHERE FUNDING CAN BE GIVEN England and Wales.

WHO CAN BENEFIT Charitable organisations; schools; hospitals.

WHAT IS FUNDED General charitable purposes with a preference for the following: children and young people; older people; people with disabilities; medical research; maritime charities; the armed forces; education; religion; sport and recreation; social welfare; animals and wildlife; religion.

RANGE OF GRANTS Mostly up to £2,500.

SAMPLE GRANTS WaterAid (£3,000); Beating Bowel Cancer (£2,500); Action on Hearing Loss, Addaction, Newcastle Foodbank and Sustrans (£2,000 each).

FINANCES *Financial year end* 30/09/2019
Income £617,200 *Total grants* £553,400
Grants to organisations £553,400
Assets £15,610,000

TRUSTEES Sir Anthony Smith; William Waites; Mr R. M. Read; David Cook; William Smith; Ugo Fagandini.

OTHER INFORMATION Grants were made to 360 organisations during the year. The 2018/19 accounts were the latest available at the time of writing (June 2021).

HOW TO APPLY Contact the correspondent for further information.

CONTACT DETAILS The Trustees, c/o Joseph Miller, Floor A, Milburn House, Dean Street, Newcastle upon Tyne NE1 1LE *Tel.* 0191 232 8065 *Email* jsf@joseph-miller.co.uk

■ The Sudborough Foundation

CC NO 272323 **ESTABLISHED** 1976

WHERE FUNDING CAN BE GIVEN Northamptonshire.

WHO CAN BENEFIT Registered charities and educational establishments.

WHAT IS FUNDED Education and training; general charitable purposes.

WHAT IS NOT FUNDED Individuals; non-registered charities; political or pressure groups; individual fundraising, including expeditions or overseas travel; religious groups; statutory authorities; national charities (with the exception of local branches for local projects).

RANGE OF GRANTS Up to £20,000.

SAMPLE GRANTS British Psychotherapy Foundation (£10,200); Home-Start Northampton (£10,000); Northamptonshire Rape Crisis (£5,000); Northampton District Scout Council and The Museum of Leathercraft (£1,000 each); Action Medical Research (£500); Bottoms Up (£200).

FINANCES *Financial year end* 05/04/2020
Income £40,100 *Total grants* £122,000
Grants to organisations £122,000
Assets £1,740,000

TRUSTEES Rachel Engel; Susan Leathem; Hugh Lowther; Marilyn Woolfson; Richard Engel; Simon Powis; Tim Parker; Lucy Watson; Elisabeth Engel.

OTHER INFORMATION Grants were awarded to 20 organisations during the year.

HOW TO APPLY An application form can be downloaded from the foundation's website and should be submitted by post or email.

CONTACT DETAILS Richard Engel, Trustee, 8 Hazelwood Road, Northampton, Northamptonshire NN1 1LP *Email* applications@sudborough.org *Website* https://sites.google.com/site/sudborough2/home

■ Suffolk Community Foundation

CC NO 1109453 **ESTABLISHED** 2005

WHERE FUNDING CAN BE GIVEN Suffolk.

WHO CAN BENEFIT Small and medium-sized registered charities; voluntary and community groups. Some funds are open to social enterprises and CICs.

WHAT IS FUNDED General charitable purposes, including the following: health and well-being; people who are disadvantaged; community development; older people; children and young people.

WHAT IS NOT FUNDED See the 'Guidelines and Policies' page of the website for a list of general exclusions. Each funding programme has further specific exclusions.

TYPE OF GRANT Core costs; project costs; one-off; capital costs.

RANGE OF GRANTS £100 to £225,000.

SAMPLE GRANTS Green Light Trust (£225,000); The Befriending Scheme (£180,000); BSC Multicultural Services (£69,900); Ipswich and District Citizens Advice (£35,000); Musicians' Union (£20,000); Woodbridge Town Council (£5,000); East Anglia's Children's Hospice (£2,000); Lighthouse Women's Aid (£1,000); Capel Parish Nurses (£500).

FINANCES *Financial year end* 30/06/2020
Income £6,210,000 *Total grants* £4,690,000
Grants to organisations £4,690,000
Assets £18,250,000

TRUSTEES Jordan Holder; Selina Hopkins; William Kendall; Peter Newnham; Susan Gull; Gulshanbir Kayembe; George Vestey; Neil Walmsley; Louisa Shelton; Jonathan Agar; Terence Ward.

OTHER INFORMATION This is one of the 46 UK community foundations, which distribute funding for a wide range of purposes. As with all community foundations, there are a number of donor-advised funds managed on behalf of individuals, families and charitable trusts. Grant schemes tend to change frequently; consult the foundation's website for details of current programmes and up-to-date deadlines. In 2019/20, the foundation awarded 855 grants to organisations. A full list of beneficiaries can be found on the website.

HOW TO APPLY The foundation's website has details of the grant schemes currently being administered and how to apply.

CONTACT DETAILS Grants Team, The Old Barn, Peninsula Business Centre, Wherstead, Ipswich, Suffolk IP9 2BB *Tel.* 01473 602602 *Email* info@suffolkcf.org.uk *Website* suffolkcf.org.uk

■ The Suffolk Historic Churches Trust

CC NO 267047 **ESTABLISHED** 1973

WHERE FUNDING CAN BE GIVEN Suffolk.

WHO CAN BENEFIT Churches and chapels which are in regular use as a place of worship.

WHAT IS FUNDED The preservation, repair, maintenance, restoration and improvement of churches.

WHAT IS NOT FUNDED Furnishings and fittings, brasses and bells, monuments or redecoration, unless needed as part of an eligible project.

TYPE OF GRANT Grants towards capital projects.

RANGE OF GRANTS £300 to £10,000.

SAMPLE GRANTS Previous beneficiaries have included: St John the Baptist – Needham Market (£10,000); St Mary – Bacton (£8,000); St Michael's – Beccles (£3,000); Felixstowe

Methodist Church (£2,000); St Mary – Raydon (£500).

FINANCES *Financial year end* 05/04/2019
Income £185,500 *Total grants* £79,600
Grants to organisations £79,600
Assets £816,700

TRUSTEES Patrick Grieve; Martin Favell; Hon. Charles Boscawen; Christopher Spicer; Simon Tennent; Celia Stephens; Nicholas Pearson; Edward Bland; Tim Allen; Geoffrey Probert; David King; John Devaux; David Gould; Revd Anthony Redman; Michael Kiely.

OTHER INFORMATION The 2018/19 accounts were the latest available at the time of writing (May 2021).

HOW TO APPLY Application forms can be downloaded from the trust's website. Grants committee meetings are held four times a year and deadlines for applications are posted on the trust's website.

CONTACT DETAILS Assistant Secretary, Brinkleys, Hall Street, Long Melford, Suffolk CO10 9JR
Tel. 01787 883884 *Email* shct@btconnect.com
Website www.shct.org.uk

The Summerfield Charitable Trust

CC NO 802493 **ESTABLISHED** 1989

WHERE FUNDING CAN BE GIVEN Gloucestershire.

WHO CAN BENEFIT Registered charities; community groups; not-for-profit limited companies; voluntary groups; CICs.

WHAT IS FUNDED The arts; museums and built heritage; the environment; community projects; education; sport and recreation; social welfare; climate change.

WHAT IS NOT FUNDED Medical research; private education; animal welfare; trips abroad; retrospective projects; individuals; churches; charities which have already received a grant in the last two years.

TYPE OF GRANT Capital costs; seed funding; start-up funding; unrestricted funding.

RANGE OF GRANTS £500 to £30,000.

SAMPLE GRANTS Previous beneficiaries have included: Scrubditch Care Farm (£20,000); Art Couture Festival Ltd (£10,000); Cirencester Foodbank (£8,500); Court Barn Museum, Kempsford Village Hall and Make Believe CIC (£5,000 each); Contact the Elderly (£3,000); Future Trees Trust (£2,000); Charlton Kings Cricket Club (£1,000); Birdlip School PTA (£550).

FINANCES *Financial year end* 31/12/2020
Income £416,700 *Total grants* £305,900
Grants to organisations £305,900
Assets £11,040,000

TRUSTEES David Owen; Roger Mortlock; Katrina Beach; Antonia Shield; Vanessa Arbuthnott.

OTHER INFORMATION Grants were made to 37 organisations during the year and distributed as follows: disadvantaged and vulnerable sectors (£203,800); arts, museums and built heritage (£48,700); community work (£20,400); the environment and natural heritage (£19,000); education, sport and recreation (£14,000).

HOW TO APPLY Applications should be made using the trust's online application form.

CONTACT DETAILS The Trustees, PO Box 287, Cirencester, Gloucestershire GL7 9FB
Tel. 01285 721211 *Email* admin@summerfield.org.uk *Website* www.summerfield.org.uk

Sumner Wilson Charitable Trust

CC NO 1018852 **ESTABLISHED** 1992

WHERE FUNDING CAN BE GIVEN UK.

WHO CAN BENEFIT Registered charities.

WHAT IS FUNDED Charitable organisations.

TYPE OF GRANT Capital costs; general funding.

RANGE OF GRANTS £1,000 to £51,000.

SAMPLE GRANTS Hope and Homes for Children (£51,000); Macmillan Cancer Support (£50,000); The Magic Future Foundation (£30,000); The Nelson Trust (£15,000); St James's Place Charitable Foundation (£13,600); Allegra's Ambition and The Charlie Waller Foundation (£10,000 each); The Tongole Foundation and Supporting Wounded Veterans (£5,000 each); Youth Action Wiltshire (£3,000); Cyclone Iolai Relief (£1,000).

FINANCES *Financial year end* 05/04/2020
Income £208,700 *Total grants* £349,800
Grants to organisations £349,800
Assets £5,110,000

TRUSTEES Amanda Sumner Christie; Anne-Marie Challen; Davina Longsdon.

OTHER INFORMATION Grants were awarded to 26 organisations during the year.

HOW TO APPLY The trust will not be making any grants or donations to unsolicited applications for the foreseeable future.

CONTACT DETAILS The Trustees, Mercer and Hole, 72 London Road, St Albans AL1 1NS
Tel. 01727 869141
Email sumnerwilsoncharity@gmail.com
Website https://www.sumnerwilson.uk

The Bernard Sunley Foundation

CC NO 1109099 **ESTABLISHED** 1960

WHERE FUNDING CAN BE GIVEN England and Wales.

WHO CAN BENEFIT Registered charities; exempt charities; schools; hospices; religious bodies/institutions.

WHAT IS FUNDED The foundation's funding themes are community, education, health and social welfare.

WHAT IS NOT FUNDED A full list of exclusions is available on the foundation's website. It includes, but is not limited to: individuals; charities registered outside England or Wales or with an income over £10 million; core costs; NHS hospitals or mainstream schools, colleges or universities; project costs of under £5,000 or over £5 million.

TYPE OF GRANT Capital costs.

RANGE OF GRANTS Typically up to £10,000.

SAMPLE GRANTS Crusader Community Boating (£100,000); Royal Horticultural Society (£50,000); Louie's Helping Hands (£25,000); Alder Hey Children's Charity and Exeter Gateway Centre (£10,000 each); Durham Wildlife Trust and Trussell Trust (£5,000 each); Manchester City Galleries Trust (£3,000); St Wilfrid's Hospice (£1,000); Marie Curie (£500).

FINANCES *Financial year end* 31/03/2020
Income £2,980,000 *Total grants* £3,420,000
Grants to organisations £3,420,000
Assets £118,180,000

TRUSTEES Dr Brian Martin; Bella Sunley; Anabel Knight; William Tice; Inigo Paternina; Lucy Evans.

OTHER INFORMATION During 2019/20 the trust made 378 grants totalling £3.42 million, distributed as follows: community (£1.98 million); social welfare (£693,000); education (£621,000); health (£252,000). 22% of grants were small grants (under £5,000).

HOW TO APPLY The trust invites applicants to discuss their project before applying. Applicants must undertake an online eligibility check before completing the online application form. There are no deadlines and the application process may take up to six months.

CONTACT DETAILS Sue Davies, Director, 20 Berkeley Square, London W1J 6LH *Tel.* 020 3036 0090 *Email* office@bernardsunley.org *Website* www.bernardsunley.org

■ The Sunrise Foundation CIO

CC NO 1172756 **ESTABLISHED** 2017

WHERE FUNDING CAN BE GIVEN UK, with a preference for Bristol; Peru.

WHO CAN BENEFIT Registered and unregistered charities; co-operatives; friendly societies; industrial and provident societies; not-for-profit companies; not-for-profit unincorporated associations; educational establishments; health bodies (including NHS hospital trusts, clinical commissioning groups and foundation hospitals).

WHAT IS FUNDED People who are disadvantaged.

SAMPLE GRANTS Previous beneficiaries have included: Asociacion Yanapasun Peru (£50,000); Caring in Bristol and Changes Bristol (£25,000 each); Newlife – Cannock (£23,500); Kids – Bristol (£15,400).

FINANCES *Financial year end* 30/06/2020
Income £253,400 *Total grants* £282,600
Grants to organisations £282,600
Assets £1,980,000

TRUSTEES Bryan Glastonbury; Maggie Glastonbury; Paul Salmons; Sophie Brooke; Richard Barnes.

OTHER INFORMATION Grants of under £5,000 totalled £18,400.

HOW TO APPLY Expressions of interest can be submitted by email or post. Full details of the application process can be found on the charity's website.

CONTACT DETAILS The Trustees, 8 Grange Road, Clifton, Bristol BS8 4EA *Tel.* 07950 809012 *Email* info@sunrisefoundation.org.uk *Website* sunrisefoundation.org.uk

■ The Support Foundation

CC NO 1167827 **ESTABLISHED** 2016

WHERE FUNDING CAN BE GIVEN UK and India.

WHO CAN BENEFIT Charitable organisations.

WHAT IS FUNDED General charitable purposes; care; education; children and young people; older people.

SAMPLE GRANTS A list of beneficiaries was not included in the annual report and accounts.

FINANCES *Financial year end* 31/03/2020
Income £97,500 *Total grants* £67,000
Grants to organisations £67,000
Assets £40,600

TRUSTEES Andrew Lane; John Alflatt; Mahesh Patel.

HOW TO APPLY Contact the correspondent for further information.

CONTACT DETAILS Mahesh Patel, Chair, CSL Partnership, 238 Station Road, Addlestone KT15 2PS *Tel.* 01932 848163

■ Surgo Foundation UK Ltd

CC NO 1157510 **ESTABLISHED** 2014

WHERE FUNDING CAN BE GIVEN UK; India; America.

WHO CAN BENEFIT Charitable organisations; universities.

WHAT IS FUNDED General charitable purposes; healthcare and health research, with a focus on financially developing countries.

TYPE OF GRANT Project funding.

RANGE OF GRANTS Up to around £1 million.

SAMPLE GRANTS Harvard University (£1.14 million); Clinton Health Access Initiative (£395,800).

FINANCES *Financial year end* 31/12/2019
Income £114,300 *Total grants* £1,540,000
Grants to organisations £1,540,000
Assets £41,060,000

TRUSTEES Mala Gaonkar; Emmanuel Roman; Oliver Haarman; Malcolm Gladwell.

OTHER INFORMATION The financial information has been converted from USD using the exchange rate applicable at the time of writing (June 2021).

HOW TO APPLY Contact the correspondent for further information.

CONTACT DETAILS The Trustees, c/o Withers LLP, Third Floor, 20 Old Bailey, London EC4M 7AN *Tel.* 020 7597 6000

■ Community Foundation for Surrey

CC NO 1111600 **ESTABLISHED** 2005

WHERE FUNDING CAN BE GIVEN Surrey.

WHO CAN BENEFIT Registered charities; unregistered charities; hospices; social enterprises; schools; CICs; PTAs.

WHAT IS FUNDED General charitable purposes including: health and well-being; arts, culture and heritage; education and employability; community cohesion; isolation and disadvantage; the environment and public spaces.

WHAT IS NOT FUNDED For-profit businesses; national programmes without a specific benefit to Surrey; faith groups where the project is exclusively for the benefit of members or for proselytising; projects that are based outside Surrey; projects which have already occurred or items purchased prior to or during a grant application; unspecified expenditure and general appeals; core costs for CICs; fundraising events/activities; funding to enable your group to make grants to others; requests to build reserves; funding for statutory obligations; political activities. Organisations which hold a high level of free reserves are unlikely to be funded.

TYPE OF GRANT Core/revenue costs; capital costs; project funding; seed funding/start-up funding.

RANGE OF GRANTS The average grant size was £5,700.

SAMPLE GRANTS Guilford Action for Community Care (£41,500); Patchworking Garden Project (£20,000); Age Concern Mole Valley (£10,000); Matrix Trust (£7,000); Food Matters Foundation (£5,000); Camberly Cricket Club (£1,000); Farnham Malting Association Ltd (£250).

FINANCES *Financial year end* 31/03/2020
Income £2,860,000 *Total grants* £2,078,800
Grants to organisations £2,030,000
Assets £13,090,000

TRUSTEES Vibhaker Baxi; Elaine Tisdall; Emma Walker; Michael Hayman; Julie Llewelyn; Bridget Bidddell; William Dawson; Peter Cluff; Nigel Gillott; Paul Downes; William Glover; Holly Murnieks.

OTHER INFORMATION This is one of the 46 UK community foundations, which distribute funding for a wide range of purposes. As with all community foundations, there are a number of donor-advised funds managed on behalf of individuals, families and charitable trusts. Grant schemes tend to change frequently; consult the foundation's website for details of current programmes and up-to-date deadlines. Grants to organisations were broken down as follows: health and well-being (£844,100); disadvantage and exclusion (£454,000); stronger communities (£430,800); education and skills (£226,900); arts, culture and heritage (£59,000); the environment (£18,000). Grants to 118 individuals totalled £48,800.

HOW TO APPLY Potential applicants are advised to visit the community foundation's website or contact its grants team to find the most suitable funding stream.

CONTACT DETAILS Grants Team, Millmead House, Millmead, Guilford, Surrey GU2 4BB *Tel.* 01483 478092 *Email* info@cfsurrey.org.uk *Website* www.cfsurrey.org.uk

The Sussex Community Foundation

CC NO 1113226 **ESTABLISHED** 2006

WHERE FUNDING CAN BE GIVEN East Sussex, West Sussex and Brighton and Hove.

WHO CAN BENEFIT Registered charities; CICs; social enterprises; PTAs; amateur sports clubs; hospices; individuals. There is a preference for supporting grassroots charities and community groups.

WHAT IS FUNDED General charitable purposes.

WHAT IS NOT FUNDED See the foundation's website for a detailed list of exclusions.

TYPE OF GRANT Capital costs; core costs; revenue costs; seed funding; start-up funding; project funding; unrestricted funding.

RANGE OF GRANTS Mostly up to £5,000; occasionally larger grants.

SAMPLE GRANTS Age UK West Sussex (£75,900); South East Dance (£25,000); Eastbourne Food Bank (£20,000); Feedback and Low Carbon Trust (£10,000 each).

FINANCES *Financial year end* 31/03/2020 *Income* £3,970,000 *Total grants* £2,430,000 *Grants to organisations* £2,430,000 *Assets* £23,460,000

TRUSTEES Pamela Stiles; Rodney Buse; Martin Roberts; Patrick Stevens; Charles Drayson; Consuelo Brooke; Jonica Fox; Margaret Burgess; Keith Hollis; Julia Carrette; Nicola Glover; Mark Spofforth.

OTHER INFORMATION This is one of the 46 UK community foundations, which distribute funding for a wide range of purposes. As with all community foundations, there are a number of donor-advised funds managed on behalf of individuals, families and charitable trusts. Grant schemes tend to change frequently – consult the foundation's website for details of current programmes and up-to-date deadlines.

HOW TO APPLY Applications should be made using the online application process, after checking the guidelines, eligibility criteria and deadlines for the relevant fund. Alternatively, email or call the office for a copy of the application form.

CONTACT DETAILS Grants Team, 15 Western Road, Lewes, East Sussex BN7 1RL *Tel.* 01273 409440 *Email* grants@sussexgiving.org.uk *Website* www.sussexgiving.org.uk

The Sutasoma Trust

CC NO 803301 **ESTABLISHED** 1990

WHERE FUNDING CAN BE GIVEN UK and overseas.

WHO CAN BENEFIT Charitable organisations; individuals.

WHAT IS FUNDED Education; humanitarian work; the arts.

TYPE OF GRANT Project funding.

SAMPLE GRANTS The New Art Studio (£15,000); Helen Bamber Foundation (£13,500); Exceed Worldwide (£2,700); Amnesty International (£1,800); Haverford College – USA (£1,000).

FINANCES *Financial year end* 30/09/2019 *Income* £100,700 *Total grants* £108,400 *Grants to organisations* £108,400 *Assets* £3,160,000

TRUSTEES Sally Wolfe; Sundar Sarukkai; Prof. Bruce Kepferer; Prof. Piers Vitebsky; Mandy Fish; Angela Hobart.

OTHER INFORMATION The 2018/19 accounts were the latest available at the time of writing (June 2021).

HOW TO APPLY Apply in writing to the correspondent.

CONTACT DETAILS Trust Administrator, PO Box 157, Haverhill, Suffolk CB9 1AH *Email* sutasoma.trust@btinternet.com *Website* www.sutasoma.org

Sabina Sutherland Charitable Trust

CC NO 1163074 **ESTABLISHED** 2015

WHERE FUNDING CAN BE GIVEN UK.

WHO CAN BENEFIT Charitable organisations.

WHAT IS FUNDED Religion; arts, culture, heritage and science; the environment and conservation; the prevention or relief of poverty; general charitable purposes.

RANGE OF GRANTS Mostly up to £10,000.

SAMPLE GRANTS Chalfleet Church (£50,000); Berkshire Record Office (£9,900); The Art Fund (£5,000); Bristol Children's Help Society (£2,000); Felix Road Adventure Playground (£1,500); St Margaret – Northam (£1,000); National Churches Trust (£300).

FINANCES *Financial year end* 30/06/2019 *Income* £38,300 *Total grants* £230,500 *Grants to organisations* £230,500 *Assets* £1,090,000

TRUSTEES Dr Peter Durrant; Sophie Shepherd; Julia Elton.

OTHER INFORMATION During the year, grants were awarded to 18 organisations for the following purposes: arts, culture, heritage or science (£108,500); religion (£93,100); poverty (£14,900); the environment (£9,500); education (£4,500). The 2018/19 accounts were the latest available at the time of writing (February 2021).

HOW TO APPLY Contact the correspondent for further information.

CONTACT DETAILS The Trustees, 84 Beech Lane, Earley, Reading, Berkshire RG6 5QE *Tel.* 07940 266478

Sutton Coldfield Charitable Trust

CC NO 218627 **ESTABLISHED** 1528

WHERE FUNDING CAN BE GIVEN The former borough of Sutton Coldfield, comprising four electoral wards: New Hall, Four Oaks, Trinity and almost all of Vesey ward.

WHO CAN BENEFIT Organisations benefitting local residents; individuals.

WHAT IS FUNDED General charitable purposes including: social welfare; education; the arts, culture, heritage and science; religion; health; community development; amateur sport; environmental protection.
WHAT IS NOT FUNDED No awards are given to individuals or organisations outside the area of benefit, unless the organisations are providing essential services in the area.
TYPE OF GRANT Project funding.
SAMPLE GRANTS St Chad's Church (£45,000); Our Place Support CIC (£38,000); FoodCycle (£13,500); MeDAL (£2,800).
FINANCES *Financial year end* 30/09/2020 *Income* £1,710,000 *Total grants* £1,260,000 *Grants to organisations* £1,260,000 *Assets* £64,320,000
TRUSTEES Cllr Diane Donaldson; Malcolm Cornish; Inge Kettner; Jayne Luckett; Andrew Morris; Andrew Burley; Keith Dudley; Cllr Jane Mosson; Ranjan Hoath; Dr Francis Murray; Cllr Francis Murray; Cllr Simon Ward; Revd William Routh; Anthony Andrews; Dr Stephen Martin.
OTHER INFORMATION Grants were broken down as follows: relief in need (£524,800); citizenship and community development (£181,400); amateur sport (£174,300); education (£146,000); health (£101,100); advancement of religion (£45,000); arts, science, culture and heritage (£27,500); environmental protection and improvement (£9,600).
HOW TO APPLY Contact the Grants Manager to make an application or to discuss further details.
CONTACT DETAILS David Cole, Grants Manager, Lingard House, Fox Hollies Road, Sutton Coldfield, West Midlands B76 2RJ *Tel.* 0121 794 0970 *Email* davidcole@suttoncharitabletrust.org *Website* www.suttoncoldfieldcharitabletrust.com

■ Swan Mountain Trust

CC NO 275594 **ESTABLISHED** 1978
WHERE FUNDING CAN BE GIVEN UK.
WHO CAN BENEFIT Charitable organisations.
WHAT IS FUNDED Refugees and asylum seekers, with an emphasis on the mental health of young people in these groups.
RANGE OF GRANTS Typically £1,000 to £4,000.
SAMPLE GRANTS Boabab Centre, Gatwick Detainees Welfare Group and Migrateful (£4,000); Methodist Asylum Project (MAP) and Refugee Information Bus (£3,000 each); Asylum Welcome (£2,500); Refugee Support Network (£1,500); The Compass Collective (£1,000).
FINANCES *Financial year end* 05/04/2020 *Income* £64,700 *Total grants* £62,500 *Grants to organisations* £62,500 *Assets* £1,390,000
TRUSTEES Jan Hargreaves; Dodie Cater; Peter Kilgarriff; Andrew Cowan.
OTHER INFORMATION The trust periodically reviews its funding priorities and at the time of writing (March 2021), the trustees were focused on supporting organisations working with refugees and asylum seekers, especially those working to improve the mental health of young people in those groups.
HOW TO APPLY Applications should be submitted via email or in writing to the correspondent. Applications may be submitted at any time but the trustees typically meet three times per annum (February, June and October).
CONTACT DETAILS Jan Hargreaves, Chair, 7 Mount Vernon, London NW3 6QS *Tel.* 01235 861326 *Email* Jan.swanmountaintrust@gmail.com *Website* swanmountaintrust.org.uk

■ The Swann-Morton Foundation

CC NO 271925 **ESTABLISHED** 1976
WHERE FUNDING CAN BE GIVEN UK, with a preference for South Yorkshire.
WHO CAN BENEFIT Charitable organisations; hospitals; individuals; employees or former employees of W. R. Swann and Co. Ltd.
WHAT IS FUNDED Medical and surgical research; education; social welfare; ill health and disability; general charitable purposes.
TYPE OF GRANT Projects; research and publication of research; bursaries and scholarships.
RANGE OF GRANTS Up to £6,000.
SAMPLE GRANTS Sheffield Children's Hospital (£8,000); Bluebell Wood Children's Hospital, Sheffield Teaching Hospitals and St Luke's Hospice (£6,000 each); University of Sheffield School of Medicine (£2,000); Whirlow Farm Trust (£1,000).
FINANCES *Financial year end* 30/06/2020 *Income* £80,000 *Total grants* £87,800 *Grants to organisations* £72,800 *Assets* £100,700
TRUSTEES Judith Gilmour; Michael McGinley; George Rodgers.
OTHER INFORMATION The accounts listed ten beneficiaries of grants above £999. Other donations totalled £33,400. During the year, student grants and electives totalled £15,000.
HOW TO APPLY Apply in writing to the correspondent. The 2019/20 accounts state: 'The charity invites applications for funding of projects from hospitals, charities and students. Applicants are invited to submit a summary of their proposals in a specific format. The applications are reviewed against specific criteria and research objectives which are set by the trustees.'
CONTACT DETAILS The Trustees, Swann-Morton Ltd, Owlerton Green, Sheffield, South Yorkshire S6 2BJ *Tel.* 0114 234 4231

■ Swansea and Brecon Diocesan Board of Finance Ltd

CC NO 249810 **ESTABLISHED** 1968
WHERE FUNDING CAN BE GIVEN Diocese of Swansea and Brecon (Neath Port Talbot, Powys and Swansea).
WHO CAN BENEFIT Places of worship and Christian organisations.
WHAT IS FUNDED Promoting Christian values and services for the benefit of the community; providing facilities for public worship; maintenance of church buildings; spiritual, moral and intellectual development.
WHAT IS NOT FUNDED Grants are not awarded for applications from outside the diocese.
TYPE OF GRANT Seed funding/start-up funding; project funding; development funding; capital costs.
RANGE OF GRANTS Small grants (£100 to £999); medium grants (£1,000 to £9,999); large grants (over £10,000). Matched funding requirements for each level of grant are listed on the website.
SAMPLE GRANTS A list of beneficiaries was not included in the annual report and accounts.
FINANCES *Financial year end* 31/12/2019 *Income* £3,810,000 *Total grants* £230,800 *Grants to organisations* £230,800 *Assets* £5,900,000
TRUSTEES Gwyn Lewis; The Venerable Johnathan Davies; Sonia Jones; Revd Albert Shackerley; Sir Paul Silk; Sir Andrew Large; Louise Pearson; The Venerable Alan Jevons.

OTHER INFORMATION Grants were awarded for a number of Christian causes, such as: from the Mission Fund, which funds new/pilot scheme mission projects (£43,600); social responsibility (£33,700); church repairs (£25,100); emergency repairs (£16,700); parish assistance (£10,000); and from the Transformation Fund, which awards seed corn funding for collaborative outreach projects and ministerial training (£9,500). A full breakdown of funds awarded is available in the charity's accounts.
HOW TO APPLY Applications are invited for the Mission Fund and the Transformation Fund. Application forms can be downloaded from the charity's helpful website where you can find further information on what to include with your application.
CONTACT DETAILS The Trustees, Diocesan Centre, Cathedral Close, Brecon, Powys LD3 9DP *Tel.* 01874 623716 *Email* diocese.swanbrec@churchinwales.org.uk *Website* https://swanseaandbrecon.churchinwales.org.uk/en/resources/mission-and-transformation-grants

■ The John Swire (1989) Charitable Trust

CC NO 802142 **ESTABLISHED** 1989
WHERE FUNDING CAN BE GIVEN UK.
WHO CAN BENEFIT Charitable organisations, universities, schools.
WHAT IS FUNDED General charitable purposes including: social welfare; health; the environment; arts.
SAMPLE GRANTS Brain and Spine Foundation (£150,000); Action for ME (£10,000); Petty Pool Trust (£5,000); Crundale Fair (£4,000); Meningitis Now (£1,500); Essex Wildlife Trust (£1,000).
FINANCES *Financial year end* 31/12/2019 *Income* £1,830,000 *Total grants* £1,890,000 *Grants to organisations* £1,890,000 *Assets* £43,860,000
TRUSTEES Barnaby Swire; Jonathan Swire; Rebecca Fitzgerald.
OTHER INFORMATION The trust is one of the four organisations that make up the Swire Family Charitable Trusts (Charity Commission. no 270726).
HOW TO APPLY The 2019 annual report states: 'Although the Trustees make some grants without a formal application, they normally require organisations to submit a request explaining how the funds could be used and what would be achieved.'
CONTACT DETAILS The Trustees, c/o John Swire & Sons Ltd, Swire House, 59 Buckingham Gate, London SW1E 6AJ *Tel.* 020 7834 7717 *Email* info@scts.org.uk

■ The Swire Charitable Trust

CC NO 270726 **ESTABLISHED** 1975
WHERE FUNDING CAN BE GIVEN UK.
WHO CAN BENEFIT UK-registered charities.
WHAT IS FUNDED General charitable purposes, with a focus on opportunities for disadvantaged and marginalised people (specifically ex-service people, victims of slavery and trafficking, and children and young people); the environment; heritage; education and training. For further detail on each of these areas, refer to the guidance on the trust's website.
WHAT IS NOT FUNDED See the trust's website for a full list of exclusions to the core funding programmes. The trust's Discretionary Fund is not subject to the same exclusions.
TYPE OF GRANT Unrestricted; project costs; core costs; capital costs; salaries. Mostly one-year grants, occasionally up to three years.
RANGE OF GRANTS There is no minimum or maximum grant size. Grants ranged up to £53,300 in 2019.
SAMPLE GRANTS The Passage (£53,300); The Snowdrop Project (£25,000); Heritage of London Trust (£20,000); The Lowry Centre (£15,000); Bletchley Park Trust and Halo Trust (£10,000 each); Ecobirmingham (£6,000); Dame Vera Lynn Children's Charity (£5,000); Lowe Syndrome Trust and University of East Anglia (£2,500 each); Hands Up Foundation (£500).
FINANCES *Financial year end* 31/12/2019 *Income* £3,230,000 *Total grants* £3,893,200 *Grants to organisations* £2,970,000 *Assets* £8,810,000
TRUSTEES Barnaby Swire; John Swire; Merlin Swire; Samuel Swire; Martha Allfrey; Rupert Hogg.
OTHER INFORMATION Grants were made to 232 organisations in 2019. Only organisations receiving grants of over £1,000 were listed as beneficiaries in the trust's accounts. Grants of less than £1,000 totalled £1,260. There were also 32 grants to individuals, totalling £923,200, in the form of educational scholarships. Alongside its core programmes, the trust's Discretionary Fund makes donations to charities that fall outside the funding criteria but where the cause is championed by the staff and other stakeholders of John Swire & Sons Ltd.
HOW TO APPLY Applicants should read the guidelines and FAQs on the trust's website first, then complete the eligibility test. If eligible, applications can be made using the online form. Requests for less than £25,000 are considered at monthly meetings, with larger requests being considered quarterly (usually in January, April, July and October). Applications sent by post or email will not be considered.
CONTACT DETAILS Sarah Irving, Grants Manager, Swire House, 59 Buckingham Gate, London SW1E 6AJ *Tel.* 020 7834 7717 *Email* info@scts.org.uk *Website* www.swirecharitabletrust.org.uk

■ The Adrian Swire Charitable Trust

CC NO 800493 **ESTABLISHED** 1988
WHERE FUNDING CAN BE GIVEN UK and overseas.
WHO CAN BENEFIT Charitable organisations; schools and colleges; universities; hospitals; hospices.
WHAT IS FUNDED General charitable purposes, including, but not limited to: opportunities for disadvantaged people; the environment; heritage.
WHAT IS NOT FUNDED The following exclusions apply to the core funding programme, though not necessarily to unrestricted funding: applications received by post or email; non-registered charities; activities outside the UK; individuals; retrospective expenditure; work primarily targeting individuals with physical or learning disabilities; statutory bodies; scholarships or bursaries.
TYPE OF GRANT Unrestricted; core/revenue costs; capital costs; salaries.
RANGE OF GRANTS Around £1,000 to £50,000.
SAMPLE GRANTS Julia's House (£60,600); Central London Samaritans (£50,000); Diverse Abilities, Thames Valley Air Ambulance and The Brain

Tumour Charity (£20,000 each); BRS Education Ltd, Home-Start Southwark and Women for Women International (£10,000 each); Be Free Young Carers and Olive Ridley Project (£5,000 each); Wantage Summer Arts Festival (£1,000); Bayford PCC (£100).

FINANCES *Financial year end* 31/12/2019
Income £1,690,000 *Total grants* £1,650,000
Grants to organisations £1,650,000
Assets £34,000,000

TRUSTEES Lady Judith Swire; Martha Allfrey; Merlin Swire; Richard Leonard; Samuel Swire; James Kidner.

OTHER INFORMATION In 2019 the trust made grants to 129 organisations. A number of these organisations also received funding in 2018.

HOW TO APPLY Applications must be made via the Swire Charitable Trust's website, not in writing or via email. Potential applicants should read the trust's funding guidelines and FAQs before beginning the process. The guidance includes an eligibility test and funding request form. Applications should include your latest inspected accounts, bank statement or other supporting materials.

CONTACT DETAILS Jo Trew, Grants and Administration Officer, Swire House, 59 Buckingham Gate, London SW1E 6AJ *Tel.* 020 7834 7717 *Email* info@scts.org.uk *Website* https://www.swirecharitabletrust.org.uk

■ The Syder Foundation

CC NO 1119373 **ESTABLISHED** 2007

WHERE FUNDING CAN BE GIVEN South East England, with a preference for Berkshire and surrounding counties.

WHO CAN BENEFIT Registered charities.

WHAT IS FUNDED General charitable purposes.

WHAT IS NOT FUNDED Animal welfare; research; individuals' education.

TYPE OF GRANT Capital funding is preferred.

SAMPLE GRANTS Previous beneficiaries have included: Hampshire Medical Fund; National Horseracing Museum; Prince's Countryside Trust; Salisbury Samaritans; The Wheelyboat Trust; Whitchurch Silk Mill.

FINANCES *Financial year end* 30/09/2020
Income £352,600 *Total grants* £469,200
Grants to organisations £469,200
Assets £14,780,000

TRUSTEES Charlotte Syder; Timothy Syder.

OTHER INFORMATION Large grants of around £50,000 are awarded to ten or fewer organisations each year. In addition, a total of around £100,000 each year is awarded in small grants to charities in Berkshire, Hampshire and Wiltshire. Some Surrey, Oxfordshire and Buckinghamshire charities are also supported. National charities are unlikely to be funded.

HOW TO APPLY For large grants the trustees prefer to proactively identify projects of interest; however, the foundation still welcomes contact from projects that fit the criteria (a formal application is not required). Applications for small grants should be no longer than two A4 pages and should include your most recent year's income and expenditure, the cost of raising funds annually and the intended impact of your project. Applications should preferably be emailed to the correspondent, with your latest accounts attached.

CONTACT DETAILS The Trustees, PO Box 6277, Newbury, Berkshire RG14 9PN
Email syderfoundation@gmail.com
Website https://www.syderfoundation.org

■ The Sir Hugh and Lady Sykes Charitable Trust

CC NO 327648 **ESTABLISHED** 1987

WHERE FUNDING CAN BE GIVEN Principally South Yorkshire, also Derbyshire.

WHO CAN BENEFIT Registered charities.

WHAT IS FUNDED General charitable purposes.

SAMPLE GRANTS A list of beneficiaries was not included in the annual report and accounts.

FINANCES *Financial year end* 05/04/2020
Income £154,700 *Total grants* £288,700
Grants to organisations £288,700
Assets £1,980,000

TRUSTEES Sir Hugh Sykes; Lady Ruby Sykes; Brian Evans.

HOW TO APPLY Contact the correspondent for further information.

CONTACT DETAILS The Trustees, Brookfield Manor, Hathersage, Hope Valley, Derbyshire S32 1BB *Tel.* 01433 651190 *Email* info@brookfieldmanor.com

■ The Charles and Elsie Sykes Trust

CC NO 206926 **ESTABLISHED** 1954

WHERE FUNDING CAN BE GIVEN UK for medical grants; Yorkshire for non-medical grants.

WHO CAN BENEFIT Registered charities only.

WHAT IS FUNDED A wide range of general charitable purposes, including: blind and partially sighted people; children and young people; cultural and environmental heritage; deaf or hard of hearing people and individuals with speech impairment; disability; education; medical research; medical welfare; mental health and well-being; older people; overseas aid; the armed forces; social welfare.

WHAT IS NOT FUNDED Individuals; building maintenance projects; projects without either a medical link or link to Yorkshire; recently established charities; applications for overseas work.

RANGE OF GRANTS Mainly under £5,000.

SAMPLE GRANTS Ripon Community Link (£14,000); St Peter's Church (£10,000); Alzheimer's Research UK (£5,000); Clothing Solutions for Disabled People – Bradford (£4,000); Harold Styan Charity for Youth – Harrogate (£2,500); Caring for Life – Leeds (£2,000); Juvenile Diabetes Research Foundation (£1,500); Positive Action for Refugees and Asylum Seekers – Leeds (£1,000); York Hospital Radio (£500).

FINANCES *Financial year end* 31/12/2019
Income £641,000 *Total grants* £376,000
Grants to organisations £376,000
Assets £18,400,000

TRUSTEES John Ward; Martin Coultas; Barry Kay; Dr Rosemary Livingstone; Sara Buchan; Dr Michael McEvoy; Sean Rushton; Elaine Morrison; David Mead.

OTHER INFORMATION A total of 401 grants were awarded during the year. The trust has sub-committees to consider both medical and non-medical grants.

HOW TO APPLY Application forms can be downloaded from the website, along with a checklist, and should be sent by post along with a copy of your latest accounts and annual report, and any other relevant information. Further guidance on what to include is given on the website. The trustees meet in March, June, September and December, and applications should be submitted by the last Friday of January, April, July and October, respectively.

CONTACT DETAILS Neil Shaw, Secretary, c/o LCF Barber Titleys, First Floor, The Exchange, Harrogate, North Yorkshire HG1 1TS *Tel.* 01423 851122 *Email* helen.hawley@lcf.co.uk *Website* www.charlesandelsiesykestrust.co.uk

■ The Hugh Symons Charitable Trust

CC NO 1137778 **ESTABLISHED** 2010

WHERE FUNDING CAN BE GIVEN UK; overseas.

WHO CAN BENEFIT Registered charities.

WHAT IS FUNDED Health; social welfare; overseas development; the environment.

SAMPLE GRANTS British Red Cross and Oxfam (£50,000 each); FareShare (£7,500); Crisis (£2,500); Mercy Ships (£2,000); Lepra and Trio Uganda (£1,500 each).

FINANCES *Financial year end* 05/04/2020 *Income* £208,200 *Total grants* £370,300 *Grants to organisations* £370,300 *Assets* £4,950,000

TRUSTEES Katherine Roper; Geoffrey Roper; Lester Aldridge Trust Company; Pauline Roper.

OTHER INFORMATION Hugh Symons is an information management company with offices in Bradford and Poole. Grants were made to 38 organisations during the year.

HOW TO APPLY Contact the correspondent for further information.

CONTACT DETAILS Geoffrey Roper, Trustee, Stubhampton House, Stubhampton, Blandford Forum DT11 8JU *Tel.* 01258 830135

■ The Syncona Foundation

CC NO 1149202 **ESTABLISHED** 2012

WHERE FUNDING CAN BE GIVEN UK.

WHO CAN BENEFIT Registered charities.

WHAT IS FUNDED Medical causes, particularly oncology.

SAMPLE GRANTS A list of beneficiaries was not included in the annual report and accounts.

FINANCES *Financial year end* 31/03/2020 *Income* £2,640,000 *Total grants* £3,030,000 *Grants to organisations* £3,030,000 *Assets* £321,000

TRUSTEES James Maltin; Thomas Henderson; Rupert Adams; Nigel Keen.

OTHER INFORMATION This is the corporate charity of Syncona Ltd. In 2019/20, £2.87 million in grants was awarded to core charities and £163,000 in grants was awarded to other charities.

HOW TO APPLY Grantees are chosen by shareholders. Unsolicited applications are unlikely to be successful.

CONTACT DETAILS The Trustees, 1st Floor, Shropshire House, 179 Tottenham Court Road, London W1T 7NZ *Tel.* 020 7801 6306 *Email* th@bacit.co.uk *Website* https://www.synconaltd.com/about-us/charities

■ T. and S. Trust Fund

CC NO 1095939 **ESTABLISHED** 2002
WHERE FUNDING CAN BE GIVEN UK, with a preference for Greater London, Gateshead and Manchester city.
WHO CAN BENEFIT Jewish organisations; occasionally individuals.
WHAT IS FUNDED Advancement of the Orthodox Jewish religion and education; relief of poverty.
RANGE OF GRANTS Up to £57,900.
SAMPLE GRANTS Beneficiaries were specified as follows in the accounts: relief of poverty grants (£57,900); religious grants (£16,900); BCR (£10,500); GJLS (£10,000); community grants (£6,500).
FINANCES *Financial year end* 31/10/2019 *Income* £86,200 *Total grants* £139,500 *Grants to organisations* £139,500 *Assets* £43,200
TRUSTEES Shoshana Sandler; Aron Sandler.
OTHER INFORMATION Grants of under £5,000 totalled £47,700. The 2018/19 accounts were the latest available at the time of writing (April 2021).
HOW TO APPLY Contact the correspondent for further information.
CONTACT DETAILS Mrs S. Sandler, Company Secretary/Trustee, 96 Whitehall Road, Gateshead, Tyne and Wear NE8 4ET *Tel.* 0191 482 5050

■ The T.K. Maxx and Homesense Foundation

CC NO 1162073 **ESTABLISHED** 2015
WHERE FUNDING CAN BE GIVEN UK; Germany; Poland; the Republic of Ireland.
WHO CAN BENEFIT National and local charities.
WHAT IS FUNDED Helping vulnerable children and young people in local communities achieve their potential.
TYPE OF GRANT The 2019/20 annual report states: 'Donations may be awarded over multiple grants in relation to numerous local projects by national and local charities.'
SAMPLE GRANTS The Prince's Trust (£264,000); British Red Cross (£145,000); Cancer Research UK (£44,000); Mind (£19,000).
FINANCES *Financial year end* 01/02/2020 *Income* £1,540,000 *Total grants* £821,000 *Grants to organisations* £821,000 *Assets* £5,080,000
TRUSTEES Deborah Dolce; Louise Greenlees; Erica Farrell.
OTHER INFORMATION Formerly known as the TJX UK Foundation, this charity is the charitable arm of TJX UK. During the year, the foundation awarded 444 grants. Only four beneficiaries were listed in the accounts. The remaining grants were awarded to a variety of local and national charities.
HOW TO APPLY Contact the correspondent for further information.
CONTACT DETAILS The Trustees, 50 Clarendon Road, Watford, WD17 1TX *Tel.* 01923 47300 *Email* TJX_Foundation@tjxeurope.com

■ Tabeel Trust

CC NO 266645 **ESTABLISHED** 1974
WHERE FUNDING CAN BE GIVEN Worldwide, with a preference for Clacton (Essex).
WHO CAN BENEFIT Registered charities; religious bodies/institutions.
WHAT IS FUNDED Evangelical Christian charitable purposes, where the trustees have an existing interest.
WHAT IS NOT FUNDED Short-term gap year initiatives.
TYPE OF GRANT Capital costs; seed funding/start-up funding.
RANGE OF GRANTS Up to £20,000.
SAMPLE GRANTS BMS World Mission (£20,000); St Michael's, Paris (£18,000); Tearfund (£15,000); Gurnell Grove Community Trust (£9,000); Selkirk Baptist Church (£5,000); Evangelical Alliance (£4,000); Gideons (£800).
FINANCES *Financial year end* 31/10/2019 *Income* £27,800 *Total grants* £200,800 *Grants to organisations* £200,800 *Assets* £977,000
TRUSTEES Douglas Brown; Barbara Carter; Dr Mary Clark; Jean Richardson; James Davey; Sarah Taylor; Nigel Davey, Edward Clark.
OTHER INFORMATION The 2018/19 accounts were the latest available at the time of writing (May 2021). The trust made 41 grants during the year.
HOW TO APPLY Only charities with which a trustee already has contact should apply. Grants are considered at trustees' meetings, which are usually in May and October.
CONTACT DETAILS The Trustees, East Dalcove House, Kelso, Scottish Borders TD5 7PD *Tel.* 01573 460395

■ The Tabhair Charitable Trust

OSCR NO SC043357 **ESTABLISHED** 2012
WHERE FUNDING CAN BE GIVEN UK and Ireland.
WHO CAN BENEFIT Registered charities.
WHAT IS FUNDED Education, training and community action.
TYPE OF GRANT Project funding, core costs.
RANGE OF GRANTS Mostly £500 to £5,000.
SAMPLE GRANTS Oxygen (£10,000); Broomhouse and Cairns Counselling (£5,000 each); Connect and Co. (£3,000); Second Chance (£2,000).
FINANCES *Financial year end* 30/09/2020 *Income* £85,400 *Total grants* £60,000 *Grants to organisations* £60,000 *Assets* £1,290,000
OTHER INFORMATION Grants were made to 11 organisations. The trust's website states that it welcomes applications from charities that 'combine support services with enterprising mission to improve social well-being and employment opportunities in the lives of the disengaged and disadvantaged'.
HOW TO APPLY Applications can be made via the trust's website or in writing to the correspondent.
CONTACT DETAILS The Trustees, c/o Chiene and Tait LLP, 61 Dublin Street, Edinburgh EH3 6NL *Website* www.tabhair.org.uk

■ The Ashley Tabor-King Foundation

CC NO 1178634 **ESTABLISHED** 2018
WHERE FUNDING CAN BE GIVEN England and Wales.
WHO CAN BENEFIT Charitable organisations.
WHAT IS FUNDED Organisations and projects supporting first responders who suffer from

post-traumatic stress disorder or physical harm associated with their employment; activities which develop young people's skills and enable them to participate in society as mature and responsible individuals.

RANGE OF GRANTS £25,000 to £300,000.

SAMPLE GRANTS Taigh Mor Foundation (£300,000); Westminster Synagogue (£25,000).

FINANCES *Financial year end* 05/04/2020 *Income* £418,800 *Total grants* £325,000 *Grants to organisations* £325,000 *Assets* £85,700

TRUSTEES The Lord Allen of Kensington; Ashley Tabor; Emma Bradley; Stephen Miron.

OTHER INFORMATION Grants were awarded to two organisations during the year.

HOW TO APPLY Contact the correspondent for further information.

CONTACT DETAILS The Trustees, c/o Global Media and Entertainment Ltd, 29–30 Leicester Square, London WC2H 7LA *Tel.* 020 7766 6000

■ Taca

CCNI NO NIC101092 **ESTABLISHED** 2014

WHERE FUNDING CAN BE GIVEN Northern Ireland.

WHO CAN BENEFIT Irish language nurseries, schools and groups.

WHAT IS FUNDED Promotion of the Irish language and traditional Irish culture.

TYPE OF GRANT Running costs; capital costs (provision of materials); staff costs.

RANGE OF GRANTS Grants range from £400 up to £40,000.

SAMPLE GRANTS Iontaobhas Na Gaelscolaíochta (£40,000); Gaelscoil Éanna (£11,300); Coláiste Feirste (£9,300); Naíscoil Ghreanacháin (£4,000).

FINANCES *Financial year end* 31/03/2019 *Income* £121,300 *Total grants* £107,600 *Grants to organisations* £107,600 *Assets* £11,700

TRUSTEES Pilib Ó Ruanaí; Pilib Mistéil; Pádraig Ó Ceallaigh.

OTHER INFORMATION The 2018/19 accounts were the latest available at the time of writing (February 2021).

HOW TO APPLY Contact the correspondent for information regarding the application process.

CONTACT DETAILS Páid Ó Cianáin, An Cultúrlann, 216 Falls Road, Belfast, County Antrim BT12 6AH *Tel.* 028 9032 3237 *Email* eolas@taca.ie *Website* www.taca.ie

■ The Tajtelbaum Charitable Trust

CC NO 273184 **ESTABLISHED** 1974

WHERE FUNDING CAN BE GIVEN UK, with some preference given to London, Gateshead, Leeds, Manchester, Salford and Scotland.

WHO CAN BENEFIT Orthodox Jewish synagogues and educational establishments; care homes; UK-registered charities.

WHAT IS FUNDED Advancement of the Orthodox Jewish religion and education; relief of poverty and ill health.

SAMPLE GRANTS A list of beneficiaries was not included in the annual report and accounts.

FINANCES *Financial year end* 05/04/2020 *Income* £586,600 *Total grants* £839,000 *Grants to organisations* £839,000 *Assets* £5,840,000

TRUSTEES Emanuel Tajtelbaum; Henry Frydenson; Shoshana Tajtelbaum; Hannah Prager.

HOW TO APPLY Contact the correspondent for further information.

CONTACT DETAILS The Trustees, PO Box 33911, London NW9 7ZX *Tel.* 020 8202 3464

■ The Gay and Keith Talbot Trust

CC NO 1102192 **ESTABLISHED** 2004

WHERE FUNDING CAN BE GIVEN UK, Nepal, Bangladesh, Nigeria, Uganda, South Sudan, Tanzania and Ethiopia.

WHO CAN BENEFIT Registered charities.

WHAT IS FUNDED Medical research, currently funding fistula work in particular; humanitarian aid; asylum seekers; general charitable purposes.

TYPE OF GRANT Capital costs; research and development; project funding.

SAMPLE GRANTS Although a list of beneficiaries was not provided in the accounts, the trustees state that they have continued funding fistula work in Nigeria, Uganda, South Sudan, Tanzania and Ethiopia. The trust also funded other medical projects in Nepal and Bangladesh, and provided grants for the support of refugees and asylum seekers in the UK and for research into cystic fibrosis.

FINANCES *Financial year end* 29/02/2020 *Income* £134,400 *Total grants* £109,000 *Grants to organisations* £109,000 *Assets* £170,000

TRUSTEES Keith Talbot; Gay Talbot.

OTHER INFORMATION Grants were distributed in the following areas: fistula work (£78,000); other medical purposes (£11,500); research and development (£10,000); grants for asylum seekers (£9,000); general charitable purposes (£500).

HOW TO APPLY Contact the correspondent for further information.

CONTACT DETAILS Gay Talbot, Trustee, Fold Howe, Kentmere, Kendal, Cumbria LA8 9JW *Tel.* 01539 821504 *Email* gay_talbot@hotmail.com

■ The Talbot Trusts

CC NO 221356 **ESTABLISHED** 1928

WHERE FUNDING CAN BE GIVEN Sheffield and immediate surrounding areas.

WHO CAN BENEFIT Registered charities; CICs; constituted community groups; social workers, GPs and practice nurses (see the trust's annual report for further detail).

WHAT IS FUNDED Health; mental health; disability; older people (social/physical isolation); children and young people; social welfare (including food poverty, domestic violence and homelessness); BAMER communities.

WHAT IS NOT FUNDED Research; educational projects; major fundraising and general appeals; non-registered charities or other organisations; individuals; recurrent grants.

TYPE OF GRANT One-off grants for items, services and facilities (capital and project funding).

RANGE OF GRANTS £500 to £5,000.

SAMPLE GRANTS British Refugee Council, Rethink Mental Illness and Sheffield Churches Council for Community Care (£5,000 each); Mums In Need and South Yorkshire Eating Disorders Association (£2,500 each); Sheffield Stroke Survivors (£2,000); British Blind Sport (£1,500); REACT (Rapid Effective Assistance for Children with potentially Terminal illness) (£1,000); Mobility Trust (£500).

FINANCES *Financial year end* 31/03/2020 *Income* £85,900 *Total grants* £87,300 *Grants to organisations* £87,300 *Assets* £1,960,000

TRUSTEES Tim Plant; Dr Zackary McMurray; Melanie Russell; Dr Mike Sawkins; Maria Flude; Mark Wilde; Sam Caldwell.

OTHER INFORMATION Grants made during the year were broken down as follows: physical well-being of people with mental health issues (£53,700); nutrition and isolation issues facing elderly people (£13,100); small grants fund (£10,600); GP and social worker grants (£5,000); other (£5,000).

HOW TO APPLY Application forms can be downloaded from the trust's helpful website during open funding periods and should be returned via email. Check the website for deadlines. The trustees meet in June and December to consider applications.

CONTACT DETAILS Gill Newman, Clerk to the Trustees, 3 Willow Tree Drive, Clowne, Chesterfield, North Derbyshire S43 4UP *Tel.* 07773 660552 *Email* admin@thetalbottrusts.com *Website* www.thetalbottrusts.com

■ The Talbot Village Trust

CC NO 249349 **ESTABLISHED** 1850

WHERE FUNDING CAN BE GIVEN Christchurch; Bournemouth; Poole; East Dorset; Isle of Purbeck.

WHO CAN BENEFIT Registered charities; churches; educational institutions.

WHAT IS FUNDED General charitable purposes, including: disability; social welfare; local community projects; young people; older people; educational and employment opportunities.

WHAT IS NOT FUNDED Running costs; revenue costs; salaries; uniforms; regular maintenance; retrospective expenditure. The trustees will not normally consider an application unless at least 25–33% of the total amount required has been raised or pledged.

TYPE OF GRANT Grants and loans for capital costs only.

RANGE OF GRANTS Up to £28,000 in 2019, but there is no upper limit.

SAMPLE GRANTS Christchurch Open Awards Centre (three grants totalling £49,000); Sturts Community Trust (£20,000); Dorset Blind Society (£15,000); Purbeck Youth Centre and St Edward's Secondary School – Poole (£10,000 each); Hurting 2 Healing (£5,800); Safewise (£3,100); St Marks Church (£1,500); Bus Stop Club (£420).

FINANCES *Financial year end* 31/12/2019
Income £2,850,000 *Total grants* £222,500
Grants to organisations £222,500
Assets £66,000,000

TRUSTEES Sir Thomas Salt; James Fleming; Christopher Lees; Russell Rowe; Earl of Shaftesbury; George Meyrick.

OTHER INFORMATION Grants were paid to 28 organisations during the year. A further 38 grants totalling £760,800 were authorised but unpaid.

HOW TO APPLY Applications can be made using the online application form or by post and must include the information specified in the guidelines on the website. The trustees meet twice a year to consider applications and applicants are notified of the outcome within a couple of weeks of a meeting.

CONTACT DETAILS Darryl Tidd, Director, c/o Savills, Wessex House, Priors Walk, Wimbourne BH21 1PB *Tel.* 07813 881053 *Email* darryl.tidd@talbotvillagetrust.org *Website* https://www.talbotvillagetrust.org

■ Tallow Chandlers Benevolent Fund No. 2

CC NO 246255 **ESTABLISHED** 1966

WHERE FUNDING CAN BE GIVEN Greater London.

WHO CAN BENEFIT Charitable organisations, schools and universities. There is a preference for charities where a liveryman or freeman is actively involved.

WHAT IS FUNDED Children and young people; education; health and medical research; people with disabilities; social welfare.

WHAT IS NOT FUNDED Large or national charities; charities operating overseas; charities that do not have a connection to London; individuals that apply to the charity directly.

TYPE OF GRANT One-off grants; three-year grants.

RANGE OF GRANTS One-off grants from £250 to £2,000; larger grants up to three years.

SAMPLE GRANTS Greig City Academy (£77,500 in two grants); The Halley Academy (£50,000 in two grants); Cubitt Town Junior School (£39,300 in two grants); Federation of London Youth Clubs (£20,000); The Bridge School (£10,000); Clean Break Theatre Company (£4,000); Build Up Foundation (£1,500).

FINANCES *Financial year end* 05/04/2020
Income £902,200 *Total grants* £425,000
Grants to organisations £425,000
Assets £8,650,000

TRUSTEE The Worshipful Company of Tallow Chandlers.

OTHER INFORMATION During the year, the charity awarded 62 grants to organisations.

HOW TO APPLY Apply in writing to the correspondent, who considers all requests. Details of what to include in an application are available on the charity's website.

CONTACT DETAILS Education and Charity Manager, Tallow Chandlers Hall, 4 Dowgate Hill, London EC4R 2SH *Tel.* 020 7248 4726 *Email* Jenna@tallowchandlers.org *Website* www.tallowchandlers.org

■ Talteg Ltd

CC NO 283253 **ESTABLISHED** 1981

WHERE FUNDING CAN BE GIVEN UK, with a preference for Scotland.

WHO CAN BENEFIT Registered charities; Jewish organisations.

WHAT IS FUNDED Orthodox Jewish religion; education; relief of poverty.

RANGE OF GRANTS £5,000 to £75,000.

SAMPLE GRANTS Clive Jay Berkley Foundation (£75,000); UJIA (£20,000); The Central British Fund for World Jewish Relief (£6,000); JNF KKL Scotland (£5,500).

FINANCES *Financial year end* 31/12/2019
Income £84,800 *Total grants* £216,000
Grants to organisations £216,000
Assets £3,790,000

TRUSTEES Adam Berkley; Delia Berkley.

HOW TO APPLY Contact the correspondent for further information.

CONTACT DETAILS The Trustees, 90 Mitchell Street, Glasgow G1 3NQ *Tel.* 0141 564 5155

■ The David Tannen Charitable Trust

CC NO 280392 **ESTABLISHED** 1974

WHERE FUNDING CAN BE GIVEN Israel and the UK, with a preference for Barnet, Hackney and Haringey.

WHO CAN BENEFIT Charitable organisations; schools.

WHAT IS FUNDED Jewish causes; social welfare; education.
RANGE OF GRANTS £10,000 to £30,000.
SAMPLE GRANTS The ABC Trust (£30,000); The Telz Talmudical Academy (£15,000); Halacha Lemoshe Trust (£13,000); Friends of Beis Chinuch Lebanos Trust, Friends of Beis Soroh Schneirer, Mifal Hachesed Vehatzedokoh and North West London Communal Mikvah Ltd (£10,000 each).
FINANCES *Financial year end* 30/06/2020
Income £3,150,000 *Total grants* £123,400
Grants to organisations £123,400
Assets £20,870,000
TRUSTEES David Tannen; Jonathan Miller; Martin Irving Tannen; Daniel Asher Tannen.
OTHER INFORMATION Grants to unspecified organisations totalled £24,900.
HOW TO APPLY Contact the correspondent for further information.
CONTACT DETAILS The Trustees, c/o Sutherland House, 70–78 West Hendon Broadway, London NW9 7BT *Tel.* 020 8202 1066

■ Tanner Trust

CC NO 1021175 **ESTABLISHED** 1993
WHERE FUNDING CAN BE GIVEN UK and overseas, with a preference for the south of England.
WHO CAN BENEFIT Registered charities; hospitals; schools.
WHAT IS FUNDED Conservation and the countryside; youth projects; health; older people and people with disabilities; culture and preservation of buildings; overseas aid.
WHAT IS NOT FUNDED Individuals.
TYPE OF GRANT Development funding; project funding; capital costs.
RANGE OF GRANTS Grants range from £250 to £20,000.
SAMPLE GRANTS Help Tibet Trust (£20,000); Cornwall Air Ambulance (£10,000); West Dean (£8,000); Helford River Children's Sailing Trust (£6,000); Tree Aid (£3,000); Lepra (£2,000); Denchworth Village Hall (£250).
FINANCES *Financial year end* 31/03/2020
Income £575,800 *Total grants* £444,700
Grants to organisations £444,700
Assets £9,880,000
TRUSTEES Alice Williams; Lucie Nottingham.
OTHER INFORMATION In the financial year 2019/20, a total of 103 grants were grants awarded to charitable organisations.
HOW TO APPLY The trust states that unsolicited applications are, without exception, not considered. Support is only given to charities personally known to the trustees.
CONTACT DETAILS The Trustees, c/o Blake Morgan, Harbour Court, Compass Road, Portsmouth, Hampshire PO6 4ST *Tel.* 023 9222 1122 *Email* Charity.Admin@blakemorgan.co.uk

■ Tay Charitable Trust

OSCR NO SC001004 **ESTABLISHED** 1951
WHERE FUNDING CAN BE GIVEN UK, with a focus on Scotland, particularly Dundee.
WHO CAN BENEFIT Registered charities.
WHAT IS FUNDED General charitable purposes, including the relief of poverty, the advancement of education or religion or other purposes beneficial to the community.
WHAT IS NOT FUNDED Individuals.
TYPE OF GRANT Core/revenue costs; seed funding/start-up funding; unrestricted funding.
RANGE OF GRANTS Grants range from £500 up to £5,000.
SAMPLE GRANTS Dundee Heritage Trust, Cambo Heritage Trust and Scottish Stroke Care Audit (£5,000 each); Tayside Opera (£3,000); Eagles Wings Trust (£2,000); Diabetes UK (£1,000); I WORK 4 ME (£500).
FINANCES *Financial year end* 05/04/2020
Income £292,400 *Total grants* £296,300
Grants to organisations £296,300
Assets £6,170,000
OTHER INFORMATION Grants of under £1,000 were awarded to 88 organisations totalling £44,000.
HOW TO APPLY Contact the correspondent for further information.
CONTACT DETAILS Mrs Z. Martin, Trustee, 87 Godstow Road, Wolvercote, Oxford OX2 8PF

■ C. B. and H. H. Taylor 1984 Trust

CC NO 291363 **ESTABLISHED** 1984
WHERE FUNDING CAN BE GIVEN Birmingham and the West Midlands; Ireland; UK-based organisations working overseas. Quaker work is supported regardless of location.
WHO CAN BENEFIT Projects with a defined link to Quaker work; registered charities.
WHAT IS FUNDED Work of the Religious Society of Friends; social welfare including children and young people, older people, people with disabilities, homelessness, women-led initiatives, counselling and mediation and hospice and bereavement services; education including adult literacy schemes, employment training, youth work and mental health education; penal affairs including work with offenders and ex-offenders and their families, police-backed initiatives and youth projects. Aid for humanitarian emergencies is always considered.
WHAT IS NOT FUNDED Individuals; projects or groups outside the trust's geographical focus; annual grants for revenue costs; repeat applications within a two-year period.
TYPE OF GRANT Project funding; development funding.
RANGE OF GRANTS Up to £72,000 but mainly £1,000 or less.
SAMPLE GRANTS Britain Yearly Meeting (£72,000); Caplor Horizons (£40,000); Friends of Hlekweni (£5,000); Book Aid International, Hope for Justice and Project Harar Ethiopia (£1,000 each); Disability Africa and The Heart of England Forest (£500 each).
FINANCES *Financial year end* 05/04/2019
Income £550,600 *Total grants* £478,800
Grants to organisations £478,800
Assets £14,620,000
TRUSTEES Constance Penny; Elizabeth Birmingham; Clare Norton; John Taylor; Thomas Penny; Robert Birmingham; Simon Taylor; Camilla Middleton.
OTHER INFORMATION Around 60% of grants made are for the work of the Religious Society of Friends. Grants were made to 160 organisations during the year. The 2018/19 accounts were the latest available at the time of writing (January 2021).
HOW TO APPLY Applications can be made by post or online via the foundation's website. According to the website, international support is given through a separate strategic fundraising agreement and unsolicited applications are unlikely to be successful.
CONTACT DETAILS The Trustees, Rokesley, Bristol Road, Selly Oak, Birmingham, West Midlands B29 6QF *Email* cbandhhtaylortrust.info@gmail.com *Website* www.cbandhhtaylortrust.com

■ The Taylor Family Foundation

CC NO 1118032 **ESTABLISHED** 2007

WHERE FUNDING CAN BE GIVEN UK, with a particular focus on Merton.

WHO CAN BENEFIT Registered charities.

WHAT IS FUNDED Disadvantaged children and young people aged 11–25; the arts; social inclusion.

WHAT IS NOT FUNDED Individuals.

TYPE OF GRANT Project funding.

RANGE OF GRANTS Generally £5,000 to £50,000, with some larger grants.

SAMPLE GRANTS Cancer Research UK (£1.5 million); Royal Opera House Convent Garden Foundation (£500,000); Polka Theatre (£150,000); Centrepoint (£50,000); Rainbow Trust Children's Charity (£25,000); University of Stirling (£20,000); Home-Start Merton (£10,000); Wimbledon Music Festival (£5,000); AFC Wimbledon Foundation (£4,300).

FINANCES *Financial year end* 24/03/2020 *Income* £2,060,000 *Total grants* £2,820,000 *Grants to organisations* £2,820,000 *Assets* £3,180,000

TRUSTEES Lisa Vaughan; Cristina Taylor; Neville Shepherd.

OTHER INFORMATION During the year, 32 grants were awarded to organisations. For smaller projects, the foundation has a particular focus on the London Borough of Merton.

HOW TO APPLY Applicants should complete the contact form on the foundation's website with a summary of the project's aims, beneficiaries and location. The trustees will then arrange to discuss eligibility and whether the project is something they may fund. The applicant may then be asked to complete a full application form.

CONTACT DETAILS The Trustees, Hill Place House, 55A High Street, Wimbledon, London SW19 5BA *Tel.* 020 8605 2629 *Email* info@thetaylorfamilyfoundation.co.uk *Website* www.thetaylorfamilyfoundation.co.uk

■ Stephen Taylor Foundation

CC NO 1168032 **ESTABLISHED** 2016

WHERE FUNDING CAN BE GIVEN Worldwide, mostly England.

WHO CAN BENEFIT Charitable organisations; educational institutions.

WHAT IS FUNDED Education; improving life chances in urban areas; inequality; the environment; young people; community.

TYPE OF GRANT Project funding; development funding; capital and building costs.

SAMPLE GRANTS Deptford Ragged Trust (£608,100); King's College Cambridge (£578,500); Age UK (£150,000); Institute for Public Policy Research (£50,000); Stephen Lawrence Day Foundation (£35,000); Youth First Ltd (£15,600); Montessori Education for Autism (£10,000).

FINANCES *Financial year end* 31/07/2020 *Income* £269,300 *Total grants* £1,550,000 *Grants to organisations* £1,550,000 *Assets* £22,270,000

TRUSTEES Lisa Taylor; Richard Walker; Martin Taylor.

OTHER INFORMATION Grants were awarded to ten organisations in 2019/20, of which six had not been supported in the previous year. A final payment of £578,500 was made to King's College, Cambridge for the completion of a halls of residence building. The foundation also awarded £608,000 to the Deptford Ragged Trust to purchase the freehold of a building which, according to the annual report, 'will then unlock public body grants to convert this building into both a community space and low cost rental housing for the disadvantaged'. The remaining grants awarded were for between £10,000 and £150,000.

HOW TO APPLY Contact the correspondent via email for information regarding the application process. The trustees will not reply to any queries received by post.

CONTACT DETAILS The Trustees, c/o Farrer and Co., 65–66 Lincoln's Inn Fields, London WC2A 3LH *Tel.* 020 3375 7000 *Email* contact@stf.london *Website* stf.london

■ A. P. Taylor Trust

CC NO 260741 **ESTABLISHED** 1969

WHERE FUNDING CAN BE GIVEN The parishes of Hayes and Harlington.

WHO CAN BENEFIT Charitable organisations; youth groups; amateur sports clubs.

WHAT IS FUNDED Medical causes; the arts; sport; children and young people; older people; women; youth groups, including Scouts and Guides.

WHAT IS NOT FUNDED Organisations outside the Hayes and Harlington area.

RANGE OF GRANTS Mostly under £400.

SAMPLE GRANTS A list of beneficiaries was not included in the annual report and accounts.

FINANCES *Financial year end* 31/03/2019 *Income* £88,800 *Total grants* £60,700 *Grants to organisations* £60,700 *Assets* £1,300,000

TRUSTEES Alan Woodhouse; Sean Fitzpatrick; Timothy McCarthy; Peter Chidwick.

OTHER INFORMATION Grants were awarded to 94 organisations during the year. The 2018/19 accounts were the latest available at the time of writing (January 2021).

HOW TO APPLY Application forms are available to download from the trust's website. Completed forms plus a copy of the previous year's accounts should be sent to the trust by 31 January of each year. Grants are distributed in May.

CONTACT DETAILS Tim McCarthy, Secretary, 14 Berwick Avenue, Hayes, Middlesex UB14 0NF *Tel.* 01895 812811 *Email* enquiries@aptaylortrust.org.uk *Website* www.aptaylortrust.org.uk

■ The Tedworth Charitable Trust

CC NO 328524 **ESTABLISHED** 1990

WHERE FUNDING CAN BE GIVEN UK and overseas.

WHO CAN BENEFIT Registered charities; CICs; schools; universities.

WHAT IS FUNDED Parenting; child development; family welfare; the arts; rural arts; the environment; organic gardening; sustainable living; general charitable purposes.

WHAT IS NOT FUNDED Individuals.

TYPE OF GRANT Core/running costs; salaries; project funding; development and strategic funding.

SAMPLE GRANTS Schumacher College (£55,000); University of Oxford – Worcester College (£54,100); Ashden Sustainable Solutions and Family Links (£20,000 each); Best Beginnings (£15,000); Tree Sisters (£10,000); Women's Environmental Network (£6,500); Poetry School (£5,000).

FINANCES *Financial year end* 05/04/2020 *Income* £339,100 *Total grants* £289,600 *Grants to organisations* £289,600 *Assets* £9,970,000

TRUSTEES Judith Portrait; Timothy Sainsbury; Jessica Sainsbury; Margaret Sainsbury.
OTHER INFORMATION The trust is one of the Sainsbury Family Charitable Trusts which share a common administration – see www.sftc.org.uk for more information. During the year, the trust made grants to 20 organisations for the following purposes: arts and the environment (£141,500); general charitable purposes (£75,600); parenting, family welfare and child development (£72,500).
HOW TO APPLY Unsolicited applications are not accepted.
CONTACT DETAILS Robert Bell, Director, The Peak, 5 Wilton Road, London SW1V 1AP *Tel.* 020 7410 0330 *Email* info@sfct.org.uk *Website* www.sfct.org.uk

■ Tees Valley Community Foundation

CC NO 1111222 **ESTABLISHED** 1988
WHERE FUNDING CAN BE GIVEN The former county of Cleveland, which covers the local authority areas of Hartlepool, Middlesbrough, Redcar and Cleveland and Stockton-on-Tees.
WHO CAN BENEFIT Registered charities; constituted community groups; schools; CICs; individuals.
WHAT IS FUNDED General charitable purposes, benefitting communities in Tees Valley. The foundation makes grants from various different funds, each with its own criteria – refer to the website for information on current programmes.
WHAT IS NOT FUNDED Each fund has separate exclusions which are available on the foundation's website.
TYPE OF GRANT One-off.
RANGE OF GRANTS Usually up to £1,000.
SAMPLE GRANTS Previous beneficiaries have included: Poot Rigg Training Centre Ltd (£60,000); Billingham Environment Link Programme (£16,000); Headland Festivals Group (£3,000); Groundwork North East and Cumbria (£1,000); The Recover Advocates and Consultants TRAC (£850); T.O.F.Y Club (The Over Fifties Youth Club) (£180).
FINANCES *Financial year end* 31/03/2020 *Income* £614,500 *Total grants* £436,000 *Grants to organisations* £436,000 *Assets* £13,390,000
TRUSTEES Wendy John; Keith Smith; Jeffrey Taylor; Neil Kenley; Emma Read; Nigel Williams; Heather O'Driscoll.
OTHER INFORMATION The grant total includes grants to individuals. As with all community foundations, grant schemes change frequently. Contact the foundation or check its website for details of current programmes and their deadlines.
HOW TO APPLY Application forms are available on the foundation's helpful website.
CONTACT DETAILS Grants Administrator, Wallace House, Falcon Court, Preston Farm, Stockton-on-Tees, Durham TS18 3TX *Tel.* 01642 260860 *Email* info@teesvalleyfoundation.org *Website* www.teesvalleyfoundation.org

■ Tegham Ltd

CC NO 283066 **ESTABLISHED** 1981
WHERE FUNDING CAN BE GIVEN UK, with a preference for Barnet.
WHO CAN BENEFIT Registered charities; individuals.
WHAT IS FUNDED Promotion of the Orthodox Jewish faith and the relief of poverty.
SAMPLE GRANTS A list of beneficiaries was not included in the annual report and accounts.
FINANCES *Financial year end* 31/03/2020 *Income* £258,500 *Total grants* £439,800 *Grants to organisations* £439,800 *Assets* £2,800,000
TRUSTEES Nizza Fluss; Daniel Fluss.
OTHER INFORMATION Grants were awarded to organisations and individuals during the year, but the breakdown was not specified in the accounts.
HOW TO APPLY Contact the correspondent for further information.
CONTACT DETAILS The Trustees, 13 Garrick Avenue, London NW11 9AR *Email* admin@geraldkreditor.co.uk

■ The Templeton Goodwill Trust

OSCR NO SC004177 **ESTABLISHED** 1938
WHERE FUNDING CAN BE GIVEN Glasgow and the west of Scotland (the Glasgow postal area).
WHO CAN BENEFIT Scottish registered charities.
WHAT IS FUNDED General charitable purposes; social welfare; health; community development.
WHAT IS NOT FUNDED Projects or organisations outside Scotland; individuals.
SAMPLE GRANTS Previous beneficiaries have included: Alzheimer's Scotland – Action for Dementia; Church of Scotland Lodging House Mission; City of Glasgow Society of Social Services; Girl Guides Association; Glasgow Hospital Broadcasting Service; Muscular Dystrophy Group; Scottish Autistic Society; Scottish Furniture Trades Benevolent Association; The Urban Fox Programme.
FINANCES *Financial year end* 31/03/2020 *Income* £231,500 *Total grants* £215,700 *Grants to organisations* £215,700 *Assets* £5,250,000
HOW TO APPLY Apply in writing to the correspondent, preferably including a copy of your latest accounts. The trustees have previously stated applications should be received by April as the trustees meet once a year, at the end of April or in May. An sae is required from applicants to receive a reply.
CONTACT DETAILS Mr P. Ferguson, Trustee, 5 Park View, Kilbarchan, Johnstone, Renfrewshire PA10 2LW

■ Tenovus Cancer Care

CC NO 1054015 **ESTABLISHED** 1996
WHERE FUNDING CAN BE GIVEN UK, with a preference for Wales.
WHO CAN BENEFIT Research organisations and universities.
WHAT IS FUNDED Innovative projects that have real benefits for cancer patients and their loved ones.
TYPE OF GRANT Research, salaries and project funding.
SAMPLE GRANTS University of Cardiff (£440,100); Swansea Bay UHLB (Lymphoedema Network Wales) (£57,000); University of Swansea (£37,700); Velindre Cancer Care (£9,500).
FINANCES *Financial year end* 31/03/2020 *Income* £8,690,000 *Total grants* £530,000 *Grants to organisations* £530,000 *Assets* £4,200,000
TRUSTEES Hugh O'Sullivan; Prof. Malcolm Mason; Prof. Deborah Fitzsimmons; Prof. Geraint Williams; Anne-Marie Koukourava; Michael Borrill; Dr Christopher Thomson; Huw George;

Roberta Fleet; Simon Finch; Prof. Peter Barrett-Lee.

OTHER INFORMATION The charity has a number of different funding streams including: iGrants; PhD Studentships; Research Strategy Grants; RCBC Projects and KESS Studentships. Further details on each separate funding stream can be found on the charity's website.

HOW TO APPLY Application processes vary depending upon the grant programme. Full guidance for all open grant programmes is available on the charity's website, where prospective applicants can register to receive updates about new programmes and funding calls.

CONTACT DETAILS The Trustees, Gleider House, Ty Glas Road, Cardiff CF14 5BD *Tel.* 029 2076 8850 *Email* post@tenovus.org.uk *Website* www.tenovus.org.uk

■ Tenovus Scotland

OSCR NO SC009675 **ESTABLISHED** 1967

WHERE FUNDING CAN BE GIVEN Scotland.

WHO CAN BENEFIT Universities, health bodies and research organisations; researchers and students.

WHAT IS FUNDED Research in the fields of medicine, dentistry, nursing, the medical sciences and allied professions. According to the charity's helpful website, grants are given in the following categories: small pilot grants; large grants (Tayside only); scholarships and awards through universities and medical schools. Further details are provided on the website.

WHAT IS NOT FUNDED Applications which are not properly certificated; work outside the beneficial area; partial funding for projects; applications that fail to provide evidence of appropriate ethical permission or statistical justification for sample/cohort sizes (where appropriate); equipment for routine patient care or for assessment of new products, which the manufacturer might be expected to finance. The following are not usually funded: applications from established investigators for work within their usual field of expertise; applications from PhD students; applications for follow-on work previously funded by Tenovus Scotland, except in exceptional circumstances.

TYPE OF GRANT Research projects – equipment, consumables, running costs, salaries, studentships; evaluations or start-up costs.

RANGE OF GRANTS Small grants of up to £20,000; large grants of up to £100,000.

SAMPLE GRANTS A list of beneficiaries was not included in the annual report and accounts.

FINANCES *Financial year end* 31/03/2020 *Income* £1,470,000 *Total grants* £1,340,000 *Grants to organisations* £1,340,000 *Assets* £2,230,000

TRUSTEES Prof. Derek Bell; Prof. Andrew Calder; Colin Black; Prof. John Connell; Prof. James Grieve; Mary Marquis; Francis McCrossin; Malcolm McIver; Prof. Kenneth Paterson; Graham Philips; Dr Heather Reid.

OTHER INFORMATION The grant total includes the total expenditure on 'research projects and awards' during the year.

HOW TO APPLY An application form can be requested from the relevant regional correspondent – refer to the website for contact details. Application deadlines are also posted on the website.

CONTACT DETAILS Francis McCrossin, Trustee, The Royal College of Physicians and Surgeons of Glasgow, 232–242 St Vincent Street, Glasgow G2 5RJ *Tel.* 0141 221 6268 *Email* general.secy@tenovus-scotland.org.uk *Website* www.tenovus-scotland.org.uk

■ The Thales Charitable Trust

CC NO 1000162 **ESTABLISHED** 1990

WHERE FUNDING CAN BE GIVEN UK.

WHO CAN BENEFIT Registered charities.

WHAT IS FUNDED Young people; technology; education; health, in particular care for permanent or terminal conditions; general charitable purposes.

SAMPLE GRANTS British Heart Foundation; Combat Stress; Dream Holidays; Lennox Children's Cancer Fund; Primary Engineers; Scope; Supporting Wounded Veterans; Together for Short Lives.

FINANCES *Financial year end* 31/12/2019 *Income* £175,000 *Total grants* £209,800 *Grants to organisations* £209,800 *Assets* £75,600

TRUSTEES John Howe; Michael Seabrook; Craig Stevenson; Stuart Boulton; Stephen Murray.

OTHER INFORMATION This trust is the corporate charity of aerospace and defence company, Thales UK Ltd. In 2019 the trust awarded grants to 58 charities.

HOW TO APPLY The 2019 annual report states that the trust 'does not generally solicit requests other than for major donations'. The trustees meet on a quarterly basis.

CONTACT DETAILS Michael Seabrook, Trustee and Secretary, c/o Thales UK Ltd, 350 Longwater Avenue, Green Park, Reading, Berkshire RG2 6GF *Tel.* 0118 943 4500 *Email* mike.seabrook@uk.thalesgroup.com

■ the7stars Foundation

CC NO 1168240 **ESTABLISHED** 2016

WHERE FUNDING CAN BE GIVEN UK.

WHO CAN BENEFIT Registered charities; charitable organisations.

WHAT IS FUNDED Young people experiencing abuse, addiction or homelessness; young people who are carers.

WHAT IS NOT FUNDED Organisations with a turnover above £1.5 million are not eligible for Project funding and Shine Bright funding; organisations with a turnover above £500,000 are not eligible for Star Start funding.

TYPE OF GRANT Project funding; grants to individuals.

RANGE OF GRANTS Typically up to £2,500.

SAMPLE GRANTS A list of beneficiaries was not included in the annual report and accounts.

FINANCES *Financial year end* 31/03/2020 *Income* £217,200 *Total grants* £159,100 *Grants to organisations* £159,100 *Assets* £167,300

TRUSTEES Nick Maddison; Liam Mullins; Rhiannon Murphy; Jenny Biggam; Helen Rose; Anuschka Clarke.

OTHER INFORMATION In 2019/20, the foundation awarded grants to two charities supporting young people who have been abused, two charities supporting child carers, and one charity supporting homeless individuals. Individuals are supported indirectly, through grants made on their behalf to professionals.

HOW TO APPLY Apply using the form for the relevant funding stream on the foundation's website.

CONTACT DETAILS Alexandra Taliadoros, Foundation Director, 6–9 Bush House, North West Wing, Aldwych, London WC2B 4PJ *Email* alexandra@

the7starsfoundation.co.uk *Website* www.the7starsfoundation.co.uk

■ The Theatres Trust Charitable Fund

CC NO 274697 **ESTABLISHED** 1976
WHERE FUNDING CAN BE GIVEN UK.
WHO CAN BENEFIT Theatres.
WHAT IS FUNDED Capital improvements for theatres.
TYPE OF GRANT Capital costs; capacity building.
RANGE OF GRANTS Up to £25,000. The grant size is dependent on the scheme.
SAMPLE GRANTS Swindon Mechanics (£23,400); Unicorn Theatre (£19,100); Eden Court Theatre (£16,200); Pleasance Theatre Trust (£10,000); Story Museum and Unity Theatre (£5,000 each); The Yard Theatre Ltd (£4,000); 2 Northdown Ltd (£3,000).
FINANCES *Financial year end* 31/03/2020 *Income* £1,090,000 *Total grants* £313,400 *Grants to organisations* £313,400 *Assets* £1,080,000
TRUSTEES Annie Hampson; Paul Cartwright; Tim Eyles; Katherine Town; Richard Johnston; Gary Kemp; Patrick Dillon; Richard Baldwin; Truda Spruyt; Jane Spiers.
OTHER INFORMATION This charity is the national advisory public body for theatres. It currently has three open programmes: small grants programme (up to £5,000); Theatre Improvement Scheme (up to £20,000); Theatres at Risk Capacity Building Programme (up to £25,000). It also provides advocacy, advice and other support.
HOW TO APPLY Application forms and eligibility guidelines for each scheme can be found on the charity's website.
CONTACT DETAILS Tom Stickland, Theatres Advisor, 22 Charing Cross Road, London WC2H 0QL *Tel.* 020 7836 8591 *Email* info@theatrestrust.org.uk or tom.stickland@theatrestrust.org.uk *Website* www.theatrestrust.org.uk

■ The Thirty Percy Foundation

CC NO 1177514 **ESTABLISHED** 2018
WHERE FUNDING CAN BE GIVEN England and Wales.
WHO CAN BENEFIT Charitable organisations; CICs; social enterprises; research institutions; innovative projects; individuals.
WHAT IS FUNDED Sustainable development; environmental conservation and research; community development; social welfare.
TYPE OF GRANT Dependent on fund: core funding; project funding; rapid-response funding; development and strategic funding; flexible grants; multi-year grants.
RANGE OF GRANTS Mostly £2,000 to £160,000.
SAMPLE GRANTS The Maggie Keswick Jencks Cancer Caring Centres Trust (£550,000); British Red Cross (£160,000); Cheltenham Festivals (£125,000); Planet Tracker (£100,000); European Climate Foundation (£70,000); Greenpeace UK (£45,000); Land Workers' Alliance (£10,000); Young Gloucestershire (£2,000).
FINANCES *Financial year end* 31/03/2020 *Income* £4,760,000 *Total grants* £2,391,000 *Grants to organisations* £2,230,000 *Assets* £7,150,000
TRUSTEES Mark Phillip-Sorensen; Anne Mann; Katharine Hill; Derek Bardowell.
OTHER INFORMATION In 2019/20 the foundation awarded grants to 28 organisations and individuals through four funds: Systems Fund (£1.18 million); Discretionary Fund (£916,000); Leaders Fund (£171,000); Place-based Fund (£127,000). See foundation's annual report for a full list of grants awarded through each fund. There is no open general fund, as the foundation is keen to explore and test new, innovative ideas and collaborate with others. Grants to individuals totalled £161,000.
HOW TO APPLY Contact the correspondent for further information. There is also an option to subscribe to updates through the website.
CONTACT DETAILS Nikki Clegg, Director of Operations and Grants, 30 Percy Street, London W1T 2DB *Tel.* 020 7514 3052 *Email* hello@thirtypercy.org *Website* https://thirtypercy.org

■ The David Thomas Charitable Trust

CC NO 1083257 **ESTABLISHED** 2000
WHERE FUNDING CAN BE GIVEN UK, in particular Gloucester and surrounding districts.
WHO CAN BENEFIT Registered charities.
WHAT IS FUNDED General charitable purposes.
SAMPLE GRANTS Previous beneficiaries have included: Friends of the Cotswolds, HF Trust Ltd, Holy Trinity Minchinhampton, Tetbury Music Festival and The Butterfly Garden.
FINANCES *Financial year end* 05/04/2020 *Income* £18,100 *Total grants* £127,000 *Grants to organisations* £127,000
TRUSTEES James Davidson; Charles Clark; Mary-Jane Clark; Jane Davidson.
OTHER INFORMATION Full accounts were not available to view on the Charity Commission's website due to the trust's low income. We have therefore estimated the grant total based on the trust's total expenditure.
HOW TO APPLY Contact the correspondent for further information.
CONTACT DETAILS The Trustees, 15 Suffolk Street, London SW1Y 4HG *Tel.* 020 3696 6721 *Email* charities@rftrustee.com

■ The Thompson Family Charitable Trust

CC NO 326801 **ESTABLISHED** 1985
WHERE FUNDING CAN BE GIVEN UK.
WHO CAN BENEFIT Registered charities.
WHAT IS FUNDED General charitable purposes.
SAMPLE GRANTS Royal National Theatre (£600,000); East Anglia's Children's Hospices (£300,000); National Gallery (£250,000); Mind (£100,000); National Literacy Trust (£50,000); The Encephalitis Society (£20,000); British Horse Society (£10,000); Kettering General Hospital (£500).
FINANCES *Financial year end* 31/01/2020 *Income* £7,540,000 *Total grants* £6,950,000 *Grants to organisations* £6,950,000 *Assets* £123,110,000
TRUSTEES Patricia Thompson; Katharine Woodward; Roy Copus.
HOW TO APPLY Apply in writing to the correspondent. The trust's 2019/20 accounts state: 'The trustees meet as regularly as is necessary to assess grant applications. Applications for donations are invited from all categories of registered charity. Applications should be in writing in the first instance, and sent to the Trustees at the Charity's address.'

CONTACT DETAILS The Trustees, 15 Totteridge Common, London N20 8LR *Tel.* 01608 676789 *Email* roycopus@btconnect.com

■ Scott Thomson Charitable Trust

OSCR NO SC004071 **ESTABLISHED** 1965
WHERE FUNDING CAN BE GIVEN UK and overseas.
WHO CAN BENEFIT Christian charitable organisations.
WHAT IS FUNDED General charitable purposes, including: relief of poverty; social welfare; education; advancement of the Christian religion.
RANGE OF GRANTS Up to £5,000.
SAMPLE GRANTS Scripture Union (£4,500); Glasgow City Mission (£3,000); St Luke's Church (£2,400); Habitat for Humanity (£2,000); Bethany Trust (£1,000); Leprosy Mission (£500); Global Justice Now (£100).
FINANCES *Financial year end* 05/04/2020 *Income* £83,200 *Total grants* £61,700 *Grants to organisations* £61,700 *Assets* £143,500
HOW TO APPLY Contact the correspondent for further information.
CONTACT DETAILS The Trustees, 33 Douglas Muir Drive, Glasgow G62 7RJ

■ Sir Jules Thorn Charitable Trust

CC NO 233838 **ESTABLISHED** 1964
WHERE FUNDING CAN BE GIVEN UK.
WHO CAN BENEFIT Registered charities; universities; hospitals; hospices.
WHAT IS FUNDED Medical research; medicine; serious illness; people who are disadvantaged; hospices.
WHAT IS NOT FUNDED Refer to the trust's website for exclusions from each specific grant scheme.
TYPE OF GRANT Capital costs; core and revenue costs; project funding; research.
SAMPLE GRANTS Cornwall Hospice Care (£10,000); Cope Children's Trust (£5,000); Cherry Trees (£1,300); British Blind Sport (£1,000); Boccia England and Unseen UK (£800 each); Central England Lipreading Trust (£500).
FINANCES *Financial year end* 31/12/2019 *Income* £1,600,000 *Total grants* £3,270,000 *Grants to organisations* £3,270,000 *Assets* £121,870,000
TRUSTEES William Sporborg; Elizabeth Charal; Mark Lever; Julian Frederick; Prof. David Russell-Jones; Prof. Sir Ravinder Maini; John Rhodes.
OTHER INFORMATION Grants were broken down as follows: medical research grants (£1.8 million); medically related grants (£1.07 million); small donations scheme (£414,200); Hospice Fund (£243,900).
HOW TO APPLY Apply via the trust's website.
CONTACT DETAILS The Director, 24 Manchester Square, London W1U 3TH *Tel.* 020 7487 5851 *Email* info@julesthorntrust.org.uk or donations@julesthorntrust.org.uk *Website* www.julesthorntrust.org.uk

■ The Thornton Foundation

CC NO 326383 **ESTABLISHED** 1983
WHERE FUNDING CAN BE GIVEN UK.
WHO CAN BENEFIT Registered charities; individuals.
WHAT IS FUNDED General charitable purposes.
TYPE OF GRANT One-off and multi-year grants.
RANGE OF GRANTS Up to £50,000. The majority of grants are between £1,000 and £10,000.
SAMPLE GRANTS St Paul's Knightsbridge Foundation (£1 million); Institute of Cancer Research (£42,700); Cirdan Sailing Trust and Prisoners of Conscience (£7,000 each); National Gallery Trust (£5,000); Books Abroad and Breast Cancer Haven (£2,000 each); Guide Dogs (£1,000).
FINANCES *Financial year end* 05/04/2020 *Income* £91,200 *Total grants* £1,110,000 *Grants to organisations* £1,110,000 *Assets* £3,480,000
TRUSTEES Anthony Isaacs; Henry Thornton; Susan Thornton.
OTHER INFORMATION During 2019/20, grants were awarded to 20 organisations totalling £1.11 million. This included an outlier grant of £1 million to St Paul's Knightsbridge Foundation. The trustees also make occasional educational grants to individuals.
HOW TO APPLY The trust does not accept unsolicited applications.
CONTACT DETAILS Daniel Valentine, Jordans, Eashing Lane, Godalming, Surrey GU7 2QA *Tel.* 01580 713055 *Email* danielvalentine@begbiesaccountants.co.uk

■ The Thornton Trust

CC NO 205357 **ESTABLISHED** 1962
WHERE FUNDING CAN BE GIVEN England and Wales.
WHO CAN BENEFIT Charitable organisations.
WHAT IS FUNDED Promotion and furthering of education and evangelical Christian faith; social welfare; health; young people.
SAMPLE GRANTS A list of beneficiaries was not included in the annual report and accounts.
FINANCES *Financial year end* 05/04/2020 *Income* £44,200 *Total grants* £51,500 *Grants to organisations* £51,500 *Assets* £692,500
TRUSTEES James Thornton; Vivienne Thornton; Catherine Awelan.
HOW TO APPLY The trust has previously stated that it identifies organisations and projects it wishes to support and does not respond to speculative grant applications.
CONTACT DETAILS The Trustees, 25 Castle Street, Hertford, Hertfordshire SG14 1HH *Tel.* 01992 306767 *Email* jim@AshbyPLC.com

■ The Three Guineas Trust

CC NO 1059652 **ESTABLISHED** 1996
WHERE FUNDING CAN BE GIVEN UK.
WHO CAN BENEFIT Charitable organisations; universities.
WHAT IS FUNDED Projects in the field of autistic spectrum disorder (ASD) which include service users in decision-making; disability; prevention of violence; access to justice.
WHAT IS NOT FUNDED Capital projects; individuals; research.
TYPE OF GRANT Project funding; research; core costs.
RANGE OF GRANTS Up to £300,000.
SAMPLE GRANTS Trussell Trust (£1 million); Respond (£300,000); London Community Foundation (£250,000); Stay Safe East (£196,300); Sunbeams Play (£100,000); Project Artworks (£68,000); Resources for Autism (£20,000); University of Bath (£10,000).
FINANCES *Financial year end* 05/04/2020 *Income* £1,870,000 *Total grants* £1,410,000 *Grants to organisations* £1,410,000 *Assets* £21,550,000
TRUSTEES Clare Sainsbury; David Wood; Dominic Flynn.

OTHER INFORMATION The trust is one of the Sainsbury Family Charitable Trusts which share a common administration – see www.sftc.org.uk for more information. During 2019/20, grants were awarded to 54 organisations under the following themes: disability, violence and access to justice (£755,700); autism (£603,400); general (£55,500).

HOW TO APPLY The trustees will only consider applications for proposals in the field of ASD. Application forms can be completed on The Sainsbury Family Charitable Trusts' website.

CONTACT DETAILS Robert Bell, Director, The Sainsbury Family Charitable Trusts, The Peak, 5 Wilton Road, London SW1V 1AP *Tel.* 020 7410 0330 *Email* info@sfct.org.uk *Website* www.sfct.org.uk

■ Three Monkies Trust

CC NO 1164342 **ESTABLISHED** 2015

WHERE FUNDING CAN BE GIVEN UK.

WHO CAN BENEFIT Small to medium-sized charitable and non-profit organisations. Funds are also sometimes granted to projects based within larger organisations where the programme of which it is a part has a budget of less than £500,000.

WHAT IS FUNDED Music and performing arts education; disadvantaged children; affordable housing for key workers in London.

SAMPLE GRANTS A list of beneficiaries was not included in the trust's annual report and accounts.

FINANCES *Financial year end* 31/03/2020 *Income* £2,400,000 *Total grants* £143,100 *Grants to organisations* £143,100 *Assets* £9,400,000

TRUSTEES Anna Higgins; Nigel Higgins; Sanya Polescuk.

OTHER INFORMATION Grants were distributed as follows: music and arts (£117,000); children and young people (£20,600); other (£3,500) affordable accommodation (£2,000).

HOW TO APPLY Applications can be made in writing by post or email. Full details of what should be included in the application can be found on the trust's website. Applications are generally considered at trustees' meetings in June/July and December/January. The deadline for applications is the 31st of May and the 30th of November.

CONTACT DETAILS The Trustees, c/o Belize Court Garages, Belize Lane, Hampstead, London NW3 5AJ *Tel.* 07928 746013 *Email* info@threemonkiestrust.org *Website* https://www.threemonkiestrust.org

■ The Thriplow Charitable Trust

CC NO 1025531 **ESTABLISHED** 1993

WHERE FUNDING CAN BE GIVEN Worldwide.

WHO CAN BENEFIT Registered charities; universities.

WHAT IS FUNDED Academic research; exhibitions and expeditions; wildlife conservation/environmental research; publishing of research; conservation of manuscripts/textiles; musical training; teacher training and resources in less financially developed countries; early career development; undergraduate and graduate bursaries.

WHAT IS NOT FUNDED Capital projects; individuals; primary, secondary and early years education.

TYPE OF GRANT Core/revenue costs; seed funding/start-up funding; project funding.

RANGE OF GRANTS £1,000 to £5,000.

SAMPLE GRANTS Previous beneficiaries have included: Academy of Ancient Music; African Child Trust; British Council for the Prevention of Blindness; Open Book Publishers; Spinal Research; Royal Scottish Conservatoire; Textile Conservation Foundation; University of West of England; Zoological Society of London.

FINANCES *Financial year end* 05/04/2020 *Income* £395,600 *Total grants* £138,000 *Grants to organisations* £138,000 *Assets* £114,500

TRUSTEES Prof. Lord Robert Mair; Dr Harriet Crawford; Prof. David McKitterick; Prof. Dame Jean Thomas; Prof. Dame Caroline Humphrey.

HOW TO APPLY Application forms are available to download from the trust's website and should be submitted by post together with a covering letter and any supporting material. The trustees meet regularly to consider and approve grants.

CONTACT DETAILS Catharine Walston, Secretary, PO Box 225, Royston, Hertfordshire SG8 1BG *Tel.* 01763 260391 *Email* catharinewalston@gmail.com *Website* www.thriplowcharitabletrust.org

■ Mrs R. P. Tindall's Charitable Trust

CC NO 250558 **ESTABLISHED** 1966

WHERE FUNDING CAN BE GIVEN UK and the Republic of Ireland; Egypt; Israel; Lebanon, Madagascar; Sudan; Tanzania.

WHO CAN BENEFIT Charitable organisations; churches; schools and colleges; individuals; members of the clergy.

WHAT IS FUNDED The Christian Church; education; music; health; social welfare; overseas aid. The trust also supports the welfare of Christian clergy and their dependants.

TYPE OF GRANT Project costs; capital costs; core/revenue costs.

RANGE OF GRANTS Typically up to £5,000.

SAMPLE GRANTS Sarum College (£36,000); Germinate, Salisbury-Sudan Medical Link and The Diocese of Antsiranana (£5,000 each); Salisbury Diocesan Board of Finance (£3,750); Embrace the Middle East (£3,000); Chess UK, Church of England Pensions Board and The Footprints Project (£2,500 each).

FINANCES *Financial year end* 31/12/2019 *Income* £118,100 *Total grants* £106,900 *Grants to organisations* £104,500 *Assets* £3,780,000

TRUSTEES Giles Fletcher; Michael Newman; Canon Philp; Nicola Halls; Claire Newman.

OTHER INFORMATION In 2019, 41 grants were made across the following categories: education (£42,000); welfare (£21,500); Christian Church (£16,000); medical causes (£15,000); Madagascar and Africa (£5,800); music (£4,300). The trust also made grants to individuals for educational purposes totalling £2,400.

HOW TO APPLY According to the trust's annual report, the trustees invite applications for funding by advertising in charitable trusts' registers. Contact the correspondent for further information.

CONTACT DETAILS The Trustees, Appletree House, Wishford Road, Middle Woodford, Salisbury, Wiltshire SP4 6NG *Tel.* 01722 782329

The Tobacco Pipe Makers and Tobacco Trade Benevolent Fund

CC NO 1135646 **ESTABLISHED** 2010

WHERE FUNDING CAN BE GIVEN London.

WHO CAN BENEFIT Charities and educational organisations.

WHAT IS FUNDED General charitable purposes; disadvantaged children; education.

RANGE OF GRANTS £500 to £20,000.

SAMPLE GRANTS Pembroke Music and Dance projects (£30,000); Spitalfields Crypt Trust (£11,000); The London Regiment Welfare Fund (£2,500); The Company of Hackney Carriage Drivers (£1,400); ABF The Soldiers' Charity (£1,000); Royal British Legion (£500); The Wellington Trust (£250).

FINANCES *Financial year end* 31/03/2020 *Income* £448,900 *Total grants* £304,200 *Grants to organisations* £139,700 *Assets* £7,220,000

TRUSTEES Nicola Snook; Simon Orlik; Jonathan Fell; Ralph Edmondson; Katherine Golding; Martine Petetin-Munn; Susan Curran; Tony Scanlan; Mark Gower-Smith.

OTHER INFORMATION During 2019/20, grants were awarded to 25 organisations and 8 individuals. The charity provides assistance to individuals who have worked in the tobacco trade in any capacity and their dependants through the welfare fund.

HOW TO APPLY Application forms for the general fund and the welfare fund can be found on the charity's website.

CONTACT DETAILS The Trustees, 2 Spa Close, Brill, Aylesbury, Buckinghamshire HP18 9RZ *Tel.* 01844 238655 *Email* benevolentfund@tobaccolivery.org *Website* https://www.tobaccolivery.org/our-charitable-activities.html

The Tolkien Trust

CC NO 1150801 **ESTABLISHED** 1977

WHERE FUNDING CAN BE GIVEN UK, with some preference for Oxfordshire; overseas, including Malawi, Rwanda, Democratic Republic of Congo, Haiti and Europe.

WHO CAN BENEFIT Registered charities.

WHAT IS FUNDED Arts; education; the environment; homelessness; international development; international relations and peace building; migration; prison reform; health; medical research.

WHAT IS NOT FUNDED Individuals.

RANGE OF GRANTS £5,000 to £217,000.

SAMPLE GRANTS Pesticide Action Network UK (£217,000); Operation Fistula (£150,000); Greenpeace Environmental Trust (£80,300); Asylum Welcome (£40,000); Uganda Childbirth Injury Fund (£30,000); Reading List Foundation (£20,000); Bloemfontein Cathedral (£5,000).

FINANCES *Financial year end* 31/12/2019 *Income* £5,180,000 *Total grants* £3,370,000 *Grants to organisations* £3,370,000 *Assets* £33,340,000

TRUSTEES Priscilla Tolkien; Michael Tolkien; Baillie Tolkien.

OTHER INFORMATION The total number of grants awarded in 2019 was 80. The trust also provides matched funding.

HOW TO APPLY Unsolicited applications are not accepted; the trustees request applications from chosen charities.

CONTACT DETAILS Nerissa Martin, Prama House, 267 Banbury Road, Oxford, Oxfordshire OX2 7HT *Tel.* 01865 339330 *Email* nerissa.martin@tolkientrust.org *Website* www.tolkientrust.org

The Tomoro Foundation

CC NO 1178061 **ESTABLISHED** 2018

WHERE FUNDING CAN BE GIVEN UK and overseas.

WHO CAN BENEFIT Registered charities.

WHAT IS FUNDED General charitable purposes; children and young people's education; the environment; social welfare.

RANGE OF GRANTS £5,000 to £25,000.

SAMPLE GRANTS Bowel Cancer UK (£25,000); Greenhouse Sports (£15,000); Arts for Dementia and Riding for the Disabled (£7,500 each); West London Synagogue of British Jews (£5,000).

FINANCES *Financial year end* 05/04/2020 *Income* £1,850,000 *Total grants* £110,000 *Grants to organisations* £110,000 *Assets* £2,700,000

TRUSTEES Nadine Jayes; Michael Rembaum; Tanya Rembaum.

HOW TO APPLY Contact the correspondent for further information.

CONTACT DETAILS Martin Pollock, Administrator, 42 Berkeley Square, London W1J 5AW

The Tompkins Foundation

CC NO 281405 **ESTABLISHED** 1980

WHERE FUNDING CAN BE GIVEN UK, with a preference for the parish of Hampstead Norreys in Berkshire and the parish of West Grinstead in West Sussex.

WHO CAN BENEFIT Registered charities; schools; theatres; hospitals; hospices; places of worship.

WHAT IS FUNDED General charitable purposes; education and training; recreation; religious causes; health.

WHAT IS NOT FUNDED Individuals.

TYPE OF GRANT One-off and recurring.

RANGE OF GRANTS Up to £25,000.

SAMPLE GRANTS Arthroplasty for Arthritis, Royal Marsden Cancer Charity and The Police Foundation (£25,000 each); Maggie's (£10,000); Douglas Macmillan Hospice and Families United Network (£5,000 each); The National Rheumatoid Arthritis Society (£1,000).

FINANCES *Financial year end* 05/04/2020 *Income* £340,100 *Total grants* £296,000 *Grants to organisations* £296,000 *Assets* £11,620,000

TRUSTEES Peter Vaines; Elizabeth Tompkins; Victoria Brenninkmeijer.

OTHER INFORMATION Grants were made to 15 organisations in 2019/20.

HOW TO APPLY Apply in writing to the correspondent. Unsolicited applications are unlikely to be successful as the foundation has a regular list of charities that receive support.

CONTACT DETAILS The Trustees, 7 Belgrave Square, London SW1X 8PH *Tel.* 020 7235 9322

The Tory Family Foundation

CC NO 326584 **ESTABLISHED** 1984

WHERE FUNDING CAN BE GIVEN Worldwide, with a preference for East Kent.

WHO CAN BENEFIT Charitable organisations.

WHAT IS FUNDED General charitable purposes; education and training; Christian causes; social welfare; medical causes.
TYPE OF GRANT Capital costs; research.
SAMPLE GRANTS Previous beneficiaries have included: Ashford YMCA, Bletchley Park, Canterbury Cathedral, Concern Worldwide, Deal Festival, Disability Law Service, Folk Rainbow Club, Foresight, Friends of Birzett, Gurkha Welfare, Kent Cancer Trust, Royal British Legion, Uppingham Foundation and Youth Action Wiltshire.
FINANCES *Financial year end* 30/04/2020 *Income* £153,200 *Total grants* £82,600 *Grants to organisations* £82,600 *Assets* £4,010,000
TRUSTEES James Tory; Paul Tory; S. Tory; David Callister; Jill Perkins.
HOW TO APPLY Apply in writing to the correspondent. Only successful applicants will be notified.
CONTACT DETAILS Paul Tory, Trustee, Etchinghill Golf Club, Canterbury Road, Etchinghill, Folkestone, Kent CT18 8FA *Tel.* 01303 862280

■ The Tottenham Grammar School Foundation

CC NO 312634 **ESTABLISHED** 1989
WHERE FUNDING CAN BE GIVEN Haringey.
WHO CAN BENEFIT Schools and colleges; charities; voluntary groups; organisations working with young people; individuals up to the age of 25.
WHAT IS FUNDED Education of young people (under 25 years old).
WHAT IS NOT FUNDED The employment of staff; the construction, adaptation, repair and maintenance of school buildings; the repair and maintenance of school equipment; the direct delivery of the national curriculum; the purchase of vehicles.
TYPE OF GRANT Project costs; capital costs; equipment.
RANGE OF GRANTS Up to £124,000 but mostly under £20,000.
SAMPLE GRANTS Haringey Sports Development Trust (£124,700); Haringey Young Musicians (£20,000); Crowland Primary School (£15,300); Haringey Police and Community Amateur Boxing Club (£10,000); Action for Kids (£9,000); Lubavitch Youth Groups (£6,000); St Paul's and All Hallows Federation (£4,000).
FINANCES *Financial year end* 31/08/2020 *Income* £551,100 *Total grants* £1,091,200 *Grants to organisations* £766,000 *Assets* £24,900,000
TRUSTEES Frederick Gruncell; Keith Brown; Paul Compton; Terry Clarke; Victoria Phillips; John Fowl; Andrew Krokou; Graham Kantorowicz; David Kaplan; Barbara Blake; Derek Levy.
OTHER INFORMATION The foundation made 183 grants to schools and other organisations during 2019/20. Grants to individuals during the year totalled £325,200. Only organisations receiving the 51 largest grants were listed as beneficiaries in the accounts.
HOW TO APPLY Application packs can be requested by email from grantsform@tgsf.info. Upcoming deadlines can be found on the foundation's website.
CONTACT DETAILS The Trustees, PO Box 34098, London N13 5XU *Tel.* 020 8882 2999 *Email* info@tgsf.info *Website* www.tgsf.info

■ Tower Hill Trust

CC NO 206225 **ESTABLISHED** 1934
WHERE FUNDING CAN BE GIVEN Tower Hill and Tower Hamlets.
WHO CAN BENEFIT Charities; community organisations; schools.
WHAT IS FUNDED The development and provision of gardens and open spaces; biodiversity projects by schools and community groups in school grounds, around housing estates or in community gardens. Grants are also occasionally made for sport and leisure facilities, education and social welfare.
WHAT IS NOT FUNDED Activities that do not directly benefit Tower Hill and the London Borough of Tower Hamlets.
TYPE OF GRANT Preference is given for equipment/ capital costs. Project funding is also available.
RANGE OF GRANTS Biodiversity grants: £100 to £2,000. Main grants: generally around £1,000 to £15,000.
SAMPLE GRANTS Trees for Cities (two grants totalling £22,000); Shadwell Community Project (£15,000); Cleanup UK (£10,000); First Love Foundation (£6,000); Bikeworks (£5,000); Tower Hamlets Youth Sport Foundation (£4,500); Vallance Community Sports Association (£1,800); George Green's Secondary School (£580).
FINANCES *Financial year end* 30/04/2020 *Income* £220,200 *Total grants* £151,900 *Grants to organisations* £151,900 *Assets* £7,600,000
TRUSTEES Susan Wood; Davina Walter; Ken Clunie; Jonathan Solomon; Les Chapman; Edward Walter; Colonel Richard Harrold.
OTHER INFORMATION There were 21 grants awarded under the Main Grant Programme during the year and 11 grants awarded under the Biodiversity Grant Programme. The trust also pays for three bursaries for pupils from Tower Hamlets at the City of London School for Girls. The trust prioritises projects that meet two or more of its objects.
HOW TO APPLY Applications for both grant programmes can be made through the application portal on the trust's website. Applications will not be accepted by post or email. Grant deadlines can be found on the website.
CONTACT DETAILS Elaine Crush, Grant Officer, Marshall House, 66 Newcomen Street, London SE1 1YT *Email* enquiries@towerhilltrust.org.uk *Website* www.towerhilltrust.org.uk

■ The Toy Trust

CC NO 1001634 **ESTABLISHED** 1991
WHERE FUNDING CAN BE GIVEN UK and Ireland; overseas.
WHO CAN BENEFIT Children's charities registered in the UK and Ireland that have been operating for at least one year; international organisations with a UK office.
WHAT IS FUNDED The welfare of disadvantaged children (up to 13 years old); emergency aid for any crisis involving children.
WHAT IS NOT FUNDED Salaries; research; running costs; books, publishing or individual cases (unless there is a compelling reason).
TYPE OF GRANT Equipment; project funding; services.
RANGE OF GRANTS Mainly under £5,000. Occasionally larger grants are made.
SAMPLE GRANTS Action for Kids and Over The Wall (£30,000 each); Bag Books (£5,100); The Children's Foundation (£4,600); Yorda

Playhouse Adventurers (£3,000); Children in Hunger and Three Ways School (£2,500 each).

FINANCES *Financial year end* 31/12/2019
Income £210,300 *Total grants* £167,700
Grants to organisations £167,700
Assets £131,500

TRUSTEES British Toy and Hobby Association Ltd; Jon Diver; Graham Canning; Phil Ratcliffe; Simon Pilkington.

OTHER INFORMATION This trust was registered in 1991 to centralise the giving of the British Toy and Hobby Association. During 2019, grants were made or committed to 42 organisations. Only organisations receiving grants of over £2,500 were listed as beneficiaries in the charity's accounts. Grants of under £2,500 totalled £38,900.

HOW TO APPLY Application forms can be found on the trust's website. Completed applications should be sent to the trust's office, along with an extra photocopy, to be considered at the next meeting. The trustees meet four times a year. Application guidelines and upcoming deadlines can be found on the website.

CONTACT DETAILS Tracey Butcher, Office and Services Manager, British Toy and Hobby Association, BTHA House, 142–144 Long Lane, London SE1 4BS *Tel.* 020 7701 7271 *Email* tracey@btha.co.uk *Website* https://toytrust.co.uk

■ The Toye Foundation

CC NO 1147256 **ESTABLISHED** 2011

WHERE FUNDING CAN BE GIVEN UK and overseas.

WHO CAN BENEFIT Charitable organisations; individuals.

WHAT IS FUNDED Christian causes; general charitable purposes. According to its website, the foundation supports 'Christian Ministry in the UK and abroad by giving grants to assist with mission, ministry and evangelism'.

TYPE OF GRANT One-off; recurrent.

RANGE OF GRANTS £20 to £28,000.

SAMPLE GRANTS Previous beneficiaries have included: Gangs Unite CIC (£28,000); IBA Boxing and Premier Christian Radio (£15,000 each); Padarom Ltd – Bangles play financing (£11,000); Goldings Church (£6,000); European Christian Mission (£3,000); Giddeons International (£500).

FINANCES *Financial year end* 31/01/2020
Income £18,800 *Total grants* £59,000
Grants to organisations £59,000

TRUSTEES William Toye; Rosemarie Toye; John Worby; Jeremy Sandy.

OTHER INFORMATION Full accounts were not available to view on the Charity Commission's website due to the foundation's low income. We have therefore estimated the grant total based on the foundation's total expenditure.

HOW TO APPLY Contact the correspondent for further information.

CONTACT DETAILS The Trustees, c/o Goldings Church, England's Lane, Loughton, Essex IG10 2QX *Tel.* 01763 247371 *Email* admin@thetoyefoundation.com or use the contact form on the website. *Website* https://www.thetoyefoundation.com

■ Toyota Manufacturing UK Charitable Trust

CC NO 1124678 **ESTABLISHED** 2008

WHERE FUNDING CAN BE GIVEN Burnaston; Deeside.

WHO CAN BENEFIT Registered charities; local community groups; sports and leisure clubs.

WHAT IS FUNDED Community; road safety; social inclusion; social welfare; health and medical research. Support may also be given to charities with which Toyota employees are involved.

WHAT IS NOT FUNDED Full exclusion criteria for Member Grants can be found on the trust's website.

RANGE OF GRANTS Generally up to £5,000.

SAMPLE GRANTS St John Ambulance (£5,000); Starr in the Community (£4,400); Multi Faith Centre (£3,000); Darley Abbey Cricket Club and Newlife Charity (£2,000 each); Osbourne Trust and Rainbows Hospice (£1,000 each); Teenage Cancer Trust (£500); 1st Chellaston Guides (£400); Claire House Hospice (£120).

FINANCES *Financial year end* 31/12/2019
Income £355,100 *Total grants* £106,600
Grants to organisations £106,600
Assets £534,000

TRUSTEES Sarah Overson; Kevin Reader; Gary Newington; Dave Richards; Kevin Potter; Tim Freeman.

OTHER INFORMATION This is the charitable trust of Toyota Motor Manufacturing (UK) Ltd. Income is largely derived from fundraising activities by the company's employees. The trust also provides matched funding for its employees ('members'). During the year, grants were awarded to 73 organisations. Grants were distributed through the following programmes: Community Grants (£46,100); Member Grants (£41,700); Member Match Funding (£12,400). Member grants are for charities which have an employee involved in their activities. Funding was also awarded for three apprentice volunteering projects (£6,500).

HOW TO APPLY Application forms for Member Grants can be downloaded from the website. Beneficiaries of Community Grant Awards are nominated by company employees. Contact the trust for further information.

CONTACT DETAILS The Trustees, c/o Toyota Motor Manufacturing (UK) Ltd, Derby, Derbyshire DE1 9TA *Tel.* 01332 283611 *Email* charitabletrust@toyotauk.com *Website* www.toyotauk.com/the-toyota-charitable-trust/charitable-trust-overview.html

■ The Trades House of Glasgow

OSCR NO SC040548 **ESTABLISHED** 1920

WHERE FUNDING CAN BE GIVEN Glasgow.

WHO CAN BENEFIT Charitable organisations; individuals.

WHAT IS FUNDED General charitable purposes; children and young people; social welfare; education.

WHAT IS NOT FUNDED Funding is not provided outside Glasgow and the surrounding areas (there is a postcode checker available on the charity's website indicating eligible areas). Political, municipal and ecclesiastical causes cannot be funded.

TYPE OF GRANT Project costs; capital costs.

RANGE OF GRANTS The majority of grants are for under £3,000.

SAMPLE GRANTS Voluntary Tutors Organisation (£29,700); First Steps Future (£7,500); Glasgow Disabled Scouts (£6,000); Glasgow Bute Benevolent Society (£5,000); Street League (£4,000); Linkes (£3,500).

FINANCES *Financial year end* 30/09/2020 *Income* £1,110,000 *Total grants* £414,500 *Grants to organisations* £163,200 *Assets* £21,170,000

TRUSTEES Tom McInally; Ken Dalgleish; Dr Alistair Dorward; Bruce Reidford; Keith Brown; Billy Birse-Stewart; Ewen Mackie.

OTHER INFORMATION Grants totalling £163,200 were made to 63 organisations and 528 individuals received grants totalling £251,300. Only organisations receiving grants of over £3,000 were listed as beneficiaries in the charity's accounts. Grants of under £3,000 totalled £80,200 and were awarded to 51 organisations.

HOW TO APPLY Application forms are available to download from the website, where further guidance about what to include and upcoming deadlines are also provided.

CONTACT DETAILS John Gilchrist, Chief Executive and Clerk, Trades Hall, 85 Glassford Street, Glasgow G1 1UH *Tel.* 0141 553 1605 *Email* john.gilchrist@tradeshouse.org.uk *Website* www.tradeshouse.org.uk

■ David William Traill Cargill Fund

OSCR NO SC012703 **ESTABLISHED** 1939

WHERE FUNDING CAN BE GIVEN UK and overseas.

WHO CAN BENEFIT Registered charities; universities; hospices.

WHAT IS FUNDED General charitable purposes.

WHAT IS NOT FUNDED Individuals.

SAMPLE GRANTS Previous beneficiaries have included: City of Glasgow Society of Social Service; Colquhoun Bequest Fund for Incurables; Crathie Opportunity Holidays; Glasgow and West of Scotland Society for the Blind; Glasgow City Mission; Greenock Medical Aid Society; Lead Scotland; North Glasgow Community Forum; Scottish Maritime Museum – Irvine; Scottish Episcopal Church; Scottish Motor Neurone Disease Association; Three Towns Blind Bowling/Social Club.

FINANCES *Financial year end* 30/11/2019 *Income* £418,500 *Total grants* £268,000 *Grants to organisations* £268,000 *Assets* £10,630,000

OTHER INFORMATION The 2018/19 accounts were the latest available at the time of writing (June 2021). A list of beneficiaries was not included in the annual report and accounts.

HOW TO APPLY Applications may be made in writing to the correspondent, supported by up-to-date accounts. The trustees meet quarterly.

CONTACT DETAILS The Trustees, Miller Beckett and Jackson Ltd, 190 St Vincent Street, Glasgow G2 5SP

■ Annie Tranmer Charitable Trust

CC NO 1044231 **ESTABLISHED** 1989

WHERE FUNDING CAN BE GIVEN Suffolk and adjacent counties.

WHO CAN BENEFIT Charitable organisations; individuals.

WHAT IS FUNDED General charitable purposes; education and training; children and young people.

RANGE OF GRANTS Up to £5,000 but mostly £500 to £2,000.

SAMPLE GRANTS Age UK Suffolk (£2,000); Tall Ships Youth Trust (£1,500); Strong Bones (£1,200); Asthma UK and Rainbow Trust (£1,000 each); Great Ormond Street Hospital Children's Charity and Happy Days (£500 each).

FINANCES *Financial year end* 05/04/2020 *Income* £132,100 *Total grants* £101,400 *Grants to organisations* £79,800 *Assets* £3,150,000

TRUSTEES Patrick Grieve; Mary Allen; Nigel Bonham Carter; Hector Wykes-Sneyd; Valerie Lewis.

OTHER INFORMATION Grants were made to 81 organisations in 2019/20. Grants to 30 individuals during the year totalled £21,700.

HOW TO APPLY Apply in writing to the correspondent. The 2019/20 accounts state: 'The charity receives applications for funding from institutions and individuals. The trustees review the applications against the objectives of the charity before deciding whether or not to authorise the application and make the grant.'

CONTACT DETAILS Mrs A. Williams, Trust Administrator, 55 Dobbs Lane, Kesgrave, Ipswich, Suffolk IP5 2QA *Tel.* 07801 556002 *Email* amwilliams7903@gmail.com

■ The Constance Travis Charitable Trust

CC NO 294540 **ESTABLISHED** 1986

WHERE FUNDING CAN BE GIVEN UK and overseas, with a preference for Northamptonshire.

WHO CAN BENEFIT Registered charities.

WHAT IS FUNDED General charitable purposes including: health; social welfare; housing; arts and culture; animal welfare; economic and community development; education and training; disability; overseas aid; religious activities; sport and recreation; the environment, conservation and heritage.

TYPE OF GRANT One-off grants for core, capital and project support.

RANGE OF GRANTS Generally up to £20,000.

SAMPLE GRANTS Northamptonshire Community Foundation (£5.29 million); Maggie's (£100,000); People's Dispensary for Sick Animals (£60,000); Age UK Northamptonshire (£50,000); Royal Opera House (£20,000).

FINANCES *Financial year end* 31/12/2019 *Income* £2,390,000 *Total grants* £7,620,000 *Grants to organisations* £7,620,000 *Assets* £156,750,000

TRUSTEES Ernest Travis; Peta Travis; Matthew Travis.

OTHER INFORMATION The grant total includes a donation of £5.29 million to the trust's named endowment fund with Northamptonshire Community Foundation.

HOW TO APPLY Apply in writing to the correspondent. The trustees meet at least quarterly to consider grants. The trust does not welcome contact prior to application.

CONTACT DETAILS The Chair of Trustees, 86 Drayton Gardens, London SW10 9SB *Email* travistrust86@yahoo.co.uk

■ The Treeside Trust

CC NO 1061586 **ESTABLISHED** 1997

WHERE FUNDING CAN BE GIVEN UK; Oldham.

WHO CAN BENEFIT Registered charities; unregistered charities; schools; universities; religious bodies/institutions.

WHAT IS FUNDED General charitable purposes.

TYPE OF GRANT Capital costs; core/revenue costs.

RANGE OF GRANTS Up to £5,000.

SAMPLE GRANTS A list of beneficiaries was not included in the annual report and accounts.

FINANCES *Financial year end* 31/03/2020 *Income* £25,600 *Total grants* £53,000 *Grants to organisations* £53,000 *Assets* £1,160,000

TRUSTEES Catherine Gould; Diana Ives; Richard Gould; Roger Gould; Richard Ives.

HOW TO APPLY Contact the correspondent for further information.

CONTACT DETAILS Roger Gould, Trustee, 4 The Park, Grasscroft, Oldham, Lancashire OL4 4ES *Tel.* 01457 876422

■ The Trefoil Trust

CC NO 1044101 **ESTABLISHED** 1995

WHERE FUNDING CAN BE GIVEN UK.

WHO CAN BENEFIT Charitable organisations.

WHAT IS FUNDED Medicine; children and young people; people with disabilities; the arts; the armed forces.

WHAT IS NOT FUNDED Individuals.

RANGE OF GRANTS £1,000 to £8,000.

SAMPLE GRANTS WaterAid (£8,000); The Smile Train (£5,500); FareShare and SSAFA (£5,000 each); Sage House (£4,000); Horatio's Garden and Spinal Injuries Association (£2,000 each); Port Isaac Village Hall and The Family Haven (£1,000 each).

FINANCES *Financial year end* 31/12/2019 *Income* £48,600 *Total grants* £69,000 *Grants to organisations* £69,000 *Assets* £995,700

TRUSTEE Trefoil Trustees Ltd.

OTHER INFORMATION Grants were made to 27 organisations during 2019.

HOW TO APPLY Applications should be made in writing to the correspondent. The trust's 2019 accounts state: 'Applications to the Charity for donations will only be considered if received in writing and accompanied by the charitable organisation's latest report and full accounts.'

CONTACT DETAILS The Trustees, Brook Farm, Little Marcle, Ledbury, Herefordshire HR8 2JY *Tel.* 07740 007606

■ The Tresanton Trust

CC NO 1103150 **ESTABLISHED** 2003

WHERE FUNDING CAN BE GIVEN UK; overseas.

WHO CAN BENEFIT Charitable organisations.

WHAT IS FUNDED Social justice; social welfare; medical research; children and young people; wildlife and the environment.

SAMPLE GRANTS Honeypot Children's Charity (£230,500); Liberty Kitchen and The Prince's Trust (£75,000 each); Water Harvest (£60,000); LATCH (£10,000).

FINANCES *Financial year end* 30/11/2019 *Income* £9,800,000 *Total grants* £960,600 *Grants to organisations* £960,600 *Assets* £8,860,000

TRUSTEES Claire Orton; Silke Meixner; Shelley Lawson; Jerry Lawson.

OTHER INFORMATION Grants were distributed as follows: children and youth welfare (£448,100); social justice and poverty (£284,000); medical research (£131,800); wildlife and environmental (£96,700). The 2018/19 accounts were the latest available at the time of writing (June 2021).

HOW TO APPLY Contact the correspondent for further information.

CONTACT DETAILS The Trustees, Birch Hall, Church Road, Windlesham GU20 6BN *Email* info@tresantontrust.com

■ The Triangle Trust (1949) Fund

CC NO 222860 **ESTABLISHED** 1949

WHERE FUNDING CAN BE GIVEN UK, with some preference for Northern Ireland, Scotland and Wales.

WHO CAN BENEFIT Community and voluntary organisations.

WHAT IS FUNDED Support for young carers; rehabilitation of young offenders and ex-offenders.

WHAT IS NOT FUNDED Restorative justice initiatives; crime prevention initiatives; non-project specific core costs; overseas projects; non-UK-registered organisations; individuals; general appeals; emergency funding; capital projects; academic research; promotion of religion; disaster relief; organisations which have more than one year's worth of unrestricted reserves; organisations which have made an unsuccessful application to the trust in the last two years. The trust wants to fund existing projects.

TYPE OF GRANT Core/revenue costs; seed funding/start-up funding; development funding.

RANGE OF GRANTS Up to £30,000 per year for up to two years.

SAMPLE GRANTS Circles UK (£35,000); Scarborough and Ryedale Carers Resource (£26,900); Promas Caring for People CIC (£25,000); Family Tree Wirral (£20,000); Harrow Carers (£14,900); The Reasons Why Foundation (£10,800); Carers Milton Keynes (£7,400); Open Gates (£3,200).

FINANCES *Financial year end* 31/03/2020 *Income* £737,400 *Total grants* £555,800 *Grants to organisations* £544,000 *Assets* £19,800,000

TRUSTEES Andrew Pitt; Julian Weinberg; Karen Drury; Doreen Foster; Dr James Anderson; Alison Hope; James Marshall; David Loudon.

OTHER INFORMATION In total, 31 grants were awarded to organisations throughout the year in two categories: carers (£287,300) and rehabilitation (£256,700). Also, 11 grants were awarded to individuals for the relief of poverty. The trust has now narrowed its focus to young carers and offenders/ex-offenders. A detailed summary of the grants given can be downloaded from the trust's helpful website.

HOW TO APPLY There are two rounds of funding each year: one for organisations working with young carers and another for organisations working with young offenders/ex-offenders. Opening and closing dates for each round of funding are published on the website. There is also a mailing list that organisations can sign up for, to be notified when applications open. The application process is in two stages. Following the submission of an initial online application, shortlisted applicants will be asked to host a visit from the trust where they will be required to present their strategic plan for the next few years.

CONTACT DETAILS Annie Corpe, Grants Assistant, Brighton Junction, 1A Isetta Square, 35 New England Street, Brighton BN1 4GQ *Tel.* 01273 810263 (Monday to Thursday) *Email* info@triangletrust.org.uk *Website* www.triangletrust.org.uk

■ Tropical Health and Education Trust

CC NO 1113101 **ESTABLISHED** 1988

WHERE FUNDING CAN BE GIVEN UK; Africa; Asia.

WHO CAN BENEFIT Medical institutions; universities; health charities.

WHAT IS FUNDED The training of health workers in low- and middle-income countries.
TYPE OF GRANT Project costs.
RANGE OF GRANTS £37,000 to £67,000.
SAMPLE GRANTS Addenbrooke Charitable Trust (£67,200); University College London Hospitals Charity (£50,600); Birmingham City University (£48,500); Sheffield Health and Social Care NHS Foundation Trust (£41,000); Standing Voice (£37,100).
FINANCES *Financial year end* 31/12/2019 *Income* £3,610,000 *Total grants* £830,500 *Grants to organisations* £830,500 *Assets* £1,770,000
TRUSTEES Gerard Byrne; Dr Titilola Banjoko; Prof. Irene May Leigh; Jonathan Roland; Dr Anne Austen; Prof. Judith Ellis; Claire Hammond; Dr Jemima Dennis-Antwi; Hugh Risebrow; Michael McKirdy; Janice Barber; Roda Ahmed.
OTHER INFORMATION Grants awarded during the year were to institutions only.
HOW TO APPLY Application forms are available on the charity's website.
CONTACT DETAILS Jacqueline Mutibwa, Secretary, Tropical Health and Education Trust, 1 St Andrews Place, London NW1 4LE *Tel.* 07908 455228 *Email* info@thet.org *Website* www.thet.org

■ The Troutsdale Charitable Trust

CC NO 1165224 **ESTABLISHED** 2015
WHERE FUNDING CAN BE GIVEN England.
WHO CAN BENEFIT Charitable organisations; children and young people.
WHAT IS FUNDED Social welfare; medical research; children and young people; religious buildings; animal welfare.
SAMPLE GRANTS A list of beneficiaries was not included in the annual report and accounts.
FINANCES *Financial year end* 05/04/2020 *Income* £50,500 *Total grants* £128,300 *Grants to organisations* £128,300 *Assets* £1,570,000
TRUSTEES Richard Guthrie; John Guthrie; Peter Guthrie; Leslie Guthrie.
OTHER INFORMATION Grants were broken down as follows: the personal and educational development of children and young people (£69,000); medical research (£32,500); social welfare (£21,300); animal welfare (£3,500); religious buildings (£2,000).
HOW TO APPLY Contact the correspondent for further information.
CONTACT DETAILS The Trustees, c/o Moore Stephens, 12–13 Alma Square, Scarborough YO11 1JU *Tel.* 01723 360361

■ The True Colours Trust

CC NO 1089893 **ESTABLISHED** 2001
WHERE FUNDING CAN BE GIVEN UK and Africa.
WHO CAN BENEFIT Registered charities.
WHAT IS FUNDED Improving access to palliative care for babies, children and young people in the UK: enabling children and young people with disabilities to live their lives to the full; improving access to pain relief and palliative care in Africa.
TYPE OF GRANT One-off small grants for capital costs. Large grants are available for: project funding; development funding; core costs; capital costs.
RANGE OF GRANTS Small grants of up to £10,000.
SAMPLE GRANTS King's College London (£500,000); International Children's Palliative Care Network and Little Village (£20,000 each); Breakthro Llanelli (£5,000); Bromley Parent Voice (£4,000); Pathfield Activities Club (£2,000).
FINANCES *Financial year end* 05/04/2020 *Income* £1,780,000 *Total grants* £2,350,000 *Grants to organisations* £2,350,000 *Assets* £11,440,000
TRUSTEES Lucy Sainsbury; Tim Price; Dominic Flynn; David Wood.
OTHER INFORMATION The trust is one of the Sainsbury Family Charitable Trusts which share a common administration – see www.sftc.org.uk for more information. Grants were made for the following purposes: palliative care in Africa (£938,400); children and young people in the UK (£862,900); small grants in the UK (£196,900).
HOW TO APPLY The trustees only consider unsolicited applications for their Small Grants programme. Applications can be made via the trust's website.
CONTACT DETAILS The Trustees, The Peak, 5 Wilton Road, London SW1V 1AP *Tel.* 020 7410 0330 *Email* info@sfct.org.uk *Website* www.truecolourstrust.org.uk

■ Truedene Co. Ltd

CC NO 248268 **ESTABLISHED** 1966
WHERE FUNDING CAN BE GIVEN UK and overseas.
WHO CAN BENEFIT Jewish organisations.
WHAT IS FUNDED Jewish religious education; support for Jewish people who are in need.
RANGE OF GRANTS £25,000 to £52,000.
SAMPLE GRANTS Yetev Lev London Jerusalem Trust (£52,000); Ora Vesimcha (£36,000); Beis Ruchel D'Satmar (London) Ltd (£35,000); Chasdei Moshe Zvi Charitable Trust (£30,000); Society of Friends of the Torah (£25,000).
FINANCES *Financial year end* 31/03/2019 *Income* £430,000 *Total grants* £422,000 *Grants to organisations* £422,000 *Assets* £7,240,000
TRUSTEES Sarah Klein; Samuel Berger; Solomon Laufer; Sije Berger; Zelda Sternlicht.
OTHER INFORMATION The 2018/19 accounts were the latest available at the time of writing (May 2021).
HOW TO APPLY Contact the correspondent for further information.
CONTACT DETAILS The Trustees, Truedene Co. Ltd, Cohen Arnold, New Burlington House, 1075 Finchley Road, London NW11 0PU *Tel.* 020 8731 0777

■ The Truemark Trust

CC NO 265855 **ESTABLISHED** 1973
WHERE FUNDING CAN BE GIVEN UK.
WHO CAN BENEFIT Registered charities, with a preference for small local charities.
WHAT IS FUNDED Social welfare and disadvantage. There is a preference for neighbourhood-based community projects and innovative work with less popular groups.
RANGE OF GRANTS Mostly £1,000 to £5,000.
SAMPLE GRANTS Dorset Children's Fund (£15,000); Canine Partners (£10,000); Young Carers Development Trust (£6,000); Beckton Skills Centre, Cruse Bereavement Care and Hargreaves Narrowboat Trust (£5,000 each); Holy Trinity Parish Church (£3,000); Hands of Hope (£2,000); Conquest Art (£1,000).

FINANCES *Financial year end* 05/04/2020 *Income* £700,100 *Total grants* £391,500 *Grants to organisations* £391,500 *Assets* £18,110,000

TRUSTEES Sharon Knight; Judy Hayward; Jane Dunham; Shirley Vening; Paul Summerfield; Stephen Collins.

OTHER INFORMATION During the year, grants were awarded to 98 organisations.

HOW TO APPLY Contact the correspondent for further information.

CONTACT DETAILS The Trustees, PO Box 2, Liss, Hampshire GU33 6YP *Tel.* 07970 540015 *Email* truemark.trust01@ntlworld.com

■ Truemart Ltd

CC NO 1090586 **ESTABLISHED** 1984

WHERE FUNDING CAN BE GIVEN UK.

WHO CAN BENEFIT Charitable organisations.

WHAT IS FUNDED Orthodox Jewish faith; relief of poverty; general charitable purposes.

TYPE OF GRANT Capital costs, project costs, strategic funding, development funding.

SAMPLE GRANTS Yeshivas Lev Simcha (£15,000); CMZ Ltd (£10,000); Start Upright and Tchabe Kollel (£7,000 each).

FINANCES *Financial year end* 31/03/2020 *Income* £203,400 *Total grants* £230,800 *Grants to organisations* £230,800 *Assets* £51,000

TRUSTEES S. Heitner; Ian Heitner.

OTHER INFORMATION Grants of less than £10,000 totalled £85,400.

HOW TO APPLY Contact the correspondent for further information.

CONTACT DETAILS The Trustees, 34 The Ridgeway, London NW11 8QS *Tel.* 020 8455 4456

■ Trumros Ltd

CC NO 285533 **ESTABLISHED** 1982

WHERE FUNDING CAN BE GIVEN UK and Israel.

WHO CAN BENEFIT Charitable organisations.

WHAT IS FUNDED Jewish causes; education and training; social welfare; health.

TYPE OF GRANT Capital costs; development funding; project funding; strategic funding.

RANGE OF GRANTS £300 to £105,000.

SAMPLE GRANTS Torah Vochessed (£118,500); One Heart Lev Echod (£105,600); Beis Abanbaruch (£83,000); Torah Lishmah (£50,000); Kollel Beis Yisroel (£31,000); YAM (£20,000); Yeshivat Chochmat Shlomo (£16,800); British Friends of Chavei Hevron (£3,600); Beis Avrohom Synagogue (£350).

FINANCES *Financial year end* 31/12/2019 *Income* £1,700,000 *Total grants* £1,280,000 *Grants to organisations* £1,280,000 *Assets* £9,680,000

TRUSTEES Hannah Hofbauer; Ronald Hofbauer.

OTHER INFORMATION Grants of under £15,000 totalled £256,300.

HOW TO APPLY Contact the correspondent for further information.

CONTACT DETAILS Hannah Hofbauer, Trustee/Secretary, 282 Finchley Road, London NW3 7AD *Tel.* 020 7431 3282 *Email* r.hofbauer@btconnect.com

■ Trust for London

CC NO 205629 **ESTABLISHED** 2004

WHERE FUNDING CAN BE GIVEN London.

WHO CAN BENEFIT Voluntary, community and other not-for-profit organisations; registered charities; bodies providing advice, information and advocacy; educational and training institutions; new initiatives; shelters and re-settlement homes; CICs and social enterprises. While most recipients are registered charities this is not a requirement. Priority is given to smaller and medium-sized organisations with an income of under £2 million.

WHAT IS FUNDED Relief and prevention of poverty; social welfare; disability; cultural equality; religion.

WHAT IS NOT FUNDED Work outside London; applications for funding of services which are the primary responsibility of statutory funders or to subsidise services delivered through statutory contracts; schools and hospitals; individuals; organisations with fewer than three people on their governing body; promotion of religion; organisations seeking to distribute grants on the trust's behalf; work that has already taken place; general appeals; large capital appeals; applicants rejected in the last 12 months. See the trust's guidelines for a full list of exclusions and preferences.

TYPE OF GRANT Campaigning; research; core/revenue costs; salaries; small capital costs.

RANGE OF GRANTS Usually up to £150,000.

SAMPLE GRANTS Child Poverty Action Group (£179,000); Solace Women's Aid (£160,000); Global Action Plan (£147,000); On Road Ltd (£100,000); Flat Justice CIC (£80,000); Interlink Foundation (£60,000); Resolution Foundation (£40,000); Police Foundation (£32,000); Centre for London (£25,000); Citizens UK (£12,800); Emmaus Greenwich (£7,500).

FINANCES *Financial year end* 31/12/2019 *Income* £10,740,000 *Total grants* £16,300,000 *Grants to organisations* £16,300,000 *Assets* £342,480,000

TRUSTEE Trust for London Trustee.

OTHER INFORMATION During the year, 128 grants were awarded to organisations from the Central Fund for the relief of poverty. The Central Fund has seven funding programmes: Good Homes and Neighbourhoods; Better Work; Decent Living Standards; Shared Wealth; Pathways to Settlement; Stronger Voices; Connected Communities. See the trust's website for guidelines for each programme. Grants made for the furtherance of religion, including the City Church Fund, totalled £6.25 million. A full list of beneficiaries can be downloaded from the website. The sample of beneficiaries includes grants to be paid over multiple years.

HOW TO APPLY Full funding guidelines and closing dates are available on the trust's website. Applications should be made using the online portal. All shortlisted applicants will be visited by one of the grants staff. Prospective applicants can book an appointment to speak with a grant manager to discuss their application if desired – the eligibility quiz must be completed first.

CONTACT DETAILS The Trustees, Fourth Floor, 4 Chiswell Street, London EC1Y 4UP *Tel.* 020 7606 6145 *Email* info@trustforlondon.org.uk *Website* www.trustforlondon.org.uk

The Trusthouse Charitable Foundation

CC NO 1063945 **ESTABLISHED** 1997

WHERE FUNDING CAN BE GIVEN UK and overseas.

WHO CAN BENEFIT Charitable organisations including CICs, social enterprises, not-for-profit registered companies and voluntary organisations.

WHAT IS FUNDED The foundation has two overarching themes – rural issues and urban deprivation. Within these themes, the foundation's major grants programme currently focuses on family support projects (e.g. early intervention, work with families coping with addiction and prisoners' families). The foundation's small grants programme currently focuses on community support projects (see the foundation's website for examples). Projects must be based in areas of high deprivation (see website for details).

WHAT IS NOT FUNDED A full list of exclusions can be found on the foundation's website.

TYPE OF GRANT General costs including core costs, salaries and project costs.

RANGE OF GRANTS Major grants: £10,000 to £100,000. Small grants: £2,000 to £10,000.

SAMPLE GRANTS Alternatives Trust East London (£60,000); Stonebridge City Farm (£50,000); Barton Bendish Village Hall Trust (£40,000); People's Orchestra (£36,000); Front Lounge Ltd (£28,900); New Futures Project (£18,200); Women Acting in Today's Society (£10,000); Fighting Words Belfast (£7,000); Reader Organisations (£2,000); Cornwall Historic Churches Trust (£1,000); Squash Nutrition (£750).

FINANCES *Financial year end* 30/06/2020 *Income* £942,000 *Total grants* £2,540,000 *Grants to organisations* £2,540,000 *Assets* £81,700,000

TRUSTEES Crispian Collins; Carole Milner; The Hon. Olga Polizzi; Patrick Reve; Sir John Nutting; Revd Rose Hudson-Wilkin; Philippa Hamilton; Nicholas Melhuish; Charlie Peyton; Revd Paul Gismondi; Nicholas Acland.

OTHER INFORMATION During the year, grants were awarded to 143 organisations. Major grants totalled £2.17 million, small grants totalled £235,200 and grants made at the trustees' discretion totalled £125,000. Major grants up to £100,000 can be paid as a single grant or over a maximum of three years. Small grants are one-off.

HOW TO APPLY Applications can be made through the foundation's website, following the completion of a brief eligibility questionnaire, which also identifies which type of grant may be most suitable.

CONTACT DETAILS Jessica Brown, Grants Director, Kings Buildings, 16 Smith Square, London SW1P 3HQ *Tel.* 020 3150 4517 *Email* grants@trusthousecharitablefoundation.org.uk *Website* www.trusthousecharitablefoundation.org.uk

The James Tudor Foundation

CC NO 1105916 **ESTABLISHED** 2004

WHERE FUNDING CAN BE GIVEN UK and overseas.

WHO CAN BENEFIT Registered charities; charities with exempt status; CIOs.

WHAT IS FUNDED Palliative care; medical research; health education; relief of human sickness.

WHAT IS NOT FUNDED A full list of exclusions can be found in the foundation's 'Application Guidelines', which are available to download from the website.

TYPE OF GRANT Core costs; project funding.

RANGE OF GRANTS £500 to £30,000.

SAMPLE GRANTS National Eye Research Centre (£29,000); University of Bristol – bowel cancer research (£20,000); Hospice Care Exeter (£15,000); Sense International (£10,000); Crohn's and Colitis (£9,300); The Children's Liver Disease Foundation (£4,300); Carlisle Youth Zone (£1,500); Macmillan/Jake Skinner (£260).

FINANCES *Financial year end* 30/09/2019 *Income* £1,110,000 *Total grants* £854,500 *Grants to organisations* £854,500 *Assets* £30,930,000

TRUSTEES Cedric Nash; Richard Esler; Susan Evans; Anne McPherson; Stephanie Wren; Linda Hooper; Michael Daw.

OTHER INFORMATION The 2018/19 accounts were the latest available at the time of writing (April 2021). A total of 117 grants were awarded to organisations during the year. Grants were distributed as follows: relief of sickness (£291,300); medical research (£171,200); palliative care (£166,100); health education (£132,600); overseas (£93,300). A full list of beneficiaries is available to view on the foundation's website.

HOW TO APPLY In the first instance, applicants should use the eligibility checker on the foundation's website. If eligible, applicants should then submit a one-page summary and a completed application cover sheet. Further information and a breakdown of the application process are available from the foundation's website.

CONTACT DETAILS Sarah Stewart, Foundation Director, Suite 8 Clifton Business Centre, Somerset House, 18 Canynge Road, Bristol BS8 3JX *Tel.* 0117 440 7340 *Email* admin@jamestudor.org.uk *Website* www.jamestudor.org.uk

The Tudor Trust

CC NO 1105580 **ESTABLISHED** 1955

WHERE FUNDING CAN BE GIVEN UK and Africa.

WHO CAN BENEFIT Registered charities; unregistered charities; CICs; social enterprises; religious bodies/institutions.

WHAT IS FUNDED Work that makes a direct difference to the lives of marginalised people. There are three categories of eligibility criteria through which the trust considers applications: display positive organisational characteristics; address marginalisation; make a difference. Full details of each of these categories are given on the trust's website. The trust also works proactively supporting ecological agriculture in sub-Saharan Africa.

WHAT IS NOT FUNDED A full list of exclusions can be found on the trust's website.

TYPE OF GRANT Core/revenue costs; capital costs; project funding, development funding.

RANGE OF GRANTS There is no minimum or maximum grant; grants are usually £10,000 or more. In 2019/20 the average grant was £60,900.

SAMPLE GRANTS Corra Foundation (£200,000); Barrow Cadbury Trust (£150,000); Asylum Justice (£130,000); Growing Sudley CIC (£88,000); London Renters Union (£60,000); Road to Recovery Trust (£50,000); Voice of Domestic Workers (£40,000); Sustainable Living Initiative (£30,000); Hope House Church (£25,000); Local Trust (£15,000); The School and Family Works (£3,000).

FINANCES *Financial year end* 31/03/2020
Income £6,200,000 *Total grants* £18,760,000
Grants to organisations £18,760,000
Assets £227,110,000

TRUSTEES Shilpa Shah; Francis Runacres; Elizabeth Crawshaw; Rosalind Dunwell; Carey Weeks; Ben Dunwell; Nell Bucker; Louise Collins; Monica Barlow; Jonathan Bell; James Long; Holly Baxter Baine; Catherine Antcliff; Christopher Graves; Matt Dunwell.

OTHER INFORMATION During the year, the trust committed 344 grants totalling £20.94 million. Grants paid during the year totalled £18.76 million. Grants committed were broken down as follows: community (£10.4 million); overseas (£2.43 million); youth (£1.92 million); mental health (£1.6 million); relationships (£1.43 million); housing (£1.3 million); criminal justice (£957,000); financial security (£371,000); older people (£365,000); learning (£106,000); substance misuse (£50,000). During the year, 92% of grants were for core costs.

HOW TO APPLY The trust makes grants on a rolling basis so there are no deadlines. There is a two-stage application process. Firstly, a basic online form will need to be completed and you will be asked to upload three accompanying documents: an introductory letter, answers to five questions and a copy of your most recent accounts. If successful, you will be introduced to a grants manager who will discuss the next steps. Full application guidelines can be found on the trust's website. The trust's funding guidelines for April 2020–March 2022 include COVID-19 guidance.

CONTACT DETAILS The Grants Team, 7 Ladbroke Grove, London W11 3BD *Tel.* 020 7727 8522 *Email* There is no email address for general enquiries as the trust prefers contact via telephone. However, if you have communication difficulties, email access@tudortrust.org.uk. *Website* www.tudortrust.org.uk

■ The Tudwick Foundation

CC NO 1184459 **ESTABLISHED** 2019

WHERE FUNDING CAN BE GIVEN Essex; Suffolk.

WHO CAN BENEFIT Charitable organisations.

WHAT IS FUNDED Health; social welfare; education.

WHAT IS NOT FUNDED General appeals to directly promote religious or political agendas; charities registered outside the UK.

TYPE OF GRANT Project funding; core funding.

RANGE OF GRANTS £300 to £3,000.

SAMPLE GRANTS Chronically Awesome and Halstead Day Centre (£3,000 each); Essex Youth Build (£2,400); Offshoot Foundation (£1,200); 1st Whiston Scout Group (£750).

FINANCES *Financial year end* 31/07/2020
Income £2,060,000 *Total grants* £50,300
Grants to organisations £50,300
Assets £1,620,000

TRUSTEES Julia Endacott; Valerie Shaikly; Timothy Bennett; Colin Bennett.

OTHER INFORMATION The foundation typically supports charities with an income under £500,000. New organisations are encouraged to apply.

HOW TO APPLY Application forms can be downloaded from the foundation's website.

CONTACT DETAILS The Trustees, 17 James Chester Road, Colchester CO3 9XA *Tel.* 01206 587000 *Email* thetudwickfoundation@gmail.com *Website* https://www.tudwickfoundation.org.uk

■ The Tufton Charitable Trust

CC NO 801479 **ESTABLISHED** 1989

WHERE FUNDING CAN BE GIVEN UK.

WHO CAN BENEFIT Charitable organisations; churches.

WHAT IS FUNDED Christian causes.

RANGE OF GRANTS Mostly up to £70,000.

SAMPLE GRANTS Church Revitalisation Trust (£150,000); The London Institute for Contemporary Christianity (£100,000); Alpha International (£70,000); Stowe School Foundation (£40,000); London City Mission (£30,000); Glyndebourne Productions (£22,500); Off the Fence and Rye Memorial Care Centre (£10,000 each); Catholic Faith Exploration and Kent MS Therapy Centre (£5,000 each).

FINANCES *Financial year end* 31/12/2019
Income £361,200 *Total grants* £633,400
Grants to organisations £633,400
Assets £1,860,000

TRUSTEE Wates Charitable Trustees Ltd.

OTHER INFORMATION Only organisations that received grants of £5,000 and above were listed as beneficiaries in the 2019 accounts (21 organisations). Grantsof under £5,000 totalled £13,000. The trust also provides accommodation for Christian retreats.

HOW TO APPLY Contact the correspondent for further information.

CONTACT DETAILS The Trustees, Tufton Place, Tufton Lane, Northiam, Rye TN31 6HL *Tel.* 01797 253311

■ The Tuixen Foundation

CC NO 1081124 **ESTABLISHED** 2000

WHERE FUNDING CAN BE GIVEN UK.

WHO CAN BENEFIT Registered charities; unregistered charities; hospitals; hospices; CICs; schools; universities; social enterprises. Charities receiving grants will usually have a turnover in the range of £500,000 to £5 million.

WHAT IS FUNDED Children and young people; education; people with physical or learning disabilities; mental health; hospices; homelessness; relief of poverty.

TYPE OF GRANT Core/revenue costs; unrestricted funding; project funding.

RANGE OF GRANTS Mostly £500 to £50,000.

SAMPLE GRANTS Impetus Trust (£100,000); Into University and Winston's Wish (£50,000 each); Fight for Peace (£40,000); Greenhouse (£30,000); Bristol University (£20,000); Save The Elephants and Storybook Dads (£10,000 each); University College London (£9,000); Learn to Love to Read (£7,500); Duchenne UK (£1,000); Shine Cancer Support (£500).

FINANCES *Financial year end* 05/04/2020
Income £792,900 *Total grants* £958,900
Grants to organisations £958,900
Assets £49,020,000

TRUSTEES Peter Englander; Dr Leanda Kroll; Stephen Rosefield; Paul Clements; Simon Englander.

OTHER INFORMATION In total, 38 grants were awarded to organisations during the year. The foundation's helpful website provides a detailed breakdown of the grants awarded and specifies to what purpose they were given. According to the website, approximately 20 charities are selected to receive a donation each year and some donations will be ongoing.

HOW TO APPLY The website states that unsolicited applications are not sought and the trustees will not reply to correspondence.

CONTACT DETAILS Paul Clements, Trustee, 440 Strand, London WC2R 0QS *Tel.* 020 7649 2903 *Email* Jandoole@tuixen.org.uk *Website* tuixen.org.uk

■ The Roger and Douglas Turner Charitable Trust

CC NO 1154467 **ESTABLISHED** 2013

WHERE FUNDING CAN BE GIVEN Birmingham; Dudley; Sandwell; Walsall; Wolverhampton; Worcestershire.

WHO CAN BENEFIT Registered charities; hospices.

WHAT IS FUNDED Children and young people; disability; health; the environment and heritage; the arts; community projects; social welfare.

WHAT IS NOT FUNDED Individuals; grant-making charities; CICs; social enterprises or other not-for-profit organisations; charities that have access to significant public sector funding, large investment portfolios, large defined-benefit pension fund deficits or excessive reserves; large national and international organisations.

TYPE OF GRANT Capital costs; core and revenue costs; unrestricted funding.

RANGE OF GRANTS Up to £30,000. The average grant is around £4,100.

SAMPLE GRANTS Birmingham St Mary's Hospice (£30,000); Acorns Children's Hospice Trust (£25,000); Compton Care (£20,000); Stonehouse Gang (£15,000); National Churches Trust (£10,000); St Anne's Hostel (£6,000); Listening Books and Sport 4 Life UK (£5,000 each).

FINANCES *Financial year end* 31/12/2020 *Income* £1,550,000 *Total grants* £515,000 *Grants to organisations* £515,000 *Assets* £61,100,000

TRUSTEES Ronald Middleton; Geoffrey Thomas; Peter Millward; Dawn Long; Amanda McGeever; Sharon Stotts.

OTHER INFORMATION Grants were made to 195 organisations during the year. Grants of less than £5,000 totalled £282,000. The trust has a number of regular beneficiaries which it supports on a long-term basis. Applications from new charities, if successful, tend to lead to an initial grant award of up to £3,000, often for capital appeals or specific projects.

HOW TO APPLY Application forms and guidelines can be downloaded from the trust's website. The website notes that it prefers to receive applications by email. Postal applications will be accepted but will take longer to process. All correspondence from the trust will be via email. Check the trust's website for upcoming deadlines.

CONTACT DETAILS Jenny Harris, Grants Manager, Arley House, Lion Lane, Upper Arley, Bewdley, Worcestershire DY12 1SQ *Tel.* 01299 861368 *Email* jenny@turnertrust.co.uk *Website* https://www.turnertrust.co.uk

■ G. J. W. Turner Trust

CC NO 258615 **ESTABLISHED** 1969

WHERE FUNDING CAN BE GIVEN Birmingham.

WHO CAN BENEFIT Charitable organisations.

WHAT IS FUNDED General charitable purposes.

SAMPLE GRANTS A list of beneficiaries was not included in the annual report and accounts.

FINANCES *Financial year end* 05/04/2020 *Income* £383,700 *Total grants* £410,000 *Grants to organisations* £410,000 *Assets* £10,770,000

TRUSTEES Lesley Davis; Hugh Carslake; Kate Honeyborne.

OTHER INFORMATION In 2019/20 the trust made 144 grants.

HOW TO APPLY Contact the correspondent for further information.

CONTACT DETAILS Chrissy Norgrove, Clerk to the Trustees, The Estate Office, Wharf Cottage, Broombank, Tenbury Wells, Worcestershire WR15 8NY *Tel.* 07799 784019

■ The Florence Turner Trust

CC NO 502721 **ESTABLISHED** 1973

WHERE FUNDING CAN BE GIVEN UK, with a strong preference for Leicestershire.

WHO CAN BENEFIT Charitable organisations. Smaller charities are favoured. Grants to national charities are made only when there is a clear and direct benefit to the people of Leicestershire. Grants can be made for the benefit of individuals through a referring agency such as social services, NHS trusts or similar responsible bodies.

WHAT IS FUNDED General charitable purposes.

RANGE OF GRANTS £500 to £5,000.

SAMPLE GRANTS A list of beneficiaries was not included in the annual report and accounts.

FINANCES *Financial year end* 31/03/2020 *Income* £223,000 *Total grants* £154,000 *Grants to organisations* £154,000 *Assets* £6,730,000

TRUSTEES Roger Bowder; Katherine Hall; Michael Jones.

OTHER INFORMATION Grants of between £500 and £5,000 were paid to 152 organisations; grants of below £500 were paid to 20 organisations; one organisation received a grant of over £5,000.

HOW TO APPLY Contact the correspondent for information regarding the application process. The trustees meet on a bi-monthly basis to consider grant applications.

CONTACT DETAILS Helen Pole, Administrator, c/o Shakespeare Martineau, Two Colton Square, Leicester, Leicestershire LE1 1QH *Tel.* 0116 257 4462 *Email* helen.pole@shma.co.uk

■ The Turtleton Charitable Trust

OSCR NO SC038018 **ESTABLISHED** 2007

WHERE FUNDING CAN BE GIVEN UK, with a strong preference for Scotland.

WHO CAN BENEFIT Registered charities.

WHAT IS FUNDED Arts, culture and heritage. A few grants are also made each year to charities for the purposes of education and supporting people who are disadvantaged.

WHAT IS NOT FUNDED Individuals.

RANGE OF GRANTS Mostly between £5,000 and £25,000.

SAMPLE GRANTS Optimistic Sound-Big Noise Douglas project (£20,000); Eskadale Church Restoration Fund (£15,000); Scottish Ballet, Edinburgh International Festival and Love Music Productions (£10,000 each); Sound Waves SCIO and Traverse Theatre (Scotland) (£5,000 each).

FINANCES *Financial year end* 30/06/2020 *Income* £233,300 *Total grants* £215,500 *Grants to organisations* £215,500 *Assets* £5,420,000

HOW TO APPLY Grants should be made via the application form available to download from the trust's website. If your charity does not have access to email, a hard-copy application can be sent to Hilary Sharkey at the correspondent's address. There is no need to send a copy of your annual accounts, unless they are not available online. Applications should reach the trust by email or in hard copy not later than 31 December. The trustees meet once a year in spring to decide on grants for the following 12 months and normally pay grants prior to 30 June in each year.

CONTACT DETAILS The Trustees, c/o Turcan Connell, Princes Exchange, 1 Earl Grey Street, Edinburgh EH3 9EE *Tel.* 0131 228 8111 *Email* enquiries@turcanconnell.com *Website* www.turcanconnell.com/turtleton

■ Two Ridings Community Foundation

CC NO 1084043 **ESTABLISHED** 2000

WHERE FUNDING CAN BE GIVEN North and East Yorkshire.

WHO CAN BENEFIT Charitable organisations and community groups. The foundation focuses mainly on smaller and grassroots organisations (larger organisations should contact the foundation before applying).

WHAT IS FUNDED General charitable purposes.

WHAT IS NOT FUNDED Each of the foundation's funding programmes has specific criteria, which can be found on the website. In general, grants are not given to: private businesses; general appeals or sponsorship; national organisations and their affiliates (this does not include locally constituted and managed branches of national or large charities); statutory agencies, including parish councils and schools, in the discharge of their statutory obligations; organisations that have substantial unrestricted funds; previous grant recipients who have outstanding monitoring information; organisations that mainly give funds to other organisations or individuals. Grants are not given for: the advancement of religion; activities solely benefitting animals; overseas holidays or trips; political campaigning; medical research, equipment or treatment.

TYPE OF GRANT See individual grant programmes.

RANGE OF GRANTS Mostly from £500 to £10,000. In 2019/20 the average grant was £2,218.

SAMPLE GRANTS Age UK – Hull and East Riding (£30,000); Bridlington Club for Young People (£19,900); Hull Sisters Ltd (£10,000); Emerging Voices (£8,000); Ripon Community Link (£4,000); Cherry Burton Parish Council (£3,500); Peasholme Charity (£2,000); Westgate Bowling Club (£1,300); Coast and Vale Community Action (£400); Hampsthwaite Village Society (£250).

FINANCES *Financial year end* 31/03/2020 *Income* £2,410,000 *Total grants* £1,253,200 *Grants to organisations* £998,700 *Assets* £6,610,000

TRUSTEES James Naylor; Hannah Harris; Alison Pearson; Harriet Reid; Eric Downey; Andrew Wilson; Venetia Wrigley; Anthony Collinson; Deborah Rosenberg; Revd Richard Frith; Christopher Legard; Rolline Frewen; Dr Gillian Hughes.

OTHER INFORMATION This is one of the 46 UK community foundations, which distribute funding for a wide range of purposes. As with all community foundations, there are a number of donor-advised funds managed on behalf of individuals, families and charitable trusts. Grant schemes tend to change frequently; consult the foundation's website for details of current programmes and up-to-date deadlines. During the year, grants were awarded to 252 organisations. In addition, grants to 313 individuals totalled £254,500.

HOW TO APPLY Potential applicants are advised to visit the community foundation's website or contact its grants team to find the most suitable funding stream.

CONTACT DETAILS Grants Team, Pavilion 2000, Amy Johnson Way, York, North Yorkshire YO30 4XT *Tel.* 01904 929500 *Email* info@tworidingscf.org.uk *Website* https://www.tworidingscf.org.uk

■ Community Foundation serving Tyne and Wear and Northumberland

CC NO 700510 **ESTABLISHED** 1988

WHERE FUNDING CAN BE GIVEN Tyne and Wear and Northumberland.

WHO CAN BENEFIT Charitable organisations; CICs; social enterprises.

WHAT IS FUNDED General charitable purposes. The foundation has a range of different grant programmes, which change frequently – refer to the website for information on grants currently available.

WHAT IS NOT FUNDED Contributions to general appeals or circulars; religious activity which is not for wider public benefit; replacement of statutory funding; activities where the primary benefit is the advancement of animal welfare; activities which have already taken place; grant-making, or equivalent gifts in kind, by other organisations; privately owned and profit-distributing companies or limited partnerships.

TYPE OF GRANT Projects costs; equipment and capital developments; running costs (including salaries and overheads).

RANGE OF GRANTS Mostly under £5,000.

SAMPLE GRANTS A list of beneficiaries was not included in the annual report and accounts.

FINANCES *Financial year end* 31/03/2020 *Income* £10,050,000 *Total grants* £6,630,200 *Grants to organisations* £6,540,000 *Assets* £80,930,000

TRUSTEES Lucy Winskell; Lady Anna Blackett; Claire Malcolm; Fiona Cruickshank; Patrick Melia; Geoffrey Hodgson; Neil Warwick; Andrew Haigh; Paul Farquhar; Dr Laura Warwick; Gillian Baker; Michael Brodie.

OTHER INFORMATION This is one of the 46 UK community foundations, which distribute funding for a wide range of purposes. As with all community foundations, there are a number of donor-advised funds managed on behalf of individuals, families and charitable trusts. Grant schemes tend to change frequently; consult the foundation's website for details of current programmes and up-to-date deadlines. Grants were awarded to 1,133 organisations and 123 individuals during the year.

HOW TO APPLY Potential applicants are advised to visit the community foundation's website or contact its grants team to find the most suitable funding stream.

CONTACT DETAILS The Grants Team, Philanthropy House, Woodbine Road, Gosforth, Newcastle upon Tyne NE3 1DD *Tel.* 0191 222 0945 *Email* general@communityfoundation.org.uk *Website* www.communityfoundation.org.uk

■ Tzedakah

CC NO 251897 **ESTABLISHED** 1966

WHERE FUNDING CAN BE GIVEN Worldwide, in practice mainly UK and Israel.

WHO CAN BENEFIT Charitable organisations.

WHAT IS FUNDED Jewish causes; education and training; relief of poverty.

SAMPLE GRANTS Previous beneficiaries have included: Gertner Charitable Trust; Hasmonean High School Charitable Trust; Hendon Adath Yisroel Synagogue; Society of Friends of the Torah; Medrash Shmuel Theological College; Torah Temimoh; Willow Foundation; Tifferes Girls School; Sage Home for the Aged; Wizo; Torah Movement of Great Britain.

FINANCES *Financial year end* 31/03/2019 *Income* £472,000 *Total grants* £376,500 *Grants to organisations* £376,500 *Assets* £340,500

TRUSTEES Leonard Finn; Michael Lebrett.

OTHER INFORMATION The trustees' annual report for 2018/19 states: 'The grant making programme helps over 300 smaller charities develop themselves each year. The charities are chosen by the individual members.' The 2018/19 accounts were the latest available at the time of writing (June 2021).

HOW TO APPLY Contact the correspondent for further information.

CONTACT DETAILS The Trustees, Brentmead House, Britannia Road, London N12 9RU *Tel.* 020 8446 6767 *Email* lfinnco@aol.com

The Udlington Trust

CC NO 1129443 **ESTABLISHED** 2009

WHERE FUNDING CAN BE GIVEN UK and overseas.

WHO CAN BENEFIT Registered charities.

WHAT IS FUNDED General charitable purposes.

SAMPLE GRANTS A list of beneficiaries was not included in the annual report and accounts.

FINANCES *Financial year end* 31/12/2019 *Income* £106,000 *Total grants* £55,300 *Grants to organisations* £55,300 *Assets* £12,900

TRUSTEES Bruce Blackledge; Richard Blackledge; Robert Blackledge; Rebecca Blackledge.

HOW TO APPLY Contact the correspondent for further information.

CONTACT DETAILS The Trustees, c/o Arrow County Supplies, Arrow House, Longden Road, Shrewsbury, Shropshire SY3 9AE *Tel.* 01743 283600

Ufi VocTech Trust

CC NO 1081028 **ESTABLISHED** 2000

WHERE FUNDING CAN BE GIVEN UK.

WHO CAN BENEFIT Organisations, including: charities; trade bodies; learning providers; employers; private companies; CICs; and other not-for-profit organisations.

WHAT IS FUNDED Projects that use digital methods to widen access to adult (over 16) vocational learning.

WHAT IS NOT FUNDED See the trust's FAQs web page (www.ufi.co.uk/faqs) for a full list of exclusions.

TYPE OF GRANT Seed funding; development funding; project funding.

RANGE OF GRANTS Programme dependent.

SAMPLE GRANTS Agylia Care; Century Tech; Learning Science Ltd; Playlingo; Relate; Royal British Legion Industries; Self Injury Support; Socrates Software; WAMITAB.

FINANCES *Financial year end* 31/12/2019 *Income* £1,170,000 *Total grants* £3,710,000 *Grants to organisations* £3,710,000 *Assets* £55,710,000

TRUSTEES Anthony Bravo; David Ryder; Paolo Fresia; Alexandra Cullen; Dominic Gill; Jonathan Scott; Jeffrey Greenidge; Julia Lambdon; Charlotte Kirby.

OTHER INFORMATION Each year the trust operates funding calls for a specific type of project or 'Challenge' calls where it combines funding types. At the time of writing (May 2021) funding types available included: VocTech Ignite – early-stage support for those new to grant funding or needing extra help to bring their ideas to life; VocTech Seed – seed funding of between £15,000 and £50,000 for ideas to be scoped and tested; VocTech Impact – grants of between £150,000 and £300,000 for well-developed ideas that can be delivered to large numbers of learners and have clear routes to market after the funding ends. The grant amounts awarded during the year were not detailed in the 2019 accounts.

HOW TO APPLY Grant funding calls are advertised on the trust's website and are explained in detail in the trust's 'Delivery Plan'. Applications can be made via an online portal on the website. The trust usually uses a two-stage application process, where you first give a summary of your idea (Stage 1) and then, if suitable, you will be invited to submit a more detailed, full application (Stage 2).

CONTACT DETAILS The Trustees, First Floor, 10 Queen Street Place, London EC4R 1BE *Tel.* 020 7969 5500 *Email* info@ufi.co.uk *Website* www.ufi.co.uk

UKH Foundation

CC NO 1160507 **ESTABLISHED** 2014

WHERE FUNDING CAN BE GIVEN England and Wales, with a preference for the North West and in particular the Bolton area.

WHO CAN BENEFIT Registered charities and hospices.

WHAT IS FUNDED Health; mental health; disability; children and young people; older people.

RANGE OF GRANTS £1,000 to £30,000.

SAMPLE GRANTS Previous beneficiaries have included: Royal Manchester Children's Hospital (£40,000); Chorley Youth Zone (£20,000); Bolton Community Transport (£10,000); Blind Veterans UK, Friends for Leisure and The Epiphany Trust (£5,000 each); West Coast Crash Rugby (£2,000); Bolton Hospice (£1,000).

FINANCES *Financial year end* 31/12/2019 *Income* £131,700 *Total grants* £236,800 *Grants to organisations* £236,800 *Assets* £3,610,000

TRUSTEES Julie Hulme; Andrew Redfern; David Udall; Sarah Boustoller.

OTHER INFORMATION Grants were awarded to 39 organisations during the year.

HOW TO APPLY Applications can made through the foundation's website and are considered at quarterly meetings.

CONTACT DETAILS The Trustees, Lancashire Gate, 21 Tiviot Dale, Stockport, Cheshire SK1 1TD *Tel.* 07955 197310 *Email* A contact form is available on the website. *Website* ukhfoundation.org

Ulster Garden Villages Ltd

CC NO 101248 **ESTABLISHED** 1946

WHERE FUNDING CAN BE GIVEN Northern Ireland.

WHO CAN BENEFIT Registered charities; hospices; hospitals; educational organisations; local authorities.

WHAT IS FUNDED Health (including mental health, home nursing and substance abuse); disability (including carers, sheltered accommodation, transport and advice); social and economic disadvantage; arts, culture and heritage (including restoration of buildings of historic or architectural interest); the environment; education and training (including life skills and literacy skills for disadvantaged individuals and people with disabilities); community development (including crime prevention, rehabilitation, victim support and regeneration); young people; older people. Preferred projects will be those demonstrating active participation and self-help. They should be innovative and developmental with an achievable, practical and sustainable objective.

WHAT IS NOT FUNDED Individuals; organisations whose application is not charitable and does not demonstrate public benefit; activities which are primarily the responsibility of central and local government; sponsorship or marketing appeals; promotion of religion; expeditions or overseas travel; charities which collect funds for distribution to other charities; core costs; retrospective expenditure. Considerable support is provided to umbrella organisations representing the community and voluntary sector and therefore applications from individual groups are a low priority.

TYPE OF GRANT Project costs; loans; capital costs.

RANGE OF GRANTS Mostly up to £60,000.

SAMPLE GRANTS Belfast Health and Social Care Trust (£500,000); Mencap Northern Ireland (£100,000); Northern Ireland Children's Hospice (£60,000); Camphill Community Clanabogan (£30,000); Cancer Fund for Children (£25,000); Cedar Foundation (£15,000); Belfast Charitable Society (£5,000); Larne Sea Cadets (£2,000); The Foyle Down Syndrome Trust (£1,500).

FINANCES *Financial year end* 31/12/2019 *Income* £2,080,000 *Total grants* £1,250,000 *Grants to organisations* £1,250,000 *Assets* £49,900,000

TRUSTEES Martie Boyd; Erskine Holmes; Kevin Baird; Dr Anthony Hopkins; Susan Crowe; Brian Garrett; William Webb; Dame Rotha Johnston; Colin Walsh.

OTHER INFORMATION Grants were awarded to 53 organisations during the year in the following categories: health (£658,600); disability (£277,500); education and training (£137,000); community (£93,500); culture and heritage (£85,900). The charity also provides and manages a portfolio of housing and amenities for disadvantaged and older people.

HOW TO APPLY Applications can be made via the charity's website. The most recent annual report and accounts will also be required. Applicants should first complete a short eligibility quiz in order to access the application form.

CONTACT DETAILS The Trustees, Forestview, Purdy's Lane, Newtownbreda, Belfast BT8 7AR *Tel.* 028 9049 1111 *Email* admin@ulstergardenvillages.co.uk *Website* www.ulstergardenvillages.co.uk

■ Ulting Overseas Trust

CC NO 294397 **ESTABLISHED** 1986

WHERE FUNDING CAN BE GIVEN UK and overseas (mostly, but not exclusively, Asia, Africa and South and Central America).

WHO CAN BENEFIT Christian training organisations; individuals.

WHAT IS FUNDED Theological training and work in financially developing countries.

TYPE OF GRANT Bursaries and training costs.

RANGE OF GRANTS £1,000 to £16,000.

SAMPLE GRANTS International Fellowship of Evangelical Students(£16,100); Langham Scholarships (£13,700); Scripture Union International (£12,000); Oxford Centre for Mission Studies (£7,000); Asian Theological Seminary (£5,000); South Asia Institute of Advanced Christian Studies (£2,100); Faculté de Théologie Évangélique de Bangui (£1,500).

FINANCES *Financial year end* 05/04/2020 *Income* £104,000 *Total grants* £118,400 *Grants to organisations* £117,400 *Assets* £4,230,000

TRUSTEES Tim Warren; John Heyward; Dr Sue Brown; Revd Joseph Kapolyo; Nicholas Durlacher; Roger Pearce; Jennifer Brown; Dr Carol Walker; John Whitfield; Jennifer Stewart.

OTHER INFORMATION In total, 34 grants were awarded to 33 organisations and one individual during the year.

HOW TO APPLY Apply in writing to the correspondent. Grants are reviewed and awarded on an annual basis.

CONTACT DETAILS The Trustees, Goosehill Hall, Buxton Road, Castleton, Derbyshire S33 8WP *Tel.* 01433 621826

■ The Ulverscroft Foundation

CC NO 264873 **ESTABLISHED** 1972

WHERE FUNDING CAN BE GIVEN UK; overseas.

WHO CAN BENEFIT Registered charities; unregistered charities; social enterprises; CICs; schools; universities; hospitals.

WHAT IS FUNDED Projects that help visually impaired people.

WHAT IS NOT FUNDED The foundation does not fund staff salaries or ongoing running costs for an organisation.

TYPE OF GRANT Capital costs; project funding.

RANGE OF GRANTS Grants range from £1,000 to £17,000, with some larger grants also made.

SAMPLE GRANTS Newcastle University (£125,000); IMET 2000 (£30,000); World Sight Foundation (£17,000); KACSU (£15,000); Bucks Vision (£5,000); Listening Books (£2,000); Sight Support Derbyshire (£1,000).

FINANCES *Financial year end* 31/10/2019 *Income* £10,400,000 *Total grants* £341,000 *Grants to organisations* £341,000 *Assets* £20,900,000

TRUSTEES John Sandford-Smith; Roger Crooks; Robert Gent; Rupert Clarke; Debra Hicks; Geoffrey Woodruff

OTHER INFORMATION The 2018/19 accounts were the latest available at the time of writing (June 2021). The foundation notes that while there will be an element of visual impairment in any group, grants will only be considered where the visual impairment element is significant.

HOW TO APPLY Applications can be made in writing or via email. The foundation outlines the information required on its website.

CONTACT DETAILS Joyce Sumner, Secretary, The Green, Bradgate Road, Anstey, Leicester, Leicestershire LE7 7FU *Tel.* 0116 236 1595 *Email* foundation@ulverscroft.co.uk *Website* www.foundation.ulverscroft.com

■ The Underwood Trust

CC NO 266164 **ESTABLISHED** 1973

WHERE FUNDING CAN BE GIVEN UK.

WHO CAN BENEFIT Charitable organisations.

WHAT IS FUNDED Medicine and health; social welfare; education; arts and culture; the environment and wildlife.

WHAT IS NOT FUNDED Individuals; political activities; commercial ventures or publications; the purchase of vehicles including mini-buses; overseas travel, holidays and expeditions.

TYPE OF GRANT Capital costs; core costs; project funding.

RANGE OF GRANTS Grants range from £5,000 up to £450,000.

SAMPLE GRANTS Greenpeace (Ocean Sanctuaries) (£450,000); Bristol Speech and Language Therapy Research Unit (£50,000); Wiltshire Community Foundation (£30,000); NSPCC (£25,000); Friends of the Earth and The Brooke (£20,000 each); The Open Blue Bus (£5,000).

FINANCES *Financial year end* 05/04/2020 *Income* £792,300 *Total grants* £965,000 *Grants to organisations* £965,000 *Assets* £14,260,000

TRUSTEES Robin Clark; Richard Bennison; Briony Wilson.

OTHER INFORMATION Grants were broken down in the following categories: the environment and wildlife (£560,000); social welfare (£195,000); medicine and health (£130,000); education and the arts (£80,000).

HOW TO APPLY The trust's website states: 'The trustees have decided to give annual support to a number of charities and proactively seek out certain projects. This restricts the funds available for general applications and as such the Trust is closed to unsolicited applications.' Only make an application if you have been invited to do so. The application form is available to download on the website. Once completed, you can either post or email it to the trust's office. The trustees meet on a regular basis to consider applications during the year.

CONTACT DETAILS The Trustees, 20 York Street, London W1U 6PU *Tel.* 020 7486 0100 *Email* michelej@taylorclark.co.uk *Website* www.theunderwoodtrust.org.uk

■ The Union of Orthodox Hebrew Congregations

CC NO 1158987 **ESTABLISHED** 1966

WHERE FUNDING CAN BE GIVEN UK.

WHO CAN BENEFIT Charitable organisations; individuals.

WHAT IS FUNDED Orthodox Jewish causes.

SAMPLE GRANTS CMZ Trust (£264,000); Hadras Kodesh Trust (£45,000); Kehal Chasidei Wiznitz Ltd (£33,600); Mutual Trust (£14,400); Shaarei Orah Ltd (£7,600); Hatzolas Chasanim (£6,000).

FINANCES *Financial year end* 31/12/2019 *Income* £1,790,000 *Total grants* £910,200 *Grants to organisations* £884,200 *Assets* £2,530,000

TRUSTEES Myer Rothfeld; Benzion Freshwater; Moses Bibelman; Jehudah Baumgarten; Jacob Goldman; Sydney Sinitsky; Benjamin Roth; Michael Lobenstein; Chaim Pinter; Aron Goldman; Mordechai Steren; Joshua Muller; Shalom Seidenfeld; Nathan Bindinger; Schloime Rand; Daniel Ost; Chaim Goldman; Robert Grussgott; Benjamin Stern; Ahron Klein; Benzion Goldstein; Ahron Rand; Michael Just; Abraham Schreiber; Zalman Roth; Victor Brinner.

OTHER INFORMATION Grants to individuals totalled £26,000 in 2019. Grants of under £7,500 to organisations totalled £82,000.

HOW TO APPLY Contact the correspondent for further information.

CONTACT DETAILS The Trustees, 140 Stamford Hill, London N16 6QT *Tel.* 020 8800 6833

■ The Union of the Sisters of Mercy of Great Britain

CC NO 288158 **ESTABLISHED** 1991

WHERE FUNDING CAN BE GIVEN England; Wales; Scotland; South Africa; Lebanon; Romania.

WHO CAN BENEFIT Charitable organisations; individuals.

WHAT IS FUNDED Catholic mission work; education; health; social welfare.

RANGE OF GRANTS During the year, grants ranged from £5,000 to around £40,000.

SAMPLE GRANTS Diocese of Westminster Education Department (£561,300); Daniel's Corporation-Romania (£66,300); Addo-South Africa (£40,800); Citizens UK (£30,000); CAFOD and Ashford Place (£10,000 each); Rise Theatre (£5,000).

FINANCES *Financial year end* 31/03/2020 *Income* £7,140,000 *Total grants* £1,048,600 *Grants to organisations* £930,200 *Assets* £63,380,000

TRUSTEES Sister Philomena Bowers; Sister Geraldine Lawlor; Sister Mary Horgan; Sister Monica Killeen.

OTHER INFORMATION The grant-maker states that it is inspired by gospel values to benefit the public, particularly women and children and those who are poor. During the year, grants to individuals totalled £118,400.

HOW TO APPLY Contact the correspondent for further information.

CONTACT DETAILS The Trustees, Mercy Union Generalate, 11 Harewood Avenue, London NW1 6LD *Tel.* 020 7723 3221 *Email* admin@mercyunion.org.uk *Website* sistersofmercyunion.org.uk

■ United Jewish Israel Appeal

CC NO 1060078 **ESTABLISHED** 1996

WHERE FUNDING CAN BE GIVEN Israel and UK.

WHO CAN BENEFIT Registered charities; schools and colleges; universities.

WHAT IS FUNDED Jewish causes, including: (in particular) education and children and young people; social welfare; older people.

RANGE OF GRANTS £89,000 to £830,000.

SAMPLE GRANTS UJIA Israel (£831,000); Jewish Agency for Israel (£749,000); Federation of Zionist Youth (£171,000); Atidim (£120,000); Equaliser (£105,000); Danciger High School (£89,000).

FINANCES *Financial year end* 30/09/2020 *Income* £9,780,000 *Total grants* £5,180,000 *Grants to organisations* £5,180,000 *Assets* £6,320,000

TRUSTEES Raphael Addlestone; Melvin Berwald; Steven Kaye; Hilton Nathanson; Karen Goodkind; Brian May; David Pliener; Marc Lester; Nicola Wertheim; Warren Persky; Louise Jacobs; Miles Webber; Jonathan Morris.

OTHER INFORMATION Grants were awarded to 132 organisations during the year. £3.5 million was given to organisations in Israel and £1.5 million to organisations in the UK. There were no grants given to individuals.

HOW TO APPLY For further information, email the correspondent.

CONTACT DETAILS The Trustees, 1 Torriano Mews, London NW5 2RZ *Tel.* 020 7424 6400 *Email* info@ujia.org *Website* www.ujia.org

■ The United Reformed Church (Wessex) Trust Ltd

CC NO 282729 **ESTABLISHED** 1980

WHERE FUNDING CAN BE GIVEN UK.

WHO CAN BENEFIT Churches of the United Reform Church; Christian organisations, particularly the Wessex Synod of the United Reform Church.

WHAT IS FUNDED Supporting local churches of the United Reform Church in their outreach and mission.

TYPE OF GRANT Capital costs; core costs; project funding; strategic funding.

RANGE OF GRANTS In 2019 grants ranged from £5,000 to £323,200.

SAMPLE GRANTS Previous beneficiaries have included: Winton – Bournemouth and the Bournemouth International Church (£323,200); Winton (£227,200); Immanuel – Southbourne,

Cumnor – Oxford, Skinner Street – Poole (£10,000 each); Aston Tirrold (£5,000).

FINANCES *Financial year end* 31/12/2019 *Income* £1,920,000 *Total grants* £723,500 *Grants to organisations* £723,500 *Assets* £42,900,000

TRUSTEES Revd Nigel Appleton; Susan Brown; Margaret Smith; Revd Clare Downing; Raymond Dunnett; Andrew Gibb; Revd Julian Macro; Colin MacBean; Revd Dr Romilly Micklem; Peter Pay; Peter Stevenson; Revd Anthea Wickens; John Sinclair.

OTHER INFORMATION Some examples of projects for which grants were awarded include: building works; renovation works; employment of a children's worker; audio visual installation.

HOW TO APPLY Contact the correspondent for further information.

CONTACT DETAILS The Trustees, 120 Alma Road, Southampton, Hampshire SO14 6UW *Tel.* 023 8067 4515 *Email* trust@urcwessex.org.uk *Website* https://wessexsynodurc.org.uk

■ United St Saviour's Charity

CC NO 1103731 **ESTABLISHED** 2004

WHERE FUNDING CAN BE GIVEN North Southwark and Bermondsey.

WHO CAN BENEFIT Local charitable organisations, including: charities; social enterprises; companies limited by guarantee (with a social purpose); faith-based organisations (where activities are not specifically connected with religion); tenants' and residents' associations; CICs.

WHAT IS FUNDED Social welfare; community development; social justice; older people.

WHAT IS NOT FUNDED Projects where the main beneficiaries are living or working outside the charity's area of benefit; individuals (including sole traders); for-profit private companies; local authorities; purely religious activity; political or animal welfare activity.

TYPE OF GRANT Project funding; capital costs; core funding; strategic funding.

RANGE OF GRANTS Mostly £5,000 to £60,000.

SAMPLE GRANTS Change Please – Cafe and Training Centre (£100,000); Salmon Youth Centre (£90,000); Duckie Ltd and London Bubble Theatre (£60,000 each); Southwark Citizens Advice Service (£40,000); Southwark Law Centre (£25,000); Brandon Estate (£10,000).

FINANCES *Financial year end* 31/03/2020 *Income* £3,000,000 *Total grants* £1,120,000 *Grants to organisations* £970,000 *Assets* £48,650,000

TRUSTEES Shane Holland; Stephen Burns; Lord Roy Kennedy; Kathryn Ogunbona; Nicola Steuer; Claire Treanor; Dr Ben Johnson; Lucinda Glover; Izabela Szmidt; Dwight Pile-Gray.

OTHER INFORMATION The charity awards grants on the basis of three priority themes: positive ageing; strong resilient communities; levelling the playing field. There are two open-access grant programmes: large grants of over £5,000 and small grants of under £5,000. Grants were awarded to over 63 organisations during the year as follows: large grants programme (13 grants totalling £702,500); strategic grants programme (6 grants totalling £148,000); small grants programme (44 grants totalling £104,900); micro grants (£15,400). The charity also manages two sheltered housing schemes: St Saviour's Court and Hopton Gardens Almshouses. During the year, grants to individuals (almshouse residents) totalled £150,000.

HOW TO APPLY Apply via the link on the charity's helpful website to the 'Flexigrant' online portal. At the time of writing (May 2021) the charity did not intend to open the large grant programme during 2021 due to the COVID-19 pandemic – see the website for updates.

CONTACT DETAILS Matthew Allgood, Grants Manager, 16 Crucifix Lane, London SE1 3JW *Tel.* 020 7089 9014 *Email* Matthew.Allgood@ustsc.org.uk or info@ustsc.org.uk *Website* www.ustsc.org.uk

■ Universal Music UK Sound Foundation

CC NO 1104027 **ESTABLISHED** 1997

WHERE FUNDING CAN BE GIVEN UK and Ireland.

WHO CAN BENEFIT Schools and individuals.

WHAT IS FUNDED The improvement of young people's access to music education. Support is given to: schools, teachers and individuals for the purchase of musical instruments and/or equipment. The foundation has also created bursaries at 11 conservatoires and music colleges to assist music students in need of financial support.

WHAT IS NOT FUNDED Music studios/businesses; private music centres; community projects.

TYPE OF GRANT Equipment costs; bursaries.

RANGE OF GRANTS Up to £1,500.

SAMPLE GRANTS A list of beneficiaries was not included in the annual report and accounts.

FINANCES *Financial year end* 31/07/2020 *Income* £434,600 *Total grants* £164,700 *Grants to organisations* £79,500 *Assets* £7,020,000

TRUSTEES Charles Aschcroft; Keith Harris; Paul Gambaccini; Mr D. Hughes; Rupert Perry; J. Hibbert; Adam Barker; James Beach; Tony Wadsworth; Leslie Hill; Laura Arowolo; The Hon. Richard Lyttelton.

OTHER INFORMATION Grants to individuals totalled £85,200.

HOW TO APPLY Application forms for instruments and equipment grants can be downloaded from the foundation's website, along with guidance notes.

CONTACT DETAILS The Trustees, Universal Music, 4 Pancras Square, Kings Cross, London N1C 4AG *Tel.* 020 3932 6101 *Email* umuksoundfoundation@umusic.com *Website* https://www.umuksoundfoundation.com

■ UnLtd (Foundation for Social Entrepreneurs)

CC NO 1090393 **ESTABLISHED** 2001

WHERE FUNDING CAN BE GIVEN UK.

WHO CAN BENEFIT Social entrepreneurs and those looking to start a social enterprise project. To be eligible, individuals must be: over the age of 16; resident in the UK; willing to participate in a learning experience; working to benefit people living in the UK. The project has to have a real social impact, fulfil a clear need and demand, and have clear outputs and goals.

WHAT IS FUNDED Support for social entrepreneurs to start, grow or develop a social enterprise initiative. Projects must: benefit the public or a community in the UK; require an UnLtd award to be successful; offer a learning opportunity for applicants; be a new initiative. There are a number of different award schemes with different criteria – refer to the charity's website for information on what is currently available.

WHAT IS NOT FUNDED According to the charity's website, applications will not be accepted if: making the request is part of the applicant's paid employment; the project involves political or religious campaigning, activities outside the law or against public policy or anything that encourages ethnic, religious or commercial disharmony; the activity is mainly for the benefit of the social entrepreneur and/or others to achieve academic qualifications.

TYPE OF GRANT Award winners receive a complete, tailored package of funding, training and advice for their project.

SAMPLE GRANTS A list of beneficiaries was not included in the annual report and accounts.

FINANCES *Financial year end* 31/03/2020 *Income* £6,310,000 *Total grants* £1,860,000 *Grants to organisations* £1,860,000 *Assets* £2,620,000

TRUSTEES Lynne Berry; Susan Charteris; Stephen Bediako; Nicolas Farhi; Elizabeth Sideris; Amma Mensah; Nicholas Petford; Rachel Barton; Krishna Vishnubhotla; James Lawson; Tim Davies-Pugh; Anne Glover.

OTHER INFORMATION Grants were awarded to 425 organisations and individuals during the year.

HOW TO APPLY Refer to the UnLtd website to find the relevant scheme for your initiative and complete an expression of interest form. Deadlines, eligibility criteria and further guidance are given on the website for each award scheme. The website states: 'We are only able to fund a limited amount of Awards per year. This means the application process is extremely competitive and we are not able to provide individual feedback to applicants who do not pass the initial assessment stage.'

CONTACT DETAILS Mark Norbury, Chief Executive, 123 Whitecross Street, Islington, London EC1Y 8JJ *Tel.* 020 7566 1100 *Email* info@unltd.org.uk *Website* www.unltd.org.uk

■ UPP Foundation

CC NO 1166323 **ESTABLISHED** 2015

WHERE FUNDING CAN BE GIVEN UK.

WHO CAN BENEFIT Registered UK charities; universities; non-registered groups with a clear social purpose; social enterprises; community groups.

WHAT IS FUNDED Education; social and economic disadvantage; unemployment; cultural equality.

WHAT IS NOT FUNDED Individuals.

TYPE OF GRANT Project funding.

RANGE OF GRANTS Generally between £5,000 and £20,000, though larger grants will occasionally be considered if greater impact and value can be demonstrated.

SAMPLE GRANTS A list of beneficiaries was not included in the annual report and accounts.

FINANCES *Financial year end* 31/08/2019 *Income* £278,000 *Total grants* £184,000 *Grants to organisations* £184,000 *Assets* £222,000

TRUSTEES Prof. Mary Stuart; Jonathan Wakeford; Andrew Percival; Chris Skidmore; Alexandra Slater; Karen Morgan; Eleanor Rapley.

OTHER INFORMATION The UPP Foundation was created in 2016 by University Partnerships Programme (UPP), a provider of on-campus student accommodation infrastructure and support services in the UK. UPP is the sole funder of the UPP Foundation. The UPP Foundation is an autonomous charity and all of its grants are reviewed and authorised by its board of trustees. The 2018/19 accounts were the latest available at the time of writing (April 2021).

HOW TO APPLY Application forms can be requested via email. Check the foundation's website for information on funding opening dates.

CONTACT DETAILS Richard Brabner, Director, 40 Gracechurch Street, London EC3V 0BT *Tel.* 020 7398 7200 *Email* upp-foundation@upp-ltd.com *Website* upp-foundation.org

■ The Michael Uren Foundation

CC NO 1094102 **ESTABLISHED** 2002

WHERE FUNDING CAN BE GIVEN UK and overseas.

WHO CAN BENEFIT Registered charities; hospitals; universities.

WHAT IS FUNDED The armed forces; medical research; animal welfare; education; heritage.

TYPE OF GRANT Project funding; research.

SAMPLE GRANTS International Animal Rescue (£3.79 million); Sherbourne School (£1 million); Moorfields Eye Hospital (£600,000); Cool Earth (£400,000); Combat Stress (£200,000); St Mildred's Church Tentterden (£100,000); The Royal British Legion (£20,000); Rye Harbour Discovery Appeal (£5,000).

FINANCES *Financial year end* 05/04/2020 *Income* £2,570,000 *Total grants* £8,020,000 *Grants to organisations* £8,020,000 *Assets* £32,850,000

TRUSTEES Anne Gregory-Jones; Janis Bennett; Roger Gould; David Uren; Robert Uren.

OTHER INFORMATION Grants were made to 22 organisations in 2019/20.

HOW TO APPLY The foundation does not consider unsolicited applications.

CONTACT DETAILS The Trustees, c/o haysmacintyre, Thames Exchange, 10 Queen Street Place, London EC4R 1AG *Tel.* 020 7969 5500 *Email* mpattenden@haysmacintyre.com

■ The David Uri Memorial Trust

CC NO 327810 **ESTABLISHED** 1988

WHERE FUNDING CAN BE GIVEN Worldwide.

WHO CAN BENEFIT Charitable organisations.

WHAT IS FUNDED General charitable purposes, particularly: Jewish causes; social welfare; education.

WHAT IS NOT FUNDED Individuals.

SAMPLE GRANTS A list of beneficiaries was not included in the annual report and accounts.

FINANCES *Financial year end* 31/03/2020 *Income* £229,100 *Total grants* £86,800 *Grants to organisations* £86,800 *Assets* £6,380,000

TRUSTEES Benjamin Blackman; Bianca Roden; Sandra Blackman.

HOW TO APPLY Contact the correspondent for further information.

CONTACT DETAILS The Trustees, 244 Vauxhall Bridge Road, London SW1V 1AU *Tel.* 020 7828 8899 *Email* dumt@duvt.com

■ Utermann Charitable Trust

CC NO 1155083 **ESTABLISHED** 2013

WHERE FUNDING CAN BE GIVEN Worldwide.

WHO CAN BENEFIT This charity supports organisations and individuals.

WHAT IS FUNDED General charitable purposes.

RANGE OF GRANTS £800 to £41,000.

SAMPLE GRANTS North London Collegiate School (£41,700); Donmar Warehouse Project

(£12,000); The Royal Horticultural Society (£5,000); Hampstead Theatre (£800).
FINANCES *Financial year end* 05/04/2020 *Income* £127,600 *Total grants* £59,500 *Grants to organisations* £59,500 *Assets* £270,100
TRUSTEES Andreas Utermann; Claudia Utermann.
OTHER INFORMATION Grants were awarded to four organisations during the year.
HOW TO APPLY Contact the correspondent for further information.
CONTACT DETAILS Claudia Utermann, Trustee, 13 Bracknell Gardens, London NW3 7EE *Tel.* 020 7435 1125

■ The Utley Foundation

CC NO 1157399 **ESTABLISHED** 2014
WHERE FUNDING CAN BE GIVEN UK; overseas.
WHO CAN BENEFIT Charitable organisations.
WHAT IS FUNDED General charitable purposes; music and dementia; veterans; children and young people; international aid.
SAMPLE GRANTS A list of beneficiaries was not included in the annual report and accounts.
FINANCES *Financial year end* 31/03/2020 *Income* £1,670,000 *Total grants* £951,100 *Grants to organisations* £951,100 *Assets* £19,750,000
TRUSTEES Melvyn Sims; Nicky Utley; Neil Utley; Raja Balasuriya.
OTHER INFORMATION Grants were broken down as follows: music and dementia (£533,500); children (£175,000); veterans (£111,100); international aid (£98,400); other (£33,000).
HOW TO APPLY Contact the correspondent for further information.
CONTACT DETAILS Lizzie Cody, Foundation Manager, Larkins Farm, 199 Nine Ashes Road, Ingatestone, Essex CM4 0JY *Tel.* 01277 821338 *Email* lizzie@utleyfoundation.org.uk *Website* utleyfoundation.org.uk/index.html

■ The Vail Foundation

CC NO 1089579 **ESTABLISHED** 2001

WHERE FUNDING CAN BE GIVEN UK and overseas.

WHO CAN BENEFIT Charitable organisations.

WHAT IS FUNDED General charitable purposes; Jewish causes.

SAMPLE GRANTS KKL Charity Accounts (£379,500); London School of Jewish Studies (£65,000); United Synagogue and WIZO UK (£5,000 each); Chicken Soup Shelter (£2,000); Friends of Yeshivat Shefa (£1,000).

FINANCES *Financial year end* 30/09/2019 *Income* £87,100 *Total grants* £457,500 *Grants to organisations* £457,500 *Assets* £4,180,000

TRUSTEES Michael Bradfield; Peggy Brett; Michael Goldstein.

OTHER INFORMATION Accounts for 2018/19 were the latest available at the time of writing (June 2021). Grants were awarded to six organisations during the year.

HOW TO APPLY Contact the correspondent for further information.

CONTACT DETAILS Michael Bradfield, Trustee, 5 Fitzhardinge Street, London W1H 6ED *Tel.* 020 7317 3000

■ The Valentine Charitable Trust

CC NO 1001782 **ESTABLISHED** 1990

WHERE FUNDING CAN BE GIVEN UK and overseas, with a preference for Dorset.

WHO CAN BENEFIT Registered charities; hospitals.

WHAT IS FUNDED General charitable purposes; medical research.

TYPE OF GRANT Core costs; development funding; project funding; strategic funding.

RANGE OF GRANTS Grants range from £500 to £25,000.

SAMPLE GRANTS Dorset Natural History Museum (£25,000); Inspire Foundation and Safewise (£15,000 each); Poole Forum Foundation (£10,000); Prisoners Abroad (£15,000); YMCA (£5,000); Purbeck Strings (£500).

FINANCES *Financial year end* 30/09/2019 *Income* £1,230,000 *Total grants* £1,070,000 *Grants to organisations* £1,070,000 *Assets* £36,990,000

TRUSTEES Douglas Neville-Jones; Peter Leatherdale; Susan Patterson; Roger Gregory; Diana Tory; Wing Cdr Donald Jack; Susan Ridley.

OTHER INFORMATION The 2018/19 accounts were the most recent available at the time of writing (June 2021). The trust has previously noted that it is willing to contribute to core/running costs. The trustees generally look for guarantees that any grants awarded to organisations related to the NHS are for projects or equipment which have no likelihood of being provided out of central funds in the foreseeable future. The trust has also offered matched funding in the past.

HOW TO APPLY Apply in writing to the correspondent. The trust notes that, over recent years, it has operated a policy of not considering applications unless there is an established relationship with the applicant. However, there have been exceptions, particularly in the case of local applicants.

CONTACT DETAILS The Trustees, Hinton House, Hinton Road, Bournemouth, Dorset BH1 2EN *Tel.* 01202 292424

■ The Valiant Charitable Trust

CC NO 1135810 **ESTABLISHED** 2010

WHERE FUNDING CAN BE GIVEN Hitchin and surrounding areas.

WHO CAN BENEFIT Registered charities.

WHAT IS FUNDED General charitable purposes.

TYPE OF GRANT Project funding; capital costs.

RANGE OF GRANTS Grants range from £1,500 up to £50,000.

SAMPLE GRANTS Keech Hospice (£50,000); Home-Start Hertfordshire (£35,000); Scout Association (£30,000); Dyspraxia Association (£25,000); Daisychains (£20,000); RNLI (£10,000); East Anglian Air Ambulance (£5,000).

FINANCES *Financial year end* 05/04/2020 *Income* £601,000 *Total grants* £290,500 *Grants to organisations* £290,500 *Assets* £4,170,000

TRUSTEES Lady Valerie Dixon; Roger Woolfe; Paul Brenham.

OTHER INFORMATION Grants were made to 15 organisations throughout the year. The trust also provided an interest-free loan of £90,000 to Hitchin Rugby Club Ltd towards costs relating to the club's redevelopment project.

HOW TO APPLY Contact the correspondent for further information.

CONTACT DETAILS The Trustees, c/o Collyer Bristow LLP, 140 Brompton Road, London SW3 1HY *Tel.* 020 7242 7363 *Email* andrew.mason@collyerbristow.com

■ The Albert Van Den Bergh Charitable Trust

CC NO 296885 **ESTABLISHED** 1987

WHERE FUNDING CAN BE GIVEN UK and overseas.

WHO CAN BENEFIT Charitable organisations.

WHAT IS FUNDED General charitable purposes, particularly medical research and care for patients with cancer, multiple sclerosis, Parkinson's and other diseases and disabilities. Organisations that care for elderly people and children's charities are also supported.

SAMPLE GRANTS A list of beneficiaries was not included in the annual report and accounts.

FINANCES *Financial year end* 05/04/2020 *Income* £160,100 *Total grants* £149,300 *Grants to organisations* £149,300 *Assets* £3,060,000

TRUSTEES Jane Hartley; Nicola Glover; David Webster.

OTHER INFORMATION Grants were awarded in the following categories: help in the community (£64,000); overseas (£21,000); disability (£20,000); medical research, care and support (£12,300); conservation (£9,000); disadvantaged people (£6,000); cultural charities and sport in the community (£4,000 each); older people (£3,000); hospices and servicemen and women (£2,000 each); homelessness and churches (£1,000 each).

HOW TO APPLY Contact the correspondent for further information.

CONTACT DETAILS Jane Hartley, Trustee, Trevornick Farmhouse, Holywell Bay, Newquay, Cornwall TR8 5PW *Tel.* 01637 830272 *Email* trustees@albertvandenbergh.org

■ The Van Mesdag Fund

CC NO 1166453 **ESTABLISHED** 2013

WHERE FUNDING CAN BE GIVEN UK and overseas.

WHO CAN BENEFIT Charitable organisations.

WHAT IS FUNDED General charitable purposes; health; disability; education; animal welfare; social welfare.

SAMPLE GRANTS A list of beneficiaries was not included in the annual report and accounts.

FINANCES *Financial year end* 30/06/2020 *Income* £131,800 *Total grants* £153,000 *Grants to organisations* £153,000 *Assets* £5,390,000

TRUSTEES Milo Maarten Van Mesdag; Rozemarijn Van Mesdag; Savanna Van Mesdag; Ewen Gilmour.

OTHER INFORMATION Grants were distributed as follows: health and disability (£44,000); prevention or relief of poverty and general charitable purposes (£33,000 each); education (£25,000); animal welfare (£18,000).

HOW TO APPLY Apply in writing to the correspondent. The 2019/20 annual report states: 'The trustees consider grant applications on an individual basis.'

CONTACT DETAILS The Trustees, 310 Lanark Road, Edinburgh, London EH14 2LJ *Tel.* 0131 443 6796 *Email* rvmesdag@gmail.com

■ The Van Neste Foundation

CC NO 201951 **ESTABLISHED** 1959

WHERE FUNDING CAN BE GIVEN UK; financially developing countries.

WHO CAN BENEFIT Registered charities; CICs.

WHAT IS FUNDED Children and young people; community projects focusing on marginalised people and environmental improvement.

WHAT IS NOT FUNDED National appeals; large NGOs.

RANGE OF GRANTS Grants range from £1,000 up to £50,000.

SAMPLE GRANTS Bristol and Bath Capital (£50,000); Be on Board (£38,000); Larchfield Homes (£20,000); Child.org (£10,000); Chiboza Community Trust (£6,300); The Ishboume Foundation and Heart of Africa (£5,000 each).

FINANCES *Financial year end* 05/04/2020 *Income* £381,700 *Total grants* £473,700 *Grants to organisations* £473,700 *Assets* £8,100,000

TRUSTEES Benedict Appleby; Jeremy Lyons; Tom Appleby; Joanna Dickens; Michael Delaney; Lucy Appleby.

OTHER INFORMATION Grants were made to 38 organisations during the year.

HOW TO APPLY Application forms can be downloaded from the foundation's website. Grant applications are assessed three times a year, usually in January, June and October.

CONTACT DETAILS The Secretary, 15 Alexandra Road, Clifton, Bristol BS8 2DD *Tel.* 0117 973 5167 *Email* secretary@vanneste.org.uk *Website* vanneste.org.uk

■ The Vandervell Foundation

CC NO 255651 **ESTABLISHED** 1968

WHERE FUNDING CAN BE GIVEN UK.

WHO CAN BENEFIT Charitable organisations.

WHAT IS FUNDED General charitable purposes, particularly education, medical care and research, the performing arts, environmental regeneration and social welfare.

WHAT IS NOT FUNDED The foundation does not accept applications from individuals.

RANGE OF GRANTS Grants range up to £15,000.

SAMPLE GRANTS British Exploring Society and Arts Education School Tring Park (£15,000 each); University of Exeter (£7,500); London's Air Ambulance (£7,000); English National Ballet and The Anne Frank Trust UK (£5,000 each).

FINANCES *Financial year end* 31/12/2019 *Income* £294,600 *Total grants* £361,000 *Grants to organisations* £361,000 *Assets* £8,050,000

TRUSTEE The Vandervell Foundation Ltd.

OTHER INFORMATION Grants were distributed in the following categories in 2019: social welfare (59 grants); medical care and research (27 grants); performing arts (six grants); education (six grants); environmental regeneration (two grants).

HOW TO APPLY Apply in writing to the correspondent. The trustees meet every other month to consider grant applications.

CONTACT DETAILS Valerie Kaye, Administrator, Hampstead Town Hall Centre, 213 Haverstock Hill, London NW3 4QP *Tel.* 020 7435 7546 *Email* vandervell@btconnect.com

■ The Vardy Foundation

CC NO 328415 **ESTABLISHED** 1987

WHERE FUNDING CAN BE GIVEN UK and overseas, with a preference for the North East.

WHO CAN BENEFIT Registered charities.

WHAT IS FUNDED Education; religion; welfare; arts.

RANGE OF GRANTS Grants range from £25,000 up to £200,000.

SAMPLE GRANTS Durham Cathedral (£200,000); Caring for Life and Foundation of Light (£100,000 each); Charlie House (£51,000); Emmanuel Church (£50,000); Urban Saints (£35,000): Hope Next Generation (£25,000).

FINANCES *Financial year end* 05/04/2020 *Income* £2,230,000 *Total grants* £1,845,000 *Grants to organisations* £1,770,000 *Assets* £32,530,000

TRUSTEES Lady Margaret Vardy; Sir Peter Vardy; Richard Vardy; Victoria Vardy; Peter Vardy.

OTHER INFORMATION In 2019/20, the foundation distributed 207 grants as follows: welfare (£1.15 million); religion (£673,600); education (£13,000); arts (£15,400); relief (£1,500). Grants of under £25,000 totalled £904,600. The foundation has two designated funds – Peter Vardy Foundation and The Jigsaw Foundation – which are primarily focused on charitable activities in Scotland but also support some international programmes.

HOW TO APPLY Apply in writing to the correspondent. The trustees meet every three months to review grants.

CONTACT DETAILS The Trustees, 19 Seafield Road East, Edinburgh EH15 1ED *Tel.* 0131 468 7301

■ Variety, the Children's Charity

CC NO 209259 **ESTABLISHED** 1962

WHERE FUNDING CAN BE GIVEN UK.

WHO CAN BENEFIT Charitable organisations; youth clubs; hospitals; hospices; individuals.

WHAT IS FUNDED Support for children and young people in the areas of: disability; health; social and economic disadvantage.

WHAT IS NOT FUNDED The charity does not fund: standard household equipment or furnishings; repayment of loans; garden adaptations; garden sheds or summerhouses; the cost of a family/ wheelchair-adapted vehicle; computer hardware; maintenance or ongoing costs; travel costs; therapy sessions; reimbursement of funds already paid out; hire/rental costs or down payments; trikes/bikes or buggies; trips abroad or holiday costs; trampolines; medical treatment; or education or tuition fees.

TYPE OF GRANT Capital costs.

RANGE OF GRANTS £5,000 to £370,000.

SAMPLE GRANTS Green Meadows School (£371,300); Springwater School (£155,500); Sir Charles Parsons School (£40,000); Birtenshaw School (£35,900); Bollon Playing for Success (£32,000); Brackenfield Special School (£20,000); The Golf Trust (£10,000); Foxgloves (£5,000).

FINANCES *Financial year end* 31/12/2019 *Income* £7,660,000 *Total grants* £4,000,000 *Grants to organisations* £2,860,000 *Assets* £3,970,000

TRUSTEES Dilaram Kitchlew-Williamson; Pamela Sinclair; Ronald Sinclair; Prof. Jonathan Shalit; Ronald Nathan; Stanley Salter; Anthony Harris; Tesula Mohindra; Tushar Prabhu; Jason Lewis; Malcolm Brenner.

OTHER INFORMATION In total, 330 grants were awarded during the year. Grants are generally awarded for the purposes of providing equipment for organisations that fit the criteria of Variety's charitable objectives.

HOW TO APPLY All grant applications are initially assessed by the charity's staff to ensure they fall within the charity's funding guidelines. They are then passed to a committee of volunteers to assess the impact of the equipment and the financial situation of the applicant. The final decision for each grant rests with the committee of volunteers. Application forms are available to download from the charity's helpful website, along with full guidelines and further information.

CONTACT DETAILS Stanley Salter, Secretary, Variety Club House, 93 Bayham Street, London NW1 0AG *Tel.* 020 7428 8100 *Email* info@variety.org.uk *Website* www.variety.org.uk

■ The Vaughan Williams Charitable Trust

CC NO 1123968 **ESTABLISHED** 2000

WHERE FUNDING CAN BE GIVEN Worldwide.

WHO CAN BENEFIT Classical music-based organisations; individuals.

WHAT IS FUNDED The promotion of knowledge about Ralph Vaughan Williams (VW) and performance of his works. Specifically in the following areas, specified on the trust's website: the publication of unpublished work of VW; performance of works by VW; recording of neglected VW works, especially the creation of DVDs of the operas; research into the music of VW; the acquisition by public institutions of VW research material, such as autograph manuscripts or original correspondence.

TYPE OF GRANT Normally, one-off project costs.

RANGE OF GRANTS Grants range from £250 up to £13,000.

SAMPLE GRANTS Dutton-Vocalion (£13,000); Newbury Spring Festival and Big Screen Live (£10,000 each); Three Chairs Festival Association and Royal Choral Society (£5,000 each); St Marylebone Parish Church (£1,000); Bewick Orchestra (£250).

FINANCES *Financial year end* 31/10/2019 *Income* £365,600 *Total grants* £97,900 *Grants to organisations* £94,900 *Assets* £4,320,000

TRUSTEES Andrew Dixon; Arthur Searle; Bernard Watson; Eva Hornstein; Sally Groves; Dr Joyce Kennedy; Dr Nicholas Bell.

OTHER INFORMATION The 2018/19 accounts were the latest available at the time of writing (June 2021). Grants were awarded to 36 organisations during the year.

HOW TO APPLY Apply in writing to the correspondent. Applicants will be informed of the decision on their application as soon as possible. The trustees normally meet twice a year, in March and September/October. However, most applications for grants can be dealt with by the trust's director, consulting trustees as necessary, soon after receipt. A detailed list of what the application should include is provided on the trust's website.

CONTACT DETAILS Hugh Cobbe, Director, Fox House, North End, Newbury, Berkshire RG20 0AY *Tel.* 01635 253190 *Email* vwct@hughcobbe.com *Website* www.vwct.org.uk

■ The Velvet Foundation

CC NO 1169789 **ESTABLISHED** 2015

WHERE FUNDING CAN BE GIVEN England and Wales; Israel.

WHO CAN BENEFIT Charitable organisations and individuals; medical institutions; educational establishments.

WHAT IS FUNDED General charitable purposes; social welfare; health; education; Jewish causes.

RANGE OF GRANTS Up to £30,000.

SAMPLE GRANTS British Friends of The Sheba Medical Centre at Tel Hashomer (£26,700); Beis Hamedrash Nishmas Yisroel Ltd (£25,300); Ahavot Shalom (£20,600); Beth Hamedrash Knesset Yehezkel (£20,000); Mercaz Hatorah Netzach Yisroel (£10,000). Grants to unspecified organisations totalled £20,500.

FINANCES *Financial year end* 30/09/2019 *Income* £250,000 *Total grants* £123,100 *Grants to organisations* £123,100 *Assets* £150,600

TRUSTEES Chee Choong Cheah; David Rodney; Michael Aaronson.

OTHER INFORMATION Grants were broken down as follows: the advancement of education (£94,400); the advancement of health (£26,700); relief of poverty (£2,000). The 2018/19 accounts were the latest available at the time of writing (May 2021).

HOW TO APPLY Contact the correspondent for further information.

CONTACT DETAILS David Rodney, Trustee, c/o Melinek Fine LLP, First Floor Winston House, 349 Regents Park Road, London N3 1DH *Tel.* 020 8458 9223 *Email* davidrodney@velvetfoundation.org.uk

■ The Veneziana Fund

CC NO 1061760 **ESTABLISHED** 1997

WHERE FUNDING CAN BE GIVEN Venice and the UK.

WHO CAN BENEFIT Registered charities; exempt charities; churches.

WHAT IS FUNDED Historic buildings; fixtures and fittings; works of art.

TYPE OF GRANT Capital costs.

RANGE OF GRANTS Grants range from £1,000 to £37,600.

SAMPLE GRANTS Venice in Peril (£37,600); Venice in Peril – Acqua Alta 2019 Appeal (£25,000); St John's Church Heritage Group (£2,000); The Silton's PCC (£1,000).

FINANCES *Financial year end* 30/06/2020 *Income* £91,300 *Total grants* £65,600 *Grants to organisations* £65,600 *Assets* £95,300

OTHER INFORMATION According to its Charity Commission record, the fund gives 50% of its income (after expenses) to the Venice in Peril Fund. The remaining 50% is given to other charities.

HOW TO APPLY Grant criteria and an application form can be requested by contacting the fund's administrator through an online form on the website.

CONTACT DETAILS Alexandra Magri, Fund Administrator, c/o Pothecary Witham Weld Solicitors, The Office Group, Thomas House, 84 Eccleston Square, London SW1V 1PX *Tel.* 020 7821 8211 *Email* charities@pwwsolicitors.co.uk *Website* https://www.pwwsolicitors.co.uk/charity-grants

■ The William and Patricia Venton Charitable Trust

CC NO 1103884 **ESTABLISHED** 2004

WHERE FUNDING CAN BE GIVEN UK.

WHO CAN BENEFIT Charitable organisations.

WHAT IS FUNDED Relief in need for older people, particularly day centre provision; and the prevention of cruelty and suffering among animals.

SAMPLE GRANTS Age UK Nottingham (£61,400); Age UK Plymouth (£45,300); Age Concern Eastbourne (£30,000); RSPCA Cornwall (£27,400).

FINANCES *Financial year end* 31/03/2020 *Income* £95,900 *Total grants* £164,100 *Grants to organisations* £164,100 *Assets* £2,790,000

OTHER INFORMATION The 2019/20 accounts note that the trust had a quiet year due to the ill health of the chair.

HOW TO APPLY Apply in writing to the correspondent. Following an initial approach, eligible applicants will be sent the relevant application forms, to be returned with the appropriate documentation and then reviewed by trustees. The trustees favour applications from charities with which the trust's founders had a connection, but all applications meeting the trust's objectives are considered.

CONTACT DETAILS The Trustees, Broadlands Gate, Broadlands Road, Brockenhurst, Hampshire SO42 7SX *Tel.* 01590 623818 *Email* johngriffiths@wpventontrust.org.uk

■ The Veolia Environmental Trust

CC NO 1064144 **ESTABLISHED** 1997

WHERE FUNDING CAN BE GIVEN UK. Projects should be near a Veolia site. There is a postcode checker on the trust's website.

WHO CAN BENEFIT Constituted not-for-profit groups or charitable organisations.

WHAT IS FUNDED Community and environmental projects. More specifically, capital projects in the following categories: community buildings and rooms; outdoor spaces; play and recreation spaces; environmental improvements; biodiversity.

WHAT IS NOT FUNDED Each programme has its own specific exclusions. See the trust's website for further information.

TYPE OF GRANT Capital projects with a total cost of less than £250,000.

RANGE OF GRANTS £10,000 to £75,000.

SAMPLE GRANTS Watford Borough Council (£238,000); Shropshire Wildlife Trust (£100,000); Alt Valley Community Trust (£59,000); Plantlife International (£56,000).

FINANCES *Financial year end* 31/03/2020 *Income* £5,820,000 *Total grants* £4,870,000 *Grants to organisations* £4,870,000 *Assets* £4,139,000

OTHER INFORMATION Grants were made to 105 organisations and broken down as follows: community rooms (£3.07 million); nature reserves and woodlands (£922,800); play and recreation facilities (£637,200); parks and gardens (£355,400); sporting facilities (£314,100); pathways (£225,700); waterways (£75,000).

HOW TO APPLY After completing the online postcode checker and eligibility checker, a stage 1 application can be made using the form on the trust's website, where guidelines are also provided. See the trust's website for application deadlines.

CONTACT DETAILS The Trustees, Ruthdene, Station Road, Four Ashes, Wolverhampton, West Midlands WV10 7DG *Tel.* 020 3567 6820 *Email* UK.Trust@veolia.com *Website* www.veoliatrust.org

■ Versus Arthritis

CC NO 207711 **ESTABLISHED** 2017

WHERE FUNDING CAN BE GIVEN UK.

WHO CAN BENEFIT Universities; research institutions.

WHAT IS FUNDED Research into the cure and prevention of arthritis and related musculoskeletal diseases.

TYPE OF GRANT Project funding; research funding; capital costs; salaries.

RANGE OF GRANTS £1,000 to £940,000.

SAMPLE GRANTS Keele University (£940,000); King's College London (£919,000); Queen Mary University of London (£852,000); Cardiff University (£563,000); Newcastle University (£403,000); Nottingham University Hospitals NHS Trust (£246,000); Addenbrookes Hospital (£108,000); Cambridge University Hospitals NHS Foundation Trust (£87,000); Queen's University Belfast (£44,000); Manchester Metropolitan University (£18,000); Medical Research Council (£5,000); National Institute for Health Research (£1,000).

FINANCES *Financial year end* 31/03/2020
Income £25,240,000
Total grants £16,800,000
Grants to organisations £16,800,000
Assets £181,660,000

TRUSTEES Clare Reid; Prof. David Isenberg; Dr Rodger Macmillan; Prof. Martijn Steultjens; Vincent Noinville; Karin Hogsander; Dr Andrew Holford; Prof. Sarah Lamb; Juliette Scott; Phillip Gray; Prof. Jonathan Cohen.

OTHER INFORMATION The charity made 53 new awards of over £10,000 during the year.

HOW TO APPLY Details of all open grant programmes can be found on the 'Types of grants' section of the charity's website. All applications should be made via the online application portal.

CONTACT DETAILS Research Department, Copeman House, St Mary's Court, St Mary's Gate, Chesterfield S41 7TD *Tel.* 0300 790 0400 *Email* research@versusarthritis.org *Website* https://www.versusarthritis.org

■ The Veterans' Foundation

CC NO 1166953 **ESTABLISHED** 2016

WHERE FUNDING CAN BE GIVEN UK.

WHO CAN BENEFIT Registered charities; not-for-profit organisations; voluntary groups; any organisation that is supporting the armed forces community.

WHAT IS FUNDED Support for serving armed forces personnel, veterans, operationally qualified seafarers and their immediate families.

WHAT IS NOT FUNDED Organisations that do not support the armed forces or seafaring communities; gap years; study trips; fundraising expeditions; sponsorship; housing associations and corporations (unless activities and costs are clear and charitable); activities that result in profit; organisations requiring payments to be sent to bank accounts outside the UK.

TYPE OF GRANT Project funding; capital costs; strategic funding; development funding; multi-year awards.

RANGE OF GRANTS Up to £30,000.

SAMPLE GRANTS Association of Royal Navy Officers; Blue Van Veterans Drop-In; Help for Homeless Veterans; Housing Options Scotland; Launchpad; Macrobet Arts Centre; Scotty's Little Soldiers; The Warrior Programme.

FINANCES *Financial year end* 30/06/2020
Income £4,350,000 *Total grants* £1,924,000
Grants to organisations £1,920,000
Assets £122,300

TRUSTEES Peter Mountford; Eline Lofgren; Bruce Walker; Mungo Tulloch; Richard Farndale.

OTHER INFORMATION During 2019/20, 124 grants were awarded to 104 organisations, the majority of which were registered charities. Grants are occasionally made to individuals. Priority is given to small and medium-sized charities.

HOW TO APPLY Applications can be made online after creating an account on the foundation's website. Completed applications should be submitted by the end of the month preceding the grants committee meeting. Meetings are usually held in December, May, September and March; however, check the website for current deadlines. Full guidelines are also available to download from the foundation's website.

CONTACT DETAILS The Trustees, Thistle Court (Room 5), Thistle Street, Edinburgh EH2 1DD *Tel.* 0333 999 3899 *Email* enquiries@veteransfoundation.org.uk *Website* https://www.veteransfoundation.org.uk

■ VHLT Ltd

CC NO 1101241 **ESTABLISHED** 2002

WHERE FUNDING CAN BE GIVEN London and Israel.

WHO CAN BENEFIT Registered charities.

WHAT IS FUNDED Jewish causes.

RANGE OF GRANTS £20,000 to £350,000.

SAMPLE GRANTS Vaad Harabonim Israel (£353,600); Mosdos Satmar (£166,500); Yad Ezra (£23,000); Olam Chesed Yiboneh (£20,400).

FINANCES *Financial year end* 31/08/2019
Income £693,600 *Total grants* £624,100
Grants to organisations £599,400
Assets £96,600

TRUSTEES Avrohom Streicher; Yoel Marmorstein; Yehiel Frand; Raymond Frand.

OTHER INFORMATION Grants were awarded to individuals and organisations during the year. The 2018/19 accounts were the latest available at the time of writing (April 2021).

HOW TO APPLY Contact the correspondent for further information.

CONTACT DETAILS The Trustees, 61 Fairholt Road, London N16 5EW *Tel.* 020 8809 5700

■ Vinci UK Foundation

CC NO 1171871 **ESTABLISHED** 2015

WHERE FUNDING CAN BE GIVEN Projects near to Vinci offices throughout the UK and the Republic of Ireland.

WHO CAN BENEFIT Small and medium-sized registered community interest or non-profit organisations.

WHAT IS FUNDED Access to employment; housing; mobility; community development.

WHAT IS NOT FUNDED Individuals; profit-based organisations; statutory bodies, federations; political or religious organisations/groups.

TYPE OF GRANT Capital costs.

SAMPLE GRANTS Raw Workshop (£15,000); Chelmsford Chess (£12,600); Friends of the Castle (£10,000); The Daisy Garland (£8,200).

FINANCES *Financial year end* 31/12/2019
Income £185,000 *Total grants* £204,200
Grants to organisations £204,200
Assets £41,000

TRUSTEES Pascal Mercier; Philip Horton; Philip Hines; Tom Jones; Scott Wardop; Jean-Yves Cojean; Francois Pogu; Rochdi Ziyat; Russell Matthews.

OTHER INFORMATION The foundation is the UK corporate charity of the Vinci Group, a construction company based in France. Projects should actively involve Vinci employees. Only beneficiaries receiving grants of over £7,500 have been included in the accounts.

HOW TO APPLY The foundation has detailed guidance for potential applicants, including deadlines, eligibility criteria and examples of past projects, on its website.

CONTACT DETAILS Ayyub Dedat, Unit 2050 The Crescent, Birmingham Business Park, Birmingham B37 7YE *Email* contact@vinci-uk-foundation.co.uk *Website* www.vinci-uk-foundation.co.uk

■ Nigel Vinson Charitable Trust

CC NO 265077 **ESTABLISHED** 1973

WHERE FUNDING CAN BE GIVEN UK.

WHO CAN BENEFIT Charitable organisations; universities; religious organisations.

WHAT IS FUNDED General charitable purposes, including: arts, culture, heritage or science; Christianity; disability; economic/community development and citizenship; education; health; the environment.

WHAT IS NOT FUNDED Individuals.

RANGE OF GRANTS Typically up to £20,000.

SAMPLE GRANTS Institute of Economic Affairs (£60,000); Civitas (£23,300); Buckingham University (£20,000); Institute for Policy Research (£11.500); Hampden Trust (£6,000); Alnwick District Playhouse (£5,000); Humanitarian and Relief Trust (£2,000).

FINANCES *Financial year end* 30/06/2020
Income £93,700 *Total grants* £161,800
Grants to organisations £161,800
Assets £3,630,000

TRUSTEES Bettina Witheridge; The Hon. Rowena Cowan; Lord Nigel Vinson; Thomas Harris; Hon. Antonia Bennett; Hoare Trustees.

OTHER INFORMATION Grants of more than £1,000 were made to 11 organisations as follows: education (£129,800); citizenship/community development (£17,000); arts, culture, heritage or science (£5,000). An unspecified number of grants for less than £1,000 totalled £10,000.

HOW TO APPLY Apply in writing to the correspondent. The trustees meet periodically to consider applications for grants. Decisions on smaller grants may be approved by a single trustee, whereas larger grants require the approval of a number of trustees.

CONTACT DETAILS Hoare Trustees, c/o C. Hoare and Co., 37 Fleet Street, London EC4Y 1BT *Tel.* 020 7353 4522

The Vintners' Foundation

CC NO 1015212 **ESTABLISHED** 1992

WHERE FUNDING CAN BE GIVEN Greater London, with a preference for inner London.

WHO CAN BENEFIT Registered charities; schools.

WHAT IS FUNDED People who are homeless or disadvantaged in Greater London, alleviating the social effects of alcohol abuse or misuse; young people; education and training.

WHAT IS NOT FUNDED Applications relating to the rest of the UK or overseas; medical research; restoration of buildings; individuals.

TYPE OF GRANT Project funding.

RANGE OF GRANTS Normally in the range of £3,000 to £5,000.

SAMPLE GRANTS Oasis Charitable Trust (£30,700); Hackney Pirates (£20,000); Counselling Pastoral Trust (£10,000); St Mary Le Bow Young Homeless Charity and Swan Lifeline (£5,000 each); Caris Camden Trust (£4,000); The Children's Literacy Project (£3,500); St Paul's Cathedral (£1,000).

FINANCES *Financial year end* 31/03/2020
Income £526,300 *Total grants* £289,000
Grants to organisations £289,000
Assets £3,200,000

TRUSTEES Christopher Davey; Ann Hill; Anthony Fairbank; Edward Berry.

OTHER INFORMATION The foundation states that most of the grants it awards are to its current selected charities. However, some limited funds are available for new organisations. Only organisations receiving grants of over £1,000 were listed as beneficiaries in the foundation's accounts. Grants of under £1,000 totalled £3,000 and were awarded to seven organisations.

HOW TO APPLY Applications can be made via the foundation's website. The grants committee meets four times a year, usually in March, June, September and December.

CONTACT DETAILS Charity Secretary, The Vintners' Company, Vintners' Hall, 68 Upper Thames Street, London EC4V 3BG *Tel.* 020 7651 0753 *Email* charity@vintnershall.co.uk *Website* www.vintnershall.co.uk

Virgin Atlantic Foundation

CC NO 1097580 **ESTABLISHED** 2003

WHERE FUNDING CAN BE GIVEN UK; overseas.

WHO CAN BENEFIT Registered charities.

WHAT IS FUNDED Education; health; social welfare.

TYPE OF GRANT Capital costs; development funding; project funding.

RANGE OF GRANTS £3,000 to £795,400.

SAMPLE GRANTS WE (£795,400); Save The Children (£25,600); Chestnut Tree House (£4,700); Summer Hill School (£3,300).

FINANCES *Financial year end* 30/04/2020
Income £947,000 *Total grants* £829,000
Grants to organisations £829,000
Assets £2,800

TRUSTEES Ian De Sousa; Estelle Hollingsworth; Suzanne Roddie.

OTHER INFORMATION In total, four grants were awarded during the year. A grant of £795,400 was awarded to WE – the foundation's long-term partner. This is a yearly grant that is not subject to change through the application process.

HOW TO APPLY Contact the correspondent for further information.

CONTACT DETAILS K. Bristoll, Secretary, c/o Virgin Atlantic Airways Ltd, The VHQ, Fleming Way, Crawley, West Sussex RH10 9DF *Tel.* 01293 747128 *Email* community.investment@fly.virgin.com *Website* https://corporate.virginatlantic.com/gb/en/sustainability/programme-overview/partners.html

The Virgin Money Foundation

CC NO 1161290 **ESTABLISHED** 2014

WHERE FUNDING CAN BE GIVEN UK, with a preference for Glasgow, Sheffield, Edinburgh, Norwich, Manchester, Cardiff, London, Leeds and the North East.

WHO CAN BENEFIT Registered charities; social enterprises; CICs.

WHAT IS FUNDED The sustainable regeneration of communities; social enterprise; children and young people. See the foundation's website for current funding programmes.

WHAT IS NOT FUNDED See individual grant programmes for specific exclusions.

TYPE OF GRANT Running costs/core costs; project costs.

RANGE OF GRANTS Up to £100,000.

SAMPLE GRANTS CF TW&N (£100,000); Linskill and North Tyneside Community Development Trust (£50,000); YMCA Newcastle (£20,000); The Junction Foundation (£10,000); The Avenues Youth Project (£1,200); Saxon Juniors Football Club and Yorkshire Imperial Band (£500 each).

FINANCES *Financial year end* 30/09/2020
Income £1,600,000 *Total grants* £984,200
Grants to organisations £984,200
Assets £1,980,000

TRUSTEES Edward Wakefield; Mandip Kaur Sahota; Keith Merrin; Lorna Bennie; Hannah Underwood; Gregory Aldridge; Joanne Curry; Keith Burge; Edward Younger; Catherine Guthrie.

OTHER INFORMATION In 2020 the foundation changed the date of its financial year-end from 31 December to 30 September. As a result, the 2019/20 accounts cover a nine-month period.

HOW TO APPLY Some grant programmes are open to applications and others are invitation only. The foundation's website provides further information on each fund, including application deadlines and detailed eligibility criteria.

CONTACT DETAILS Richard Walton, Programme Manager, Jubilee House, Gosforth, Newcastle upon Tyne, Tyne and Wear NE3 4PL *Tel.* 0330 123 3624 *Email* info@virginmoneyfoundation.org.uk *Website* https://virginmoneyfoundation.org.uk

■ Viridor Credits Environmental Company

CC NO 1096538 **ESTABLISHED** 2003

WHERE FUNDING CAN BE GIVEN England and Scotland – in areas near Viridor landfill sites.

WHO CAN BENEFIT Charitable organisations; places of worship.

WHAT IS FUNDED Community projects; heritage projects.

WHAT IS NOT FUNDED A list of exclusions can be found in the guidance notes for applicants available on the grant-maker's website.

TYPE OF GRANT Capital costs; project funding.

RANGE OF GRANTS £50,000 to £100,000.

SAMPLE GRANTS All Saints' Church (£100,000); Temple Park Centre (£99,400); Shepherd's Lodge Pond (£77,200); St Michael and All Angels Church (£68,500); Mollington, Backford and District Village Hall (£50,000).

FINANCES *Financial year end* 31/03/2020 *Income* £5,380,000 *Total grants* £4,970,000 *Grants to organisations* £4,970,000 *Assets* £1,820,000

TRUSTEES Simon Catford; Peter Renshaw; David Robertson; Mary Prior; Dan Cooke.

OTHER INFORMATION Grants made may require a contributing third-party payment, which is the equivalent of 10% of any funds awarded. See the 'Contributing Third Party' section of the grant-maker's website for further information.

HOW TO APPLY Contact the correspondent for further information. Full details on the application process can be found on the grant-maker's website.

CONTACT DETAILS Grants Officer, PO Box 977, Taunton, Somerset TA1 9PQ *Tel.* 01823 476476 *Email* enquiries@viridor-credits.co.uk *Website* www.viridor-credits.co.uk

■ Vision Foundation

CC NO 1074958 **ESTABLISHED** 1999

WHERE FUNDING CAN BE GIVEN London.

WHO CAN BENEFIT This charity supports registered CIOs, charitable companies and CICs limited by guarantee.

WHAT IS FUNDED Projects that are collaborative and designed in partnership with blind and partially sighted people. Services that have been proven to be effective, are valued by their users or can demonstrate evidence for demand. New, innovative and untested work that has a significant positive impact on people living with or are at risk of sight loss.

WHAT IS NOT FUNDED Educational establishment charities and individuals are not supported.

TYPE OF GRANT Project costs; core costs; one-off awards.

RANGE OF GRANTS £10,000 to £50,000.

SAMPLE GRANTS Eye Heroes (£40,000); Queens Crescent Community Association, SeeAbility and Blind in Business (£20,000 each); The Change Foundation (£15,000); The Amber Trust (£13,600); Jewish Care, Panathlon and Wood Street Wall CIC (£6,000 each); Talking News Islington (£2,000); Merton Sports and Social Club (£1,700).

FINANCES *Financial year end* 31/03/2020 *Income* £3,230,000 *Total grants* £371,800 *Grants to organisations* £371,800 *Assets* £2,110,000

TRUSTEES Anna Tylor; Keith Felton; Sharon Petrie; Heather Goodhew; Andy Gregson; Elizabeth Honer; Bob Hughes; Ly Lam; Susanette Mansour.

OTHER INFORMATION Grants were awarded to 41 organisations during the year.

HOW TO APPLY See the foundation's website for details of open grant programmes.

CONTACT DETAILS Lin Richardson, Director of Grants and Impact, 11–12 Whitehorse Mews, 37 Westminster Bridge Road, London SE1 7QD *Tel.* 020 7620 2066 *Email* hello@visionfoundation.org.uk *Website* https://www.visionfoundation.org.uk

■ Vivdale Ltd

CC NO 268505 **ESTABLISHED** 1974

WHERE FUNDING CAN BE GIVEN UK.

WHO CAN BENEFIT Jewish people.

WHAT IS FUNDED Advancement of the Orthodox Jewish faith.

SAMPLE GRANTS Previous beneficiaries have included: Achisomach Aid Company Ltd, Beis Soroh Schneirer, Beis Yaakov Town, Beis Yisroel Tel Aviv, Comet Charities Ltd, Friends of Harim Bnei Brak, Jewish Teachers' Training College Gateshead, Mosdos Bnei Brak, Torah Vechesed Ashdod and Woodstock Sinclair Trust.

FINANCES *Financial year end* 05/04/2020 *Income* £178,400 *Total grants* £145,900 *Grants to organisations* £145,900 *Assets* £3,577,000

TRUSTEES David Marks; Loretta Marks.

HOW TO APPLY Contact the correspondent for further information.

CONTACT DETAILS The Trustees, 133 Leeside Crescent, Golders Green, London NW11 0JN *Tel.* 020 8458 0900 *Email* aepton@goldwins.co.uk

■ The Vodafone Foundation

CC NO 1089625 **ESTABLISHED** 2001

WHERE FUNDING CAN BE GIVEN UK and overseas (where Vodafone operates).

WHO CAN BENEFIT Registered charities and charitable organisations.

WHAT IS FUNDED Projects which use mobile connectivity and technology to promote a healthier, safer and more sustainable society.

SAMPLE GRANTS A list of beneficiaries was not included in the annual report and accounts.

FINANCES *Financial year end* 31/03/2020 *Income* £18,170,000 *Total grants* £12,800,000 *Grants to organisations* £12,800,000 *Assets* £6,120,000

TRUSTEES Nick Land; Elizabeth Filkin; Rosemary Martin; Joakim Reiter; John Otty; Patricia Ithau; Leanne Wood; Maria Amparo Moraleda Martinez.

OTHER INFORMATION Grants were broken down as follows: Vodafone local foundations (£7.74 million); digital health (£1.9 million); other activities (£1.09 million); digital education (£779,500); gender equality (£775,200); UK employee matched funding (£515,300).

HOW TO APPLY The foundation usually approaches charitable organisations which it believes can help with the delivery of its charitable aims.
CONTACT DETAILS The Trustees, 1 Kingdom Street, Paddington Central, London W2 6BY *Email* groupfoundation@vodafone.com *Website* www.vodafonefoundation.org

■ Volant Charitable Trust

OSCR NO SC030790 **ESTABLISHED** 2000
WHERE FUNDING CAN BE GIVEN Scotland
WHO CAN BENEFIT Registered charities; CICs; community organisations.
WHAT IS FUNDED Social deprivation, particularly where it affects women, children and young people; international disaster relief.
WHAT IS NOT FUNDED Individuals; projects not based in Scotland; fundraising activities; major capital projects; retrospective expenditure. A full list of exclusions can be found on Foundation Scotland's website (www.foundationscotland.org.uk).
TYPE OF GRANT Project funding; core costs; equipment (COVID-19 Response Fund only); one-off; multi-year (up to three years).
RANGE OF GRANTS Up to £15,000 per year for three years.
SAMPLE GRANTS Foundation Scotland (£1 million); Médecins Sans Frontières (£200,000); ActionAid and Save the Children (£100,000 each); Citizens UK (£62,500); Plan International UK and Oxfam (£50,000 each).
FINANCES *Financial year end* 05/04/2020 *Income* £1,400,000 *Total grants* £2,140,000 *Grants to organisations* £2,140,000 *Assets* £56,800,000
OTHER INFORMATION This trust was established by the author J. K. Rowling. Grants paid during 2019/20 totalled £2.14 million. Grants committed during the year totalled £1.56 million and were distributed for the following purposes: social deprivation (£1.06 million); international aid (£500,000). Only beneficiaries receiving major grants were listed in the trust's accounts.
HOW TO APPLY Applications can be made online via the Foundation Scotland website. Applicants should first complete an initial enquiry form. Once Foundation Scotland has reviewed the form, organisations may then be invited to submit a full application. Further guidance is available on the website.
CONTACT DETAILS The Trustees, c/o Turcan Connell, Princes Exchange, 1 Earl Grey Street, Edinburgh EH3 9EE *Tel.* 0141 341 4964 *Email* Enquiry form via the trust's website or jennifer@foundationscotland.org.uk. *Website* https://www.volanttrust.org

■ The Georg and Emily Von Opel Foundation

CC NO 1172977 **ESTABLISHED** 2017
WHERE FUNDING CAN BE GIVEN UK; overseas.
WHO CAN BENEFIT UK-registered charities.
WHAT IS FUNDED Social welfare; health; education; nature and the environment; the advancement of the Roman Catholic faith.
SAMPLE GRANTS Natare West London Swimming Club (£944,200); The Latymer Foundation (£500,000); WaterAid (£360,000); Child's Dream Association (£310,000); The Lemon Tree Trust (£7,900).
FINANCES *Financial year end* 31/12/2019 *Income* £2,090,000 *Total grants* £2,500,000 *Grants to organisations* £2,500,000 *Assets* £247,000
TRUSTEES Emily Von Opel; Right Hon. Candida Viscountess Petersham; George Von Opel.
OTHER INFORMATION Georg Von Opel is a German-born Swiss billionaire and great-grandson of Adam Opel, founder of the German car manufacturer.
HOW TO APPLY Contact the correspondent for further information.
CONTACT DETAILS The Trustees, GVO Asset Management AG, Bundesplatz 14, 6300 Zug, Switzerland *Tel.* +415 264 70219

■ The VTCT Foundation

CC NO 1155360 **ESTABLISHED** 2013
WHERE FUNDING CAN BE GIVEN UK.
WHO CAN BENEFIT UK-based organisations; medical research organisations; universities.
WHAT IS FUNDED Medical research in the field of disfigurement; providing support to organisations helping those living with visible difference.
WHAT IS NOT FUNDED Projects that have commercial interests.
TYPE OF GRANT Project funding; research; capacity building; seed funding; one-off; multi-year.
RANGE OF GRANTS Up to £200,000.
SAMPLE GRANTS The University of Oxford – Wilkie Fellowship (£197,000); Alopecia UK (£24,800); Centre for Appearance Research (£20,000); DEBRA (£13,800); Dan's Fund for Burns (£9,000); The Appearance Collective (£4,600); Lipodystrophy UK (£640).
FINANCES *Financial year end* 31/07/2020 *Income* £117,700 *Total grants* £337,700 *Grants to organisations* £337,700 *Assets* £5,000,000
TRUSTEES Dr Wendy Edwards; Anthony Walker; Prof. Naiem Moiemen; Prof. Nichola Rumsey; Rosanna Preston.
OTHER INFORMATION Grants were awarded to seven organisations during 2019/20.
HOW TO APPLY To request further information and/or an application form, contact the correspondent.
CONTACT DETAILS The Trustees, Aspire House, Annealing Close, Eastleigh, Hampshire SO50 9PX *Tel.* 023 8068 4500 *Email* companysecretary@vtctfoundation.org.uk *Website* www.vtctfoundation.org.uk

■ Sylvia Waddilove Foundation UK

CC NO 1118097 **ESTABLISHED** 2007

WHERE FUNDING CAN BE GIVEN UK.

WHO CAN BENEFIT Registered charities; unregistered charities; CICs; hospitals; hospices.

WHAT IS FUNDED Education, particularly organic farming, animal husbandry, veterinary science, animal welfare and surgery and research into animal surgery; visual and performing arts; medical research; the relief of disability or illness; the preservation of buildings of architectural or historical significance; accommodation for those in need.

WHAT IS NOT FUNDED Individuals (except medical research projects).

TYPE OF GRANT Capital costs; staff costs and overheads (specifically for the COVID-19 emergency funding).

RANGE OF GRANTS Typically £1,000 to £5,000.

SAMPLE GRANTS National Trust (£50,000); English Heritage (£25,000); Alzheimer's Research UK and Bedfordshire Opportunities for Learning Disabilities (£5,000 each); Chelsea Physic Garden and Horatio's Garden (£4,000 each); The Holiday Homes Trust and The Institute of Cancer Research (£3,000 each); Corran Dean CIC and The Brain Charity (£2,500); St Peters Community Centre (£1,000); Fire and Ice Theatre Company Ltd (£500).

FINANCES *Financial year end* 31/12/2019
Income £85,800 *Total grants* £232,500
Grants to organisations £232,500
Assets £2,940,000

TRUSTEES Gerald Kidd; Peter Spencer.

OTHER INFORMATION In 2019, the trust made 57 grants to organisations totalling £232,500, distributed as follows: Allocated Grant Programme (£87,500); relief of disability and illness (£40,000); medical research (£38,500); preservation of buildings (£36,500); visual and performing arts (£26,000); accommodation for those in need (£10,000); education (£8,400). The number of grants made was unusually low for this reporting period, due to a lower number of trustees' meetings held.

HOW TO APPLY Application forms, alongside guidance notes, are available from the foundation administrator's website and must be returned by email; applications or correspondence by post are not accepted. Typically, the trustees meet quarterly.

CONTACT DETAILS The Trustees, c/o Pothecary Witham Weld Solicitors, 70 St George's Square, London SW1V 3RD *Tel.* 020 7821 8211 *Email* waddilove@pwwsolicitors.co.uk *Website* https://www.pwwsolicitors.co.uk/charity-grants/13-the-sylvia-waddilove-foundation-uk

■ Wade's Charity

CC NO 224939 **ESTABLISHED** 1530

WHERE FUNDING CAN BE GIVEN Leeds, within the pre-1974 boundary of the city (approximately LS1 to LS17 postcode areas).

WHO CAN BENEFIT Registered charities; unregistered charities; charitable organisations.

WHAT IS FUNDED Recreational activities; the preservation of public open spaces. The main grants programme (£300 or above) considers applications supporting all or any section of the community, including: children and young people; older people; wider community; the arts; open spaces. There is also a small grants programme (up to £300) for small community groups and charities.

WHAT IS NOT FUNDED Applications from outside the area of benefit; non-charitable organisations; individuals; church repairs; general appeals from high-profile national charities; activities which fall outside the charity's objectives; activities which are the responsibility of statutory bodies or local authorities, particularly in health and education; salaries; core costs; projects which have already taken place.

TYPE OF GRANT Capital costs; seed funding/start-up funding; project funding; unrestricted funding.

RANGE OF GRANTS Up to £20,000. The average grant for the main grants programme was £2,551.

SAMPLE GRANTS Leeds City Council Ranger Program (£20,000); Central Yorkshire County Scout Council (£6,500); Leeds Children's Charity (£5,000); Flourishing Families (£3,400); Asha Neighbourhood Project (£3,000); Archway Renew Leeds (£2,000); Vamos Festival (£1,000); Wortley PCC (£210).

FINANCES *Financial year end* 31/12/2019
Income £309,700 *Total grants* £190,900
Grants to organisations £190,900
Assets £9,080,000

TRUSTEES Cllr Jacqueline Shemilt; Hilary Finnigan; Revd Canon Sam Corley; Tim Barber; Bernard Atha; Timothy Ward; Nicholas Mercer; Cllr Mohammed Rafique; Susan Reddington; Bruce Smith; John Stoddart-Scott; Mark Pullan; John Roberts; Cllr Colin Campbell; John Pike; John Tinker; David Richardson.

OTHER INFORMATION During 2019, grants were awarded to 63 organisations and distributed in the following categories: provision of facilities for recreation (£160,700); provision and maintenance of open spaces (£30,200).

HOW TO APPLY Applications to the main grants programme should preferably be submitted by email, including all the required information given in the guidelines on the charity's website. Applicants will then be contacted by the Grants Adviser to arrange a meeting, after which applications are considered by the trustees at meetings in April, July and November. Early applications are encouraged as it can take 4–6 weeks to process an application. The charity welcomes contact to discuss ideas before submitting an application. Applications to the small grants programme should be made through Voluntary Action Leeds (https://doinggoodleeds.org.uk/wades-charity-small-grants).

CONTACT DETAILS Kathryn Hodges, Grants Adviser and Administrator, Mount Villa, 306 Tadcaster Road, York, North Yorkshire YO24 1HE *Tel.* 01904 702384 *Email* info@wadescharity.org *Website* www.wadescharity.org

■ The Scurrah Wainwright Charity

CC NO 1002755 **ESTABLISHED** 1991

WHERE FUNDING CAN BE GIVEN UK, with a preference for Yorkshire; South Africa and Zimbabwe.

WHO CAN BENEFIT Registered charities; unregistered charities; CICs; social enterprises.

WHAT IS FUNDED Social reform.

WHAT IS NOT FUNDED Individuals; large and national charitable organisations unless specifically working in the Yorkshire region and providing local control and access to the grant; organisations with an annual income/ expenditure that exceeds around £250,000; animal welfare; buildings; medical research or support for individual medical conditions; substitution for government funding (e.g. in education and health); unsolicited general appeal letters; activities that have already taken place; organisations without a UK bank account into which a grant can be paid.

TYPE OF GRANT Capital costs; core and revenue costs; seed funding; start-up funding; unrestricted funding.

RANGE OF GRANTS Typically £1,000 to £5,000, but in 'cases of exceptional merit' larger grants may be awarded.

SAMPLE GRANTS Leeds North and East Circuit of the Methodist Church (£11,500); Creating Better Futures and Trellis Foundation (£5,000 each); Open Country Harrogate (£3,500); Independent Research Unit – Addingham (£3,400); South Yorkshire Refugee Law and Justice (£2,500); Alive and Kicking Theatre Co. Ltd (£2,000); Survivors of Torture Activity Fund (£1,000); SY Arts – Sheffield (£900).

FINANCES *Financial year end* 05/04/2020 *Income* £124,500 *Total grants* £175,300 *Grants to organisations* £175,300 *Assets* £2,450,000

TRUSTEES Hilary Wainwright; Hugh Scott; Martin Wainwright; Penny Wainwright; Tessa Wainwright.

OTHER INFORMATION During 2019/20, grants were distributed as follows: projects in the north of England (£131,400); UK national projects (£27,400); projects in Zimbabwe and South Africa (£16,500). The Wainwright family also runs The Andrew Wainwright Reform Trust Ltd, a non-charitable organisation that focuses on 'work for a just and democratic society and to redress political and social injustices'. It funds projects that are ineligible for charitable funding.

HOW TO APPLY In the first instance, check the eligibility criteria and deadlines on the charity's website. Applicants should then submit a preliminary registration form to register their interest, which can be found on the website. If the trustees are interested in the proposal, applicants will be asked to submit their most recent audited accounts together with a full application to the correspondent via post or email. The trustees usually meet in March, July and November, and applications should be submitted by 14 January, 14 May or 14 September, respectively. Applicants may contact the administrator by email with any queries.

CONTACT DETAILS Kerry McQuade, Administrator, 19 Wadsworth Lane, Hebden Bridge, West Yorkshire HX7 8DL *Tel.* 01422 845085 *Email* admin@wainwrighttrusts.org.uk *Website* www.wainwrighttrusts.org.uk

■ The Bruce Wake Charitable Trust

CC NO 1018190 **ESTABLISHED** 1993

WHERE FUNDING CAN BE GIVEN UK.

WHO CAN BENEFIT Charities; not-for-profit organisations; CICs; individuals.

WHAT IS FUNDED Grants to fund leisure activities for people with disabilities, particularly activities which aim to improve access to sport or leisure activities for people who use a wheelchair.

RANGE OF GRANTS Mostly under £5,000.

SAMPLE GRANTS Wheelpower (£25,000); Charity Link Leicester (£21,000); Disability Snowsport UK (£10,000); Revitalise Respite Holidays (£6,000).

FINANCES *Financial year end* 05/04/2020 *Income* £197,000 *Total grants* £859,300 *Grants to organisations* £714,300 *Assets* £7,060,000

TRUSTEES Penny Wake; John Gilboy; Robert Rowley; Peter Hems.

OTHER INFORMATION Grants were made to 251 organisations during the year. Grants to individuals totalled £145,000.

HOW TO APPLY Apply via the trust's website.

CONTACT DETAILS The Trustees, c/o Grant Thornton UK LLP, Regent House, 80 Regent Road, Leicester LE1 7NH *Tel.* 0344 879 3349 *Email* info@brucewaketrust.co.uk *Website* www.brucewaketrust.co.uk

■ Wakefield and Tetley Trust

CC NO 1121779 **ESTABLISHED** 2008

WHERE FUNDING CAN BE GIVEN London boroughs of Tower Hamlets, Southwark and the City of London.

WHO CAN BENEFIT Registered charities; unregistered charities; CICs.

WHAT IS FUNDED Projects that improve the lives of people and communities experiencing disadvantage. Previously, grants have been given towards: people living with disabilities and ill health; vulnerable women and families; BAME communities, advice and welfare support initiatives; children and young people; asylum seekers and refugees. At the time of writing (May 2021), the trust's grant-making priorities were temporarily changed as a result of the COVID-19 pandemic. Check the website for the latest information.

WHAT IS NOT FUNDED See the trust's website for a full list of exclusions.

TYPE OF GRANT Core/revenue costs; seed funding/ start-up funding; project funding; unrestricted funding.

RANGE OF GRANTS Main grants average around £8,500; fast-track grants range up to £5,000.

SAMPLE GRANTS Women's Trust (£10,000); Toucan Employment (£5,000); Neighbours in Poplar (£3,500); Black Women's Health and Family Support (£2,500); Smiley's Playtime (£1,200); Pelier Tenants and Residents (£900); Southwark Park Association 1869 (£400).

FINANCES *Financial year end* 31/12/2019 *Income* £402,000 *Total grants* £226,700 *Grants to organisations* £226,700 *Assets* £11,390,000

TRUSTEES Stuart Morgenstein; Sue Smith; Peter Delaney; Patrick Kelly; Clare Murphy; Lawrence Kilshaw; Dawn Plimmer; Tim McNally.

OTHER INFORMATION During 2019, the trust approved 13 main grants and 18 fast-track grants. The trust makes an annual grant to All Hallows Church.

HOW TO APPLY The trust's online application portal can be accessed at wtt.flexigrant.com. Applications are not accepted by post or email.

CONTACT DETAILS Elaine Crush, Clerk to the Trustees (joint with Cherry Bushell), Marshall House, 66 Newcomen Street, London SE1 1YT *Tel.* 07926 927861 *Email* enquiries@wakefieldtrust.org.uk *Website* www.wakefieldtrust.org.uk

■ The Wakeham Trust

CC NO 267495 **ESTABLISHED** 1974

WHERE FUNDING CAN BE GIVEN UK.

WHO CAN BENEFIT Registered charities. The trust is especially interested in helping organisations that are starting up and require small grants.

WHAT IS FUNDED Education; community service by young people.

WHAT IS NOT FUNDED National appeals and round-robin letters; medical projects, including counselling, family therapy or self-help projects; arts and performance projects; projects outside the UK; individuals; equipment; large projects that rely on paid staff – the trust prefers to build volunteer capacity.

TYPE OF GRANT Seed funding/start-up funding.

RANGE OF GRANTS £120 to £2,500.

SAMPLE GRANTS A list of beneficiaries was not included in the annual report and accounts.

FINANCES *Financial year end* 30/06/2020 *Income* £18,300 *Total grants* £50,000 *Grants to organisations* £50,000

TRUSTEES Harold Carter; Barnaby Newbolt; Tess Silkstone.

OTHER INFORMATION Full accounts were not available to view on the Charity Commission's website due to the trust's low income. We have therefore estimated the grant total based on the trust's total expenditure.

HOW TO APPLY Applications can be made by email. Full guidelines are available on the trust's website.

CONTACT DETAILS The Trustees, Wakenham Lodge, Rogate, Petersfield, Hampshire GU31 5EJ *Tel.* 01730 821274 *Email* TheWakehamTrust@icloud.com *Website* https://thewakehamtrust.org

■ The Walcot Foundation

CC NO 312800 **ESTABLISHED** 1990

WHERE FUNDING CAN BE GIVEN The London Borough of Lambeth.

WHO CAN BENEFIT Schools; registered charities, social enterprises, community groups and other voluntary organisations; individuals.

WHAT IS FUNDED Social welfare and education. The aim of the foundation is to help individuals along the key paths of educational achievement, employment/employability and financial self-sufficiency.

WHAT IS NOT FUNDED Activities that are the responsibility of central or local government, or schools; organisations that cannot show they are working with Lambeth residents in financial need; debt repayments; crisis funding to solve an organisation's financial problems; research; capital projects.

TYPE OF GRANT Revenue funding; project funding.

RANGE OF GRANTS Up to £25,000 per year for three years.

SAMPLE GRANTS Battersea Arts Centre (£80,000); Chance UK and Mosaic Clubhouse (£25,000 each); Ebony Horse Club (£23,000); Timewise Foundation (£20,000); Granton Primary School (£10,000).

FINANCES *Financial year end* 31/03/2020 *Income* £2,770,000 *Total grants* £2,001,000 *Grants to organisations* £1,770,000 *Assets* £102,370,000

TRUSTEE The Walcot and Hayle's Trustee.

OTHER INFORMATION The Lambeth Endowed Charities, with roots dating back to the 17th century, is an umbrella title for what are now three charities: The Walcot Educational Foundation, Hayle's Charity and The Walcot Non-Educational Charity. Grants are also made to individuals.

HOW TO APPLY Refer to the website to check if the grants scheme for organisations is currently open. Potential applicants should initially contact a member of the Grants Team to discuss whether their proposal is eligible and obtain an application form. Deadlines are posted on the website.

CONTACT DETAILS Grants Team, 127 Kennington Road, London SE11 6SF *Tel.* 020 7735 1925 *Email* grants@walcotfoundation.org.uk *Website* www.walcotfoundation.org.uk

■ The Community Foundation in Wales

CC NO 1074655 **ESTABLISHED** 1999

WHERE FUNDING CAN BE GIVEN Wales.

WHO CAN BENEFIT Registered charities, community groups and other voluntary organisations.

WHAT IS FUNDED General charitable purposes.

RANGE OF GRANTS The majority of grants awarded are under £5,000.

SAMPLE GRANTS Examples of projects supported by the foundation can be found on its website.

FINANCES *Financial year end* 31/03/2020 *Income* £4,530,000 *Total grants* £2,951,000 *Grants to organisations* £2,880,000 *Assets* £10,440,000

TRUSTEES Geraint Jewson; Tanwen Grover; Sarah Jennings; Nigel Annett; Samsunear Ali; Alun Evans; Lt Col Andrew Tuggey; Annabel Lloyd; Kathryn Morris; Gwyn Own; Emma Metcalfe; Sarah Corser.

OTHER INFORMATION This is one of the 46 UK community foundations. The foundation administers a number of different grant programmes, which may open and close at different times. For information on what is currently available, refer to its website.

HOW TO APPLY Potential applicants are advised to visit the community foundation's website or contact its grants team to find the most suitable funding stream.

CONTACT DETAILS Grants Team, St Andrews House, 24 St Andrews Crescent, Cardiff CF10 3DD *Tel.* 029 2037 9580 *Email* info@communityfoundationwales.org.uk *Website* www.cfiw.org.uk

■ Robert and Felicity Waley-Cohen Charitable Trust

CC NO 272126 **ESTABLISHED** 1976

WHERE FUNDING CAN BE GIVEN England and Wales, with a preference for North Oxfordshire, Warwickshire and South Northamptonshire.

WHO CAN BENEFIT Charitable organisations; hospitals; places of worship; museums.

WHAT IS FUNDED General charitable purposes, particularly: physical and mental health of young people; the arts.

WHAT IS NOT FUNDED Individuals.

RANGE OF GRANTS Typically £100 to £15,000.

SAMPLE GRANTS UBS Optimus Foundation UK (£63,000); Parenting Project (£33,000); Tate Foundation (£10,000); Greenhouse Sports and MK Gallery (£5,000 each); Child Bereavement UK, Royal Marsden Cancer Charity and Victoria and Albert Museum (£1,000 each); Hands Up Foundation and The Art Angel Trust (£500 each); Moorcroft Racehorse Welfare Centre and Starlight Children's Foundation (£100 each).

FINANCES *Financial year end* 05/04/2020 *Income* £294,200 *Total grants* £202,800 *Grants to organisations* £202,800 *Assets* £2,040,000

TRUSTEES Robert Waley-Cohen; Hon. Felicity Waley-Cohen.

OTHER INFORMATION Grants were made to 28 organisations in 2019/20, with £137,700 dedicated to the Thomas Fund which supports the mental well-being of young people.

HOW TO APPLY Contact the correspondent for more information. The trust's 2019/20 annual report states it is 'unlikely' that funding will be available for new applicants for the foreseeable future.

CONTACT DETAILS The Trustees, 27 South Terrace, London SW7 2TB *Tel.* 020 7581 6710 *Email* jeg@Uptonviva.com

■ The Walker Trust

CC NO 215479 **ESTABLISHED** 1897

WHERE FUNDING CAN BE GIVEN Shropshire.

WHO CAN BENEFIT Registered charities; unregistered charities; hospices; individuals.

WHAT IS FUNDED Health and disability; education.

TYPE OF GRANT Capital costs.

RANGE OF GRANTS Up to £50,000 but mostly £1,000 to £5,000.

SAMPLE GRANTS Flaxmill Shrewsbury (£50,000); University Centre Shrewsbury (£25,000); Museum of the Gorge (£7,500); Education Kids Outdoors (£3,000); RNIB and The Fire Fighters Charity (£2,000 each); Bliss (£1,500); Shropshire Council Camping – equipment (£500).

FINANCES *Financial year end* 31/03/2020 *Income* £175,800 *Total grants* £161,800 *Grants to organisations* £145,600 *Assets* £5,410,000

TRUSTEES Sir Algernon Heber-Percy; Carolin Paton-Smith; Vince Hunt; Shirley Reynolds; Lady Lydia Forester; Ann Hartley.

OTHER INFORMATION In 2019/20 a total of £126,600 was awarded to schools and other organisations and £19,000 was awarded to health and disability organisations. Grants to individuals totalled £16,200.

HOW TO APPLY Contact the correspondent for further information.

CONTACT DETAILS Edward Hewitt, Clerk, 2 Breidden Way, Bayston Hill, Shrewsbury, Shropshire SY3 0LN *Tel.* 01743 873866 *Email* edward.hewitt@btinternet.com

■ Walton Foundation

OSCR NO SC004005 **ESTABLISHED** 1965

WHERE FUNDING CAN BE GIVEN Glasgow and the west of Scotland.

WHO CAN BENEFIT Charitable organisations.

WHAT IS FUNDED Education; medical causes; community care. There appears to be some preference for Jewish causes.

TYPE OF GRANT Often recurrent.

RANGE OF GRANTS Up to £15,000 per year.

SAMPLE GRANTS Previous beneficiaries have included: University of Strathclyde (£100,000); Cosgrove Care (£15,100); UJIA (£10,200); Friends of Lubavitch Scotland and Kinship Care Initiative (£5,000 each); Jewish Care Scotland (£1,500); Canine Partners (£500).

FINANCES *Financial year end* 31/12/2018 *Income* £196,400 *Total grants* £321,100 *Grants to organisations* £321,100 *Assets* £3,410,000

OTHER INFORMATION The 2018 accounts were the latest available at the time of writing (June 2021). The foundation made grants to 24 organisations during the year.

HOW TO APPLY Contact the correspondent for further information.

CONTACT DETAILS The Trustees, c/o Martin Aitken and Co., Caledonia House, 89 Seaward Street, Glasgow G41 1HJ

■ Walton-on-Thames Charity

CC NO 1185959 **ESTABLISHED** 1963

WHERE FUNDING CAN BE GIVEN Borough of Elmbridge, Surrey.

WHO CAN BENEFIT Registered charities; social enterprises; CICs.

WHAT IS FUNDED Social welfare. The charity's Community Grants programme offers grants to organisations which provide a range of services to the local community. There is a particular focus on the following themes: social isolation and inequality in Elmbridge; housing enablement; current needs; grassroots community organisations; organisational capability and capacity; carer support. Further guidance is given on the charity's website.

TYPE OF GRANT Project funding; core/revenue costs; seed funding/start-up funding.

RANGE OF GRANTS Grants have previously ranged from £4,000 to £37,000 (average grant just over £5,000).

SAMPLE GRANTS Previous beneficiaries have included: Burwood Pre-school, Citizens Advice Elmbridge West, Elmbridge Borough Council, Elmbridge Youth Support Services, Surrey Fire and Rescue Service, Surrey SATRO, Thames Riverboat Project, The Delight Charity and Walton Oak School.

FINANCES *Financial year end* 31/03/2020 *Income* £1,300,000 *Total grants* £337,500 *Grants to organisations* £280,400 *Assets* £31,630,000

TRUSTEES Nick Stuart; Juliet Hobbs; David Easson; Elizabeth Kennedy; Graham Mann; Paul Tajasque; James Vizzini; Robert Mills; Alexandra Fitzpatrick; Andrew Button-Stephens; Sarah Tomkins; Dennis Pillay; Kellie Scott.

OTHER INFORMATION The charity also makes grants to individuals and provides sheltered housing. It also provides other support to local voluntary sector organisations, such as office space, training and advice. Grants were broken down as follows: community (£158,200); schools (£36,100); residents (£29,300); individual crisis (£28,800); COVID-19 (£18,400); community projects (£6,600); learning and development (£2,900). The financial information is for the period between 12 September 2019 and 31 March 2020.

HOW TO APPLY Contact the correspondent via the online form available on the charity's website.

CONTACT DETAILS Caroline Davies, Community Grants and Projects, Walton-on-Thames Charity, Charities House, 1–2 The Quintet, Churchfield Road, Walton-on-Thames, Surrey KT12 2TZ *Tel.* 01932 220242 *Email* admin@waltoncharity.org.uk *Website* www.waltoncharity.org.uk

■ War Memorials Trust

CC NO 1062255 **ESTABLISHED** 1997

WHERE FUNDING CAN BE GIVEN UK; Channel Islands; Isle of Man.

WHO CAN BENEFIT Individuals; organisations; councils.

WHAT IS FUNDED The repair and conservation of war memorials.

WHAT IS NOT FUNDED See the trust's website for a full list of exclusions.

RANGE OF GRANTS Grants are usually 25% to 75% of eligible costs up to a maximum of £30,000.

SAMPLE GRANTS A list of beneficiaries was not included in the annual report and accounts.

FINANCES *Financial year end* 31/03/2020 *Income* £438,400 *Total grants* £186,000 *Grants to organisations* £186,000 *Assets* £491,700

TRUSTEES Peter McCormick; John Peat; Russell Walters; Dr Roger Bowdler; Lord Mauley; Margaret Goodall; Randolph Churchill.

HOW TO APPLY Applications can be submitted via the trust's website.

CONTACT DETAILS The Grants Team, 14 Buckingham Palace Road, London SW1W 0QP *Tel.* 020 7834 0200 *Email* grants@warmemorials.org *Website* www.warmemorials.org

■ The Ward Blenkinsop Trust

CC NO 265449 **ESTABLISHED** 1972

WHERE FUNDING CAN BE GIVEN UK, with a special interest in Merseyside and surrounding counties.

WHO CAN BENEFIT Charitable organisations.

WHAT IS FUNDED General charitable purposes, medicine, social welfare, arts, education.

SAMPLE GRANTS Pervious beneficiaries have included: Action on Addiction; Chase Children's Hospice; Clatterbridge Cancer Research; Comic Relief; Depaul; Halton Autistic Family Support Group; Hope HIV; Infertility Network; George Martin Music Foundation; Royal Academy of Dance; St Joseph's Family Centre; Strongbones Children's Charitable Trust; Wirral Holistic Care Services.

FINANCES *Financial year end* 31/03/2020 *Income* £123,500 *Total grants* £88,800 *Grants to organisations* £88,800 *Assets* £1,480,000

TRUSTEES Andrew Blenkinsop; Charlotte Blenkinsop; Frances Stormer; Haidee Millin; Sarah Blenkinsop.

HOW TO APPLY Contact the correspondent for further information.

CONTACT DETAILS The Trustees, PO Box 28840, London SW13 0WZ *Tel.* 020 8878 9975

■ The Barbara Ward Children's Foundation

CC NO 1089783 **ESTABLISHED** 2001

WHERE FUNDING CAN BE GIVEN Mainly UK, but also overseas.

WHO CAN BENEFIT Charitable organisations, particularly smaller charities. According to its website, the foundation prefers to make grants to 'financially healthy children's charities where funding is not forthcoming from statutory bodies, where incomes and fund balances are constantly put to good use and where administration overheads are kept to a minimum'.

WHAT IS FUNDED Grants are awarded to organisations serving children who are disadvantaged in some respect. Purposes that have previously been funded include: educational projects; holidays; support, care and respite; health and well-being; and sport, play and leisure. Grants may also be given to charities supporting adults with learning disabilities.

WHAT IS NOT FUNDED Grants are not given to religious charities.

TYPE OF GRANT One-off grants; project costs for up to five years.

RANGE OF GRANTS Up to £15,000.

SAMPLE GRANTS Sebastian's Action Trust (£15,000); REACT (Rapid Effective Assistance for Children with potentially Terminal illness) (£12,800); Capital Kids Cricket and Life Cycle UK (£4,000 each); Cheshire Autism Practical Support (£3,800); Sunny Days Children's Fund and The Therapy Garden (£3,000 each); TAG Youth Club (£2,000); Leeds Community Trust (£500).

FINANCES *Financial year end* 31/12/2019 *Income* £531,300 *Total grants* £380,300 *Grants to organisations* £380,300 *Assets* £12,070,000

TRUSTEES Barbara Ward; Chris Banks; Brian Walters; Ken Parker; David Bailey; Mark Waight; Christopher Brown.

OTHER INFORMATION Grants were made to 68 organisations in 2019.

HOW TO APPLY Apply in writing to the correspondent detailing the purpose for which the grant is requested. Your application should also include the latest annual report and set of audited financial statements. Beneficiaries or applicants may be visited by trustees, who usually meet on a quarterly basis to review and award grants (though sub-groups may meet more frequently to assess applications).

CONTACT DETAILS The Trustees, 85 Fleet Street, London EC4 1AE *Tel.* 020 7222 7040 *Email* info@bwcf.org.uk *Website* www.bwcf.org.uk

■ Warwick Relief in Need Charity

CC NO 256447 **ESTABLISHED** 1976

WHERE FUNDING CAN BE GIVEN Warwick.

WHO CAN BENEFIT Individuals in need and organisations assisting such people.

WHAT IS FUNDED Social welfare.

TYPE OF GRANT Project costs.

RANGE OF GRANTS In 2019 grants ranged from £540 up to £45,000.

SAMPLE GRANTS Percy Estate – 'The Gap' (£45,000); Lord Leycester Hospital (£15,000); Warwick Apprenticing Charities (£10,000); Graham Fulford Charitable Trust (£6,000); Molly Olly's Wishes (£5,000); Music Life Foundation (£2,000); New Life Church (£540).

FINANCES *Financial year end* 31/12/2019 *Income* £190,500 *Total grants* £138,000 *Grants to organisations* £120,800 *Assets* £4,150,000

TRUSTEES Anthony Atkins; Janet Honnoraty; Revd Dr Vaughan Roberts; Diana Thompson; Sheila Brown; Martyn Ashford; Revd Linda Duckers; John Atkinson; Sarah Hunt; Richard Eddington; Parminder Singh Birdi; Mandy Littlejohn.

HOW TO APPLY Apply in writing to the correspondent or by downloading an application form from the charity's website.

CONTACT DETAILS Christopher Houghton, Clerk to the Trustees, c/o Moore and Tibbits, 34 High Street, Warwick, Warwickshire CV34 4BE *Tel.* 01926 491181 *Email* choughton@moore-tibbits.co.uk *Website* www.warwickreliefinneed.org.uk

The Warwickshire Masonic Charitable Association Ltd

CC NO 211588 **ESTABLISHED** 1945

WHERE FUNDING CAN BE GIVEN Warwickshire; West Midlands.

WHO CAN BENEFIT Charitable organisations; Masonic organisations.

WHAT IS FUNDED Masonic organisations; general charitable purposes.

RANGE OF GRANTS £250 to £100,000.

SAMPLE GRANTS Masonic Charitable Foundation 2023 Festival (£100,000); 2nd Warwick Sea Scouts (£10,000); Marie Curie Cancer Care Hospice (£5,000); Midlands Air Ambulance (£5,000); St Giles Hospice (£4,000); Salvation Army (£2,000); Norman Laud Centre (£1,250); Coventry and Warwickshire Mind (£500); St Chads Sanctuary (£250).

FINANCES *Financial year end* 31/12/2019 *Income* £1,180,000 *Total grants* £282,800 *Grants to organisations* £282,800 *Assets* £8,920,000

TRUSTEES Howard Smith; David Greenwood; Stephen Tranter; John Harris; Nigel Hawkins; John Hayward; Peter Britton; William Clark; Christopher Grove; Mervyn Kimberly; Eric Rymer; Phillip Hall; Richard Baker; Peter Manning; Gordon Law; Stanley Butterworth; Nigel Burton; Geoffrey Walker; Michael Morris; David Butcher; Stuart Esworthy.

OTHER INFORMATION Grants were awarded to 137 non-Masonic charities and nine Masonic charities.

HOW TO APPLY Contact the correspondent for further information.

CONTACT DETAILS D. A. Lodge, Secretary, Yenton Assembly Rooms, 73–75 Gravelly Hill North, Erdington, Birmingham, West Midlands B23 6BJ *Tel.* 0121 454 0554 *Email* dalec@warwickshirepgl.org *Website* www.warwickshirepgl.org.uk

Mrs Waterhouse Charitable Trust

CC NO 261685 **ESTABLISHED** 1967

WHERE FUNDING CAN BE GIVEN UK, with an interest in the North West and particularly the Lancashire area.

WHO CAN BENEFIT Charitable institutions and organisations.

WHAT IS FUNDED General charitable purposes, particularly: medical causes and health; welfare in the community; the environment and wildlife; churches and heritage.

WHAT IS NOT FUNDED Individuals.

RANGE OF GRANTS £3,000 to £30,000.

SAMPLE GRANTS Amend (£30,000); Maggie's (£20,000); Caritas, Francis House and National Trust Lake District (£15,000 each); Alzheimer's Research, Prevent Breast Cancer and Scope (£10,000 each); Contact, Doorway and The Prince's Trust (£5,000 each).

FINANCES *Financial year end* 05/04/2020 *Income* £357,000 *Total grants* £354,500 *Grants to organisations* £354,500 *Assets* £7,920,000

TRUSTEES Alistair Dunn; Helen Dunn.

OTHER INFORMATION In 2019/20 the trust made 31 grants.

HOW TO APPLY Contact the correspondent for further information.

CONTACT DETAILS The Trustees, 2nd Floor, Parkgates, Bury New Road, Prestwich, Manchester M25 0TL *Tel.* 0161 904 9942 *Email* houghtondunnct@gmail.com

The Waterloo Foundation

CC NO 1117535 **ESTABLISHED** 2007

WHERE FUNDING CAN BE GIVEN UK and overseas, with a preference for Wales.

WHO CAN BENEFIT Charitable organisations. There is a preference for projects that help globally, particularly in the areas of the disparity of opportunities and wealth and the unsustainable use of the world's natural resources.

WHAT IS FUNDED World development; the environment; development of children. In Wales: employment, carers and education.

WHAT IS NOT FUNDED The promotion of religious or political causes; development of children. In Wales: employment, carers and education.

SAMPLE GRANTS A list of beneficiaries was not included in the annual report and accounts.

FINANCES *Financial year end* 31/12/2019 *Income* £9,530,000 *Total grants* £8,500,000 *Grants to organisations* £8,500,000 *Assets* £180,390,000

TRUSTEES Heather Stevens; David Stevens; Caroline Oakes.

OTHER INFORMATION Grants were awarded to 267 organisations during the year.

HOW TO APPLY Application guidelines, criteria and deadlines for each of the grant programmes are available on the foundation's website. Potential applicants are encouraged to read full details before making an application. Applications are welcomed from organisations with a clear charitable purpose. There is no application form and all applications should be submitted via email to applications@waterloofoundation.org.uk.

CONTACT DETAILS The Trustees, c/o 46–48 Cardiff Road, Llandaff, Cardiff CF5 2DT *Tel.* 029 2083 8980 *Email* info@waterloofoundation.org.uk *Website* www.waterloofoundation.org.uk

G. R. Waters Charitable Trust 2000

CC NO 1091525 **ESTABLISHED** 2000

WHERE FUNDING CAN BE GIVEN Mainly UK, with some support given overseas.

WHO CAN BENEFIT Registered charities; human rights organisations.

WHAT IS FUNDED General charitable purposes; community services; adults with severe disabilities; human rights.

TYPE OF GRANT Core costs; project funding; capital costs.

RANGE OF GRANTS £1,000 to £78,900.

SAMPLE GRANTS Tides Centre – Palestine Legal (£78,900); First Look Media (£30,800), Nuhanovic Foundation (£19,400); NAACP Legal Defence and Education Fund (£15,400); Tools For Solidarity (£10,000); A Jewish Voice for Peace (£4,000); Amnesty International UK (£1,000).

FINANCES *Financial year end* 05/04/2020 *Income* £88,400 *Total grants* £186,300 *Grants to organisations* £167,100 *Assets* £1,300,000

TRUSTEES Mark Fenwick; Christopher Organ.

OTHER INFORMATION In 2019/20 the trust awarded grants to eight organisations. The trust's accounts for 2019/20 show that grants are generally awarded 'towards regular activities'. Grants were also made to two individuals totalling £19,200.

HOW TO APPLY The trustees do not respond to unsolicited applications.

CONTACT DETAILS The Trustees, 7 Melbray Mews, 158 Hurlingham Road, London SW6 3NS *Tel.* 020 7499 7275

■ Wates Family Enterprise Trust

CC NO 1126007 **ESTABLISHED** 2008

WHERE FUNDING CAN BE GIVEN UK.

WHO CAN BENEFIT Registered charities; unregistered charities; schools; universities; social enterprises; CICs; amateur sports clubs; hospices; religious bodies/institutions; individuals.

WHAT IS FUNDED General charitable purposes, including: communities; education, training and employment; sustainability; social enterprise; thought leadership.

TYPE OF GRANT Core/revenue costs; project funding; unrestricted funding.

RANGE OF GRANTS Mostly up to £40,000.

SAMPLE GRANTS City Year UK (Life Opportunities for Young People) (£100,000); Creating Futures (£50,000); Build Yourself 2019 (£36,000); All Saints Enterprise CIC (£24,000); Noah Enterprise (£10,000); Serious About Youth (£5,000); Shelter (Gen 5) (£250).

FINANCES *Financial year end* 31/12/2019 *Income* £1,500,000 *Total grants* £793,300 *Grants to organisations* £787,300 *Assets* £192,600

TRUSTEES Andrew Wates; Paul Wates; Tim Wates; James Wates; Andy Wates; Michael Wates; Charles Wates; Jonathan Wates.

OTHER INFORMATION The trust runs the Wates Giving programme, which supports causes with which Wates employees or the Wates family are involved. There are a number of schemes, including: major awards; matched funding; employee awards; family awards; client supply chain fund; Give As You Earn scheme; sports sponsorship.

HOW TO APPLY Unsolicited applications are not considered – the trust only supports organisations where a Wates employee or family member has direct involvement on a regular basis.

CONTACT DETAILS Felicity Mallam, Director, Wates House, Station Approach, Leatherhead, Surrey KT22 7SW *Tel.* 01372 861250 *Email* director@watesfoundation.org.uk *Website* https://www.wfet.org.uk

■ The Wates Foundation

CC NO 247941 **ESTABLISHED** 1966

WHERE FUNDING CAN BE GIVEN Southern England.

WHO CAN BENEFIT Registered charities; social enterprises; community groups.

WHAT IS FUNDED Building social values; education and employment; community health; life transitions; safer communities; strengthening the charitable and voluntary sector.

WHAT IS NOT FUNDED Promotion of religion; individuals; statutory bodies; other grant-makers; organisations with an income over £3 million; capital projects; general appeals; continuation funding or new bids on behalf of organisations already in receipt of an award from the foundation.

TYPE OF GRANT Core costs; salaries; project funding.

RANGE OF GRANTS £5,000 to £30,000.

SAMPLE GRANTS Previous beneficiaries have included: First Steps ED, Imagine If Theatre Company, INQUEST, Life 2009, National Cancer Research Institute, Oxfordshire Association for the Blind, Reach Learning Disability, Ride High Ltd, Startuponline, The Children's Literacy Charity and West London Action for Children.

FINANCES *Financial year end* 31/03/2020 *Income* £431,300 *Total grants* £453,700 *Grants to organisations* £453,700 *Assets* £18,450,000

TRUSTEES Andy Wates; Jonathan Heynes; Neil Wates; Victoria Tanner; Luke Wates; Nichola Adams.

OTHER INFORMATION Grants were distributed as follows: community health (£155,000); education and employment (£131,200); building family values (£90,000); strengthening the voluntary sector (£47,500); safer communities (£30,000).

HOW TO APPLY Unsolicited applications are not accepted. The foundation is a proactive grant-maker.

CONTACT DETAILS The Director, Wates House, Station Approach, Leatherhead, Surrey KT22 7SW *Tel.* 01372 861250 *Email* director@watesfoundation.org.uk *Website* www.watesfoundation.org.uk

■ The William Wates Memorial Trust

CC NO 1011213 **ESTABLISHED** 1992

WHERE FUNDING CAN BE GIVEN London and the South East. The trust will also support projects throughout the UK proposed by the trust's Le Loop riders.

WHO CAN BENEFIT Registered charities and not-for-profit enterprises.

WHAT IS FUNDED Projects that encourage young people (5 to 19 years old) experiencing severe disadvantage to keep away from anti-social behaviour and criminal activity, enabling them to fulfil their potential.

TYPE OF GRANT Project funding.

RANGE OF GRANTS The trust's website states: 'Generally, our individual grants are around £30,000 over 3 years.'

SAMPLE GRANTS GRIT Breakthrough (£120,000); Envision (£30,000); Islington Boat Club (£20,000); Pilton Youth and Children's Project (£19,000); Ride High (£6,300); BIRD (£2,500); BoxnSkills (£500).

FINANCES *Financial year end* 31/08/2019 *Income* £764,600 *Total grants* £247,300 *Grants to organisations* £247,300 *Assets* £842,500

TRUSTEES Andrew Wates; Sarah Wates; Jonathon Wates; Richard Wates; Monty Wates; Timothy Wates; Susan Laing.

OTHER INFORMATION The 2018/19 accounts were the latest available at the time of writing (May 2021). During the year, grants were made to ten organisations and were distributed within the following themes: personal development (£122,000); mentoring (£64,000); sports (£58,800); arts (£2,500). The trust's primary fundraising event, Le Loop, gives riders the opportunity to tackle up to 21 stages of the Tour de France.

HOW TO APPLY Applications can be made through the trust's website, where information about current submission dates can be found. Applications made before submission dates are announced will not be processed. The trustees meet three times per year.

CONTACT DETAILS Jane Lowe, Wates House, Station Approach, Leatherhead, Surrey KT22 7SW *Tel.* 01372 861051 *Email* wwmt@wates.co.uk *Website* https://wwmt.rideleloop.org

■ The Geoffrey Watling Charity

CC NO 1025258 **ESTABLISHED** 1993

WHERE FUNDING CAN BE GIVEN Norfolk and the Waveney area of Suffolk.

WHO CAN BENEFIT Charitable organisations.

WHAT IS FUNDED Social welfare; churches and historic buildings; education; the arts; health; sport; the environment.

WHAT IS NOT FUNDED The charity will not consider grant applications from organisations which have not submitted their annual accounts/ annual return to the Charity Commission or Companies House.

TYPE OF GRANT Project funding.

RANGE OF GRANTS Up to £30,000.

SAMPLE GRANTS Centre 81 Ltd (£50,000); University of East Anglia (£30,000); Norfolk Community Sports Foundation, Ted Ellis Trust and St Martins (£10,000 each).

FINANCES *Financial year end* 30/09/2020 *Income* £726,400 *Total grants* £446,200 *Grants to organisations* £446,200 *Assets* £15,870,000

TRUSTEES Susan Watling; Richard Marks; David Lundean; Alan Charles

OTHER INFORMATION The charity made 124 grants, which were broken down as follows: social and welfare (£280,200); education and arts (£52,500); medical causes (£51,500); churches and historic buildings (£43,000); the environment (£25,500); sport (£17,500); infrastructure (£9,000).

HOW TO APPLY Applications can be made via the charity's website, where there are detailed guidelines for prospective applicants. The trustees meet quarterly to consider applications and make decisions on the grants to be awarded in accordance with the charity's objectives. The guidelines for applicants state that applications for funding 'towards a specific project are more likely to be looked on favourably by the trustees than those to help core costs or salaries'.

CONTACT DETAILS The Trustees, 8A Ber Street, Norwich, Norfolk NR1 3EJ *Email* enquiries@geoffreywatling.org.uk *Website* www.geoffreywatling.org.uk

■ Blyth Watson Charitable Trust

CC NO 1071390 **ESTABLISHED** 1996

WHERE FUNDING CAN BE GIVEN UK.

WHO CAN BENEFIT Registered charities.

WHAT IS FUNDED Humanitarian causes based in the UK and other general charitable purposes.

TYPE OF GRANT One off; recurrent.

RANGE OF GRANTS Up to £7,000.

SAMPLE GRANTS Foundling Museum, Royal Trinity Hospice and Society for the Relief of Distress (£5,000 each); Streets of London (£4,000); Haringey Law Centre (£3,000); Battens Disease Family Association (£2,000); Home-Start (£1,000); Access Sport (£500).

FINANCES *Financial year end* 30/06/2020 *Income* £141,000 *Total grants* £105,000 *Grants to organisations* £105,000 *Assets* £4,860,000

TRUSTEES Alastair Collett; Elizabeth Neale.

OTHER INFORMATION Grants were made to 45 organisations during 2019/20.

HOW TO APPLY Apply in writing to the correspondent. The trustees meet twice a year, usually in June and December, to consider applications.

CONTACT DETAILS The Trustees, c/o BDB Pitmans, One Bartholomew Close, London EC1A 7BL *Tel.* 020 7227 7000

■ The Watson Family Charitable Trust

CC NO 1159965 **ESTABLISHED** 2015

WHERE FUNDING CAN BE GIVEN Northern England; overseas.

WHO CAN BENEFIT Registered charities.

WHAT IS FUNDED General charitable purposes; health; humanitarian causes.

RANGE OF GRANTS £1,000 to £50,000.

SAMPLE GRANTS Whickham School and Sports College (£50,000); St George's Church Jesmond – for the community of Jesmond (£11,500); Alan Shearer Foundation (£9,000); Percy Hedley Foundation (£4,500); Jessica's Sarcoma Awareness (£1,000).

FINANCES *Financial year end* 31/03/2020 *Income* £11,100 *Total grants* £76,000 *Grants to organisations* £70,000 *Assets* £577,000

TRUSTEES Claire Watson; Ian Watson; Mark Watson; Hugh Welch; Craig Watson.

OTHER INFORMATION Grants were awarded to five organisations during the year.

HOW TO APPLY Applications can be made in writing to the correspondent.

CONTACT DETAILS Ian Watson, Trustee, Hadrian Offices, Unit 3, Keel Row, The Watermark, Gateshead, Tyne and Wear NE11 9SZ *Tel.* 0191 460 5219 *Email* Enquiries@WatsonCharitableTrust.co.uk

■ John Watson's Trust

OSCR NO SC014004 **ESTABLISHED** 1984

WHERE FUNDING CAN BE GIVEN Scotland, with a strong preference for Lothian.

WHO CAN BENEFIT Registered charities; schools; PTAs; amateur sports clubs; universities; individuals.

WHAT IS FUNDED Grants are made for educational purposes for children and young people under the age of 21 who have a physical or learning disability or are socially disadvantaged.

WHAT IS NOT FUNDED Grants are not given for general running costs or salaries.

TYPE OF GRANT Grants can be made for any aspect of charitable organisations' work that will contribute to the education of children who are disadvantaged or have a disability. Grants are often made for trips, equipment and activities.

RANGE OF GRANTS Generally, £100 to £2,000.

SAMPLE GRANTS Pilton Retreat (£2,700); Roses Charitable Trust (£2,000); Street League (£1,400); Strange Town (£1,000).

FINANCES *Financial year end* 31/12/2019 *Income* £183,500 *Total grants* £156,900 *Grants to organisations* £69,200 *Assets* £4,910,000

TRUSTEES Robin Garrett; John Harding-Edgar; Richard Murray; Karen Phillips; Kenneth Mackay; Amanda Laurie; Cllr Alison Dickie; Andrew Cochrane; David Hill; Gordon Wylie; Janet Morton; Susie Jamieson.

OTHER INFORMATION During the year, grants of less than £1,000 to organisations totalled £18,500. Grants to 95 individuals totalled £87,700.

HOW TO APPLY Apply online via the trust's website.

CONTACT DETAILS James Hamilton, The Signet Library, Parliament Square, Edinburgh EH1 1RF *Tel.* 0131 220 3249 *Email* jhamilton@wssociety.co.uk *Website* www.wssociety.co.uk

■ The Weavers' Company Benevolent Fund

CC NO 266189 **ESTABLISHED** 1973

WHERE FUNDING CAN BE GIVEN UK.

WHO CAN BENEFIT Registered charities or organisations in the process of applying for registration.

WHAT IS FUNDED The fund lists the following as areas of interest: young offenders (particularly those under 30 years of age); prisoners and ex-prisoners; young disadvantaged people, especially those at risk of criminal involvement.

WHAT IS NOT FUNDED Sponsorship, marketing or other fundraising activities; endowment funds, bursaries or long-term capital projects; grant-giving charities; work that has been completed or will be completed while the application is being considered; work that should be covered by statutory funding; building work; capital projects to provide access in compliance with the Disability Discrimination Act; collaborative/partnership projects with large organisations; organisations outside the UK; overseas expeditions; individuals.

TYPE OF GRANT Project funding; core costs; capital costs.

RANGE OF GRANTS £100 to £90,000.

SAMPLE GRANTS Knife Crime Projects (£90,000); Safer Living Foundation (£15,000); The Reasons Why Foundation (£12,500); bthechange (£10,000); Innercity Films (£5,000); Sheriffs' and Recorder's Fund (£1,000); City of London Police Widows' and Orphans' Fund (£150).

FINANCES *Financial year end* 31/12/2019 *Income* £648,300 *Total grants* £298,900 *Grants to organisations* £298,900 *Assets* £15,270,000

TRUSTEE Bailiffs, wardens and assistants of the Worshipful Company of Weavers.

OTHER INFORMATION The grant-maker is composed of four funds: the charitable grants fund, which is administered by the charitable grants committee; the millennial fund, which was launched in 1995 with the aim of building a significant new charitable fund by 2130; the primary schools fund, which is administered by the primary schools committee; and the textile fund, which is administered by the textile committee.

HOW TO APPLY Applications can be made via the grant-maker's website, where information on upcoming deadlines can also be found. Applications must arrive by midday on the closing date. Any late applications will be held over for consideration at the next closing date.

CONTACT DETAILS Anne Howe, Charities Officer, Saddlers House, 40 Gutter Lane, London EC2V 6BR *Tel.* 020 7606 1155 *Email* charity@weavers.org.uk *Website* www.weavers.org.uk

■ The William Webster Charitable Trust

CC NO 259848 **ESTABLISHED** 1969

WHERE FUNDING CAN BE GIVEN The North East, principally Northumberland, Tyne and Wear, Durham and Cleveland.

WHO CAN BENEFIT Registered charitable organisations.

WHAT IS FUNDED General charitable purposes.

TYPE OF GRANT One-off grants for capital projects.

SAMPLE GRANTS A list of beneficiaries was not included in the annual report and accounts.

FINANCES *Financial year end* 05/04/2020 *Income* £87,000 *Total grants* £89,000 *Grants to organisations* £89,000 *Assets* £2,130,000

TRUSTEE Kimcote and Walton Parish Council.

HOW TO APPLY Apply in writing to the correspondent. Our previous research suggests that applications should include details of the costings of capital projects and of funding already raised, a set of the latest annual accounts and details of the current charity registration.

CONTACT DETAILS The Trustees, Zedra UK Trusts, Booths Hall, Booths Park 3, Chelford Road, Knutsford, Cheshire WA16 8GS *Tel.* 01565 748813 *Email* charities@zedra.com

■ The Linda and Michael Weinstein Charitable Trust

CC NO 1000637 **ESTABLISHED** 1990

WHERE FUNDING CAN BE GIVEN UK and Israel.

WHO CAN BENEFIT Charitable organisations.

WHAT IS FUNDED Jewish causes; general charitable purposes.

RANGE OF GRANTS Typically less than £5,000.

SAMPLE GRANTS UK Gives Ltd (£25,000); The Jerusalem Foundation UK (£22,700); University Jewish Chaplaincy Board (£20,000); Chana Charity Ltd (£13,000); The Work Avenue Foundation (£5,000); British Friends of Shalva (£3,000); British Friends of the Jaffa Institute (£1,800); SOFT (Support Organisation for Trisomy) (£1,400); Lolev CT (£790).

FINANCES *Financial year end* 05/04/2020 *Income* £7,900 *Total grants* £80,000 *Grants to organisations* £80,000

TRUSTEES Michael Weinstein; Linda Weinstein; Philip Keane.

OTHER INFORMATION Full accounts were not available to view on the Charity Commission's website due to the trust's low income. We have therefore estimated the grant total based on the trust's total expenditure.

HOW TO APPLY Contact the correspondent for further information.

CONTACT DETAILS The Trustees, 32 Fairholme Gardens, London N3 3EB *Tel.* 020 8346 1257

■ The Weinstock Fund

CC NO 1150031 **ESTABLISHED** 2012

WHERE FUNDING CAN BE GIVEN UK.

WHO CAN BENEFIT Registered charities.

WHAT IS FUNDED General charitable purposes, particularly: medical care and treatment, including respite care and hospices; care for adults and children with disabilities; education and training for adults and children with disabilities; care and support of older people; care and support of children; social welfare; music and the arts.

WHAT IS NOT FUNDED Research projects; projects based outside the UK. The trustees prefer to support smaller charities or projects.

TYPE OF GRANT Capital costs; core/revenue costs; unrestricted funding.

SAMPLE GRANTS A list of beneficiaries was not included in the annual report and accounts.

FINANCES *Financial year end* 05/04/2020
Income £694,700 *Total grants* £671,700
Grants to organisations £671,700
Assets £15,130,000

TRUSTEES Susan Lacroix; The Hon. Clare Renton; The Hon. Laura Weinstock.

OTHER INFORMATION Grants were made to 182 organisations and were broken down as follows: disability (£184,500); arts (£168,700); medical causes (£127,900); cultural and environmental (£65,000); education (£46,300); community (£40,300); hardship alleviation (£39,000).

HOW TO APPLY Apply via the charity's website, where guidance information on what to include is provided.

CONTACT DETAILS Sally Barber, The Administrator, PO Box 5369, Wincanton BA9 0BG
Email enquiries@weinstockfund.org.uk
Website www.weinstockfund.org.uk

■ The Colin Weir Charitable Foundation

OSCR NO SC049161 **ESTABLISHED** 2019

WHERE FUNDING CAN BE GIVEN Scotland.

WHO CAN BENEFIT Charitable organisations.

WHAT IS FUNDED General charitable purposes.

RANGE OF GRANTS £5,000 to £25,000.

SAMPLE GRANTS A list of beneficiaries was not included in the annual report and accounts.

FINANCES *Financial year end* 31/03/2020
Income £291,800 *Total grants* £242,200
Grants to organisations £236,200
Assets £38,300

OTHER INFORMATION Grants were made to 12 organisations and one individual.

HOW TO APPLY Contact the correspondent for further information.

CONTACT DETAILS The Trustees, 3 Glenfinlas Street, Edinburgh EH3 6AQ

■ The Weir Charitable Trust

OSCR NO SC043187 **ESTABLISHED** 2013

WHERE FUNDING CAN BE GIVEN Scotland.

WHO CAN BENEFIT Small Scottish charities and community groups with an income of less than £125,000.

WHAT IS FUNDED Sport and recreational activities; animal welfare; health; Scottish culture.

WHAT IS NOT FUNDED Individuals; commercial activities; research; educational establishments; social enterprises; governing bodies; public sector bodies; pilot projects; sponsorship.

TYPE OF GRANT Capital projects; running costs; one-off projects; core costs; salaries. All awards are for one year or less.

RANGE OF GRANTS Less than £25,000.

SAMPLE GRANTS Larger awards included: Duncan Mackinnon Music and Arts (£15,000); South of Scotland Wildlife Hospital (£10,000); St Ronans Bowling Club (£8,100), The Weekend Respite Project (£6,000); Edina Hibs (£5,000).

FINANCES *Financial year end* 19/12/2019
Income £223,200 *Total grants* £199,500
Grants to organisations £199,500
Assets £5,171,000

OTHER INFORMATION Grants were broken down as follows: health (£103,700); sport (£31,700); culture (£28,500); animal welfare (£19,000); recreational facilities (£16,600). The 2018/19 accounts were the latest available at the time of writing (April 2021).

HOW TO APPLY Applications can be made through the trust's website or on an application form available from the website. Details of application deadlines are also published on the website. Applications for grants of over £25,000 will not be considered.

CONTACT DETAILS Trust Manager, Unit 201, Ettrick Riverside, Dunsdale Road, Selkirk, Scottish Borders TD7 5EB *Tel.* 01750 505262
Email enquiries@weircharitabletrust.com
Website www.weircharitabletrust.com

■ The James Weir Foundation

CC NO 251764 **ESTABLISHED** 1967

WHERE FUNDING CAN BE GIVEN UK, with a preference for Ayrshire and Glasgow.

WHO CAN BENEFIT UK-registered charities.

WHAT IS FUNDED Education and training; health; disability.

WHAT IS NOT FUNDED Individuals; overseas organisations.

TYPE OF GRANT Capital costs; core/revenue costs.

RANGE OF GRANTS £1,000 to £5,000.

SAMPLE GRANTS Mencap, Support Dogs, Target Ovarian Cancer and Young Enterprise Scotland (£5,000 each); British Blind Sport and Meningitis Research Foundation (£3,000 each); PSP Association (£2,000); Action for Pulmonary Fibrosis and Textile Conservation Foundation (£1,000 each).

FINANCES *Financial year end* 31/12/2019
Income £351,700 *Total grants* £272,000
Grants to organisations £272,000
Assets £9,320,000

TRUSTEES Elizabeth Bonham; William Ducas.

HOW TO APPLY Applications should be sent by post with supporting evidence and a copy of the applicant's latest annual report. Emailed applications will not be considered.

CONTACT DETAILS Louisa Lawson, Secretary to the Trustees, PO Box 72361, London SW18 9NB *Tel.* 01727 869141 *Email* info@jamesweirfoundation.org
Website jamesweirfoundation.org

■ The Welland Trust

CC NO 1181775 **ESTABLISHED** 2018

WHERE FUNDING CAN BE GIVEN England; Wales.

WHO CAN BENEFIT Charitable organisations.

WHAT IS FUNDED People who have experienced care.

TYPE OF GRANT Project funding.

SAMPLE GRANTS A list of beneficiaries was not included in the annual report and accounts.

FINANCES *Financial year end* 31/12/2019
Income £11,020,000 *Total grants* £365,600
Grants to organisations £345,600
Assets £10,460,000

TRUSTEES Polly Jones; Isabelle Murphy; Sarah Saunders; Janet Rees.

HOW TO APPLY Contact the charity via email or using the form available on its website. Applicants will need to provide a full project plan indicating how the grant will be used and the expected outcomes and benefits for adults who have experienced care.

CONTACT DETAILS The Trustees, Craftsman House, De Salis Drive, Hampton Lovett, Droitwich, Worcestershire WR9 0QE *Email* enquiries@thewellandtrust.org *Website* https://www.thewellandtrust.org

■ Wellbeing of Women

CC NO 239281 **ESTABLISHED** 1964

WHERE FUNDING CAN BE GIVEN UK and Ireland.

WHO CAN BENEFIT Medical research organisations, primarily universities; individuals.

WHAT IS FUNDED Research into women's reproductive and gynaecological health. The charity runs various grant programmes, including: research grants; research training fellowships; entry-level research fellowships; entry-level midwifery scholarships; postdoctoral research fellowships.

WHAT IS NOT FUNDED See the charity's website for a full list of exclusions for each scheme.

TYPE OF GRANT Research projects; training and research fellowships; scholarships.

RANGE OF GRANTS Grants range up to £255,300.

SAMPLE GRANTS University College London (£255,300); Lancaster University (£161,800); University of London (£144,300); University of Bedfordshire (£98,900); Birmingham University (£69,700); University of Edinburgh (£26,200); University of Sunderland (£4,800).

FINANCES *Financial year end* 31/12/2019 *Income* £1,900,000 *Total grants* £1,110,000 *Grants to organisations* £1,110,000 *Assets* £2,020,000

TRUSTEES Philip Jansen; David Moffat; Eve Pollard; Lynn Hiestand; Prof. Mary Lumsden; Debra White; Sir Ian Powell; Margaret Horvath; Lady Helen Ward; Prof. Dame Lesley Regan.

OTHER INFORMATION Applications are extremely competitive; of the 36 applications made across the various grant programmes in 2019, five new research project grants and six new research training grants were awarded.

HOW TO APPLY Application forms are available to download from the charity's website, where you will also find research guidelines and dates of open application periods for each scheme.

CONTACT DETAILS Jeremy Barratt, Head of Research, 1st Floor, Fairgate House, 78 New Oxford Street, London WC1A 1HB *Tel.* 020 3697 7000 *Email* jbarratt@wellbeingofwomen.org.uk *Website* https://www.wellbeingofwomen.org.uk

■ The Wellcome Trust

CC NO 210183 **ESTABLISHED** 1936

WHERE FUNDING CAN BE GIVEN UK and overseas.

WHO CAN BENEFIT Academic researchers; research institutions; charitable organisations.

WHAT IS FUNDED Improving health through research and activities in: biomedical science; population health; humanities and social science; public engagement and creative industries; education; product development and applied research.

WHAT IS NOT FUNDED Specific criteria and exclusions for each funding programme are detailed on the trust's website.

TYPE OF GRANT A wide range of grants including: research grants; fellowships; starter grants; funding for PhD and master's degrees; undergraduate scholarships; equipment and resources.

SAMPLE GRANTS University of Oxford (£128.1 million); University of Cambridge (£70.9 million); Rosalind Franklin Institute (£20.2 million); Novartis AG – Switzerland (£15.2 million); Liverpool School of Tropical Medicine (£10 million); European Bioinformatics Institute (£8.1 million); Cardiff University (£7.1 million).

FINANCES *Financial year end* 30/09/2020 *Income* £463,600,000 *Total grants* £759,500,000 *Grants to organisations* £759,500,000 *Assets* £27,820,000

TRUSTEES Governors: Baroness Eliza Manningham-Buller; Prof. Sir Michael Ferguson; Prof. Tobias Bonoeffer; Williams Burns; Dame Amelia Fawcett; Richard Gillingwater; Prof. Bryan Grenfell; Prof. Fiona Powrie; Dame Cilla Snowball; Elhadj As Sy; Alan Brown; Naguib Kheraj; Prof. Dame Anne Johnson.

OTHER INFORMATION The Wellcome Trust is one of the world's leading biomedical research charities and is the UK's largest non-governmental source of funds for biomedical research. The grant total is taken from the organisation's consolidated accounts and refers to grants awarded by the trust. Grants were broken down as follows: science (£644 million); culture and society (£49.2 million); priority areas (£332.3 million); innovations (£79.1 million).

HOW TO APPLY Applications can be made via the trust's website.

CONTACT DETAILS The Grants Team, Gibbs Building, 215 Euston Road, London NW1 2BE *Tel.* 020 7611 8888 *Email* gtsupport@wellcome.org *Website* www.wellcome.ac.uk

■ Wellington Management UK Foundation

CC NO 1167369 **ESTABLISHED** 2016

WHERE FUNDING CAN BE GIVEN UK, Germany, Luxembourg and Switzerland.

WHO CAN BENEFIT Registered charities.

WHAT IS FUNDED Improvement of academic performance and behaviour, reduction in absenteeism and development of life skills for economically disadvantaged young people (up to the age of 26).

WHAT IS NOT FUNDED The foundation does not support scholarship programmes.

TYPE OF GRANT Unrestricted (although not scholarship programmes).

SAMPLE GRANTS Primary Shakespeare Co. (£40,000); Doorstep Library Network (£30,000); Street League and Westminster City School (£20,000 each); Action for Kids (£18,500); London Youth Rowing and Just Like Us (£15,000 each).

FINANCES *Financial year end* 31/12/2019 *Income* £567,200 *Total grants* £613,500 *Grants to organisations* £613,500 *Assets* £57,300

TRUSTEES Damian Bloom; John Dickinson; Nicola Staunton; Joanne Carey; Richard van Lienden; Anna Lunden; Thomas Horsey; James Stoll.

OTHER INFORMATION Grants were awarded to 25 organisations during the year.

HOW TO APPLY In 2021, the foundation was not accepting any grant applications from charities that have not received funding previously. All charities that have been funded by the foundation but that do not have multi-year grants will need to re-apply for funding in 2021. For more information read the section describing the foundation's grant-making process and application deadlines on the website. If you have any questions about the foundation's application process, email wmukf@wellington.com.

CONTACT DETAILS The Trustees, 80 Victoria Street, London SW1E 5JL *Tel.* 020 7126 6000 *Email* wmukf@wellington.com *Website* https://www.wellington.com/en-gb/community-engagement

The Welsh Church Act Fund

CC NO 506658 **ESTABLISHED** 1976

WHERE FUNDING CAN BE GIVEN Rhondda Cynon Taff, Bridgend and Merthyr Tydfil county borough councils.

WHO CAN BENEFIT Charitable organisations; churches.

WHAT IS FUNDED General charitable purposes; education; social welfare; health; arts, culture and heritage; social and recreational activities; medical and social research; probation; older people; blind people; places of worship; emergency and disaster relief.

WHAT IS NOT FUNDED Students; individuals; clubs with a liquor licence; projects operating outside the area of benefit; regular running expenses.

TYPE OF GRANT Capital costs; project costs.

RANGE OF GRANTS Typically up to £10,000.

SAMPLE GRANTS Friends of Aberdare Park and St Elvan's Church – Aberdare (£50,000 each); ASD Rainbows – Perthcelyn (£33,900); YMCA – Hirwaun (£28,000); Hope Rescue – Llanharan and St George's Church – Cwmparc (£10,000 each); New Life Community Church – Tonyrefail (£6,400); Green Street Methodist Church – Aberdare (£5,000); St Bride's Minor Church – Bridgend (£4,100); Cwmparc Community Association (£2,000).

FINANCES *Financial year end* 31/03/2020 *Income* £427,000 *Total grants* £798,400 *Grants to organisations* £798,400 *Assets* £12,140,000

TRUSTEES Christopher Lee; Rhondda Cynon Taff County Borough Council.

OTHER INFORMATION Grants of more than £2,000 require a minimum of 10% matched funding from non-Welsh Church Fund sources (20% for grants exceeding £10,000). Those grants which are structural in nature are only considered where a professional assessment for the necessary works has been made. Grants were made to 57 organisations in 2019/20, of which two were under £2,000 and together totalled £3,650.

HOW TO APPLY Apply in writing to the correspondent, submitting your application together with estimates, accounts and constitution. The 2019/20 annual report states: 'Recommendations for grant awards are made by officers in an Assessment Round Report, which is considered at special meetings regularly throughout the year on approximately a monthly basis.'

CONTACT DETAILS Chris Bradshaw, Chief Executive, c/o Rhondda Cynon Taff County Borough Council, Council Offices, Bronwydd, Porth, Rhondda Cynon Taf CF39 9DL *Tel.* 01443 680734 *Email* treasurymanagement@rctcbc.gov.uk

Wembley National Stadium Trust

CC NO 1072392 **ESTABLISHED** 1998

WHERE FUNDING CAN BE GIVEN England, with a preference for the London Borough of Brent.

WHO CAN BENEFIT Registered charities; local authorities; schools, colleges and educational establishments; amateur sports clubs; CICs; not-for-profit organisations; social enterprises; community groups.

WHAT IS FUNDED Sports and recreation; disability sports projects; football projects for women and girls.

WHAT IS NOT FUNDED Individuals; items already purchased or ordered, or works already undertaken; core PE school curricula; activities which promote religion.

TYPE OF GRANT Capital grants; strategic funding; projects.

RANGE OF GRANTS Mostly up to £36,000.

SAMPLE GRANTS EFL (£530,000); Sheffield Hallam University (£36,000); Brent Youth Football League (£25,000); Capital City Academy (£11,000); Chance to Shine (£10,000); Phoenix Canoe Club (£9,900); Welsh Harp Sailing Club (£970).

FINANCES *Financial year end* 31/03/2019 *Income* £828,200 *Total grants* £824,500 *Grants to organisations* £824,500 *Assets* £350,100

TRUSTEES Dinah Cox; Gordon Haines; Baroness Tanni Grey-Thompson; Peter Ackerley; Lynsey Edwards; Khilna Shah; Andrew Douglass.

OTHER INFORMATION Grants were awarded to 90 organisations during the year. The 2018/19 accounts were the latest available at the time of writing (June 2021).

HOW TO APPLY At the time of writing (June 2021), the LB Brent grants programme, LB Brent Capital grants programme and LB Haringey Small grants programme were closed. Check the trust's website for the latest information.

CONTACT DETAILS Stewart Goshawk, Chief Executive Officer, Guildhall, PO Box 270, London EC2P 2EJ *Tel.* 020 7332 1055 *Email* info@wnst.org.uk *Website* www.wnst.org.uk

West Derby Waste Lands Charity

CC NO 223623 **ESTABLISHED** 1753

WHERE FUNDING CAN BE GIVEN West Derby, Merseyside.

WHO CAN BENEFIT Charitable organisations; amateur sports clubs; uniformed groups; individuals.

WHAT IS FUNDED General charitable purposes; community development; social welfare; older people; children and young people.

RANGE OF GRANTS Grants range from £430 to £6,000.

SAMPLE GRANTS Bradbury Fields (£6,000); Bridge Community Centre (£4,000); Rosce Primary School (£3,000); Ronald McDonald House (£2,000); Beautiful New Beginnings (£1,000); Christ Church Tuebrook (£600); 446th St Pauls Brownies (£430).

FINANCES *Financial year end* 31/12/2019 *Income* £73,800 *Total grants* £65,000 *Grants to organisations* £63,000 *Assets* £2,250,000

TRUSTEES Joan Driscoll; Barbara Kerr; Peter North; Barbara Shacklady; Derek Corlett; Brenda Antrobus; Anthony Heath; John Hudson; Peter Rooney; Julia Casimo.

OTHER INFORMATION Grants were made to 36 organisations during the year. Grants to individuals totalled £2,000.

HOW TO APPLY You can download an application form for a personal grant from the charity's website or use the contact form on the website to request the secretary to send you one via post. There is also an FAQ section which provides more information on eligibility requirements.

CONTACT DETAILS Lawrence Downey, Secretary, Ripley House, 56 Freshfield Road, Formby,

Liverpool, Merseyside L37 3HW *Tel.* 01704 879330 *Email* lawrencedowney@btconnect.com *Website* www.westderbywastelands.co.uk

■ West Herts Charity Trust Ltd

CC NO 278891 **ESTABLISHED** 1992

WHERE FUNDING CAN BE GIVEN Hertfordshire.

WHO CAN BENEFIT Charities and community groups.

WHAT IS FUNDED Donations of vehicles and minibuses.

SAMPLE GRANTS Previous beneficiaries have included: Abbotts Langley Primary School; Batchworth Sea Scouts; Brockswood Primary and Nursery School.

FINANCES *Financial year end* 31/07/2020 *Income* £260,000 *Total grants* £265,600 *Grants to organisations* £265,600 *Assets* £3,670,000

TRUSTEES Michael Humphreys; Peter Miller; R. D. Minashi; Paul Miller; Matthew Humphreys.

HOW TO APPLY Application forms can be downloaded from the charity's website. Completed forms should be returned by email.

CONTACT DETAILS Mike Humphreys, The Weather House, Croxley Green, Croxley Hall Woods, Rickmansworth, Hertfordshire WD3 3BE *Email* info@whct.org.uk *Website* westhertscharitytrust.co.uk

■ The Westcroft Trust

CC NO 212931 **ESTABLISHED** 1947

WHERE FUNDING CAN BE GIVEN UK, with a special interest in Shropshire.

WHO CAN BENEFIT Registered charities; religious bodies/institutions.

WHAT IS FUNDED Society of Friends (Quaker) activities across the UK; international understanding, peace and reconciliation and associated education and counselling; social care and community development, particularly in Shropshire; international medical relief and aid; people with disabilities and special needs, particularly in Shropshire.

TYPE OF GRANT Seed funding/start-up funding.

RANGE OF GRANTS Grants of mostly £1,000 to £2,000.

SAMPLE GRANTS Budiriro Trust (£5,000); British Epilepsy Association (£3,500); Oasis of Peace, Fae Dromgool – Ethos Group Oswestry (£2,000 each); The Toybox Charity (£1,100); Mercy Ships (£1,000); Bunhitt Fields Meeting House (£700).

FINANCES *Financial year end* 05/04/2020 *Income* £75,300 *Total grants* £113,400 *Grants to organisations* £113,400 *Assets* £2,200,000

TRUSTEES Mary Cadbury; Richard Cadbury; James Cadbury; Erica Cadbury.

OTHER INFORMATION Grants were distributed as follows: international medical and relief aid (£29,200); international understanding, peace, reconciliation, education and counselling (£24,000); people with disabilities (£23,600); religious society of friends (£21,900); social care and community development in Shropshire (£9,300).

HOW TO APPLY Apply in writing to the correspondent. Applications should consist of no more than two pages of A4 and include: clearly stated aims of the project and how it meets the trust's objectives; the time scale of the project; details of any funding received so far; information about the organisation.

CONTACT DETAILS The Trustees, 32 Hampton Road, Oswestry, Shropshire SY11 1SJ *Tel.* 01743 231604 *Email* westcroft32@btinternet.com

■ The Westfield Health Charitable Trust

CC NO 246057 **ESTABLISHED** 1965

WHERE FUNDING CAN BE GIVEN UK.

WHO CAN BENEFIT Medical, NHS-related or health and well-being charities registered with the Charity Commission for England and Wales, the Charity Commission for Northern Ireland, the Office of the Scottish Charity Regulator or the Association of Jersey Charities.

WHAT IS FUNDED Health, well-being and medical causes.

TYPE OF GRANT Capital costs; project funding.

RANGE OF GRANTS Up to £100,500; many grants are of under £5,000.

SAMPLE GRANTS The Children's Hospital Charity (£100,500); Ashgate Hospice (£50,000); Cathedral Archer Project (£30,000); Helen's Trust (£21,000); Wigan and Leigh Hospice (£10,500); Alzheimer's Society (£250); The Grace Kelly Childhood Cancer Trust (£130).

FINANCES *Financial year end* 05/04/2020 *Income* £570,900 *Total grants* £670,300 *Grants to organisations* £670,300 *Assets* £188,204

TRUSTEES Graham Moore; David Whitney; Lynn Clarke.

OTHER INFORMATION The trust was previously known as The Sheffield and District Hospital Services Charitable Fund.

HOW TO APPLY Apply in writing to charity@westfieldhealth.com. Applications should include a covering letter detailing the specifics of what you are applying for, any supporting information that you feel is relevant and a breakdown of costs. There are no deadlines, applications are considered throughout the year.

CONTACT DETAILS The Trustees, Westfield House, 60 Charter Row, Sheffield, South Yorkshire S1 3FZ *Tel.* 0114 250 2079 *Email* charity@westfieldhealth.com *Website* https://www.westfieldhealth.com/charitable-trust

■ Westhill Endowment

CC NO 1104736 **ESTABLISHED** 2004

WHERE FUNDING CAN BE GIVEN Worldwide, with a preference for the UK.

WHO CAN BENEFIT Registered charities; churches.

WHAT IS FUNDED Formal and informal religious education projects and faith-motivated activities that enable people to transform their lives and the life of their communities.

WHAT IS NOT FUNDED According to the charity's website, the following are not likely to be successful: 'capital appeals for building projects; requests for contributions towards ongoing salary costs, although Westhill does consider applications to fund the costs of sessional, part-time or project staff; where the beneficiaries of the project do not involve humans, i.e. projects that work exclusively for the benefit of animals or for the environment; if the activity to be funded is a statutory responsibility of the state; if the project is to take place overseas and the organisation/charity does not have an accountable UK-based partner organisation; if Westhill has provided a grant to the same applicant within the past 12 months; requests for funding that seek to persuade people of one faith/political belief or none to adopt another faith/political belief; if the expected impact of the project is unclear or considered to be very unlikely to be achievable; if it is clear that the applicant has sufficient unrestricted reserves to self-fund the project; requests for grants for payments to individuals.'

TYPE OF GRANT Project funding, mostly for a one-year period.

RANGE OF GRANTS Generally between £1,000 and £20,000.

SAMPLE GRANTS Greenbelt (£24,000); NASACRE (£20,000); Hull Community Church (£11,000); C2C Social Action, Chaiya Trust and Diocese of Manchester (£10,000 each).

FINANCES *Financial year end* 31/07/2020 *Income* £448,000 *Total grants* £258,200 *Grants to organisations* £258,200 *Assets* £13,160,000

TRUSTEES Sarah Evans; Revd Edward Coleman; Peter Ullathorne; Lorna Hewitt; Andrew Morris; Julie Grove; Margaret Rendle; Philip White; David Slade; Dr Aisha Ahmad; Dr Rachael Royal; Shivaji Shiva; Revd Leonora Jagessar-Visser't Hooft.

HOW TO APPLY See the charity's website for details on how to apply.

CONTACT DETAILS Diane Webb, Trust Office Manager, The Lodge Westhill, South Drive, Selly Oak, Birmingham, West Midlands B29 6WE *Tel.* 0121 472 8000 *Email* admin@westhilltrust.com *Website* www.westhillendowment.org

■ Westminster Almshouses Foundation

CC NO 226936 **ESTABLISHED** 2007

WHERE FUNDING CAN BE GIVEN City of Westminster.

WHO CAN BENEFIT Charitable organisations. Grants of up to £500 are also made to individuals.

WHAT IS FUNDED Accommodation for older people; relief in need, particularly for social isolation; education/training for young people on low incomes in the City of Westminster.

WHAT IS NOT FUNDED Organisations with large financial reserves will not be funded.

TYPE OF GRANT Projects; capital grants.

RANGE OF GRANTS Grants of up to £30,000.

SAMPLE GRANTS Harris Academy 6th Form (£27,000); St Matthew's Primary School (£19,900); I Can and North Paddington Foodbank (£10,100 each); St Andrew's Club (£7,000); Avenues Youth Project (£5,000); Westminster Medical School Science Conference (£2,600).

FINANCES *Financial year end* 31/12/2019 *Income* £157,200 *Total grants* £280,800 *Grants to organisations* £157,200 *Assets* £31,490,000

TRUSTEES Revd Graham Buckle; Cllr Rachael Robathan; Charles Lillis; Lady Joanna Knatchbull; Lucy Slater; Cllr Selina Short; Xavier Villers; Dr Robert Linton; Cllr Jim Glen; Susan Ford.

HOW TO APPLY Apply in writing to the correspondent. Large grants are considered by the grants committee, which meets four times a year in February, June, September and November.

CONTACT DETAILS Tony Reid, Clerk to the Trustees, Palmer's House, 42 Rochester Row, London SW1P 1BU *Tel.* 020 7828 3131 *Email* clerk@westminsteralmshouses.com *Website* www.westminsteralmshouses.com

■ Westminster Amalgamated Charity

CC NO 207964 **ESTABLISHED** 1961

WHERE FUNDING CAN BE GIVEN City of Westminster.

WHO CAN BENEFIT Registered charities; individuals in need. Applications from national charities are only considered if they can demonstrate that their project or service will benefit a significant number of residents in need in Westminster.

WHAT IS FUNDED Social welfare; addiction; children and young people; community; older people; health and disability; homelessness.

WHAT IS NOT FUNDED Retrospective grants; emergency cash grants or crisis loans.

TYPE OF GRANT Specific capital costs; revenue funding and core costs; specific project/service costs. One-off grants only.

RANGE OF GRANTS Grants range from £500 to £10,000.

SAMPLE GRANTS A list of beneficiaries was not included in the annual report and accounts.

FINANCES *Financial year end* 31/12/2018 *Income* £363,200 *Total grants* £317,400 *Grants to organisations* £287,700 *Assets* £7,300,000

TRUSTEES Jenny Bianco; A. Gardner; Jean Rymer; Linda McHugh; Graham Mordue; Simon Carruth; David Cavaye; Kate Bowyer; Geraldine Elliot; Toby Jameson-Till; Matthew Keane.

OTHER INFORMATION Grants were made to 47 organisations during the year. The charity also makes grants to individuals in need who live, work or study in the London Borough of Westminster or if they have previously lived or worked in this borough for a total of five years or more. Grants were made to 154 individuals totalling £29,700. The 2018 accounts were the latest available at the time of writing (June 2021).

HOW TO APPLY Applications can be made using the online form on the charity's website, where deadlines for submission are also posted.

CONTACT DETAILS Julia Moorcroft, Grants Administrator, School House, Drury Lane, London WC2B 5SU *Tel.* 020 7395 9460 *Email* wac@3chars.org.uk *Website* www.w-a-c.org.uk

■ Westminster Foundation

CC NO 267618 **ESTABLISHED** 1974

WHERE FUNDING CAN BE GIVEN Westminster (parts of the Old Metropolitan Borough of Westminster); Cheshire West and Cheshire; rural North West Lancashire (near Forest of Bowland); and North West Sutherland.

WHO CAN BENEFIT Registered charities.

WHAT IS FUNDED Social welfare. The foundation is currently focusing its grant-making on issues around poverty in the UK, in the following themes: supporting communities in need; vulnerable groups; building resilience; crisis intervention. Further detail on eligibility criteria is given on the foundation's website. The foundation also makes some grants overseas, but these are not open to application.

WHAT IS NOT FUNDED Individuals, including student fees and bursaries; projects benefitting only one school or college; holidays or trips including respite programmes; projects that are overtly political or religious; gifts and prizes for events and auctions; organisations that have applied to the foundation unsuccessfully within the previous 12 months; capital costs in isolation.

TYPE OF GRANT One-off grants; core cost; project grants.

RANGE OF GRANTS Grants range from £20,000 up to £160,000.
SAMPLE GRANTS The Country Trust (£160,000); Platform for Life (£99,700); Westminster Children's University (£84,300); Future Men (£50,000); Family House Tokyo (£37,900); Cheshire Young Carers and Positive View (£20,000 each).
FINANCES *Financial year end* 31/12/2019 *Income* £4,500,000 *Total grants* £2,110,000 *Grants to organisations* £2,110,000 *Assets* £110,730,000
TRUSTEES James Hanbury; Mark Preston; Victoria Hornby; The Duke of Westminster.
OTHER INFORMATION Only organisations receiving grants of over £20,000 were listed as beneficiaries in the charity's accounts. Grants of under £20,000 totalled £625,900.
HOW TO APPLY Check the foundation's website for details on eligibility. Applications for the Small Grant Programme can be made online. Charities can also join the waiting list for office space online. Partnership grants are by invitation only.
CONTACT DETAILS Tom Mansell, Grants Manager, The Grosvenor Office, 70 Grosvenor Street, London W1K 3JP *Tel.* 020 7408 0988 *Email* westminster.foundation@grosvenor.com *Website* www.westminsterfoundation.org.uk

■ Westway Trust

CC NO 1123127 **ESTABLISHED** 2008
WHERE FUNDING CAN BE GIVEN The Royal Borough of Kensington and Chelsea, with particular focus on North Kensington, in and around the Westway.
WHO CAN BENEFIT Social enterprises; charitable, voluntary and community organisations.
WHAT IS FUNDED Isolation; spaces for young people; recreation and exercise; economic participation; arts and culture; the environment.
WHAT IS NOT FUNDED See the grant-maker's website for exclusions relevant to each grants programme.
TYPE OF GRANT Projects costs; capital costs; core costs. As part of the Community Grants programme, the trust will also pledge up to £4,000 for larger projects and initiatives which commit to undertake a crowdfunding campaign to raise further funds – refer to the website for more information.
RANGE OF GRANTS Grants range from £500 up to £32,660.
SAMPLE GRANTS Kensington and Chelsea Social Council (£50,600 in three grants); Swinbrook Estate T&RA (£20,000); Midaye Somali Development Network (£15,000); FerArts CIC (£5,000); Lancaster West Residents Association (£2,000); Westway Community Transport (£730); The Learning Club Community Association (£500).
FINANCES *Financial year end* 31/03/2020 *Income* £6,060,000 *Total grants* £826,000 *Grants to organisations* £695,700 *Assets* £63,940,000
TRUSTEES Angela Spence; Sheraine Williams; Marie-Therese Rossi; Eve Wedderburn; Alexander Korda; Tobias Laurent Belson; Thomas Fitch; Dr Marwan Elnaghi; Huey Walker.
OTHER INFORMATION The trust was previously known as Westway Development Trust. Grants to individuals totalled £130,300 during the year.
HOW TO APPLY See the trust's website for the latest information on grant programmes.
CONTACT DETAILS The Trustees, Westway Trust Office, 1 Thorpe Close, London W10 5XL *Tel.* 020 8962 5720 *Email* info@westway.org *Website* www.westway.org

■ The Barbara Whatmore Charitable Trust

CC NO 283336 **ESTABLISHED** 1981
WHERE FUNDING CAN BE GIVEN UK, with some preference for East Anglia.
WHO CAN BENEFIT Registered charities.
WHAT IS FUNDED Arts, music and relief of poverty, focusing mainly on cultural and heritage projects, particularly in East Anglia. Eligible areas of support include: classical music education; conservation and crafts training; education projects in museums, the theatre and poetry; conservation of endangered historic artefacts and of the natural heritage environment, as well as preventive projects to protect historic or natural collections.
WHAT IS NOT FUNDED Repair work to the fabric of buildings or structures; the purchase of musical instruments or works of art; choral societies; festivals; individuals; organisations without registered charitable status.
TYPE OF GRANT Project funding; general funding.
RANGE OF GRANTS Up to £5,000.
SAMPLE GRANTS Edward James Foundation (£5,000); City and Guilds of London Art School, Edward Barnsley Educational Trust and Royal School of Needlework (£4,000 each); Blandford Parish Church (£3,500); Prince's Foundation (£3,000); Dartington International Summer School (£2,000); New Lanark Conservation and Sherborne Douzelage (£500 each).
FINANCES *Financial year end* 05/04/2020 *Income* £91,200 *Total grants* £103,200 *Grants to organisations* £103,200 *Assets* £1,534,000
TRUSTEES David Eldridge; Denis Borrow; Gillian Lewis; Luke Gardiner; Patricia Cooke-Yarborough; Sally Carter; Stephen Bate.
OTHER INFORMATION Grants were awarded to 34 organisations in 2019/20.
HOW TO APPLY Apply in writing to the correspondent, either by post or email. Applications can be submitted at any time but no later than 15 March or 15 September for consideration at the meetings in April and October, respectively.
CONTACT DETAILS Denise Gardiner, 3 Honeyhanger, Hindhead Road, Hindhead, Surrey GU26 6BA *Tel.* 07762 942914 *Email* denise@bwct.org

■ The Wheeler Family Charitable Trust

CC NO 1156928 **ESTABLISHED** 2014
WHERE FUNDING CAN BE GIVEN England and Wales.
WHO CAN BENEFIT Registered charities.
WHAT IS FUNDED The advancement of education.
SAMPLE GRANTS Previous beneficiaries have included: Place2Be (£154,500); Buckinghamshire Community Foundation and Eton College Charitable Trust (£100,000 each); Best Beginnings (£30,000); Child Bereavement UK (£20,000); Peter Jones Foundation (£10,000); Wellington College (£1,400).
FINANCES *Financial year end* 30/06/2020 *Income* £10,300 *Total grants* £453,800 *Grants to organisations* £453,800
TRUSTEES Belinda Wheeler; Nicholas Wheeler.
OTHER INFORMATION Full accounts were not available to view on the Charity Commission's website

due to the trust's low income. We have therefore estimated the grant total based on the trust's total expenditure.

HOW TO APPLY Contact the correspondent for further information.

CONTACT DETAILS The Trustees, RSM, Fifth floor, Central Square, 29 Wellington Street, Leeds, West Yorkshire LS1 4DL *Tel.* 0113 285 5000

■ The Whinfell Charitable Fund

CC NO 267333 **ESTABLISHED** 1973

WHERE FUNDING CAN BE GIVEN UK, in particular Bolton and Manchester.

WHO CAN BENEFIT Registered charities and charitable organisations, particularly those based in Bolton or Manchester. The trust has specific regular allocations, including the RNLI, with opportunities to add further charities.

WHAT IS FUNDED General charitable purposes; the advancement of the Christian religion; education; the advancement of health; saving lives.

TYPE OF GRANT Mainly recurrent grants to established beneficiaries.

SAMPLE GRANTS A list of beneficiaries was not included in the annual report and accounts.

FINANCES *Financial year end* 31/01/2020
Income £115,200 *Total grants* £151,600
Grants to organisations £151,600
Assets £5,520,000

TRUSTEES Jennifer Mitchell; Katherine Duff; Sarah Bowles.

HOW TO APPLY Contact the correspondent for further information.

CONTACT DETAILS The Trustees, 35 Westgate, Huddersfield HD1 1PA *Tel.* 01484 423691

■ The Whitaker Charitable Trust

CC NO 234491 **ESTABLISHED** 1964

WHERE FUNDING CAN BE GIVEN UK, with a preference for Nottinghamshire, the East Midlands and Scotland.

WHO CAN BENEFIT Registered charities.

WHAT IS FUNDED General charitable purposes with a preference for: local charities in Nottinghamshire and the East Midlands; music; agricultural and silvicultural education; countryside conservation; Scottish charities.

RANGE OF GRANTS Grants range up to £27,000 but mostly £1,000 to £5,000.

SAMPLE GRANTS Atlantic College (£27,000); School of Artisan Food (£18,000); Royal Forestry Society (£15,000); Game and Wildlife Conservation Trust (£10,000); Nottinghamshire and Nottingham Refugee Forum (£5,000); Bassetlaw Hospice (£3,000); Alcohol Education Trust (£1,000).

FINANCES *Financial year end* 31/03/2020
Income £161,200 *Total grants* £184,500
Grants to organisations £184,500
Assets £9,130,000

TRUSTEES Edward Perks; Lady Elizabeth Whitaker; Sir Jack Whitaker.

HOW TO APPLY Apply in writing to the correspondent. The trustees meet regularly to review grant applications.

CONTACT DETAILS The Trustees, c/o Currey and Co., 33 Queen Anne Street, London W1G 9HY *Tel.* 020 7802 2700

■ Colonel W. H. Whitbread Charitable Trust

CC NO 210496 **ESTABLISHED** 1953

WHERE FUNDING CAN BE GIVEN UK, with an interest in Gloucestershire.

WHO CAN BENEFIT Charitable organisations; educational institutions; sports organisations.

WHAT IS FUNDED The trust supports: education, particularly for those who are disadvantaged, as well as for pupils at Aldenham School and in support of Corpus Christi College, Cambridge; amateur sports, particularly those enjoyed by the settlor (ocean racing, Finn Class sailing, National Hunt racing, flying, field sports, eventing and polo); health and welfare of service personnel; conservation projects.

RANGE OF GRANTS Grants of £500 and upwards.

SAMPLE GRANTS Previous beneficiaries have included: 1st Queen's Dragon Guards Regimental Trust, Abbey School Tewkesbury, Army Benevolent Fund, CLIC Sargent, Disasters Emergency Committee Tsunami Earthquake Appeal, Friends of Alderman Knights School, Gloucestershire Historic Churches Trust, Great Ormond Street Hospital Children's Charity, Household Cavalry Museum Appeal, Hunt Servants' Fund, Queen Mary's Clothing Guild, Royal Hospital Chelsea and St Richard's Hospice.

FINANCES *Financial year end* 31/12/2019
Income £243,300 *Total grants* £179,000
Grants to organisations £179,000
Assets £850,200

TRUSTEES Mr H. F. Whitbread; Jeremy Barkes; Rupert Foley.

HOW TO APPLY Contact the correspondent for further information.

CONTACT DETAILS Susan Smith, Secretary, Fir Tree Cottage, World's End, Grimley, Worcestershire WR2 6NN *Tel.* 07812 454321
Email whwhitbread.trust@googlemail.com

■ The Melanie White Foundation Ltd

CC NO 1077150 **ESTABLISHED** 1999

WHERE FUNDING CAN BE GIVEN Mainly UK.

WHO CAN BENEFIT Charitable organisations.

WHAT IS FUNDED General charitable purposes, particularly: health; medicine; social welfare.

SAMPLE GRANTS One Bahamas Foundation (£813,600); University of Buckingham – Institute of Sports Humanities (£90,000); CLIC Sargent (£25,000); Association Aquitaine (£5,400); Great Ormond Street Hospital (£1,500); Lady Garden Foundation (£200).

FINANCES *Financial year end* 05/04/2020
Income £312,800 *Total grants* £1,180,000
Grants to organisations £1,180,000
Assets £11,050,000

TRUSTEES Melanie White; Andrew White; Adrian de la Touche.

OTHER INFORMATION The foundation awarded 15 grants to organisations in 2019/20. The foundation supports CLIC Sargent on a recurrent basis.

HOW TO APPLY The foundation does not accept unsolicited applications as the trustees proactively identify beneficiaries themselves.

CONTACT DETAILS The Trustees, 61 Grosvenor Street, London W1K 3JE *Tel.* 020 3011 1100
Email melaniewhitefoundation@gmail.com

White Stuff Foundation

CC NO 1134754 **ESTABLISHED** 2010

WHERE FUNDING CAN BE GIVEN UK.

WHO CAN BENEFIT Registered charities.

WHAT IS FUNDED General charitable purposes.

TYPE OF GRANT Unrestricted funding.

RANGE OF GRANTS Grants range from £3,000 up to £87,400.

SAMPLE GRANTS ID Care Trust (£87,400); The Spires Centre (£43,300); Soft Touch Arts (£7,800); National Flood Forum (£7,000); The Laura Centre (£3,700); Penhaligons Friend (£3,500); South London Care (£3,000).

FINANCES *Financial year end* 02/05/2020 *Income* £316,100 *Total grants* £326,300 *Grants to organisations* £326,300 *Assets* £191,100

TRUSTEES Rebecca Kong; Victoria Hodges; Sean Thomas; Matthew Scott; Joanne Jenkins; Naomi Howgate.

OTHER INFORMATION Grants were made to 149 charities in 2019/20. Smaller grants totalled £167,600 during the year. Types of grant include one-off discretionary grants; Community Chest grants to promote local community engagement; matched funding for employee-supported charities; local charity partnership grants. Volunteer support from White Stuff employees may also be offered to partner charities.

HOW TO APPLY The foundation supports regular partner charities, making ad hoc grants to other charities, where the trustees consider it appropriate. Contact the correspondent for information regarding how to apply to be a partner charity or to request an ad hoc grant.

CONTACT DETAILS Foundation Manager, Canterbury Court, 1–3 Brixton Road, London SW9 6DE *Tel.* 020 7735 8133 *Email* community@whitestuff.com *Website* https://www.whitestuff.com/our-foundation

The Norman Whiteley Trust

CC NO 226445 **ESTABLISHED** 1963

WHERE FUNDING CAN BE GIVEN Worldwide, with a preference for Cumbria.

WHO CAN BENEFIT Christian evangelical organisations; individuals.

WHAT IS FUNDED Evangelical Christian causes. The trust's objects are to fund activities which further the spread of the Gospel, relieving poverty and assisting with education.

RANGE OF GRANTS Up to £8,000, typically less than £3,000.

SAMPLE GRANTS Marantha Christian Outreach Ministries (£8,000); Jesus Christ International Ministries (£5,000); Malcolm and Trish Morgan and Mark Bimson (£3,600 each); New Life Church (£3,000); Openwell (£2,000); Windermere Deanery (£1,000).

FINANCES *Financial year end* 29/02/2020 *Income* £142,000 *Total grants* £122,800 *Grants to organisations* £96,300 *Assets* £3,090,000

TRUSTEES Derek Dickson; Paul Whiteley; Pippa Guidera.

OTHER INFORMATION The grant total includes awards to organisations and individuals.

HOW TO APPLY Contact the correspondent for further information.

CONTACT DETAILS The Trustees, Brookside, Vicarage Lane, Childswickham, Broadway, Worcestershire WR12 7HL *Tel.* 01253 798812 *Email* normanwhiteleytrust@gmail.com

Whitley Animal Protection Trust

CC NO 236746 **ESTABLISHED** 1964

WHERE FUNDING CAN BE GIVEN UK and overseas.

WHO CAN BENEFIT Registered charities only.

WHAT IS FUNDED Animal welfare and conservation.

WHAT IS NOT FUNDED Grants are not made to non-registered charities.

TYPE OF GRANT Core and project grants; one-off grants are made, but most are recurrent grants that last for several years.

RANGE OF GRANTS Generally £250 to £20,000, although larger grants may also be awarded.

SAMPLE GRANTS Whitley Fund for Nature (£131,100); Oxford WildCRU (£30,000): RSPB Scotland – Acquisition of Coll land (£20,000); Sustainable Inshore Fisheries Trust (£10,000); Blue Marine Trust (£7,000); Campaign to Protect Rural England (£5,000); Orangutan Foundation (£1,000).

FINANCES *Financial year end* 31/12/2019 *Income* £352,000 *Total grants* £300,400 *Grants to organisations* £300,400 *Assets* £10,960,000

TRUSTEES Edward John Whitley; Edward Whitley; Jeremy Whitley; Penelope Whitley; Vivien Thompson.

HOW TO APPLY The trustees meet twice a year to decide on grants to be made. The trust's 2019 annual report states: 'A majority of the grants undertaken are repeat donations, however, the Trustees do provide essential core funding to these smaller charities without which they would find it hard to maintain their activities. The Charity does also make one-off grants, but a majority of the grants are in respect of longer-term commitments.' Contact the correspondent for more information.

CONTACT DETAILS The Trustees, Padmore House, Hall Court, Hall Park Way, Telford, Shropshire TF3 4LX *Tel.* 01952 641651

Charity of Sir Richard Whittington

CC NO 1087167 **ESTABLISHED** 1424

WHERE FUNDING CAN BE GIVEN UK, particularly London and disadvantaged areas in the east of England and the North East.

WHO CAN BENEFIT Charitable organisations; individuals; churches and faith-based organisations; secular community-based organisations.

WHAT IS FUNDED Social welfare; young people; education; older people; families; homelessness and housing.

TYPE OF GRANT Dependent on grant programme.

RANGE OF GRANTS Mostly £9,000 to £90,000.

SAMPLE GRANTS Young people and education programme: National Literacy Trust (£239,100); Ministry of Stories (£115,000); The Education Policy Institute (£44,300). Older people and housing programme: The Cares Family Ltd (£70,000); Age UK – East London (£44,700); Hackney Caribbean Elderly Organisation (£25,000); Face Front Inclusive Theatre (£4,800). Church and communities programme: Southwark Diocesan WellCare (£49,700); Feeding Britain (£22,700); In Deep Community Task Force (£8,000).

FINANCES *Financial year end* 31/03/2020 *Income* £3,950,000 *Total grants* £2,852,900 *Grants to organisations* £2,660,000 *Assets* £104,040,000

TRUSTEE The Mercers' Company.

OTHER INFORMATION Grants were made to 75 organisations during the year. Grants were channelled through three programmes: young people and education (£1.28 million); older people and housing (£723,100); church and communities (£660,700). Grants to 163 individuals totalling £192,900 were made through the older people and housing programme. The charity also provides accommodation to 215 residents in its six almshouses.

HOW TO APPLY The charity is an associated charitable trust of The Mercers' Company. Application guidelines and grant programme deadlines can be found on the Mercers' Company website.

CONTACT DETAILS The Trustees, c/o The Mercers' Company, 6 Frederick's Place, London EC2R 8AB *Tel.* 020 7776 7250 *Email* grants@mercers.co.uk *Website* https://www.mercers.co.uk/philanthropy

■ The Wigoder Family Foundation

CC NO 1086806 **ESTABLISHED** 2000

WHERE FUNDING CAN BE GIVEN England and Wales.

WHO CAN BENEFIT Registered charities.

WHAT IS FUNDED General charitable purposes; Jewish causes.

RANGE OF GRANTS Grants range from £1,600 up to £150,000.

SAMPLE GRANTS Previous beneficiaries have included: Jewish Learning Exchange (£150,000); The Chicken Soup Kitchen (£80,000); Lord Mayor's Appeal (£35,000); Norwood (£25,000); Jewish Care (£15,000); Chai Cancer Care (£6,000); Centre for Jewish Life (£1,600).

FINANCES *Financial year end* 30/11/2019 *Income* £6,170,000 *Total grants* £536,100 *Grants to organisations* £536,100 *Assets* £52,830,000

TRUSTEES Elizabeth Wigoder; Charles Wigoder; Martin Rose.

OTHER INFORMATION The 2018/19 accounts were the latest available at the time of writing (May 2021).

HOW TO APPLY Apply in writing to the correspondent. According to the 2018/19 annual report, 'the trustees meet as many times as deemed appropriate but not less than twice a year to discuss grants, based on applications received throughout the year'.

CONTACT DETAILS The Trustees, 22 Lyndhurst Road, London W2 2LT *Tel.* 020 8955 5000

■ The Felicity Wilde Charitable Trust

CC NO 264404 **ESTABLISHED** 1972

WHERE FUNDING CAN BE GIVEN UK.

WHO CAN BENEFIT Charitable organisations.

WHAT IS FUNDED Children's charities; medical research, particularly into the cause and cure of asthma.

SAMPLE GRANTS Previous beneficiaries have included: Asthma UK (£10,000); Sparks (£4,000); Douglas Bader Foundation and The George Coller Memorial Fund (£2,000 each); Bliss, Crackerjack Children's Trust, Hearing Dogs for Deaf People, Kidney Research UK, Martin House Children's Hospice and Motability (£1,000 each).

FINANCES *Financial year end* 09/05/2020 *Income* £75,200 *Total grants* £106,500 *Grants to organisations* £106,500 *Assets* £2,010,000

TRUSTEE Zedra Trust Company (UK) Ltd.

HOW TO APPLY Contact the correspondent for further information.

CONTACT DETAILS The Trustees, Zedra UK Trusts, Booths Hall, Booths Park, 3 Chelford Road, Knutsford, Cheshire WA16 8GS *Tel.* 01565 748814 *Email* charities@zedra.com

■ Joan Wilkinson Charitable Trust

CC NO 1162954 **ESTABLISHED** 2014

WHERE FUNDING CAN BE GIVEN England.

WHO CAN BENEFIT Charitable organisations.

WHAT IS FUNDED The education, advancement and welfare of children.

RANGE OF GRANTS Mostly £1,000 to £5,000.

SAMPLE GRANTS Keech Hospice Care (£5,100); Dorset Children's Foundation (£4,000); 4 Cancer Group (£3,000); Sense (£1,600); The Brainwave Centre (£1,000).

FINANCES *Financial year end* 02/06/2019 *Income* £54,300 *Total grants* £120,700 *Grants to organisations* £120,700 *Assets* £1,530,000

TRUSTEE Kimcote and Walton Parish Council.

OTHER INFORMATION The 2018/19 accounts were the latest available at the time of writing (May 2021).

HOW TO APPLY Contact the correspondent for further information.

CONTACT DETAILS The Trustees, Zedra UK Trusts, Booths Hall, Booths Park 3, Chelford Park, Knutsford WA16 8GS *Tel.* 01565 748808 *Email* charities@zedra.com

■ The Will Charitable Trust

CC NO 801682 **ESTABLISHED** 1989

WHERE FUNDING CAN BE GIVEN UK.

WHO CAN BENEFIT UK-registered or exempt charities.

WHAT IS FUNDED Care of and services for blind people, and the prevention and cure of blindness; care of people with learning disabilities; the long-term care of people with learning disabilities; care of and services for people suffering from cancer, and their families.

WHAT IS NOT FUNDED A full list of exclusions can be found on the trust's website.

TYPE OF GRANT Capital costs; project funding; one-off.

RANGE OF GRANTS Grants range from £3,000 to £30,000.

SAMPLE GRANTS Henshaws (£25,000); IMPACT UK (£20,000); St Luke's Hospice (Basildon) (£15,000); Price of Wales Hospice (£12,500); Bloodwise (£10,000); Enhanceable (£7,500); Alington House Community Association (£3,000).

FINANCES *Financial year end* 05/04/2020 *Income* £668,900 *Total grants* £697,800 *Grants to organisations* £697,800 *Assets* £18,080,000

TRUSTEES Alastair McDonald; Rodney Luff; Vanessa Reburn; Joanna Dyson.

OTHER INFORMATION Grants were made to 57 organisations during the year and distributed as follows: care of people with learning disabilities (£225,000); care of blind people (£210,800); care of cancer patients (£196,000); exceptional grants fund (£66,000). The trustees may occasionally consider larger exceptional grants, but this is unusual and generally confined to charities that the trustees know well and have supported for some time.

HOW TO APPLY Applications should be made in writing to the correspondent and sent by post – emailed applications will not be accepted.

Guidance on what to include in your application is given on the trust's website, along with more detailed eligibility criteria. There are separate deadlines for each area of focus.

CONTACT DETAILS The Grants Administrator, Bridge House, 11 Creek Road, East Molesey KT8 9BE *Tel.* 020 8941 0450 *Email* admin@willcharitabletrust.org.uk *Website* willcharitabletrust.org.uk

■ The Williams Charitable Trust

CC NO 1086668 **ESTABLISHED** 2001

WHERE FUNDING CAN BE GIVEN UK; overseas.

WHO CAN BENEFIT Charitable organisations; individuals.

WHAT IS FUNDED General charitable purposes including: education and training; arts and theatre; the advancement of medicine; the environment; heritage.

RANGE OF GRANTS Up to £40,000 but mainly under £15,000.

SAMPLE GRANTS Pratt Contemporary – Anne Pacheco Sculpture (£40,000); Viva Arts and Community Group (£15,000); Towner Gallery (£12,500); Arts Educational Schools and London Firebird Orchestra (£10,000 each); British Film Institute (£3,900); Stage One (£2,000).

FINANCES *Financial year end* 30/06/2020 *Income* £93,300 *Total grants* £142,300 *Grants to organisations* £141,300 *Assets* £2,230,000

TRUSTEES Stuart Williams; Hilary Williams; Andrew Williams; Matthew Williams; Keith Eyre-Varnier.

OTHER INFORMATION During 2019/20, grants were awarded to 25 organisations and two individuals. Only organisations receiving grants of over £1,000 were listed as beneficiaries in the trust's accounts. Grants of £1,000 or less totalled £12,500 and were awarded to 13 organisations.

HOW TO APPLY Unsolicited applications are not accepted. The 2019/20 annual report states: 'Trustees adopt a proactive approach in seeking worthy causes requiring support.'

CONTACT DETAILS The Trustees, Flat 85, Capital Wharf, 50 Wapping High Street, London E1W 1LY *Tel.* 020 7488 0314

■ Alfred Williams Charitable Trust

CC NO 266652 **ESTABLISHED** 1974

WHERE FUNDING CAN BE GIVEN Suffolk.

WHO CAN BENEFIT Registered charities; CICs.

WHAT IS FUNDED Environmental and heritage causes including repair and development, conservation and restoration. Social causes are also supported. This includes voluntary care, education, theatre, music, youth projects and community projects. The trust has a preference for the preservation or regeneration of the built heritage, amenity and landscape of Suffolk.

TYPE OF GRANT Capital costs; seed funding/start-up funding.

RANGE OF GRANTS £50 to £12,500.

SAMPLE GRANTS My Wish Charity (£12,500); Woodland Heritage (£3,000); Churches Conservation Trust (£2,500); East Anglian Traditional Music Trust (£2,000); Battisford and District Cricket Club (£1,500); St Elizabeth Hospice (£1,000); Clare Community Bees (£500); Suffolk Historic Churches Trust (£50).

FINANCES *Financial year end* 05/04/2020 *Income* £91,400 *Total grants* £90,400 *Grants to organisations* £90,400 *Assets* £2,680,000

TRUSTEES Jonathan Penn; Paul Clarke; Robert Williams; Dr Luke Williams.

OTHER INFORMATION Grants totalling £90,400 were made to 49 organisations in 2019/20.

HOW TO APPLY Application forms can be downloaded from the trust's website. The trustees meet three times a year to consider grant applications. Applications must be received by the end of January, May and September.

CONTACT DETAILS Kate Bowe, Administrator, Haughley Park, Stowmarket, Suffolk IP14 3JY *Tel.* 07917 509009 *Email* alfredwilliamscharitabletrust@gmail.com *Website* https://alfredwilliamscharitabletrust.org

■ The Williams Family Foundation

CC NO 1157478 **ESTABLISHED** 2014

WHERE FUNDING CAN BE GIVEN Flintshire; Wrexham; Denbighshire; Cheshire (to the west of the M6).

WHO CAN BENEFIT Registered charities; CIOs.

WHAT IS FUNDED Health and saving lives; arts, culture, heritage and science; environmental protection or improvement; relief in need; young people; older people; people with disabilities or illnesses.

WHAT IS NOT FUNDED General appeals from national charities; small contributions to large appeals for vehicles or buildings; animal charities; religious organisations; any part of a request for a grant that would involve the payment of salaries or remuneration.

TYPE OF GRANT Project funding; equipment; refurbishment costs.

SAMPLE GRANTS A list of beneficiaries was not included in the annual report and accounts.

FINANCES *Financial year end* 31/12/2019 *Income* £200,000 *Total grants* £253,600 *Grants to organisations* £253,600 *Assets* £65,300

TRUSTEES John Gregory; Amy Sheppard; Barbara Williams; Mark Williams; Thomas Williams.

OTHER INFORMATION The 2018/19 accounts were the latest available at the time of writing (May 2021).

HOW TO APPLY Applications can be made through the foundation's website. Alternatively, application forms can be downloaded from the website to be completed and returned to applications@williamsfamilyfoundation.org.uk.

CONTACT DETAILS The Trustees, PO Box 3809, Chester CH1 9ZW *Tel.* 01244 570292 *Email* enquiries@williamsfamilyfoundation.org.uk *Website* www.williamsfamilyfoundation.org.uk

■ The Willmott Dixon Foundation

CC NO 326530 **ESTABLISHED** 1984

WHERE FUNDING CAN BE GIVEN UK.

WHO CAN BENEFIT Registered charities.

WHAT IS FUNDED The education of children and young people; people with disabilities.

TYPE OF GRANT Project funding.

RANGE OF GRANTS £100 to £62,000.

SAMPLE GRANTS Chestnut Tree House (£62,900); Key4Life (£25,300); The Talent Foundry Trust (£13,100); Action Medical Research (£10,000); Cancer Research UK (£4,800); Watergate Co-operative Trust (£2,500); Links International (£1,600).

FINANCES *Financial year end* 05/04/2020 *Income* £204,300 *Total grants* £186,900 *Grants to organisations* £186,900 *Assets* £46,300

TRUSTEES Richard Willmott; Colin Enticknap; Wendy McWilliams.

OTHER INFORMATION Willmott Dixon Group is a privately owned construction, housing and property development business based in Hertfordshire. During 2019/20, support was given to 21 projects. Only organisations receiving grants of over £2,500 were listed as beneficiaries in the charity's accounts. Grants of under £2,500 totalled £6,200.
HOW TO APPLY Contact the correspondent for further information.
CONTACT DETAILS The Trustees, Spirella 2, Icknield Way, Letchworth Garden City, Hertfordshire SG6 4GY *Tel.* 07974 457508 *Email* company.secretarial@willmottdixon.co.uk *Website* https://www.willmottdixon.co.uk/the-willmott-dixon-foundation

■ The HDH Wills 1965 Charitable Trust

CC NO 1117747 **ESTABLISHED** 1965
WHERE FUNDING CAN BE GIVEN Predominantly UK.
WHO CAN BENEFIT Registered, exempt or excepted charities only.
WHAT IS FUNDED General charitable purposes; the environment; wildlife. The trust makes two types of grant: monthly and large. Monthly grants are used to make grants for general charitable purposes, the environment and wildlife conservation; large grants operate on a seven-year funding priority cycle. In years 1, 2, 5, 6 and 7 of this cycle, grants are made to specified institutions; in years 3 and 4, favour is given to environmental and wildlife conservation and external applications are accepted.
WHAT IS NOT FUNDED Organisations that have been supported in the previous 24 months; individuals.
TYPE OF GRANT Revenue, capital or project expenditure.
RANGE OF GRANTS Grants from the monthly fund are typically £250 to £2,000, occasionally up to £5,000. Large grants range from £5,000 to £50,000.
SAMPLE GRANTS Ditchley Foundation (£573,000); Sandford St Martin (Church of England) Trust (£150,000); The Sunshine Centre (£50,000); Flexicare (£20,000); The Community Foundation for Staffordshire (£10,000); Farms for City Children and The National Horse Racing Museum (£5,000 each); Katharine House Hospice (£2,000); Gamekeepers Welfare Trust (£1,000).
FINANCES *Financial year end* 31/03/2020 *Income* £2,990,000 *Total grants* £1,250,000 *Grants to organisations* £1,250,000 *Assets* £89,070,000
TRUSTEES John Carson; Dr Catherine Wills; Charles Francklin; Martin Fiennes; Tom Nelson; Richard Tulloch.
OTHER INFORMATION A total of 140 grants were made from the monthly grants fund for general charitable purposes, wildlife conservation and the environment in 2019/20, of which 121 were for less than £1,000. A further £1.12 million was expended on large grants at the discretion of the trustees.
HOW TO APPLY Monthly grants can be applied for using the online form on the trust's website, or by downloading a form to send by post or email. Applications should be accompanied by supporting documents. Details on what should be included are given on the website. The large grants scheme was closed at the time of writing (April 2021). The website states: 'The next time applications for Large Grants for wildlife and the environment will be accepted are from January 2023 through to December 2024.'
CONTACT DETAILS Sue Trafford, Trust Administrator, Henley Knapp Barn, Fulwell, Chipping Norton, Oxfordshire OX7 4EN *Tel.* 01608 678051 *Email* trust@hdhwills.org *Website* www.hdhwills.org

■ Dame Violet Wills Charitable Trust

CC NO 219485 **ESTABLISHED** 1955
WHERE FUNDING CAN BE GIVEN UK and overseas.
WHO CAN BENEFIT Registered charities.
WHAT IS FUNDED Evangelical Christian activities.
RANGE OF GRANTS Mainly £500 to £1,000.
SAMPLE GRANTS Previous beneficiaries have included: AWMedia, Bristol International Student Centre, Evangelists Fund, Lee Abbey Small Missional Communities, Missionary Aviation Fellowship, True Freedom Trust.
FINANCES *Financial year end* 31/12/2019 *Income* £76,300 *Total grants* £74,500 *Grants to organisations* £74,500 *Assets* £2,170,000
TRUSTEES Julian Marsh; Revd Dr Ernest Lucas; Revd Ray Lockhart; Derek Cleave; Rosalind Peskett; Rachel Daws; Revd David Caporn; Mrs E. Street; Yme Potjewijd; John Norris; John Hollman.
OTHER INFORMATION Grants were made to 70 organisations.
HOW TO APPLY Contact the correspondent for further information.
CONTACT DETAILS Julian Marsh, Trustee, 3 Cedar Way, Portishead, Bristol BS20 6TT *Tel.* 01275 848770

■ The Dame Violet Wills Will Trust

CC NO 262251 **ESTABLISHED** 1965
WHERE FUNDING CAN BE GIVEN Bristol; Somerset; Gloucestershire.
WHO CAN BENEFIT Registered charities.
WHAT IS FUNDED General charitable purposes, with a strong preference for projects for children and medical causes.
SAMPLE GRANTS A list of beneficiaries was not included in the annual report and accounts.
FINANCES *Financial year end* 31/03/2020 *Income* £146,700 *Total grants* £103,200 *Grants to organisations* £103,200
TRUSTEES Guy Biggin; Tim Baines; Mark Naughton.
OTHER INFORMATION The trust made 62 grants during the year. We were unable to ascertain the trust's assets.
HOW TO APPLY Contact the correspondent for further information.
CONTACT DETAILS The Trustees, Red Roofs, Station Road, Flax Bourton, Bristol BS48 1UA *Tel.* 07367 095245

■ The Wilmcote Charitrust

CC NO 503837 **ESTABLISHED** 1974
WHERE FUNDING CAN BE GIVEN Midlands.
WHO CAN BENEFIT Registered charities and voluntary organisations.
WHAT IS FUNDED General charitable purposes including: ex-service personnel; medical causes; children and young people; religion; older people.
RANGE OF GRANTS Mostly £250, £500 or £1,000.
SAMPLE GRANTS Previous beneficiaries have included: England and Wales Blind Golf and

Sunny Days Children's Fund (£1,000 each); Troop Aid, Wide Horizons and Willow Foundation (£500 each); Dudley Hospital Radio and Marine Conservation Society (£250 each).

FINANCES *Financial year end* 05/04/2020 *Income* £22,500 *Total grants* £57,000 *Grants to organisations* £57,000

TRUSTEES Jean King; Anabel Murphy; Rosamond Whiteside; Graham Beach.

OTHER INFORMATION Full accounts were not available to view on the Charity Commission's website. We have therefore estimated the charity's grant total based on its total expenditure.

HOW TO APPLY Contact the correspondent for further information.

CONTACT DETAILS Graham Beach, Trustee, Warren Chase, Billesley Road, Wilmcote, Stratford-upon-Avon, Warwickshire CV37 9XG *Tel.* 01789 298472 *Email* graham@leighgraham.co.uk

■ Brian Wilson Charitable Trust

CC NO 1059736 **ESTABLISHED** 1996

WHERE FUNDING CAN BE GIVEN Cheshire.

WHO CAN BENEFIT Charitable organisations.

WHAT IS FUNDED General charitable purposes.

SAMPLE GRANTS Previous beneficiaries have included: Cross Roads Care – North Wales, Help for Heroes, Leonard Cheshire Disability Support, St Luke's Cheshire Hospice and The Friends of Russett School.

FINANCES *Financial year end* 31/12/2019 *Income* £134,600 *Total grants* £159,500 *Grants to organisations* £159,500 *Assets* £4,250,000

TRUSTEES John Pickup; Vivien Roberts; Ruth Downes.

OTHER INFORMATION The trust made 33 grants totalling £159,500 during 2019.

HOW TO APPLY Apply in writing to the correspondent. The trustees meet on a quarterly basis to consider requests and approve grants.

CONTACT DETAILS John Pickup, Trustee, 36 Landswood Park, Hartford, Northwich, Cheshire CW8 1NF *Tel.* 01606 74970

■ The Wilson Foundation

CC NO 1074414 **ESTABLISHED** 1999

WHERE FUNDING CAN BE GIVEN Northamptonshire.

WHO CAN BENEFIT Charities; community organisations; CICs; schools; individuals.

WHAT IS FUNDED Young people (under 21 years old) in Northamptonshire, particularly those facing disadvantage. Grants are given to both organisations and individuals, for a range of projects and purposes, including youth projects and trips that provide opportunities for character building.

TYPE OF GRANT Capital projects and grants to individuals.

RANGE OF GRANTS Mostly up to £10,000.

SAMPLE GRANTS Pacesetter Sports (three grants totalling £27,800); Crusader Community Boating (£10,000); Starlight Children's Foundation (£5,000); Thorplands Primary School (£3,000); Growing Together Northampton (£2,000); 13th Northampton Scouts (£1,000); Teenage Cancer Trust (£500); Brixworth Music Festival (£250).

FINANCES *Financial year end* 05/04/2019 *Income* £103,300 *Total grants* £159,600 *Grants to organisations* £141,900 *Assets* £7,840,000

TRUSTEES Giles Wilson; Nicholas Wilson; Fiona Wilson; Adam Welch; Pollyanna Wilson; Anthony Hewitt.

OTHER INFORMATION The 2018/19 accounts were the latest available at the time of writing (June 2021). During the year, the foundation made 36 grants to 34 organisations. There were also 45 grants made to individuals totalling £17,700.

HOW TO APPLY Applications can be made via the foundation's website.

CONTACT DETAILS Pollyanna Wilson, Trustee, The Maltings, Tithe Farm, Moulton Road, Holcot, Northamptonshire NN6 9SH *Tel.* 01604 782240 *Email* polly@tithefarm.com *Website* https://www.thewilsonfoundation.org.uk

■ J. and J. R. Wilson Trust

OSCR NO SC007411 **ESTABLISHED** 1989

WHERE FUNDING CAN BE GIVEN Scotland, particularly Glasgow and the west coast of Scotland.

WHO CAN BENEFIT Registered charities; hospices.

WHAT IS FUNDED Care for older people; care for animals and birds (either domestic or wild).

TYPE OF GRANT Capital costs; core/revenue costs; general funding; project funding; seed funding/start-up funding; unrestricted funding.

RANGE OF GRANTS £1,000 to £10,000.

SAMPLE GRANTS Glasgow's Golden Generation (£10,000); The Salvation Army (£5,000); Whale and Dolphin Conservation Trust (£3,000); Cowal Elderly Befrienders (£1,500); Bumblebee Conservation Trust, Crossroads Caring Scotland and St Andrew's Hospice – Airdrie (£1,000 each).

FINANCES *Financial year end* 09/02/2020 *Income* £159,800 *Total grants* £145,000 *Grants to organisations* £145,000 *Assets* £4,510,000

OTHER INFORMATION During 2019/20, grants were distributed as follows: care of older people (£98,000); charities in support of animals and birds (£43,000). A further £4,000 was paid in accordance with commitments made in previous years.

HOW TO APPLY Apply in writing to the correspondent. The 2019/20 annual report states: 'Requests for donations are investigated carefully and, where appropriate, the Trustees visit the charities concerned to check the carrying out of the purposes of the donation.'

CONTACT DETAILS The Trustees, c/o Tho and JW Barty Solicitors, 61 High Street, Dunblane, Perthshire FK15 0EH

■ Wiltshire Community Foundation

CC NO 1123126 **ESTABLISHED** 1991

WHERE FUNDING CAN BE GIVEN Wiltshire and Swindon only.

WHO CAN BENEFIT Registered charities; unregistered charities; individuals.

WHAT IS FUNDED General charitable purposes.

WHAT IS NOT FUNDED Each programme may have specific exclusions. However, our previous research suggests that, in general, the foundation will not support: groups with more than 12 months' running costs in unrestricted reserves; projects outside the County of Wiltshire or Borough of Swindon; organisations which deliver services in Wiltshire or Swindon but do not have a local governance structure (e.g. management committee or board of trustees) for the project; projects which will not start within six months of a grant award; projects where only a minority of beneficiaries would be considered disadvantaged; one-off events or sponsored events; general large appeals; advancement of religion; medical research and equipment; animal welfare; party political activities; substitution of funding that should be provided by the statutory sector or local authority institutions, including schools or academies (though PTAs can apply if the project concerned does not overlap with statutory responsibilities and benefits the wider community); promotion of religion or exclusion of beneficiaries based on religion; running costs for Community Area Partnerships.

TYPE OF GRANT Capital costs; core/revenue costs; unrestricted funding; project funding.

RANGE OF GRANTS See individual grant programmes.

SAMPLE GRANTS Swindon Borough Council – RESPECT (£71,000); Wiltshire Wildlife Trust (£29,800); Tick Tock Playgroup (£20,000); Arts Together and Back on Track – Stroke Rehab Service (£15,000 each); Wroughton Infant School (£12,500); Swindon Women's Aid (£11,100); Youth Adventure Trust (£10,000).

FINANCES *Financial year end* 31/03/2020
Income £1,790,000 *Total grants* £1,278,500
Grants to organisations £893,800
Assets £23,000,000

TRUSTEES Jason Dalley; Ashley Truluck; Angus Macpherson; Andy Tait; Susan Webber; Ian Thomas; Steve Wall; Junab Ali; David Wray; Oliver Jones-Davies; Samantha O'Sullivan; Lisa Lewis.

OTHER INFORMATION This is one of the 46 UK community foundations, which distribute funding for a wide range of purposes. As with all community foundations, there are a number of donor-advised funds managed on behalf of individuals, families and charitable trusts. Grant schemes tend to change frequently; consult the foundation's website for details of current programmes and up-to-date deadlines. In 2019/20, the foundation awarded 155 grants to organisations and 391 grants to individuals. Grants of under £10,000 totalled £349,500.

HOW TO APPLY Potential applicants are advised to visit the community foundation's website or contact its grants team to find the most suitable funding stream.

CONTACT DETAILS Grants Team, Sandcliff House, 21 Northgate Street, Devizes, Wiltshire SN10 1JT *Tel.* 01380 738985 *Email* info@wiltshirecf.org.uk *Website* https://wiltshirecf.org.uk

■ The Wimbledon Foundation

CC NO 1156996 **ESTABLISHED** 2014

WHERE FUNDING CAN BE GIVEN The London boroughs of Merton and Wandsworth and overseas.

WHO CAN BENEFIT Registered charities; community groups; amateur sports clubs.

WHAT IS FUNDED The three main focus areas of the foundation are: the London boroughs of Merton and Wandsworth; charities associated with or promoted by key groups involved in The Championships; projects and charities that use the power of sport (and particularly tennis) to provide opportunities to assist people, especially young individuals, with education and personal development.

SAMPLE GRANTS ABF The Soldiers' Charity; Battersea Arts Centre; Carers Support Merton; Filmanthropy; Junction Community Trust; Leonard Cheshire Disability; Mayor of Merton's Fund; Tennis First; Uptown Youth Services; Wimbledon Foodbank; Youth Sport Trust.

FINANCES *Financial year end* 31/07/2020
Income £2,090,000 *Total grants* £1,820,000
Grants to organisations £1,820,000
Assets £1,770,000

TRUSTEES Sir Nicholas Young; Nicholas Bitel; I. L. Hewitt; Sir Keith Ajegbo; Kevin Havelock; Anne Bretherton; Henry Weatherill.

OTHER INFORMATION During the year, grants were distributed through the following funds: COVID-19 Fund (£495,000); other (£432,000); The Championships and Club-related grants (£255,000); The Roof for All homelessness fund (£77,000); Strengthening Our Local Community (£122,000); Emergency Relief Fund (£100,000); Get Set, Get Active Fund (£63,000); The Health and Wellbeing Fund (£62,000); Arts and Community Engagement Fund (£15,000). Check the website for open funding programmes.

HOW TO APPLY Details of open funding rounds and application procedures are published on the foundation's website as they arise.

CONTACT DETAILS The Trustees, Church Road, Wimbledon, London SW19 5AE *Tel.* 020 8971 2702 *Email* foundation@aeltc.com *Website* www.wimbledon.com/en_GB/foundation/index.html

■ The Benjamin Winegarten Charitable Trust

CC NO 271442 **ESTABLISHED** 1976

WHERE FUNDING CAN BE GIVEN UK.

WHO CAN BENEFIT Charitable organisations; individuals; Jewish organisations.

WHAT IS FUNDED Jewish religious education; social welfare.

SAMPLE GRANTS Previous beneficiaries have included: Hechal Hatovah Institute, the Jewish Educational Trust, the Mechinah School, Merkaz Lechinuch Torani Zichron Ya'akov, Ohr Someach Friends, Or Akiva Community Centre, Yeshivo Hovomo Talmudical College and ZSVT.

FINANCES *Financial year end* 05/04/2020
Income £280,100 *Total grants* £151,600
Grants to organisations £147,600
Assets £2,080,000

TRUSTEES Esther Winegarten; Simon Winegarten; Miriam Schwab; Leah Chontow.

HOW TO APPLY Contact the correspondent for further information.

CONTACT DETAILS The Trustees, 25 St Andrews Grove, Stoke Newington, London N16 5NF *Tel.* 07817 212952

■ W. Wing Yip and Brothers Foundation

CC NO 326999 **ESTABLISHED** 1985

WHERE FUNDING CAN BE GIVEN Within 25 miles of Wing Yip stores in Birmingham, Manchester, Croydon and Cricklewood.

WHO CAN BENEFIT Registered charities (preference for small charities); educational organisations; community bodies. Our research suggests there is a preference for those organisations with a Chinese connection.

WHAT IS FUNDED General charitable purposes, including: education; community welfare; medical research; care for people with illnesses.

WHAT IS NOT FUNDED Very large charitable organisations; projects and travel undertaken by individuals or religious organisations; individuals; applications that fall within two calendar months of proposed events.

RANGE OF GRANTS Most under £3,000.

SAMPLE GRANTS Loughborough University (£39,000); University Hospitals Birmingham – Parkinson's Monitors (£17,500); Chinese Community Health Information Centre (£5,900); Insight Counselling (£1,000); Nechells Community Centre (£500); Sunny Days Children's Fund (£300); Chinese Education Cultural Community Centre (£200).

FINANCES *Financial year end* 31/07/2020
Income £109,500 *Total grants* £74,400
Grants to organisations £74,400
Assets £1,350,000

TRUSTEES Joseph Bates; Brian Wing Yip; Jenny Loynton; Albert Yip; Ennevor Yap; David Wing Yip; Kenny Yap.

OTHER INFORMATION During 2019/20, grants were distributed as follows: educational (£42,700); medical research and relief of suffering (£24,800); community welfare (£6,900). The foundation also funds the Wing Yip Scholarship at Loughborough University to support students from under-represented areas of the UK.

HOW TO APPLY Application forms can be downloaded from the foundation's website. Completed applications should be printed and physically signed before returning to the foundation with any relevant documents, by email or post.

CONTACT DETAILS The Trustees, W. Wing Yip plc, The Wing Yip Centre, 375 Nechells Park Road, Birmingham B7 5NT *Tel.* 0121 327 6618 *Email* foundation@wingyip.com *Website* www.wingyip.com/Supporting-our-communities/Wing-Yip-Foundation

The Wingate Foundation

CC NO 264114 **ESTABLISHED** 1960

WHERE FUNDING CAN BE GIVEN UK and overseas.

WHO CAN BENEFIT Registered charities; academic organisations specialising in Jewish subjects; museums and libraries promoting Jewish culture.

WHAT IS FUNDED Jewish life and learning; performing arts; music; education and social exclusion; overseas aid; medical research (travel grants).

WHAT IS NOT FUNDED Individuals; gap years, Duke of Edinburgh awards or similar; large charities (including local branch offices of large organisations); funding for stage productions.

TYPE OF GRANT Project and development funding.

RANGE OF GRANTS Mostly up to £10,000.

SAMPLE GRANTS World ORT Trust (£17,500); Theatre Royal Stratford East (£10,000); Beth Shalom Ltd (£6,000); Holocaust Educational Trust and Mountview Academy of Theatre Arts (£5,000 each); Young Classical Artists (£4,000); British Library (£3,500); University of Sheffield (£1,000); Hope Housing Training and Support Ltd (£900).

FINANCES *Financial year end* 05/04/2020
Income £52,000 *Total grants* £331,600
Grants to organisations £331,600
Assets £5,510,000

TRUSTEES Roger Wingate; Prof. Robert Cassen; Prof. Jonathan Drori; Daphne Hyman; Emily Kasriel; Dr Richard Wingate; Barbara Arnold; Melanie Morris.

OTHER INFORMATION In 2019/20, grants were given to 70 organisations across the following categories: performing arts (32%); Jewish life and learning (28%); music (26%); education and social exclusion (6%); literary prizes (6%); development projects (1%); medical research (1%). Further detail on the areas the foundation supports is given on its website.

HOW TO APPLY Application forms are available to download on the foundation's website. Once completed, forms should be returned to the administrator by email only as the foundation is moving to an online system. Applications should include supporting documentation and your most recent accounts. The trustees usually meet quarterly to consider grant applications. Details of upcoming meetings can be seen on the website.

CONTACT DETAILS Administrator, Somerset House, South Wing, Strand, London WC2R 1LA *Tel.* 020 3701 7479 *Email* admin@wingate.org.uk *Website* www.wingatefoundation.org.uk

The Francis Winham Foundation

CC NO 278092 **ESTABLISHED** 1979

WHERE FUNDING CAN BE GIVEN England.

WHO CAN BENEFIT Registered charities; exempt charitable organisations.

WHAT IS FUNDED Grants to organisations working to improve the quality of life of older people.

RANGE OF GRANTS Typically up to £20,000.

SAMPLE GRANTS Age UK (16 grants totalling £102,500); Care and Repair (23 grants totalling £24,900); Wiltshire Community Foundation (£15,000); Stroke Association (£10,000); London Hearts (£7,500); FareShare, Katharine House Hospice and The Seeing Dogs Alliance (£5,000 each).

FINANCES *Financial year end* 05/04/2020
Income £994,300 *Total grants* £991,000
Grants to organisations £991,000
Assets £76,700,000

TRUSTEES Josephine Winham; Elsa Peters; Desmond Corcoran; Fuschia Peters.

OTHER INFORMATION The foundation made 259 grants to organisations during 2019/20. Only organisations receiving grants of more than £5,000 were listed as beneficiaries in the foundation's accounts. Grants of under £5,000 were made to 90 organisations and totalled £168,400.

HOW TO APPLY Contact the correspondent for information regarding the application process.

CONTACT DETAILS The Trustees, 18 Gilston Road, London SW10 9SR *Tel.* 020 7795 1261 *Email* francinetrust@outlook.com

The Michael and Anna Wix Charitable Trust

CC NO 207863 **ESTABLISHED** 1955

WHERE FUNDING CAN BE GIVEN UK.

WHO CAN BENEFIT UK-registered charities.

WHAT IS FUNDED General charitable purposes, particularly medical causes and social welfare.

WHAT IS NOT FUNDED Individuals. Grants are generally awarded to national bodies rather than local branches or local groups.

TYPE OF GRANT Unrestricted.

RANGE OF GRANTS Between £100 and £5,000.

SAMPLE GRANTS British Friends of the Hebrew University (£5,000); Leukaemia UK (£2,000); Breast Cancer Care and Breast Cancer Now (£1,000); Brain Research UK, Leonard Cheshire and Marie Curie (£500 each); Carers UK and Inter Care (£200 each); Bag Books (£100).

FINANCES *Financial year end* 05/04/2020
Income £131,100 *Total grants* £104,900
Grants to organisations £104,900
Assets £1,770,000

TRUSTEES Janet Bloch; Dominic Flynn; Judith Portrait.

OTHER INFORMATION Grants were awarded to 320 organisations in 2019/20.

HOW TO APPLY Apply in writing to the trustees. Applications are considered half-yearly. Only applications from registered charities are acknowledged.

CONTACT DETAILS The Trustees, c/o Portrait Solicitors, 21 Whitefriars Street, London EC4Y 8JJ *Tel.* 020 7092 6985

■ The Wixamtree Trust

CC NO 210089 **ESTABLISHED** 1949

WHERE FUNDING CAN BE GIVEN Bedfordshire.

WHO CAN BENEFIT Registered or exempt charities; mainly local charities, with a small number of national charities supported.

WHAT IS FUNDED General charitable purposes, including: social welfare; the environment and conservation; medicine and health; the arts; education; training and employment; sports and leisure; and overseas work.

RANGE OF GRANTS Usually between £1,000 and £10,000, with a small number of donations outside this range. The trust's Small Grants Programme awards grants of up to £3,000.

SAMPLE GRANTS A list of beneficiaries was not included in the annual report and accounts.

FINANCES *Financial year end* 05/04/2020
Income £1,200,000 *Total grants* £1,050,000
Grants to organisations £1,050,000
Assets £27,240,000

TRUSTEES Harry Whitbread; Charles Whitbread; Paul Patten; Arthur Polhill; Marion Stern.

OTHER INFORMATION Grants were paid to over 180 organisations during the year. 'Grants payable' were broken down as follows: social welfare (£454,200); medicine and health (£114,800); the environment and conservation (£114,300); education (£107,100); the arts (£87,000); sports and leisure (£55,600); training and employment (£6,000); international (£3,500).

HOW TO APPLY Applications can be made via the trust's website where deadlines and guidance can also be found.

CONTACT DETAILS Mia Duddridge, Clerk to the Trustees, 6 Trull Farm Buildings, Tetbury, Gloucestershire GL8 8SQ *Tel.* 020 8777 4140 *Email* wixamtree@thetrustpartnership.com *Website* www.wixamtree.org

■ Friends of Wiznitz Ltd

CC NO 255685 **ESTABLISHED** 1948

WHERE FUNDING CAN BE GIVEN Hackney; Haringey; Israel; USA.

WHO CAN BENEFIT Jewish organisations; individuals.

WHAT IS FUNDED Orthodox Jewish religious education; the advancement of the Orthodox Jewish religion; the relief of poverty.

SAMPLE GRANTS Mosdos Viznitz (£2.4 million); Igud Mosdot Wiznitz (£1.43 million); Lehachzikom (£570,000); Kollel Viznitz London (£70,000); Vishnitz Girls School Ltd (£62,000); Ahavat Israel Synagogue (£54,000).

FINANCES *Financial year end* 31/03/2020
Income £4,700,000 *Total grants* £5,445,000
Grants to organisations £5,400,000
Assets £7,000,000

TRUSTEES Heinrich Feldman; Shulom Feldman; Ephraim Gottesfeld.

OTHER INFORMATION Grants were broken down as follows: religious education (£4.23 million); relief of poverty (£870,000); advancement of religion (£250,500); social welfare (£16,500). Grants of under £50,000 totalled £370,100.

HOW TO APPLY The 2019/20 annual report advises: 'In general the trustees select the institutions to be supported according to their personal knowledge of work of the institution. While not actively inviting applications, they are always prepared to accept any application which will be carefully considered and help given according to circumstances and funds then available. Applications by individuals must be accompanied by a letter of recommendation by the applicant's minister or other known religious leader.'

CONTACT DETAILS The Trustees, 8 Jessam Avenue, London E5 9DU *Tel.* 020 8806 0017

■ The Maurice Wohl Charitable Foundation

CC NO 244519 **ESTABLISHED** 1965

WHERE FUNDING CAN BE GIVEN UK and Israel.

WHO CAN BENEFIT Jewish organisations; registered charities.

WHAT IS FUNDED Health and medical sciences; welfare within the Jewish community; Jewish education.

WHAT IS NOT FUNDED Ongoing maintenance projects; individuals; scholarships.

RANGE OF GRANTS £14,000 to £1 million.

SAMPLE GRANTS Maggie's Cancer Caring Centres (£1 million); The National Gallery (£425,000); The Warburg Institute (£300,000); Norwood (£277,000); Bikur Cholim (£150,000); Reshet, Jewish Leadership Council and Youth Aliyah (£50,000 each); discretionary grant (£14,000).

FINANCES *Financial year end* 31/12/2019
Income £1,640,000 *Total grants* £3,770,000
Grants to organisations £3,770,000
Assets £83,470,000

TRUSTEES Ella Latchman; Martin Paisner; Prof. David Latchman; Sir Ian Gainsford; Daniel Dover.

OTHER INFORMATION The foundation is part of the Wohl Legacy, a group of three charitable foundations established by Maurice and Vivienne Wohl.

HOW TO APPLY The foundation does not accept unsolicited applications, as the trustees work with full-time staff to identify suitable projects.

CONTACT DETAILS Joseph Houri, Secretary, Fitzrovia House, 2nd Floor, 153–157 Cleveland Street, London W1T 6QW *Tel.* 020 7383 5111 *Email* jh@wohl.org.uk *Website* www.wohl.org.uk

■ The Charles Wolfson Charitable Trust

CC NO 238043 **ESTABLISHED** 1960

WHERE FUNDING CAN BE GIVEN Worldwide, mainly UK.

WHO CAN BENEFIT Registered charities, hospitals, schools and similar charitable organisations.

WHAT IS FUNDED Medicine; education; social welfare. The 2019/20 annual report states that 'particular, but not exclusive, regard is given to the needs of the Jewish community'

WHAT IS NOT FUNDED Individuals.

TYPE OF GRANT Mostly capital or fixed-term projects. The trust also provides rent-free premises to charities, and occasionally loans.

RANGE OF GRANTS Typically up to £250,000.

SAMPLE GRANTS Royal Marsden Cancer Charity (£875,000); Music in Secondary Schools Trust (£350,000); Imperial College London (£250,000); Central Synagogue (£168,000); Diabetes UK (£100,000); Street Action (£75,000); Meningitis Now Foundation (£60,000); Cornwall Air Ambulance Trust and Institute for Policy Research (£50,000 each).

FINANCES *Financial year end* 05/04/2020
Income £10,290,000 *Total grants* £6,350,000
Grants to organisations £6,350,000
Assets £220,600,000

TRUSTEES Lord Simon Wolfson; Dr Sara Levene; The Hon. Andrew Wolfson; Lord David Wolfson; Deborah Edwards; Lord Jonathan Mendelsohn.

OTHER INFORMATION Grants were distributed as follows: education (£2.73 million); medicine (£2.03 million); welfare (£1.6 million). Only organisations receiving grants of £50,000 and above were listed as beneficiaries in the trust's accounts. Grants of £50,000 and above totalled £4.83 million. Grants made between £10,000 and £49,999 totalled £1.39 million. Grants made between £5,000 and £9,999 totalled £91,000. Grants of less than £5,000 totalled £37,200.

HOW TO APPLY Contact the correspondent for further information.

CONTACT DETAILS Joanne Cowan, 8/10 Hallam Street, London W1W 6NS *Tel.* 020 7079 2506 *Email* admin@cwctcharity.org.uk

■ The Wolfson Family Charitable Trust

CC NO 228382 **ESTABLISHED** 1958

WHERE FUNDING CAN BE GIVEN UK and Israel.

WHO CAN BENEFIT Universities and hospitals in Israel; UK organisations serving the Jewish community. Applicants should be registered charities or organisations with equivalent charitable status, and have an income of more than £50,000.

WHAT IS FUNDED In the UK – culture and heritage (especially historic synagogues), education and Jewish community projects with a focus on older people and people with disabilities; in Israel – science, medicine, health, cultural organisations and people with disabilities.

WHAT IS NOT FUNDED According to the trust's website, ineligible projects and costs include: 'the purchase of land or existing buildings (including a building's freehold); grants direct to individuals; grants through conduit organisations; overheads, maintenance costs, VAT; non-specific appeals (including circulars) and endowment funds; costs of meetings, exhibitions, concerts, expeditions, conferences, etc.; film or promotional materials; repayment of loans; projects that have already been completed or will be by the time of award'.

TYPE OF GRANT Capital projects (new buildings, refurbishment or specialist equipment).

RANGE OF GRANTS £10,000 to £50,000. Applicants are expected to provide matched funding.

SAMPLE GRANTS Rambam Health Care Campus – Israel (£160,000); Rabin Medical Centre – Israel (£120,000); Bevis Marks Synagogue – London (£54,000); The Fed – Manchester (£50,000); SOAS University of London (£25,000); Sandys Row Synagogue – London (£15,000); Prism – London (£9,600).

FINANCES *Financial year end* 31/03/2020
Income £990,000 *Total grants* £1,680,000
Grants to organisations £1,680,000
Assets £32,850,000

TRUSTEES Martin Paisner; Sir Ian Gainsford; Sir Bernard Rix; The Hon. Laura Wolfson Townsley; Dame Jane Wolfson de Botton; Lord Turnberg; The Hon. Elizabeth Wolfson Peltz; Alexandra Wolfson Halamish; Sir Michael Pepper.

OTHER INFORMATION Grants were committed to 22 organisations during the year. Grants paid during the year were broken down as follows: science and medicine (£1.12 million); health and disability (£415,000); arts and humanities (£110,000); education (£35,000).

HOW TO APPLY There is a two-stage application process for grants in the UK. A stage 1 application can be submitted on the trust's website, where guidance is also provided. All requests are responded to and eligible organisations will be invited to submit a stage 2 application. Unsolicited applications are not accepted for grants in Israel.

CONTACT DETAILS The Trustees, 8 Queen Anne Street, London W1G 9LD *Tel.* 020 7323 5730 *Email* grants@wolfson.org.uk *Website* https://www.wfct.org

■ The Lord Leonard and Lady Estelle Wolfson Foundation

CC NO 1148663 **ESTABLISHED** 2012

WHERE FUNDING CAN BE GIVEN UK.

WHO CAN BENEFIT Universities; hospitals; registered charities; arts organisations; cultural organisations.

WHAT IS FUNDED Medical research and related initiatives in preventative healthcare. The foundation states that an area of focus is the role that art, music and literature can play in preventing and mitigating certain illnesses and in creating innovative healthcare delivery mechanisms.

WHAT IS NOT FUNDED The foundation outlines a list of exclusions via the grant application information document on the foundation's website.

TYPE OF GRANT Research funding; project funding.

RANGE OF GRANTS Up to £180,000.

SAMPLE GRANTS Alcohol Health Alliance (£180,000); University of Liverpool (£100,000); Victoria and Albert Museum (£60,000); Chai Cancer Care (£25,000); Great Ormond Street Hospital Children's Charity (£15,000); Noah's Ark Children's Hospice and Maggie's (£10,000 each); The Prince's Trust (£5,000).

FINANCES *Financial year end* 31/03/2020
Income £486,600 *Total grants* £848,900
Grants to organisations £848,900
Assets £24,150,000

TRUSTEES Ian Burman; Lord Ara Darzi of Denham; Lady Estelle Wolfson of Marylebone; Sir Ian Gilmore; Antoinette Jackson.

OTHER INFORMATION Grants totalling £522,500 and £326,400 were awarded to medical research and well-being, respectively. The foundation's website states that the trustees have placed a temporary halt on new applications due to the COVID-19 pandemic, although guidance for future applications can be found on the foundation's website.

HOW TO APPLY An application information document can be found on the foundation's website.

CONTACT DETAILS Mr M.S. Feldman, Administrator, 74 Portland Place, London W1B 1NR *Tel.* 020 7636 6446 *Email* admin@lordandladywolfson.org.uk *Website* https://lordandladywolfson.org.uk

■ The Wolfson Foundation

CC NO 1156077 **ESTABLISHED** 1955

WHERE FUNDING CAN BE GIVEN UK.

WHO CAN BENEFIT Charities; hospices; places of worship; libraries, museums, galleries and libraries; schools, colleges and universities.

WHAT IS FUNDED Disability; mental health; older people; historic buildings and landscapes;

hospices and palliative care; places of worship; libraries and archives; museums and galleries; performing arts; public engagement with science; the teaching of science, computer science, design and technology, art, languages and performing arts; schools and colleges for children and young people with special educational needs; universities and research institutions.

WHAT IS NOT FUNDED Exclusions differ for each grant programme. A full list of exclusions is available on the foundation's website.

TYPE OF GRANT Capital infrastructure (new buildings, refurbishment and equipment).

RANGE OF GRANTS Grant sizes vary depending on programme.

SAMPLE GRANTS Grants committed during the year include: University of Manchester (£5 million); The Francis Crick Institute (£1 million); National Galleries of Scotland (£500,000); Coventry Cathedral (£250,000); West Bridgford School (£100,000); Trinity College – Oxford (£50,000); Wigan and Leigh Hospice (£16,500); University of Exeter (£5,000).

FINANCES *Financial year end* 31/03/2020
Income £21,170,000
Total grants £29,860,000
Grants to organisations £29,860,000
Assets £688,950,000

TRUSTEES Lord McColl; The Hon. Laura Wolfson Townsley; Prof. Sir David Cannadine; Dame Janet Wolfson de Botton; Rebecca Marks; Lord Turnberg; Prof. Dame Jean Olwen Thomas; Dame Hermione Lee; Sir Michael Pepper; Sir Peter Ratcliffe; Charles Wolfson Townsley.

OTHER INFORMATION The grant total includes bursaries, scholarships, fellowships and prizes paid to organisations on behalf of individuals. Applicants with a total project cost of more than £50,000 are expected to provide matched funding.

HOW TO APPLY There is a two-stage application process. A stage 1 application can be submitted on the foundation's website, where guidance is also provided. Eligible organisations will be invited to submit a stage 2 application. Applications can usually be submitted at two points during the year. Check the foundation's website for the latest application deadlines.

CONTACT DETAILS Paul Ramsbottom, Chief Executive, 8 Queen Anne Street, London W1G 9LD *Tel.* 020 7323 5730 *Email* grants@wolfson.org.uk *Website* www.wolfson.org.uk

■ Women's Fund for Scotland

OSCR NO SC049217 **ESTABLISHED** 2013

WHERE FUNDING CAN BE GIVEN Scotland.

WHO CAN BENEFIT Charities and community groups.

WHAT IS FUNDED Projects that encourage women's growth, self-sufficiency and social economic equality.

TYPE OF GRANT Project funding.

RANGE OF GRANTS Up to £10,000.

SAMPLE GRANTS Women's Business Station and Edinburgh Women's Aid (£10,000 each); Access to Industry (£4,900); Young Mums Group (£4,800); Broomhouse Centre (£3,500).

FINANCES *Financial year end* 31/03/2020
Income £702,000 *Total grants* £288,200
Grants to organisations £288,200
Assets £372,900

TRUSTEES Sue Robertson; Judy Russell; Adrian Bell; Anne Meikle; Jan Torrance; Sally Wainwright.

OTHER INFORMATION Grants are available for organisations with an annual income of less than £1 million (priority is given to those with an income of less than £500,000).

HOW TO APPLY Apply via the fund's website.

CONTACT DETAILS Shona Blakeley, Executive Director, 17–21 East Mayfield, Edinburgh EH9 1SE *Email* shona@womensfundscotland.org *Website* https://www.womensfundscotland.org

■ The James Wood Bequest Fund

OSCR NO SC000459 **ESTABLISHED** 1932

WHERE FUNDING CAN BE GIVEN Scotland.

WHO CAN BENEFIT Charitable organisations.

WHAT IS FUNDED General charitable purposes.

WHAT IS NOT FUNDED Individuals.

TYPE OF GRANT Capital costs; project funding.

RANGE OF GRANTS £500 to £4,000.

SAMPLE GRANTS Church of Scotland Fabric Fund (£4,000); Macular Society (£2,500); The National Autistic Society (£2,000); Combat Stress and Scottish Opera Young Company (£1,000 each); Teapot Trust and Visibility (£500 each).

FINANCES *Financial year end* 30/06/2019
Income £88,000 *Total grants* £85,000
Grants to organisations £85,000
Assets £2,140,000

OTHER INFORMATION The 2018/19 accounts were the latest available at the time of writing (May 2021). The fund awarded 61 grants during the financial year.

HOW TO APPLY Apply in writing to the correspondent. According to our previous research, applications should include, if possible, a copy of your latest accounts, a budget for the project, sources of funding received and other relevant financial information. The trustees meet four times a year, usually in January, April, July and October to consider applications. Applications should be received by the preceding month.

CONTACT DETAILS The Trustees, c/o Mitchells Roberton Solicitors, George House, 36 North Hanover Street, Glasgow G1 2AD

■ The Wood Foundation

OSCR NO SC037957 **ESTABLISHED** 2007

WHERE FUNDING CAN BE GIVEN Scotland; sub-Saharan Africa.

WHO CAN BENEFIT Charitable organisations; individuals.

WHAT IS FUNDED Economic and community development; education; young people.

TYPE OF GRANT Project funding.

SAMPLE GRANTS A list of beneficiaries was not included in the annual report and accounts.

FINANCES *Financial year end* 31/03/2020
Income £3,450,000 *Total grants* £3,345,000
Grants to organisations £3,340,000
Assets £107,920,000

TRUSTEES Sir Ian Wood; Lady Helen Wood; Garreth Wood; Graham Good.

OTHER INFORMATION Grants were awarded to 204 organisations and six individuals in 2019/20 and were distributed as follows: miscellaneous grants (£4.58 million); developing young people in Scotland (£2.59 million); venture philanthropy transforming livelihoods in Africa (£737,000); volunteering overseas (£15,000).

HOW TO APPLY The foundation independently seeks beneficiaries rather than inviting open applications. However, there is an open application process for organisations and individuals looking for sources of funding for young people to volunteer overseas. Application forms can be downloaded from the website.

CONTACT DETAILS The Trustees, Blenheim House, Fountainhall Road, Aberdeen, Aberdeenshire AB15 4DT *Tel.* 01224 619862 *Email* info@thewoodfoundation.org.uk *Website* www.thewoodfoundation.org.uk

■ The Victoria Wood Foundation

CC NO 1170494 **ESTABLISHED** 2016

WHERE FUNDING CAN BE GIVEN UK, with a preference for the North West and London.

WHO CAN BENEFIT Charitable organisations.

WHAT IS FUNDED The arts.

WHAT IS NOT FUNDED Individuals; courses of study; expeditions and foreign travel; general appeals; youth and community associations; retrospective expenditure; statutory bodies; places of worship or which promote religion; animal, wildlife, heritage and environmental causes.

SAMPLE GRANTS A list of beneficiaries was not included in the annual report and accounts.

FINANCES *Financial year end* 05/04/2020 *Income* £151,700 *Total grants* £275,000 *Grants to organisations* £275,000 *Assets* £3,440,000

TRUSTEES Davina Walter; Nigel Lilley; Jane Wymark; Piers Wenger; Charlotte Scott; Lucy Ansbro; Roger Glossop.

OTHER INFORMATION The foundation was established in memory of the late comedian Victoria Wood, who died from cancer in April 2016.

HOW TO APPLY Contact the administrator who will take you through the application process.

CONTACT DETAILS Catherine Edis, Administrator, Plumpton House, Bents Drive, Sheffield, South Yorkshire S11 9RN *Email* info@victoriawoodfoundation.org.uk *Website* https://victoriawoodfoundation.org.uk

■ Wooden Spoon Society

CC NO 326691 **ESTABLISHED** 1983

WHERE FUNDING CAN BE GIVEN UK and Ireland.

WHO CAN BENEFIT Organisations with a legal status such as charities, schools or clubs.

WHAT IS FUNDED Transforming young people's lives through rugby. Projects must enhance and support the lives of children and young people under the age of 25 who are disadvantaged physically, mentally or socially. Grants are given in the following categories: special equipment and facilities; playground; education, skills and training; sensory rooms and gardens; health and well-being; transport.

WHAT IS NOT FUNDED See the grant-maker's website for exclusions relating to different types of project.

TYPE OF GRANT Mostly capital costs and equipment; project costs; some salaries and core costs.

RANGE OF GRANTS Grants are unlikely to be of less than £5,000.

SAMPLE GRANTS Previous beneficiaries have included: RFL (£80,000); 999 Club (£58,500); Quarriers Epilepsy Centre (£50,000); Camphill School (£29,000); Claytons Primary School (£23,000); Greenbank Sports Academy (£15,000); Horseworld (£11,000); PACT (£10,000); Printfield Community Project (£6,500); Scottish Spina Bifida Association (£5,000); Our Lady of Walsingham School (£1,000).

FINANCES *Financial year end* 31/03/2020 *Income* £3,360,000 *Total grants* £1,350,000 *Grants to organisations* £1,350,000 *Assets* £1,270,000

TRUSTEES Christine Braithwaite; Callum Whitton; Brett Bader; Graham Allen; Jane Harwood; Joanna Coombs; John Gibson; Mark McCafferty; Quentin Smith; George Whitefoot.

OTHER INFORMATION During 2019/20, grants were made to 82 organisations. A significant grant of £100,000 was awarded to HITZ, a programme delivered by the Premiership Rugby.

HOW TO APPLY The charity recommends first submitting an Expression of Wish form, which can be completed on its website. Eligible applicants may then complete an application form, which can also be downloaded from the website. Applications will be sent to the regional committee for approval.

CONTACT DETAILS Projects Team, Sentinel House, Ancells Business Park, Harvest Crescent, Fleet, Hampshire GU51 2UZ *Tel.* 01252 773720 *Email* projects@woodenspoon.org.uk *Website* www.woodenspoon.org.uk

■ Woodlands Green Ltd

CC NO 277299 **ESTABLISHED** 1979

WHERE FUNDING CAN BE GIVEN Worldwide.

WHO CAN BENEFIT Charitable organisations.

WHAT IS FUNDED Orthodox Jewish faith; relief of poverty.

WHAT IS NOT FUNDED Individuals, expeditions or scholarships.

RANGE OF GRANTS Up to around £40,000.

SAMPLE GRANTS Talmud Torah D'Chasidei Gur Ltd (£37,200); Revach Vehazola Trust (£20,000); Balstraw Ltd and Kollel Viznitz London (£10,000 each); British Friends of Mosdos Tchernobel (£7,000); Society of Friends of the Torah (£5,800); Broom Foundation; The J. and R. Margulies Charitable Trust and The Gateshead Cheder Ltd (£5,000 each).

FINANCES *Financial year end* 05/04/2019 *Income* £317,400 *Total grants* £162,200 *Grants to organisations* £162,200 *Assets* £2,550,000

TRUSTEES Daniel Ost; Edith Ost; Jospeh Ost; Arie Hepner.

OTHER INFORMATION Grants of under £5,000 totalled £57,200. The 2018/19 accounts were the latest available at the time of writing (May 2021).

HOW TO APPLY Contact the correspondent for further information.

CONTACT DETAILS The Trustees, 75 Woodlands, London NW11 9QS *Tel.* 020 8209 1458

■ Woodroffe Benton Foundation

CC NO 1075272 **ESTABLISHED** 1988

WHERE FUNDING CAN BE GIVEN UK.

WHO CAN BENEFIT UK-based charitable organisations; educational organisations.

WHAT IS FUNDED Relief of hardship; care of older people; education and youth development; the environment and conservation; physical well-being.

WHAT IS NOT FUNDED See the grant-maker's website for a full list of exclusions.

TYPE OF GRANT Core costs; project costs.

RANGE OF GRANTS £500 to £2,500.

SAMPLE GRANTS A list of beneficiaries was not included in the annual report and accounts.

FINANCES *Financial year end* 02/12/2019
Income £314,200 *Total grants* £342,600
Grants to organisations £342,600
Assets £8,280,000

TRUSTEES James Hope; Richard Page; Jill Wesley; Edward White; Chiyo Rimington.

OTHER INFORMATION The 2018/19 accounts were the latest available at the time of writing (May 2021). During the financial year, the foundation awarded a total of 220 grants. Within this, 169 were small grants (from 720 applications – the only grants programme open to unsolicited applications) totalling £142,800. The foundation also awards annual grants to specific charities and a number of other grants at the discretion of the trustees.

HOW TO APPLY Applications must be made via an online form on the foundation's website. At the time of writing (May 2021), the foundation had temporarily suspended its small grants programme while it reviewed the grant-making policy. Check the website for the latest information.

CONTACT DETAILS Joanna Noles, Secretary to the Trustees, PO Box 309, Cirencester, Gloucestershire GL7 9HA *Email* secretary@woodroffebenton.org.uk *Website* www.woodroffebenton.org.uk

■ The Woodward Charitable Trust

CC NO 299963 **ESTABLISHED** 1988

WHERE FUNDING CAN BE GIVEN The UK.

WHO CAN BENEFIT UK-registered charities; CICs. The trustees favour small-scale, locally based initiatives.

WHAT IS FUNDED Children and young people; prisoners and ex-offenders; disadvantaged women and families; community cohesion particularly among minority groups including refugees and Travellers; disability; arts outreach. A budget is set aside each year for summer play-schemes that take place during the summer holidays for disadvantaged children and young people (aged 5–16).

WHAT IS NOT FUNDED Charities whose annual income exceeds £200,000; charities only registered or working overseas; construction projects such as playgrounds, village halls and disability access; hospices; individuals; medical research; exclusively education-based charities; arts organisations without a social purpose. For summer play schemes, the trustees will also not fund: trips that are only social (the trustees prefer to fund trips that are educational and motivational); organisations with an annual turnover exceeding £100,000; overseas projects; playgroups.

TYPE OF GRANT Core costs.

RANGE OF GRANTS There are three grant levels: small grants (up to £3,000); large grants (over £3,000 and only given to charities known to the trustees); children's summer play scheme grants (£250 to £1,000).

SAMPLE GRANTS Dragon School Trust Ltd (£20,000); Human Dignity Trust (£10,000); Royal Opera House Covent Garden Foundation (£5,000); Off the Streets (£4,000); Carefree Kids (£2,000); Immediate Theatre (£1,800); Women's Health Information and Support Centre (£750); WyePlay (£250).

FINANCES *Financial year end* 05/04/2020
Income £169,700 *Total grants* £306,000
Grants to organisations £306,000
Assets £10,160,000

TRUSTEES Camilla Woodward; Shaun Woodward; Eleanor Mills; Olivia Woodward; Katherine Woodward; Thomas Hunniwood.

OTHER INFORMATION The trust is one of the Sainsbury Family Charitable Trusts which share a common administration – see www.sftc.org.uk for more information. In 2019/20, grants were made for the following purposes: community and social welfare (111 grants totalling £137,100); disability and health (59 grants totalling £72,400); arts (30 grants totalling £34,800); summer schemes (65 grants totalling £34,200); education (10 grants totalling £27,500).

HOW TO APPLY Applications must be completed using the online form on the trust's website. Applications can only be made during open grant rounds, details of which can be found on the 'diary' page on the website. General grants are allocated following the trustees' meetings, which usually happen in February/March and October/November each year. Children's Summer Playscheme grants are considered in April/May. Full criteria and guidelines can also be found on the trust's website.

CONTACT DETAILS Karin Hooper, Administrator, The Peak, 5 Wilton Road, London SW1V 1AP *Tel.* 020 7410 0330 *Email* contact@woodwardcharitabletrust.org.uk *Website* www.woodwardcharitabletrust.org.uk

■ The Woosnam Foundation

CC NO 1171136 **ESTABLISHED** 2016

WHERE FUNDING CAN BE GIVEN UK.

WHO CAN BENEFIT Charitable organisations.

WHAT IS FUNDED Education; research, with some preference for medical research; animal welfare.

TYPE OF GRANT Research.

RANGE OF GRANTS £20,000 to £80,000.

SAMPLE GRANTS Macmillan Cancer Care (£60,000); Rays of Sunshine (£20,000).

FINANCES *Financial year end* 31/12/2020
Income £77,200 *Total grants* £80,000
Grants to organisations £80,000
Assets £3,512,600

TRUSTEES Ian Burman; Michael Feldman.

OTHER INFORMATION The trust made only two grants during 2020; in 2019 it made seven grants. However, the accounts state that 'the trustees intend to launch a number of new grant-making initiatives during the year. The charity's activities will be subject to all applicable COVID19 related restrictions.'

HOW TO APPLY Contact the correspondent for more information.

CONTACT DETAILS Ian Burman, Trustee, c/o Laytons Solicitors, 2 More London Riverside, London SE1 2AP *Tel.* 020 7842 8000 *Email* ian.burman@laytons.com

■ Worcester Municipal Charities (CIO)

CC NO 1166931 **ESTABLISHED** 1836

WHERE FUNDING CAN BE GIVEN Worcester.

WHO CAN BENEFIT Charitable organisations; individuals.

WHAT IS FUNDED Social welfare and the relief of hardship.

WHAT IS NOT FUNDED Healthcare-related organisations.

TYPE OF GRANT Running costs; recurrent; salaries.

RANGE OF GRANTS Mainly under £35,000.

SAMPLE GRANTS Citizens Advice Worcester and WHABAC (£168,700); Tudor House Museum (£35,200); Armchair (£16,000); Dancefest (£10,800); All Sorts of Performing Arts (£10,000); Shopmobility (£7,000); John Palmer Educational Foundation (£950).

FINANCES *Financial year end* 31/12/2019 *Income* £995,600 *Total grants* £450,200 *Grants to organisations* £392,100 *Assets* £17,350,000

TRUSTEES Ruth Heywood; Ron Rust; Richard Boorn; Margaret Panter; Roger Berry; Sue Osborne; Margaret Jones; Geraint Thomas; Martyn Saunders; Brenda Sheridan; Roger Knight; Paul Griffith; Michael Johnson; Graham Hughes; Jennifer Barnes; Paul Denham; Mel Kirk.

OTHER INFORMATION During 2019, grants were made to 11 organisations. The charity also made grants totalling £58,100 to 159 individuals. The charity also owns almshouses and provides in-kind support such as free furniture, advice and legal aid.

HOW TO APPLY At the time of writing (May 2021), the charity's website stated: 'Due to financial constraints, the trustees have resolved not to consider applications from organisations that are new i.e. not currently, or very recently, in receipt of a grant. The charity currently provides major financial assistance to the organisations listed.' Grants are given to eight organisations, listed on the website, on an ongoing regular basis. However, there is an application form on the website, and the page states: 'If having read the advice above you wish to apply complete the form.'

CONTACT DETAILS Office Administration, Kateryn Heywood House, Berkeley Court, The Foregate, Worcester, Worcestershire WR1 3QG *Tel.* 01905 317117 *Email* admin@wmcharities.org.uk *Website* www.wmcharities.org.uk

■ Worcestershire Community Foundation

CC NO 1102266 **ESTABLISHED** 2003

WHERE FUNDING CAN BE GIVEN Worcestershire.

WHO CAN BENEFIT Grants are awarded to both organisations and individuals.

WHAT IS FUNDED Projects that promote the well-being of the local communities in Worcestershire.

WHAT IS NOT FUNDED Each funding programme has its own set of exclusions, refer to the foundation's website for further information.

RANGE OF GRANTS £4,000 on average.

SAMPLE GRANTS Previous beneficiaries have included: Eastham Memorial Hall, Footsteps, Jestaminute, Malvern Community Forest, Redditch Boxing Academy and St Mary's Pickersleigh.

FINANCES *Financial year end* 30/09/2019 *Income* £125,300 *Total grants* £125,200 *Grants to organisations* £125,200 *Assets* £1,490,000

TRUSTEES Prof. Tamar Thompson; Robert Sykes; Jeremy Clarke-Morris; Roger Britton; David Shaw; Nick Stanley; Mark Yates; Robert Capper.

OTHER INFORMATION This is one of the 46 UK community foundations, which distribute funding for a wide range of purposes. As with all community foundations, there are a number of donor-advised funds managed on behalf of individuals, families and charitable trusts. Grant schemes tend to change frequently – consult the foundation's website for details of current programmes and up-to-date deadlines. The 2018/19 accounts were the latest available at the time of writing (June 2021).

HOW TO APPLY Potential applicants are advised to visit the community foundation's website or contact its grants team to find the most suitable funding stream. Application forms are available on the foundation's website. Each funding programme has its own set of exclusions and deadlines, refer to the website for further information. The grant panel will usually meet within eight weeks of the grant programme's application deadline.

CONTACT DETAILS Emma Buckingham, Grants and Communications Officer, c/o Community First, First Floor, Unit 3 Harmac House, Chequers Close, Enigma Business Park, Malvern, Worcestershire WR14 1GP *Tel.* 01684 892666 *Email* emmab@comfirst.org.uk *Website* https://www.worcscf.org.uk

■ Worth Waynflete Foundation

CC NO 1068892 **ESTABLISHED** 1986

WHERE FUNDING CAN BE GIVEN UK, with a strong preference for Lincolnshire.

WHO CAN BENEFIT Lincolnshire-based charities and organisations (including schools, churches, sports clubs and community groups); national charities and organisations benefitting Lincolnshire residents; individual projects and initiatives.

WHAT IS FUNDED General charitable purposes particularly in South Lincolnshire; community projects; rural projects that enhance the landscape and ecology; heritage preservation; school initiatives (including IT equipment).

WHAT IS NOT FUNDED Individuals.

TYPE OF GRANT Training of existing staff; training of new volunteers; core costs, running costs and special requirements; start-up initiatives and additional stages.

SAMPLE GRANTS Previous beneficiaries have included: Lincolnshire Blind Society (£6,000); Canine Partners, Lincolnshire and Nottinghamshire Air Ambulance and the Order of St John (£4,000 each); Deafblind UK (£2,500); Action for Kids, Gurkha Welfare Trust and Marine Conservation Society (£1,000); Braille Chess Association, Children's Safety Education Foundation and Royal National Lifeboat Fund (£500 each); Mouth and Foot Painting Artists (£100).

FINANCES *Financial year end* 31/12/2019 *Income* £0 *Total grants* £783,800 *Grants to organisations* £783,800

TRUSTEES Michael Worth; Graham Scrimshaw; Hubert Lewczuk-Tilley.

OTHER INFORMATION Full accounts were not available to view on the Charity Commission's website. We have therefore estimated the foundation's grant total based on its total expenditure. Note that in 2019 the foundation's expenditure was considerably higher at £787,000 than in previous years, when it averaged at around £413,400.

HOW TO APPLY Applicants should contact the foundation by email or post, providing their name, address, organisation, contact details and a brief outline of their activities and proposal. Alternatively, contact one of the foundation managers, details of which can be found on the website.

CONTACT DETAILS Margaret Dawson, Foundation Manager, PO Box 9986, Grantham, Lincolnshire

NG31 0FJ *Tel.* 01400 250210 *Email* info@waynfletecharity.com or margaretdawson@waynfletecharity.com *Website* www.waynfletecharity.com

■ The Edward and Catherine Wray Charitable Trust

CC NO 1160375 **ESTABLISHED** 2015

WHERE FUNDING CAN BE GIVEN UK; South Africa.

WHO CAN BENEFIT Charitable organisations.

WHAT IS FUNDED General charitable purposes.

SAMPLE GRANTS Gold Peer and Royal Foundation (£200,000 each).

FINANCES *Financial year end* 13/01/2020 *Income* £118,100 *Total grants* £200,000 *Grants to organisations* £200,000 *Assets* £5,370,000

TRUSTEES Coutts & Co.; Catherine Wray; James Wray.

OTHER INFORMATION Grants were made to two organisations during the year.

HOW TO APPLY Apply by letter to the correspondent.

CONTACT DETAILS The Trustees, Coutts & Co. Trustee Department, 1st Floor, Trinity Quay 1, Avon Street, Bristol BS2 0PT *Tel.* 0345 304 2424

■ The Eric Wright Charitable Trust

CC NO 1002966 **ESTABLISHED** 1990

WHERE FUNDING CAN BE GIVEN UK, with a preference for the North West.

WHO CAN BENEFIT Community and voluntary service organisations.

WHAT IS FUNDED Young people; older people; education and training; health; carers' support.

TYPE OF GRANT According to the trust's website: 'The Trustees are willing to consider a range of applications, both capital and revenue, but with emphasis on applications that will either build capacity and therefore sustainability within the applicant organisation or which will broaden the range of its target beneficiaries.'

RANGE OF GRANTS Major grants from £10,000 to £25,000; community grants from £5,000 to £10,000; and minor grants from £500 to £5,000.

SAMPLE GRANTS Galloway Society for the Blind (£50,000); Age UK Lancashire, Blackburn Youth Zone, Lancashire Mind, The Children's Adventure Farm Trust and Wigan Boys and Girls Club (£25,000 each).

FINANCES *Financial year end* 31/12/2019 *Income* £236,860,000 *Total grants* £904,000 *Grants to organisations* £904,000 *Assets* £78,030,000

TRUSTEES Alan Sturrock; Michael Collier; Hugh MacDonald; Alison Wright; Martin Newsholme; Janette Collier; Catherine Wilson.

OTHER INFORMATION A high volunteer involvement in the applicant organisation is likely to be influential although not essential. Only organisations receiving grants of over £25,000 were listed as beneficiaries in the charity's accounts. Grants of under £25,000 totalled £569,000.

HOW TO APPLY Major grants are by invitation only. In regards to applications for community grants and minor grants the trust's website states: 'If you would like to apply, we would strongly advise you in the first instance to contact the Trust to discuss the nature of your application and the process involved.'

CONTACT DETAILS Michael Collier, Trustee, Sceptre House, Sceptre Way, Bamber Bridge, Preston, Lancashire PR5 6AW *Tel.* 01772 694698 *Email* rebeccam@ericwright.co.uk *Website* https://www.ericwright.co.uk/charitable-trust

■ WWDP (World Day of Prayer National Committee for England, Wales and Northern Ireland)

CC NO 233242 **ESTABLISHED** 1964

WHERE FUNDING CAN BE GIVEN UK and overseas.

WHO CAN BENEFIT Christian charities.

WHAT IS FUNDED Promotion of the Christian faith; women and children.

TYPE OF GRANT Project costs; core grants; development funding. Mostly one-off but also some recurrent awards.

RANGE OF GRANTS Mostly £5,000 and under.

SAMPLE GRANTS World Day of Prayer International Committee (£17,900); 28 Too Many (£5,000); Global Care (£4,400); Toxteth Women's Centre (£3,000); Bryngwenith Chapel (£500); Catholic Agency for Overseas Development (£2,500); St David's Church, Cardiff (£75).

FINANCES *Financial year end* 31/12/2020 *Income* £435,400 *Total grants* £163,700 *Grants to organisations* £163,700 *Assets* £428,900

TRUSTEES Dr Elizabeth Burroughs; Nicola Hoskin-Stone; Revd Carole Bourne.

OTHER INFORMATION Grants were awarded to 55 organisations during 2020.

HOW TO APPLY Further information can be obtained by contacting the trustees by post or email.

CONTACT DETAILS The Trustees, Commercial Road, Tunbridge Wells, Kent TN1 2RR *Tel.* 01892 541411 *Email* office@wwdp.org.uk *Website* https://www.wwdp.org.uk/grants

■ Wychdale Ltd

CC NO 267447 **ESTABLISHED** 1974

WHERE FUNDING CAN BE GIVEN UK and overseas.

WHO CAN BENEFIT Jewish organisations; charitable organisations.

WHAT IS FUNDED Orthodox Jewish religion; general charitable purposes.

RANGE OF GRANTS Up to £40,000.

SAMPLE GRANTS The ABC Foundation (£40,000); Mosdos Bobov (£30,000); Midal Hachesed Vehatzdokoh (£28,000); United Talmudical Associates Ltd (£25,000); Keren Hatzolos Doros Alei Siach (£23,000).

FINANCES *Financial year end* 31/03/2019 *Income* £266,000 *Total grants* £238,000 *Grants to organisations* £238,000 *Assets* £1,115,000

TRUSTEES Chaskel Schlaff; Jacob Schlaff; Ziporah Schlaff.

OTHER INFORMATION The 2018/19 accounts were the latest available at the time of writing (May 2021). The following breakdown of grants was provided in the accounts: advancement of religion (£125,000); relief of poverty (£43,000); education (£37,500); social welfare (£22,000); general purposes (£10,200).

HOW TO APPLY The 2018/19 annual report states: 'In general the trustees select the institutions to be supported according to their personal knowledge of work of the institution. While not actively inviting applications, they are always prepared to accept any application which will be carefully considered and help given according to circumstances and funds then available.' Contact the correspondent for further information.

CONTACT DETAILS The Trustees, c/o Sugarwhite Meyer Accountants Ltd, First Floor, 94 Stamford Hill, London N16 6XS *Tel.* 020 8880 8910

■ Wychville Ltd

CC NO 267584 **ESTABLISHED** 1973

WHERE FUNDING CAN BE GIVEN Throughout England and Wales.

WHO CAN BENEFIT Charitable organisations.

WHAT IS FUNDED The advancement of the Orthodox Jewish faith; education; general charitable purposes.

RANGE OF GRANTS Up to £260,000.

SAMPLE GRANTS Friends of Mercaz Hatorah Belz Machnivka (£260,100); Mifal Hachesed Vehatzdokoh (£66,500); One Heart – Lev Echod (£53,000); Friends of Beis Chinuch Lebonos (£51,300); Beis Aharon Trust Ltd (£42,300); Friends of Beis Soroh Schneirer (£23,800).

FINANCES *Financial year end* 31/03/2020 *Income* £533,000 *Total grants* £540,500 *Grants to organisations* £540,500 *Assets* £61,000

TRUSTEES E. Englander; B. R. Englander.

OTHER INFORMATION Grants were awarded to more than six organisations, with smaller grants totalling £43,500.

HOW TO APPLY Contact the correspondent for further information.

CONTACT DETAILS The Trustees, 44 Leweston Place, London N16 6RH *Tel.* 020 8802 3948

■ The Wyfold Charitable Trust

CC NO 1157483 **ESTABLISHED** 2014

WHERE FUNDING CAN BE GIVEN England and Wales.

WHO CAN BENEFIT UK-registered charities.

WHAT IS FUNDED General charitable purposes, including: social welfare; health; arts, culture, heritage or science; education; citizenship or community development; the environment; sport; animal welfare; religion.

TYPE OF GRANT One-off; recurrent.

RANGE OF GRANTS Up to £30,000.

SAMPLE GRANTS Oxford Health Charity (£30,000); Normandy Memorial Trust and Young Epilepsy (£20,000 each); The Fleming-Wyfold Art Foundation (£12,500); Arts4Dementia, Friends of the National Libraries, Racing Welfare and Villiers Park Education Trust (£10,000 each).

FINANCES *Financial year end* 31/03/2020 *Income* £382,100 *Total grants* £344,000 *Grants to organisations* £344,000 *Assets* £9,000,000

TRUSTEES Hermione Fleming; Adam Fleming; Roderick Fleming; Nicholas Powell; Angus Fleming.

OTHER INFORMATION During 2019/20, grants were made to 47 organisations. Only organisations receiving grants of over £10,000 were listed as beneficiaries in the trust's accounts. Grants of under £10,000 totalled £134,000.

HOW TO APPLY Our previous research suggests that applications should be made in writing on no more than two sides of A4 and sent to the correspondent by post along with any supporting documentation. The Wyfold Charitable Trust should be referenced in the application. The trustees meet twice during the year to consider applications.

CONTACT DETAILS The Trustees, c/o RF Trustee Co. Ltd, 15 Suffolk Street, London SW1Y 4HG *Tel.* 020 3696 6721 *Email* charities@rftrustee.com

■ Sir Graham Wylie Foundation

CC NO 1165447 **ESTABLISHED** 2016

WHERE FUNDING CAN BE GIVEN The North East.

WHO CAN BENEFIT Organisations in North East England that assist young people.

WHAT IS FUNDED Projects that allow young people to participate in healthy educational and recreational activities that they could not otherwise afford. Projects that assist in the treatment and care of young people in the North East England suffering from mental or physical illness of any description.

SAMPLE GRANTS A list of beneficiaries was not included in the annual report and accounts.

FINANCES *Financial year end* 31/12/2019 *Income* £492,600 *Total grants* £168,000 *Grants to organisations* £168,000 *Assets* £621,500

TRUSTEES Andrea Wylie; Graham Wylie; Rachael Garden.

OTHER INFORMATION All grants awarded during the year were to organisations.

HOW TO APPLY Application forms can be downloaded from the 'Who we help' page of the foundation's website and should be returned by post.

CONTACT DETAILS The Trustees, Nelson House, Burdon Terrace, Newcastle upon Tyne, Tyne and Wear NE2 3AE *Tel.* 0191 212 5140 *Email* info@grahamwyliefoundation.org.uk *Website* www.grahamwyliefoundation.org.uk

■ The Wyndham Charitable Trust

CC NO 259313 **ESTABLISHED** 1969

WHERE FUNDING CAN BE GIVEN UK and financially developing countries.

WHO CAN BENEFIT Registered charities; universities; hospitals; hospices; religious bodies/institutions.

WHAT IS FUNDED General charitable purposes, in particular: the elimination of modern-day slavery; medical research, particularly cancer; support for people in financially developing countries.

WHAT IS NOT FUNDED Individuals.

TYPE OF GRANT Unrestricted funding; capital costs; core/revenue costs.

RANGE OF GRANTS Mostly under £10,000.

SAMPLE GRANTS Anti-Slavery International (£16,000); Institute of Cancer Research (£8,000); The Royal College of Surgeons of England (£4,000); Liverpool School of Tropical Medicine (£1,200); Church Mission Society (£800); Asthma UK (£700); Boldre PCC (£45).

FINANCES *Financial year end* 20/07/2020 *Income* £199,600 *Total grants* £83,900 *Grants to organisations* £83,900 *Assets* £1,760,000

TRUSTEES John Gaselee; Julie Gaselee; David Gaselee; Sarah Gaselee.

HOW TO APPLY The trustees have previously stated that they do not encourage unsolicited requests.

CONTACT DETAILS The Trustees, 34A Westfield Road, Lymington, Hampshire SO41 3QA *Email* wyndham_ct@yahoo.co.uk *Website* www.wyndham-ct.org

■ The Wyseliot Rose Charitable Trust

CC NO 257219 **ESTABLISHED** 1968

WHERE FUNDING CAN BE GIVEN UK.

WHO CAN BENEFIT Registered charities only.

WHAT IS FUNDED Health and medical causes; the arts; social welfare; disability.

WHAT IS NOT FUNDED Individuals.

TYPE OF GRANT Recurrent funding; core costs; capital costs; project costs.

RANGE OF GRANTS £2,000 to £6,000.

SAMPLE GRANTS Street Games and Time and Talent Association (£6,000 each); Alzheimer's Research UK and FareShare (£5,000 each); Centrepoint Soho, Cystic Fibrosis Trust and Gingerbread (£4,000 each); Interact Stroke Support and Macmillan Cancer Support (£3,500 each); Runnymede Trust (£3,000); Child Action Nepal (£2,500); Andover Child Contact Centre (£2,000).

FINANCES *Financial year end* 05/04/2020
Income £139,600 *Total grants* £129,000
Grants to organisations £129,000
Assets £2,245,400

TRUSTEES Jonathan Rose; Adam Raphael; William Rose; Lucy Rose.

HOW TO APPLY Apply in writing to the correspondent. The trustees have previously stated that many of the same charities are supported each year, with perhaps one or two changes. It is unlikely new charities sending circular appeals will be supported.

CONTACT DETAILS The Trustees, 17 Chelsea Square, London SW3 6LF *Tel.* 01273 562563

■ Yankov Charitable Trust

CC NO 1106703 **ESTABLISHED** 2004

WHERE FUNDING CAN BE GIVEN Worldwide.

WHO CAN BENEFIT Charitable organisations, particularly Jewish organisations.

WHAT IS FUNDED Advancement of the Jewish religion and religious education and culture among the Jewish community.

TYPE OF GRANT Research.

SAMPLE GRANTS Zichron Tamar (£65,600); Yeshivat Hiyun Hatalmud (£51,000); Yeshivas Nesivos Hatorah (£32,000); Yeshivas Toras Moshe (£20,400); Zichron Nachum (£20,000); Igud Hakollelim (£15,000).

FINANCES *Financial year end* 30/09/2019 *Income* £404,000 *Total grants* £238,000 *Grants to organisations* £238,000 *Assets* £335,500

TRUSTEES Jacob Schonberg; Julian Lewin; Aryeh Schonberg.

OTHER INFORMATION The 2018/19 accounts were the latest available at the time of writing (May 2021). According to the 2018/19 annual report, the grant total includes a grant of £51,000 to Yeshivat Hiyun Hatalmud 'to support monthly grants to research students studying under the Tiferes Chaim project' and £34,000 in grants of under £10,000.

HOW TO APPLY Contact the correspondent for further information.

CONTACT DETAILS The Trustees, 88 Castlewood Road, London N16 6DH *Tel.* 020 8202 7948

■ The Yapp Charitable Trust

CC NO 1076803 **ESTABLISHED** 1999

WHERE FUNDING CAN BE GIVEN England and Wales.

WHO CAN BENEFIT Registered charities.

WHAT IS FUNDED Older people; children and young people (aged 5–25); people with physical disabilities, learning disabilities or mental health challenges; social welfare, particularly people trying to overcome life-limiting problems of a social nature (such as addiction, relationship difficulties, abuse and offending); education and learning, particularly adults or children who are educationally disadvantaged.

WHAT IS NOT FUNDED According to the charity's website, the following are excluded: charities with a total annual expenditure of more than £40,000; charities that are not registered with the Charity Commission in England and Wales (unless you are excepted); industrial provident societies; CICs; work that is not based in England or Wales; charities with unrestricted reserves worth more than 12 months' expenditure; branches of national charities (you must have your own charity number and not a shared one); new organisations (you must have been operating as a fully constituted organisations for at least three years prior to applying, although note that you may have registered as a charity more recently); new work that has not been occurring for at least a year; new paid posts; additional activities, expansion or development plans; special events, trips or outings; capital expenditure (equipment, buildings, renovations, furnishings, minibuses, etc.); work exclusively with children under the age of five; childcare; holidays and holiday centres; core funding of charities that benefit the wider community (such as general advice services and community centres unless a significant element of their work focuses on one of the trust's priority groups); bereavement support; debt advice; community safety initiatives; charities raising money to give to other organisations (such as schools or hospitals, or other voluntary groups); individuals (including charities raising funds to purchase equipment for or make grants to individuals).

TYPE OF GRANT Core/revenue costs.

RANGE OF GRANTS £500 to £9,000.

SAMPLE GRANTS Autism Networks (£9,000); Bivol Trust (£7,500); Learning Plus (£6,000); Oadby Youth Centre (£4,500); Norfolk SEN Network (£3,000); York Women's Counselling Service (£2,000); West View Project – Children and Young People's Activity Centre (£1,000); 7th Camborne Guides (£500).

FINANCES *Financial year end* 30/09/2020 *Income* £179,900 *Total grants* £259,300 *Grants to organisations* £259,300 *Assets* £6,330,000

TRUSTEES Jane Fergusson; Ron Lis; Lisa Bone; Alfred Hill; Liz Islam; Jacqui Orchard.

OTHER INFORMATION The trust gives priority to work that is unattractive to the general public or unpopular with other funders, particularly when it helps improve the lives of marginalised, disadvantaged or isolated people. Preference is also given to charities that can demonstrate the effective use of volunteers, an element of self-sustainability, or preventative work which aims to create change through raising awareness and campaigning. Grants were made to 48 organisations and distributed as follows: children and young people (£61,500 in 11 grants); disability (£60,500 in 12 grants); social welfare (£41,000 in seven grants); older people (£33,500 in seven grants); education (£22,500 in four grants).

HOW TO APPLY An application form and further guidelines are available on the trust's website. Pre-application enquires can be made to the correspondent via phone or email.

CONTACT DETAILS Joanne Anderson, Trust Secretary, 1st Floor, Mile House, Bridge End, Chester Le Street, County Durham DH3 3RA *Tel.* 0191 389 3300 *Email* info@yappcharitabletrust.org.uk *Website* www.yappcharitabletrust.org.uk

■ York Children's Trust

CC NO 222279 **ESTABLISHED** 1976

WHERE FUNDING CAN BE GIVEN Within 20-mile radius of York.

WHO CAN BENEFIT Registered charities; schools and special schools; community organisations; local authorities; care trusts; individuals.

WHAT IS FUNDED Children and young people. Grants are given in the following categories: educational; social and medical welfare; travel and fostering talents; children's groups.

WHAT IS NOT FUNDED National charities; organisations without a clear link to York.

RANGE OF GRANTS £1,000 to £5,000.

SAMPLE GRANTS Ebor Academy Trust (£7,700); 1st Easingwold Scout Group (£5,000); Koplin Violins York (£3,500); York Family Mediation Service (£3,000); Home-Start York (£2,500); Pathfinder Multi Academy (£2,100); The Sick Children's Trust (£1,000); Sun and Moon Play Therapy (£960).

FINANCES *Financial year end* 31/12/2019 *Income* £114,300 *Total grants* £89,600 *Grants to organisations* £50,600 *Assets* £2,970,000

TRUSTEES Lenore Hill; Keith Hayton; Peter Watson; Alan Ward; Lorraine Kerr; Kathy Pickard; Kitty Lamb; John Corden; Dr Michael Harran; Anne Clark; Maggie Soper; Yvette Bent; Steve Flatley; Mark Sessions.

OTHER INFORMATION Grants were made to 29 organisations during the year, distributed as follows: children's groups (£33,400); education (£14,100); social and medical welfare (£3,000). Grants were also made to 101 individuals during the year, totalling £39,000.

HOW TO APPLY Contact the correspondent for information regarding the application process.

CONTACT DETAILS The Trustees, 29 Whinney Lane, Harrogate, North Yorkshire HG2 9LS *Tel.* 01423 504765 *Email* yorkchildrenstrust@hotmail.co.uk

■ Yorkshire Building Society Charitable Foundation

CC NO 1069082 **ESTABLISHED** 1998

WHERE FUNDING CAN BE GIVEN UK, with a preference for areas local to the society's branches.

WHO CAN BENEFIT UK-registered charities.

WHAT IS FUNDED General charitable purposes, with priority areas: alleviating poverty; improving health/saving lives. There is a particular focus on beneficiary groups that are vulnerable or disadvantaged, such as children, people with disabilities or serious illness, older people and people who are homeless.

WHAT IS NOT FUNDED Charities serving only a specific sector of the community selected on the basis of political or religious grounds/advancement; animal welfare charities; charities with beneficiaries not in the UK; CICs and community or voluntary organisations that are not registered charities; individuals. See the charity's guidance notes for full exclusions.

TYPE OF GRANT Specific projects; purchase of specific capital items.

RANGE OF GRANTS £250 to £2,000.

SAMPLE GRANTS Appley Bridge Community Association, Chartwell Cancer Trust, Fulham Good Neighbour Service, Mulberry Centre, Sheffield Wildlife Trust, The Bromley Homeless Shelter, United Churches Healing Ministry Ltd and Welsh Air Ambulance Charitable Trust (£2,000 each).

FINANCES *Financial year end* 31/12/2019 *Income* £334,700 *Total grants* £382,000 *Grants to organisations* £382,000 *Assets* £62,400

TRUSTEES Richard Brown; Vanessa White; Sarah Jackson; Gordon Rogers. Lloyd Latibeaudiere.

OTHER INFORMATION During the year, grants were made to 355 organisations. Only organisations receiving grants of £2,000 and above were listed as beneficiaries in the charity's accounts.

HOW TO APPLY To be eligible for a grant you must be recommended by one of the building society's members or colleagues. If you are a member and would like the foundation to consider supporting a charity, an online application form can be found on the foundation's webpage. All applications are reviewed on a quarterly basis by the trustees. Deadlines are 31 March, 30 June, 30 September and 31 December annually. You can expect to hear back within three months of submitting an application.

CONTACT DETAILS Ms D. Colley, Secretary, Yorkshire House, Yorkshire Drive, Bradford, West Yorkshire BD5 8LJ *Tel.* 0345 166 9271 *Email* corporateresponsibility@ybs.co.uk *Website* https://www.ybs.co.uk/your-society/charitable-foundation/index.html

■ Yorkshire Cancer Research

CC NO 516898 **ESTABLISHED** 1985

WHERE FUNDING CAN BE GIVEN Yorkshire.

WHO CAN BENEFIT Universities; research organisations; health bodies.

WHAT IS FUNDED Cancer research, including: education around lifestyle decisions; early diagnosis; research-led innovation; improvement in cancer services. The research strategy is available to view on the charity's website.

WHAT IS NOT FUNDED Refer to the guidance notes on the website for specific exclusions.

TYPE OF GRANT Research projects, programmes and facilities; development funding; strategic funding.

RANGE OF GRANTS Dependent on funding call. Mostly up to £300,000 in 2019/20.

SAMPLE GRANTS University of Leeds (£3.33 million in 15 grants); University of Hull (£301,100 in three grants); University of Sheffield (£236,000 in five grants); University College London (£159,500 in two grants); Northumbria University (£96,600); Leeds Beckett University (£36,100); University of York (£3,700).

FINANCES *Financial year end* 31/03/2020 *Income* £18,720,000 *Total grants* £5,300,000 *Grants to organisations* £5,300,000 *Assets* £56,570,000

TRUSTEES Sandra Dodson; Graham Berville; Catherine Rustomji; Dr Yvette Oade; Elizabeth Richards; Bobby Ndawula; Rosemary Crook; Christopher Slater; Clare Field; Dr James Rice; Craig Bonnar.

OTHER INFORMATION During the year, 55 grants were awarded to approximately 15 organisations.

HOW TO APPLY Our previous research suggests that each year the charity opens a targeted funding round for research projects, the details of which are posted on the charity's website. Refer to the website for information on current funding rounds, as well as deadlines, guidance and application forms. Contact services@ycr.org.uk for information about funding for health initiatives and services.

CONTACT DETAILS Research Team, Jacob Smith House, 7 Grove Park Court, Harrogate, North Yorkshire HG1 4DP *Tel.* 01423 501269 *Email* hq@ycr.org.uk *Website* https://yorkshirecancerresearch.org.uk

■ The Yorkshire Dales Millennium Trust

CC NO 1061687 **ESTABLISHED** 1996

WHERE FUNDING CAN BE GIVEN The Yorkshire Dales.

WHO CAN BENEFIT Voluntary organisations, community groups, farmers and other individuals, Yorkshire Dales National Park Authority, estates, parish councils and district councils.

WHAT IS FUNDED The environment; conservation; heritage; rural communities.

TYPE OF GRANT Project funding; capital costs.

RANGE OF GRANTS £900 to £165,000.

SAMPLE GRANTS Stories in Stone (£165,600); Capital Grants Woodlands (£65,400); Westmorland Dales Haytime (£25,000); Green Futures (YEAF) (£4,600).

FINANCES *Financial year end* 31/03/2020 *Income* £1,530,000 *Total grants* £428,100 *Grants to organisations* £310,100 *Assets* £1,500,000

TRUSTEES Prof. Christine Leigh; Carl Lis; Mark Cunliffe-Lister; Jane Roberts; His Hon. Peter Charlesworth; Stephen Macare; Thomas Wheelwright; Andrew Campbell; Karen Cowley; Eileen Spencer; Heather McQue; Tracy Walker; Eloise Brown.

OTHER INFORMATION A total of £459,700 in grants was awarded to seven organisations and four individuals during the year.

HOW TO APPLY Application processes may vary depending upon the specific programme. Guidance and application forms for all current grant programmes can be downloaded from the trust's website. The trustees meet at regular intervals six times during the financial year for full board plus additional meetings.

CONTACT DETAILS Josephine Boulter, Company Secretary, Main Street, Clapham, Lancaster, Lancashire LA2 8DP *Tel.* 01524 251002 *Email* info@ydmt.org *Website* www.ydmt.org

■ The Yorkshire Historic Churches Trust

CC NO 1175099 **ESTABLISHED** 1988

WHERE FUNDING CAN BE GIVEN Yorkshire (pre-1974 boundaries).

WHO CAN BENEFIT Churches.

WHAT IS FUNDED The repair and restoration of churches. Most grants are given for repairs to the main fabric of the church. Grants are also given for the preservation of individual items such as bells, monuments and organs.

WHAT IS NOT FUNDED All work in connection with facilities for people with disabilities; all work in connection with heating or electrical installations (including upgrading); all new work in connection with improvements or re-ordering, including extensions; projects where work has either commenced or been completed.

TYPE OF GRANT Capital costs.

RANGE OF GRANTS £250 to £112,500.

SAMPLE GRANTS Heeley, Christ Church (£8,500); Alne, St Mary the Virgin (£8,000); Newton-on-Ouse, All Saints (£7,000); Bierley, St John the Evangelist (£4,000); Newby, St Mark (£3,000); Wetherby, St James (£2,000); Whixley, Church of the Ascension (£1,000).

FINANCES *Financial year end* 31/12/2019 *Income* £145,200 *Total grants* £113,700 *Grants to organisations* £113,700 *Assets* £1,100,000

TRUSTEES Rory Wardroper; Peter Johnston; Sylvia Johnson; Thomas Ramsden; Richard Bailey; Jane Crease; Moira Fulton; Christopher Wildblood; Clive Lloyd; Dr Katherine Giles.

OTHER INFORMATION 30 grants were awarded during the year.

HOW TO APPLY Applications should be made using the form available to download on the trust's website.

CONTACT DETAILS Mr J. K. Stamp, Grants Secretary, Yorkshire Historic Churches Trust, 2 Dalton Terrace, York YO24 4DA *Tel.* 01904 643943 *Email* vanbarassociates@gmail.com *Website* www.yhct.org.uk

■ The William Allen Young Charitable Trust

CC NO 283102 **ESTABLISHED** 1978

WHERE FUNDING CAN BE GIVEN UK, with a preference for London.

WHO CAN BENEFIT Registered charities.

WHAT IS FUNDED Health; community; education; culture; human rights; animal welfare; social welfare.

TYPE OF GRANT One-off.

RANGE OF GRANTS Up to £41,600 but mostly £1,000 to £5,000.

SAMPLE GRANTS The Halow Project (£41,600); Anti-Slavery International and Shelter (£20,000 each); Imperial College London (£10,000); Shire Horse Society (£5,000); Alzheimer's Society (£4,000); Smallwood Primary School (£300).

FINANCES *Financial year end* 05/04/2020 *Income* £698,000 *Total grants* £546,500 *Grants to organisations* £546,500 *Assets* £35,070,000

TRUSTEES Torquil Sligo-Young; James Young; Caroline Chelton.

OTHER INFORMATION Grants were broken down as follows: medical causes (£240,800); community (£142,100); social welfare (£50,500); education (£45,900); culture (£31,800); human rights (£23,000); animals (£12,500).

HOW TO APPLY The 2019/20 annual report notes: 'The trustees aim to support those organisations they have supported in the past on an ongoing basis although one-off donations are considered.'

CONTACT DETAILS The Trustees, Young and Co. Brewery plc, 26 Osiers Road, Wandsworth, London SW18 1NH *Tel.* 020 8875 7000 *Email* claire.hill@youngs.co.uk

■ Youth Music

CC NO 1075032 **ESTABLISHED** 1999

WHERE FUNDING CAN BE GIVEN England, Wales and Scotland.

WHO CAN BENEFIT Registered charities; CICs; constituted community groups; schools.

WHAT IS FUNDED Youth Music funds projects that provide musical opportunities and activities for children and young people (under 25), working towards greater inclusion of young people in musical activities, across all genres and styles. It funds developmental music projects for children and young people in challenging circumstances, as well as strategic work to support the workforce and organisations in the sector. Its priority groups are: early years; special educational needs and/or disabilities; young people facing barriers; young adults; youth justice; organisations and the workforce; cold spots of access to diverse music-making opportunities.

WHAT IS NOT FUNDED See the grant-maker's website for a full list of funding exclusions relevant to the fund being applied to.

TYPE OF GRANT Project costs; core costs; salaries; capital costs; development funding (programme dependent). Funding can be given for projects lasting from one year up to three years and beyond.

RANGE OF GRANTS £2,000 to £200,000; matched funding of 10–25% is required, depending on the fund.

SAMPLE GRANTS A list of beneficiaries was not included in the annual report and accounts.

FINANCES *Financial year end* 31/03/2020 *Income* £13,320,000 *Total grants* £9,430,000 *Grants to organisations* £9,430,000 *Assets* £3,860,000

OTHER INFORMATION This trust is funded each year by the National Lottery, channelled through Arts Council England and the People's Postcode Lottery. Grants are awarded from Fund A (grants of £2,000 to £30,000), Fund B (grants of £30,001 to £200,000) and Fund C (grants of up to £160,000 per year), depending on the grant size and duration of the project. Other funds are advertised on the trust's website as they arise. In 2019/20, grants were given to 189 organisations to support 191 projects. The charity was previously known as National Foundation for Youth Music.

HOW TO APPLY The three main funds from which grants are awarded each differ in their funding criteria and application process. Potential applicants are advised to refer to the Youth Music Network website for up-to-date criteria, priorities, guidelines and deadlines. Applications should be made online, via the website. Note: At the time of writing (May 2021) Fund C was 'closed for applications until further notice'. Guidance on other current funds not mentioned here can also be found on the website.

CONTACT DETAILS Angela Linton, Chief Operating Officer, Suites 3–5, Swan Court, 9 Tanner Street, London SE1 3LE *Tel.* 020 7902 1095 *Email* angela.linton@youthmusic.org.uk *Website* https://www.youthmusic.org.uk

■ The Elizabeth and Prince Zaiger Trust

CC NO 282096 **ESTABLISHED** 1981

WHERE FUNDING CAN BE GIVEN UK; some preference for Somerset, Dorset and the South West.

WHO CAN BENEFIT Registered charities; hospitals; hospices; occasionally individuals.

WHAT IS FUNDED General charitable purposes; social welfare; older people; people with disabilities; education of children and young people; care and protection of animals.

RANGE OF GRANTS £2,000 to £50,000.

SAMPLE GRANTS The Stars Appeal (£50,000); Variety, the Children's Charity (£25,000); Treloar Trust (£17,000); King's College Hospital Charity (£15,000); Children's Hospice South West (£14,000); Whizz-Kidz (£10,000); Spark Somerset (£7,000); Guide Dogs for the Blind Association, Leeds Women's Aid and Prostate Cancer UK (£5,000 each); Arts Emergency, Escape Support Group and The Brain Tumour Charity (£3,000 each).

FINANCES *Financial year end* 31/03/2020 *Income* £698,700 *Total grants* £690,000 *Grants to organisations* £690,000 *Assets* £17,900,000

TRUSTEES John Davidge; Peter Harvey; Derek Long; Edward Parry; Dr Robin Keyte.

OTHER INFORMATION The trust awarded 92 grants to organisations during 2019/20. Since the establishment of the trust in 1981, a total of £12.64 million has been awarded in grants.

HOW TO APPLY The trust's Charity Commission record states: 'This trust does not respond to unsolicited applications for funds. Don't apply – it wastes your time and money.'

CONTACT DETAILS The Trustees, Gatesmoor, Hawkridge, Spaxton, Bridgwater, Somerset TA5 1AL *Tel.* 01278 671353

■ The Marjorie and Arnold Ziff Charitable Foundation

CC NO 249368 **ESTABLISHED** 1964

WHERE FUNDING CAN BE GIVEN UK, with a preference for Leeds.

WHO CAN BENEFIT Jewish causes and organisations.

WHAT IS FUNDED General charitable purposes, including education, healthcare, the arts and social welfare; in practice, Jewish causes.

TYPE OF GRANT Capital costs.

RANGE OF GRANTS Up to £75,000.

SAMPLE GRANTS UJIA (£75,000); Leeds Jewish Welfare Board (£64,900); Lubavitch UK (£36,000); Chief Rabbinate Trust (£22,500); Friends of Brodetsky (£10,000); Norwood (£5,000); ORT UK (£1,000); Lifelites Charity (£250); Macmillan Cancer Support (£25).

FINANCES *Financial year end* 05/04/2020 *Income* £766,800 *Total grants* £542,700 *Grants to organisations* £542,700 *Assets* £6,600,000

TRUSTEES Dr Marjorie Ziff; Michael Ziff; Edward Ziff; Ann Manning.

OTHER INFORMATION Grants were awarded to 53 organisations in 2019/20.

HOW TO APPLY Apply in writing to the correspondent. The trust has previously stated that funds available are limited and requests not previously supported are unlikely to be successful. Initial telephone calls are welcome but applicants should note the foregoing comments. Replies will only be given to a request accompanied by an sae.

CONTACT DETAILS The Trustees, Town Centre House, The Merrion Centre, Leeds, West Yorkshire LS2 8LY *Tel.* 0113 222 1234

■ The Zochonis Charitable Trust

CC NO 274769 **ESTABLISHED** 1978

WHERE FUNDING CAN BE GIVEN UK, particularly Greater Manchester; overseas, particularly Africa.

WHO CAN BENEFIT Registered charities only.

WHAT IS FUNDED A range of charitable purposes including: welfare; education; children and young people; homelessness; community work; the armed forces; older people; rescue services.

SAMPLE GRANTS A list of beneficiaries was not included in the annual report and accounts.

FINANCES *Financial year end* 05/04/2020 *Income* £5,070,000 *Total grants* £5,030,000 *Grants to organisations* £5,030,000 *Assets* £111,830,000

TRUSTEES Christopher Green; Archibald Calder; Paul Milner.

OTHER INFORMATION Grants were distributed as follows: education (£1.4 million); health (£923,300); emergency (£630,000); children and young people (£491,000); homelessness (£479,500); overseas (£460,000); social provision (£186,500); community (£155,500); families (£74,000); the armed forces (£62,500); older people (£45,100); rescue services (£35,000).

HOW TO APPLY Contact the correspondent for further information.

CONTACT DETAILS The Trustees, Manchester Business Park, 3500 Aviator Way, Manchester M22 5TG *Tel.* 0161 435 1005 *Email* enquiries@zochonischaritabletrust.com

■ Zurich Community Trust (UK) Ltd

CC NO 266983 **ESTABLISHED** 1973

WHERE FUNDING CAN BE GIVEN UK and overseas, with priority given to locations where the company has offices.

WHO CAN BENEFIT Registered charities, voluntary organisations; NGOs.

WHAT IS FUNDED Communities and people that are disadvantaged. The trust's grant-making comes under a number of programmes. At a national level, the Zurich Cares programme provides grants to three partner charities chosen by employees. At a local level, the programme awards grants to charities in the communities local to Zurich offices and employees, with local and regional grant funds available (refer to the trust's website for further information on eligibility). Overseas, Zurich Cares programme provides support via grants to UK-registered charities. The Strategic Funding programmes are specific targeted projects, funded by the annual donation made to the trust by Zurich UK (applications for this scheme are by invitation only).

WHAT IS NOT FUNDED See the trust's website for a full list of exclusions for each funding programme.

TYPE OF GRANT Multi-year partnership grants; project costs; core cost; salaries; seed funding; capital.

RANGE OF GRANTS Mostly £100 to £5,000 for UK grants; £2,000 to £10,000 for grants overseas. Strategic grants may be much larger.

SAMPLE GRANTS The Openwork Foundation (£448,000); Aston Villa Foundation (£203,000); Greenwich Leisure Ltd (£160,000); Saints Foundation (£133,000); Dementia UK and Place2Be (£76,000 each); Mental Health Foundation (£22,000); Action for Kids (£40,000); University of Bath (£15,000); Addaction (£5,000).

FINANCES *Financial year end* 31/12/2019 *Income* £3,750,000 *Total grants* £2,440,000 *Grants to organisations* £2,440,000 *Assets* £5,170,000

TRUSTEES Tim Culling; Wayne Myslik; Andrew Jepp; Tulsi Naidu; Richard Peden; Stephen Collinson.

OTHER INFORMATION Only organisations receiving over £30,000 were listed as beneficiaries in the trust's accounts. Grants of under £30,000 totalled £1.26 million.

HOW TO APPLY Application processes vary between grant schemes and different locations. Prospective applicants should see the trust's website for details on how to apply for a given scheme. Application opening/closing dates are also published on the website. Multi-year partners are nominated by Zurich Insurance employees.

CONTACT DETAILS Steve Grimmett, Head of ZCT (UK), PO Box 1288, Swindon, Wiltshire SN1 1FL *Tel.* 07875 886341 *Email* steve.grimmett@zct.org.uk *Website* www.zct.org.uk

Take your knowledge further with the Fundraising Series

www.dsc.org.uk/cfr

www.dsc.org.uk/lin

www.dsc.org.uk/fst

www.dsc.org.uk/cmf